Small Business Sourcebook

ISSN 0883-3397

Small Business Sourcebook

The Entrepreneur's Resource

THIRTIETH EDITION

Volume 5

General Small Business Topics
General Small Business Resources
(Includes State Sections)

(Entries 43316-55539)

Sonya D. Hill
Project Editor

GALE
CENGAGE Learning®

Detroit • New York • San Francisco • New Haven, Conn • Waterville, Maine • London

GALE
CENGAGE Learning®

Small Business Sourcebook, 30th edition

Project Editor: Sonya D. Hill

Editorial Support Services: Charles Beaumont

Composition and Electronic Prepress: Gary Leach

Manufacturing: Rita Wimberley

For product information and technology assistance, contact us at
Gale Customer Support, 1-800-877-4253.
For permission to use material from this text or product,
submit all requests online at **www.cengage.com/permissions.**
Further permissions questions can be emailed to
permissionrequest@cengage.com

Gale
27500 Drake Rd.
Farmington Hills, MI, 48331-3535

ISBN-13: 978-1-4144-7957-6 (set)
ISBN-10: 1-4144-7957-3 (set)
ISBN-13: 978-1-4144-7958-3 (vol. 1)
ISBN-10: 1-4144-7958-1 (vol. 1)
ISBN-13: 978-1-4144-7959-0 (vol. 2)
ISBN-10: 1-4144-7959-X (vol. 2)
ISBN-13: 978-1-4144-7960-6 (vol. 3)
ISBN-10: 1-4144-7960-3 (vol. 3)
ISBN-13: 978-1-4144-7961-3 (vol. 4)
ISBN-10: 1-4144-7961-1 (vol. 4)
ISBN-13: 978-1-4144-7962-0 (vol. 5)
ISBN-10: 1-4144-7962-X (vol. 5)
ISBN-13: 978-1-4144-7963-7 (vol. 6)
ISBN-10: 1-4144-7963-8 (vol. 6)

ISSN 0883-3397

Printed in the United States of America
1 2 3 4 5   17 16 15 14 13

Contents

The appeal of small business ownership remains perpetually entrenched in American culture as one of the most viable avenues for achieving the American Dream. To many entrepreneurs going into business for themselves represents financial independence, an increased sense of identity and self-worth, and the fulfillment of personal goals. Small business owners strive to make their mark in today's competitive marketplace by establishing healthy businesses that can, over time, become legacies handed down from one generation to the next. Entrepreneurs from each generation tackle the obstacles and adversities of the current business and economic climate to test their business savvy and generate opportunities. Today's entrepreneurs face many of the problems of their predecessors, as well as some distinctly new challenges.

With the rightsizing, downsizing, and reorganization of corporate America, many individuals have decided to confront the risks of developing and operating their own businesses. Small business ownership is rapidly becoming a viable alternative to what is perceived as an equally unstable corporate environment. These entrepreneurs, many of whom have firsthand experience with the problems and inefficiencies inherent in today's large corporations, seek to improve upon an archaic business model and to capitalize on their own ingenuity and strengths. Led by their zeal, many would-be entrepreneurs let their desire, drive, and determination overshadow the need for business knowledge and skill. Ironically, aids in obtaining these components of entrepreneurial success are widely available, easily accessible, and often free of charge.

Small Business Sourcebook (*SBS*) is a six-volume annotated guide to more than 21,310 listings of live and print sources of information designed to facilitate the start-up, development, and growth of specific small businesses, as well as over 26,280 similar listings on general small business topics. An additional 12,367 state-specific listings and over 2,220 U.S. federal government agencies and offices specializing in small business issues, programs, and assistance are also included. *SBS* covers 340 specific small business profiles and 99 general small business topics.

Features of This Edition

This edition of *Small Business Sourcebook* has been revised and updated, incorporating thousand of changes to names, addresses, contacts, and descriptions of listings from the previous edition.

Contents and Arrangement

The geographical scope of *SBS* encompasses the United States and Canada, with expanded coverage for resources pertaining to international trade and for resources that have a U.S. or Canadian distributor or contact. Internet sites that are maintained outside of the U.S. and Canada are also included if they contain relevant information for North American small businesses. Resources that do not relate specifically to small businesses are generally not included.

The information presented in *SBS* is grouped within four sections: Specific Small Business Profiles, General Small Business Topics, State Listings, and Federal Government Assistance. Detailed outlines of these sections may be found in the Users' Guide following this Introduction. Also included is a Master Index to Volumes 1 through 6.

Specific Small Business Profiles This section includes the following types of resources: start-up information, associations and other organizations, educational programs, directories of educational programs, reference works, sources of supply, statistical sources, trade periodicals, videocassettes/audiocassettes, trade shows and conventions, consultants, franchises and business opportunities, computerized databases, computer systems/software, Internet databases, libraries, and research centers-all arranged by business type. Entries range from Accounting Service to Word Processing Service, and include such businesses as Airbag Replacement Service Centers, Computer Consulting, Damage Restoration Service, and Web Site Design.

General Small Business Topics This section offers such resources as associations, books, periodicals, articles, pamphlets, educational programs, directories of educational programs, videocassettes/audiocassettes, trade shows and conventions, consultants, computerized databases, Internet databases, software, libraries, and research centers, arranged alphabetically by business topic.

State Listings Entries include government, academic, and commercial agencies and organizations, as well as select coverage of relevant state-specific publications; listings are arranged alphabetically by state, territory, and Canadian province. Some examples include small business development consultants, educational programs, financing and loan programs, better business bureaus, and chambers of commerce.

Federal Government Assistance Listings specializing in small business issues, programs, assistance, and policyare arranged alphabetically by U.S. government agency or office; regional or branch offices are listed alphabetically by state.

Master Index All entries in Volumes 1 through 6 are arranged in one alphabetic index for convenience.

Entries in *SBS* include (as appropriate andavailable):

- Organization, institution, or product name

- Contact information, including contact name, address and phone, toll-free, and fax numbers

- Author/editor, date(s), and frequency

- Availability, including price

- Brief description of purpose, services, or content

- Company and/or personal E-mail addresses

- Web site addresses

SBS also features the following:

Guide to Publishers—An alphabetic listing of 2,470 companies, associations, institutions, and individuals that publish the periodicals, directories, guidebooks, and other publications noted in the Small Business Profiles and General Topics sections. Users are provided with full contact information, including address, phone, fax,and e-mail and URL when available. The Guide to Publishers facilitates contact with publishers and provides a one- stop resource for valuable information.

Method of Compilation

SBS was compiled by consulting small business experts and entrepreneurs, as well as a variety of resources, including direct contact with the associations, organizations, and agencies through telephone surveys, Internet research, or through materials provided by those listees; government resources; and data obtained from other relevant Gale directories. *SBS* was reviewed by a team of small business advisors, all of whom have numerous years of expertise in small business counseling and identification of small business information resources. The last and perhaps most important resource we utilize is direct contact with our readers, who provide valuable comments and suggestions to improve our publication. *SBS* relies on these comprehensive market contacts to provide today's entrepreneurs with relevant, current, and accurate informationon all aspects of small business.

Available in Electronic Formats

Licensing. Small Business Sourcebook is available for licensing. The complete database is provided in a fielded format and is deliverable on such media as disk or CD-ROM. For more information, contact Gale's Business Development Group at1-800-877-GALE, or visit our website at www.gale.com/bizdev.

Comments and Suggestions Welcome

Associations, agencies, business firms, publishers, and other organizations that provide assistance and information to the small business community are encouraged to submit material about their programs, activities, services, or products. Comments and suggestions from users of this directory are also welcomed and appreciated. Please contact:

Project Editor
Small Business Sourcebook
Gale, Cengage Learning
27500 Drake Rd.
Farmington Hills, MI 48331-3535
Phone: (248) 699-4253
Fax: (248) 699-8070
E-mail: BusinessProductsgale.com
URL: www.gale.com

Small Business Sourcebook (*SBS*) provides information in a variety of forms and presentations for comprehensive coverage and ease of use. The directory contains four parts within two volumes:

- Specific Small Business Profiles
- General Small Business Topics
- State Listings
- Federal Government Assistance

Information on specific businesses is arranged by type of business; the many general topics that are of interest to the owners, operators, or managers of all small businesses are grouped in a separate section for added convenience. Users should consult the various sections to benefit fully from the information *SBS* offers. For example, an entrepreneur with a talent or interest in the culinary arts could peruse a number of specific small business profiles, such as Restaurant, Catering, Cooking School, Specialty Food/Wine Shop, Bakery/Doughnut Shop, Healthy Restaurant, or Candy/Chocolate Store. Secondly, the General Small Business Topics section could be consulted for any applicable subjects, such as Service Industry, Retailing, Franchising, and other relevant topics. Then, the appropriate state within the State Listings section would offer area programs and offices providing information and support to small businesses, including venture capital firms and small business development consultants. Finally, the Federal Government Assistance section could supply relevant government offices, such as procurement contacts.

Features Included in Volumes 1 through 3

List of Small Business Profiles. This list provides an alphabetic outline of the small businesses profiled, with cross-references for related profiles and for alternate names by which businesses may be identified. The page number for each profile is indicated.

Standard Industrial Classification (SIC) Codes for Profiled Small Businesses. This section lists four-digit SIC codes and corresponding classification descriptions for the small businesses profiled in this edition. The SIC system, which organizes businesses by type, is a product of the Statistical Policy Division of the U.S. Office of Management and Budget. Statistical data produced by government, public, and private organizations is usually categorized according to SIC codes, thereby facilitating the collection, comparison, and analysis of data as well as providing a uniform method for presenting statistical information. Hence, knowing the SIC code for a particular small business increases access and the use of a variety of statistical data from many sources.

Guide to Publishers. This resource lists alphabetically the companies, associations, institutions, and individuals that publish the periodicals, directories, guidebooks, and other publications noted in the "Small Business Profiles" and "General Topics" sections. Users are provided with full contact information, including address, phone, fax, and e-mail and URL when available. The "Guide" facilitates contact with publishers and provides a one-stop resource for valuable information.

Glossary of Small Business Terms. This glossary defines nearly 400 small business terms, including financial, governmental, insurance, procurement, technical, and general business definitions. Cross-references and acronyms are also provided.

Small Business Profiles A-Z. A total of 340 small businesses is represented in volumes 1 through 3. Profiles are listed alphabetically by business name. Entries within each profile are arranged alphabetically by resource type, within up to 17 subheadings. These subheadings are detailed below:

- *Start-up Information*—Includes periodical articles, books, manuals, book excerpts, kits, and other sources of information. Entries offer title; publisher; address; phone, fax, toll-free numbers; company e-mail and URL addresses; and a description. Bibliographic data is provided for cited periodical articles whenever possible.

- *Associations and Other Oganizations*—Includes trade and professional associations whose members gather and disseminate information of interest to small business owners. Entries offer the association's name; address; phone, toll-free and fax numbers; company e-mail address; contact name; purpose and objective; a description of membership; telecommunication services; and a listing of its publications, including publishing frequency.

- **Educational Programs**—Includes university and college programs, schools, training opportunities, association seminars, correspondence courses, and other educational programs.Entries offer name of program or institution, sponsor name, address, phone, toll-free and fax numbers, e-mail and URL addresses; and description of program.

- **Directories of Educational Programs**—Includes directories and other publications that list educational programs. Entries offer name of publication; publisher name, address, and phone, toll-free and fax numbers; editor; frequency or date of publication; price; and description of contents, including directory arrangement and indexes.

- **Reference Works**—Includes handbooks, manuals, textbooks, guides, directories, dictionaries, encyclopedias, and other published reference materials. Entries offer name of publication; publisher name, address, and phone, toll-free and fax numbers; e-mail and URL addresses; and, when available, name of author or editor, publication year or frequency, and price. A brief description is often featured.

- **Sources of Supply**—Includes buyer's guides,directories, special issues of periodicals, and other publications that list sources of equipment, supplies, and services related to the operation of the profiled small business. Entries offer publication name; publisher name, address, and phone, toll-free and fax numbers; e-mail and URL addresses; and, when available, editor's name, frequency or publication year, and price. A brief description of the publication, including directory arrangement and indexes, is often provided.

- **Statistical Sources**—Includes books, reports, pamphlets, and other sources of statistical data of interest to an owner, operator or manager of the profiled small business, such as wage, salary, and compensation data; financial and operating ratios; prices and costs; demographics; and other statistical information. Entries offer publication/data source name; publisher (if applicable); address; phone, toll-free and fax numbers of data source; publication date or frequency; and price. A brief description of the publication/data source is often provided.

- **Trade Periodicals**—Includes trade journals, newsletters, magazines, and other serials that offer information about the management and operation of the profiled small business. Such periodicals often contain industry news; trends and developments; reviews; articles about new equipment and supplies;

and other information related to business operations. Entries offer publication name; publisher name, address, phone, toll-free and fax numbers, and e-mail and URL addresses; editor name; publication frequency; andprice. A brief description of the publication's content is also included, when known.

- **Videocassettes/Audiocassettes**—Includes videocassettes, audiocassettes, and other audiovisual media offering information on the profiled small business. Entries offer program title; distributor name, address, phone, toll-free and fax numbers, and e-mail and URL addresses; description of program; release date; price; and format(s).

- **Trade Shows and Conventions**—Includes tradeshows, exhibitions, expositions, conventions, and other industry meetings that provide prospective and existing business owners with the opportunity to meet and exchange information with their peers, review commercial exhibits, establish business or sales contacts, and attend educational programs. Entries offer event name; sponsor or management company name, address, phone, toll-free and fax numbers, and e-mail and URL addresses; a description of the event, including audience, frequency, principal exhibits, and dates and locations of event for as many years ahead as provided by the event's sponsor.

- **Consultants**—Includes consultants and consulting organizations that provide services specifically related to the profiled small business. Entries offer individual consultant or consulting organization name, address, and phone, toll-free and fax numbers; company and individual e-mail addresses; and a brief description of consulting services. (For e-mail and URL addresses, see the Small Business Development Consultants subheadings in the State Listings section in Volume 2.)

- **Franchises and Business Opportunities**—Includes companies granting franchise licenses for enterprises falling within the scope of the profiled small business, as well as other non-franchised business opportunities that operate within a given network or system. Entries offer franchise name, address, phone, toll-free and fax numbers, and e-mail and URL addresses, as well as a description of the franchise or business opportunity, which has been expanded whenever possible to include the number of existing franchises, the founding date of the franchise, franchise fees, equity capital requirements, royalty fees, any managerial assistance offered, and available training.

- **Computerized Databases**—Includes diskettes, magnetic tapes, CD-ROMs, online systems, and other computer-readable databases. Entries offer database name; producer name, address, phone, toll-free and fax numbers, e-mail and URL addresses; description; and available format(s), including vendor name.

(Many university and public libraries offer online information retrieval services that provide searches of databases, including those listed in this category.)

- *Computer Systems/Software*—Includes software-eand computerized business systems designed to assist in the operation of the profiled small business. Entries offer name of the software or system; publisher name, address, phone, toll-free and fax-numbers; price; and description.

- *Libraries*—Includes libraries and special collections that contain material especially applicable to the profiled small business. Entries offer library or collection name; parent organization (where applicable); address; phone, toll-free and fax numbers; e-mail and URL addresses; contact name and title; scope of collection; and description of holdings, subscriptions, and services.

- *Research Centers*—Includes university-related and independently operated research institutes and information centers that generate, through their research programs, data related to the operation of the profiled small business. Also listed are associations and other business-related organizations that conduct research programs. Entries offer name of organization; address; phone, toll-free and fax numbers; company web site address; contact name and personale-mail; a description of principal fields of research or services; publications, including title and frequency; and related conferences.

Features Included in Volumes 2 through 6

General Small Business Topics. This section offers chapters on different topics in the operation of any small business, for example, venture capital and other funding, or compensation. Chapters are listed alphabetically by small business topic; entries within each chapter are arranged alphabetically, within up to 14 subheadings, by resource type:

- *Associations and Other Organizations*—Includes trade and professional associations that gather and disseminate information of interest to small business owners. Entries offer the association's name; address; phone, toll-free and fax numbers; organization e-mail and URL addresses; contact name;purpose and objectives; a description of membership; telecommunication services; and a listing of its publications, including publishing frequency.

- *Educational Programs*—Includes university and college programs, schools, training opportunities, association seminars, correspondence courses, and other educational programs. Entries offer name of program or institution, sponsor name, address, phone, toll-free and fax numbers, e-mail and URL addresses, and description of program.

- *Directories of Educational Programs*—Includes directories and other publications that list educational programs. Entries offer name of publication; publisher name, address, phone, toll-free and fax numbers, and e-mail and URL addresses; editor; frequency or date of publication; price; and description of contents, including arrangement and indexes.

- *Reference Works*—Includes articles, handbooks, manuals, textbooks, guides, directories, dictionaries, encyclopedias, and other published reference materials. Entries offertitle of article, including bibliographic information; name of publication; publisher name, address, phone, toll-free and fax numbers, and e-mail and URL addresses; and, when available, name of author oreditor, publication year or frequency, and price. A brief descriptionis often featured.

- *Sources of Supply*—Includes buyer's guides,directories, special issues of periodicals, and other publications that list sources of equipment, supplies, and services. Entries offer publication name; publisher name, address, phone, toll-free and fax numbers, and e-mail and URL addresses; editor's name, frequency or publication year, price, and a brief description of the publication, when available.

- *Statistical Sources*—Includes books, reports, pamphlets, and other sources of statistical data of interest to an owner, operator, or manager of a small business, such as wage, salary, and compensation data; financial and operating ratios; prices and costs; demographics; and other statistical information. Entries offer publication/data source name; publisher (if applicable); address; phone, toll-free and fax numbers of data source; publication date or frequency; and price. A brief description is often provided.

- *Trade Periodicals*—Includes journals, newsletters, magazines, and other serials. Entries offer name of publication; publisher name, address, phone, toll-free and fax numbers, and e-mail and URL addresses; and name of editor, frequency, and price.A brief description of the periodical's content is included when known.

- *Videocassettes/Audiocassettes*—Includes videocassettes, audiocassettes, and other audiovisual media. Entries offer program title; distributor name, address, phone, toll-free and fax numbers, and e-mail and URL addresses; price; description of program; release date; and format(s).

- *Trade Shows and Conventions*—Includes tradeshows, exhibitions, expositions, seminars, and conventions. Entries offer event name; sponsor or management company name, address, phone, toll-free and fax numbers, and e-mail and URL addresses; frequency of event; and dates and locations of the event for as many years ahead as known.

- *Consultants*—Includes consultants and consulting organizations. Entries offer individual consultant or-consulting organization name, address, and phone, toll-free and fax numbers; company and individual e-mail addresses; and a brief description of consulting services. (See also Consultants in the State Listings section.)

- *Computerized Databases*—Includes diskettes, CD-ROMs, magnetic tape, online systems and other computer-readable databases. Entries offer database name; producer, address, phone, toll-free and fax numbers, and e-mail and URL addresses; description; and available format(s), including vendor name. (Many university and public libraries offer online information retrieval services that provide searches of databases, including those listed in this category.)

- *Computer Systems/Software*—Includes software and computerized business systems. Entries offer name of the software or system; publisher name, address, phone, toll-free and fax numbers, and e-mail and URL addresses; price; and description.

- *Libraries*—Includes libraries and special collections that contain material applicable to the small business topic. Entries offer library or collection name, parent organization (where applicable), address, phone and fax numbers, e-mail and URL addresses, scope of collection, and description of holdings and services.

- *Research Centers*— Includes university-related and independently operated research institutes and information centers that generate, through their research programs, data related to specific small business topics. Entries offer name of organization, address, phone, toll-free and fax numbers, e-mail and URL addresses, a description of principal fields of research or services, and related conferences.

State Listings. This section lists various sources of information and assistance available within given states, territories, and Canadian provinces; entries include governmental, academic, and commercial agencies, and are arranged alphabetically within up to 15 subheadings by resource type:

- *Small Business Development Center Lead Office*— Includes the lead small business development center (SBDC) for each state.

- *Small Business Development Centers*—Includes any additional small business development centers (SBDC) in the state, territory, or province. SBDCs provide support services to small businesses, including individual counseling, seminars, conferences, and learning center activities.

- *Small Business Assistance Programs*—Includes state small business development offices and other programs offering assistance to small businesses.

- *SCORE Offices*—Includes SCORE office(s) for each state. The Service Corps of Retired Executives Association (SCORE), a volunteer program sponsored by the Small Business Administration, offers counseling, workshops, and seminars across the U.S. for small business entrepreneurs.

- *Better Business Bureaus*—Includes various better business bureaus within each state. By becoming a member of the local Better Business Bureau, a small business owner can increase the prestige and credibility of his or her business within the community, as well as make valuable business contacts.

- *Chambers of Commerce*—Includes various chambers of commerce within each state. Chambers of Commerce are valuable sources of small business advice and information; often, local chambers sponsor SCORE counseling several times per month for a small fee, seminars, conferences, and other workshops to its members. Also, by becoming a member of the local Chamber of Commerce, a small business owner can increase the prestige and credibility of his or herbusiness within the community, as well as make valuable business contacts.

- *Minority Business Assistance Programs*—Includes minority business development centers and other sources of assistance for minority-owned business.

- *Financing and Loan Programs*—Includes venture capital firms, small business investment companies (SBIC), minority enterprise small business investment companies (MESBIC), and other programs that provide funding to qualified small businesses.

- *Procurement Assistance Programs*—Includes state services such as counseling, set-asides, and sheltered-market bidding, which are designed to aid small businesses in bidding on government contracts.

- *Incubators/Research and Technology Parks*— Includes small business incubators, which provide newly established small business owners with work sites, business services, training, and consultation; also includes research and technology parks, which sponsor research and facilitate commercialization of new technologies.

- *Educational Programs*—Includes university and college programs, as well as those sponsored by other organizations that offer degree, nondegree, certificate, and correspondence programs in entrepreneurship and in small business development.

- *Legislative Assistance*—Includes committees, subcommittees, and joint committees of each state's senate and house of representatives that are concerned with small business issues and regulations.

- *Consultants*—Includes consultants and consulting firms offering expertise in small business development.

- *Publications*—Includes publications related to small business operations within the profiled state.

- *Publishers*—Includes publishers operating in or for the small business arena within the profiled state.

Federal Government Assistance. This section lists federal government agencies and offices, many with additional listings for specific offices, as well as regional or district branches. Main agencies or offices are listed alphabetically; regional, branch, ordistrict offices are listed after each main office or agency.

Master Index. This index provides an alphabetic listing of all entries contained in Volumes 1 throgh 6. Citations are referenced by their entry numbers. Publication titles are rendered in italics.

Acknowledgements

The editors would like to extend sincere thanks to the following members of the Small Business Sourcebook advisory board for their expert guidance, recommendations, and suggestions for the ongoing development of this title:

Susan C. Awe
Assistant Director,
William J. Parish Memorial Business Library

Jill Clever
Business Technology Specialist,
Toledo-Lucas County Public Library

Jules Matsoff
District Manager,
Service Corps of Retired Executives (SCORE) Milwaukee Chapter

Ken MacKenzie
President,
Southeast Business Appraisal

The editors would also like to thank the individuals from associations and other organizations who provided information for the compilation of this directory.

This section covers sources of assistance applicable to a variety of small businesses. Resources are arranged by topic and include associations, educational programs, directories of educational programs, reference works, sources of supply, statistical sources, periodicals, videocassettes/audiocassettes, trade shows and conventions, consultants, computerized databases, computer systems/software, Internet databases, libraries, and research centers.

START-UP INFORMATION

43316 ■ *How to Start and Run Your Own Corporation: S-Corporations For Small Business Owners*
Pub: HCM Publishing
Ed: Peter I. Hupalo. **Released:** March 6, 2003. **Price:** $22.95. **Description:** Basics of corporate business structure are explained. Topics include discovering the best business structure for your company; how to decided between an S-Corporation and LLC; choosing the state in which to incorporate, how to form a corporation, angel investing, special issues for one-person corporations, the role of bylaws and corporate minutes, board of directors, taxes, workers' compensation issues, retirement plans, and more.

43317 ■ *Structuring Your Business*
Pub: Adams Media Corporation
Contact: Gary Krebs, Director
E-mail: swatrous@adamsmedia.com
Ed: Michele Cagan. **Released:** 2004. **Price:** $19.95. **Description:** Accountant and author shares insight into starting a new company. The guide assists entrepreneurs through the process, whether it is a corporation, an LLC, a sole proprietorship, or a partnership. Tax codes, accounting practices and legislation affecting every business as well as tips on managing finances are among the topics covered.

REFERENCE WORKS

43318 ■ *"All Indicators in Michigan Innovation Index Drop in 4Q" in Crain's Detroit Business (Vol. 25, June 22, 2009, No. 25, pp. 9)*
Pub: Crain Communications Inc. - Detroit
Ed: Ryan Beene. **Description:** Economic indicators that rate Michigan's innovation fell in the fourth quarter of 2008. The index of trademark applications, SBA loans, venture capital funding, new incorporations and other indicators traced dropped 12.6 points.

43319 ■ *"Angel Investments Tripled in 2009" in Austin Business JournalInc. (Vol. 29, January 8, 2010, No. 44, pp. 1)*
Pub: American City Business Journals
Ed: Christopher Calnan. **Description:** Central Texas Angel Network (CTAN) has invested $3.5 million in 12 ventures, which include 10 in Austin, Texas in 2009 to triple the amount it invested during 2008. The largest recipient of CTAN's investments is life sciences, which attracted 20 percent of the capital, while software investments fell to 18 percent. The new screening process that helps startups secure CTAN capital is explored.

43320 ■ *"Attend To Your Corporate Housekeeping" in Women Entrepreneur (December 4, 2008)*
Pub: Entrepreneur Media Inc.
Ed: Nina Kaufman. **Description:** Business owners can lose all the benefits and privileges of the corporate form if they do not follow proper corporate formalities such as holding an annual meeting, elect-ing officers and directors and adopting or passing corporate resolutions. Creditors are able to take from one's personal assets if such formalities have not been followed.

43321 ■ *Breaking Free: How to Work at Home with the Perfect Small Business Opportunity*
Pub: Lulu.com
Ed: Brian Armstrong. **Released:** June 2007. **Price:** $24.95. **Description:** Three ways to smooth the transition from working for someone else to starting your own business are outlined. Seven exercises to help discover the type of business you should start, how to incorporate, get important tax benefits, and start accepting payments immediately are examined.

43322 ■ *Choosing the Right Legal Form of Business: The Complete Guide to Becoming a Sole Proprietor, Partnership, LLC, or Corporation*
Pub: Atlantic Publishing Company
Ed: Pat Mitchell. **Released:** January 1, 2009. **Price:** $24.95. **Description:** According to the U.S. Small Business Administration, nearly 250,000 new businesses start up annually; currently there are over nine million small companies in the nation. The importance of choosing the proper legal form of business is stressed.

43323 ■ *"A Conversation with Mark Lange" in Crain's Detroit Business (Vol. 26, January 18, 2010, No. 3, pp. 9)*
Pub: Crain Communications Inc.
Ed: Nancy Kaffer. **Description:** Second-stage companies have different needs from other kinds of startups since they often are moving very fast and dealing with several complex problems at the same time.

43324 ■ *Entrepreneurial Finance*
Pub: Pearson Education, Limited
Contact: Steven A. Dowling, President
Ed: Philip J. Adelman; Alan M. Marks. **Released:** July 2006. **Price:** $87.35. **Description:** Financial aspects of running a small business are covered; topics include sole proprietorships, partnerships, limited liability companies, and private corporations.

43325 ■ *Fast-Track Business Start-Up Kit: California*
Pub: DP Group, Incorporated
Ed: Carolyn Usinger. **Released:** September 2006. **Price:** $29.00. **Description:** Step-by-step guide for starting and running a business in California, including information on sole proprietors, partnerships, limited liability companies, S and C corporations, as well as details concerning business entities, sales taxes, environmental issues, human resources, and more.

43326 ■ *Getting Rich In Your Underwear: How To Start and Run a Profitable Home-Based Business*
Pub: HCM Publishing
Ed: Peter I. Hupalo. **Released:** April 1, 2005. **Price:** $17.95. **Description:** Book offers insight into starting a home-based business. Entrepreneurs will learn about business models and the home business; distribution and fulfillment of product or service; marketing and sales; how to overcome the fear of starting a business; personal success characteristics; naming a business; zoning and insurance; intellectual capital; copyrights, trademarks, and patents; limited liability companies and S-corporations; business expenses and accounting; taxes; fifteen basic steps for starting a home-based business, state resources for starting a home company; and seven home-based business ideas.

43327 ■ *How to Form Your Own Corporation without a Lawyer for Under $75.00*
Pub: Dearborn Trade Publishing Inc.
Contact: Roy Lipner, President
Ed: Ted Nicholas; Sean P. Melvin. **Price:** $19.95.

43328 ■ *Incorporate Your Business: A 50 State Legal Guide to Forming a Corporation*
Pub: Nolo
Ed: Anthony Mancuso. **Released:** January 2004. **Description:** Legal guide to incorporating a business in the U.S., covering all 50 states.

43329 ■ *Own Your Own Corporation: Why the Rich Own Their Own Companies and Everyone Else Works for Them*
Pub: Business Plus
Ed: Garrett Sutton; Robert T. Kiyosaki; Ann Blackman. **Released:** June 2008. **Price:** $17.99 paperback. **Description:** Part of the Rich Dad Advisor's Series, this edition shows how individuals can incorporate themselves and their businesses to save thousands of dollars in taxes and protect against financial disaster.

43330 ■ *Simplified Incorporation Kit*
Pub: Nova Publishing Company
Ed: Daniel Sitarz. **Released:** March 2007. **Price:** $19.95. **Description:** Kit includes all the forms, instructions, and information necessary for incorporating any small business in any state (CD-ROM included).

43331 ■ *"Test Your Structural Integrity" in Entrepreneur (Vol. 37, August 2009, No. 8, pp. 60)*
Pub: Entrepreneur Media, Inc.
Ed: Jennifer Lawler. **Description:** Tax considerations can be important when choosing a business structure. For example, profits are taxed to the corporation in a C corp while profits are taxed only once at an S corp or a limited liability company. Meeting a tax professional should be done prior to switching to a different structure.

43332 ■ *"To Be or Not To Be an S Corporation" in Modern Machine Shop (Vol. 84, September 2011, No. 4, pp. 38)*
Pub: Gardner Business Media, Inc.
Contact: Richard G. Kline, President
E-mail: rkline@gardnerweb.com
Ed: Irving L. Blackman. **Description:** The definitions of both C corporations and S corporations are defined to help any machine shop discover which best suits the owner's business plan.

TRADE PERIODICALS

43333 ■ *Taxes--The Tax Magazine*
Pub: CCH Inc.
Contact: Mike Sabbatis, President
URL(s): onlinestore.cch.com/productdetail.asp?productid=591. **Ed:** Shannon Jett Fischer. **Released:** Monthly **Price:** $349, Individuals.

COMPUTERIZED DATABASES

43334 ■ *Federal Income Taxation of S Corporations*
2395 Midway Rd.
Carrollton, TX 75006
Free: 800-431-9025
Co. E-mail: ria@thomson.com
URL: http://ria.thomsonreuters.com
Availability: Online: Thomson Reuters - RIA Tax & Accounting Unit. **Type:** Full-text.

LIBRARIES

43335 ■ **Cornell University - Johnson Graduate School of Management Library**
101 Sage Hall
Ithaca, NY 14853
Ph: (607)255-3389
Fax: (607)255-8633
Co. E-mail: akh8@cornell.edu
URL: http://www.library.cornell.edu/johnson
Contact: Angela Horne, Director
Scope: Business administration and management science, finance, investment, accounting, marketing, managerial economics, operations management and quantitative analysis. **Services:** Interlibrary loan.

Founded: 1949. **Holdings:** 164,000 volumes; 1096 non-book materials; 860,000 microfiche; 2800 microfilm; 450 CD-ROMs. **Subscriptions:** 1300 journals and other serials; 23 newspapers.

RESEARCH CENTERS

43336 ■ **Jackson State University - Bureau of Business and Economic Research**
1230 Raymond Rd., Box 500
Jackson, MS 39204
Ph: (601)979-2795
Fax: (601)914-0833
Co. E-mail: lurlene.irvin@jsums.edu
URL: http://www.jsums.edu/business/bber
Contact: Lurlene Irvin, Director
Services: Consulting for local business. **Founded:** 1985. **Publications:** *Annual Demographic Databook* (Annual); *Economic Indicators* (Monthly); *Bureau of Business and Economic Research Reports.* **Educational Activities:** College of Business Annual Research Symposiums; Seminars in areas of finance, marketing, management, accounting, and secretarial education, for business personnel and entrepreneurs in the Jackson area. **Awards:** Minigrants; Bureau of Business and Economic Research Research Awards, for faculty; Three paid internships.

43337 ■ **St. Francis Xavier University - Coady International Institute**
PO Box 5000
Antigonish, NS, Canada B2G 2W5
Ph: (902)867-3960
Free: 866-820-7835
Fax: (902)867-3907
Co. E-mail: jgaventa@stfx.ca
URL: http://www.coady.stfx.ca
Contact: John Gaventa, Director
Founded: 1959. **Publications:** *Coady Connection* (Biennial); *Coady International Institute Newsletters*;

Coady International Institute Annual report. **Telecommunication Services:** coady@stfx.ca.

43338 ■ **University of Maryland at College Park - Dingman Center for Entrepreneurship**
2518 Van Munching Hall
Robert H. Smith School of Business
College Park, MD 20742
Ph: (301)405-9545
Fax: (301)314-7971
Co. E-mail: aepstein@rhsmith.umd.edu
URL: http://www.rhsmith.umd.edu/dingman
Contact: Asher Epstein, Managing Director

Services: Assistance: to emerging growth firms through mentor program; Business Plan Reviews. **Founded:** 1986. **Publications:** *Newsletters for the entrepreneurial community and for volunteers* (Monthly). **Educational Activities:** Dingman Day Lunches; Dingman Jumpstart (Biennial), three week program aimed at getting students comfortable with start-up culture within the center's experiential learning environment and bringing their business ideas to life; Industry forums; Networking breakfasts; Dingman Center for Entrepreneurship Seminars; Speaker events, in entrepreneurship and entrepreneurship concentration in MBA curriculum; Venture Capital Forums. **Awards:** Pitch Dingman (Monthly), includes $2,500 in start-up funds to any 5- to 8-minute power point presentation directed towards an investor audience; Dingman Scholarships, to MBA students; Dingman Center for Entrepreneurship Internships, for graduate business students with area emerging growth firms; Lamone Scholars Program, for MBA students. **Telecommunication Services:** dingman@rhsmith.umd.edu.

START-UP INFORMATION

43339 ■ *Design and Launch Your Online Boutique in a Week*
Pub: Entrepreneur Press
Ed: Melissa Campanelli. **Released:** June 26, 2008. **Price:** $17.95. **Description:** Tips for starting an on-line boutique in a short amount of time are given. The books shows how to build the online boutique with designer goods or your own product, ways to create eye-catching content, online tools to handle payments and accept orders, marketing and advertising techniques, and customer service.

43340 ■ *"Five Low-Cost Home Based Startups" in Women Entrepreneur (December 16, 2008)*
Pub: Entrepreneur Media Inc.
Ed: Lesley Spencer Pyle. **Description:** During tough economic times, small businesses have an advantage over large companies because they can adjust to economic conditions more easily and without having to go through corporate red tape that can slow the implementation process. A budding entrepreneur may find success by taking inventory of his or her skills, experience, expertise and passions and utilizing those qualities to start a business. Five low-cost home-based startups are profiled. These include starting an online store, a virtual assistant service, web designer, sales representative and a home staging counselor.

43341 ■ *"Follow the Numbers: It's the Best Way To Spot Problems Before They Become Life-Threatening" in Inc. (January 2008, pp. 63-64)*
Pub: Gruner & Jahr USA Publishing
Ed: Norm Brodsky. **Description:** It is important for any small business to track monthly sales and gross margins by hand for the first year or two. When writing the numbers, be sure to break them out by product category or service type and by customer.

43342 ■ *Mommy Millionaire: How I Turned My Kitchen Table Idea Into a Million Dollars and How You Can, Too!*
Pub: St. Martin's Press LLC
Ed: Kim Lavine. **Released:** February 19, 2008. **Price:** $14.95. **Description:** Advice, secrets and lessons for making a million dollars from a mom who turned her kitchen into a successful business; tools cover developing and patenting an idea, cold calling, trade shows, QVC, big retailers, manufacturing, and raising venture capital.

ASSOCIATIONS AND OTHER ORGANIZATIONS

43343 ■ **Canadian Professional Sales Association (CPSA)—L'association Canadienne des Professionnels de la Vente**
655 Bay St., Ste. 400
Toronto, ON, Canada M5G 2K4
Ph: (416)408-2685

Free: 888-267-2772
Fax: (416)408-2684
Co. E-mail: csteinke@cpsa.com
URL: http://www.cpsa.com
Contact: Harvey Copeman, President
Description: Professional salespeople. Promotes professional advancement of members. Represents members' interests before government agencies, industrial organizations, and the public. Conducts continuing professional education programs. **Scope:** sales and marketing. **Founded:** 1874. **Subscriptions:** 5000. **Publications:** *Contact* (Quarterly). **Awards:** Charles H. Barnes Award; Corporate Ambassador for Sales Excellence (Annual); CPSA Sales Hall of Fame (Annual); CPSA Travel Awards (Annual); Sales Excellence Award (Annual). **Telecommunication Services:** contact@cpsa.com.

43344 ■ *Contact*
655 Bay St., Ste. 400
Toronto, ON, Canada M5G 2K4
Ph: (416)408-2685
Free: 888-267-2772
Fax: (416)408-2684
Co. E-mail: csteinke@cpsa.com
URL: http://www.cpsa.com
Contact: Harvey Copeman, President
Released: Quarterly **Price:** included in membership dues.

43345 ■ **Direct Selling Association**
1667 K St. NW, Ste. 1100
Washington, DC 20006
Ph: (202)452-8866
Fax: (202)452-9010
Co. E-mail: info@dsa.org
URL: http://www.dsa.org
Contact: Mr. Joseph N. Mariano, President
Description: Manufacturers and distributors selling consumer products through person-to-person sales, by appointment, and through home-party plans. Products include food, gifts, house wares, dietary supplements, cosmetics, apparel, jewelry, decorative accessories, reference books, and telecommunications products and services. Offers specialized education; conducts research programs; compiles statistics. Maintains hall of fame. Sponsors Direct Selling Education Foundation. **Scope:** direct selling. **Subscriptions:** archival material audiovisuals books clippings monographs periodicals. **Publications:** *Direct Selling Association State Status Sheet* (Weekly); *Direct Selling Association--Directory* (Annual). **Awards:** Hall of Fame (Annual); Innovation (Annual); Vision for Tomorrow (Annual); Hall of Fame Award; Vision for Tomorrow Award; Partnership Award; Success Award; Distinguished Service Award; DSEF Circle of Honor Award.

43346 ■ **Direct Selling Education Foundation (DSEF)**
1667 K St. NW, Ste. 1100
Washington, DC 20006-1660
Ph: (202)452-8866

Fax: (202)452-9015
Co. E-mail: info@dsef.org
URL: http://www.dsef.org
Contact: Robin Diamond, Director
E-mail: rdiamond@dsef.org
Description: Serves the public interest with education, information, and research, thereby enhancing acceptance and public awareness of direct selling in the global marketplace. **Scope:** direct selling. **Founded:** 1973. **Subscriptions:** archival material books. **Publications:** *Who's Who in Direct Selling* (Quarterly); *Direct Selling Association--Active Member List* (Quarterly); *Moral Suasion*; *DSEF: A Foundation That Works*. **Educational Activities:** Direct Selling Education Foundation Seminar. **Awards:** Circle of Honor (Annual).

43347 ■ **Marketing Agencies Association Worldwide (MAA)**
89 Woodland Cir.
Minneapolis, MN 55424-1454
Ph: (952)922-0130
Fax: (760)437-4141
Co. E-mail: keith.mccracken@maaw.org
URL: http://www.maaw.org
Contact: David Ploughman, President
Description: Represents the interests of CEOs, presidents, managing directors and principals of top marketing services agencies. Provides opportunity for marketing professionals to meet with peers, raise company profile on both a national and a global platform, and influence the future of industry. Fosters networking through conferences. **Founded:** 1969. **Educational Activities:** Marketing Agencies Association Worldwide Conference (Semiannual). **Awards:** MAA Worldwide Awards - The Globes (Annual).

43348 ■ **Professional Society for Sales and Marketing Training (SMT)**
2885 Sanford Ave. SW, No. 17425
Grandville, MI 49418-1342
Free: 877-763-2948
Co. E-mail: info@smt.org
URL: http://www.smt.org
Contact: Teresa Hiatt, President
Description: Directors of training. Seeks to improve sales, marketing and customer relations through training. Conducts educational conferences and sales training clinics. **Founded:** 1940.

43349 ■ **World Federation of Direct Selling Associations (WFDSA)**
1667 K St. NW, Ste. 1100
Washington, DC 20006
Ph: (202)452-8866
Fax: (202)452-9010
Co. E-mail: info@wfdsa.org
URL: http://www.wfdsa.org
Description: Organized for the purpose of promoting the common business interests of its members. Exchanges information among members. Fosters highest standards of direct selling practices, consumer protection and ethics in the marketplace, by adoption and promotion of the Codes of Conduct for Direct Selling. Improves communications through sponsorship of World Congress of direct selling.

Encourages personal relationships and cooperation among people in direct selling. Promotes education internationally through programs and funding, relying on the United States Direct Selling Education Foundation (USDSEF) to help it towards this objective. **Founded:** 1978. **Publications:** *Direct Selling World Directory* (Continuous); *Direct Selling Association World Federation News*; *WFDSA World Federation News* (Bimonthly). **Awards:** WFDSA Distinguished Service Award (Triennial).

EDUCATIONAL PROGRAMS

43350 ■ Advanced Sales Management (Onsite)
American Management Association
600 AMA Way
Saranac Lake, NY 12983-5534
Ph: (212)586-8100
Free: 877-566-9441
Fax: (518)891-0368
Co. E-mail: customerservice@amanet.org
URL: http://www.amaseminars.org
Price: $2,545.00 for non-members; $2,295.00 for AMA members; and $1,965.00 for General Services Administration (GSA) members. **Description:** Covers increasing productivity and efficiency through team building, adapting to a changing environment, and decision, and problem solving techniques. **Dates and Locations:** Chicago, IL; and New York, NY.

43351 ■ Cracking New Accounts: High Pay-Off Prospecting (Onsite)
Seminar Information Service, Inc.
20 Executive Park, Ste. 120
Irvine, CA 92614
Ph: (949)261-9104
Free: 877-SEM-INFO
Fax: (949)261-1963
Co. E-mail: info@seminarinformation.com
URL: http://www.seminarinformation.com
Price: $499.00. **Description:** Covers building relationships, winning against competition and maximizing your sales and profit potentials in today's crowded marketplace, including 50 power prospecting techniques and why 85% or more of all sales calls are wasted and how to gain access to anybody at any time. **Dates and Locations:** Cities throughout the United States.

43352 ■ The Distinct Advantage (Onsite)
Seminar Information Service, Inc.
20 Executive Park, Ste. 120
Irvine, CA 92614
Ph: (949)261-9104
Free: 877-SEM-INFO
Fax: (949)261-1963
Co. E-mail: info@seminarinformation.com
URL: http://www.seminarinformation.com
Price: $1,399.00. **Description:** Provides valuable, innovative, measurable skills that can be put into immediate practice and can dramatically impact the chances of closing a sale-and ultimately the organization's bottom line. **Dates and Locations:** Cleveland, OH.

43353 ■ Fundamental Selling Techniques for the New or Prospective Salesperson Level I (Onsite)
Seminar Information Service, Inc.
20 Executive Park, Ste. 120
Irvine, CA 92614
Ph: (949)261-9104
Free: 877-SEM-INFO
Fax: (949)261-1963
Co. E-mail: info@seminarinformation.com
URL: http://www.seminarinformation.com
Price: $2,095.00; $1,895.00 for AMA members. **Description:** Gain the skills and confidence to sell your product or service successfully, including listening and prospecting skills. **Dates and Locations:** Chicago, IL; New York, NY; and San Francisco, CA..

43354 ■ Mastering the Complex Sale (Onsite)
Seminar Information Service, Inc.
20 Executive Park, Ste. 120
Irvine, CA 92614
Ph: (949)261-9104

Free: 877-SEM-INFO
Fax: (949)261-1963
Co. E-mail: info@seminarinformation.com
URL: http://www.seminarinformation.com
Price: $1,595.00. **Description:** Seminar that combines the best university level learning with the best of street-smart selling into a proven system for success in the high-stakes sale.

43355 ■ Principles of Professional Selling (Onsite)
American Management Association
600 AMA Way
Saranac Lake, NY 12983-5534
Ph: (212)586-8100
Free: 877-566-9441
Fax: (518)891-0368
Co. E-mail: customerservice@amanet.org
URL: http://www.amaseminars.org
Price: $2,345.00 for non-members; $2,095.00 for AMA members; and $1,794.00 for General Services Administration (GSA) members. **Description:** Three-day seminar for seasoned sales professionals; covers consultative selling, planning the sales process, building relationships with customers, the sales process, utilizing technology, listening skills, telephone techniques, and time management. **Dates and Locations:** New York, NY; Chicago, IL; Atlanta, GA; and Los Angeles, CA..

43356 ■ Prospecting Strategies to Build a Qualified Pipeline (Onsite)
Seminar Information Service, Inc.
20 Executive Park, Ste. 120
Irvine, CA 92614
Ph: (949)261-9104
Free: 877-SEM-INFO
Fax: (949)261-1963
Co. E-mail: info@seminarinformation.com
URL: http://www.seminarinformation.com
Price: $1,995.00. **Description:** Learn a proactive approach to successful prospecting by first perfecting your lead qualification followed by practicing your prospecting skills through role-plays, applying your new insights to determine what has value to your qualified customer.

43357 ■ Retail Automobile Sales (Onsite)
Seminar Information Service, Inc.
20 Executive Park, Ste. 120
Irvine, CA 92614
Ph: (949)261-9104
Free: 877-SEM-INFO
Fax: (949)261-1963
Co. E-mail: info@seminarinformation.com
URL: http://www.seminarinformation.com
Price: $395.00. **Description:** Main areas covered are overcoming objections, advanced inter-personal communications skills, and things to do to avoid job burn-out, stay enthusiastic and motivated, and how to positively influence the emotional states of those around them. **Dates and Locations:** Portland, OR; and Phoenix, AZ.

43358 ■ Selling to Major Accounts: A Strategic Approach (Onsite)
American Management Association
600 AMA Way
Saranac Lake, NY 12983-5534
Ph: (212)586-8100
Free: 877-566-9441
Fax: (518)891-0368
Co. E-mail: customerservice@amanet.org
URL: http://www.amaseminars.org
Price: $2,345.00 for non-members; $2,095.00 for AMA members; and $1,794.00 for (GSA) members. **Description:** Covers strategies for developing successful relationships with major accounts. **Dates and Locations:** Chicago, IL; and Las Vegas, NV.

43359 ■ Strategic Sales Negotiations (Onsite)
American Management Association
600 AMA Way
Saranac Lake, NY 12983-5534
Ph: (212)586-8100
Free: 877-566-9441

Fax: (518)891-0368
Co. E-mail: customerservice@amanet.org
URL: http://www.amaseminars.org
Price: $2,095.00 for non-members; $1,895.00 for AMA members; and $1,623.00 for General Services Administration (GSA) members. **Description:** Covers the tools, techniques, and negotiation tactics for effectively influencing a buyer's perception of cost, benefits, and value. **Dates and Locations:** Chicago, IL; and San Francisco, CA.

43360 ■ Successful Sales Skills (Onsite)
Seminar Information Service, Inc.
20 Executive Park, Ste. 120
Irvine, CA 92614
Ph: (949)261-9104
Free: 877-SEM-INFO
Fax: (949)261-1963
Co. E-mail: info@seminarinformation.com
URL: http://www.seminarinformation.com
Price: Contact for fees. **Description:** Learn how to enhance their ability to deal with buying objections, and refine their skills in closing sales and negotiating win-win agreements leading to long-term relationships with customers.

43361 ■ Territory and Time Management for Salespeople (Onsite)
American Management Association
600 AMA Way
Saranac Lake, NY 12983-5534
Ph: (212)586-8100
Free: 877-566-9441
Fax: (518)891-0368
Co. E-mail: customerservice@amanet.org
URL: http://www.amaseminars.org
Price: $2,095.00 for non-members; $1,895.00 for AMA members; and $1,623.00 for General Services Administration (GSA) members. **Description:** Two-day seminar covers setting goals, attitude, organizational skills, developing a territory strategy, and increasing productivity. **Dates and Locations:** San Francisco, CA; and Chicago, IL.

43362 ■ Track Selling System Workshop (Onsite)
Seminar Information Service, Inc.
20 Executive Park, Ste. 120
Irvine, CA 92614
Ph: (949)261-9104
Free: 877-SEM-INFO
Fax: (949)261-1963
Co. E-mail: info@seminarinformation.com
URL: http://www.seminarinformation.com
Price: $1,895.00 per person; $1,845.00 each for 2 attending the same program. **Description:** Teaches salespeople to be customer oriented rather than product-centered, how to translate product/service features into customer benefits, using role playing extensively, and orients and motivates participants towards sales as a profession, and introduces a consultative selling process and a guaranteed method of closing. **Dates and Locations:** Seattle, WA; and Chicago, IL.

REFERENCE WORKS

43363 ■ "$1M Home Sales Spike" in Business Courier (Vol. 27, December 3, 2010, No. 31, pp. 1)
Pub: Business Courier
Ed: Tom Demeropolis. **Description:** Cincinnati Area Board of Realtors reported the increase of sales of multi-million dollar Tri-State homes in 2010, particularly in Indian Hill where sales surged nearly 60 percent. Sales of homes of $1 million and above are up 21 percent through November in Hamilton County with 58 homes sales.

43364 ■ The 4 Routes to Entrepreneurial Success
Pub: Berrett-Koehler Publishers
Ed: John B. Miner. **Price:** $18.95. **Description:** After researching one hundred successful entrepreneurs, the author discovered there are basically four personality types of entrepreneurs: the personal achiever, the super salesperson, the real manager, and the expert idea generator.

43365 ■ *31 Days to Greeting Card Marketing Mastery*
Pub: Desktop Wings Inc.
Ed: Bruce Brown. **Released:** February 19, 2010. **Price:** $17.95. **Description:** The use of simple greeting cards for marketing and increasing sales is explained.

43366 ■ *49 Marketing Secrets (That Work) to Grow Sales*
Pub: Morgan James Publishing, LLC
Ed: Ronald Finklestein. **Released:** October 2007. **Price:** $19.95/. **Description:** This book was written to fill the void on marketing books and is tailored to the small business owner. The author helps the small business owner to understand marketing and who they can trust while doing business. The book includes information to help entrepreneurs discover winning marketing strategies, branding and corporate image, media strategies, networking tips, technology-based marketing ideas, event strategies, and sales strategies.

43367 ■ *"2009 Real Estate in Review: Median Prices Drop, Sales Up" in Bellingham Business Journal (Vol. February 2010, pp. 15)*
Pub: Sound Publishing Inc.
Ed: Isaac Bonnell. **Description:** Bellingham and Whatcom County, Washington saw a rise in home sales in 2008. Single family home sales were up 3.3 percent in Bellingham and 0.5 percent for the entire county. Statistical data included.

43368 ■ *"2010 Book of Lists" in Austin Business JournalInc. (Vol. 29, December 25, 2009, No. 42, pp. 1)*
Pub: American City Business Journals
Description: Rankings of companies and organizations within the business services, finance, healthcare, hospitality and travel, insurance, marketing and media, professional services, real estate, education and technology industries in Austin, Texas are presented. Rankings are based on sales, business size, and other statistics.

43369 ■ *"2010 Book of Lists" in Tampa Bay Business Journal (Vol. 30, December 22, 2009, No. 53, pp. 1)*
Pub: American City Business Journals
Description: Rankings of companies and organizations within the human resources, banking and finance, business services, healthcare, real estate, technology, hospitality and travel, and education industries in the Greater Tampa Bay area are presented. Rankings are based on sales, business size, and more.

43370 ■ *"A&E Networks" in Brandweek (Vol. 49, April 21, 2008, No. 16, pp. SR9)*
Pub: VNU Business Media, Inc.
Ed: Anthony Crupi. **Description:** Provides contact information for sales and marketing personnel for the A&E Networks as well as a listing of the station's top programming and an analysis of the current season and the target audience for those programs running in the current season. A&E has reinvented itself as a premium entertainment brand over the last five years and with its $2.5 million per episode acquisition of The Sopranos, the station signaled that it was serious about getting back into the scripted programming business. The acquisition also helped the network compete against other cable networks and led to a 20 percent increase in prime-time viewers.

43371 ■ *"ABC" in Brandweek (Vol. 49, April 21, 2008, No. 16, pp. SR6)*
Pub: VNU Business Media, Inc.
Ed: John Consoli. **Description:** Provides contact information for sales and marketing personnel for the ABC network as well as a listing of the station's top programming and an analysis of the current season and the target audience for those programs running in the current season.

43372 ■ *The Accidental Entrepreneur: The 50 Things I Wish Someone Had Told Me About Starting a Business*
Pub: AMACOM
Ed: Susan Urquhart-Brown. **Released:** March 2008. **Price:** $17.95. **Description:** Advice is offered to any would-be entrepreneur, including eight questions to

ask before launching a new business, ten traits of a successful entrepreneur, how to obtain licenses and selling permits, best way to create a business plan, ten ways to get referrals, six secrets of marketing, investment and financial information, ways to avoid burnout, and the seven biggest pitfalls to avoid.

43373 ■ *"Active Sales" in Green Industry Pro (Vol. 23, September 2011)*
Pub: Cygnus Business Media
Ed: Gregg Wartgow. **Description:** Craig den Hartog, owner of Emerald Magic Lawn Care located in Holtsville, New York, describes the various marketing tactics he has developed to increase sales in the current economic environment. Statistical data included.

43374 ■ *"Add Aquatics to Boost Business" in Pet Product News (Vol. 64, December 2010, No. 12, pp. 20)*
Pub: BowTie Inc.
Ed: David Lass. **Description:** Pet stores are encouraged to add aquatics departments to increase profitability through repeat sales. This goal can be realized by sourcing, displaying, and maintaining high quality live fish. Other tips regarding the challenges associated with setting up an aquatics department are presented.

43375 ■ *Advanced Selling for Dummies*
Pub: John Wiley and Sons, Inc.
Ed: Ralph R. Roberts; Joe Kraynak (As told to). **Released:** September 2007. **Price:** $21.99. **Description:** This book explores topics such as: visualizing success (includes exercises), investing and reinvesting in your own success, harnessing media and multimedia outlets, calculating risks that stretch your limits, creating lasting relationships, finding balance to avoid burnout and more. This guide is for salespeople who have already read 'Selling for Dummies' and now want forward-thinking, advanced strategies for recharging and reenergizing their careers and their lives. Blogging, Internet leads and virtual assistants are also discussed.

43376 ■ *Advancing Research on Minority Entrepreneurship*
Pub: SAGE Publications USA
Contact: Blaise R. Simqu, President
Ed: James H. Johnson Jr.; Timothy Bates; William E. Jackson III; James H. Johnson; William E. Jackson. **Released:** September 2007. **Price:** $34.00. **Description:** Although minorities are more likely to engage in start-up businesses than others, minority entrepreneurs are less likely to get their enterprises off the ground or succeed in growing their businesses. The higher failure rates, lower sales and profits and less employment are among topics discussed.

43377 ■ *Alpha Dogs: How Your Small Business Can Become a Leader of the Pack*
Pub: HarperInformation
Ed: Donna Fenn. **Released:** May 2007. **Price:** $14.95. **Description:** Ways for an entrepreneur to outsmart competitors in the marketplace, to generate higher sales, and earn lasting customer and employee loyalty.

43378 ■ *"Angels for the Jobless; Church Volunteer Groups Give Career Guidance" in Crain's Detroit Business (Vol. 24, March 31, 2008, No. 13)*
Pub: Crain Communications, Inc.
Ed: Sherri Begin. **Description:** St. Andrew Catholic Church, located in Rochester, offers the St. Andrew Career Mentoring Ministry, a program that brings in professionals who volunteer to aid those seeking jobs or, in numerous cases, new careers.

43379 ■ *"Art of the Online Deal" in Farm Industry News (March 25, 2011)*
Pub: Penton Business Media Inc.
Description: Farmers share advice for shopping online for machinery; photos, clean equipment, the price, equipment details, and online sources topped their list.

43380 ■ *"Ask Inc" in Inc. (February 2008, pp. 52)*
Pub: Gruner & Jahr USA Publishing
Ed: James Dyson. **Description:** Owner of a consulting firm seeks advice to help his sales staff become more successful.

43381 ■ *"avVaa World Health Care Products Rolls Out Internet Marketing Program" in Health and Beauty Close-Up (September 18, 2009)*
Pub: Close-Up Media
Description: avVaa World Health Care Products, Inc., a biotechnology company, manufacturer and distributor of nationally branded therapeutic, natural health care and skin products, has signed an agreement with Online Performance Marketing to launch of an Internet marketing campaign in order to broaden its presence online. The impact of advertising on the Internet to generate an increase in sales is explored.

43382 ■ *"Back to Business for Bishop Museum" in Hawaii Business (Vol. 54, August 2008, No. 2, pp. 53)*
Pub: Hawaii Business Publishing
Ed: Shara Enay. **Description:** Bishop Museum, ranked 224 in Hawaii Business' top 250 companies for 2008, had $29.5 million in gross sales for 2007, up 52.8 percent from the $19.3 million gross sales in 2006. The company has cut 24 positions in a restructuring effort for the museum's sustainability. Grants, artifacts and plans for sustainable operations are discussed.

43383 ■ *Baseline Selling*
Pub: AuthorHouse
Ed: Dave Kurlan. **Released:** November 2005. **Price:** $18.49. **Description:** Training manual for sales people that provides methods for 'baseline selling'. This practice involves a process similar to baseball, where a deal is worked from one base to the next until the deal is closed. First base is the appointment, second means the prospect wants what you are selling, third base shows two parties are qualified to do business together, home base is presenting a winning solution and making the sale.

43384 ■ *"BayTSP, NTT Data Corp. Enter Into Reseller Pact to Market Online IP Monitoring" in Professional Services Close-Up (Sept. 11, 2009)*
Pub: Close-Up Media
Description: Due to incredible interest from distributors and content owners across Asia, NTT Data Corp. will resell BayTSP's online intellectual property monitoring, enforcement, business intelligence and monetization services in Japan.

43385 ■ *Be the Elephant: Build a Bigger, Better Business*
Pub: Workman Publishing Company
Ed: Steve Kaplan. **Price:** $19.95. **Description:** Entrepreneur and author sets out an accessible, no-frills plan for business owners, managers, and other industrialists to grow their businesses into elephants: big and strong but also smart. Advice is given on fostering a growth mind-set, assessing risk, and creating unique selling propositions.

43386 ■ *Behind the Cloud*
Pub: Jossey-Bass
Ed: Marc Benioff, Carlye Adler. **Released:** 2010. **Price:** $27.95. **Description:** Salesforce.com is the world's most successful business-to-business cloud-computing company that sells an online service that helps businesses manage sales, customer service, and marketing functions.

43387 ■ *"Being all a-Twitter" in Canadian Business (Vol. 81, December 8, 2008, No. 21, pp. 22)*
Pub: Rogers Media Ltd.
Ed: Andrew Wahl. **Description:** Marketing experts suggest that advertising strategies have to change along with new online social media. Companies are advised to find ways to incorporate social software because workers and customers are expected to continue its use.

43388 ■ *"Best Value Stocks" in Canadian Business (Vol. 82, Summer 2009, No. 8, pp. 30)*
Pub: Rogers Media
Ed: Calvin Leung. **Description:** Canadian companies that are believed to have the best value stocks are suggested. Suggestions include publishing firm

Glacier Media, which has reported a four-fold growth in sales in the last three years. While publishers like Glacier Media face challenges such as declining circulation, the firm's industry diversification is expected to help it weather the economic downturn.

43389 ■ "The Best and Worst Economic Times" in Agency Sales Magazine (Vol. 39, December 2009, No. 11, pp. 22)
Pub: MANA
Ed: Mark Young. **Description:** U.S. gross domestic product grew 3.5 percent and the stock market has improved but manufacturers are cutting commissions or dropping sales representatives. Despite these challenges, it can a good time for salespeople because clients need them more than ever. Salesmen should find new ways to do business for their clients during this current challenging environment.

43390 ■ "Better Business: Get Ready (Marketing Strategies for Better Sales Performance)" in Entrepreneur (Vol. 35, October 2007, No. 10)
Pub: Entrepreneur Media Inc.
Ed: Gwen Moran. **Description:** Good sales practice increases sales performance and revenue. Sales consultant Paul S. Goldner believes that salespeople should research prospective clients before negotiating with them, while another consultant, Chet Holmes thinks that companies should support their salespeople and set sales performance standards. Other proven effective marketing strategies are presented.

43391 ■ "Better Made's Better Idea: Diversify Despite Rising Costs" in Crain's Detroit Business (Vol. 24, September 22, 2008, No. 38, pp. 18)
Pub: Crain Communications Inc.
Ed: Nathan Skid. **Description:** Better Made Snack Foods Inc. is planning to expand its product lines and market reach as well as boost manufacturing capability during a time in which the company is being buffeted by rising commodity and fuel costs. The company feels that diversification is the key to maintain sales and growth.

43392 ■ "Big Trouble at Sony Ericsson" in Barron's (Vol. 88, March 24, 2008, No. 12, pp. M9)
Pub: Dow Jones & Company, Inc.
Ed: Angelo Franchini. **Description:** Sony Ericsson is facing trouble as it warned that its sales and net income before taxes will fall by nearly half for the first quarter of 2008. The joint venture of Sony and Ericsson has a global mobile phone market share of nine percent as of 2007, fourth largest in the world.

43393 ■ "BMW Revs Up for a Rebound" in Barron's (Vol. 89, July 13, 2009, No. 28, pp. M7)
Pub: Dow Jones & Co., Inc.
Ed: Jonathan Buck. **Description:** Investors may like BMW's stocks because the company has maintained its balance sheet strength and has an impressive production line of new models that should boost sales in the next few years. The company's sales are also gaining traction, although their vehicle delivery was down 1.7 percent year on year on June 2009, this was still the best monthly sales figure for 2009.

43394 ■ "Book of Lists 2010" in Philadelphia Business Journal (Vol. 28, December 25, 2009, No. 45, pp. 1)
Pub: American City Business Journals
Description: Rankings of companies and organizations within the banking, biotechnology, economic development, healthcare, hospitality, law and accounting, marketing and media, real estate, and technology industries in the Philadelphia, Pennsylvania area are presented. Rankings are based on sales, business size, and more.

43395 ■ "Boom and Bust in the Book Biz" in Canadian Business (Vol. 83, August 17, 2010, No. 13-14, pp. 16)
Pub: Rogers Media Ltd.
Ed: Jordan Timm. **Description:** Electronic book marketplace is booming with Amazon.com's e-book sales for the Kindle e-reader exceeding the hardcover

sales. Kobo Inc. has registered early success with its Kobo e-reader and has partnered with Hong Kong telecom giant on an e-book store.

43396 ■ "Boosting Worried Customers' Confidence" in Gallup Management Journal (November 8, 2011)
Pub: Gallup
Ed: Jessica Tyler, Patrick Whiston. **Description:** While customers fear a double-dip recession and US economic confidence is low, leading edge firms have found a timely and creative way to win customers: they are improving their wellbeing.

43397 ■ "Boosting Your Merchant Management Services With Wireless Technology" in Franchising World (Vol. 42, August 2010, No. 8, pp. 27)
Pub: International Franchise Association
Ed: Michael S. Slominski. **Description:** Franchises should have the capability to accept credit cards away from their businesses. This technology will increase sales.

43398 ■ "Bottoms Up!" in Entrepreneur (Vol. 36, April 2008, No. 4, pp. 128)
Pub: Entrepreneur Media, Inc.
Ed: Amanda C. Kooser. **Description:** Jill Bernheimer launched her online alcohol business Domaine547 in 2007, and encountered challenges as legal issues over the licensing and launching of the business took about seven months to finish. Domain547 features blog and forum areas. Marketing strategy that connects to the social community is one of the ways to reach out to customers.

43399 ■ "Brite-Strike Tactical Launches New Internet Marketing Initiatives" in Internet Wire (September 15, 2009)
Pub: Comtex News Network, Inc.
Description: Brite-Strike Tactical Illumination Products, Inc. has enlisted the expertise of Internet marketing guru Thomas J. McCarthy to help revamp the company's Internet campaign. An outline of the Internet marketing strategy is provided.

43400 ■ "Building Your Business: A Strong Web Presence Is a Must" in Black Enterprise (Vol. 38, December 2007, No. 5, pp. 74)
Pub: Earl G. Graves Publishing Co. Inc.
Ed: Tennille M. Robinson. **Description:** Building a strong presence on the Internet is crucial to any growing business. Websites can provide information or sell merchandise, but the site must also make sure the customer knows how to use and navigate around within the site. Common mistakes to avoid when designing a small business Website are outlined.

43401 ■ Business Black Belt: Develop the Strength, Flexibility and Agility to Run Your Company
Pub: Career Press, Inc.
Ed: Burke Franklin. **Released:** November 1, 2010. **Price:** $15.99. **Description:** Manual offering insights that will enable anyone to become successful in small business. Seventy short chapters included topics such as attitude, management, marketing, selling, employees, money, MBAs, lawyers, consultants, and investors.

43402 ■ "The Business Case for Mobile Content Acceleration" in Streaming Media (November 2011, pp. 78)
Pub: Information Today Inc.
Ed: Dan Rayburn. **Description:** Last holiday season, eBay became a mobile commerce (m-commerce) giant when sales rose by 134 percent, as most online retailers offered customers the ability to purchase items using their mobile devices.

43403 ■ "Business Forecast: Stormy and Successful" in Women In Business (Vol. 62, June 2010, No. 2, pp. 12)
Pub: American Business Women's Association
Ed: Kathleen Leighton. **Description:** Stormy Simon, vice president of customer service at Overstock.com is a self-made career woman who started out as a temporary employee in the company in 2001. She

was not able to attend college because she had two sons to care for after her divorce. Simon got involved in advertising and media buying and shares her love for business.

43404 ■ "The Business Value of Social Networks" in Agency Sales Magazine (Vol. 39, July 2009, No. 7, pp. 44)
Pub: MANA
Ed: Daniel Burrus. **Description:** Personal and business uses of several Web 2.0 tools for salespeople are discussed. Leading questions which will guide salespeople in finding out if one particular tool will benefit them are presented.

43405 ■ Business Warrior: Strategy for Entrepreneurs
Pub: Clearbridge Publishing
Ed: Sun Tzu. **Released:** September 2006. **Price:** $19.95. **Description:** Advice to help entrepreneurs understand competitive strategies in order to succeed, focusing on sales, marketing, and personnel management.

43406 ■ Buying In: The Secret Dialogue Between What We Buy and Who We Are
Pub: Random House
Ed: Rob Walker. **Released:** 2008. **Price:** $25.00. **Description:** The book offers a look at the state of advertising today and shows why even those who feel like they see through marketing feel attached to specific brands as a way to both project and foster their identities.

43407 ■ Buying and Selling a Business
Pub: Entrepreneur Press
Ed: Ira Nottonson. **Released:** April 2008. **Price:** $32.95. **Description:** Tips for negotiating sales are presented. Attorney, Ira Nottonson presents both sides of negotiations by presenting the both buyer's and seller's perspectives. Critical steps in the sale process, including presentation, negotiation and documentations are discussed. The book teaches how to gain the upper hand, minimize financial risk and be a winner regardless of side.

43408 ■ "Calling All Recruiters: Agent HR Puts Staffing Agents In Charge" in Black Enterprise (Vol. 38, December 2007, No. 5, pp. 72)
Pub: Earl G. Graves Publishing Co. Inc.
Ed: Chana Garcia. **Description:** Recruiting and staffing agencies are seeing a drop in services due to slow economic growth. AgentHR partners with full-service recruiters who have three to five year's experience-specialists soliciting their own clients, provide staffing services, and manage their own accounts, thus combining the roles of recruiter and salesperson.

43409 ■ "Can You Hear Them Now?" in Hawaii Business (Vol. 54, August 2008, No. 2, pp. 48)
Pub: Hawaii Business Publishing
Ed: Jason Ubay. **Description:** Coral Wireless LLC (dba Mobi PCS) is ranked 237 in Hawaii Business' list of the state's top 250 companies for 2008. The company is a local wireless phone provider, which has expanded its market to Oahu, Maui and the Big Island since opening in 2006, offering 13 phones and unlimited texts and calls. Details on the company's sales are provided.

43410 ■ "Cash in Your Attic: Is Your Junk Someone Else's Treasure?" in Black Enterprise (Vol. 37, November 2006, No. 4, pp. 156)
Pub: Earl G. Graves Publishing Co. Inc.
Ed: Angela P. Moore-Thorpe. **Description:** Selling items accumulated over the years or purchased at auctions or garage sales can be a lucrative way to make extra cash. Advice and resources on auctions, collecting, and consignment shops included.

43411 ■ "CBS" in Brandweek (Vol. 49, April 21, 2008, No. 16, pp. SR6)
Pub: VNU Business Media, Inc.
Ed: John Consoli. **Description:** Provides contact information for sales and marketing personnel for the CBS network as well as a listing of the station's top

programming and an analysis of the current season and the target audience for those programs running in the current season.

43412 ■ *"CBS Television Distribution"* in *Brandweek (Vol. 49, April 21, 2008, No. 16, pp. SR13)*
Pub: VNU Business Media, Inc.
Ed: Marc Berman. **Description:** Provides contact information for sales and marketing personnel for CBS Television Distribution as well as a listing of the station's top programming and an analysis of the current season and the target audience for those programs running in the current season. Due to the unprecedented, decade-plus advantage of first-run leaders such as Wheel of Fortune, Oprah, Judge Judy and Entertainment Tonight, CBS is poised to remain a leader among the syndicates.

43413 ■ *"Channeling for Growth"* in *The Business Journal-Serving Greater Tampa Bay (Vol. 28, July 11, 2008, No. 29, pp. 1)*
Pub: American City Business Journals, Inc.
Ed: Margie Manning. **Description:** HSN Inc., one of the largest employers in Tampa Bay, Florida, is expected to spend an additional $9.7 million annually as it plans to hire more accounting, internal audit, legal, treasury and tax personnel after its spin-off to a public company. Details on the company's sales growth are provided.

43414 ■ *"Characteristics of Great Salespeople"* in *Agency Sales Magazine (Vol. 39, November 2009, No. 10, pp. 40)*
Pub: MANA
Ed: Paul Pease. **Description:** Tips for managers in order to maximize the performance of their sales personnel are presented through several vignettes. Using performance based commission that rewards success, having business systems that support sales activity, and having an organizational culture that embraces sales as a competitive edge are some suggestions.

43415 ■ *"Charged Up for Sales"* in *Charlotte Business Journal (Vol. 25, October 15, 2010, No. 30, pp. 1)*
Pub: Charlotte Business Journal
Ed: Susan Stabley. **Description:** Li-Ion Motors Corporation is set to expand its production lines of electric cars in Sacramento, California. The plan is seen to create up to 600 jobs. The company's total investment is seen to reach $500 million.

43416 ■ *"Cheap Thrills: Where to Look When You're Craving a Low-Price Wine"* in *Chicago Tribune (January 12, 2009)*
Pub: McClatchy-Tribune Information Services
Ed: Bill Daley. **Description:** Wines priced $15 and above are being hit the hardest by the economic downturn while cheaper wines, specifically those priced between $3 and $6, are seeing a growth in sales.

43417 ■ *"Click Here to Book"* in *Caterer & Hotelkeeper (October 28, 2011, No. 288)*
Pub: Reed Reference Publishing
Ed: Ross Bentley. **Description:** Customers expectations are determined by the quality of a Website when booking hotel rooms.

43418 ■ *Clued In*
Pub: Financial Times/Prentice Hall
Contact: Richard Stagg, Director
Ed: Lewis Carbone. **Released:** May 24, 2004. **Price:** $34.99. **Description:** Tips for providing excellent customer service that keeps clients coming back are shared. Brand management and Experience Value Management are defined.

43419 ■ *"Comcast Networks"* in *Brandweek (Vol. 49, April 21, 2008, No. 16, pp. SR9)*
Pub: VNU Business Media, Inc.
Ed: Anthony Crupi. **Description:** Provides contact information for sales and marketing personnel for the Comcast networks as well as a listing of the station's top programming and an analysis of the current

season and the target audience for those programs running in the current season. Experts believe Comcast will continue to acquire more stations into their portfolio.

43420 ■ *"Come Together"* in *Pet Product News (Vol. 64, December 2010, No. 12, pp. 28)*
Pub: BowTie Inc.
Ed: Lizett Bond. **Description:** Pet supply retailers have posted improved sales and improved customer service by bundling their offerings. Bundling pertains to grouping related items such as collars and leashes into a single unit for marketing purposes. Aside from providing convenience and enhanced product information to customers, bundling has facilitated more efficient purchases.

43421 ■ *The Complete Guide to Google Adwords: Secrets, Techniques, and Strategies You Can Learn to Make Millions*
Pub: Atlantic Publishing Company
Released: December 1, 2010. **Price:** $24.95. **Description:** Google AdWords, when it launched in 2002 signaled a fundamental shift in what the Internet was for so many individuals and companies. Learning and understanding how Google AdWords operates and how it can be optimized for maximum exposure, boosting click through rates, conversions, placement, and selection of the right keywords, can be the key to a successful online business.

43422 ■ *"Condo Markdown"* in *Boston Business Journal (Vol. 27, November 30, 2007, No. 44, pp. 1)*
Pub: American City Business Journals Inc.
Ed: Michelle Hillman. **Description:** Boston real estate market is softening, and condominium developers such as Beacon Communities LLC are sending out various incentives like markdowns and unit upgrades. Developers have also held auctions and even offered brand new cars to lure buyers. Other perks being offered by various Boston developers are discussed.

43423 ■ *Consumer Behavior*
Pub: Prentice Hall Business Publishing
Contact: Jerome Grant, President
Ed: Leon Schiffman, Leslile Kanuk. **Released:** August 7, 2009. **Price:** $180.00. **Description:** Consumer behavior is central to the planning, development and implementation of marketing strategies.

43424 ■ *Content Rich: Writing Your Way to Wealth on the Web*
Pub: 124 S Mercedes Rd.
Ed: Jon Wuebben. **Released:** April 2008. **Price:** $19. 95. **Description:** A definitive search engine optimization (SEO) copywriting guide for search engine rankings and sales conversion. It includes topics not covered in other books on the subject and targets the small to medium sized business looking for ways to maximize online marketing activities as well as designers and Web developers seeking to incorporate more SEO techniques into design and content.

43425 ■ *"Contractors Debate Maximizing Green Opportunities, Education"* in *Contractor (Vol. 56, November 2009, No. 11, pp. 3)*
Pub: Penton Media, Inc.
Ed: Robert P. Mader. **Description:** Attendees at the Mechanical Service Co ntractors Association convention were urged to get involved with their local U.S. Green Building Council chapter by one presenter. Another presenter says that one green opportunity for contractors is the commissioning of new buildings.

43426 ■ *"Contractors Fret Over Credit, People, Government"* in *Contractor (Vol. 57, February 2010, No. 2, pp. 7)*
Pub: Penton Media, Inc.
Ed: Robert P. Mader. **Description:** Telephone interviews with 22 plumbing and HVAC contractors reveal that only two had sales increases for 2009 and that overall, contractors were down anywhere from seven to 25 percent. In the repair/service market, the residential sector was holding its own but the commercial portion was lagging behind.

43427 ■ *"Contracts"* in *Agency Sales Magazine (Vol. 39, September-October 2009, No. 9, pp. 7)*
Pub: MANA
Description: One session at the MANAfest conference provided suggestions to sales representatives when negotiating a contract with their principals. New sales representatives need to stand their ground and to negotiate a fair and balanced contract with every principal that they sign on with.

43428 ■ *"Coping With a Shrinking Planet"* in *Agency Sales Magazine (Vol. 39, December 2009, No. 11, pp. 46)*
Pub: MANA
Ed: Mark Young. **Description:** China and India are forcing big changes in the world and are posing a huge threat to U.S. manufacturers and their sales representatives. Reps may want to consider expanding into these territories. Helping sell American products out of the country presents an opportunity for economic expansion.

43429 ■ *"Counting on Cornhole: Popular Bean Bag Game Brings Crowds to Bars"* in *Boston Business Journal (Vol. 29, July 15, 2011, No. 10, pp. 1)*
Pub: American City Business Journals Inc.
Ed: Alexander Jackson. **Description:** Cornhole game is being used by bars to spur business as the games hikes beer and food sales on slow weekdays. The game is played with two cornhole boards facing each other and is played with one or two people on one team who try to place a bag on the board.

43430 ■ *"Courier 250 Companies Hope to Rebound From 2009"* in *Business Courier (Vol. 27, July 16, 2010, No. 11, pp. 1)*
Pub: Business Courier
Ed: Dan Monk, Jon Newberry. **Description:** Private companies that are featured in the Courier 250 publication have lost almost $4 billion in revenue, while combined sales dropped by 11 percent to 32 billion in 2009. Courier 250 is a guide to public companies, large nonprofits, private firms, and other related entities in Ohio's Cincinnati region.

43431 ■ *"Covington's Business Owners Get Bridge Relief"* in *Business Courier (Vol. 27, October 29, 2010, No. 26, pp. 1)*
Pub: Business Courier
Ed: Dan Monk. **Description:** Engineers of Brent Spence Bridge have developed a new 'second chance' exit that preserves highway access to Covington, Kentucky's main business districts. It is believed that the planned ramp off Interstate 75 represents a compromise between highway planners, who wish to maintain continuous traffic for interstate users.

43432 ■ *Craft Inc: Turn Your Creative Hobby into a Business*
Pub: Chronicle Books LLC
Ed: Meg Mateo Ilasco. **Released:** September 2007. **Price:** $16.95. **Description:** Guide to help any crafter turn their hobby into a successful business. The book covers all aspects including pricing, sales and marketing, trade shows, as well as interviews with successful craft artisans Jonathan Adler, Lotta Jansdotter, Denyse Schmidt and Jill Bliss.

43433 ■ *"Creative Marketing: How to Cultivate a Network of Endless Referrals"* in *Agency Sales Magazine (Vol. 39, July 2009, No. 7, pp. 38)*
Pub: MANA
Ed: Bob Burg. **Description:** Tips on how a salesperson can build a network of people that will bring them referrals are presented. Asking a person about their business and re-introducing one's self to an earlier acquaintance while remembering their names are some elements in the process of building this network.

43434 ■ *Crossing the Chasm: Marketing and Selling Disruptive Products to Mainstream Customers*
Pub: HarperInformation
Ed: Geoffrey A. Moore. **Released:** September 2002. **Price:** $17.95. **Description:** A guide for marketing in high-technology industries, focusing on the Internet.

43435 ■ *"The CW" in Brandweek (Vol. 49, April 21, 2008, No. 16, pp. SR8)*
Pub: VNU Business Media, Inc.
Ed: John Consoli. **Description:** Provides contact information for sales and marketing personnel for the CW network as well as a listing of the station's top programming and an analysis of the current season and the target audience for those programs running in the current season. Purchases of advertising feel that Warner Bros. and CBS made a mistake merging The WB and UPN into the new CW rather than folding UPN into the more-established WB; compared to last season ratings are down more than 20 percent across the board.

43436 ■ *"Cyber Thanksgiving Online Shopping a Growing Tradition" in Marketing Weekly News (December 12, 2009, pp. 137)*
Pub: Investment Weekly News
Description: According to e-commerce analysts, Thanksgiving day is becoming increasingly important to retailers in terms of online sales. Internet marketers are realizing that consumers are already searching for Black Friday sales and if they find deals on the products they are looking for, they are highly likely to make their purchase on Thanksgiving day instead of waiting.

43437 ■ *"Dealers Fight To Steer Course" in The Business Journal-Serving Metropolitan Kansas City (Vol. 27, November 7, 2008, No. 9, pp. 1)*
Pub: American City Business Journals, Inc.
Ed: Steve Vockrodt. **Description:** One local automobile dealer says that their sales are down by 30 to 40 percent and that car financing is now in the low 60 percentile from 85 to 88 percent. The National Automobile Dealers Association says that 700 dealerships are likely to be lost for 2008.

43438 ■ *"Dealers Trying Not to Fold" in Business First Columbus (Vol. 25, December 5, 2008, No. 15, pp. A1)*
Pub: American City Business Journals
Ed: Dan Eaton. **Description:** Increase in the number of automobile dealer closures in Ohio is seen to impact the state's economy. The trend of consolidation is forecasted to adversely affect employment and sales. Statistical data included.

43439 ■ *"Dear Customer: Managing E-Mail Campaigns" in Inc. (March 2008, pp. 58-59)*
Pub: Gruner & Jahr USA Publishing
Ed: Ryan Underwood. **Description:** Internet services that help firms manage their online business including email marketing, to manage subscriber lists, comply with spam regulations, monitor bouncebacks, and track potential customers are profiled. Constant Contact, MobileStorm Stun, Campaign Monitor, Pop Commerce, Emma, and StrongMail E-mail Server are among software and services highlighted.

43440 ■ *"Deskside Story: As the Latest Buzzword Suggests, PR Firms Are Happy To Drop By" in Inc. (December 2007, pp. 70, 73)*
Pub: Gruner & Jahr USA Publishing
Ed: Nitasha Tiku. **Description:** Setting up a meeting between a company's CEO and a journalist is known as deskside and is becoming popular again whereby a publicist offers clients deskside visits, briefings and alerts to help promote public relations for a company.

43441 ■ *"Discovery Networks" in Brandweek (Vol. 49, April 21, 2008, No. 16, pp. SR9)*
Pub: VNU Business Media, Inc.
Ed: Anthony Crupi. **Description:** Provides contact information for sales and marketing personnel for the Discovery networks as well as a listing of the station's top programming and an analysis of the current season and the target audience for those programs running in the current season. The networks flagship station returned to the top 10 in 2007, averaging 1.28 million viewers.

43442 ■ *"Disney-ABC Domestic Television Distribution" in Brandweek (Vol. 49, April 21, 2008, No. 16, pp. SR13)*
Pub: VNU Business Media, Inc.
Ed: Marc Berman. **Description:** Provides contact information for sales and marketing personnel for Disney-ABC Domestic Television Distribution as well as a listing of the station's top programming and an analysis of the current season and the target audience for those programs running in the current season.

43443 ■ *"Do You Really Know Who Your Best Salespeople Are?" in Harvard Business Review (Vol. 88, December 2010, No. 12, pp. 34)*
Pub: Harvard Business School Publishing
Ed: Lynette Ryals, Iain Davies. **Description:** Eight salesperson performance types are identified and charted using statistics of their effectiveness in given scenarios.

43444 ■ *"Don't Cry For Me?" in Canadian Business (Vol. 83, July 20, 2010, No. 11-12, pp. 47)*
Pub: Rogers Media Ltd.
Ed: Joe Castaldo. **Description:** Canada's theaters are faced with low ticket sales, donations and endowments. The industry is producing popular works as a response to the situation.

43445 ■ *"The Don't Do Lists" in Inc. (Vol. 33, October 2011, No. 8, pp. 65)*
Pub: Inc. Magazine
Ed: Jennifer Alsever, Adam Bluestein. **Description:** Ten business leaders and experts share their don't do lists, the things that should be avoided when going on sales calls, planning business lunches, motivating employees and more are presented.

43446 ■ *"Dow Jones Gives Apple-Loving Sales Professionals a Boost" in Information Today (Vol. 26, February 2009, No. 2, pp. 30)*
Pub: Information Today, Inc.
Description: Dow Jones Sales Triggers for iPhone and iPod program helps sales professionals stay current to prospects and customers in their fields by providing real-time news on business changes, including management moves, mergers, and new investments. The application presents events that trigger best opportunities and allows users to look up companies and executives to retrieve information.

43447 ■ *"Down by the Bay" in Canadian Business (Vol. 81, December 8, 2008, No. 21, pp. 15)*
Pub: Rogers Media Ltd.
Ed: Calvin Leung. **Description:** Hudsons Bay Company chief executive Jeffrey Sherman believes that his vast experience in retail will help him find the company's customer base. Sales are estimated to increase 3.6 percent in 2009 after posting average annual retail sales increases of 5 percent between 2006 and 2008.

43448 ■ *"Dozens 'Come Alive' in Downtown Chicago" in Green Industry Pro (July 2011)*
Pub: Cygnus Business Media
Ed: Gregg Wartgow. **Description:** Highlights from the Come Alive Outside training event held in Chicago, Illinois July 14-15, 2011 are shared. Nearly 80 people representing 38 landscape companies attended the event that helps contractors review their services and find ways to sell them in new and various ways.

43449 ■ *"Dream Big! When the Going Gets Tough, Reps Work Harder and Smarter" in Agency Sales Magazine (Vol. 39, July 2009, No. 7, pp. 22)*
Pub: MANA
Ed: John Chapin. **Description:** Sales representatives should use the tough economy as a warning and motivation to work harder and smarter. Reps should improve their selling by reading books, listening to tapes and CDs. They should also keep a good attitude and build relationships.

43450 ■ *"Drug-Maker Plans IPO" in Business Courier (Vol. 24, November 23, 2008, No. 32, pp. 1)*
Pub: American City Business Journals, Inc.
Ed: James Ritchie; Steve Watkins. **Description:** Xanodyne Pharmaceuticals Inc. filed plans with the Securities and Exchange Commission on November 9, 2007 for an initial public offering. The company, with annual sales of $75 million, had lost $222 million since it was founded in 2001.

43451 ■ *eBay Business the Smart Way*
Pub: AMACOM
Ed: Joseph T. Sinclair. **Released:** June 6, 2007. **Price:** $17.95. **Description:** eBay commands ninety percent of all online auction business. Computer and software expert and online entrepreneur shares information to help online sellers get started and move merchandise on eBay. Tips include the best ways to build credibility, find products to sell, manage inventory, create a storefront Website, and more.

43452 ■ *EBay Business Start-up Kit: 100s of Live Links to All the Information and Tools You Need*
Pub: NOLO
Ed: Richard Stim. **Released:** July 2008. **Price:** $24.99. **Description:** Interactive kit that connects user directly to EBay is presented.

43453 ■ *EBay Income: How ANYONE of Any Age, Location, and/or Background Can Build a Highly Profitable Online Business with eBay*
Pub: Atlantic Publishing Company
Released: December 1, 2010. **Price:** $24.95. **Description:** A complete overview of eBay is given and guides any small company through the entire process of creating the auction and auction strategies, photography, writing copy, text and formatting, multiple sales, programming tricks, PayPal, accounting, creating marketing, merchandising, managing email lists, advertising plans, taxes and sales tax, best time to list items and for how long, sniping programs, international customers, opening a storefront, electronic commerce, buy-it now pricing, keywords, Google marketing and eBay secrets.

43454 ■ *Ebay the Smart Way: Selling, Burying, and Profiting on the Web's Number One Auction Site*
Pub: AMACOM
Ed: Joseph T. Sinclair. **Released:** May 2007. **Price:** $17.95. **Description:** Resource to help individuals sell, buy and profit using the Internet auction site Ebay.

43455 ■ *"Economic Crises Calls For Better Marketing Plans" in Entrepreneur (October 1, 2008)*
Pub: Entrepreneur Media Inc.
Ed: Tim Berry. **Description:** Revising one's business plan is essential, especially during times of economic crisis; sales and marketing plans should be reviewed, analyzed and changed in an attempt to survive the economic downturn.

43456 ■ *"Economic Trends for Small Business" in Small Business Economic Trends (April 2008, pp. 1)*
Pub: National Federation of Independent Business
Ed: William C. Dunkelberg, Holly Wade. **Description:** Summary of economic trends for small businesses in the U.S. is presented. Economic indicators such as capital spending, inventories and sales, inflation, and profits are given. Analysis of credit markets is also provided.

43457 ■ *"Effective Use of Field Time" in Agency Sales Magazine (Vol. 39, July 2009, No. 7, pp. 40)*
Pub: MANA
Description: Sales representatives need to consider the value of field visits to themselves and their customers ahead of time. Several anecdotes about field visits from the perspective of manufacturers and sale representatives are presented.

43458 ■ *Electronic Commerce*
Pub: Course Technology
Ed: Gary Schneider, Bryant Chrzan, Charles McCormick. **Released:** May 1, 2010. **Price:** $117.95. **Description:** E-commerce can open the door to more opportunities than ever before for small business. Packed with real-world examples and cases, the book delivers comprehensive coverage of emerging online technologies and trends and their influence on the

electronic marketplace. It details how the landscape of online commerce is evolving, reflecting changes in the economy and how business and society are responding to those changes. Balancing technological issues with the strategic business aspects of successful e-commerce, the new edition includes expanded coverage of international issues, social networking, mobile commerce, Web 2.0 technologies, and updates on spam, phishing, and identity theft.

43459 ■ "Emack & Bolio" in Ice Cream Reporter (Vol. 23, October 20, 2010, No. 11, pp. 8)
Pub: Ice Cream Reporter
Description: Emack & Bolio's is engaging in scent marketing using various odors to help boost sales by attracting consumers with scents appropriate to their products.

43460 ■ Exceptional Selling: How the Best Connect and Win in High Stakes Sales
Pub: John Wiley & Sons, Incorporated
Ed: Jeff Thull. **Released:** August 18, 2006. **Price:** $24.95. **Description:** New approach to B2B selling, called diagnostic selling to help sales professionals achieve.

43461 ■ The Facebook Era: Tapping Online Social Networks to Build Better Products, Reach New Audiences, and Sell More Stuff
Pub: Prentice Hall
Ed: Clara Shih. **Price:** $24.99. **Description:** The '90s were about the World Wide Web of information and the power of linking Web pages. Today it's about the World Wide Web of people and the power of the social graph. Online social networks are fundamentally changing the way we live, work, and interact. They offer businesses immense opportunities to transform customer relationships for profit: opportunities that touch virtually every business function, from sales and marketing to recruiting, collaboration to executive decision-making, product development to innovation.

43462 ■ "Feet on the Street: Reps Are Ready to Hit the Ground Running" in Agency Sales Magazine (Vol. 39, July 2009, No. 7, pp. 12)
Pub: MANA
Ed: Jack Foster. **Description:** One of the major benefits to manufacturers in working with sales representatives is the concept of synergistic selling where the rep shows his mettle. The rep of today is a solution provider that anticipates and meets the customer's needs.

43463 ■ "First: Package Deal" in Entrepreneur (Vol. 35, October 2007, No. 10, pp. 114)
Pub: Entrepreneur Media Inc.
Ed: Nichole L. Torres. **Description:** Unique packaging of Me! Bath's products proved to be an effective marketing strategy for the company, which has over $3 million dollar sales yearly. Their ice cream-looking bath products have become popular and are much appreciated by vendors. Details of how packaging can affect sales are presented.

43464 ■ "Five Distinct Divisions, One Collective Focus" in Green Industry Pro (Vol. 23, October 2011)
Pub: Cygnus Business Media
Ed: Gregg Wartgow. **Description:** Profile of ACLS Inc., an amalgamation of All Commercial Landscape Service (commercial maintenance), All Custom Landscape Service (design/build), Fresno Tree Service, Certified Water Consulting (irrigation), and Tractor Service (disking and flailing services on everything from one-acre lots to hundreds of acres of open land). The firm discusses its rebranding effort in order to increase sales.

43465 ■ "For Gilead, Growth Beyond AIDS" in Barron's (Vol. 88, June 30, 2008, No. 26, pp. 18)
Pub: Dow Jones & Co., Inc.
Ed: Jay Palmer. **Description:** First-quarter 2008 revenue for Gilead Sciences grew by 22 percent and an earnings gain of 19 percent thanks to their HIV-treatment drugs that comprised over two-thirds of the

company's sales in 2007. An analyst has a 12-month target from June, 2008 of 65 per share. The factors behind the company's prospects are also discussed.

43466 ■ "Formaspace Finds a Bigger Home" in Austin Business JournalInc. (Vol. 29, December 4, 2009, No. 39, pp. 1)
Pub: American City Business Journals
Ed: Kate Harrington. **Description:** Formaspace Technical Furniture has signed a lease for 56,700 square feet in Harris Ridge Business Center at Northeast Austin, Texas, which represents one of the area's largest leases for 2009. The new lease enables Formaspace to hire new employees, invest in new equipment, and take advantage of a taxing designation created for manufacturers.

43467 ■ "Formula for Success: Dispelling the Age-Old Myths" in Agency Sales Magazine (Vol. 39, July 2009, No. 7, pp. 26)
Pub: MANA
Ed: Douglas Smith. **Description:** Common misperceptions about selling and salespeople include the idea that anyone can be successful in selling if they work hard enough and that successful salespeople are born that way. In fact, top performers take risks and they invest in themselves.

43468 ■ "Fox" in Brandweek (Vol. 49, April 21, 2008, No. 16, pp. SR3)
Pub: VNU Business Media, Inc.
Ed: John Consoli. **Description:** Provides contact information for sales and marketing personnel for the Fox network as well as a listing of the station's top programming and an analysis of the current season and the target audience for those programs running in the current season. In terms of upfront advertising dollars, it looks as if Fox will be competing against NBC for third place due to its success at courting the 18-49-year-old male demographic.

43469 ■ "Fox Cable Entertainment Networks" in Brandweek (Vol. 49, April 21, 2008, No. 16, pp. SR10)
Pub: VNU Business Media, Inc.
Ed: Anthony Crupi. **Description:** Provides contact information for sales and marketing personnel for the Fox Cable Entertainment networks as well as a listing of the station's top programming and an analysis of the current season and the target audience for those programs running in the current season.

43470 ■ "Funds "Friend" Facebook" in Barron's (Vol. 89, July 27, 2009, No. 30, pp. 30)
Pub: Dow Jones & Co., Inc.
Ed: Leslie P. Norton. **Description:** Mutual-fund companies are the latest entrants to the 'social media' space and several companies have already set up Facebook and Twitter pages. The use of this technology pose special challenges for compliance and regulators especially since the Financial Industry Regulatory Authority reminds companies that advertising, sales and literature are governed by regulations.

43471 ■ "Funny Business" in Canadian Business (Vol. 82, April 27, 2009, No. 7, pp. 27)
Pub: Rogers Media
Ed: Rachel Pulfer. **Description:** Companies are advised to use humor in marketing to drive more revenue. IBM Canada, for example, commissioned Second City Communications for a marketing campaign that involved humor. While IBM Canada declined to give sales or traffic figures, firm executives rank the marketing campaign as an overall success.

43472 ■ "Gain the 'Come Alive Outside' Selling Edge" in Green Industry Pro (July 2011)
Pub: Cygnus Business Media
Ed: Jim Paluch. **Description:** Marketing the 'Come Alive Outside' slogan can help landscapers to increase their market share by identifying and applying these elements to each customer as well as their workers.

43473 ■ "Games Gone Wild: City's Newest Public Company Aims for the Sky" in Business Courier (Vol. 27, September 24, 2010, No. 21, pp. 1)
Pub: Business Courier
Ed: Dan Monk. **Description:** Video game company Zoo Entertainment Inc., which is based in Norwood near Cincinnati, Ohio aims to build a strong company and to position itself for future growth. The company reported $27.6 million in revenue for the first half of 2010 and analysts project $100 million in sales for 2011.

43474 ■ "Get Back To Business Planning Fundamentals" in Entrepreneur (October 24, 2008)
Pub: Entrepreneur Media Inc.
Ed: Tim Berry. **Description:** During a recession it is important to know what adjustment to make to your business plan. Some fundamentals to remember include: watching things more closely by tracking progress on cash, sales, new projects, customer satisfaction, ad spending and expenses; looking for built-in indicators such as what drives sales or expenses; watching what drives cash flow; and do not make mistakes such as laying off experienced employees too soon.

43475 ■ "Get Personal" in Entrepreneur (Vol. 36, April 2008, No. 4)
Pub: Entrepreneur Media, Inc.
Ed: Romanus Wolter. **Description:** Customers appreciate personal contact, and communicating with them can help business owners' customer relations. Some ways on how to keep a personal touch with customers and improve business dealings include blending technology with personal interaction and knowing what the customers want. Other tips are provided.

43476 ■ "Get Sold On eBay" in Entrepreneur (Vol. 36, March 2008, No. 3, pp. 94)
Pub: Entrepreneur Media Inc.
Ed: Marcia Layton Turner. **Description:** Entrepreneurs are increasingly using eBay to sell products. Some tips to start selling products through eBay include: starting with used items, developing a niche to sell specific products, and researching product pricing. Other tips with regard to starting an eBay business are covered.

43477 ■ Getting Clients and Keeping Clients for Your Service Business
Pub: Atlantic Publishing Company
Ed: Anne M. Miller; Gail Brett Levine. **Released:** August 28, 2008. **Price:** $24.95 paperback. **Description:** Tips are offered to help any small service business identify customers, brand and grow the business, as well as development of logos, brochures and Websites.

43478 ■ "Getting a Grip on the Saddle: Chasms or Cycles?" in Journal of Marketing (Vol. 75, July 2011, No. 4, pp. 21)
Pub: American Marketing Association
Ed: Deepa Chandrasekaran, Gerald J. Tellis. **Description:** A study of the saddle's generality across products and countries is presented. The saddle is fairly pervasive based on empirical analysis of historical sales data from ten products across 19 countries. The results indicate chasms and technological cycles for information/entertainment products while business cycles and technological cycles affect kitchen/laundry products.

43479 ■ Getting More: How to Negotiate to Achieve Your Goals in the Real World
Pub: Crown Business Books
Ed: Stuart Diamond. **Released:** December 28, 2010. **Price:** $26.00. **Description:** When negotiating, people fail to meet their goals due to focusing on power and the 'win-win' instead of on relationships and perceptions, thus not finding enough things to trade. They think others should be rational when they are dealing with emotions and they get distracted from the real goal.

43480 ■ *Getting Rich In Your Underwear: How To Start and Run a Profitable Home-Based Business*
Pub: HCM Publishing
Ed: Peter I. Hupalo. **Released:** April 1, 2005. **Price:** $17.95. **Description:** Book offers insight into starting a home-based business. Entrepreneurs will learn about business models and the home business; distribution and fulfillment of product or service; marketing and sales; how to overcome the fear of starting a business; personal success characteristics; naming a business; zoning and insurance; intellectual capital; copyrights, trademarks, and patents; limited liability companies and S-corporations; business expenses and accounting; taxes; fifteen basic steps for starting a home-based business, state resources for starting a home company; and seven home-based business ideas.

43481 ■ *"Give It Your All, and Don't Worry About the Rest" in Inc. (Vol. 33, November 2011, No. 9, pp. 37)*
Pub: Inc. Magazine
Ed: Norm Brodsky. **Description:** In the early stage of a service company, the owners sell themselves to the customers.

43482 ■ *The Golden 120 Seconds of Every Sales Call: A Fresh Innovative Look at the Sales Process*
Pub: NorlightsPress.com
Ed: Peter G. Dennis. **Released:** October 28, 2009. **Price:** $15.95. **Description:** Salespeople who want to find their personal style, gain confidence, and avoid deal-killing mistakes must read this book. It will show both new and experienced sales professionals how to use key fundamentals with every call, every selling interaction, and every opportunity to make something happen. Anyone who sells for a living has experienced the magic moments that can make or break a sales. Advice is given to help recognize, and learn to cultivate, this vital part of the sales process.

43483 ■ *"Good Questions and the Basics of Selling" in Agency Sales Magazine (Vol. 39, September-October 2009, No. 9, pp. 14)*
Pub: MANA
Ed: Dave Kahle. **Description:** Six basic elements to enhance the job of a sales person in regards to his relationship to a customer are presented.

43484 ■ *"Graceful Landing" in Entrepreneur (Vol. 37, November 2009, No. 11, pp. 59)*
Pub: Entrepreneur Media, Inc.
Ed: Mikal E. Belicove. **Description:** Successful marketers regularly use Website landing pages to capture qualified leads and make sales. It is believed that an effective landing page devoted to a single product or service offering can significantly boost leads and conversion rates. Organizations can create a top-notch landing page by anticipating customer expectations and focusing on a clear call to action.

43485 ■ *"Harness the Internet to Boost Equipment Sales" in Indoor Comfort Marketing (Vol. 70, July 2011, No. 7, pp. 24)*
Pub: Industry Publications Inc.
Ed: Richard Rutigliano. **Description:** Advice is given to increase HVAC/R equipment sales using the Internet.

43486 ■ *"Hawaii Business 2008 SB Success Awards" in Hawaii Business (Vol. 53, February 2008, No. 8, pp. 43)*
Pub: Hawaii Business Publishing
Description: Winners in the Hawaii Business 2008 SB Success Awards are presented; the awards give recognition for Hawaii small businesses with less than 100 employees and are based on four criteria, namely: unique service or product; rapid expansion or sales growth; longevity; and competency in overcoming challenges.

43487 ■ *Heads in Beds*
Pub: Prentice Hall PTR
Ed: Ivo Raza. **Released:** May 28, 2004. **Description:** Advice is given to help build brands, generate sales and grow profits through marketing for any hospitality or tourism business.

43488 ■ *"Heavy Duty: The Case Against Packing Lightly" in Crain's Chicago Business (Vol. 31, April 21, 2008, No. 16, pp. 29)*
Pub: Crain Communications, Inc.
Ed: Sarah A. Klein. **Description:** Penelope Biggs, a Northern Trust executive who manages sales teams in North America, Europe and Asia gives advice on traveling abroad for business including time management skills, handling time-zone hops and avoiding jet-lag.

43489 ■ *"Help Customers Choose Full Service Over Discount" in Indoor Comfort Marketing (Vol. 70, September 2011, No. 9, pp. 10)*
Pub: Industry Publications Inc.
Ed: Richard Rutigliano. **Description:** Marketing strategies for HVAC/R firms to use in 2011 and 2012 heating seasons are outlined, focusing on oil heat.

43490 ■ *"Helping Customers Fight Pet Waste" in Pet Product News (Vol. 64, November 2010, No. 11, pp. 52)*
Pub: BowTie Inc.
Ed: Sandy Robins. **Description:** Pet cleaning products manufacturers have been enjoying high sales figures by paying attention to changing pet ownership trends and environmental awareness. Meanwhile, the inclusion of user-friendly features in these products has also been boosted by the social role of pets and the media attention to pet waste. How manufacturers have been responding to this demand is explored.

43491 ■ *High Trust Selling: Make More Money, in Less Time, with Less Stress*
Pub: Nelson Business
Ed: Todd Duncan. **Released:** April 2007. **Price:** $14.99. **Description:** Laws governing salesmanship are divided into two sections. The first deals with attitudes, aptitudes, and abilities required for successful selling; the second with communication, courtship, camaraderie and commitments between salespeople and their clients.

43492 ■ *A History of Small Business in America*
Pub: University of North Carolina Press
Contact: Kate Douglas Torrey, Director
E-mail: kate_torrey@unc.edu
Ed: Mansel G. Blackford. **Released:** May 2003. **Price:** $22.95. **Description:** History of American small business from the colonial era to present, showing how it has played a role in the nation's economic, political, and cultural development across manufacturing, sales, services and farming.

43493 ■ *"Ho, Ho, Ho!" in Retail Merchandiser (Vol. 51, September-October 2011, No. 5, pp. 10)*
Pub: Phoenix Media Corporation
Ed: Ted Vaughan. **Description:** Despite consumer caution and economic woes, retail leaders are expecting a high volume holiday selling season for 2011 Christmas. Statistical data covering holiday sales expectations is included.

43494 ■ *"Hoover's Mobile, MobileSP Now Available" in Information Today (Vol. 26, February 2009, No. 2, pp. 29)*
Pub: Information Today, Inc.
Description: Hoover's Inc. introduced its Hoover's Mobile for iPhone, BlackBerry and Windows Mobile smartphones along with Hoover's MobileSP for BlackBerry and Windows Mobile. Both products allow users to access customer, prospect, and partner information; analyze competitors; prepare for meetings; and find new opportunities. In addition, MobileSP adds one-click calling to executives, GPS-enabled location searches, advanced search and list building, and a custom call queue and a 'save to contacts' capabilities.

43495 ■ *"How to Dominate in Residential Maintenance" in Green Industry Pro (Vol. 23, October 2011)*
Pub: Cygnus Business Media
Ed: Gregg Wartgow. **Description:** Lawn care services were ranked among the most expendable consumer expenditures, according to the National

Retail Federation data accumulated in early 2011. This makes it critical for any landscape firm to target sales efforts toward higher-income households and higher-value homes.

43496 ■ *"How Good Advice 'Online' Can Attract Customers" in Indoor Comfort Marketing (Vol. 70, August 2011, No. 8, pp. 20)*
Pub: Industry Publications Inc.
Ed: Richard Rutigliano. **Description:** Online marketing tips for heating and cooling small businesses are explained.

43497 ■ *"How to Keep Your Sales from Running Out of Gas" in Agency Sales Magazine (Vol. 39, July 2009, No. 7, pp. 30)*
Pub: MANA
Ed: John Graham. **Description:** Salespeople can let the good times deceive them into thinking that success will go on forever. Salespeople and businesses should see prospecting as a strategy for creating a continuing flow of business.

43498 ■ *How to Make Money with Social Media: Using New and Emerging Media to Grow Your Business*
Pub: FT Press
Ed: Jamie Turner, Reshma Shah. **Released:** October 1, 2010. **Price:** $24.99. **Description:** Marketers, executives, entrepreneurs are shown more effective ways to utilize Internet social media to make money. This guide brings together both practical strategies and proven execution techniques for driving maximum value from social media marketing.

43499 ■ *How to Market and Sell Your Art, Music, Photographs, and Handmade Crafts Online*
Pub: Atlantic Publishing Group, Inc.
Ed: Lee Rowley. **Released:** May 2008. **Price:** $24.95. **Description:** The book provides all the basics for starting and running an online store selling arts, crafts, photography or music. There are more than 300 Websites listed to help anyone market and promote their arts and/or crafts online.

43500 ■ *How to Open and Operate a Financially Successful Bookstore on Amazon and Other Web Sites: With Companion CD-ROM*
Pub: Atlantic Publishing Company
Released: December 1, 2010. **Price:** $39.95. **Description:** This book was written for every used book aficionado and bookstore owner who currently wants to take advantage of the massive collection of online resources available to start and run your own online bookstore business.

43501 ■ *"How to Plan and Execute Effective Sales Meetings" in Agency Sales Magazine (Vol. 39, August 2009, No. 8, pp. 8)*
Pub: MANA
Ed: Jack Foster. **Description:** Basic guide to successful representative-manufacturer sales meetings based on effective planning is presented. The representative and the manufacturer will reap the benefits of a productive meeting only when they both focus on what's going to transpire before, during and after the event. Insights from industry players are also presented.

43502 ■ *"How a Unique Culture Proposition Became a USP" in Business Strategy Review (Vol. 21, Spring 2010, No. 1, pp. 52)*
Pub: Wiley-Blackwell
Ed: Adam Kingl. **Description:** How can you transform the way you do things into a compelling sales proposition? Zurich Insurance has created a Unique Culture Proposition which may be its Unique Selling Point.

43503 ■ *"The Human Approach" in Entrepreneur (Vol. 37, September 2009, No. 9, pp. 30)*
Pub: Entrepreneur Media, Inc.
Description: Focusing on customer's needs is seen to result in better sales performance. Understanding customer needs is a question of emotional and social intelligence. Such sales competencies are seen as learned capabilities.

43504 ■ *"Hyundai's Hitting Its Stride"* in *Barron's (Vol. 89, July 20, 2009, No. 29, pp. M7)*
Pub: Dow Jones & Co., Inc.
Ed: Assif Shameen. **Description:** Hyundai Motors has kept growing by producing better products, enabling it to increase its sales and market share despite the weaker automotive market. The shares of Hyundai and Kia are poised to rise due to their improved finances.

43505 ■ *"I Hear You're Interested In a.."* in *Inc. (January 2008, pp. 40-43)*
Pub: Gruner & Jahr USA Publishing
Ed: Leah Hoffmann. **Description:** Four tips to help any small business generate sales leads online are examined.

43506 ■ *"An Ice Boost in Revenue; Wings Score With Expanded Corporate Sales"* in *Crain's Detroit Business (Vol. 25, June 1, 2009, No. 22)*
Pub: Crain Communications Inc. - Detroit
Ed: Bill Shea. **Description:** Stanley Cup finals always boost business for the Detroit area, even during a recession. The Red Wings corporate office reported corporate sponsorship revenue luxury suite rentals, Legends Club seats and advertising were up 40 percent this year over 2008.

43507 ■ *"If the Opportunity is There, Move Boldly"* in *Indoor Comfort Marketing (Vol. 70, March 2011, No. 3, pp.)*
Pub: Industry Publications Inc.
Ed: Rich Rutigliano. **Description:** Suggestions are offered to help improve air conditioning sales.

43508 ■ *"Indulgent Parsimony: an Enduring Marketing Approach"* in *Strategy and Leadership (Vol. 39, March-April 2011, No. 2, pp. 36)*
Pub: Emerald Group Publishing Inc.
Ed: Kenneth Alan Grossberg. **Description:** Indulgent parsimony (IP), a marketing strategy employed on consumers that are affected by recession, is found to be a relevant and appropriate approach that can help encourage buying. IP involves the selling of cheaper goods and services that allow consumers experience comfort and relief from stress.

43509 ■ *Influence: The Psychology of Persuasion*
Pub: HarperCollins Publishers
Ed: Robert B. Cialdini. **Released:** June 2, 2009. **Price:** $17.99. **Description:** Whether you are the consumer or the salesperson, this book will help you understand the psychological foundations of marketing.

43510 ■ *"Info Junkie"* in *Crain's Chicago Business (Vol. 34, October 24, 2011, No. 42, pp. 35)*
Pub: Crain Communications Inc.
Ed: Christina Le Beau. **Description:** Greg Colando, president of Flor Inc., an eco-friendly carpet company located I Chicago discusses his marketing program to increase sales.

43511 ■ *Instant Cashflow: Hundreds of Proven Strategies to Win Customers, Boost Margins and Take More Money Home*
Pub: McGraw-Hill Companies Inc.
Contact: Deven Sharma, President
Ed: Bradley J. Sugars. **Released:** December 2005. **Price:** $17.95 (US), $22.95 (Canadian). **Description:** Nearly 300 proven marketing and sales strategies are shared by the author, a self-made millionaire. Advice on creating the proper mindset, generating new leads, boosting the conversion rate of leads to sales, maximizing the value of the average sale, and measuring results is included.

43512 ■ *Instant Income*
Pub: McGraw-Hill Inc.
Ed: Janet Switzer. **Released:** February 2007. **Price:** $30.95 (CND). **Description:** Book covers small business advertising techniques, marketing, joint ventures, and sales.

43513 ■ *"Insuraprise Growing Fast"* in *Austin Business Journal (Vol. 31, April 22, 2011, No. 7, pp. 1)*
Pub: American City Business Journals Inc.
Ed: Sandra Zaragoza. **Description:** Austin, Texas-based Insuraprise Inc. is finalizing the purchase of a 24,000-square-foot office at 12116 Jekel Circle. The firm, with 23 salespeople and sales that are growing nearly 300 percent over the past 18 months, will now have room to grow. Insuraprise plans to hire 35 new salespersons for its call center.

43514 ■ *"Internet Marketing 2.0: Closing the Online Chat Gap"* in *Agent's Sales Journal (November 2009, pp. 14)*
Pub: Summit Business Media
Ed: Jeff Denenholz. **Description:** Advice regarding the implementation of an Internet marketing strategy for insurance agencies includes how and why to incorporate a chat feature in which a sales agent can communicate in real-time with potential or existing customers. It is important to understand if appropriate response mechanisms are in place to convert leads into actual sales.

43515 ■ *"Is the Generation Gap Gone?"* in *Agency Sales Magazine (Vol. 39, November 2009, No. 10, pp. 3)*
Pub: MANA
Ed: Bryan C. Shirley. **Description:** Four generations are working side-by-side in the workplace for the first time in history and this is a big opportunity to get different perspectives and views on life. In the sales representatives business, there is a need to better understand the upcoming generations and understand their specific abilities to their risk/reward business.

43516 ■ *Island of Profit in a Sea of Red Ink Why 40 Percent of Your Business Is Unprofitable and How to Fix It*
Pub: Portfolio
Ed: Jonathan L.S. Byrnes. **Released:** October 14, 2010. **Price:** $27.95. **Description:** Top companies from around the world turn to Jonathan Byrnes to figure out where to find profit for their companies. He shows which parts of a business are worth expanding, and which are just a drain on resources. He has found that roughly 40 percent of any new client's business is unprofitable, and that profit increases of thirty percent or more are within reach.

43517 ■ *"It's Not About You"* in *Entrepreneur (Vol. 35, November 2007, No. 11, pp. 102)*
Pub: Entrepreneur Media Inc.
Ed: Barry Farber. **Description:** Companies should focus on the customers' need and show them that they care about them. Listening to and learning about your customers can make selling easier; tips on how to stay focused on the customers' needs are outlined.

43518 ■ *"Jay Berkowitz to Present Making Social Media Money Seminar at Affiliate Summit West"* in *Entertainment Close-Up (January 15, 2010)*
Pub: Close-Up Media
Description: Highlights of Jay Berkowitz's conference, 'Making Social Media Make Money' include ways in which to develop Internet marketing strategies that will maximize Website traffic and convert that traffic to sales.

43519 ■ *"Keeping Tabs"* in *Entrepreneur (Vol. 36, February 2008, No. 2, pp. 38)*
Pub: Entrepreneur Media Inc.
Ed: Robert Kiyosaki. **Description:** Measuring and reporting the number of customers being served by a business can help in the company's growth. Details on this idea are discussed.

43520 ■ *"Keys to Overcome Fear of Follow-Up"* in *Agency Sales Magazine (Vol. 39, December 2009, No. 11, pp. 26)*
Pub: MANA
Ed: Judy Garmaise. **Description:** In order to be more successful at making follow-up calls, salespeople should not take rejection personally and never assume that they are going to annoy prospects if they follow-up. Those that follow-up with prospects stand out among others since few salespeople do this.

43521 ■ *Knock Your Socks Off Selling*
Pub: Amacom
Ed: Jeffrey Gitomer. **Released:** May 1999. **Price:** $17.95. **Description:** Tips for salespeople to succeed in a competitive sales environment.

43522 ■ *"Last Founder Standing"* in *Conde Nast Portfolio (Vol. 2, June 2008, No. 6, pp. 124)*
Pub: Conde Nast Publications
Contact: David Carey, President
Ed: Kevin Maney. **Description:** Interview with Amazon CEO Jeff Bezos in which he discusses the economy, the company's new distribution center and the hiring of employees for it, e-books, and the overall vision for the future of the firm.

43523 ■ *"Let Emerging Market Customers Be Your Teachers"* in *Harvard Business Review (Vol. 88, December 2010, No. 12, pp. 115)*
Pub: Harvard Business School Publishing
Ed: Guillermo D'Andrea, David Marcotte, Gwen Dixon Morrison. **Description:** Examination of effective strategies for emerging markets is presented. These include helping educate customers as well as selling to them, adapting to customers' habits, and focusing brands appropriately. Magazine Luiza, a chain store in Brazil, is used to illustrate these points.

43524 ■ *"Let's Go Team: When a Retail Professional Leads by Example, Everyone Benefits"* in *Black Enterprise (Vol. 41, November 2010, No. 4)*
Pub: Earl G. Graves Publishing Co. Inc.
Ed: Aisha I. Jefferson. **Description:** Profile of Derek Jenkins, senior vice president of Target Stores Northeast Region is presented. Jenkins oversees the management of 450 retail stores with nearly 75,000 workers. He shares insight into managing by making sure every interaction with his team counts.

43525 ■ *"Lifetime Networks"* in *Brandweek (Vol. 49, April 21, 2008, No. 16, pp. SR10)*
Pub: VNU Business Media, Inc.
Ed: Anthony Crupi. **Description:** Provides contact information for sales and marketing personnel for the ABC network as well as a listing of the station's top programming and an analysis of the current season and the target audience for those programs running in the current season. Lifetime will still produce its original signature movies but will now focus its emphasis more clearly on series development in order to appeal to a younger, hipper female demographic.

43526 ■ *"Lombard Leaves Starbucks"* in *Black Enterprise (Vol. 38, July 2008, No. 12, pp. 28)*
Pub: Earl G. Graves Publishing Co. Inc.
Ed: Tamara E. Holmes. **Description:** Ken Lombard stepped down from his position as head of Starbuck's entertainment division; the company is restructuring its entertainment unit in an attempt to revitalize sales and reduce costs.

43527 ■ *"Loseley Dairy Ice Cream"* in *Ice Cream Reporter (Vol. 23, November 20, 2010, No. 12, pp. 8)*
Pub: Ice Cream Reporter
Description: Neil Burchell has been named managing director of Loseley Dairy Ice Cream, one of the UK's largest independent producers. Burchell, with over 30 years experience in the food industry, was recently managing director of Rachel's, the leading organic dairy foods company in the UK, where he is credited with driving a sixfold increase in sales.

43528 ■ *"A Love of Likes"* in *Boston Business Journal (Vol. 31, July 8, 2011, No. 24, pp. 1)*
Pub: Boston Business Journal
Ed: Lisa van der Pool. **Description:** An increasing number of companies in Boston, Massachusetts have been keen on getting Facebook 'likes' from people.

Business owners realize that Facebook 'likes' could generate sales and based on some studies, equate to specific dollar values.

43529 ■ "Loyalty Cards Score Points" in Crain's Cleveland Business (Vol. 30, June 8, 2009, No. 22, pp. 1)
Pub: Crain Communications, Inc.

Ed: Chuck Soder. **Description:** Northeast Ohio retailers are promoting loyalty and rewards programs in order to attract and maintain loyal customers.

43530 ■ Lucrative List Building
Pub: Morgan James Publishing, LLC

Ed: Glen Hopkins. **Released:** July 2006. **Price:** $13.95. **Description:** List building guaranteed to double profits is outlined.

43531 ■ "Make Relationships Count: CRM Software That Works" in Black Enterprise (Vol. 38, February 2008, No. 7, pp. 60)
Pub: Earl G. Graves Publishing Co. Inc.

Ed: Fiona Haley. **Description:** Customer relationship management (CRM) software can help any small business keep track of clients. Descriptions of the latest CRM software offered are profiled, including Salesforce.com, Microsoft Dynamics, and Saga Software.

43532 ■ "MANAfest Provides Reps with Tools for the Future" in Agency Sales Magazine (Vol. 39, September-October 2009, No. 9, pp. 36)
Pub: MANA

Ed: Jack Foster. **Description:** Former Harley Davidson director of communications Ken Schmidt was the keynote speaker at the MANAfest conference; he discussed how the company delivered itself from bankruptcy. Selling Power magazine publisher Gerhard Gschwandtner also made a presentation; he believes that there will be opportunities for sales people involved in relationship selling.

43533 ■ "Marathon Money" in Hawaii Business (Vol. 53, December 2007, No. 6, pp. 127)
Pub: Hawaii Business Publishing

Ed: Jolyn Okimoto Rosa. **Description:** Discusses the effects of the Honolulu Marathon on small businesses' sales. The Running Room, for instance, experience growth in sales starting from the training season up to the end of the race, as a surge of Hawaiian residents and tourists come into the store for items such as running shoes and blister kits. The marathon's impact on Hawaii's tourism is examined as well.

43534 ■ "Marketing in the Digital World: Here's How to Craft a Smart Online Strategy" in Black Enterprise (Vol. 40, July 2010, No. 12, pp. 47)
Pub: Earl G. Graves Publishing Co. Inc.

Ed: Sonya A. Donaldson. **Description:** Social media is an integral part of any small business plan in addressing marketing, sales, and branding strategies.

43535 ■ Marketing for Entrepreneurs
Pub: FT Press

Ed: Jurgen Wolff. **Released:** December 9, 2010. **Price:** $24.99. **Description:** This text identifies marketing as the entire process of researching, creating, distributing and selling a product or service. It isn't about theory and metrics, rather it is a practical guide that starts with the basics of all marketing aspects.

43536 ■ "Marketing: 'Twill Be the Season" in Entrepreneur (Vol. 35, October 2007, No. 10, pp. 108)
Pub: Entrepreneur Media Inc.

Ed: Kim T. Gordon. **Description:** Entrepreneurs should plan ahead in order to promote products for the holiday season, since it is peak sales time. They can unify their business theme, use customer incentives, advertise early using TV or radio, and reorganize the company Website. Other ways to market for the holiday season are provided.

43537 ■ Marketing Without Money for Small and Midsize Businesses: 300 FREE and Cheap Ways to Increase Your Sales
Pub: Halle House Publishing

Contact: Nicholas E. Bade, Publisher

Ed: Nicholas E. Bade. **Released:** July 2005. **Price:** $16.95. **Description:** Three hundred practical low-cost or no-cost strategies to increase sales, focusing on free advertising, free marketing assistance, and free referrals to the Internet.

43538 ■ Mastering the Complex Sales: How to Compete and Win When the Stakes Are High!
Pub: John Wiley & Sons, Incorporated

Ed: Jeff Thull. **Released:** May 2003. **Price:** $24.95. **Description:** Guide to compete for and win in complex selling, the business-to-business transactions involving multiple decisions by multiple people from multiple perspectives.

43539 ■ Masters of Sales: Secrets from Top Sales Professionals That Will Transform You Into a World Class Salesman
Pub: Entrepreneur Press

Ed: Ivan R. Misner; Don Morgan. **Released:** August 15, 2007. **Price:** $19.95. **Description:** Eighty successful salespeople share insight into selling.

43540 ■ Maximum Marketing, Minimum Dollars: The Top 50 Ways to Grow Your Small Business
Pub: Kaplan Books

Ed: Kim Gordon. **Released:** April 2006. **Price:** $24.00. **Description:** Marketing tips to increase sales are presented. Small business owners will learn to maximize marketing with 50 innovative and affordable methods, including online marketing.

43541 ■ "Mini Melts" in Ice Cream Reporter (Vol. 23, August 20, 2010, No. 9, pp. 8)
Pub: Ice Cream Reporter

Description: Mini Melts appointed David S. Tade to position of director of sales USA in order to cultivate existing distributors and add new partners to its distribution network.

43542 ■ "More Ad Shops Link Payment to Results" in Boston Business Journal (Vol. 30, November 12, 2010, No. 42, pp. 1)
Pub: Boston Business Journal

Ed: Lisa van der Pool. **Description:** A growing number of advertising firms are proposing a 'value-based' payment scheme where they are paid a base fee plus a bonus if certain sales goals or other targets are met. The proposed shift in payment scheme is seen as reminiscent of the dot-com boom about ten years ago. Advertising firms are traditionally paid by the hour.

43543 ■ "More Leading Retailers Using Omniture Conversion Solutions to Boost Sales and Ecommerce Performance" in Internet Wire (Sept. 22,2009)
Pub: Comtex News Network, Inc.

Description: Many retailers are utilizing Omniture conversion solutions to improve the performance of their ecommerce businesses; recent enhancements to Omniture Merchandising and Omniture Recommendations help clients drive increased conversion to their Internet ventures.

43544 ■ "More Leading Retailers Using Omniture Conversion Solutions to Boost Sales and Ecommerce Performance" in Internet Wire (Sept. 22,2009)
Pub: Comtex News Network, Inc.

Description: Many retailers are utilizing Omniture conversion solutions to improve the performance of their ecommerce businesses; recent enhancements to Omniture Merchandising and Omniture Recommendations help clients drive increased conversion to their Internet ventures.

43545 ■ "More Sales Leads, Please: Or, What Happened When Frontline Selling Started Practicing What It Preaches" in Inc.

(November 2007)
Pub: Gruner & Jahr USA Publishing

Description: Frontline Selling located in Oakland, New Jersey helps train sales teams to generate and convert sales leads. The consulting firm doubled their marketing budget to increase their own sales.

43546 ■ More Than a Pink Cadillac
Pub: McGraw-Hill

Ed: Jim Underwood. **Released:** 2002. **Price:** $23.95. **Description:** Profile of Mary Kay Ash who turned her $5,000 investment into a billion-dollar corporation. Ash's nine principles that form the foundation of her company's global success are outlined. Stories from her sales force leaders share ideas for motivating employees, impressing customers and building a successful company. The book emphasizes the leadership skills required to drive performance in any successful enterprise.

43547 ■ "MTV Networks" in Brandweek (Vol. 49, April 21, 2008, No. 16, pp. SR10)
Pub: VNU Business Media, Inc.

Ed: Anthony Crupi. **Description:** Provides contact information for sales and marketing personnel for the MTV networks as well as a listing of the station's top programming and an analysis of the current season and the target audience for those programs running in the current season. MTV networks include MTV, VH1, Nickelodeon and Comedy Central.

43548 ■ "NBC" in Brandweek (Vol. 49, April 21, 2008, No. 16, pp. SR6)
Pub: VNU Business Media, Inc.

Ed: John Consoli. **Description:** Provides contact information for sales and marketing personnel for the NBC network as well as a listing of the station's top programming and an analysis of the current season and the target audience for those programs running in the current season. NBC also devised a new strategy of announcing its prime-time schedule 52 weeks in advance which was a hit for advertisers who felt this gave them a better opportunity to plan for product placement. Even with the station's creative sales programs, they could face a challenge from Fox in terms of upfront advertisement purchases.

43549 ■ "NBC Universal Cable" in Brandweek (Vol. 49, April 21, 2008, No. 16, pp. SR11)
Pub: VNU Business Media, Inc.

Ed: Anthony Crupi. **Description:** Provides contact information for sales and marketing personnel for the NBC Universal Cable networks as well as a listing of the station's top programming and an analysis of the current season and the target audience for those programs running in the current season. The network's stations include USA, Sci Fi and Bravo. Ad revenue for the network grew 30 percent in the first quarter.

43550 ■ "NBC Universal Domestic Television Distribution" in Brandweek (Vol. 49, April 21, 2008, No. 16, pp. SR13)
Pub: VNU Business Media, Inc.

Ed: Marc Berman. **Description:** Provides contact information for sales and marketing personnel for NBC Universal Domestic Television Distribution as well as a listing of the station's top programming and an analysis of the current season and the target audience for those programs running in the current season.

43551 ■ "Network Marketing Strategies for Marketing Professionals" in Black Enterprise (Vol. 38, October 2007, No. 3, pp. 70)
Pub: Earl G. Graves Publishing Co. Inc.

Description: Network marketing programs are redefining the sales business and leveraging opportunities in the ever-expanding global, highly networked, and ultra-specialized marketplace.

43552 ■ "A New Challenge Facing Reps: The Generation Gap!" in Agency Sales Magazine (Vol. 39, November 2009, No. 10, pp. 9)
Pub: MANA

Ed: Roger Ralston. **Description:** Different generations in the workplace is one of the many drivers of change that reps are facing today. Pre-boomers and boomers historically put work first while Gen-Xers and Millennials think lifestyle before work. A sales rep should listen and learn, while providing a strong sense of flexibility in this environment.

43553 ■ *"The Next Dimension"* in *Entrepreneur (Vol. 35, November 2007, No. 11, pp. 62)*
Pub: Entrepreneur Media Inc.
Ed: Heather Clancy. **Description:** Entrepreneurs can make use of virtual worlds like Second Life to promote their products or services. Details and cautions on the use of virtual worlds are discussed.

43554 ■ *"North American Pet Health Insurance Market Poised for Growth"* in *Pet Product News (Vol. 64, December 2010, No. 12, pp. 4)*
Pub: BowTie Inc.
Ed: David Lummis. **Description:** The pet health insurance market is expected to further grow after posting about $350 million in sales in 2009, a gain of more than $40 million. Pet insurance firms have offered strategies such as product humanization in response to this growth forecast. Meanwhile, pet insurance shoppers have been provided more by insurance firms with wider choices.

43555 ■ *"Norvax University Health Insurance Sales Training and Online Marketing Conference"* in *Internet Wire (January 27, 2010)*
Pub: Comtex News Network, Inc.
Description: Overview of the Norvax University Marketing and Sales Success Conference Tour which includes insurance sales training seminars, proven and innovative online marketing techniques and a host of additional information and networking opportunities.

43556 ■ *"Not All Contracts a Good Fit for Fashion Reps"* in *Agency Sales Magazine (Vol. 39, September-October 2009, No. 9, pp. 10)*
Pub: MANA
Ed: Jack Foster. **Description:** Difficult situations regarding the relationship between sales representatives and their principals in the fashion industry are presented and suggestions on how to create contracts that seek to prevent potential problems are provided. Sales reps should make sure that manufacturer has a viable business that is well thought-out and adequately financed.

43557 ■ *"A Novel Approach to the Market"* in *Agency Sales Magazine (Vol. 39, December 2009, No. 11, pp. 10)*
Pub: MANA
Ed: Jack Foster. **Description:** R/B Sales created a 'merchandising specialist' position that travels their territory and works with distributor counter sales teams. This puts them ahead of their competition as it increases their visibility, appeal and mix of products in their area.

43558 ■ *"Nowspeed and OneSource to Conduct Webinar"* in *Internet Wire (December 14, 2009)*
Pub: Comtex News Network, Inc.
Description: OneSource, a leading provider of global business information, and Nowspeed, an Internet marketing agency, will conduct a webinar titled 'How to Develop Social Media Content That Gets Results' in order to provide marketers insight into how to develop and optimize effective social media content to get consumer results that translate into purchases and lead generation.

43559 ■ *"On Beyond Powerpoint: Presentations Get a Wake-Up Call"* in *Inc. (November 2007, pp. 58-59)*
Pub: Gruner & Jahr USA Publishing
Ed: Michael Fitzgerald. **Description:** New software that allows business presentations to be shared online are profiled, including ProfCast, audio podcasts for sales, marketing, and training; SmartDraw2008, software that creates professional graphics; Dimdim, an open-Web conferencing tool; Empressr, a hosted Web service for creating, managing, and sharing multimedia presentations; Zentation, a free tool that

allows users to watch slides and a videos of presenter; Spresent, a Web-based presentation tool for remote offices or conference calls.

43560 ■ *"On the Go: a Busy Executive Is Always Well-Equipped for Travel"* in *Black Enterprise (Vol. 40, July 2010, No. 12, pp. 106)*
Pub: Earl G. Graves Publishing Co. Inc.
Ed: Sonia Alleyne. **Description:** Successful sales executive, Henry Watkins, shares tips on business travel.

43561 ■ *"The One Thing You Must Get Right When Building a Brand"* in *Harvard Business Review (Vol. 88, December 2010, No. 12, pp. 80)*
Pub: Harvard Business School Publishing
Ed: Patrick Barwise, Sean Meehan. **Description:** Four uses for new media include: communicating a clearly defined customer promise, creating trust via delivering on the promise, regularly improving on the promise, and innovating past what is familiar.

43562 ■ *"Online All the Time"* in *Retail Merchandiser (Vol. 51, July-August 2011, No. 4, pp. 18)*
Pub: Phoenix Media Corporation
Description: Ecommerce sales are rising at a steady pace and for cross-channel retailers it is boosting sales in the weak economy. Online sales are expected to reach $188 billion in 2011, boasting a 13.7 rate of growth.

43563 ■ *"Online Book Sales Surpass Bookstores"* in *Information Today (Vol. 28, September 2011, No. 8, pp. 11)*
Pub: Information Today, Inc.
Ed: Cindy Martine. **Description:** Online book sales outpaced bookstore purchases in the United States, signaling a shift in the US book industry. Statistical data included.

43564 ■ *"Options Abound in Winter Wares"* in *Pet Product News (Vol. 64, November 2010, No. 11, pp. 1)*
Pub: BowTie Inc.
Ed: Maggie M. Shein. **Description:** Pet supply manufacturers emphasize creating top-notch construction and functional design in creating winter clothing for pets. Meanwhile, retailers and pet owners seek human-inspired style, quality, and versatility for pets' winter clothing. How retailers generate successful sales of pets' winter clothing outside of traditional brand marketing is also examined.

43565 ■ *Our Daily Meds: How the Pharmaceutical Companies Transformed Themselves into Slick Marketing Machines*
Pub: Farrar, Straus and Giroux
Ed: Melody Petersen. **Released:** 2009. **Price:** $26.00. **Description:** Petersen, using industry memos, transcripts of meetings, and other sources shows how some drug companies are more concerned with the bottom line than with helping patients. Some of these firms are actually inventing 'diseases' in order to sell marginal medicines.

43566 ■ *"Paid to Persuade: Careers in Sales"* in *Occupational Outlook Quarterly (Vol. 55, Summer 2011, No. 2, pp. 24)*
Pub: U.S. Bureau of Labor Statistics
Ed: Ilka Maria Torpey. **Description:** Sales workers are paid to persuade others to buy goods and services. There were over 13 million wage and salary sales workers in the US in 2010. Wages in sales careers can vary and some become lucrative, lifelong career positions. Seven sales occupations with annual wages higher than $33,000 are profiled.

43567 ■ *"P&G to Mine E-Commerce Potential"* in *Business Courier (Vol. 26, September 18, 2009, No. 21, pp. 1)*
Pub: American City Business Journals, Inc.
Ed: Lisa Biank Fasig. **Description:** Procter & Gamble (P&G) is looking to turn the hits to the company's Websites into increased sales. The program will include a shop now option to track all emerging sales.

43568 ■ *"Pay or Play: Do Nice (Sales) Guys Finish Last?"* in *Agency Sales Magazine (Vol. 39, August 2009, No. 8, pp. 8)*
Pub: MANA
Ed: Julia M. Rahn. **Description:** How positive interpersonal relationships among salespersons, program coordinators, and other business-related professions will pay in terms of business success is presented. Business people should know the ideal customers, promise only what they can do, refer out when needed, and follow through with any stated promise. Further insight into these ideas is presented.

43569 ■ *"Perfecting Customer Services"* in *Pet Product News (Vol. 64, November 2010, No. 11, pp. 18)*
Pub: BowTie Inc.
Description: Pet supply retailers are encouraged to emphasize customer experience and sales representatives' knowledge of the store's product offerings to foster repeat business. Employee protocols could be implemented to improve customer interaction. Other guidelines on developing a pet supply retail environment that advances repeat business are presented.

43570 ■ *Playing Bigger Than You Are: How to Sell Big Accounts Even If You're David in a World of Goliaths*
Pub: John Wiley & Sons, Inc.
Ed: William T. Brooks, William P.G. Brooks. **Released:** November 1, 2009. **Price:** $18.99. **Description:** Small and mid-size companies are shown how to compete with larger firms and sell big accounts.

43571 ■ *"Point, Click, Buy"* in *Barron's (Vol. 90, September 6, 2010, No. 36, pp. 11)*
Pub: Barron's Editorial & Corporate Headquarters
Ed: Vito J. Racanelli. **Description:** Non-travel online retail sales from January to July 2010 increased nine percent which indicates that online shopping for the coming holidays will be good. Online sales are outpacing traditional shopping, but pricing is still critical.

43572 ■ *"Power Up"* in *Entrepreneur (Vol. 35, November 2007, No. 11, pp. 140)*
Pub: Entrepreneur Media Inc.
Ed: Amanda C. Kooser. **Description:** PowerSeller is a status in the Internet company eBay, wherein sellers average at least $1,000 in sales per month for three consecutive months. There are five tiers in the PowerSeller status, which ranges from Bronze to Titanium. Launching startups at eBay can help entrepreneurs pick up a wide customer base, but getting and maintaining PowerSeller status is a challenge.

43573 ■ *Prepare to Be a Teen Millionaire*
Pub: Health Communications, Inc.
Contact: Peter Vegso, President
Ed: Robyn Collins; Kimberly Spinks Burleson. **Released:** April 1, 2008. **Price:** $16.95. **Description:** Business reference for any teenager wishing to become a successful entrepreneur; advice is given from successful teenage millionaires. Topics covered include: choosing a business name, type, and location; use of the Internet; legal issues; branding, sales, and marketing; funding and financial management; return on investment; retirement; development of a sound business plan; and certification for minority or women-owned companies.

43574 ■ *"Private Label Manufacturers Association"* in *Ice Cream Reporter (Vol. 23, July 20, 2010, No. 8, pp. 7)*
Pub: Ice Cream Reporter
Description: Branded frozen dessert manufacturers sold more frozen desserts in terms of sales volume and revenue and market share in 2009. Statistical details included.

43575 ■ *"Promotions Create a Path to Better Profit"* in *Pet Product News (Vol. 64, December 2010, No. 12, pp. 1)*
Pub: BowTie Inc.
Ed: Joan Hustace Walker. **Description:** Pet store retailers can boost small mammal sales by launching creative marketing and promotions such as social networking and adoption days.

43576 ■ *"Pssst! Buzz About Target"* in *Barron's (Vol. 89, July 27, 2009, No. 30, pp. 15)*
Pub: Dow Jones & Co., Inc.
Ed: Katherine Cheng. **Description:** Target rebutted the rumor that they will disassociate themselves from a line of clothing inspired by the television show 'Gossip Girl'. Target's spokesman says that the retailer intends to remain closely identified with the show. Target's sales should benefit from the hotly anticipated clothing line.

43577 ■ *"Psst..Spread the Word"* in *Boston Business Journal (Vol. 27, November 23, 2007, No. 43, pp. 1)*
Pub: American City Business Journals Inc.
Ed: Lisa van der Pool. **Description:** More and more Boston companies are using word-of-mouth marketing to boost sales, and spending on it rose to $981 million in 2006. It is projected that spending on word-of-mouth marketing will reach $1.4 billion in 2007, and marketing companies using this type of method are getting higher funding. Trends in word-of-mouth marketing are discussed.

43578 ■ *"Real Estate Wheeling and Dealing Picks Up"* in *Business Journal Portland (Vol. 27, October 29, 2010, No. 35, pp. 1)*
Pub: Portland Business Journal
Ed: Wendy Culverwell. **Description:** LoopNet has listed 33 prominent commercial properties for sale in Portland, Oregon's real estate market. However, reasons for the sales rush are not totally clear, but speculations point to the end of the Bush tax cuts in 2010 that prompted real estate investors to close the deals and avoid the increase in capital gains taxes.

43579 ■ *"Recovery a Ruse?"* in *Baltimore Business Journal (Vol. 28, August 6, 2010, No. 13, pp. 1)*
Pub: Baltimore Business Journal
Ed: Scott Dance. **Description:** Baltimore, Maryland-area businesses have remained cautious as their optimism faded along with the latest indicators on economic recovery. Economists believe they might be justified with their concern since sales were better, but there is no security that they will stay that way.

43580 ■ *"Rediscovering the Land of Opportunity"* in *Green Industry Pro (July 2011)*
Pub: Cygnus Business Media
Ed: Gregg Wartgow. **Description:** Landscape contractors need to discover new strategies that will generate leads and convert those leads into sales.

43581 ■ *"Refreshing"* in *Canadian Business (Vol. 79, September 11, 2006, No. 18, pp. 22)*
Pub: Rogers Media
Ed: Joe Castaldo. **Description:** Turnaround strategies and initiatives adopted by Canadian Beverage Corp. to boost its declining sales are presented.

43582 ■ *"Reinventing Your Rep Training Program"* in *Agency Sales Magazine (Vol. 39, August 2009, No. 8, pp. 40)*
Pub: MANA
Description: Tips on how to encourage manufacturer's representatives to attend scheduled training sessions are given. Manufacturers should learn the value of keeping the training program up-to-date and communicate with the sales team to know what needs to be revamped. Problems faced by representatives with inside sales staff should also be addressed by the manufacturer.

43583 ■ *"Renewed Vision"* in *Hawaii Business (Vol. 54, August 2008, No. 2, pp. 49)*
Pub: Hawaii Business Publishing
Ed: Jason Ubay. **Description:** Saint Francis Healthcare System of Hawaii, ranked 81 in Hawaii's top 250 companies for 2008, has been rebranding to focus on senior community healthcare and sold some of its operations, which explains the decline in gross sales from $219.5M in 2006 to $122.7M in 2007. The system's senior services and home hospice service expansion are provided.

43584 ■ *"Rep Contracts: Simple, Clear, Fair"* in *Agency Sales Magazine (Vol. 39, September-October 2009, No. 9, pp. 3)*
Pub: MANA
Ed: Bryan C. Shirley. **Description:** Things that a manufacturer and a sales representative needs to strive for when creating an Agreement for Representation includes an agreement that is simple and complete, one that covers all the needs of both parties and is fair, equitable, and balanced. Sales representatives need to make more sales calls and find new opportunities during this recession.

43585 ■ *"Rep Vs. Direct: Always an Interesting Story"* in *Agency Sales Magazine (Vol. 39, July 2009, No. 7, pp. 3)*
Pub: MANA
Ed: Bryan C. Shirley. **Description:** Manufacturers benefit from outsourcing their field sales to professional sales representatives in the areas of multi-line selling and customer knowledge and relationship. Some misperceptions about sales reps include the belief that they are an additional 'channel' in sales.

43586 ■ *"Reps Continue to Move to International Trade"* in *Agency Sales Magazine (Vol. 39, September-October 2009, No. 9, pp. 24)*
Pub: MANA
Ed: Jack Foster. **Description:** Sales representatives should get involved and look into international trade if they want to be successful in the future. The weak U.S. dollar, labor costs, and the low cost of transportation are factors that drive the trend towards international trade.

43587 ■ *"Reps Have Needs Too!"* in *Agency Sales Magazine (Vol. 39, December 2009, No. 11, pp. 16)*
Pub: MANA
Ed: Bill Heyden. **Description:** There is common information that a sales representatives needs to know prior to choosing a manufacturer to represent. Both parties must keep promises made to customers and prospects. Reps also need the support from the manufacturers and to clear matters regarding their commission. Interviewing tips for representatives to get this vital information are presented.

43588 ■ *"Reps Vs. Factory Direct Sales Force..Which Way to Go?"* in *Agency Sales Magazine (Vol. 39, September-October 2009, No. 9, pp. 28)*
Pub: MANA
Ed: Eric P. Johnson. **Description:** Hiring independent manufacturers' sales representative is a cost-effective alternative to a direct sales force. Sales reps have predictable sales costs that go up and down with sales, stronger local relationships and better market intelligence.

43589 ■ *"Reps Vs. Factory Direct Sales Force..Which Way to Go?"* in *Agency Sales Magazine (Vol. 39, September-October 2009, No. 9, pp. 28)*
Pub: MANA
Ed: Eric P. Johnson. **Description:** Hiring independent manufacturers' sales representative is a cost-effective alternative to a direct sales force. Sales reps have predictable sales costs that go up and down with sales, stronger local relationships and better market intelligence.

43590 ■ *"Revisiting Rep Coping Strategies"* in *Agency Sales Magazine (Vol. 39, December 2009, No. 11, pp. 32)*
Pub: MANA
Ed: Jack Foster. **Description:** Independent manufacturers representatives should become a well-rounded and complete businessman with continued education. The new type of representative is a problem solver and the resource for answering questions. Employing the concept of synergistic selling is also important to salespeople.

43591 ■ *"Right From the Start"* in *Small Business Opportunities (July 2010)*
Pub: Harris Publications Inc.
Ed: Ed Krug. **Description:** Ed Krug from Pitch Blue provides sales support services by partnering with small and mid-sized companies to set and reach new revenue targets.

43592 ■ *"The Rise of Pompei"* in *Retail Merchandiser (Vol. 51, September-October 2011, No. 5, pp. 13)*
Pub: Phoenix Media Corporation
Description: Soho creative consulting group follows its C3 philosophy to create an invigorated brand experience that transforms customers from consumers to empowered buyers. Pompei AD is a leading creative consultancy that specializes in design and branding for retail, museum, hospitality, and other sectors.

43593 ■ *"Sales and the Absolute Power of Information"* in *Agency Sales Magazine (Vol. 39, July 2009, No. 7, pp. 16)*
Pub: MANA
Ed: Dave Kahle. **Description:** Having good information can help a sales representative deliver effective sales performance. A process for collecting information about customers, prospects, and competitors is discussed.

43594 ■ *Sales Bible*
Pub: Collins Publications
Contact: Rachel Anderson, Director
Ed: Jeffery Gitomer. **Released:** May 6, 2008. **Price:** $29.95. **Description:** An expert in sales provides the definitive sales reference.

43595 ■ *"Sales Communications in a Mobile World"* in *Business Communication Quarterly (December 2007, pp. 492)*
Pub: SAGE Publications USA
Contact: Blaise R. Simqu, President
Ed: Daniel T. Norris. **Description:** Salespeople can take advantage of the latest mobile technologies while maintaining a personal touch with clients and customers through innovation, formality in interactions, client interactions, and protection and security of mobile data.

43596 ■ *"Sales Force Expertise: A Competitive Advantage"* in *Agency Sales Magazine (Vol. 39, November 2009, No. 10, pp. 10)*
Pub: MANA
Ed: Ken Valla. **Description:** Maintaining an expert sales force is a competitive advantage that sales leaders can count on. The skills that the sales force need to have include 'consultative selling' or the ability to understand and link to a customer's business priorities, conducting a process conversation, and asking discovery questions.

43597 ■ *"Sales Gave W&S Record '07"* in *Business Courier (Vol. 24, March 14, 2008, No. 49, pp. 1)*
Pub: American City Business Journals, Inc.
Ed: Jon Newberry. **Description:** Western & Southern Financial Group was able to achieve a record $365 million in net income thanks in large part to the double-digit increases in profits by its W&S Agency Group field offices and non-insurance businesses. The sale of their Integrated Investment Services Subsidiary and shares in several Marriot hotels also added to the record profit.

43598 ■ *Salesforce.com Secrets of Success: Best Practices for Growth and Profitability*
Pub: Prentice Hall Business Publishing
Contact: Jerome Grant, President
Ed: David Taber. **Released:** May 15, 2009. **Price:** $34.99. **Description:** Guide for using Salesforce.com; it provides insight into navigating through user groups, management, sales, marketing and IT departments in order to achieve the best results.

43599 ■ *"Say Goodbye to Voicemail"* in *Agency Sales Magazine (Vol. 39, November 2009, No. 10, pp. 3)*
Pub: MANA
Description: Salespeople should think twice before leaving a voicemail. The emerging modern etiquette is to send a text message or to e-mail the customer or client. Communication suggestions for both salespeople and their principals are presented.

43600 ■ *"Scripps Networks" in Brandweek (Vol. 49, April 21, 2008, No. 16, pp. SR12)*
Pub: VNU Business Media, Inc.
Ed: Anthony Crupi. **Description:** Provides contact information for sales and marketing personnel for the Scripps networks as well as a listing of the station's top programming and an analysis of the current season and the target audience for those programs running in the current season. Scripps networks include HGTV and the Food Network. HGTV boasts on of the industry's best commercial-retention averages, keeping nearly 97 percent of its viewers during advertising breaks.

43601 ■ *"The Secret Strategy for Meaningful Sales Meetings" in Agency Sales Magazine (Vol. 39, December 2009, No. 11, pp. 40)*
Pub: MANA
Ed: Dave Kahle. **Description:** Sales meetings can be made more meaningful by focusing on the end results that the meeting seeks to achieve. Describing the changed behavior that is sought from the sales force and working backwards from there also help make a sales meeting more meaningful.

43602 ■ *"Sell: Going Zen" in Entrepreneur (Vol. 35, October 2007, No. 10, pp. 106)*
Pub: Entrepreneur Media Inc.
Ed: Barry Farber. **Description:** Principles of Zen can actually be used to improve selling skills. Some of the Zen values such as being prepared, keeping silent, and practicing open-mindedness are applicable in the marketing world. Details on what salespeople can learn from Zen are provided.

43603 ■ *Sell More of Anything to Anyone: Sales Tips for Individuals, Business Owners and Sales Professionals*
Pub: Allen & Unwin
Ed: Andrew Griffiths. **Released:** May 10, 2010. **Price:** $16.95. **Description:** Tips are shared to help anyone improve sales skills while providing strong customer service.

43604 ■ *Selling the Invisible: A Field Guide to Modern Marketing*
Pub: Business Plus
Ed: Harry Beckwith. **Price:** $22.95. **Description:** Tips for marketing and selling intangibles such as health care, entertainment, tourism, legal services, and more are provided.

43605 ■ *Selling Online: Canada's Bestselling Guide to Becoming a Successful E-Commerce Merchant*
Pub: John Wiley and Sons Canada Ltd.
Ed: Jim Carroll; Rick Broadhead. **Released:** September 6, 2002. **Description:** Helps individuals build online retail enterprises; this updated version includes current tools, information and success strategies, how to launch an online storefront, security, marketing strategies, and mistakes to avoid.

43606 ■ *"Selling With Strengths; Talent Trumps Training" in Gallup Management Journal (March 24, 2011)*
Pub: Gallup
Description: What are the strengths of salespeople, and how can organizations develop them? What do great sales managers do differently? The authors of, 'Strengths Based Selling' answer these questions and others, including: why money is overrated as a motivator.

43607 ■ *Selling to Zebras: How to Close 90 Percent of the Business You Pursue Faster, More Easily and More Profitably*
Pub: Greenleaf Book Group Press
Ed: Jeff Koser, Chad Koser. **Released:** October 1, 2008. **Price:** $19.95. **Description:** Authors argue that the key to closing more sales is to spend more time researching and meeting with clients.

43608 ■ *"Shoestring-Budget Marketing" in Women Entrepreneur (January 5, 2009)*
Pub: Entrepreneur Media Inc.
Ed: Maria Falconer. **Description:** Pay-per-click search engine advertising is the traditional type of e-marketing that may not only be too expensive for certain kinds of businesses but also may not attract

the quality customer base a business looking to grow needs to find. Social networking websites have become a mandatory marketing tool for business owners who want to see growth in their sales; tips are provided for utilizing these networking websites in order to gain more visibility on the Internet which can, in turn, lead to the more sales.

43609 ■ *"Should You Invest in the Long Tail?' in Harvard Business Review (Vol. 86, July-August 2008, No. 8, pp. 88)*
Pub: Harvard Business School Press
Ed: Anita Elberse. **Description:** Relevance of the long tail, or the sustainability of sales after a given product's launch is examined. It is posited that niche sales are not as sustainable as those for products with broader appeal.

43610 ■ *"The Simon Cowell of Sales" in Inc. (March 2008, pp. 81-82)*
Pub: Gruner & Jahr USA Publishing
Ed: Norm Brodsky. **Description:** Successful selling tips to help anyone trying to close a deal are examined.

43611 ■ *"Single Most Important Problem" in Small Business Economic Trends (September 2010, pp. 18)*
Pub: National Federation of Independent Business
Ed: William C. Dunkelberg, Holly Wade. **Description:** A table of the single most important problem among small businesses surveyed in the U.S. in August 2010 is presented. 'Poor sales' was selected by 31 percent of firms as the single most important problem, followed by taxes at 21 percent. Graphs comparing selected single most important problem from January 1986 to August 2010 are also provided.

43612 ■ *"Single Most Important Problem" in Small Business Economic Trends (July 2010, pp. 18)*
Pub: National Federation of Independent Business
Description: A table showing the single most important problem among small businesses surveyed in the U.S. for June 2010 is presented. Poor sales was selected by 30 percent of firms as the single most important problem, followed by taxes and government requirements and red tape. Graphs comparing selected single most important problem from January 1986 to June 2010 are also given.

43613 ■ *Six SIGMA for Small Business*
Pub: Entrepreneur Press
Ed: Greg Brue. **Released:** October 2005. **Price:** $19.95 (US), $26.95 (Canadian). **Description:** Jack Welch's Six SIGMA approach to business covers accounting, finance, sales and marketing, buying a business, human resource development, and new product development.

43614 ■ *"Six Tips To Maximize Networking Opportunities" in Women Entrepreneur (November 3, 2008)*
Pub: Entrepreneur Media Inc.
Ed: Tamara Monosoff. **Description:** Networking events fall into the realm of business development as opposed to immediate sales opportunities. It is important to remember that these events provide a chance to build relationships that may someday help one's business. Tips to help make the most out of networking events are provided.

43615 ■ *"Skinner's No Drive-Thru CEO" in Crain's Chicago Business (Vol. 31, April 28, 2008, No. 17, pp. 1)*
Pub: Crain Communications, Inc.
Ed: David Sterrett. **Description:** Profile of James Skinner who was named CEO for McDonald's Corp. in November 2004 and has proved to be a successful leader despite the number of investors who doubted him when he came to the position. Mr. Skinner has overseen three years of unprecedented sales growth and launched the biggest menu expansion in 30 years.

43616 ■ *"The Small 300" in Canadian Business (Vol. 81, Summer 2008, No. 9, pp. 137)*
Pub: Rogers Media Ltd.
Description: Small cap-companies are ranked based on market capitalization and stock performance. Calgary-based Grande Cache Coal Corp. topped the

roster with 1,000 percent of return resulting from strong sales. A table showing the 2008 rankings of the companies is presented.

43617 ■ *"Small Budget, Big Impact" in Small Business Opportunities (Summer 2010)*
Pub: Harris Publications Inc.
Ed: Hilary J.M. Topper. **Description:** Ways to use social media to get in from of a target audience for small businesses are examined.

43618 ■ *Small Business Desk Reference*
Pub: Penguin Books USA Inc.
Ed: Gene Marks. **Released:** December 2004. **Description:** Comprehensive guide for starting or running a successful small business, focusing on buying a business or franchise, writing a business plan, financial management, accounting, legal issues, human resources management, operations, marketing, sales, customer service, taxes, insurance, and ethics. Information for launching a restaurant, property management firm, retail outlet, consulting firm, and service business is included.

43619 ■ *The Small Business Owner's Manual: Everything You Need to Know to Start Up and Run Your Business*
Pub: Career Press, Incorporated
Ed: Joe Kennedy. **Released:** June 2005. **Price:** $19.99 (US), $26.95 (Canadian). **Description:** Comprehensive guide for starting a small business, focusing on twelve ways to obtain financing, business plans, selling and advertising products and services, hiring and firing employees, setting up a Web site, business law, accounting issues, insurance, equipment, computers, banks, financing, customer credit and collection, leasing, and more.

43620 ■ *"Small Business Prices" in Small Business Economic Trends (April 2008, pp. 8)*
Pub: National Federation of Independent Business
Ed: William C. Dunkelberg, Holly Wade. **Description:** Two tables and a graph presenting the price changes and price plans of small businesses in the U.S. are provided. The net percentage of planned and actual prices includes data from 1968 to 2008.

43621 ■ *"Small Business Prices" in Small Business Economic Trends (March 2008, pp. 8)*
Pub: National Federation of Independent Business
Ed: William C. Dunkelberg. **Description:** Two tables and a graph presenting the price changes and price plans of small businesses in the U.S. are provided. The net percentage of planned and actual prices includes data from 1986 to 2008.

43622 ■ *"Small Business Prices" in Small Business Economic Trends (February 2008, pp. 8)*
Pub: National Federation of Independent Business
Ed: William C. Dunkelberg. **Description:** Two tables and a graph presenting the price changes and price plans of small businesses in the U.S. are provided. The net percentage of planned and actual prices includes data from 1974 to 2008.

43623 ■ *"Small Business Prices" in Small Business Economic Trends (January 2008, pp. 8)*
Pub: National Federation of Independent Business
Description: Graph from a survey of small businesses in the U.S. is given representing business prices from January 1986 to December 2007. Actual prices (last three months) and planned prices (next three months) were compared in the graph. Tables of actual price changes and price plans from January 2002 to December 2007 are also supplied.

43624 ■ *"Small Business Sales" in Small Business Economic Trends (April 2008, pp. 7)*
Pub: National Federation of Independent Business
Ed: William C. Dunkelberg, Holly Wade. **Description:** Two tables and a graph resenting sales figures of small businesses in the U.S. is presented. Statistics for sales changes and sales expectations are provided. The figures in the graph include data from 1986 to 2008.

43625 ■ *"Small Business Sales" in Small Business Economic Trends (March 2008, pp. 7)*
Pub: National Federation of Independent Business
Ed: William C. Dunkelberg, Holly Wade. **Description:** Two tables and a graph that present sales figures for small businesses in the U.S. are given. Statistics for sales changes and sales expectations are provided. The figures in the graph include data from 1986 to 2008.

43626 ■ *"Small Business Sales" in Small Business Economic Trends (February, pp. 7)*
Pub: National Federation of Independent Business
Ed: William C. Dunkelberg, Holly Wade. **Description:** Two tables and a graph that present sales figures for small businesses in the U.S. are given. Statistics for sales changes and sales expectations are provided. The figures in the graph include data from 1974 to 2008.

43627 ■ *"Small Business Sales" in Small Business Economic Trends (January, pp. 7)*
Pub: National Federation of Independent Business
Description: Graph from a survey of small businesses in the U.S. is given, representing sales from January 1986 to December 2007. Actual sales (prior three months) and expected sales (next three months) were compared in the graph. Tables of actual sales changes and sales expectations from January 2002 to December 2007 are also given.

43628 ■ *"Small Business Sales" in Small Business Economic Trends (September 2010, pp. 7)*
Pub: National Federation of Independent Business
Ed: William C. Dunkelberg, Holly Wade. **Description:** A graph from a survey of small businesses in the U.S. is given, representing sales from January 1986 to August 2010. Actual sales (prior three months) and expected sales (next three months) were compared in the graph. Tables of actual sales changes and sales expectations from January 2005 to August 2010 are also given.

43629 ■ *"Small Business Sales" in Small Business Economic Trends (July 2010, pp. 7)*
Pub: National Federation of Independent Business
Description: A graph from a survey of small businesses in the U.S. is given representing sales from January 1986 to June 2010. Actual sales (prior three months) and expected sales (next three months) were compared in the graph. Tables of actual sales changes and sales expectations from January 2005 to June 2010 are also given.

43630 ■ *"Smart Car Sales Take Big Hit in Recession" in Business Journal-Milwaukee (Vol. 28, December 10, 2010, No. 10, pp. A1)*
Pub: Milwaukee Business Journal
Ed: Stacey Vogel Davis. **Description:** Sales of smart cars in Milwaukee declined in 2010. Smart Center Milwaukee sold only 52 new cars through October 2010. Increased competition is seen as a reason for the decline in sales.

43631 ■ *"Smarts Drive Sales" in Pet Product News (Vol. 64, December 2010, No. 12, pp. 1)*
Pub: BowTie Inc.
Ed: Karen Shugart. **Description:** Retailers could make smart decisions by deciding how to best attract customers into their stores or resolving whether to nurture in-store or buy herps (reptiles) from suppliers. Paying attention to these smart decisions could help boost customer interest in herps and address customer demands.

43632 ■ *The Social Media Bible: Tactics, Tools, and Strategies for Business Success*
Pub: John Wiley & Sons, Inc.
Ed: Lon Safko, David Brake. **Released:** June 17, 2009. **Price:** $29.95. **Description:** Information is given to build or transform a business into social media, where customers, employees, and prospects connect, collaborate, and champion products and services in order to increase sales and to beat the competition.

43633 ■ *"Solar Hot Water Sales Are Hot, Hot, Hot" in Contractor (Vol. 56, December 2009, No. 12, pp. 22)*
Pub: Penton Media, Inc.
Ed: Dave Yates. **Description:** Plumbing contractors in the United States can benefit from the increased sales of solar thermal water systems. Licensed plumbers have the base knowledge on the risks associated from heating and storing water. Safety issues associated with solar water heaters are also included.

43634 ■ *"Sony Pictures Television" in Brandweek (Vol. 49, April 21, 2008, No. 16, pp. SR13)*
Pub: VNU Business Media, Inc.
Ed: Marc Berman. **Description:** Provides contact information for sales and marketing personnel for Sony Pictures Television Distribution as well as a listing of the station's top programming and an analysis of the current season and the target audience for those programs running in the current season.

43635 ■ *"Sound Check" in Agency Sales Magazine (Vol. 39, August 2009, No. 8, pp. 14)*
Pub: MANA
Ed: Dave Kahle. **Description:** Most customers believe salespersons are unable to do well in terms of listening, which is one of the four fundamental competencies of a sales person. Listening is the primary tool to uncover deeper and more powerful needs and motivations of the customer. A guide on how to listen better and improve listening effectiveness is presented.

43636 ■ *"Spillover Effects" in Crain's Detroit Business (Vol. 24, October 6, 2008, No. 40, pp. 29)*
Pub: Crain Communications, Inc.
Description: Earlier this year, the Detroit Regional Chamber estimated that the Detroit Tiger's baseball team's 81 home games would have a $277 million positive economic impact on the region. Due to the poor performance of the team, fewer fans are spending money on tickets, which translates into fewer dollars coming into the region. Lower viewership on television has also been a result of the Tiger's losing season.

43637 ■ *"Sponsorship, Booths Available for Spring Business Showcase" in Bellingham Business Journal (Vol. February 2010, pp. 3)*
Pub: Sound Publishing Inc.
Description: Third Annual Spring Business Showcase still have space available for vendors and sponsors. The event gives local businesses the opportunity to increase their visibility and provides a means to increase sales and build relationships.

43638 ■ *"Stop Trying to Delight Your Customers" in Harvard Business Review (Vol. 88, July-August 2010, No. 7-8, pp. 116)*
Pub: Harvard Business School Publishing
Ed: Matthew Dixon, Karen Freeman, Nicholas Toman. **Description:** Importance of resolving issues for customers is key to increasing their loyalty, rather than by exceeding customer expectations. Areas to address include decreasing customer need for follow-up calls, switching service channels, and the potential for negative emotional response.

43639 ■ *Streetwise Small Business Book of Lists: Hundreds of Lists to Help You Reduce Costs, Increase Revenues, and Boost Your Profits!*
Pub: Adams Media Corporation
Contact: Gary Krebs, Director
E-mail: swatrous@adamsmedia.com
Ed: Gene Marks. **Released:** September 2006. **Price:** $25.95. **Description:** Strategies to help small business owners locate services, increase sales, and lower expenses.

43640 ■ *"Suited for Success" in Retail Merchandiser (Vol. 51, July-August 2011, No. 4, pp. 6)*
Pub: Phoenix Media Corporation
Description: MyBestFit is a size-matching body scanner that helps consumers find the perfect size clothing for themselves, giving brick and mortar retailers an edge on ecommerce competitors.

43641 ■ *"Summary. Economic Trends for Small Business" in Small Business Economic Trends (March 2008, pp. 1)*
Pub: National Federation of Independent Business
Ed: William C. Dunkelberg, Holly Wade. **Description:** Summary of economic trends for small businesses in the U.S. is provided. Economic indicators such as capital spending, inventories and sales, inflation, and profits are given. Analysis of credit markets is also provided.

43642 ■ *"Summary. Economic Trends for Small Business" in Small Business Economic Trends (February 2008, pp. 1)*
Pub: National Federation of Independent Business
Ed: William C. Dunkelberg, Holly Wade. **Description:** Summary of economic trends for small businesses in the U.S. is provided. Economic indicators such as capital spending, inventories and sales, inflation, and profits are given. Analysis of credit markets is also provided.

43643 ■ *"Super Success" in Small Business Opportunities (November 2008)*
Pub: Entrepreneur Press
Contact: Perlman Neil, President
Description: Profile of PromoWorks LLC, a company founded by Michael Kent, that distributes samples of food at grocery stores for clients like Kraft Foods, Inc. and Kellogg Co. and also handles the logistics, provides the employees and tracks the products' sales.

43644 ■ *"Suppliers Look to Rack Up Big Sales to Distributors" in The Business Journal-Serving Metropolitan Kansas City (August 15, 2008)*
Pub: American City Business Journals, Inc.
Ed: James Dornbrook. **Description:** Suppliers of shelving units, conveyor systems and other equipment used in distribution facilities are expecting new business opportunities along with the planned intermodal projects in the Kansas City area. Suppliers have already observed that small distributors have started to relocate to the city because of the intermodal projects. Demand for shelves and lifts have also increased.

43645 ■ *"Sustaining Health" in Pet Product News (Vol. 64, November 2010, No. 11, pp. 28)*
Pub: BowTie Inc.
Ed: Angela Pham. **Description:** How pet supply retailers have responded to dog owners' interest in health supplements and their ingredients is discussed. Dog owners are showing interest in the ingredients inside the supplements and are reading labels. Retailers must now prove the beneficial effects of these ingredients in order to make the sale.

43646 ■ *"Sweet Harmony" in Canadian Business (Vol. 82, April 27, 2009, No. 7, pp. 6)*
Pub: Rogers Media
Description: Canada will harmonize its 5 percent federal goods and services tax wit the 8 percent provincial sales tax effective July 1, 2010. Meanwhile, provinces like Ontario and Quebec have switched the sales taxes that are charged in new investments into a value-added tax. The conversion has led to an 11 percent increase in investments in Quebec and the three other provinces that made the conversion.

43647 ■ *"Sweet Tea; Neil Golden" in Advertising Age (Vol. 79, November 17, 2008, No. 43, pp. 4)*
Pub: Crain Communications, Inc.
Ed: Emily Bryson York. **Description:** McDonald's launch of iced coffee and sweat tea, which were promoted via price cuts over the summer, helped to boost sales at the fast-food chain.

43648 ■ *"Take Out the Garbage" in Entrepreneur (Vol. 37, August 2009, No. 8, pp. 26)*
Pub: Entrepreneur Media, Inc.
Ed: Michael Port. **Description:** Canned 1-2-3 sales tactics should be ditched since consumers express their values with the products and services they buy. Sales people should instead work their call list and become a masterful permission marketer, make

relevant sales offers proportionate to the trust they have earned, and build credibility with the people they are meant to serve.

43649 ■ *"Taking a Chance"* in *Baltimore Business Journal (Vol. 28, July 16, 2010, No. 10, pp. 1)*
Pub: Baltimore Business Journal
Ed: Scott Dance. **Description:** North Avenue in Baltimore, Maryland is considered a rough neighborhood due to the dangers of prostitution and drug dealing. However, some entrepreneurs have taken the risk of building their businesses on North Avenue as revitalization efforts grow. One of the challenges for businesses in rough neighborhoods is bringing customers to their stores or offices.

43650 ■ *"Tap Into Food Truck Trend to Rev Up Sales, Build Buzz"* in *Nation's Restaurant News (Vol. 45, February 7, 2011, No. 3, pp. 18)*
Pub: Penton Media, Inc.
Ed: Brian Sacks. **Description:** Food truck trend is growing, particularly in New York City, Philadelphia, Washington DC, and Los Angeles, California. Man entrepreneurs are using a mobile food component to market their food before opening a restaurant.

43651 ■ *"Teachable Moments: Worth Every Penny"* in *Pet Product News (Vol. 64, December 2010, No. 12, pp. 34)*
Pub: BowTie Inc.
Ed: Cheryl Reeves. **Description:** Pet bird retailers can attain both outreach to customers and enhanced profitability by staging educational events such as the annual Parrot Palooza event of Burlington, New Jersey-based Bird Paradise. Aside from attracting a global audience, Parrot Palooza features seminars, workshops, classes, and bird-related contests.

43652 ■ *"Technically Speaking"* in *Black Enterprise (Vol. 38, February 2008, No. 7, pp. 64)*
Pub: Earl G. Graves Publishing Co. Inc.
Ed: Sonia Alleyne. **Description:** Marketing manager for Texas Instruments discusses the Strategic Marketing of Technology Products course offered at the California Institute of Technology. The course helps turn products into profits.

43653 ■ *"Telemundo"* in *Brandweek (Vol. 49, April 21, 2008, No. 16, pp. SR8)*
Pub: VNU Business Media, Inc.
Ed: John Consoli. **Description:** Provides contact information for sales and marketing personnel for the Telemundo network as well as a listing of the station's top programming and an analysis of the current season and the target audience for those programs running in the current season.

43654 ■ *"Tell Us What You Really Think Collecting Customer Feedback"* in *Inc. (Vol. 30, December 2008, No. 12, pp. 52)*
Pub: Mansueto Ventures LLC
Ed: Ryan Underwood. **Description:** According to a recent survey, nearly 77 percent of online shoppers review consumer-generated reviews of products before making a purchase.

43655 ■ *"That's the Spirit"* in *Entrepreneur (Vol. 36, March 2008, No. 3, pp. 78)*
Pub: Entrepreneur Media Inc.
Ed: Barry Farber. **Description:** Tips on how to maintain confidence and deal with challenges when it is difficult to sell a product.

43656 ■ *"Thomas Industrial Network Unveils Custom SPEC"* in *Entertainment Close-Up (March 3, 2011)*
Pub: Close-Up Media
Description: Thomas Industrial Network assists custom manufacturers and industrial service providers a complete online program called Custom SPEC which includes Website development and Internet exposure.

43657 ■ *Titanium EBay: A Tactical Guide to Becoming a Millionaire PowerSeller*
Pub: Penguin Group Incorporated
Ed: Skip McGrath. **Released:** June 2006. **Price:** $24.95. **Description:** Advice is given to help anyone selling items on eBay to become a Power Seller, an award presented based on monthly gross merchandise sales.

43658 ■ *"Title Creep: The Chief Revenue Officer"* in *Inc. (March 2008, pp. 28)*
Pub: Gruner & Jahr USA Publishing
Ed: The title, Chief Revenue Officer, is growing. The marketing function of the CRO is to oversee sales, new product development, and pricing.

43659 ■ *"TiVo, Domino's Team to Offer Pizza Ordering by DVR"* in *Advertising Age (Vol. 79, November 17, 2008, No. 43, pp. 48)*
Pub: Crain Communications, Inc.
Ed: Brian Steinberg. **Description:** Domino's Pizza and TiVo are teaming up to make it possible for customers to order from the restaurant straight from their DVR. The companies see that this kind of interactive television and consumer experience will only serve to generate more sales as the customer can be exposed to a fuller range of menu selections and will not have to interrupt their viewing, while workers can spend more time making the product.

43660 ■ *"Tofutti Brands"* in *Ice Cream Reporter (Vol. 23, September 20, 2010, No. 10, pp. 6)*
Pub: Ice Cream Reporter
Description: Tofutti Brands announced net sales at $4.5 million for second quarter 2010.

43661 ■ *"Toss the Gum Before You Speak"* in *Agency Sales Magazine (Vol. 39, July 2009, No. 7, pp. 34)*
Pub: MANA
Ed: Stephen D. Boyd. **Description:** When preparing to present to a prospective principal, a salesperson should anticipate the speaking situation and find out in advance the program events that occur around their speech. They should also practice their material in front of a friend or colleague.

43662 ■ *"Training: an Investment in Performance Improvement"* in *Franchising World (Vol. 42, September 2010, No. 9, pp. 22)*
Pub: International Franchise Association
Ed: Catherine Monson. **Description:** Advantages of training provided by franchisors that are available to franchisees and their employees is discussed.

43663 ■ *Treasure Hunt*
Pub: Penguin Group Incorporated
Ed: Michael J. Silverstein; John Butman. **Released:** May 4, 2006. **Description:** Explanation of people's spending habits and how to capitalize on retail sales.

43664 ■ *"Tripped by Trump?"* in *The Business Journal-Serving Greater Tampa Bay (Vol. 28, July 25, 2008, No. 31, pp. 1)*
Pub: American City Business Journals, Inc.
Ed: Michael Hinman. **Description:** Jean Shahnasarian, a buyer of the Trump Tower Tampa, filed cases against Donald Trump, The Trump Organization Inc., and Trump Tower Tampa for giving misleading information about Trump's involvement in the project. She wants a return of her $278,000 deposit and does not want to take part in the sale of the project.

43665 ■ *"Turner Broadcasting System"* in *Brandweek (Vol. 49, April 21, 2008, No. 16, pp. SR13)*
Pub: VNU Business Media, Inc.
Ed: Anthony Crupi. **Description:** Provides contact information for sales and marketing personnel for the Turner Broadcasting System networks as well as a listing of the station's top programming and an analysis of the current season and the target audience for those programs running in the current season. Recent acquisitions are also discussed.

43666 ■ *"Twentieth Television"* in *Brandweek (Vol. 49, April 21, 2008, No. 16, pp. SR16)*
Pub: VNU Business Media, Inc.
Ed: Marc Berman. **Description:** Provides contact information for sales and marketing personnel for Twentieth Television as well as a listing of the station's top programming and an analysis of the current season and the target audience for those programs running in the current season.

43667 ■ *"Two Ways to Find New Customers"* in *Inc. (Vol. 31, January-February 2009, No. 1, pp. 41)*
Pub: Mansueto Ventures LLC
Description: Latest software programs that help sales staff connect to new leads are profiled. Salesconx provides online leads while Demandbase reports users on a particular Website.

43668 ■ *The Ultimate Guide to Electronic Marketing for Small Business: Low-Cost/High Return Tools and Techniques That Really Work*
Pub: John Wiley & Sons, Incorporated
Ed: Tom Antion. **Released:** June 2005. **Price:** $19.95 (US), $25.99 (Canadian). **Description:** Online marketing techniques for small business to grow and increase sales.

43669 ■ *The Ultimate Sales Machine: Turbocharge Your Business With Relentless Focus on 12 Key Strategies*
Pub: Penguin Group
Ed: Chet Holmes. **Released:** June 21, 2007. **Price:** $24.95. **Description:** Offers insight and step-by-step instructions to build a strong sales force.

43670 ■ *The Ultimate Small Business Marketing Toolkit: All the Tips, Forms, and Strategies You'll Ever Need!*
Pub: McGraw-Hill Inc.
Ed: Beth Goldstein. **Released:** July 2007. **Price:** $27.95. **Description:** An all-in-one sales and marketing resource for entrepreneurs to grow a business.

43671 ■ *Understanding Exporting in the Small and Micro Enterprise*
Pub: Nova Science Publishers, Inc.
Ed: Densil A. Williams. **Released:** April 1, 2009. **Price:** $79.00. **Description:** An examination into the reasons why some small and micro locally-owned businesses choose to sell a portion of their goods abroad while others facing similar market conditions remain focused on the domestic market.

43672 ■ *"Understanding Persuasive Online Sales Messages from eBay Auctions"* in *Business Communication Quarterly (December 2007, pp. 482)*
Pub: SAGE Publications USA
Contact: Blaise R. Simqu, President
Ed: Barbara Jo White, Daniel Clapper, Rita Noel, Jenny Fortier, Pierre Grabolosa. **Description:** eBay product listings were studied to determine the requirements of persuasive sales writing. Potential sellers should use the proper keywords and make an authentic description with authentic photographs of the item being auctioned.

43673 ■ *"Univision"* in *Brandweek (Vol. 49, April 21, 2008, No. 16, pp. SR8)*
Pub: VNU Business Media, Inc.
Ed: John Consoli. **Description:** Provides contact information for sales and marketing personnel for the Univision network as well as a listing of the station's top programming and an analysis of the current season and the target audience for those programs running in the current season. Univision is the No. 1 network on Friday nights in the 18-34 demographic, beating all English-language networks.

43674 ■ *"Unleashing the Power of Marketing"* in *Harvard Business Review (Vol. 88, October 2010, No. 10, pp. 90)*
Pub: Harvard Business School Publishing
Ed: Beth Comstock, Ranjay Gulati, Stephen Liguori. **Description:** Chronicle of the development of General Electric's marketing framework that focused on three key factors: Principles, people and process. GE determined that successful marketing fulfills four functions: instigating, innovating, implementing, and integrating.

43675 ■ *Up the Loyalty Ladder*
Pub: HarperCollins Publishers Inc.
Ed: Murray Rephel; Neil Raphel. **Released:** September 1996. **Description:** Marketing consultants share insight into growing any retail business and gain customer loyalty.

43676 ■ "Use Social Media to Enhance Brand, Business" in Contractor (Vol. 56, December 2009, No. 12, pp. 14)
Pub: Penton Media, Inc.
Ed: Elton Rivas. Description: Advice on how plumbing contractors should use online social networks to increase sales is presented including such issues as clearly defining goals and target audience. An additional advantage to this medium is that advertisements can easily be shared with other users.

43677 ■ Use What You've Got
Pub: Portfolio Publishing
Ed: Barbara Corcoran, Bruce Littlefield. Released: 2003. Price: $24.95. Description: Founder and chairman of New York's premier real estate company, the Corcoran Group, shares her successes in the real estate industry. The book offers tips and pointers to salespeople, entrepreneurs and business people alike. Corcoran explains how she went from waiting tables and borrowed $1,000 from a boyfriend to build her real estate company into the industry's powerhouse.

43678 ■ Values Sell: Transforming Purpose into Profit through Creative Sales and Distribution Strategies
Pub: Berrett-Koehler Publishers, Incorporated
Ed: Nadine A. Thompson; Angela E. Soper. Released: March 28, 2007. Price: $16.95. Description: Sales and distribution are the lifeblood of any business, socially responsible businesses are no different.

43679 ■ "VC Boosts WorkForce; Livonia Software Company to Add Sales, Marketing Staff" in Crain's Detroit Business (March 24, 2008)
Pub: Crain Communications, Inc.
Ed: Tom Henderson. Description: WorkForce Software Inc., a company that provides software to manage payroll processes and oversee compliance with state and federal regulations and with union rules, plans to use an investment of $5.5 million in venture capital to hire more sales and marketing staff.

43680 ■ "Warner Bros. Domestic Television Distribution" in Brandweek (Vol. 49, April 21, 2008, No. 16, pp. SR16)
Pub: VNU Business Media, Inc.
Ed: Marc Berman. Description: Provides contact information for sales and marketing personnel for Warner Bros. Domestic Television Distribution as well as a listing of the station's top programming and an analysis of the current season and the target audience for those programs running in the current season.

43681 ■ "Web-Based Marketing Excites, Challenges Small Business Use" in Colorado Springs Business Journal (January 20, 2010)
Pub: Dolan Media Co.
Ed: Becky Hurley. Description: Business-to-business and consumer-direct firms alike are using the fast-changing Web technologies to increase sales, leads and track consumer behavior but once a company commits to an Online marketing plan, experts believe, they must be prepared to consistently tweak and overhaul content and distribution vehicles in order to keep up.

43682 ■ "What Are You Doing Differently?" in Agency Sales Magazine (Vol. 39, December 2009, No. 11, pp. 3)
Pub: MANA
Ed: Bryan C. Shirley. Description: Strategies that sales representatives can do to plan for a good year include professional development, networking with other reps, and making more sales calls and seeing more people. The end of the year is the perfect time for reps to write or re-write their mission statement and to conduct line profitability.

43683 ■ "When Are Sales Representatives Also Franchisees?" in Franchise Law Journal (Vol. 27, Winter 2008, No. 3, pp. 151)
Pub: American Bar Association
Contact: Carolyn Lamm, President
Ed: John R.F. Baer, David A. Beyer, Scott P. Weber. Description: Review of the traditional definitions of sales representatives along with information on how these distribution models could fit into various legal tests for a franchise.

43684 ■ "When Success Isn't Enough" in Entrepreneur (Vol. 35, November 2007, No. 11, pp. 78)
Pub: Entrepreneur Media Inc.
Ed: Chris Penttila. Description: Companies that achieve success can often times continue to push for more growth. Details on planning expansion and boosting sales of several companies are explored.

43685 ■ Who's Your Gladys?: How to Turn Even the Most Difficult Customer into Your Biggest Fan
Pub: AMACOM
Ed: Marilyn Suttle, Lori Jo Vest. Released: September 9, 2009. Price: $22.95. Description: Every customer oriented business has a hard-to-satisfy client. This book shows how to serve customers who require a higher degree of skill to manage.

43686 ■ "Why You Need a New-Media 'Ringmaster" in Harvard Business Review (Vol. 88, December 2010, No. 12, pp. 78)
Pub: Harvard Business School Publishing
Ed: Patrick Spenner. Description: The concept of ringmaster is applied to brand marketing. This concept includes integrative thinking, lean collaboration skills, and high-speed decision cycles.

43687 ■ "Will mCommerce Make Black Friday Green?" in Retail Merchandiser (Vol. 51, September-October 2011, No. 5, pp. 8)
Pub: Phoenix Media Corporation
Ed: Scott Miller. Description: Retailers speculate the possibilities of mobile commerce and are implementing strategies at their stores. Consumers using mobile devices accounted for only 0.1 percent of visits to retail Websites on Black Friday 2009 and rose to 5.6 percent in 2010; numbers are expected to rise for 2011.

43688 ■ "William Barr III; President, Co-Founder, Universal Windows Direct, 33" in Crain's Cleveland Business (November 19, 2007)
Pub: Crain Communications, Inc.
Ed: David Bennett. Description: Profile of William Barr III, the president and co-founder of Universal Windows Direct, a manufacturer of vinyl windows and siding, whose successful salesmanship and leadership has propelled his company forward.

43689 ■ "With New Listings, Business Brokers See Hope" in Business Courier (Vol. 27, September 3, 2010, No. 18, pp. 1)
Pub: Business Courier
Ed: Lucy May. Description: Business brokers in Cincinnati, Ohio are expecting better prices in view of the strengthening economy.

43690 ■ "Women Clicking to Earn Virtual Dollars" in Sales and Marketing Management (November 11, 2009)
Pub: Nielsen Business Media, Inc.
Ed: Stacy Straczynski. Description: According to a new report from Internet marketing firm Q Interactive, women are increasingly playing social media games where they are able to click on an ad or sign up for a promotion to earn virtual currency. Research is showing that this kind of marketing may be a potent tool, especially for e-commerce and online stores.

43691 ■ "Women Workers Spend Lunchtime on Fridays Shopping Online" in Marketing to Women (Vol. 23, November 2010, No. 11, pp. 8)
Pub: EPM Communications Inc.
Contact: Ira Mayer, President
E-mail: imayer@epmcom.com
Description: Forty percent of women shop online during work hours, particularly on Fridays. The largest number of women make these purchases during their lunch break. Demographics are included.

43692 ■ "YoCream" in Ice Cream Reporter (Vol. 23, September 20, 2010, No. 10, pp. 6)
Pub: Ice Cream Reporter
Description: YoCream reported a sales increase for third quarter 2010 at 15.6 percent and net income increasing 25 percent to $2,141,000 for that quarter.

43693 ■ "You Can't Beat Habit" in Entrepreneur (Vol. 37, July 2009, No. 7, pp. 61)
Pub: Entrepreneur Media, Inc.
Ed: Neale Martin. Description: Customers are changing their spending behavior because of the financial meltdown, and this poses an opportunity for businesses to change their marketing practices in order to regain customers. Being flexible is one way to reestablish purchase behavior, along with paying attention to customer feedback.

43694 ■ "Young Adult, Childless May Help Fuel Post-Recession Rebound" in Pet Product News (Vol. 64, November 2010, No. 11, pp. 4)
Pub: BowTie Inc.
Description: Pet industry retailers and marketers are encouraged to tap into the young adult and childless couple sectors to boost consumer traffic and sales to pre-recession levels. Among young adult owners, pet ownership increased from 40 percent in 2003 to 49 percent in 2009. Meanwhile, the childless couple sector represented 63 percent of all dog/cat owners in 2009.

43695 ■ "Your Booming Business: How You Can Align Sales and Marketing for Dynamic Growth" in Small Business Opportunities (Spring 2008)
Pub: Harris Publications Inc.
Ed: Voss W. Graham. Description: Voss Graham, founder and CEO of Inneractive Consulting Group Inc., works with companies to develop and hire successful sales teams. A checklist from the American Bankers Association to help write a business plan is included.

43696 ■ "Your Turn in the Spotlight" in Inc. (Volume 32, December 2010, No. 10, pp. 57)
Pub: Inc. Magazine
Ed: John Brandon. Description: Examples of three video blogs created by entrepreneurs to promote their businesses and products are used to show successful strategies. Wine Library TV promotes a family's wine business; SHAMA.TV offers marketing tips and company news; and Will It Blend? promotes sales of a household blender.

43697 ■ "Zebra's Changing Stripes" in Crain's Chicago Business (Vol. 31, November 17, 2008, No. 46, pp. 4)
Pub: Crain Communications, Inc.
Ed: John Pletz. Description: Zebra Technologies Corp., the world's largest manufacturer of bar-code printers is profiled; the company's stock has plunged with shares declining 40 percent in the past three months grinding the firm's growth to a halt. Zebra's plans to regain revenue growth are also discussed.

TRADE PERIODICALS

43698 ■ Counterman: Dedicated to Successful Parts Distribution
Pub: Babcox
URL(s): www.babcox.com/site/our-brands/counterman www.counterman.com/. Ed: Mark Phillips. Released: Monthly Price: Free.

43699 ■ The Selling Advantage
Pub: Progressive Business Publications
Ed: Phil Ahr, Editor. Released: Semimonthly. Price: $94.56, individuals. Description: Explores new strategies and proven techniques to improve sales performance. Recurring features include book reviews and a column titled Tale of the Sale.

43700 ■ Selling Power: Solutions for sales management
Pub: Personal Selling Power Inc.
Contact: Gerhard Gschwandtner, Chief Executive Officer
E-mail: gerhardpsp@aol.com
URL(s): www.sellingpower.com/magazine. Released: 10/yr. Price: $10, Individuals U.S.

43701 ■ *Selling to Seniors*
Pub: CD Publications
Ed: Jean Van Ryzin, Editor. **Released:** Monthly. **Price:** $294, individuals. **Description:** Suggests effective ways to reach the 'over 50' market by emphasizing successful marketing strategies. Recurring features include interviews, case studies, and demographic data. Remarks: Incorporates the former Maturity Market Perspectives and Mature Market Report. Editor: Allison Patterson.

43702 ■ *Targets*
Pub: Salesforce Training & Consulting Inc.
Ed: Lorraine Jeffrey, Editor, lorraine@salesforcetraining.com. **Released:** Quarterly. **Price:** Free. **Description:** Provides sales professionals with information on developments and improvements within the marketing, sales, and advertising industries. Recurring features include columns titled Publishers Podium, Guest Column, Hints-Tips-Ideas, and Sales Manager's Corner.

43703 ■ *What's Working in Sales Management*
Pub: Progressive Business Publications
Contact: Ron McRae, Editor-in-Chief
Ed: Steve Trimble, Editor. **Released:** 22x/Year. **Price:** $264, individuals. **Description:** Acts as a time-saving resource for busy sales managers. Recurring features include interviews, news of research, a calendar of events, and news of educational opportunities.

VIDEOCASSETTES/ AUDIOCASSETTES

43704 ■ *Achieve Success by Prospecting with Phillip Wexler*
Instructional Video
2219 C St.
Lincoln, NE 68502
Ph: (402)475-6570
Free: 800-228-0164
Fax: (402)475-6500
Co. E-mail: feedback@insvideo.com
URL: http://www.insvideo.com
Released: 19??. **Price:** $95.00. **Description:** Phillip Wexler offers prospecting training program for sales people. Only available in the U.S. **Availability:** VHS.

43705 ■ *American Business Sales Series*
Instructional Video
2219 C St.
Lincoln, NE 68502
Ph: (402)475-6570
Free: 800-228-0164
Fax: (402)475-6500
Co. E-mail: feedback@insvideo.com
URL: http://www.insvideo.com
Released: 19??. **Description:** Business education series aimed at improving phone-selling skills. **Availability:** VHS.

43706 ■ *Ask for the Order. . .and Get It!*
Dartnell Corp.
2222 Sedwick Dr.
Durham, NC 34112
Ph: (239)417-2079
Free: 800-223-8720
Fax: (800)508-2592
Co. E-mail: customerservice@dartnellcorp.com
URL: http://www.dartnellcorp.com
Contact: Kenneth F. Kahn, Publisher
Released: 1972. **Description:** Hammers home a key principle of salesmanship—to get an order you must ask for it; from the "Tough-Minded Salesmanship" series. **Availability:** VHS; 3/4 U; Special order formats.

43707 ■ *Ask for the Order. . .and Get It!?Revised*
Excellence in Training Corp.
c/o ICON Training
804 Roosevelt St.
Polk City, IA 50226

Free: 800-609-0479
Co. E-mail: info@icontraining.com
URL: http://www.icontraining.com
Released: 1991. **Price:** $469.00. **Description:** An updated look at the timeless issues of selling. **Availability:** VHS; 3/4 U; Special order formats.

43708 ■ *Bakery Merchandising 101*
International Dairy-Deli-Bakery Association (IDDBA)
PO Box 5528
Madison, WI 53705-0528
Ph: (608)310-5000
Fax: (608)238-6330
Co. E-mail: iddba@iddba.org
URL: http://www.iddba.org
Contact: Steve Beekhuizen, President
Released: 19??. **Price:** $50.00. **Description:** Discusses ways for successful promotion and product appeal to help increase bakery sales. **Availability:** VHS.

43709 ■ *Bakery Merchandising Certificate Program*
International Dairy-Deli-Bakery Association (IDDBA)
PO Box 5528
Madison, WI 53705-0528
Ph: (608)310-5000
Fax: (608)238-6330
Co. E-mail: iddba@iddba.org
URL: http://www.iddba.org
Contact: Steve Beekhuizen, President
Released: 19??. **Price:** $160.00. **Description:** Examines the benefits of suggestive selling, sampling, displays, and event merchandising. **Availability:** VHS.

43710 ■ *Beware the Naked Man Who Offers You His Shirt*
PBS Home Video
Catalog Fulfillment Center
Charlotte, NC 28275-1089
Ph: (800)531-4727
Free: 800-645-4PBS
Co. E-mail: info@pbs.org
URL: http://www.pbs.org
Released: 1990. **Price:** $395.00. **Description:** The author of "Swim With the Sharks Without Being Eaten Alive" offers insights and advice on increasing sales productivity. **Availability:** VHS; 3/4 U.

43711 ■ *Business Library Series: Sales and Motivation*
Instructional Video
2219 C St.
Lincoln, NE 68502
Ph: (402)475-6570
Free: 800-228-0164
Fax: (402)475-6500
Co. E-mail: feedback@insvideo.com
URL: http://www.insvideo.com
Released: 19??. **Price:** $19.95. **Description:** Offers humorous look at the fundamental elements of executing a sale. Emphasizes planning and determination as the essence of everyday success. **Availability:** VHS.

43712 ■ *Clean, Fresh & Friendly*
International Dairy-Deli-Bakery Association (IDDBA)
PO Box 5528
Madison, WI 53705-0528
Ph: (608)310-5000
Fax: (608)238-6330
Co. E-mail: iddba@iddba.org
URL: http://www.iddba.org
Contact: Steve Beekhuizen, President
Released: 19??. **Price:** $160.00. **Description:** Deli customer service training video. **Availability:** VHS.

43713 ■ *The Cold Call*
Video Arts, Inc.
c/o Aim Learning Group
8238-40 Lehigh
Morton Grove, IL 60053-2615
Free: 877-444-2230

Fax: (416)252-2155
Co. E-mail: service@aimlearninggroup.com
URL: http://www.aimlearninggroup.com
Released: 1976. **Price:** $695.00. **Description:** This program demonstrates the specific skills and disciplines of telephone selling, and the dangers of ignoring them. **Availability:** VHS; 8 mm; 3/4 U; Special order formats.

43714 ■ *The Competitive Edge*
Film Library/National Safety Council California Chapter
4553 Glencoe Ave., Ste. 150
Marina Del Rey, CA 90292
Ph: (310)827-9781
Free: 800-421-9585
Fax: (310)827-9861
Co. E-mail: California@nsc.org
URL: http://www.nsc.org/nsc_near_you/FindYourLocalChapter/Pages/California.aspx
Released: 1989. **Description:** This program emphasizes finding out your customer's most immediate concern, and selling to that concern. **Availability:** VHS; 3/4 U.

43715 ■ *Customer-Responsive Selling*
Excellence in Training Corp.
c/o ICON Training
804 Roosevelt St.
Polk City, IA 50226
Free: 800-609-0479
Co. E-mail: info@icontraining.com
URL: http://www.icontraining.com
Released: 19??. **Price:** $995.00. **Description:** A comprehensive program for increasing sales, customer satisfaction, and the corporate image. Workshop materials are available. **Availability:** VHS; 3/4 U; Special order formats.

43716 ■ *Customer Service 101*
International Dairy-Deli-Bakery Association (IDDBA)
PO Box 5528
Madison, WI 53705-0528
Ph: (608)310-5000
Fax: (608)238-6330
Co. E-mail: iddba@iddba.org
URL: http://www.iddba.org
Contact: Steve Beekhuizen, President
Released: 19??. **Price:** $50.00. **Description:** Teaches how to build repeat business, increase sales, and maximize productivity. **Availability:** VHS.

43717 ■ *Dealing with Difficult Prospects*
American Management Association (AMA)
1601 Broadway
New York, NY 10019-7420
Ph: (212)586-8100
Free: 877-566-9441
Fax: (212)903-8168
Co. E-mail: customerservice@amanet.org
URL: http://www.amanet.org
Contact: Charles R. Craig, Chairman
Released: 19??. **Price:** $495.00. **Description:** Contains information and techniques on how to sell successfully, even to the most difficult prospect. **Availability:** VHS.

43718 ■ *The Effective Manager*
Nightingale-Conant Corp.
6245 W. Howard St.
Niles, IL 60714
Ph: (847)647-0300
Free: 800-560-6081
URL: http://www.nightingale.com
Released: 19??. **Price:** $95.00. **Description:** A series of award-winning programs designed to promote effective management and help increase sales. Audio tapes and booklets are included, and the series can be purchased individually or as a set. **Availability:** VHS.

43719 ■ *Explode Those Sales Myths*
Dartnell Corp.
2222 Sedwick Dr.
Durham, NC 34112
Ph: (239)417-2079
Free: 800-223-8720

Fax: (800)508-2592
Co. E-mail: customerservice@dartnellcorp.com
URL: http://www.dartnellcorp.com
Contact: Kenneth F. Kahn, Publisher
Released: 1976. **Description:** Designed to explode misleading old tales and beliefs that negatively affect salesmanship. **Availability:** VHS; 3/4 U; Special order formats.

43720 ■ *Five Steps to Successful Selling*
Cambridge Educational
c/o Films Media Group
132 West 31st Street, 17th Floor
Ste. 124
New York, NY 10001
Free: 800-257-5126
Fax: (609)671-0266
Co. E-mail: custserve@films.com
URL: http://www.cambridgeol.com
Released: 1990. **Price:** $54.95. **Description:** Zig Ziglar condenses his years of selling experience down to this presentation on sales techniques. **Availability:** VHS.

43721 ■ *Follow-Up: Proven Methods & Strategies That Will Covert Your Contacts into Closings*
Tapeworm Video Distributors
25876 The Old Road #141
Stevenson Ranch, CA 91381
Ph: (661)257-4904
Fax: (661)257-4820
Co. E-mail: sales@tapeworm.com
URL: http://www.tapeworm.com
Released: 19??. **Price:** $29.95. **Description:** Sales education training program that offers tips on how to become a successful multiple call salesperson, including skills that will help with follow through and follow-up until the sale is final. **Availability:** VHS.

43722 ■ *Friendly Persuasion: The Art of Converting Objections into Sales*
American Media, Inc.
4621 121st St.
Urbandale, IA 50323-2311
Ph: (515)224-0919
Free: 888-776-8268
Fax: (515)327-2555
Co. E-mail: custsvc@ammedia.com
URL: http://www.ammedia.com
Released: 1985. **Description:** Salesman Joe Batten outlines the objection-into-sales theories that profit salesman best in any area. **Availability:** VHS; 3/4 U.

43723 ■ *Handling Objections*
American Management Association (AMA)
1601 Broadway
New York, NY 10019-7420
Ph: (212)586-8100
Free: 877-566-9441
Fax: (212)903-8168
Co. E-mail: customerservice@amanet.org
URL: http://www.amanet.org
Contact: Charles R. Craig, Chairman
Released: 19??. **Price:** $695.00. **Description:** Presents a three step process on the secrets of successful selling. **Availability:** VHS.

43724 ■ *A Happy Beginning*
Resources for Education & Management, Inc.
1804 Montreal Ct., Ste. A
Tucker, GA 30084
Released: 1971. **Description:** An examination of closing the sale, asking for the order, and answering the customer's objections. How to become a confident sale closer. **Availability:** VHS; 3/4 U.

43725 ■ *How to Close the Sale*
Dartnell Corp.
2222 Sedwick Dr.
Durham, NC 34112
Ph: (239)417-2079
Free: 800-223-8720

Fax: (800)508-2592
Co. E-mail: customerservice@dartnellcorp.com
URL: http://www.dartnellcorp.com
Contact: Kenneth F. Kahn, Publisher
Released: 1981. **Description:** This program shows salespeople how to ask for the order, and how to get it. **Availability:** VHS; 3/4 U; Special order formats.

43726 ■ *How to Find New Customers*
Instructional Video
2219 C St.
Lincoln, NE 68502
Ph: (402)475-6570
Free: 800-228-0164
Fax: (402)475-6500
Co. E-mail: feedback@insvideo.com
URL: http://www.insvideo.com
Released: 19??. **Price:** $39.95. **Description:** Top sales professionals furnish advice on how to be successful in sales. Includes Leroy Leale, sales rep. from Shearson Lehman Bros.; Jim Kilcoyne, account executive for SARNS/3M; and Elaine Bailey, sales rep. for Connect Software. **Availability:** VHS.

43727 ■ *How to Raise Your Batting Average in Selling*
Dartnell Corp.
2222 Sedwick Dr.
Durham, NC 34112
Ph: (239)417-2079
Free: 800-223-8720
Fax: (800)508-2592
Co. E-mail: customerservice@dartnellcorp.com
URL: http://www.dartnellcorp.com
Contact: Kenneth F. Kahn, Publisher
Released: 1968. **Description:** Dr. Peale shows how any salesman can operate at peak efficiency that will eventually help improve sales average. **Availability:** VHS; 3/4 U; Special order formats.

43728 ■ *How to Take the Butt Out of a Sales Rebuttal*
Dartnell Corp.
2222 Sedwick Dr.
Durham, NC 34112
Ph: (239)417-2079
Free: 800-223-8720
Fax: (800)508-2592
Co. E-mail: customerservice@dartnellcorp.com
URL: http://www.dartnellcorp.com
Contact: Kenneth F. Kahn, Publisher
Released: 1967. **Description:** A look at how to cope with the difficult problem of rebutting a customer's objection-without being objectionable. **Availability:** VHS; 3/4 U; Special order formats.

43729 ■ *Knowing the Prospect*
Resources for Education & Management, Inc.
1804 Montreal Ct., Ste. A
Tucker, GA 30084
Released: 1971. **Description:** Shows the relationship of product or service benefits to the sales prospect's personal goals, and illustrates the value of knowing a prospect's needs. Ignores the fast-talking sales pitch. **Availability:** VHS; 3/4 U.

43730 ■ *Making It Live*
Resources for Education & Management, Inc.
1804 Montreal Ct., Ste. A
Tucker, GA 30084
Released: 1971. **Description:** This tape demonstrates a key to sales success-knowing your product or service and telling your story with enthusiasm and conviction. **Availability:** VHS; 3/4 U.

43731 ■ *Manage Your Time to Build Your Territory*
Dartnell Corp.
2222 Sedwick Dr.
Durham, NC 34112
Ph: (239)417-2079
Free: 800-223-8720

Fax: (800)508-2592
Co. E-mail: customerservice@dartnellcorp.com
URL: http://www.dartnellcorp.com
Contact: Kenneth F. Kahn, Publisher
Released: 1974. **Description:** An examination of time thieves that rob salespeople of both hours and sales volume. From the "Tough-Minded Salesmanship" series. **Availability:** VHS; 3/4 U; Special order formats.

43732 ■ *Managing Sales Stress*
American Management Association (AMA)
1601 Broadway
New York, NY 10019-7420
Ph: (212)586-8100
Free: 877-566-9441
Fax: (212)903-8168
Co. E-mail: customerservice@amanet.org
URL: http://www.amanet.org
Contact: Charles R. Craig, Chairman
Released: 19??. **Price:** $495.00. **Description:** Outlines techniques on handling stress from day-to-day sales. **Availability:** VHS.

43733 ■ *Million Dollar Sales Strategy*
Nightingale-Conant Corp.
6245 W. Howard St.
Niles, IL 60714
Ph: (847)647-0300
Free: 800-560-6081
URL: http://www.nightingale.com
Released: 19??. **Price:** $39.95. **Description:** Jim Cathcart and Dr. Tony Alessandra share tips on time management, prospecting, closing, and successful customer relations. **Availability:** VHS.

43734 ■ *Negotiating Profitable Sales*
Video Arts, Inc.
c/o Aim Learning Group
8238-40 Lehigh
Morton Grove, IL 60053-2615
Free: 877-444-2230
Fax: (416)252-2155
Co. E-mail: service@aimlearninggroup.com
URL: http://www.aimlearninggroup.com
Released: 197?. **Price:** $695.00. **Description:** The first program in this two-part series exposes and analyzes the most-frequent and costly errors of untrained negotiators and shows a salesman being briefed by his superiors. The second program shows the prepared salesman actually negotiating with the buyer. The programs are available individually. Also available as a seminar kit. **Availability:** VHS; 8 mm; 3/4 U; Special order formats.

43735 ■ *The New Selling with Service*
RMI Media
1365 N. Winchester St.
Olathe, KS 66061-5880
Ph: (913)768-1696
Free: 800-745-5480
Fax: (800)755-6910
Co. E-mail: actmedia@act.org
URL: http://www.actmedia.com
Released: 1993. **Price:** $89.95. **Description:** Philip Wexler explains how to implement a marketing philosophy to maintain and increase customers. **Availability:** VHS.

43736 ■ *Overcoming Objections*
Film Library/National Safety Council California Chapter
4553 Glencoe Ave., Ste. 150
Marina Del Rey, CA 90292
Ph: (310)827-9781
Free: 800-421-9585
Fax: (310)827-9861
Co. E-mail: California@nsc.org
URL: http://www.nsc.org/nsc_near_you/FindYourLocalChapter/Pages/California.aspx
Released: 198?. **Description:** This film emphasizes the importance of understanding the customer's point of view. **Availability:** VHS; 3/4 U.

43737 ■ *Path to Profit*
International Dairy-Deli-Bakery Association (IDDBA)
PO Box 5528
Madison, WI 53705-0528
Ph: (608)310-5000

Fax: (608)238-6330
Co. E-mail: iddba@iddba.org
URL: http://www.iddba.org
Contact: Steve Beekhuizen, President
Released: 19??. **Price:** $160.00. **Description:** Analyzes strategies for increasing bakery impulse sales and bottom-line profitability. Discusses how to control shrink and effectively schedule labor. **Availability:** VHS.

43738 ■ Prescription for Complaints
Video Arts, Inc.
c/o Aim Learning Group
8238-40 Lehigh
Morton Grove, IL 60053-2615
Free: 877-444-2230
Fax: (416)252-2155
Co. E-mail: service@aimlearninggroup.com
URL: http://www.aimlearninggroup.com
Released: 1975. **Price:** $695.00. **Description:** This program shows a six-step, objective method for dealing with customer complaints. **Availability:** VHS; 8 mm; 3/4 U; Special order formats.

43739 ■ Presenting the Story
Resources for Education & Management, Inc.
1804 Montreal Ct., Ste. A
Tucker, GA 30084
Released: 1971. **Description:** How a salesman can best communicate benefits to a customer. Emphasis is on preparation of the story and practice. **Availability:** VHS; 3/4 U.

43740 ■ The Real Estate Success Series
Council of Real Estate Brokerage Managers
430 N. Michigan Ave.
Chicago, IL 60611
Free: 800-621-8738
Fax: (312)329-8882
Co. E-mail: info@crb.com
URL: http://www.crb.com
Released: 1981. **Description:** This training series, designed to increase skills and profitability through proven training techniques, concentrates on building sales skills step-by-step. **Availability:** VHS; 3/4 U.

43741 ■ Real Selling: How to Increase Sales in Growing Companies
Excellence in Training Corp.
c/o ICON Training
804 Roosevelt St.
Polk City, IA 50226
Free: 800-609-0479
Co. E-mail: info@icontraining.com
URL: http://www.icontraining.com
Released: 1990. **Price:** $495.00. **Description:** A five-part sales training program that shows how to make more sales, more effectively. Workbooks are included. **Availability:** VHS; 3/4 U; Special order formats.

43742 ■ The Sales Film
American Media, Inc.
4621 121st St.
Urbandale, IA 50323-2311
Ph: (515)224-0919
Free: 888-776-8268
Fax: (515)327-2555
Co. E-mail: custsvc@ammedia.com
URL: http://www.ammedia.com
Released: 1982. **Description:** Fundamental sales techniques are covered for new, as well as seasoned salespeople. This program includes in-field and industrial sales practices, with methods that bring results. **Availability:** VHS; 3/4 U.

43743 ■ The Sales Professionals: Building Your Clients' Confidence
Video Arts, Inc.
c/o Aim Learning Group
8238-40 Lehigh
Morton Grove, IL 60053-2615
Free: 877-444-2230

Fax: (416)252-2155
Co. E-mail: service@aimlearninggroup.com
URL: http://www.aimlearninggroup.com
Released: 1991. **Price:** $790.00. **Description:** The need for long-term client trust is emphasized in this video, which focuses on how to be a consultant, problem solver, and partner. **Availability:** VHS; 8 mm; 3/4 U; Special order formats.

43744 ■ Self-Motivation in Selling
Learning Communications L.L.C.
5520 Trabuco Rd.
Irvine, CA 92620-5705
Free: 800-622-3610
Fax: (949)727-4323
Co. E-mail: sales@learncom.com
URL: http://www.learncom.com
Contact: Lloyd W. Singer, President
Released: 1979. **Description:** A look at how to avoid sales slumps and maintain peak performances. Four untitled programs cover frustrations and turndowns, seeking feedback, how to keep personal problems from affecting performance, and how sales managers can keep their people motivated. **Availability:** VHS; 3/4 U.

43745 ■ Selling in the '90s
Nightingale-Conant Corp.
6245 W. Howard St.
Niles, IL 60714
Ph: (847)647-0300
Free: 800-560-6081
URL: http://www.nightingale.com
Released: 1990. **Price:** $95.00. **Description:** Sales guru Larry Wilson offers this guide to maintaining a competitive edge in sales. Included is a look at what consumers really want, the keys to partnership selling, and how to deliver a product through dreams and solutions. Two audio cassettes and two workbooks are included. **Availability:** VHS.

43746 ■ Selling Skills: Have I Got a Deal for You!
Cambridge Educational
c/o Films Media Group
132 West 31st Street, 17th Floor
Ste. 124
New York, NY 10001
Free: 800-257-5126
Fax: (609)671-0266
Co. E-mail: custserve@films.com
URL: http://www.cambridgeol.com
Released: 1991. **Price:** $79.00. **Description:** For maximum effectiveness, learn to match sales style with the product being sold. Real-life dramatic skits bring different sales techniques to life. **Availability:** VHS.

43747 ■ Selling: The Power of Confidence
Film Library/National Safety Council California Chapter
4553 Glencoe Ave., Ste. 150
Marina Del Rey, CA 90292
Ph: (310)827-9781
Free: 800-421-9585
Fax: (310)827-9861
Co. E-mail: California@nsc.org
URL: http://www.nsc.org/nsc_near_you/FindYourLocalChapter/Pages/California.aspx
Released: 1989. **Description:** Pride makes for the most successful sales staff, and this program explains how to achieve it. **Availability:** VHS; 3/4 U.

43748 ■ Service That Sells
International Dairy-Deli-Bakery Association (IDDBA)
PO Box 5528
Madison, WI 53705-0528
Ph: (608)310-5000
Fax: (608)238-6330
Co. E-mail: iddba@iddba.org
URL: http://www.iddba.org
Contact: Steve Beekhuizen, President
Released: 19??. **Price:** $160.00. **Description:** Bakery customer service training video. **Availability:** VHS.

43749 ■ Sharpen Your Sales Presentation: Make It a Winner
Dartnell Corp.
2222 Sedwick Dr.
Durham, NC 34112
Ph: (239)417-2079
Free: 800-223-8720
Fax: (800)508-2592
Co. E-mail: customerservice@dartnellcorp.com
URL: http://www.dartnellcorp.com
Contact: Kenneth F. Kahn, Publisher
Released: 1981. **Description:** Gaining attention, arousing interest, key benefit selling, the demonstration, and closing on cue are among the sales techniques outlined and defined by Joe Batten. **Availability:** VHS; 3/4 U; Special order formats.

43750 ■ So You Want to Be a Success at Selling?
Video Arts, Inc.
c/o Aim Learning Group
8238-40 Lehigh
Morton Grove, IL 60053-2615
Free: 877-444-2230
Fax: (416)252-2155
Co. E-mail: service@aimlearninggroup.com
URL: http://www.aimlearninggroup.com
Released: 1982. **Price:** $790.00. **Description:** Four videos that describe the fundamental skills of selling, from the initial research to the close. Part 1 focuses on the preparation, including client research and product knowledge. Part 2 looks at the skills and techniques of sales presentation. Part 3 shows how to deal with problem clients. Part 4 demonstrates the tactics for successfully closing a sale. Also available as a complete seminar kit. **Availability:** VHS; 8 mm; 3/4 U; Special order formats.

43751 ■ Suggestive Selling 101
International Dairy-Deli-Bakery Association (IDDBA)
PO Box 5528
Madison, WI 53705-0528
Ph: (608)310-5000
Fax: (608)238-6330
Co. E-mail: iddba@iddba.org
URL: http://www.iddba.org
Contact: Steve Beekhuizen, President
Released: 19??. **Price:** $50.00. **Description:** Teaches how to understand and encourage impulse sales, increase sales, and close sales using product samples. **Availability:** VHS.

43752 ■ Time Is Money!
Aspen Publishers, Inc.
7201 McKinney Cir.
Frederick, MD 21704
Ph: (301)698-7100
Free: 800-234-1660
Fax: (800)901-9075
Co. E-mail: customerservice@aspenpublisher.com
URL: http://www.aspenpublishers.com
Contact: Robert Becker, President
Released: 197?. **Description:** Helps solve salespeople's time problems by teaching them good habits, and provides them with timesaving techniques so they'll spend their time more profitably. **Availability:** VHS; 3/4 U.

43753 ■ Time and Territory Management
American Management Association (AMA)
1601 Broadway
New York, NY 10019-7420
Ph: (212)586-8100
Free: 877-566-9441
Fax: (212)903-8168
Co. E-mail: customerservice@amanet.org
URL: http://www.amanet.org
Contact: Charles R. Craig, Chairman
Released: 19??. **Price:** $495.00. **Description:** Instructs salespeople to take full advantage of prime selling time and how to turn downtime into productive time. **Availability:** VHS.

43754 ■ Tony Alessandra, Ph.D.: On Collaborative Selling
Instructional Video
2219 C St.
Lincoln, NE 68502

Ph: (402)475-6570
Free: 800-228-0164
Fax: (402)475-6500
Co. E-mail: feedback@insvideo.com
URL: http://www.insvideo.com
Released: 19??. **Price:** $95.00. **Description:** Part of the Tony Alessandra, Ph.D. Series. Offers advice on how to change from persuading, telling, and selling to problem-solving, asking, and helping. Also discusses how to develop your competitive advantage statement, explore customer needs, assure customer satisfaction, and how to question, listen, create, and select options. **Availability:** VHS.

43755 ■ The Unorganized Salesperson
Video Arts, Inc.
c/o Aim Learning Group
8238-40 Lehigh
Morton Grove, IL 60053-2615
Free: 877-444-2230
Fax: (416)252-2155
Co. E-mail: service@aimlearninggroup.com
URL: http://www.aimlearninggroup.com
Released: 199?. **Price:** $790.00. **Description:** These two videos show how to organize one's time and skills to be more effective in selling. **Availability:** VHS; 8 mm; 3/4 U; Special order formats.

43756 ■ What Is Salesmanship?
Resources for Education & Management, Inc.
1804 Montreal Ct., Ste. A
Tucker, GA 30084
Released: 1971. **Description:** This tape introduces the idea that selling can be broken down into identifiable steps, each of which can improve selling success. **Availability:** VHS; 3/4 U.

43757 ■ When You're Turned Down—Turn On!
Dartnell Corp.
2222 Sedwick Dr.
Durham, NC 34112
Ph: (239)417-2079
Free: 800-223-8720
Fax: (800)508-2592
Co. E-mail: customerservice@dartnellcorp.com
URL: http://www.dartnellcorp.com
Contact: Kenneth F. Kahn, Publisher
Released: 1977. **Description:** Examines the question: When is a turndown a true rejection and when is it just a disguised objection?; from the "Tough—Minded Salesmanship" series. **Availability:** VHS; 3/4 U; Special order formats.

43758 ■ Zig Ziglar: 5 Steps to Successful Selling
Nightingale-Conant Corp.
6245 W. Howard St.
Niles, IL 60714
Ph: (847)647-0300
Free: 800-560-6081
URL: http://www.nightingale.com
Released: 19??. **Price:** $54.95. **Description:** Ziglar examines the personality traits that are shared by the nation's top salespersons, and offers a program to develop these traits. **Availability:** VHS.

43759 ■ Zig Ziglar: Selling, a Great Way to Reach the Top
Nightingale-Conant Corp.
6245 W. Howard St.
Niles, IL 60714
Ph: (847)647-0300
Free: 800-560-6081
URL: http://www.nightingale.com
Released: 1987. **Price:** $49.95. **Description:** Ziglar offers this guide to developing winning sales skills, including relating to the client, presenting a product and closing the deal. **Availability:** VHS.

CONSULTANTS

43760 ■ 4th Generation Systems
113 N Grant St.
Barrington, IL 60010
Ph: (847)381-7797
Free: 800-227-4332

Fax: (847)381-7301
Co. E-mail: Dirk@4thgenerationsystems.com
URL: http://www.4thgenerationsystems.com
Contact: Dirk Beveridge, President
E-mail: dirk@4thgenerationsystems.com
Scope: Sales, marketing and management consultants. Special emphasis on the development of professional, sophisticated selling skills as well as modern sales management systems. **Founded:** 1969. **Publications:** "Sales Management: Why the Best are Better," Walsworth, 1992; "The Superman Syndrome"; "Sustaining Resource Selling Skills". **Seminars:** BOSS-The Mandatory Business Operating System Standards; Sales Management Why The Best Are Better; Proactive Customer Focused Sales; Marketing In The Age Of Technology; Marketing - The Perception of Difference; Why Successful Businesses Don't Stay; Everyone is Part of the Sales Promise. **Telecommunication Services:** cari@dirkbeveridge.com.

43761 ■ Coyne Associates
4010 E Lake St.
Minneapolis, MN 55406-2201
Ph: (612)724-1188
Fax: (612)722-1379
Contact: John T. Coyne, Chief Executive Officer
Scope: A marketing and public relations consulting firm that specializes in assisting architectural, engineering, and contractor/developer firms. Services include: marketing plains and audits, strategic planning, corporate identity, turnarounds, and sales training. **Founded:** 2008.

43762 ■ Harding & Co.
511 Harvard Ave.
Swarthmore, PA 19081
Ph: (610)544-9005
Fax: (973)763-9347
Co. E-mail: fharding@hardingco.com
URL: http://www.hardingco.com
Contact: Mimi Spangler, President
E-mail: mspangler@hardingco.com
Scope: Specializes in sales management, client development and employee training. **Founded:** 1993. **Publications:** "Cross-Selling Success: A Rainmakers Guide to Professional Account Development," Aug, 2002; "Rain Making: The Professional's Guide to Attracting New Clients"; "Creating Rainmakers: The Managers Guide to Training Professionals to Attract New Clients". **Telecommunication Services:** mspangler@hardingco.com.

43763 ■ High Probability Selling
103 Chesley Dr., Ste. 200
Media, PA 19063
Ph: (610)566-1535
Free: 800-394-7762
Fax: (610)891-2711
Co. E-mail: contact_us@highprobsell.com
URL: http://www.highprobsell.com
Contact: Jacques Werth, President
Scope: Consultancy transforms sales training into a model of integrity which eliminates sales resistance and establishes relationships of trust and respect, sales management and target marketing. Industries served: All. **Founded:** 1989. **Publications:** "Features vs. Benefits"; "Training the 'D Team'"; "Top 6 Pitfalls of Leaving Voice Mail Messages"; "Building Rapport: Don't"; "The One-Call Close"; "Getting Real About Sales Training"; "Top 10 Reasons Sales Managers Fail"; "Top 10 Reasons Salespeople Fail"; "A Clearly Defined Sales Process Yields Big Results"; "Being 'Right' vs. Being Rich"; "Poison Words: The Top 6 Words that Sabatoge Sales"; "Overcoming Question Reluctance"; "Top Producers- How They Get There". **Seminars:** High Probability Selling; High Probability Prospecting and The Power of Experiential Learning; HPS Telecourse: Training in the Basic Process; Overcoming Skepticism and Distrust; How to Turn Cold-Calls into Warm Calls.

43764 ■ Keiei Senryaku Corp.
19191 S Vermont Ave., Ste. 530
Torrance, CA 90502-1049
Ph: (310)366-3331
Free: 800-951-8780

Fax: (310)366-3330
Co. E-mail: takenakaes@earthlink.net
Contact: Kurt Miyamoto, President
Scope: Offers consulting services in the areas of strategic planning; feasibility studies; profit enhancement; organizational development; start-up businesses; mergers and acquisitions; joint ventures; divestitures; executive searches; sales management; and competitive analysis. **Founded:** 1989.

43765 ■ William E. Kuhn & Associates
234 Cook St.
Denver, CO 80206-5305
Ph: (303)322-8233
Fax: (303)331-9032
Co. E-mail: billkuhn1@cs.com
Contact: William E. Kuhn, Owner
E-mail: billkuhn1@cs.com
Scope: Firm specializes in strategic planning; profit enhancement; small business management; mergers and acquisitions; joint ventures; divestitures; human resources management; performance appraisals; team building; sales management; appraisals and valuations. **Founded:** 1980. **Publications:** "Creating a High-Performance Dealership," Office SOLUTIONS & Office DEALER, Jul-Aug, 2006.

43766 ■ Marketing Resource Group
31 Valley Forge Way
Foxboro, MA 02035
Ph: (508)543-8452
Fax: (508)842-7252
Contact: Candace la Chapelle, Vice President
E-mail: candacemrg@aol.com
Scope: Customized sales skills and field training systems for sales people, sales managers, executives and non-selling staff. Curriculum can be developed and branded for in-house program to be used with future trainees and new hires. Offers pre-screening of sales candidates and strategic consulting. **Founded:** 1995. **Seminars:** Basic Sales Skills; Consultative Selling; Relationship Selling; Networking to Maximize Your Business; Six Critical Steps for Every Sales Call; Selling Skills for the Non-Sales Professional; Effective Sales Management; Maximizing Revenue.

43767 ■ Max Sacks International (MSI)
2442 NW Market St., Ste. 409
Seattle, WA 98107
Ph: (206)706-4119
Free: 800-488-4629
Fax: (206)706-5359
Co. E-mail: info@maxsacks.com
URL: http://www.maxsacks.com
Contact: Roy E. Chitwood, President
Scope: Offers sales and sales management training and consulting. Industries served: all. **Founded:** 1958. **Publications:** "Ultimate Success -7 Secrets to Spiritually-based Leadership"; "Don't repeat seven deadly sins of customer service"; "Creating a true business partnership with customers"; "The logistics of merging sales and marketing"; "Toughest job in management: The sales manager"; "Time to erase the lack of respect felt by the sales profession"; "Civility plays a huge role in salesperson's success," 2007. **Seminars:** Track Selling System, 2006; The Guaranteed Close A Scientific Selling Procedure; World Class Selling; Sales Management Clinic and Coaching; Telemarketing; World Class Customer Service; Track Selling Graduate Program. **Telecommunication Services:** contact@maxsacks.com. **Special Services:** The Track Selling System™; Online Track Selling™; WorldClass Selling™; The Guaranteed Close: A Scientific Selling Procedure™; The Seven Steps To Closing More Sales™; World Class Customer Service™; Track Selling Graduate Program™.

43768 ■ Porter Henry & Company Inc.
455 E 86th St., Ste. 37c
New York, NY 10028
Ph: (212)953-5544
Co. E-mail: sales@porterhenry.com
URL: http://www.porterhenry.com
Contact: Bill Voelkel, President
Scope: Consulting and custom-designed training in sales and sales management. Work includes sales force studies and needs analyses, systems design, and visual sales presentations. Have 25 validated

sales and sales management training programs. **Founded:** 1945. **Publications:** "The Sales Strategist-6 Breakthrough Strategies to Win New Business". **Seminars:** AccountAbility; ManageAbility; SalesAbility: Totaling 25 off- the-shelf programs. Mobliesales/motivation, 1999. Infield reinforcement selling skills and motivational program for sales people.

43769 ■ James J. Prihoda & Associates
400 Island Way, Ste. 707
Clearwater Beach, FL 33767
Ph: (727)446-4082
Contact: James J. Prihoda, President
Scope: Specializes in marketing and sales.

43770 ■ The Tactix Group
1619 N 102 St.
Omaha, NE 68114
Ph: (402)393-3800
Fax: (402)393-5151
Co. E-mail: info@thetactixgroup.com
URL: http://www.thetactixgroup.com
Contact: Douglas R. Little, President
E-mail: dlittle@tactixinc.com
Scope: Offers integrated marketing system design and implementation, for customer relationship management. Serves manufacturing, distributing, high-tech, banking, and executive benefit industries. **Founded:** 1987. **Special Services:** Saleslogix (Client Server) Sales Automation Software.

43771 ■ Westlife Consultants & Counsellors
95 October Ln.
Aurora, ON, Canada L4G 7A1
Ph: (905)867-0686
Fax: (416)799-5242
Co. E-mail: westlifeconsultant@hotmail.com
URL: http://www.westlifeconsultants.com
Contact: Dr. Syed N. Hussain, President
E-mail: westlifeconsultant@hotmail.com
Scope: Provider of entrepreneurs and businesses with a highly commercial and global perspectives on the international business development ideas under consideration. **Founded:** 1990. **Publications:** "Innovative Management"; "Team Building and Leadership"; "Financial Planning"; "Estate Planning"; "Risk Management"; "Export/Import Trade Finance Mechanics"; "Marketing and Sales Management"; "What Your Banker Needs to Know"; "Building A Successful Financial Plan".

43772 ■ William Blades L.L.C.
101 North Regulator Dr.
Cambridge, MD 21613
Ph: (443)477-0061
Co. E-mail: wblades@aol.com
URL: http://www.williamblades.com
Contact: William H. Blades, President
E-mail: wblades@aol.com
Scope: A business consulting firm with expertise in marketing and sales. Presents seminars, workshops and keynotes on the following topics: re-energizing the organization; professional selling and marketing; corporate culture; proactive leadership; world-class customer service; creativity; great teamwork. **Founded:** 1988. **Publications:** "Selling-The Mother of All Enterprise"; "Leadership Defined"; "Why Do We

Make Change So Hard"; "10 Crucial Steps for Sales Management Success"; "In Sales, it's all About Accountability"; "Conversations Of Success"; "Celebrate Selling"; "Vision: Help Your Mind"; "Leadership Defined"; "Managing to Improve: 10 Areas of Emphasis for Workplace Leaders"; "Creativity: Let the Juices Flow in the Workplace"; "Get Bill Blades Philosophy on Boot Camps"; "Great Leadership Grows From a Mixed Bag"; "Self Improvement - The Million Dollar Equation". **Seminars:** Sales Leadership Culture Creativity; Sales and Management; Coaching for Executives and Sales Managers; Sales and Marketing Action Plans.

FRANCHISES AND BUSINESS OPPORTUNITIES

43773 ■ DEI Franchise Systems
PO Box 20169
Cincinnati, OH 45230
Ph: (212)581-7390
Free: 800-224-2140
Fax: (212)245-7897
Co. E-mail: franchise@dei-sales.com
URL: http://www.dei-sales.com
Description: Sales training industry. **No. of Franchise Units:** 32. **No. of Company-Owned Units:** 1. **Founded:** 1979.. **Franchised:** 2003. **Equity Capital Needed:** $60,000-$75,000. **Franchise Fee:** $50,000. **Royalty Fee:** 7%. **Training:** Offers 2 weeks home-based training and 2 weeks at headquarters with ongoing support.

43774 ■ DEI Sales Training Systems
DEI Franchise Systems, Inc.
250 W 57th St., Ste. 2217
New York, NY 10107
Ph: (212)581-7390
Free: 800-224-2140
Fax: (212)245-7897
Description: Selling and delivering of sales training programs. **No. of Franchise Units:** 31. **Founded:** 1979.. **Franchised:** 2003. **Equity Capital Needed:** $99,400-$153,700. **Franchise Fee:** $50,000. **Royalty Fee:** 7%. **Financial Assistance:** Limited in-house financial assistance available. **Training:** Provides 2 weeks at headquarters and ongoing support. **Telecommunication Services:** smulch@dei-sales.com.

43775 ■ Sandler Training (Vancouver, Canada)
3625 McGill St.
Vancouver, BC, Canada V5K 1J3
Ph: (604)254-4341
Free: 800-669-3537
Fax: (604)251-8060
URL: http://www.sandler.com
Description: Sales and sales management training. Provides ongoing incremental reinforced sales and management training for individuals and companies. **No. of Franchise Units:** 16. **No. of Company-Owned Units:** 216. **Founded:** 1967.. **Franchised:** 1983. **Equity Capital Needed:** $80,000. **Franchise Fee:** $68,000. **Training:** Provides personal coaching, ongoing reinforced training and coaching support with excellent products and programs.

LIBRARIES

43776 ■ Canadian Professional Sales Association - Sales Resource Centre
655 Bay St., Ste. 400
Toronto, ON, Canada M5G 2K4
Ph: (416)408-2685
Free: 888-267-2772
Fax: (416)408-2684
Co. E-mail: asksrc@cpsa.com
URL: http://www.cpsa.com
Contact: Anna Fredericks, Manager
URL(s): www.cpsa.com/src. **Scope:** Sales - management, negotiation, selling skills, training, marketing, presentations, meetings, conventions, industry directories, speakers bureau. **Services:** Interlibrary loan; copying; library open to the public by permission only. **Founded:** 1993. **Holdings:** 2500 books; 400 audiocassettes; 400 videotapes. **Subscriptions:** 8 journals and other serials.

43777 ■ Point-of-Purchase Advertising International Information Center—POPAI Information Center.
1600 Duke St., Ste. 400
Alexandria, VA 22314
Ph: (703)373-8809
Fax: (703)373-8801
Co. E-mail: info@popai.com
URL: http://www.popai.com
Contact: Dietra Brandon, Executive Officer
Scope: Point-of-purchase research information, slide and videotape presentation. **Founded:** 1936. **Holdings:** 162 volumes; reports; surveys; 10 research publications; 10 reference guides; 200 audio seminars. **Subscriptions:** 90 journals and other serials; 10 newspapers. **Telecommunication Services:** dbrandon@popai.com.

43778 ■ University of Akron - Fisher Institute of Professional Selling - Sales Education Learning Library
College of Business Administration
259 S. Broadway
Akron, OH 44325-4805
Ph: (330)972-6303
URL: http://www.uakron.edu
Scope: Selling and sales management. **Services:** Library open to students. **Holdings:** Books; audiotapes; CDs; videos.

RESEARCH CENTERS

43779 ■ University of Akron - Fisher Institute for Professional Selling
259 S Broadway St.
Akron, OH 44325
Ph: (330)972-5447
Fax: (330)972-5798
Co. E-mail: linda@uakron.edu
URL: http://www.uakron.edu/cba/cba-home/dept-cent-inst/fisher/
Contact: Prof. Linda Orr, Director (Acting)
Services: Consulting; Corporate training. **Founded:** 1992. **Educational Activities:** Fisher Institute for Professional Selling Seminars; Continuing education courses, and management development courses for sales executives. **Awards:** Fisher Scholarships.

START-UP INFORMATION

43780 ■ *Entrepreneurship: Frameworks and Empirical Investigations from Forthcoming Leaders of European Research*
Pub: Elsevier Science and Technology Books
Ed: Johan Wiklund; Dimo Dimov; Jerome A. Katz; Dean Shepherd. **Released:** July 2006. **Price:** $99. 95. **Description:** Entrepreneurial research and theory cover the early growth of research-based startups and the role of learning in international entrepreneurship, focusing on Europe.

43781 ■ *"Incubator Cooking Up Expansion Plans"* in Business First Columbus (Vol. 25, December 5, 2008, No. 15, pp.)
Pub: American City Business Journals
Ed: Kevin Kemper. **Description:** United States-based Science and Technology Campus Corporation is planning to build additional office space in Columbus, Ohio. The site is designed to accommodate three large tenants. Comment from company executives are presented.

43782 ■ *"Troy Patent Law Firm Launches Rent-Free Tech Incubator"* in Crain's Detroit Business (Vol. 25, June 8, 2009, No. 23, pp. 4)
Pub: Crain Communications Inc. - Detroit
Ed: Tom Henderson. **Description:** Young Basile Hanlon MacFarlane & Helmholdt PC, a patent law firm located in Troy, Michigan has created a small, rent-free technology incubator on site. The incubator will be called North Woodward Tech Incubator and has room for four or five startups. The incubator is for the earliest or pre-seed stage for entrepreneurs who have not yet gotten significant investment capital.

43783 ■ *"The Ultimate Cure"* in Conde Nast Portfolio (Vol. 2, June 2008, No. 6, pp. 110)
Pub: Conde Nast Publications
Contact: David Carey, President
Ed: David Ewing Duncan. **Description:** Small upstarts as well as pharmaceutical giants are developing drugs for the neurotechnology industry; these firms are attempting to adapt groundbreaking research into the basic workings of the brain to new drugs for ailments ranging from multiple sclerosis to dementia to insomnia.

43784 ■ *"Wanted: Angels in the Country"* in Austin Business JournalInc. (Vol. 28, July 18, 2008, No. 18, pp. 1)
Pub: American City Business Journals
Ed: Laura Hipp. **Description:** A proposal is being pushed forward by managers of Texas' Emerging Technology Fund to create an angel investors' network. The proposal is asking that tax credits for those who invest in research and development projects be granted in order to boost the number of technology companies in the state.

ASSOCIATIONS AND OTHER ORGANIZATIONS

43785 ■ **Federation of American Scientists (FAS)**
1725 DeSales St. NW, 6th Fl.
Washington, DC 20036

Ph: (202)546-3300
Fax: (202)675-1010
Co. E-mail: fas@fas.org
URL: http://www.fas.org
Contact: Gilman Louie, Chairman
Description: Natural and social scientists, engineers, and individuals concerned with problems of science and society. Aims to "act on public issues where the opinions of scientists are relevant, those which affect science or in which the experience or perspective of scientists is a needed guide." Functions through testimony to Congress and government agencies, public statements, and articles. Maintains the Federation of American Scientists Fund, a research and education arm of the association. **Founded:** 1945. **Publications:** *FAS Public Interest Report* (Bimonthly). **Awards:** Hans Bethe Science in Public Service Award (Annual); Public Service Award (Annual).

REFERENCE WORKS

43786 ■ *"13D Filings: Investors Report to the SEC"* in Barron's (Vol. 88, July 4, 2008, No. 28, pp. M10)
Pub: Dow Jones & Co., Inc.
Description: Robino Stortini Holdings will seek control of Investors Capital Holdings either alone or with members of the company's management. Discovery Group I will withhold its votes at the nomination of directors for TESSCO Technologies while JMB Capital Partners Master Fund plans to nominate a slate of candidates to the board of Maguire Properties.

43787 ■ *"100-BU. Beans"* in Farm Industry News (Vol. 42, January 1, 2009, No. 1)
Pub: Penton Media Inc.
Contact: John French, President
Ed: Lynn Grooms. **Description:** Demand for soybeans has increased and growers are seeing an increase in yields as well due to breeders that are using molecular-assisted selection; other aspects of the soybean market are presented.

43788 ■ *"2011 U.S. Smart Grid - Saving Energy/Saving Money"* in Ecology,Environment & Conservation Business (October 8, 2011, pp. 3)
Pub: HighBeam Research
Description: Highlights of the '2011 U.S. Smart Grid —Saving Energy/Saving Money Customers' Prospective Demand-Response assesses residential energy consumers' willingness to decrease their power consumption in order to mitigate power issues. Statistical details included.

43789 ■ *"Abaddon Acquires Pukaskwa Uranium Properties in NW Ontario"* in Canadian Corporate News (May 16, 2007)
Pub: Comtex News Network Inc.
Description: Rubicon Minerals Corp. has entered into an Option Agreement with Consolidated Abaddon Resources Inc. for the acquisition of Pukaskwa uranium properties and plans to conduct an extensive exploration program to prove out the resource and geological potential of the area. Statistical data included.

43790 ■ *"Abraxis Bets On Biotech Hub"* in Business Journal-Serving Phoenix and the Valley of the Sun (Vol. 10, November 9, 2007, No. 28)
Pub: American City Business Journals, Inc.
Ed: Angela Gonzales. **Description:** Abraxis BioScience Inc. purchased a 200,000 square foot manufacturing facility in Phoenix, Arizona from Watson Pharmaceuticals Inc. The company has the technology to allow chemotherapy drugs to be injected directly into tumor cell membranes. A human protein, albumin, is used to deliver the chemotherapy.

43791 ■ *"Aggenix Completes Merger with German Giant"* in Houston Business Journal (Vol. 40, December 25, 2009, No. 33, pp. 2)
Pub: American City Business Journals
Ed: Mary Ann Azevedo. **Description:** Agennix Inc. has completed its transformation into a German company after Germany-based GPC Biotech merged into the former publicly traded Agennix AG. One quarter of Agennix's 60 employees will remain in Houston. Details on Agennix's drug trials are examined.

43792 ■ *"Angel Investments Tripled in 2009"* in Austin Business JournalInc. (Vol. 29, January 8, 2010, No. 44, pp. 1)
Pub: American City Business Journals
Ed: Christopher Calnan. **Description:** Central Texas Angel Network (CTAN) has invested $3.5 million in 12 ventures, which include 10 in Austin, Texas in 2009 to triple the amount it invested during 2008. The largest recipient of CTAN's investments is life sciences, which attracted 20 percent of the capital, while software investments fell to 18 percent. The new screening process that helps startups secure CTAN capital is explored.

43793 ■ *"Angiotech to Buy Top Medical Devices Company"* in Globe & Mail (February 1, 2006, pp. B1)
Pub: CTVglobemedia Publishing Inc.
Ed: Leonard Zehr. **Description:** The details on Angiotech Pharmaceuticals Inc.'s acquisition of American Medical Instruments Holdings Inc. are presented.

43794 ■ *"Apples, Decoded: WSU Scientist Unraveling the Fruit's Genetics"* in Puget Sound Business Journal (Vol. 29, September 5, 2008, No. 20)
Pub: American City Business Journals
Ed: Clay Holtzman. **Description:** Washington State University researcher is working to map the apple's genome in order to gain information about how the fruit grows, looks and tastes. His work, funded by a research grant from the US Department of Agriculture and the Washington Apple Commission is crucial to improving the state's position as an apple-producing region.

43795 ■ *"Ardesta Venture-Capital Fund Folds"* in Crain's Detroit Business (Vol. 24, September 22, 2008, No. 38, pp. 24)
Pub: Crain Communications Inc.
Ed: Tom Henderson. **Description:** Due to the downturn in the local economy, Ann Arbor-based Ardesta LLC, a venture-capital firm specializing in micro- and nanotechnology research, has pulled the plug on its planned fund of $100 million and said no to an investment of up to $15 million from the state.

43796 ■ *"Asterand Eyes Jump to Ann Arbor; TechTown Tenant"* in Crain's Detroit Business (Vol. 25, June 22, 2009)
Pub: Crain Communications Inc. - Detroit
Ed: Tom Henderson. **Description:** Asterand PLC is considering a move to Ann Arbor from its current location as anchor tenant at TechTown, an incubator and technology park associated with Wayne State University. The university believes the Ann Arbor location's rent is too expensive for the tissue bank company.

43797 ■ *"ASU Explores Russian Partnership"* in The Business Journal - Serving Phoenix and the Valley of the Sun (Vol. 28, September 5, 2008)
Pub: American City Business Journals, Inc.
Ed: Mike Sunnucks. **Description:** Arizona State University is planning to partner with Russia-based St. Petersburg State University (SPSU) regarding research, faculty and student exchange, and other joint efforts. SPSU is one of Russia's leading scientific and research institutions. Arizona State's partnerships with other foreign colleges are also mentioned.

43798 ■ *"ATI Now Ready to Pounce on Biotech"* in Austin Business JournalInc. (Vol. 28, August 22, 2008, No. 23, pp. 1)
Pub: American City Business Journals
Ed: Laura Hipp. **Description:** Austin Technology Incubator has entered the biotechnology sector through a program of the University of Texas incubator. The company's bioscience program was set off by a grant from the City of Austin worth $125,000. The growth of Austin's biotechnology sector is examined.

43799 ■ *"Atlantis-Resistant Figures on the Up"* in Farmer's Weekly (March 28, 2008, No. 320)
Pub: Reed Business Information
Contact: Jeff Greisch, President
Description: Researches are studying the number of cases in which blackgrass became resistant to Atlantis to determine if the resistance is due mainly to the ALS target-site mechanism or enhanced metabolism.

43800 ■ *"Attorney Guides Biotech Company in $6 Million Initial Public Offering"* in Miami Daily Business Review (March 26, 2008)
Pub: ALM Media Inc.
Description: In order to raise capital to engage in a full-scale trial of MyoCell to receive clinical approval, Bioheart Inc., launched an initial public offering. Bioheart researches and develops cell therapies to treat heart damage.

43801 ■ *"Auctions and Bidding: a Guide for Computer Scientists"* in ACM Computing Surveys (Vol. 43, Summer 2011, No. 2, pp. 10)
Pub: Association for Computing Machinery
Ed: Simon Parsons, Juan A. Rodriguez-Aguilar, Mark Klein. **Description:** There are various actions: single dimensional, multi-dimensional, single-sided, double-sided, first-price, second-price, English, Dutch, Japanese, sealed-bid, and these have been extensively discussed and analyzed in economics literature. This literature is surveyed from a computer science perspective, primarily from the viewpoint of computer scientists who are interested in learning about auction theory, and to provide pointers into the economics literature for those who want a deeper technical understanding. In addition, since auctions are an increasingly important topic in computer science, the article also looks at work on auctions from the computer science literature. The aim is to identify what both bodies of work tell us about creating electronic auctions.

43802 ■ *"Banking on Cord Blood"* in Business Journal-Serving Phoenix & the Valley of the Sun (Vol. 31, September 10, 2010, No. 1, pp. 1)
Pub: Phoenix Business Journal
Ed: Angela Gonzales. **Description:** Celebration Stem Cell Centre obtained contracts from Mercy Gilbert Medical Center and its two sister hospitals, St. Joseph Hospital and Medical Center in Phoenix, Arizona and Chandler Regional Medical Center. The contract will facilitate the donation of unused umbilical cord blood for research.

43803 ■ *"Being Big By Design"* in Canadian Business (Vol. 82, April 27, 2009, No. 7, pp. 39)
Pub: Rogers Media
Ed: Andrew Wahl. **Description:** Gennum expects that its planned acquisition of Tundra Semiconductor will expand its market presence and leverage its research and development better than working alone. The proposed friendly acquisition could challenge Zarlink Semiconductor as the largest Canadian semiconductor firm in terms of revenue. The merger could expand Gennum's addressable market to about $2 billion.

43804 ■ *"Biotechnology Wants a Lead Role"* in Business North Carolina (Vol. 28, March 2008, No. 3, pp. 14)
Pub: Business North Carolina
Description: According to experts, North Carolina is poised as a leader in the biotechnology sector. Highlights of a recent roundtable discussion sponsored by the North Carolina Biotechnology Center in Research Triangle Park are presented.

43805 ■ *"Blood Bank"* in Canadian Business (Vol. 80, February 12, 2007, No. 4, pp. 36)
Pub: Rogers Media
Ed: Erin Pooley. **Description:** The plan of Insception Biosciences to popularize stem cell banks, which can store stem cells, is discussed.

43806 ■ *"Bloomberg Law Upgraded Its Online Legal Research Platform"* in Information Today (Vol. 28, September 2011, No. 8, pp. 28)
Pub: Information Today, Inc.
Description: Bloomberg Law upgraded its online legal research platform for law practices. The new services includes a redesigned interface, improved search capabilities, and expanded collaboration and workflow features, while maintaining it comprehensive law resources such as mergers and acquisitions, antitrust, and securities.

43807 ■ *"Border Boletin: UA to Take Lie-Detector Kiosk to Poland"* in Arizona Daily Star (September 14, 2010)
Pub: Arizona Daily Star
Ed: Brady McCombs. **Description:** University of Arizona's National Center for Border Security and Immigration Research will send a team to Warsaw, Poland to show border guards from 27 European Union countries the center's Avatar Kiosk. The Avatar technology is designed for use at border ports and airports to assist Customs officers detect individuals who are lying.

43808 ■ *"Born of Culture of Innovation"* in Canadian Business (Vol. 81, October 27, 2008, No. 18, pp. 98)
Pub: Rogers Media Ltd.
Description: MaRS, an independent nonprofit organization, aims to better capture the relevant commercial potential of Ontario's research and to connect the worlds of science, business, and capital as well as to stimulate a culture of innovation. Profile of MaRS and its 'MaRS Innovation' program is included.

43809 ■ *Borrowing Brilliance: The Six Steps to Business Innovation by Building on the Ideas of Others*
Pub: Gotham
Ed: David Kord Murray. **Price:** $26.00. **Description:** The author builds the case that cherry-picking the ideas of others is a vital part of the research and development process for any small firm.??.

43810 ■ *"Bridging the Worlds"* in Academy of Management Journal (Vol. 50, No. 5, October 2007, pp. 1043)
Pub: Academy of Management
Contact: Ming-Jer Chen, President
Ed: Lise Saari. **Description:** Need to transfer human resource research information published in journals to practitioners and organizations is investigated, along with suggestions on ways of achieving this goal.

43811 ■ *"Bristol-Myers Close to Settling Lawsuit"* in Globe & Mail (January 23, 2006, pp. B6)
Pub: CTVglobemedia Publishing Inc.
Ed: Barbara Martinez. **Description:** The details of shareholder case against Bristol-Myers Squibb Co. are presented. The dispute is over the company's claim on the efficiency of Vanlev drug.

43812 ■ *"California Company Suing City's Lupin Over its Generic Diabetes Drug"* in Baltimore Business Journal (Vol. 27, January 1, 2010)
Pub: American City Business Journals
Ed: Gary Haber. **Description:** California-based Depomed Inc. is suing Baltimore, Maryland-based Lupin Pharmaceuticals Inc. and its parent company in India over the patents to a diabetes drug. Lupin allegedly infringed on Depomed's four patents for Glumetza when it filed for permission to sell its own version of the drug with the US Food and Drug Administration. Details on generic pharmaceutical manufacturer tactics are discussed.

43813 ■ *"Can America Invent Its Way Back?"* in Business Week (September 22, 2008, No. 4100, pp. 52)
Pub: McGraw-Hill Companies, Inc.
Description: Business leaders as well as economists agree that innovative new products, services and ways of doing business may be the only way in which America can survive the downward spiral of the economy; innovation economics may be the answer and may even provide enough growth to enable Americans to prosper in the years to come.

43814 ■ *"Canadian Research Generates Innovation and Prosperity"* in Canadian Business (Vol. 81, October 27, 2008, No. 18, pp. 87)
Pub: Rogers Media Ltd.
Description: Universities play a key role in helping Canadians achieve prosperity, competitiveness, and quality of life by conducting more than a third of Canada's research. Research in universities help train graduates to apply sophisticated knowledge to real problems.

43815 ■ *"Cancer Care's Quantum Leap"* in Hawaii Business (Vol. 53, October 2007, No. 4, pp. 17)
Pub: Hawaii Business Publishing
Ed: Cathy S. Cruz-George. **Description:** Tomo-Therapy is an innovative device for cancer treatment that gives high-intensity radiation to more accurate parts of the body compared to conventional treatments. Hawaii has one of the 70 TomoTherapy machines in the nation, and it is expected to help advance cancer care in the area. Details on how the machine works are provided.

43816 ■ *"Cancer-Fighting Entrepreneurs"* in Austin Business Journal (Vol. 31, August 5, 2011, No. 22, pp. 1)
Pub: American City Business Journals Inc.
Ed: Sandra Zaragoza. **Description:** Cancer Prevention and Research Institute of Texas has invested $10 million in recruiting known faculty to the University of Texas. The move is seen to bolster Austin's position as a major cancer research market. The institute has awarded grants to researchers Jonghwan Kim, Guangbin Dong and Kyle Miller.

43817 ■ *"Cancer Therapy Raises Debate Over Shared Technology"* in Crain's Detroit

Business (Vol. 24, March 10, 2008, No. 10, pp. 1)
Pub: Crain Communications, Inc.
Ed: Jay Greene. **Description:** Overview of a proposed collaborative approach among select hospitals that would allow the consortium to utilize proton-beam accelerators in order to treat cancer patients; this expensive new technology is possibly a better way to destroy cancers by using the proton beams to direct high dosages of radiation to destroy small tumors.

43818 ■ "Cannabis Science Signs Exclusive and Non-Exclusive Agreement with Prescription Vending Machines" in Benzinga.com (October 29, 2011)
Pub: Benzinga.com
Ed: Benzinga Staff. **Description:** Cannabis Science Inc., a biotech company developing pharmaceutical cannabis products has partnered with Prescription Vending Machines Inc. and its principal Vincent Meddizadeh to provide industry specific consulting and advisory services to Cannabis Science.

43819 ■ "Caterpillar to Expand Research, Production in China" in Chicago Tribune (August 27, 2008)
Pub: McClatchy-Tribune Information Services
Ed: James P. Miller. **Description:** Caterpillar Inc., the Peoria-based heavy-equipment manufacturer, plans to establish a new research-and-development center at the site of its rapidly growing campus in Wuxi.

43820 ■ "Chicago Botanic Garden Builds Green Research Facility" in Contractor (Vol. 56, December 2009, No. 12, pp. 5)
Pub: Penton Media, Inc.
Ed: Candace Roulo. **Description:** Chicago Botanic Garden has built a laboratory and research facility in Illinois. The facility is set to receive a United States Green Building Council LEED Gold certification. The building features a solar photovoltaic array, radiant flooring and water-conserving plumbing products.

43821 ■ "Chief Boo Boo Officer" in Marketing to Women (Vol. 21, February 2008, No. 2, pp. 1)
Pub: EPM Communications Inc.
Contact: Ira Mayer, President
E-mail: imayer@epmcom.com
Ed: Ellen Neuborne. **Description:** Pharmaceutical companies are reaching out to women through innovative marketing techniques.

43822 ■ "Clean Wind Energy Tower Transitions from R&D Stage Company" in Professional Services Close-Up (September 30, 2011)
Pub: Close-Up Media
Description: Clean Wind Energy designed and is developing large downdraft towers that use benevolent, non-toxic natural elements to generate electricity and clean water. The firm is closing its internally staffed engineering office in Warrenton, Virginia and transitioning a development team to oversee and coordinate industry consultants and advisors to construct their first dual renewable energy tower.

43823 ■ "Cleaner and Greener" in Canadian Business (Vol. 80, February 12, 2007, No. 4, pp. 45)
Pub: Rogers Media
Ed: Zena Olijnyk. **Description:** Canadian research and government investments in clean coal technology is discussed.

43824 ■ "A Click In the Right Direction: Website Teaches Youth Financial Literacy" in Black Enterprise (Vol. 38, December 2007, No. 5)
Pub: Earl G. Graves Publishing Co. Inc.
Ed: Nicole Norfleet. **Description:** Profile of Donald Lee Robinson who launched SkillsThatClick, a Website that teaches young individuals ages 12 to 15 about money management. Robinson shares how he used his Navy career as a model for designing the site.

43825 ■ "The CMO of Consequence" in Business Strategy Review (Vol. 21, Autumn 2010, No. 3, pp. 42)
Pub: Wiley-Blackwell
Ed: D. Eric Boyd, Rajesh K. Chandy, Marcus Cunha. **Description:** Do chief marketing officers matter? Some say that CMOs have limited effect on corporate performance and don't add significant value to the firm. The authors agree that the job in many firms is in great peril, but their research has uncovered why the contributions of some CMOs are invaluable.

43826 ■ "The Code-Cracker" in Business Courier (Vol. 24, January 11, 2008, No. 40, pp. 1)
Pub: American City Business Journals, Inc.
Ed: James Ritchie. **Description:** Michael Kennedy, a professor in the chemistry and biochemistry department at the Miami University, is a part of the Protein Structure Initiative, a project that is aimed at forming a catalog of three-dimensional protein structures. The initiative is a project of the Northeast Structural Genomics consortium, of which the Miami University is a member. The impacts of the research on drug development are discussed.

43827 ■ "Colt Capital Corp. Acquires Two Uranium Properties From DIAGNOS" in Canadian Corporate News (May 16, 2007)
Pub: Comtex News Network Inc.
Description: DIAGNOS Inc., a leader in the use of artificial intelligence and advanced knowledge extraction techniques, announced an agreement with Colt Capital Corp., a Canadian mineral exploration company that will grant an exclusive option in two uranium properties.

43828 ■ "Connectors for Space, Mil/Aero and Medical Applications" in Canadian Electronics (Vol. 23, June-July 2008, No. 4, pp. 13)
Pub: Action Communication Inc.
Ed: Gilles Parguey. **Description:** Product information on electrical connectors for use in space, military, aeronautics, and medical applications is provided. These connectors are built to withstand the extreme conditions offered by the harsh working environments in those applications.

43829 ■ "Cost Remains Top Factor In Considering Green Technology" in Canadian Sailings (June 30, 2008)
Pub: UBM Global Trade
Contact: Leonard J. Corallo, President
Ed: Julie Gedeon. **Description:** Improving its environmental performance remains a priority in the shipping industry; however, testing new technologies can prove difficult due to the harsh conditions that ships endure as well as installation which usually requires a dry dock.

43830 ■ "Craig Muhlhauser" in Canadian Business (Vol. 81, September 15, 2008, No. 14-15, pp. 6)
Pub: Rogers Media Ltd.
Ed: Andrew Wahl. **Description:** Interview with Craig Muhlhauser who is the CEO of Celestica, a manufacturing company that provides services for the electronics sector; Muhlhauser discusses the company's restructuring program, which he feels was the secret to their surprising first-quarter results. Muhlhauser states that the company is operating with more forward visibility and that understanding the opportunities during the current economic situation presents the biggest challenge.

43831 ■ "A Curious Appeal (Market for Scientific Toys)" in Playthings (Vol. 106, October 1, 2008, No. 9, pp. 26)
Pub: Reed Business Information
Contact: Jeff Greisch, President
Ed: Pamela Brill. **Description:** Science and nature toys are still popular with children. Kits allow kids to make candy, soap, grow miniature gardens, catch bugs and more. These hands-on kits have manufacturers watching trends to create more toys in this category.

43832 ■ "Dean Foods" in Ice Cream Reporter (Vol. 23, September 20, 2010, No. 10, pp. 8)
Pub: Ice Cream Reporter
Description: Dean Foods promoted Joseph Scalzo to President and Chief Operating Officer to oversee the firm's operational turnaround and near-term strategic initiatives as well as business units. Key functions will include worldwide supply chain and research and development.

43833 ■ "Deere to Open Technology Center in Germany" in Chicago Tribune (September 3, 2008)
Pub: McClatchy-Tribune Information Services
Ed: James P. Miller. **Description:** Deere & Co. plans to open a technology and innovation center in Germany; details of the company's expansion plans are discussed.

43834 ■ "Defense Contractor May Expand Locally; BAE Systems Ramps Up Vehicle Prototypes" in Crain's Detroit Business (March 24, 2008)
Pub: Crain Communications, Inc.
Ed: Chad Halcom. **Description:** Profile of BAE Systems, a defense contractor, that has built a prototype in the highly competitive Joint Light Tactical Vehicle project; the company has also completed its prototype RG33L Mine Resistant Recovery Maintenance Vehicle and has plans for expansion.

43835 ■ "A Different Kind of Waiting List" in Canadian Business (Vol. 80, April 9, 2007, No. 8, pp. 17)
Pub: Rogers Media
Ed: Erin Pooley. **Description:** The adverse impact on drug companies' profitability due to regulatory delays in approving drugs is discussed.

43836 ■ "The Doctor Is In" in Canadian Business (Vol. 80, February 12, 2007, No. 4, pp. 38)
Pub: Rogers Media
Ed: Erin Pooley. **Description:** The research at McMaster University to make a pill having imaging devices to takes pictures of any possible cancerous cells in the human body is discussed.

43837 ■ "Dow AgroSciences Buys Wheat Breeding Firm in Pacific Northwest" in Farm Industry News (July 29, 2011)
Pub: Penton Business Media Inc.
Description: Dow AgroSciences purchased Northwest Plant Breeding Company, a cereals breeding station in Washington in 2011. The acquisition will help Dow expand its Hyland Seeds certified wheat seed program foundation in the Pacific Northwest. Financial terms of the deal were not disclosed.

43838 ■ "Drug Trial Halt at YM Sets Stage for Selloff" in Globe & Mail (January 31, 2007, pp. B3)
Pub: CTVglobemedia Publishing Inc.
Ed: Leonard Zehr. **Description:** The decision of YM Biosciences Inc. to stop its trial of cancer drug tesmilifene and stocks following government concern over the safety of the drug is discussed.

43839 ■ "DuPontas Pioneer Hi-Bred, Evogene to Develop Rust-Resistant Soybean Varieties" in Farm Industry News (November 22, 2011)
Pub: Penton Business Media Inc.
Ed: Karen McMahon. **Description:** DuPont and Evogene have signed a new contract to work together to develop resistance in soybeans to rust. Financial terms of the agreement were not disclosed.

43840 ■ "Eco-Preneuring" in Small Business Opportunities (July 2008)
Pub: Entrepreneur Media Inc.
Ed: Mary C. Pearl. **Description:** Profile of Wildlife Trust, a rapidly growing global organization dedicated to innovative conservation science linking health and ecology. With partners in nearly twenty countries, Wildlife Trust draws on global strengths in order to respond to well-defined local needs. In the Dominican Republic, they are working with the community and local biologists in order to restore fishing and create jobs in the field of ecotourism.

43841 ■ *"Ed Otto, Director of Biotechnology at RCCC"* in *Charlotte Observer* (February 8, 2007)
Pub: Knight-Ridder/Tribune Business News
Ed: Gail Smith-Arrants. **Description:** Profile of Ed Otto, director of biotechnology at Rowan-Cabarrus Community College. Before taking the position at RCCC, Otto directed the Food and Drug Administration office responsible for regulating cellular, tissue and gene therapies products.

43842 ■ *"Electronic Design and a Greener Environment"* in *Canadian Electronics* (Vol. 23, June-July 2008, No. 4, pp. 6)
Pub: Action Communication Inc.
Ed: Nicholas Deeble. **Description:** Companies seeking to minimize their environmental impact are using Design methodologies of Cadence Design Systems Ltd. The company's Low Power Format and Low Power Design Flow help reduce carbon dioxide emissions.

43843 ■ *"EMU, Spark Plan Business Incubator for Ypsilanti"* in *Crain's Detroit Business* (Vol. 23, October 15, 2007, No. 42, pp. 3)
Pub: Crain Communications Inc. - Detroit
Ed: Chad Halcom. **Description:** Eastern Michigan University is seeking federal grants and other funding for a new business incubator program that would be in cooperation with Ann Arbor Spark. The site would become a part of a network of three Spark incubator programs with a focus on innovation in biotechnology and pharmaceuticals.

43844 ■ *"Ending the Ebola Death Sentence"* in *Canadian Business* (Vol. 83, August 17, 2010, No. 13-14, pp. 22)
Pub: Rogers Media Ltd.
Ed: Michael McCullough. **Description:** US Army Medical Research Institute of Infectious Diseases made a $140 million agreement with Tekmira Pharmaceuticals Corporation to develop both a drug delivery system and delivery technology for curing the Ebola virus. Tekmira's delivery technology, which has been shown to halt Ebola in laboratory animals, might be the key to finding a cure.

43845 ■ *"Entrepreneurial Orientation and Firm Performance"* in *Journal of Small Business and Entrepreneurship* (Vol. 23, Winter 2010, No. 1)
Pub: Canadian Council for Small Business and Entrepreneurship
Description: The article develops a theoretical model of the relationship between firm-level entrepreneurship and firm performance. This model is intended to further clarify the consequences of an 'entrepreneurial orientation', paying particular attention to the differential relationship that exists between the three sub-dimensions of entrepreneurial orientation and firm performance. Included in the theoretical model are other important variables (such as organizational structure and environmental characteristics) that may impact the EO-performance relationship. Propositions are developed regarding the various configurations of the sub-dimensions of EO and organizational structure that would be most appropriate in a given environmental context. Future research may also benefit from considering the important role that organizational strategy and life cycle stage play in this model. The implications of this model for both researchers and managers are discussed.

43846 ■ *"eResearch Issues Initiating Report on Aldershot Resources Ltd."* in *Canadian Corporate News* (May 14, 2007)
Pub: Comtex News Network Inc.
Description: Overview of Bob Weir and Michael Wood's Initiating Report on Aldershot Resources Ltd., a junior Canadian-based uranium exploration company with prospective projects in Canada, Zambia, Australia, and a base metals project in Chile.

43847 ■ *"The Executive Brain"* in *Canadian Business* (Vol. 80, October 22, 2007, No. 21, pp. 41)
Pub: Rogers Media
Ed: Rachel Pulfer. **Description:** Studies by Jordan Petersen, Frank Schmidt, and John Hunter show that leaders have highly evolved capacities to think using

the prefrontal cortex of the brain. Inspirational leadership ability is located in the parietal lobe. Other details of the research are discussed.

43848 ■ *"Executive Decision: Just What the Doctor Ordered"* in *Globe & Mail* (February 11, 2006, pp. B3)
Pub: CTVglobemedia Publishing Inc.
Ed: Leonard Zehr. **Description:** The leadership ability of chief executive William Hunter of Angiotech Pharmaceuticals Inc., who acquired American Medical Instruments Holdings Inc. for $785 million, is discussed.

43849 ■ *"Family Business Research"* in *International Journal of Entrepreneurship and Small Business* (Vol. 12, December 3, 2010, No. 1)
Pub: Publishers Communication Group
Ed: A. Bakr Ibrahim, Jean B. McGuire. **Description:** Assessment of the growing field of family business and suggestions for an integrated framework. The paper addresses a number of key issues facing family business research.

43850 ■ *"Fast-Release Calcium Could Help Control Club Root"* in *Farmer's Weekly* (March 28, 2008, No. 320)
Pub: Reed Business Information
Contact: Jeff Greisch, President
Description: According to initial observations from a new HGCA club root research study, applications of fertilizers that rapidly release calcium may help improve performance of both susceptible and resistant oilseed rape varieties.

43851 ■ *"Federal Fund Valuable Tool For Small-Biz Innovators"* in *Crain's Detroit Business* (Vol. 24, September 29, 2008, No. 39, pp. 42)
Pub: Crain Communications Inc.
Ed: Nancy Kaffer. **Description:** Grants from the Small Business Innovation Research Program, or SBIR grants, are federal funds that are set aside for 11 federal agencies to allocate to tech-oriented small-business owners. Firms such as Biotechnology Business Consultants help these companies apply for SBIR grants.

43852 ■ *Federal Research in Progress (FEDRIP)*
Pub: Office of Product Management National Technical Information Service—NTIS
URL(s): grc.ntis.gov/fedrip.htm. **Released:** Monthly **Price:** $450, single user subscription; $625, 1 network; $950, 2-5 networks; $1400, 6-10 networks. **Database covers:** more than 150,000 federally-funded research projects currently in progress in the physical sciences, engineering, health, agriculture, and life sciences areas. **Database includes:** Project title, starting date, principal investigator, performing and sponsoring organization, detailed abstract, description of the research, objective, and findings (when available). **Availability:** Online: ProQuest LLC - Dialog; U.S. Department of Commerce - Technology Administration - National Technical Information Service; Innovaro Inc. - Knowledge Express. **Type:** Directory.

43853 ■ *"FinOvation 2009"* in *Farm Industry News* (Vol. 42, January 1, 2009, No. 1)
Pub: Penton Media Inc.
Contact: John French, President
Ed: Karen McMahon; David Hest; Mark Moore. **Description:** New and innovative products and technologies are presented.

43854 ■ *"First Venture Reports Proprietary Yeasts Further Reduce Ethyl Carbamate in Sake"* in *Canadian Corporate News* (May 16, 2007)
Pub: Comtex News Network Inc.
Description: First Ventures Technologies Corp., a biotechnology company that develops and commercializes advanced yeast products, confirmed that two of their proprietary yeasts used in the making of sake have yielded reductions in ethyl carbamate compared to previous sake brewing trials.

43855 ■ *"Five New Scientists Bring Danforth Center $16 Million"* in *Saint Louis Business Journal* (Vol. 32, October 7, 2011, No. 6, pp. 1)
Pub: Saint Louis Business Journal
Ed: E.B. Solomont. **Description:** Donald Danforth Plant Science Center's appointment of five new lead scientists has increased its federal funding by $16 million. Cornell University scientist Tom Brutnell is one of the five new appointees.

43856 ■ *"Flu is a Booster for Firms Here"* in *Philadelphia Business Journal* (Vol. 28, September 25, 2009, No. 32, pp. 1)
Pub: American City Business Journals
Ed: John George. **Description:** GlaxoSmithKline, AstraZeneca, CSL Biotherapies, and Sanofi Aventis were awarded contract by the US Government to supply swine flu vaccines. It is estimated that global sales of the vaccine could reach billions of dollars.

43857 ■ *"Flue Vaccines are Going Green"* in *Canadian Business* (Vol. 83, September 14, 2010, No. 15, pp. 24)
Pub: Rogers Media Ltd.
Ed: Angelia Chapman. **Description:** Quebec-based Medicago has found a solution to the bottleneck in the production of influenza vaccines by using plant-based processes instead of egg-based systems. Medicago's US Department of Defense funded research has produced the technology that speeds up the production time for vaccines by almost two-thirds. Insights into Medicago's patented process are also given.

43858 ■ *"For Gilead, Growth Beyond AIDS"* in *Barron's* (Vol. 88, June 30, 2008, No. 26, pp. 18)
Pub: Dow Jones & Co., Inc.
Ed: Jay Palmer. **Description:** First-quarter 2008 revenue for Gilead Sciences grew by 22 percent and an earnings gain of 19 percent thanks to their HIV-treatment drugs that comprised over two-thirds of the company's sales in 2007. An analyst has a 12-month target from June, 2008 of 65 per share. The factors behind the company's prospects are also discussed.

43859 ■ *"From OTC Sellers to Surgeons, Healthcare Marketers Target Women to Achieve Growth"* in *Marketing to Women* (February 2008)
Pub: EPM Communications Inc.
Contact: Ira Mayer, President
E-mail: imayer@epmcom.com
Description: Healthcare companies are targeting women with ad campaigns, new product development and new technology in order to reach and develop brand loyalty.

43860 ■ *"FSU's OGZEB Is Test Bed for Sustainable Technology"* in *Contractor* (Vol. 56, October 2009, No. 10, pp. 1)
Pub: Penton Media, Inc.
Ed: Candace Roulo. **Description:** Florida State University has one of 14 off-grid zero emissions buildings (OGZEB) in the U.S.; it was built to research sustainable and alternative energy systems. The building produces electricity from 30 photovoltaic panels and it also has three AET water heating solar panels on the roof.

43861 ■ *"Funding Drought Stalls Biotech Incubators"* in *Saint Louis Business Journal* (Vol. 31, July 29, 2011, No. 49, pp. 1)
Pub: Saint Louis Business Journal
Ed: Angela Mueller. **Description:** Economic slowdown took its toll on cash-strapped startups that fill incubators such as the Bio-Research and Development Growth (BRDG) Park in Creve Coeur, Missouri and the Center for Emerging Technologies in Midtown St. Louis. BRDG put a hold on construction of of its two buildings.

43862 ■ *"The Future of Work"* in *Business Strategy Review* (Vol. 21, Autumn 2010, No. 3, pp. 16)
Pub: Blackwell Publishers Ltd.
Ed: Lynda Gratton. **Description:** Work is universal. But how, why, where and when we work has never been so open to individual interpretation. The certain-

ties of the past have been replaced by ambiguity, questions and the steady hum of technology. Now, in a groundbreaking research project covering 21 global companies and more than 200 executives, the author is making sense of the future of work.

43863 ■ *"Galvanizing the Scientific Community" in Information Today (Vol. 26, February 2009, No. 2, pp. 20)*
Pub: Information Today, Inc.
Ed: Barbara Brynko. **Description:** Profile of John Haynes, newly appointed vice president of publishing for the American Institute of Physics; the Institute consists of ten organizations specializing in STM publishing as well as providing publishing services for over 170 science and engineering journals.

43864 ■ *"Giving Biotech Startups a Hand" in Philadelphia Business Journal (Vol. 28, January 8, 2010, No. 47, pp. 1)*
Pub: American City Business Journals
Ed: John George. **Description:** Elkins Park, Pennsylvania-based BioStrategy Partners is a virtual life sciences incubator that is seeking to improve the dull ranking of Philadelphia in the small business vitality index of life sciences. BioStrategy provides technology and business development services to startup life sciences companies and university-based research projects.

43865 ■ *"Good for Business: Houston is a Hot Spot for Economic Growth" in Black Enterprise (Vol. 37, October 2006, No. 3, pp. 216)*
Pub: Earl G. Graves Publishing Co. Inc.
Ed: Jeanette Valentine. **Description:** Fast-growing sectors in the biotechnology and healthcare industries are among the driving forces of Houston's economic growth. More than 76,000 small businesses in the area employ about one in four area workers, according to the Small Business Administration. Housing and business costs are 26 and 11 percent below the national average, respectively, garnering the attention of corporate giants.

43866 ■ *"Growing Field" in Crain's Detroit Business (Vol. 26, January 11, 2010, No. 2, pp. 3)*
Pub: Crain Communications Inc.
Description: Detroit's TechTown was awarded a combination loan and grant of $4.1 million from the U.S. Department of Housing and Urban Development to build a 15,000-square-foot stem cell center, a collection of laboratories that will be available to both for-profit companies and university researchers.

43867 ■ *"Henry Ford Health Leases Lab Space at TechTown" in Crain's Detroit Business (Vol. 24, March 31, 2008, No. 13, pp. 5)*
Pub: Crain Communications, Inc.
Ed: Tom Henderson. **Description:** Henry Ford Health System has signed a seven-year lease at TechTown, the high-tech incubator and research park affiliated with Wayne State University, to take over 14,000 square feet of space for four research groups and laboratories. Construction has already begun and Henry Ford officials hope to take occupancy as early as June 1.

43868 ■ *"High Energy: Gaurdie Banister Joins Aera As President and CEO" in Black Enterprise (Vol. 38, July 2008, No. 12, pp. 30)*
Pub: Earl G. Graves Publishing Co. Inc.
Ed: Brenda Porter. **Description:** Gaurdie Banister Jr. has been appointed president and CEO of Aera Energy L.L.C., becoming one of the first African Americans in the nation to run a major energy corporation. His plans for the firm include utilizing new, sophisticated technologies in order to unlock the 3-1/2 billion barrels of resources the company has on their books in a safe and environmentally friendly way. He also hopes to increase production and maintain cost leadership.

43869 ■ *"The Hired Guns" in Business Courier (Vol. 26, November 13, 2009, No. 29, pp. 1)*
Pub: American City Business Journals, Inc.
Ed: Lisa Biank Fasig. **Description:** YourForce has nearly 6,000 retired scientists and researchers who work together in helping Procter & Gamble (P&G)

and other companies in addressing various project needs. Operating as an online innovation community, YourEncore is a result of P&G's Connect Develop program.

43870 ■ *"Hopkins' Security, Reputation Face Challenges in Wake of Slaying" in Baltimore Business Journal (Vol. 28, August 6, 2010, No. 13)*
Pub: Baltimore Business Journal
Ed: Gary Haber. **Description:** The slaying of Johns Hopkins University researcher Stephen Pitcairn has not tarnished the reputation of the elite school in Baltimore, Maryland among students. Maintaining Hopkins' reputation is important since it is Baltimore's largest employer with nearly 32,000 workers. Insights on the impact of the slaying among the Hopkins' community are also given.

43871 ■ *"Hopkins, UMd Worry Reduced NIH Budget Will Impact Research" in Boston Business Journal (Vol. 29, August 19, 2011, No. 15, pp. 1)*
Pub: American City Business Journals Inc.
Ed: Scott Dance. **Description:** The budget for the National Institutes of Health (NIH) is slated to be cut by at least 7.9 percent to $2.5 billion in 2013. This will have a big negative effect on medical and biotech research in Maryland, especially Johns Hopkins University and University of Maryland, Baltimore which could face stiffer completion for grants from the NIH.

43872 ■ *"Hospitals See Major Shift To Outpatient Care" in The Business Journal-Milwaukee (Vol. 25, September 12, 2008, No. 51, pp. A1)*
Pub: American City Business Journals, Inc.
Ed: Corrinne Hess. **Description:** Statistics show that the revenue of Wisconsin hospitals from outpatient medical care is about to surpass revenue from hospital patients who stay overnight. This revenue increase is attributed to new technology and less-invasive surgery. Trends show that the shift toward outpatient care actually started in the late 1980s and early 1990s.

43873 ■ *"How Green Is The Valley?" in Barron's (Vol. 88, July 4, 2008, No. 28, pp. 13)*
Pub: Dow Jones & Co., Inc.
Description: San Jose, California has made a good start towards becoming a leader in alternative energy technology through the establishment of United Laboratories' own lab in the city. The certification process for photovoltaic cells will be dramatically shortened with this endeavor.

43874 ■ *"How Pixar Fosters Collective Creativity" in Harvard Business Review (Vol. 86, September 2008, No. 9, pp. 64)*
Pub: Harvard Business School Press
Ed: Ed Catmull. **Description:** Pixar Animation Studios illustrates peer-culture methods for fostering product development. These include allowing any employee to communicate with any other employee, providing a safe environment for new ideas, and watching the academic community closely for innovations.

43875 ■ *"Human Activity Analysis: a Review" in ACM Computing Surveys (Vol. 43, Fall 2011, No. 3, pp. 16)*
Pub: Association for Computing Machinery
Ed: J.K. Aggarwal, M.S. Ryoo. **Description:** Human activity recognition is an important area of computer vision research and is studied in this report.

43876 ■ *"Human Bone Breakthrough" in Houston Business Journal (Vol. 40, January 8, 2010, No. 35, pp. 1)*
Pub: American City Business Journals
Ed: Casey Wooten. **Description:** Biotech startup company Osteosphere in Houston, Texas aims to market a technology in which laboratory-grown bone tissues can be processed to appear like a real human bone tissue. The technology was developed by a co-founder of the startup and it can be applied to

bone disease and injury treatment. Osteophere's future plans, such as the search for possible investors, is also outlined.

43877 ■ *"Ian Delaney" in Canadian Business (Vol. 81, Summer 2008, No. 9, pp. 168)*
Pub: Rogers Media Ltd.
Ed: Joe Castaldo. **Description:** Interview with Ian Delaney who is the executive chairman of chemical company Sherritt International Corp.; Delaney previously worked as chief executive for a holding company owned by Peter Munk. Details of his beliefs, profession and family life are discussed.

43878 ■ *"IMRA's Ultrafast Lasers Bring Precision, profits; Ann Arbor Company Eyes Expansion" in Crain's Detroit Business (March 10, 2008)*
Pub: Crain Communications, Inc.
Ed: Tom Henderson. **Description:** IMRA America Inc. plans to expand its headquarters and has applied for permits to build a fourth building that will house research and development facilities and allow the company more room for manufacturing; the company plans to add about 20 more employees that would include research scientists, manufacturing and assembly workers, engineers and salespeople. The growth is due mainly to a new technology of ultrafast fiber lasers that reduce side effects for those getting eye surgeries and help manufacturers of computer chips to reduce their size and cost.

43879 ■ *"In Search of the Next Big Thing: It's Out There - Just Waiting For You To Find It" in Inc. (Volume 32, December 2010, No. 10, pp. 34)*
Pub: Inc. Magazine
Ed: April Joyner. **Description:** Innovation is the future for small business. A new book, Inside Real Innovation: How the Right Approach Can Move Ideas from R&D to Market - And Get the Economy Moving helps to break down the process by which innovation occurs.

43880 ■ *"The Innovator: Rob McEwen's Unique Vision of Philanthropy and Business" in Canadian Business (Vol. 81, November 10, 2008, No. 19)*
Pub: Rogers Media Ltd.
Ed: Alex Mlynek. **Description:** Rob McEwen says that his donation to the Schulich School of Business is his first large donation. He went to the University Health Network and was told about their pan for regenerative medicine, helping him make the decision. McEwan wants to be involved in philanthropy in the areas of leadership and education.

43881 ■ *International Research Centers Directory*
Pub: Cengage Learning Inc.
Contact: Ronald Dunn, President
URL(s): www.gale.cengage.com. **Released:** Annual; Latest edition 27th; November, 2011. **Price:** $916, Individuals. **Covers:** Over 9,500 research and development facilities maintained outside the United States by governments, universities, or independent organizations, and concerned with all areas of physical, social, and life sciences, technology, business, military science, public policy, and the humanities. **Entries include:** Facility name, address, phone, fax, telex, e-mail, URLs, name of parent agency or other affiliation, date established, number of staff, type of activity and fields of research, special research facilities, publications, educational activities, services, and library holdings. **Arrangement:** Subject. **Indexes:** Master, subject, personal name and country.

43882 ■ *"Inventive Doctor New Venture Partner" in Houston Business Journal (Vol. 40, January 29, 2010, No. 38, pp. A2)*
Pub: American City Business Journals
Ed: Ford Gunter. **Description:** Dr. Billy Cohn, a surgeon from Houston, Texas has been named as venture partner for venture firm Sante Ventures LLC of Austin, Texas. Cohn will be responsible for seeing marketable developing technologies in the medical industry. The motivation for Cohn's naming as venture partner is his development of a minimally invasive therapy for end-stage renal disease.

43883 ■ *"Iron Man Forges New Path"* in *Canadian Business (Vol. 80, February 12, 2007, No. 4, pp. 41)*
Pub: Rogers Media
Ed: Rachel Pulfer. Description: The research of Donald Sadoway of Massachusetts Institute of Technology in making iron in an environmentally friendly method using electrolysis is discussed.

43884 ■ *"Is Your Employees' BMI Your Business?"* in *Canadian Business (Vol. 83, September 14, 2010, No. 15, pp. 98)*
Pub: Rogers Media Ltd.
Ed: Jacqueline Nelson. Description: Canada's Public Health Agency's research shows that there is a solid business case for companies to promote active living to their employees. However, employers must toe the line between being helpful and being invasive. Insights into the issues faces by companies when introducing health programs are discussed.

43885 ■ *"Key FDA Approval Yanked for Avastin"* in *Wall Street Journal Eastern Edition (November 19 , 2011, pp. B1)*
Pub: Dow Jones & Company Inc.
Ed: Thomas M. Burton, Jennifer Corbett Dooren. Description: Avastin, a drug manufactured by Genetech Inc. and used in the treatment of metastatic breast cancer in women, has had its approval by the US Food and Drug Administration withdrawn by the agency, which says there is no evidence the widely-used drug is successful in increasing the longevity of breast cancer patients.

43886 ■ *"Lack of Support Drives Scientists Away from Valley"* in *The Business Journal - Serving Phoenix and the Valley of the Sun (Vol. 28, August 1, 2008, No. 48, pp. 1)*
Pub: American City Business Journals, Inc.
Ed: Angela Gonzales. Description: Lack of support for scientists has caused scientists like Dietrich Stephan to depart from the city. Stephan is expected to relocate to California where he has found funding for his company Navigenics. Other views and information on the rising rate of the departure of scientists are presented.

43887 ■ *"Lawrence: Larger than Life Sciences"* in *Business Journal-Serving Metropolitan Kansas City (Vol. 26, November 2, 2007, No. 8, pp. 1)*
Pub: American City Business Journals, Inc.
Ed: Rob Roberts. Description: Greater Kansas City Community Foundation has more than $1 billion to spend on life sciences initiatives and chairwoman Sandra Lawrence will unveil a multimillion-dollar master plan for Children's Mercy Hospitals and Clinics. Details regarding Lawrence's dedication to the foundation are discussed.

43888 ■ *"Letting the Sunshine In"* in *Barron's (Vol. 89, July 6, 2009, No. 27, pp. 11)*
Pub: Dow Jones & Co., Inc.
Ed: Katherine Cheng. Description: Solar energy industry leaders believe the industry needs aid from the US government regarding the funding of its research efforts and lowering solar energy costs. The climate change bill passed by the US House of Representatives signifies the US government's desire to significantly reduce carbon dioxide emissions.

43889 ■ *"The Life Changers"* in *Canadian Business (Vol. 81, October 27, 2008, No. 18, pp. 86)*
Pub: Rogers Media Ltd.
Description: The first season of 'The Life Changers' was produced in September 2007 to feature stories about research and development (R&D) efforts by universities in Atlantic Canada. The program addresses the need to inform the public about university R&D and its outcomes.

43890 ■ *"Life Sciences Become State's Growth Powerhouse"* in *Crain's Detroit Business (Vol. 25, June 1, 2009, No. 22, pp. M008)*
Pub: Crain Communications Inc. - Detroit
Ed: Amy Lane. Description: According to a study conducted by Anderson Economic Group, Michigan's University Research Corridor has helped grow the life sciences industry. Statistical details included.

43891 ■ *"Lifebank Grants Stock Options"* in *Canadian Corporate News (May 16, 2007)*
Pub: Comtex News Network Inc.
Description: Lifebank, a biomedical service company that provides processing cryogenic storage of umbilical cord blood stem cells, announced that, under its stock option plan, it has granted incentive stock options to directors, officers, and consultants of the company.

43892 ■ *"The Little Insect"* in *Canadian Electronics (Vol. 23, June-July 2008, No. 4, pp. 6)*
Pub: Action Communication Inc.
Ed: Tim Gouldson. Description: Electronics designers should not be underestimated because they can manufacture technologies vital to saving lives and bringing peace. They have designed robots and other electronic equipment that are as small as insects.

43893 ■ *"Local Researchers Get Cash Infusion"* in *Business Courier (Vol. 26, October 9, 2009, No. 24, pp. 1)*
Pub: American City Business Journals, Inc.
Ed: James Ritchie. Description: Cincinnati's Children's Hospital Medical Center and the University of Cincinnati researchers are set to receive at least $56 million from the stimulus bill. The cash infusion has reenergized research scientists and enhances Cincinnati's national clout as a major research center.

43894 ■ *"Major Tech Employers Pulling Out"* in *Sacramento Business Journal (Vol. 25, August 1, 2008, No. 22, pp. 1)*
Pub: American City Business Journals, Inc.
Ed: Celia Lamb. Description: Biotechnology company Affymetrix Inc. is planning to close its West Sacramento, California plant and lay off 110 employees. The company said it will expand a corporate restructuring plan. Affymetrix also plans to lease out or sell its building at Riverside Parkway.

43895 ■ *"Making Waves"* in *Business Journal Portland (Vol. 27, November 26, 2010, No. 39, pp. 1)*
Pub: Portland Business Journal
Ed: Erik Siemers. Description: Corvallis, Oregon-based Columbia Power Technologies LLC is about to close a $2 million Series A round of investment initiated by $750,000 from Oregon Angel Fund. The wave energy startup company was formed to commercialize the wave buoy technology developed by Oregon State University researchers.

43896 ■ *"mChip: Claros Diagnostics"* in *Inc. (Vol. 33, November 2011, No. 9, pp. 42)*
Pub: Inc. Magazine
Ed: Christine Lagorio. Description: Harvard University researchers have developed a device called the mChip that produces accurate blood tests in about 10 minutes. Plans to apply for FDA approval for the mChip in the US should happen in 2012.

43897 ■ *"Meet UT's New Business Mind"* in *Austin Business Journal (Vol. 31, May 13, 2011, No. 10, pp. A1)*
Pub: American City Business Journals Inc.
Ed: Sandra Zaragoza. Description: University of Texas (UT) chief commercialization officer, Dr. Richard Miller, has opened a satellite office in Silicon Valley, California in the hopes of luring Californian investors to the science and technology at UT. The satellite office is just one of Miller's efforts to reshape and widen the commercialization of UT-Austin. Insights into Miller's long-term view approach to commercialization are also covered.

43898 ■ *"Mexican Companies to Rent Space in TechTown, Chinese Negotiating"* in *Crain's Detroit Business (Vol. 24, September 29, 2008, No. 39)*
Pub: Crain Communications Inc.
Ed: Tom Henderson. Description: Wayne State University's TechTown, the business incubator and research park, has signed an agreement with the Mexican government that will provide temporary office space to 25 Mexican companies looking to find customers or establish partnerships in Michigan. TechTown's executive director is negotiating with

economic development officials from China. To accommodate foreign visitors the incubator is equipping offices with additional equipment and resources.

43899 ■ *"MIR Growing With Help From Former Pfizer Workers"* in *Crain's Detroit Business (Vol. 24, January 28, 2008, No. 4, pp. 33)*
Pub: Crain Communications Inc. - Detroit
Ed: Tom Henderson. Description: Molecular Imaging Research Inc. helps fund research at its parent firm, Molecular Therapeutics Inc. The company provides imaging services and other in vivo and in vitro services to help pharmaceutical companies test new compounds.

43900 ■ *"Monsanto Acquires Targeted-Pest Control Technology Start-Up; Terms Not Disclosed"* in *Benzinga.com (, 2011)*
Pub: Benzinga.com
Ed: Benzinga Staff. Description: Monsanto Company acquired Beelogics, a firm that researches and develops biological tools that control pests and diseases. Research includes a product that will help protect bee health.

43901 ■ *"More Pain"* in *Canadian Business (Vol. 81, December 24, 2007, No. 1, pp. 12)*
Pub: Rogers Media
Ed: Lauren McKeon. Description: Manufacturing sector in Canada is sinking with a forecast by as much as 23 percent for 2008, which can be offset as manufacturers say they plan to increase productivity by 25 percent. Details on the sector's competitiveness, workforce, importing of machinery from the U.S. and financial needs for research and development are examined.

43902 ■ *"Mosaid Grants First Wireless Parent License To Matsushita"* in *Canadian Electronics (Vol. 23, June-July 2008, No. 5, pp. 1)*
Pub: Action Communication Inc.
Description: Matsushita Electric Industrial Co. Ltd. has been granted a six-and-a-half-year license by Mosaid Technologies Inc. to manufacture the latter's products. The patent portfolio license agreement covers Mosaid's Wi-Fi, Wi-Max, CDMA-enabled notebook computers and other products.

43903 ■ *"MPI Expansion Goes Back to Family Roots"* in *Crain's Detroit Business (Vol. 25, June 1, 2009, No. 22, pp. M007)*
Pub: Crain Communications Inc. - Detroit
Ed: Sherri Begin Welch. Description: William Parfet, grandson of Upjohn Company founder, is expanding MPI Research's clinical and early clinical research operations into two buildings in Kalamazoo, land which was once part of his grandfather's farm.

43904 ■ *"Nanoready?"* in *Entrepreneur (Vol. 36, May 2008, No. 5, pp. 20)*
Pub: Entrepreneur Media, Inc.
Ed: Andrea Cooper. Description: Experts predict that the medicine and energy sectors are among those that will see nanotechnology innovations in the coming years, and that nanotechnology will produce significant commercial value in new products. Some entrepreneurs are investing in nanotech and are partnering with universities. Details on nanotech funding concerns are discussed.

43905 ■ *"NASA Taps Younger Talent Pool to Supplement Aging Work Force"* in *Crain's Cleveland Business (Vol. 30, June 22, 2009, No. 24, pp. 1)*
Pub: Crain Communications, Inc.
Ed: Chuck Soder. Description: NASA's Glenn Research Center has reversed the trend towards hiring older workers with more experience by recruiting for entry-level positions as part of a pilot program to attract younger talent.

43906 ■ *"Neuromed Strikes Major Merck Deal"* in *Globe & Mail (March 21, 2006, pp. B1)*
Pub: CTVglobemedia Publishing Inc.
Ed: Leonard Zehr. Description: Neuromed Pharmaceuticals Ltd., a spin off of British Columbia University,

has struck a drug research deal valued at up to $500 million (U.S) with giant Merck &Co. Inc., the biggest collaboration in Canada. Details of the deal are presented.

43907 ■ *"New Drug Could Revitalize Amgen"* in Barron's (Vol. 88, July 7, 2008, No. 27, pp. 23)
Pub: Dow Jones & Co., Inc.

Ed: Johanna Bennett. **Description:** Shares of the biotechnology company Amgen could receive a boost from the release of the anti-osteoporosis drug denosumab. The shares, priced at $48.84 each, are trading at 11 times expected earnings for 2008 and could also be boosted by cost cutting measures.

43908 ■ *"New Institutional Accounting and IFRS"* in Accounting and Business Research (Vol. 41, Summer 2011, No. 3, pp. 309)
Pub: American Institute of Certified Public Accountants
Contact: Barry C. Melancon, President
E-mail: bmelancon@aicpa.org

Ed: Peter Wysocki. **Description:** A new framework for institutional accounting research is presented. It has five fundamental components — efficient versus inefficient results, interdependencies, causation, level of analysis, and institutional structure. The use of the framework for evaluation accounting institutions such as the international financial reporting standards is discussed.

43909 ■ *"New Life for Old Chemistries"* in Farm Industry News (Vol. 42, January 1, 2009, No. 1)
Pub: Penton Media Inc.
Contact: John French, President

Ed: Mark Moore. **Description:** To expand the uses of familiar crop protection products, chemical companies are utilizing biotechnology research and development tools; many off-patent products are being rejuvenated with small changes to make the product even better than it was when originally conceived.

43910 ■ *"The Next Big Thing"* in Farm Industry News (Vol. 42, January 1, 2009, No. 1)
Pub: Penton Media Inc.
Contact: John French, President

Ed: David Hest. **Description:** Communication technology that allows farmers to detect equipment location, travel speed and real-time fuel and sprayer/combine tank levels will pay off with better machine use efficiency, improved maintenance and reduced downtime. These telemetry systems will be widely available in the next few years.

43911 ■ *"Nine Sectors to Watch: Biotech"* in Canadian Business (Vol. 81, December 24, 2007, No. 1, pp. 48)
Pub: Rogers Media

Ed: Calvin Leung. **Description:** Forecasts on the Canadian biotechnology sector for 2008 are presented. Details on the increase in the number of biotechnology companies and prediction on the government's plan for business incentives are discussed.

43912 ■ *"No Lines, No Waiting"* in The Business Journal-Serving Greater Tampa Bay (Vol. 28, August 15, 2008, No. 34, pp. 1)
Pub: American City Business Journals, Inc.

Ed: Jane Meinhardt. **Description:** Voda LLC, which was founded to commercialize developments by David Fries, develops outdoor sensor networks used for environmental monitoring by markets like research, the security industry, and the government. Fries already licensed 12 technologies for clients for about $130,000 per technology. Other information on Voda LLC is presented.

43913 ■ *"No-Shed Dogs Lead the Way to Big Growth"* in Business Courier (Vol. 26, January 8, 2010, No. 38, pp. 1)
Pub: American City Business Journals, Inc.

Ed: Lucy May. **Description:** Ed Lukacevic of Grant County, Kentucky is developing Dinovite, a dietary supplement that minimizes shedding and scratching in dogs. Statistical data included.

43914 ■ *"OccuLogix Shares Plummet 65 Percent"* in Globe & Mail (February 4, 2006, pp. B5)
Pub: CTVglobemedia Publishing Inc.

Ed: Leonard Zehr. **Description:** The shares of OccuLogix drop by 65% in Canada. The decline in share price is attributed to failure of blood filtering system.

43915 ■ *"The One Thing That's Holding Back Your Wellness Program"* in Employee Benefit News (Vol. 25, December 1, 2011, No. 15, pp. 8)
Pub: SourceMedia Inc.

Ed: Kelley M. Butler. **Description:** A 13-year study shows that women who sat for more than six hours a day were 94 percent more likely to die during the study period. Most women sit at their desks an average of 7.7 hours while at work.

43916 ■ *"OPEC Exposed"* in Hawaii Business (Vol. 54, September 2008, No. 3, pp. 2)
Pub: Hawaii Business Publishing

Ed: Serena Lim. **Description:** Organization of the Petroleum Exporting Countries (OPEC) has said that their effort in developing an alternative energy source has driven prices up. The biofuel sector is criticizing the statement, saying that a research study found that biofuels push petroleum prices down by 15 percent. Details on the effect of rising petroleum prices are discussed.

43917 ■ *"Optimal Awarded US $256 Thousand Contract to Conduct LiDAR Survey for a Major Electric Utility in the Southwest"* in Canadian Corporate News
Pub: Comtex News Network Inc.

Description: Optimal Geomatics, a company specializing in the science and technology of analyzing, gathering, interpreting, distributing, and using geographic information, was awarded a new contract from a long-standing electric utility customer in the Southwest to conduct a LiDAR survey for a part of the utility's overhead transmission line system.

43918 ■ *Our Daily Meds: How the Pharmaceutical Companies Transformed Themselves into Slick Marketing Machines*
Pub: Farrar, Straus and Giroux

Ed: Melody Petersen. **Released:** 2009. **Price:** $26.00. **Description:** Petersen, using industry memos, transcripts of meetings, and other sources shows how some drug companies are more concerned with the bottom line than with helping patients. Some of these firms are actually inventing 'diseases' in order to sell marginal medicines.

43919 ■ *"PA Tax Reforms See Some Progress"* in Philadelphia Business Journal (Vol. 28, October 16, 2009, No. 35, pp. 1)
Pub: American City Business Journals

Ed: Athena D. Merritt. **Description:** It was reported that Pennsylvania's $27.8 billion budget arrived 101 days late, but business groups are encouraged that progress continues to be made on long-called-for tax reforms. The Research and Development Tax Credit, currently at $40 million, will drop to $20 million in 2009-2010.

43920 ■ *"P&G vs. IRS: Split Decision"* in Business Courier (Vol. 27, July 16, 2010, No. 11, pp. 1)
Pub: Business Courier

Ed: Jon Newberry. **Description:** Implications of a court ruling in a $435 million legal dispute between Procter & Gamble Company (P&G) and the Internal Revenue Service (IRS) are discussed. A $21 million win has been realized for P&G for its interpretation of research and development tax credits. However, the said case might involve more than $700 million in P&G tax deductions from 2001 through 2004 that the IRS had disállowed.

43921 ■ *"Paralysis Foundation has Big Plans"* in Austin Business JournalInc. (Vol. 29, December 11, 2009, No. 40, pp. 1)
Pub: American City Business Journals

Ed: Sandra Zaragoza. **Description:** Lone Star Paralysis Foundation revealed plans to launch a fund-raising effort for the advancement of cures for spinal

cord injuries via adult stem cells and also fund a new spinal injury rehabilitation center. Efforts to raise about $3 million will begin as soon as the adult stem cell research study by Dr. Wise Young receives Food and Drug Administration approval.

43922 ■ *"Past Promises Haunt Project"* in The Business Journal-Portland (Vol. 25, August 1, 2008, No. 21, pp. 1)
Pub: American City Business Journals, Inc.

Ed: Aliza Earnshaw. **Description:** Oregon University System and Oregon Health and Science University will face the state Legislature to defend their request for a $250 million in state bonds to fund a life-sciences collaborative research building. The project is meant to help grow the Oregon bioscience industry. Comments from industry observers and legislators are also presented.

43923 ■ *"Physics for Females"* in Occupational Outlook Quarterly (Vol. 55, Summer 2011, No. 2, pp. 22)
Pub: U.S. Bureau of Labor Statistics

Description: Free resources to help females investigate careers in medical physics and health physics are available from the American Physical Society. The booklet is designed for girls in middle and high school and describes the work of 15 women who use physics to solve medical mysteries, discover planets, research new materials, and more.

43924 ■ *"The Power of Innovation"* in Canadian Business (Vol. 81, March 17, 2008, No. 4, pp. 57)
Pub: Rogers Media

Ed: Andrew Wahl. **Description:** Canada ranks badly in terms innovation yardsticks that directly translate to economic growth such as business R&D as a percentage of GDP and R&D per capita. Canada's reliance on natural resources does not provide incentives to innovate unlike smaller countries with little natural resources. Canada could spur innovation through regulations that encourage industrial research.

43925 ■ *"The Price Is Right: What You Can Learn From the Wine Industry"* in Advertising Age (Vol. 88, February 11, 2008, No. 6, pp. 14)
Pub: Crain Communications, Inc.

Ed: Lenore Skenazy. **Description:** In California a wine study was conducted in which participants' brains were hooked up to an MRI so researchers could watch what was happening in both the taste centers as well as the pleasure centers; the participants were given three different wines but were told that the samples were from a variety of wines that differed radically in price; surprisingly, the differences did not affect the taste centers of the brain, however, when the participants were told that a sample was more expensive, the pleasure centers were greatly affected.

43926 ■ *"Providing Expertise Required to Develop Microsystems"* in Canadian Electronics (Vol. 23, February 2008, No. 1, pp. 6)
Pub: CLB Media Inc.

Ed: Ian McWalter. **Description:** CMC Microsystems, formerly Canadian Microelectronics Corporation, is focused on empowering microelectronics and Microsystems research in Canada. Microsystems offers the basis for innovations in the fields of science, environment, technology, automotives, energy, aerospace and communications technology. CMC's strategy in developing Microsystems in Canada is described.

43927 ■ *"Putting 'Extra' in Extra-Silky Shampoo"* in Crain's Chicago Business (Vol. 31, April 28, 2008, No. 17, pp. 37)
Pub: Crain Communications, Inc.

Ed: Phuong Ly. **Description:** Profile of HallStar Co., a Chicago-based company which develops and manufactures specialty chemicals to upgrade existing products such as hair dye, lotion and deodorant. HallStar has seen its annual earnings rise more than 30 percent since 2002.

**43928 ■ "The Quest for the Smart Prosthetic"
in Canadian Business (Vol. 83, October 12,
2010, No. 17, pp. 26)**
Pub: Rogers Media Ltd.
Ed: Jacqueline Nelson. **Description:** Information
about a two-year research project led by Southern
Methodist University (SMU) and funded by the
Defense Advance Research Projects Agency
(DARPA) is provided. The agency aims to create a
'smart prosthetic' which will improve the lives of
military amputees. The planned prosthetic will use a
sensor that can carry nerve signals through synthetic
channels.

**43929 ■ "A Questionable Chemical Romance"
in Barron's (Vol. 88, July 14, 2008, No. 28, pp.
28)**
Pub: Dow Jones & Co., Inc.
Ed: Andrew Bary. **Description:** Dow Chemical paid
$78-a-share for the surprise takeover of Rohm &
Haas. The acquisition is reducing Dow Chemical's
financial flexibility at a time when chemical companies
are being affected by high costs and a weak U.S.
economy.

**43930 ■ "Radiant Commences In-Lab Testing
for US Air Mobility Command" in Canadian
Corporate News (May 16, 2007)**
Pub: Comtex News Network Inc.
Description: The Boeing Company will be conducting in-lab infrared material testing for the Radiant
Energy Corporation, developer and marketer of In-
fraTek, the environmentally friendly, patented infrared
pre-flight aircraft deicing system.

**43931 ■ "Reading the Public Mind" in Harvard
Business Review (Vol. 88, October 2010, No.
10, pp. 27)**
Pub: Harvard Business School Publishing
Ed: Andrew O'Connell. **Description:** Examination of
the various methods for obtaining public opinion and
consumer preferences is provided; an outline of the
disadvantages and benefits of both are also given.

**43932 ■ "Rebels' Cause: Adult Stem Cell" in
Austin Business Journal (Vol. 31, June 3,
2011, No. 13, pp. 1)**
Pub: American City Business Journals Inc.
Ed: Sandra Zaragoza. **Description:** MedRebels
Foundation was launched in February 2011 with the
goal of providing millions of dollars for research funding, education and advocacy for adult stem cell-
focused medicine. The foundation, whose major
contributor is SpineSmith LP, is a collaboration of
other adult stem cell-related companies and nonprofit
partners. It hopes to raise $200,000 by the end of
2011.

**43933 ■ "Region to Be Named Innovation
Hub" in Business Courier (Vol. 27, July 2,
2010, No. 9, pp. 1)**
Pub: Business Courier
Ed: Dan Monk. **Description:** The selection of Cincinnati's consumer-marketing cluster as a 'Hub of Innovation' by the Ohio Department of Development
could boost Cincinnati's chances of receiving $100
million in grants from Ohio's Third Frontier program
and other funding sources. Implications of the
University of Cincinnati's designation as a Center of
Excellence in Advanced Transportation and Aerospace are also discussed.

**43934 ■ "Region Ready to Dig Deeper into
Tech Fund" in Business Courier (Vol. 26,
October 30, 2009, No. 27, pp. 1)**
Pub: American City Business Journals, Inc.
Ed: James Ritchie. **Description:** Southwest Ohio
region aims for a bigger share in the planned renewal
of Ohio's Third Frontier technology funding program.
Meanwhile, University of Cincinnati vice president
Sarah Degen will be appointed to the program's
advisory board if the renewal proceeds.

**43935 ■ "Rehab Will Turn Hospital Into
Incubator" in The Business Journal-Serving
Metropolitan Kansas City (Vol. 26, September
12, 2008)**
Pub: American City Business Journals, Inc.
Ed: Rob Roberts. **Description:** Independence
Regional Health Center will be purchased by CEAH
Realtors and be converted into the Independence

Regional Entrepreneurial Center, a business incubator that will house startups and other tenants. Other
details about the planned entrepreneurial center are
provided.

**43936 ■ "Renewable Energy Market
Opportunities: Wind Testing" in PR Newswire
(September 22, 2011)**
Pub: United Business Media
Description: Global wind energy test systems
markets are discussed. Research conducted covers
both non-destructive test equipment and condition
monitoring equipment product segments.

**43937 ■ Research Centers Directory: A Guide
to about 13,600 University-Related and Other
Nonprofit Research Organizations
Established on a Permanent Basis. . .**
Pub: Cengage Learning Inc.
Contact: Ronald Dunn, President
URL(s): www.gale.cengage.com. **Released:** Annual;
Latest edition 41st; October, 2011. **Price:** $1071,
Individuals paperback. **Covers:** About 14,800 university, government, and other nonprofit research
organizations established on a permanent basis to
carry on continuing research programs in all areas of
study; includes research institutes, laboratories,
experiment stations, research parks, technology
transfer centers, and other facilities and activities;
coverage includes Canada. **Entries include:** Unit
name, name of parent institution, address, phone,
fax, name of director, e-mail addresses, URLs, year
founded, governance, staff, educational activities,
public services, sources of support, annual volume of
research, principal fields of research, publications,
special library facilities, special research facilities. **Arrangement:** Classified by broad subjects, then
alphabetical by unit name. **Indexes:** Alphabetical
(includes centers, institutions, and keywords), subject,
geographical, personal name.

**43938 ■ "Research Note" in International
Journal of Globalisation and Small Business
(Vol. 4, September 21, 2010, No. 1, pp. 92)**
Pub: Publishers Communication Group
Ed: Alexander Bode, Tobias B. Talmon l'Armee, Simon Alig. **Description:** The cluster concept has
steadily increased its importance during the past
years both from practitioners' and reearchers' points
of view. Simultaneously, many corporate networks
are established. Researchers from different areas
(business management, economic social and geographical science) are trying to explain both phenom-
ena.

**43939 ■ "Research Reports" in Barron's (Vol.
88, March 24, 2008, No. 12, pp. M10)**
Pub: Dow Jones & Company, Inc.
Description: Investors are recommending purchasing shares of Ampco Pittsburgh due to an expected
surge in earnings. Deteriorating credit quality presents
problems for the shares of BankAtlantic Bancorp,
whose price targets have been lowered from $7 to $5
each. Shares of Helicos Biosciences are expected to
move sideways from their $6 level. Statistical data
included.

**43940 ■ "Research Reports: How Analysts
Size Up Companies" in Barron's (Vol. 90,
August 23, 2010, No. 34, pp. M13)**
Pub: Barron's Editorial & Corporate Headquarters
Description: Shares of Sirius XM Radio, Target and
Deere and Company received an eBuyE rating, while
shares of Research in Motion got an eNeutralE rat-
ing.

**43941 ■ "The Right Remedy: Entrepreneur's
Success Is a Matter of Life and Death" in
Black Enterprise (Vol. 38, February 2008, No.
7, pp. 46)**
Pub: Earl G. Graves Publishing Co. Inc.
Ed: Tamara E. Holmes. **Description:** Profile of Leah
Brown, whose company conducts clinical trials to
determine if specific drugs will relieve particular
symptoms. Her company will also visit physician's offices to make certain doctors are following proper
protocol for a clinical trial or will collect data from
patients.

**43942 ■ "Rimfire Minerals Corporation: Jake
Gold Project-Drilling Planned for 2007" in
Canadian Corporate News (May 16, 2007)**
Pub: Comtex News Network Inc.
Description: Rimfire Minerals Corporation and Island
Arc Exploration Corporation formed a partnership to
explore the Jake Property, a high-grade gold prospect
with previously unrecognized potential to host
economic gold mineralization, located 13 kilometers
west of Clearwater, British Columbia.

**43943 ■ "Rising in the East; Research and
Development" in The Economist (Vol. 390,
January 3, 2009, No. 8612, pp. 47)**
Pub: The Economist Newspaper Inc.
Description: Impressive growth of the technological
research and development in Asian countries is
discussed. Statistical data included.

**43944 ■ "The Role for Canada's Research
Universities" in Canadian Business (Vol. 81,
October 27, 2008, No. 18, pp. 84)**
Pub: Rogers Media Ltd.
Description: Great students tend to be the foundation of a great research-intensive university, enabling
it to attract great teachers and researchers. Success
is likely to attract the brightest graduate students to
do research, leading to further success.

**43945 ■ "Roswell Park Researcher Gets
$1.5M From M&T" in Business First Buffalo
(October 19, 2007, pp. 1)**
Pub: American City Business Journals, Inc.
Ed: Annmarie Franczyk. **Description:** Roswell Park
Cancer Institute researcher Dr. Thomas Tomasi has
received the M&T Bank Endowed Chair in Cancer
Research, wherein $1.5 million in research funds is
included. The funding is an addition to Roswell Park's
Leaders for Life endowment campaign which aims to
raise $20 for research. Tomasi's plans and back-
ground are also given.

**43946 ■ "RS Information Systems Signs
Buyout Deal" in Black Enterprise (February
2008)**
Pub: Earl G. Graves Publishing Co. Inc.
Ed: Alan Hughes. **Description:** Details of the RS
Information Systems buyout by Wyle, a privately held
provider of high-tech aerospace engineering, testing,
and research services.

**43947 ■ "Rumor Has It" in Entrepreneur (Vol.
35, October 2007, No. 10, pp. 30)**
Pub: Entrepreneur Media Inc.
Ed: Chris Penttila. **Description:** Some entrepreneurs
like Ren Moulton and Dan Scudder regard rumor
sites and product blogs as great sources of market
research. However, there are legal issues that must
be studied before using these Internet sites in marketing and product development. The use and limitations of rumor sites and product blogs are provided.

**43948 ■ "Safer Ammonium-Nitrate-Based
Fertilizer" in Farm Industry News (Vol. 42,
January 1, 2009, No. 1)**
Pub: Penton Media Inc.
Contact: John French, President
Description: Honeywell has patented a new technol-
ogy which it will use to develop a highly effective,
safer ammonium-nitrate-based fertilizer that has a
significantly lower potential for explosion.

**43949 ■ "Saudi Overtures" in The Business
Journal-Portland (Vol. 25, August 15, 2008,
No. 23, pp. 1)**
Pub: American City Business Journals, Inc.
Ed: Aliza Earnshaw. **Description:** Saudi Arabia's
huge revenue from oil is creating opportunities for
Oregon companies as the country develops new cities, industrial zones, and tourism centers. Oregon
exported only $46.8 million worth of goods to Saudi
Arabia in 2007 but the kingdom is interested in green
building materials and methods, renewable energy
and water quality control, and nanotechnology all of
which Oregon has expertise in.

43950 ■ *"Scanning the Field" in Business Courier (Vol. 26, January 8, 2010, No. 38, pp. 1)*
Pub: American City Business Journals, Inc.
Ed: Jon Newberry. **Description:** Anti-terror detection systems developer Valley Force Composite Technologies Inc. of Kentucky plans to enter the market with its high-resolution ODIN and Thor-LVX screening systems. These systems are expected to meet the increasing demand for airport security equipment.

43951 ■ *Science Lessons: What the Business of Biotech Taught Me About Management*
Pub: Harvard Business School Press
Ed: Gordon Binder, Philip Bashe. **Released:** 2009. **Price:** $29.95. **Description:** Former CFO of biotechnology startup Amgen and veteran of Ford Motor Company provides a universal guide to management based on some of the same scientific principles used to create new drugs.

43952 ■ *Science et Technologie au Quebec*
Pub: Quebec Dans Le Monde
Contact: Alain Prujiner, President
URL(s): www.quebecmonde.com. **Released:** Biennial; Latest edition 2011-2012. **Price:** $52.95, Individuals. **Covers:** over 1,150 scientific associations, periodicals, research and development facilities, and research centers in Quebec. **Entries include:** Organization name, address, phone, fax, toll-free phone, description of services. **Arrangement:** Alphabetical. **Indexes:** Subject.

43953 ■ *"Scientific American Builds Novel Blog Network" in Information Today (Vol. 28, September 2011, No. 8, pp. 12)*
Pub: Information Today, Inc.
Ed: Kurt Schiller. **Description:** Scientific American launched a new blog network that joins a diverse lineup of bloggers cover various scientific topics under one banner. The blog network includes 60 bloggers providing insights into the ever-changing world of science and technology.

43954 ■ *"Selling Michigan; R&D Pushed as Reason For Chinese To Locate In State" in Crain's Detroit Business (Vol. 24, January 14, 2008)*
Pub: Crain Communications Inc. - Detroit
Ed: Marti Benedetti. **Description:** Southeast Michigan Economic Development organizations are working to develop relationships with Chinese manufacturers so they will locate their automotive research and development operations in the state.

43955 ■ *"The Service Imperative" in Business Horizons (Vol. 51, January-February 2008, No. 1, pp. 39)*
Pub: Elsevier Advanced Technology Publications
Ed: Mary Jo Bitner, Stephen W. Brown. **Description:** The importance of services is growing in developing countries like India and China, but little attention is given to service research, education and innovation. The 'service imperative' seeks to promote the advancement of services. The scope, objectives and philosophy of the service imperative platform are outlined.

43956 ■ *"Shipbuilding & Defence" in Canadian Sailings (July 7, 2008)*
Pub: UBM Global Trade
Contact: Leonard J. Corallo, President
Ed: Sharon Hobson. **Description:** Overview of the Joint Support Ship Project whose initial budget was set at $2.1 billion for the acquisition of the ships required for the Canadian navy; another $800 million was allotted for 20 years of in-service support. Four teams of competitors bid for the contract and the Department of National Defence decided to fund two teams for the project definition phase of the competition.

43957 ■ *"Shire Seeking New Digs for Headquarters" in Philadelphia Business Journal (Vol. 30, September 2, 2011, No. 29, pp. 1)*
Pub: American City Business Journals Inc.
Ed: Natalie Kostelni. **Description:** Dublin, Ireland-based Shire PLC announced plans to relocate its North American headquarters from Chesterbrook

Corporate Center in Wayne, Pennsylvania and currently evaluating their options. The specialty biopharmaceutical firm is also considering a move to New Jersey or Delaware.

43958 ■ *"Slick Science" in Canadian Business (Vol. 81, September 15, 2008, No. 14-15, pp. 55)*
Pub: Rogers Media Ltd.
Ed: Andrew Nikiforuk. **Description:** N-Solv Corp's John Nenniger has discovered a better alternative to steam-assisted gravity drainage methods for extracting bitumen. Nenniger's technique also relies on gravity but replaces steam with propane, which leaves behind impurities like asphaltenes and heavy metals that are too dirty to burn.

43959 ■ *"Slow but Steady into the Future" in Barron's (Vol. 88, July 7, 2008, No. 27, pp. M)*
Pub: Dow Jones & Co., Inc.
Ed: Mark Veverka. **Description:** Investors are advised to maintain their watch on the shares of business software company NetSuite. The company's chief executive officer, Zach Nelson, claims that the company has a 10-year lead on its competitors with the development of software-as-a service.

43960 ■ *"Smart Medicine" in Canadian Business (Vol. 80, February 26, 2007, No. 5, pp. 73)*
Pub: Rogers Media
Ed: Zena Olijnyk. **Description:** The stock price stability and future earnings prospects of Canadian biotechnology firm YM Biosciences are analyzed.

43961 ■ *"Some Relief Possible Following Painful Week" in Barron's (Vol. 88, July 14, 2008, No. 28, pp. M3)*
Pub: Dow Jones & Co., Inc.
Ed: Kopin Tan. **Description:** Dow Chemical is offering a 74 percent premium to acquire Rohm & Haas' coatings and electronics materials operations. Frontline amassed a 5.6 percent stake in rival Overseas Shipholding Group and a merger between the two would create a giant global fleet with pricing power. Highlights of the U.S. stock market during the week that ended in July 11, 2008 are discussed. Statistical data included.

43962 ■ *"Sophia Siskel; CEO, Chicago Botanic Garden" in Crain's Chicago Business (Vol. 31, May 5, 2008, No. 18, pp. 36)*
Pub: Crain Communications, Inc.
Ed: John Rosenthal. **Description:** Profile of Sophia Siskel who is the CEO of the Chicago Botanic Garden and is overseeing the $100 million expansion which will put the Botanic Garden at the forefront of plant conservation science; Ms. Siskel is also an efficient marketer and researcher.

43963 ■ *"Southwestern Resources Project Update" in Canadian Corporate News (May 14, 2007)*
Pub: Comtex News Network Inc.
Description: Southwestern Resoures Corp. provides a quarterly update on its various exploration projects in both Peru and China.

43964 ■ *"STAR TEC Incubator's Latest Resident Shows Promise" in The Business Journal-Serving Greater Tampa Bay (August 8, 2008)*
Pub: American City Business Journals, Inc.
Ed: Jane Meinhardt. **Description:** Field Forensics Inc., a resident of the STAR Technology Enterprise Center, has grown after being admitted into the business accelerator. The producer of defense and security devices and equipment has doubled 2007 sales as of 2008.

43965 ■ *"The Start of a Beautiful Friendship: Partnering with Your Customers on R&D" in Inc. (March 2008, pp. 37-38)*
Pub: Gruner & Jahr USA Publishing
Ed: Leigh Buchanan. **Description:** Joint research and development projects between customers and suppliers are a growing trend in the small business community; these ventures can help keep new

product development costs lower. Four tips to maintain a good working relationship in these ventures are outlined.

43966 ■ *"The Stem Cell Revolution" in Canadian Business (Vol. 79, November 20, 2006, No. 23, pp. 31)*
Pub: Rogers Media
Ed: Erin Pooley. **Description:** The commercial prospects and the future of stem cell therapeutics are presented. The use of stem cell therapy to heal the chronic conditions of patients is also discussed.

43967 ■ *"Stronger Corn? Take It Off Steroids, Make It All Female" in Farm Industry News (December 5, 2011)*
Pub: Penton Business Media Inc.
Ed: Brian Wallheimer. **Description:** Purdue University researcher found that higher improvements in corn crops, and possibly other crops, were yielded when steroids were discontinued.

43968 ■ *"Study Puts Hub On Top of the Tech Heap" in Boston Business Journal (Vol. 30, November 26, 2010, No. 44, pp. 1)*
Pub: Boston Business Journal
Ed: Galen Moore. **Description:** The Ewing Marion Kauffman Foundation ranked Massachusetts at the top in its evaluations of states' innovative industries, government leadership, and education. Meanwhile, research blog formDs.com also ranked Massachusetts number one in terms of venture-capital financings per capita.

43969 ■ *"Sundt, DPR Score $470 Million Biotech Project" in The Business Journal - Serving Phoenix and the Valley of the Sun (Vol. 29, September 19, 2008, No. 3, pp. 1)*
Pub: American City Business Journals, Inc.
Ed: Jan Buchholz. **Description:** Sundt Inc. and DPR Construction Inc. were awarded the winning joint-venture contract to develop the second phase of the Arizona Biomedical Collaborative on the Phoenix Biomedical Campus. Both firms declined to comment, but an employee of the Arizona Board of Regents confirmed that the firms won the bidding. Views and information on the development project are presented.

43970 ■ *"Superior Completes Second Vertical Hole Through Morin Kimberlite and Intersects 141 Metres of Crater Facies Material at the Ville Marie Project" in*
Pub: Comtex News Network Inc.
Description: Superior Diamonds Inc., a junior Canadian exploration company that primarily searches for diamonds in the highly prospective and under-explored regions of the Canadian Shield, announced completion of a second vertical hole through the western side of Superior's Morin kimberlite pipe to try to determine the type and thickness of the kimberlite material.

43971 ■ *"Tabular Dreams" in Canadian Business (Vol. 80, February 12, 2007, No. 4, pp. 36)*
Pub: Rogers Media
Ed: Christina Campbell. **Description:** The research of Raymor Industries in developing carbon nanotubes by bonding carbon atoms using high technology is discussed.

43972 ■ *"The Tech 100" in Canadian Business (Vol. 81, July 21, 2008, No. 11, pp. 48)*
Pub: Rogers Media Ltd.
Ed: Calvin Leung. **Description:** Absolute Software Corp. Day4 Energy Inc., Sandvine Corp., Norsat International Inc. and Call Genie Inc. are the five technology firms included in the annual ranking of top companies in Canada by market capitalization. The services and the one-year total return potential of the companies are presented.

43973 ■ *"Tech Coalition Warns Takeover Spree is Nigh" in Globe & Mail (February 6,*

2007, pp. B1)
Pub: CTVglobemedia Publishing Inc.
Ed: Steven Chase. **Description:** The declaration by an alliance of technology-rich companies, that the huge credits that these companies have to endure due to research and development activities may lead to company takeovers, is discussed.

43974 ■ *Technological Entrepreneurship*
Pub: Edward Elgar Publishing, Incorporated
Ed: Donald Siegel. **Released:** October 2006. **Price:** $230.00. **Description:** Technological entrepreneurship at universities is discussed. The book covers four related topics: university licensing and patenting; science parks and incubators; university-based startups; and the role of academic science in entrepreneurship.

43975 ■ *"Testing Firm to Add Jobs"* in Business Courier (Vol. 26, December 11, 2009, No. 33, pp. 1)
Pub: American City Business Journals, Inc.
Ed: Dan Monk. **Description:** Cincinnati-based Q Laboratories announced plans to add dozens of jobs with the $1.6 million stimulus assisted expansion. The company hired Michael Lichtenberg & Sons Construction Co. to build a new 9,000 square foot laboratory building.

43976 ■ *"Thinking Aloud"* in Business Strategy Review (Vol. 21, Summer 2010, No. 2, pp. 47)
Pub: Wiley-Blackwell
Ed: Yiorgos Mylonadis. **Description:** In each issue we ask an academic to explain the big question on which their research hopes to shed light. Yiorgos Mylonadis looks at how people define and solve problems.

43977 ■ *"Thinking Aloud: Julian Franks"* in Business Strategy Review (Vol. 21, Autumn 2010, No. 3, pp. 35)
Pub: Blackwell Publishers Ltd.
Ed: Stuart Crainer. **Description:** Julian Franks is Academic Director of the Centre for Corporate Governance at London Business School and lead investigator for a 1.4 million (sterling pounds) grand for research into corporate governance.

43978 ■ *"Thinking Aloud: Julian Franks"* in Business Strategy Review (Vol. 21, Autumn 2010, No. 3, pp. 35)
Pub: Wiley-Blackwell
Ed: Stuart Crainer. **Description:** Julian Franks is academic director of the Centre for Corporate Governance at London Business School and lead investigator for a (pounds sterling) 1.4 million grant for research into corporate governance.

43979 ■ *"To Build for the Future, Reach Beyond the Skies"* in Canadian Business (Vol. 83, June 15, 2010, No. 10, pp. 11)
Pub: Rogers Media Ltd.
Ed: Richard Branson. **Description:** Richard Branson says that tackling an engineering challenge or a scientific venture is a real adventure for an entrepreneur. Branson discusses Virgin's foray into the aviation business and states that at Virgin, they build for the future.

43980 ■ *"Top 50 in the Capital Market"* in Canadian Business (Vol. 81, Summer 2008, No. 9, pp. 117)
Pub: Rogers Media Ltd.
Description: Research in Motion Ltd. topped the list of companies in Canada in terms of market capitalization. The company's share prices surge to 119.8 percent in the year ended April 4. A table showing the top 50 Canadian companies in terms of market capitalization is presented.

43981 ■ *"Top Worst Weeds in Corn"* in Farm Industry News (November 29, 2011)
Pub: Penton Business Media Inc.
Ed: John Pocock. **Description:** Effective weed control for profitable crops is discussed with information from leading weed scientists from the University of Illinois Extension. It is important for farmers to know what their worst weed is in order to choose the best product, or mix of products, to control them.

43982 ■ *"Tweaking On-Board Activities, Equipment Saves Fuel, Reduces CO2"* in Canadian Sailings (June 30, 2008)
Pub: UBM Global Trade
Contact: Leonard J. Corallo, President
Description: Optimizing ship activities and equipment uses less fuel and therefore reduces greenhouse gas emissions. Ways in which companies are implementing research and development techniques in order to monitor ship performance and analyze data in an attempt to become more efficient are examined.

43983 ■ *"UA, BP Test Unmanned Aircraft"* in Alaska Business Monthly (Vol. 27, October 2011, No. 10, pp. 8)
Pub: Alaska Business Publishing Company
Ed: Nancy Pounds. **Description:** University of Alaska Fairbanks Geophysical Institute and BP Exploration Alaska tested the oil-spill capabilities of an unmanned aircraft. The aircraft will be used to gather 3-D ariel data to aid in oil-spill cleanup.

43984 ■ *"UC Lobbies for Big Chunk of New Funds"* in Business Courier (Vol. 24, February 22, 2008, No. 46, pp. 1)
Pub: American City Business Journals, Inc.
Ed: Laura Baverman. **Description:** Discusses the University of Cincinnati (UC) which has requested $192 million funding from the Ohio Innovation Partnership. The program was launched by governor Stickland in an attempt to drive research and innovation in the studies of biotechnology, aeronautics, and other fields that reflects Ohio's strengths. Details of UC's grant proposals are supplied.

43985 ■ *"USM Focuses on Turning Science Into New Companies, Cash"* in Boston Business Journal (Vol. 29, July 1, 2011, No. 8, pp. 1)
Pub: American City Business Journals Inc.
Ed: Alexander Jackson. **Description:** University System of Maryland gears up to push for its plan for commercializing its scientific discoveries which by 2020 could create 325 companies and double the $1.4 billion the system's eleven schools garner in yearly research grants. It is talking with University of Utah and University Maryland, Baltimore to explore ways to make this plan a reality.

43986 ■ *Values and Opportunities in Social Entrepreneurship*
Pub: Palgrave Macmillan
Ed: Kai Hockerts. **Released:** November 1, 2009. **Price:** $90.00. **Description:** Social entrepreneurship has grown as a research field. This book discusses social entrepreneurship as well as the identification and exploitation of social venturing opportunities.

43987 ■ *"Voices: Breaking the Corruption Habit"* in Business Strategy Review (Vol. 21, Autumn 2010, No. 3, pp. 67)
Pub: Wiley-Blackwell
Ed: David De Cremer. **Description:** In times of crisis, it seems natural that people will work together for the common good. David De Cremer cautions that, on the contrary, both economic and social research prove otherwise. He proposes steps for organizations to take to prevent corrupt behaviors.

43988 ■ *"Water Distiller"* in Canadian Business (Vol. 81, September 29, 2008, No. 16, pp. 52)
Pub: Rogers Media Ltd.
Ed: Matthew McClearn. **Description:** Les Fairn's invention of a water distiller called a Solarsphere was recognized in the Great Canadian Invention Competition. Fairn's invention resembles a buoy that uses the sun's energy to vaporize dirty water then leaves the impurities behind in a sump. The invention has an application for producing potable water in impoverished countries.

43989 ■ *"The Way to the Market's Heart?"* in Canadian Business (Vol. 80, March 26, 2007, No. 7, pp. 74)
Pub: Rogers Media
Ed: Erin Pooley. **Description:** The financial and stock performance of Canadian biotechnology companies Medicure Inc. and Angiotech Pharmaceuticals Inc. are analyzed.

43990 ■ *"Where the Future is Made"* in Indoor Comfort Marketing (Vol. 70, May 2011, No. 5, pp. 48)
Pub: Industry Publications Inc.
Description: Research being performed at Brookhaven National Laboratory, located in Upton, New York, is discussed, focusing on new energy sources for our nation.

43991 ■ *"Where the Money Is"* in Conde Nast Portfolio (Vol. 2, June 2008, No. 6, pp. 113)
Pub: Conde Nast Publications
Contact: David Carey, President
Description: Revenue generated from treatments for common brain disorders that are currently on the market are listed.

43992 ■ *"Whistling in the Dark"* in Canadian Business (Vol. 79, September 25, 2006, No. 19, pp. 17)
Pub: Rogers Media
Ed: Jack Mintz. **Description:** Increasing subsidies for research projects in Canada is discussed.

43993 ■ *"Young-Kee Kim; Deputy Director, Fermi National Accelerator Laboratory"* in Crain's Chicago Business (Vol. 31, May 5, 2008, No. 18)
Pub: Crain Communications, Inc.
Ed: Phuong Ly. **Description:** Profile of Young-Kee Kim who is the deputy director of Fermilab, a physics lab where scientists study the smallest particles in the universe; Ms. Kim was a researcher at Fermilab before becoming deputy director two years ago; Fermilab is currently home to the most powerful particle accelerator in the world and is struggling to compete with other countries despite cuts in federal funding.

TRADE PERIODICALS

43994 ■ *Alloy Digest*
Pub: ASM International
Contact: Larry Wagner, President
URL(s): www.asminternational.org/portal/site/www/store/journals/alloydigest /. **Released:** Bimonthly **Price:** $749, Nonmembers; $328, Members.

43995 ■ *The Anatomical Record: Advances in Integrative Anatomy and Evolutionary Biology*
Pub: John Wiley & Sons Inc.
Contact: Stephen M. Smith, President
URL(s): onlinelibrary.wiley.com/journal/10.1002/(-ISSN)1932-8494. **Ed:** Kurt H. Albertine. **Released:** Monthly **Price:** $8214, Institutions print; $8382, Institutions, Canada print; $8466, Institutions, other countries print.

43996 ■ *Applied Engineering in Agriculture*
Pub: American Society of Agricultural Engineers
Contact: Scott Cedarquist, Director
E-mail: cedarq@asabe.org
URL(s): www.asabe.org/publications/publications-catalog/periodicals.aspx. **Released:** Bimonthly **Price:** $79, Members; $157, Nonmembers; $29, Nonmembers outside U.S.; $20, Members outside United States.

43997 ■ *Biochemistry and Cell Biology*
Pub: National Research Council Canada, NRC Research Press NRC Corporate Communications
URL(s): www.nrcresearchpress.com/journal/bcb. **Ed:** Dr. James R. Davie. **Released:** Bimonthly **Price:** $880, Institutions print; $740, Institutions electronic; $1100, Institutions print & electronic; $100, Institutions satellite; $210, Individuals electronic; $280, Individuals print & electronic; $114, Individuals airmail.

43998 ■ *Biopolymers*
Pub: John Wiley & Sons Inc.
Contact: Stephen M. Smith, President
URL(s): onlinelibrary.wiley.com/journal/10.1002/(-ISSN)1097-0282. **Released:** Semimonthly **Price:** $11491, Institutions print or online; $11827, Institutions, Canada and Mexico print only; $11995, Institutions, other countries print only.

43999 ■ Bioscience Technology: Tools and Techniques for Life Science Researchers
Pub: Advantage Business Media L.L.C.
Contact: George Fox, President
URL(s): www.biosciencetechnology.com/Default.aspx?CommonCount=0. **Released:** Monthly **Price:** Free.

44000 ■ BioTechniques
Pub: Eaton Publishing
URL(s): www.biotechniques.com. **Released:** Monthly

44001 ■ Biotechnology Advances: Research Reviews and Patent Abstracts
Pub: Elsevier Science B.V.
URL(s): www.elsevier.com/wps/find/journaldescription.cws_home/525455/descri ption#description. **Ed:** E.A. Bayer, M. Butler. **Released:** 6/yr. **Price:** $2236.80, Institutions online; $227, Individuals print; $2237, Institutions print.

44002 ■ Biotechnology & Bioengineering
Pub: John Wiley & Sons Inc.
Contact: Stephen M. Smith, President
URL(s): onlinelibrary.wiley.com/journal/10.1002/(-ISSN)1097-0290. **Ed:** Elmer L. Gaden, Jr. **Released:** 18/yr. **Price:** $9539, Institutions print only; $9791, Institutions, Canada and Mexico print only; $9917, Institutions, other countries print only.

44003 ■ Birth Defects Research Part B: Developmental and Reproductive Toxicology
Pub: John Wiley & Sons Inc.
Contact: Stephen M. Smith, President
URL(s): onlinelibrary.wiley.com/journal/10.1002/(-ISSN)1542-9741. **Ed:** George P. Daston. **Released:** Bimonthly

44004 ■ Brain, Behavior, and Immunity
Pub: Elsevier Science B.V.
URL(s): www.elsevier.com/wps/find/journaldescription.cws_home/622800/descri ption#description. **Released:** 8/yr. **Price:** $1190.40, Institutions online; $453, Individuals print; $1190, Institutions print; $55200, Individuals.

44005 ■ Canadian Journal of Chemistry
Pub: National Research Council Canada, NRC Research Press NRC Corporate Communications
URL(s): www.nrcresearchpress.com/journal/cjc. **Ed:** Dr. Derek G. Leaist. **Released:** Monthly **Price:** $1710, Institutions print only; $1430, Institutions electronic; $2145, Institutions print & electronic; $200, Institutions satellite; $416, Individuals electronic; $560, Individuals print & electronic.

44006 ■ Cereal Chemistry
Pub: AACC International
Contact: David H. Hann, President
URL(s): www.aaccnet.org/Pages/default.aspx. **Released:** Bimonthly **Price:** $117, Single issue U.S.; $128, Single issue elsewhere; $667, Individuals print; $712, Elsewhere print; $124, Single issue back issue; $135, Elsewhere back issue.

44007 ■ Chemical Engineering Research and Design (ChERD)
Pub: Mosby An Imprint of Elsevier Science Inc. Elsevier Inc. Health Sciences
URL(s): www.icheme.org/www.elsevier.com/wps/find/journaldescription.cws_home/713871/description#description. **Released:** Monthly **Price:** $1936, Institutions, other countries.

44008 ■ Chemical and Petroleum Engineering
Pub: Springer-Verlag New York Inc.
Contact: Ruediger Gebauer, President
URL(s): www.springer.com/chemistry/journal/10556. **Released:** Monthly **Price:** €5047, Institutions print or online; €6056, Institutions print & enchanced access.

44009 ■ Communication Outlook: Quarterly International Magazine
Pub: Artificial Language Laboratory Michigan State University
URL(s): www.msu.edu/~artlang/CommOut.html. **Ed:** Rebecca Ann Baird. **Released:** Quarterly **Price:** $18, Individuals North and South America; $24, Other countries; $5, Single issue.

44010 ■ Computer Animation & Virtual Worlds
Pub: John Wiley & Sons Inc.
Contact: Stephen M. Smith, President
URL(s): onlinelibrary.wiley.com/journal/10.1002/(-ISSN)1546-427X. **Ed:** T.L. Kunii. **Released:** Bimonthly **Price:** $1964, Institutions online only; $1964, Institutions, other countries online only; €1266, Institutions online only; £1002, Institutions online only; $1964, Institutions, Canada and Mexico online only.

44011 ■ Computing in Science and Engineering
Pub: Institute of Electrical and Electronics Engineers Inc.
Contact: Jack Howell, Director
URL(s): www.computer.org/portal/web/cise/home. **Released:** Quarterly **Price:** $47, Members; $78, Nonmembers; $625, Institutions.

44012 ■ Corrosion: The Journal of Science and Engineering
Pub: NACE International: The Corrosion Society
Contact: Chris Fowler, President
E-mail: chris.fowler@nace.org
URL(s): www.nace.org/Publications/CORROSION-Journal/. **Ed:** Dr. J.R. Scully. **Released:** Monthly **Price:** $85, Members online access only; $175, Nonmembers online access only; $560, Institutions online access only; $105, Members print and online access; international; $60, Students member -printed and online access; $235, Nonmembers U.S. non-member-printed and online access; $300, Other countries non-member-printed and online access; $780, Institutions printed and online access; $860, Institutions, other countries; Free student member; online access only.

44013 ■ Cytoskeleton
Pub: John Wiley & Sons Inc.
Contact: Stephen M. Smith, President
URL(s): onlinelibrary.wiley.com/journal/10.1002/(-ISSN)1949-3592/issues. **Released:** Monthly **Price:** $6265, Institutions print; $6433, Institutions, Canada and Mexico print; $6517, Institutions, other countries print.

44014 ■ Diesel & Gas Turbine Worldwide: The Marine & Stationary Power Authority
Pub: Diesel & Gas Turbine Publications
URL(s): www.dieselpub.com/ers/rdr_login.asp?magradio=WW. **Ed:** Brent Haight. **Released:** Monthly; (Jan /Feb., July/Aug. issues combined). **Price:** $65, Individuals.

44015 ■ DISCOVERY
Pub: Office of Research and Creative Activity
Ed: Annette Trinity-Stevens, Editor, annettet @montana.edu. **Released:** Monthly, during the academic year. **Price:** Free. **Description:** Features news of University research in agriculture, engineering, life sciences, and the humanities.

44016 ■ DNA and Cell Biology
Pub: Mary Ann Liebert Inc. Publishers
URL(s): www.liebertpub.com/publication.aspx?pub_id=13. **Released:** Monthly **Price:** $993, Individuals print and online; $1192, Other countries print and online; $984, Individuals online only; $4480, Institutions print and online; $5152, Institutions, other countries print and online; $3925, Institutions print only; $4514, Institutions, other countries print only; $4267, Institutions online only.

44017 ■ Earth and Mineral Sciences
Pub: Pennsylvania State University
URL(s): www.ems.psu.edu. **Released:** Semiannual **Price:** Free.

44018 ■ Electric Power Components and Systems
Pub: Taylor & Francis Group Journals
Contact: Kevin J. Bradley, President
URL(s): www.tandfonline.com/toc/uemp20/current. **Released:** 16/yr. **Price:** $3269, Institutions print & online; $2942, Institutions online; $1370, Individuals print only.

44019 ■ Electrical Engineering in Japan
Pub: John Wiley & Sons Inc.
Contact: Stephen M. Smith, President
URL(s): onlinelibrary.wiley.com/journal/10.1002/(-ISSN)1520-6416. **Ed:** Tatsuki Okamoto. **Released:** 16/yr. **Price:** $10869, Institutions print only; $11093, Institutions, Canada and Mexico print only; $11205, Institutions, other countries print only; $12499, Institutions print with online; $12723, Institutions, Canada and Mexico print with online; $12835, Institutions, other countries print with online.

44020 ■ Environmental Toxicology and Chemistry: An International Journal
Pub: Society of Environmental Toxicology and Chemistry
Contact: Paul Van den Brink, President
URL(s): www.setacjournals.org/view/0/index.htmlonlinelibrary.wiley.com/journal/10.1002/(ISSN)1552-8618/homepage/Pro ductInformation.html. **Released:** Monthly **Price:** $2152, Institutions print & online; $1871, Institutions online only; $1871, Institutions print only; $2152, Institutions, other countries print & online; $1871, Institutions, other countries online.

44021 ■ Experimental Heat Transfer
Pub: Taylor & Francis Group Journals
Contact: Kevin J. Bradley, President
URL(s): www.tandfonline.com/toc/ueht20/current. **Ed:** Ishwar K. Puri, Prof. J.P. Meyer, J.W. Rose, J.H. Lienhard, Suresh V. Garimella. **Released:** Quarterly **Price:** $809, Institutions print & online; $728, Institutions online only; $383, Individuals.

44022 ■ Gear Technology: The Journal of Gear Manufacturing
Pub: Randall Publishing Inc.
Contact: Ross Deneau, Manager
E-mail: rdeneau@engineeredtools.com
URL(s): www.geartechnology.com/. **Released:** Bimonthly **Price:** $15, Single issue back issue; Free U.S., Mexico and Canada; $70, Other countries; $115, Other countries two years.

44023 ■ Geomicrobiology Journal
Pub: Taylor & Francis Group Journals
Contact: Kevin J. Bradley, President
URL(s): www.tandfonline.com/toc/ugmb20/current. **Ed:** William C. Ghiorse, Henry Ehrlich. **Released:** 10/yr. **Price:** $514, Individuals online only; $1512, Institutions online only; $1680, Institutions print & online.

44024 ■ Human Mutation
Pub: John Wiley & Sons Inc.
Contact: Stephen M. Smith, President
URL(s): onlinelibrary.wiley.com/journal/10.1002/(-ISSN)1098-1004. **Ed:** Dr. Haig H. Kazazian, Jr., Dr. Richard G.H. Cotton. **Released:** Monthly **Price:** $1786, Institutions print only; $1954, Institutions, Canada and Mexico print only; $2038, Institutions, other countries print only.

44025 ■ IBM Journal of Research and Development
Pub: International Business Machines Corp.
Contact: Virginia Rometty, President
URL(s): www.research.ibm.com/journal/rdindex.html. **Ed:** Rachel Henriquez. **Released:** Bimonthly **Price:** $995, Libraries online.

44026 ■ International Journal of Adaptive Control and Signal Processing
Pub: John Wiley & Sons Inc.
Contact: Stephen M. Smith, President
URL(s): onlinelibrary.wiley.com/journal/10.1002/(-ISSN)1099-1115. **Ed:** Angelo Alessandri, Brian D.O. Anderson. **Released:** 12/yr. **Price:** $3189, Institutions print only; $3189, Institutions, other countries print only; €2057, Institutions print only; £1627, Institutions print only; $3189, Institutions, Canada and Mexico print only.

44027 ■ International Journal on Artificial Intelligence Tools
Pub: World Scientific Publishing Company Inc.
Contact: Leon Wang, Manager
URL(s): www.worldscinet.com/ijait/ijait.shtml. **Released:** Bimonthly **Price:** $1091, Institutions print + electronic; $992, Institutions electronic only; £751,

Institutions print + electronic; £683, Institutions electronic only; $1729, Institutions print + electronic; $1572, Institutions electronic only.

44028 ■ International Journal of Computer Integrated Manufacturing
Pub: Taylor & Francis Group Journals
Contact: Kevin J. Bradley, President
URL(s): www.tandfonline.com/toc/tcim20/current. **Ed:** Prof. David J. Williams, Paul Kenneth Wright, George Huang, Paul G. Ranky. **Released:** 12/yr. **Price:** $2748, Institutions online only; $3053, Institutions print and online.

44029 ■ International Journal of Computer Simulation
Pub: University of Wisconsin-Eau Claire Department of English
URL(s): portal.acm.org/citation.cfm?id=202926. **Ed:** Vijay K. Madisetti, Giorgio Casinovi, George W. Zobrist. **Released:** Quarterly

44030 ■ International Journal of Energy Research
Pub: John Wiley & Sons Inc.
Contact: Stephen M. Smith, President
URL(s): onlinelibrary.wiley.com/journal/10.1002/(-ISSN)1099-114X. **Ed:** Prof. J.T. McMullan, Prof. P. Lund. **Released:** 15/yr. **Price:** $7064, Institutions print only; $7064, Institutions, other countries print only; €4558, Institutions, other countries print only; £3606, Institutions print only; $7064, Institutions, Canada and Mexico print only.

44031 ■ International Journal of Hyperthermia
Pub: Informa Healthcare
URL(s): informahealthcare.com/hth. **Released:** 8/yr. **Price:** £2050, Institutions; $3575, Institutions; €2860, Institutions.

44032 ■ International Journal of Intelligent Systems
Pub: John Wiley & Sons Inc.
Contact: Stephen M. Smith, President
URL(s): onlinelibrary.wiley.com/journal/10.1002/(-ISSN)1098-111X. **Ed:** Ronald R. Yager. **Released:** Monthly **Price:** $3985, Institutions print and online; $4153, Institutions, Canada and Mexico print and online; £1899, Institutions print only; $3465, Institutions print only; $3633, Institutions, Canada and Mexico print only; $3717, Institutions, other countries print only; €2399, Institutions print only; £2185, Institutions print and online; €2760, Institutions, other countries print and online; $4237, Institutions, other countries print and online.

44033 ■ Journal of the American Oil Chemists' Society
Pub: AOCS Press
Contact: Richard Cantrill, Director
E-mail: richard.cantrill@aocs.org
URL(s): www.aocs.org/Journals/jaocs.cfm. **Released:** Monthly **Price:** $165, Members.

44034 ■ Journal of Andrology
Pub: American Society of Andrology
Contact: Wendy J. Weiser, Executive Director
URL(s): www.andrologyjournal.org. **Released:** Bimonthly **Price:** $390, Institutions print only; $420, Institutions, other countries print only; $510, Institutions print and online; $380, Individuals print and online; $540, Institutions, other countries print and online; $410, Other countries print and online; $450, Institutions online only; $320, Individuals online only.

44035 ■ Journal of Biochemical and Molecular Toxicology
Pub: John Wiley & Sons Inc.
Contact: Stephen M. Smith, President
URL(s): onlinelibrary.wiley.com/journal/10.1002/(-ISSN)1099-0461. **Ed:** Ernest Hodgson. **Released:** Bimonthly **Price:** $1070, Institutions print only; $1154, Institutions, Canada and Mexico print only; $1196, Institutions, other countries print only; $1232, Institutions print with online; $1316, Institutions, Canada and Mexico print with online; $1358, Institutions, other countries print with online.

44036 ■ Journal of Bioenergetics and Biomembranes
Pub: Springer Netherlands
Contact: Zachary Rolnik, Managing Director
E-mail: zrolnik@wkap.com
URL(s): www.springerlink.com/content/0145-479X. **Ed:** Dr. Peter L. Pedersen. **Released:** Bimonthly **Price:** €1163, Institutions print or online; €1396, Institutions print & enchanced access.

44037 ■ Journal of Biological Rhythms
Pub: SAGE Publications USA
Contact: Blaise R. Simqu, President
URL(s): www.sagepub.com/journalsProdDesc.nav?prodId=Journal200933&. **Released:** Bimonthly **Price:** $1180, Institutions combined (print & e-access); $1298, Institutions combined plus backfile; $1062, Institutions e-access; $1180, Institutions e-access plus backfile; $1174, Institutions e-access (content through 1998); $1156, Institutions print only; $232, Individuals print only; $212, Institutions single print; $50, Individuals single print.

44038 ■ Journal of Cellular Biochemistry
Pub: John Wiley & Sons Inc.
Contact: Stephen M. Smith, President
URL(s): onlinelibrary.wiley.com/journal/10.1002/(-ISSN)1097-4644. **Released:** 18/yr. **Price:** $11319, Institutions print only; $11535, Institutions, Canada and Mexico print only; $11661, Institutions, other countries print only.

44039 ■ Journal of Chemical Ecology: Official Journal of the International Society of Chemical Ecology
Pub: Springer Netherlands
Contact: Zachary Rolnik, Managing Director
E-mail: zrolnik@wkap.com
URL(s): www.springerlink.com/content/0098-0331. **Released:** Monthly **Price:** €2380, Institutions print & online; €2856, Institutions print & enchanced access.

44040 ■ Journal of Chemical Technology and Biotechnology: International Research in Process, Environmental, and Monitoring Technology
Pub: John Wiley & Sons Inc.
Contact: Stephen M. Smith, President
URL(s): onlinelibrary.wiley.com/journal/10.1002/(-ISSN)1097-4660. **Released:** Monthly **Price:** €1849, Institutions, other countries print only; £1461, Institutions print only; $2864, Institutions, other countries print only; €2127, Institutions, other countries print with online; £1681, Institutions print with online; $3294, Institutions, other countries print with online.

44041 ■ Journal of Clinical Microbiology
Pub: ASM Journals
URL(s): jcm.asm.org/. **Released:** Monthly **Price:** $139, Members print; $185, Members print & online; $184, Members Canada, print; $230, Members Canada, print & online.

44042 ■ Journal of Communications Technology and Electronics
Pub: John Wiley & Sons Inc.
Contact: Stephen M. Smith, President
URL(s): www.maik.rssi.ru/cgi-perl/journal.pl?name=comtech&page=main. **Released:** Monthly **Price:** $4012, U.S. and Canada; $4613; $4613, Other countries.

44043 ■ Journal of Environmental Engineering
Pub: American Society of Civil Engineers Architectural Engineering Institute
Contact: D. Wayne Klotz, President
URL(s): ascelibrary.org/eeo. **Ed:** Raymond A. Ferrara, Dionysios D. Dionysiou. **Released:** Monthly **Price:** $820, Institutions print & online; $850, Institutions, other countries print & online; $719, Institutions print; $749, Institutions, other countries print; $631, Institutions online; $631, Institutions, other countries online; $205, Members print & online; $235, Members other countries; print & online; $180, Members print; $210, Members other countries; print.

44044 ■ Journal of Investigative Surgery
Pub: Taylor & Francis Group
Contact: Kevin J. Bradley, President
URL(s): informahealthcare.com/page/Description?journalCode=ivs. **Released:** 6/yr. **Price:** $494, Individuals print only; $1084, Institutions online only; $1141, Institutions print & online; £690, Institutions print & online; £655, Institutions online only; £300, Individuals print only.

44045 ■ Journal of Labelled Compounds and Radiopharmaceuticals
Pub: John Wiley & Sons Inc.
Contact: Stephen M. Smith, President
URL(s): onlinelibrary.wiley.com/journal/10.1002/(-ISSN)1099-1344. **Ed:** B. Langstrom, W.J. Wheeler, T. Moenius. **Released:** 14/yr. **Price:** €3687, Institutions print only; $5714, Institutions, other countries print only; £2916, Institutions print only; €4240, Institutions, other countries print with online; £3354, Institutions print with online; $6571, Institutions, other countries print with online.

44046 ■ Journal of Materials in Civil Engineering
Pub: American Society of Civil Engineers Architectural Engineering Institute
Contact: D. Wayne Klotz, President
URL(s): ascelibrary.org/journal/jmcee7. **Released:** Monthly **Price:** $1080, Institutions print & online; $1140, Institutions, other countries print & online; $947, Institutions print; $1007, Institutions, other countries print; $831, Institutions online; $831, Institutions, other countries online; $270, Members print & online; $330, Members other countries; print & online; $237, Members print; $297, Members other countries; print.

44047 ■ Journal of Morphology
Pub: John Wiley & Sons Inc.
Contact: Stephen M. Smith, President
URL(s): onlinelibrary.wiley.com/journal/10.1002/(-ISSN)1097-4687. **Ed:** Matthias J. Starck. **Released:** Monthly **Price:** $7184, Institutions print only; $7352, Institutions, Canada and Mexico print only; $7436, Institutions, other countries print only.

44048 ■ Journal of Natural History
Pub: Taylor & Francis Group Journals
Contact: Kevin J. Bradley, President
URL(s): www.tandfonline.com/toc/tnah20/current. **Ed:** A. Polaszek, L. Allcock. **Released:** Semimonthly **Price:** $9236, Institutions online only; $10263, Institutions print and online.

44049 ■ Journal of Neurochemistry: Official Journal of the International Society for Neurochemistry
Pub: Blackwell Publishing Inc.
Contact: Gordon Tibbitts, President
URL(s): www.blackwellpublishing.com/jnc_enhanced/default.asp. **Released:** Bimonthly **Price:** $1027, Individuals print and online; $977, Individuals online only; $5326, Institutions print & online; £613, Individuals print & online; $4631, Institutions print, online; $20, Members online only.

44050 ■ Journal of Pharmaceutical Sciences
Pub: American Pharmacists Association
Contact: Thomas E. Menighan, Chief Executive Officer
E-mail: tmenighan@aphanet.org
URL(s): onlinelibrary.wiley.com/journal/10.1002/(-ISSN)1520-6017. **Ed:** Bradley D. Anderson, Harry Brittain. **Released:** Monthly **Price:** $351, Individuals print; $408, Other countries print; $1859, Institutions print only; $1916, Institutions, other countries print only; $2139, Institutions print and online; $2196, Institutions, other countries print and online.

44051 ■ Journal of Polymer Science: Part A: Polymer Chemistry
Pub: John Wiley & Sons Inc.
Contact: Stephen M. Smith, President
URL(s): onlinelibrary.wiley.com/journal/10.1002/(-ISSN)1099-0518. **Ed:** Craig J. Hawker, Mitsuo Sawamoto, Virgil Percec, Karen L. Wooley, Herman F. Mark. **Released:** 48/yr. **Price:** $20000, Institutions print only; $20336, Institutions, Canada print only; $20504, Institutions, other countries print only;

$23000, Institutions print with online; $23336, Institutions, Canada print with online; $23504, Institutions, other countries print with online.

44052 ■ Journal of Pressure Vessel Technology
Pub: American Society of Mechanical Engineers
Contact: Allan Kirkpatrick, Manager
E-mail: allan@engr.colostate.edu
URL(s): asmedl.aip.org/PressureVesselTech. Ed: G.E. Otto Widera. Released: Quarterly Price: $60, Members USA; print & online; $107, Members international; print & online; $51, Members internet only; $509, Nonmembers U.S. and Canada; print & online; $556, Nonmembers international; print & online.

44053 ■ Journal of Software: Improvement and Practice
Pub: John Wiley & Sons Inc.
Contact: Stephen M. Smith, President
URL(s): onlinelibrary.wiley.com/journal/10.1002/(-ISSN)2047-7481. Released: 7/yr. Price: £209, Individuals print; $363, Other countries print; $727, Institutions, other countries print; €469, Institutions, other countries print; £370, Institutions print.

44054 ■ Journal of Turbomachinery
Pub: American Society of Mechanical Engineers
Contact: Allan Kirkpatrick, Manager
E-mail: allan@engr.colostate.edu
URL(s): scitation.aip.org/ASMEJournals/Turbomachinery/. Ed: David C. Wisler. Released: Quarterly Price: $50, Members print and online; $88, Members international; print and online; $43, Members internet only; $391, Nonmembers U.S. and Canada; print and online; $429, Nonmembers international; print and online.

44055 ■ Machine Design: Proven America's Most Useful Design Engineering Magazine
Pub: Penton Media Inc.
URL(s): machinedesign.com/. Ed: Leland E. Teschler. Released: 22/yr.

44056 ■ Microbiology Abstracts Section A: Industrial and Applied Microbiology
Pub: Cambridge Scientific Abstracts L.P.
Contact: Chris Jahn, Manager
URL(s): www.csa.com/factsheets/microbiology-a-set-c.php. Released: Monthly; except December.

44057 ■ Microscopy Research and Technique
Pub: John Wiley & Sons Inc.
Contact: Stephen M. Smith, President
URL(s): onlinelibrary.wiley.com/journal/10.1002/(-ISSN)1097-0029. Released: Monthly Price: $9270, Institutions print; $9438, Institutions, Canada and Mexico print; $9522, Institutions, other countries print.

44058 ■ Molecular Physics: An International Journal in the Field of Chemical Physics
Pub: Taylor & Francis Group Journals
Contact: Kevin J. Bradley, President
URL(s): www.tandfonline.com/toc/tmph20/current. Ed: Prof. Jean-Pierre Hansen. Released: Semimonthly Price: $8440, Institutions online only; $9378, Institutions print and online.

44059 ■ Neurobiology of Learning and Memory
Pub: Elsevier Science B.V.
URL(s): www.elsevier.com/wps/find/journaldescription.cws_home/622924/descri ption#description. Ed: J.L. McGaugh. Released: 8/yr. Price: $1627.20, Institutions online; $711, Individuals print; $1627, Institutions print.

44060 ■ Numerical Heat Transfer, Part A: Applications: An International Journal of Computation and Methodology
Pub: Taylor & Francis Group Journals
Contact: Kevin J. Bradley, President
URL(s): www.tandfonline.com/toc/unht20/current. Released: 24/yr. Price: $8902, Institutions print and online; $3290, Individuals; $8012, Institutions online only.

44061 ■ Particulate Science and Technology: An International Journal
Pub: Taylor & Francis Group Journals
Contact: Kevin J. Bradley, President
URL(s): www.tandf.co.uk/journals/titles/02726351.asp. Released: Quarterly Price: $475, Individuals print only; $1089, Institutions online only; $1210, Individuals print and online.

44062 ■ The Plant Cell
Pub: American Society of Plant Biologists
Contact: Dr. Crispin Taylor, Executive Director
URL(s): www.plantcell.org. Released: Monthly Price: $215, Members print; $150, Students print; $450, Nonmembers.

44063 ■ Progress in Photovoltaics: Research and Applications
Pub: John Wiley & Sons Inc.
Contact: Stephen M. Smith, President
URL(s): onlinelibrary.wiley.com/journal/10.1002/(-ISSN)1099-159X. Released: 8/yr. Price: $2609, Institutions print with online; $2269, Institutions, other countries print only; €1464, Institutions print only; £1158, Institutions print only.

44064 ■ The Quarterly Review of Biology
Pub: University of Chicago Press
Contact: Garrett P. Kiely, Director
E-mail: gkiely@press.uchicago.edu
URL(s): www.jstor.org/action/showPublication?journalCode=quarrevibiol. Ed: John J. Wiens, James D. Thomson. Released: Quarterly Price: $56, Individuals print and electronic; $46, Individuals electronic only; $48, Individuals print only; $28, Students electronic only; $101, Two years print and electronic; $50, Students electronic only, two years; $143, Individuals print and electronic, three years.

44065 ■ R & D Magazine
Pub: Advantage Business Media L.L.C.
Contact: George Fox, President
URL(s): www.rdmag.com. Released: Monthly Price: Free.

44066 ■ Random Structures & Algorithms
Pub: John Wiley & Sons Inc.
Contact: Stephen M. Smith, President
URL(s): onlinelibrary.wiley.com/journal/10.1002/(-ISSN)1098-2418. Ed: Joel Spencer. Released: 8/yr. Price: $1662, Institutions print; $1774, Institutions, Canada and Mexico print; $1914, Institutions, other countries print; $1912, Institutions print with online; $2024, Institutions, Canada and Mexico print with online; $2164, Institutions, other countries print with online.

44067 ■ Rapid Communications in Mass Spectrometry
Pub: John Wiley & Sons Inc.
Contact: Stephen M. Smith, President
URL(s): onlinelibrary.wiley.com/journal/10.1002/(-ISSN)1097-0231. Ed: Prof. Kermit K. Murray, Dr. David Goodlett, Prof. John J. Monaghan. Released: Semimonthly Price: €5172, Institutions print; £4090, Institutions print; $8014, Institutions, other countries print; €5948, Institutions print with online; £4704, Institutions print with online; $9216, Institutions, other countries print with online.

44068 ■ Reviews in Medical Virology
Pub: John Wiley & Sons Inc.
Contact: Stephen M. Smith, President
URL(s): onlinelibrary.wiley.com/journal/10.1002/(-ISSN)1099-1654/homepage/Edi torialBoard.html. Ed: Dr. Richard R. Whitley, Dr. Yiming Shao. Released: Bimonthly Price: £491, Individuals print only; $878, Other countries print only; $1458, Institutions, other countries print only; €942, Institutions print only; £745, Institutions print only; €1084, Institutions, other countries print with online; £857, Institutions print with online; $1677, Institutions, other countries print with online.

44069 ■ Rubber Chemistry and Technology: Papers on Fundamental Research, Technical Developments and Chemical Engineering on
Rubber and Allied Substances
Pub: Rubber Division American Chemical Society
URL(s): www.rubber.org/publications/rct/index.htm. Released: 4/yr. Price: $550, Institutions print only; $450, Nonmembers print only; $350, Members print only; $450, Other countries member; print only; $650, Institutions, other countries print only.

44070 ■ Sensor Technology
Pub: Technical Insights
Ed: Leo O'Connor, Editor. Released: Monthly. Price: $650, U.S. and Canada year; $710, elsewhere year. Description: Informs readers of the latest scientific and technological developments in the field of sensors. Focuses on process and machine control, including robotics; also covers environmental and medical uses. Recurring features include a calendar of events, news of research, book reviews, and columns titled Key Patents and Keep an Eye On.

44071 ■ Strategic S&T
Pub: EPRI
Ed: Gail McCarthy, Editor. Released: 3/year. Description: Profiles research projects, results, and activities of the SS&T program. Recurring features include news of research, reports of meetings, and listing of SS&T reports with ordering information.

44072 ■ Systems and Computers in Japan
Pub: John Wiley & Sons Inc.
Contact: Stephen M. Smith, President
URL(s): www3.interscience.wiley.com/journal/51986/home. Ed: Shoji Shinoda. Released: 14/yr.

44073 ■ Yeast
Pub: John Wiley & Sons Inc.
Contact: Stephen M. Smith, President
URL(s): onlinelibrary.wiley.com/journal/10.1002/(-ISSN)1097-0061. Ed: S.G. Oliver, John Armstrong. Released: Monthly Price: $3790, Institutions, other countries print only; €2446, Institutions print only; £1935, Institutions print only; €2814, Institutions print with online; £2225, Institutions print with online; $4359, Institutions, other countries print with online.

44074 ■ Zoo Biology
Pub: John Wiley & Sons Inc.
Contact: Stephen M. Smith, President
URL(s): onlinelibrary.wiley.com/journal/10.1002/(-ISSN)1098-2361. Ed: Terry L. Maple, Donald G. Lindburg, Mandi Vick, Dan Wharton. Released: Bimonthly Price: $326, U.S., Canada, and Mexico print only; $368, Other countries print only; $2488, Institutions print only; $2572, Institutions, Canada and Mexico print only; $2614, Institutions, other countries print only.

VIDEOCASSETTES/ AUDIOCASSETTES

44075 ■ The Science of Energy
Human Relations Media
41 Kensico Dr.
Mount Kisco, NY 10549
Ph: (914)244-0486
Free: 800-431-2050
Fax: (914)244-0485
Co. E-mail: orders@hrmvideo.com
URL: http://www.hrmvideo.com

Released: 1994. Price: $189. Description: Introduces students to biology and physics, touching on the scientific history of energy from Galileo to Einstein, thermodynamics, the sun as the Earth's energy source, photosynthesis and respiration. Complete with teacher's resource book. Availability: VHS.

44076 ■ Science on Ice: Research in Antarctica
Encyclopedia Britannica
331 N. LaSalle St.
Chicago, IL 60654
Ph: (312)347-7159
Free: 800-323-1229

Fax: (312)294-2104
URL: http://www.britannica.com
Released: 1988. **Price:** $59.00. **Description:** Illustrates the advantages of researching in the Antarctica and provides information on some of the current research taking place in the region. **Availability:** VHS; 3/4 U; SVS.

44077 ■ Technical Studies
Home Vision Cinema
c/o Image Entertainment
20525 Nordhoff St., Ste. 200
Chatsworth, CA 91311
Co. E-mail: inquiries@image-entertainment.com
URL: http://www.homevision.com
Released: 1981. **Description:** This series is designed to illustrate the practical application of concepts in materials and engineering science. **Availability:** VHS; 3/4 U.

TRADE SHOWS AND CONVENTIONS

44078 ■ American Technical Education Association National Conference on Technical Education
American Technical Education Association
c/o North Dakota State College of Science
800 N. 6th St.
Wahpeton, ND 58076-0002
Ph: (701)671-2301
Fax: (701)671-2260
URL: http://www.ateaonline.org
Contact: Betty M. Krump, Executive Director
E-mail: betty.krump@ndscs.edu
URL(s): www.ateaonline.org. **Frequency:** Annual. **Audience:** Technical educators and administrators of post-secondary technical education. **Principal Exhibits:** Supplies and services related to post secondary technical education. **Telecommunication Services:** deeann.bilben@ndscs.edu.

44079 ■ Estuarine Research Federation Conference
Estuarine Research Federation
University of Southwest Louisiana
Dept. of Biology
Port Republic, MD 20676
Ph: (410)326-7467
Fax: (410)326-7466
Co. E-mail: info@erf.org
URL: http://www.erf.org
Contact: Linda Schaffner, President
E-mail: Linda@vims.edu
URL(s): www.sgmeet.com. **Frequency:** Biennial. **Principal Exhibits:** Exhibits for persons actively engaged in biological, hydrographic, or related investigations of estuarine problems.

CONSULTANTS

44080 ■ Bio-Technical Resources L.P. (BTR)
1035 S 7th St.
Manitowoc, WI 54220-5301
Ph: (920)684-5518
Fax: (920)684-5519
Co. E-mail: info@biotechresources.com
URL: http://www.biotechresources.com
Contact: Tom Jerrell, President
Scope: Services include strain improvement, process development and metabolic engineering. Solutions are also offered for the development of biotechnology products and processes through contract services in research and development, bio process scale-up, pilot scale manufacturing, technology and economic assessments. Target audience: pharmaceutical, biotechnology, chemical and food and feed industries. Client base may be global leaders as well as small companies and startups. **Founded:** 1962. **Publications:** "A Novel Fungus for the Production of Efficient Cellulases and Hemi-Cellulases," Jun, 2009; "Linoleic Acid Isomerase from Propionibacterium acnes: Purification, Characterization, Molecular Cloning, and Heterologous Expression," 2007; "Purification and Characterization of a Membrane-Bound Linoleic Acid Isomerase from Clostridium sporogenes," 2007;

"Metabolic Engineering of Sesquiterpene Metabolism in Yeast," 2007; "Purification and Characterization of a Membrane-Bound Linoleic AcidIsomerase from Clostridium sporogenes," 2007; "Reduction of Background Interference in the Spectrophotometric Assay of Mevalonate Kinase," 2006; "A Soluble Form of Phosphatase in Saccharomyces cerevisiae Capable of Converting Farnesyl Diphosphate to E, E-Farnesol," 2006; "Ascorbate Biosynthesis: A Diversity of Pathways," BIOS Scientific Publishers, 2004; "The Biotechnology of Ascorbic Acid Manufacture," BIOS Scientific Publishers, 2004; "Detection of Farnesyl Diphosphate Accumulation in YeastERG9 Mutants," 2003; "Reverse Two-Hybrid System: Detecting Critical Interaction Domains and Screening for Inhibitors," Eaton Publishing, 2000. **Seminars:** Metabolic Engineering for Industrial Production of Glucosamine and N-Acetylglucosamine, Aug, 2003; Metabolic Engineering of E. coli for the Industrial Production of Glucosamine, Apr, 2003.

44081 ■ BioChem Technology Inc.
3620 Horizon Dr., Ste. 200
King of Prussia, PA 19406
Ph: (610)768-9360
Fax: (610)768-9363
Co. E-mail: sales@biochemtech.com
URL: http://www.biochemtech.com
Contact: George Lee, President
Scope: A process consultation firm specializing in the monitoring, optimization and control of wastewater treatment processes. The technological optimization services include assessment of treatment capacities, facility re-rating, optimization services, debottlenecking services, flow dynamics/mixing pattern analysis. **Founded:** 1979. **Publications:** "Process Evaluation Provides Optimization and Energy Reduction"; "Effect of Ionic Strength on Ion Selective Electrodes in the Activated Sludge Process"; "DO Control Based on On-line Ammonia Measurement"; "Energy Savings at Phoenix 23rd Avenue Wastewater Treatment Plant Using Feed-Forward Process Control"; "A Novel Approach for Monitoring and Control of Denitrification in a Biological Nutrient Removal Facility," Oct, 1999; "A Unique Approach for Assessing the Capacity of a Biological Nutrient Removal Facility," Oct, 1999; "Enhancing Competitiveness of an Operations Staff: Five Years Experience with a BNR Wastewater Treatment Facility," Oct, 1998; "Optimization of Nitrification Process By On-Line Monitoring of Nitrification Time," Jun, 1997; "Monitoring and Control of the Nitrification Process Marine Park Water Reclamation Facility, City of Vancouver, WA," Oct, 1997; "Operational Improvements in a Biological Nutrient Removal Facility Using an Innovative Biological Activity Meter," May, 1996; "Operator Education and an Innovative Monitoring Technology Improve Performance of a Biological Nutrient Removal Facility," Oct, 1996; "Performance Enhancement of a BNR Wastewater Treatment Facility Utilizing a Microcosm Reactor Equipped With a Biological Activity Meter," Oct, 1996; "Optimization of Biological Denitrification Through Biological Activity Monitoring: System Development," Jun, 1995. **Seminars:** A Five Year Case Study of a Feed Forward Nitrogen Reduction Process Control System, Jun, 2009; Alternate DO Control Based on On-line Ammonia Measurement, Jun, 2009.

44082 ■ Education Development Center Inc. (EDC)
43 Foundry Ave.
Waltham, MA 02453-8313
Ph: (617)969-7100
Free: 800-225-4276
Fax: (617)969-5979
Co. E-mail: comment@edc.org
URL: http://www.edc.org
Contact: Luther Luedtke, President
Description: Seeks to build bridges among research, policy and practice; programs and products, developed in collaboration with partners worldwide, consistently advance learning and health development for individuals of all ages; manages 335 projects in 50 countries; works to strengthen nearly every facet of society, including early child development, K-12 education, health promotion, workforce preparation, community development, learning technologies, basic and adult education, institutional reform, and

social justice. **Scope:** Services include research, training, educational materials and strategy, with activities ranging from seed projects to large-scale national and international initiatives. Specialize in program and fiscal management. Serves to design, deliver and evaluate innovative programs to address some of the world's most urgent challenges in education, health, and economic opportunity. Renders services to U.S. and foreign government agencies, private foundations, healthcare sectors, educational institutions, nonprofit organizations, universities, and corporations. **Founded:** 1958. **Publications:** "A Call to Action: HIV/AIDS, Health, Safety, and the Youth Employment Summit"; "A Case Against "Binge" as the Term of Choice: How to Get College Students to Personalize Messages about Dangerous Drinking"; "A Description of Foundation Skills Interventions for Struggling Middle-Grade Readers in Four Urban Northeast and Islands Region School Districts"; "A Guide to Facilitating Cases in Education"; "A Look at Social, Emotional, and Behavioral Screening Tools for Head Start and Early Head Start"; "A Multifaceted Social Norms Approach to Reduce High-Risk Drinking: Lessons from Hobart and William Smith Colleges"; "The New Media Literacy Handbook"; "Helping Children Outgrow War"; "Worms, Shadows, and Whirlpools: Science in the Early Childhood Classroom"; "Teacher Leadership in Mathematics and Science Casebook and Facilitator's Guide"; "Teachers' Professional Development and the Elementary Mathematics Classroom: Bringing Understandings to Light". **Seminars:** Designed to Introduce the Materials; To Guide Schools Through the Issues. **Telecommunication Services:** contact@edc.org; lluedtke@edc.org.

44083 ■ Flett Research Ltd.
440 DeSalaberry Ave.
Winnipeg, MB, Canada R2L 0Y7
Ph: (204)667-2505
Fax: (204)667-2505
Co. E-mail: flett@flettresearch.ca
URL: http://www.flettresearch.ca
Contact: Dr. Robert Flett, President
E-mail: flett@flettresearch.ca
Scope: Provider of environmental audits and assessments. Offers contract research and consultation on environmental topics, specializing in limnology, with emphasis in microbiology, bio-geochemistry and radio-chemistry. Performs dating of sediments via Pb-210 and CS-137 methods, to determine sediment accumulation rates in lakes. One of a handful of labs in the world able to carry out total mercury and methyl mercury analyses at the sub-nanogram and L concentration in water. **Founded:** 1978. **Seminars:** Comparison of Two Methods for the Measurement of Methyl Mercury Concentrations in Penobscot River Sediments.

44084 ■ Innovative Scientific Analysis & Computing (ISAac)
6168 Flagstaff Rd.
Boulder, CO 80302
Ph: (303)440-7673
Fax: (303)545-6674
Co. E-mail: ros5e@isaac.com
URL: http://www.ros5e.com
Contact: Charlie E. Rose, President
E-mail: ros5e@isaac.com
Scope: Engineering services includes mathematical analysis specializing in optimal estimation, scientific programming, and database design and development, data encryption and security. **Founded:** 1993.

44085 ■ Midwest Research Institute (MRI)
425 Volker Blvd.
Kansas City, MO 64110-2241
Ph: (816)753-7600
Fax: (816)753-8420
Co. E-mail: info@mriresearch.org
URL: http://www.mriresearch.org
Contact: James L. Spigarelli, President
Scope: Independent not-for-profit research institute offering scientific services in the areas of national defense, health sciences, agriculture and food safety, engineering, energy, and infrastructure. Services include biomedical electronics, remote sensing, automation and control electromagnetic radiation, environmental sampling and analysis programs for

industry and government, program management, engineering studies, exposure and risk assessment, waste management strategies, contaminant identification, pollution prevention, and waste minimization. Expertise in highway safety/accident analysis, chemometrics/pattern recognition/neural networks, statistical support, process and product engineering. **Founded:** 1943. **Telecommunication Services:** bduncan@mriresearch.org.

44086 ■ Technology Management Group Co.—Ratafia Ventures
PO Box 3260
New Haven, CT
Ph: (203)387-1430
Fax: (203)387-1470
Co. E-mail: info@commtechsoftware.com
URL: http://www.ratafia.net
Contact: Manny Ratafia, President
E-mail: manny@commtechsoftware.com
Scope: Consulting services include analysis of market opportunities; product introductions; new ventures; acquisitions analysis; licensing, joint ventures, and OEM arrangements. Emphasis on polymers, medical devices, biotechnology, pharmaceuticals, and chemicals. **Founded:** 1981. **Telecommunication Services:** manny@ratafia.net. **Special Services:** CommTechPowerSearch®.

COMPUTERIZED DATABASES

44087 ■ *BooksInPrint.com® Professional (BIP)*
630 Central Ave.
New Providence, NJ 07974
Ph: (908)268-1090
Free: 888-269-5372
Fax: (908)665-3528
Co. E-mail: customerservice@bowker.com
URL: http://www.bowker.com
Availability: Online: ProQuest LLC - Dialog; Colorado Alliance of Research Libraries; R.R. Bowker LLC. CD-ROM: R.R. Bowker LLC. **Type:** Bibliographic.

RESEARCH CENTERS

44088 ■ American Defense Institute (ADI)
1055 N Fairfax St., Ste. 200
Alexandria, VA 22314
Ph: (703)519-7000
Fax: (703)519-8627
Co. E-mail: ebm1@americandefinst.org
URL: http://www.ojc.org/adi/
Contact: Eugene McDaniel, President
Services: National speakers' bureau. **Founded:** 1983. **Publications:** *ADI Briefs*; *ADI Newsletter*; *ADI*

Security Review. **Educational Activities:** National Security Leadership Seminar (Annual), in Washington; POW awareness campaign. **Awards:** Outstanding Leadership Award, for individual citizens committed to America's national defense; Fellowship in National Security Studies (Annual), to qualified graduate student; Undergraduate internship. **Telecommunication Services:** rdt2@americandefinst.org.

44089 ■ New Mexico State University - Arts and Sciences Research Center
PO Box 30001, MSCRC
Las Cruces, NM 88003
Ph: (575)646-7441
Fax: (575)646-4188
Co. E-mail: rczernia@nmsu.edu
URL: http://artsci.nmsu.edu/Research/
Contact: Dr. Robert J. Czerniak, Director
Founded: 1959.

44090 ■ Polytechnic University - Institute for Technology and Enterprise (ITE)
New York Information Technology Ctr.
55 Broad St., Ste. 13B
New York, NY 10004
Ph: (212)547-7030
Fax: (212)547-7029
Co. E-mail: horwitch@poly.edu
URL: http://www.ite.poly.edu
Contact: Prof. Mel Horwitch, Director
Founded: 1997. **Educational Activities:** Round Tables (Periodic); ITE Workshops (Periodic); ITE Conferences (Occasionally).

44091 ■ San Diego State University - Mount Laguna Observatory (MLO)
Department of Astronomy
5500 Campanile Dr.
San Diego, CA 92182-1221
Ph: (619)594-6182
Fax: (619)594-1413
Co. E-mail: etzel@sciences.sdsu.edu
URL: http://mintaka.sdsu.edu
Contact: Prof. Paul B. Etzel, Director
Founded: 1968. **Publications:** *MLOA Newsletter* (3/year). **Educational Activities:** Planetarium shows, lectures, and telescope viewing (Semiannual), on campus, for general public; Summer Star Party, for the public viewing Friday and Saturday nights in the summer; Mount Laguna Observatory Associates Meeting, for graduate students. **Awards:** MLOA Scholarship, for undergraduates. **Telecommunication Services:** astro@mintaka.sdsu.edu.

44092 ■ State University of New York at Binghamton - Institute for Materials Research (IMR)
Vestal Pky. E
Binghamton, NY 13902-6000

Ph: (607)777-4623
Fax: (607)777-4623
Co. E-mail: stanwhit@binghamton.edu
URL: http://materials.binghamton.edu
Contact: Prof. M. Stanley Whittingham, Director
Founded: 1988. **Publications:** *Papers, books, and reviews*.

44093 ■ Syracuse University - Center for Technology and Information Policy (CTIP)
419 Crouse-Hinds Hall
Maxwell School of Citizenship & Public Affairs
900 S Crouse Ave.
Syracuse, NY 13244-2130
Ph: (315)443-1890
Fax: (315)443-1075
Co. E-mail: sibretsc@maxwell.syr.edu
URL: http://ctip.maxwell.syr.edu
Contact: Stuart Bretschneider, Director
Founded: 1983. **Publications:** *TIPP Working Paper series*. **Educational Activities:** CTIP Seminars; CTIP Conferences. **Telecommunication Services:** ctip@maxwell.syr.edu.

44094 ■ University of Delaware - Center for Molecular and Engineering Thermodynamics (CMET)
Colburn Laboratory
Department of Chemical Engineering
150 Academy St.
Newark, DE 19716
Ph: (302)831-4500
Fax: (302)831-4466
Co. E-mail: furst@udel.edu
URL: http://www.che.udel.edu/cmet
Contact: Prof. Eric M. Furst, Director
Founded: 1992. **Telecommunication Services:** sboulden@udel.edu.

44095 ■ University of Toronto - Institute for the History and Philosophy of Science and Technology (IHPST)
Victoria College, Rm. 316
91 Charles St. W
Toronto, ON, Canada M5S 1K7
Ph: (416)978-5397
Fax: (416)978-3003
Co. E-mail: anjan.chakravartty@utoronto.ca
URL: http://www.hps.utoronto.ca
Contact: Anjan Chakravartty, Director
Founded: 1967. **Educational Activities:** Colloquia and public lectures (Biweekly), historic-scientific experiments, open to the University of Toronto community and public. **Awards:** Postdoctoral Fellowship in the History of Mathematics (Semiannual). **Telecommunication Services:** ihpst.info@utoronto.ca.

START-UP INFORMATION

44096 ■ *"Firefighter Wins ABC's American Inventor" in Hispanic Business (September 2007, pp. 94)*
Pub: Hispanic Business
Description: Greg Chavez, firefighter, won ABC televisions American Inventor award of $1 million for his Guardian Angel invention. The device makes Christmas trees safer.

44097 ■ *"Options Abound in Winter Wares" in Pet Product News (Vol. 64, November 2010, No. 11, pp. 1)*
Pub: BowTie Inc.
Ed: Maggie M. Shein. **Description:** Pet supply manufacturers emphasize creating top-notch construction and functional design in creating winter clothing for pets. Meanwhile, retailers and pet owners seek human-inspired style, quality, and versatility for pets' winter clothing. How retailers generate successful sales of pets' winter clothing outside of traditional brand marketing is also examined.

REFERENCE WORKS

44098 ■ *"Austin to Make it Easier for Stores to Just Pop In" in Austin Business Journal (Vol. 31, August 19, 2011, No. 24, pp. A1)*
Pub: American City Business Journals Inc.
Ed: Vicky Garza. **Description:** Temporary retail stores may soon become common in Austin as City Council has urged the city manager to look into the possibility of amending the city codes to permit businesses to temporarily fill the vacant spaces downtown.

44099 ■ *"Discount Shopping: Holiday Shopping Meets Social Media" in Employee Benefit News (Vol. 25, December 1, 2011, No. 15)*
Pub: SourceMedia Inc.
Ed: Rob J. Thurston. **Description:** Offering employees access to discount shopping using social media sites for Christmas bonuses, could be the gift that keeps on giving.

44100 ■ *"Early Spring Halts Drilling Season" in Globe & Mail (March 14, 2007, pp. B14)*
Pub: CTVglobemedia Publishing Inc.
Ed: Norval Scott. **Description:** Decreased petroleum productivity in Canadian oil drilling rigs due to early spring season in western regions is discussed.

44101 ■ *"eBay and Jonathan Adler Team to Launch 'The eBay Inspiration Shop"* in Entertainment Close-Up (October 25, 2011)*
Pub: Close-Up Media
Description: Designer Jonathan Adler partnered with eBay to create a collection of new must-have merchandise for the fall season. Top trendsetters, including actors, designers, bloggers, stylists, editors, photographers, models and musicians helped curate the items being featured in the windows by sharing their shopping wish lists with users.

44102 ■ *"Farming Season Starts in December" in Farm Industry News (November 29, 2011)*
Pub: Penton Business Media Inc.
Ed: Kent Lock. **Description:** One farmer suggests the season starts in December because one third of his seed and fertilizer for the following year has already been bought and paid for and his cropping mix changes little from one year to another.

44103 ■ *"Freak Weather Dampens Intrawest Forecast" in Globe & Mail (February 8, 2006, pp. B3)*
Pub: CTVglobemedia Publishing Inc.
Ed: Peter Kennedy. **Description:** Intrawest Corp. dropped its earnings forecast by 7 percent. The impact of weather on earnings is discussed.

44104 ■ *"Ghouls, Goblins, and Harry Potter: Cashing In On Halloween" in Inc. (Vol. 33, October 2011, No. 8, pp. 24)*
Pub: Inc. Magazine
Ed: Darren Dahl. **Description:** Costume Craze, an online costume retailer reports $13.2 million in sales last year. Originally the family business started out as a software company called StaticAdvantage, but switched gears.

44105 ■ *"Help Customers Choose Full Service Over Discount" in Indoor Comfort Marketing (Vol. 70, September 2011, No. 9, pp. 10)*
Pub: Industry Publications Inc.
Ed: Richard Rutigliano. **Description:** Marketing strategies for HVAC/R firms to use in 2011 and 2012 heating seasons are outlined, focusing on oil heat.

44106 ■ *"Ho, Ho, Ho!" in Retail Merchandiser (Vol. 51, September-October 2011, No. 5, pp. 10)*
Pub: Phoenix Media Corporation
Ed: Ted Vaughan. **Description:** Despite consumer caution and economic woes, retail leaders are expecting a high volume holiday selling season for 2011 Christmas. Statistical data covering holiday sales expectations is included.

44107 ■ *"Marketing: 'Twill Be the Season" in Entrepreneur (Vol. 35, October 2007, No. 10, pp. 108)*
Pub: Entrepreneur Media Inc.
Ed: Kim T. Gordon. **Description:** Entrepreneurs should plan ahead in order to promote products for the holiday season, since it is peak sales time. They can unify their business theme, use customer incentives, advertise early using TV or radio, and reorganize the company Website. Other ways to market for the holiday season are provided.

44108 ■ *"Mattel's Got a Monster Holiday Hit, But Will Franchise Have Staying Power?" in Advertising Age (Vol. 81, December 6, 2010, No. 43)*
Pub: Crain Communications, Inc.
Ed: Beth Snyder Bulik. **Description:** Monster High transmedia play expands beyond dolls to merchandise, apparel and entertainment.

44109 ■ *"Oilheating Delivery Issues" in Indoor Comfort Marketing (Vol. 70, September 2011, No. 9, pp. 14)*
Pub: Industry Publications Inc.
Ed: John Levey. **Description:** Tools and techniques for delivery heating oil to customers this season are discussed.

44110 ■ *"Playfair Receives Drill Permit for Risby, Yukon Tungsten Deposit" in Canadian Corporate News (May 16, 2007)*
Pub: Comtex News Network Inc.
Description: Playfair Mining announced that it has received a 5 year Class III land use permit from the Mineral Resources Branch, Yukon which will allow the company to carry out a drill program during the upcoming drill season on the company-owned Risby, Yukon tungsten deposit. Statistical data included.

44111 ■ *"Point, Click, Buy" in Barron's (Vol. 90, September 6, 2010, No. 36, pp. 11)*
Pub: Barron's Editorial & Corporate Headquarters
Ed: Vito J. Racanelli. **Description:** Non-travel online retail sales from January to July 2010 increased nine percent which indicates that online shopping for the coming holidays will be good. Online sales are outpacing traditional shopping, but pricing is still critical.

44112 ■ *"Sabathia Deal Makes Dollars and Sense" in The Business Journal-Milwaukee (Vol. 25, July 11, 2008, No. 42, pp. A1)*
Pub: American City Business Journals, Inc.
Ed: Mark Kass. **Description:** It was reported that the Milwaukee Brewers' acquisition of CC Sabathia will mean that the team will pick up an estimated $5 million in salary that Sabathia is owed for the remainder of the season. Because of this, the team will not make a profit in 2008. The acquisition of Sabathia is expected to cause an increase in attendance and merchandise revenue over the remainder of the season.

44113 ■ *"Scream Therapy: A Chain of New York City Beauty Stores Perfect Halloween Pop-Ups" in Inc. (Vol. 33, October 2011, No. 8, pp. 99)*
Pub: Inc. Magazine
Ed: Amy Barrett. **Description:** Ricky's Halloween stores will open 30 temporary stores for about two months, 28 of which are permanent beauty supply shops the rest of the year.

44114 ■ *"Seasonal Franchises" in Franchising World (Vol. 42, August 2010, No. 8, pp. 50)*
Pub: International Franchise Association
Ed: Jennifer Lemcke. **Description:** Seasonal franchises, such as tax businesses can be slow during the summer months. Restaurants are slow during the months of January and February. The various challenges faced by seasonal franchises are examined.

44115 ■ *"Strathmore Receives Permit to Drill oca Honda Project in New Mexico" in*

Canadian Corporate News (May 14, 2007)
Pub: Comtex News Network Inc.
Description: New Mexico's Mining and Minerals Division approved a permit to allow Strathmore Minerals Corp. to conduct drilling at its Roca Honda Project located in McKinley County, New Mexico.

44116 ■ *"Uranerz Acquires Additional Uranium Property Adjoining Nichols Ranch" in Canadian Corporate News (May 14, 2007)*
Pub: Comtex News Network Inc.
Description: Uranerz Energy Corporation announced the successful leasing of the fee mineral lands that appear to host the 'nose' of the oxidation-rduction geochemical front and has the potential for increasing the known uranium mineralization at the Nichols Ranch project which lies west of and adjacent to Uranerz's Nichols Ranch ISR uranium project.

44117 ■ *"What Dead Zone?" in Entrepreneur (Vol. 37, October 2009, No. 10, pp. 128)*
Pub: Entrepreneur Media, Inc.
Ed: Jason Daley. **Description:** Joe Purifico, Halloween Adventure franchises co-owner and chief executive officer, discusses the Halloween superstore phenomenon. Malls allow seasonal leasing for Halloween stores due to the high number of customers these stores attract.

44118 ■ *"Why Oil Fell, and How It May Rise" in Globe & Mail (January 18, 2007, pp. B2)*
Pub: CTVglobemedia Publishing Inc.
Ed: Eric Reguly. **Description:** The causes of the decline in oil prices in Canada are discussed, along with prospects of an increase in the same.

44119 ■ *"Will mCommerce Make Black Friday Green?" in Retail Merchandiser (Vol. 51,*

September-October 2011, No. 5, pp. 8)
Pub: Phoenix Media Corporation
Ed: Scott Miller. **Description:** Retailers speculate the possibilities of mobile commerce and are implementing strategies at their stores. Consumers using mobile devices accounted for only 0.1 percent of visits to retail Websites on Black Friday 2009 and rose to 5.6 percent in 2010; numbers are expected to rise for 2011.

REFERENCE WORKS

44120 ■ *"Avoiding Invention Scams" in Black Enterprise (Vol. 37, January 2007, No. 6, pp. 46)*
Pub: Earl G. Graves Publishing Co. Inc.
Ed: James C. Johnson. **Description:** Invention promotion firms provide inventors assistance in developing a prototype for product development. It is important to research these companies before making a commitment to work with them because there are a number of these firms that are not legitimate and have caused independent inventors to lose thousands of dollars by making false claims as to the market potential of the inventions.

44121 ■ *Behind the Cloud*
Pub: Jossey-Bass
Ed: Marc Benioff, Carlye Adler. **Released:** 2010.
Price: $27.95. **Description:** Salesforce.com is the world's most successful business-to-business cloud-computing company that sells an online service that helps businesses manage sales, customer service, and marketing functions.

44122 ■ *"Benchmark Makes Granduca Entrance" in Houston Business Journal (Vol. 40, January 8, 2010, No. 35, pp. 2)*
Pub: American City Business Journals
Ed: Jennifer Dawson. **Description:** Houston, Texas-based Interfin Company, owner of the Hotel Granduca, has tapped the services of Benchmark Hospitality International to manage the property. The hiring of Benchmark is part of Interfin's efforts to develop Granduca hotels in other markets. Statistical data included.

44123 ■ *It's Not Who You Know - It's Who Knows You!: The Small Business Guide to Raising Your Profits by Raising Your Profile*
Pub: John Wiley & Sons, Inc.
Ed: David Avrin. **Released:** November 9, 2010.
Price: $24.95. **Description:** When it comes to promoting a small business or a brand, it is essential to know how valuable high-profile attention can be. But for most small companies, the cost of hiring an outside firm to increase attention can be too expensive.

44124 ■ *"Legal Aid: Sample Legal Documents can Lower Your Attorney Fees" in Black Enterprise (Vol. 37, October 2006, No. 3, pp. 210)*
Pub: Earl G. Graves Publishing Co. Inc.
Ed: Tamara E. Holmes. **Description:** FreeLegalForms.net provides thousands of free legal forms. These forms are not a substitute for consultation with an attorney but the sample documents can help save you time and money.

44125 ■ *"Online Self-Publishing Services" in Black Enterprise (Vol. 37, November 2006, No. 4, pp. 90)*
Pub: Earl G. Graves Publishing Co. Inc.
Description: Profiles of five online self-publishing services.

CONSULTANTS

44126 ■ **Expense Control Systems Inc.**
117 E Butler Ave.
Ambler, PA 19002
Ph: (215)643-4610
Fax: (215)643-4614
Contact: John F. Frustaci, Sr., President
Scope: Telecommunications consulting service specializing in voice and data network analyses, equipment evaluations and accounting services. Serves all industries nationwide. **Founded:** 1979.

RESEARCH CENTERS

44127 ■ **Indiana Small Business Development Center (ISBDC)**
1 N Capitol Ave., Ste. 900
Indianapolis, IN 46204
Ph: (317)234-2082
Free: 888-472-3244
Fax: (317)232-8872
Co. E-mail: leadcenter@isbdc.org
URL: http://www.isbdc.org
Contact: Jeff Heinzmann, Director
Services: Management consulting, business evaluation, and assistance with identification: of business and management problems. **Founded:** 1983. **Educational Activities:** ISBDC Conferences and workshops, for small business owners and those starting new businesses; co-sponsors are universities, professionals, I.E., attorneys, and CPAs; Specialized training and individual consultation, in business management, marketing, and finance; Workshops and forums.

REFERENCE WORKS

44128 ■ *"ACE Aims High With Spinoff of Repair Unit" in Globe & Mail (January 31, 2007, pp. B15)*
Pub: CTVglobemedia Publishing Inc.

Ed: Brent Jang. **Description:** The decision of ACE Aviation Holdings Inc. to sell its aircraft maintenance division and add workforce at its El Salvador plant is discussed.

44129 ■ *"Algoma Resolves Hedge Fund Fight" in Globe & Mail (March 8, 2006, pp. B1)*
Pub: CTVglobemedia Publishing Inc.

Ed: Greg Keenan. **Description:** Algoma Steel Inc. has ended a dispute with Paulson and Co., a New York hedge fund, by offering to pay $200 million special dividend, appointing new directors, and continue to go for a sale.

44130 ■ *American Bar Association Legal Guide for Small Business: Everything You Need to Know About Small Business*
Pub: Random House Information Group
Contact: Markus Dohle, Accountant

Ed: American Bar Association. **Released:** June 10, 2010. **Description:** The American Bar Association provides insight into financial, health and family issues affecting small business, including start up issues, employment laws, financing a business, and selling a business.

44131 ■ *"Apartment Tower in River North Fetches More Than $90 Million" in Crain's Chicago Business (Vol. 34, October 24, 2011, No. 42, pp. 17)*
Pub: Crain Communications Inc.

Ed: Alby Gallun. **Description:** Apartment tower in River North was sold for over $90 million to a Texas pension fund adviser. Details are included.

44132 ■ *"Ask Inc." in Inc. (November 2007, pp. 70)*
Pub: Gruner & Jahr USA Publishing

Description: Advice is given for any entrepreneur considering the sale of a company.

44133 ■ *"Attention, Please" in Entrepreneur (Vol. 36, April 2008, No. 4, pp. 52)*
Pub: Entrepreneur Media, Inc.

Ed: Andrea Cooper. **Description:** Gurbaksh Chahal created his own company ClickAgents at the age of 16, and sold it two years later for $40 million to ValueClick. He then founded BlueLithium, an online advertising network on behavioral targeting, which Yahoo! Inc. bought in 2007 for $300 million. Chahal, now 25, talks about his next plans and describes how BlueLithium caught Yahoo's attention.

44134 ■ *"Auxilium Drug's New Use: Putting Squeeze On Cellulite" in Philadelphia Business Journal (Vol. 30, September 16,*
2011, No. 31, pp. 1)
Pub: American City Business Journals Inc.

Ed: John George. **Description:** Auxilium Pharmaceuticals and BioSpecifics Technologies are getting on with their plans of finding new uses for their drug Xiaflex, a possible treatment for cellulite. The two firms have dismissed their pending litigations and mapped out an amended licensing agreement for their search for the potential uses of the drug.

44135 ■ *"Big Sell-Off At Sunwest" in The Business Journal-Portland (Vol. 25, July 25, 2008, No. 20, pp. 1)*
Pub: American City Business Journals, Inc.

Ed: Robin J. Moody. **Description:** Oregon's largest operator of assisted living facilities Sunwest Management Inc. is expected to sell 132 of its properties. The planned sale, which is believed to be worth more than $1 billion, will help Sunwest pay creditors and investors. Other views and information on the planned sale, as well as on Sunwest's services which include adult day care, are presented.

44136 ■ *"Black On Black Business: Moorehead Buys Hank Aaron's Toyota Dealership" in Black Enterprise (Vol. 38, February 2008, No. 7, pp. 28)*
Pub: Earl G. Graves Publishing Co. Inc.

Ed: Brenda Porter. **Description:** In a move to expand his automotive business, Thomas A. Moorehead, CEO of BMW/MINI of Sterling, Georgia bought Hank Aaron's Toyota automobile dealership in McDonough, Georgia. Moorehead stated that he will call the new store Toyota of McDonough.

44137 ■ *"BofA May Part With U.S. Trust" in Boston Business Journal (Vol. 31, May 20, 2011, No. 17, pp. 1)*
Pub: Boston Business Journal

Ed: Tim McLaughlin. **Description:** Bank of America Corporation is willing to sell its U.S. Trust private banking division to improve its capital ratio. The unit remains to be the corporation's core asset and posted $696 million revenue in the first quarter 2010 in contract with Merrill Lynch Global Wealth Management's $3.5 billion. Analysts say that U.S. Trust would fetch more than $3 billion.

44138 ■ *Building a Dream: A Canadian Guide to Starting Your Own Business*
Pub: McGraw-Hill Ryerson Ltd.

Ed: Walter S. Good. **Released:** 2005. **Description:** Topics covered include evaluating business potential, new business ideas, starting or buying a business, franchise opportunities, business organization, protecting an idea, arranging financing, and developing a business plan.

44139 ■ *"Business For Sale: Your Cold Calling?" in Inc. (December 2007, pp. 34)*
Pub: Gruner & Jahr USA Publishing

Ed: Elaine Appleton Grant. **Description:** Profile of a recreational outfitting company in northern New England with an asking price of $6.185 million, with gross revenue of $9.4 million in 2007.

44140 ■ *Buying and Selling a Business*
Pub: Entrepreneur Press

Ed: Ira Nottonson. **Released:** April 2008. **Price:** $32.95. **Description:** Tips for negotiating sales are presented. Attorney, Ira Nottonson presents both sides of negotiations by presenting the both buyer's and seller's perspectives. Critical steps in the sale process, including presentation, negotiation and documentations are discussed. The book teaches how to gain the upper hand, minimize financial risk and be a winner regardless of side.

44141 ■ *"Calista Sells Rural Newspapers" in Alaska Business Monthly (Vol. 27, October 2011, No. 10, pp. 8)*
Pub: Alaska Business Publishing Company

Ed: Nancy Pounds. **Description:** Calista sold its six newspapers, a magazine, shoppers and its printing house. Details of the sales are given.

44142 ■ *"CanWest Plotting Buyback of Newspaper Income Trust" in Globe & Mail (February 7, 2007, pp. B1)*
Pub: CTVglobemedia Publishing Inc.

Ed: Sinclair Stewart; Boyd Erman; Grant Robertson. **Description:** The CanWest Global Communications Corp.'s decision to sell its media assets in Australia and New Zealand in order to finance its plans of repurchasing its newspaper income trust CanWest MediaWorks Income Fund is discussed.

44143 ■ *"Carveouts Back in Vogue" in Mergers & Acquisitions: The Dealmaker's Journal (March 1, 2008)*
Pub: SourceMedia, Inc.

Ed: Ken MacFadyen. **Description:** Discusses ways in which companies look for hidden assets that they can exploit in worsening economic times; oftentimes firms try to sell off assets or in other instances they will look to unlock value through public spinoffs or through internal reorganizations.

44144 ■ *"Coca-Cola Bottler Up for Sale: CEO J. Bruce Llewellyn Seeks Retirement" in Black Enterprise (Vol. 37, December 2006, No. 5, pp. 31)*
Pub: Earl G. Graves Publishing Co. Inc.

Ed: Marcia A. Wade. **Description:** J. Bruce Llewellyn of Brucephil Inc., the parent company of the Philadelphia Coca-Cola Bottling Co. has agreed to sell its remaining shares to Coca-Cola Co., which previously owned 31 percent of Philly Coke. Analysts believe that Coca-Cola will eventually sell its shares to another bottler.

44145 ■ *The Complete Guide to Buying a Business*
Pub: NOLO

Ed: Fred S. Steingold. **Released:** November 2007. **Price:** $24.99. **Description:** Key steps in buying a business are highlighted, focusing on legal issues, tax considerations, approaches for valuing a business, financing, structuring the deal, along with forms and documents for taking ownership are included.

44146 ■ The Complete Guide to Selling a Business
Pub: NOLO
Ed: Fred S. Steingold. Released: November 2007. Price: $34.99. Description: When selling a business it is critical that a sales agreement covers all key concerns from price and payment terms to liability protection and restrictions on future competition.

44147 ■ "A Counter Offer" in Inc. (February 2008, pp.)
Pub: Gruner & Jahr USA Publishing
Ed: Elaine Appleton Grant. Description: Online retailer offering a line of kitchen and home products has upgraded its Website in order to make the business more attractive to possible buyers of the company. The firm is asking $9.9 million and reported gross revenue of $12.7 in 2007. The owner suggests that a buyer add product lines geared towards more rooms of the home than currently offer on the retail site.

44148 ■ "Cyberwise" in Black Enterprise (Vol. 41, September 2010, No. 2, pp. 49)
Pub: Earl G. Graves Publishing Co. Inc.
Ed: Marcia Wade Talbert. Description: Advice is given to assist in selling an online store called theupscalegaragesale.com. A listing of business brokers specializing in the sale of Internet businesses is included.

44149 ■ "Defer Tax with Installment Sale Election" in Business Owner (Vol. 35, September-October 2011, No. 5, pp. 12)
Pub: DL Perkins Company
Description: It is critical to consult with a tax professional before selling any high-value asset in order to minimize taxes.

44150 ■ "For Hospitals, a Dating Game" in Business Courier (Vol. 26, December 4, 2009, No. 32, pp. 1)
Pub: American City Business Journals, Inc.
Ed: James Ritchie. Description: Drake Center, Fort Hamilton Hospital, and West Chester Medical Center are among the members of Cincinnati's Health Alliance looking for potential buyers or partners. Meanwhile, Jewish Hospital, another member of the Alliance, will be bought by Mercy Health Partners by January 7, 2010.

44151 ■ "For the Seasoned Buyer" in Inc. (Vol. 30, November 2008, No. 11, pp. 32)
Pub: Mansueto Ventures LLC
Ed: Darren Dahl. Description: Dominick Fimiano shares his plans to sell his ten-year-old business that manufactures and sells frozen pizza dough and crusts as well as a variety of topped pizzas. Products are purchased by schools, hospitals, bowling alleys and amusement parks. The business sale includes the buyer's taking on Fimiano's son the firm's most senior employee.

44152 ■ "Fred Weber CEO Tom Dunne: Sales Talks Confidential" in Saint Louis Business Journal (Vol. 32, September 23, 2011, No. 4, pp. 1)
Pub: Saint Louis Business Journal
Ed: Evan Binns. Description: Fred Weber Inc. CEO Tom Dunne Sr. signed a letter of confidentiality as part of an inquiry made by interested party to the construction company. However, Dunne denied the company is in a fire sale and has been continuing to bid for work and has not stopped securing projects.

44153 ■ "A Graceful (and Lucrative) Exit" in Black Enterprise (Vol. 38, November 2007, No. 4, pp. 108)
Pub: Earl G. Graves Publishing Co. Inc.
Ed: Tamara E. Holmes. Description: BlueKey Business Brokerage helps clients buy, grow or sell a business. Four key points are examined in order to successfully exit a business.

44154 ■ "Harleysville Eyes Growth After Nationwide Deal" in Philadelphia Business Journal (Vol. 30, October 7, 2011, No. 34, pp. 1)
Pub: American City Business Journals Inc.
Ed: Jeff Blumenthal. Description: Harleysville Group announced growth plans after the company was sold to Columbus, Ohio-based Nationwide Mutual Insur-ance Company for about $1.63 billion. Nationwide gained an independent agency platform in 32 states with the Harleysville deal.

44155 ■ "Hartco Income Fund Announces the Completion of the CompuSmart Strategic Review" in Canadian Corporate News (May 14, 2007)
Pub: Comtex News Network Inc.
Description: Hartco Income Fund announced that it has completed the process of exploring strategic options for CompuSmart and found that it should implement a plan to sell select stores and assets while consolidating remaining CompuSmart locations over the next sixty days.

44156 ■ "Health Alliance Could Sell Group" in Business Courier (Vol. 27, June 18, 2010, No. 7, pp. 1)
Pub: Business Courier
Ed: James Ritchie. Description: Health Alliance could sell the 31-doctor Greater Cincinnati Associated Physicians Group. The group has seen several members withdraw ever since the group filed a complaint asking to be released from services to Health Alliance.

44157 ■ "Hospital Fighting for Its Life; Board of St. Anthony Scrambles to Stem Losses" in Crain's Chicago Business (April 28, 2008)
Pub: Crain Communications, Inc.
Ed: Mike Colias. Description: Chicago's Catholic health chain was looking to sell the money-losing hospital St. Anthony Hospital on the West Side but with the financial picture improving and no merger offers in the works the investment bank hired to shop the hospital is hoping to operate the 111-year-old facility as an independent entity. St. Anthony serves as a 'safety net' for the region since an increasing number of its patients are uninsured or on public aid, which pays far less than commercial insurers.

44158 ■ How to Buy and/or Sell a Small Business for Maximum Profit: A Step-by-Step Guide
Pub: Atlantic Publishing Company
Ed: Rene V. Richards. Released: January 2006. Price: $24.95. Description: Suggestions, insights and techniques for buying and selling small businesses, includes advice on when to buy or sell, how to market the business, explanation of legal and financial documents involved in the sale and closing of a deal.

44159 ■ "How I Did It: Laurel Touby Mediabistro" in Inc. (March 2008, pp. 124-126)
Pub: Gruner & Jahr USA Publishing
Ed: Eric Schine. Description: Profile of Laurel Touby and her business plan; Touby started Mediabistro as a series of parties that turned into an influential job listing and training Website for journalists. Last year she sold it for $23 million.

44160 ■ "Imax in Play as It Explores Options" in Globe & Mail (March 10, 2006, pp. B3)
Pub: CTVglobemedia Publishing Inc.
Ed: Shirley Won. Description: Imax Corp. has put up itself for sale, and has also confirmed that it has received unsolicited offers for purchase.

44161 ■ "Inmet Selling Nunavut Mining Properties" in Globe & Mail (February 15, 2006, pp. B6)
Pub: CTVglobemedia Publishing Inc.
Ed: Allan Robinson. Description: The details on Wolfden Resources Inc.'s acquisition of mining assets of Inmet Mining Corp. are presented.

44162 ■ "Intel to Buy McAfee Security Business for 768B" in eWeek (August 19, 2010)
Pub: Ziff Davis Enterprise
Description: Intel will acquire security giant McAfee for approximately $7.68 billion, whereby McAfee would become a wholly owned subsidiary of Intel and would report to Intel's Software and Services Group.

44163 ■ "Intrawest Puts Itself on Market" in Globe & Mail (March 1, 2006, pp. B1)
Pub: CTVglobemedia Publishing Inc.
Ed: Elizabeth Church. Description: The reasons behind the decision of Intrawest Corp. to go for sale or seek partnerships are presented. The company appointed Goldman Sachs & Co. to meet the purpose.

44164 ■ "Kerry Steel to Sell Inventory, Close Business After 30 Years" in Crain's Detroit Business (Vol. 24, March 17, 2008, No. 11, pp. 26)
Pub: Crain Communications, Inc.
Ed: Brent Snavely. Description: Kerry Steel Inc. has confirmed that it is selling all of its inventory and equipment and is going out of business; the company, which was once one of the largest steel service centers in the Midwest, has sustained financial losses and is in violation of its loan agreements.

44165 ■ "Legacy Hotels Looks for a Buyer" in Globe & Mail (March 2, 2007, pp. B3)
Pub: CTVglobemedia Publishing Inc.
Ed: Elizabeth Church. Description: Legacy Hotels Real Estate Investment Trust, which has a portfolio of 25 properties, plans to sell its businesses. The shares of the real estate investment trust climbed $13.21, as the sales news was delivered.

44166 ■ "Major Tech Employers Pulling Out" in Sacramento Business Journal (Vol. 25, August 1, 2008, No. 22, pp. 1)
Pub: American City Business Journals, Inc.
Ed: Celia Lamb. Description: Biotechnology company Affymetrix Inc. is planning to close its West Sacramento, California plant and lay off 110 employees. The company said it will expand a corporate restructuring plan. Affymetrix also plans to lease out or sell its building at Riverside Parkway.

44167 ■ "McIntosh Family Sells Car Dealership" in Black Enterprise (Vol. 38, December 2007, No. 5)
Pub: Earl G. Graves Publishing Co. Inc.
Ed: Brenda Porter. Description: Seattle's McIntosh family sold its Kirkland Chrysler Jeep dealership to private equity firm Cerberus Capital Management. Details of the deal are given.

44168 ■ Mergers and Acquisitions from A to Z
Pub: Amacom
Ed: Andrew J. Sherman, Milledge A. Hart. Released: January 2006. Price: $35.00. Description: Guide for the entire process of mergers and acquisitions, including taxes, accounting, laws, and projected financial gain.

44169 ■ "Milton Touts ACE Unit to Would-Be Buyers" in Globe & Mail (February 10, 2007, pp. B6)
Pub: CTVglobemedia Publishing Inc.
Ed: Brent Jang. Description: The decision of Air Canada chairman Robert Milton to sell Air Canada Technical Services unit is presented. ACE Aviation Holdings Inc. is the parent company of Air Canada.

44170 ■ "Murdock Carrousel Sold" in Charlotte Observer (January 31, 2007)
Pub: Knight-Ridder/Tribune Business News
Ed: Bob Fliss. Description: Details on the sale of the Murdock Carrousel shopping center are highlighted. The deal was reported at $281 million.

44171 ■ "My Day" in Business Strategy Review (Vol. 21, Autumn 2010, No. 3, pp. 77)
Pub: Blackwell Publishers Ltd.
Ed: Julie Meyer. Description: Profile of Julie Meyer, who rose to prominence as cofounder of the entrepreneurial network, First Tuesday; Meyer sold the firm for $50 million in 2000.

44172 ■ "My Day" in Business Strategy Review (Vol. 21, Autumn 2010, No. 3, pp. 77)
Pub: Wiley-Blackwell
Ed: Julie Meyer. Description: Julie Meyer shot to prominence as cofounder of the entrepreneurial network, First Tuesday. The firm was sold for $50 million in 2000.

44173 ■ *"NexCen Brands Sells Chains and Will Liquidate" in Ice Cream Reporter (Vol. 23, August 20, 2010, No. 9, pp. 1)*
Pub: Ice Cream Reporter
Description: NexCen Brands is closing the sale of its franchise businesses, which include the frozen dessert chains MaggieMoo's and Marbel Slab Creamery, to Global Franchise Group.

44174 ■ *"The Next Chapter" in Business Courier (Vol. 26, November 20, 2009, No. 30, pp. 1)*
Pub: American City Business Journals, Inc.
Ed: Lucy May. **Description:** Eric Browne and Mel Gravely purchased controlling interest in TriVersity Construction Group from CM-GC CEO Schuyler Murdoch and MBJ Consultants President Monroe Barnes. One third of the company was still owned by Cincinnati-based Messer and TriVersity and will continue to be a certified minority business enterprise.

44175 ■ *"Nursing Home Group Put on the Block" in Globe & Mail (February 23, 2006, pp. B1)*
Pub: CTVglobemedia Publishing Inc.
Ed: Elizabeth Church. **Description:** The reasons behind the decision of Exetendicare Inc. to go for sale are presented.

44176 ■ *"On the Cutting Edge" in Inc. (November 2007, pp. 28)*
Pub: Gruner & Jahr USA Publishing
Ed: Elaine Appleton Grant. **Description:** Information is provided about a Nashville-area glass and glazing company that is on the market for $8.2 million. The owner started the company from the back of his truck in 2990 with $2,200. The firm has $9 million worth of contracts signed through 2008. Statistical data included.

44177 ■ *"P/Kaufmann Sells Bennettsville" in Home Textiles Today (Vol. 31, May 24, 2011, No. 13, pp. 6)*
Pub: Reed Business Information
Contact: Jeff Greisch, President
Description: Decorative Screen Printers purchased the printing and finishing facility of P/Kaufmann in Bennettsville, South Carolina. However, the firm will continue its focus on its core business, a vat printing facility for home furnishings fabrics.

44178 ■ *"Pocket Change?" in Inc. (Vol. 30, December 2008, No. 12, pp. 28)*
Pub: Mansueto Ventures LLC
Ed: Ryan McCarthy. **Description:** Owner of a chain of nine retail billiard showrooms grew his business by starting to deliver pool tables for Sears. The company, consisting of seven retail locations and two warehouses, is now for sale. Details are included.

44179 ■ *"Points of Light Sells MissionFish to eBay" in Non-Profit Times (Vol. 25, May 15, 2011, No. 7, pp. May 15, 2011)*
Pub: NPT Publishing Group Inc.
Contact: John McIlquham, President
Description: eBay purchased MissionFish, a subsidiary of Points of Light Institute for $4.5 million. MissionFish allows eBay sellers to give proceeds from sales to their favorite nonprofit organization and helps nonprofits raise funds by selling on eBay.

44180 ■ *"Portland's Hilton For Sale" in Business Journal Portland (Vol. 27, October 22, 2010, No. 34, pp. 1)*
Pub: Portland Business Journal
Ed: Wendy Culverwell. **Description:** Hilton Portland & Executive Tower, Portland's biggest hotel, is being sold by Cornerstone Real Estate Advisers LLC. Cornerstone hopes to close the deal for the 782-room complex by the end of 2010. Cornerstone contracted Jones Lang LaSalle to manage the sale, but terms to the deal are not available.

44181 ■ *"Potash Sale Must Be Blocked" in Canadian Business (Vol. 83, October 12, 2010, No. 17, pp. 24)*
Pub: Rogers Media Ltd.
Ed: Kasey Coholan. **Description:** Chief executive officers (CEOs) and corporate leaders in Canada are concerned about the possible sale of Potash Corporation to foreign buyers. A Compas Inc. poll recently asked CEOs whether the Canadian Government should step in to block the sale of the country's largest fertilizer firm.

44182 ■ *"Roy MacDowell Jr." in Boston Business Journal (Vol. 31, June 10, 2011, No. 20, pp. 1)*
Pub: Boston Business Journal
Ed: Craig M. Douglas. **Description:** Real estate developer Roy MacDowell is selling his Boston, Massachusetts estate. The asking price for the property is $21.8 million. MacDowell recently suffered setbacks in his finances.

44183 ■ *"RS Information Systems Signs Buyout Deal" in Black Enterprise (February 2008)*
Pub: Earl G. Graves Publishing Co. Inc.
Ed: Alan Hughes. **Description:** Details of the RS Information Systems buyout by Wyle, a privately held provider of high-tech aerospace engineering, testing, and research services.

44184 ■ *"Sale of Solo Cup Plant Pending" in Boston Business Journal (Vol. 29, June 17, 2011, No. 6, pp. 1)*
Pub: American City Business Journals Inc.
Ed: Daniel J. Sernovitz. **Description:** Baltimore developers Vanguard Equities Inc. and Greenberg Gibbons Commercial have contracted to buy the Solo Cup Company facility in Owing Mills and are now considering several plans for the property. Sale should be completed by September 2011 but no proposed sale terms are disclosed.

44185 ■ *The Secret of Exiting Your Business Under Your Terms!*
Pub: Outskirts Press, Incorporated
Ed: Gene H. Irwin. **Released:** August 2005. **Price:** $29.95. **Description:** Topics include how to sell a business for the highest value, tax laws governing the sale of a business, finding the right buyer, mergers and acquisitions, negotiating the sale, and using a limited auction to increase future value of a business.

44186 ■ *Sell Your Business Your Way: Getting Out, Getting Rich, and Getting on with Your Life*
Pub: American Management Association
Contact: Charles R. Craig, Chairman
Ed: Rick Rickertsen; Robert Gunther. **Released:** 2006. **Price:** $27.95.

44187 ■ *"Selling Your Company" in Inc. (March 2008, pp. 78)*
Pub: Gruner & Jahr USA Publishing
Ed: Myra Goodman. **Description:** Owner of a safety consulting company seeks advice for selling the firm.

44188 ■ *"Serial Starter" in Entrepreneur (Vol. 36, April 2008, No. 4, pp. 17)*
Pub: Entrepreneur Media, Inc.
Ed: Andrea Cooper. **Description:** Some entrepreneurs are engaged in serial entrepreneurship as they feel that they are no longer satisfied with their business and they decide to sell it. Others start out new businesses because they believe they can try out and be successful in different kinds of businesses. Details on how to identify and handle new entrepreneurial opportunities are discussed.

44189 ■ *"Sign, Sign, Everywhere a Sign: How I Did It: Richard Schaps" in Inc. (October 2007, pp. 128)*
Pub: Gruner & Jahr USA Publishing
Ed: Stephanie Clifford. **Description:** Richard Schaps shares the story of selling his outdoor-advertising firm, Van Wagner for $170 million and sharing the wealth with his employees. Schaps then started another outdoor-sign company.

44190 ■ *"Silverdome Bidders Bring New Proposals" in Crain's Detroit Business (Vol. 24, March 17, 2008, No. 11, pp. 23)*
Pub: Crain Communications, Inc.
Ed: Daniel Duggan. **Description:** Discusses the seven plans which have been proposed as part of the third round of bidding for the Pontiac Silverdome; proposals range from Global Baseball Inc., a baseball league that would pit a team from every country against one another, to an Indian casino, a musical 'hall of fame', a convention center, a horse track, a hotel and an indoor water park.

44191 ■ *"S.M. Whitney Co. (1868-2010)" in Canadian Business (Vol. 83, October 12, 2010, No. 17, pp. 27)*
Pub: Rogers Media Ltd.
Ed: Angelina Chapin. **Description:** A history of S.M. Whitney Company is presented. The cotton company was opened in 1868. The cotton is sold to textile manufacturers after crops have been picked, ginned and baled. The company closed down in 2010 after chief executive officer Barry Whitney decided to sell his last bale of cotton.

44192 ■ *"Souled Out" in Canadian Business (Vol. 81, March 3, 2008, No. 3, pp. 35)*
Pub: Rogers Media
Ed: Calvin Leung. **Description:** According to a survey of over 100 entrepreneurs, 78 percent responded that selling their business was emotionally draining for them. Greig Clark, for example, says that one of the toughest times of his life was selling College Pro Painters, after putting 18 years into that business. The economic impacts of selling out are also examined.

44193 ■ *"Speedway Explored Sale" in Business Courier (Vol. 24, October 12, 2008, No. 26, pp. 1)*
Pub: American City Business Journals, Inc.
Ed: Jon Newberry. **Description:** Court records revealed that Kentucky Speedway discussed a possible sale of its Gallatin County track to International Speedway Corp. (ISC) before it sued NASCAR and ISC in 2005 for monopolizing bigtime racing. Kentucky Speedway chairman Jerry Carroll explained in a sworn statement that ISC was only interested in the sale if it can buy the track for a cheap price. The court proceedings and the sale allegations are discussed.

44194 ■ *Stop Working: Start a Business, Globalize It, and Generate Enough Cash Flow to Get Out of the Rat Race*
Pub: Eye Contact Media
Ed: Rohan Hall. **Released:** November 2004. **Price:** $15.99. **Description:** Advice is given to small companies to compete in the global marketplace by entrepreneur using the same strategy for his own business.

44195 ■ *"Suitors Circling Chrysler as Sale Likely" in Globe & Mail (February 19, 2007, pp. B1)*
Pub: CTVglobemedia Publishing Inc.
Ed: Jason Singer. **Description:** DaimlerChrysler AG is planning to sell or spin-off the Chrysler Group, as a cost cutting strategy. Chrysler reported a 40 percent drop in fourth quarter profit because of the $1.5 billion operating loss.

44196 ■ *"Sullivan Led Bucyrus through Unforgettable Year" in Business Journal-Milwaukee (Vol. 28, December 17, 2010, No. 11, pp. A1)*
Pub: Milwaukee Business Journal
Ed: Rich Rovito. **Description:** Bucyrus International's president and CEO, Tim Sullivan, was chosen as Milwaukee, Wisconsin's Executive of the Year for 2010. Sullivan led Bucyrus through a year of dramatic change which started with the acquisition of the mining business of Terex Corporation and culminating with a deal to sell Caterpillar Inc.

44197 ■ *"Sunwest Vies To Stave Off Bankruptcy" in The Business Journal-Portland (Vol. 25, August 15, 2008, No. 23, pp. 1)*
Pub: American City Business Journals, Inc.
Ed: Robin J. Moody. **Description:** Sunwest Management Inc. is teetering on the edge of bankruptcy as creditors start foreclosure on nine of their properties. This could potentially displace residents of the as-

sisted living operator. Sunwest is trying to sell smaller packages of properties to get a $100 million bridge loan to maintain operations.

44198 ■ "Symantic Completes Acquisition of VeriSign's Security Business" in Internet Wire (August 9, 2010)
Pub: Comtex
Description: Symantec Corporation acquired VeriSign's identity and authentication business, which includes Secure Sockets Layer (SSL) and Code Signing Certificate Services, the Managed Public Key Infrastructure (MPKI) Services, the VeriSign Trust Seal, the VeriSign Identity Protection (VIP) Authentication Service and the VIP Fraud Protection Service (FDS). The agreement also included a majority stake in VeriSign Japan.

44199 ■ "Tampa Condo Conversion Sells for $14.8 Million Less" in The Business Journal-Serving Greater Tampa Bay (Vol. 28, September 5, 2008)
Pub: American City Business Journals, Inc.
Ed: Janet Leiser. **Description:** Former apartment complex Village Oaks at Tampa, which was converted to condominiums, has been sold to Tennessee-based real estate investment trust Mid-America Apartment Communities Inc. for $21.2 million in August 2008. The amount was $14.2 million less than what developer Radco Management LLC paid for in 2005.

44200 ■ "Tektronix Buys Arbor Networks for Security Business" in eWeek (August 9, 2010)
Pub: Ziff Davis Enterprise
Description: Tektronix Communications, provider of communications test and network intelligence solutions will acquire Arbor Networks. The deal will help Tektronix build a brand in security. Details of the transaction are included.

44201 ■ "To Sell or Not To Sell" in Inc. (December 2007, pp. 80)
Pub: Gruner & Jahr USA Publishing
Ed: Patrick J. Sauer. **Description:** Owner of a private equity discusses the challenges he faces when deciding to sell his family's business.

44202 ■ "Today's Business Sale Climate" in Business Owner (Vol. 35, September-October 2011, No. 5, pp. 10)
Pub: DL Perkins Company
Description: Despite the weak economy, there is a surplus of individuals wanting to purchase a small business. The Small Business Administration loan guarantees program helps with its loans for purchase/sale of business assistance.

44203 ■ Ultimate Guide to Buying or Selling Your Business
Pub: Entrepreneur Press
Ed: Ira N. Nottonson. **Released:** September 2004. **Price:** $24.95 (US), $35.95 (Canadian). **Description:** Proven strategies to evaluate, negotiate, and buy or sell a small business. Franchise and family business succession planning is included.

44204 ■ "The VC Shakeout" in Harvard Business Review (Vol. 88, July-August 2010, No. 7-8, pp. 21)
Pub: Harvard Business School Publishing
Ed: Joseph Ghalbouni, Dominque Rouzies. **Description:** Authors argue that in order to be successful, venture capital needs to focus less on how to sell a newly acquired investment and more on ways to grow a good company.

44205 ■ "Welcome Back" in Canadian Business (Vol. 82, April 27, 2009, No. 7, pp. 25)
Pub: Rogers Media
Ed: Sarka Halas. **Description:** Some Canadian companies such as Gennum Corporation have taken advantage of corporate sale-leasebacks to raise money at a time when credit is hard to acquire. Corporate sale-leasebacks allow companies to sell their property assets while remaining as tenants of the building. Sale-leasebacks allow firms to increase capital while avoiding the disruptions that may result with moving.

44206 ■ "With New Listings, Business Brokers See Hope" in Business Courier (Vol. 27, September 3, 2010, No. 18, pp. 1)
Pub: Business Courier
Ed: Lucy May. **Description:** Business brokers in Cincinnati, Ohio are expecting better prices in view of the strengthening economy.

44207 ■ "Wrap It Up" in Entrepreneur (Vol. 36, April 2008, No. 4, pp. 84)
Pub: Entrepreneur Media, Inc.
Ed: Barry Farber. **Description:** Tips on how to manage and get through the closing of a business sale are presented. Focus on what solutions you can bring and not on emotional attachments that can show your eagerness for the sale. Having a track of positive accomplishments can also help.

44208 ■ "Your Turn in the Spotlight" in Inc. (March 2008, pp. 30)
Pub: Gruner & Jahr USA Publishing
Ed: Elaine Appleton Grant. **Description:** Profile of a Tennessee business that produces events and concerts. The company offers a complete package of services handling staging, lighting, video, musical instrument rentals, and audio support. The founder has decided to sell the business and details of the asking price, price rationale, the pros and cons of buying the firm and its bottom line are examined.

CONSULTANTS

44209 ■ The Blaine Group Inc.
8665 Wilshire Blvd., Ste. 301
Beverly Hills, CA 90211-2975
Ph: (310)360-1499
Fax: (310)360-1498
Co. E-mail: devon@blainegroupinc.com
URL: http://www.blainegroupinc.com
Contact: Devon Blaine, President
E-mail: devon@blainegroupinc.com
Scope: The firm provides a variety of special communications services to its clients. These include managing crisis situations conceiving, coordinating seminars and press conferences, event and party planning, developing master plans and collateral materials, proposal, article, letter and speech writing, conducting surveys and publishing newsletters and brochures. **Founded:** 1975. **Publications:** "They Don't Want You to Know About".

44210 ■ Business Brokers Hawaii L.L.C. (BBH)
3230 Pikai Way
Kihei, HI 96753
Ph: (808)879-8833
Free: 866-239-1567
Fax: (808)879-5966
URL: http://www.business-brokers.com
Contact: Milton Docktor, Chief Executive Officer
E-mail: md@business-brokers.com
Scope: Offers buying or selling existing businesses, creation of new businesses, business evaluation and appraisal, assistance to clients on expansion and mergers, consultation with owners of businesses in trouble, and consultation on Unites States, Japan and Chinese commerce. **Founded:** 1983. **Seminars:** How to Start Your Own Business; How to Make a Sick Business Well Again; How to do Fiscal Forecasting and Cash Flow Projections.

44211 ■ Business Team
1901 S Bascom Ave., Ste. 400
Campbell, CA 95008
Ph: (408)246-1102
Fax: (408)246-2219
Co. E-mail: sanjose@business-team.com
URL: http://www.business-team.com
Contact: William L. Kramer, Vice President
Scope: Business consulting services offered to companies looking for buyers. Specializes in mergers and acquisitions, business brokerage, and valuations. **Founded:** 1980. **Seminars:** Business Valuation Enhancing the Value of Your Company.

44212 ■ The Change Agents
145 Columbia Ave.
Holland, MI 49423-2978

Ph: (616)392-5564
Contact: William G. Garlough, Managing Director
Scope: Provider of consulting services related to mergers, acquisitions and divestitures. Services offered include: Assisting acquiring companies in establishing and managing effective acquisition programs; representing sellers in the sale of their companies, and bringing buyers and sellers together. Additional consulting services include: Advising on the structure of leveraged buy-outs; mediating sales between partners or in family succession; business valuations; due diligence examination of the marketing function; post-acquisition integration advice; and corporate strategy and planning. **Founded:** 1983.

44213 ■ James W. Davidson Company Inc.
23 Forest View Rd.
Wallingford, PA 19086
Ph: (610)566-1462
Co. E-mail: jwdmsd@comcast.net
Contact: James W. Davidson, President
E-mail: jwdmsd@comcast.net
Scope: Offers counsel to clients to improve business strategy, organization, controls, management effectiveness and profits. Provides planning, problem-analysis and implementation assistance. Also performs thorough, in-depth executive recruiting and acquisition and divestment search and analysis. Experienced with large and small manufacturing and service companies, including new ventures. **Founded:** 1973.

44214 ■ DeVries & Company Inc.
800 W 47th St.
Kansas City, MO 64112
Ph: (816)756-0055
Fax: (816)756-0061
Contact: Robert J. de Vries, President
Scope: Investment banking/financial consulting firm which helps companies solve financial problems and achieve growth and diversification goals. Helps established companies raise capital and assists new and developing companies secure venture capital and create public markets for their stocks. Provides confidential services to companies who want to sell or merge, aids companies in acquiring other companies, helps individuals and companies structure and negotiate leveraged buyouts, provides financial guidance, shapes business strategy and develops operating and financial strategies. Also performs business valuations for estate and gift tax and ESOPS. Renders fairness opinions and expert witness services. **Founded:** 1984.

44215 ■ Hampton Group
7172 Regional St., Ste. 290
Dublin, CA 94568
Ph: (925)830-3447
Free: 800-820-6424
Fax: (925)831-8194
Co. E-mail: dataforpeter@hotmail.com
Contact: Peter Siegel, Owner
E-mail: dataforpeter@hotmail.com
Scope: Consults on the buying and selling of small and medium-sized businesses. **Founded:** 1991.

44216 ■ Management Services & Development Ltd.—Groundhog New Media
103 Carmalt Ave.
Punxsutawney, PA 15767-2502
Ph: (814)938-8170
Free: 800-633-0688
Fax: (814)938-8177
Co. E-mail: rdm@mergermentor.com
URL: http://www.mergermentor.com
Contact: Richard D. Mowrey, President
E-mail: rdm@mergermentor.com
Scope: Specializes in valuation and financial services for acquisition or sale of businesses. Performs appraisals and facilitates the actual transfer of business ownership. Also specializes in the sale of privately owned manufacturing businesses. Professional intermediaries who handle all phases of the project including initial analysis, planning, valuating, qualifying of prospective buyers, negotiations and execution of the transaction. Industries served: Businesses, manufacturing firms and government agencies. Serves United States and Canada. **Founded:** 1979. **Publications:** "Business Owner's Journal". **Semi-**

nars: Exit Planning; How to Determine the Value of Your Business; How to Maximize the Value of Your Business; Success without Stress. **Special Services:** XL Template for Assessment Business Valuation Process.

44217 ■ Mertz Associates Inc.
N1629 County Road P
Rubicon, WI 53078
Ph: (262)523-4200

Fax: (262)523-4202
Co. E-mail: mertz@mertz.com
URL: http://www.mertz.com
Contact: Linda Mertz, Chief Executive Officer
E-mail: l.mertz@mertz.com
Scope: A merger and acquisition consulting firm representing either dedicated buyers or sellers of companies across the U.S. Clients range from small privately held companies to large public companies in all industries. **Publications:** "Why Successful Companies are Launching Acquisition Searches Now"; "On the Block"; "Selling Troubled Divisions and Companies"; "Don't Fear the D Word"; "M and A Multiples: A Key to Value Or a Distraction"; "Savvy CPA Levels the Playing Field"; "M and A Trends Strategic Focus Drives Success".

FRANCHISES AND BUSINESS OPPORTUNITIES

44218 ■ Upside Group Franchise Consulting Corp.
11445 E Via Linda, Ste. 2-495
Scottsdale, AZ 85259
Ph: (888)445-2882
Fax: (480)664-1627
Description: Full franchise consulting/sales development. **Founded:** 2000.. **Training:** Yes.

REFERENCE WORKS

44219 ■ *"On Target' in Canadian Business (Vol. 81, July 22, 2008, No. 12-13, pp. 45)*
Pub: Rogers Media Ltd.

Ed: Calvin Leung. **Description:** Companies such as LavalifePRIME, a dating website devoted to singles 45 and older, discuss the value of marketing and services aimed at Canada's older consumers. One-third of Canada's 33 million people are 50-plus, controlling 77 percent of the countries wealth.

44220 ■ *"A Second Chance to Make a Living' in The Business Journal-Milwaukee (Vol. 25, September 19, 2008, No. 52, pp. A1)*
Pub: American City Business Journals, Inc.

Description: Unemployed workers and baby boomers are driving interest in purchasing small businesses. BizBuySell general manager Mike Handelsman reveals that the supply of small businesses for sale is decreasing due to the increased demand. The trends in the small business market are analyzed.

LIBRARIES

44221 ■ **Virginia Commonwealth University - Virginia Center on Aging - Information**
Resources Center
730 E. Broad St.
Theatre Row Building
Richmond, VA 23219
Ph: (804)828-1525
Fax: (804)828-7905
Co. E-mail: eansello@vcu.edu
URL: http://www.sahp.vcu.edu/vcoa
Contact: Dr. Edward F. Ansello, Director
Scope: Gerontology, mental health, sociology and the politics of aging, geriatrics, family relationships, long-term care, lifelong learning. **Services:** Library open to the public with restrictions (audio/visual materials available to Virginia residents only). **Founded:** 1978. **Holdings:** 1500 books; 4 archives; 120 AV items. **Subscriptions:** 6 journals and other serials.

START-UP INFORMATION

44222 ■ *"Business Start-Up a Learning Experience for Young Bellingham Entrepreneur" in Bellingham Herald (July 18, 2010)*
Pub: Bellingham Herald
Ed: Dave Gallagher. **Description:** Profile of 21-year-old entrepreneur, Chase Larabee, who developed an online program that helps airport fixed-based operators handle refueling, hotel and transportation reservations and other requests from private airplane pilots.

44223 ■ *"Fast-Forward Fortune" in Small Business Opportunities (July 2010)*
Pub: Harris Publications Inc.
Description: Profile of Steve Dalbec and his home-based Home Video Studio where he earns income by offering a wide variety of video services to clients from duplicating CDs, video to DVD transfer, sports videos and more. Dalbec believes this is the perfect home-based business.

44224 ■ *"Fixing Up the Area: Leo Piatz Opens General Repair Business" in The Dickinson Press (November 16, 2010)*
Pub: Dickinson Press
Ed: Ashley Martin. **Description:** Profile of Leo Piatz, owner of Leo's Repair in Dickinson, North Dakota; Piatz provides welding and fabricating services to farmers and ranchers in the area.

44225 ■ *Foreclosure Cleanout Business: High Profits — Low Start Up Cost*
Pub: James R. Tolliver
Ed: James Tolliver. **Released:** October 11, 2011. **Price:** $17.99. **Description:** Foreclosure cleanout business is booming. This manual teaches how to start a foreclosure firm, who to contact, what to charge, services provided and more.

44226 ■ *Getting Rich In Your Underwear: How To Start and Run a Profitable Home-Based Business*
Pub: HCM Publishing
Ed: Peter I. Hupalo. **Released:** April 1, 2005. **Price:** $17.95. **Description:** Book offers insight into starting a home-based business. Entrepreneurs will learn about business models and the home business; distribution and fulfillment of product or service; marketing and sales; how to overcome the fear of starting a business; personal success characteristics; naming a business; zoning and insurance; intellectual capital; copyrights, trademarks, and patents; limited liability companies and S-corporations; business expenses and accounting; taxes; fifteen basic steps for starting a home-based business, state resources for starting a home company; and seven home-based business ideas.

44227 ■ *How to Make Money While You Look for a Job*
Pub: Booklocker.com, Incorporated
Ed: Donna Boyette. **Released:** March 2005. **Price:** $11.95. **Description:** Six steps to make money while searching for employment are outlined, from setting up a home-based office to selling a service.

44228 ■ *"Online Fortunes" in Small Business Opportunities (Fall 2008)*
Pub: Entrepreneur Media Inc.
Description: Fifty hot, e-commerce enterprises for the aspiring entrepreneur to consider are featured; virtual assistants, marketing services, party planning, travel services, researching, web design and development, importing as well as creating an online store are among the businesses featured.

44229 ■ *Small Business Desk Reference*
Pub: Penguin Books USA Inc.
Ed: Gene Marks. **Released:** December 2004. **Description:** Comprehensive guide for starting or running a successful small business, focusing on buying a business or franchise, writing a business plan, financial management, accounting, legal issues, human resources management, operations, marketing, sales, customer service, taxes, insurance, and ethics. Information for launching a restaurant, property management firm, retail outlet, consulting firm, and service business is included.

44230 ■ *Start Your Own Net Services Business*
Pub: Entrepreneur Press
Contact: Perlman Neil, President
Released: February 1, 2009. **Price:** $17.95. **Description:** Web design, search engine marketing, new-media online, and blogging, are currently the four most popular web services available. This book provides information to start a net service business.

44231 ■ *Your Million-Dollar Idea: From Concept to Marketplace*
Pub: Adams Media Corporation
Ed: Sandy Abrams. **Released:** March 1, 2010. **Price:** $14.95. **Description:** Self-taught entrepreneur provides a 12-step plan to make a new product or service a profitable reality.

ASSOCIATIONS AND OTHER ORGANIZATIONS

44232 ■ **Coalition of Service Industries (CSI)**
1090 Vermont Ave. NW, Ste. 420
Washington, DC 20005-4968
Ph: (202)289-7460
Fax: (202)379-9864
URL: http://uscsi.org
Contact: William J. Toppeta, Chairman
Description: Increases attention to measurement of productivity in services and revises national economic indicators to account for services. Represents US service sector in multilateral trade negotiations. Works with interested groups internationally. **Founded:** 1982.

REFERENCE WORKS

44233 ■ *"2010 Book of Lists" in Austin Business JournalInc. (Vol. 29, December 25,* 2009, No. 42, pp. 1)
Pub: American City Business Journals
Description: Rankings of companies and organizations within the business services, finance, healthcare, hospitality and travel, insurance, marketing and media, professional services, real estate, education and technology industries in Austin, Texas are presented. Rankings are based on sales, business size, and other statistics.

44234 ■ *"2010 Book of Lists" in Business Courier (Vol. 26, December 26, 2009, No. 36, pp. 1)*
Pub: American City Business Journals, Inc.
Description: Rankings of companies and organizations within the business services, education, finance, health care, hospitality and tourism, real estate, and technology industries in the Cincinnati, Ohio-Northern Kentucky area are presented. Rankings are based on sales, business size, or other statistics.

44235 ■ *"2010 Book of Lists" in Tampa Bay Business Journal (Vol. 30, December 22, 2009, No. 53, pp. 1)*
Pub: American City Business Journals
Description: Rankings of companies and organizations within the human resources, banking and finance, business services, healthcare, real estate, technology, hospitality and travel, and education industries in the Greater Tampa Bay area are presented. Rankings are based on sales, business size, and more.

44236 ■ *"ABM Janitorial Services Receives Service Excellence Award from Jones Lang LaSalle" in Investment Weekly News (July 16, 2011, pp. 75)*
Pub: NewsRX
Description: ABM Janitorial Services was awarded the 2010 Jones Lang LaSalle Distinction award in the category of Service Excellence. LaSalle is a leading financial and professional services firm that specializes in real estate services and investment management. The program recognizes supplier partners who play a vital role in LaSalle's aim to provide the highest quality of services, value and innovation to clients.

44237 ■ *"ACE Agrees to Pay Out $266 Million to Investors" in Globe & Mail (February 17, 2006, pp. B1)*
Pub: CTVglobemedia Publishing Inc.
Ed: Brent Jang. **Description:** Canada-based commercial aviation firm ACE Aviation Holdings has agreed to pay 266 million dollars to its investors after filing a bankruptcy one year ago. Complete details of this pay off are discussed.

44238 ■ *Achieving Planned Innovation: A Proven System for Creating Successful New Products and Services*
Pub: Simon and Schuster
Ed: Frank R. Bacon. **Released:** August 2007. **Price:** $16.95. **Description:** Planned innovation is a disciplined and practical step-by-step sequence of procedures for reaching the intended destination point: successful products. This easy-to-read book explains

the system along with an action-oriented program for continuous success in new-product innovations. Five steps outlined include: a disciplined reasoning process; lasting market orientation; proper selection criteria that reflect both strategic and tactical business objectives and goals along with dynamic matching of resources to present and future opportunities, and positive and negative requirements before making major expenditures; and proper organizational staffing. The author explains what to do and evaluating the potential of any new product or service, ranging from ventures in retail distribution to the manufacture of goods as diverse as bicycles, motorcycles, aerospace communication and navigation equipment, small business computers, food packaging, and medical products.

44239 ■ *"Actiontec and Verizon Team Up for a Smarter Home" in Ecology,Environment & Conservation Business (November 5, 2011, pp. 3)*
Pub: HighBeam Research

Description: Verizon is implementing Actiontec Electronics' SG200 Service Gateway as a basic component of its Home Monitoring and Control service. This new smart home service allows customers to remotely check their homes, control locks and appliances, view home-energy use and more using a smartphone, PC, or FiOS TV.

44240 ■ *"Active Sales" in Green Industry Pro (Vol. 23, September 2011)*
Pub: Cygnus Business Media

Ed: Gregg Wartgow. **Description:** Craig den Hartog, owner of Emerald Magic Lawn Care located in Holtsville, New York, describes the various marketing tactics he has developed to increase sales in the current economic environment. Statistical data included.

44241 ■ *"Age-Old System of Bartering Is Being Revolutionized by Phoenix Company, Premier Barter" in Internet Wire (July 12, 2010)*
Pub: Comtex

Description: Premier Barter is helping entrepreneurs rediscover the system of bartering as a method of exchanging goods and services without cash or credit.

44242 ■ *"Air Canada to Slash 600 Non-Union Jobs" in Globe & Mail (February 11, 2006, pp. B3)*
Pub: CTVglobemedia Publishing Inc.

Ed: Brent Jang. **Description:** The reasons behind workforce reduction by ACE Aviation Holdings Inc. at Air Canada are presented.

44243 ■ *"Air Canada, WestJet Fill More Seats" in Globe & Mail (January 6, 2006, pp. B3)*
Pub: CTVglobemedia Publishing Inc.

Ed: Brent Jang. **Description:** The reasons behind the increase in passenger for Air Canada and WestJet Airlines Ltd. are presented.

44244 ■ *"Air Canada's Flight Plan for 777s Excludes India" in Globe & Mail (March 28, 2007, pp. B5)*
Pub: CTVglobemedia Publishing Inc.

Ed: Brent Jang. **Description:** The decision of Air Canada to exclude India and to fly its Boeing 777s due to poor economic returns is discussed.

44245 ■ *"Airline Mergers: United Next?" in Crain's Chicago Business (Vol. 31, April 21, 2008, No. 16, pp. 12)*
Pub: Crain Communications, Inc.

Description: Discusses a potential merger between United and Continental airlines; unions representing 48,900 pilots, mechanics, flight attendants, ticket agents and ramp workers at United have put the management on notice that they expect to be a factor in any merger discussions if the company wants their cooperation.

44246 ■ *"Airlines Mount PR Push to Win Public Support Against Big Oil" in*

Advertising Age (Vol. 79, July 14, 2008, No. 7, pp. 1)
Pub: Crain Communications, Inc.

Ed: Michael Bush. **Description:** Top airline executives from competing companies have banded together in a public relations plan in which they are sending e-mails to their frequent fliers asking for aid in lobbying legislators to put a restriction on oil speculation.

44247 ■ *"All Bundled Up" in Entrepreneur (Vol. 35, November 2007, No. 11, pp. 104)*
Pub: Entrepreneur Media Inc.

Ed: Kim T. Gordon. **Description:** Bundling is a marketing strategy that combines a variety of features to present products and services as a whole. Tips on how to handle bundling are outlined.

44248 ■ *"All the Trimmings" in Green Industry Pro (Vol. 23, March 2011, No. 3, pp. 29)*
Pub: Cygnus Business Media

Ed: Gregg Wartgow. **Description:** When choosing lawn mowing equipment, it is advised to purchase commercial-grade 21-inch walk mowers rather than less expensive consumer-grade mowers. John Deere is reentering the commercial 21-inch walk behind mower market after a five-year hiatus.

44249 ■ *"Ann Alexander; Senior Attorney, Natural Resources Defense Council" in Crain's Chicago Business (Vol. 31, May 5, 2008, No. 18)*
Pub: Crain Communications, Inc.

Ed: Emily Stone. **Description:** Profile of Ann Alexander who is the senior attorney at the Natural Resources Defense Council and is known for her dedication to the environment and a career spent battling oil companies, steelmakers and the government to change federal regulations. One recent project aims to improve the Bush administration's fuel economy standards for SUVs. Past battles include her work to prevent permits from slipping through the cracks such as the proposal by London-based BP PLC to dump 54 percent more ammonia and 35 percent more suspended solids from its Whiting, Indiana refinery into Lake Michigan-the source of drinking water for Chicago and its surrounding communities.

44250 ■ *"Anybody Out There?" in Canadian Business (Vol. 81, July 21 2008, No. 11, pp. 31)*
Pub: Rogers Media Ltd.

Ed: Andrew Wahl. **Description:** Virtual offices or shared office services provide solutions to companies that can no longer accommodate additional workspaces. The alternative working arrangement allows the company to have a kind of distributed work system. The disadvantages of employing virtual offices are presented.

44251 ■ *"App Time: Smartphone Applications Aren't Just for Fun and Games Anymore" in Inc. (Volume 32, December 2010, No. 10, pp. 116)*
Pub: Inc. Magazine

Ed: Jason Del Rey. **Description:** Smart phone technology can help any small business market their products and services.

44252 ■ *"Astral Media Set to Broadcast Coast to Coast" in Globe & Mail (February 24, 2007, pp. B5)*
Pub: CTVglobemedia Publishing Inc.

Ed: Grant Robertson. **Description:** The decision of Astral Media Inc. to acquire Standard Broadcasting Corp. Ltd. for $1.2 billion, with a view to increase its broadcast coverage, is discussed.

44253 ■ *"AT&T Wins Networking Deal from GM Worth $1 Billion" in Globe & Mail (February 22, 2007, pp. B14)*
Pub: CTVglobemedia Publishing Inc.

Description: AT&T Inc., the largest telephone company in the United States, won a $1 billion contract from General Motors Corp. to provide communications services to integrate the automaker's networks.

44254 ■ *"Aussie Rules" in Canadian Business (Vol. 79, Winter 2006, No. 24, pp. 45)*
Pub: Rogers Media

Ed: Jeff Sanford. **Description:** The efforts of the Toronto-based private equity firm Onex, to acquire the Australian national airline, Qantas Airways Ltd., are described.

44255 ■ *"Auxis Introduces Services for Government Contracting" in Entertainment Close-Up (December 22, 2010)*
Pub: Close-Up Media

Description: Profile of Auxis Inc., a management consulting and outsourcing company has launched a new service for companies involved in or bidding for government contracts. Details of the program are provided.

44256 ■ *"A Banking Play Without Banking Plagues" in Barron's (Vol. 88, March 31, 2008, No. 13, pp. 26)*
Pub: Dow Jones & Company, Inc.

Ed: Jack Willoughby. **Description:** Fiserv's shares have been dragged down by about 20 percent which presents an appealing entry point since the shares could rise by 30 percent or more by 2009. The company enables banks to post and open new checks and keeps track of loans which are not discretionary processes of banks.

44257 ■ *"Bankruptcies" in Crain's Detroit Business (Vol. 24, March 24, 2008, No. 12, pp. 6)*
Pub: Crain Communications, Inc.

Description: Current list of business that filed for Chapter 7 or 11 protection in U.S. Bankruptcy Court in Detroit include a construction company, a medical care company, a physical therapy firm and a communications firm.

44258 ■ *"Bankruptcies" in Crain's Detroit Business (Vol. 24, October 6, 2008, No. 40, pp. 26)*
Pub: Crain Communications, Inc.

Description: Current businesses that have filed for Chapter 7 or 11 protection in U.S. Bankruptcy Court include an auto dealership, a gun range and a grocery service.

44259 ■ *"Banks Fall Short in Online Services for Savvy Traders" in Barron's (Vol. 88, March 17, 2008, No. 11, pp. 35)*
Pub: Dow Jones & Company, Inc.

Ed: Theresa W. Carey. **Description:** Banc of America Investment Services, WellsTrade, and ShareBuilder are at the bottom of the list of online brokerages because they offer less trading technologies and product range. Financial shoppers miss out on a lot of customized tools and analytics when using these services.

44260 ■ *"Barbarians Set Bar Low With Lowly Canadian Telco" in Globe & Mail (March 31, 2007, pp. B1)*
Pub: CTVglobemedia Publishing Inc.

Ed: Derek DeCloet. **Description:** The efforts of the private equity fund Kohlberg, Kravis, Roberts and Co. to acquire the Canadian telecommunications firm BCE are described.

44261 ■ *"Bartering Trades on Talents" in Reading Eagle (June 20, 2010)*
Pub: Reading Eagle/Reading Times

Ed: Tony Lucia. **Description:** Bartering is not just a way of trading goods and services, it can be an essential tool for small business to survive in a bad economy.

44262 ■ *"BCE's Aliant Trust Spinoff Valued at About $8.5 Billion" in Globe & Mail (March 8, 2006, pp. B1)*
Pub: CTVglobemedia Publishing Inc.

Ed: Catherine McLean. **Description:** The details pertaining to the spinoff of Aliant Inc.'s landline business into an income trust by BCE Inc. are presented. The trust is valued at $8.5 billion.

44263 ■ *"Be Innovative In Other Ways"* in *Green Industry Pro (Vol. 23, March 2011, No. 3, pp. 4)*
Pub: Cygnus Business Media
Ed: Rod Dickens. **Description:** Emphasis is put on the importance of putting the customer first in order to successfully market any product or service. Six marketing ideas are presented to promote a landscaping business.

44264 ■ *"Beam My Data Up"* in *Canadian Business (Vol. 80, February 12, 2007, No. 4, pp. 42)*
Pub: Rogers Media
Ed: Marlene Rego. **Description:** Innovations in the field of teleportation since its invention by Gilles Brassard in 1992 is discussed.

44265 ■ *Behind the Cloud*
Pub: Jossey-Bass
Ed: Marc Benioff, Carlye Adler. **Released:** 2010. **Price:** $27.95. **Description:** Salesforce.com is the world's most successful business-to-business cloud-computing company that sells an online service that helps businesses manage sales, customer service, and marketing functions.

44266 ■ *"The Bell Tolls for Thee"* in *Canadian Business (Vol. 81, March 3, 2008, No. 3, pp. 36)*
Pub: Rogers Media
Ed: Andrew Wahl. **Description:** Bell Canada has formed the Canadian Coalition for Tomorrow's IT Skills to solve the shortage of technology talent in the country. Canada's total workforce has only around 4%, or 600,000 people employed in information technology-related fields. The aims of the Bell-led coalition, which is supported by different industry associations and 30 corporations, are investigated.

44267 ■ *"Benchmark Makes Granduca Entrance"* in *Houston Business Journal (Vol. 40, January 8, 2010, No. 35, pp. 2)*
Pub: American City Business Journals
Ed: Jennifer Dawson. **Description:** Houston, Texas-based Interfin Company, owner of the Hotel Granduca, has tapped the services of Benchmark Hospitality International to manage the property. The hiring of Benchmark is part of Interfin's efforts to develop Granduca hotels in other markets. Statistical data included.

44268 ■ *"Bernier Open to Telecom Changes"* in *Globe & Mail (March 22, 2006, pp. B1)*
Pub: CTVglobemedia Publishing Inc.
Ed: Simon Tuck. **Description:** Federal Industry Minister Maxime Bernier of Canada says that he is open to scrapping restrictions on foreign ownership in telecommunications. His views on telecom industry are detailed.

44269 ■ *Beyond Booked Solid: Your Business, Your Life, Your Way-It's All Inside*
Pub: John Wiley and Sons, Inc.
Ed: Michael Port. **Released:** April 2008. **Price:** $24.95. **Description:** Professional service providers and small business owners will discover tactics and strategies for growing and expanding their companies while allowing them to find time to relax and enjoy their lives. Owners will learn to attract new clients and grow profits.

44270 ■ *"Big Sell-Off At Sunwest"* in *The Business Journal-Portland (Vol. 25, July 25, 2008, No. 20, pp. 1)*
Pub: American City Business Journals, Inc.
Ed: Robin J. Moody. **Description:** Oregon's largest operator of assisted living facilities Sunwest Management Inc. is expected to sell 132 of its properties. The planned sale, which is believed to be worth more than $1 billion, will help Sunwest pay creditors and investors. Other views and information on the planned sale, as well as on Sunwest's services which include adult day care, are presented.

44271 ■ *"Big Trouble at Sony Ericsson"* in *Barron's (Vol. 88, March 24, 2008, No. 12, pp. M9)*
Pub: Dow Jones & Company, Inc.
Ed: Angelo Franchini. **Description:** Sony Ericsson is facing trouble as it warned that its sales and net income before taxes will fall by nearly half for the first

quarter of 2008. The joint venture of Sony and Ericsson has a global mobile phone market share of nine percent as of 2007, fourth largest in the world.

44272 ■ *"Bill Lee's Auto Repair Business Chugs Along Despite Life's Obstacles"* in *Bradenton Herald (August 22, 2010)*
Pub: Bradenton Herald
Ed: Grace Gagliano. **Description:** Profile of Bill Lee's Professional Automotive Services located in Bradenton, Florida. The auto repair business was opened 26 years ago and provides repair for an assortment of fleet vehicles, including truck repair.

44273 ■ *"Black Gold"* in *Canadian Business (Vol. 79, August 14, 2006, No. 16-17, pp. 57)*
Pub: Rogers Media
Ed: Erin Pooley. **Description:** A list of the top ten jobs in the petroleum industry in Canada along with pay and nature of jobs, is presented.

44274 ■ *"Blockbuster Launches Internet Movie Downloads to Compete Against Netflix, Others"* in *Chicago Tribune (December 3, 2008)*
Pub: McClatchy-Tribune Information Services
Ed: Eric Benderoff. **Description:** Blockbuster Inc., the DVD rental giant, has launched a new service that delivers movies to their customer's homes via the Internet in an attempt to compete against Netflix and other competitors.

44275 ■ *"Blood Bank"* in *Canadian Business (Vol. 80, February 12, 2007, No. 4, pp. 36)*
Pub: Rogers Media
Ed: Erin Pooley. **Description:** The plan of Insception Biosciences to popularize stem cell banks, which can store stem cells, is discussed.

44276 ■ *"Bombardier Wins Chinese Rail Deal"* in *Globe & Mail (March 20, 2006, pp. B1)*
Pub: CTVglobemedia Publishing Inc.
Ed: Geoffrey York. **Description:** Bombardier Inc. has won a $68 million (U.S) contract to provide railway cars for rapid transit-link between Beijing and its international airport for 2008 Olympics in China. Details of the contract are presented.

44277 ■ *"Bookkeeping Service Opens First Sacramento Franchise"* in *Sacramento Bee (April 13, 2011)*
Pub: Sacramento Bee
Ed: Mark Glover. **Description:** Franchise bookkeeping service called BookKeeping Express opened its new office in Roseville, California; its first shop in the area.

44278 ■ *"Bountiful Barrels: Where to Find $140 Trillion"* in *Barron's (Vol. 88, July 14, 2008, No. 28, pp. 40)*
Pub: Dow Jones & Co., Inc.
Ed: Andrew Bary. **Description:** Surge in oil prices has caused a large transfer of wealth to oil-producing countries thereby reshaping the global economy. Oil reserves of oil exporting countries are now valued at $140 trillion. Economist Stephen Jen believes that this wealth will be transformed into paper assets as these countries invest in global stocks and bonds.

44279 ■ *"Brief: Janitorial Company Must Pay Back Wages"* in *Buffalo News (September 24, 2011)*
Pub: The Buffalo News
Ed: Jonathan D. Epstein. **Description:** Knights Facilities Management, located in Michigan, provides grounds maintenance and janitorial services at the Ralph Wilson Stadium in Buffalo, New York. The US Department of Labor ordered the firm to pay $22,000 in back wages and damages to 26 employees for overtime and minimum wage compensation. Details of the company's violation of the Fair Labor Standards Act are included.

44280 ■ *Building Buzz to Beat the Big Boys*
Pub: Greenwood Publishing Group, Inc.
Ed: Steve O'Leary; Kim Sheehan. **Released:** March 30, 2008. **Price:** $39.95. **Description:** Seventy to eighty percent of small retail stores fail within the first five years of opening due to competition from big-box

retailers and online stores. Service providers and small retailers should capitalize on the fact that they are local and can connect on a personal level with customers in a way the big stores cannot. Word of mouth marketing methods are very critical to any small retail or service company. This book is designed to help any small business compete against large competitors.

44281 ■ *"Bumpy Ride Ahead for United"* in *Crain's Chicago Business (Vol. 31, May 5, 2008, No. 18, pp. 3)*
Pub: Crain Communications, Inc.
Ed: John Pletz. **Description:** Continental Airlines Inc. walked away from merger talks with United Airlines last week. Now the choices facing United boil down to going it alone in an increasingly stormy airline business or a less-desirable merger with US Airways Group Inc. Analysts expect United to lose $977 million this year due, mainly, to the high price of fuel.

44282 ■ *"Burton Group Answers Industry Need for Practical Data Center Advice"* in *Canadian Corporate News (May 14, 2007)*
Pub: Comtex News Network Inc.
Description: Burton Group, an IT research firm focused on in-depth technical analysis of enterprise IT infrastructures, launched a new service providing practical advice for IT professionals facing critical data center decisions which due to technological advances can be more efficient while reducing costs.

44283 ■ *"Business Diary"* in *Crain's Detroit Business (Vol. 24, October 6, 2008, No. 40, pp. 23)*
Pub: Crain Communications, Inc.
Description: Detailed listing of acquisitions, expansions, new products, new services, business contracts and startups from the Detroit area is provided.

44284 ■ *"Businesses Band Together in Destin Bartering to Keep Heads Above Water"* in *Destin Log (July 24, 2010)*
Pub: The Destin Log
Ed: Andrew Metz. **Description:** Profile of The Barter Company located in Destin, Florida, whose owner believes that bartering for goods and services can help small companies in a down economy.

44285 ■ *"Butane Heated Pressure Washer Offers Diverse Cleaning Options"* in *Product News Network (March 8, 2011)*
Pub: Product News Network
Description: Profile of the Super Max (TM) 6000B power sprayer the can clean with cold or heated water and wet steam. Daimer Industries, provider of janitorial supplies, announced the availability of the machine that offers a variety of cleaning options for a range of applications.

44286 ■ *"Call of Prepaid Heard by More"* in *Chicago Tribune (November 26, 2008)*
Pub: McClatchy-Tribune Information Services
Ed: Wailin Wong. **Description:** Due to the economic downturn, more consumers are switching to no-contract, prepaid cell phone service. Customers find that the cost savings, flexibility and lack of contract are appealing in such uncertain times.

44287 ■ *"Can You Hear Them Now?"* in *Hawaii Business (Vol. 54, August 2008, No. 2, pp. 48)*
Pub: Hawaii Business Publishing
Ed: Jason Ubay. **Description:** Coral Wireless LLC (dba Mobi PCS) is ranked 237 in Hawaii Business' list of the state's top 250 companies for 2008. The company is a local wireless phone provider, which has expanded its market to Oahu, Maui and the Big Island since opening in 2006, offering 13 phones and unlimited texts and calls. Details on the company's sales are provided.

44288 ■ *"The Case of the Deflated IPO"* in *Boston Business Journal (Vol. 29, June 24, 2011, No. 7, pp. 1)*
Pub: American City Business Journals Inc.
Ed: Scott Dance. **Description:** IPO market is on the rebound from the recession but for some companies in Maryland, the time is not yet ripe to go public. One

of the companies that chooses to wait for better timing is SafeNet Inc. and it is eyeing some possible acquisitions while doing so.

44289 ■ "The Caterer and Hotelkeeper Interview Patrick Harbour and Nathan Jones" in Caterer & Hotelkeeper (October 28, 2011, No. 288)
Pub: Reed Reference Publishing

Description: Profiles of Patrick Harbour and Nathan Jones who quit their jobs to start their own catering business. The partners discuss their business strategy when launching their boutique catering firm and ways they are adapting to the slow economy in order to remain successful.

44290 ■ "Cell Phone the Ticket on American Airlines" in Chicago Tribune (November 14, 2008)
Pub: McClatchy-Tribune Information Services

Ed: Julie Johnsson. **Description:** American Airlines is testing a new mobile boarding pass at O'Hare International Airport. Travelers on American can board flights and get through security checkpoints by flashing a bar code on their phones. Passengers must have an Internet-enabled mobile device and an active e-mail address in order to utilize this service.

44291 ■ "Certification Experts Germanischer Lloyd Wind Energy Assist NaiKun's Offshore Wind Project" in Canadian Corporate News (May 14, 2007)
Pub: Comtex News Network Inc.

Description: Germanischer Lloyd Wind Energy (GL Wind) will examine, inspect, and provide quality management services for the engineering, design, and construction of the offshore wind project planned by NaiKun Wind Development Inc. in northwest British Columbia.

44292 ■ "Certified Technicians can Increase Bottom Line" in Contractor (Vol. 56, September 2009, No. 9, pp. 37)
Pub: Penton Media, Inc.

Ed: Ray Isaac. **Description:** Certified technicians increase the value of HVAC firms, a survey by Service Round Table has reported. The increased value has been attributed to fewer callbacks, less warranty work and greater ability to educate consumers. Meanwhile, consumers are willing to pay more for the services of certified technicians.

44293 ■ "Check Provider Says It Plans to Close Call Center in Charlotte" in Charlotte Observer (February 6, 2007)
Pub: Knight-Ridder/Tribune Business News

Ed: Rick Rothacker. **Description:** Clarke American Checks Inc. is closing its call center located in Charlotte, North Carolina. Clarke provides checks and other services to financial institutions and customers.

44294 ■ "City a Pawn in Airlines' Chess Game" in Business Courier (Vol. 24, January 18, 2008, No. 41, pp. 1)
Pub: American City Business Journals, Inc.

Ed: Lisa Biank Fasig. **Description:** Delta Air Lines is under negotitaions with Northwest Airlines and UAL Corp. for a proposed merger. The deal will have a negative impact on Cincinnati as a hub regardless whether it goes to UAL or Northwest. The impacts of the planned merger on Cincinnati's labor market and airport traffic are discussed.

44295 ■ "City Seeks More Minorities" in Austin Business Journal Inc. (Vol. 28, November 7, 2008, No. 34, pp. A1)
Pub: American City Business Journals

Ed: Jean Kwon. **Description:** Austin, Texas is planning to increase the participation of minority- and women-owned businesses in government contracts. Contractors are required to show 'good faith' to comply with the specified goals. The city is planning to effect the changes in the construction and professional services sector.

44296 ■ "Columbia's JPB Raising $175M to Acquire Companies, Real Estate" in Boston

Business Journal (Vol. 29, May 27, 2011, No. 3, pp. 1)
Pub: American City Business Journals Inc.

Ed: Gary Haber. **Description:** JPB Enterprises is preparing to raise $175 million in its goal of acquiring companies and real estate that are major names in America. The $75 million will be raised for a buyout fund that will target wide range of industries while the $100 million will be used for land investment projects in the Florida Panhandle. Baltimore firms are expected to benefit from this deal.

44297 ■ "Compelling Opportunities" in Barron's (Vol. 88, March 10, 2008, No. 10, pp. 39)
Pub: Dow Jones & Company, Inc.

Ed: Neil A. Martin. **Description:** Michael L. Reynal, portfolio manager of Principal International Emerging Markets Fund, is bullish on the growth prospects of stocks in emerging markets. He is investing big on energy, steel, and transportation companies.

44298 ■ "Complete Discovery Source, Inc. (CDS) Receives Minority Owned Business Certification" in Internet Wire (December 14, 2010)
Pub: Comtex

Description: Complete Discovery Source Inc. (CDS) was granted Minority-Owned Business Enterprise status by the New York State Department of Economic Development. The certification provides CDS, an end-to-end eDiscovery services provider, with access to contracting opportunities with 130 government agencies throughout New York state.

44299 ■ The Concierge Manual: A Step-by-Step Guide to Starting Your Own Concierge Service or Lifestyle Management Company
Pub: New Road Publishing

Ed: Katharine C. Giovanni. **Released:** September 9, 2010. **Price:** $23.00. **Description:** Answering some of the biggest questions about the logistics of running a concierge business, this guide provides all the tools necessary to create a successful concierge, lifestyle management, errand service, or personal assistant company.

44300 ■ "Conquering Your Fear of Fees" in Entrepreneur (Vol. 37, October 2009, No. 10, pp. 86)
Pub: Entrepreneur Media, Inc.

Ed: Rosalind Resnick. **Description:** Entrepreneurs should study money management charges carefully before investing. They should understand how different forms of investments work and how much money managers and mutual funds charge for their services.

44301 ■ "CoolBrands" in Canadian Business (Vol. 83, September 14, 2010, No. 15, pp. 25)
Pub: Rogers Media Ltd.

Ed: Joe Castaldo. **Description:** CoolBrands International Inc.'s merger with Swisher International Inc., a US hygiene products and services company, has formally erased the last traces of the former ice cream company. CoolBrands began as a frozen yogurt stand in 1986 and flourished across the world. How the string of acquisitions and poor corporate governance led to its demise are cited.

44302 ■ "Count Out The Consumer" in Barron's (Vol. 88, July 7, 2008, No. 27, pp. 10)
Pub: Dow Jones & Co., Inc.

Description: American consumers are not expected to give the US economy its much-needed boost as the rising food and energy prices are taking their toll. US consumers have cut spending on utilities and food and are increasing their use of credit cards.

44303 ■ "CPI Corporation Acquires Assets of Bella Pictures" in Benzinga.com (January 28, 2011)
Pub: Benzinga.com

Ed: Benzinga Staff. **Description:** CPI Corporation acquired assets of Bella Pictures Inc., a leading provider of branded wedding photography services. Details of the acquisition are explained.

44304 ■ "CPR-CN Deal to Ease Vancouver Logjam" in Globe & Mail (January 27, 2006, pp. B4)
Pub: CTVglobemedia Publishing Inc.

Ed: Brent Jang. **Description:** In a bid to lessen West coast port grid lock Canadian Pacific Railway Ltd and Canadian National Railway Co. has agreed to share tracks in the Vancouver region. This will allow the trains to operate more efficiently from the Vancouver Port.

44305 ■ "CPR Signals a Switch in Strategy to Narrow Competitive Gap With CN" in Globe & Mail (January 20, 2006, pp. B3)
Pub: CTVglobemedia Publishing Inc.

Ed: Brent Jang. **Description:** The reasons behind the restructuring efforts of Canadian Pacific Railway Ltd. are presented.

44306 ■ "Customer Retention is Proportionate to Employee Retention" in Green Industry Pro (Vol. 23, September 2011)
Pub: Cygnus Business Media

Description: Presented in a question-answer format, information is provided to help retain customers as well as keeping workers happy.

44307 ■ "Customized Before Custom Was Cool" in Green Industry Pro (July 2011)
Pub: Cygnus Business Media

Ed: Gregg Wartgow. **Description:** Profile of Turf Care Enterprises and owner Kevin Vogeler, who discusses his desire to use more natural programs using little or no chemicals in 1986. At that time, that sector represented 20 percent of his business, today it shares 80 percent.

44308 ■ "The Data Drivers" in Canadian Business (Vol. 81, September 15, 2008, No. 14-15, pp. 1)
Pub: Rogers Media Ltd.

Ed: Andrew Wahl. **Description:** Canadian regulators hope that an auction of telecommunications companies will inject more competition into the industry; however, newcomers may not be able to rely on lower prices in order to gain market share from the three major telecommunications companies that already have a stronghold on the market. Analysts feel that providing additional data service is the key to surviving market disruptions.

44309 ■ "Data Firm Growth 'Opportunistic" in Tampa Bay Business Journal (Vol. 30, January 29, 2010, No. 6, pp. 1)
Pub: American City Business Journals

Ed: Michael Hinman. **Description:** E Solutions Corporation is experiencing growth amid the economic downturn, with its Park Tower data center occupancy in Tampa Florida expanding from 14,000 square feet to 20,000 square feet. Details on the increased operations fueled by demand for information storage and management services offered by the company are discussed.

44310 ■ "Daycare Dollars" in Small Business Opportunities (Winter 2009)
Pub: Entrepreneur Media Inc.

Description: Profile of Maui Playcare, a franchise that provides parents drop-in daycare for their children without having to purchase a membership, make reservations or pay costly dues; the company is expanding beyond its Hawaiian roots onto the mainland and is expected to have between 40 and 50 locations signed by the end of 2010.

44311 ■ "Dear Customer: Managing E-Mail Campaigns" in Inc. (March 2008, pp. 58-59)
Pub: Gruner & Jahr USA Publishing

Ed: Ryan Underwood. **Description:** Internet services that help firms manage their online business including email marketing, to manage subscriber lists, comply with spam regulations, monitor bouncebacks, and track potential customers are profiled. Constant Contact, MobileStorm Stun, Campaign Monitor, Pop Commerce, Emma, and StrongMail E-mail Server are among software and services highlighted.

44312 ■ *"Debt-Collection Agency to Lay Off 368 in Hampton Center"* in Virginian-Pilot (December 4, 2010)
Pub: Virginian-Pilot
Ed: Tom Shean. Description: NCO Financial Systems Inc., provider of debt-collection and outsourcing services will permanently lay off 368 workers at its Hampton call center in 2011.

44313 ■ *"Deep in the Heart of Drought"* in Green Industry Pro (Vol. 23, October 2011)
Pub: Cygnus Business Media
Ed: Gregg Wartgow. Description: Challenges faced by landscape contractors during the recent drought in Texas are explored. Despite these challenges, opportunity for contractors providing irrigation services has risen.

44314 ■ *Delivering Knock Your Socks Off Service, 4th Edition*
Pub: American Management Association
Contact: Charles R. Craig, Chairman
Ed: Performance Research Associates. Released: 2006.

44315 ■ *"Descartes Launches Ocean Shipment Management Suite"* in Canadian Corporate News (May 16, 2007)
Pub: Comtex News Network Inc.
Description: Descartes Systems Group, a global on-demand software-as-a-service (SaaS) logistics solutions provider, launched the latest release of its Descartes Ocean Shipment Management Suite. The release integrates customs compliance services with Descartes' Rate Builder solution, a central database for global shipment and rate information, and Descartes Global Logistics Network (GLN) messaging capabilities.

44316 ■ *"Do the Right Thing"* in Contractor (Vol. 56, December 2009, No. 12, pp. 16)
Pub: Penton Media, Inc.
Ed: Robert P. Mader. Description: Applewood Plumbing, Heating and Electric has won Contractor magazine's 2009 Contractor of the Year Award. The company has ranked eighth among more than 300 service companies in the United States. A brief history of the company is also provided.

44317 ■ *"Dollar General Selects GSI Commerce to Launch Its eCommerce Business"* in Benzinga.com (October 29, 2011)
Pub: Benzinga.com
Ed: Benzinga Staff. Description: Dollar General Corporation chose GSI Commerce, a leading provider of ecommerce and interactive marketing solutions, to launch its online initiative. GSI Commerce is an eBay Inc. company.

44318 ■ *"Don't' Hang Up On FairPoint"* in Barron's (Vol. 88, July 7, 2008, No. 27, pp. M5)
Pub: Dow Jones & Co., Inc.
Ed: Fleming Meeks. Description: Shares of FairPoint Communications, priced at $6.63 each, are undervalued and should be worth over $12 each. The company increased its size by more than five times by acquiring Verizon's local telephone operations in Vermont, New Hampshire, and Maine, but must switch customers in those areas into their system by the end of September 2007.

44319 ■ *"Don't' Hate the Cable Guy"* in Saint Louis Business Journal (Vol. 31, August 5, 2011, No. 50, pp. 1)
Pub: Saint Louis Business Journal
Ed: Angela Mueller. Description: Charter Communications named John Birrer as senior vice president of customer experience. The company experienced problems with its customer services.

44320 ■ *"Dozens 'Come Alive' in Downtown Chicago"* in Green Industry Pro (July 2011)
Pub: Cygnus Business Media
Ed: Gregg Wartgow. Description: Highlights from the Come Alive Outside training event held in Chicago, Illinois July 14-15, 2011 are shared. Nearly

80 people representing 38 landscape companies attended the event that helps contractors review their services and find ways to sell them in new and various ways.

44321 ■ *"Drilling Deep and Flying High"* in Barron's (Vol. 88, June 30, 2008, No. 26, pp. 34)
Pub: Dow Jones & Co., Inc.
Ed: Kenneth Rapoza. Description: Shares of Petrobras could rise another 25 percent if the three deepwater wells that the company has found proves as lucrative as some expect. Petrobras will become an oil giant if the reserves are proven.

44322 ■ *"DST Turns to Banks for Credit"* in The Business Journal-Serving Metropolitan Kansas City (Vol. 27, October 3, 2008, No. 3, pp. 1)
Pub: American City Business Journals, Inc.
Ed: Rob Roberts. Description: Kansas City, Missouri-based DST Systems Inc., a company that provides sophisticated information processing, computer software services and business solutions, has secured a new five-year, $120 million credit facility from Enterprise Bank and Bank of the West. The deal is seen to reflect that the region and community-banking model remain stable. Comments from executives are also provided.

44323 ■ *"eBay Inc. Completes Acquisition of Zong"* in Benzinga.com (October 29, 2011)
Pub: Benzinga.com
Ed: Benzinga Staff. Description: eBay Inc. acquired Zong, a provider of payments through mobile carrier billing. Terms of the agreement are outlined.

44324 ■ *"eBay and Jonathan Adler Team to Launch 'The eBay Inspiration Shop"* in Entertainment Close-Up (October 25, 2011)
Pub: Close-Up Media
Description: Designer Jonathan Adler partnered with eBay to create a collection of new must-have merchandise for the fall season. Top trendsetters, including actors, designers, bloggers, stylists, editors, photographers, models and musicians helped curate the items being featured in the windows by sharing their shopping wish lists with users.

44325 ■ *"Embarq Sale Sets New Tone"* in The Business Journal-Serving Metropolitan Kansas City (Vol. 27, October 31, 2008, No. 8, pp. 1)
Pub: American City Business Journals, Inc.
Ed: Suzsanna Stagemeyer. Description: CenturyTel Inc. has agreed to acquire Embarq Corp., a large phone company based in Overland Park. The acquisition deal is valued at $11.6 billion. The potential impacts of the deal on Kansas City's economy are analyzed.

44326 ■ *"EnCana Gets Top Dollar for Gas Depot Division"* in Globe & Mail (March 7, 2006, pp. B6)
Pub: CTVglobemedia Publishing Inc.
Ed: Dave Ebner. Description: The details on acquisition of natural gas storage assets of EnCana Corp. by Carlyle/Riverstone Global Energy and Power Fund II LP and Carlyle Group LP are presented.

44327 ■ *"EnCana Surpasses All Canadian Profit Records"* in Globe & Mail (February 16, 2007, pp. B5)
Pub: CTVglobemedia Publishing Inc.
Ed: David Ebner. Description: Canada-based energy giant EnCana Corp. has reported $5.65 billion profits for the fiscal year 2006. The company has outpaced expectations by this impressive figure.

44328 ■ *"Energy, MLPs: Pipeline to Profits"* in Barron's (Vol. 89, July 27, 2009, No. 30, pp. 9)
Pub: Dow Jones & Co., Inc.
Ed: Dimitra DeFotis. Description: Energy master limited partnership stocks are range-bound in the next few months from July 2009 but there are some opportunities that remain. These include Energy Transfer Equity, Enterprise GP holdings, NuStar GP Holdings, and Plains All American Pipeline.

44329 ■ *"Energy Sparks Job Growth"* in The Business Journal-Serving Greater Tampa Bay (Vol. 28, August 8, 2008, No. 33, pp. 1)
Pub: American City Business Journals, Inc.
Ed: Margie Manning. Description: Energy infrastructure projects in Tampa Bay, Florida, are increasing the demand for labor in the area. Energy projects requiring an increase in labor include TECO Energy Inc.'s plan for a natural gas pipeline in the area and the installation of energy management system in Bank of America's branches in the area.

44330 ■ *"Everett Dowling"* in Hawaii Business (Vol. 54, August 2008, No. 2, pp. 32)
Pub: Hawaii Business Publishing
Ed: Jason Ubay. Description: Real estate developer Everett Dowling, president of Dowling Company Inc., talks about the company's sustainable management and services. The company's office has been retrofitted to earn a Leadership in Energy and Environmental Design (LEED) certification. Dowling believes that real estate development can be part of the sustainable solution.

44331 ■ *Exceptional Service, Exceptional Profit: The Secrets of Building a Five-Star Customer Service Organization*
Pub: AMACOM
Ed: Leonard Inghilleri, Micah Solomon. Released: April 1, 2010. Price: $21.95. Description: Team of insiders share exclusive knowledge of the loyalty-building techniques pioneered by the world's most successful service leaders, including brick-and-mortar stars such as The Ritz-Carlton and Lexus and online success stories such as Netflix and CD Baby.

44332 ■ *"Exxon Braving the Danger Zones"* in Globe & Mail (March 8, 2007, pp. B1)
Pub: CTVglobemedia Publishing Inc.
Ed: Shawn McCarthy. Description: The plans of Exxon Mobil Corp. to increase its revenues through the expansion of its operations in Asia, Africa, and the Middle East are discussed.

44333 ■ *"Facebook, Adobe, Kenshoo, Outright and Cignex Datamatics Sign On to X.commerce"* in Entertainment Close-Up (October 24, 2011)
Pub: Close-Up Media
Description: Facebook, Adobe, Kenshoo, Outright and Cignex Datamatics have all partnered with X.commerce's ecosystem, where developers build and merchants can come to shop for new technologies and services.

44334 ■ *"Fairfax Announces Acquisition of William Ashley"* in Benzinga.com (August 16, 2011)
Pub: Benzinga.com
Ed: Benzinga Staff. Description: Fairfax Financial Holdings Limited acquired the family-owned William Ashley China company, leader within the dinnerware and wedding registry industries and was the first company in North America to introduce a computerized wedding registry system.

44335 ■ *"Family Throne"* in Hawaii Business (Vol. 53, March 2008, No. 9, pp. 51)
Pub: Hawaii Business Publishing
Ed: Cathy S. Cruz-George. Description: Jeanette and George Grace inherited Paradise Lua Inc., a portable toilet company founded by George's father. The toilets are rented by Aloha Stadium during football season and St. Patrick's Day block party among others. The company has 2,500 toilets and 20 pumping trucks and had earnings of $1.3 million in 2007.

44336 ■ *"A Few Points of Contention"* in Barron's (Vol. 88, July 14, 2008, No. 28, pp. 3)
Pub: Dow Jones & Co., Inc.
Ed: Michael Santoli. Description: Headline inflation tends to revert to the lower core inflation, which excludes food and energy in its calculation over long periods. Prominent private equity figures believe that regulators should allow more than the de facto 10 percent to 25 percent limit of commercial banks to hasten the refunding of the financial sector.

44337 ■ *"Fifth Third Spinoff" in Business Courier (Vol. 27, July 16, 2010, No. 11, pp. 1)*
Pub: Business Courier

Ed: Dan Monk, Steve Watkins. **Description:** Electronic-funds transfer company Fifth Third Solutions (FTPS), a spinoff of Fifth Third Bancorp, is seeking as much as 200,000 square feet of new office space in Ohio. The bank's sale of 51 percent ownership stake to Boston-based Advent International Corporation has paved the way for the growth of FTPS. How real estate brokers' plans have responded to FTPS' growth mode is discussed.

44338 ■ *"Finding a Way to Continue Growing" in Green Industry Pro (Vol. 23, March 2011, No. 3, pp. 31)*
Pub: Cygnus Business Media

Description: Profile of Brett Lemcke, VP of R.M. Landscape located in Rochester, New York. Lemcke tells how his Landscape Industry Certified credentials helped him to grow his business and beat out his competition.

44339 ■ *"Five Distinct Divisions, One Collective Focus" in Green Industry Pro (Vol. 23, October 2011)*
Pub: Cygnus Business Media

Ed: Gregg Wartgow. **Description:** Profile of ACLS Inc., an amalgamation of All Commercial Landscape Service (commercial maintenance), All Custom Landscape Service (design/build), Fresno Tree Service, Certified Water Consulting (irrigation), and Tractor Service (disking and flailing services on everything from one-acre lots to hundreds of acres of open land). The firm discusses its rebranding effort in order to increase sales.

44340 ■ *"Fix-It Career: Jobs in Repair" in Occupational Outlook Quarterly (Vol. 54, Fall 2010, No. 3, pp. 26)*
Pub: U.S. Bureau of Labor Statistics

Ed: Elka Maria Torpey. **Description:** Auto mechanics and HVAC technician occupations require repair skills. Advantages for individuals with proper skills are outlined.

44341 ■ *"Flat or Slight Decline Seen for Nortel 2007 Revenue" in Globe & Mail (March 17, 2007, pp. B3)*
Pub: CTVglobemedia Publishing Inc.

Ed: Catherine McLean. **Description:** The forecast about Nortel Network Corp's decrease in the 2007 revenue and its restructuring to reduce costs is discussed.

44342 ■ *"Flight of Capital?" in Canadian Business (Vol. 80, February 26, 2007, No. 5, pp. 76)*
Pub: Rogers Media

Description: The economic reasons, which forced Air Canada to pullback its direct daily service from Toronto to New Delhi, India, are presented. The views of Michael Treacy, United States' entrepreneur, on the economic conditions of Canada are also presented.

44343 ■ *"Flights of Fancy" in Crain's Chicago Business (Vol. 31, April 21, 2008, No. 16, pp. 27)*
Pub: Crain Communications, Inc.

Ed: Sarah A. Klein. **Description:** Due to the competition for business travelers, who account for 30 percent of airline revenue, airlines are offering a number of luxury amenities, especially on long-haul routes.

44344 ■ *"Flying High Down Under" in Entrepreneur (Vol. 37, August 2009, No. 8, pp. 16)*
Pub: Entrepreneur Media, Inc.

Ed: Dan Oko. **Description:** V Australia offers direct flights from Los Angeles International Airport to Brisbane, Melbourne, and Sydney in Australia. Their Boeing 777-300ER aircrafts has a fully stocked sit-down bar in the business class, touch screens with audio and video on demand and passengers get to perk up with Bulgari toiletries kits.

44345 ■ *"Flying the Unfriendly Skies" in Crain's Chicago Business (Vol. 31, April 21, 2008, No. 16, pp. 26)*
Pub: Crain Communications, Inc.

Ed: Sarah A. Klein. **Description:** Due to the number of Chicago companies and entrepreneurs who are traveling overseas more frequently in order to strengthen ties with customers, companies and oftentimes even business partners, the number of flights leaving O'Hare International Airport for destinations abroad has surged; In 2007, international passengers departing O'Hare totaled 5.7 million, up from 2.4 million in 1990.

44346 ■ *"The Fort" in Hawaii Business (Vol. 53, November 2007, No. 5, pp. 19)*
Pub: Hawaii Business Publishing

Ed: Jason Ubay. **Description:** DRFortress' flagship data center The Fort located at Honolulu's Airport Industrial Park provides companies a place to store their servers in an ultra-secure environment. Anything stored in here that requires power has a back up and in case of an outage generators can supply power up to 80 hrs. The Fort caters to major carriers and Internet service providers.

44347 ■ *"Fortis Snaps Up Terasen's Gas Utility Business" in Globe & Mail (February 27, 2007, pp. B1)*
Pub: CTVglobemedia Publishing Inc.

Ed: Wendy Stueck. **Description:** The acquisition of Terasen Inc. from Kinder Morgan Inc. by Fortis Inc. is described.

44348 ■ *"Forward Motion" in Green Industry Pro (July 2011)*
Pub: Cygnus Business Media

Ed: Gregg Wartgow. **Description:** Several landscape contractors have joined this publication's Working Smarter Training Challenge over the last year. This process is helping them develop ways to improve work processes, boost morale, drive out waste, reduce costs, improve customer service, and be more competitive.

44349 ■ *"Free Your Mind" in Entrepreneur (Vol. 37, October 2009, No. 10, pp. 24)*
Pub: Entrepreneur Media Inc.

Ed: Joe Robinson. **Description:** Writer Chris Anderson believes that firms in the digital age should allow products and services to initially be sold for free. These companies could then charge for premium versions of these products and services after the free versions have gained attention.

44350 ■ *"Friedland's Next Frontier: Drilling for Oil in Iraq" in Globe & Mail (April 20, 2007, pp. B1)*
Pub: CTVglobemedia Publishing Inc.

Ed: Wendy Stueck. **Description:** The decision of the Canadian oil and gas company Ivanhoe Energy Inc. to partner with the Japanese oil and gas firm INPEX Corp. for the development of heavy oil fields in north central Iraq is discussed.

44351 ■ *"Fuel for Thought; Canadian Business Leaders on Energy Policy" in Canadian Business (Vol. 81, September 15, 2008, No. 14-15, pp. 12)*
Pub: Rogers Media Ltd.

Ed: Joe Castaldo. **Description:** Most Canadian business leaders worry about the unreliability of the oil supply but feel that Canada is in a better position to benefit from the energy supply crisis than other countries. Many respondents also highlighted the need to invest in renewable energy sources.

44352 ■ *"The Future of Work" in Black Enterprise (Vol. 41, August 2010, No. 1, pp. 65)*
Pub: Earl G. Graves Publishing Co. Inc.

Ed: Annya M. Lott. **Description:** Technology, globalization, and outsourcing will continue to shape the future of work. Social media is a means for small companies to market goods and services.

44353 ■ *"Gain the 'Come Alive Outside' Selling Edge" in Green Industry Pro (July 2011)*
Pub: Cygnus Business Media

Ed: Jim Paluch. **Description:** Marketing the 'Come Alive Outside' slogan can help landscapers to increase their market share by identifying and applying these elements to each customer as well as their workers.

44354 ■ *"Get Paid and Get Moving" in Entrepreneur (Vol. 37, October 2009, No. 10, pp. 38)*
Pub: Entrepreneur Media, Inc.

Description: GoPayments application from Intuit allows mobile telephones to process payments like credit card terminals. The application costs $19.95 a month and can be used on the Internet browsers of mobile telephones.

44355 ■ *Getting Clients and Keeping Clients for Your Service Business*
Pub: Atlantic Publishing Company

Ed: Anne M. Miller; Gail Brett Levine. **Released:** August 28, 2008. **Price:** $24.95 paperback. **Description:** Tips are offered to help any small service business identify customers, brand and grow the business, as well as development of logos, brochures and Websites.

44356 ■ *"Getting In On the Ground Floor" in Entrepreneur (Vol. 37, September 2009, No. 9, pp. 90)*
Pub: Entrepreneur Media, Inc.

Description: Franchise businesses in the United States are listed. Franchise services are mentioned. Statistical data and contact information included.

44357 ■ *"The GHG Quandary: Whose Problem Is It Anyway?" in Canadian Business (Vol. 81, September 15, 2008, No. 14-15, pp. 72)*
Pub: Rogers Media Ltd.

Ed: Matthew McClearn. **Description:** Nongovernmental organizations were able to revoke the permit for Imperial Oil Ltd's Kearl oilsands project on the grounds of its expected greenhouse gas emission but the court's ruling was rendered irrelevant by bureaucratic paper-shuffling shortly after. The idea of an environmental impact assessment as a guide to identify the consequences of a project is also discussed.

44358 ■ *"Give It Your All, and Don't Worry About the Rest" in Inc. (Vol. 33, November 2011, No. 9, pp. 37)*
Pub: Inc. Magazine

Ed: Norm Brodsky. **Description:** In the early stage of a service company, the owners sell themselves to the customers.

44359 ■ *"Give This Pooch a Home" in Advertising Age (Vol. 78, August 13, 2007, No. 32, pp. 4)*
Pub: Crain Communications, Inc.

Ed: Kimberly D. Williams. **Description:** Overview of FlexPetz, a pet-sharing program that targets customers that live in metropolitan areas and travel frequently, who want to have a dog but cannot care for one on a full time basis.

44360 ■ *"Giving Biotech Startups a Hand" in Philadelphia Business Journal (Vol. 28, January 8, 2010, No. 47, pp. 1)*
Pub: American City Business Journals

Ed: John George. **Description:** Elkins Park, Pennsylvania-based BioStrategy Partners is a virtual life sciences incubator that is seeking to improve the dull ranking of Philadelphia in the small business vitality index of life sciences. BioStrategy provides technology and business development services to startup life sciences companies and university-based research projects.

44361 ■ *"Global Pain: Alberta's Gain" in Canadian Business (Vol. 79, August 14, 2006, No. 16-17, pp. 60)*
Pub: Rogers Media

Ed: Jeff Sanford. **Description:** Political problems and conflicts in oil-rich countries like Iran, Venezuela, and Russia among others, which have benefited the petroleum industry in Alberta, is discussed.

44362 ■ *"Good Going, Partners: Energy-Asset Firms Do Their Parents Proud"* in *Barron's (Vol. 89, July 27, 2009, No. 30, pp. M8)*

Pub: Dow Jones & Co., Inc.

Ed: Shirley A. Lazo. **Description:** Four master limited partnerships boosted their dividends. Sunoco Logistics raised theirs by 11.2 percent, El Paso Pipeline by 12 percent, Holly Energy upped their dividends by a penny, and Western Gas hiked their dividend to 31 cents per unit.

44363 ■ *"Good Things Happen When We Buy Local"* in *Crain's Detroit Business (Vol. 24, October 6, 2008, No. 40, pp. 7)*

Pub: Crain Communications, Inc.

Description: Michigan is facing incredibly difficult economic times. One way in which each one of us can help the state and the businesses located here is by purchasing our goods and services from local vendors. The state Agriculture Department projected that if Michigan households earmarked $10 per week in their grocery purchases to made-in-Michigan products, this would generate $30 million a week in economic impact.

44364 ■ *"Grace Puma; Senior Vice-President of Strategic Sourcing, United Airlines"* in *Crain's Chicago Business (May 5, 2008)*

Pub: Crain Communications, Inc.

Ed: John Rosenthal. **Description:** Profile of Grace Puma who is the senior vice-president of strategic sourcing at United Airlines and is responsible for cutting costs at the company in a number of ways including scheduling safety inspections at the same time as routine maintenance, thereby reducing the downtime of each aircraft by five days as well as replacing a third of her staff with outside talent.

44365 ■ *"Grave Concerns"* in *Canadian Business (Vol. 81, July 21 2008, No. 11, pp. 25)*

Pub: Rogers Media Ltd.

Ed: Andrew Nikiforuk. **Description:** Air pollution control regulations to reduce greenhouse gasses have been implemented by the Canadian government. The federal government is planning to construct a carbon funeral industry that will store the global warming gases, however the expenditure for the project will be shifted to the taxpayers. Details of the Bruce Peachy's initiative on how to reduce GHGs are presented.

44366 ■ *"Green Assets Powering Boralex Shares"* in *Globe & Mail (March 30, 2007, pp. B10)*

Pub: CTVglobemedia Publishing Inc.

Ed: Richard Blackwell. **Description:** The impact of econ-friendly power plant portfolio on the stock performance of Kingsey Falls-based Boralex Inc. is analyzed.

44367 ■ *"The Green Industry Jobs Gap"* in *Green Industry Pro (Vol. 23, October 2011)*

Pub: Cygnus Business Media

Ed: Gregg Wartgow. **Description:** According to the U.S. Bureau of Labor Statistics, the landscaping industry employs over 829,000 workers. According to another private study, the industry would employ more if they were able to find more people interested in performing the required work.

44368 ■ *"Greg Stringham"* in *Canadian Business (Vol. 81, March 3, 2008, No. 3, pp. 8)*

Pub: Rogers Media

Ed: Michelle Magnan. **Description:** Canadian Association of Petroleum Producers' Greg Stringham thinks that the new royalty plan will result in companies pulling out their investments for Alberta's conventional oil and gas sector. Stringham adds that Alberta is losing its competitive advantage and companies must study their cost profiles to retrieve that advantage. The effects of the royalty system on Alberta's economy are examined further.

44369 ■ *"Groomers Eye Profit Growth Through Services"* in *Pet Product News (Vol. 64, December 2010, No. 12, pp. 26)*

Pub: BowTie Inc.

Ed: Kathleen M. Mangan. **Description:** Pet groomers can successfully offer add-on services by taking into account insider customer knowledge, store im-

age, and financial analysis in the decision-making process. Many pet groomers have decided to add services such as spa treatments and training due to a slump in the bathing and grooming business. How some pet groomers gained profitability through add-on services is explored.

44370 ■ *"Growing Subscriber Base Fuels Roger's Rosy Outlook for 2007"* in *Globe & Mail (February 16, 2007, pp. B3)*

Pub: CTVglobemedia Publishing Inc.

Ed: Catherine McLean. **Description:** Canada-based Rogers Communications Inc. has projected increased profits for the 2007 fiscal year. The company has increased its market share by 14 percent with fourth quarter revenues of $176 million.

44371 ■ *"Have Tag, Will Travel"* in *Inc. (Vol. 33, November 2011, No. 9, pp. 48)*

Pub: Inc. Magazine

Ed: Abram Brown. **Description:** Truleytag and Boomerangit are provide services to protect luggage while traveling. Turlytag provides brightly colored ID tags and stickers that attach to any item and feature words Return Me along with the company's contact information. Boomerangit's ID tags and labels feature the words Return for Reward along with their information.

44372 ■ *"Hawaii Business 2008 SB Success Awards"* in *Hawaii Business (Vol. 53, February 2008, No. 8, pp. 43)*

Pub: Hawaii Business Publishing

Description: Winners in the Hawaii Business 2008 SB Success Awards are presented; the awards give recognition for Hawaii small businesses with less than 100 employees and are based on four criteria, namely: unique service or product; rapid expansion or sales growth; longevity; and competency in overcoming challenges.

44373 ■ *"Headwinds From the New Sod Slow Aer Lingus"* in *Barron's (Vol. 88, March 10, 2008, No. 10, pp. M6)*

Pub: Dow Jones & Company, Inc.

Ed: Sean Walters; Arindam Nag. **Description:** Aer Lingus faces a drop in its share prices with a falling US market, higher jet fuel prices, and lower long-haul passenger load factors. British media companies Johnston Press and Yell Group are suffering from weaker ad revenue and heavier debt payments due to the credit crunch.

44374 ■ *"The Heat Is On"* in *Crain's Chicago Business (Vol. 31, April 28, 2008, No. 17, pp. 4)*

Pub: Crain Communications, Inc.

Ed: Steve Daniels. **Description:** Discusses Nicor Inc., a natural-gas utility serving 2 million customers in Chicago's suburbs, and its potential acquirers; shares of the company have dropped 17 percent this year making Nicor the second-worst among 31 utilities in an index tracked by Standrd & Poor's. Statistical data included.

44375 ■ *"Hey, You Can't Do That"* in *Green Industry Pro (Vol. 23, September 2011)*

Pub: Cygnus Business Media

Ed: Rod Dickens. **Description:** Manufacturers of landscape equipment are making better use of energy resources, such as the use of fuel-injection systems instead of carburetors, lightweight materials, better lubricants, advanced battery technology, and innovative engine designs.

44376 ■ *"H.I.G. Capital Announces Acquisition of Next Generation Vending"* in *Benzinga.com (October 29, 2011)*

Pub: Benzinga.com

Ed: Benzinga Staff. **Description:** H.I.G. Capital LLC, a leader in global private investments, acquired Next Generation Vending and Food Service Inc. Next Generation is a provider of vending services for corporate and institutional clients in Northeastern United States.

44377 ■ *"Higher Freight Rates Keep CPR Rolling in Profit"* in *Globe & Mail (February 1,*

2006, pp. B3)

Pub: CTVglobemedia Publishing Inc.

Ed: Brent Jang. **Description:** Canadian Pacific Railway Ltd. posted $135.4 million in revenues for fourth quarter 2005. The company's earnings projections for 2006 and workforce reduction plans are presented.

44378 ■ *"Hispanic Business 100 Fastest-Growing Companies"* in *Hispanic Business (July-August 2009, pp. 16-18)*

Pub: Hispanic Business

Ed: Joshua Molina. **Description:** Despite the recession, the 100 fastest growing companies profiled are able to maintain their competitive edge; federal contracts are key to their success. Service companies are at the top of the list and Texas and Florida are the states in which the top are located.

44379 ■ *A History of Small Business in America*

Pub: University of North Carolina Press

Contact: Kate Douglas Torrey, Director

E-mail: kate_torrey@unc.edu

Ed: Mansel G. Blackford. **Released:** May 2003. **Price:** $22.95. **Description:** History of American small business from the colonial era to present, showing how it has played a role in the nation's economic, political, and cultural development across manufacturing, sales, services and farming.

44380 ■ *"Hot For All The Wrong Reasons"* in *Canadian Business (Vol. 81, March 31, 2008, No. 5, pp. 19)*

Pub: Rogers Media

Ed: Andrea Jezovit. **Description:** Soaring platinum prices are due to South Africa's platinum mining industry's safety issues and power supply disruptions that exacerbate the metal's supply problems. South Africa supplies 80 percent of the world's platinum. South Africa's power utility has said that it cannot guarantee the industry's power needs until 2013.

44381 ■ *"Hotel Tax Eyed For Waukesha"* in *The Business Journal-Milwaukee (Vol. 25, August 29, 2008, No. 49, pp. A1)*

Pub: American City Business Journals, Inc.

Ed: Rich Kirchen. **Description:** Midwest Airlines Center chairman Frank Gimbel wants Waukesha County to help in the funding of the $200-million expansion of the convention center through a hotel room tax. The Waukesha hotel industry is expected to oppose the new room tax. Other views and information on the planned new room tax in Waukesha are presented.

44382 ■ *"How Dell Will Dial for Dollars"* in *Austin Business JournalInc. (Vol. 29, December 4, 2009, No. 39, pp. 1)*

Pub: American City Business Journals

Ed: Christopher Calnan. **Description:** Dell Inc. revealed plans to launch a Mini3i smartphone in China which could enable revenue sharing by bundling with wireless service subscription. Dell's smartphone plan is similar to the netbook business, which Dell sold with service provided by AT&T Inc.

44383 ■ *"How to Dominate in Residential Maintenance"* in *Green Industry Pro (Vol. 23, October 2011)*

Pub: Cygnus Business Media

Ed: Gregg Wartgow. **Description:** Lawn care services were ranked among the most expendable consumer expenditures, according to the National Retail Federation data accumulated in early 2011. This makes it critical for any landscape firm to target sales efforts toward higher-income households and higher-value homes.

44384 ■ *"How Growers Buy"* in *Farm Industry News (Vol. 42, January 1, 2009, No. 1)*

Pub: Penton Media Inc.

Contact: John French, President

Ed: Karen McMahon. **Description:** According to a survey regarding the buying habits among large commercial growers, most prefer to purchase from local retailers, customer service is important concerning their decision on who to buy products from, and price and convenience seem to be more important then brand.

44385 ■ *"How Our Picks Beat The Bear"* in *Barron's (Vol. 88, July 14, 2008, No. 28, pp. 18)*
Pub: Dow Jones & Co., Inc.
Ed: Andrew Bary. **Description:** Performance of the stocks that Barron's covered in the first half of 2008 is discussed; some of the worst picks and most rewarding pans have been in the financial sector while the best plays were in the energy, materials, and the transportation sectors.

44386 ■ *"How to Plug in to the Wireless Revolution"* in *Globe & Mail (March 11, 2006, pp. B3)*
Pub: CTVglobemedia Publishing Inc.
Ed: Catherine McLean. **Description:** The plans of president David Dobbin of Toronto Hydro Telecom Inc., to establish WiFi service, are presented.

44387 ■ *"How To Turn Your Efforts Into Results"* in *Green Industry Pro (Vol. 23, September 2011)*
Pub: Cygnus Business Media
Ed: Bob Coulter. **Description:** Working Smarter Training Challenge teaches that leaders are able to carry out solutions directly into their organization, develop skills and drive business results in key areas by creating a culture of energized workers who are able to take ownership of their performance as well as the performance of the company as a whole.

44388 ■ *"Huberman Failing to Keep CTA on Track"* in *Crain's Chicago Business (Vol. 31, April 21, 2008, No. 16, pp. 22)*
Pub: Crain Communications, Inc.
Description: Discusses the deplorable service of CTA, the Chicago Transit Authority, as well as CTA President Ron Huberman who, up until last week had riders hoping he had the management skills necessary to fix the system's problems; Tuesday's event left hundreds of riders trapped for hours and thousands standing on train platforms along the Blue Line waiting for trains that never came.

44389 ■ *"In Surging Oil Industry, Good Fortune Comes In Stages"* in *Barron's (Vol. 88, July 7, 2008, No. 27, pp. 12)*
Pub: Dow Jones & Co., Inc.
Ed: Sandra Ward. **Description:** Shares of US land oil and gas driller Helmerich and Payne, priced at $69 each, are estimated to be at peak levels. The shares are trading at 17 times 2008 earnings and could be in for some profit taking.

44390 ■ *"Industrial Evolution"* in *Entrepreneur (Vol. 35, November 2007, No. 11, pp. 142)*
Pub: Entrepreneur Press
Contact: Perlman Neil, President
Ed: Nichole L. Torres. **Description:** Businesses often target specific customer bases, but it is possible that your business does not fit a particular industry as your services may also be needed in other fields. Details with regard to expanding businesses into other industries are discussed.

44391 ■ *"Ingrian and Channel Management International Sign Distribution Agreement"* in *Canadian Corporate News (May 16, 2007)*
Pub: Comtex News Network Inc.
Description: Channel Management International (CMI), a Canadian channel management and distribution company, and Ingrian Networks, Inc., the leading provider of data privacy solutions, announced a Canadian distribution agreement to resell Ingrian encryption solutions to the Canadian market.

44392 ■ *"Intel to Buy McAfee Security Business for 768B"* in *eWeek (August 19, 2010)*
Pub: Ziff Davis Enterprise
Description: Intel will acquire security giant McAfee for approximately $7.68 billion, whereby McAfee would become a wholly owned subsidiary of Intel and would report to Intel's Software and Services Group.

44393 ■ *"It's Back to Business for the Ravens"* in *Boston Business Journal (Vol. 29, July 29, 2011, No. 12, pp. 1)*
Pub: American City Business Journals Inc.
Ed: Scott Dance. **Description:** The Baltimore Ravens football team has been marketing open sponsorship packages following the end of the National Football League lockout. Team officials are working to get corporate logos and slogans on radio and television commercials and online advertisements.

44394 ■ *"Jack Be Nimble"* in *Business Courier (Vol. 24, October 26, 2008, No. 28, pp. 1)*
Pub: American City Business Journals, Inc.
Ed: Laura Baverman. **Description:** Cincinnati Bell is losing around 47,000 phone lines a year due to the advent of wireless technology and increased competition from cable companies.

44395 ■ *"Jacksonville-based Interline Expanding in Janitorial-Sanitation Market"* in *Florida Times-Union (May 10, 2011)*
Pub: Florida Times-Union
Ed: Mark Basch. **Description:** Interline Brands Inc., located in Jacksonville, Florida, aims to grow its business with two recent acquisitions of firms that distribute janitorial and sanitation products. Interline markets and distributes maintenance, repair and operations products.

44396 ■ *"Janitorial Equipment and Supplies US Market"* in *PR Newswire (October 24, 2011)*
Pub: PR Newswire
Description: United States demand for janitorial equipment and supplies (excluding chemical products) is predicted to rise 2.4 percent per year to $7.6 billion in 2013. New product development will lead to increased sales of higher-value goods in the industry.

44397 ■ *"Juiced on Energy"* in *Barron's (Vol. 88, July 14, 2008, No. 28, pp. 33)*
Pub: Dow Jones & Co., Inc.
Ed: Leslie P. Norton. **Description:** Brad Evans and his team at Heartland Value Plus were able to outperform their peers by significantly undercommitting to financials and overexposing themselves with energy stocks. Brad Evans believes that there is a lot of value left in energy stocks such as natural gas.

44398 ■ *"Just Be Nice"* in *Canadian Business (Vol. 79, October 9, 2006, No. 20, pp. 141)*
Pub: Rogers Media
Ed: Joe Castaldo. **Description:** The customer relationship management strategies on customer retention and satisfaction adopted by WestJet are discussed.

44399 ■ *"Just Hang Up"* in *Barron's (Vol. 88, March 10, 2008, No. 10, pp. 45)*
Pub: Dow Jones & Company, Inc.
Ed: Tiernan Ray. **Description:** Sprint's shares are expected to continue falling while the company attempts to attract subscribers by cutting prices, cutting earnings in the process. The company faces tougher competition from better-financed AT&T and Verizon Communications.

44400 ■ *"Keeping Railcars 'Busy At All Times' At TTX"* in *Crain's Chicago Business (Vol. 31, April 28, 2008, No. 17, pp. 6)*
Pub: Crain Communications, Inc.
Ed: Bob Tita. **Description:** Profile of the president of Chicago railcar pool operator TTX Co. and his business plan for the company which includes improving fleet management and car purchasing through better use of data on railroad demand.

44401 ■ *"Kenyans Embrace Moving Money By Text Message"* in *Chicago Tribune (October 7, 2008)*
Pub: McClatchy-Tribune Information Services
Ed: Laurie Goering. **Description:** Cell phone banking services are becoming more common, especially for foreign residents; customers are able to establish

a virtual cell phone bank account through companies such as M-Pesa which allows their customers to pay bills, withdraw cash, pay merchants or text money to relatives.

44402 ■ *"Kerry Steel to Sell Inventory, Close Business After 30 Years"* in *Crain's Detroit Business (Vol. 24, March 17, 2008, No. 11, pp. 26)*
Pub: Crain Communications, Inc.
Ed: Brent Snavely. **Description:** Kerry Steel Inc. has confirmed that it is selling all of its inventory and equipment and is going out of business; the company, which was once one of the largest steel service centers in the Midwest, has sustained financial losses and is in violation of its loan agreements.

44403 ■ *"The King of Kincardine"* in *Canadian Business (Vol. 79, October 9, 2006, No. 20, pp. 101)*
Pub: Rogers Media
Ed: Paul Webster. **Description:** Motives of Duncan Hawthorne, president and chief executive officer of Bruce Power Ltd., behind investing in nuclear power plant in Ontario, Canada through private financing are discussed.

44404 ■ *"Know It All Finds Applicants are Stretching the Truth"* in *Philadelphia Business Journal (Vol. 28, September 11, 2009, No. 30, pp. 1)*
Pub: American City Business Journals
Ed: Athena D. Merritt. **Description:** Know It All Background Research Services has reported that discrepancies in background checks reached 19.8 percent in 2009. Reports show that 42 percent of the discrepancies involve lying about previous employment, and 37 percent involve education information. Marc Bourne, the company's vice president, believes that employers have cause to be concerned.

44405 ■ *"Knox County Schools Debate Outsourcing Janitorial Services"* in *(March 29, 2011)*
Pub: Knoxville News Sentinel
Ed: Lola Alapo. **Description:** Custodial services of Knox County Schools in Tennessee may be outsourced in move to save money for the school district. Details of the proposed program are included.

44406 ■ *"Labor of Love"* in *Green Industry Pro (Vol. 23, March 2011, No. 3, pp. 14)*
Pub: Cygnus Business Media
Ed: Gregg Wartgow. **Description:** Profile of CLS Landscape Management in Chino, California and its owner who started the company when he was 21 years old. Kevin Davis built his landscape firm into a $20 million a year business without using any dedicated salesperson.

44407 ■ *"Leasing Midway; Look for Higher Parking Fees, More Retail Under Private Airport Operator"* in *Crain's Chicago Business (May 5, 2008)*
Pub: Crain Communications, Inc.
Ed: Paul Merrion. **Description:** According to experts, bids for the first privatization of a major U.S. airport could run as high as $3.5 billion. Information-gathering and negotiations will soon get under way with some or all of the six major international investor groups that recently expressed interest in running Midway.

44408 ■ *"Lifebank Grants Stock Options"* in *Canadian Corporate News (May 16, 2007)*
Pub: Comtex News Network Inc.
Description: Lifebank, a biomedical service company that provides processing cryogenic storage of umbilical cord blood stem cells, announced that, under its stock option plan, it has granted incentive stock options to directors, officers, and consultants of the company.

44409 ■ *"Live and Learn: Lionel Hurtubise"* in *Canadian Business (Vol. 80, January 29, 2007, No. 3, pp. 64)*
Pub: Rogers Media
Ed: Andy Holloway. **Description:** The views of Lionel Hurtubise, the chairman of SR Telecom, PolarSat, and STP, on his life and the growth of the Canadian telecommunications industry are presented.

44410 ■ *"Local Firms Will Feel Impact Of Wall St. Woes"* in *The Business Journal-Milwaukee (Vol. 25, September 19, 2008, No. 52, pp. A1)*
Pub: American City Business Journals, Inc.
Ed: Rich Kirchen. **Description:** Wall Street's crisis is expected to affect businesses in Wisconsin, in terms of decreased demand for services and products and increased financing costs. Businesses in Milwaukee area may face higher interest rates and tougher loan standards. The potential impacts of the Wall Street crisis on local businesses are examined further.

44411 ■ *"Local Hotels Brace for Downturn"* in *Crain's Chicago Business (Vol. 31, March 31, 2008, No. 13, pp. 3)*
Pub: Crain Communications, Inc.
Ed: Bob Tita. **Description:** Chicago hotels are seeing a noticeable drop in business-related guests so far this year due to a slumping national economy, tighter corporate expense budgets and higher airfares.

44412 ■ *"Locally Based Stocks Escape Worst of Market's Turmoil"* in *Crain's Detroit Business (Vol. 24, September 22, 2008, No. 38, pp. 4)*
Pub: Crain Communications Inc.
Ed: Daniel Duggan. **Description:** Locally-based companies did not take as big a hit as might be expected with the shock to the financial markets last week; this is due mainly to the fact that the region does not have heavy exposure to energy or capital markets.

44413 ■ *"A Look Ahead Into 2007"* in *Canadian Business (Vol. 80, December 25, 2006, No. 1, pp. 40)*
Pub: Rogers Media
Description: The 2007 forecasts for various industrial sectors like telecom, information technology, manufacturing, retail, financial and energy among others is discussed.

44414 ■ *"Losses Threaten Comp Care's Future Viability"* in *The Business Journal-Serving Greater Tampa Bay (Vol. 28, August 15, 2008, No. 34)*
Pub: American City Business Journals, Inc.
Ed: Margie Manning. **Description:** Comprehensive Care Corp. expressed that it may have to cease or drastically curtail its operations if it won't be able to raise additional funding in the next two or three months. The firm, which provides managed behavioral health care services, is also believed to be exploring a sale. Other views and information on Comprehensive Care's finances and plans are presented.

44415 ■ *Low-Budget Online Marketing for Small Business*
Pub: International Self-Counsel Press, Limited
Ed: Holly Berkley. **Released:** July 2005. **Price:** $14.95. **Description:** Low-cost, effective online marketing tips for small companies selling products or services over the Internet.

44416 ■ *Low-Budget Online Marketing for Small Business*
Pub: Self-Counsel Press, Incorporated
Ed: Holley Berkley. **Released:** July 2005. **Price:** $14.95, CD-Rom. **Description:** Low-cost, effective online marketing tips for small companies selling products or services over the Internet.

44417 ■ *"Lower Prices No Shoo-In as Telcos Near Deregulation"* in *Globe & Mail (March 28, 2007, pp. B1)*
Pub: CTVglobemedia Publishing Inc.
Ed: Catherine McLean. **Description:** The fall in market share and low quality of service among other issues that may disallow telecommunication industries in Canada from setting their phone rates is discussed.

44418 ■ *"Madeleine Paquin"* in *Canadian Business (Vol. 81, March 3, 2008, No. 3, pp. 92)*
Pub: Rogers Media
Ed: Regan Ray. **Description:** Madeleine Paquin, chief executive officer and president of Logistec Corp., talks about how she balanced her career and

her life as a mother to two girls. Paquin thinks that working mothers need to focus on some things instead of trying to do everything. Her career in the marine cargo handling industry is also discussed.

44419 ■ *"Making Visitors Out Of Listeners"* in *Hawaii Business (Vol. 54, July 2008, No. 1, pp. 18)*
Pub: Hawaii Business Publishing
Ed: Casey Chin. **Description:** Japanese workers are subscribing to the Official Hawaii Podcast in iTunes, which offers a free 20-minute, Japanese-language audio content on different topics, such as dining reviews and music from local artists. The concept is a way to attract Japanese travelers to come to Hawaii.

44420 ■ *Marketing for Entrepreneurs*
Pub: FT Press
Ed: Jurgen Wolff. **Released:** December 9, 2010. **Price:** $24.99. **Description:** This text identifies marketing as the entire process of researching, creating, distributing and selling a product or service. It isn't about theory and metrics, rather it is a practical guide that starts with the basics of all marketing aspects.

44421 ■ *"Maryland Senate Gets Read to Talk Taxes"* in *Boston Business Journal (Vol. 29, July 1, 2011, No. 8, pp. 1)*
Pub: American City Business Journals Inc.
Ed: Scott Dance. **Description:** Maryland Senate Budget and Taxation Committee will meet July 26, 2011 to discuss some of business community's concerns including sales tax expansion to cover services, a restructuring of the corporate income tax brackets and an answer to questions regarding transportation funding project.

44422 ■ *"May I Handle That For You?"* in *Inc. (March 2008, pp. 40, 42)*
Pub: Gruner & Jahr USA Publishing
Ed: Taylor Mallory. **Description:** According to a recent survey, 53 percent of all companies outsource a portion of their human resources responsibilities. Ceridian, Administaff, Taleo, KnowledgeBank, and CheckPoint HR are among the companies profiled.

44423 ■ *"mChip: Claros Diagnostics"* in *Inc. (Vol. 33, November 2011, No. 9, pp. 42)*
Pub: Inc. Magazine
Ed: Christine Lagorio. **Description:** Harvard University researchers have developed a device called the mChip that produces accurate blood tests in about 10 minutes. Plans to apply for FDA approval for the mChip in the US should happen in 2012.

44424 ■ *"Mergers Mean Woe for Fliers; Airline Hookups Boost Fares, Diminish Service"* in *Crain's Chicago Business (April 21, 2008)*
Pub: Crain Communications, Inc.
Ed: John Pletz. **Description:** Discusses the impact airline mergers will have on customer service, pricing and business travel, particularly at Chicago's O'Hare International Airport.

44425 ■ *"Microsoft Clicks Into High Speed"* in *Hispanic Business (Vol. 30, July-August 2008, No. 7-8, pp. 54)*
Pub: Hispanic Business, Inc.
Ed: Derek Reveron. **Description:** Microsoft's diversity hiring and vendor diversity program to capture more Hispanic consumer and business-to-business market is described. One of the main goals of these programs is to hire more Hispanic executives and managers who will help the company develop and market products and services that will appeal and benefit Hispanic consumers.

44426 ■ *"Midwest Looks 'Back to the Future"* in *The Business Journal-Milwaukee (Vol. 25, July 18, 2008, No. 43, pp. A1)*
Pub: American City Business Journals, Inc.
Ed: Rich Rovito. **Description:** Midwest Air Group Inc. announced plans to reduce their work force by 40 percent or 1,200 employees after an earlier announcement of a drastic fleet reduction. These steps

are being taken by the company in an effort to avoid filing bankruptcy since this would cost the airline millions of dollars in legal and other professional fees.

44427 ■ *"Midwest Seeks Concessions From Creditors"* in *The Business Journal-Milwaukee (Vol. 25, July 25, 2008, No. 44, pp. A1)*
Pub: American City Business Journals, Inc.
Ed: Rich Rovito. **Description:** Midwest Airlines Inc. is turning to creditors and lease holders for the financial aspect of its restructuring, which involves going back to serving popular business destinations. Chief executive officer Timothy believes that the company can survive in a niche market as long as it provides quality service. He discusses Midwest's restructuring plan.

44428 ■ *"Milton Touts ACE Unit to Would-Be Buyers"* in *Globe & Mail (February 10, 2007, pp. B6)*
Pub: CTVglobemedia Publishing Inc.
Ed: Brent Jang. **Description:** The decision of Air Canada chairman Robert Milton to sell Air Canada Technical Services unit is presented. ACE Aviation Holdings Inc. is the parent company of Air Canada.

44429 ■ *"A Mixed-Bag Quarter"* in *Barron's (Vol. 88, July 7, 2008, No. 27, pp. 19)*
Pub: Dow Jones & Co., Inc.
Ed: Shirley A. Lazo. **Description:** Seven component companies of the Dow Jones Industrial Average increased their dividend payouts in the second quarter of 2008 despite the weak performance of the index. Five companies in the Dow Jones Transportation index and three in the Dow Jones Utilities also increased their dividends.

44430 ■ *"Mobile: Juanes Fans Sing for Sprint"* in *Advertising Age (Vol. 79, November 3, 2008, No. 41, pp. 22)*
Pub: Crain Communications, Inc.
Ed: Laurel Wentz. **Description:** Marketers are appealing to the Hispanic market since they are more prone to use their cell phones to respond to contests, download videos, ringtones, or other data activity. Sprint recently sponsored a contest inviting people to sing like Colombian megastar Juanes; the participants filmed and sent their videos using their cell phones rather than laptops or camcorders illustrating the Hispanic overindex on mobile-phone technology. The contest generated hundreds of thousands of dollars in additional fee revenue, as monthly downloads increased 63 percent.

44431 ■ *"Monopoly Money Madness"* in *Canadian Business (Vol. 81, March 17, 2008, No. 4, pp. 9)*
Pub: Rogers Media
Description: Enbridge was given permission by the Ontario Energy Board to collect $22 million it spent on an out-of-court settlement for charging unfair fees from 1994 to 2002. Customers are essentially being gouged twice in this scenario. The monopoly of Enbridge should end and the consumers should not have to pay for the system's faults.

44432 ■ *"Monsanto Acquires Targeted-Pest Control Technology Start-Up; Terms Not Disclosed"* in *Benzinga.com (, 2011)*
Pub: Benzinga.com
Ed: Benzinga Staff. **Description:** Monsanto Company acquired Beelogics, a firm that researches and develops biological tools that control pests and diseases. Research includes a product that will help protect bee health.

44433 ■ *"Montgomery & Barnes: a Service-Disabled, Veteran-Owned Small Business"* in *Underground Construction (Vol. 65, October 2010, No. 10)*
Pub: Oildom Publishing Company of Texas Inc.
Description: Gary Montgomery, chairman of Montgomery and Barnes announced that President Wendell (Buddy) Barnes is now majority owner, thus making the Houston-based civil engineering and consulting services firm, eligible to quality as a Service-Disabled Veteran-Owned Small Business (SDVOSB).

44434 ■ *"The Moral Legitimacy of NGOs as Partners of Corporations"* in *Business Ethics Quarterly (Vol. 21, October 2011, No. 4, pp. 579)*
Pub: Society for Business Ethics
Contact: Jeff Frooman, Executive Director
Ed: Dorothea Baur, Guido Palazzo. **Description:** Partnerships between companies and NGOs have received considerable attention in CSR in the past years. However, the role of NGO legitimacy in such partnerships has thus far been neglected. The article argues that NGOs assume a status as special stakeholders of corporations which act on behalf of the common good. This role requires a particular focus on their moral legitimacy. An introduction to the conceptual framework analyzing the moral legitimacy of NGOs along three dimensions, building on the theory of deliberative democracy.

44435 ■ *"More Callers Are Cutting Their Landlines"* in *Chicago Tribune (December 30, 2008)*
Pub: McClatchy-Tribune Information Services
Ed: Eric Benderoff. **Description:** Despite sporadic outages for cell phone users, the trend for consumers to cut out the expense of a landline does not appear to be slowing; experts believe that the recession will further increase the number of consumers who decide to go completely wireless.

44436 ■ *"Most Popular Tools? The Survey Says"* in *Contractor (Vol. 57, February 2010, No. 2, pp. 1)*
Pub: Penton Media, Inc.
Ed: Robert P. Mader. **Description:** According to a survey of individuals in the field, mechanical contractors are purchasing more of their tools at home centers and they are also increasingly working in the service, repair, and retrofit markets. The survey also found that the reciprocating saw is the most used corded power tool. Additional purchasing habits of mechanical contractors are listed.

44437 ■ *"My Favorite Tool for Managing Expenses"* in *Inc. (Volume 32, December 2010, No. 10, pp. 60)*
Pub: Inc. Magazine
Ed: J.J. McCorvey. **Description:** Web-based service called Expensify is outlined. The service allows companies to log expenses while away from the office using the service's iPhone application.

44438 ■ *"A Nasty Russian Tale"* in *Canadian Business (Vol. 81, March 3, 2008, No. 3, pp. 85)*
Pub: Rogers Media
Ed: Andrew Nikiforuk. **Description:** Billionaires Alex Shnaider and Michael Shtaif entered a partnership for an oil venture which ended in a slew of litigations. Cases of breach of contract, injurious falsehood and other related lawsuits were filed against Shnaider. Details of the lawsuits and the other parties involved in the disputes are presented.

44439 ■ *"Network Like A Boy Scout"* in *Women Entrepreneur (January 15, 2009)*
Pub: Entrepreneur Media Inc.
Ed: Merrily Orsini. **Description:** Marketing for businesses that provide products or services that people only seek during emergencies or natural disasters such as hurricanes can be a challenge; tips for branding such businesses, networking and establishing a strong customer base that will refer your business to others are given.

44440 ■ *"New Boss at Nortel Mines GE for New Executives"* in *Globe & Mail (February 6, 2006, pp. B1)*
Pub: CTVglobemedia Publishing Inc.
Ed: Catherine McLean. **Description:** Chief executive officer Mike Zafirovski of Nortel Networks Corp. appoints executives Dennis Carey, Joel Hackney and Don McKenn of GE Electric Co. The managerial abilities of Mike are discussed.

44441 ■ *"The New Face of Detroit"* in *Inc. (Vol. 33, October 2011, No. 8, pp. 6)*
Pub: Inc. Magazine
Ed: Elizabeth Sile. **Description:** Basketball legend Magic Johnson has joined Detroit Venture Partners and Detroit will be one of the firm's three inaugural

cities to host fellows from Venture for America, a new organization that places recent college graduates in start-up companies.

44442 ■ *"New Sprint Phone Whets Appetite for Applications"* in *The Business Journal-Serving Metropolitan Kansas City (Vol. 26, July 25, 2008)*
Pub: American City Business Journals, Inc.
Ed: Suzanna Stagemeyer. **Description:** Firms supporting the applications of the new Samsung Instinct, which was introduced by Sprint Nextel Corp. in June 2008, have reported usage rates increase for their products. Handmark, whose mobile services Pocket Express comes loaded with Instinct, has redirected employees to meet the rising demand for the services. Other views and information on Instinct, are presented.

44443 ■ *"New Tax Sends Biz Scrambling; Service Levy Will Affect 16,000 Businesses"* in *Crain's Detroit Business (October 8, 2007)*
Pub: Crain Communications Inc. - Detroit
Ed: Amy Lane. **Description:** Legislation that imposes a tax on services in Michigan has business leaders upset. The new law exerts a 6 percent tax on 57 categories of services that affects 16,000 businesses in the state.

44444 ■ *"A New Way to Tell When to Fold"* in *Barron's (Vol. 88, July 7, 2008, No. 27, pp. 27)*
Pub: Dow Jones & Co., Inc.
Ed: Theresa W. Carey. **Description:** Overview of the Online trading company SmartStops, a firm that aims to tell investors when to sell the shares of a particular company. The company's Web site categorizes stocks as moving up, down, or sideways, and calculates exit points for individual stocks based on an overall market trend.

44445 ■ *Niche and Grow Rich*
Pub: Entrepreneur Press
Ed: Jennifer Basye Sander; Peter Sander. **Released:** 2003. **Description:** Consultants share insight to entrepreneurs wishing to find a profitable niche market. Authors write that good niche businesses are easy to start and easy to defend from competitors. They also report that finding a successful niche can attract and maintain good customers who are willing to pay more for unique goods and services.

44446 ■ *"Niche Markets, Green Will Be Okay in 2010"* in *Contractor (Vol. 57, January 2010, No. 1, pp. 1)*
Pub: Penton Media, Inc.
Ed: Robert P. Mader . **Description:** Mechanical contractors will see most of their work stemming from niche markets, such as green work, as well as service work in 2010. It is said that things will turn around for the industry in 2012 and 2013 and one forecast believes that anything outside of the institutional or more public sector work could be down 15 to 30 percent.

44447 ■ *"Nighttime Shuttle to Connect Detroit, Ferndale, Royal Oak"* in *Crain's Detroit Business (Vol. 24, October 6, 2008, No. 40, pp. 24)*
Pub: Crain Communications, Inc.
Ed: Nancy Kaffer. **Description:** With hopes of bridging the social gap between the cities and suburbs, Chris Ramos has launched The Night Move, a new shuttle service that will ferry passengers between Royal Oak, Ferndale and downtown Detroit. The cost for a round trip ticket is $12.

44448 ■ *"Nortel Makes Customers Stars in New Campaign"* in *Brandweek (Vol. 49, April 21, 2008, No. 16, pp. 8)*
Pub: VNU Business Media, Inc.
Ed: Mike Beirne. **Description:** Nortel has launched a new television advertising campaign in which the business-to-business communications technology provider cast senior executives in 30-second TV case studies that show how Nortel's technology helped their businesses innovate.

44449 ■ *"Nortel Outlook Shows Recovery Won't Come Quickly"* in *Globe & Mail (March 20, 2007, pp. B4)*
Pub: CTVglobemedia Publishing Inc.
Ed: Catherine McLean. **Description:** The forecast about the unlikely recovery of Nortel Networks Corp. from decrease in its share prices is discussed.

44450 ■ *"Nothing Plus Nothing"* in *Entrepreneur (Vol. 37, October 2009, No. 10, pp. 25)*
Pub: Entrepreneur Media, Inc.
Ed: Joe Robinson. **Description:** Jason Fried and David Heinemeier Hansson of Web application firm 37signals believe that free Web services will never become profitable in the long term. They believe that Web service providers should charge a fair price on such services.

44451 ■ *"NovAtel Inc. Licensed to Sell Galileo Receivers"* in *Canadian Corporate News (May 14, 2007)*
Pub: Comtex News Network Inc.
Description: NovAtel Inc., a leading provider of precision Global Navigation Satellite System (GNSS) components and subsystems that afford its customers rapid integration of precise positioning technology, has received a license valid for ten years that allows NovAtel to sell receivers that track Galileo signals.

44452 ■ *"Nuclear Plans May Stall on Uranium Shortage"* in *Globe & Mail (March 22, 2007, pp. B4)*
Pub: CTVglobemedia Publishing Inc.
Ed: Shawn McCarthy. **Description:** The poor investments in uranium production and enrichment despite growing demand for it for nuclear energy is discussed.

44453 ■ *"Oce Business Services: Discovery Made Easy"* in *Information Today (Vol. 26, February 2009, No. 2, pp. 31)*
Pub: Information Today, Inc.
Ed: Barbara Brynko. **Description:** Oce Business Services provides document process management and electronic discovery through its CaseData repertoire of legal management solutions.

44454 ■ *"OK, Bring in the Lawyers"* in *Crain's Chicago Business (Vol. 31, November 17, 2008, No. 46, pp. 26)*
Pub: Crain Communications, Inc.
Ed: Daniel Rome Levine. **Description:** Bankruptcy attorneys are finding the economic and credit crisis a benefit for their businesses due to the high number of business owners and mortgage holders that are need of their services. One Chicago firm is handling ten times the number of cases they did the previous year and of that about 80 percent of their new clients are related to the real estate sector.

44455 ■ *"The Old Railway is on a Roll"* in *Globe & Mail (January 26, 2006, pp. B1)*
Pub: CTVglobemedia Publishing Inc.
Description: The reasons behind 5 percent rise in shares for Canadian National Railway Co. are presented.

44456 ■ *"Omniplex on the Case"* in *Black Enterprise (Vol. 37, December 2006, No. 5, pp. 38)*
Pub: Earl G. Graves Publishing Co. Inc.
Ed: Glenn Townes. **Description:** Office of Personnel Management in Washington D.C. recently awarded a service contract to Omniplex World Services Corp. Virginia-based, The Chantilly, will perform security investigations and background checks on current and prospective federal employees and military personnel and contractors.

44457 ■ *"On Policy: Where Talk is Cheap"* in *Canadian Business (Vol. 80, January 29, 2007, No. 3, pp. 19)*
Pub: Rogers Media
Ed: Jack Mintz. **Description:** The comparative analysis of the telecommunications policy of Canada and the United States of America is presented. The methods of improving Canada's telecommunications policy are discussed.

44458 ■ *"On Target" in Canadian Business (Vol. 81, July 22, 2008, No. 12-13, pp. 45)*
Pub: Rogers Media Ltd.
Ed: Calvin Leung. **Description:** Companies such as LavalifePRIME, a dating website devoted to singles 45 and older, discuss the value of marketing and services aimed at Canada's older consumers. One-third of Canada's 33 million people are 50-plus, controlling 77 percent of the countries wealth.

44459 ■ *"Open Skies: Opportunity, Challenge for Airlines" in Crain's Chicago Business (April 21, 2008)*
Pub: Crain Communications, Inc.
Ed: Paul Merrion. **Description:** Discusses the new aviation agreement between Europe and the United States known as Open Skies; the pact creates opportunities for U.S. carriers to fly to new destinations in Europe from more U.S. cities; it also allows carriers to fly between European cities, something they have not been able to do until now.

44460 ■ *"Open the Telecom Market" in Canadian Business (Vol. 80, April 23, 2007, No. 9, pp. 80)*
Pub: Rogers Media
Description: The effects of federal telecommunication law on foreign investments in telecommunication industry are presented.

44461 ■ *"Optima Public Relations Gains Partners" in Alaska Business Monthly (Vol. 27, October 2011, No. 10, pp. 10)*
Pub: Alaska Business Publishing Company
Ed: Nancy Pounds. **Description:** OPrima Public Relations has partnered with Gogerty Marriott of Seattle and Seattle Design Group.

44462 ■ *"Optimal Awarded US $256 Thousand Contract to Conduct LiDAR Survey for a Major Electric Utility in the Southwest" in Canadian Corporate News*
Pub: Comtex News Network Inc.
Description: Optimal Geomatics, a company specializing in the science and technology of analyzing, gathering, interpreting, distributing, and using geographic information, was awarded a new contract from a long-standing electric utility customer in the Southwest to conduct a LiDAR survey for a part of the utility's overhead transmission line system.

44463 ■ *"Ordering Pizza Hut From Your Facebook Page?" in Advertising Age (Vol. 79, November 10, 2008, No. 42, pp. 50)*
Pub: Crain Communications, Inc.
Ed: Emily Bryson York. **Description:** Fast-food chains are experimenting with delivery/takeout services via social networks such as Facebook and iPhone applications. This also allows the chains to build valuable databases of their customers.

44464 ■ *"OSHA Proposes Historic Safety Penalty on BP" in Workforce Management (Vol. 88, November 16, 2009, No. 12, pp. 8)*
Pub: Crain Communications Inc.
Ed: Mark Schoeff Jr. **Description:** Labor Secretary Hilda Solis has warned that she aims to toughen the enforcement of workplace laws; OSHA, the Occupational Safety and Health Administration, an agency within the Department of Labor, is penalizing BP Products North America Inc. for their failure to improve workplace safety.

44465 ■ *"Our Gadget of the Week: Easy as a Snap" in Barron's (Vol. 90, September 13, 2010, No. 37, pp. 35)*
Pub: Barron's Editorial & Corporate Headquarters
Ed: Jay Palmer. **Description:** SanMyPhotos.com offers a service whereby people can receive an empty box they can fill with photos then send back to the company to be stored digitally. The photos are returned to the customer with a disc containing the digital photographs. The service costs $150 for one box and $300 for three boxes.

44466 ■ *"Owning the Right Risks" in Harvard Business Review (Vol. 86, September 2008, No. 9, pp. 102)*
Pub: Harvard Business School Press
Ed: Kevin Bueler; Andrew Freeman; Ron Hulme. **Description:** TXU Corp. is used to illustrate methods for successful risk management. The electric utility's practices include determining which risks are natural, embedding risk in all processes and decisions, and organizing corporate governance around risk.

44467 ■ *"Panel to Call for Reduced Restraints on Telecom Sector" in Globe & Mail (March 17, 2006, pp. B1)*
Pub: CTVglobemedia Publishing Inc.
Ed: Simon Tuck. **Description:** A federal panel called to adopt a more market-friendly approach to the lucrative telecommunications sector in Canada. Details of the report are presented.

44468 ■ *"Panel Calls for 'Fundamental' Change to Telecom Regulation" in Globe & Mail (March 23, 2006, pp. B1)*
Pub: CTVglobemedia Publishing Inc.
Ed: Catherine McLean. **Description:** A federal panel review at Ottawa called for a shakeup of regulations and policies that govern telecommunications companies to contend with sweeping technological changes. Details of the panel review are presented.

44469 ■ *"Patients to Elect to Cut Care" in The Business Journal-Serving Metropolitan Kansas City (Vol. 27, November 21, 2008, No. 11, pp. 1)*
Pub: American City Business Journals, Inc.
Ed: Rob Roberts. **Description:** Patients in Kansas City, Missouri are cutting down on health care services due to the economic crisis. A decline in diagnostic procedures has been observed at Northland Cardiology. Elective reconstructive procedures have also been reduced by 25 percent. Additional information and statistics regarding the healthcare sector is included.

44470 ■ *"PDAs Are Great - As Long As You Can Find Them" in Crain's Chicago Business (Vol. 31, May 5, 2008, No. 18, pp. 41)*
Pub: Crain Communications, Inc.
Ed: Jennifer Olvera. **Description:** Discusses a new service from Global Lost & Found Inc. in which after paying a one-time fee, customers receive a label with an identification number and a toll free phone number so if they lose a gadget such as a cell phone, PDA or laptop the finder can return the device and are rewarded with a gift card.

44471 ■ *"PDX Bucks National Trend" in The Business Journal-Portland (Vol. 25, August 1, 2008, No. 21, pp. 1)*
Pub: American City Business Journals, Inc.
Ed: Erik Siemers. **Description:** Portland International Airport could face problems as air carriers are planning to reduce capacity at the airport. The airport is showing signs of growth despite the slowdown in the airline industry. Other airlines that are planning to reduce seating capacity at the airport are also presented.

44472 ■ *"The Phone-Service Test" in Canadian Business (Vol. 79, October 9, 2006, No. 20, pp. 137)*
Pub: Rogers Media
Ed: Rachel Pulfer. **Description:** Suggestions to improve the customer services provided by airlines through call centers are discussed.

44473 ■ *"Pioneering Strategies for Entrepreneurial Success" in Business Horizons (Vol. 51, January-February 2008, No. 1, pp. 21)*
Pub: Elsevier Advanced Technology Publications
Ed: Candida G. Brush. **Description:** Entrepreneurs are known for new products, services, processes, markets and industries. In order to achieve success, they have to develop a clear vision, creatively manage finances, and use social skills to persuade others to commit to the venture. Pioneering strategies and their implementation are examined.

44474 ■ *"Pioneers Get All The Perks" in Canadian Business (Vol. 81, March 3, 2008, No. 3, pp. 18)*
Pub: Rogers Media
Description: Suncor Energy Inc. will face royalty payments from 25% to 30% of net profits as it signs a new deal with Alberta. Biovail Corp., meanwhile, is under a U.S. grand jury investigation for supposed improprieties in Cardizem LA heart drug launch. The Conference Board of Canada's proposal to impose taxes on greenhouse gas emissions and other developments in the business community are discussed.

44475 ■ *"Plans for Coal-Fired Electricity Could Go Up in Smoke" in Globe & Mail (March 5, 2007, pp. B7)*
Pub: CTVglobemedia Publishing Inc.
Ed: Steve James. **Description:** The coal-fired power project initiated by Texas-based utility company TXU Corp. is receiving legal challenges from green groups. The possible disasters caused by the coal-fired plant are presented.

44476 ■ *"Poisoning Relationships: Perceived Unfairness in Channels of Distribution" in Journal of Marketing (Vol. 75, May 2011, No. 3, pp. 99)*
Pub: American Marketing Association
Ed: Stephen A. Samaha, Robert W. Palmatier, Rajiv P. Dant. **Description:** The effects of perceived unfairness on the relationships among members of distribution channels are examined. Perceived unfairness is found to directly damage relationships, aggravate the negative effects of conflict and opportunism, and undermine the benefits of the contract.

44477 ■ *"Poor Economy Inspires Rich Alternatives In a Modern, and Tax-Free, Twist on Bartering" in Houston Chronicle (June 7, 2010)*
Pub: Houston Chronicle Publishing Company
Ed: Michael Rubinkam. **Description:** Time banking helps individuals and firms receive goods or services by depositing time dollars into a bank reserved for receipt of goods and services.

44478 ■ *"Population Growing Faster Than Retail, Service Sector" in Crain's New York Business (Vol. 24, January 14, 2008, No. 2, pp. 30)*
Pub: Crain Communications, Inc.
Ed: Andrew Marks. **Description:** Downtown Manhattan is seeing more residential development; however, as more families call the area home the need for more retail and services is becoming evident.

44479 ■ *"Post-Prison Center Idea Rankles OTR" in Business Courier (Vol. 26, November 27, 2009, No. 31, pp. 1)*
Pub: American City Business Journals, Inc.
Ed: Lucy May. **Description:** Cincinnati officials and community leaders oppose Firetree Ltd.'s plan to launch a residential program for federal offenders near the School for the Creative and Performing Arts in Over-the-Rhine. Firetree, a Pennsylvania-based reentry center services firm, proposed a five-year contract with the Federal Bureau of Prisons based on a letter to Cincinnati Police Chief Thomas Streicher.

44480 ■ *"Powder River Reports First Quarter Revenues Over 5 Million" in Canadian Corporate News (May 16, 2007)*
Pub: Comtex News Network Inc.
Description: Financial report for Powder River Basin Gas Corp., a revenue generating producer, marketer, and acquirer of crude oil and natural gas properties. Statistical data included.

44481 ■ *"The Power Brokers" in Crain's Chicago Business (Vol. 31, April 28, 2008, No. 17, pp. 41)*
Pub: Crain Communications, Inc.
Ed: Samantha Stainburn. **Description:** Profile of BlueStar Energy Services Inc., one of the first suppliers to cash in on the deregulation f the electricity market by the Illinois Legislature; last year BlueStar's revenue was $171.1 million, up from $600,000 in 2002, the year the company was founded.

44482 ■ *"The Price of Profitability" in Green Industry Pro (Vol. 23, March 2011, No. 3, pp. 18)*
Pub: Cygnus Business Media
Ed: Tony Bass. **Description:** Profit Builder Process is used to help landscaping companies be more competitive. Landscape contractors report pricing

among their largest challenges and although the economy is improving, homeowners are paying closer attention to quality and service.

44483 ■ *"Pride Lands Janitorial Work at New Terminal" in Sacramento Business Journal (Vol. 28, June 10, 2011, No. 15, pp. 1)*
Pub: Sacramento Business Journal
Ed: Kelly Johnson. **Description:** Pride Industries Inc. won the five-year $9.4 million contract to clean the Sacramento International Airport's new Terminal B, which will open in fall 2011. The nonprofit organization posts a revenue of $191 million for 2011 and currently employs more than 2,400 people with disabilities. The contract is expected to provide savings of over $3 million a year to the airport.

44484 ■ *"Prime-Time Exposure" in Inc. (March 2008, pp. 66, 68)*
Pub: Gruner & Jahr USA Publishing
Ed: Adam Bluestein. **Description:** Product placement in television shows has increase sales for many companies. Tips for placing products or services into TV shows are explained: consider hiring an agency, target efforts, dream up a plot point, be ready to go on short notice, and work the niches.

44485 ■ *Professional Services Marketing: How the Best Firms Build Premier Brands*
Pub: John Wiley & Sons, Inc.
Ed: Mike Schultz, John Doerr. **Released:** July 27, 2009. **Price:** $27.95. **Description:** Research based on best practices and processes for the professional services industry is presented. The book covers five key areas: creating a custom marketing and growth strategy, establishing a brand, implementing a marketing communications program, developing a lead strategy, and winning new clients.

44486 ■ *"Put Power in Your Direct Mail Campaigns" in Contractor (Vol. 56, September 2009, No. 9, pp. 64)*
Pub: Penton Media, Inc.
Ed: Matt Michel. **Description:** Advice on how members of the United States plumbing industry should manage direct mail marketing campaigns are offered. Determining the purpose of a campaign is recommended. Focusing on a single message, product or service is also encouraged.

44487 ■ *"Put Your Heating Cap On.." in Indoor Comfort Marketing (Vol. 70, September 2011, No. 9, pp. 26)*
Pub: Industry Publications Inc.
Ed: George Carey. **Description:** Tools and techniques for HVAC/R technicians servicing boilers are outlined.

44488 ■ *"Putting the Service-Profit Chain to Work" in Harvard Business Review (Vol. 86, July-August 2008, No. 8, pp. 118)*
Pub: Harvard Business School Press
Ed: James L. Heskett; Thomas O. Jones; Gary W. Loveman; W. Earl Sasser Jr.; Leonard A. Schlesinger. **Description:** Advice is given on how to foster profitability in service businesses. Topics include the link between employee satisfaction and customer satisfaction, internal service quality, external service value, and revenue growth.

44489 ■ *"Q&A" in Canadian Business (Vol. 81, July 22, 2008, No. 12-13, pp. 8)*
Pub: Rogers Media Ltd.
Ed: Michelle Magnan. **Description:** Interview with Scott Saxberg who discusses Crescent Point Energy Trust's discovery of resources in Saskatchewan and believes that this is a once-in-a-lifetime type of event. Crescent Point holds 75 percent of its resources in Saskatchewan; this new finding being considered the second-largest pool discovered since the 1950s. Saxberg's other views as well as information on Crescent Point's services are presented.

44490 ■ *"Quicksilver Resources Receives Favorable Judgement" in Canadian Corporate News (May 16, 2007)*
Pub: Comtex News Network Inc.
Description: The 236th Judicial District Court of Texas ruled in favor of Quicksilver Resources Inc., a crude oil and natural gas exploration and production company, in the litigation between Quicksilver and CMS Marketing Services and Trading Company regarding the sale and purchase of 10,000 million British thermal units of natural gas per day at a minimum price of $2.47 per MMbtu, with the condition that the parties share any upside equally. The Court has rescinded the contract, rendering it void.

44491 ■ *"Race-Week Schedule Filling Up With Galas, Nonprofit Fundraisers" in Boston Business Journal (Vol. 29, July 22, 2011, No. 11, pp. 1)*
Pub: American City Business Journals Inc.
Ed: Alexander Jackson. **Description:** Baltimore, Maryland-based businesses and nonprofit groups have been planning their own events to coincide with the Baltimore Grand Prix during the Labor Day weekend. They also plan to partner with others in hopes of drumming up new business, raising money or to peddle their brands.

44492 ■ *"Ready for the Worst? How to Disaster-Proof Your Business" in Inc. (Vol. 33, September 2011, No. 7, pp. 38)*
Pub: Inc. Magazine
Ed: J.J. McCorvey, Dave Smith. **Description:** Twelve products to and services designed to help small businesses run smoothly in the event of a disaster are outlined.

44493 ■ *"Recipe for Disaster?" in Sacramento Business Journal (Vol. 25, July 4, 2008, No. 18, pp. 1)*
Pub: American City Business Journals, Inc.
Ed: Mark Anderson. **Description:** Restaurateurs are challenged with balancing rising operating costs and what customers are willing to pay for their services. Flour prices in 2008 have increased by 46 percent from April 2007. Other views on the situation, as well as trends, forecasts and statistics on sales, outlook on economic conditions, consumer price index, and the typical split of restaurant revenue, are presented.

44494 ■ *"Red Tape Ties Detroit Housing Rehab Plan" in Crain's Detroit Business (Vol. 24, September 22, 2008, No. 38, pp. 1)*
Pub: Crain Communications Inc.
Ed: Ryan Beene. **Description:** Venture-capital firm Wilherst Oxford LLC is a Florida-based company that has purchased 300 inner-city homes which were in foreclosure in Detroit. Wilherst Oxford is asking the city to forgive the existing tax and utility liens so the firm can utilize the money for home improvements. The city, however, is reluctant but has stated that they are willing to negotiate.

44495 ■ *"Rediscovering the Land of Opportunity" in Green Industry Pro (July 2011)*
Pub: Cygnus Business Media
Ed: Gregg Wartgow. **Description:** Landscape contractors need to discover new strategies that will generate leads and convert those leads into sales.

44496 ■ *"Renren Partners With Recruit to Launch Social Wedding Services" in Benzinga.com (June 7, 2011)*
Pub: Benzinga.com
Ed: Benzinga Staff. **Description:** Renren Inc. and Recruit Company Ltd. partnered to build a wedding social media catering to engaged couples and newlyweds in China. The platform will integrate online wedding related social content and offline media such as magazine and wedding exhibitions.

44497 ■ *"Renren Partnership With Recruit to Launch Social Wedding Services" in Benzinga.com (June 7, 2011)*
Pub: Benzinga.com
Ed: Benzinga Staff. **Description:** Renren Inc., the leading real name social networking Internet platform in China has partnered with Recruit Company Limited, Japan's largest human resource and classified media group to form a joint venture to build a wedding social media catering to the needs of engaged couples and newlyweds in China.

44498 ■ *"Reports of Banks' Revival were Greatly Exaggerated" in Barron's (Vol. 88, July 7, 2008, No. 27, pp. L14)*
Pub: Dow Jones & Co., Inc.
Ed: Jack Willoughby. **Description:** Performance of mutual funds improved for the second quarter of 2008 compared to the previous quarter, registering an average gain of 0.13 percent; funds focusing on natural resources rose the highest, their value rising by an average of 24.50 percent.

44499 ■ *"Research Reports" in Barron's (Vol. 88, March 10, 2008, No. 10, pp. M13)*
Pub: Dow Jones & Company, Inc.
Description: Research reports on different company stocks by investment analysts are given. Shares of Cal Dive are rated Outperform by analysts, citing the shares' continued attractiveness and the company's acquisition of Horizon. Analysts recommend buying the shares of California Water Service Group.

44500 ■ *"Research Reports: How Analysts Size Up Companies" in Barron's (Vol. 88, March 31, 2008, No. 13, pp. M13)*
Pub: Dow Jones & Company, Inc.
Ed: Anita Peltonen. **Description:** Sirius Satellite's shares are ranked Outperform as it awaits approval from the Federal Communications Commission in its merger with XM. TiVo's shares are ranked Avoid as the company is in a sector that's being commoditized. Verizon Communications' rising dividend yield earns it a Focus List ranking. The shares of Bear Stearns, Churchill Downs, Corning, and Deerfield Triarc Capital are also reviewed. Statistical data included.

44501 ■ *"Research Reports: How Analysts Size Up Companies" in Barron's (Vol. 88, July 14, 2008, No. 28, pp. M13)*
Pub: Dow Jones & Co., Inc.
Ed: Anita Peltonen. **Description:** Shares of Bankrate and AutoZone both get a 'Buy' rating from analysts while Zions Bancorporation's shares are downgraded from 'Outperform' to 'Neutral'. The shares of Jet Blue Airline and Deckers Outdoor, a manufacturer of innovative footwear, are also rated and discussed. Statistical data included.

44502 ■ *"'Resume Mining' Services Can Save Time, Money" in HR Specialist (Vol. 8, September 2010, No. 9, pp. 7)*
Pub: Capitol Information Group Inc.
Description: Low-cost resume mining services can help human resource departments save time and money by searching online resume databases for candidates matching specific job qualifications.

44503 ■ *"Retail Woes: The Shoe Doesn't Fit for Gerald Loftin's Stock Picks" in Black Enterprise (Vol. 38, July 2008, No. 12, pp. 40)*
Pub: Earl G. Graves Publishing Co. Inc.
Ed: Steve Garmhausen. **Description:** Each of the three stocks that Gerald Loftin picked in May 2007 have lost money; DSW, the designer shoe retailer, fell by 63.7 percent; paint and coatings retailer Sherwin-Williams Co. fell by 7.2 percent; and Verizon Communications Inc. fell by 1.4 percent. Statistical data included.

44504 ■ *Riches in Niches: How to Make It Big in a Small Market*
Pub: Career Press, Inc.
Ed: Susan Friedmann. **Released:** May 10, 2007. **Price:** $21.99. **Description:** The multiple factors that separate the experts from the service professionals who may actually have betters skills, but are never heard about, are discussed. The seven secrets every entrepreneur should know are listed.

44505 ■ *"Right From the Start" in Small Business Opportunities (July 2010)*
Pub: Harris Publications Inc.
Ed: Ed Krug. **Description:** Ed Krug from Pitch Blue provides sales support services by partnering with small and mid-sized companies to set and reach new revenue targets.

44506 ■ "Ring Ka-Ching" in Canadian Business (Vol. 79, November 6, 2006, No. 22, pp. 106)
Pub: Rogers Media
Description: A brief profile of Jajah including its web activated telephone services is presented.

44507 ■ "The Role of Human and Financial Capital in the Profitability and Growth of Women-Owned Small Firms" in Journal of Small Business Management
Pub: Blackwell Publishing Inc.
Contact: Gordon Tibbitts, President
Ed: Susan Coleman. **Description:** Examines the relationship between the human and financial capital in both men and women-owned businesses and firm performance in the service and retail sectors.

44508 ■ "Russia Eyes Nuclear Power Co-Operation With Canada" in Globe & Mail (April 2, 2007, pp. B1)
Pub: CTVglobemedia Publishing Inc.
Ed: Shawn McCarthy. **Description:** The plans of the Russian nuclear energy agency, Federal Atomic Energy Agency, to enter into a partnership with its Canadian counterpart Atomic Energy of Canada Ltd. for the generation of electric power are discussed.

44509 ■ "The Rypple Effect; Performance Management" in The Economist (Vol. 390, January 3, 2009, No. 8612, pp. 48)
Pub: The Economist Newspaper Inc.
Description: New companies such as Rypple, a new, web-based service, claim that they can satisfy the Net Generation's need for frequent assessments while easing the burden this creates for management.

44510 ■ "S2C Global Installs Its First Mass Production Aquaduct Unit in North America" in Canadian Corporate News (May 16, 2007)
Pub: Comtex News Network Inc.
Description: S2C Global Systems, a leader of distributing 5-gallon bottled water units to the consumer, has announced the installation of its first mass production Aquaduct in Surrey, British Columbia.

44511 ■ "S3 Entertainment Group Partners with WFW International for Film Services in Michigan" in Michigan Vue (July-August 2008)
Pub: Entrepreneur Media Inc.
Description: William F. White (WFW), one of North America's largest production equipment providers has partnered with S3 Entertainment Group (S3EG), a Michigan-based full-service film production services company due to the new incentives package which currently offers the highest incentives in the United States, up to 42 percent. S3EG will actively store, lease, manage, distribute and sell WFW's equipment to the growing number of production teams that are filming in the state.

44512 ■ "St. Luke's Gets Shot in the Arm From Outpatient Services" in Saint Louis Business Journal (Vol. 31, August 19, 2011, No. 52, pp. 1)
Pub: Saint Louis Business Journal
Ed: Angela Mueller, E.B. Solomont. **Description:** St. Louis, Missouri-based St. Luke's Hospital benefited from investing in outpatient services as contained in its latest bond offering. Fitch Ratings gave the bond issuance an A rating.

44513 ■ "Screening for the Best Stock Screens" in Barron's (Vol. 90, September 13, 2010, No. 37, pp. 36)
Pub: Barron's Editorial & Corporate Headquarters
Ed: Mike Hogan. **Description:** Pros and cons of the new and revised stock screening tools from Zack, Finviz.com, and GuruFocus are discussed. FinVix.com is more capable for screening through stocks and the service is free.

44514 ■ "Sean Durfy" in Canadian Business (Vol. 80, April 23, 2007, No. 9, pp. 14)
Pub: Rogers Media
Ed: Michelle Magnan. **Description:** Sean Durfy, president of WestJet Airlines Ltd., feels that marketing is essential factor for growth of airline industry.

44515 ■ "Secrets To Trade Show Success" in Women Entrepreneur (September 12, 2008)
Pub: Entrepreneur Media Inc.
Ed: Lesley Spencer Pyle. **Description:** Trade shows require an enormous amount of work, but they are an investment that can pay off handsomely because they allow a business to get their product or service in front of their target market. Advice regarding trade shows is given including selecting the correct venue, researching the affair and following up on leads obtained at the event.

44516 ■ "Self-Employment in the United States" in Montly Labor Review (Vol. 133, September 2010, No. 9, pp. 17)
Pub: Bureau of Labor Statistics
Description: Self employment in 2009 in the U.S. continued to be more common among men, Whites, Asians, and older workers and in the agriculture, construction, and services industries.

44517 ■ Selling the Invisible: A Field Guide to Modern Marketing
Pub: Business Plus
Ed: Harry Beckwith. **Price:** $22.95. **Description:** Tips for marketing and selling intangibles such as health care, entertainment, tourism, legal services, and more are provided.

44518 ■ "The Service Imperative" in Business Horizons (Vol. 51, January-February 2008, No. 1, pp. 39)
Pub: Elsevier Advanced Technology Publications
Ed: Mary Jo Bitner, Stephen W. Brown. **Description:** The importance of services is growing in developing countries like India and China, but little attention is given to service research, education and innovation. The 'service imperative' seeks to promote the advancement of services. The scope, objectives and philosophy of the service imperative platform are outlined.

44519 ■ Services in Canada
Pub: Routledge Inc.
Ed: W.R. Frisbee. **Released:** March 29, 1990. **Price:** $215.00. **Description:** Profiles of the services industry in Canada.

44520 ■ "Shaw, Telus Take Up Battle Positions" in Globe & Mail (January 1, 2006, pp. B1)
Pub: CTVglobemedia Publishing Inc.
Ed: Catherine McKLean. **Description:** The competition between Shaw Communications Inc. and Telus Corp. over voice over Internet protocol offer for customers is presented.

44521 ■ "Ship Shape" in Hawaii Business (Vol. 53, January 2008, No. 7, pp. 46)
Pub: Hawaii Business Publishing
Ed: David K. Choo. **Description:** Ship Maintenance LLC is in charge of repairing and maintaining the U.S. Navy ships at Pearl Harbor's Middle Noch, having renewed a five-year contract with the navy. Cleaning a ship is a difficult process, which involves degreasing and removal of sensitive items such as guns and missiles. The awards given to Ship Maintenance are also discussed.

44522 ■ "Shipping 2.0" in Entrepreneur (Vol. 36, April 2008, No. 4, pp. 54)
Pub: Entrepreneur Media, Inc.
Ed: Heather Clancy. **Description:** Doggypads.com contacted with Web 2.0 service provider Shipwire to handle its warehouse concerns. The service works by paying a rent to Shipwire and they will store the client's items. The client's customers can continue to order from the client's website and Shipwire will take care of delivery. Doggypads was able to save up on costs by using Shipwire.

44523 ■ "Show and Tell" in Entrepreneur (Vol. 36, May 2008, No. 5, pp. 54)
Pub: Entrepreneur Media, Inc.
Ed: Heather Clancy. **Description:** FreshStart Telephone uses recorded video testimonials of customers, by using Pure Digital Flip Video that downloads content directly to the computer, and uploads it in the company's website to promote their wireless phone service.

44524 ■ "A Simple Old Reg that Needs Dusting Off" in Barron's (Vol. 88, June 30, 2008, No. 26, pp. 35)
Pub: Dow Jones & Co., Inc.
Ed: Gene Epstein. **Description:** Senator Joe Lieberman has a point when he accused speculators of inflating the prices of food and fuel futures but introducing legislation to address speculation has an alternative. The senator's committee should instead demand that the Commodity Futures Trading Commission enforce position limits on the maximum number of contracts in a given market per speculative entity.

44525 ■ "The Skype's the Limit" in Canadian Business (Vol. 80, February 12, 2007, No. 4, pp. 70)
Pub: Rogers Media
Ed: Gerry Blackwell. **Description:** The increase in the market share of Skype Technologies S.A.'s Internet phone service to 171 million users is discussed.

44526 ■ "Slow but Steady into the Future" in Barron's (Vol. 88, July 7, 2008, No. 27, pp. M)
Pub: Dow Jones & Co., Inc.
Ed: Mark Veverka. **Description:** Investors are advised to maintain their watch on the shares of business software company NetSuite. The company's chief executive officer, Zach Nelson, claims that the company has a 10-year lead on its competitors with the development of software-as-a service.

44527 ■ "Small Business Unsure of Impact of New Tax Law" in Crain's Detroit Business (Vol. 23, October 15, 2007, No. 42, pp. 13)
Pub: Crain Communications Inc. - Detroit
Ed: Sheena Harrison. **Description:** Small business owners in Michigan are concerned with issues surrounding the proposed increases in state taxes geared at small business, which includes a 6 percent service tax.

44528 ■ "Small Firms Punch Ticket for Growth" in Houston Business Journal (Vol. 40, January 29, 2010, No. 38, pp. 1)
Pub: American City Business Journals
Ed: Allison Wollam. **Description:** Independent ticket agencies anticipate growth as American and Canadian authorities approved a merger between Ticketmaster and concert promoter Live Nation. Expansion of service offerings and acquisition of venues have also been done by independent ticket agencies in light of the merger. Details of the merger are included.

44529 ■ "SoBran Partners with U.S. Navy" in Black Enterprise (Vol. 37, October 2006, No. 3, pp. 38)
Pub: Earl G. Graves Publishing Co. Inc.
Ed: Glenn Townes. **Description:** SoBran Inc., partnered with Lockheed Martin and signed a three-Tear production service contract with the Naval Aviation Depot in Jacksonville, Florida. The $44 million contract will allow SoBran to transport and warehouse materials for Navy facilities.

44530 ■ The Social Media Bible: Tactics, Tools, and Strategies for Business Success
Pub: John Wiley & Sons, Inc.
Ed: Lon Safko, David Brake. **Released:** June 17, 2009. **Price:** $29.95. **Description:** Information is given to build or transform a business into social media, where customers, employees, and prospects connect, collaborate, and champion products and services in order to increase sales and to beat the competition.

44531 ■ "A Socko Payout Menu: Rural Phone Carrier Plots to Supercharge Its Shares" in Barron's (Vol. 88, June 30, 2008, No. 26, pp. M5)
Pub: Dow Jones & Co., Inc.
Ed: Shirley A. Lazo. **Description:** CenturyTel boosted its quarterly common payout to 70 cents from 6.75 cents per share die to its strong cash flows and solid balance sheet. Eastman Kodak's plan for a buyback will be partially funded by its $581 million tax refund. CME Group will buyback stocks through 2009 worth $1.1 billion.

44532 ■ *"Sprint Tries to Wring Out Positives"* in *The Business Journal-Serving Metropolitan Kansas City (Vol. 26, August 8, 2008, No. 48)*
Pub: American City Business Journals, Inc.
Ed: Suzanna Stagemeyer. **Description:** Sprint Nextel Corp. reported that 901,000 subscribers left the company in the quarter ending June 30, 2008; fewer than the nearly 1.1 million it lost in the previous quarter. Customer turnover also dropped to just less than 2 percent, compared to 2.45 percent in the first quarter of 2008.

44533 ■ *"Staffing Firms are Picking Up the Pieces, Seeing Signs of Life"* in *Milwaukee Business Journal (Vol. 27, February 5, 2010, No. 19)*
Pub: American City Business Journals
Ed: Rich Rovito. **Description:** Milwaukee, Wisconsin-based staffing firms are seeing signs of economic rebound as many businesses turned to temporary employees to fill the demands for goods and services. Economic observers believe the growth in temporary staffing is one of the early indicators of economic recovery.

44534 ■ *"Staples Advantage Receives NJPA National Contract for Janitorial Supplies"* in *Professional Services Close-Up (April 22, 2011)*
Pub: Close-Up Media
Description: Staples Advantage, the business-to-business division of Staples Inc. was awarded a contract for janitorial supplies to members of the National Joint Powers Alliance (NJPA). NJPA is a member-owned buying cooperative serving public and private schools, state and local governments, and nonprofit organizations.

44535 ■ *"Still in the Jet Set"* in *Barron's (Vol. 89, July 13, 2009, No. 28, pp. 13)*
Pub: Dow Jones & Co., Inc.
Ed: Brad Davis. **Description:** Coastal Jet Service will be offering coast-to-coast flights and a one way ride on their Cessna Citation X will cost $4,600 plus tax. The service is a compromise between a corporate jet and a first-class seat on a commercial flight and the jets fly out of Westchester County, New York and land in Burbank, California.

44536 ■ *"Stockerts Open Repair Business"* in *Dickinson Press (July 13, 2010)*
Pub: Dickinson Press
Ed: Ashley Martin. **Description:** Ed Stockert is opening his new appliance repair firm in Dickinson, North Dakota with his wife Anna.

44537 ■ *"Stoneham Drilling Trust Announces Cash Distribution for May 2007"* in *Canadian Corporate News (May 16, 2007)*
Pub: Comtex News Network Inc.
Description: Stoneham Drilling Trust, an income trust that provides contract drilling services to natural gas and oil exploration and production companies operating in western Canada, announced that its cash distribution for the period from May 1, 2007 to May 31, 2007 will be $0.15 per trust unit ($1.80 per annum).

44538 ■ *"Study: New Moms Build A Lot of Brand Buzz"* in *Brandweek (Vol. 49, April 21, 2008, No. 16, pp. 7)*
Pub: VNU Business Media, Inc.
Description: According to a new survey which sampled 1,721 pregnant women and new moms, this demographic is having 109 word-of-mouth conversations per week concerning products, services and brands. Two-thirds of these conversations directly involve brand recommendations. The Internet is driving these word-of-mouth, or W-O-M, conversations among this segment, beating out magazines, television and other forms of media.

44539 ■ *"Suits Keep Flying in Wireless Service Marketing Wars"* in *Globe & Mail (March 22, 2007, pp. B3)*
Pub: CTVglobemedia Publishing Inc.
Ed: Catherine McLean. **Description:** The suit filed by Telus Corp. against BCE Mobile Communications Inc. over the latter's alleged misleading advertisement in the press is discussed.

44540 ■ *"The Sure Thing That Flopped"* in *Harvard Business Review (Vol. 86, July-August 2008, No. 8, pp. 29)*
Pub: Harvard Business School Press
Ed: Gerald Zaltman; Lindsay Zaltman. **Description:** Fictitious brand extension scenario is presented, with contributors providing suggestions and advice. The company's struggles with expanding the brand may be alleviated by improving consumer research, focusing on emotional responses to products and services.

44541 ■ *"Survey Distorts Cost of Capitals"* in *Canadian Business (Vol. 83, October 12, 2010, No. 17, pp. 22)*
Pub: Rogers Media Ltd.
Ed: Matthew McClearn. **Description:** Swiss bank UBS publishes a study comparing the costs of goods and services in megalopolises every three years. The study ranked Toronto and Montreal outside the Top 30 in 2009, but the two cities jumped to eighth and ninth in a recent update. This change can be contributed to the conversion of prices into Euros before making comparisons.

44542 ■ *"Sweet Harmony"* in *Canadian Business (Vol. 82, April 27, 2009, No. 7, pp. 6)*
Pub: Rogers Media
Description: Canada will harmonize its 5 percent federal goods and services tax wit the 8 percent provincial sales tax effective July 1, 2010. Meanwhile, provinces like Ontario and Quebec have switched the sales taxes that are charged in new investments into a value-added tax. The conversion has led to an 11 percent increase in investments in Quebec and the three other provinces that made the conversion.

44543 ■ *"Take This Job and Love It"* in *Green Industry Pro (Vol. 23, October 2011)*
Pub: Cygnus Business Media
Ed: Gregg Wartgow. **Description:** Details of the lawsuit filed by the Professional Landcare Network (PLANET) against the U.S. Department of Labor are explained. Challenges faced by landscape firms because of employment costs are outlined. Statistical data included.

44544 ■ *"Teachers, U.S. Fund Providence Made Moves On BCE Buyout"* in *Globe & Mail (April 10, 2007, pp. B17)*
Pub: CTVglobemedia Publishing Inc.
Ed: Boyd Erman; Sinclair Stewart; Jacquie McNish. **Description:** The Ontario Teachers Pension Plan, the largest shareholder of telecommunications firm BCE Inc., has called for a partnership with buyout firm Providence Equity Partners Inc. in order to acquire BCE Inc.

44545 ■ *"A Team Sport"* in *Business Courier (Vol. 26, October 2, 2009, No. 23, pp. 1)*
Pub: American City Business Journals, Inc.
Ed: Lisa Biank Fasig. **Description:** Procter & Gamble (P&G) revised the way it works with marketing, design and public relations firms. Creative discussions will be managed by only two representatives, the franchise leader and the brand agency leader in order for P&G to simplify operations as it grows larger and more global.

44546 ■ *"Telesat's New Rocket Man"* in *Canadian Business (Vol. 80, January 29, 2007, No. 3, pp. 21)*
Pub: Rogers Media
Ed: Andrew Wahl. **Description:** The plans of Dan Goldberg, the chief executive officer of Telesat Canada, for the enhancement of the company's services are discussed.

44547 ■ *"TELUS Drawing More Power From Its Wireless Operations"* in *Globe & Mail (February 17, 2007, pp. B3)*
Pub: CTVglobemedia Publishing Inc.
Ed: Catherine McLean. **Description:** TELUS Corp., the fast-growing wireless business company, posted tripled profits in the fourth quarter of 2006. The revenues of the company increased 8 percent in the same period.

44548 ■ *"Thomas Industrial Network Unveils Custom SPEC"* in *Entertainment Close-Up (March 3, 2011)*
Pub: Close-Up Media
Description: Thomas Industrial Network assists custom manufacturers and industrial service providers a complete online program called Custom SPEC which includes Website development and Internet exposure.

44549 ■ *"Time to Fight Back"* in *Green Industry Pro (Vol. 23, March 2011, No. 3, pp. 8)*
Pub: Cygnus Business Media
Ed: Rod Dickens. **Description:** Lawn care operators in the United States must learn from Canada that a shift to socialism will impact their industry in a negative way. Government regulation over the application of control products regarding environmental health in Canada has been a death sentence for small lawn care businesses.

44550 ■ *"Time for State Tax Restructure?"* in *Crain's Detroit Business (Vol. 26, January 18, 2010, No. 3, pp. 3)*
Pub: Crain Communications Inc.
Ed: Amy Lane. **Description:** Business Leaders for Michigan, a statewide CEO group, launched a proposal to cut the Michigan Business Tax by about $1.1 billion and replace the revenue by taxing services. Statistical data included.

44551 ■ *"Tiny Telecom Big Prize in Bell Aliant Bid Battle"* in *Globe & Mail (April 4, 2007, pp. B1)*
Pub: CTVglobemedia Publishing Inc.
Ed: Catherine McLean. **Description:** The competition between Bell Aliant Regional Communications Income Fund of BCE Inc. and Bragg Communications Inc. to bid for acquiring Amtelecom Income Fund is discussed.

44552 ■ *"To JM On Its 75th Anniversary"* in *Journal of Marketing (Vol. 75, July 2011, No. 4, pp. 129)*
Pub: American Marketing Association
Ed: Ruth M. Bolton. **Description:** How the Journal of Marketing influenced the marketing science and practice is presented. The Marketing Science Institute's 50th anniversary coincides with the journal's 75th anniversary and both have collaborated to tackle important marketing issues identified in MSI's priorities. The mind-set of managers worldwide was also influenced by ideas in the journal's articles.

44553 ■ *"To Keep Freight Rolling, Springfield Must Grease the Hub"* in *Crain's Chicago Business (Vol. 31, April 21, 2008, No. 16, pp. 22)*
Pub: Crain Communications, Inc.
Ed: Paul O'Connor. **Description:** Discusses the importance of upgrading Chicago's continental-hub freight rail system which is integral to moving international products as well as domestic ones. Global tonnage is expected to double by 2020 and unless more money is designated to upgrade the infrastructure the local and national economy will suffer.

44554 ■ *"Top 50 By 1-Year Return"* in *Canadian Business (Vol. 81, Summer 2008, No. 9, pp. 121)*
Pub: Rogers Media Ltd.
Description: Table showing the top 50 Canadian companies ranked in terms of one-year return is presented. Toronto, Canada-based Timminco Ltd. topped the roster with a 1,294.2 percent in one-year return. However, the share prices of the company were affected by the recent controversy in its silicon purification process.

44555 ■ *"Top 100 Consolidate Gains"* in *Hispanic Business (Vol. 30, July-August 2008, No. 7-8, pp. 30)*
Pub: Hispanic Business, Inc.
Ed: Richard Kaplan. **Description:** Data developed by HispanTelligence on the increase in revenue posted by the top 100 fastest-growing U.S. Hispanic firms over the last five years is reported. Despite the

economic downturn, the service sector, IT and health suppliers showed an increase in revenue whereas construction companies showed a marginal slump in revenue growth.

44556 ■ *Trade-Off: The Ever-Present Tension Between Quality and Conscience*
Pub: Crown Business Books
Ed: Kevin Maney. **Released:** August 17, 2010. **Price:** $15.00. **Description:** The tension between fidelity (the quality of a consumer's experience) and convenience (the ease of getting and paying for a product) are shown to be the forces that determine the success or failure of new products and services in the marketplace.

44557 ■ *"Traffic Slows at O'Hare; As Airlines Cut Flights, City Tries to Push Expansion Forward"* in Crain's Chicago Business (April 28, 2008)
Pub: Crain Communications, Inc.
Ed: Paul Merrion; John Pletz. **Description:** O'Hare International Airport is seeing a decline in passenger traffic just as the city of Chicago presses cash-strapped airlines to fund the second phase of the airport's expansion which would include the extension of one runway, the relocation of two others and the construction of a new western terminal.

44558 ■ *"A Train of Our Own"* in Canadian Business (Vol. 79, July 17, 2006, No. 14-15, pp. 71)
Pub: Rogers Media
Ed: Victor Dwyer. **Description:** The luxuries and pleasure of traveling in private rail road cars are discussed.

44559 ■ *"TransCanada Builds on Proud Olympic History by Joining Vancouver 2010"* in Canadian Corporate News (May 14, 2007)
Pub: Comtex News Network Inc.
Description: TransCanada is the official supplier in the Natural Gas Pipeline Operator category for the Vancouver 2010 Olympic and Paralympic Winter Games.

44560 ■ *"Transportation: Laidlaw's Chief Driver"* in Canadian Business (Vol. 80, January 29, 2007, No. 3, pp. 14)
Pub: Rogers Media
Ed: Michelle Magnan. **Description:** The role of Kevin Benson in the restructuring and growth of the bankrupt transportation company Laidlaw Inc. is described. The increase in the revenues of the restructures company is discussed.

44561 ■ *"Travel Leery"* in Crain's Chicago Business (Vol. 31, March 31, 2008, No. 13, pp. 3)
Pub: Crain Communications, Inc.
Description: Due to the rise in airline prices and a possible recession, many companies are starting to change their travel policies and limit travel spending.

44562 ■ *"The Traveler's Traveler"* in Entrepreneur (Vol. 37, September 2009, No. 9, pp. 22)
Pub: Entrepreneur Media, Inc.
Ed: Kim Orr. **Description:** Business travel columnist Joe Sharkey says technology may someday replace business travel. Airlines are realizing that a part of the business travel market has disappeared. Sharkey also says airlines can never get those customers back.

44563 ■ *"Trend: Tutors to Help You Pump Up the Staff"* in Business Week (September 22, 2008, No. 4100, pp. 45)
Pub: McGraw-Hill Companies, Inc.
Ed: Reena Janaj. **Description:** High-level managers are turning to innovation coaches in an attempt to obtain advice on how to better sell new concepts within their companies. Individuals as well as consulting firms are now offering this service.

44564 ■ *"Turbulent Skies"* in The Business Journal-Portland (Vol. 25, August 29, 2008, No. 25, pp. 1)
Pub: American City Business Journals, Inc.
Ed: Erik Siemers. **Description:** Small airlines are struggling to keep their commercial services amid the troubled commercial airline sector. Small communi-

ties, for example, were expected to pony up about $650,000 in revenue guarantees each in order to convince SkyWest Airlines to offer two direct flights to Portland daily beginning October 12, 2008. The trends in the commercial airline industry are analyzed.

44565 ■ *"The Turkey Has Landed"* in Canadian Business (Vol. 79, November 20, 2006, No. 23, pp. 38)
Pub: Rogers Media
Ed: Erik Heinrich. **Description:** The design and construction of Toronto Pearson International Airport to handle domestic, international and transborder flights in one facility is discussed.

44566 ■ *"TV Revenue Slide Hits CanWest Profit"* in Globe & Mail (January 13, 2006, pp. B3)
Pub: CTVglobemedia Publishing Inc.
Ed: Grant Robertson. **Description:** CanWest Global Communications Corp. posted drop in profits by 14 percent for first quarter 2006. The downward trend in profits is attributed to low television revenues.

44567 ■ *"U Overhauling Its Janitorial Program, but Custodians Taking Exception"* in Saint Paul Pioneer Press (August 20, 2011)
Pub: McClatchy-Tribune Regional News
Ed: Mila Koumpilova. **Description:** University of Minnesota developed a new team cleaning approach for its campus. The new custodian program will save $3.1 million annually while providing a cleaner campus. The union representing the custodians questions both claims.

44568 ■ *"U.S. Savvy Helps Fuel TD's Fortunes"* in Globe & Mail (February 23, 2007, pp. B1)
Pub: CTVglobemedia Publishing Inc.
Ed: Andrew Willis; Tavia Grant. **Description:** The rise in the revenues of Toronto-Dominion Bank due to its acquisition of American financial service providers and the rise in its domestic retail banking revenues are disussed.

44569 ■ *"United's Next Hurdle: Costly Repairs"* in Crain's Chicago Business (Vol. 31, April 14, 2008, No. 15, pp. 1)
Pub: Crain Communications, Inc.
Ed: John Pletz. **Description:** Discusses the recent crackdown by aviation regulators concerning airline safety at United Airlines as well as other carriers. Maintenance costs at United for the upkeep on the company's older planes is severely affecting its bottom line which is already sagging under heavy fuel costs.

44570 ■ *"Utilities Report Lower Customer Growth Rate, Power Use"* in The Business Journal - Serving Phoenix and the Valley of the Sun (Vol. 28, August 8, 2008, No. 49, pp. 1)
Pub: American City Business Journals, Inc.
Ed: Patrick O'Grady. **Description:** Arizona Public Service Co. and Salt River Project are experiencing sharp decrease in customer growth rates due to less movement of people to the Valley. Arizona Public Service Co. expects a further decline of just 1 percent customer growth by the end of 2008 while Salt River Project expects this to grow between 1 to 2 percent for the two years ahead of 2008.

44571 ■ *"VC-Heavy, Revenue-Light Sensicore Sold to GE Division"* in Crain's Detroit Business (Vol. 24, April 14, 2008, No. 15, pp. 28)
Pub: Crain Communications Inc.
Ed: Tom Henderson. **Description:** General Electric has acquired Sensicore Inc., which although one of Michigan's most successful companies in raising venture capital was unable to generate significant revenue from its handheld water-testing devices. GE is capable of penetrating a larger market than a private company and will be able to take the devices to the municipal marketplace.

44572 ■ *"Ventura Police Install Electronic Kiosk to Access Services"* in Ventura County

Star (October 28, 2010)
Pub: Ventura County Star
Description: Ventura Police Department installed a kiosk in the front lobby of its building in order to provide services to the public. The kiosk allows access to the Department's Website; to retrieve a collision report, file an abandoned vehicle report, receive a permit for an oversized vehicle, or filing a citizen's complaint; information can be obtained about alarms, programs and permits; users can pay a parking ticket and review calls for services on an interactive map.

44573 ■ *"Virgin Mobile has Big Plans for Year Two"* in Globe & Mail (March 6, 2006, pp. B5)
Pub: CTVglobemedia Publishing Inc.
Ed: Catherine McLean. **Description:** The business growth plans of Virgin Mobile Canada are presented.

44574 ■ *"Vista-Based NCV Bought by Canteen Vending"* in North County Times (October 18, 2011)
Pub: Lee Enterprises Inc.
Ed: Pat Maio. **Description:** Details of North Carolina-based Canteen Vending Services' acquisition of NCV Refreshment Services, are given.

44575 ■ *"Wall Street Is No Friend to Radical Innovation"* in Harvard Business Review (Vol. 88, July-August 2010, No. 7-8, pp. 28)
Pub: Harvard Business School Publishing
Ed: Julia Kirby. **Description:** Research indicates that investors are skittish about backing a business that proposes significant changes to its product or service status quo.

44576 ■ *"War Veteran Hit Payoff with Repair Business"* in Tulsa World (July 28, 2010)
Pub: Tulsa World
Ed: Tim Stanley. **Description:** Profile of Sam Melton, Korean War veteran and retired Air Force staff sergeant, launched appliance repair stores in the Tulsa, Oklahoma area 50 years ago.

44577 ■ *"Warning Lights Flashing for Air Canada: Carty's Back"* in Globe & Mail (February 22, 2006, pp. B1)
Pub: CTVglobemedia Publishing Inc.
Ed: Brent Jang. **Description:** Air Canada's rival, Donald Carty, former chief executive officer at American Airlines and new chairman of Toronto based Regco Holdings Inc., launches Porter Airlines Inc. out of Toronto City Center Airport this fall.

44578 ■ *"Waste Not"* in Entrepreneur (Vol. 36, April 2008, No. 4, pp. 21)
Pub: Entrepreneur Media, Inc.
Ed: JJ Ramberg. **Description:** RecycleBank is a company that provides homes with carts in which recyclables are thrown. An identification chip measures the amount of recyclables and converts them into points, which can be redeemed in stores, such as Starbucks and Whole Foods. RecycleBank earns revenue from cities that save landfill waste spending with the use of the program.

44579 ■ *"Water Treatment Play Zenon Goes to GE"* in Globe & Mail (March 15, 2006, pp. B1)
Pub: CTVglobemedia Publishing Inc.
Ed: Leonard Zehr. **Description:** General Electric Co. acquires Ontario-based company, Zenon Environmental Inc., a technology giant in purifying water in northern Canada.

44580 ■ *"Way More Than Mowing"* in Green Industry Pro (Vol. 23, September 2011)
Pub: Cygnus Business Media
Ed: Rod Dickens. **Description:** Shipp Shape Lawn Services located in Sylvester, Georgia now offers aeration, fertilizing and weed control, mulching, yard renovation, flowerbed maintenance, landscaping, as well as irrigation repairs and installation in order to diversify the business and stay competitive.

44581 ■ *"Web Translation Made Simple"* in Inc. (Vol. 33, October 2011, No. 8, pp. 44)
Pub: Inc. Magazine
Ed: Adam Baer. **Description:** Smartling is a Web-based service that translates sites into more than 50 foreign languages. The software will begin translation right after setting up the account.

44582 ■ *"Website Backup Made Simple"* in *Inc.* (Vol. 33, September 2011, No. 7, pp. 52)
Pub: Inc. Magazine

Ed: John Brandon. **Description:** Tools to back up content on a Website are profiled. Vaultpress works only with sites that run on the WordPress publishing platform and CodeGuard works with a variety of publishing platforms and hosting services.

44583 ■ *"Welcome to a New Kind of Cubicle Culture"* in *Boston Business Journal* (Vol. 29, August 19, 2011, No. 15, pp. 1)
Pub: American City Business Journals Inc.

Ed: Alexander Jackson. **Description:** Beehive Baltimore offers a co-working space where independent freelancers and entrepreneurs can work. There are two other companies that provide the same service and the value of these services to these professional is that it provides them with an office that is both convenient and affordable aside from letting them network with peers.

44584 ■ *"WestJet Gears Up for Domestic Dogfight"* in *Globe & Mail* (May 1, 2007, pp. B6)
Pub: CTVglobemedia Publishing Inc.

Ed: Brent Jang. **Description:** The effort of WestJet Airlines Ltd. to compete with Air Canada for greater market share of passengers is discussed.

44585 ■ *"WestJet Ponders Growth Plan Following Record Profit"* in *Globe & Mail* (February 15, 2007, pp. B15)
Pub: CTVglobemedia Publishing Inc.

Ed: Brent Jang. **Description:** The Calgary-based WestJet Airlines Ltd., which reported a record $114.7 million profit last year, is planning to expand its operations by 2010. The airline is planning new services and carriers.

44586 ■ *"What Will Green Power Cost? Surcharge, Spending Cap Considered"* in *Crain's Detroit Business* (Vol. 24, March 10, 2008, No. 10, pp. 1)
Pub: Crain Communications, Inc.

Ed: Amy Lane. **Description:** Due to a proposed mandate, which states that 10 percent of power will have to come from renewable sources by 2015 in the state of Michigan, concern is being raised about the higher electricity prices this legislation will undoubtedly cause to business and residential customers.

44587 ■ *"Why Change?"* in *Canadian Business* (Vol. 80, October 8, 2007, No. 20, pp. 9)
Pub: Rogers Media

Ed: Joe Chidley. **Description:** The need for economic change in Canada is discussed. Despite the country's economic growth and low unemployment rate, economic reform is needed in order to maximize its economic potential in the future. Other reasons for the need to further develop its economy, such as the rise of manufacturing and service industries in Asia and the emergence of regional trade pacts in South America are also tackled.

44588 ■ *"Why-Max?"* in *Canadian Business* (Vol. 81, July 22, 2008, No. 12-13, pp. 19)
Pub: Rogers Media Ltd.

Ed: Andrew Wahl. **Description:** Nascent technology known as LTE (Long Term Evolution) is expected to challenge Intel's WiMax wireless technology as the wireless broadband standard. LTE , which is believed to be at least two years behind WiMax in development, is likely to be supported by wireless and mobile-phone carriers. Views and information on WiMax and LTE are presented.

44589 ■ *"Wild-Goose Chaser"* in *Entrepreneur* (Vol. 37, September 2009, No. 9, pp. 96)
Pub: Entrepreneur Media, Inc.

Ed: Jason Daley. **Description:** Geese Police owner David Marcks says he discovered that trained collies could chase geese off golf courses, which started his business. He gives new franchises two dogs to start their business. The company has fared well even during the economic crisis.

44590 ■ *"Will Work for Equity"* in *Inc.* (March 2008, pp. 50, 52)
Pub: Gruner & Jahr USA Publishing

Ed: Ryan McCarthy. **Description:** Profile of Dave Graham and his information technology company; Graham built his business by taking equity in client firms rather than charging fees. Four tips to consider before signing a work-for-equity business deal are outlined.

44591 ■ *"Women as 21st Century Leaders"* in *Women In Business* (Vol. 63, Summer 2011, No. 2, pp. 26)
Pub: American Business Women's Association

Ed: Leigh Elmore. **Description:** American Business Women's Association and Park University have partnered to provide a leadership training program to attendees of the 2011 National Women's Leadership Conference. The courses will incorporate introduction to concepts, development of critical thinking skills and direct application through exercises. Comments from executives are also included.

44592 ■ *"Women Losing IT Ground"* in *Marketing to Women* (Vol. 21, February 2008, No. 2, pp. 6)
Pub: EPM Communications Inc.
Contact: Ira Mayer, President
E-mail: imayer@epmcom.com

Description: According to a study conducted by The National Center for Women & Information Technology, women in technology are losing ground. Statistical data included.

44593 ■ *"Work Smarter"* in *Entrepreneur* (Vol. 36, April 2008, No. 4, pp. 70)
Pub: Entrepreneur Media, Inc.

Ed: Amanda C. Kooser. **Description:** Online applications that address a business' particular needs are presented. These web applications offer email services, collaboration services of sharing and editing documents and presentations, and tie-ups with online social networking sites. Details on various web applications are provided.

44594 ■ *"XM Mulls Betting the Bank in Competitive Game of Subscriber Growth"* in *Globe & Mail* (March 18, 2006, pp. B3)
Pub: CTVglobemedia Publishing Inc.

Ed: Grant Robertson. **Description:** Canadian Satellite Radio Inc., XM Canada, president and Chief Operating Officer Stephen Tapp feel that establishing a profile in satellite radio to attract subscribers is a very big challenge. His views on the Canadian radio market are detailed.

44595 ■ *"Xtium Has Its Head in the Clouds"* in *Philadelphia Business Journal* (Vol. 30, September 23, 2011, No. 32, pp. 1)
Pub: American City Business Journals Inc.

Ed: Peter Key. **Description:** Philadelphia-based cloud computing firm Xtium LLC received an $11.5 million first-round investment from Boston-Massachusetts-based OpenView Venture Partners. Catering to midsize businesses and unit of bigger firms, Xtium offers disaster-recovery, hosting, and managed-information-technology-infrastructure services.

44596 ■ *"Yammer Gets Serious"* in *Inc.* (Volume 32, December 2010, No. 10, pp. 58)
Pub: Inc. Magazine

Ed: Eric Markowitz. **Description:** Yammer, an internal social network for companies, allows coworkers to share ideas and documents in real-time. Details of this service are included.

44597 ■ *"You Won't Go Broke Filling Up On These Stocks"* in *Barron's* (Vol. 88, July 14, 2008, No. 28, pp. 38)
Pub: Dow Jones & Co., Inc.

Ed: Assif Shameen. **Description:** Due to high economic growth, pro-business policies and a consumption boom, the Middle East is a good place to look for equities. The best ways in which to gain exposure to this market include investing in the real estate industry and telecommunications markets as well as large banks that serve corporations and consumers.

44598 ■ *"Young Giants"* in *Canadian Business* (Vol. 79, August 14, 2006, No. 16-17, pp. 47)
Pub: Rogers Media

Ed: Brad Purdy. **Description:** New generations of young chiefs of oil and gas companies in Canada, are featured.

44599 ■ *"Your Next Big Customer"* in *Business Owner* (Vol. 35, November-December 2011, No. 6, pp. 7)
Pub: DL Perkins Company

Description: Learn how to sell goods and services to the Federal Government. The Office of Government Contracting is the agency responsible for coordinating government purchases.

44600 ■ *"You're a What? Wind Turbine Service Technician"* in *Occupational Outlook Quarterly* (Vol. 54, Fall 2010, No. 3, pp. 34)
Pub: U.S. Bureau of Labor Statistics

Ed: Drew Liming. **Description:** Profile of Brandon Johnson, former member of the Air Force, found a career as a wind turbine service technician.

44601 ■ *"Zeon Solutions Teams with Endeca for SaaS Version of Endeca InFront"* in *Entertainment Close-Up* (October 25, 2011)
Pub: Close-Up Media

Description: Zeon Solutions, an enterprise e-commerce and Website development firm announced a special licensing partnership with Endecca Technologies. Endeca is an information management software company that provides small and mid-size retailers with high-performance Customer Experience Management technology.

FRANCHISES AND BUSINESS OPPORTUNITIES

44602 ■ ACFN - The ATM Franchise Business
ACFN Franchised Inc.
111 Saint John St., 6th Fl.
San Jose, CA 95113
Ph: (888)444-2236
Fax: (888)708-8600
Co. E-mail: franchising@acfn.info
URL: http://www.acfnfranchised.com

Description: The ATM FRANCHISE business. Develop & operate your own private network of ATM machines in hotels and Other travel & entertainment based businesses. Potential to earn significant long term residual income. Proven business plan with impressive list of corporate clients. Prior experience not necessary. **No. of Franchise Units:** 210. **Founded:** 1996.. **Franchised:** 2003. **Equity Capital Needed:** $40,000. **Franchise Fee:** $25,000. **Financial Assistance:** Financial assistance available for $10,000 of the franchise fee. **Training:** 1 week at corporate office in California and ongoing support in all aspects of operating your ATM network.

44603 ■ Advanced Maintenance
2820 Kerr Ave.
Wilmington, NC 28405
Ph: (888)452-9206
Fax: (910)251-0095

Description: Onsite fleet vehicle services. **No. of Franchise Units:** 6. **No. of Company-Owned Units:** 3. **Founded:** 2000.. **Franchised:** 2005. **Equity Capital Needed:** $117,900-$175,450, franchise fee discount for Honorable Discharge Veterans. **Franchise Fee:** $35,000. **Training:** Yes.

44604 ■ ChemDry Canada Ltd.
8472 Harvard Pl.
Chilliwack, BC, Canada V2P 7Z5
Free: 888-243-6379
Fax: (604)795-7071
Co. E-mail: franchisesales@chemdry.ca
URL: http://www.chemdry.ca

Description: Carpet and upholstery cleaning service. **No. of Franchise Units:** 77. **Franchised:** 1978. **Equity Capital Needed:** $20,000-$60,000 total investment; $20,000 startup capital required. **Franchise Fee:** $815/month. **Training:** Provides 5 days training, including travel and accommodation.

44605 ■ College Hunks Hauling Junk
4836 W Gandy Blvd.
Tampa, FL 33611
Free: 800-586-5872
Fax: (301)881-5865
Description: Junk removal service. **No. of Franchise Units:** 132. **No. of Company-Owned Units:** 16. **Founded:** 2003.. **Franchised:** 2007. **Equity Capital Needed:** $100,000-$167,950. **Franchise Fee:** $35,000-$40,000. **Royalty Fee:** 7%. **Financial Assistance:** Third party financing available. **Training:** Provides 7-10 days training at headquarters, 3 days onsite and ongoing support.

44606 ■ DoodyCalls
114 4th St. SE, No. A
Charlottesville, VA 22902
Free: 800-366-3922
Fax: (703)995-0601
URL: http://www.doodycalls.com
Description: Pet waste removal service. **No. of Franchise Units:** 46. **No. of Company-Owned Units:** 8. **Founded:** 2000.. **Franchised:** 2004. **Equity Capital Needed:** $35,612-$52,875. **Franchise Fee:** $24,500. **Royalty Fee:** 9%. **Financial Assistance:** In-house financial assistance with franchise fee. **Training:** Offers 30 hours training at headquarters and ongoing training as needed.

44607 ■ ease e-waste
3016 S Halladay St., Ste. F
Santa Ana, CA 92705
Free: 866-548-8100
Fax: (775)871-5259
Description: Electronic waste collection and recycling services. **No. of Franchise Units:** 1. **No. of Company-Owned Units:** 2. **Founded:** 2003.. **Franchised:** 2005. **Equity Capital Needed:** $134,800-$224,100. **Franchise Fee:** $50,000. **Royalty Fee:** 5%. **Training:** Provides 1 week training at headquarters, 1 week onsite and ongoing support.

44608 ■ Flamingo A Friend
FAF Franchising Inc.
110 Crosscut Rd.
Alabaster, AL 35007
Ph: (205)621-7400
Description: Special occasion yard decorations. **No. of Franchise Units:** 8. **Founded:** 1994.. **Franchised:** 1998. **Equity Capital Needed:** $5,000 down; balance paid end of 12 months. **Franchise Fee:** $2,500 and up. **Financial Assistance:** Yes. **Training:** Yes.

44609 ■ 4Refuel
9440 202nd St., Ste. 215
Langley, BC, Canada V1M 4A6
Ph: (604)881-4445
Free: 888-473-3835
Fax: (604)881-4446
Co. E-mail: jvaleriote@4refuel.com
URL: http://www.4refuel.com
Description: 4Refuel has evolved from being a product provider to being a complete service and solutions provider (diesel fuel, environmentally friendly, timely and safe delivery, information/data collection and reporting.) We reinvented our company and are ready to grow into new markets and attract thousands of new clients because no one else in the world does what we do. **No. of Franchise Units:** 59. **No. of Company-Owned Units:** 6. **Founded:** 1995.. **Franchised:** 1995. **Equity Capital Needed:** $100,000-$150,000. **Franchise Fee:** $75,000.

44610 ■ The Franchise Co., Inc.
5397 Eglinton Ave. W, Ste. 108
Etobicoke, ON, Canada M9C 5K6
Ph: (416)620-4700
Fax: (416)620-9955
Co. E-mail: info@thefranchisecompany.com
URL: http://www.thefranchisecompany.com
Description: Focus is on home and business services with six distinct systems as California Closets, Certa ProPainters, Stained Glass Overlay, Paul Davis Restoration (US), College Pro Painters, Action Window Cleaners and Nutri-Lawn. **No. of Franchise Units:** 1,800. **Founded:** 1992.. **Equity Capital Needed:** Varies.

44611 ■ The Gutter Guys
The Gutter Guys Franchisor, Inc.
2547 Fire Rd., Ste. E-5
Egg Harbor Township, NJ 08234
Ph: (609)646-4888
Fax: (609)646-7283
URL: http://www.thegutterguys.com
Description: Seamless gutter manufacturing, installation and maintenance. **No. of Franchise Units:** 10. **No. of Company-Owned Units:** 4. **Founded:** 1988.. **Franchised:** 2000. **Equity Capital Needed:** $36,500 liquid; $90,000 total investment range. **Franchise Fee:** $15,000. **Training:** Yes.

44612 ■ Ident-A-Kid
Ident-A-Kid Franchising Corp.
2810 Scherer Dr., Ste. 100
St. Petersburg, FL 33716
Free: 800-890-1000
Fax: (727)576-8258
Co. E-mail: franchise@ident-a-kid.com
URL: http://www.Ident-A-Kid.com
Description: Provides laminated child ID cards that contain photograph, fingerprints, and physical description. Program is marketed through public and private schools. **No. of Franchise Units:** 208. **Founded:** 1986. **Franchised:** 2000. **Equity Capital Needed:** $24,900 total investment, including equipment, software, supplies, and training. **Franchise Fee:** $24,900. **Financial Assistance:** Yes. **Training:** Provides 2 day training session at the distributor's residence. Training includes: The identification process, equipment operation, computer and marketing techniques.

44613 ■ InfantHouse.com
6101 Long Prarie, Ste. 744-115
Flower Mound, TX 75028
Free: 866-463-2685
Fax: (972)691-8807
Description: Baby proofing. **No. of Company-Owned Units:** 1. **Founded:** 2005.. **Franchised:** 2007. **Equity Capital Needed:** $23,500-$26,000. **Franchise Fee:** $7,000. **Royalty Fee:** 7%. **Training:** 1 week training at headquarters and ongoing support.

44614 ■ Jon'Ric International Spas
PO Box 1856
Deland, FL 32721
Ph: (888)609-0123
Fax: (407)358-5421
Description: Medical, dental and day spas. **No. of Franchise Units:** 52. **No. of Company-Owned Units:** 2. **Founded:** 1983.. **Franchised:** 2003. **Equity Capital Needed:** $95,000-$350,000. **Franchise Fee:** $29,500. **Financial Assistance:** Yes. **Training:** Yes.

44615 ■ Mr. Appliance
1010 N University Parks Dr.
Waco, TX 76707
Ph: (800)290-1422
Fax: (800)209-7621
Co. E-mail: steven.cox@dwyergroup.com
URL: http://www.mrappliancefranchise.com
Description: Home and commercial appliance repair and maintenance. **No. of Franchise Units:** 10. **Founded:** 1996.. **Franchised:** 1996. **Equity Capital Needed:** $24,000 investment required; $30,000 start-up capital required. **Franchise Fee:** $24,000 per 100,000 population. **Training:** Initial, onsite, intranet and ongoing support.

44616 ■ On Track Power Window Repair
On Track Franchising, LLC
4616 Popular Level Rd.
Louisville, KY 40213
Ph: (502)777-0114
Fax: (502)962-6250
Co. E-mail: john@ontrackrepair.com
URL: http://www.OnTrackRepair.com
Description: Power window repair. This is virtually an untapped multi-billion dollar market. There is a continuous supply of window systems to repair. **No. of Company-Owned Units:** 1. **Founded:** 2002.. **Franchised:** 2007. **Equity Capital Needed:** $64,200-$77,900. **Franchise Fee:** $32,000. **Royalty Fee:** 7%.

Training: Provides 2 weeks hands on training and in depth technical instruction as it relates to power and manual window, door locks, mirrors, latches and door handles.

44617 ■ 1-800-Radiator
4401 Park Rd.
Benicia, CA 94510
Ph: (707)580-5318
Free: 866-780-9392
Fax: (707)747-7401
Co. E-mail: kellyg@1800radiator.com
URL: http://www.1800radiator.com
Description: Each franchise operation is typically comprised of a 2,000 to 3,000 square foot warehouse stocked with approximately 1,200 radiators. You and your staff of 1 to 3 people will make field sales calls, take phone orders, manage inventory, dispatch drivers and deliver products within 3 hours of orders being taken. You will typically be open 9 hours per day, 5 1/2 days per week. Your ability to call on new prospective customers and service them to high levels will be the key to your success. **No. of Franchise Units:** 230. **No. of Company-Owned Units:** 5. **Founded:** 1983.. **Franchised:** 2003. **Equity Capital Needed:** $172,000. **Franchise Fee:** $45,000. **Royalty Fee:** 8%.

44618 ■ Pet Butler
HomeTask
1800 SW 152nd St., Ste. 100
Seattle, WA 98166
Ph: (206)763-6800
Free: 800-PET-BUTLER
Fax: (206)763-6883
Description: Pet waste cleanup, removal & more. **No. of Franchise Units:** 36. **Founded:** 1988.. **Franchised:** 2005. **Equity Capital Needed:** $17,000-$29,000. **Franchise Fee:** $15,000. **Financial Assistance:** Yes. **Training:** Yes.

44619 ■ Pirtek USA
501 Haverty Ct.
Rockledge, FL 32955
Ph: (321)504-4422
Description: Offers industrial services. **No. of Franchise Units:** 373. **No. of Company-Owned Units:** 2. **Founded:** 1980.. **Franchised:** 1985. **Equity Capital Needed:** $125,000 minimum. **Franchise Fee:** $49,000. **Training:** Yes.

44620 ■ Play N Trade Franchise Inc.
1330 Calle Avanzado, 2nd Fl.
San Clemente, CA 92673
Ph: (888)895-2156
Fax: (866)260-7261
URL: http://www.playntrade.com
URL(s): www.playntradevideogamefranchise.com.
Description: New & used video games. **No. of Franchise Units:** 133. **No. of Operating Units:** 163. **Founded:** 2001. **Franchised:** 2003. **Equity Capital Needed:** $134,500-$255,000. **Franchise Fee:** $30,000. **Royalty Fee:** 5%. **Financial Assistance:** Limited third party and in-house financing available. **Training:** Training available at headquarters, at franchisee's location and ongoing including distance learning.

44621 ■ Precision Door Service
Precision Holdings of Brevard, Inc.
2395 S Washington Ave., Ste. 5
Titusville, FL 32780
Ph: (321)225-3500
Free: 800-985-1430
Fax: (321)225-3511
Co. E-mail: edresser@precisiondoor.net
URL: http://www.precisiondoor.net
Description: Garage door repair and installation service. **No. of Franchise Units:** 68. **Founded:** 1997.. **Franchised:** 1999. **Equity Capital Needed:** $200,000. **Franchise Fee:** $10,000-$200,000. **Training:** Complete training and ongoing support.

44622 ■ Receil it Professional Ceiling Restoration
175 Liberty St., Ste. B
Copiague, NY 11726
Ph: (631)842-0099
Free: 800-234-5464

Fax: (631)980-7668
Co. E-mail: info@receilit.com
URL: http://www.receilit.com
Description: Restoration or cleaning of drop ceilings. **No. of Franchise Units:** 2. **No. of Company-Owned Units:** 1. **Founded:** 1992. **Franchised:** 2003. **Equity Capital Needed:** $38,900-$58,900. **Franchise Fee:** $17,500. **Royalty Fee:** 7%. **Training:** Provides 5-6 days training at headquarters and ongoing support.

44623 ■ Servicemaster of Canada Limited
5462 Timberlea Blvd.
Mississauga, ON, Canada L4W 2T7
Ph: (905)670-0000
Free: 800-263-5928
Fax: (905)670-0077
URL: http://www.servicemaster.com
Description: Offers a variety of services including disaster restoration, commercial carpet and upholstery cleaning, residential carpet and upholstery cleaning, contract janitorial services. **No. of Franchise Units:** 180. **Founded:** 1948.. **Franchised:** 1950. **Equity Capital Needed:** $25,000-$100,000. **Franchise Fee:** $24,000-$67,000. **Training:** Offers 2

weeks at ServiceMaster Academy then ongoing support out of Canadian Head Office.

44624 ■ Squeegee Squad
Jack & Joes Franchising Inc.
8862 Zealand Ave. N., Ste. A
Minneapolis, MN 55445
Ph: (763)780-0492
Fax: (763)780-7372
Description: Residential & new construction window cleaning. **No. of Franchise Units:** 28. **No. of Company-Owned Units:** 1. **No. of Operating Units:** 31. **Founded:** 1999.. **Franchised:** 2005. **Equity Capital Needed:** $25,300-$70,110. **Franchise Fee:** $14,900. **Royalty Fee:** 7-5%. **Financial Assistance:** Assistance with franchise fee. **Training:** Yes.

44625 ■ Suspended In Time, Inc.
122 S Mountainway Dr.
Orem, UT 84058
Ph: (801)227-0075
Free: 866-756-0059
Fax: (801)221-1003
Co. E-mail: info@suspendedintime.com
URL: http://www.suspendedintime.com
Description: With the remarkable discovery of Suspended in Time's technology in floral preserva-

tion over the last 10 years, we are expanding our business opportunities. This is not a Freeze Dry Method. We offer an excellent dealership package with low start-up fees. This preservation process only takes an average of 3-5 days to complete. **No. of Franchise Units:** 47. **Founded:** 1997.. **Equity Capital Needed:** $4,886. **Training:** Training provided at the corporate location 3, 10 hour days, which includes lunch - large discount on room accommodations and ongoing support as long as needed.

44626 ■ Worldwide Wireless
Worldwide Wireless Franchise Services LLC
1000 Eagle Ridge Dr.
Schererville, IN 46375
Ph: (219)864-9991
Free: 877-346-3999
Fax: (219)864-9992
URL: http://www.worldwidewirelessinc.com
Description: Exclusive Sprint dealership. **Founded:** 1999.. **Franchised:** 2006. **Equity Capital Needed:** $75,000-$150,000. **Franchise Fee:** $30,000. **Financial Assistance:** Yes. **Training:** Yes.

START-UP INFORMATION

44627 ■ *The Canadian Small Business Survival Guide: How to Start and Operate Your Own Successful Business*
Pub: Dundurn Group

Ed: Benj Gallander. FRQ June 2002. **Price:** $26.99. **Description:** Ideas for starting and running a successful small business. Topics include selecting a business, financing, government assistance, locations, franchises, and marketing ideas.

44628 ■ *The Complete Idiot's Guide to Starting and Running a Thrift Store*
Pub: Alpha Publishing House

Ed: Ravel Buckley, Carol Costa. **Released:** January 5, 2010. **Price:** $18.95. **Description:** Thrift stores saw a 35 percent increase in sales during the falling economy in 2008. Despite the low startup costs, launching and running a thrift store is complicated. Two experts cover the entire process, including setting up a store on a nonprofit basis, choosing a location, funding, donations for saleable items, recruiting and managing staff, sorting items, pricing, and recycling donations.

44629 ■ *"Geo-Marketing: Site Selection by the Numbers" in Franchising World (Vol. 42, September 2010, No. 9, pp.)*
Pub: International Franchise Association

Ed: Kellen Vaughan. **Description:** Site location is critical when starting a new franchise. Information to help franchisees choose the right location is included.

44630 ■ *"Head West, Young Startup?" in Boston Business Journal (Vol. 30, October 22, 2010, No. 39, pp. 1)*
Pub: Boston Business Journal

Ed: Galen Moore. **Description:** Startup companies Lark Technologies, Baydin and E la Cart Inc. are planning to leave Boston, Massachusetts for Silicon Valley. Lark has developed a vibrating wrist strap that syncs with a mobile phone's alarm clock.

44631 ■ *"Where to be an Entrepreneur: Ten Startup-Friendly Cities" in Entrepreneur (Vol. 37, August 2009, No. 8, pp. 49)*
Pub: Entrepreneur Media, Inc.

Ed: Jason Daley. **Description:** Ten U.S. cities that embody the entrepreneurial spirit are presented. These cities are ideal for startup companies and profiles of businesses that are making it in these cities are discussed.

44632 ■ *Working for Yourself: An Entrepreneur's Guide to the Basics*
Pub: Kogan Page, Limited

Contact: Ben Glover, Director of Marketing

Ed: Jonathan Reuvid. **Released:** September 2006. **Description:** Guide for starting a new business venture, focusing on raising financing, legal and tax issues, marketing, information technology, and site location.

REFERENCE WORKS

44633 ■ *"Aeronautics Seeking New HQ Site" in The Business Journal-Milwaukee (Vol. 25, September 5, 2008, No. 50, pp. 1)*
Pub: American City Business Journals, Inc.

Ed: Rich Kirchen. **Description:** Milwaukee, Wisconsin-based Aeronautics Corp. of America is planning to move its headquarters to a new site. The company has started to search for a new site. It also plans to consolidate its operations under one roof.

44634 ■ *"Aircraft Maker May Land Here" in Austin Business Journal (Vol. 31, April 15, 2011, No. 6, pp. 1)*
Pub: American City Business Journals Inc.

Ed: Jacob Dirr. **Description:** Icon Aircraft Inc. is planning to build a manufacturing facility in Austin, Texas. The company needs 100,000 square feet of space in a new or renovated plant. Executive comments are included.

44635 ■ *"Allen Tate Expanding to Research Triangle Park: Firm Expects Raleigh Market to Grow Faster" in Charlotte Observer (January 31, 2007)*
Pub: Knight-Ridder/Tribune Business News

Ed: Doug Smith; Dudley Price. **Description:** Allen Tate Realtors expanded its operations to the Research Triangle area. The firm is predicting a strong market and growth in Charlotte, North Carolina.

44636 ■ *"AMC Scouts Downtown for New HQ" in Business Journal-Serving Metropolitan Kansas City (Vol. 26, October 19, 2007, No. 6, pp. 1)*
Pub: American City Business Journals, Inc.

Ed: Jim Davis. **Description:** AMC Entertainment Inc. is seeking a new 100,000 square foot office in downtown Kansas City. The new headquarters is expected to bring additional employment and revenue to the city. AMC's stay on Main Street since 2002 is discussed.

44637 ■ *"Another California Firm On Way" in Austin Business Journal (Vol. 31, May 6, 2011, No. 9, pp. 1)*
Pub: American City Business Journals Inc.

Ed: Christopher Calnan. **Description:** Main Street Hub Inc. is planning to build a facility in Austin, Texas. The company helps businesses manage their online reputations. Main Street has selected Aquila Commercial LLC as its real estate broker.

44638 ■ *"Aquila HQ Hits the Market" in The Business Journal-Serving Metropolitan Kansas City (Vol. 26, July 25, 2008, No. 46, pp. 1)*
Pub: American City Business Journals, Inc.

Ed: Rob Roberts. **Description:** Commercial real estate experts believe that Aquila Inc.'s former headquarters will be hard to rent out. The historic value of the building, being Kansas City's first skyscraper, is not expected to add value to the price of the rent. Other views and information on the building, as well as on Aquila, are presented.

44639 ■ *"The Asian Decade" in Hawaii Business (Vol. 53, January 2008, No. 7, pp. 19)*
Pub: Hawaii Business Publishing

Ed: Cathy S. Cruz-George. **Description:** Chaney Brooks, a Hawaiian real estate company, has affiliated with commercial real estate network NAI Global. The NAI partnership will improve Hawaii's international business, particularly its Asian investments. Hawaii's diverse workforce is evaluated, with regards to being an asset for international businesses.

44640 ■ *"Asterand Eyes Jump to Ann Arbor; TechTown Tenant" in Crain's Detroit Business (Vol. 25, June 22, 2009)*
Pub: Crain Communications Inc. - Detroit

Ed: Tom Henderson. **Description:** Asterand PLC is considering a move to Ann Arbor from its current location as anchor tenant at TechTown, an incubator and technology park associated with Wayne State University. The university believes the Ann Arbor location's rent is too expensive for the tissue bank company.

44641 ■ *"Austin Ponders Annexing F1 Racetrack" in Austin Business Journal (Vol. 31, July 8, 2011, No. 18, pp. 1)*
Pub: American City Business Journals Inc.

Ed: Vicky Garza. **Description:** City planners in Austin, Texas are studying the feasibility of annexing the land under and around the Circuit of the Americas Formula One Racetrack being constructed east of the city. The annexation could generate at least $13 million in financial gain over 25 years from property taxes alone.

44642 ■ *"BancVue to Expand" in Austin Business JournalInc. (Vol. 29, November 27, 2009, No. 38, pp. 1)*
Pub: American City Business Journals

Ed: Kate Harrington. **Description:** Significant growth of BancVue in the past six years has prompted the company to look for a site that could increase its office space from 25,000 square feet to 65,000 square feet. BancVue offers bank and credit union software solutions and is planning to lease or buy a property in Austin, Texas.

44643 ■ *"Bank Bullish on Austin" in Austin Business JournalInc. (Vol. 29, November 13, 2009, No. 36, pp. A1)*
Pub: American City Business Journals

Ed: Kate Harrington. **Description:** American Bank's presence in Austin, Texas has been boosted by new management and a new 20,000 square foot building. This community bank intends to focus on building relationship with commercial banking customers. American Bank also plans to extend investment banking, treasury management, and commercial lending services.

44644 ■ *"Before Signing a Lease" in Business Owner (Vol. 35, September-October*

2011, No. 5, pp. 14)
Pub: DL Perkins Company
Description: The following terms are essential to investigate before renewing or negotiating a lease for a small business: Term, Neighbors, Actual Usable Space, Gross or Net, Tenant Improvements, Renewal Option, Purchase Option, Cancelation Option, Sublease or Assignment, Security Deposit, Code Restrictions and Zoning, Parking, Relief and Lease Agreement.

44645 ■ *"Betting On Slots" in Baltimore Business Journal (Vol. 28, November 19, 2010, No. 28, pp. 1)*
Pub: Baltimore Business Journal
Ed: Rachel Bernstein. **Description:** Penn National Gaming Company's Hollywood Casino in Perryville, Maryland has been betting on the slot machines to lure slot players to the region to boost the town's growth. The success of Maryland's first casino is expected to lead to the development of land in the area.

44646 ■ *"Biz Assesses 'Textgate' Fallout; Conventions, Smaller Deals Affected" in Crain's Detroit Business (Vol. 24, March 31, 2008)*
Pub: Crain Communications, Inc.
Ed: Tom Henderson. **Description:** Businesspeople who were trying to measure the amount of economic damage is likely to be caused due to Mayor Kwame Kilpatrick's indictment on eight charges and found that: automotive and other large global deals are less likely to be affected than location decisions by smaller companies and convention site decisions. Also being affected are negotiations in which Mexican startup companies were planning a partnership with the TechTown incubator to pursue opportunities in the auto sector; those plans are being put on hold while they look at other sites.

44647 ■ *"Boeing's Next Flight May Well Be to the South" in Puget Sound Business Journal (Vol. 29, November 21, 2008, No. 31, pp.)*
Pub: American City Business Journals
Ed: Steve Wilhelm. **Description:** Southern states in the U.S. are luring Boeing Company to locate a new plant in their region which is experiencing a growing industrial base while offering permissive labor laws as selling points.

44648 ■ *"Bond Hill Cinema Site To See New Life" in Business Courier (Vol. 27, October 29, 2010, No. 26, pp. 1)*
Pub: Business Courier
Ed: Dan Monk. **Description:** Avondale, Ohio's Corinthian Baptist Church will redevelop the 30-acre former Showcase Cinema property to a mixed-use site that could feature a college, senior home, and retail. Corinthian Baptist, which is one of the largest African-American churches in the region, is also planning to relocate the church.

44649 ■ *"A Bright Spot: Industrial Space in Demand Again" in Sacramento Business Journal (Vol. 28, October 21, 2011, No. 34, pp. 1)*
Pub: Sacramento Business Journal
Ed: Michael Shaw. **Description:** Sacramento, California's industrial sites have been eyed by potential tenants who are actively seeking space larger than 50,000 square feet.

44650 ■ *"Brokerages Seek a Foothold in Local Real Estate Market" in Charlotte Business Journal (Vol. 25, October 15, 2010, No. 30, pp. 1)*
Pub: Charlotte Business Journal
Ed: Will Boye. **Description:** Charlotte, North Carolina has become an attractive destination for out-of-town brokerage firms. Colliers International has signed an affiliate deal with Anthony and Company to set up shop in Charlotte. Grubb and Ellis Company, on the other hand, is planning to open an office in the city.

44651 ■ *"Business Plan Refines Focus" in Business Journal Portland (Vol. 27, December 10, 2010, No. 41, pp. 1)*
Pub: Portland Business Journal
Ed: Wendy Culverwell. **Description:** Organizers of the Oregon Business Plan's Leadership Summit 2010 seek the opinions of nearly 1,000 business, educa-

tion, political, and civic leaders in an effort to address how to rehabilitate Oregon's economy. The opinion-seeking actions recognize the organizers' belief that the economic fate of the state depends on rural Oregon.

44652 ■ *"Challenges, Responses and Available Resources" in Journal of Small Business and Entrepreneurship (Vol. 23, Winter 2010, No. 1)*
Pub: Canadian Council for Small Business and Entrepreneurship
Ed: Lynne Siemens. **Description:** Rural communities and their residents are exploring the potential of small business and entrepreneurship to address the economic changes they are facing. While these rural areas present many opportunities, business people in these areas face challenges which they must navigate to operate successfully.

44653 ■ *"Chinese Solar Panel Manufacturer Scopes Out Austin" in Austin Business JournalInc. (Vol. 29, October 30, 2009, No. 34, pp. 1)*
Pub: American City Business Journals
Ed: Jacob Dirr. **Description:** China's Yingli Green Energy Holding Company Ltd. is looking for a site in order to construct a $20 million photovoltaic panel plant. Both Austin and San Antonio are vying to house the manufacturing hub. The project could create about 300 jobs and give Austin a chance to become a player in the solar energy market. Other solar companies are also considering Central Texas as an option to set up shop.

44654 ■ *"Chuy's Gears Up to Serve Atlants, Other Untapped Cities" in Austin Business Journal (Vol. 31, June 17, 2011, No. 15, pp. 1)*
Pub: American City Business Journals Inc.
Ed: Cody Lyon. **Description:** Chuy's Holdings Inc. plans to expand into the Southeastern United States, particularly in Atlanta, Georgia. The restaurant, which secured $67.5 million in debt financing in May 2011, added 20 stores in five years and plans to open eight locations in 2011.

44655 ■ *"Cities Work to Attract Small Biz" in Crain's Detroit Business (Vol. 25, June 8, 2009, No. 23, pp. 20)*
Pub: Crain Communications Inc. - Detroit
Ed: Nancy Kaffer. **Description:** Royal Oak and other metropolitan cities are trying to attract small companies to their towns.

44656 ■ *"City Wooing Red Roof Inn for Return of Corporate HQ" in Business First-Columbus (October 19, 2007, pp. A1)*
Pub: American City Business Journals, Inc.
Description: Department of Development of Columbus, Ohio offered Red Roof Inns Inc. a four-year, 40 percent jobs growth initiative to entice the company to move its corporate headquarters into the city from Dallas, Texas. The Watermark Island office building off Dublin Road and Grandview Avenue will be the headquarters of the company if it accepts the offer.

44657 ■ *"City's Streetcar Utility Estimate Way Off Mark" in Business Courier (Vol27, November 19, 2010, No. 29. , pp. 1)*
Pub: Business Courier
Ed: Dan Monk, Lucy May. **Description:** Duke Energy Corporation has released new estimates that show moving electric and gas lines alone for Cincinnati, Ohio's proposed streetcar project could cost more than $20 million. However, the city has only estimated the relocation to cost $5 million in federal grant applications.

44658 ■ *"Conversation: Historian Geoffrey Jones On Why Knowledge Stays Put" in Harvard Business Review (Vol. 86, July-August 2008, No. 8)*
Pub: Harvard Business School Press
Ed: Gardiner Morse. **Description:** Geoffrey Jones, Harvard Business School's professor of business history, discusses factors that cause knowledge to concentrate in particular regions, rather than disperse, such as the location of wealth.

44659 ■ *"Coors Execs Listen to Milwaukee Pitch" in Business Journal-Milwaukee (Vol. 25, November 2, 2007, No. 5, pp. A1)*
Pub: American City Business Journals, Inc.
Ed: Rich Rovito. **Description:** Coors Brewing Company officials met with Wisconsin Governor Jim Doyle and Milwaukee Mayor Tom Barnett about putting the MillerCoors corporate headquarters in Milwaukee. The city is competing with Denver, Colorado for the headquarters of the joint venture.

44660 ■ *"Could This Be Your Next Office Building?" in Austin Business Journal (Vol. 31, May 13, 2011, No. 10, pp. A1)*
Pub: American City Business Journals Inc.
Ed: Cody Lyon. **Description:** Falcon Containers moved to a 51-acre site in Far East Austin, Texas and started construction of a 2,500-square-foot headquarters made from eight 40-foot shipping containers. Falcon's CEO Stephen Shang plans to use his headquarters building as a showroom to attract upscale, urban hipsters. Insights on the construction's environmental and social impact are shared.

44661 ■ *"Could UNCC Be Home to Future Med School Here?" in Charlotte Business Journal (Vol. 25, July 23, 2010, No. 18, pp. 1)*
Pub: Charlotte Business Journal
Ed: Jennifer Thomas. **Description:** University of North Carolina, Charlotte chancellor Phil Dubois is proposing that a medical school be established at the campus. The idea began in 2007 and Dubois' plan is for students to spend all four years in Charlotte and train at the Carolinas Medical Center.

44662 ■ *"Cupcake Maker Grabs Outpost" in Crain's New York Business (Vol. 27, August 15, 2011, No. 33, pp. 16)*
Pub: Crain Communications, Inc.
Ed: Jermaine Taylor. **Description:** Family-owned miniature cupcake maker, Baked by Melissa, singed a ten-year lease, expanding their stores to five. The business was started three years ago by advertising executive Melissa Bushell.

44663 ■ *"Deal Made for Pontiac Home of Film Studio" in Crain's Detroit Business (Vol. 25, June 1, 2009, No. 22, pp. 3)*
Pub: Crain Communications Inc. - Detroit
Ed: Daniel Duggan. **Description:** Details of the $75 million movie production and training facility in Pontiac, Michigan are revealed.

44664 ■ *"Delta Looks at Downtown Departure" in Business Courier (Vol. 27, October 1, 2010, No. 22, pp. 1)*
Pub: Business Courier
Ed: Dan Monk. **Description:** Delta Air Lines Inc. has been looking for a smaller office for its reservations center in downtown Cincinnati, Ohio. Delta has informed the city of its plan to seek proposals on office space alternatives in advance of the 2011 lease expiration. Insights on the current employment status at the reservations center are also given.

44665 ■ *"Denver Will Put Up Fight for MillerCoors HQ" in Business Journal-Milwaukee (Vol. 25, October 19, 2007, No. 3, pp. A1)*
Pub: American City Business Journals, Inc.
Ed: Rich Rovito. **Description:** A contention exists between Milwaukee and Denver over which city will become the new location of the Miller Brewing Company (Milwaukee) and Coors Brewing Company (Colorado) joint venture MillerCoors. Leaders of the breweries since the announcement of the merger, have contended frantically to prepare strategies to back up their own cities. The advantages and disadvantages of both cities are presented.

44666 ■ *"Downtown Detroit Needs More Retail" in Crain's Detroit Business (Vol. 24, March 10, 2008, No. 10, pp. 9)*
Pub: Crain Communications, Inc.
Ed: Robin Boyle; James Bieri. **Description:** Although Detroit is doing well with event-driven traffic, the city remains far off the site selection rosters of major national retailers as well as smaller retail outlets.

44667 ■ *"Downtown Retail Site Sold to ATCO"* *in Austin Business JournalInc. (Vol. 29, November 20, 2009, No. 37, pp. 1)*
Pub: American City Business Journals
Ed: Kate Harrington. **Description:** New York-based real estate company ATCO Advisory Services purchased a 13,700 square foot retail space in Austin, Texas from 360 Condominiums. The selection of the retail space, named the Shops at 360 has been attributed to the local tenant mix and its location in downtown Austin. Meanwhile, ATCO may continue investing in the area in the near future.

44668 ■ *"Drawn to York County: Less-Expensive Homes, Good Schools Attract Charlotteans"* *in Charlotte Observer (February 4, 2007)*
Pub: Knight-Ridder/Tribune Business News
Ed: Taylor Bright. **Description:** York County, North Carolina offers low-priced homes and good schools, making it attractive to workers and small business.

44669 ■ *The Emerging Digital Economy: Entrepreneurship, Clusters, and Policy*
Pub: Springer
Ed: Borje Johansson; Charlie Karlsson; Roger Stough. **Released:** August 2006. **Price:** $119.00. **Description:** The new economy, or digital economy, and its impact on the way industries and firms choose to locate and cluster geographically.

44670 ■ *"Exiting Stage Left"* *in Baltimore Business Journal (Vol. 28, June 18, 2010, No. 6, pp. 1)*
Pub: Baltimore Business Journal
Ed: Scott Dance. **Description:** Film professionals including crew members and actors have been leaving Maryland to find work in other states such as Michigan, Louisiana, and Georgia where bigger budgets and film production incentives are given. Other consequences of this trend in local TV and film production are discussed.

44671 ■ *"Feds, Not City, Will Pick GSA Office Site"* *in Business Journal-Serving Metropolitan Kansas City (Vol. 26, November 30, 2007, No. 12)*
Pub: American City Business Journals, Inc.
Ed: Jim Davis. **Description:** Mark Funkhouser wants the federal government to decide the location of the General Services Administration building site. The act of the Mayor enraged the executive director of Kansas City Port Authority, Vincent Gauthier. Details of the GSAs building location plans are discussed.

44672 ■ *"Fifth Third Spinoff"* *in Business Courier (Vol. 27, July 16, 2010, No. 11, pp. 1)*
Pub: Business Courier
Ed: Dan Monk, Steve Watkins. **Description:** Electronic-funds transfer company Fifth Third Solutions (FTPS), a spinoff of Fifth Third Bancorp, is seeking as much as 200,000 square feet of new office space in Ohio. The bank's sale of 51 percent ownership stake to Boston-based Advent International Corporation has paved the way for the growth of FTPS. How real estate brokers' plans have responded to FTPS' growth mode is discussed.

44673 ■ *"Formaspace Finds a Bigger Home"* *in Austin Business JournalInc. (Vol. 29, December 4, 2009, No. 39, pp. 1)*
Pub: American City Business Journals
Ed: Kate Harrington. **Description:** Formaspace Technical Furniture has signed a lease for 56,700 square feet in Harris Ridge Business Center at Northeast Austin, Texas, which represents one of the area's largest leases for 2009. The new lease enables Formaspace to hire new employees, invest in new equipment, and take advantage of a taxing designation created for manufacturers.

44674 ■ *"Franchises with an Eye on Chicago"* *in Crain's Chicago Business (Vol. 34, March 14, 2011, No. 11, pp. 20)*
Pub: Crain Communications Inc.
Description: Profiles of franchise companies seeking franchisees for the Chicago area include: Extreme Pita, a sandwich shop; Hand and Stone, offering massage, facial and waxing services; Molly Maid, home-

cleaning service; Primrose Schools, private accredited schools for children 6 months to 6 hears and after-school programs; Protect Painters, residential and light-commercial painting contractor; and Wingstop, a restaurant offering chicken wings in nine flavors, fries and side dishes.

44675 ■ *"Furniture Chain Moving to Harford"* *in Baltimore Business Journal (Vol. 27, January 22, 2010, No. 38, pp. 1)*
Pub: American City Business Journals
Ed: David J. Sernovitz. **Description:** Manchester, Connecticut-based Bob's Discount Furniture signed a lease for 672,000 square feet of space in Harford County, Maryland. The site will become the discount furniture retailer's distribution center in mid-Atlantic US. As many as 200 jobs could be generated when the center opens.

44676 ■ *"Game Changer"* *in Canadian Business (Vol. 83, June 15, 2010, No. 10, pp. 52)*
Pub: Rogers Media Ltd.
Ed: Jordan Timm. **Description:** Ubisoft chose Ontario to be the site for its new development studio and it has appointed Jade Raymond as its managing director. Raymond was born in Montreal in 1975 and studied computer science at McGill. Raymond is said to possess the understanding of the game industry's technical, art, and business components.

44677 ■ *Getting Rich In Your Underwear: How To Start and Run a Profitable Home-Based Business*
Pub: HCM Publishing
Ed: Peter I. Hupalo. **Released:** April 1, 2005. **Price:** $17.95. **Description:** Book offers insight into starting a home-based business. Entrepreneurs will learn about business models and the home business; distribution and fulfillment of product or service; marketing and sales; how to overcome the fear of starting a business; personal success characteristics; naming a business; zoning and insurance; intellectual capital; copyrights, trademarks, and patents; limited liability companies and S-corporations; business expenses and accounting; taxes; fifteen basic steps for starting a home-based business, state resources for starting a home company; and seven home-based business ideas.

44678 ■ *"Good for Business: Houston is a Hot Spot for Economic Growth"* *in Black Enterprise (Vol. 37, October 2006, No. 3, pp. 216)*
Pub: Earl G. Graves Publishing Co. Inc.
Ed: Jeanette Valentine. **Description:** Fast-growing sectors in the biotechnology and healthcare industries are among the driving forces of Houston's economic growth. More than 76,000 small businesses in the area employ about one in four area workers, according to the Small Business Administration. Housing and business costs are 26 and 11 percent below the national average, respectively, garnering the attention of corporate giants.

44679 ■ *"Green Firm Scouts Sites in Tri-State"* *in Business Courier (Vol. 27, July 23, 2010, No. 12, pp. 1)*
Pub: Business Courier
Ed: Dan Monk. **Description:** CresaPartners is searching for a manufacturing facility in Cincinnati, Ohio. The company is set to tour about ten sites in the area.

44680 ■ *"Hispanic Business 100 Fastest-Growing Companies"* *in Hispanic Business (July-August 2009, pp. 16-18)*
Pub: Hispanic Business
Ed: Joshua Molina. **Description:** Despite the recession, the 100 fastest growing companies profiled are able to maintain their competitive edge; federal contracts are key to their success. Service companies are at the top of the list and Texas and Florida are the states in which the top are located.

44681 ■ *"Hispanic Businesses Try to Drum Up Cash to Battle Crime Spree"* *in Baltimore*

Business Journal (Vol. 28, September 3, 2010, No. 17)
Pub: Baltimore Business Journal
Ed: Scott Dance. **Description:** Hispanic businesses in Baltimore, Maryland have been raising funds to pay off-duty police officers to patrol a few blocks of Broadway in Fells Point to help curb crime. Efforts to make the area a Latin Town have failed owing to muggings, prostitution and drug dealing. Comments from small business owners are also given.

44682 ■ *"Horizon Acquires Significant Working Interest in High Impact Prospect in Southeast Texas"* *in Canadian Corporate News (May 14, 2007)*
Pub: Comtex News Network Inc.
Description: Horizon Industries Ltd., an emerging gas and oil exploration and production company, announced that it has entered into a Joint Venture agreement with Pan American Development Company, Inc. in which they will begin a drilling program in San Jacinto County, Texas.

44683 ■ *How to Start and Run Your Own Corporation: S-Corporations For Small Business Owners*
Pub: HCM Publishing
Ed: Peter I. Hupalo. **Released:** March 6, 2003. **Price:** $22.95. **Description:** Basics of corporate business structure are explained. Topics include discovering the best business structure for your company; how to decided between an S-Corporation and LLC; choosing the state in which to incorporate, how to form a corporation, angel investing, special issues for one-person corporations, the role of bylaws and corporate minutes, board of directors, taxes, workers' compensation issues, retirement plans, and more.

44684 ■ *"In Addition, Pinkberry Reports It Is Opening a New Shop in Sunnyvale, CA"* *in Ice Cream Reporter (Vol. 23, October 20, 2010)*
Pub: Ice Cream Reporter
Description: Pinkberry opened a new shop in Sunnyvale, California, its fourth opening in the South Bay and its 101st location worldwide.

44685 ■ *"Incentives In Play for Astronautics"* *in Business Journal-Milwaukee (Vol. 28, November 5, 2010, No. 5, pp. A1)*
Pub: Milwaukee Business Journal
Ed: Sean Ryan. **Description:** Astronautics Corporation was offered incentives by local government officials in Milwaukee, Wisconsin and by Brewery Project LLC to move into a building in The Brewery in the city. The company's officials remain indecisive over the offers and incentives.

44686 ■ *"Insitu Looks to Oregon"* *in Business Journal Portland (Vol. 27, October 29, 2010, No. 35, pp. 1)*
Pub: Portland Business Journal
Ed: Erik Siemers. **Description:** Bingen, Washington-based Insitu Inc. announced that it has narrowed the search for a new corporate campus into five locations within the Columbia Gorge region. However, state economic development officials are curious whether the company will land in Oregon or Washington. Insights on economic impact of Insitu's decision are also given.

44687 ■ *"Insuraprise Growing Fast"* *in Austin Business Journal (Vol. 31, April 22, 2011, No. 7, pp. 1)*
Pub: American City Business Journals Inc.
Ed: Sandra Zaragoza. **Description:** Austin, Texas-based Insuraprise Inc. is finalizing the purchase of a 24,000-square-foot office at 12116 Jekel Circle. The firm, with 23 salespeople and sales that are growing nearly 300 percent over the past 18 months, will now have room to grow. Insuraprise plans to hire 35 new salespersons for its call center.

44688 ■ *"It's Not Perfect; But Illinois a Good Home for Business"* *in Crain's Chicago Business (Vol. 34, October 24, 2011, No. 42, pp. 18)*
Pub: Crain Communications Inc.
Description: Focusing on all factors that encompass Illinois' business environment, findings show that Illinois is a good place to start and grow a business.

The study focused on corporate income tax rates and the fact that talent, access to capital and customers along with transportation connections are among the important factors the state has for small businesses.

44689 ■ "Kellog Pores Over KC Sites" in Business Journal-Serving Metropolitan Kansas City (Vol. 26, November 23, 2007, No. 11, pp. 1)
Pub: American City Business Journals, Inc.
Ed: Jim Davis. Description: Kellog Company is searching Kansas City for a parcel about 1.3 million square feet to build its product distribution center. According to brokers, a selection might come by end of November 2007. Some of the potential sites are detailed.

44690 ■ "Kodiak Bucks Bear Market" in Austin Business JournalInc. (Vol. 29, December 18, 2009, No. 41, pp. 1)
Pub: American City Business Journals
Ed: Kate Harrington. Description: Austin, Texas-based Kodiak Assembly Solutions LLC, a company that installs components into printed circuit boards for product or evaluation tool kit prototyping purposes, will expand despite the recession. It will relocate from a 28,000 square foot space to a 42,000 square foot space in North Austin. The firm will also increase its workforce by 20 employees.

44691 ■ "KXAN Seeks Larger Studio, Office Space" in Austin Business Journal (Vol. 31, May 27, 2011, No. 12, pp. A1)
Pub: American City Business Journals Inc.
Ed: Cody Lyon. Description: Austin NBC affiliate KXAN Television is opting to sell its property north of downtown and relocate to another site. The station is now inspecting possible sites to house its broadcasting facility and employees totaling as many as 200 people. Estimated cost of the construction of the studios and offices is $13 million plus another million in moving the equipment.

44692 ■ "Law Firm Jones Day Coming to Boston" in Boston Business Journal (Vol. 30, November 19, 2010, No. 43, pp. 1)
Pub: Boston Business Journal
Ed: Lisa van der Pool. Description: Jones Day is set to open an office in Boston, Massachusetts. The company will be the largest law firm to enter Boston since 2007. The firm will open with at least three partners.

44693 ■ "Local Green Technology on Display" in Crain's Detroit Business (Vol. 26, January 18, 2010, No. 3, pp. 1)
Pub: Crain Communications Inc.
Ed: Ryan Beene. Description: Detroit's 2010 North American International Auto Show put the newest, most innovative green technologies on display showing that the Southeast Michigan automobile industry is gaining traction with its burgeoning e-vehicle infrastructure. Think, a Norwegian electric city-car manufacturer is eyeing sites in Southeast Michigan in which to locate its corporate headquarters and technical center for its North American branch.

44694 ■ "Luxury Still Sells Well" in Puget Sound Business Journal (Vol. 29, September 5, 2008, No. 20, pp. 1)
Pub: American City Business Journals
Ed: Jeanne Lang Jones. Description: High fashion retailers are planning to open stores in the Puget Sound area despite the economic slowdown, citing high incomes in the area despite the weak U.S. dollar.

44695 ■ "Magpower May Build Solar Panels Here" in Austin Business Journal (Vol. 31, May 13, 2011, No. 10, pp. A1)
Pub: American City Business Journals Inc.
Ed: Christopher Calnan. Description: RRE Austin Solar LLC CEO Doven Mehta has revealed plans to partner with Portugal-based Magpower SA, only if Austin energy buys electricity from planned solar energy farm in Pflugerville. Austin Energy has received 100 bids from 35 companies to supply 200 megawatts of solar- and wind-generated electricity.

44696 ■ "Mandel Site Favored For UWM Hall" in The Business Journal-Milwaukee (Vol. 25, September 19, 2008, No. 52, pp. A1)
Pub: American City Business Journals, Inc.
Description: University of Wisconsin-Milwaukee student residence hall's leading location is a site pushed by Mandel Group Inc. Real estate sources say that the developer's proposal offers the best opportunity for business development and the least conflict with nearby neighborhoods. Plans for the Mandel site are presented.

44697 ■ "M&T On the March?" in Baltimore Business Journal (Vol. 28, November 12, 2010, No. 27, pp. 1)
Pub: Baltimore Business Journal
Ed: Gary Haber. Description: Information on the growth of M&T Bank, as well as its expansion plans are presented. M&T recently acquired Wilmington Trust and took over $500 million in deposits from the failed K Bank. Analysts believe that M&T would continue its expansion through Washington DC and Richmond, Virginia, especially after a bank executive acknowledged that the markets in those areas are attractive.

44698 ■ "Mapping Out a Career" in Occupational Outlook Quarterly (Vol. 54, Fall 2010, No. 3, pp. 12)
Pub: U.S. Bureau of Labor Statistics
Ed: Audrey Watson. Description: Geographic distribution of occupations is studied, along with lifestyle considerations when choosing a career.

44699 ■ "Mayor Unveils Business Plan" in Boston Business Journal (Vol. 29, September 16, 2011, No. 19, pp. 1)
Pub: American City Business Journals Inc.
Ed: Gary Haber. Description: Mayor Stephanie Rawlings-Blake of Baltimore, Maryland unveiled her plan to push the economy forward. Her key objectives include giving more support for the city's technology companies and refocusing the Baltimore Development Corporation on job creation and retention.

44700 ■ "Meet UT's New Business Mind" in Austin Business Journal (Vol. 31, May 13, 2011, No. 10, pp. A1)
Pub: American City Business Journals Inc.
Ed: Sandra Zaragoza. Description: University of Texas (UT) chief commercialization officer, Dr. Richard Miller, has opened a satellite office in Silicon Valley, California in the hopes of luring Californian investors to the science and technology at UT. The satellite office is just one of Miller's efforts to reshape and widen the commercialization of UT-Austin. Insights into Miller's long-term view approach to commercialization are also covered.

44701 ■ "Mission: Poach California" in Business Journal Portland (Vol. 26, December 11, 2009, No. 40, pp. 1)
Pub: American City Business Journals Inc.
Ed: Andy Giegerich. Description: Leaders of Greenlight Greater Portland, a privately funded economic development organization, will visit California five times in 2010 in an attempt to lure California businesses to expand or relocate in Oregon.

44702 ■ "More Offices Planned For Percheron Square" in The Business Journal-Milwaukee (Vol. 25, August 22, 2008, No. 48, pp. A1)
Pub: American City Business Journals, Inc.
Ed: Pete Millard. Description: More office projects are under way at Percheron Square. Ryan Cos. US Inc., for example, plans to build over 200,000 square feet of office space at the area. Details of new office projects in Wisconsin are presented.

44703 ■ "Move South Could Bring Big Benefits" in Business Journal-Portland (Vol. 24, November 9, 2007, No. 36, pp. 1)
Pub: American City Business Journals Inc.
Ed: Matthew Kish. Description: Freightliner LLC has announced that it would move around one-tenth of its jobs to Fort Mill, South Carolina, but stated that immediate plans for headquarters relocation have not

been made. The relocation of its headquarters is expected to earn $100 million in economic incentives. The benefits of moving to the area, aside from the economic incentives, are discussed.

44704 ■ "Moving On: What's It Worth?" in Entrepreneur (Vol. 36, February 2008, No. 2, pp. 32)
Pub: Entrepreneur Media Inc.
Ed: Jacquelyn Lynn. Description: An area's cost of living should be considered by business owners when relocating, as it can affect operating costs and salary expenses, among other issues. Details on how to decide on business relocation with regard to cost of living concerns are examined.

44705 ■ "N.E.'s Largest Solar Site Set for Scituate Landfill" in Boston Business Journal (Vol. 30, December 17, 2010, No. 47, pp. 1)
Pub: Boston Business Journal
Ed: Kyle Alspach. Description: A closed 12-acre landfill in Scituate, Massachusetts is the proposed site for a 2.4-megawatt solar power plant. The town government will buy the power at a discounted rate, saving it $200,000 annually.

44706 ■ "New Kittinger Showroom Twice the Size of the Last One" in Business First Buffalo (December 7, 2007, pp. 4)
Pub: American City Business Journals, Inc.
Ed: Tracey Drury. Description: Kittinger Furniture Company, an upscale furniture maker, has opened a 6,000 square foot retail outlet at the Transit Road, New York. The company's moved to attract suburban and affluent customers for its high-end furniture products.

44707 ■ "Nordstrom Points for Richmond Heights" in Saint Louis Business Journal (Vol. 31, August 5, 2011, No. 50, pp. 1)
Pub: Saint Louis Business Journal
Ed: E.B. Solomont. Description: Nordstrom is set to upgrade its offerings for its second full-line store in St. Louis, Missouri. The new store is expected to benefit nearby shops.

44708 ■ "Novi Eyed for $11 Million, 100-Bed Medilodge" in Crain's Detroit Business (Vol. 25, June 1, 2009, No. 22, pp. M032)
Pub: Crain Communications Inc. - Detroit
Description: Novi, Michigan is one of the cities being considered for construction of a new 110-bed skilled nursing facility. Details of the project are included.

44709 ■ "Ohio Business Incentives Lag Offerings By Other States" in Crain's Cleveland Business (Vol. 30, May 18, 2009, No. 20, pp. 1)
Pub: Crain Communications, Inc.
Ed: Jay Miller. Description: Incentives designed to attract business and promote business expansion in Ohio has not done their job. According to a new study, despite tax changes made four years ago, the state's ability to attract new business has gone unchanged.

44710 ■ "Ohio's Reputation Lags Its Business Ranking" in Business Courier (Vol. 24, November 23, 2008, No. 32, pp. 1)
Pub: American City Business Journals, Inc.
Ed: Jon Newberry. Description: Site Selection magazine's annual ranking of the top states for new business facilities has ranked Ohio and Kentucky in seventh and eight place respectively, but an opinion survey of real estate executives had placed Ohio much lower at 14. The survey asked 6,000 executives if Ohio's conditions were best for new building projects.

44711 ■ "Old Ford Plant to Sign New Tenants" in Business Courier (Vol. 27, August 13, 2010, No. 15, pp. 1)
Pub: Business Courier
Ed: Dan Monk. Description: Ohio Realty Advisors LLC, a company handling the marketing of the 1.9 million-square-foot former Ford Batavia plant is on the brink of landing one distribution and three

manufacturing firms as tenants. These tenants are slated to occupy about 20 percent of the facility and generate as many as 250 jobs in Ohio.

44712 ■ *"Organic Chain Scouting Tri-State Sites, Including Kenwood" in Business Courier (Vol. 27, December 3, 2010, No. 31, pp. 1)*
Pub: Business Courier

Ed: Tom Demeropolis. **Description:** Asheville, North Carolina-based Earth Fare has been planning to add a total of six stores in 2011, including the potential opening of more than one store in the Greater Cincinnati area market. Earth Fare has not named specific locations but Kenwood area was reportedly being considered for its first location. Insights on growing trends toward health food stores are also given.

44713 ■ *"PNC Begins Search for New Local HQ" in Baltimore Business Journal (Vol. 28, June 4, 2010, No. 4, pp. 1)*
Pub: Baltimore Business Journal

Ed: Daniel J. Sernovitz. **Description:** PNC Financial Services Group Inc. is searching for a new headquarters building in Greater Baltimore, Maryland. The company is seeking about 150,000 square feet for its regional operations. However, PNC could also end up moving out of Baltimore for space in the surrounding suburbs.

44714 ■ *"Portland Wooing Under Armour to West Coast Facility" in Baltimore Business Journal (Vol. 27, January 29, 2010, No. 39, pp. 1)*
Pub: American City Business Journals

Ed: Andy Giegerich. **Description:** Baltimore, Maryland sports apparel maker, Under Armour, is planning a west coast expansion with Portland, Oregon among the sites considered to house its apparel and footwear design center. Portland officials counting on the concentration of nearly 10,000 activewear workers in the city will help lure the company to the city.

44715 ■ *Prepare to Be a Teen Millionaire*
Pub: Health Communications, Inc.

Contact: Peter Vegso, President
Ed: Robyn Collins; Kimberly Spinks Burleson. **Released:** April 1, 2008. **Price:** $16.95. **Description:** Business reference for any teenager wishing to become a successful entrepreneur; advice is given from successful teenage millionaires. Topics covered include: choosing a business name, type, and location; use of the Internet; legal issues; branding, sales, and marketing; funding and financial management; return on investment; retirement; development of a sound business plan; and certification for minority or women-owned companies.

44716 ■ *"Priced-Out Tenants Flocking to Class B" in Boston Business Journal (Vol. 27, October 19, 2007, No. 38, pp. 1)*
Pub: American City Business Journals Inc.

Ed: Michelle Hillman. **Description:** Tenants who usually rent top-tier office buildings are migrating to building that are not as expensive. The shift from Class A to Class B buildings is influenced by the high rental cost of the flashy office towers.

44717 ■ *"Restaurateurs Follow High-End Apartments Into Kendall Square" in Boston Business Journal (Vol. 31, July 22, 2011, No. 26, pp. 3)*
Pub: Boston Business Journal

Ed: Lisa van der Pool. **Description:** Kendall Square in Cambridge, Massachusetts is attracting restaurants, 16 of which have opened since 2009. The influx of restaurants is being driven by lower commercial rents.

44718 ■ *"River Plan in Disarray" in Business Journal Portland (Vol. 26, December 4, 2009, No. 39, pp. 1)*
Pub: American City Business Journals Inc.

Ed: Andy Giegerich. **Description:** Portland's proposed rules on a waterfront development plan for the Willamette River calls for fees intended for river bank preservation, a move that could drive industrial

manufacturers away. The manufacturers, under the Working Waterfront Coalition, claim that the proposals could increase riverfront building costs by 15 percent.

44719 ■ *"Roseville Investing Big in Downtown" in Sacramento Business Journal (Vol. 28, September 2, 2011, No. 27, pp. 1)*
Pub: Sacramento Business Journal

Ed: Michael Shaw. **Description:** The city of Roseville, California is planning to invest in downtown development projects. The plan includes a new town square, a venue for a farmers market and an interactive water fountain.

44720 ■ *"Roundy' Pushing Chicago Expansion" in Milwaukee Business Journal (Vol. 27, February 12, 2010, No. 20, pp. A1)*
Pub: American City Business Journals

Ed: Rich Kirchen. **Description:** Roundy Supermarkets Inc. is expanding in Chicago, Illinois as the Milwaukee-based company is set to open one store in downtown Chicago and another in the Arlington suburb. The store openings have been pushed back to spring and early summer in 2010 due to the economic downturn.

44721 ■ *"Running the Numbers" in Entrepreneur (Vol. 37, July 2009, No. 7, pp. 87)*
Pub: Entrepreneur Media, Inc.

Ed: Carol Tice. **Description:** Ways in which entrepreneurs can assess if they are ready to be a multi-unit franchisee are presented. Choosing the right locations, knowing how much assistance they can get from the franchisor, and financing are the key considerations when planning additional franchise units. Examples of success in multi-unit operations and multi-unit terms are also presented.

44722 ■ *"The Secret's Out About Kansas City" in Women In Business (Vol. 61, August-September 2009, No. 4, pp. 26)*
Pub: American Business Women's Association

Ed: Leigh Elmore. **Description:** Missouri's Kansas City offers various attractions, such as public fountains, the 18th and Vine Historic Districts for jazz enthusiasts, and the Crossroads Arts District with a variety of art galleries. Details on other cultural attractions and neighborhoods in the city are presented.

44723 ■ *"Shire Seeking New Digs for Headquarters" in Philadelphia Business Journal (Vol. 30, September 2, 2011, No. 29, pp. 1)*
Pub: American City Business Journals Inc.

Ed: Natalie Kostelni. **Description:** Dublin, Ireland-based Shire PLC announced plans to relocate its North American headquarters from Chesterbrook Corporate Center in Wayne, Pennsylvania and currently evaluating their options. The specialty biopharmaceutical firm is also considering a move to New Jersey or Delaware.

44724 ■ *"The Silvery Moon Moves to Larger Space" in Bellingham Business Journal (Vol. March 2010, pp. 5)*
Pub: Sound Publishing Inc.

Description: Jewelry store, the Silvery Moon, moved to a larger location in order to expand its business. The new location was chosen because it offers the firm more visibility. The store offers find silver and gold pieces and specializes in Pacific Northwest native jewelry.

44725 ■ *"Sobering Consequences" in The Business Journal-Milwaukee (Vol. 25, July 11, 2008, No. 42, pp. A1)*
Pub: American City Business Journals, Inc.

Ed: Rich Rovito. **Description:** Milwaukee Mayor Tom Barrett and Wisconsin Governor Jim Doyle met with MillerCoors management in an effort to convince the company to locate its corporate headquarters in the city. The company is expected to announce its decision by mid-July 2008. It was revealed that the decision-making process is focusing on determining an optimal location for the headquarters.

44726 ■ *"Solo, But Not Alone" in Entrepreneur (Vol. 37, October 2009, No. 10, pp. 99)*
Pub: Entrepreneur Media, Inc.

Ed: David Port. **Description:** Co-working spaces are emerging in different US cities, allowing entrepreneurs and other independent workers to co-exist. These work spaces, which can be availed for about $500 a month or $25 a day, also afford networking opportunities.

44727 ■ *"Soured Relationship Plays Out in Courts" in The Business Journal-Serving Greater Tampa Bay (Vol. 28, September 19, 2008, No. 39)*
Pub: American City Business Journals, Inc.

Ed: Janet Leiser. **Description:** Heirs of developer Julian Hawthorne Lifset won a court battle to end a 50-year lease with Specialty Restaurants Corp. in Rocky Point. The decision opens the Tampa Bay prime waterfront property for new development.

44728 ■ *"South Park Draws Brewers, Vintners" in Puget Sound Business Journal (Vol. 29, August 29, 2008, No. 19, pp. 1)*
Pub: American City Business Journals

Ed: Heidi Dietrich. **Description:** Craft breweries and wineries are moving into Seattle, Washington's South Park neighborhood due to the area's low rents, convenience, and ample equipment space. These industries bring a more upscale flavor to the heavily industrial area and the tastings and festivals draw people from throughout the Seattle region.

44729 ■ *"Southwestern Resources Project Update" in Canadian Corporate News (May 14, 2007)*
Pub: Comtex News Network Inc.

Description: Southwestern Resoures Corp. provides a quarterly update on its various exploration projects in both Peru and China.

44730 ■ *Start and Run a Delicatessen: Small Business Starters Series*
Pub: How To Books

Ed: Deborah Penrith. **Released:** November 9, 2010. **Price:** $30.00. **Description:** Information for starting and running a successful delicatessen is provided. Insight is offered into selecting a location, researching the market, writing a business plan and more.

44731 ■ *"State Center Lease Deal High for Md." in Baltimore Business Journal (Vol. 28, August 6, 2010, No. 13, pp. 1)*
Pub: Baltimore Business Journal

Ed: Daniel J. Sernovitz. **Description:** The proposed $1.5 billion State Center development project in Midtown Baltimore might cause the State of Maryland to pay the most expensive rental rates in the city. The state will have to pay an effective rental rate of $34 per square foot, including expenses, on the leasing. Other details of the redevelopment project are discussed.

44732 ■ *"State Film Business Tops $1.3 Billion" in The Business Journal-Portland (Vol. 25, August 22, 2008, No. 24, pp. 1)*
Pub: American City Business Journals, Inc.

Ed: Andy Giegerich. **Description:** Oregon's film industry has generated $1.39 billion in direct and indirect economic impact in 2007, a 55 percent rise from 2005 levels. The growth of the industry is attributed to tax incentives issued in 2007, which attracted film production companies from other states.

44733 ■ *"Still on the Block" in Entrepreneur (Vol. 35, November 2007, No. 11, pp. 22)*
Pub: Entrepreneur Media Inc.

Ed: Laura Tiffany. **Description:** Neighborhoods where business enterprises are located sometimes go into decline, particularly in low-income communities with high crime rates. Some entrepreneurs share stories about getting involved to help revive the community and keep their businesses thriving.

44734 ■ *"Stimulus 'Loser' Won't Build Plant in Mass." in Boston Business Journal (Vol. 30, November 5, 2010, No. 41, pp. 1)*
Pub: Boston Business Journal

Ed: Kyle Alspach. **Description:** Boston-Power Inc. no longer plans to build an electric vehicle battery plant in Massachusetts after it failed to obtain stimulus funds from the federal government. The company is instead looking to build a lithium-ion battery plant in China and possibly Europe.

44735 ■ *"Suppliers May Follow Fiat" in Crain's Detroit Business (Vol. 25, June 15, 2009, No. 24, pp. 1)*

Pub: Crain Communications Inc. - Detroit

Ed: Ryan Beene. **Description:** Italian suppliers to Fiat SpA are looking toward Detroit after the formation of Chrysler Group LLC, the Chrysler-Fiat partnership created from Chrysler's bankruptcy. The Italian American Alliance for Business and Technology is aware of two Italy-based powertrain component suppliers that are considering a move to Detroit.

44736 ■ *"Taking a Chance" in Baltimore Business Journal (Vol. 28, July 16, 2010, No. 10, pp. 1)*

Pub: Baltimore Business Journal

Ed: Scott Dance. **Description:** North Avenue in Baltimore, Maryland is considered a rough neighborhood due to the dangers of prostitution and drug dealing. However, some entrepreneurs have taken the risk of building their businesses on North Avenue as revitalization efforts grow. One of the challenges for businesses in rough neighborhoods is bringing customers to their stores or offices.

44737 ■ *"Taylor Tests Land Grant Program" in Austin Business Journal (Vol. 31, June 3, 2011, No. 13, pp. 1)*

Pub: American City Business Journals Inc.

Ed: Vicky Garza. **Description:** Taylor Economic Development Corporation implemented a land grant program called Build On Our Lot to lure businesses to Taylor City, Austin, Texas. They are targeting small businesses, especially those in the renewable energy, advanced manufacturing, technical services and food products. Program details are included.

44738 ■ *"UC May Expand into Old Ford Plant" in Business Courier (Vol. 26, December 25, 2009, No. 35, pp. 1)*

Pub: American City Business Journals, Inc.

Ed: Dan Monk. **Description:** Developer Stuart Lichter is planning to acquire University of Cincinnati (UC) as a tenant at a two-story office building on a 132-acre site where a vacant Ford transmission plant is located. Details of the transaction are outlined.

44739 ■ *"U.S. Playing Card Might Shuffle HQ" in Business Courier (Vol. 24, March 21, 2008, No. 50, pp. 1)*

Pub: American City Business Journals, Inc.

Ed: Jon Newberry. **Description:** United States Playing Card Co. is considering the possibility of relocating. It is expected that the company will finalize its decision by June 2008. According to Phil Dolci, the company's president, the firm is looking at certain locations in Ohio, Kentucky, and Indiana. He also revealed that the plan to relocate was prompted by the desire to improve the company's manufacturing facilities.

44740 ■ *"Uniting Spring in OP Could Reduce Static" in Business Journal-Serving Metropolitan Kansas City (October 19, 2007)*

Pub: American City Business Journals, Inc.

Ed: Jim Davis, Steve Vockrodt. **Description:** Sprint Nextel, the result of Sprint Corporation and Nextel Communications Inc. has been using Nextel's Reston office as corporate headquarters. The consolidation of Sprint Nextel's headquarters is expected to result in saving on cost of living and leases. The benefits of choosing Kansas City as the headquarters are evaluated.

44741 ■ *"Wal-Mart Sharpens Focus on Roxbury" in Boston Business Journal (Vol. 31, July 8, 2011, No. 24, pp. 1)*

Pub: Boston Business Journal

Ed: Mary Moore. **Description:** Wal-Mart Stores is boosting its search for a possible location in the Roxbury section of Boston, Massachusetts. The search is focused on underserved communities in terms of jobs and access to reasonably-priced merchandise.

The extent Boston's African American community has clashed with Mayor Thomas M. Menino over the accommodations of the retailer in Roxbury is discussed.

44742 ■ *"Water Company Eyeing Region for a New Plant" in Charlotte Business Journal (Vol. 25, December 10, 2010, No. 38, pp. 1)*

Pub: Charlotte Business Journal

Ed: Ken Elkins. **Description:** California-based Niagara Bottling Company is hoping to find a site in Charlotte, North Carolina where it can build a water bottling plant that would employ 70 workers. The investment is expected to cost about $25 million to $40 million.

44743 ■ *"Wattles Plugs Back Into State" in Business Journal Portland (Vol. 27, November 19, 2010, No. 38, pp. 1)*

Pub: Portland Business Journal

Ed: Wendy Culverwell. **Description:** Denver, Colorado-based Ultimate Electronics Inc.'s first store in Oregon was opened in Portland and the 46th store in the chain of electronic superstores is expected to employ 70-80 workers. The venture is the latest for Mark Wattles, one of Oregon's most successful entrepreneurs, who acquired Ultimate from bankruptcy.

44744 ■ *"Welcome: From the Chamber of Commerce" in Inside Business (Vol. 13, September-October 2011, No. 5, pp. SS5)*

Pub: Great Lakes Publishing Co.

Ed: Diane Helbig. **Description:** Diane Helbig, Chairperson for the Lakewood Chamber of Commerce in Ohio touts the areas as the best place to start and run a small company. Two colleges, real estate, and culture are among the reasons cited.

44745 ■ *"Welcome to the Neighborhood" in Hawaii Business (Vol. 53, October 2007, No. 4, pp. 48)*

Pub: Hawaii Business Publishing

Ed: Jolyn Okimoto Rosa. **Description:** Finance Factors is planning to build branches in Manoa, and Liliha, as part of its strategy to position itself in high-yield areas. The company chose Manoa and Liliha due to thee sites' rich deposits. Its strategy with regards to the branches' location and to the building design is discussed.

44746 ■ *"Who's Next?" in Boston Business Journal (Vol. 27, November 16, 2007, No. 42, pp. 1)*

Pub: American City Business Journals Inc.

Ed: Lisa van der Pool. **Description:** Boston, Massachusetts' burgeoning technology and biotech industries along with rising billing rates make it a unique legal market. Law firms cross the threshold either by merging with or acquiring a smaller law firm. Boston as a unique legal market is discussed.

44747 ■ *Who's Your City? How the Creative Economy is Making Where to Live the Most Important Decision of Your Life*

Pub: Basic Books

Ed: Richard Florida. **Released:** 2009. **Price:** $26.95. **Description:** Richard Florida disagrees with the notion that under globalization, a leveling has taken away the economic advantages of any place in particular. Florida believes that globalization has also created higher-level economic activities such as innovation, design, finance, and media to cluster in a smaller number of locations.

TRADE PERIODICALS

44748 ■ *Business Facilities: The Source for Corporate Site Selectors*

Pub: Group C Communications Inc.

Contact: Lyle Connor, Manager

E-mail: lconnor@groupc.com

URL(s): www.businessfacilities.com/. **Released:** Monthly **Price:** Free.

44749 ■ *Expansion Management: Growth Strategies for Companies on the Move*

Pub: Penton Media Inc.

URL(s): www.expansionmanagement.com. **Released:** 6/yr.

44750 ■ *Site Selection Magazine*

Pub: Conway Data Inc.

Contact: Laura Lyne, President

URL(s): www.siteselection.com/. **Released:** Bi-monthly **Price:** $95, Individuals; $135, Other countries; $160, Two years; $246, Two years other countries.

44751 ■ *Urban Land Magazine*

Pub: Urban Land Institute

URL(s): www.uli.orgurbanland.uli.org/About-Urban-Land. **Released:** 11/yr.

CONSULTANTS

44752 ■ **Architectural Research Consultants Inc. (ARC)**

220 Gold Ave. SW

Albuquerque, NM 87102

Ph: (505)842-1254

Fax: (505)766-9269

Co. E-mail: jppetronis@arcplanning.com

URL: http://www.arcplanning.com

Contact: John P. Petronis, President

E-mail: jppetronis@arcplanning.com

Scope: Specializes in feasibility studies, site selection, site development plans, zoning, and specialized management consulting services. It serves private industries and government agencies. **Founded:** 1976. **Publications:** "Post-Occupancy Evaluation and edited Facility Programming"; "Programming the Built Environment"; "Building Evaluation"; "Pueblo Style and Regional Architecture"; "Design Intervention: Toward A More Humane Architecture"; "Professional Practice in Facility Programming"; "Design Review: Challenging Urban Aesthetic Control"; "New Directions in Urban Public Housing"; "Directions in Person-Environment Research and Practice"; "Universal Design Handbook"; "Assessing Building Performance"; "Designing for Designers".

44753 ■ **LSA Associates Inc.**

20 Executive Pk., Ste. 200

Irvine, CA 92614

Ph: (949)553-0666

Fax: (949)553-8076

Co. E-mail: irvine@lsa-assoc.com

URL: http://www.lsa-assoc.com

Contact: Rob McCann, President

E-mail: rob.mccann@lsa-assoc.com

Scope: Provides environmental planning and assessment services to public and private clients. Offers professional services in environmental assessment, community planning, natural resources analysis, transportation, cultural resources, noise and air quality analysis and GIS. **Founded:** 1976.

44754 ■ **Pomeroy Appraisal Associates Inc.—Pomeroy Organization Inc.**

Pomeroy Pl., 225 W Jefferson St.

Syracuse, NY 13202-2334

Ph: (315)422-7106

Fax: (315)476-1011

Co. E-mail: info@pomeroyappraisal.com

URL: http://www.pomeroyappraisal.com

Contact: Donald A. Fisher, President

E-mail: dfisher@pomeroyappraisal.com

Scope: Advises clients on commercial and industrial properties, site analysis, real estate tax problems, land development and all types of real estate valuation problems and projects. **Founded:** 1964.

44755 ■ **Space Management Programs Inc.**

55 W Wacker Dr., Ste. 600

Chicago, IL 60601-1609

Ph: (312)263-0700

Fax: (312)263-1228

Contact: Michael J. Cohen, President

E-mail: mcohen@ghk.net

Scope: A facilities and technology consulting firm experienced in all aspects of design and corporate relocation. Available for site evaluation, strategic planning through the writing of briefs, or architectural programs through space planning, design and construction documents. **Founded:** 1973.

Small Business Development

START-UP INFORMATION

44756 ■ *"Big Bucks In Pet-ty Cash"* in *Small Business Opportunities (Fall 2008)*
Pub: Entrepreneur Media Inc.
Description: Twenty-five ways in which to start a business that caters to pets by either creating a product or a service that pet owners desire are profiled.

44757 ■ *"Bottoms Up!"* in *Entrepreneur (Vol. 36, April 2008, No. 4, pp. 128)*
Pub: Entrepreneur Media, Inc.
Ed: Amanda C. Kooser. **Description:** Jill Bernheimer launched her online alcohol business Domaine547 in 2007, and encountered challenges as legal issues over the licensing and launching of the business took about seven months to finish. Domain547 features blog and forum areas. Marketing strategy that connects to the social community is one of the ways to reach out to customers.

44758 ■ *"Business Diary"* in *Crain's Detroit Business (Vol. 24, October 6, 2008, No. 40, pp. 23)*
Pub: Crain Communications, Inc.
Description: Detailed listing of acquisitions, expansions, new products, new services, business contracts and startups from the Detroit area is provided.

44759 ■ *"A Class Act"* in *Hawaii Business (Vol. 53, March 2008, No. 9, pp. 25)*
Pub: Hawaii Business Publishing
Ed: Cathy S. Cruz-George. **Description:** UBoost is a startup company that offers online content for the educational magazine 'Weekly Reader'. The website features quizzes and allows users to accumulate points and redeem rewards afterward. Other details about the company are discussed.

44760 ■ *"Confessions Of Serial Entrepreneurs"* in *Entrepreneur (January 8, 2009)*
Pub: Entrepreneur Media Inc.
Ed: Jennifer Wang. **Description:** Serial entrepreneurs are those individuals that are able to start business after business. These individuals enjoy the process of starting a company then handing off the finished product and starting over with a new endeavor. Several serial entrepreneurs are profiled.

44761 ■ *"Find the Upside to a Down Economy"* in *Women Entrepreneur (September 30, 2008)*
Pub: Entrepreneur Media Inc.
Ed: Tamara Monosoff. **Description:** Starting a new business in this economic crisis may not be as daunting of a pursuit as one might think. Aspiring entrepreneurs may find success by looking for opportunities in unusual places and relying on what they do best.

44762 ■ *"Five Low-Cost Home Based Startups"* in *Women Entrepreneur (December 16, 2008)*
Pub: Entrepreneur Media Inc.
Ed: Lesley Spencer Pyle. **Description:** During tough economic times, small businesses have an advantage over large companies because they can adjust to economic conditions more easily and without having to go through corporate red tape that can slow the implementation process. A budding entrepreneur may find success by taking inventory of his or her skills, experience, expertise and passions and utilizing those qualities to start a business. Five low-cost home-based startups are profiled. These include starting an online store, a virtual assistant service, web designer, sales representative and a home staging counselor.

44763 ■ *"Friends With Money"* in *Entrepreneur (Vol. 37, August 2009, No. 8, pp. 74)*
Pub: Entrepreneur Media, Inc.
Ed: Asheesh Advani. **Description:** Providing a strong introduction to an investor will maximize a startup's chances of getting a second meeting. Startups should also pick an achievable fund raising goal and to keep track of their labor-adjusted net capital when fund raising.

44764 ■ *"Fun And Easy Gold Mines"* in *Small Business Opportunities (Fall 2008)*
Pub: Entrepreneur Media Inc.
Description: Twenty-five businesses that cater to the booming children's market are profiled; day care services, party planning, special events videomaking, tutoring, personalized children's toys and products and other services geared toward the kids market are included.

44765 ■ *"Getting Others To Take Your Startup Seriously"* in *Women Entrepreneur (August 1, 2008)*
Pub: Entrepreneur Media Inc.
Ed: Tamara Monosoff. **Description:** Writing a serious business plan is essential if you want others to take your startup endeavor seriously. As friends, family and acquaintances see you taking positive steps toward your goal they will begin to lend their support and may even help get the business off the ground.

44766 ■ *"Home Grown"* in *Hawaii Business (Vol. 53, November 2007, No. 5, pp. 51)*
Pub: Hawaii Business Publishing
Ed: Jolyn Okimoto Rosa. **Description:** Discusses a program that focuses on Native Hawaiian entrepreneurs and offers business training at the Kapiolani Community College; upon completion of the program, participants may apply for a loan provided by the Office of Hawaiian Affairs (OHA) to help them start their business. OHA plans to present the restructured loan program in November 2007, with aims of shortening the loan process.

44767 ■ *"Home Work"* in *Black Enterprise (Vol. 37, October 2006, No. 3, pp. 78)*
Pub: Earl G. Graves Publishing Co. Inc.
Ed: James C. Johnson. **Description:** Information on starting a resume-writing service is profiled.

44768 ■ *"I Have A Business Idea. What Now?"* in *Women Entrepreneur (October 15, 2008)*
Pub: Entrepreneur Media Inc.
Ed: Cheryl Isaac. **Description:** Four pre-planning steps to take before launching a new business are discussed in detail.

44769 ■ *"Is Entrepreneurship Right For You?"* in *Women Entrepreneur (July 25, 2008)*
Pub: Entrepreneur Media Inc.
Ed: Bonnie Price. **Description:** Assessing the marketplace, evaluating your skills and sizing up your passions are three necessary elements to examine before starting a business.

44770 ■ *"The New Orleans Saints"* in *Entrepreneur (Vol. 37, August 2009, No. 8, pp. 40)*
Pub: Entrepreneur Media, Inc.
Ed: Jason Meyers. **Description:** Idea Village is a nonprofit group that fosters entrepreneurship in New Orleans, Louisiana. Entrepreneurship is indeed growing in the city during a time when the city is still recovering from the damage of hurricane Katrina.

44771 ■ *"The New Orleans Saints"* in *Entrepreneur (Vol. 37, August 2009, No. 8, pp. 40)*
Pub: Entrepreneur Media, Inc.
Ed: Jason Meyers. **Description:** Idea Village is a nonprofit group that fosters entrepreneurship in New Orleans, Louisiana. Entrepreneurship is indeed growing in the city during a time when the city is still recovering from the damage of hurricane Katrina.

44772 ■ *"Online Fortunes"* in *Small Business Opportunities (Fall 2008)*
Pub: Entrepreneur Media Inc.
Description: Fifty hot, e-commerce enterprises for the aspiring entrepreneur to consider are featured; virtual assistants, marketing services, party planning, travel services, researching, web design and development, importing as well as creating an online store are among the businesses featured.

44773 ■ *"The Perfect Formula to Build Your Brand"* in *Entrepreneur (Vol. 37, July 2009, No. 7, pp. 70)*
Pub: Entrepreneur Media, Inc.
Ed: Susan J. Linder. **Description:** Combining a product with expertise and a promise is the formula in building a brand for startups. The product will not sell itself, so one must consider what makes the product truly unique. Meanwhile, establishing trust and a foundation for a brand can be achieved by making a promise to the consumer and fulfilling it.

44774 ■ *"Recession-Proof Your Startup"* in *Crain's Chicago Business (Vol. 31, November 10, 2008, No. 45, pp. 24)*
Pub: Crain Communications, Inc.
Description: Detailed information concerning ways in which to start a business during an economic crisis is provided. Ways in which to find financing, the importance of a solid business plan, customer service, problem-solving and finding the right niche for the region are also discussed.

44775 ■ *"Rehab Will Turn Hospital Into Incubator"* in *The Business Journal-Serving*

Metropolitan Kansas City (Vol. 26, September 12, 2008)
Pub: American City Business Journals, Inc.
Ed: Rob Roberts. **Description:** Independence Regional Health Center will be purchased by CEAH Realtors and be converted into the Independence Regional Entrepreneurial Center, a business incubator that will house startups and other tenants. Other details about the planned entrepreneurial center are provided.

44776 ■ *"Serial Starter" in Entrepreneur (Vol. 36, April 2008, No. 4, pp. 17)***
Pub: Entrepreneur Media, Inc.
Ed: Andrea Cooper. **Description:** Some entrepreneurs are engaged in serial entrepreneurship as they feel that they are no longer satisfied with their business and they decide to sell it. Others start out new businesses because they believe they can try out and be successful in different kinds of businesses. Details on how to identify and handle new entrepreneurial opportunities are discussed.

44777 ■ *"Should You Go Into Business With Your Spouse?" in Women Entrepreneur (September 1, 2008)***
Pub: Entrepreneur Media Inc.
Ed: Tamara Monosoff. **Description:** Things to consider before starting a business with one's spouse are discussed. Compatible work ethics, clear expectations of one another, long-term goals for the company and the status of the relationship are among the things to consider before starting a business endeavor with a spouse.

44778 ■ *"So You Want to Start a Business?" in Women Entrepreneur (August 5, 2008)***
Pub: Entrepreneur Media Inc.
Ed: Cynthia McKay. **Description:** Advice for taking an idea and turning it into a legitimate business is given.

44779 ■ *"Spread Your Wings" in Canadian Business (Vol. 81, March 17, 2008, No. 4, pp. 31)***
Pub: Rogers Media
Ed: Megan Harman. **Description:** Financing from angel investors is one avenue that should be explored by startups. Angel investors are typically affluent individuals who invest their own money. Angel investors usually want at least 10 times their initial investment within eight years but they benefit the businesses through their help in decision-making and the industry expertise they provide.

44780 ■ *"Take the Plunge" in Small Business Opportunities (July 2008)***
Pub: Entrepreneur Press
Contact: Perlman Neil, President
Description: Resources are provided for starting a new business venture for under $500 as well as fifteen different suggestions for different kinds of businesses that can be created with minimal expense.

44781 ■ *"Three Weeks To Startup" in Entrepreneur (December 19, 2008)***
Pub: Entrepreneur Media Inc.
Ed: Tim Berry; Sabrina Parsons. **Description:** Breakdown for realistically starting a business in three weeks is provided in detail.

44782 ■ *"Time for a Leap Of Faith?" in Women Entrepreneur (November 18, 2008)***
Pub: Entrepreneur Media Inc.
Ed: Cynthia McKay. **Description:** Starting a new business, despite the downturn in the economy, can prove to be a successful endeavor if one has the time, energy and most importantly a good idea.

44783 ■ *"UM-Dearborn to Launch Program for Entrepreneurs" in Crain's Detroit Business (Vol. 24, April 14, 2008, No. 15, pp. 7)***
Pub: Crain Communications Inc.
Ed: Chad Halcom. **Description:** Starting this fall the University of Michigan-Dearborn will begin its Product Realization and Technology Commercialization Program for entrepreneurs and innovators with lab-tested, high-technology products. Ultimately, 20 businesses will each work with the university in creating

a customer base, commercializing a new high-tech product or process and connecting with venture capitalists who may invest in the new companies.

44784 ■ *"Victoria Colligan; Co-Founder, Ladies Who Launch Inc., 38" in Crain's Cleveland Business (Vol. 28, November 19, 2007, No. 46)***
Pub: Crain Communications, Inc.
Ed: Jay Miller. **Description:** Profile of Victoria Colligan who is the co-founder of Ladies Who Launch Inc., an organization with franchises in nearly 50 cities; the company offers women entrepreneurs workshops and a newsletter to help women balance their businesses with other aspects of their lives. Ms. Colligan found that women were learning about being business owners differently than men and she felt that there was a need to create opportunities for networking for women launching businesses that had more of a lifestyle purpose.

44785 ■ *"What Are You Afraid Of?" in Entrepreneur (Vol. 37, July 2009, No. 7, pp. 79)***
Pub: Entrepreneur Media, Inc.
Ed: Lindsay Holloway. **Description:** According to a survey of entrepreneurs in the US, failure, economic uncertainty, not having enough personal time, being their own boss, and staying afloat are the biggest fears when starting a business. Advice on how to deal with these fears is also given.

44786 ■ *"Where to be an Entrepreneur: Ten Startup-Friendly Cities" in Entrepreneur (Vol. 37, August 2009, No. 8, pp. 49)***
Pub: Entrepreneur Media, Inc.
Ed: Jason Daley. **Description:** Ten U.S. cities that embody the entrepreneurial spirit are presented. These cities are ideal for startup companies and profiles of businesses that are making it in these cities are discussed.

44787 ■ *"Your Startup may be Worth Less than You Think" in Entrepreneur (Vol. 37, October 2009, No. 10, pp. 96)***
Pub: Entrepreneur Media, Inc.
Ed: Asheesh Advani. **Description:** Valuations of startups at the idea stage are dropping due to the effects of the recession. This drop is due to the decreasing availability of investment capital, the reduction in portfolio values of investors, and the increase in early stage startups.

ASSOCIATIONS AND OTHER ORGANIZATIONS

44788 ■ Action for Enterprise (AFE)
4600 North Fairfax Dr., Ste. 304
Arlington, VA 22203
Ph: (703)243-9172
Fax: (703)243-9123
URL: http://www.actionforenterprise.org
Contact: Frank Lusby, Executive Director
Description: Seeks to design and implement small enterprise development programs, based on a comprehensive analysis of business sectors and the interrelationships of enterprises that function with them. Initiates efforts to develop sustainable business development service providers at the local level. **Founded:** 1991.

44789 ■ Association of Small Business Development Centers (ASBDC)
8990 Burke Lake Rd., 2nd Fl.
Burke, VA 22015
Ph: (703)764-9850
Fax: (703)764-1234
Co. E-mail: tee.rowe@asbdc-us.org
URL: http://www.asbdc-us.org
Contact: C. Edward Rowe, III, President
Description: Local centers providing advice for those planning to establish a small business. Aims to facilitate information exchange among members and to represent their interests before the federal government. Informs the Small Business Administration on issues of interest to the small business community.

Founded: 1980. **Publications:** *Business Plan Workbook for Special Use Permits.* **Educational Activities:** Professional Development Conference.

44790 ■ BEST Employers Association (BEA)
2505 McCabe Way
Irvine, CA 92614
Free: 866-706-2225
URL: http://www.beassoc.org
Description: Provides small independent businesses with managerial, economic, financial and sales information helpful for business improvement. Organizes and sponsors healthcare alliances for small employers. (The acronym BEST stands for Beneficial Employees Security Trust). **Founded:** 1980.

44791 ■ Canadian Association of Family Enterprise (CAFE)—Association Canadienne des Entreprises Familiales
465 Morden Rd., Ste. 112
Oakville, ON, Canada L6K 3W6
Ph: (905)337-8375
Free: 866-849-0099
Fax: (905)337-0572
Co. E-mail: office@cafenational.org
URL: http://www.cafecanada.ca
Contact: Peter G. White, Director
Description: Family-owned businesses. Seeks to "encourage, educate, and inform members in disciplines unique to the family business." Fosters increased understanding of the importance of family-owned enterprises in the national economy among government agencies and the public. Gathers and disseminates information of interest to members. Conducts educational and lobbying activities. Provides technical support and advisory services to small businesses in areas including succession planning, taxation, family law, and arbitration and mediation. Maintains network of Family Councils, which serve as a forum for discussion of family and business matters. **Scope:** business, personal wellness, family business. **Founded:** 1983. **Subscriptions:** books. **Publications:** *Family Business Magazine* (Quarterly); *Family Enterpriser* (Quarterly); *International Magazine for Family Businesses* (Bimonthly); *Canadian Association of Family Enterprise--Annual Membership Directory.* **Educational Activities:** National Symposium for Families in Business (Semiannual). **Awards:** Family Enterprise of the Year Award.

44792 ■ Canadian Federation of Independent Business (CFIB)—Federation Canadienne de l'Entreprise Independante
401-4141 Yonge St., Ste. 401
Toronto, ON, Canada M2P 2A6
Ph: (416)222-8022
Free: 888-234-2232
Fax: (416)222-6103
Co. E-mail: cfib@cfib.ca
URL: http://www.cfib-fcei.ca/english/index.html
Contact: Danny Kelly, President
Description: Independent businesses. Promotes economic well-being of members and seeks to maintain a healthy domestic business climate. Represents members' interests before government agencies, labor and industrial organizations, and the public. **Scope:** entrepreneurship, economic policy, small business, public policy. **Founded:** 1971. **Subscriptions:** 4000 books periodicals reports. **Publications:** *Mandate* (Quarterly); *Quarterly Business Barometer* (3/year). **Awards:** Canada Awards for Excellence.

44793 ■ Employers of America (EofA)
310 Meadow Ln.
Mason City, IA 50401
Ph: (641)424-3187
Free: 800-728-3187
Fax: (641)424-3187
Co. E-mail: employer@employerhelp.org
URL: http://www.employerhelp.org
Contact: Mr. Jim Collison, President
Description: Assists employers, managers, and supervisors in keeping their businesses profitable by maintaining the best possible workplace policies and practices, and to deal safely, effectively, and profit-

ably with employees. Publishes e-Letter to help members achieve more with their employees. **Founded:** 1976. **Publications:** *Empowered @ Work* (Monthly).

44794 ■ Entrepreneurs' Organization (EO)
500 Montgomery St., Ste. 500
Alexandria, VA 22314
Ph: (703)519-6700
Fax: (703)519-1864
Co. E-mail: info@eonetwork.org
URL: http://www.eonetwork.org
Contact: Samer Kurdi, Chairman
Description: Entrepreneurs under the age of 50 who have either founded, co-founded, are a controlling shareholder of, or own a firm with annual gross revenues exceeding $1,000,000 (membership is by invitation only). Engages leading entrepreneurs to learn and grow. Serves as a focal point for networking and development of members through small group learning sessions, regular local chapter social and learning events, and global conference-based education programs. **Founded:** 1987. **Publications:** *Octane* (Quarterly); *Overdrive* (Monthly). **Educational Activities:** Universities and Leadership Conference (Annual); Universities and Leadership Conference (Periodic).

44795 ■ The Entrepreneurship Institute (TEI)
3700 Corporate Dr., Ste. 145
Columbus, OH 43231
Ph: (614)895-1153
Co. E-mail: info@tei.net
URL: http://www.tei.net
Contact: Dr. Jan W. Zupnick, President
Description: Provides encouragement and assistance to entrepreneurs who operate companies with revenue in excess of $1 million. Unites financial, legal, and community resources to help foster the success of companies. Promotes sharing of information and interaction between members. Operates President's forums and projects which are designed to improve communication between businesses, develop one-to-one business relationships between small and mid-size businesses and local resources, provide networking, and stimulate the growth of existing companies. **Scope:** growth strategies, accounting, finance, investments 401K. **Founded:** 1976. **Subscriptions:** audiovisuals books software. **Publications:** *The President's Forum* (Monthly). **Educational Activities:** The Entrepreneurship Institute Meeting (Periodic).

44796 ■ *Family Business Magazine*
465 Morden Rd., Ste. 112
Oakville, ON, Canada L6K 3W6
Ph: (905)337-8375
Free: 866-849-0099
Fax: (905)337-0572
Co. E-mail: office@cafenational.org
URL: http://www.cafecanada.ca
Contact: Peter G. White, Director
Released: Quarterly

44797 ■ *Family Enterpriser*
465 Morden Rd., Ste. 112
Oakville, ON, Canada L6K 3W6
Ph: (905)337-8375
Free: 866-849-0099
Fax: (905)337-0572
Co. E-mail: office@cafenational.org
URL: http://www.cafecanada.ca
Contact: Peter G. White, Director
Released: Quarterly

44798 ■ *International Magazine for Family Businesses*
465 Morden Rd., Ste. 112
Oakville, ON, Canada L6K 3W6
Ph: (905)337-8375
Free: 866-849-0099
Fax: (905)337-0572
Co. E-mail: office@cafenational.org
URL: http://www.cafecanada.ca
Contact: Peter G. White, Director
Released: Bimonthly

44799 ■ *Mandate*
401-4141 Yonge St., Ste. 401
Toronto, ON, Canada M2P 2A6
Ph: (416)222-8022
Free: 888-234-2232
Fax: (416)222-6103
Co. E-mail: cfib@cfib.ca
URL: http://www.cfib-fcei.ca/english/index.html
Contact: Danny Kelly, President
Released: Quarterly

44800 ■ National Association for Business Organizations (NAFBO)
5432 Price Ave.
Baltimore, MD 21215
Ph: (410)367-5309
Co. E-mail: nahbb@msn.com
URL: http://www.ameribizs.com/global
Contact: Rudolph Lewis, President
Description: Business organizations that develop and support small businesses that have the capability to provide their products or services on a national level. Promotes small business in a free market system; represents the interests of small businesses to government and community organizations on small business affairs; monitors and reviews laws that affect small businesses; promotes a business code of ethics. Supplies members with marketing and management assistance; encourages joint marketing services between members. Operates a Home Based Business Television Network that provides an affordable audio/visual media for small and home based businesses. **Founded:** 1986. **Awards:** Entrepreneur Certificate.

44801 ■ National Association for the Self-Employed (NASE)
PO Box 241
Annapolis Junction, MD 20701-0241
Free: 800-232-6273
Fax: (800)551-4446
Co. E-mail: advocacy@nase.org
URL: http://www.nase.org
Contact: Kristie Arslan, President
Description: Self-employed and small independent businesspersons. Acts as an advocate at the state and federal levels for self-employed people. Provides discounts on products and services important to self-employed and small business owners. **Founded:** 1981. **Publications:** *Self-Employed*; *Self-Employed America* (Bimonthly); *Washington Watch* (Weekly). **Awards:** Future Entrepreneur (Annual); NASE Future Entrepreneur Scholarships; National Association for the Self-Employed Scholarships.

44802 ■ National Business Association (NBA)
5151 Beltline Rd., Ste. 1150
Dallas, TX 75254
Ph: (972)458-0900
Free: 800-456-0440
Fax: (972)960-9149
Co. E-mail: info@nationalbusiness.org
URL: http://www.nationalbusiness.org
Contact: Raj Nisankarao, President
Description: Employed owners of small businesses. Promotes and assists the growth and development of small businesses. Aids members in obtaining government small business and education loans; makes available insurance policies and software in conjunction with the U.S. Small Business Administration. Maintains career, educational institution, and scholarship information program for members and their dependents. Offers over 100 benefits, services and programs in the areas of Business, Health, Lifestyle and Education. **Founded:** 1982. **Publications:** *Biz Corner* (Weekly); *NBA boss* (Bimonthly).

44803 ■ National Business Incubation Association (NBIA)
20 E Circle Dr., No. 37198
Athens, OH 45701-3571
Ph: (740)593-4331

Fax: (740)593-1996
Co. E-mail: info@nbia.org
URL: http://www.nbia.org
Contact: David Monkman, President
Description: Incubator developers and managers; corporate joint venture partners, venture capital investors; economic development professionals. (Incubators are business assistance programs providing business consulting services and financing assistance to start-up and fledgling companies.) Helps newly formed businesses to succeed. Educates businesses and investors on incubator benefits; offers specialized training in incubator formation and management. Conducts research and referral services; compiles statistics; maintains speakers' bureau; publishes information relevant to business incubation and growing companies. **Scope:** business incubation, entrepreneurship. **Founded:** 1985. **Publications:** *NBIA Insights* (Monthly); *NBIA Memberabilia* (Biweekly); *NBIA Review* (Bimonthly); *NBIA Business Incubation Industry Directory* (Annual); *Business Incubators of North America* (Biennial). **Educational Activities:** International Conference on Business Incubation (Annual). **Awards:** Incubator Innovation Award; Incubator of the Year; Outstanding Incubator Client Award; Outstanding Incubator Graduate Award; Incubator Innovation Award (Annual); Incubator of the Year (Annual); Outstanding Incubator Client (Annual); Outstanding Incubator Graduate (Annual).

44804 ■ National Small Business Association (NSBA)
1156 15th St. NW, Ste. 1100
Washington, DC 20005
Ph: (202)293-8830
Free: 800-345-6728
Fax: (202)872-8543
Co. E-mail: membership@nsba.biz
URL: http://www.nsba.biz
Contact: Chris Holman, Chairman
Description: Small businesses including manufacturing, wholesale, retail, service, and other firms. Works to advocate at the federal level on behalf of smaller businesses. **Founded:** 1937. **Publications:** *Advocate* (Bimonthly). **Educational Activities:** Small Business Meetup Day (Monthly). **Awards:** Lewis I. Shattuck Advocate of the Year Award (Annual).

44805 ■ *Quarterly Business Barometer*
401-4141 Yonge St., Ste. 401
Toronto, ON, Canada M2P 2A6
Ph: (416)222-8022
Free: 888-234-2232
Fax: (416)222-6103
Co. E-mail: cfib@cfib.ca
URL: http://www.cfib-fcei.ca/english/index.html
Contact: Danny Kelly, President
Released: 3/year

44806 ■ Support Services Alliance (SSA)
PO Box 340
Cobleskill, NY 12043
Free: 800-909-2772
Co. E-mail: info@ssamembers.com
URL: http://www.ssamembers.com
Contact: Steven C. Cole, President
Description: Represents small businesses (less than 50 employees), the self-employed, and associations of such individuals. Provides services and programs such as group purchasing discounts, health coverage, legislative advocacy, and business and financial support services. **Founded:** 1977. **Publications:** *Capital Crier*; *Small-Biz Growth* (Monthly). **Educational Activities:** Small Biz (Annual).

REFERENCE WORKS

44807 ■ *"The 100 Fastest-Growing Companies" in Hispanic Business (Vol. 30, July-August 2008, No. 7-8, pp. 22)*
Pub: Hispanic Business, Inc.
Ed: Michael Bowker. **Description:** CEO's of the five fastest growing Hispanic-owned companies discuss the success of their companies; most of them attribute their success to proper investment and diversification, effective innovations and seeing growth opportunities where others see roadblocks.

44808 ■ *"Analyzing the Analytics"* in *Entrepreneur (Vol. 37, October 2009, No. 10, pp. 42)*
Pub: Entrepreneur Media, Inc.
Ed: Mikal E. Belicove. **Description:** Startups can maximize Web analytics by using them to monitor traffic sources and identify obstacles to converting them into targeted behaviors . Startups should set trackable Web site goals and continuously track traffic and conversion rates.

44809 ■ *"Athletes Face Wins and Losses After Pro Sport"* in *The Business Journal - Serving Phoenix and the Valley of the Sun (Vol. 29, September 19, 2008, No. 3, pp. 1)*
Pub: American City Business Journals, Inc.
Ed: Chris Casacchia. **Description:** Professional athletes like hockey star Jeremy Roenick start businesses, while others like Joel Adamson work to boost local communities. Former athletes were found to be particularly interested with real estate businesses. Other views and information on former athletes and their life after sports are presented.

44810 ■ *"Bailout May Force Cutbacks, Job Losses"* in *The Business Journal - Serving Phoenix and the Valley of the Sun (Vol. 29, September 26, 2008, No. 4, pp. 1)*
Pub: American City Business Journals, Inc.
Ed: Mike Sunnucks. **Description:** Economists say the proposed $700 billion bank bailout could affect Arizona businesses as banks could be forced to reduce the amount and number of loans it has thereby forcing businesses to shrink capital expenditures and then jobs. However, the plan could also stimulate the economy by taking bad loans off banks balance sheets according to another economist.

44811 ■ *"Bangles, BMWs Elbow Out Delis and Discount Shops"* in *Crain's New York Business (Vol. 24, January 14, 2008, No. 2, pp. 35)*
Pub: Crain Communications, Inc.
Ed: Wendy Davis. **Description:** Lured by a growing number of affluent residents and high-earning professionals, a number of upscale retailers have opened locations downtown which is driving up rents and forcing out longtime independent merchants.

44812 ■ *"'Biggest Loser' Adds Bit of Muscle to Local Economy"* in *Crain's Detroit Business (Vol. 26, January 4, 2010, No. 1, pp. 1)*
Pub: Crain Communications Inc.
Ed: Chad Halcom. **Description:** NBC's weight-loss reality show, 'The Biggest Loser' has helped the local economy and generated a new crop of local startup businesses due to past contestants that were from the Detroit area.

44813 ■ *"Book Smart"* in *Hawaii Business (Vol. 53, December 2007, No. 6, pp. 39)*
Pub: Hawaii Business Publishing
Ed: David K. Choo. **Description:** Different parts of a biography entry in the Black Book are examined in relation to their usage in starting a conversation with an executive. The second part, which is the educational background, is considered the most significant of all, due to the amount of information given. The importance of making connections in Hawaii is discussed.

44814 ■ *"Breaking the Mold"* in *Entrepreneur (Vol. 37, September 2009, No. 9, pp. 87)*
Pub: Entrepreneur Media, Inc.
Ed: Tracy Stapp. **Description:** Profiles of top franchise businesses in the United States are presented. Hey Buddy! Pet Supply Vending Co. offers pet supply vending machines. Home Health Mates, on the other hand, provides professional medical care at home.

44815 ■ *"Bryan Berg"* in *Hawaii Business (Vol. 53, March 2008, No. 9, pp. 28)*
Pub: Hawaii Business Publishing
Ed: David K. Choo. **Description:** Bryan Berg, senior vice president at Target Corp.'s Region 1, shares his thoughts about entering the Hawaiian market and Target representatives bringing malasadas when visiting a business in the state. Berg finds the state's

aloha spirit interesting and feels that it is important to be respectful of the Hawaiian culture and traditions in doing their business there.

44816 ■ *"Business Diary"* in *Crain's Detroit Business (Vol. 26, January 11, 2010, No. 2, pp. 16)*
Pub: Crain Communications Inc.
Description: Listing of local businesses involved in acquisitions, contracts, expansions, new products and services as well as startups in the region.

44817 ■ *"The Business End of Staying in Business"* in *Contractor (Vol. 56, September 2009, No. 9, pp. 51)*
Pub: Penton Media, Inc.
Ed: Al Schwartz. **Description:** Advice on how to manage a new plumbing business in the United States are offered. The transition from being a workman to an employer is seen as one that accompanies a steep learning curve. The importance of managing cash flow is also highlighted.

44818 ■ *"Can America Invent Its Way Back?"* in *Business Week (September 22, 2008, No. 4100, pp. 52)*
Pub: McGraw-Hill Companies, Inc.
Description: Business leaders as well as economists agree that innovative new products, services and ways of doing business may be the only way in which America can survive the downward spiral of the economy; innovation economics may be the answer and may even provide enough growth to enable Americans to prosper in the years to come.

44819 ■ *"Capital Ideas: Regions to Lansing: Focus on Taxes, Reform, Keeping Talent"* in *Crain's Detroit Business (Vol. 24, October 6, 2008)*
Pub: Crain Communications, Inc.
Ed: Amy Lane. **Description:** Michigan must make bold and dramatic changes in public policy regarding business legislation. The tax structure, unemployment issues and attracting and retaining talent are among the issues the state must confront, especially in this tough economic climate.

44820 ■ *"Celebrate Success. Embrace Innovation"* in *Black Enterprise (Vol. 37, February 2007, No. 7, pp. 145)*
Pub: Earl G. Graves Publishing Co. Inc.
Description: 2007 Women of Power Summit provides networking opportunities, empowerment sessions, and nightly entertainment. More than 500 executive women of color are expected to attend this inspiring summit in Phoenix, February 7-10.

44821 ■ *"City Sets Yamhill Makeover"* in *The Business Journal-Portland (Vol. 25, July 4, 2008, No. 17, pp. 1)*
Pub: American City Business Journals, Inc.
Ed: Andy Giegerich. **Description:** City government is scheduled to redevelop Peterson's property on Yamhill Street in Portland. The redevelopment is seen as a way to better developing commercial properties in the area. Problems associated with the project, which include cost and developer selection, are also discussed.

44822 ■ *"Conversation: Historian Geoffrey Jones On Why Knowledge Stays Put"* in *Harvard Business Review (Vol. 86, July-August 2008, No. 8)*
Pub: Harvard Business School Press
Ed: Gardiner Morse. **Description:** Geoffrey Jones, Harvard Business School's professor of business history, discusses factors that cause knowledge to concentrate in particular regions, rather than disperse, such as the location of wealth.

44823 ■ *"A Conversation with Mark Lange"* in *Crain's Detroit Business (Vol. 26, January 18, 2010, No. 3, pp. 9)*
Pub: Crain Communications Inc.
Ed: Nancy Kaffer. **Description:** Second-stage companies have different needs from other kinds of startups since they often are moving very fast and dealing with several complex problems at the same time.

44824 ■ *"Deep Thoughts: Getting Employees to Think Better Requires a Bit of Creative Thinking Itself"* in *Canadian Business (March 17, 2008)*
Pub: Rogers Media
Ed: Lauren McKeon. **Description:** Discusses the reason a company needs to make their employees understand that ideas are the stuff of life. For employees to be more creative, they need to cultivate spark moments, play with possibilities, and venture into the unknown.

44825 ■ *Directory of Venture Capital and Private Equity Firms*
Pub: Grey House Publishing
Contact: Richard Gottlieb, President
E-mail: rhg2@greyhouse.com

URL(s): www.greyhouse.com/venture.htm. **Released:** Latest edition 2011. **Price:** $685, Individuals Softcover; $450, Libraries softcover. **Covers:** 2,300 domestic and international venture capital and private equity firms. **Entries include:** Firm name, address, phone, fax, e-mail, URL, description of services, names and titles of key personnel. **Indexes:** Geographic; Executive Name; Portfolio Company; Industry Preference; College & University.

44826 ■ *"The Early Bird Gets the Worm"* in *Black Enterprise (Vol. 37, January 2007, No. 6, pp. 111)*
Pub: Earl G. Graves Publishing Co. Inc.
Ed: Tykisha N. Lundy. **Description:** General Motors hosts the Black Enterprise Conference And Expo: Where Deals Are Made at Walt Disney World's Swan and Dolphin Resort, May 9-12. The conference will offer great information to entrepreneurs.

44827 ■ *"Federal Fund Valuable Tool For Small-Biz Innovators"* in *Crain's Detroit Business (Vol. 24, September 29, 2008, No. 39, pp. 42)*
Pub: Crain Communications Inc.
Ed: Nancy Kaffer. **Description:** Grants from the Small Business Innovation Research Program, or SBIR grants, are federal funds that are set aside for 11 federal agencies to allocate to tech-oriented small-business owners. Firms such as Biotechnology Business Consultants help these companies apply for SBIR grants.

44828 ■ *"Five More Great Books on Entrepreneurship"* in *Entrepreneur (Vol. 37, July 2009, No. 7, pp. 19)*
Pub: Entrepreneur Media, Inc.
Description: 800-CEO-Read founder, Jack Covert, and president, Todd Sattersten, share five books that would have been included in the book, 'The 100 Business Books of All Time' if space was not an issue. 'You Need to Be a Little Crazy,' 'Oh, the Places You'll Go!,' 'Founders at Work,' 'The Innovator's Dilemma,' and 'Purple Cow' are highly recommended for entrepreneurs.

44829 ■ *"Five Steps to an Effective Business Call"* in *Hawaii Business (Vol. 53, October 2007, No. 4, pp. 64)*
Pub: Hawaii Business Publishing
Ed: Matthew K. Ing. **Description:** University of Hawaii professor Libda Patrylak believes that communication skills are integral to business success, which is why businesses should know how to properly handle phone conversations. Presented are five ways of achieving effective business phone calls, such as setting rules for employees to follow with regards to answering calls and providing undivided attention to the other speaker.

44830 ■ *"Five Steps to an Effective Meeting"* in *Hawaii Business (Vol. 53, March 2008, No. 9, pp. 55)*
Pub: Hawaii Business Publishing
Ed: Jason Ubay. **Description:** Identifying goals and writing them down can help in knowing what needs get done. Engaging everyone is a way to get cooperation in reaching the goals set. Other tips on how to have an effective meeting are discussed.

44831 ■ *"Five Steps for Handling Independent Contractors"* in *Hawaii Business (Vol. 53, January 2008, No. 7, pp. 49)*
Pub: Hawaii Business Publishing
Ed: Jason Ubay. **Description:** Small companies should be cautious in dealing with independent contractors. They must understand that they cannot dictate specific operational procedures, job duties, standards of conduct and performance standards to the contractors, and they cannot interfere with the evaluation and training of the contractors' employees. Tips on negotiating with independent contractors are given.

44832 ■ *"Five Steps to Killer Business Ideas"* in *Hawaii Business (Vol. 53, December 2007, No. 6, pp. 135)*
Pub: Hawaii Business Publishing
Ed: Jason Ubay. **Description:** Five ways to formulating good business concepts are presented. The importance of keeping an open mind and analyzing the market is discussed.

44833 ■ *"From Craft Biz To Wholesale Giant"* in *Women Entrepreneur (January 19, 2009)*
Pub: Entrepreneur Media Inc.
Ed: Maria Falconer. **Description:** Advice is given on how to turn a small craft business into a full-time venture; tips to help one transition from a part-time designer to a full-time wholesaler and brand are also included.

44834 ■ *"From War Zone to Franchise Zone"* in *Entrepreneur (Vol. 37, August 2009, No. 8, pp. 104)*
Pub: Entrepreneur Media, Inc.
Ed: Jason Daley. **Description:** Ross Paterson says that he realized that the material he used in the Growth Coach franchise could give the people of Afghanistan the systematic model they need. Paterson says that the Afghans are very business-oriented people but that they work in a different system than Americans.

44835 ■ *"George Cohon"* in *Canadian Business (Vol. 79, November 20, 2006, No. 23, pp. 70)*
Pub: Rogers Media
Ed: Zena Olijnyk. **Description:** George Cohon, the founder of McDonald's in Canada and Russia, speaks about the Canadian market and the experience of starting McDonald's in Canada.

44836 ■ *"Going to Bat"* in *Canadian Business (Vol. 80, February 26, 2007, No. 5, pp. S7)*
Pub: Rogers Media
Description: Various strategies to make the business loan lending process simple and faster are presented.

44837 ■ *"'Groundhog Day' B & B Likely Will Be Converted Into One In Real Life"* in *Chicago Tribune (October 21, 2008)*
Pub: McClatchy-Tribune Information Services
Ed: Carolyn Starks. **Description:** Everton Martin and Karla Stewart Martin have purchased the Victorian house that was featured as a bed-and-breakfast in the 1993 hit move 'Groundhog Day'; the couple was initially unaware of the structure's celebrity status when they purchased it with the hope of fulfilling their dream of owning a bed-and-breakfast.

44838 ■ *"A Growing Dilemma"* in *Crain's Cleveland Business (Vol. 28, October 8, 2007, No. 40, pp. 19)*
Pub: Crain Communications, Inc.
Ed: Kimberly Bonvissuto. **Description:** Discusses small business owners who often have to grapple with the decision on whether or not to expand their operations and the importance of a business plan which may help owners with that decision.

44839 ■ *"Have High-Tech Tax Credits Helped or Hurt Hawaii?"* in *Hawaii Business (Vol. 53, December 2007, No. 6, pp. 28)*
Pub: Hawaii Business Publishing
Description: Presents the opinons of Channel Capital LLC's Walter R. Roth and Hawaii Venture Capital Association's Bill Spencer concerning the impacts of tax credits. Roth thinks that Act 221 appeals to investors who can earn despite business failure while Spencer thinks that the legislation promotes investments in innovative technology firms. The need to support tax credits is also discussed.

44840 ■ *"Hawaii Business 2008 SB Success Awards"* in *Hawaii Business (Vol. 53, February 2008, No. 8, pp. 43)*
Pub: Hawaii Business Publishing
Description: Winners in the Hawaii Business 2008 SB Success Awards are presented; the awards give recognition for Hawaii small businesses with less than 100 employees and are based on four criteria, namely: unique service or product; rapid expansion or sales growth; longevity; and competency in overcoming challenges.

44841 ■ *"Hawaii's Identity Crisis"* in *Hawaii Business (Vol. 53, November 2007, No. 5, pp. 10)*
Pub: Hawaii Business Publishing
Ed: Kelli Abe Trifonovitch. **Description:** Some Hawaiians have shown that the Superferry controversy makes it seem to the rest of the world as if they do not know what they are doing, and intensifies several issues regarding the stability of investing in Hawaii. With or without the Superferry, there is still no evidence that investors are afraid to put their money in Hawaii.

44842 ■ *"Head of the Class"* in *Entrepreneur (Vol. 37, October 2009, No. 10, pp. 59)*
Pub: Entrepreneur Media, Inc.
Description: Top 25 graduate and undergraduate entrepreneurship programs in the US for 2009 as ranked by The Princeton Review are listed. Babson College in Wellesley, Massachusetts topped both categories.

44843 ■ *"How Green Is The Valley?"* in *Barron's (Vol. 88, July 4, 2008, No. 28, pp. 13)*
Pub: Dow Jones & Co., Inc.
Description: San Jose, California has made a good start towards becoming a leader in alternative energy technology through the establishment of United Laboratories' own lab in the city. The certification process for photovoltaic cells will be dramatically shortened with this endeavor.

44844 ■ *"Intrepid Souls: Meet a Few Who've Made the Big Leap"* in *Crain's Chicago Business (Vol. 31, November 10, 2008, No. 45, pp. 26)*
Pub: Crain Communications, Inc.
Ed: Meredith Landry. **Description:** Advice is given from entrepreneurs who have launched businesses in the last year despite the economic crisis. Among the types of businesses featured are a cooking school, a child day-care center, a children's clothing store and an Internet-based company.

44845 ■ *"Kid-Friendly Business Sources"* in *Black Enterprise (Vol. 37, January 2007, No. 6, pp. 40)*
Pub: Earl G. Graves Publishing Co. Inc.
Ed: Carolyn M. Brown. **Description:** Financial or business camps are a great way to encourage a child who interested in starting his or her own business. A number of these camps are available each year including Kidpreneurs Conference and Bull and Bear Investment Camp. Other resources are available online. Resources included.

44846 ■ *"Legislators Must Cut Cost of Government"* in *Crain's Detroit Business (Vol. 24, October 6, 2008, No. 40, pp. 6)*
Pub: Crain Communications, Inc.
Description: Southeast and West Michigan business leaders are setting aside their differences and have proposed clear agendas, ranging from eliminating the Michigan Business Tax to overhauling public employee and retiree benefits and pensions. Lawmakers must also come together to find solutions for the state's economy and discover an entirely new vision for the future of Michigan business.

44847 ■ *"Live and Learn"* in *Canadian Business (Vol. 80, April 23, 2007, No. 9, pp. 76)*
Pub: Rogers Media
Ed: Chris Buck. **Description:** Paul Anka, a musician, feels that ground work is essential before establishing a company.

44848 ■ *"Local Knowledge"* in *Hawaii Business (Vol. 53, December 2007, No. 6, pp. 40)*
Pub: Hawaii Business Publishing
Ed: David K. Choo. **Description:** Rules and facts business professionals need to know about the local life in Hawaii are presented. The important components in island life include knowledge Hawaiian high schools' histories and image, the local sports scene, special events, potluck ethics, and locals' favorite destination, which is Las Vegas.

44849 ■ *"Look Before You Lease"* in *Women Entrepreneur (February 3, 2009)*
Pub: Entrepreneur Media Inc.
Ed: Nina L. Kaufman. **Description:** Top issues to consider before leasing an office space are discussed including: additional charges that may be expected on top of the basic rental price; determining both short- and long-term goals; the cost of improvements to the space; the cost of upkeep; and the conditions of the lease.

44850 ■ *"Mandel Site Favored For UWM Hall"* in *The Business Journal-Milwaukee (Vol. 25, September 19, 2008, No. 52, pp. A1)*
Pub: American City Business Journals, Inc.
Description: University of Wisconsin-Milwaukee student residence hall's leading location is a site pushed by Mandel Group Inc. Real estate sources say that the developer's proposal offers the best opportunity for business development and the least conflict with nearby neighborhoods. Plans for the Mandel site are presented.

44851 ■ *"Minority Auto Suppliers Get Help Diversifying"* in *Crain's Detroit Business (Vol. 26, January 11, 2010, No. 2, pp. 3)*
Pub: Crain Communications, Inc.
Ed: Sherri Welch. **Description:** Displaced minority auto suppliers are being given assistance by the Kauffman's Foundation Urban Entrepreneur Partnership Detroit program, a three-year effort to assist 150 of the region's suppliers into more diversified businesses.

44852 ■ *"More Offices Planned For Percheron Square"* in *The Business Journal-Milwaukee (Vol. 25, August 22, 2008, No. 48, pp. A1)*
Pub: American City Business Journals, Inc.
Ed: Pete Millard. **Description:** More office projects are under way at Percheron Square. Ryan Cos. US Inc., for example, plans to build over 200,000 square feet of office space at the area. Details of new office projects in Wisconsin are presented.

44853 ■ *"Northern Kentucky Adds 1,355 Jobs in '07"* in *Business Courier (Vol. 24, February 15, 2008, No. 45, pp. 3)*
Pub: American City Business Journals, Inc.
Ed: Lucy May. **Description:** Jobs generated by new and expanding businesses in Northern Kentucky in 2007 totaled to 1,355, which boosted total business sales to $410 million. The ripple effects of the businesses are expected to create 5,432 new jobs and increase business sales to more than $888 million.

44854 ■ *"Ohio's Reputation Lags Its Business Ranking"* in *Business Courier (Vol. 24, November 23, 2008, No. 32, pp. 1)*
Pub: American City Business Journals, Inc.
Ed: Jon Newberry. **Description:** Site Selection magazine's annual ranking of the top states for new business facilities has ranked Ohio and Kentucky in seventh and eight place respectively, but an opinion survey of real estate executives had placed Ohio much lower at 14. The survey asked 6,000 executives if Ohio's conditions were best for new building projects.

44855 ■ *"Part-Time Office Space" in Hawaii Business (Vol. 53, December 2007, No. 6, pp. 132)*
Pub: Hawaii Business Publishing

Ed: Ashley Hamershock. **Description:** My Office is one of the companies that are renting space office not only by the month, but by the hour. Such setup is beneficial to small businesses that do not need a whole office all to themselves, and are interested in cutting the cost of office space rental. The prices of office space in Hawaii are mentioned.

44856 ■ *"People/Calendar" in Brandweek (Vol. 49, April 21, 2008, No. 16, pp. 30)*
Pub: VNU Business Media, Inc.

Description: Listing of current conferences, tradeshows and events concerning the marketing industry.

44857 ■ *"Pick A Name, Not Just Any Name" in Women Entrepreneur (December 17, 2008)*
Pub: Entrepreneur Media Inc.

Ed: Maria Falconer. **Description:** Craft business owners must choose a name that sounds personal since customers who buy hand-made products want to feel that they are buying from an individual rather than an institution. Tips for choosing a name are provided.

44858 ■ *"Playing to Win" in Entrepreneur (Vol. 36, May 2008, No. 5, pp. 40)*
Pub: Entrepreneur Media, Inc.

Ed: Robert Kiyosaki. **Description:** Four personality types needed by entrepreneurs to drive their leadership in business are given. 'I must be liked' are social directors and go-betweens; 'I must be comfortable' are those who seek job security and are not at ease with deadlines; I must be right are those strong in opinion; and 'I must win' are people in charge.

44859 ■ *"Population Growing Faster Than Retail, Service Sector" in Crain's New York Business (Vol. 24, January 14, 2008, No. 2, pp. 30)*
Pub: Crain Communications, Inc.

Ed: Andrew Marks. **Description:** Downtown Manhattan is seeing more residential development; however, as more families call the area home the need for more retail and services is becoming evident.

44860 ■ *"Region and City Need Influx of Youth" in Crain's Detroit Business (Vol. 24, April 14, 2008, No. 15, pp. 8)*
Pub: Crain Communications Inc.

Description: Discusses an upcoming report from Michigan Future Inc. which finds that young professionals, including those with children, are interested in living in an active urban environment. It also states that because many of those young professionals are entrepreneurial in nature, oftentimes businesses follow.

44861 ■ *"Resource Line" in Black Enterprise (Vol. 37, January 2007, No. 6, pp. 6)*
Pub: Earl G. Graves Publishing Co. Inc.

Description: Interactive Media Editor, Philana Patterson, writes a column for blackenterprise.com that offers advice and provides resources for entrepreneurs, corporate executives, business owners, and budding investors.

44862 ■ *"SBA-Backed Lending Slides; Economy, Close Scrutiny of Applications Cited" in Crain's Detroit Business (March 10, 2008)*
Pub: Crain Communications, Inc.

Ed: Nancy Kaffer. **Description:** Due to the state of the economy and a closer scrutiny on applications, Small Business Administration-backed loans are down by a significant margin in one loan program and have decreased slightly across the board. Statistical data included.

44863 ■ *"Scottsdale Bank Plans 4Q Opening" in The Business Journal - Serving Phoenix and the Valley of the Sun (Vol. 28, August 15,*
2008, No. 50)
Pub: American City Business Journals, Inc.

Ed: Chris Casacchia. **Description:** Arizona's Department of Financial Institutions has approved Scottsdale Business Bank, a community bank which plans to open in the fourth quarter of 2008. The bank, which is to be located near McCormick Ranch in Scottsdale, Arizona, will cater to small business owners in the professional sector, such as accountants and doctors.

44864 ■ *"The Seat-Of-The-Pants School of Marketing" in Brandweek (Vol. 49, April 21, 2008, No. 16, pp. 24)*
Pub: VNU Business Media, Inc.

Ed: David Vinjamuri. **Description:** Excerpt from the book 'Accidental Branding: How Ordinary People Build Extraordinary Brands,' by David Vinjamuri, discusses six shared principles for creating a brand that is unique and will be successful over the long-term.

44865 ■ *"A Second Chance to Make a Living" in The Business Journal-Milwaukee (Vol. 25, September 19, 2008, No. 52, pp. A1)*
Pub: American City Business Journals, Inc.

Description: Unemployed workers and baby boomers are driving interest in purchasing small businesses. BizBuySell general manager Mike Handelsman reveals that the supply of small businesses for sale is decreasing due to the increased demand. The trends in the small business market are analyzed.

44866 ■ *"Senate OKs Funds for Promoting Tourism" in Crain's Detroit Business (Vol. 24, March 31, 2008, No. 13, pp. 6)*
Pub: Crain Communications, Inc.

Ed: Amy Lane. **Description:** Discusses the Senate proposal which allocates funds for Michigan tourism and business promotion as well as Michigan's No Worker Left Behind initiative, a program that provides free tuition at community colleges and other venues to train displaced workers for high-demand occupations.

44867 ■ *"Setting Out on Your Own? Think Franchises" in Crain's Cleveland Business (Vol. 28, October 8, 2007, No. 40, pp. 20)*
Pub: Crain Communications, Inc.

Description: Franchisers are targeting baby boomers due to their willingness to put up some of their own money to open their own business. According to local franchising expert, Joel Libava, entrepreneurs should expect to pay about 15 to 30 percent of the total cost of starting the franchise out of their own pocket.

44868 ■ *"Seven Ways to Fail Big" in Harvard Business Review (Vol. 86, September 2008, No. 9, pp. 82)*
Pub: Harvard Business School Press

Ed: Paul B. Carroll; Chunka Mui. **Description:** Seven factors involved in business failures are identified, and ways to avoid them are described. These factors include flawed financial engineering, hurrying into consolidation, and investing in technology that is not a good fit.

44869 ■ *"Sharing the Micro Wealth" in Entrepreneur (Vol. 37, July 2009, No. 7, pp. 46)*
Pub: Entrepreneur Media, Inc.

Ed: Jennie Dorris. **Description:** Step-by-step guide is presented on how Kiva.org, a website which allows people to make microloans to entrepreneurs across the world, works. The website, founded by Matt Flannery, raises $1 million weekly and it will add U.S. entrepreneurs to its list of loan recipients in June 2010. Other features of Kiva.org are discussed.

44870 ■ *"Shoe's On Other Foot" in Business Courier (Vol. 24, November 30, 2008, No. 33, pp. 1)*
Pub: American City Business Journals, Inc.

Description: Ronald Hummons was fresh out of prison for felony in 2000, and through the help of spiritual non-profit group the Lord's Gym he was able to turn his life around and start his own company Grapevine Ltd. LLC, which makes C-town athletic shoes.

44871 ■ *"Six Tips To Maximize Networking Opportunities" in Women Entrepreneur (November 3, 2008)*
Pub: Entrepreneur Media Inc.

Ed: Tamara Monosoff. **Description:** Networking events fall into the realm of business development as opposed to immediate sales opportunities. It is important to remember that these events provide a chance to build relationships that may someday help one's business. Tips to help make the most out of networking events are provided.

44872 ■ *"Small-Business Agenda: Increase Capital, Education, Tax Breaks" in Crain's Detroit Business (Vol. 24, March 17, 2008)*
Pub: Crain Communications, Inc.

Ed: Nancy Kaffer. **Description:** Discusses the policy suggestions detailed in the Small Business Association of Michigan's entrepreneurial agenda which include five main categories of focus: making entrepreneurial education a higher state priority; increasing capital available to entrepreneurs; using the state's tax structure as an incentive for entrepreneurial growth; getting university research from the lab to the market; and limiting government regulation that's burdensome to small businesses and getting legislative support of entrepreneurial assistance efforts.

44873 ■ *"Small Business: Just When Hopes Were High" in Business Week (January 8, 2007)*
Pub: McGraw-Hill Companies

Ed: James Mehring. **Description:** Overview of the reasons for a fall in confidence concerning the economy among small businesses and the affect this could have in the coming year.

44874 ■ *"The Solution" in Entrepreneur (Vol. 37, October 2009, No. 10, pp. 71)*
Pub: Entrepreneur Media, Inc.

Ed: Jennifer Wang. **Description:** Ford's 2010 Transit Connect is a compact commercial van developed specifically for small business owners. The compact van offers an integrated in-dash computer system providing a cellular broadband connection.

44875 ■ *"Soured Relationship Plays Out in Courts" in The Business Journal-Serving Greater Tampa Bay (Vol. 28, September 19, 2008, No. 39)*
Pub: American City Business Journals, Inc.

Ed: Janet Leiser. **Description:** Heirs of developer Julian Hawthorne Lifset won a court battle to end a 50-year lease with Specialty Restaurants Corp. in Rocky Point. The decision opens the Tampa Bay prime waterfront property for new development.

44876 ■ *"Spending on Innovation Down Sharply in State" in Crain's Detroit Business (Vol. 24, March 10, 2008, No. 10, pp. 7)*
Pub: Crain Communications, Inc.

Ed: Chad Halcom. **Description:** Due to such issues as Michigan's uncertain tax structure, a shaky national economy, the credit crunch and mortgage lending crisis, investments in innovation for the state have sharply declined.

44877 ■ *"Start or Buy? It's a Tough Question for Eager Entrepreneurs" in Crain's Cleveland Business (Vol. 28, October 8, 2007, No. 40)*
Pub: Crain Communications, Inc.

Ed: David Prizinsky. **Description:** Discusses different approaches to becoming a small business owner.

44878 ■ *"Success Products" in Black Enterprise (Vol. 37, February 2007, No. 7, pp. 135)*
Pub: Earl G. Graves Publishing Co. Inc.

Ed: Tanisha A. Sykes. **Description:** Using innovative resources that are already at your fingertips instead of trying to reach out to companies first is a great way to discover whether you have a viable idea or product. Be motivated to start an e-newsletter letting people know about your products and attend conferences like The Motivation Show, the world's largest exhibition of motivational products and services related to performance in business.

44879 ■ *"Survive the Small-to-Big Transition"* *in Entrepreneur (November 4, 2008)*
Pub: Entrepreneur Media Inc.
Ed: Elizabeth Wilson. **Description:** Transitioning a small company to a large company can be a challenge, especially during the time when it is too big to be considered small and too small to be considered big. Common pitfalls during this time are discussed as well as techniques business owners should implement when dealing with this transitional period.

44880 ■ *"Tee Off Online"* *in Black Enterprise (Vol. 37, January 2007, No. 6, pp. 52)*
Pub: Earl G. Graves Publishing Co. Inc.
Ed: James C. Johnson. **Description:** The E-Com Resource Center is one of many resources that are available for those interested in starting an e-commerce business. One of the first steps is to create a business plan, of which there are free samples available at BPlans.com.

44881 ■ *"The Thinker"* *in Canadian Business (Vol. 81, March 31, 2008, No. 5, pp. 52)*
Pub: Rogers Media
Ed: Andrew Wahl. **Description:** Mihnea Moldoveanu provides much of the academic rigor that underpins Roger Martin's theories on how to improve the way business leaders think. Moldoveanu is also a classically trained pianist and founder of Redline Communications and has a mechanical engineering degree from MIT on top of his astounding knowledge on many academic fields.

44882 ■ *"TMC Development Closes $1.1 Million Real Estate Purchase"* *in Internet Wire (September 17, 2009)*
Pub: Comtex News Network, Inc.
Description: TMC Development announced the closing of a $1.1 million real estate purchase for Mansa, LLC dba Kwikee Mart, a Napa-based convenience store; TMC helped the company secure a Small Business Administration 504 loan in order to purchase the acquisition of a 3,464 square foot building. SBA created the 504 loan program to provide financing for growing small and medium-sized businesses.

44883 ■ *"Top of the Food Chain"* *in Entrepreneur (Vol. 37, October 2009, No. 10, pp. 19)*
Pub: Entrepreneur Media Inc.
Ed: Jennifer Wang. **Description:** Television producer Mark Burnett discusses his latest reality television production, Shark Tank. The show pits venture capitalists against entrepreneurs in a contest to obtain business funding.

44884 ■ *"Transform Your Life"* *in Black Enterprise (Vol. 37, January 2007, No. 6, pp. 14)*
Pub: Earl G. Graves Publishing Co. Inc.
Description: Through the magazine, television and radio programs, events, and the website, the various platforms of Black Enterprise will provide the tools necessary to achieve success in business ventures, career aspirations, and personal goals.

44885 ■ *"Tying the Knot"* *in Entrepreneur (Vol. 36, April 2008, No. 4, pp. 48)*
Pub: Entrepreneur Media, Inc.
Ed: Guy Kawasaki. **Description:** Tips to consider when forming business partnerships are presented.

44886 ■ *"The Union of Town and Gown"* *in Entrepreneur (Vol. 37, October 2009, No. 10, pp. 47)*
Pub: Entrepreneur Media, Inc.
Ed: Jason Daley. **Description:** Ten of the best entrepreneurial initiatives involving cities and local universities in the US are described. Cities and universities are joining up for these efforts to strengthen local economies and stop brain drain.

44887 ■ *"Venture Capital's Capital Infusion: Federal Incentives Mean More Money for VC Firms"* *in Entrepreneur (August 2009)*
Pub: Entrepreneur Media, Inc.
Ed: Carol Tice. **Description:** American Recovery and Reinvestment Act of 2009 changed the rules for the Small Business Investment Corporations (SBIC) program under the Small Business Authority. The

rule changes are meant to put more money from the program into circulation and it increases funding to existing SBICs.

44888 ■ *"Venture Capital's Capital Infusion: Federal Incentives Mean More Money for VC Firms"* *in Entrepreneur (Vol. 37, August 2009)*
Pub: Entrepreneur Media, Inc.
Ed: Carol Tice. **Description:** American Recovery and Reinvestment Act of 2009 changed the rules for the Small Business Investment Corporations (SBIC) program under the Small Business Authority. The rule changes are meant to put more money from the program into circulation and it increases funding to existing SBICs.

44889 ■ *"Venture Gap"* *in Canadian Business (Vol. 81, March 17, 2008, No. 4, pp. 82)*
Pub: Rogers Media
Ed: Joe Castaldo. **Description:** Money raised by Canadian venture capitalist firms has been declining since 2001. A strong venture capital market is important if Canada is to build innovative companies. Fixing Canada's tax policy on foreign investments is a start in reviving the industry.

44890 ■ *"Wait a Minute!"* *in Entrepreneur (Vol. 37, September 2009, No. 9, pp. 76)*
Pub: Entrepreneur Media, Inc.
Ed: Jennifer Wang. **Description:** Advice on how entrepreneurs in the United States should secure funding in view of the economic crisis is presented. Enough interest should be stimulated so as to secure a follow-up meeting. Investors should be asked questions that would encourage them to tell stories related to the downturn.

44891 ■ *"Wayne, Oakland Counties Create Own 'Medical Corridor"* *in Crain's Detroit Business (Vol. 24, October 6, 2008, No. 40, pp. 8)*
Pub: Crain Communications, Inc.
Ed: Jay Greene. **Description:** Woodward Medical Corridor that runs along Woodward Avenue and currently encompasses twelve hospitals and is rapidly growing with additional physician offices, advanced oncology centers and new hospitals. Beaumont Hospital is building a $160 million proton-beam therapy cancer center on its Royal Oak campus in a joint venture with Procure Treatment Centers of Bloomington Ind. That is expected to open in 2010 and will employ approximately 145 new workers.

44892 ■ *"What Are Your Party's Legislative Priorities for 2008?"* *in Hawaii Business (Vol. 53, January 2008, No. 7, pp. 22)*
Pub: Hawaii Business Publishing
Description: Discusses the Democratic Party of Hawaii which will prioritize giving more opportunities to earn a living a wage in 2008, according to the party chairwoman Jeani Withington. The Republican Party chairman Willes K. Lee, meanwhile, states that his party will seek to enhance the local business climate. The political parties' plans for Hawaii for the year 2008 are presented in detail.

44893 ■ *"What's Cooking?"* *in Entrepreneur (Vol. 36, April 2008, No. 4, pp. 98)*
Pub: Entrepreneur Media, Inc.
Ed: Eileen Figure Sandlin. **Description:** Unique and unusual restaurants have the potential to attract customers and provide them with fresh menu options. Outlining goals, strategies and details on proposed concept and target market can also help in restaurant planning. Other tips on how to plan launching your own restaurant are provided.

44894 ■ *"The WIN Library"* *in Women In Business (Vol. 61, August-September 2009, No. 4, pp. 36)*
Pub: American Business Women's Association
Ed: Leigh Elmore. **Description:** Women's Instructional Network (WIN) offers members of the American Business Women's Association with information about the organization and 15 Team Tools learning modules to help further the learning of business women. Other training programs and services offered by WIN are presented.

44895 ■ *"Your Guide to Local Style Business"* *in Hawaii Business (Vol. 53, December 2007, No. 6, pp. 36)*
Pub: Hawaii Business Publishing
Ed: David K. Choo. **Description:** Discusses the importance of studying the Hawaiian culture when doing business locally. It was observed that geographical aspects increase emphasis on culture and lifestyle more than the need to rectify false imaging do. Details of how locals adhere to their culture are supplied.

TRADE PERIODICALS

44896 ■ *Business Opportunities Journal*
Pub: Business Service Corp.
URL(s): www.boj.com. **Ed:** Mark Adkins. **Released:** Monthly

44897 ■ *Entrepreneur Magazine*
Pub: Entrepreneur Press
Contact: Perlman Neil, President
URL(s): www.entrepreneur.com/magazine/entrepreneur/index.html. **Released:** Monthly **Price:** $11.97, Individuals.

44898 ■ *Entrepreneurship Theory and Practice*
Pub: Baylor University Dept. of Management
URL(s): www.baylor.edu/business/etp/www.wiley.com/bw/subs.asp?ref=1042-2587. **Ed:** Barbara Bird. **Released:** Bimonthly **Price:** $602, Institutions Americas, print & online; £464, Institutions UK, print & online; $908, Institutions, other countries print & online; €589, Institutions Europe; print & online; $133, Individuals Americas, print & online; £126, Institutions U.K. print & online; €126, Individuals Europe (non-Euro zone) print & online; €188, Individuals Europe (Euro zone) print & online; $523, Institutions Americas, online only.

44899 ■ *SBANE Enterprise*
Pub: Smaller Business Association of New England
Contact: Robert A. Baker, President
E-mail: bob@sbane.org
Ed: Julie Scofield, Editor. **Released:** 8-9/year. **Price:** Included in membership; $49, nonmembers. **Description:** Reports on matters of concern to those who are engaged in small businesses in the New England area. Includes news of government actions and legislation and economic trends. Recurring features include items on business education opportunities, members, and Association activities.

44900 ■ *The Small Business Advisor*
Pub: Small Business Advisors Inc.
Contact: Joseph Gelb, Publisher
Ed: Ann Liss, Editor. **Released:** Monthly. **Price:** $35. **Description:** Seeks to help emerging growth companies increase profits. Considers small business issues, including marketing sales, finance, taxes, organizing, competition, management, and human resources. Recurring features include letters to the editor, interviews, and columns titled Info Bank, In the Mail Box, Taxes, Human Resources, Marketing, Insurance, and Law. Remarks: Publication suspended in 1980; resumed publication Fall 1993.

44901 ■ *Small Business Opportunities: Money Making Ideas for Entrepreneurs*
Pub: Harris Publications Inc.
URL(s): www.sbomag.com/. **Ed:** Susan Rakowski. **Released:** Bimonthly; (plus 4 special editions). **Price:** $14.97, U.S. and Canada; $29.94, Other countries.

VIDEOCASSETTES/ AUDIOCASSETTES

44902 ■ *American Institute of Small Business: Setting Up a Home-Based Business*
American Institute of Small Business
23075 Highway 7, Ste. 200
Shorewood, MN 55331
Ph: (952)545-7001
Free: 800-328-2906

Fax: (952)545-7020
Co. E-mail: judy@aisb.biz
URL: http://www.pfa.com/AISB.htm
Released: 199?. **Price:** $69.95. **Description:** Step-by-step guide to operating a business out of your home. **Availability:** VHS.

44903 ■ American Institute of Small Business: Starting a Business—Advice from Experts
American Institute of Small Business
23075 Highway 7, Ste. 200
Shorewood, MN 55331
Ph: (952)545-7001
Free: 800-328-2906
Fax: (952)545-7020
Co. E-mail: judy@aisb.biz
URL: http://www.pfa.com/AISB.htm
Released: 199?. **Price:** $69.95. **Description:** Business commentators from Money, Fortune, and Newsweek magazines give tips on taxes, obtaining financing, and other issues. **Availability:** VHS.

44904 ■ Beyond Start-Up: Management Lessons for Growing Companies
Video Arts, Inc.
c/o Aim Learning Group
8238-40 Lehigh
Morton Grove, IL 60053-2615
Free: 877-444-2230
Fax: (416)252-2155
Co. E-mail: service@aimlearninggroup.com
URL: http://www.aimlearninggroup.com
Released: 1989. **Price:** $395.00. **Description:** Don't settle for being a small company—find out what it takes to expand your business. **Availability:** VHS; 3/4 U.

44905 ■ The Entrepreneurs: Risk Takers
RMI Media
1365 N. Winchester St.
Olathe, KS 66061-5880
Ph: (913)768-1696
Free: 800-745-5480
Fax: (800)755-6910
Co. E-mail: actmedia@act.org
URL: http://www.actmedia.com
Released: 1989. **Price:** $70.00. **Description:** College and high school students gain a special understanding of small business from this series. **Availability:** VHS; 3/4 U.

44906 ■ Finding a Niche: Determining Business Potential
Instructional Video
2219 C St.
Lincoln, NE 68502
Ph: (402)475-6570
Free: 800-228-0164
Fax: (402)475-6500
Co. E-mail: feedback@insvideo.com
URL: http://www.insvideo.com
Released: 19??. **Price:** $99.00. **Description:** Outlines the process of selecting an appropriate market for your product, including profile development of potential customers and planning and implementing a feasability study. **Availability:** VHS.

44907 ■ Growing a Business
Ambrose Video Publishing, Inc.
145 W. 45th St., Ste. 1115
New York, NY 10036
Ph: (212)768-7373
Free: 800-526-4663
Fax: (212)768-9282
Co. E-mail: customerservice@ambrosevideo.com
URL: http://www.ambrosevideo.com
Released: 1989. **Price:** $1295.00. **Description:** This video shows the steps taken by different people to start up a business. **Availability:** VHS.

44908 ■ How to Start Your Own Successful Business
Instructional Video
2219 C St.
Lincoln, NE 68502
Ph: (402)475-6570
Free: 800-228-0164

Fax: (402)475-6500
Co. E-mail: feedback@insvideo.com
URL: http://www.insvideo.com
Released: 19??. **Price:** $29.95. **Description:** Illustrates correct procedures for establishing and maintaining an effective business. Covers marketing, managing, financing, business insurance, buying an existing business, franchising, home-based business, youth entrepreneurial business, negotiating deals, and projecting your ideas. **Availability:** VHS.

44909 ■ I Can Do It! Stew Leonard
Direct Cinema Ltd.
PO Box 10003
Santa Monica, CA 90410-1003
Ph: (310)636-8200
Free: 800-525-0000
Fax: (310)636-8228
Co. E-mail: orders@directcinemalimited.com
URL: http://www.directcinema.com
Released: 1985. **Description:** The dairy king explains the details and knowledge he used to devise a phenomenonally successful business. **Availability:** VHS; 3/4 U; Special order formats.

44910 ■ Inc. Magazine Business Success Programs
Cambridge Educational
c/o Films Media Group
132 West 31st Street, 17th Floor
Ste. 124
New York, NY 10001
Free: 800-257-5126
Fax: (609)671-0266
Co. E-mail: custserve@films.com
URL: http://www.cambridgeol.com
Released: 1987. **Price:** $99.95. **Description:** These four programs contain a step-by-step explanation of what must be done to succeed in business. **Availability:** VHS; CC.

44911 ■ Inc. Magazine's How to Really Start Your Own Business
Cambridge Educational
c/o Films Media Group
132 West 31st Street, 17th Floor
Ste. 124
New York, NY 10001
Free: 800-257-5126
Fax: (609)671-0266
Co. E-mail: custserve@films.com
URL: http://www.cambridgeol.com
Released: 1986. **Price:** $29.95. **Description:** An authoritative guide to starting a small business, including tips on investment acquisition, business planning, financing and more. **Availability:** VHS.

44912 ■ Inside Business Today
GPN Educational Media
1550 Executive Drive
Elgin, IL 60123
Ph: (402)472-2007
Free: 800-228-4630
Fax: (800)306-2330
Co. E-mail: askgpn@smarterville.com
URL: http://www.shopgpn.com
Released: 1989. **Description:** Leaders in business and industry tell their success stories in this extensive series. **Availability:** VHS; 3/4 U.

44913 ■ Inside Business Today. . .The '90s
GPN Educational Media
1550 Executive Drive
Elgin, IL 60123
Ph: (402)472-2007
Free: 800-228-4630
Fax: (800)306-2330
Co. E-mail: askgpn@smarterville.com
URL: http://www.shopgpn.com
Released: 1990. **Price:** $2765.00. **Description:** Second part of the Inside Business series. Contains 30 sections which discuss various areas of business concerns in the 1990s. **Availability:** VHS.

44914 ■ New or Used? Buying a Firm or Starting Your Own
Instructional Video
2219 C St.
Lincoln, NE 68502

Ph: (402)475-6570
Free: 800-228-0164
Fax: (402)475-6500
Co. E-mail: feedback@insvideo.com
URL: http://www.insvideo.com
Released: 19??. **Price:** $99.00. **Description:** Details the different options open to anyone wanting to start or obtain their own business. Discusses the various factors to be considered when putting a value on a company, negotiating price and terms, and closing the deal. **Availability:** VHS.

44915 ■ Small Business in a Big World
Instructional Video
2219 C St.
Lincoln, NE 68502
Ph: (402)475-6570
Free: 800-228-0164
Fax: (402)475-6500
Co. E-mail: feedback@insvideo.com
URL: http://www.insvideo.com
Released: 19??. **Price:** $99.00. **Description:** Demonstrates how small business has contributed to the overall economy. Includes profiles of small retail, service, manufacturing, professional, high tech, wholesale, and warehousing operations at work. **Availability:** VHS.

44916 ■ Understanding Business Valuation
Chesney Communications
2302 Martin St., Ste. 125
Irvine, CA 92612
Ph: (949)263-5500
Free: 800-223-8878
Fax: (949)263-5506
Co. E-mail: videocc@aol.com
URL: http://www.videocc.com
Released: 1987. **Description:** A look for the small businessman at how to plan the future of his company-growth, reinvestment and possible sale. **Availability:** VHS; 3/4 U.

CONSULTANTS

44917 ■ 2010 Fund 5
24351 Spartan St.
Mission Viejo, CA 92691-3920
Ph: (949)583-1992
Fax: (949)583-0474
Contact: Wally Eater, Principal
Scope: Funds in formation that will invest in technologies licensed from 30 universities. **Founded:** 1982.

44918 ■ Aurora Management Partners Inc.
4485 Tench Rd., Ste. 340
Suwanee, GA 30024
Ph: (770)904-5209
Fax: (770)904-5226
Co. E-mail: rturcotte@auroramp.com
URL: http://www.auroramp.com
Contact: William A. Barbee, Director
E-mail: abarbee@auroramp.com
Scope: Specializes in turnaround management and reorganization consulting. Firm develop strategic initiatives, organize and analyze solutions, deal with creditor issues, review organizational structure and develop time frames for decision making. Turnaround services offered include Recovery plans and their implementation, Viability analysis, Crisis management, Financial restructuring, Corporate and organizational restructuring, Facilities rationalization, Liquidation management, Loan workout, Litigation support and Expert testimony, Contract renegotiation, Sourcing loan refinancing and Sourcing equity investment. **Founded:** 2005. **Publications:** "TMA Turnaround of the Year Award, Small Company, Honorable Mention," Nov, 2005; "Back From The Brink - Bland Farms," Progressive Farmer, Oct, 2004; "New Breed of Turnaround Managers," Catalyst Magazine, Aug, 2004; "Key Performance Drivers - Bland Farms," The Produce News, Apr, 2004; "Corporate Governance: Averting Crisis's Before They Happen," ABJ journal, Feb, 2004.

44919 ■ Biomedical Management Resources (BMR)
PO Box 521125
Salt Lake City, UT 84152-1125

Ph: (801)272-4668
Fax: (801)277-3290
Co. E-mail: SeniorManagement@BiomedicalMan-
agement.com
URL: http://www.biomedicalmanagement.com
Contact: Ping Fong, Jr., President
E-mail: pingfong@biomedicalmanagement.com
Scope: Provides business development, interim management, and executive search services. Assists companies in strategic alliances, corporate partnering, business acquisition. Demonstrated success in identifying recruiting, and placing key managers in difficult to hire positions. **Founded:** 1993.

44920 ■ BPT Consulting Associates Ltd.
12 Parmenter Rd., Ste. B-6
Londonderry, NH 03053
Ph: (603)437-8484
Free: 888-278-0030
Fax: (603)434-5388
Contact: John Kuczynski, Managing Director
Scope: Provides management consulting expertise and resources to cross-industry clients with services for: Business Management consulting, People/Human Resources Transition and Training programs, and a full cadre of multi-disciplined Technology Computer experts. Virtual consultants with expertise in e-commerce, supply chain management, organizational development, and business application development consulting. **Founded:** 1991.

44921 ■ CEO Advisors
848 Brickell Ave., Ste. 603
Miami, FL 33131
Ph: (305)371-8560
Fax: (305)371-8563
Co. E-mail: ciaizpurua@ceoadvisors.us
URL: http://www.ceoadvisors.us
Contact: Roberto J. Arguello, President
E-mail: rjarguello@ceoadvisors.us
Scope: Business consulting firm offering clients services in strategy, mergers and acquisitions, corporate finance, corporate advisory, supply chain management, government relations and public affairs. Specializes in strategic planning, profit enhancement, start-up businesses, venture capital, appraisals and valuations. **Founded:** 1989.

44922 ■ Chamberlain & Cansler Inc.
2251 Perimeter Park Dr.
Atlanta, GA 30341
Ph: (770)457-5699
Contact: Charles L. Cansler, Owner
Scope: Firm specializes in strategic planning; profit enhancement; small business management; interim management; crisis management; turnarounds. **Founded:** 1986.

44923 ■ Chartered Management Co.
10 S Riverside Plz., Ste. 1800
Chicago, IL 60606
Ph: (312)214-2575
Contact: William B. Avellone, President
Scope: Operations improvement consultants. Specializes in strategic planning; feasibility studies; management audits and reports; profit enhancement; start-up businesses; mergers and acquisitions; joint ventures; divestitures; interim management; crisis management; turnarounds; business process re-engineering; venture capital; and due diligence. **Founded:** 1985.

44924 ■ Clayton/Curtis/Cottrell
1722 Madison Ct.
Louisville, CO 80027-1121
Ph: (303)665-2005
Contact: Robert Cottrell, President
Scope: Market research firm specializes in providing consultations for packaged goods, telecommunications, direct marketing and printing, and packaging industries. Services include strategic planning; profit enhancement; startup businesses; mergers and acquisitions; joint ventures; divestitures; interim management; crisis management; turnarounds; market size, segmentation and rates of growth; competitor intelligence; image and reputation, and competitive analysis. **Founded:** 1981. **Publications:** "Turn an attitude into a purchase," Jul, 1995; "Mixed results for private label; price assaults by the national

brands are getting heavy, but there's still a place for private label," Jun, 1995; "In-store promotion goes high-tech: is the conventional coupon destined for obsolescence?," Jun, 1995.

44925 ■ Colmen Menard Company Inc. (CMCI)
The Woods, 994 Old Eagle School Rd., Ste. 1000
Wayne, PA 19087
Ph: (484)367-0300
Fax: (484)367-0305
Co. E-mail: cmci@colmenmenard.com
URL: http://www.colmenmenard.com
Contact: David W. Menard, President
E-mail: dmenard@colmenmenard.com
Scope: Merger and acquisition corporate finance and business advisory services for public and private companies located in North America. **Founded:** 1982. **Publications:** "Success in Selling a Troubled Company," Nov, 2002; "Savvy Dealmakers," May, 2001; "Success in Selling a Troubled Company feature article from The Technology Times bimonthly newspaper," Apr, 2002; "Truisms," M&A Today, Nov, 2000.

44926 ■ Comer & Associates L.L.C.—Energy Alliance Group
5255 Holmes Pl.
Boulder, CO 80303
Ph: (303)786-7986
Free: 888-950-3190
Fax: (303)895-2347
Co. E-mail: jerry@comerassociates.com
URL: http://www.comerassociates.com
Contact: Jerry C. Comer, President
E-mail: jerry@comerassociates.com
URL(s): www.energyalliance.biz. **Scope:** Specialize in developing markets and businesses. Marketing support includes: Developing and writing strategic and tactical business plans; developing and writing focused, effective market plans; researching market potential and competition; implementing targeted marketing tactics to achieve company objectives; conducting customer surveys to determine satisfaction and attitudes toward client. Organization development support includes: Executive management training programs; executive coaching; team building; developing effective organization structures; and management of change in dynamic and competitive environments; individual coaching for management and leadership effectiveness. **Founded:** 1993. **Seminars:** Developing a Strategic Market Plan; Market Research: Defining Your Opportunity; Management and Leadership Effectiveness; Team Building; Developing a Business Plan; How to Close; Using Questions to Sell; Sales System Elements and Checklist; Working With Independent Reps; Features vs. Benefits; Overcoming Objections; Sales Force Automation.

44927 ■ The Corlund Group L.L.C. (CG)
101 Federal St., Ste. 310
Boston, MA 02110
Ph: (617)423-9364
Fax: (617)423-9371
Co. E-mail: info@corlundgroup.com
URL: http://www.corlundgroup.com
Contact: Wilmot J. Gravenslund, Director
E-mail: wgravenslund@corlundgroup.com
Scope: Boutique firm offering services in the areas of leadership, governance, and change with a particular focus on CEO and senior executive succession planning, including assessment, development, and orchestrating succession processes with management and Boards of Directors. Also Board governance effectiveness. **Founded:** 1996. **Publications:** "Are You Rolling the Dice on CEO Succession?" Center for Healthcare Governance, 2006; "Leadership Due Diligence: The Neglected Governance Frontier," Directorship, Sep, 2001; "Leadership Due Diligence: Managing the Risks," The Corporate Board, Aug, 2001; "Succession: The need for detailed insight," Directors and Boards, 2001; "CEO Succession: Who's Doing Due Diligence?," 2001. **Telecommunication Services:** corlund@corlundgroup.com.

44928 ■ Corporate Consulting Inc.
3333 Belcaro Dr.
Denver, CO 80209-4912

Ph: (303)698-9292
Fax: (303)698-9292
Co. E-mail: corpcons@compuserve.com
Contact: Devereux C. Josephs, President
Scope: Specializes in feasibility studies, organizational development, small business management, mergers and acquisitions, joint ventures, divestitures, interim management, crisis management, turnarounds, financing, appraisals valuations and due diligence studies. **Founded:** 1983.

44929 ■ Crystal Clear Communications Inc.
1633 W Winslow Dr., Ste. 210
Mequon, WI 53092
Ph: (262)240-0072
Fax: (262)240-0073
Co. E-mail: contact@crystalclear1.com
URL: http://www.crystalclear1.com
Contact: Barry J. Moze, Partner
E-mail: barrymoze@crystalclearl.com
Scope: Specialize in helping executives identify impediments to success, and then develop strategies to surmount them. Serves to identify core problems, suggest appropriate business changes, work with the organization to support these changes, and help executives articulate the behavior that will uphold these changes. Specializes in strategic planning; organizational development; small business management; executive coaching. **Founded:** 1986. **Publications:** "Weakest Link"; "Aware Leadership"; "Integrity"; "When Your Plate is Full"; "Problem Solving"; "Strategic Thinking".

44930 ■ Development Resource Consultants (DRC)
PO Box 118
Rancho Cucamonga, CA 91729
Ph: (909)902-7655
Fax: (909)476-6942
Co. E-mail: drc@gotodrc.com
URL: http://www.gotodrc.com
Contact: Jerry R. Frey, Business Manager
E-mail: jfrey@gotodrc.com
Scope: Specializes in office re-organization, employee training in office organization, communication skills, sales training and career counseling. **Founded:** 1985. **Publications:** "Institute of Management Consultants Southern California Chapter," Jan, 2006.

44931 ■ Dimond Hospitality Consulting Group Inc.
5710 Stoneway Trl.
Nashville, TN 37209
Ph: (615)353-0033
Fax: (615)352-5290
Co. E-mail: drew@dimondhotelconsulting.com
URL: http://www.dimondhotelconsulting.com
Contact: Drew W. Dimond, President
E-mail: drew@dimondhotelconsulting.com
Scope: Specializes in strategic planning; start-up businesses; business process re-engineering; team building; competitive analysis; venture capital; competitive intelligence; and due diligence. Offers litigation support. Comprehensive hospitality consulting firm that serves as an adviser to leading hotel companies, independent hotels, lending institutions, trustees, law firms, investment companies and municipalities in the areas of: Asset management, Acquisition due diligence, Arbitration, Disposition advisory services, Exit strategies, Financial review and analysis, Impact studies, Mediation. **Founded:** 1985. **Publications:** "The distressed debt conundrum," Jul, 2009; "How to buy distressed assets," Apr, 2009; "Cmbs Loans: A History and the Future," Apr, 2009; "Opportunity Knocks," Apr, 2009; "Another Reality Check," Mar, 2009; "An Inkling of Hope," Mar, 2009; "Strong World Tourism Growth in 2007," 2007; "Les U.S. Construction Pipeline Sets Another Record at 5011 Hotels with 654503 Rooms"; "Hotel Capitalization Rates Hold for Now"; "Winning Cornell Hotel and Restaurant Administration Quarterly Article Provides Hotel Brand Analysis"; "Breaking News for Lifestyle Hotels. Ian Schrager and Bill Marriott Announce Their Marriage Will the Schrager-Marriott Marriage Lead to Eternal Bliss Or End in Divorce What Will the M Hotels Children Be Named"; "Brands Vs Independents"; "Nyu Conf Takes Industry Temp"; "Economy Hotel Performance Indication of Travel

Trends"; "Hotel Sales Continue at Brisk Pace"; "Fundamentals Strong, Weakening Undercurrent"; "Hotel Investments: Where Do We Go From Here"; "On the Road: Aahoa Panel Commits to Change"; "Cuba Not Ready, But Expecting U.S. Tourists".

44932 ■ donphin.com Inc.
1001 B Ave., Ste. 200
Coronado, CA 92118
Ph: (619)550-3533
Free: 800-234-3304
Fax: (619)600-0096
Co. E-mail: inquiry@donphin.com
URL: http://www.donphin.com
Contact: Vito Tanzi, President
Scope: Offers a comprehensive approach to understanding and applying a broad range of business principles: legal compliance issues, management concerns, health and safety, customer service, marketing, information management. Industries served: All developing small businesses. **Publications:** "Doing Business Right!"; "HR That Works!"; "Lawsuit Free! How to Prevent Employee Lawsuits!"; "Building Powerful Employment Relationships!"; "Victims, Villains and Heroes: Managing Emotions in The Workplace". **Seminars:** Doing Business Right!; HR That Works!; Building Powerful Employment Relationships; Lawsuit Free!.

44933 ■ Dubuc Lucke & Company Inc.—Adventa Global Intermediaries
120 W 5th St.
Cincinnati, OH 45202-2713
Ph: (513)579-8330
Fax: (513)241-6669
Contact: Kenneth E. Dubuc, President
Scope: Provides consulting services in the areas of profit enhancement; small business management; mergers and acquisitions; joint ventures; divestitures; interim management; crisis management; turnarounds; appraisals; valuations; due diligence; and international trade. **Founded:** 1999.

44934 ■ The DuMond Group
5282 Princeton Ave.
Westminster, CA 92683-2753
Ph: (714)373-0610
Contact: Adrianne H. Geiger-Dumond, President
Scope: Human resources and executive search consulting firm that specializes in organizational development; small business management; employee surveys and communication; performance appraisals; and team building. **Founded:** 1992.

44935 ■ Dunelm International
437 Colebrook Ln.
Bryn Mawr, PA 19010-3216
Ph: (610)989-0144
Fax: (610)964-9524
Co. E-mail: jecdunelm@worldnet.att.net
Contact: John E. Crowther, President
E-mail: Jecdunelm@dunelm.org.uk
Scope: Firm specializes in feasibility studies; start-up businesses; interim management; crisis management; turnarounds; business process re-engineering; sales forecasting; supply chain solution and project management. **Founded:** 1988.

44936 ■ Facility Directions Inc.
PO Box 761
Manchester, MO 63011
Ph: (636)256-4400
Free: 800-536-0044
Fax: (636)227-2868
Co. E-mail: walty@facilitydirections.com
URL: http://www.facilitydirections.com
Contact: Walter E. Yesberg, President
E-mail: walty@facilitydirections.com
Scope: Specializes in service to financial institutions; strategic planning; feasibility studies; facility and space planning; attitude surveys; site selection. **Founded:** 1990.

44937 ■ First Strike Management Consulting Inc.—FSMC Inc.
4001 Loblolly Ave.
Little River, SC 29566-1188
Ph: (843)385-6338

Fax: (843)390-1004
Co. E-mail: info@fsmc.com
URL: http://www.fsmc.com
Contact: J. D. Lewis, Chief Executive Officer
E-mail: jd.lewis@fsmc.com
Scope: Offers proposal management and program management services. Specializes in enterprise systems, management systems, and staff augmentation. Serves the following industries: Nuclear/Fossil Power, Petro-Chemical, Aerospace and Defense, Telecommunications, Engineering and Construction, Information Technology, Golf Course Construction/Management, Utility Engineering/Construction, Civil Works, and Housing Development. **Founded:** 1991. **Publications:** "Project Management for Executives"; "Project Risk Management"; "Project Communications Management"; "Winning Proposals, Four Computer Based Training (CBT) courses"; "Principles of Program Management". **Seminars:** Preparing Winning Proposals in Response to Government RFPs.

44938 ■ Global Technology Transfer L.L.C.
1500 Dixie Hwy.
Park Hills, KY 41011-2819
Ph: (859)431-1262
Fax: (859)431-5148
Contact: Anthony Zembrodt, President
Scope: Firm specializes in product development; quality assurance; new product development; and total quality management focusing on household chemical specialties, especially air fresheners. Utilizes latest technology from global resources. Specializes in enhancement products for home and automobile. **Founded:** 1992.

44939 ■ Great Lakes Consulting Group Inc.
54722 Little Flower Trl.
Mishawaka, IN 46545
Ph: (574)287-4500
Fax: (574)233-2688
Contact: James E. Schrager, President
Scope: Provides consulting services in the areas of strategic planning; feasibility studies; start-up businesses; small business management; mergers and acquisitions; joint ventures; divestitures; interim management; crisis management; turnarounds; business process re-engineering; venture capital; and international trade. **Founded:** 1989.

44940 ■ Grimmick Consulting Services (GCS)
455 Donner Way
San Ramon, CA 94582
Ph: (925)735-1036
Fax: (925)735-1100
Co. E-mail: hank@grimmickconsulting.com
URL: http://www.grimmickconsulting.com
Contact: Henry Grimmick, President
E-mail: hank@grimmickconsulting.com
Scope: Provider of consulting services in the areas of strategic planning; organizational assessment; organizational development; leadership and management development Baldridge criteria, process improvement and balanced scorecards and team dynamics. **Founded:** 1993.

44941 ■ Health Strategy Group Inc.
46 River Rd.
Chatham, NY 12037
Ph: (518)392-6770
Contact: Cameron Battley, President
Scope: Provides consulting services in the areas of strategic planning, feasibility studies, start-up businesses, organizational development, market research, customer service audits, new product development, marketing, public relations. **Founded:** 1981. **Publications:** "Online Consumer Surveys as a Methodology for Assessing the Quality of the United States Health Care System," 2004.

44942 ■ Hewitt Development Enterprises (HDE)
1717 N Bayshore Dr., Ste. 2154
Miami, FL 33132
Ph: (305)372-0941

Fax: (305)372-0941
Co. E-mail: info@hewittdevelopment.com
URL: http://www.hewittdevelopment.com
Contact: Robert G. Hewitt, Principal
E-mail: bob@hewittdevelopment.com
Scope: Specializes in strategic planning; profit enhancement; start-up businesses; interim management; crisis management; turnarounds; production planning; just-in-time inventory management; and project management. Serves senior management (CEOs, CFOs, division presidents, etc.) and acquirers of distressed businesses. **Founded:** 1985.

44943 ■ Holt Capital
1916 Pike Pl., Ste. 12-344
Seattle, WA 98101
Ph: (206)484-0403
Fax: (206)789-8034
Co. E-mail: info@holtcapital.com
URL: http://www.holtcapital.com
Contact: Marilyn J. Holt, Chief Executive Officer
E-mail: mjholt@holtcapital.com
Scope: Registered investment advisory firm. Services include: Debt planning, private equity, mergers, divestitures and acquisitions, transaction support services. Connects companies with capital. **Founded:** 1980. **Publications:** "Early Sales Key to Early-Stage Funding"; "Financial Transactions: Who Should Be At Your Table"; "Get the Deal Done: The Four Keys to Successful Mergers and Acquisitions"; "Is Your First Paragraph a Turn-off"; "Bubble Rubble: Bridging the Price Gap for an Early-Stage Business"; "Are You Ready For The new Economy"; "Could I Get Money or Jail Time With That The Sarbanes-Oxley Act Of 2002 gives early-stage companies More Risks". **Seminars:** Attracting Private Investors; Five Proven Ways to Finance Your Company; How to Get VC Financing; Venture Packaging; How to Finance Company Expansion.

44944 ■ The Institute for Management Excellence
PO Box 5459
Lacey, WA 98509-5459
Ph: (360)412-0404
Co. E-mail: pwoc@itstime.com
URL: http://www.itstime.com
Contact: Michael Anthony, Director
Scope: Management consulting and training focuses on improving productivity, using practices and creative techniques. Practices based on the company's theme: It's time for new ways of doing business. Industries served: public sector, law enforcement, finance or banking, non profit, computers or high technology, education, human resources, utilities. **Founded:** 1995. **Publications:** "Income Without a Job," 2008; "The Other Side of Midnight, 2000: An Executive Guide to the Year 2000 Problem"; "Concordance to the Michael Teachings"; "Handbook of Small Business Advertising"; "The Personality Game"; "How to Market Yourself for Success". **Seminars:** The Personality Game; Power Path Seminars; Productivity Plus; Sexual Harassment and Discrimination Prevention; Worker's Comp Cost Reduction; Americans with Disabilities Act; In Search of Identify: Clarifying Corporate Culture.

44945 ■ Interminds & Federer Resources Inc.
106 E 6th St., Ste. 310
Austin, TX 78701-3659
Ph: (512)476-8800
Fax: (512)476-8811
Co. E-mail: yesyoucan@interminds.com
URL: http://www.interminds.com
Contact: Frank Federer, President
E-mail: ffederer@integra100.com
Scope: Specializes in feasibility studies; startup businesses; small business management; mergers and acquisitions; joint ventures; divestitures; interim management; crisis management; turnarounds; production planning; team building; appraisals and valuations. **Founded:** 1985. **Publications:** "Yes You Can: How To Be A Success No Matter Who You Are Or Where You're From".

44946 ■ Johnston Co.
78 Bedford St.
Lexington, MA 02420
Ph: (781)862-7595

Fax: (781)862-9066
Co. E-mail: info@johnstoncompany.com
URL: http://www.johnstoncompany.com
Contact: Claire Sehringer, Manager
Scope: Specializes in management audits and reports; start-up businesses; small business management; mergers and acquisitions; joint ventures; divestitures; interim management; crisis management; turnarounds; cost controls; financing; venture capital; controller services; financial management, strategic and advisory services. **Founded:** 1987. **Publications:** "Why are board meetings such a waste of time," Boston Business Journal, Apr, 2004.

44947 ■ Keiei Senryaku Corp.
19191 S Vermont Ave., Ste. 530
Torrance, CA 90502-1049
Ph: (310)366-3331
Free: 800-951-8780
Fax: (310)366-3330
Co. E-mail: takenakaes@earthlink.net
Contact: Kurt Miyamoto, President
Scope: Offers consulting services in the areas of strategic planning; feasibility studies; profit enhancement; organizational development; start-up businesses; mergers and acquisitions; joint ventures; divestitures; executive searches; sales management; and competitive analysis. **Founded:** 1989.

44948 ■ Management Resource Partners
181 2nd Ave., Ste. 542
San Mateo, CA 94401
Ph: (650)401-5850
Fax: (650)401-5850
Contact: John C. Roberts, Owner
Scope: Firm specializes in strategic planning; small business management; mergers and acquisitions; joint ventures; divestitures; interim management; crisis management; turn around; venture capital; appraisals and valuations. **Founded:** 1981.

44949 ■ Mefford, Knutson & Associates Inc. (MK)
6437 Lyndale Ave. S, Ste. 103
Richfield, MN 55423-1465
Ph: (612)869-8011
Free: 800-831-0228
Fax: (612)869-8004
Co. E-mail: info@mkaonline.net
URL: http://www.mkaonline.net
Contact: Jeanette Mefford, Director
E-mail: jmefford@mkaonline.com
Scope: A consulting and licensed business brokerage firm specializing in start-up businesses; strategic planning; mergers and acquisitions; joint ventures; divestitures; business process re-engineering; personnel policies and procedures; market research; new product development and cost controls. **Founded:** 1990.

44950 ■ Miller, Hellwig Associates
150 W End Ave.
New York, NY 10023-5713
Ph: (212)799-0471
Fax: (212)877-0186
Co. E-mail: millerhelwig@earthlink.net
Contact: Ernest C. Miller, President
Scope: Consulting services in the areas of start-up businesses; small business management; employee surveys and communication; performance appraisals; executive searches; team building; personnel policies and procedures; market research. Also involved in improving cross-cultural and multi-cultural relationships, particularly with Japanese clients. **Founded:** 1984. **Seminars:** Objectives and standards/recruiting for boards of directors.

44951 ■ Murray Dropkin & Associates—Dropkin Consulting
390 George St.
New Brunswick, NJ 08901
Ph: (732)828-3211
Fax: (732)828-4118
Co. E-mail: murray@dropkin.com
URL: http://www.dropkin.com
Contact: Murray Dropkin, President
E-mail: murray@dropkin.com
Scope: Specializes in feasibility studies; business management; business process re-engineering; and team building, health care and housing. **Founded:**

1969. **Publications:** "Bookkeeping for Nonprofits," Jossey Bass, 2005; "Guide to Audits of Nonprofit Organizations," PPC; "The Nonprofit Report," Warren, Gorham & Lamont; "The Budget Building Book for Nonprofits," Jossey-Bass; "The Cash Flow Management Book for Nonprofits," Jossey-Bass.

44952 ■ Parker Consultants Inc.
230 Mason St.
Greenwich, CT 06830-6633
Ph: (203)861-6698
Contact: Donald L. Parker, President
Scope: Firm specializes in strategic planning; organizational development; small business management; performance appraisals; executive searches; team building; and customer service audits. **Founded:** 1988.

44953 ■ Partners for Market Leadership L.L.C.
400 Galleria Pky., Ste. 1500
Atlanta, GA 30339
Ph: (770)850-1409
Free: 800-984-1110
Co. E-mail: dcarpenter@market-leadership.com
URL: http://www.market-leadership.com
Contact: Nancy Surdyka, Manager
E-mail: nsurdyka@market-leadership.com
Scope: Boutique consulting firm focused on assisting clients to develop sustainable market leadership in geographic, practice area and/or industry markets. Provides consulting on market leadership, revenue enhancement, strategic development and change facilitation. Additional services are offered to legal, accounting, valuation and financial firms. **Founded:** 1995.

44954 ■ Performance Consulting Group Inc.
8031 SW 35th Terr.
Miami, FL 33155-3443
Ph: (305)264-5577
Fax: (305)264-9079
Contact: Patrick J. O'Brien, President
Scope: Firm provides consulting services in the areas of strategic planning; profit enhancement; product development; and production planning. **Founded:** 1980.

44955 ■ Rose & Crangle Ltd.
117 N 4th St.
Lincoln, KS 67455
Ph: (785)524-5050
Fax: (785)524-3130
Co. E-mail: rcltd@nckcn.com
URL: http://www.roseandcrangle.com
Contact: Robert D. Crangle, President
E-mail: rcltd@nckcn.com
Scope: Provider of evaluation, planning and policy analyzes for universities, associations, foundations, governmental agencies and private companies engaged in scientific, technological or educational activities. Special expertise in the development of new institutions. Special skills in providing planning and related group facilitation workshops. **Founded:** 1984. **Publications:** "Preface to Bulgarian Integration Into Europe and NATO: Issues of Science Policy And research Evaluation Practice," Ios Press, 2006; "Allocating Limited National Resources for Fundamental Research," 2005.

44956 ■ Rothschild Strategies Unlimited L.L.C.
19 Thistle Rd.
Norwalk, CT 06851-1909
Ph: (203)846-6898
Fax: (203)847-1426
Co. E-mail: bill@strategyleader.com
URL: http://www.strategyleader.com
Contact: Stephen M. Rothschild, President
Scope: Consults with senior management and business level strategy teams to develop overall strategic direction, set priorities and creates sustainable competitive advantages and differentiators. Enables organizations to enhance their own strategic thinking and leadership skills so that they can continue to develop and implement profitable growth strategies. **Founded:** 1983. **Publications:** "Putting It All Together-a guide to strategic thinking"; "Competitive

Advantage"; "Ristaker, Caretaker, Surgeon & Undertaker four faces of strategic leadership"; "The Secret to GE's Success"; "Having the Right Strategic Leader and Team".

44957 ■ Sklar and Associates Inc.
242 Laurel Bay Dr.
Murrells Inlet, SC 29576
Ph: (843)798-0412
Fax: (843)651-3090
Co. E-mail: sklarincdc@aol.com
URL: http://www.sklarinc.com
Contact: Tim Sklar, President
Scope: Provider of consulting services for business acquisitions, business development and project finance. Provides audit oversight services to listed corporations on Sarbanes-Oxley compliance. Services include: Due diligence analyses and corporate governance. Industries served: transportation sectors, energy sector and commercial real estate industries. **Seminars:** Financial Analysis in MBA; Emerging Company Finance; Due Diligence in Business Acquisition; Business Valuation.

44958 ■ Harvey C. Skoog
7151 E Addis Ave.
Prescott Valley, AZ 86314
Ph: (928)772-1448
Scope: Firm has expertise in taxes, payroll, financial planning, budgeting, buy/sell planning, business start-up, fraud detection, troubled business consulting, acquisition, and marketing. Serves the manufacturing, construction, and retailing industries in Arizona. **Founded:** 1977.

44959 ■ Turnaround Inc.
3415 A St. NW
Gig Harbor, WA 98335
Ph: (253)857-6730
Fax: (253)857-6344
Co. E-mail: info@turnround-inc.com
URL: http://www.turnaround-inc.com
Contact: Miles Stover, President
E-mail: mstover@turnaround-inc.com
Scope: Provider of interim executive management assistance and management advisory to small, medium and family-owned businesses that are not meeting their goals. Services include acting as an interim executive or on-site manager. Extensive practices in arena of bankruptcy management. **Founded:** 1997. **Publications:** "How to Identify Problem and Promising Management"; "How to Tell if Your Company is a Bankruptcy Candidate"; "Signs that Your Company is in Trouble"; "The Turnaround Specialist: How to File a Petition Under 11 USC 11". **Seminars:** Competitive Intelligence Gathering.

44960 ■ ValueNomics Value Specialists
50 W San Fernando St., Ste. 600
San Jose, CA 95113
Fax: (408)200-6401
Co. E-mail: info@amllp.com
Contact: Gary E. Jones, Chief Executive Officer
Scope: Consulting is offered in the areas of financial management, process re-engineering, growth business services; governance, risk/compliance, SOX readiness and compliance, SAS 70, enterprise risk management, system security, operational and internal audit; business advisory services; valuation services; CORE assessment; contract assurance; transaction advisory services, IT solutions and litigation support services. **Founded:** 1993. **Publications:** "Dueling Appraisers: How Differences in Input and Assumptions May Control the Value," Apr, 2005; "The Business of Business Valuation and the CPA as an expert witness"; "The Business of Business Valuation," McGraw-Hill Professional Publishers Inc.

44961 ■ Venture Marketing Associates L.L.C.
800 Palisade Ave., Ste. 907
Fort Lee, NJ 07024
Ph: (201)924-7435
Fax: (201)224-8757
Co. E-mail: venturemkt@aol.com
URL: http://www.venturemarketingassociates.com
Contact: Brian Furber, Market Analyst Director, Marketing
Scope: Provider of consulting services in business development and franchising. Provides hands-on assistance in planning and implementing strategic

marketing/management plans. Clients include franchisers, small business owners and individuals. Cost-effective fees for those in transition, facing unemployment, researching a franchise or starting a business. Industries served: service, retail and distribution. **Seminars:** Franchise Your Business; How to Research a Franchise Services.

44962 ■ Young & Associates Inc.
121 E Main St.
Kent, OH 44240
Ph: (330)678-0524
Free: 800-525-9775
Fax: (330)678-6219
Co. E-mail: online@younginc.com
URL: http://www.younginc.com
Contact: Gary J. Young, Chief Executive Officer
E-mail: gyoung@younginc.com
Scope: Provider of a variety of management consulting, outsourcing, educational, and research services, including strategic planning, risk management, capital planning, mergers and acquisitions, internal audit, branching and expansion, loan review, information technology, marketing, market research, human resources planning and management, site/location feasibility studies, development of business plans, and organizational analysis and development and regulatory compliance. Specialists in small and mid-size companies. Industries served: financial institutions, manufacturers (business-to-business and consumer), banking, healthcare (hospitals and practitioners), retailers, and services. **Founded:** 1978. **Publications:** "An Avalanche of New Compliance Regulations," Oct, 2009; "Fair Lending Risk Assessment," May, 2009. **Special Services:** The Compliance Monitoring System™; Compliance Monitoring Update Service™; The Compliance Review Program™; Compliance Review Program Update Service™.

COMPUTERIZED DATABASES

44963 ■ SBA Online
409 3rd St. SW
Washington, DC 20416
Ph: (202)606-4000
Free: 800-U-ASK-SBA
Fax: (202)205-6901
Co. E-mail: answerdesk@sba.gov
URL: http://www.sba.gov
Contact: Dr. Winslow Sargeant, Manager
Availability: Online: U.S. Small Business Administration. **Type:** Bulletin board; Full-text; Directory.

COMPUTER SYSTEMS/ SOFTWARE

44964 ■ Business Simulator
6 Tower Bridge, Ste. 540
Conshohocken, PA 19428
Ph: (484)391-2900
Free: 800-445-7089
Co. E-mail: rommin.adl@smginc.com
URL: http://www.smginc.com
Price: $69.95. **Description:** Software program allowing the user to simulate running a start-up company through the various phases of development.

LIBRARIES

44965 ■ Boston Public Library - Kirstein Business Branch
700 Boylston St.
Boston, MA 02116
Ph: (617)859-2142
Co. E-mail: ask@bpl.org
URL: http://www.bpl.org/kbl
Contact: Laura Pattison, Librarian
Scope: Business administration, retailing, advertising, finance, marketing, real estate, insurance, banking, taxation, accounting, investments, economics, business law, small business. **Services:** Copying is available through the library's interlibrary loan department; reference faxing up to three pages. **Founded:** 1930. **Holdings:** Moody's Manuals (1935 to present in print; 1909-1997 in microfiche); Commercial and

Financial Chronicle, 1957-1987; Bank and Quotation Record, 1928-1987; Standard and Poor's Daily Stock Price Record: New York and American Stock Exchanges, 1962 to present; over-the-counter stocks, 1968 to present; domestic and foreign trade directories; city directories; telephone directories for New England and U.S. cities with populations over 100,000 for New England cities and towns; Standard Stock Market Service, 1921-1922; Standard Stock Offerings, 1925-1939; National Stock Summary, 1927 to present; Standard & Poor's Stock Guide, 1943 to present; New York and American Stock Exchange companies Annual and 10K reports on microfiche (1987-1996); Wall Street Journal on microfilm (latest 10 years); Wall Street Transcript on microfilm (latest 5 years); D-U-N-S Business Identification Service (November 1973 -1995). **Subscriptions:** 700 journals and other serials; 13 newspapers. **Telecommunication Services:** kirstein@bpl.org.

44966 ■ Business Development Bank of Canada Research & Information Centre
5 Place Ville Marie, Ste. 300
Montreal, QC, Canada H3B 5E7
Ph: (514)283-7632
Free: 877-232-2269
Fax: (514)283-2304
URL: http://www.bdc.ca
Contact: Odette Lavoie, Specialist
Scope: Small business, management, Canadian business and industry, banking and finance, development banking. **Services:** Interlibrary loan; Library not open to the public. **Founded:** 1977. **Holdings:** 5000 books. **Subscriptions:** 100 journals and other serials; 7 newspapers.

44967 ■ Carnegie Library of Pittsburgh - Downtown & Business
612 Smithfield St.
Pittsburgh, PA 15222-2506
Ph: (412)281-7141
Fax: (412)471-1724
Co. E-mail: downtown@carnegielibrary.org
URL: http://www.carnegielibrary.org/locations/ downtown
Contact: Karen Rossi, Department Head
Scope: Investments, small business, entrepreneurship, management, marketing, insurance, advertising, personal finance, accounting, real estate, job and career, International business. **Services:** Library open to the public. **Founded:** 1924. **Holdings:** 13,000 business volumes; VF materials; microfilm; looseleaf services; AV materials.

44968 ■ Chicago Public Library Central Library - Business/Science/Technology Division
Harold Washington Library Center
400 S. State St., 4th Fl.
Chicago, IL 60605
Ph: (312)747-4450
Fax: (312)747-4975
URL: http://www.chipublib.org/branch/details/library/ harold-washington/p/Bst
Scope: Small business, marketing, technology, corporate reports, investments, management, personnel, patents, physical and biological sciences, medicine, health, computer science, careers, environmental information, gardening, cookbooks. **Services:** Interlibrary loan; copying; division open to the public. **Founded:** 1977. **Holdings:** 415,000 books; 52,100 bound periodical volumes; 33,000 reels of microfilm; Securities and Exchange Commission (SEC) reports; federal specifications and standards; American National Standards Institute standards; corporate Annual reports. **Subscriptions:** 4000 journals and other serials; 8 newspapers.

44969 ■ Employment Support Center Library
1556 Wisconsin Ave., NW
Washington, DC 20007
Ph: (202)628-2919
Fax: (703)790-1469
Co. E-mail: escjobclubs@yahoo.com
URL: http://jobclubs.angelfire.com/
Contact: Ellie Wegener, Executive Director
Scope: Employment networking, self-esteem, starting your own business, setting up job clubs, training facilitators, maintaining a large job bank, providing

job-searching skills. **Services:** Library open to the public. **Founded:** 1984. **Holdings:** 150 articles; books; periodicals; videos on job search; interviews; reports; manuscripts. **Subscriptions:** 4 journals and other serials; 2 newspapers.

44970 ■ Greater Oviedo Chamber of Commerce Business Library
PO Box 621236
Oviedo, FL 32765
Ph: (407)365-6500
Fax: (407)365-6587
Co. E-mail: cory@oviedowintersprings.org
URL: http://www.oviedowintersprings.org
Contact: Corydon G. Skeates, Executive Director
Scope: Small business; central Florida business. **Services:** Copying; library open to the public. **Founded:** 1995. **Holdings:** 3 books; 10 reports; periodicals. **Subscriptions:** 3 newspapers.

44971 ■ Indian River Area Library
PO Box 160
Indian River, MI 49749
Ph: (231)238-8581
Fax: (231)238-9494
Co. E-mail: indrivl@northland.lib.mi.us
URL: http://www.libnet.org/iriver
Contact: Cindy Lou Poquette, Director
Scope: Small business, careers, fine arts, music, dance. **Services:** Interlibrary loan; copying; library open to the public (fee for non-residents to check out materials). **Founded:** 1976. **Holdings:** 52,000 books; 32,000 videocassettes and DVDs; 2000 microfiche; sound cassettes; DVDs; CDs; periodicals; large print books. **Subscriptions:** 80 journals and other serials; 3 newspapers.

44972 ■ National Small Business Benefits Association Library
2244 N. Grand Ave., E.
Springfield, IL 62702
Ph: (217)544-0881
Fax: (217)544-5816
Co. E-mail: t-shirtz@t-shirtz.com
URL: http://www.t-shirtz.com
Scope: Small businesses. **Services:** Copying; library open to the public with restrictions. **Holdings:** 300 volumes. **Telecommunication Services:** honkeytown@t-shirtz.com.

44973 ■ Nations Bank - Business Resource Center
3401 Westend Ave., Ste. 110
Nashville, TN 37203
Ph: (615)749-4088
Fax: (615)749-3685
Co. E-mail: Lillie.Taylor@NationsBank.com
Contact: Lillie Taylor, Librarian
Scope: Small business. **Services:** Copying; Library open to the public with restrictions. **Founded:** 1976. **Holdings:** 2000 books; 6 VF drawers of archives. **Subscriptions:** 160 journals and other serials.

44974 ■ New York State Small Business Development Center - Research Network
State University Plaza
22 Corporate Woods Bldg., 3rd Fl.
Albany, NY 12246
Ph: (518)443-5398
Free: 800-732-SBDC
Co. E-mail: james.king@nyssbdc.org
URL: http://www.nyssbdc.org/resources/researchnetwork.html
Contact: Mr. James King, Director
Scope: Small business. **Services:** Copying; faxing; document delivery. **Founded:** 1992. **Holdings:** 1000 books; 20 CD-ROMs. **Subscriptions:** 40 journals and other serials; 10 newspapers.

44975 ■ Newfoundland Department of Industry, Trade and Technology - Registry
PO Box 8700
St. John's, NL, Canada A1B 4J6
Ph: (709)729-5982
Fax: (709)729-5936
Scope: Economics, energy, small business, oil and gas. **Holdings:** Figures not available.

44976 ■ Newfoundland and Labrador Business Service Centre
West Block, Confederation Bldg.
St. John's, NL, Canada A1B 4J6
Ph: (709)729-7000
Fax: (709)729-0654
Co. E-mail: mike.howley@acoa-apeca.gc.ca
URL: http://www.intrd.gov.nl.ca/intrd/department/
   branches/sibd/cnlbsc.html
Contact: Mike Howley, Manager
Scope: Marketing, small business, economic and regional development. **Services:** Copying; SDI; centre open to the public. **Founded:** 1973. **Holdings:** 10,000 books; 20 VF drawers of subject files; Standard Industrial Classification (SIC) files. **Subscriptions:** 300 journals and other serials.

44977 ■ Piedmont Technical College Library
Lex Walters Campus
Bldg. K, 2nd Fl.
Greenwood, SC 29648-1467
Ph: (864)941-8441
Free: 800-868-5528, x8441
Fax: (864)941-8558
Co. E-mail: librarian@ptc.edu
URL: http://www.ptc.edu/library/
Contact: Meredith Daniel, Dean
Scope: Economics, technology, allied health, nursing, small business, computer science, criminal justice. **Services:** Interlibrary loan; copying; library open to the public. **Founded:** 1966. **Holdings:** 30,000 books; 400 bound periodical volumes; 3500 reels of microfilm; 2000 AV programs. **Subscriptions:** 325 journals and other serials; 10 newspapers. **Telecommunication Services:** daniel.m@ptc.edu; wilde.m@ptc.edu.

44978 ■ Saskatchewan Research Council - Information Services
125-15 Innovation Blvd.
Saskatoon, SK, Canada S7N 2X8
Ph: (306)933-5400
Fax: (306)933-7446
Co. E-mail: info@src.sk.ca
URL: http://www.src.sk.ca
Contact: Colleen Marshall, Coordinator, Information
Scope: Agriculture, biotechnology and food, alternative energy and manufacturing, energy, the environment and forestry, mining and minerals. **Services:** Interlibrary loan. **Founded:** 1947. **Holdings:** 8600 monographs; 3300 SRC-authored publications. **Subscriptions:** 55 periodicals.

44979 ■ South College Library
3904 Lonas Dr.
Knoxville, TN 37909
Ph: (865)251-1800

Fax: (865)637-0127
Co. E-mail: mmchugh@southcollegetn.edu
URL: http://www.southcollegetn.edu/library/
Contact: Mel McHugh, Librarian
Scope: Business, physical therapy, occupational therapy, administration, medical administration, legal administration, small business, secretarial science, paralegal, hotel and restaurant management. **Services:** Interlibrary loan; copying; printing; SDI; library open to South College staff and students. **Holdings:** 6700 books; 10 VF drawers; 214 volumes on microfilm; 1 cabinet of microfiche. **Subscriptions:** 106 journals and other serials. **Telecommunication Services:** scref@southcollegetn.edu.

44980 ■ U.S.D.A. National Agricultural Library - Rural Information Center—RIC.
10301 Baltimore Ave., Rm. 132
Beltsville, MD 20705
Ph: (301)504-5547
Free: 800-633-7701
Fax: (301)504-5181
Co. E-mail: ric@nal.usda.gov
URL: http://ric.nal.usda.gov
Contact: William Thomas, Coordinator
Scope: Economic development; small business development; city and county government services; government and private grants and funding sources; rural communities; community leadership; natural resources. **Services:** Copying; center open to the public. **Founded:** 1987. **Holdings:** Figures not available. **Telecommunication Services:** william. thomas@ars.usda.gov.

44981 ■ University of Colorado--Boulder - William M. White Business Library
Leeds School of Business
Campus Box 184
Boulder, CO 80309-0184
Ph: (303)492-8367
Fax: (303)735-0333
Co. E-mail: buslib@colorado.edu
URL: http://ucblibraries.colorado.edu/business
Contact: Jennie Gerke, Director
Scope: Ethics, information systems, business policy, economics and law, small business, management and Organization, finance and accounting, marketing, transportation, management science, real estate, insurance, taxation. **Services:** Interlibrary loan; copying; Library open to the public. **Founded:** 1970. **Holdings:** 80,000 volumes; 160,000 microforms. **Subscriptions:** 660 journals; 15 newspapers. **Telecommunication Services:** joseph.grobelny@colorado. edu.

44982 ■ Warren County Community College Library Special Collections
475 Rte. 57 W.
Washington, NJ 07882-4343
Ph: (908)835-2336
Co. E-mail: reference@warren.edu
URL: http://www.warren.edu
Contact: Ariana Baker, Librarian, Reference
URL(s): warren.libguides.com/content.php-?pid=218828. **Scope:** Business, humanities, American history, law. **Services:** Interlibrary loan; Q&ANJ, copying; services for the deaf; closed-captioned videos available; library open to the public. **Founded:** 1984. **Holdings:** 26,600 books; 18 lin.ft. of archival materials; 1100 videos/DVD; 45 CDs. **Subscriptions:** 200 journals and other serials.

RESEARCH CENTERS

44983 ■ Laval University - Centre for Entrepreneurship and Small Business—Laval University - Centre d'Entrpreneuriat et de PME (CEPME)
Faculty of Science of the Administration
Pavilion Palasis Prince, local 1663
Sainte Foy, QC, Canada G1K 7P4
Ph: (418)656-2490
Fax: (418)656-2624
Co. E-mail: mariejosee.drapeau@fsa.ulaval.ca
URL: http://www.fsa.ulaval.ca/cepme
Contact: Yvon Gasse, Director
E-mail: yvon.gasse@fsa.ulaval.ca
Founded: 1993. **Educational Activities:** Training sessions and seminars; Centre for Entrepreneurship and Small Business Conferences. **Telecommunication Services:** centre.pme@fsa.ulaval.ca.

44984 ■ University of Quebec at Trois-Rivieres - Research Institute for Small and Medium-Sized Enterprises
Pavillon Desjardins-Hydro-Quebec
3351, Blvd. des Forges
Trois-Rivieres, QC, Canada G9A 5H7
Ph: (819)376-5235
Fax: (819)376-5138
Co. E-mail: inrpme@uqtr.ca
URL: http://oraprdnt.uqtr.uquebec.ca/pls/public/
   gscw030?owa_no_site=861
Contact: Claire V. de la Durantaye, Director
Founded: 1997. **Publications:** *Revue Internationale PME Scientific Magazine* (3/year). **Educational Activities:** Postgraduate assistance; Weekly research seminars, in fall and winter terms. **Telecommunication Services:** claire.v.de.la.durantaye@uqtr.ca.

START-UP INFORMATION

44985 ■ *The 100 Best Businesses to Start When You Don't Want To Work Hard Anymore*
Pub: Career Press Inc.
Ed: Lisa Rogak. **Price:** $16.99. **Description:** Author helps burned-out workers envision a new future as a small business owner. Systems analysis, adventure travel outfitting, bookkeeping, food delivery, furniture making, and software development are among the industries examined.

44986 ■ *"Aptitudes for Apps" in Boston Business Journal (Vol. 31, July 1, 2011, No. 23, pp. 3)*
Pub: Boston Business Journal
Ed: Kyle Alspach. **Description:** Startups Apperian Inc. and Kinvey Inc. are aiming to accelerate the development and deployment of mobile applications and have received fund pledges from Boston-area venture capital firms.

44987 ■ *"Local Startup Hits Big Leagues" in Austin Business JournalInc. (Vol. 28, December 19, 2008, No. 40, pp. 1)*
Pub: American City Business Journals
Ed: Christopher Calnan. **Description:** Qcue LLC, an Austin, Texas-based company founded in 2007 is developing a software system that can be used by Major League Baseball teams to change the prices of their single-game tickets based on variables affecting demand. The company recently completed a trial with the San Francisco Giants in 2008.

44988 ■ *"OtherInbox Ready for Revenue: Software Startup Expects Profits in '09" in Austin Business JournalInc. (Vol. 28, January 2, 2009)*
Pub: American City Business Journals
Ed: Christopher Calnan. **Description:** Founder of Austin, Texas-based OtherBox Inc. expects the company to generate revenue through subscriptions and advertising and also reach profitability in 2009. The company's email management tool sends secondary mail to an alternate location thereby freeing up the work inbox for more urgent messages.

44989 ■ *"Probability Processing Chip: Lyric Semiconductor" in Inc. (Volume 32, December 2010, No. 10, pp. 52)*
Pub: Inc. Magazine
Ed: Christine Lagorio. **Description:** Lyric Semiconductor, a start up located in Cambridge, Massachusetts, has developed a computer chip that also uses values that fall between zero and one, resulting in a chip that can process information using probabilities, considering many possible answers that find the best fit.

ASSOCIATIONS AND OTHER ORGANIZATIONS

44990 ■ **Business Software Alliance (BSA)**
1150 18th St. NW, Ste. 700
Washington, DC 20036
Ph: (202)872-5500
Fax: (202)872-5501
Co. E-mail: info@bsa.org
URL: http://www.bsa.org
Contact: Robert Holleyman, II, President
Description: Computer software publishers. Promotes the free world trade of business software by combating international software piracy, advancing intellectual property protection, and increasing market access. **Founded:** 1988. **Publications:** *Guide to Software Management* (Annual); *Software Review* (Quarterly).

44991 ■ **TechAmerica**
601 Pennsylvania Ave., NW
Washington, DC 20004
Ph: (202)682-9110
Fax: (202)682-9111
URL: http://www.techamerica.org
Contact: Phil Bond, President
E-mail: pbond@itaa.org
Description: A division of the Information Technology Association of America; software companies involved in the development or marketing of software for personal, midrange, and mainframe computers. Promotes the software industry and addresses specific problems of the industry. Represents the industry before various governmental units; provides educational programs to members; conducts research and makes available legal services. Develops standards. **Founded:** 1961. **Publications:** *ITAA Software Industry Briefing Book*; *Software Industry Executive Newsletter* (Bimonthly); *Information Technology Association of America--Membership Directory* (Annual); *VAR/Vendor Directory*; *Quality Goes Global: An ITAA Guide to ISO 9,000 Standard Series for Information Technology Companies*; *Financial Operating Ratios for Software Companies*. **Awards:** Customer Support Quality Award (Annual); Documentation/Training Materials Quality Award (Annual); Total Quality Award (Annual).

EDUCATIONAL PROGRAMS

44992 ■ **Accessible Web Design: Complying with Section 508**
EEI Communications
8945 Guilford Rd., Ste. 145
Columbia, MD 21046
Ph: (410)309-8200
Free: 888-253-2762
Fax: (410)630-3980
Co. E-mail: train@eeicom.com
URL: http://www.eeicom.com/eei-training-services
Price: $425.00. **Description:** Covers what the law is and whom it applies, using HTML and CSS coding techniques to meet the guidelines, creating fluid design that adapts to user needs, using free validation to check site for accessibility, and putting the compliance icon on completed site. **Dates and Locations:** Silver Spring, MD; Alexandria, VA; Hunt Valley, MD; and Columbia, MD.

44993 ■ **Adobe Acrobat 9 for Legal Professionals**
EEI Communications
8945 Guilford Rd., Ste. 145
Columbia, MD 21046
Ph: (410)309-8200
Free: 888-253-2762
Fax: (410)630-3980
Co. E-mail: train@eeicom.com
URL: http://www.eeicom.com/eei-training-services
Price: $425.00. **Description:** Designed for lawyers and paralegals who need to incorporate specific legal procedures into their document workflow, including Redaction and Bates numbering. **Dates and Locations:** Alexandria, VA; Silver Spring, MD; Hunt Valley, MD; and Columbia, MD.

44994 ■ **Adobe Acrobat II (Onsite)**
EEI Communications
8945 Guilford Rd., Ste. 145
Columbia, MD 21046
Ph: (410)309-8200
Free: 888-253-2762
Fax: (410)630-3980
Co. E-mail: train@eeicom.com
URL: http://www.eeicom.com/eei-training-services
Price: $797.00. **Description:** Seminar that covers the advanced features of Adobe Acrobat, focusing on making documents accessible and flexible, incorporating digital signatures and security settings, creating and modifying PDF forms and multimedia presentations, using the engineering and technical features, and using Adobe Acrobat for professional publishing. **Dates and Locations:** Silver Spring, MD; and Alexandria, VA.

44995 ■ **Adobe Acrobat Section 508 Accessibility (Onsite)**
EEI Communications
8945 Guilford Rd., Ste. 145
Columbia, MD 21046
Ph: (410)309-8200
Free: 888-253-2762
Fax: (410)630-3980
Co. E-mail: train@eeicom.com
URL: http://www.eeicom.com/eei-training-services
Price: $425.00. **Description:** Covers the regulations by the Federal Government's Section 508 accessibility and the features of Adobe Acrobat software designed to meet the regulations, including definition of accessibility, authoring for accessibility, working with existing PDF files, forms, and scanned documents, using the accessibility checker, and tags palette, and testing your PDF files for accessibility. **Dates and Locations:** Alexandria, VA.

44996 ■ **Adobe After Effects II (Onsite)**
EEI Communications
66 Canal Ctr. Plz., Ste. 200
Alexandria, VA 22314-5507
Ph: (703)683-7453
Free: 888-253-2762

Fax: (703)683-7310
Co. E-mail: train@eeicom.com
URL: http://www.eeicom.com/training
Price: $1,097.00. **Description:** Seminar that builds on the foundation of After Effects I that covers the techniques that production environments use and learn to reverse-engineer popular effects seen on TV, including working with Rotoscoping techniques, keying and mattes, motion matching and video stabilization, 3D layers, cameras, and lights, titling effects and filters, altering time and displacement, and rendering the movies and batching. **Dates and Locations:** Silver Spring, MD; and Columbia, MD.

44997 ■ Adobe Bridge
EEI Communications
8945 Guilford Rd., Ste. 145
Columbia, MD 21046
Ph: (410)309-8200
Free: 888-253-2762
Fax: (410)630-3980
Co. E-mail: train@eeicom.com
URL: http://www.eeicom.com/eei-training-services
Price: $425.00. **Description:** Learn the many useful features hidden in Adobe Bridge, the command central for your Creative Suite 4 software, include the settings that help you get the most out of workflow. **Dates and Locations:** Alexandria, VA.

44998 ■ Adobe Captivate 3
EEI Communications
66 Canal Ctr. Plz., Ste. 200
Alexandria, VA 22314-5507
Ph: (703)683-7453
Free: 888-253-2762
Fax: (703)683-7310
Co. E-mail: train@eeicom.com
URL: http://www.eeicom.com/training
Price: $745.00. **Description:** Seminar that teaches how to create professional quality, interactive simulations and software demonstrations without any programming or multimedia knowledge, including basics, captions and timelines, images, pointer paths, buttons, and highlight boxes, movies, rollover captions and rollover images, slide labels and notes, audio, animation, and question slides. **Dates and Locations:** Alexandria, VA.

44999 ■ Adobe ColdFusion II (Onsite)
EEI Communications
8945 Guilford Rd., Ste. 145
Columbia, MD 21046
Ph: (410)309-8200
Free: 888-253-2762
Fax: (410)630-3980
Co. E-mail: train@eeicom.com
URL: http://www.eeicom.com/eei-training-services
Price: $745.00. **Description:** Seminar that covers advanced programming techniques, including complex programming concepts such as arrays and loops, deploy application-level security, read information from and write information to text files on server, use the Verify search engine, schedule templates to run on a recurring basis, perform multiple queries as a transaction, and build intelligent 'agents' for the Web. **Dates and Locations:** Alexandria, VA.

45000 ■ Adobe Creative Suite 5 Bootcamp Training (Onsite)
EEI Communications
8945 Guilford Rd., Ste. 145
Columbia, MD 21046
Ph: (410)309-8200
Free: 888-253-2762
Fax: (410)630-3980
Co. E-mail: train@eeicom.com
URL: http://www.eeicom.com/eei-training-services
Price: $797.00. **Description:** Covers the interoperability and productively possible between Adobe Photoshop, Illustrator, InDesign, and Acrobat PDF. **Dates and Locations:** Silver Spring, MD; and Alexandria, VA.

45001 ■ Adobe Fireworks II
EEI Communications
8945 Guilford Rd., Ste. 145
Columbia, MD 21046
Ph: (410)309-8200
Free: 888-253-2762

Fax: (410)630-3980
Co. E-mail: train@eeicom.com
URL: http://www.eeicom.com/eei-training-services
Price: $745.00. **Description:** Covers Web page designs, including masks to create photomontages, create vector graphics, slicing advanced page designs, generate HTML and JavaScript code, swap images, and create pop-up images. **Dates and Locations:** Silver Spring, MD.

45002 ■ Adobe Flash III (Onsite)
EEI Communications
66 Canal Ctr. Plz., Ste. 200
Alexandria, VA 22314-5507
Ph: (703)683-7453
Free: 888-253-2762
Fax: (703)683-7310
Co. E-mail: train@eeicom.com
URL: http://www.eeicom.com/training
Price: $797.00. **Description:** Covers project creation from planning and development, working with XML, advanced animation and interaction concepts and sound applications, and integrating video with Flash. **Dates and Locations:** Alexandria, VA.

45003 ■ Adobe Flash Media Server
EEI Communications
8945 Guilford Rd., Ste. 145
Columbia, MD 21046
Ph: (410)309-8200
Free: 888-253-2762
Fax: (410)630-3980
Co. E-mail: train@eeicom.com
URL: http://www.eeicom.com/eei-training-services
Price: $745.00. **Description:** Provides experienced Flash developers with the knowledge and hands-on experience they need to build and deliver Streaming and Social Media applications with Flash Media Server 3, with focus on Server Side ActionScript, ActionScript 3 and Flash skills required to build real-world media applications with audio, video, and data that interact with the user. **Dates and Locations:** Alexandria, VA.

45004 ■ Adobe Flex I - Developing Rich Internet Client Applications
EEI Communications
8945 Guilford Rd., Ste. 145
Columbia, MD 21046
Ph: (410)309-8200
Free: 888-253-2762
Fax: (410)630-3980
Co. E-mail: train@eeicom.com
URL: http://www.eeicom.com/eei-training-services
Price: $1,245.00. **Description:** Introduction to the Flex technology teaches how to develop fully functional, well architected front end for a Rich Internet Application (RIA). **Dates and Locations:** Alexandria, VA.

45005 ■ Adobe Flex II - Data and Communications
EEI Communications
8945 Guilford Rd., Ste. 145
Columbia, MD 21046
Ph: (410)309-8200
Free: 888-253-2762
Fax: (410)630-3980
Co. E-mail: train@eeicom.com
URL: http://www.eeicom.com/eei-training-services
Price: $995.00. **Description:** Learn how your Flex applications exchange data and communicate with remote objects in this hands-on course. **Dates and Locations:** Alexandria, VA.

45006 ■ Adobe Flex III - Building Dashboard Applications
EEI Communications
8945 Guilford Rd., Ste. 145
Columbia, MD 21046
Ph: (410)309-8200
Free: 888-253-2762
Fax: (410)630-3980
Co. E-mail: train@eeicom.com
URL: http://www.eeicom.com/eei-training-services
Price: $995.00. **Description:** Learn how to build dashboard applications using Adobe Flex 3 to create highly interactive charts and graphs for data visualiza-

tion, including creating interactive charts and dynamically controlling the chart data. **Dates and Locations:** Alexandria, VA.

45007 ■ Adobe FrameMaker I (Onsite)
EEI Communications
8945 Guilford Rd., Ste. 145
Columbia, MD 21046
Ph: (410)309-8200
Free: 888-253-2762
Fax: (410)630-3980
Co. E-mail: train@eeicom.com
URL: http://www.eeicom.com/eei-training-services
Price: $1,097.00. **Description:** Learn how to design FrameMaker publication in its entirety, as well as work on a variety of FrameMaker documents. Some topics include understanding FrameMaker interface and screen elements, using paragraph designer to control paragraph formatting, working with character designer, adding color to character and paragraph formats, working with master pages and anchored frames, creating running headers and footers, creating and editing variables and working with table designer and customizing tables. **Dates and Locations:** Silver Spring, MD.

45008 ■ Adobe FrameMaker III: Structured
EEI Communications
8945 Guilford Rd., Ste. 145
Columbia, MD 21046
Ph: (410)309-8200
Free: 888-253-2762
Fax: (410)630-3980
Co. E-mail: train@eeicom.com
URL: http://www.eeicom.com/eei-training-services
Price: $745.00. **Description:** Seminar using Adobe FrameMaker as an authoring tool for creating XML documents, including structured interface and add and edit elements and attributes, documents with structured content EDD (Element Definition Document) and DTD (Document Type Definitions), converting unstructured documents, and the latest tools availible for cross-media publishing. **Dates and Locations:** Alexandria, VA.

45009 ■ Adobe InDesign CS4 Master Class for Designers Training (Onsite)
EEI Communications
8945 Guilford Rd ., Ste. 145
MD 21046
Ph: (410)309-8200
Free: 888-253-2762
Fax: (410)630-3980
Co. E-mail: train@eeicom.com
URL: http://www.eeicom.com/eei-training-services
Price: $895.00. **Description:** Master Adobe InDesign CS4's styles, text processing capabilities, table-creation tools, automation features, and in-document creativity enhancements to free up countless hours from smaller tasks and concentrate on designing. **Dates and Locations:** Silver Spring, MD; Hunt Valley, MD; Columbia, MD; and Alexandria, VA.

45010 ■ Adobe InDesign III (Onsite)
EEI Communications
8945 Guilford Rd., Ste. 145
Columbia, MD 21046
Ph: (410)309-8200
Free: 888-253-2762
Fax: (410)630-3980
Co. E-mail: train@eeicom.com
URL: http://www.eeicom.com/eei-training-services
Price: $797.00. **Description:** 2-day seminar that explores the advanced features within Adobe InDesign, including transparency features, feathering, and drop shadows, hyperlinks for PDF or DHTML, create a book list, formatting an index, generate a table of contents, advanced frame techniques and color management, and XML and other cross-media publishing support. **Dates and Locations:** Alexandria, VA.

45011 ■ Adobe InDesign with InCopy for Workgroups Training (Onsite)
EEI Communications
8945 Guilford Rd., Ste. 145
Columbia, MD 21046
Ph: (410)309-8200
Free: 888-253-2762

Fax: (410)630-3980
Co. E-mail: train@eeicom.com
URL: http://www.eeicom.com/eei-training-services
Price: $425.00. **Description:** Learn a professional writing and editing program that tightly integrates with Adobe InDesign for a complete solution, including assigning editors to work on parts of pages, spreads, or entire documents in parallel with designers, significantly decreasing the production time for projects. **Dates and Locations:** Alexandria, VA.

45012 ■ Adobe InDesign IV (Onsite)
EEI Communications
8945 Guilford Rd., Ste. 145
Columbia, MD 21046
Ph: (410)309-8200
Free: 888-253-2762
Fax: (410)630-3980
Co. E-mail: train@eeicom.com
URL: http://www.eeicom.com/eei-training-services
Price: $797.00. **Description:** Examine ways to speed up productivity in your workflow by taking advantage of the many advanced features throughout InDesign CS4, including an interactive Data Merge project for joining graphic design with data from an external file. **Dates and Locations:** Alexandria, VA.

45013 ■ Adobe InDesign for Long Documents I (Onsite)
EEI Communications
8945 Guilford Rd., Ste. 145
Columbia, MD 21046
Ph: (410)309-8200
Free: 888-253-2762
Fax: (410)630-3980
Co. E-mail: train@eeicom.com
URL: http://www.eeicom.com/eei-training-services
Price: $797.00. **Description:** Learn to publish long documents, such as books or annual reports. Also, explore Adobe InDesign CS4 options in numbering, position figures in relation to text automatically, create running headers or footers, and much more. **Dates and Locations:** Alexandria, VA; and Silver Spring, MD.

45014 ■ Adobe InDesign for Long Documents II (Onsite)
EEI Communications
8945 Guilford Rd., Ste. 145
Columbia, MD 21046
Ph: (410)309-8200
Free: 888-253-2762
Fax: (410)630-3980
Co. E-mail: train@eeicom.com
URL: http://www.eeicom.com/eei-training-services
Price: $797.00. **Description:** Learn all you need to know to work effectively with InDesign CS4, including advanced features. **Dates and Locations:** Silver Spring, MD; and Alexandria, VA.

45015 ■ Adobe InDesign for Long Documents III (Onsite)
EEI Communications
8945 Guilford Rd., Ste. 145
Columbia, MD 21046
Ph: (410)309-8200
Free: 888-253-2762
Fax: (410)630-3980
Co. E-mail: train@eeicom.com
URL: http://www.eeicom.com/eei-training-services
Price: $795.00. **Description:** Learn to fully exploit all the advanced featured of InDesign CS4 as your integrated workflow and publishing environment. **Dates and Locations:** Alexandria, VA.

45016 ■ Adobe Lightroom Photo Workflow
EEI Communications
8945 Guilford Rd., Ste. 145
Columbia, MD 22314
Ph: (410)309-8200
Free: 888-253-2762
Fax: (410)6303980
Co. E-mail: train@eeicom.com
URL: http://www.eeicom.com/eei-training-services
Price: $745.00. **Description:** Covers importing and arranging photos, quick edits, developing modules' array of image correction controls, tone curves, black and white conversions, working with Photoshop,

slideshow's customizable features, exporting images, and print controls and custom print layouts. **Dates and Locations:** Silver Spring, MD; and Alexandria, VA.

45017 ■ Adobe Photoshop for Beginners (Onsite)
Seminar Information Service, Inc.
20 Executive Park, Ste. 120
Irvine, CA 92614
Ph: (949)261-9104
Free: 877-SEM-INFO
Fax: (949)261-1963
Co. E-mail: info@seminarinformation.com
URL: http://www.seminarinformation.com
Price: $199.00. **Description:** Learn how to manipulate images, retouch photos, and cut down time through the entire design process. **Dates and Locations:** Houston, TX; Dallas, TX; Cromwell, CT; and Boston, MA.

45018 ■ Adobe Photoshop Channels and Masks (Onsite)
EEI Communications
8945 Guilford Rd., Ste. 145
Columbia, MD 21046
Ph: (410)309-8200
Free: 888-253-2762
Fax: (410)630.3980
Co. E-mail: train@eeicom.com
URL: http://www.eeicom.com/eei-training-services
Price: $745.00. **Description:** Learn how to make masks using channels in Adobe Photoshop CS3 to create high quality and accurate selections like the professionals do. **Dates and Locations:** Alexandria, VA.

45019 ■ Adobe Photoshop Digital Mastery I (Onsite)
EEI Communications
145 Guilford Rd., Ste. 145
Columbia, MD 21046
Ph: (410)309-8200
Free: 888-253-2762
Fax: (410)630-3980
Co. E-mail: train@eeicom.com
URL: http://www.eeicom.com/eei-training-services
Price: $797.00. **Description:** Covers techniques for photo recovery, image enhancements, and professional portrait work. **Dates and Locations:** Silver Spring, MD.

45020 ■ Adobe Photoshop Digital Painting (Onsite)
EEI Communications
8945 Guilford Rd., Ste. 145
Columbia, MD 22314
Ph: (410)309-8200
Free: 888-253-2762
Fax: (410)630-3980
Co. E-mail: train@eeicom.com
URL: http://www.eeicom.com/eei-training-services
Price: $745.00. **Description:** Learn digital painting techniques from adding colors and effects to line art to creating full-on digital paintings in various artistic styles, including watercolor and oil. **Dates and Locations:** Silver Spring, MD; Hunt Valley, MD; Columbia, MD; and Alexandria, VA.

45021 ■ Adobe Photoshop Extended
EEI Communications
8945 Guilford Rd., Ste. 145
Alexandria, MD 21046
Ph: (410)309-8200
Free: 888-253-2762
Fax: (410)630-3980
Co. E-mail: train@eeicom.com
URL: http://www.eeicom.com/eei-training-services
Price: $425.00. **Description:** Covers 3D compositing and texture editing, enhanced vanishing point with 3D support, movie paint, the new animation palette, importing and playing video in Photoshop, video layers, using 2D and 3D measurement tools, scale marker, count tool and combining image stacks. **Dates and Locations:** Silver Spring, MD; Hunt Valley, MD; Columbia, MD; and Alexandria, VA.

45022 ■ Advanced Training for Microsoft Excel (Onsite)
Padgett-Thompson Seminars
Rockhurst University CEC
14502 W. 105th St.
Lenexa, KS 66215
Free: 800-349-1935
URL: http://www.findaseminar.com/tpd/Padgett-Thompson-Seminars.asp
Price: $179.00. **Description:** An intensive one-day seminar that teaches the most advanced features of Microsoft Excel. **Dates and Locations:** Albuquerque, NM; Burbank, CA; Ontario, CA; and Long Beach, CA.

45023 ■ AJAX Development I (Onsite)
EEI Communications
145 Guilford Rd., Ste. 145
Columbia, MD 21046
Ph: (410)309-8200
Free: 888-253-2762
Fax: (410)630-3980
Co. E-mail: train@eeicom.com
URL: http://www.eeicom.com/eei-training-services
Price: $745.00. **Description:** Learn how to make dynamic and interactive Web applications using Asynchronous JavaScript and XML (AJAX), including a review of the essential elements of XHTML, CSS, and XML. **Dates and Locations:** Alexandria, VA.

45024 ■ AJAX Development II (Onsite)
EEI Communications
66 Canal Center Plz., Ste. 200
Alexandria, VA 22314
Ph: (703)683-7453
Free: 888-253-2762
Fax: (703)683-7310
Co. E-mail: train@eeicom.com
URL: http://www.eeicom.com/training
Price: $745.00. **Description:** In this advanced class explore AJAX in greater depth through topics that include addressing security concerns inherent to AJAX, using XPath and XSLT in your AJAX development, validating form data, managing user sessions, and explore the available AJAX frameworks. **Dates and Locations:** Alexandria, VA.

45025 ■ Apple DVD Studio Pro I (Onsite)
EEI Communications
66 Canal Ctr. Plz., Ste. 200
Alexandria, VA 22314-5507
Ph: (703)683-7453
Free: 888-253-2762
Fax: (703)683-7310
Co. E-mail: train@eeicom.com
URL: http://www.eeicom.com/training
Price: $745.00. **Description:** Seminar that covers creating menus within DVD Studio Pro, creating slide shows, adding subtitles and closed captioning, multiple language/audio streams, DVD-ROM content and Internet access, options to encode high quality video, creating and working with buttons, overlays, markers, and stories, basic scripting, advanced menu design, working with and creating transitions, using alternate and mixed angles, and Dolby, surround, and PCM audio encoding. **Dates and Locations:** Alexandria, VA.

45026 ■ Apple Final Cut Pro Bootcamp (Onsite)
EEI Communications
8945 Guilford Rd., Ste. 145
Columbia, MD 21046
Ph: (410)309-8200
Free: 888-253-2762
Fax: (410)630-3980
Co. E-mail: train@eeicom.com
URL: http://www.eeicom.com/eei-training-services
Price: $1,697.00. **Description:** Course includes an introduction to Final Cut Pro Interface, basic video editing, importing and exporting video footage, introduction to Soundtrack Pro Interface, basic audio editing, post-production techniques with video, introduction to DVD Studio Pro, introduction to motion, post-production techniques with video, introduction to DVD Studio Pro, and authoring DVDs to your own specifications. **Dates and Locations:** Alexandria, VA.

45027 ■ Apple Final Cut Pro I (Onsite)

EEI Communications
66 Canal Ctr. Plz., Ste. 200
Alexandria, VA 22314-5507
Ph: (703)683-7453
Free: 888-253-2762
Fax: (703)683-7310
Co. E-mail: train@eeicom.com
URL: http://www.eeicom.com/training
Price: $797.00. **Description:** Seminar that covers editing using Apple, including working with interface, video standard and HD basics, marking and editing, timeline control, single- and double-sided trimming, master clips, subclips and working with markers, capturing video, importing and exporting assets, working with audio and mixing audio tracks, applying transitions, adding and working with filters, build a composite image, change clip speeds, create motion effects, adding text and graphics, working with and creating animated titles, and finishing and outputting. **Dates and Locations:** Alexandria, VA.

45028 ■ Apple Final Cut Pro II (Onsite)

EEI Communications
8945 Guilford Rd., Ste. 145
Columbia, MD 21046
Ph: (410)309-8200
Free: 888-253-2762
Fax: (703)630-3980
Co. E-mail: train@eeicom.com
URL: http://www.eeicom.com/eei-training-services
Price: $797.00. **Description:** Learn all you need to know to create your video from concept to completion, including working with the interface, video standard and HD basics, timeline control, single- and double-sided trimming, capturing video and much more. **Dates and Locations:** Alexandria, VA.

45029 ■ Apple Motion I (Onsite)

EEI Communications
66 Canal Ctr. Plz., Ste. 200
Alexandria, VA 22314-5507
Ph: (703)683-7453
Free: 888-253-2762
Fax: (703)683-7310
Co. E-mail: train@eeicom.com
URL: http://www.eeicom.com/training
Price: $745.00. **Description:** Covers real-time motion graphics, including using generators, working with layers and objects, use and create customized templates, particles and parameter behaviors, blend modes, nonlinear editing and motion, key-framing, audio and setting markers, and create text effects. **Dates and Locations:** Alexandria, VA.

45030 ■ ASP.NET with VB.NET and C I (Onsite)

EEI Communications
8945 Guilford Rd., Ste. 145
Columbia, MD 21046
Ph: (410)309-8200
Free: 888-253-2762
Fax: (410)630-3980
Co. E-mail: train@eeicom.com
URL: http://www.eeicom.com/eei-training-services
Price: $1,065.00. **Description:** Learn to write dynamic, high-performance Web applications with Microsoft's ASP.NET. Topics include introduction of Web forms, controls (HTML, Server, Web), ASP.NET application state management, and error handling. **Dates and Locations:** Alexandria, VA.

45031 ■ ASP.NET with VB.NET and C II

EEI Communications
8945 Guilford Rd., Ste. 145
Columbia, MD 21046
Ph: (410)309-8200
Free: 888-253-2762
Fax: (410)630-3980
Co. E-mail: train@eeicom.com
URL: http://www.eeicom.com/eei-training-services
Price: $1,065.00. **Description:** Hands-on class with those with knowledge of HTML and some programming who want to study data binding, data controls and templates, consuming and manipulating data, and creating and managing .NET components and assemblies. **Dates and Locations:** Alexandria, VA.

45032 ■ ASP.NET with VB.NET C III

EEI Communications
8945 Guilford Rd., Ste. 145
Columbia, MD 21046
Ph: (410)309-8200
Free: 888-253-2762
Fax: (410)630-3980
Co. E-mail: train@eeicom.com
URL: http://www.eeicom.com/eei-training-services
Price: $1,065.00. **Description:** Hands-on class for those with the knowledge of HTML and some programming background who want to study Web services, localization, Web accessibility, testing and debugging a Web application, and configuring a Web application. **Dates and Locations:** Alexandria, VA.

45033 ■ Auditing Business Application Systems (Onsite)

Seminar Information Service, Inc.
20 Executive Park, Ste. 120
Irvine, CA 92614
Ph: (949)261-9104
Free: 877-SEM-INFO
Fax: (949)261-1963
Co. E-mail: info@seminarinformation.com
URL: http://www.seminarinformation.com
Price: $2,150.00. **Description:** Three-day seminar attendees will learn how to audit and how to develop controls for complex automated applications which use online/real-time, distributed processing, and/or database technologies, including an opportunity to actually prepare an audit plan for a complex application system. **Dates and Locations:** Chicago, IL.

45034 ■ Business Analysis Essentials (Onsite)

Seminar Information Service, Inc.
20 Executive Park, Ste. 120
Irvine, CA 92614
Ph: (949)261-9104
Free: 877-SEM-INFO
Fax: (949)261-1963
Co. E-mail: info@seminarinformation.com
URL: http://www.seminarinformation.com
Price: $2,195.00. **Description:** Learn to define the scope of work and master requirements-gathering techniques that will work for a variety of projects and audiences. **Dates and Locations:** New York, NY; Dallas, TX; and Orlando, FL.

45035 ■ Cascading Style Sheets II

EEI Communications
8945 Guilford Rd., Ste. 145
Columbia, MD 21046
Ph: (410)309-8200
Free: 888-253-2762
Fax: (410)630-3980
Co. E-mail: train@eeicom.com
URL: http://www.eeicom.com/eei-training-services
Price: $425.00. **Description:** Covers the conversion of an HTML Web site to a site that uses Cascading Style Sheets, including text enhancements, link color control, table conversion to precise positioning, layering with text and graphics, DHTML effects, a watermark background image, and validation CSS code. **Dates and Locations:** Alexandria, VA.

45036 ■ Color Management for Adobe Creative Suite 4 (CS4)

EEI Communications
8945 Guilford Rd., Ste. 145
Columbia, MD 21046
Ph: (410)309-8200
Free: 888-253-2762
Fax: (410)630-3980
Co. E-mail: train@eeicom.com
URL: http://www.eeicom.com/eei-training-services
Price: $795.00. **Description:** Learn how to get predictable, accurate, and stable color from scratch to screen to proof and printed output, including assessing your system for improvement by calibration. **Dates and Locations:** Alexandria, VA.

45037 ■ Color Management for Digital Publishing

EEI Communications
8945 Guilford Rd., Ste. 145
Columbia, MD 21046
Ph: (410)309-8200
Free: 888-253-2762
Fax: (410)630-3980
Co. E-mail: train@eeicom.com
URL: http://www.eeicom.com/eei-training-services
Price: $795.00. **Description:** Covers color theory and color models, build and edit ICC profiles, color management at the OS level, and setup. **Dates and Locations:** Alexandria, VA.

45038 ■ Deploying Microsoft Windows Vista Business Desktops (Onsite)

Seminar Information Service, Inc.
20 Executive Park, Ste. 120
Irvine, CA 92614
Ph: (949)261-9104
Free: 877-SEM-INFO
Fax: (949)261-1963
Co. E-mail: info@seminarinformation.com
URL: http://www.seminarinformation.com
Price: $2,095.00. **Description:** Three-day training to get the knowledge and skills you needed to successfully deploy Windows Vista business desktops throughout your organization.

45039 ■ Designing and Building Great Web Pages: Hands-On (Onsite)

Seminar Information Service, Inc.
20 Executive Park, Ste. 120
Irvine, CA 92614
Ph: (949)261-9104
Free: 877-SEM-INFO
Fax: (949)261-1963
Co. E-mail: info@seminarinformation.com
URL: http://www.seminarinformation.com
Price: $2,890.00. **Description:** Learn to build powerful Web content that effectively conveys your message; Create graphical content using Photoshop CS2, Fireworks 8 and Flash 8; Develop Web page content with FrontPage and Dreamweaver 8; Generate complex Web pages using Cascading Style Sheets, tables and layers; and Enhance Web pages with special effects and DHTML.

45040 ■ Developing Effective Software Estimation Techniques (Onsite)

Seminar Information Service, Inc.
20 Executive Park, Ste. 120
Irvine, CA 92614
Ph: (949)261-9104
Free: 877-SEM-INFO
Fax: (949)261-1963
Co. E-mail: info@seminarinformation.com
URL: http://www.seminarinformation.com
Price: $2,490.00. **Description:** Learn how to prepare a software project estimate through an iterative process; Develop an initial estimate using the expert judgment method; Apply historical data for greater precision in an estimate; Refine the size or scope estimate using a component-based method; Perform Function Point calculations to determine the magnitude of a project; Translate a size or scope estimate into a time, schedule and cost estimate. **Dates and Locations:** Toronto and Ottawa, CN.

45041 ■ Developing SQL Queries for SQL Server: Hands-On (Onsite)

Seminar Information Service, Inc.
20 Executive Park, Ste. 120
Irvine, CA 92614
Ph: (949)261-9104
Free: 877-SEM-INFO
Fax: (949)261-1963
Co. E-mail: info@seminarinformation.com
URL: http://www.seminarinformation.com
Price: $2,890.00. **Description:** Learn how to develop complex and robust SQL queries for SQL Server 2005 and SQL Server 2000; Query multiple tables with inner joins, outer joins and self joins; Transform data with built-in functions; Summarize data using aggregation and grouping; Execute analytic functions to calculate ranks; Build simple and correlated subqueries. **Dates and Locations:** Cities throughout the United States.

45042 ■ Digital Scanning for Production

EEI Communications
8945 Guilford Rd., Ste. 145
Columbia, MD 21046

Ph: (410)309-8200
Free: 888-253-2762
Fax: (410)630-3980
Co. E-mail: train@eeicom.com
URL: http://www.eeicom.com/eei-training-services
Price: $745.00. **Description:** Seminar designed for those using any digital purpose, including direct reproduction or inclusion in page layout programs. **Dates and Locations:** Alexandria, VA; Silver Spring, MD; and Washington, DC.

45043 ■ Digital Video Production for Streaming and DVD (Onsite)
EEI Communications
66 Canal Ctr. Plz., Ste. 200
Alexandria, VA 22314-5507
Ph: (703)683-7453
Free: 888-253-2762
Fax: (703)683-7310
Co. E-mail: train@eeicom.com
URL: http://www.eeicom.com/training
Price: $1,065.00. **Description:** Seminar the teaches the process of producing video for distribution via the Web, CD, DVD and computer-based presentations, including writing, directing, shooting, recording, capture, edit, and encode/compress effective digital video for training, marketing, internal communications, public information, and other uses. Also, communicate effectively with internal clients/staff, video crews, and editing facilities. **Dates and Locations:** Alexandria, VA.

45044 ■ Dynamic Web Development I
EEI Communications
8945 Guilford Rd., Ste. 145
Columbia, MD 21046
Ph: (410)309-8200
Free: 888-253-2762
Fax: (410)630-3980
Co. E-mail: train@eeicom.com
URL: http://www.eeicom.com/eei-training-services
Price: $1,065.00. **Description:** Those already familiar with HTML and how to do some programming will learn to write high-performance Web applications with Microsoft's ASP.NET. Topics include Web forms, controls (HTML, server, Web), ASP.NET application state management, and error handling. **Dates and Locations:** Alexandria, VA.

45045 ■ Dynamic Web Development II
EEI Communications
8945 Guilford., Ste. 145
Columbia, MD 21046
Ph: (410)309-8200
Free: 888-253-2762
Fax: (410)630-3980
Co. E-mail: train@eeicom.com
URL: http://www.eeicom.com/eei-training-services
Price: $1,065.00. **Description:** Explore data binding, data controls and templates, consuming and manipulating data, and creating and managing .NET components and assemblies. **Dates and Locations:** Alexandria, VA.

45046 ■ Enhanced and Video Podcasts (Onsite)
EEI Communications
8945 Guilford Rd., Ste. 145
Columbia, MD 21046
Ph: (410)309-8200
Free: 888-230-3980
Fax: (703)683-7310
Co. E-mail: train@eeicom.com
URL: http://www.eeicom.com/eei-training-services
Price: $745.00. **Description:** Course includes the pros and cons of enhanced podcasts and video poscasts, creating enhanced podcasts with GarageBand (Mac), creating enhanced podcasts on a PC, creating video podcasts with Funal Cut Pro (Mac) with Adobe Audition (PC), Using QuickTime Pro (Mac/PC) in post-production, compression and other troubleshooting issues, keeping production values simple but professional, how to keep video podcasts, and quick, easy downloads. **Dates and Locations:** Alexandria, VA.

45047 ■ The Essentials Of Crystal Reports (Onsite)
Seminar Information Service, Inc.
20 Executive Park, Ste. 120
Irvine, CA 92614
Ph: (949)261-9104
Free: 877-SEM-INFO
Fax: (949)261-1963
Co. E-mail: info@seminarinformation.com
URL: http://www.seminarinformation.com
Price: $199.00. **Description:** Learn to create complex reports containing huge amounts of information to simple reports without being an expert in databases. **Dates and Locations:** Cities throughout the United States.

45048 ■ Forensic Photoshop (Onsite)
EEI Communications
8945 Guilford Rd., Ste. 145
Columbia, MD 21046
Ph: (410)309-8200
Free: 888-253-2762
Fax: (410)630-3980
Co. E-mail: train@eeicom.com
URL: http://www.eeicom.com/eei-training-services
Price: $745.00. **Description:** Designed for law enforcement and Homeland Security personnel that outlines the processes for using Photoshop in a forensic environment. **Dates and Locations:** Silver Spring, MD; Hunt Valley, MD; Columbia, MD; and Alexandria, VA.

45049 ■ How to Manage an Information Security Program (Onsite)
Seminar Information Service, Inc.
20 Executive Park, Ste. 120
Irvine, CA 92614
Ph: (949)261-9104
Free: 877-SEM-INFO
Fax: (949)261-1963
Co. E-mail: info@seminarinformation.com
URL: http://www.seminarinformation.com
Price: $2,050.00. **Description:** Learn the components of a comprehensive plan, covering access control software applications; telecom/network security measures; physical protection of the computer facility; and the legal and regulatory aspects of information security.

45050 ■ Introduction to ASP.NET 2.0 Applications
EEI Communications
8945 Guilford Rd., Ste. 145
Columbia, MD 21046
Ph: (410)309-8200
Free: 888-253-2762
Fax: (410)630-3980
Co. E-mail: train@eeicom.com
URL: http://www.eeicom.com/eei-training-services
Price: $745.00. **Description:** Seminar designed for ASP.NET programmers, includes ASP.NET 2.0 applications, master pages, Web parts and personalized API, ADO.NET 2.0 and data-bound controls, membership and role management API, and Web form wizards. **Dates and Locations:** Silver Spring, MD; Alexandria, VA; Hunt Valley, MD; and Columbia, MD.

45051 ■ Introduction to .Net and ASP.NET
EEI Communications
8945 Guilford Rd., Ste. 145
Columbia, MD 21046
Ph: (410)309-8200
Free: 888-253-2762
Fax: (410)630-3980
Co. E-mail: train@eeicom.com
URL: http://www.eeicom.com/eei-training-services
Price: $745.00. **Description:** Covers Microsoft.NET and ASP.NET Web pages in both Visual Basic.NET and C (pronounced C-sharp), including Microsoft.Net framework, common language run-time, base framework classes, ADO.NET, ASP.NET, .NET compact framework, XML Web services, and .NET languages. **Dates and Locations:** Silver Spring, MD; Alexandria, VA; Hunt Valley, MD; and Columbia, MD.

45052 ■ Introduction to PHP and MySQL
EEI Communications
8945 Guilford Rd., Ste. 145
Columbia, MD 21046
Ph: (410)309-8200
Free: 888-253-2762
Fax: (410)630-3980
Co. E-mail: train@eeicom.com
URL: http://www.eeicom.com/eei-training-services
Price: $745.00. **Description:** Seminar that covers an open-source scripting language for developing database-driven Web sites, including how to download and install PHP on Web server, using PHP to respond to HTML form submissions, sending e-mail messages with PHP, SQL and querying databases with PHP, and managing state information with cookies and sessions. **Dates and Locations:** Silver Spring, MD; Alexandria, VA; Hunt Valley, MD; and Columbia, MD.

45053 ■ Layout Software Basics (Onsite)
EEI Communications
8945 Guilford Rd., Ste. 145
Columbia, MD 21046
Ph: (410)309-8200
Free: 888-253-2762
Fax: (410)630-3980
Co. E-mail: train@eeicom.com
URL: http://www.eeicom.com/eei-training-services
Price: $425.00. **Description:** Seminar that provides an introduction to publishing and graphics software, including a step-by-step introduction through the terms and tools of applications used by graphic designers, illustrators, photographers, and editors. **Dates and Locations:** Alexandria, VA.

45054 ■ Mastering Microsoft Excel (Onsite)
Fred Pryor Seminars & CareerTrack
5700 Broadmoor St., Ste. 300
Mission, KS 66202
Free: 800-780-8476
Fax: (913)967-8849
Co. E-mail: customerservice@pryor.com
URL: http://www.pryor.com
Price: $249.00; $229.00 for groups of 3 or more. **Description:** Seminar designed to deliver the most information in the least amount of time, including how to create spreadsheets, input data, perform mathematical calculations, develop workbooks, edit cells, and use formulas, functions, Wizards, and more. **Dates and Locations:** Cities throughout the United States.

45055 ■ Microsoft Access: A 2-Day Hands-On Workshop (Onsite)
Fred Pryor Seminars & CareerTrack
5700 Broadmoor St., Ste. 300
Mission, KS 66202
Free: 800-780-8476
Fax: (913)967-8849
Co. E-mail: customerservice@pryor.com
URL: http://www.pryor.com
Price: $299.00; $279.00 for groups of 3 or more. **Description:** Learn how to use features, how to solve problems, and customize Access for the way you work. **Dates and Locations:** Cities throughout the United States.

45056 ■ Microsoft Excel
Padgett-Thompson Seminars
Rockhurst University CEC
14502 W. 105th St.
Lenexa, KS 66215
Free: 800-349-1935
URL: http://www.findaseminar.com/tpd/Padgett-Thompson-Seminars.asp
Price: $199.00. **Description:** One-day workshop covering ways to get the most out of Excel's features and functions. **Dates and Locations:** Cities throughout the United States.

45057 ■ Microsoft Excel 2007 - II (Onsite)
EEI Communications
8945 Guilford Rd., Ste. 145
Columbia, MD 21046
Ph: (410)309-8200
Free: 888-253-2762

Fax: (410)630-3980
Co. E-mail: train@eeicom.com
URL: http://www.eeicom.com/eei-training-services
Price: $797.00. **Description:** Seminar covering the advanced features of Excel, including advanced formulas, PivotTables, and analysis tools, including customizing workbook and toolbars, working with multiple data sources, edit macros, test data, and protect worksheets. **Dates and Locations:** Silver Spring, MD; and Alexandria, VA.

45058 ■ Microsoft Excel Basics (Onsite)
Fred Pryor Seminars & CareerTrack
5700 Broadmoor St., Ste. 300
Mission, KS 66202
Free: 800-780-8476
Fax: (913)967-8849
Co. E-mail: customerservice@pryor.com
URL: http://www.pryor.com
Price: $79.00; $74.00 for groups of 5 or more. **Description:** Seminar for Excel 2007 and 2010 starting with the basics and moving to more advanced features. **Dates and Locations:** Cities throughout the United States.

45059 ■ Microsoft PowerPoint 2007/2010 (Onsite)
Fred Pryor Seminars & CareerTrack
5700 Broadmoor St., Ste. 300
Mission, KS 66202
Free: 800-780-8476
Fax: (913)967-8849
Co. E-mail: customerservice@pryor.com
URL: http://www.pryor.com
Price: $149.00; $149.00 for groups of 5 or more. **Description:** Learn to put together well constructed, engaging and entertaining, pleasing to the eye, properly paced, and unmistakable clear in message presentations. **Dates and Locations:** Cities throughout the United States.

45060 ■ Microsoft Project 2007 - II (Onsite)
EEI Communications
8945 Gilford Rd. 145
Columbia, MD 21046
Ph: (410)309-8200
Free: 888-253-2762
Fax: (410)630-3980
Co. E-mail: train@eeicom.com
URL: http://www.eeicom.com/eei-training-services
Price: $797.00. **Description:** Seminar that covers workload adjustments and developing tracking skills to ensure a successful project completion, including fine-tuning task, resource, and assignment information, reorganizing phases and tasks, analyzing the critical path, leveling over-allocated resources, documenting resource details with reports, create consumption rates, track project progress, create an interim plan, and documenting the project's progress with reports. **Dates and Locations:** Silver Spring, MD.

45061 ■ Microsoft SharePoint I - Using SharePoint (Onsite)
EEI Communications
8945 Guilford Rd., Ste. 145
Columbia, MD 21046
Ph: (410)309-8200
Free: 888-253-2762
Fax: (410)630-3980
Co. E-mail: train@eeicom.com
URL: http://www.eeicom.com/eei-training-services
Price: $797.00. **Description:** Learn practical hands-on exercise techniques for using the document and project collaboration tools in Windows SharePoint Services. **Dates and Locations:** Alexandria, VA.

45062 ■ Microsoft SharePoint II - Building SharePoint Sites (Onsite)
EEI Communications
8945 Guilford Rd., Ste. 145
Columbia, MD 21046
Ph: (410)309-8200
Free: 888-253-2762

Fax: (410)630-3980
Co. E-mail: train@eeicom.com
URL: http://www.eeicom.com/ee-training-services
Price: $1,097.00. **Description:** Hands-on class you will learn the skills to design, maintain, and publish a custom SharePoint site. **Dates and Locations:** Alexandria, VA; Columbia, MD; and Silver Spring, MD.

45063 ■ Microsoft SharePoint III - Installing and Working With SharePoint Server (Onsite)
EEI Communications
8945 Guilford Rd., Ste. 145
Columbia, MD 21046
Ph: (410)309-8200
Free: 888-253-2762
Fax: (410)630-3980
Co. E-mail: train@eeicom.com
URL: http://www.eeicom.com/eei-training-services
Price: $1,097.00. **Description:** Hands-on class you learn how to create and make modifications that can be applied to all users on the site or to individual users using Microsoft SharePoint controls. **Dates and Locations:** Alexandria, VA.

45064 ■ Migrating to Structured Authoring in Adobe Framemaker (Onsite)
EEI Communications
8945 Guilford Rd. 145
Columbia, MD 22314
Ph: (410)309-8200
Free: 888-253-2762
Fax: (410)630-3980
Co. E-mail: train@eeicom.com
URL: http://www.eeicom.com/eei-training-services
Price: $797.00. **Description:** Learn to work with structured interface view, element catalogs, an understanding of elements and their attributes, edit structured documents, change, merge, split and wrapping of elements, working with paragraph, character, graphic, and table elements, validating documents, adding and editing element definitions, setting up elements with automatic insertion of children, and convert unstructured to structured documents. **Dates and Locations:** Columbia, MD.

45065 ■ Object-Oriented Programming (OOP) Boot Camp
EEI Communications
8945 Guilford Rd., Ste. 145
Columbia, MD 21046
Ph: (410)309-8200
Free: 888-253-2762
Fax: (410)630-3980
Co. E-mail: train@eeicom.com
URL: http://www.eeicom.com/eei-training-services
Price: $425.00. **Description:** Seminar that teaches what it means to give objects characteristics that can be transferred to, added to, and combined with other objects to make a complete program, including classes and objects, fields, properties, methods, and events, encapsulating, inheritance and polymorphisms, overloading, overriding, and shadowing. **Dates and Locations:** Silver Spring, MD; Alexandria, VA; Hunt Valley, MD; and Columbia, MD.

45066 ■ Professional Design Techniques with Adobe Creative Suite 4 (CS4)
EEI Communications
8945 Guilford Rd., Ste. 145
Columbia, MD 21046
Ph: (410)309-8200
Free: 888-253-2762
Fax: (410)630-3980
Co. E-mail: train@eeicom.com
URL: http://www.eeicom.com/eei-training-services
Price: $745.00. **Description:** Covers design principles and workflow techniques in real-life projects, including the management of numerous parts, such as stories, data, charts, and images. **Dates and Locations:** Alexandria, VA.

45067 ■ C Programming: Hands-On (Onsite)
Seminar Information Service, Inc.
20 Executive Park, Ste. 120
Irvine, CA 92614
Ph: (949)261-9104
Free: 877-SEM-INFO

Fax: (949)261-1963
Co. E-mail: info@seminarinformation.com
URL: http://www.seminarinformation.com
Price: $2,890.00. **Description:** Learn how to: Create, compile and run C programs using Visual Studio 2005; Write and understand C language constructs, syntax and classes; Leverage the architecture and namespaces of the .NET Framework library; Manage the Common Language Infrastructure (CLI) to integrate C with Visual Basic 2005 and C; Develop .NET components in C for desktop and distributed multi-tier applications. **Dates and Locations:** Toronto, CN; New York, NY; Los Angeles, CA; Alexandria, VA; Schaumburg, IL; Reston, VA; Ottawa, CN; and Atlanta , GA.

45068 ■ Project Management for Software Development - Planning and Managing Successful Projects (Onsite)
Seminar Information Service, Inc.
20 Executive Park, Ste. 120
Irvine, CA 92614
Ph: (949)261-9104
Free: 877-SEM-INFO
Fax: (949)261-1963
Co. E-mail: info@seminarinformation.com
URL: http://www.seminarinformation.com
Price: $2,890.00. **Description:** Learn how to: Deliver successful software projects that support your organization's strategic goals; Match organizational needs to the most effective software development model; Plan and manage projects at each stage of the software development life cycle (SDLC); Create project plans that address real-world management challenges; Develop the skills for tracking and controlling the project deliverables; Focus on key tasks for the everyday management of software projects; Build an effective and committed team and keep them motivated day to day. **Dates and Locations:** Alexandria, VA; Rockville, MD; New York, NY; Ottawa, CN; Toronto, CN; Los Angeles, CA; and Reston, VA.

45069 ■ Structured Query Language (SQL) I
EEI Communications
8945 Guilford Rd., Ste. 145
Columbia, MD 21046
Ph: (410)309-8200
Free: 888-253-2762
Fax: (410)630-3980
Co. E-mail: train@eeicom.com
URL: http://www.eeicom.com/eei-training-services
Price: $745.00. **Description:** Seminar that covers how to organize and extract information from relational databases, including design relational databases, proper syntax for SQL statements, analyze and organize data, retrieve, insert, update, and delete data, use aggregate functions, write queries from multiple tables, and normalize data. **Dates and Locations:** Silver Spring, MD; Alexandria, VA; Hunt Valley, MD; and Columbia, MD.

45070 ■ Structured Query Language (SQL) II
EEI Communications
8945 Guilford Rd., Ste. 145
Columbia, MD 21046
Ph: (410)309-8200
Free: 888-253-2762
Fax: (410)630-3980
Co. E-mail: train@eeicom.com
URL: http://www.eeicom.com/eei-training-services
Price: $745.00. **Description:** Seminar that provides critical information for writing advanced database queries using complex databases, including design sub-queries, data dictionaries, establish database security, and create manage sequences and indexes, and create stored procedures. **Dates and Locations:** Silver Spring, MD; Alexandria, VA; Hunt Valley, MD; and Columbia, MD.

45071 ■ Typography and Font Management (Onsite)
EEI Communications
8945 Guilford Rd., Ste. 145
Columbia, MD 21046
Ph: (410)309-8200
Free: 888-253-2762

Fax: (410)630-3980
Co. E-mail: train@eeicom.com
URL: http://www.eeicom.com/eei-training-services
Price: $425.00. **Description:** Covers the various electronic typefaces used in desktop publishing applications, including installing, managing, and troubleshooting fonts. **Dates and Locations:** Alexandria, VA.

45072 ■ VMware Ultimate Bootcamp

EEI Communications
8945 Guilford Rd., Ste. 145
Columbia, MD 21046
Ph: (410)309-8200
Free: 888-253-2762
Fax: (410)630-3980
Co. E-mail: train@eeicom.com
URL: http://www.eeicom.com/eei-training-services
Price: $4,500.00. **Description:** Hands-on labs designed to expose you to advanced virtualization concepts with VMware V13.5 product suite. Comprehensive class prepares students to become professional virtualization experts with the certification Certified Virtualization Expert (CVE). **Dates and Locations:** Silver Spring, MD; Alexandria, VA; and Herndon, VA.

45073 ■ Web Design with Adobe Dreamweaver and Photoshop (Onsite)

EEI Communications
8945 Guilford Rd., Ste. 145
Columbia, MD 21046
Ph: (410)309-8200
Free: 888-253-2762
Fax: (410)630-3980
Co. E-mail: train@eeicom.com
URL: http://www.eeicom.com/eei-training-services
Price: $497.00. **Description:** Learn how to create attractive navigation elements and add texture and depth to your Web design, including how to create color palettes, and design clean and well-organized Web page layouts. **Dates and Locations:** Silver Spring, MD.

45074 ■ Web Graphics with Adobe Photoshop (Onsite)

EEI Communications
8945 Guilford Rd., Ste. 145
Columbia, MD 21046
Ph: (410)309-8200
Free: 888-253-2762
Fax: (410)630-3980
Co. E-mail: train@eeicom.com
URL: http://www.eeicom.com/eei-training-services
Price: $797.00. **Description:** Covers creating high-quality, low-bandwidth graphics for the Web, including optimizing GIFs and JPEGs, creating transparent GIF graphics and animated GIFs and rollovers, create background tiles and sliced graphics, create navigation bars and buttons, image maps, and correct photographs for the Web. **Dates and Locations:** Alexandria, VA.

45075 ■ Website Optimization (Onsite)

Seminar Information Service, Inc.
20 Executive Park, Ste. 120
Irvine, CA 92614
Ph: (949)261-9104
Free: 877-SEM-INFO
Fax: (949)261-1963
Co. E-mail: info@seminarinformation.com
URL: http://www.seminarinformation.com
Price: $199.00. **Description:** Learn how to deliver exceptional service to site visitors, including a friendlier environment, obtain more leads, and integrate social media into your site. **Dates and Locations:** Oak Brook, IL; Milwaukee, WI; Madison, WI; Madison, WI; Chicago, IL; and Bloomington, MN.

45076 ■ Windows Vista: A Hands-On Introduction (Onsite)

Seminar Information Service, Inc.
20 Executive Park, Ste. 120
Irvine, CA 92614
Ph: (949)261-9104
Free: 877-SEM-INFO

Fax: (949)261-1963
Co. E-mail: info@seminarinformation.com
URL: http://www.seminarinformation.com
Price: $2,890.00. **Description:** Learn how to: Install and maintain Windows Vista in a professional environment; Navigate and configure Windows Vista; Create and manage users and groups; Protect resources with rights, access control and encryption; Implement and troubleshoot network and Internet connectivity; Improve application compatibility to maximize user productivity. **Dates and Locations:** Cities throughout the United States; Ottawa, CN; and Toronto, CN.

45077 ■ Writing for the Web II (Onsite)

EEI Communications
66 Canal Ctr. Plz., Ste. 200
Alexandria, VA 22314-5507
Ph: (703)683-7453
Free: 888-253-2762
Fax: (703)683-7310
Co. E-mail: train@eeicom.com
URL: http://www.eeicom.com/training
Price: $797.00. **Description:** Seminar for persons with 3-5 years' experience as a Web writer or editor, or have completed Writing for the Web I, covering how to define your genre and audience, develop a structure for your Web content, working with subject matter experts who aren't writers, making the most of your writing project, giving and getting feedback, writing links that work for your client, how to write menus so clients can use them, and recasting a print article for the Web. **Dates and Locations:** Columbia, MD.

45078 ■ XML Development I (Onsite)

EEI Communications
8945 Guilford Rd., Ste. 145
Columbia, MD 21046
Ph: (410)309-8200
Free: 888-253-2762
Fax: (410)630-3980
Co. E-mail: train@eeicom.com
URL: http://www.eeicom.com/eei-training-services
Price: $797.00. **Description:** Covers Extensible Markup Language (XML) that enables the Web designer to create information that is evolvable, including XML structure and syntax, create well-formed XML documents and document type definitions (DTDs) and schemas, valid XML documents, using entities, display using Cascading Style Sheets, data binding, and object model scripts. **Dates and Locations:** Silver Spring, MD; and Columbia, MD.

45079 ■ XML Development II (Onsite)

EEI Communications
8945 Gilford Rd., Ste. 145
Columbia, MD 21046
Ph: (410)309-8200
Free: 888-253-2762
Fax: (410)630-3980
Co. E-mail: train@eeicom.com
URL: http://www.eeicom.com/eei-training-services
Price: $797.00. **Description:** Covers XSLT and how it is used to convert XML data for presentational purposes, modify data structure, and to create non-XML files, including building XSLT applications, transforming XML to HTML, PDF, and Word. **Dates and Locations:** Silver Spring, MD; and Columbia, MD.

45080 ■ XML Development III (Onsite)

EEI Communications
8945 Guilford Rd., Ste. 145
Columbia, MD 21046
Ph: (410)309-8200
Free: 888-253-2762
Fax: (410)630-3980
Co. E-mail: train@eeicom.com
URL: http://www.eeicom.com/eei-training-services
Price: $1,065.00. **Description:** Covers the integration of XML into Web applications using ASP, Cold Fusion, PHP and Java, including guidelines for translating XML structure to a relational database model, rules for modeling, common techniques for storing, transmitting, and displaying content, data access mechanisms that expose relational data as XML, and how to use related technologies when processing XML data. **Dates and Locations:** Silver Spring, MD; Alexandria, VA; Hunt Valley, MD; and Columbia, MD.

45081 ■ XML Web Services (Onsite)

EEI Communications
8945 Guilford Rd., Ste. 145
Columbia, MD 22314
Ph: (410)309-8200
Free: 888-253-2762
Fax: (410)630-3980
Co. E-mail: train@eeicom.com
URL: http://www.eeicom.com/eei-training-services
Price: $1,065.00. **Description:** Learn how Web services can enhance your Web site and communication with other companies. **Dates and Locations:** Alexandria, VA.

REFERENCE WORKS

45082 ■ "Abacast, Citadel Strike Radio Ad Deal" in Business Journal Portland (Vol. 27, December 31, 2010, No. 44, pp. 3)

Pub: Portland Business Journal

Ed: Erik Siemers. **Description:** Software firm Abacast Inc. has partnered with Citadel Media to aid the latter's advertising sales. Citadel provides radio networks and syndicated programs to 4,200 affiliate stations.

45083 ■ "ACC Game Development Program Opens" in Austin Business JournalInc. (Vol. 28, October 31, 2008, No. 33, pp. 1)

Pub: American City Business Journals

Ed: Sandra Zaragoza. **Description:** Austin, Texas-based Austin Community College has launched its Game Development Institute. The institute was created to meet the gaming industry's demand for skilled workers. One hundred students have enrolled with the institute.

45084 ■ "AMT's Partner Program Enables New Security Business Models" in Internet Wire (August 12, 2010)

Pub: Comtex

Description: AMT, technical provider of physical access control Software as a Service (Saas) solutions, has developed a new Partner Program that allows partners to outsource any technical abilities lacking to AMT with no upfront fees.

45085 ■ "Angel Investments Tripled in 2009" in Austin Business JournalInc. (Vol. 29, January 8, 2010, No. 44, pp. 1)

Pub: American City Business Journals

Ed: Christopher Calnan. **Description:** Central Texas Angel Network (CTAN) has invested $3.5 million in 12 ventures, which include 10 in Austin, Texas in 2009 to triple the amount it invested during 2008. The largest recipient of CTAN's investments is life sciences, which attracted 20 percent of the capital, while software investments fell to 18 percent. The new screening process that helps startups secure CTAN capital is explored.

45086 ■ "Apps For Anybody With an Idea" in Advertising Age (Vol. 79, October 20, 2008, No. 39, pp. 29)

Pub: Crain Communications, Inc.

Ed: Beth Snyder Bulik. **Description:** Apple's new online App Store is open to anyone with an idea and the ability to write code and many of these developers are not only finding a sense of community through this venue but are also making money since the sales are split with Apple, 30/70 in the developer's favor.

45087 ■ "Arctic IT Honored" in Alaska Business Monthly (Vol. 27, October 2011, No. 10, pp. 10)

Pub: Alaska Business Publishing Company

Ed: Nancy Pounds. **Description:** Arctic Information Technology Inc. was named to Everything Channel's 2011 Computer Reseller News (CRN) Next-Generation 250 list. The firm provides business software and network infrastructure solutions.

45088 ■ "Arizona Firms In Chicago Go For Gold With '08 Games" in The Business Journal - Serving Phoenix and the Valley of

the Sun (Vol. 28, August 8, 2008, No. 49, pp. 1)
Pub: American City Business Journals, Inc.
Ed: Patrick O'Grady. **Description:** More than 20 U.S. athletes will wear Arizona-based eSoles LLC's custom-made insoles to increase their performance at the 2008 Beijing Olympics making eSoles one of the beneficiaries of the commercialization of the games. Translation software maker Auralog Inc saw a 60 percent jump in sales from its Mandarin Chinese language applications.

45089 ■ *"Attivio Brings Order to Data" in Information Today (Vol. 26, February 2009, No. 2, pp. 14)*
Pub: Information Today, Inc.
Ed: Marji McClure. **Description:** Profile of Attivio, the high tech firm offering next-generation software that helps businesses to consolidate data and eliminate enterprise silos.

45090 ■ *"AVG Introduces Security Software Suite for SMBs 551179" in eWeek (October 12, 2010)*
Pub: Ziff Davis Enterprise
Description: AVG Technologies is offering its AVG Internet Security 2011 Business Edition and AVG Anti-Virus Business Edition designed to give Internet-active SMB owners protection. The system protects online transactions and email communications as well as sensitive customer data and AVG Anti-Virus 2011 Business edition offers real-time protection against the latest online threats.

45091 ■ *"BancVue to Expand" in Austin Business JournalInc. (Vol. 29, November 27, 2009, No. 38, pp. 1)*
Pub: American City Business Journals
Ed: Kate Harrington. **Description:** Significant growth of BancVue in the past six years has prompted the company to look for a site that could increase its office space from 25,000 square feet to 65,000 square feet. BancVue offers bank and credit union software solutions and is planning to lease or buy a property in Austin, Texas.

45092 ■ *"Bar Hopping: Your Numbers At a Glance" in Inc. (January 2008, pp. 44-45)*
Pub: Gruner & Jahr USA Publishing
Ed: Michael Fitzgerald. **Description:** Software that helps any company analyze data include Crystal Xcelsius, a program that takes data from Excel documents and turns them into animated gauges, charts and graphs; CashView, a Web-based application that tracks receivables and payables; iDashboards, a Web-based programs that produces animated gauges, maps, pie charts and graphs; Corda Human Capital Management, that transforms stats like head count, productivity, and attrition into graphs and dials; NetSuite, a Web-based application that tracks key indicators; and Cognos Now, that gauges, dials, and graphs data.

45093 ■ *"BayTSP, NTT Data Corp. Enter Into Reseller Pact to Market Online IP Monitoring" in Professional Services Close-Up (Sept. 11, 2009)*
Pub: Close-Up Media
Description: Due to incredible interest from distributors and content owners across Asia, NTT Data Corp. will resell BayTSP's online intellectual property monitoring, enforcement, business intelligence and monetization services in Japan.

45094 ■ *"Behind the Scenes: Companies At the Heart of Everyday Life" in Inc. (February 2008, pp. 26-27)*
Pub: Gruner & Jahr USA Publishing
Ed: Athena Schindelheim. **Description:** Profiles of companies providing services to airports, making the environment safer and more efficient, as well as more comfortable for passengers and workers. Centerpoint Manufacturing provides garbage bins that can safely contain explosions producing thousands of pounds of pressure; Infax, whose software displays arrival and departure information on 19-foot-wide screens; Lavi Industries, whose products include security barricades, hostess stands, and salad-bar sneeze

guards; and SATech maker of rubber flooring that helps ease discomfort for workers having to stand for long periods of time.

45095 ■ *"Being all a-Twitter" in Canadian Business (Vol. 81, December 8, 2008, No. 21, pp. 22)*
Pub: Rogers Media Ltd.
Ed: Andrew Wahl. **Description:** Marketing experts suggest that advertising strategies have to change along with new online social media. Companies are advised to find ways to incorporate social software because workers and customers are expected to continue its use.

45096 ■ *"Best Managed Companies (Canada)" in Canadian Business (Vol. 82, Summer 2009, No. 8, pp. 38)*
Pub: Rogers Media
Ed: Calvin Leung. **Description:** Agrium Inc. and Barrick Gold Corporation are among those that are found to be the best managed companies in Canada. Best managed companies also include software firm Open Text Corporation, which has grown annual sales by 75 percent and annual profits by 160 percent since 1995. Open Text markets software that allow firms to manage word-based data, and has 46,000 customers in 114 countries.

45097 ■ *"Beyond Microsoft and Yahoo!: Some M&A Prospects" in Barron's (Vol. 88, March 17, 2008, No. 11, pp. 39)*
Pub: Dow Jones & Company, Inc.
Ed: Eric J. Savitz. **Description:** Weak quarterly earnings report for Yahoo! could pressure the company's board to cut a deal with Microsoft. Electronic Arts is expected to win its hostile $26-a-share bid for Take-Two Interactive Software. Potential targets and buyers for mergers and acquisitions are mentioned.

45098 ■ *"Beyond YouTube: New Uses for Video, Online and Off" in Inc. (October 2007, pp. 53-54)*
Pub: Gruner & Jahr USA Publishing
Ed: Leah Hoffmann. **Description:** Small companies are using video technology for embedding messages into email, broadcasting live interactive sales and training seminars, as well as marketing campaigns. Experts offer insight into producing and broadcasting business videos.

45099 ■ *The Big Switch*
Pub: W. W. Norton & Company, Inc.
Ed: Nicholas Carr. **Released:** January 19, 2009. **Price:** $16.95 paperback. **Description:** Today companies are dismantling private computer systems and tapping into services provided via the Internet. This shift is remaking the computer industry, bringing competitors such as Google to the forefront ant threatening traditional companies like Microsoft and Dell. The book weaves together history, economics, and technology to explain why computing is changing and what it means for the future.

45100 ■ *Business Feasibility Analysis Pro*
Pub: Prentice Hall PTR
Ed: Palo Alto Software. **Released:** August 2006. **Price:** $28.40. **Description:** Profile of software developed to support small business management and/or entrepreneurship text. Step-by-step instructions are provided.

45101 ■ *"BusinessOnLine Launches a New Web-Based Search Engine Optimization Tool" in Internet Wire (October 19, 2009)*
Pub: Comtex News Network, Inc.
Description: First Link Checker, a complimentary new search engine optimization tool that helps site owners optimize their on-page links by understanding which of those links are actually being counted in Google's relevancy algorithm, was developed by BusinessOnLine, a rapidly growing Internet marketing agency. This tool will make it easy for the average web master to ensure that their internal link structure is optimized.

45102 ■ *"A Case Study: Real-Life Business Planning" in Entrepreneur (February 3, 2009)*
Pub: Entrepreneur Media Inc.
Ed: Tim Berry. **Description:** Provides a case study of a two-day planning meeting for Palo Alto Software in which the executives of the company met for their

annual planning cycle and discussed ways in which the company needed to change in order to stay viable in today's tough economic climate.

45103 ■ *"Cerner Works the Business Circuit" in Business Journal-Serving Metropolitan Kansas City (Vol. 26, October 5, 2007, No. 4, pp. 1)*
Pub: American City Business Journals, Inc.
Ed: Rob Roberts. **Description:** Cerner Corporation is embracing the coming of the electronic medical record exchange by creating a regional health information organization (RHIO) called the CareEntrust. The RHIO convinced health insurers to share claims data with patients and clinicians. At the Center Health Conference, held October 7 to 10, Cerner will demonstrate the software it developed for CareEntrust to the 40,000 healthcare and information technology professionals.

45104 ■ *"ChemSW Software Development Services Available for Outsourcing" in Information Today (Vol. 26, February 2009, No. 2, pp. 30)*
Pub: Information Today, Inc.
Description: ChemSW software development services include requirements analysis, specification development, design, development, testing, and system documentation as an IT outsourcing solution. The company can also develop software tracking systems for satellite stockrooms, provide asset management integration solutions and more.

45105 ■ *"ClickFuel Launches New Products to Help Small and Mid-Sized Businesses Bolster Their Brand Online" in Internet Wire (Dec. 3,2009)*
Pub: Comtex News Network, Inc.
Description: Boostability, a provider of Enterprise Search Engine Optimization (SEO) software technology, has partnered with ClickFuel, a firm that designs, tracks and manages Internet marketing campaigns in order to leverage Boostability's technology in order to deliver comprehensive SEO solutions to small and mid-size businesses; three new products will also become available for these business clients to help them manage all facets of their online presence.

45106 ■ *"ClickFuel Launches New Products to Help Small and Mid-Sized Businesses Bolster Their Brand Online" in Internet Wire (Dec. 3, 2009)*
Pub: Comtex News Network, Inc.
Description: Boostability, a provider of Enterprise Search Engine Optimization (SEO) software technology, has partnered with ClickFuel, a firm that designs, tracks and manages Internet marketing campaigns in order to leverage Boostability's technology in order to deliver comprehensive SEO solutions to small and mid-size businesses; three new products will also become available for these business clients to help them manage all facets of their online presence.

45107 ■ *"ClickFuel Unveils Internet Marketing Tools for Small Businesses" in Internet Wire (October 19, 2009)*
Pub: Comtex News Network, Inc.
Description: ClickFuel, a firm that manages, designs and tracks marketing campaigns has unveiled a full software suite of affordable services and technology solutions designed to empower small business owners and help them promote and grow their businesses through targeted Internet marketing campaigns.

45108 ■ *"Clouds in the Forecast" in Information Today (Vol. 28, September 2011, No. 8, pp. 10)*
Pub: Information Today, Inc.
Ed: Paula J. Hane. **Description:** Cloud computing is software, applications, and data stored remotely and accessed via the Internet with output displayed on a client device. Recent developments in cloud computing are explored.

45109 ■ *Computer Accounting Essentials with Microsoft Office Accounting 2010*
Pub: McGraw-Hill Higher Education
Ed: Carol Yacht, Susan Crosson. **Released:** March 10, 2010. **Description:** Step-by-step guide to using Microsoft's Office Professional 2007 Accounting program.

45110 ▪ *"Cut Energy Waste" in Inc. (Vol. 31, January-February 2009, No. 1, pp. 42)*
Pub: Mansueto Ventures LLC
Description: Carbon Control, Edison, and Saver software programs help companies cut carbon emissions by reducing the amount of energy consumed by computers while they are idle.

45111 ▪ *"Dear Customer: Managing E-Mail Campaigns" in Inc. (March 2008, pp. 58-59)*
Pub: Gruner & Jahr USA Publishing
Ed: Ryan Underwood. **Description:** Internet services that help firms manage their online business including email marketing, to manage subscriber lists, comply with spam regulations, monitor bouncebacks, and track potential customers are profiled. Constant Contact, MobileStorm Stun, Campaign Monitor, Pop Commerce, Emma, and StrongMail E-mail Server are among software and services highlighted.

45112 ▪ *"Design Center Shows Quality of Digital Paper" in American Printer (Vol. 128, June 1, 2011, No. 6)*
Pub: Penton Media Inc.
Description: Digital Design Centers allows printers to customize marketing tools in order to promote their own digital printing capabilities.

45113 ▪ *"Design Programs for HVAC Sizing Solutions" in Contractor (Vol. 57, January 2010, No. 1, pp. 44)*
Pub: Penton Media, Inc.
Ed: William Feldman; Patti Feldman. **Description:** Rhvac 8 is an HVAC design program that lets users calculate peak heating and cooling load requirements for rooms, zones, systems, and entire buildings. The HVAC Pipe Sizer software for the iPhone enables quick sizing of a simple piping system.

45114 ▪ *"Don't Touch My Laptop, If You Please Mr. Customs Man" in Canadian Electronics (Vol. 23, June-July 2008, No. 4, pp. 6)*
Pub: Action Communication Inc.
Ed: Mark Borkowski. **Description:** Canadian businessmen bringing electronic devices to the US can protect the contents of their laptops by hiding their data from US border agents. They can also choose to clean up the contents of their laptop using file erasure programs.

45115 ▪ *"DST Turns to Banks for Credit" in The Business Journal-Serving Metropolitan Kansas City (Vol. 27, October 3, 2008, No. 3, pp. 1)*
Pub: American City Business Journals, Inc.
Ed: Rob Roberts. **Description:** Kansas City, Missouri-based DST Systems Inc., a company that provides sophisticated information processing, computer software services and business solutions, has secured a new five-year, $120 million credit facility from Enterprise Bank and Bank of the West. The deal is seen to reflect that the region and community-banking model remain stable. Comments from executives are also provided.

45116 ▪ *"Eagles Measure Suite Success" in Philadelphia Business Journal (Vol. 30, September 9, 2011, No. 30, pp. 1)*
Pub: American City Business Journals Inc.
Ed: John George. **Description:** Philadelphia Eagles have a new software program that helps suite holders keep track of how their suite is being used and whether they are getting a return on their investment. The software allows suite holders to better utilize and distribute their tickets.

45117 ▪ *"EBSCO Adds New Features to EBSCOhost Content Viewer" in Information Today (Vol. 26, February 2009, No. 2, pp. 31)*
Pub: Information Today, Inc.
Description: EBSCOhost Content Viewer historical digital archive collection provides a visual overview of a displayed document, highlighting search keywords on the page as well as providing a document map that shows the number of times a given keyword is mentioned in a periodical, monograph, article, or other document. For periodical content, the viewer

lets users browse multiple issues in a volume without leaving the interface; features include zoom and pan technology similar to online maps.

45118 ▪ *"Elastic Path Software Joins Canada in G20 Young Entrepreneur Summit" in Internet Wire (June 14, 2010)*
Pub: Comtex
Description: The Canadian Youth Business Foundation hosted the G20 Young Entrepreneur Summit and announced that Harry Chemko of British Columbia's Elastic Path Software will be a member of the Canadian delegation at the G20 Young Entrepreneur Summit. Details are included.

45119 ▪ *"Elemental Nabs $5.5 Million" in The Business Journal-Portland (Vol. 25, July 18, 2008, No. 19, pp. 1)*
Pub: American City Business Journals, Inc.
Ed: Aliza Earnshaw. **Description:** Elemental Technologies Inc., a Portland, Oregon-based software company got $5.5 million in new funding, bringing its total invested capital to $7.1 million in nine months since October 2008. The company plans to launch Badaboom, software for converting video into various formats, later in 2008.

45120 ▪ *"The Emergence of Governance In an Open Source Community" in Academy of Management Journal (Vol. 50, No. 5, October 2007, pp. 1079)*
Pub: Academy of Management
Contact: Ming-Jer Chen, President
Ed: Siiobhan O'Mahony, Fabrizio Ferraro. **Description:** Study examined the method of self-governance among small communities producing collective goods, focusing on an open source software community. Results revealed that a combination of bureaucratic and democratic practices helped its governance system.

45121 ▪ *"Empire of Pixels" in Entrepreneur (Vol. 37, September 2009, No. 9, pp. 50)*
Pub: Entrepreneur Media, Inc.
Ed: Jason Daley. **Description:** Entrepreneur Jack Levin has successfully grown Imageshack, an image-hosting Web service. The Website currently gets 50 million unique visitors a month. Levin has launched Y-Frog, an application that uses Imageshack to allow Twitter users to add images to their posts.

45122 ▪ *The Entrepreneurial Culture Network Advantage Within Chinese and Irish Software Firms*
Pub: Edward Elgar Publishing, Incorporated
Ed: Tsang. **Released:** October 2006. **Price:** $95.00.
Description: Ways national cultural heritage influences entrepreneurial ventures are discussed.

45123 ▪ *"Ex Libris Rosetta Hits the Market" in Information Today (Vol. 26, February 2009, No. 2, pp. 30)*
Pub: Information Today, Inc.
Description: Ex Libris Rosetta, the latest version of the Ex Libris Group's Digital Preservation System supports the acquisition, validation, ingest, storage, management, preservation, and dissemination of digital objects, allowing libraries the infrastructure and technology to preserve and facilitate access to digital collections. The firm's Ex Libris Roseta Charter Program helps users develop strategic collaboration between Ex Libris and its customers to improve the product.

45124 ▪ *"Fly Phishing" in Canadian Business (Vol. 80, October 22, 2007, No. 21, pp. 42)*
Pub: Rogers Media
Ed: Andy Holloway. **Description:** Symantec Corporation's report shows consumers and companies have effectively installed network defenses that prevent unwanted access. Phishing packages are readily available and are widely used. Other details of the Internet Security Threat Report are presented.

45125 ▪ *"The Folly of Google's Latest Gambit" in Barron's (Vol. 89, July 13, 2009, No. 28, pp. 23)*
Pub: Dow Jones & Co., Inc.
Ed: Eric J. Savitz. **Description:** Google will enter the operating systems business with the introduction of the Google Chrome OS but its success is dubious

because the project is still a year or so away while Microsoft will release an updated version of Windows by then; another problem is that Google already has another OS called Android which will overlap with the Chrome OS's market.

45126 ▪ *"German Win Through Sharing" in Canadian Business (Vol. 83, September 14, 2010, No. 15, pp. 16)*
Pub: Rogers Media Ltd.
Ed: Jordan Timm. **Description:** German economic historian Eckhard Hoffner has a two-volume work showing how German's relaxed attitude toward copyright and intellectual property helped it catch up to industrialized United Kingdom. Hoffner's research was in response to his interest in the usefulness of software patents. Information on the debate regarding Canada's copyright laws is given.

45127 ▪ *"Getting Rid of Global Glitches: Choosing Software For Trade Compliance" in Black Enterprise (Vol. 41, September 2010, No. 2, pp. 48)*
Pub: Earl G. Graves Publishing Co. Inc.
Ed: Marcia Wade Talbert. **Description:** Compliance software for trading with foreign companies must be compatible with the U.S. Census Bureau's Automated Export System (www.aesdirect.gov). It has to be current with regulatory requirements for any country in the world. Whether owners handle their own compliance or hire a logistics company, they need to be familiar with this software in order to access reports and improve transparency and efficiency of theft supply chain.

45128 ▪ *"Ghouls, Goblins, and Harry Potter: Cashing In On Halloween" in Inc. (Vol. 33, October 2011, No. 8, pp. 24)*
Pub: Inc. Magazine
Ed: Darren Dahl. **Description:** Costume Craze, an online costume retailer reports $13.2 million in sales last year. Originally the family business started out as a software company called StaticAdvantage, but switched gears.

45129 ▪ *"Global: Put It on Autopilot" in Entrepreneur (Vol. 35, October 2007, No. 10, pp. 110)*
Pub: Entrepreneur Media Inc.
Ed: Laurel Delaney. **Description:** A business that aims to enter the global market must first streamline its global supply chain (GSC). A streamlined GSC can be achieved by laying out the company's processes and by automating it with supply chain management software. Advantages of GSC automation such as credibility are provided.

45130 ▪ *"A Hacker in India Hijacked His Website Design and Was Making Good Money Selling It" in Inc. (December 2007, pp. 77-78, 80)*
Pub: Gruner & Jahr USA Publishing
Ed: Darren Dahl. **Description:** John Anton, owner of an online custom T-shirt business and how a company in India was selling software Website templates identical to his firm's Website.

45131 ▪ *"His Banking Industry Software Never Caught On, so Bill Randle is Now Targeting the Health Care Market" in Inc. (March 2008)*
Pub: Gruner & Jahr USA Publishing
Ed: Alex Salkever. **Description:** Profile of Bill Randle, bank executive turned entrepreneur; Randle tells how he changed his focus for his company from banking software to healthcare software. The firm employs ten people who secure online billing and recordkeeping systems for hospitals and insurers. Randle discusses critical decisions that will impact his firm in the coming year. Three experts offer advice.

45132 ▪ *"Holiday Sales Look Uncertain for Microsoft and PC Sellers" in Puget Sound Business Journal (Vol. 29, November 28, 2008, No. 32)*
Pub: American City Business Journals
Ed: Todd Bishop. **Description:** Personal computer makers face uncertain holiday sales for 2008 as a result of the weak U.S. economy and a shift toward

low-cost computers. Personal computer shipments for the fourth quarter 2008 are forecast to drop 1 percent compared to the same quarter 2007.

45133 ■ *"How Hard Could It Be? Adventures In Software Demol'ling" in Inc. (December 2007, pp. 99-100)*
Pub: Gruner & Jahr USA Publishing
Ed: Joel Spolsky. **Description:** Founder and CEO of Fog Creek Software, a New York City software developer shares insight into his software demo tour used to promote his firm's products.

45134 ■ *"HR Tech on the Go" in Workforce Management (Vol. 88, November 16, 2009, No. 12, pp. 1)*
Pub: Crain Communications Inc.
Ed: Ed Frauenheim. **Description:** Examination of the necessity of mobile access of human resources software applications that allow managers to recruit, schedule and train employees via their mobile devices; some industry leaders believe that mobile HR applications are vital while others see this new technology as hype.

45135 ■ *"iControl Networks Powers Comcast's XFINITY (Reg) Home Security Service" in Benzinga.com (June 9, 2011)*
Pub: Benzinga.com
Ed: Benzinga Staff. **Description:** Comcast's XFIN-ITY Home Security Service is powered by iControl Networks' OpenHome (TM) software platform. The service provides intrusion and fire protection along with interactive features such as home monitoring, home management, and energy management services with Web and mobile access.

45136 ■ *"Image Conscious" in Canadian Business (Vol. 81, March 17, 2008, No. 4, pp. 36)*
Pub: Rogers Media
Ed: Andrew Wahl. **Description:** Idee Inc. is testing an Internet search engine for images that does not rely on tags but compares its visual data to a database of other images. The company was founded and managed by Leila Boujnane as an off-shoot of their risk-management software firm. Their software has already been used by image companies to track copyrighted images and to find images within their own archives.

45137 ■ *"iMozi Integrates Esprida LiveControl for Advanced DVD Kiosk Hardware" in Wireless News (December 20, 2010)*
Pub: Close-Up Media Inc.
Description: Provider of self-service entertainment technology, iMozi Canada has partnered with Esprida to make its automated DVD Kiosk solutions Esprida-enabled. Esprida develops remote device management solutions and will offer enhanced capabilities and to improve customer experience for users.

45138 ■ *"Inside Intel's Effectiveness System for Web Marketing" in Advertising Age (Vol. 81, January 25, 2010, No. 4, pp. 4)*
Pub: Crain's Communications
Ed: Beth Snyder Bulik. **Description:** Overview of Intel's internally developed program called Value Point System in which the company is using in order to evaluate and measure online marketing effectiveness.

45139 ■ *"Intel to Buy McAfee Security Business for 768B" in eWeek (August 19, 2010)*
Pub: Ziff Davis Enterprise
Description: Intel will acquire security giant McAfee for approximately $7.68 billion, whereby McAfee would become a wholly owned subsidiary of Intel and would report to Intel's Software and Services Group.

45140 ■ *"iPhone Apps Big Business" in Austin Business JournalInc. (Vol. 28, November 14, 2008, No. 35, pp. 1)*
Pub: American City Business Journals
Ed: Christopher Calnan. **Description:** Members of the computer software industry in Austin, Texas have benefited from developing applications for Apple Inc.'s iPhone. Pangea Software Inc.'s revenues have grown by developing iPhone applications. Lexcycle LLC, on the other hand, has created an application that enables users to read books on the iPhone.

45141 ■ *"iPhone Apps In a Flash" in Entrepreneur (Vol. 37, October 2009, No. 10, pp. 38)*
Pub: Entrepreneur Media, Inc.
Description: Ansca is developing Corona, a software development kit for the Apple iPhone. The kit reduces development time and allows individuals with knowledge of software to develop iPhone applications.

45142 ■ *"Is It Time to Ban Swearing at Work?" in HR Specialist (Vol. 8, September 2010, No. 9, pp. 2)*
Pub: Capitol Information Group Inc.
Description: Screening software has been developed to identify profanity used in business correspondence.

45143 ■ *"Is It Time for a Change?" in Rental Product News (Vol. 33, October 2011)*
Pub: Cygnus Business Media
Ed: Jenny Lescohier. **Description:** Management software for running a rental business is examined.

45144 ■ *"iSymmetry's Technological Makeover Or, How a Tech Company Finally Grew Up and Discovered the World Wide Web" in Inc. (October 2007)*
Pub: Gruner & Jahr USA Publishing
Description: Profile of iSymmetry, an Atlanta, Georgia-based IT recruiting firm, covering the issues the company faces keeping its technology equipment up-to-date. The firm has devised a program that will replace its old server-based software systems with on-demand software delivered via the Internet, known as software-as-a-service. Statistical information included.

45145 ■ *"Johnny Royal of Luthier Society Unveils Archimedes 1.0 Trailer" in Internet Wire (October 22, 2009)*
Pub: Comtex News Network, Inc.
Description: Luthier Society, a social media and viral branding agency, has released the first viral video for the company's ROI weighted-value software platform named Archimedes 1.0; users of the software will be able to determine the depth of their outreach efforts, saturation rate, value of their Internet presence and the geo-spatial location of their audience; this will give a true, monetized value for ROI (Return on Investment) in social media marketing.

45146 ■ *"Keeping Up With the Joneses: Outfitting Your Company With Up-To-Date Technology is Vital" in Black Enterprise (November 2007)*
Pub: Earl G. Graves Publishing Co. Inc.
Ed: Sonya A. Donaldson. **Description:** Small businesses, whether home-based or not, need to keep up with new technological developments including hardware, software, and the Internet.

45147 ■ *"Lights, Camera, Action: Tools for Creating Video Blogs" in Inc. (Volume 32, December 2010, No. 10, pp. 57)*
Pub: Inc. Magazine
Ed: John Brandon. **Description:** A video blog is a good way to spread company news, talk about products, and stand out among traditional company blogs. New editing software can create two- to four-minute blogs using a webcam and either Windows Live Essentials, Apple iLife 2011, Powerdirector 9 Ultra, or Adobe Visual Communicator 3.

45148 ■ *"Make Relationships Count: CRM Software That Works" in Black Enterprise (Vol. 38, February 2008, No. 7, pp. 60)*
Pub: Earl G. Graves Publishing Co. Inc.
Ed: Fiona Haley. **Description:** Customer relationship management (CRM) software can help any small business keep track of clients. Descriptions of the latest CRM software offered are profiled, including Salesforce.com, Microsoft Dynamics, and Saga Software.

45149 ■ *"Media Software and Data Services" in MarketingMagazine (Vol. 115, September 27, 2010, No. 13, pp. 78)*
Pub: Rogers Publishing Ltd.
Description: Media software and data services information in Canada is presented.

45150 ■ *"Meetings Go Virtual" in HRMagazine (Vol. 54, January 2009, No. 1, pp. 74)*
Pub: Society for Human Resource Management
Contact: Henry G. Jackson, President
E-mail: hjackson@shrm.org
Ed: Elizabeth Agnvall. **Description:** Microsoft Office Live Meeting conferencing software allows companies to schedule meetings from various company locations, thus saving travel costs.

45151 ■ *"Metallics Education" in American Printer (Vol. 128, June 1, 2011, No. 6)*
Pub: Penton Media Inc.
Description: Guide 'Curious About Print: Your Guide to the World of Curious Metallics' provides hints and tips to help printers maximize selection and reproduction, advice on working with metallic and UV inks, and recommendations for gaining quantity without sacrificing quality.

45152 ■ *"Microsoft Clicks Into High Speed" in Hispanic Business (Vol. 30, July-August 2008, No. 7-8, pp. 54)*
Pub: Hispanic Business, Inc.
Ed: Derek Reveron. **Description:** Microsoft's diversity hiring and vendor diversity program to capture more Hispanic consumer and business-to-business market is described. One of the main goals of these programs is to hire more Hispanic executives and managers who will help the company develop and market products and services that will appeal and benefit Hispanic consumers.

45153 ■ *"Microsoft Goes Macrosoft" in Barron's (Vol. 89, July 27, 2009, No. 30, pp. 25)*
Pub: Dow Jones & Co., Inc.
Ed: Mark Veverka. **Description:** Microsoft reported a weak quarter on the heels of a tech rally which suggests the economy has not turned around. Marc Andreesen describes his new venture-capital fund as focused on 'classic tech' and that historical reference places him in the annals of the last millennium.

45154 ■ *"Microsoft Releases Office Security Updates" in Mac World (Vol. 27, November 2010, No. 11, pp. 66)*
Pub: Mac Publishing
Ed: David Dahlquist. **Description:** Office for Mac and Mac Business Unit are Microsoft's pair of security- and stability-enhancing updates for Office 2008 and Office 2004. The software will improve the stability and compatibility and fixes vulnerabilities that would allow attackers to overwrite Mac's memory with malicious code.

45155 ■ *Microsoft Windows Small Business Server 2003 R2 Administrator's Companion*
Pub: Microsoft Press
Ed: Charlie Russel; Sharon Crawford. **Released:** July 2006. **Price:** $80.99. **Description:** Profile of Microsoft's Small Business Server R2.

45156 ■ *"Mimosa Systems Gains 150,000 New NearPoint Users" in Information Today (Vol. 26, February 2009, No. 2, pp. 31)*
Pub: Information Today, Inc.
Description: Mimosa System's NearPoint archive solution features email and file archiving, e-discovery, archive virtualization, and disaster recovery capabilities.

45157 ■ *"MindLeaders' Online Training Courses Come to ePath Learning" in Information Today (Vol. 26, February 2009, No. 2, pp. 4)*
Pub: Information Today, Inc.
Description: MindLeaders has partnered with ePath Learning to provide clients with over 2,200 new online courses. ePath's integrated Learning Management Service (iLMS) allows organizations to create online training programs for employees.

45158 ■ *"More Leading Retailers Using Omniture Conversion Solutions to Boost Sales and Ecommerce Performance"* in *Internet Wire (Sept. 22,2009)*
Pub: Comtex News Network, Inc.

Description: Many retailers are utilizing Omniture conversion solutions to improve the performance of their ecommerce businesses; recent enhancements to Omniture Merchandising and Omniture Recommendations help clients drive increased conversion to their Internet ventures.

45159 ■ *"More Leading Retailers Using Omniture Conversion Solutions to Boost Sales and Ecommerce Performance"* in *Internet Wire (Sept. 22,2009)*
Pub: Comtex News Network, Inc.

Description: Many retailers are utilizing Omniture conversion solutions to improve the performance of their ecommerce businesses; recent enhancements to Omniture Merchandising and Omniture Recommendations help clients drive increased conversion to their Internet ventures.

45160 ■ *"My Favorite Tool for Organizing Data"* in *Inc. (Vol. 33, November 2011, No. 9, pp. 46)*
Pub: Inc. Magazine

Ed: Abram Brown. **Description:** Intelligence software firm uses Roambi, a Web-based service that turns spreadsheet data into interactive files for iPhones and iPads.

45161 ■ *"New Database Brings Doctors Out of the Dark"* in *Business Courier (Vol. 26, October 23, 2009, No. 26, pp. 1)*
Pub: American City Business Journals, Inc.

Ed: James Ritchie. **Description:** A database created by managed care consulting firm Praesentia allows doctors in Cincinnati to compare average reimbursements from health insurance companies to doctors in different areas. Specialist doctors in the city are paid an average of $172.25 for every office consultation.

45162 ■ *"New Sprint Phone Whets Appetite for Applications"* in *The Business Journal-Serving Metropolitan Kansas City (Vol. 26, July 25, 2008)*
Pub: American City Business Journals, Inc.

Ed: Suzanna Stagemeyer. **Description:** Firms supporting the applications of the new Samsung Instinct, which was introduced by Sprint Nextel Corp. in June 2008, have reported usage rates increase for their products. Handmark, whose mobile services Pocket Express comes loaded with Instinct, has redirected employees to meet the rising demand for the services. Other views and information on Instinct, are presented.

45163 ■ *"New Wave of Business Security Products Ushers in the Kaspersky Anti-Malware Protection System"* in *Internet Wire (October 26, 2010)*
Pub: Comtex

Description: Kaspersky Anti-Malware System provides anti-malware protection that requires minimal in-house resources for small businesses. The system offers a full range of tightly integrated end-to-end protection solutions, ensuring unified protection across an entire network, from endpoint and mobile device protection to file server, mail server, network storage and gateway protection. It provides flexible centralized management, immediate threat visibility and a level of responsiveness not seen in other anti-malware approaches.

45164 ■ *"Nonprofit NAIC Acquires Software Developer as For-Profit Arm"* in *Crain's Detroit Business (Vol. 25, June 22, 2009, No. 25, pp. 10)*
Pub: Crain Communications Inc. - Detroit

Ed: Sherri Begin Welch. **Description:** Details of National Association of Investors Corporation's acquisition of a Massachusetts investment software developer in order to offer more products to investment clubs and individual investors nationwide.

45165 ■ *"Not Your Father's Whiteboard"* in *Inc. (Vol. 33, November 2011, No. 9, pp. 50)*
Pub: Inc. Magazine

Ed: Adam Baer. **Description:** Sharp's new interactive whiteboard is really a 70-inch touch screen monitor with software for importing presentations from any Windows 7 computer.

45166 ■ *"Note-Taking App, Supercharged"* in *Inc. (Vol. 33, October 2011, No. 8, pp. 48)*
Pub: Inc. Magazine

Ed: Adam Baer. **Description:** Note Taker HD is an iPad app that lets the user text by typing with finger or stylus with various colors, fonts and sizes; Extensive Notes creates notes, records audio memos, and takes photos and videos; Evernote allows users to create notes, take snapshots, and record voice memos.

45167 ■ *"Nothing Like a Weak Team Or An Unrealistic Schedule To Start a Project Off Right"* in *Inc. (November 2007, pp. 85-87)*
Pub: Gruner & Jahr USA Publishing

Ed: Joel Spolsky. **Description:** Five easy ways to fail meeting a project deadline are discussed by the owner of a software development company: start with second-rate team of developers, set weekly milestones, negotiate a deadline, divide tasks equitably, and work until midnight.

45168 ■ *"OCE Boosts JetStream Productivity"* in *American Printer (Vol. 128, August 1, 2011, No. 8)*
Pub: Penton Media Inc.

Description: New Oce JetStream 1400 and 3000 digital full-color inkjet presses are profiled. The new models promise higher speed to grow print volume.

45169 ■ *"Oce Business Services: Discovery Made Easy"* in *Information Today (Vol. 26, February 2009, No. 2, pp. 31)*
Pub: Information Today, Inc.

Ed: Barbara Brynko. **Description:** Oce Business Services provides document process management and electronic discovery through its CaseData repertoire of legal management solutions.

45170 ■ *"Omniture's Next Version of SearchCenter Delivers Landing Page Optimization"* in *Internet Wire (September 24, 2009)*
Pub: Comtex News Network, Inc.

Description: Omniture, Inc., a leading provider of online business optimization software, has announced a new release of Omniture SearchCenter; this latest version will allow search engine marketers to test landing pages across campaigns and ad groups.

45171 ■ *"On Beyond Powerpoint: Presentations Get a Wake-Up Call"* in *Inc. (November 2007, pp. 58-59)*
Pub: Gruner & Jahr USA Publishing

Ed: Michael Fitzgerald. **Description:** New software that allows business presentations to be shared online are profiled, including ProfCast, audio podcasts for sales, marketing, and training; SmartDraw2008, software that creates professional graphics; Dimdim, an open-Web conferencing tool; Empressr, a hosted Web service for creating, managing, and sharing multimedia presentations; Zentation, a free tool that allows users to watch slides and a videos of presenter; Spresent, a Web-based presentation tool for remote offices or conference calls.

45172 ■ *Open Source Solutions for Small Business Problems*
Pub: Charles River Media

Ed: John Locke. **Released:** May 2004. **Price:** $35.95. **Description:** Open source software provides solutions to many small business problems such as tracking electronic documents, scheduling, accounting functions, managing contact lists, and reducing spam.

45173 ■ *"Oracle and Tauri Group Honored by Homeland Security and Defense Business*

Council" in *Wireless News (December 15, 2009)*
Pub: Close-Up Media

Description: Selected as members of the year by the Homeland Security and Defense Business Council were Oracle, a software company that has provided thought leadership and strategic insights as well as The Tauri Group, an analytical consultancy, that has demonstrated a unique understanding of the role of small business and its vital contribution to the success of the country's security.

45174 ■ *"Our Gadget of the Week"* in *Barron's (Vol. 88, March 24, 2008, No. 12, pp. 47)*
Pub: Dow Jones & Company, Inc.

Ed: Tiernan Ray. **Description:** Review of the $299 Apple Time Capsule, which is a 500-megabyte hard disk drive and a Wi-Fi router, rolled into one device. The device allows users to create backup files without the need for sophisticated file management software.

45175 ■ *"Owner of IT Firm MK2 Tying Future to Software"* in *Crain's Cleveland Business (Vol. 30, June 15, 2009, No. 23, pp. 3)*
Pub: Crain Communications, Inc.

Ed: Chuck Soder. **Description:** Donald Kasper, owner of MK2 Technologies LLC of Cleveland, Ohio discusses his recent acquisition of a portion of ProSource Solution. The move will help expand the two companies' custom software development plans.

45176 ■ *"Panda Security for Business 4.05"* in *SC Magazine (Vol. 21, July 2010, No. 7, pp. 50)*
Pub: Haymarket Media Inc.

Description: Profile of Panda Security for Business, software offering endpoint security protection for computer desktops and servers is presented.

45177 ■ *"The Paper Shredder"* in *Business Courier (Vol. 26, September 11, 2009, No. 20, pp. 1)*
Pub: American City Business Journals, Inc.

Ed: Dan Monk. **Description:** DotLoop Company, owned by entrepreneur Austin Allison, is developing the DotLoop software, which eliminates paperwork in the processing of real estate contracts. The software allows realtors to take control of the negotiation process and is adaptable to the rules of different US states.

45178 ■ *"Paperless Bookkeeping Program"* in *Fleet Owner Online (February 15, 2011)*
Pub: Penton Business Media Inc.

Description: TruckTax launched its new paperless bookkeeping system to help manage bookkeeping tasks, accounting and business tax information and filings for truckers.

45179 ■ *"PC Connection Acquires Cloud Software Provider"* in *New Hampshire Business Review (Vol. 33, March 25, 2011, No. 6, pp. 8)*
Pub: Business Publications Inc.

Description: Merrimack-based PC Connection Inc. acquired ValCom Technology, a provider of cloud-based IT service management software. Details of the deal are included.

45180 ■ *"PC Running Slowly? How to Rev Up Your Machine"* in *Inc. (Vol. 33, November 2011, No. 9, pp. 46)*
Pub: Inc. Magazine

Ed: John Brandon. **Description:** Software that keeps PCs tuned up and running smoothing are profiled: AUSLO6ICS BOOSTSPEED 5, $50; Tuneup Utilities 2011, $40; Slimware Slimcleaner 1.9, free; and IOBIT Advanced Systemcare Pro 4, $20 a year.

45181 ■ *"PopCap Games Achieves Significant Increase in Return on Ad Spend With Omniture SearchCenter"* in *Internet Wire (September 15, 2009)*
Pub: Comtex News Network, Inc.

Description: PopCap Games, a leading computer games provider, is using Omniture SearchCenter together with Omniture SiteCatalyst to increase revenue from its search engine marketing campaign. Omniture, Inc. is a leading provider of Internet business optimization software.

45182 ■ *"The Power of Negative Thinking"* in *Inc. (Volume 32, December 2010, No. 10, pp. 43)*
Pub: Inc. Magazine

Ed: Jason Fried. **Description:** A Website is software and most businesses have and need a good Website to generate business. Understanding for building a powerful Website is presented.

45183 ■ *"Power Ranger"* in *Inc. (November 2007, pp. 131)*
Pub: Gruner & Jahr USA Publishing

Ed: Nitasha Tiku. **Description:** Surveyor software is designed to power down computers when not in use, in order to save energy.

45184 ■ *Practical Tech for Your Business*
Pub: Kiplinger Books and Tapes

Ed: Michael J. Martinez. **Released:** 2002. **Description:** Advice is offered to help small business owners choose the right technology for their company. The guide tells how to get started, network via the Internet, create an office network, use database software, and conduct business using mobile technology.

45185 ■ *"Precision Crop Control with Valley Irrigation/CropMetrics Partnership"* in *Farm Industry News (January 6, 2011)*
Pub: Penton Business Media Inc.

Description: Irrigation systems have become a precision farming tool since partnering with agronomic software systems to apply products across the field by prescription. Valley Irrigation and CropMetrics have partnered in order to variably control water, fertilizer and other crop management products through a center pivot irrigation system.

45186 ■ *"Press Release: Trimble Introduces CFX-750 Display"* in *Farm Industry News (January 4, 2011)*
Pub: Penton Business Media Inc.

Description: Trimble is offering a touch screen display called the CFX-750. The new 8-inch full-color display allows farmers to choose the specific guidance, steering and precision agriculture capabilities that best fit their farm's particular needs. The display can be upgraded as business needs change, including the addition of GLONASS capabilities, or the addition of section and rate control for crop inputs such as seed, chemicals and fertilizer.

45187 ■ *"Programs Provide Education and Training"* in *Contractor (Vol. 56, September 2009, No. 9, pp. 56)*
Pub: Penton Media, Inc.

Ed: William Feldman; Patti Feldman. **Description:** Opportunity Interactive's Showroom v2 software provides uses computer graphics to provide education and training on HVAC equipment and systems. It can draw heat pump balance points for a specific home. Meanwhile, Simutech's HVAC Training Simulators provide trainees with 'hands-on' HVACR training.

45188 ■ *"Protection One Introduces Home and Business Security iPhone App"* in *Wireless News (November 13, 2009)*
Pub: Close-Up Media

Description: Protection One, Inc., a provider of security systems to business and residential customers, has developed an application that allows users to access their security panels and receive real-time updates from their iPhone or iPod touch devices.

45189 ■ *"Providers Ride First Wave of eHealth Dollars"* in *Boston Business Journal (Vol. 31, June 10, 2011, No. 20, pp. 1)*
Pub: Boston Business Journal

Ed: Julie M. Donnelly. **Description:** Health care providers in Massachusetts implementing electronic medical records technology started receiving federal stimulus funds. Beth Israel Deaconess Medical Center was the first hospital to qualify for the funds.

45190 ■ *"Publishing Technology Introduces IngentaConnect Mobile"* in *Information Today (Vol. 26, February 2009, No. 2, pp. 33)*
Pub: Information Today, Inc.

Description: College undergraduates will find Publishing Technology's newest publisher product, IngentaConnect Mobile helpful. The product allows users to read articles and abstracts on mobile devices. According to a recent study, 73 percent of young adults with wireless hand-held devices use them to access non-voice data on any given day.

45191 ■ *"Putting the App in Apple"* in *Inc. (Vol. 30, November 2008, No. 11, pp.)*
Pub: Mansueto Ventures LLC

Ed: Nitasha Tiku. **Description:** Aftermarket companies are scrambling to develop games and widgets for Apple's iPhone. Apple launched a kit for developers interested in creating iPhone-specific software along with the App Store, and an iTunes spinoff. Profiles of various software programs that may be used on the iPhone are given.

45192 ■ *QuickBooks All-in-One Desk Reference for Dummies*
Pub: John Wiley & Sons, Incorporated

Ed: Stephen L. Nelson. **Released:** January 2007. **Price:** $29.99 (US), $42.99 (Canadian). **Description:** Compilation of nine self-contained minibooks to get the most from QuickBooks accounting software. Companion Web site with sample business plan workbook and downloadable profit-volume cost analysis workbook included.

45193 ■ *QuickBooks for the New Bean Counter: Business Owner's Guide 2006*
Pub: Wheatmark

Ed: Joseph L. Catallini. **Released:** July 2006. **Price:** $21.95. **Description:** Profile of QuickBooks software, offering insight into using the software's accounting and bookkeeping functions.

45194 ■ *QuickBooks Simple Start for Dummies*
Pub: John Wiley and Sons, Inc.

Ed: Stephen L. Nelson. **Released:** October 2004. **Price:** $21.99. **Description:** Profile of Intuits new accounting software geared to micro businesses. Advice is offered on daily, monthly, and yearly accounting activities covering records, sales tax, and reports.

45195 ■ *QuickBooks X on Demand*
Pub: Que

Ed: Gail Perry. **Released:** December 2006. **Price:** $34.99. **Description:** Step-by-step training for using various small business financial software programs; includes illustrated, full color explanations.

45196 ■ *QuickBooks X for Dummies*
Pub: John Wiley & Sons, Incorporated

Ed: Stephen L. Nelson. **Released:** November 2006. **Price:** $21.99. **Description:** Key features of QuickBooks software for small business are introduced. Invoicing and credit memos, recoding sales receipts, accounting, budgeting, taxes, payroll, financial reports, job estimating, billing, tracking, data backup, are among the features.

45197 ■ *"Quickoffice's MobileFiles Pro App Enables Excel Editing On-the-Go"* in *Information Today (Vol. 26, February 2009, No. 2, pp. 31)*
Pub: Information Today, Inc.

Description: Quickoffice Inc. introduced MobileFiles Pro, which features editable Microsoft Office functionality for the iPone and iPod touch. The application allows users to edit and save Microsoft Excel files in .xls format, transfer files to and from PC and Mac desktops via Wi-Fi, and access and synchronize with Apple MobileMe accounts.

45198 ■ *"Remote Control: Working From Wherever"* in *Inc. (February 2008, pp. 46-47)*
Pub: Gruner & Jahr USA Publishing

Ed: Ryan Underwood. **Description:** New technology allows workers to perform tasks from anywhere via the Internet. Profiles of products to help connect to your office from afar include, LogMein Pro, a Web-based service that allowsaccess to a computer from anywhere; Xdrive, an online service that allows users

to store and swap files; Basecamp, a Web-based tools that works like a secure version of MySpace; MojoPac Freedom, is software that allows users to copy their computer's desktop to a removable hard drive and plug into any PC; WatchGuard Firebox X Core e-Series UTM Bundle, hardware that blocks hackers and viruses while allowing employees to work remotely; TightVNC, a free open-source software that lets you control another computer via the Internet.

45199 ■ *"RES Stakes Its Claim in Area"* in *Philadelphia Business Journal (Vol. 28, January 29, 2010, No. 50, pp. 1)*
Pub: American City Business Journals

Ed: Peter Key. **Description:** RES Software Company Inc. of Amsterdam, Netherlands appointed Jim Kirby as president for the Americas and Klaus Besier as chairman in an effort to boost the firm's presence in the US. Brief career profiles of Kirby and Besier are included. RES develops software that allows management of information flow between an organization and its employees regardless of location.

45200 ■ *"Route Optimization Impacts the Bottom Line"* in *Contractor (Vol. 56, November 2009, No. 11, pp. 48)*
Pub: Penton Media, Inc.

Ed: Dave Beaudry. **Description:** Plumbing and HVAC businesses can save a significant amount of money from route optimization. The process begins with gathering information on a fleet and a routing software tool can determine the effectiveness of current route configurations and identify preferable route plans.

45201 ■ *Salesforce.com Secrets of Success: Best Practices for Growth and Profitability*
Pub: Prentice Hall Business Publishing
Contact: Jerome Grant, President

Ed: David Taber. **Released:** May 15, 2009. **Price:** $34.99. **Description:** Guide for using Salesforce.com; it provides insight into navigating through user groups, management, sales, marketing and IT departments in order to achieve the best results.

45202 ■ *"Save the Date"* in *Barron's (Vol. 90, September 13, 2010, No. 37, pp. 35)*
Pub: Barron's Editorial & Corporate Headquarters

Ed: Mark Veverka. **Description:** Mark Hurd is the new Co-President of Oracle after being forced out at Hewlett-Packard where he faced a harassment complaint. HP fired Hurd due to expense account malfeasance. Hurd is also set to speak at an Oracle trade show in San Francisco on September 20, 2010.

45203 ■ *"Scitable Puts Nature Education on the Map"* in *Information Today (Vol. 26, February 2009, No. 2, pp. 29)*
Pub: Information Today, Inc.

Description: Nature Education, a division of the Nature Publishing Group, released its first product, Scitable, a free online resource for undergraduate biology students and educators. The service includes over 180 overviews of key genetics concepts as well as social networking features, including groups and functionality, that lets students work with classmates and others. Teachers can use the service to set up public or private groups for students.

45204 ■ *"Second Cup?"* in *Canadian Business (Vol. 81, July 21, 2008, No. 11, pp. 50)*
Pub: Rogers Media Ltd.

Ed: Calvin Leung. **Description:** Profile of James Gosling who is credited as the inventor of the Java programming language; however, the 53-year-old software developer feels ambivalent for being credited as inventor since many people contributed to the language. Netscape and Sun Microsystems incorporation of the programming language into Java is presented.

45205 ■ *"Sense of Discovery"* in *Business Journal Portland (Vol. 27, November 19, 2010, No. 38, pp. 1)*
Pub: Portland Business Journal

Ed: Erik Siemers. **Description:** Tigard, Oregon-based Exterro Inc. CEO Bobby Balachandran announced plans to go public without the help of an institutional investor. Balachandran believes Exterro could grow to a $100 million legal compliance software company in the span of three years. Insights on Exterro's growth as market leader in the $1 billion legal governance software market are also given.

45206 ■ *"Serials Solutions Launches 360 Resource Manager Consortium Edition" in Information Today (Vol. 26, February 2009, No. 2, pp. 32)*
Pub: Information Today, Inc.
Description: Serials Solutions new Serials Solutions 360 Resource Manager Consortium Edition helps consortia, groups and member libraries with their e-resource management services. The products allows users to consolidate e-resource metadata and acquisition information into one place, which enables groups to manage holdings, subscriptions, licensing, contacts, and cost information and to streamline delivery of information to members.

45207 ■ *"A Side Project Threatens To Get Totally Out of Control and I Think, 'How Fun'" in Inc. (October 2007, pp. 81-82)*
Pub: Gruner & Jahr USA Publishing
Ed: Joel Spolsky. **Description:** Profile of Fog Creek Software, makers of project-management software for other software developers. Fog Creek's owner discusses his idea to create a new product for his firm.

45208 ■ *"Skype on Steroids" in Inc. (Vol. 31, January-February 2009, No. 1, pp. 46)*
Pub: Mansueto Ventures LLC
Ed: Nitasha Tiku. **Description:** Free software called VoxOx allows users to make calls over the Internet and connects all email and IM accounts.

45209 ■ *"Slow but Steady into the Future" in Barron's (Vol. 88, July 7, 2008, No. 27, pp. M)*
Pub: Dow Jones & Co., Inc.
Ed: Mark Veverka. **Description:** Investors are advised to maintain their watch on the shares of business software company NetSuite. The company's chief executive officer, Zach Nelson, claims that the company has a 10-year lead on its competitors with the development of software-as-a service.

45210 ■ *"Small is Bountiful for Intuit" in Barron's (Vol. 90, September 13, 2010, No. 37, pp. 22)*
Pub: Barron's Editorial & Corporate Headquarters
Ed: Mark Veverka. **Description:** Finance software maker Intuit wants to tap the underserved small business market. One analyst sees Intuit's shares rising 25 percent to 55 percent in the next 12 months from September 2010.

45211 ■ *"A Software Company's Whimsical Widgets Were an Instant Hit. But Its Core Product Was Getting Overshadowed" in Inc. (Jan. 2008)*
Pub: Gruner & Jahr USA Publishing
Ed: Alex Salkever. **Description:** A widget designed as a marketing tool tuned into a hit on Facebook. Should ChipIn shift its focus?.

45212 ■ *"Software Solutions Increase Productivity" in Contractor (Vol. 57, February 2010, No. 2, pp. 26)*
Pub: Penton Media, Inc.
Ed: William Feldman; Patti Feldman. **Description:** Singletouch is a real-time data capture solution for mechanical and other contractors that work in jobs that require materials and workload tracking. Contractors get information on extreme weather and sudden changes in the cost of materials. The OptimumHVAC optimization software by Optimum Energy is designed to optimize energy savings in commercial buildings.

45213 ■ *"Software Solutions from Trane and Carrier" in Contractor (Vol. 56, July 2009, No. 7, pp. 38)*
Pub: Penton Media, Inc.
Ed: William Feldman; Patti Feldman. **Description:** Trane Trace 700 software helps HVAC contractors optimize the design of a building's HVAC system and aids in the evaluation of various key energy-saving concepts, including daylighting, high-performance glazing, and other optimization strategies. Carrier's E20-II family of software programs lets contractors increase the accuracy of an HVAC system estimate.

45214 ■ *"Software's Last Hurrah" in Canadian Business (Vol. 81, December 24, 2007, No. 1, pp. 27)*
Pub: Rogers Media
Ed: Andrew Wahl. **Description:** Canada's software industry could be facing a challenge with IBM's acquisition of Cognos, which was the country's last major independent business intelligence company and was also IBM's largest acquisition ever. Next in line to Cognos in terms of prominence is Open Text Corporation, which could also be a possible candidate for acquisition, as analysts predict.

45215 ■ *"Speaking In Tongues: Rosetta Stone's TOTALE Adds 'Social' To Language Learning" in Black Enterprise (Vol. 41, September 2010, No. 2)*
Pub: Earl G. Graves Publishing Co. Inc.
Ed: Sonya A. Donaldson. **Description:** As small businesses become more globalized, it is necessary to learn new languages in order to compete. Rosetta Stone's TOTALe is profiled.

45216 ■ *"Startup on Cusp of Trend" in Austin Business JournalInc. (Vol. 29, January 8, 2010, No. 44, pp. 1)*
Pub: American City Business Journals
Ed: Christopher Calnan. **Description:** Austin-based Socialware Inc. introduced a new business called social middleware, which is a software that is layered between the company network and social networking Website used by workers. The software was designed to give employers a measure of control over content while allowing workers to continue using online social networks.

45217 ■ *"The State of the Art in End-User Software Engineering" in ACM Computing Surveys (Vol. 43, Fall 2011, No. 3, pp. 21)*
Pub: Association for Computing Machinery
Description: Most programs today are not written by professional software developers but by people with expertise in other domains working towards goals for which they need computational support. A discussion of empirical research about end-user software engineering activities and the technologies designed to support them is presented. Several crosscutting issues in the design of EUSE tools, including the roles of risk, reward, and domain complexity, and self-efficacy in the design of EUSE tools and the potential of educating users about software engineering principles are also examined.

45218 ■ *"The Story Of Diane Greene" in Barron's (Vol. 88, July 14, 2008, No. 28, pp. 31)*
Pub: Dow Jones & Co., Inc.
Ed: Mark Veverka. **Description:** Discusses the ousting of Diane Greene as a chief executive of VMWare, a developer of virtualization software, after the firm went public; in this case Greene, a brilliant engineer, should not be negatively impacted by the decision because it is common for companies to bring in new executive leadership that is more operations oriented after the company goes public.

45219 ■ *"A Survey of Combinatorial Testing" in ACM Computing Surveys (Vol. 43, Summer 2011, No. 2, pp. 11)*
Pub: Association for Computing Machinery
Ed: Changhai Nie, Hareton Leung. **Description:** Combinatorial Testing (CT) can detect failures triggered by interactions of parameters in the Software Under Test (SUT) with a covering array test suite generated by some sampling mechanisms. Basic concepts and notations of CT are covered.

45220 ■ *"A Survey of Comparison-Based System-Level Diagnosis" in ACM Computing Surveys (Vol. 43, Fall 2011, No. 3, pp. 22)*
Pub: Association for Computing Machinery
Ed: Elias P. Duarte Jr., Roverli P. Ziwich, Luiz C.P. Albini. **Description:** The growing complexity and dependability requirements of hardware, software, and networks demand efficient techniques for discovering disruptive behavior in those systems. Comparison-based diagnosis is a realistic approach to detect faulty units based on the outputs of tasks executed by system units. This survey integrates the vast amount of research efforts that have been produced in this field.

45221 ■ *"Taking the Steps Into the Clouds" in New Hampshire Business Review (Vol. 33, March 25, 2011, No. 6, pp. 19)*
Pub: Business Publications Inc.
Ed: Tim Wessels. **Description:** Cloud services include Internet and Web security, spam filtering, message archiving, work group collaboration, IT asset management, help desk and disaster recovery backup.

45222 ■ *"Tech Deal Couples Homegrown Firms" in The Business Journal-Serving Greater Tampa Bay (Vol. 28, July 4, 2008, No. 28, pp. 1)*
Pub: American City Business Journals, Inc.
Ed: Michael Hinman. **Description:** Tampa Bay, Florida-based Administrative Partners Inc. was acquired by Tribridge Inc. resulting in the strengthening of the delivery of Microsoft products to clients. Other details of the merger of the management consulting services companies are presented.

45223 ■ *"Technology to the Rescue" in Contractor (Vol. 56, July 2009, No. 7, pp. 22)*
Pub: Penton Media, Inc.
Ed: Candace Ruolo. **Description:** Features of several products that will make the job of a mechanical contractor easier are discussed. These include Ridgid's line of drain and sewer inspection cameras and monitors, Motion Computing's Motion F5 tablet rugged tablet PC, the JobClock from Exaktime, and the TeleNav Track tool for mobile workforce management.

45224 ■ *"Technology: What Seems To Be the Problem? Self Service Gets a Tune-Up" in Inc. (February 2008, pp. 43-44)*
Pub: Gruner & Jahr USA Publishing
Ed: Darren Dahl. **Description:** Self-service software can save companies money when responding to customer service phone calls, text or email messages. More companies are relying on alternatives such as automated Web-based self-service systems.

45225 ■ *"Ted Stahl: Executive Chairman" in Inside Business (Vol. 13, September-October 2011, No. 5, pp. NC6)*
Pub: Great Lakes Publishing Co.
Ed: Miranda S. Miller. **Description:** Profile of Ted Stahl, who started working in his family's business when he was ten years old is presented. The firm makes dies for numbers and letters used on team uniforms. Another of the family firms manufactures stock and custom heat-printing products, equipment and supplies. It also educates customers on ways to decorate garments with heat printing products and offers graphics and software for customers to create their own artwork.

45226 ■ *"Tell Us What You Really Think Collecting Customer Feedback" in Inc. (Vol. 30, December 2008, No. 12, pp. 52)*
Pub: Mansueto Ventures LLC
Ed: Ryan Underwood. **Description:** According to a recent survey, nearly 77 percent of online shoppers review consumer-generated reviews of products before making a purchase.

45227 ■ *"Thinking Strategically About Technology" in Franchising World (Vol. 42, August 2010, No. 8, pp. 9)*
Pub: International Franchise Association
Ed: Bruce Franson. **Description:** Nearly 25 percent of companies waste money from their technology budget. Most of the budget is spent on non-strategic software. Ways to spend money on technology for any franchise are examined.

45228 ■ *"A Timely Boon for Small Investors" in Barron's (Vol. 88, March 24, 2008, No. 12, pp. 48)*
Pub: Dow Jones & Company, Inc.
Ed: Theresa W. Carey. **Description:** Nasdaq Data Store's new program called Market Replay allows investors to accurately track stock price movements.

The replay can be as long as a day of market time and allows investors to determine whether they executed stock trades at the best possible price.

45229 ■ "Touching the Future" in Canadian Business (Vol. 81, July 21, 2008, No. 11, pp. 41)
Pub: Rogers Media Ltd.
Ed: Matt McClearn. **Description:** Microsoft Corp. has launched a multi-touch product which is both a software and hardware technology called Microsoft Surface. The innovative product allows people to use it at the same time, however touch-based computers are reported to be around $100,000. Other features and benefits of the product are presented.

45230 ■ "Trust But Verify: FMLA Software Isn't Foolproof, So Apply a Human Touch" in HR Specialist (Vol. 8, September 2010, No. 9, pp. 3)
Pub: Capitol Information Group Inc.
Description: Employers are using software to track FMLA information, however, it is important for employers to review reasons for eligibility requirements, particularly when an employee is reportedly overstepping the bounds within leave regulations due to software error.

45231 ■ "Two Field Service Management Solutions" in Contractor (Vol. 56, November 2009, No. 11, pp. 37)
Pub: Penton Media, Inc.
Ed: William Feldman; Patti Feldman. **Description:** Bella Solutions Field Service Software v. 4.2 is a web based solution for HVAC service contractors that enables scheduling of emergency, one-time, multivisit or periodically recurring jobs with drag and drop appointments. VaZing is another web based solution that costs $99 per month for contractors. It can handle line-item discounting and invoices aside from scheduling.

45232 ■ "Two Ways to Find New Customers" in Inc. (Vol. 31, January-February 2009, No. 1, pp. 41)
Pub: Mansueto Ventures LLC
Description: Latest software programs that help sales staff connect to new leads are profiled. Salesconx provides online leads while Demandbase reports users on a particular Website.

45233 ■ "Unbound ID Raises $2 Million" in Austin Business JournalInc. (Vol. 28, December 12, 2008, No. 39, pp. 1)
Pub: American City Business Journals
Ed: Christopher Calnan. **Description:** Austin, Texas-based Unbound ID Corporation has secured $2 million in funding from venture capital firm Silverton Partners. The company has developed identity management software for network directories. The market for identity management technology is expected to grow to more than $12.3 billion by 2014.

45234 ■ "uTest Discusses the Evolution of Crowdsourcing Models at CrowdConf 2010" in Internet Wire (October 1, 2010)
Pub: Comtex
Description: World's largest software testing marketplace, uTest, announces its first conference dedicated to the emerging field of crowdsourcing along with the future of distributed work. A panel of experts will discuss common misconceptions about crowdsourcing using real-world examples.

45235 ■ "Video Surveillance Enters Digital Era, Makes Giant Strides" in Arkansas Business (Vol. 26, September 28, 2009, No. 39, pp. 1)
Pub: Journal Publishing Inc.
Ed: Jamie Walden. **Description:** Arkansas business owners are finding that the newest technology in video surveillance is leading to swift apprehension of thieves due to the high-quality digital imagery now being captured on surveillance equipment. Motion detection software for these systems is enhancing the capabilities of these systems and providing opportunities for businesses that would normally have problems integrating these systems.

45236 ■ "A Virtual Jog Mode for CAM" in Modern Machine Shop (Vol. 84, November 2011, No. 6, pp. 22)
Pub: Gardner Business Media, Inc.
Contact: Richard G. Kline, President
E-mail: rkline@gardnerweb.com
Ed: Edwin Gasparraj. **Description:** In many cases, CAM programming required a specific, user-defined path. Siemens PLMs Generic Motion Controller is an alternative that defines the tool path within CAM. The program is a virtual 'teach' mode that enables the user to capture cutter locations by jogging machines axes within CAM.

45237 ■ "Web Translation Made Simple" in Inc. (Vol. 33, October 2011, No. 8, pp. 44)
Pub: Inc. Magazine
Ed: Adam Baer. **Description:** Smartling is a Web-based service that translates sites into more than 50 foreign languages. The software will begin translation right after setting up the account.

45238 ■ "Website Backup Made Simple" in Inc. (Vol. 33, September 2011, No. 7, pp. 52)
Pub: Inc. Magazine
Ed: John Brandon. **Description:** Tools to back up content on a Website are profiled. Vaultpress works only with sites that run on the WordPress publishing platform and CodeGuard works with a variety of publishing platforms and hosting services.

45239 ■ "Wegmans Uses Database for Recall" in Supermarket News (Vol. 56, September 22, 2008, No. 38)
Pub: Penton Business Media, Inc.
Ed: Carol Angrisani. **Description:** Wegmans used data obtained through its loyalty card that, in turn, sent automated telephone calls to every customer who had purchased tainted pet food when Mars Petcare recalled dog food products.

45240 ■ "Will the Force Be With Salesforce?" in Barron's (Vol. 88, March 24, 2008, No. 12, pp. 20)
Pub: Dow Jones & Company, Inc.
Ed: Mark Veverka. **Description:** Shares of Salesforce.com are likely to drop from the $44.83-a-share level in the face of a deteriorating economy and financial sector and thus lower demand for business software. The company is unlikely to deliver on its ambitious earnings forecasts for 2008 especially with strengthening competition from Oracle.

45241 ■ "Women Losing IT Ground" in Marketing to Women (Vol. 21, February 2008, No. 2, pp. 6)
Pub: EPM Communications Inc.
Contact: Ira Mayer, President
E-mail: imayer@epmcom.com
Description: According to a study conducted by The National Center for Women & Information Technology, women in technology are losing ground. Statistical data included.

45242 ■ "Yammer Gets Serious" in Inc. (Volume 32, December 2010, No. 10, pp. 58)
Pub: Inc. Magazine
Ed: Eric Markowitz. **Description:** Yammer, an internal social network for companies, allows coworkers to share ideas and documents in real-time. Details of this service are included.

45243 ■ "Yes, No, and Somewhat Likely: Survey the World with Web Polls" in Inc. (October 2007, pp. 58-59)
Pub: Gruner & Jahr USA Publishing
Ed: Don Steinberg. **Description:** Online tools for surveying customers, employees and the general public include Zoomergan zPro and Zoomerang Sample, software designed to send surveys and allows viewing results; SurveyMonkey software creates, administers and allows viewing online surveys and results; Vizu software places a one-question poll on a particular Website; and Vovici EFM Feedback, a subscription service providing ongoing surveys to customers or employees.

45244 ■ "Zeon Solutions Teams with Endeca for SaaS Version of Endeca InFront" in Entertainment Close-Up (October 25, 2011)
Pub: Close-Up Media
Description: Zeon Solutions, an enterprise e-commerce and Website development firm announced a special licensing partnership with Endecca Technologies. Endeca is an information management software company that provides small and mid-size retailers with high-performance Customer Experience Management technology.

TRADE PERIODICALS

45245 ■ Business Computer Report
Pub: Lawrence Oakly
Ed: Lawrence Oakly, Editor. **Released:** Monthly. **Description:** Reviews business applications software and hardware for IBM and compatible computers.

45246 ■ PC Business Products
Pub: Worldwide Videotex
Released: Monthly. **Price:** $165, U.S. and Canada; $180, elsewhere outside North America. **Description:** Covers developments in software and hardware products and services. Includes list of performance ratings and prices.

45247 ■ Technology Trends
Pub: Enterprise Technology Corp.
Ed: Kevin J. Merz, Editor. **Released:** 6/year. **Description:** Discusses news on computer software technology and its perceived value to the business community.

CONSULTANTS

45248 ■ Business Resource Software Inc.
1779 Wells Branch Pky
Austin, TX 78728-7090
Ph: (512)251-7541
Free: 800-423-1228
Fax: (512)251-4401
URL: http://www.brs-inc.com
Contact: Kylon Gustin, President
Scope: Provides marketing and business planning software. Provides an evaluation of business conditions and advises the users about situations in their specific business. **Founded:** 1989. **Publications:** Plan Write for Marketing; Quick Insight; Plan Write for Business; Business Insight; Insight for Sales Strategy; Plan Write Expert Edition. **Special Services:** Plan Write?; Quick Insight?; Business Insight?.

45249 ■ CheckMark Software Inc.
724 Whalers Way, Bldg. H, Ste. 101
Fort Collins, CO 80525-7578
Ph: (970)225-0522
Free: 800-444-9922
Fax: (970)225-0611
Co. E-mail: info@checkmark.com
URL: http://www.checkmark.com
Contact: Jim Mathre, President
Scope: Developer of accounting software tools for small businesses and provides fast, easy to use, affordable accounting and payroll solutions to small and medium sized businesses. Provides payroll software and multiledger integrated accounting software. **Founded:** 1984. **Publications:** Multi-Ledger; CheckMark Payroll for Macintosh; Check-Mark Payroll for Windows. **Special Services:** Multi-Ledger™; Payroll.

45250 ■ Claremont Consulting Group
4525 Castle Ln.
La Canada, CA 91011-1436
Ph: (818)249-0584
Fax: (818)249-5811
Contact: Donald S. Remer, Partner
Scope: Consulting, coaching, training, and litigation support in project management, engineering management, system engineering and cost estimating. **Founded:** 1979. **Publications:** "What Every Engineer Should Know About Project Management"; "100% product-oriented work breakdown structures and their importance to system engineering". **Seminars:** Project Management, System Engineering and Cost Estimating.

45251 ■ DacEasy Inc.—Sage Software Inc.
1715 N Brown Rd.
Lawrenceville, GA 30043
Free: 800-222-0505
Co. E-mail: sales@daceasy.com
URL: http://www.daceasy.com
Contact: Greg Hammermaster, President
URL(s): www.sagedaceasy.com. **Scope:** Develops an accounting system for small businesses that integrates accounting, invoicing, payroll, communications, and management software into a single package. **Founded:** 1981. **Seminars:** Tech Tuesday - Sage DacAccess Query and Publisher: Creating Basic Queries and Formatting, May, 2012; Tech Tuesday - Graphics Form Designer, Mar, 2012; Tech Tuesday - Year End Processes with Sage DacEasy; DacEasy Training.

45252 ■ Global Business Consultants (GBC)
200 Lake Hills Rd.
Pinehurst, NC 28374-0776
Ph: (910)295-5991
Fax: (910)295-5991
Co. E-mail: gbc@pinehurst.net
Contact: Nan S. Leaptrott, President
E-mail: nan@yourculturecoach.com
Scope: Firm specializes in human resources management; project management; software development; and international trade. Offers litigation support. **Founded:** 1987. **Publications:** "Culture to Culture: Mission Trip Do's and Don'ts," Jul, 2005; "Rules of the Game: Global Business Protocol". **Seminars:** Cross-Cultural Training.

45253 ■ MoneySoft Inc.
1 E Camelback Rd., Ste. 550
Phoenix, AZ 85012-1650
Ph: (602)266-7710
Free: 800-966-7797
URL: http://www.moneysoft.com
Contact: Bob Machiz, President
Scope: Specializes in the publication of software for the corporate acquisition and development communities. **Founded:** 1991. **Publications:** "The Price is Right? Or is It?"; "Preparing Financial Projections and Valuations"; "Negotiating Business Acquisitions"; "Managing the Process of Buying a Business"; "The Overpayment Trap"; "Strategies to Avoid the Overpayment Trap"; "The Value, Price and Cost of an Acquisition"; "The Trouble with EBITDA". **Special Services:** Corporate Valuation Professional?; DealSense?; Buy-OutPlan?; Corporate Valuation?; Lightning Deal Reviewer?; Fixed Asset Pro?; Benchmark Pro 2006?; DealSense Plus; Mergerstat?.

45254 ■ On-Q Software Inc.
13764 SW 11 St.
Miami, FL 33184
Ph: (305)553-2400
Free: 800-553-2862
Fax: (305)220-2666
Co. E-mail: info@on-qsoftware.com
URL: http://www.on-qsoftware.com
Contact: Hermenegildo Cajigas, Treasurer
E-mail: hcajigas@on-qsoftware.com
Scope: Provider of the small business community with simple to use, feature rich software. Provides software solutions including time and fixed fee billing, due date tracking and practice manager. **Founded:** 1987.

COMPUTERIZED DATABASES

45255 ■ TecTrends™
PO Box 8120
Berkeley, CA 94707
Ph: (510)525-6220
Co. E-mail: tectrendsinfo@tectrends.com
URL: http://www.tectrends.com
Availability: Online: ProQuest LLC-Dialog; ProQuest LLC - Dialog; Information Sources Inc. - TecTrends. **Type:** Bibliographic; Directory.

Small Business Trends

START-UP INFORMATION

45256 ■ *How to Start Your Own Business for Entrepreneurs*
Pub: FT Press

Ed: Robert Ashton. **Released:** December 9, 2010. **Price:** $24.99. **Description:** More than 300,000 individuals start a business every year. That number will rise over the next year or two if the current economic downturn leads to widespread job losses.

45257 ■ *"The Next Generation: African Americans Are Successfully Launching Businesses Earlier In Life"* in *Black Enterprise (January 2008)*
Pub: Earl G. Graves Publishing Co. Inc.

Ed: Tennille M. Robinson. **Description:** According to a survey conducted by OPEN, a team dedicated small business at American Express, Generation Y individuals are three times more likely to start their own company. Three African American individuals who did just that are profiled.

ASSOCIATIONS AND OTHER ORGANIZATIONS

45258 ■ **Academy of Legal Studies in Business (ALSB)**
Miami University
Dept. of Finance
3111 Farmer School of Business
Oxford, OH 45056
Free: 800-831-2903
Co. E-mail: herrondj@muohio.edu
URL: http://www.alsb.org
Contact: Constance E. Bagley, President

URL(s): alsb.roundtablelive.org. **Description:** Teachers of business law and legal environment in colleges and universities. Promotes and encourages business law scholarship and teaching outside of the law school environment. **Founded:** 1924. **Publications:** *American Business Law Journal* (Quarterly); *Journal of Legal Studies Education* (Semiannual). **Educational Activities:** Academy of Legal Studies in Business Conference (Annual); ALSB Conference (Annual).

45259 ■ **Association for Consumer Trends (ACT)**
7076 Drinkard Way
Mechanicsville, VA 23111
Ph: (804)559-6519
Fax: (804)559-4087
Co. E-mail: info@consumerexpert.org
URL: http://www.consumerexpert.org
Contact: Ms. Kimberly Thies, Executive Director

Description: Provides global trend information and networking resources to assist members to identify and integrate trends into the design and marketing of consumer goods and services; educates businesses to interpret impact of trends on consumer needs and expectations. Hosts an annual Consumer Trends Forum with speakers addressing consumer trends.

Founded: 1998. **Publications:** *ACT Trendline* (Biweekly). **Educational Activities:** Consumer Trends Forum (Annual).

45260 ■ **Small Business Legislative Council (SBLC)**
1100 H St. NW, Ste. 540
Washington, DC 20005
Ph: (202)639-8500
Co. E-mail: email@sblc.org
URL: http://www.sblc.org
Contact: John Satagaj, President

Description: Serves as an independent coalition of trade and professional associations that share a common commitment to the future of small business. Represents the interests of small businesses in such diverse economic sectors as manufacturing, retailing, distribution, professional and technical services, construction, transportation, and agriculture. **Founded:** 1976.

REFERENCE WORKS

45261 ■ *"10 Trends That Are Shaping Global Media Consumption"* in *Advertising Age (Vol. 81, December 6, 2010, No. 43, pp. 3)*
Pub: Crain Communications, Inc.

Ed: Ann Marie Kerwin. **Description:** Ad Age offers the statistics from the TV penetration rate in Kenya to the number of World Cup watchers and more.

45262 ■ *"The ABCs of a Good Show"* in *Playthings (Vol. 106, October 1, 2008, No. 9, pp. 18)*
Pub: Reed Business Information
Contact: Jeff Greisch, President

Ed: Karyn M. Peterson. **Description:** ABC Kids Expo 2008 made a strong showing with products for babies, kids and new/expecting parents. The new Naturally Kids section promoting eco-friendly products was the highlight of the show.

45263 ■ *"Abroad, Not Overboard"* in *Entrepreneur (Vol. 36, April 2008, No. 4, pp. 68)*
Pub: Entrepreneur Media, Inc.

Ed: Crystal Detamore-Rodman. **Description:** Export-Import Bank is an agency created by the U.S. government to help exporters get credit insurance and capital loans by providing them with loan guarantees. The bank, being criticized as supporting more the bigger exporters, has allotted to smaller businesses a bigger portion of the annual credit being approved.

45264 ■ *The Age Curve: How to Profit from the Demographic Storm*
Pub: AMACOM

Ed: Kenneth W. Gronbach. **Released:** July 3, 2008. **Price:** $24.95. **Description:** Reveals how America's largest generations are redefining consumer behavior and how businesses can anticipate their growing needs more effectively.

45265 ■ *"Age-Old System of Bartering Is Being Revolutionized by Phoenix Company, Premier Barter"* in *Internet Wire (July 12, 2010)*
Pub: Comtex

Description: Premier Barter is helping entrepreneurs rediscover the system of bartering as a method of exchanging goods and services without cash or credit.

45266 ■ *"Agribusiness: How to Get Rich in Farming"* in *Canadian Business (Vol. 80, January 29, 2007, No. 3, pp. 42)*
Pub: Rogers Media

Ed: Peter Shawn Taylor. **Description:** The trends pertaining to the income of Canadian farmers are examined. The methods of increasing the profits of Canadian agribusinesses are discussed.

45267 ■ *"ALA: Hot Topics for Librarianship"* in *Information Today (Vol. 28, September 2011, No. 8, pp. 17)*
Pub: Information Today, Inc.

Ed: Barbara Brynko. **Description:** Highlights from the American Library Association Annual Conference and Exhibition are listed. Thousands of attendees sought out services, displays, demos, new product rollouts, and freebies. Emerging technology for librarians, staff development, gray literature, interlibrary loans, and next-generation interfaces were among the topics discussed.

45268 ■ *"All Eyes On Iris"* in *Canadian Business (Vol. 81, July 22, 2008, No. 12-13, pp. 20)*
Pub: Rogers Media Ltd.

Ed: Jack Mintz. **Description:** Provincial governments in Canada are believed to be awaiting Alberta Finance Minister Iris Evans' financial and investment policies as well as Evans' development of a new saving strategy. Alberta is the only Canadian province that is in position to invest in sovereign wealth funds after it eliminated its debt in 2005.

45269 ■ *"Alternative Energy Calls for Alternative Marketing"* in *Indoor Comfort Marketing (Vol. 70, June 2011, No. 6, pp. 8)*
Pub: Industry Publications Inc.

Ed: Richard Rutigliano. **Description:** Advice for marketing solar energy products and services is given.

45270 ■ *"Amid Recession, Companies Still Value Supplier Diversity Programs"* in *Hispanic Business (July-August 2009, pp. 34)*
Pub: Hispanic Business

Ed: Joshua Molina. **Description:** The decline of traditionally strong industries, from automotive manufacturing to construction, has shaken today's economy and has forced small businesses, especially suppliers and minority-owned firms, turn to diversity programs in order to make changes.

45271 ■ *"Amount Md. Pays to Unemployed Dips to Lowest Level Since '08"* in *Baltimore Business Journal (Vol. 28, November 12,*

2010, No. 27)
Pub: Baltimore Business Journal

Ed: Scott Dance. **Description:** Maryland paid out $50 million for unemployment benefits in September 2010 for its lowest payout since 2008. The drop in unemployment payout could mean lower taxes for employers who pay for the benefits. The unemployment rate in Maryland, however, increased to 7.5 percent.

45272 ■ *"Analysts: Intel Site May Be Last Major U.S.-Built Fab" in Business Journal-Serving Phoenix and the Valley of the Sun (Oct. 19, 2007)*
Pub: American City Business Journals, Inc.

Ed: Ty Young. **Description:** Intel's million-square-foot manufacturing facility, called Fab 32, is expected to open in 2007. The plant will mass-produce the 45-nanometer microchip. Industry analysts believe Fab 32 may be the last of its kind to be built in the U.S., as construction costs are higher in America than in other countries. Intel's future in Chandler is examined.

45273 ■ *"Analysts: More Mergers for the Region's Hospitals" in Boston Business Journal (Vol. 30, October 15, 2010, No. 36, pp. 1)*
Pub: Boston Business Journal

Ed: Julie M. Donnelly. **Description:** A number of hospitals in Boston, Massachusetts are engaging in mergers and acquisitions. Caritas Christi Health Care is set to be purchased by Cerberus Capital Management. The U.S. healthcare reform law is seen to drive the development.

45274 ■ *"App Time: Smartphone Applications Aren't Just for Fun and Games Anymore" in Inc. (Volume 32, December 2010, No. 10, pp. 116)*
Pub: Inc. Magazine

Ed: Jason Del Rey. **Description:** Smart phone technology can help any small business market their products and services.

45275 ■ *"Apparel" in Retail Merchandiser (Vol. 51, July-August 2011, No. 4, pp. 14)*
Pub: Phoenix Media Corporation

Description: NPD Group Inc. released current sales statistics for the women's apparel market along with men's apparel. It also reported annual shoes sales for 2010. Statistical data included.

45276 ■ *"Are Movie Theaters Doomed?" in Business Horizons (November-December 2007, pp. 491)*
Pub: Elsevier Technology Publications

Ed: Jon Silver, John McDonnell. **Description:** Theater operators must embrace new technologies and more diverse target markets if they are to stem the decline in theatergoers. Movie theaters remain highly vulnerable to trends in the home entertainment industry.

45277 ■ *"Are You Ignoring Trends That Could Shake Up Your Business?" in Harvard Business Review (Vol. 88, July-August 2010, No. 7-8, pp. 124)*
Pub: Harvard Business School Publishing

Ed: Elie Ofek, Luc Wathieu. **Description:** Ways for firms to capitalize on trends that might otherwise negatively affect their business are spotlighted. These include using certain aspects of the trend to augment traditional product/service offerings, and combining the trend with the offerings to transcend its traditional category.

45278 ■ *"As Capital Gains Tax Hike Looms, Merger Activity Percolates" in Baltimore Business Journal (Vol. 28, August 27, 2010, No. 16, pp. 1)*
Pub: Baltimore Business Journal

Ed: Scott Dance. **Description:** Concerns for higher capital gains taxes in 2011 have been provoking buyers and sellers to engage in mergers and acquisitions activity, which is expected to gain momentum before the end of 2010. Companies that had saved

cash during the recession have been taking advantage of the buyer's market. Other trends in local and national mergers and acquisitions activity are presented.

45279 ■ *"As Technology Changes, So Must African American Business" in Black Enterprise (Vol. 41, August 2010, No. 1, pp. 61)*
Pub: Earl G. Graves Publishing Co. Inc.

Ed: Sonya A. Donaldson. **Description:** Social media is essential to compete in today's business environment, especially for African American firms.

45280 ■ *"Ask Inc." in Inc. (October 2007, pp. 73-74)*
Pub: Gruner & Jahr USA Publishing

Description: An online marketing research firm investigates the use of online communities such as MySpace and Second life in order to recruit individuals to answer surveys.

45281 ■ *"Athletes Face Wins and Losses After Pro Sport" in The Business Journal - Serving Phoenix and the Valley of the Sun (Vol. 29, September 19, 2008, No. 3, pp. 1)*
Pub: American City Business Journals, Inc.

Ed: Chris Casacchia. **Description:** Professional athletes like hockey star Jeremy Roenick start businesses, while others like Joel Adamson work to boost local communities. Former athletes were found to be particularly interested with real estate businesses. Other views and information on former athletes and their life after sports are presented.

45282 ■ *"Attend To Your Corporate Housekeeping" in Women Entrepreneur (December 4, 2008)*
Pub: Entrepreneur Media Inc.

Ed: Nina Kaufman. **Description:** Business owners can lose all the benefits and privileges of the corporate form if they do not follow proper corporate formalities such as holding an annual meeting, electing officers and directors and adopting or passing corporate resolutions. Creditors are able to take from one's personal assets if such formalities have not been followed.

45283 ■ *"Attract More Online Customers: Make Your Website Work Harder for You" in Black Enterprise (Vol. 37, November 2006, No. 4, pp. 66)*
Pub: Earl G. Graves Publishing Co. Inc.

Description: Having an impressive presence on the Internet has become crucial. Detailed advice on making your website serve your business in the best way possible is included.

45284 ■ *"Attracting Veteran-Franchisees To Your System" in Franchising World (Vol. 42, November 2010, No. 11, pp. 53)*
Pub: International Franchise Association

Ed: Mary Kennedy Thompson. **Description:** As military servicemen and women return home, the franchising industry expects an increase in veterans as franchise owners. The Veterans Transition Franchise Initiative, also known as VetFran, is described.

45285 ■ *"Auto Supplier Stock Battered In Wake Of Wall Street Woes" in Crain's Detroit Business (Vol. 24, September 29, 2008, No. 39, pp. 4)*
Pub: Crain Communications Inc.

Ed: Ryan Beene. **Description:** Due to the volatility of the stock market and public perception of the $700 billion banking bailout, auto suppliers are now facing a dramatic drop in their shares. Statistical data included.

45286 ■ *"AVT Launches New ExpressPay Vending Systems" in Benzinga.com (July 13, 2011)*
Pub: Benzinga.com

Ed: Benzinga Staff. **Description:** AVT Inc. has developed a new high-tech vending system that features a touch screen interface and a cashless payment system so users can find what they want easily and pay using a credit card.

45287 ■ *"A Baby Step to the South" in Canadian Business (Vol. 81, July 22, 2008, No. 12-13, pp. 21)*
Pub: Rogers Media Ltd.

Ed: Jane Bao. **Description:** Canada's free trade agreement (FTA) with Colombia is seen as Canada's re-engagement with Latin America. Some politicians believe that the FTA is more of a political agreement than a trade agreement with Colombia. Key information on Canada's trade agreements, as well as trade with Colombia and Latin American countries, is presented.

45288 ■ *Back on the Career Track: A Guide for Stay-At-Home Moms Who Want to Return to Work*
Pub: Warner Books Inc.

Ed: Carol Fishman Cohen; Vivian Steir Rabin. **Released:** 2008. **Price:** $14.99 paperback. **Description:** For women like themselves who have rejoined the workforce after a prolonged absence, the authors detail seven main steps for reentry; profiles of six women who have successfully re-launched their careers are included.

45289 ■ *"Back on Track-Or Off the Rails?" in Business Week (September 22, 2008, No. 4100, pp. 22)*
Pub: McGraw-Hill Companies, Inc.

Ed: Peter Coy; Tara Kalwarski. **Description:** Discusses the possible scenarios the American economy may undergo due to the takeover of Fannie Mae and Freddie Mac. Statistical data included.

45290 ■ *"Bailout Forgets the 'Little Guys'" in The Business Journal-Milwaukee (Vol. 25, September 26, 2008, No. 53, pp. A1)*
Pub: American City Business Journals, Inc.

Ed: Rich Kirchen. **Description:** Community Bankers of Wisconsin and the Wisconsin Bankers Association are urging members to approach congressional representatives and remind them to include local banks in building the $700 billion bailout plan. WBA president and CEO Kurt Bauer thinks that it is only fair to include smaller institutions in the bailout. The initial bailout plan and its benefit for the smaller banks are examined.

45291 ■ *"Banking Bailout: Boost or Bust?" in Crain's Detroit Business (Vol. 24, September 29, 2008, No. 39, pp. 1)*
Pub: Crain Communications Inc.

Ed: Amy Lane. **Description:** Economic insiders discuss the banking bailout and how it might impact the state of Michigan.

45292 ■ *"Banking Crisis Rattles Local Businesses" in Puget Sound Business Journal (Vol. 29, October 10, 2008, No. 25, pp. 1)*
Pub: American City Business Journals

Ed: Kirsten Grind. **Description:** Customers of Washington Mutual in the Puget Sound region started withdrawing large sums of cash due to fears of the banks unstable condition.

45293 ■ *"Banking on Twitter" in Baltimore Business Journal (Vol. 27, February 6, 2010, No. 40, pp. 1)*
Pub: American City Business Journals

Ed: Gary Haber. **Description:** Ways that banks are using Twitter, Facebook and other social networking sites to provide customer services is discussed. First Mariner Bank is one of those banks that are finding the social media platform as a great way to reach customers. Privacy issues regarding this marketing trend are examined.

45294 ■ *"Bankruptcy Blowback" in Business Week (September 22, 2008, No. 4100, pp. 36)*
Pub: McGraw-Hill Companies, Inc.

Ed: Jessica Silver-Greenberg. **Description:** Changes to bankruptcy laws which were enacted in 2005 after banks and other financial institutions lobbied hard for them are now suffering the consequences of the laws which force more troubled borrowers to let their homes go into foreclosure; lenders suffer financially every time they have to take on a foreclosure and the laws in which they lobbied so hard to see enacted are now becoming a problem for these lending institutions. Details of the changes in the laws are outlined as are the affects on the consumer, the economy and the lenders.

45295 ■ "Banks Lower Rates on CDs, Deposits" in Baltimore Business Journal (Vol. 27, January 1, 2010, No. 35, pp. 1)
Pub: American City Business Journals
Ed: Gary Haber. Description: Greater Baltimore area banks in Maryland have lowered their rates on certificates of deposits (CDs) and money market accounts, which could indicate the incoming trend for the first half of 2010. A banking industry forecast shows that lower Federal Funds rate, low inflation, and a new Federal Deposit Insurance Corporation (FDIC) rule might cause the rates to drop even further. Details on the FDIC rule are given.

45296 ■ "Bartering Makes a Return in Hard Times" in Atlanta Journal-Constitution (October 2, 2010, pp. A15)
Pub: Atlanta Journal-Constitution
Ed: Bill York. Description: The advantages of bartering are explored.

45297 ■ "Bartering Trades on Talents" in Reading Eagle (June 20, 2010)
Pub: Reading Eagle/Reading Times
Ed: Tony Lucia. Description: Bartering is not just a way of trading goods and services, it can be an essential tool for small business to survive in a bad economy.

45298 ■ "Be Wary of Legal Advice on Internet, Lawyers Warn" in Crain's Detroit Business (Vol. 24, September 22, 2008, No. 38, pp. 16)
Pub: Crain Communications Inc.
Ed: Harriet Tramer. Description: While some lawyers feel that the proliferation of legal information on the Internet can point people in the right direction, others maintain that it simply results in giving false hope, may bring about confusion or worse yet, it sometimes makes their jobs even harder.

45299 ■ Behind the Cloud
Pub: Jossey-Bass
Ed: Marc Benioff, Carlye Adler. Released: 2010. Price: $27.95. Description: Salesforce.com is the world's most successful business-to-business cloud-computing company that sells an online service that helps businesses manage sales, customer service, and marketing functions.

45300 ■ "Beyond YouTube: New Uses for Video, Online and Off" in Inc. (October 2007, pp. 53-54)
Pub: Gruner & Jahr USA Publishing
Ed: Leah Hoffmann. Description: Small companies are using video technology for embedding messages into email, broadcasting live interactive sales and training seminars, as well as marketing campaigns. Experts offer insight into producing and broadcasting business videos.

45301 ■ Big-Box Swindle: The True Cost of Mega-Retailers and the Fight for America's Independent Businesses
Pub: Beacon Press
Ed: Stacy Mitchell. Released: October 2007. Price: $15.00. Description: Examination of the economic, environmental, and social damage done by big-box retailers like Wal-Mart, Costco, and Home Depot. Labor policies of these retailers, particularly those enforced by Wal-Mart, are discussed at length.

45302 ■ The Big Switch
Pub: W. W. Norton & Company, Inc.
Ed: Nicholas Carr. Released: January 19, 2009. Price: $16.95 paperback. Description: Today companies are dismantling private computer systems and tapping into services provided via the Internet. This shift is remaking the computer industry, bringing competitors such as Google to the forefront and threatening traditional companies like Microsoft and Dell. The book weaves together history, economics, and technology to explain why computing is changing and what it means for the future.

45303 ■ The Big Switch: Rewiring the World, From Edison to Google
Pub: W.W. Norton & Company
Ed: Nicholas Carr. Released: 2009. Price: $25.95. Description: Companies such as Google, Microsoft, and Amazon.com are building huge centers in order to create massive data centers. Together these centers form a giant computing grid that will deliver the digital universe to scientific labs, companies and homes in the future. This trend could bring about a new, darker phase for the Internet, one where these networks could operate as a fearsome entity that will dominate the lives of individuals worldwide.

45304 ■ "Bigger is Definitely Not Better When It Comes to Cooling" in Indoor Comfort Marketing (Vol. 70, May 2011, No. 5, pp. 49)
Pub: Industry Publications Inc.
Ed: Eugene Silberstein. Description: Efficiency is more important than size when installing air conditioning equipment over size of the unit. Details are provided.

45305 ■ "Bill Kaneko" in Hawaii Business (Vol. 53, December 2007, No. 6, pp. 32)
Pub: Hawaii Business Publishing
Ed: David K. Choo. Description: Hawaii Institute for Public Affairs chief executive officer and president Bill Kaneko believes that the Hawaiian economy is booming, however, he also asserts that the economy is too focused on tourism and real estate. Kaneko has also realized the that the will of the people is strong while he was helping with the Hawaiian 2050 Sustainability Plan. The difficulties of making a sustainable Hawaii are discussed.

45306 ■ "Biodiesel Poised to Regain Growth" in Farm Industry News (January 21, 2011)
Pub: Penton Business Media Inc.
Description: According to Gary Haer, vice president of sales and marketing for Renewable Energy Group, the biodiesel industry is positioned to regain growth in 2011 with the reinstatement of the biodiesel blendersa tax credt of $1 per gallon.

45307 ■ "Bioheat - Alternative for Fueling Equipment" in Indoor Comfort Marketing (Vol. 70, May 2011, No. 5, pp. 14)
Pub: Industry Publications Inc.
Ed: Gary Hess. Description: Profile of Worley and Obetz, supplier of biofuels used as an alternative for fueling industry equipment.

45308 ■ "Biotechs Are Using Back Door to Go Public" in Boston Business Journal (Vol. 31, May 27, 2011, No. 18, pp. 1)
Pub: Boston Business Journal
Ed: Julie M. Donnelly. Description: Members of Massachusetts' biotechnology sector have been engaging in reverse mergers as an alternative to initial public offerings. Reverse mergers provide access to institutional investors and hedge funds.

45309 ■ "Birdcage Optimization" in Pet Product News (Vol. 64, November 2010, No. 11, pp. 54)
Pub: BowTie Inc.
Description: Manufacturers have been emphasizing size, security, quality construction, stylish design, and quick cleaning when guiding consumers on making birdcage options. Selecting a birdcage is gaining importance considering that cage purchases have become the highest expense associated with owning a bird. Other avian habitat trends are also examined.

45310 ■ "Blue Hill Tavern to Host Baltimore's First Cupcake Camp" in Daily Record (August 10, 2011)
Pub: Dolan Company
Ed: Rachel Bernstein. Description: Cities joining the trend to host cupcake camps are listed. The camps are open to all individuals wishing to share and eat cupcakes in an open environment.

45311 ■ "Branding Your Way" in Canadian Business (Vol. 80, February 12, 2007, No. 4, pp. 31)
Pub: Rogers Media
Ed: Erin Pooley. Description: The trend in involving consumers in brand marketing by seeking their views through contests or inviting them to produce and submit commercials through Internet is discussed.

45312 ■ "Burger Market Sizzling with Newcomers" in Boston Business Journal (Vol. 29, June 10, 2011, No. 5, pp. 1)
Pub: American City Business Journals Inc.
Ed: Ryan Sharrow. Description: The burger trend in Maryland is on the rise with burger joints either opening up or expanding into several branches. Startup costs for this kind of business range between $250,000 to $400,000. With a growth rate of roughly 17 percent in 2009, this so-called better burger segment of the burger categories is expected to dominate the market for quite some time.

45313 ■ "Burner Handles Everything From #2 to B100" in Indoor Comfort Marketing (Vol. 70, May 2011, No. 5, pp. 24)
Pub: Industry Publications Inc.
Description: A new oil burner being offered by AMERIgreen Energy is profiled.

45314 ■ "Business Forecast: Stormy and Successful" in Women In Business (Vol. 62, June 2010, No. 2, pp. 12)
Pub: American Business Women's Association
Ed: Kathleen Leighton. Description: Stormy Simon, vice president of customer service at Overstock.com is a self-made career woman who started out as a temporary employee in the company in 2001. She was not able to attend college because she had two sons to care for after her divorce. Simon got involved in advertising and media buying and shares her love for business.

45315 ■ "Business Must Stand Up And Be Counted" in Crain's Detroit Business (Vol. 24, October 6, 2008, No. 40, pp. 6)
Pub: Crain Communications, Inc.
Description: Discusses the challenges that the new mayor of Detroit faces concerning business, the state of the economy and the exceptionally tight budget the city is running on, which includes a lot of red ink. It is very likely that the city is going to see tax revenues fall substantially in the next few months and business leaders may find it in their favor to lend their support to the new mayor as well as provide him with the executive talent necessary to overcome some of these crucial issues.

45316 ■ "Business Stands Firm for Reform" in Crain's Detroit Business (Vol. 26, January 4, 2010, No. 1, pp. 3)
Pub: Crain Communications, Inc.
Ed: Amy Lane. Description: As Michigan faces a new year of budgetary problems, many business groups are preparing to hold firm against tax increases and instead push for enacting spending reforms.

45317 ■ "Businesses Keep a Watchful Eye on Worker's Comp" in The Business Journal-Serving Greater Tampa Bay (September 5, 2008)
Pub: American City Business Journals, Inc.
Ed: Jane Meinhardt. Description: Pending a ruling from the Florida Supreme Court that could uphold the 2003 changes on workers' compensation law, the outcome would include restrictions on claimant attorneys' fees and allow the competitive workers' compensation insurance rates to remain low. However, insurance rates are expected to go up if the court overturns the changes.

45318 ■ "Buyers' Market" in Baltimore Business Journal (Vol. 27, November 20, 2009, No. 28, pp. 1)
Pub: American City Business Journals
Ed: Daniel J. Sernovitz. Description: Some business owners in Maryland are removing their leases and purchasing buildings due to the lower costs of real estate. This trend has enabled small business owners to avoid rent hikes, while setting equity into their companies. The pros and cons of owning buildings and how business owners assess their return on investment are examined.

45319 ■ "Buying Power of Hispanics Growing" in Austin Business JournalInc. (Vol. 29, November 27, 2009, No. 38, pp. 1)
Pub: American City Business Journals
Ed: Sandra Zaragoza. Description: Hispanic Marketing Symposium presented a report stating that the buying power of Hispanics of Austin, Texas has grown

by 54 percent in last five years to $9.4 billion in 2009. Details on the projected growth of the Hispanic market in the are is covered.

45320 ■ *"Buying Seed by Weight or By Count" in Farm Industry News (October 20, 2010)*
Pub: Penton Business Media Inc.

Ed: Mark Moore. **Description:** Soybean producers have the option of buying seeds by count or by weight; tips for either method of purchase are outlined.

45321 ■ *"Call of Prepaid Heard by More" in Chicago Tribune (November 26, 2008)*
Pub: McClatchy-Tribune Information Services

Ed: Wailin Wong. **Description:** Due to the economic downturn, more consumers are switching to no-contract, prepaid cell phone service. Customers find that the cost savings, flexibility and lack of contract are appealing in such uncertain times.

45322 ■ *"Campaigner Survey: 46 Percent of Small Businesses Use Email Marketing" in Wireless News (November 21, 2009)*
Pub: Close-Up Media

Description: Almost half (46 percent) of small businesses surveyed by Campaigner's 2009 State of Small Business Online Marketing, say that they rely on email marketing to help them find new customers, keep existing ones and grow their businesses. The survey also found that 36 percent of small businesses plan to begin using email marketing over the next year. The trend to utilize Internet marketing tools is allowing small businesses to grow faster and generate higher revenues than those that are not using these mediums.

45323 ■ *"Can HOAs Stop You From Going Green?" in Contractor (Vol. 56, July 2009, No. 7, pp. 39)*
Pub: Penton Media, Inc.

Ed: Susan Linden McGreevy. **Description:** There have been cases concerning homeowners' associations objections to the installation of wind turbines and solar panels. Precedence with the courts show that they will look at several factors when deciding to uphold restrictions on property use including whether the item encroaches on the rights of others, is likely to adversely affect property values, and also the state of enforcement.

45324 ■ *"Canada Tomorrow" in Canadian Business (Vol. 80, October 8, 2007, No. 20, pp. 14)*
Pub: Rogers Media

Ed: Donald J. Johnston. **Description:** An assessment of Canada's future in terms of its educational, social, and economic environment is presented. Concerns regarding the country's educational system such as the declining interest in science and technology and the possible lack of teachers in the future are discussed. In terms of its social and economic aspects, the need to support entrepreneurs and other qualified people is explained.

45325 ■ *"Canada's Oil Rush" in Canadian Business (Vol. 81, October 13, 2008, No. 17, pp. 58)*
Pub: Rogers Media Ltd.

Description: Excerpt from Andrew Nikiforuk's 'Tar Sands' details the exploration and development of oil sands in Alberta, Canada and its significance to the U.S. Canada has been the United State's largest supplier of oil since 2002, accounting for 18 percent of U.S. oil imports. Details regarding Canada's oil sand are examined.

45326 ■ *"Canadian Hydronics Businesses Promote 'Beautiful Heat" in Indoor Comfort Marketing (Vol. 70, September 2011, No. 9, pp. 20)*
Pub: Industry Publications Inc.

Description: Canadian hydronics companies are promoting their systems as beautiful heat. Hydronics is the use of water as the heat-transfer medium in heating and cooling system.

45327 ■ *"Capital Ideas: Regions to Lansing: Focus on Taxes, Reform, Keeping Talent" in Crain's Detroit Business (Vol. 24, October 6, 2008)*
Pub: Crain Communications, Inc.

Ed: Amy Lane. **Description:** Michigan must make bold and dramatic changes in public policy regarding business legislation. The tax structure, unemployment issues and attracting and retaining talent are among the issues the state must confront, especially in this tough economic climate.

45328 ■ *"Capturing Generation Y: Ready, Set, Transform" in Credit Union Times (Vol. 21, July 14, 2010, No. 27, pp. 20)*
Pub: Summit Business Media

Ed: Senthil Kumar. **Description:** The financial services sector recognizes that Generation Y will have a definite impact on the way business is conducted in the future. The mindset of Generation Y is social and companies need to use networking tools such as Facebook in order to reach this demographic.

45329 ■ *"Car Dealers Shift Gears to Survive" in Puget Sound Business Journal (Vol. 29, November 14, 2008, No. 30, pp. 1)*
Pub: American City Business Journals

Ed: Gregg Lamm. **Description:** Washington-based automobile dealers are offering incentives such as repairs, parts and used cars in order to supplement the decline in new car sales.

45330 ■ *"Carbon Trading: Current Schemes and Future Developments" in Energy Policy (Vol. 39, October 2011, No. 10, pp. 6040-6054)*
Pub: Reed Elsevier Reference Publishing

Ed: Slobodan Perdan, Adisa Azapagic. **Description:** Current and future developments regarding carbon trading is highlighted.

45331 ■ *The Catalyst Code: The Strategies Behind the World's Most Dynamic Companies*
Pub: Harvard Business School Press

Ed: David S. Evans; Richard Schmalensee. **Released:** May 9, 2007. **Price:** $29.95. **Description:** Economic catalysts businesses can bring consumers and merchants together in order to survive in an economy where markets, consumers and technology are always changing.

45332 ■ *"Cents and Sensibility" in Playthings (Vol. 107, January 1, 2009, No. 1, pp. 19)*
Pub: Reed Business Information
Contact: Jeff Greisch, President

Ed: Pamela Brill. **Description:** Recent concerns over safety, phthalate and lead paint and other toxic materials, as well as consumers going green, are issues discussed by toy manufacturers. Doll manufacturers also face increase labor and material costs and are working to design dolls that girls will love.

45333 ■ *Change in SMEs: The New European Capitalism*
Pub: Palgrave Macmillan

Ed: Katharina Bluhm; Rudi Schmidt. **Released:** October 2008. **Price:** $95.00. **Description:** Effects of global change on corporate governance, management, competitive strategies and labor relations in small-to-medium sized enterprises in various European countries are discussed.

45334 ■ *"Changing Fuel Compositions: What It Means To You and Your Business" in Indoor Comfort Marketing (Vol. 70, June 2011, No. 6, pp. 30)*
Pub: Industry Publications Inc.

Ed: Paul Nazzaro. **Description:** Biofuels are outlined and the way it is changing the HVAC/R industry are discussed.

45335 ■ *Chief Culture Officer: How to Create a Living, Breathing Corporation*
Pub: Basic Books

Ed: Grant McCracken. **Price:** $26.95. **Description:** Business consultant argues that corporations need to focus on 'reading' what's happening in the culture around them. Otherwise, companies will suffer the consequences, as Levi Strauss did when it missed out on the rise of hip-hop (and the baggy pants that are part of that lifestyle).

45336 ■ *"Child-Care Policy and the Labor Supply of Mothers with Young Children" in University of Chicago Press (Vol. 26, July 2008, No. 3)*
Pub: University of Chicago Press
Contact: Garrett P. Kiely, Director
E-mail: gkiely@press.uchicago.edu

Ed: Pierre Lefebvre, Philip Merrigan. **Description:** In 1997, the provincial government of Quebec, the second most populous province in Canada, initiated a new childcare policy. Licensed childcare service providers began offering day care spaces at the reduced fee of $5 per day per child for children aged four. By 2000, the policy applied to all children not in kindergarten. Using annual data (1993-2002) drawn from Statistics Canada's Survey of Labour and Income Dynamics, the results show that the policy had a large and statistically significant impact on the labor supply of mothers with preschool children.

45337 ■ *"Cincinnati's Senior Moment" in Business Courier (Vol. 27, June 11, 2010, No. 6, pp. 1)*
Pub: Business Courier

Ed: James Ritchie. **Description:** It is believed that the high demand in housing that will accompany the aging population has yet to arrive, and is not due for years to come. The next few years could lead to leaner times for long-standing independent-living properties and a slow climb for newer centers looking to build occupancy.

45338 ■ *Cities from the Arabian Desert: The Building of Jubail and Yanbu in Saudi Arabia*
Pub: Turnaround Associates

Ed: Andrea H. Pampanini. **Released:** May 2005. **Price:** $35.00. **Description:** An overview of Saudi Arabia's government to take control of the nation's natural resources and change the government, educational system, and its culture by evolving into a modern industrial society.

45339 ■ *"ClickFuel Unveils Internet Marketing Tools for Small Businesses" in Internet Wire (October 19, 2009)*
Pub: Comtex News Network, Inc.

Description: ClickFuel, a firm that manages, designs and tracks marketing campaigns has unveiled a full software suite of affordable services and technology solutions designed to empower small business owners and help them promote and grow their businesses through targeted Internet marketing campaigns.

45340 ■ *"Closing the Marketing Capabilities Gap" in Journal of Marketing (Vol. 75, July 2011, No. 4, pp. 183)*
Pub: American Marketing Association

Ed: George S. Day. **Description:** A look at the growing gap between the demands of the market and the capacity of organizations is presented. New thinking about marketing capabilities is needed to close the gap between the accelerating complexities of their market needs. The adaptive capabilities needed are vigilant market learning, adaptive market experimentation, and open marketing.

45341 ■ *"Clouds in the Forecast" in Information Today (Vol. 28, September 2011, No. 8, pp. 10)*
Pub: Information Today, Inc.

Ed: Paula J. Hane. **Description:** Cloud computing is software, applications, and data stored remotely and accessed via the Internet with output displayed on a client device. Recent developments in cloud computing are explored.

45342 ■ *"Collection Agency Issues Whitepaper on Legal and Ethical Methods of Collecting on Overdue Accounts" in Internet Wire (July 20, 2009)*
Pub: Comtex News Network, Inc.

Description: American Profit Recovery, a collection agency based in Massachusetts and Michigan, has updated and reissued a whitepaper on what businesses can and cannot do regarding conversing with their customers in an attempt to collect on overdue accounts and payments. A detailed summary on the federal laws associated with collecting on overdue accounts is outlined in such a way that any business owner, manager, or responsible party can easily understand.

45343 ■ *"Commentary. Economic Trends for Small Business" in Small Business Economic Trends (April 2008, pp. 3)*
Pub: National Federation of Independent Business
Ed: William C. Dunkelberg, Holly Wade. **Description:** Commentary on the economic trends for small businesses in the U.S. is presented. Analysis of recession possibilities is given. Reports indicate that the number of business owners citing inflation as their number one problem is at its highest point since 1982.

45344 ■ *"Commentary. On Federal Reserve's Cut of Interest Rates" in Small Business Economic Trends (January 2008, pp. 3)*
Pub: National Federation of Independent Business
Description: Federal Reserve cut interest rates and announced its economic outlook on September 18, 2007 to stimulate spending. The cut in interest rates, however, may not help in supporting consumer spending because savers may lose interest income. The expected economic impact of the interest rate cuts and the U.S. economic outlook are also discussed.

45345 ■ *"Commentary. Small Business Economic Trends" in Small Business Economic Trends (March 2008, pp. 3)*
Pub: National Federation of Independent Business
Ed: William C. Dunkelberg, Holly Wade. **Description:** Commentary on the economic trends for small businesses in the U.S. is presented. Analysis of the labor market and low interest rates is given. The effect of the Federal Reserve's policy announcement on small business owner optimism is also discussed.

45346 ■ *"Commentary. Small Business Economic Trends" in Small Business Economic Trends (February 2008, pp. 3)*
Pub: National Federation of Independent Business
Ed: William C. Dunkelberg, Holly Wade. **Description:** Commentary on the economic trends for small businesses in the U.S. is presented. Analysis of the U.S. Federal Reserve Board's efforts to prevent a recession is given. Reduction in business inventories is also discussed.

45347 ■ *"Commotion Pictures; Bill C-10: Is It Censorship or Merely Inept?" in Canadian Business (Vol. 81, March 31, 2008, No. 5, pp. 10)*
Pub: Rogers Media
Ed: Denis Seguin. **Description:** Filmmakers are claiming that Bill C-10 amounts to censorship as it could retract a production's eligibility for a tax credit if it is deemed offensive. However, the bill's backers say that the bill protects against tax dollars being directed at productions that run contrary to public policy.

45348 ■ *The Company We Keep: Reinventing Small Business for People, Community, and Place*
Pub: Chelsea Green Publishing
Ed: John Abrams, William Grieder. **Released:** June 2006. **Price:** $18.00. **Description:** The new business trend in social entrepreneurship as a business plan enables small business owners to meet the triple bottom line of profits for people (employees and owners), community, and the environment.

45349 ■ *"Competition At Last?" in Canadian Business (Vol. 81, July 22, 2008, No. 12-13, pp. 7)*
Pub: Rogers Media Ltd.
Description: Competition Policy Review Panel's 'Compete to Win' report revealed that Canada is being 'hollowed-out' by foreign acquisitions. The panel investigated competition and foreign investment policies in Canada. Key information on the report, as well as views on the Investment Canada Act and the Competition Act, is presented.

45350 ■ *"Congress Ponders Annuity Trusts" in National Underwriter Life & Health (Vol. 114, June 21, 2010, No. 12, pp. 10)*
Pub: Summit Business Media
Ed: Arthur D. Postal. **Description:** Congress is looking over several bills, including the Small Business Jobs Tax Relief Act that would significantly narrow the advantages of using grantor-retained annuity trusts (GRATs) to avoid estate and gift taxes.

45351 ■ *"Consumers Like Green, But Not Mandates" in Business Journal-Milwaukee (Vol. 28, December 10, 2010, No. 10, pp. A1)*
Pub: Milwaukee Business Journal
Ed: Sean Ryan. **Description:** Milwaukee, Wisconsin consumers are willing to spend more on green energy, a survey has revealed. Respondents also said they will pay more for efficient cars and appliances. Support for public incentives for homeowners and businesses that reduce energy use has also increased.

45352 ■ *"Consumers Who Saw a Food Truck This Summer" in Nation's Restaurant News (Vol. 45, September 26, 2011, No. 20, pp. 8)*
Pub: Penton Media Inc.
Contact: John French, President
Description: A guide to the number of customers encountering food trucks during summer 2011 is presented by region.

45353 ■ *"Convenience Store Deal for Cardtronics" in American Banker (Vol. 174, July 28, 2009, No. 143, pp. 12)*
Pub: SourceMedia, Inc.
Description: Royal Buying Group, Inc., a convenience store marketing company, has agreed to recommend automated teller machine services from Cardtronics Inc., to its clients.

45354 ■ *"Corporate Diversity Driving Profits" in Hispanic Business (Vol. 30, September 2008, No. 9, pp. 12)*
Pub: Hispanic Business, Inc.
Ed: Michael Bowker. **Description:** U.S. businesses are beginning to appreciate the importance of diversity and are developing strategies to introduce a diverse workforce that reflects the cultural composition of their customers. The realization that diversity increases profits and the use of professional networks to recruit and retain skilled minority employees are two other new trends impacting corporate diversity in the U.S.

45355 ■ *"COSE: More Small Companies Offering Wellness Plans" in Crain's Cleveland Business (Vol. 28, December 3, 2007, No. 48, pp. 22)*
Pub: Crain Communications, Inc.
Ed: Shannon Mortland. **Description:** Discusses the Council of Smaller Enterprises (COSE) which is offering incentives to companies who implement wellness programs and can show that their employees are living healthier lives.

45356 ■ *"Countdown" in Canadian Business (Vol. 81, March 3, 2008, No. 3, pp. 27)*
Pub: Rogers Media
Ed: Al Rosen. **Description:** According to a recent poll only 42 percent of portfolio managers in Canada are aware that the country is planning to adopt the International Financial Reporting Standards beginning 2011. The shift to the new standards will have significant impacts on investment values and will be the biggest revolution in Canadian financial reporting. The effects of the transition on portfolio managers and investors are analyzed.

45357 ■ *"Counter Service" in Nation's Restaurant News (Vol. 45, September 26, 2011, No. 20, pp. 8)*
Pub: Penton Media Inc.
Contact: John French, President
Description: As food trucks continue their momentum, a study was conducted showing how many consumer would visit a food truck. Nearly two thirds of 18-44 year olds would likely visit a food truck, while individuals over the age of 65 only 38 percent would eat from a food truck.

45358 ■ *"Counter Service: We Gear Up Some Food Truck Stats" in Nation's Restaurant News (Vol. 45, August 8, 2011, No. 16, pp. 6)*
Pub: Penton Media Inc.
Contact: John French, President
Description: According to a recent survey, people do not see food truck service as a trend and 84 percent of social media users said they would visit food trucks at least once a week.

45359 ■ *Creating a World without Poverty: Social Business and the Future of Capitalism*
Pub: Basic Books
Released: April 26, 2009. **Price:** $26.00. **Description:** Explanation of how microcredit lending practices and more collaborative business strategies can be used to alleviate poverty worldwide.

45360 ■ *"Credit Crunch Gives, Takes Away" in The Business Journal-Serving Metropolitan Kansas City (Vol. 27, October 17, 2008, No. 5, pp. 1)*
Pub: American City Business Journals, Inc.
Ed: Suzanna Stagemeyer. **Description:** Although many Kansas City business enterprises have been adversely affected by the U.S. credit crunch, others have remained relatively unscathed. Examples of how local businesses are being impacted by the crisis are provided including: American Trailer & Storage Inc., which declared bankruptcy after failing to pay a long-term loan; and NetStandard, a technology firm who, on the other hand, is being pursued by prospective lenders.

45361 ■ *"Credit Unions Buck Trend, Lend Millions More" in Saint Louis Business Journal (Vol. 32, September 9, 2011, No. 2, pp. 1)*
Pub: Saint Louis Business Journal
Ed: Greg Edwards. **Description:** St. Louis, Missouri-based credit unions have been making more loans despite the weak economy. Credit unions have made a total of $3.46 billion in outstanding loans as of June 30, 2011.

45362 ■ *"Credit Unions Gain: New Members Sign Up, Fleeing Banks" in Puget Sound Business Journal (Vol. 29, October 10, 2008, No. 25, pp. 1)*
Pub: American City Business Journals
Ed: Kirsten Grind. **Description:** Credit unions are gaining new members due to customers' lack of confidence in federal banks.

45363 ■ *"The Critical Need to Reinvent Management" in Business Strategy Review (Vol. 21, Spring 2010, No. 1, pp. 4)*
Pub: Wiley-Blackwell
Ed: Julian Birkinshaw. **Description:** The author believes that management is undervalued today - and for good reasons. Management, he says, has failed at the big-picture level and thinks it is time to reinvent the profession.

45364 ■ *Crowdsourcing: Why the Power of the Crowd is Driving the Future of Business*
Pub: Crown Business
Ed: Jeff Howe. **Released:** 2009. **Price:** $26.95. **Description:** Small businesses are shown how to use social networks online to promote goods and services.

45365 ■ *"Crude Awakening" in Canadian Business (Vol. 81, October 27, 2008, No. 18, pp. 14)*
Pub: Rogers Media Ltd.
Ed: Jeff Sanford. **Description:** Jim Grays believes that a global liquid fuels crisis is coming and hopes the expected transition from oil dependence will be smooth. Charles Maxwell, on the other hand, predicts that a new world economy will arrive in three waves. Views of both experts are examined.

45366 ■ *"Cupcake Craze" in Mail Tribune (March 2, 2011)*
Pub: Southern Oregon Media Group
Ed: Sarah Lemon. **Description:** Gourmet cupcake shops are sprouting up in large cities in Oregon. The Cupcake Company, a family business, is profiled.

45367 ■ *"A Curious Appeal (Market for Scientific Toys)" in Playthings (Vol. 106, October 1, 2008, No. 9, pp. 26)*
Pub: Reed Business Information
Contact: Jeff Greisch, President
Ed: Pamela Brill. **Description:** Science and nature toys are still popular with children. Kits allow kids to make candy, soap, grow miniature gardens, catch bugs and more. These hands-on kits have manufacturers watching trends to create more toys in this category.

45368 ■ *"Currency: I'm Otta Here" in Entrepreneur (Vol. 35, October 2007, No. 10, pp. 72)*
Pub: Entrepreneur Media Inc.
Ed: C.J. Prince. **Description:** Liberum Research revealed that 193 chief financial officers (CFOs) at small companies have either resigned or retired during the first half of 2007. A survey conducted by Tatum found that unreasonable expectations from the management and compliance to regulations are the main reasons why CFOs are leaving small firms. The chief executive officer's role in making CFOs stay is also discussed.

45369 ■ *Currency Internationalization: Global Experiences and Implications for the Renminbi*
Pub: Palgrave Macmillan
Ed: Wensheng Peng, Chang Shu. **Released:** January 5, 2010. **Price:** $100.00. **Description:** A collection of academic studies relating to the potential internationalization of China's remnibi. It also discusses the increasing use of China's remnibi currency in international trade and finance.

45370 ■ *"Daddy's Home! Fathers Stay Home To Watch the Kids and Build Businesses To Suit Their Values" in Black Enterprise (October 2007)*
Pub: Earl G. Graves Publishing Co. Inc.
Ed: George Alexander. **Description:** Fathers are staying home and running home-based businesses in order to spend more time with their families.

45371 ■ *"A Day Late and a Dollar Short" in Indoor Comfort Marketing (Vol. 70, March 2011, No. 3, pp. 30)*
Pub: Industry Publications Inc.
Ed: Philip J. Baratz. **Description:** A discussion involving futures options and fuel oil prices is presented.

45372 ■ *"Dealers Trying Not to Fold" in Business First Columbus (Vol. 25, December 5, 2008, No. 15, pp. A1)*
Pub: American City Business Journals
Ed: Dan Eaton. **Description:** Increase in the number of automobile dealer closures in Ohio is seen to impact the state's economy. The trend of consolidation is forecasted to adversely affect employment and sales. Statistical data included.

45373 ■ *"Death of the PC" in Canadian Business (Vol. 83, October 12, 2010, No. 17, pp. 44)*
Pub: Rogers Media Ltd.
Ed: Joe Castaldo. **Description:** The future of the personal computer (PC) is looking bleak as consumers are relying more on new mobile devices instead of their PC. A 'Wall Street Journal' article published in September 2010 reported that the iPad had cannibalized sales of laptops by as much as 50 percent. The emergence of tablet computers running alternative operating systems is also explained.

45374 ■ *"Defying Gravity?" in Canadian Business (Vol. 81, October 13, 2008, No. 17, pp. 17)*
Pub: Rogers Media Ltd.
Ed: Joe Castaldo. **Description:** Airlines around the world are expected to lose $4.1 billion in 2009, but experts believe Canadian airlines will be able to survive the economic challenges. Lower demand for air travel and uncertainty on oil prices are also expected to make the conditions more challenging. Views and key information on airlines in Canada and around the world are cited.

45375 ■ *"Despite Economic Upheaval Generation Y is Still Feeling Green: RSA Canada Survey" in CNW Group (October 28, 2010)*
Pub: CNW Group
Contact: Carolyn McGill-Davidson, President
Description: Canadian Generation Y individuals believe it is important for their company to be environmentally-friendly and one-third of those surveyed would quit their job if they found their employer was environmentally irresponsible, despite the economy.

45376 ■ *"The Digital Revolution is Over. Long Live the Digital Revolution!" in Business Strategy Review (Vol. 21, Spring 2010, No. 1, pp. 74)*
Pub: Wiley-Blackwell
Ed: Gianvito Lanzolla, Jamie Anderson. **Description:** Many businesses are now involved in the digital marketplace. The authors argue that the new reality of numerous companies offering overlapping products means that it is critical for managers to understand digital convergence and to observe the imperatives for remaining competitive.

45377 ■ *"Do the Math on Discounts" in Entrepreneur (Vol. 37, October 2009, No. 10, pp. 82)*
Pub: Entrepreneur Media, Inc.
Ed: Jennifer Lawler. **Description:** Small business owners should consider all effects of discounts before implementing them. Some entrepreneurs do not discount prices for fear of damaging brands or their company's reputation.

45378 ■ *"Docs Might Hold Cure for Real Estate, Banks" in Baltimore Business Journal (Vol. 28, November 5, 2010, No. 26, pp. 1)*
Pub: Baltimore Business Journal
Ed: Gary Haber. **Description:** Health care providers, including physicians are purchasing their office space instead of renting it as banks lower interest rates to 6 percent on mortgages for medical offices. The rise in demand offers relief to the commercial real estate market. It has also resulted in a boom in building new medical offices.

45379 ■ *"Doctors Buy In to Medical Timeshares" in Houston Business Journal (Vol. 40, December 11, 2009, No. 31, pp. 1)*
Pub: American City Business Journals
Ed: Mary Ann Azevedo. **Description:** Memorial Hermann Hospital System has leased to doctors three examination rooms and medical office space in the Memorial Hermann Medical Plaza in line with its new timeshare concept. The concept was designed to bring primary care physicians to its Texas Medical Center campus.

45380 ■ *"Doctors Eye Rating Plan With Caution" in The Business Journal-Portland (Vol. 25, July 4, 2008, No. 17, pp. 1)*
Pub: American City Business Journals, Inc.
Ed: Robin J. Moody. **Description:** Doctors in Portland, Oregon are wary of a new Providence Health Plan system that rates their performance on patients with certain medical conditions. The system is expected to discourage wasteful procedures, thereby, saving employers' money. Other mechanics of the rating system are also discussed.

45381 ■ *"DOE Proposes New Water Heater Efficiency Standards" in Contractor (Vol. 57, January 2010, No. 1, pp. 3)*
Pub: Penton Media, Inc.
Ed: Robert P. Mader. **Description:** U.S. Department of Energy is proposing higher efficiency standards for gas and electric water heaters which will not take effect until 2015. The proposal calls for gas-fired storage water heaters less than 60 gallons to have an Energy Factor of 0.675 and those larger than 60 gallons to have an Energy Factor of 0.717.

45382 ■ *"Doing the Right Thing" in Black Enterprise (Vol. 38, July 2008, No. 12, pp. 50)*
Pub: Earl G. Graves Publishing Co. Inc.
Ed: Tamara E. Holmes. **Description:** More business owners are trying to become more environmentally friendly, either due to their belief in social responsibil-

ity or for financial incentives or for both reasons. Tips for making one's business more environmentally responsible are included as well as a listing of resources that may be available to help owners in their efforts.

45383 ■ *"Doing Without" in Baltimore Business Journal (Vol. 28, June 11, 2010, No. 5, pp. 1)*
Pub: Baltimore Business Journal
Ed: Scott Graham. **Description:** Maryland Health Care Commission report figures have shown only 47,661 small businesses provided some level of health coverage to 381,517 employees in 2009. These numbers are down from 51,283 employers who offered benefits to 407,983 employees in 2008 to highlight a disturbing trend in Maryland's small-group insurance market. Reasons for the drop are discussed.

45384 ■ *"Don't Expect Quick Fix" in The Business Journal-Serving Metropolitan Kansas City (Vol. 27, October 3, 2008, No. 3, pp. 1)*
Pub: American City Business Journals, Inc.
Ed: James Dornbrook. **Description:** United States governmental entities cannot provide a quick fix solution to the current financial crisis. The economy requires a systemic change in the way people think about credit. The financial services industry should also focus on core lending principles.

45385 ■ *Earth: The Sequel*
Pub: W. W. Norton & Company, Inc.
Ed: Fred Krupp; Miriam Horn. **Released:** March 16, 2009. **Price:** $15.95. **Description:** President of the Environmental Defense Fund offers suggestions for small businesses to help solve global warming. Investigation into the new industries, jobs, and opportunities is provided.

45386 ■ *"eBay Introduces Open Commerce Ecosystem" in Entertainment Close-Up (October 24, 2011)*
Pub: Close-Up Media
Description: eBay's new X.commerce is an open commerce ecosystem that will arm developers and merchants with the technology tools required to keep pace with the ever-changing industry. X.commerce brings together the technology assets and developer communities of eBay, PayPal, Magento and partners to expand on eBays vision for enabling commerce.

45387 ■ *"Economic Outlook 2009" in Hispanic Business (January-February 2009, pp. 30, 32)*
Pub: Hispanic Business
Ed: Dr. Juan Solana. **Description:** Successful business policies of the past no longer work in this economic climate. New tools and initiatives regarding monetary policy, fiscal policy and a higher multiplier are required to survive the crisis.

45388 ■ *"Economic Trends for Small Business" in Small Business Economic Trends (April 2008, pp. 1)*
Pub: National Federation of Independent Business
Ed: William C. Dunkelberg, Holly Wade. **Description:** Summary of economic trends for small businesses in the U.S. is presented. Economic indicators such as capital spending, inventories and sales, inflation, and profits are given. Analysis of credit markets is also provided.

45389 ■ *Ecopreneuring: Putting Purpose and the Planet Before Profits*
Pub: New Society Publishers
Ed: John Ivanko; Lisa Kivirist. **Released:** July 1, 2008. **Price:** $17.95 paperback. **Description:** Ecopreneurs in America are shifting profits and market share towards green living. The book provides a guideline for ecopreneurs in the areas of eco-business basics, purposeful management, marketing in the green economy, and running a lifestyle business.

45390 ■ *"Effort Is Growing to Offer Healthier Choices in Vending Machines" in Philadelphia*

Inquirer (July 29, 2011)
Pub: Philadelphia Media Network Inc.

Ed: Don Sapatkin. **Description:** Since Boston's mayor announced a ban on the sale of all sugar sweetened beverages on city properties, it seems more cities, states, hospitals, businesses, and even park systems are following suit. Thus, vending machines are beginning to offer healthier snacks and drinks to consumers.

45391 ■ *"Election Could Undo Renewable Energy Quotas" in The Business Journal - Serving Phoenix and the Valley of the Sun (Vol. 28, July 11, 2008, No. 45, pp. 1)*
Pub: American City Business Journals, Inc.

Ed: Patrick O'Grady. **Description:** Competition for the three open seats in the Arizona Corporation Commission is intense, with 12 candidates contesting for the three slots. The commission's mandates for renewable energy and infrastructure investment will also be at stake.

45392 ■ *Electronic Commerce*
Pub: Course Technology

Ed: Gary Schneider, Bryant Chrzan, Charles McCormick. **Released:** May 1, 2010. **Price:** $117.95. **Description:** E-commerce can open the door to more opportunities than ever before for small business. Packed with real-world examples and cases, the book delivers comprehensive coverage of emerging online technologies and trends and their influence on the electronic marketplace. It details how the landscape of online commerce is evolving, reflecting changes in the economy and how business and society are responding to those changes. Balancing technological issues with the strategic business aspects of successful e-commerce, the new edition includes expanded coverage of international issues, social networking, mobile commerce, Web 2.0 technologies, and updates on spam, phishing, and identity theft.

45393 ■ *The Elephant and the Dragon: The Rise of India and China and What It Means to All of Us*
Pub: W.W. Norton & Company

Ed: Robyn Meredith. **Released:** 2008. **Price:** $15.95. **Description:** The author illustrates how both China and India have followed their own economic path, and examines the countries' similarities and considers the repercussions of their growing involvement in the world market.

45394 ■ *Emerging Business Online: Global Markets and the Power of B2B Internet Marketing*
Pub: FT Press

Ed: Lara Fawzy, Lucas Dworksi. **Released:** October 1, 2010. **Price:** $49.99. **Description:** An introduction into ebocube (emerging business online), a comprehensive proven business model for Internet B2B marketing in emerging markets.

45395 ■ *The Emerging Digital Economy: Entrepreneurship, Clusters, and Policy*
Pub: Springer

Ed: Borje Johansson; Charlie Karlsson; Roger Stough. **Released:** August 2006. **Price:** $119.00. **Description:** The new economy, or digital economy, and its impact on the way industries and firms choose to locate and cluster geographically.

45396 ■ *The Emerging Markets Century: How a New Breed of World-Class Companies is Overtaking the World*
Pub: Free Press/Simon & Schuster Inc.

Ed: Antoine van Agtmael. **Released:** 2007. **Price:** $29.00. **Description:** An exploration of how companies like Lenovo and Haier who are presently in emerging economies are already competing with household name brands like Ford and Sony, thus proving globalization is here to stay.

45397 ■ *"Eminent Domain Fight Looks Imminent" in The Business Journal-Serving Metropolitan Kansas City (Vol. 26, August 1,*

2008, No. 47)
Pub: American City Business Journals, Inc.

Ed: Rob Roberts. **Description:** Views and information on the proposed constitutional amendments that will limit the use of eminent domain in Missouri, are presented. The proposals are expected to largely ban the taking of private property for private development. It may be included in a November 4,2008 statewide vote for approval.

45398 ■ *"Employers See Workers' Comp Rates Rising" in Sacramento Business Journal (Vol. 28, April 8, 2011, No. 6, pp. 1)*
Pub: Sacramento Business Journal

Ed: Kelly Johnson. **Description:** Employers in California are facing higher workers compensation costs. Increased medical costs and litigation are seen to drive the trend.

45399 ■ *"Employers Tied in Knots" in Sacramento Business Journal (Vol. 25, August 15, 2008, No. 24, pp. 1)*
Pub: American City Business Journals, Inc.

Ed: Kathy Robertson. **Description:** Conflicting laws on same sex marriage have been posing problems for companies, and insurers in California. The court ruling that allowed gay marriages has created differences between state and federal laws. Federal laws on same-sex spouse taxation are also seen to complicate the issue.

45400 ■ *"EPA 'Finalizes' WaterSense for Homes" in Contractor (Vol. 57, January 2010, No. 1, pp. 70)*
Pub: Penton Media, Inc.

Ed: Bob Mader. **Description:** U.S. Environmental Protection Agency released its 'final' version of the WaterSense for Homes standard. The standard's provisions that affect plumbing contractors includes the specification that everything has to be leak tested and final service pressure cannot exceed 60 psi.

45401 ■ *"An Equity Fund of Their Own" in Entrepreneur (Vol. 35, October 2007, No. 10, pp. 68)*
Pub: Entrepreneur Media Inc.

Ed: Lee Gimpel. **Description:** About 100 new private equity funds have formed since 2002, proof that private equity investing is becoming popular among companies. There is also an increase in competition to close deals owing to the large number of investors that companies can choose; advantages of smaller funds over the larger one is explained.

45402 ■ *"Every Year, Thousands of People Are Killed By Pathogens In Food. William Hanson Wants To Help" in Inc. (November 2007, pp. 46-47)*
Pub: Gruner & Jahr USA Publishing

Ed: Dalia Fahmy. **Description:** OmniFresh 1000 System tests produce for pathogens such as E.coli and salmonella. The firm is able to test for these pathogens in two hours compared to traditional tests that take as many as three days. Each year some 5,000 Americans die from food-borne diseases.

45403 ■ *"Exiting Stage Left" in Baltimore Business Journal (Vol. 28, June 18, 2010, No. 6, pp. 1)*
Pub: Baltimore Business Journal

Ed: Scott Dance. **Description:** Film professionals including crew members and actors have been leaving Maryland to find work in other states such as Michigan, Louisiana, and Georgia where bigger budgets and film production incentives are given. Other consequences of this trend in local TV and film production are discussed.

45404 ■ *"Expert Sees No Radical Reform of 401(K) System" in Workforce Management (Vol. 88, November 16, 2009, No. 12, pp. 12)*
Pub: Crain Communications Inc.

Ed: Ed Frauenheim. **Description:** Although many would like to see an overhaul of the 401(k) retirement system, it is unlikely to occur anytime soon; however, the drastic stock market drop of 2008 has raised pointed questions about the 401(k) system and if it enables a secure retirement for American workers.

45405 ■ *"Experts Strive to Educate on Proper Pet Diets" in Pet Product News (Vol. 64, November 2010, No. 11, pp. 40)*
Pub: BowTie Inc.

Ed: John Hustace Walker. **Description:** Pet supply manufacturers have been bundling small mammal food and treats with educational sources to help retailers avoid customer misinformation. This action has been motivated by the customer's quest to seek proper nutritional advice for their small mammal pets.

45406 ■ *"Experts Take the Temp of Obama Plan" in The Business Journal-Serving Metropolitan Kansas City (Vol. 27, November 14, 2008, No. 10)*
Pub: American City Business Journals, Inc.

Ed: Rob Roberts. **Description:** Kansas City, Missouri-based employee benefits experts say president-elect Barack Obama's health care reform plan is on track. Insurance for children and capitalization for health information technology are seen as priority areas. The plan is aimed at reducing the number of uninsured people in the United States.

45407 ■ *"Face Values: Responsibility Inc" in Business Strategy Review (Vol. 21, Summer 2010, No. 2, pp. 66)*
Pub: Wiley-Blackwell

Ed: John Connolly. **Description:** Investment and growth in emerging markets will bring new opportunities, but with them added responsibility. Will companies be able to rise to meet the new responsibility agenda?.

45408 ■ *"Facebook: A Promotional Budget's Best Friend" in Women Entrepreneur (February 1, 2009)*
Pub: Entrepreneur Media Inc.

Ed: Tamara Monosoff. **Description:** Facebook began as a social networking website but has become a valuable marketing tool for all types of businesses, organizations and causes. Tips are provided for creating a Facebook account and growing one's network on Facebook.

45409 ■ *The Facebook Effect: The Inside Story of the Company That Is Connecting the World*
Pub: Simon & Shuster

Ed: David Kirkpatrick. **Released:** June 8, 2010. **Price:** $26.00. **Description:** There's never been a Website like Facebook: more than 350 million people have accounts, and if the growth rate continues, by 2013 every Internet user worldwide will have his or her own page. No one's had more access to the inner workings of the phenomenon than Kirkpatrick, a senior tech writer at Fortune magazine. Written with the full cooperation of founder Mark Zuckerberg, the book follows the company from its genesis in a Harvard dorm room through its successes over Friendster and MySpace, the expansion of the user base, and Zuckerberg's refusal to sell.

45410 ■ *"Fair Tax Backers Hope MBT Anger Will Bring Votes" in Crain's Detroit Business (Vol. 24, March 31, 2008, No. 13, pp. 32)*
Pub: Crain Communications, Inc.

Description: Discusses the Michigan Fair Tax Proposal which would eliminate Michigan's business taxes and income tax, raise the state sales tax to 9.75 percent and expand it to services.

45411 ■ *"Falling Local Executive Pay Could Suggest a Trend" in Tampa Bay Business Journal (Vol. 30, January 15, 2010, No. 4, pp. 1)*
Pub: American City Business Journals

Ed: Margie Manning. **Description:** Tampa Bay, Florida-based Raymond James Financial Inc. and MarineMax Inc.'s proxy statements have shown the decreasing compensation of the companies' highest paid executives. The falling trend in executive compensation was a result of intensified shareholder scrutiny and the economy.

45412 ■ *"Family Business Research" in International Journal of Entrepreneurship and*

Small Business (Vol. 12, December 3, 2010, No. 1)
Pub: Publishers Communication Group
Ed: A. Bakr Ibrahim, Jean B. McGuire. **Description:** Assessment of the growing field of family business and suggestions for an integrated framework. The paper addresses a number of key issues facing family business research.

45413 ■ *"Faster and Shorter" in Canadian Business (Vol. 81, October 13, 2008, No. 17, pp. 25)*
Pub: Rogers Media Ltd.
Ed: Terri Goveia. **Description:** Study revealed that instant messaging (IM) technologies are slowly becoming legitimate in the corporate world. IM is traditionally considered as a distraction, but it was found to let workers make targeted inquiries that gives them what they need in an instant. Other views and information about IMs is included.

45414 ■ *"Fifty Percent of Global Online Retail Visits Were to Amazon, eBay and Alibaba in June 2011" in Benzinga.com (October 29, 2011)*
Pub: Benzinga.com
Ed: Benzinga Staff. **Description:** Current statistics and future forecasts through the year 2015 for Amazon, eBay and Alibaba are explored.

45415 ■ *"Fight Against Fake" in The Business Journal-Portland (Vol. 25, July 18, 2008, No. 19, pp. 1)*
Pub: American City Business Journals, Inc.
Ed: Erik Siemers. **Description:** Companies, such as Columbia Sportswear Co. and Nike Inc., are fighting the counterfeiting of their sportswear and footwear products through the legal process of coordinating with law enforcement agencies to raid factories. Most of the counterfeiting factories are in China and India. Other details on the issue are discussed.

45416 ■ *"Film Incentives: A Hit or a Flop?" in Michigan Vue (Vol. 13, July-August 2008, No. 4, pp. 10)*
Pub: Entrepreneur Media Inc.
Description: Michigan's new film incentive legislation is fulfilling its core purpose, according to Lisa Dancsok of the Michigan Economic Development Corp. (MEDC), by kickstarting the state's entry into the multi-billion dollar industry; the initiative is considered to be very competitive with other states and countries and is thought to be a way in which to help revitalize Michigan's struggling economy.

45417 ■ *"Final State Budget Is a Mixed Bag of Key Industries" in The Business Journal - Serving Phoenix and the Valley of the Sun (Vol. 28, July 4, 2008, No. 44, pp. 3)*
Pub: American City Business Journals, Inc.
Ed: Mike Sunnucks; Patrick O'Grady. **Description:** Approved by Governor Janet Napolitano and passed by the Arizona Legislature, the $9.9 billion state budget is beneficial to some industries in the business community. The tax cap for on Arizona Lottery has been removed which is beneficial to the industry, while the solar energy industry and real estate developers stand to lose from the spending bill. Other details of the finance budget are presented.

45418 ■ *"Fitter from Twitter" in Boston Business Journal (Vol. 30, December 17, 2010, No. 47, pp. 1)*
Pub: Boston Business Journal
Ed: Lisa van der Pool. **Description:** Small businesses are increasing their use of the Twitter microblogging platform to attract and retain customers. Lisa Johnson, who owns Modern Pilates studios, managed to raise awareness of her personal brand nationally through the social media platform.

45419 ■ *"Five Ways to Make RTK Pay" in Farm Industry News (March 25, 2011)*
Pub: Penton Business Media Inc.
Ed: David Hest. **Description:** It is important for farmers to decide whether they are seeking greater accuracy or faster payback when upgrading navigation systems. The trend towards higher accuracy continues to grow.

45420 ■ *"Flying the Unfriendly Skies" in Crain's Chicago Business (Vol. 31, April 21, 2008, No. 16, pp. 26)*
Pub: Crain Communications, Inc.
Ed: Sarah A. Klein. **Description:** Due to the number of Chicago companies and entrepreneurs who are traveling overseas more frequently in order to strengthen ties with customers, companies and oftentimes even business partners, the number of flights leaving O'Hare International Airport for destinations abroad has surged; In 2007, international passengers departing O'Hare totaled 5.7 million, up from 2.4 million in 1990.

45421 ■ *"Food as Nature Intended" in Pet Product News (Vol. 64, November 2010, No. 11, pp. 30)*
Pub: BowTie Inc.
Ed: Nikki Moustaki. **Description:** Dog owners have been extending their health-consciousness to their pets by seeking natural products that will address their pets' raw food diet. Retailers response to this trend are outlined.

45422 ■ *"Foods for Thought" in Pet Product News (Vol. 64, December 2010, No. 12, pp. 16)*
Pub: BowTie Inc.
Ed: Maddy Heleine. **Description:** Manufacturers have been focused at developing species-specific fish foods due to consumer tendency to assess the benefits of the food they feed their fish. As retailers stock species-specific fish foods, manufacturers have provided in-store items and strategies to assist in efficiently selling these food products. Trends in fish food packaging and ingredients are also discussed.

45423 ■ *"For All It's Worth" in Entrepreneur (Vol. 36, April 2008, No. 4, pp. 46)*
Pub: Entrepreneur Media, Inc.
Ed: Farnoosh Torabi. **Description:** Discusses the federal estate tax system requires that 45 percent of the money beyond $2 million be given to the government. Ways on how to minimize the effects of estate tax on assets include: creating bypass trusts for married couples; setting up an irrevocable life insurance trust to avoid taxation of estate for insurance benefactors; and having annual gift tax exclusion.

45424 ■ *"For MySpace, A Redesign to Entice Generation Y" in The New York Times (October 27, 2010, pp. B3)*
Pub: The New York Times Company
Ed: Miguel Helft. **Description:** MySpace is redesigning its Website in order to attract individuals from the Generation Y group.

45425 ■ *"Franchising Lures Boomers" in Business Journal-Portland (Vol. 24, November 9, 2007, No. 36, pp. 1)*
Pub: American City Business Journals, Inc.
Ed: Wendy Culverwell. **Description:** Popularity of franchising has increased, and investors belonging to the baby boom generation contribute largely to this growth. The number of aging baby boomers is also increasing, particularly in Oregon, which means further growth of franchises can be expected. Reasons why franchising is a good investment for aging baby boomers are given.

45426 ■ *"Freshman Lawmaker Graves Keeping Busy" in Atlanta Journal-Constitution (June 20, 2010, pp. A6)*
Pub: Atlanta Journal Constitution
Ed: Bob Keefe. **Description:** Newly elected Republican Representative Tom Graves of Ranger supports the Small Business Jobs Tax Relief Act.

45427 ■ *"From Fat to Fit" in Canadian Business (Vol. 79, September 25, 2006, No. 19, pp. 100)*
Pub: Rogers Media
Ed: Graham Scott. **Description:** The increase in physical fitness clubs across Canada is discussed.

45428 ■ *"FTC Takes Aim At Foreclosure 'Rescue' Firm" in The Business Journal-Serving Greater Tampa Bay (Vol. 28,*

September 19, 2008, No. 39)
Pub: American City Business Journals, Inc.
Ed: Michael Hinman. **Description:** United Home Savers LLP has been ordered to halt its mortgage foreclosure rescue services after the Federal Trade Commission accused it of deceptive advertising. The company is alleged to have charged customers $1,200 in exchange for unfulfilled promises to keep them in their homes.

45429 ■ *"Fuel for Thought; Canadian Business Leaders on Energy Policy" in Canadian Business (Vol. 81, September 15, 2008, No. 14-15, pp. 12)*
Pub: Rogers Media Ltd.
Ed: Joe Castaldo. **Description:** Most Canadian business leaders worry about the unreliability of the oil supply but feel that Canada is in a better position to benefit from the energy supply crisis than other countries. Many respondents also highlighted the need to invest in renewable energy sources.

45430 ■ *"Fueling Business" in The Business Journal-Milwaukee (Vol. 25, July 25, 2008, No. 44, pp. A1)*
Pub: American City Business Journals, Inc.
Ed: David Doege. **Description:** Several businesses in Wisconsin's Milwaukee area are offering gas cards in order to attract customers. Examples of this include apartment manager Nancy Randle offering a $400 gas card to new tenants with a 1 year lease and dentist Perry Sukowatey giving a $25 gas card after examining patients. Other details on gas card promotions are discussed.

45431 ■ *"Funny Business" in Canadian Business (Vol. 82, April 27, 2009, No. 7, pp. 27)*
Pub: Rogers Media
Ed: Rachel Pulfer. **Description:** Companies are advised to use humor in marketing to drive more revenue. IBM Canada, for example, commissioned Second City Communications for a marketing campaign that involved humor. While IBM Canada declined to give sales or traffic figures, firm executives rank the marketing campaign as an overall success.

45432 ■ *"Furniture Making May Come Back--Literally" in Business North Carolina (Vol. 28, March 2008, No. 3, pp. 32)*
Pub: Business North Carolina
Description: Due to the weak U.S. dollar and the fact that lumber processors never left the country, foreign furniture manufacturers are becoming interested in moving manufacturing plants to the U.S.

45433 ■ *"Future Autoworkers will Need Broader Skills" in Crain's Detroit Business (Vol. 25, June 8, 2009, No. 23, pp. 13)*
Pub: Crain Communications Inc. - Detroit
Ed: Ryan Beene. **Description:** Auto industry observers report that new workers in the industry will need advanced skills and educational backgrounds in engineering and technical fields because jobs in the factories will become more technology-based and multidisciplinary.

45434 ■ *"Future of Diversity: Cultural Inclusion Is a Business Imperative" in Black Enterprise (Vol. 41, August 2010, No. 1, pp. 75)*
Pub: Earl G. Graves Publishing Co. Inc.
Ed: Annya M. Lott. **Description:** As globalization continues to make the world a smaller place, workforce diversity will be imperative to any small company in order to be sustainable.

45435 ■ *"The Future Is Another Country; Higher Education" in The Economist (Vol. 390, January 3, 2009, No. 8612, pp. 43)*
Pub: The Economist Newspaper Inc.
Description: Due to the growth of the global corporation, more ambitious students are studying at universities abroad; the impact of this trend is discussed.

45436 ■ "The Future of Work" in Black Enterprise (Vol. 41, August 2010, No. 1, pp. 65)
Pub: Earl G. Graves Publishing Co. Inc.
Ed: Annya M. Lott. **Description:** Technology, globalization, and outsourcing will continue to shape the future of work. Social media is a means for small companies to market goods and services.

45437 ■ "The Future of Work" in Business Strategy Review (Vol. 21, Autumn 2010, No. 3, pp. 16)
Pub: Wiley-Blackwell
Ed: Lynda Gratton. **Description:** Work is universal. Buy, how, why, where and when we work has never been so open to individual interpretation. The certainties of the past have been replaced by ambiguity, questions and the steady hum of technology. Research covering 21 global companies and more than 200 executives covers the future of work.

45438 ■ "Futures Shock for the CME" in Crain's Chicago Business (Vol. 31, November 10, 2008, No. 45, pp. 8)
Pub: Crain Communications, Inc.
Ed: Ann Saphir. **Description:** Chicago-based CME Group Inc., the largest futures exchange operator in the U.S., is facing a potentially radically altered regulatory landscape as Congress weighs sweeping reform of financial oversight. The possible merger of the CFTC and the Securities and Exchange Commission are among CME's concerns. Other details of possible regulatory measures are provided.

45439 ■ "Generation Y Chooses the Mobile Web" in PR Newswire (November 24, 2010)
Pub: PR Newswire Association LLC
Description: Generation Y individuals between the ages of 18 - 27 use their mobile phones to browse the Internet more often than a desktop or laptop computer, according to a survey conducted by Opera, a Web browser company.

45440 ■ "Generation Y Driving Portland Multifamily Market" in Daily Journal of Commerce, Portland (October 29, 2010)
Pub: Dolan Media Newswires
Ed: Nick Bjork. **Description:** Generation Y, young adults between the ages of 18-30, are interested in multifamily residents in the Portland, Oregon area. Developers in the area, particularly North Portland, have recognized this trend and are looking into multifamily investments.

45441 ■ "Generation Y Goes To Work; Management" in The Economist (Vol. 390, January 3, 2009, No. 8612, pp. 48)
Pub: The Economist Newspaper Inc.
Description: Unemployment rates among people in their 20s has increased significantly and there is a lower turnover in crisis-hit firms, which has made it more difficult to simply find another job if one is unsatisfied with the management style of his or her company. Managers are adopting a more command-and-control approach which is the antithesis of the open, collaborative style that younger employees prefer.

45442 ■ "Getting the Bioheat Word Out" in Indoor Comfort Marketing (Vol. 70, September 2011, No. 9, pp. 32)
Pub: Industry Publications Inc.
Description: Ways to market advanced liquid fuels to the public are outlined.

45443 ■ "The GHG Quandary: Whose Problem Is It Anyway?" in Canadian Business (Vol. 81, September 15, 2008, No. 14-15, pp. 72)
Pub: Rogers Media Ltd.
Ed: Matthew McClearn. **Description:** Nongovernmental organizations were able to revoke the permit for Imperial Oil Ltd's Kearl oilsands project on the grounds of its expected greenhouse gas emission but the court's ruling was rendered irrelevant by bureaucratic paper-shuffling shortly after. The idea of an environmental impact assessment as a guide to identify the consequences of a project is also discussed.

45444 ■ "Go Beyond Local Search With Hyper-Local" in Women Entrepreneur (October 30, 2008)
Pub: Entrepreneur Media Inc.
Ed: Lena West. **Description:** According to Forrester Research, as much as $500 billion in local spending in 2007 was influenced by the Internet and industry analysts report that consumers spend approximately 80 percent of their income within 50 miles of their home. Discussion of ways in which to capitalize on the hyper-local trend that is being driven by greater Internet connectivity and use of the web to find information is provided.

45445 ■ "Going Green, Going Slowly" in Playthings (Vol. 106, September 1, 2008, No. 8, pp. 17)
Pub: Reed Business Information
Contact: Jeff Greisch, President
Ed: Nancy Zwiers. **Description:** Sustainability and greener materials for both product and packaging in the toy industry has become important for protecting our environment. However, in a recent survey nearly 60 percent of responders stated environmental issues did not play a part in purchasing a toy or game for their children.

45446 ■ "Grave Concerns" in Canadian Business (Vol. 81, July 21 2008, No. 11, pp. 25)
Pub: Rogers Media Ltd.
Ed: Andrew Nikiforuk. **Description:** Air pollution control regulations to reduce greenhouse gasses have been implemented by the Canadian government. The federal government is planning to construct a carbon funeral industry that will store the global warming gases, however the expenditure for the project will be shifted to the taxpayers. Details of the Bruce Peachy's initiative on how to reduce GHGs are presented.

45447 ■ "Gray, Gray, & Gray: a Difficult Year for Oilheat" in Indoor Comfort Marketing (Vol. 70, September 2011, No. 9, pp. 30)
Pub: Industry Publications Inc.
Description: According to the 20th Annual Oilheat Industry Survey, 2011 will be another dismal year for the industry sector.

45448 ■ "Green Acres" in Hawaii Business (Vol. 54, September 2008, No. 3, pp. 48)
Pub: Hawaii Business Publishing
Ed: Jan Tenbruggencate. **Description:** Bill Cowern's Hawaiian Mahogany is a forestry business that processes low-value trees to be sold as wood chips, which can be burned to create biodiesel. Cowern is planning to obtain certification to market carbon credits and is also working with Green Energy Hawaii for the permit of a biomass-fueled power plant. Other details about Cowern's business are discussed.

45449 ■ Green Business: A Five-Part Model for Creating an Environmentally Responsible Company
Pub: Schiffer Publishing Ltd.
Contact: Peter B. Schiffer, President
E-mail: petes@schifferbooks.com
Ed: Amy K. Townsend. **Released:** 2006. **Price:** $29.95 paperback. **Description:** Five-part model for small companies to become a green business; the book discusses the advantages to following the current trend using environmentally-friendly practices.

45450 ■ "Green Business Push Blooms" in Charlotte Observer (February 7, 2007)
Pub: Knight-Ridder/Tribune Business News
Ed: Christopher D. Kirkpatrick. **Description:** Many energy companies are capitalizing on corporate guild about global warming. Companies offering environmental peace of mind are discussed.

45451 ■ "Green Counting" in Canadian Business (Vol. 81, October 13, 2008, No. 17, pp. 27)
Pub: Rogers Media Ltd.
Ed: Joe Castaldo. **Description:** Procter and Gamble research revealed that only 10 percent of North American consumers are willing to accept trade-offs for a greener product. Three out of four North American consumers will not accept a higher price or a decrease in a product's performance for an environmental benefit. Details on green marketing are also discussed.

45452 ■ Green Your Small Business: Profitable Ways to Become an Ecopreneur
Pub: McGraw-Hill
Ed: Scott Cooney. **Released:** November 7, 2008. **Price:** $19.95 paperback. **Description:** Advice and guidance is given to help any entrepreneur start, build or grow a green business, focusing on green business basics, market research and financing, as well as handling legal and insurance issues.

45453 ■ "Greening the Auto Industry" in Business Journal-Serving Phoenix & the Valley of the Sun (Vol. 30, July 23, 2010, No. 46, pp. 1)
Pub: Phoenix Business Journal
Ed: Patrick O'Grady. **Description:** Thermo Fluids Inc. has been recycling used oil products since 1993 and could become Arizona's first home for oil filter recycling after retrofitting its Phoenix facility to include a compaction machine. The new service could help establish Thermo Fluids as a recycling hub for nearby states.

45454 ■ "Groomers Eye Profit Growth Through Services" in Pet Product News (Vol. 64, December 2010, No. 12, pp. 26)
Pub: BowTie Inc.
Ed: Kathleen M. Mangan. **Description:** Pet groomers can successfully offer add-on services by taking into account insider customer knowledge, store image, and financial analysis in the decision-making process. Many pet groomers have decided to add services such as spa treatments and training due to a slump in the bathing and grooming business. How some pet groomers gained profitability through add-on services is explored.

45455 ■ Groundswell: Winning in a World Transformed by Social Technologies
Pub: Harvard Business School Press
Ed: Charlene Li; Josh Bernoff. **Released:** April 21, 2008. **Price:** $29.95. **Description:** Individuals are using online social technologies such as blogs, social networking sites, YouTube, and podcasts to discuss products and companies, write their own news, and find their own deals. When consumers you've never met are rating your company's products in public forums with which you have no experience or influence, your company is vulnerable. This book teaches the tools and data necessary to turn this treat into an opportunity.

45456 ■ Groundswell: Winning in a World Transformed by Social Technologies
Pub: Harvard Business School Press
Ed: Charlene Li, Josh Bernoff. **Released:** 2008. **Price:** $29.95. **Description:** Corporate executives are struggling with a new trend: people using online social technologies (blogs, social networking sites, YouTube, podcasts) to discuss products and companies, write their own news, and find their own deals.

45457 ■ Grown Up Digital: How the Net Generation Is Changing Your World
Pub: The McGraw-Hill Companies
Ed: Don Tapscott. **Released:** 2009. **Price:** $27.95. **Description:** As baby boomers retire, business needs to understand what makes the Internet work for business.

45458 ■ "H&M Offers a Dress for Less" in Canadian Business (Vol. 83, September 14, 2010, No. 15, pp. 20)
Pub: Rogers Media Ltd.
Ed: Laura Cameron. **Description:** Swedish clothing company H&M has implemented loss leader strategy by pricing some dresses at extremely low prices. The economy has forced retailers to keep prices down despite the increasing cost of manufacturing, partly due to Chinese labor becoming more expensive. How the trend will affect apparel companies is discussed.

45459 ■ *"Hank Paulson On the Housing Bailout and What's Ahead"* in *Business Week (September 22, 2008, No. 4100, pp. 19)*
Pub: McGraw-Hill Companies, Inc.

Ed: Maria Bartiromo. **Description:** Interview with Treasury Secretary Henry Paulson in which he discusses the bailout of Fannie Mae and Freddie Mac as well as the potential impact on the American economy and foreign interests and investments in the country. Paulson has faith that the government's actions will help to stabilize the housing market.

45460 ■ *"Health Job Shift Looms"* in *Boston Business Journal (Vol. 31, June 3, 2011, No. 19, pp. 3)*
Pub: Boston Business Journal

Ed: Julie M. Donnelly. **Description:** Pending health care payment reform in Massachusetts is seen to adversely impact hospital staff. Hospitals are also seen to serve more patients once the bill is approved.

45461 ■ *"Health Nuts and Bolts"* in *Entrepreneur (Vol. 36, April 2008, No. 4, pp. 24)*
Pub: Entrepreneur Media, Inc.

Ed: Jacquelyn Lynn. **Description:** Encouraging employees to develop good eating habits can promote productivity at work. Ways on how to improve employee eating habits include employers setting a good example themselves and offering employees healthy options. Other details about the topic are discussed.

45462 ■ *"Helping Customers Fight Pet Waste"* in *Pet Product News (Vol. 64, November 2010, No. 11, pp. 52)*
Pub: BowTie Inc.

Ed: Sandy Robins. **Description:** Pet cleaning products manufacturers have been enjoying high sales figures by paying attention to changing pet ownership trends and environmental awareness. Meanwhile, the inclusion of user-friendly features in these products has also been boosted by the social role of pets and the media attention to pet waste. How manufacturers have been responding to this demand is explored.

45463 ■ *"Helping Small Businesses Create Jobs"* in *America's Intelligence Wire (August 27, 2010)*
Pub: HighBeam Research

Ed: Ross Raihala. **Description:** Ways the Small Business Jobs Tax Relief Act will help small businesses create jobs are investigated.

45464 ■ *"Henry Mintzberg: Still the Zealous Skeptic and Scold"* in *Strategy and Leadership (Vol. 39, March-April 2011, No. 2, pp. 4)*
Pub: Emerald Group Publishing Inc.

Ed: Robert J. Allio. **Description:** Henry Mintzberg, professor at the McGill University in Montreal, Canada, shares his thoughts on issues such as inappropriate methods in management education and on trends in leadership and management. Mintzberg believes that US businesses are facing serious management and leadership challenges.

45465 ■ *"His Record, Not Polls, Is What Matters"* in *Bangor Daily News (October 13, 2010)*
Pub: Bangor Daily News

Ed: Nick Sambides Jr. **Description:** The Small Business Jobs Tax Relief Act could spur investment in small businesses by increasing capital gains tax cuts for investors in small business in 2010 and increase to $20,000 from $5,000 the deduction for start-up businesses.

45466 ■ *"Hispantelligence Report"* in *Hispanic Business (January-February 2009, pp. 10)*
Pub: Hispanic Business

Description: U.S. Hispanic purchasing power is expected to reach $958 billion in 2009 and projected to reach $1.25 trillion by 2015, a rate of more than two times the overall national rate. Statistical data included.

45467 ■ *"Holiday Cheer"* in *Business Journal-Serving Phoenix & the Valley of the Sun (Vol. 31, December 3, 2010, No. 13, pp. 1)*
Pub: Phoenix Business Journal

Ed: Lynn Ducey, Mike Sunnucks. **Description:** Results of a study conducted by Challenger, Gray & Christmas Inc., shows that 68 percent of companies are planning holiday parties in 2010, up slightly from 62 percent in 2009. About 53 percent of those having holiday parties are holding them on company premises.

45468 ■ *"The Hollow Debate"* in *Canadian Business (Vol. 81, March 3, 2008, No. 3, pp. 26)*
Pub: Rogers Media

Ed: Thomas Watson. **Description:** According to a report conducted by the Conference Board of Canada, the Canadian business community is not being hollowed out by acquisitions made by foreign companies. Findings further showed that local businesses are protected by dual shares and that the economy can benefit more from foreign acquisitions than local mergers. The need to relax foreign ownership restrictions and other recommendations are presented.

45469 ■ *"Holy Wasabi! Sushi Not Just For Parents Anymore"* in *Chicago Tribune (March 13, 2008)*
Pub: McClatchy-Tribune Information Services

Ed: Christopher Borrelli. **Description:** Wicker Park cooking school, The Kid's Table, specializes in cooking classes for pre-teens; Elena Marre who owns the school was surprised when she was asked to plan a children's party in which she would teach a course in sushi making. More and more adolescents and small children are eating sushi.

45470 ■ *"The Home Game"* in *Canadian Business (Vol. 80, October 8, 2007, No. 20, pp. 68)*
Pub: Rogers Media

Ed: Rachel Pulfer. **Description:** Analysis of Canada's banking industry is presented. Trends show that Canadian banks avoid risks in their investments, and usually choose to take safer paths. Experts believe these trends affect the country's economy and that Canadian banks do not play a significant role in economic development.

45471 ■ *"A Home of Her Own"* in *Hawaii Business (Vol. 53, October 2007, No. 4, pp. 51)*
Pub: Hawaii Business Publishing

Ed: Maria Torres-Kitamura. **Description:** It was observed that the number of single women in Hawaii purchasing their own home has increased, as that in the whole United States where the percentage has increased from 14 percent in 1995 to 22 percent in 2006. However, First Hawaiian Bank's Wendy Lum thinks that the trend will not continue in Hawaii due to lending restrictions. The factors that women consider in buying a home of their own are presented.

45472 ■ *"Home Improvement Marketers Target Women With New Products, New Campaigns and Plenty of Pink"* in *Marketing to Women (March 2008)*
Pub: EPM Communications Inc.
Contact: Ira Mayer, President
E-mail: imayer@epmcom.com

Description: From creating tools that fit a woman's ergonomics to designs that fit a woman's fashion sense, home improvement is finding new ways in which to market to women.

45473 ■ *"Home Sweet Home?"* in *Canadian Business (Vol. 79, September 11, 2006, No. 18, pp. 17)*
Pub: Rogers Media

Ed: David Wolf. **Description:** Fading attractiveness of the Canadian stock market for its domestic investors is discussed. Changing investor's trends toward cross-border investments are presented.

45474 ■ *"A Home's Identity in Black and White"* in *Crain's Chicago Business (Vol. 31, April 21, 2008, No. 16, pp. 35)*
Pub: Crain Communications, Inc.

Ed: Lisa Bertagnoli. **Description:** Real estate agents are finding that showing customers a written floor plan is a trend that is growing since many buyers feel that Online virtual tours distort a room. Although floor plans cost up to $500 to have drawn up, they clearly show potential buyers the exact dimensions of rooms and how they connect.

45475 ■ *Hoover's Vision*
Pub: Cengage Learning Inc.
Contact: Michael Hansen, Chief Executive Officer

Ed: Gary Hoover. **Description:** Founder of Bookstop Inc. and Hoover's Inc. provides a plan to turn an enterprise into a success by showing entrepreneurs how to address inputs with an open mind in order to see more than what other's envision. Hoover pushes business owners to create and feed a clear and consistent vision by recognizing the importance of history and trends, then helps them find the essential qualities of entrepreneurial leadership.

45476 ■ *"Hospitals See Major Shift To Outpatient Care"* in *The Business Journal-Milwaukee (Vol. 25, September 12, 2008, No. 51, pp. A1)*
Pub: American City Business Journals, Inc.

Ed: Corrinne Hess. **Description:** Statistics show that the revenue of Wisconsin hospitals from outpatient medical care is about to surpass revenue from hospital patients who stay overnight. This revenue increase is attributed to new technology and less-invasive surgery. Trends show that the shift toward outpatient care actually started in the late 1980s and early 1990s.

45477 ■ *"Hot Air"* in *Canadian Business (Vol. 81, July 22, 2008, No. 12-13, pp. 16)*
Pub: Rogers Media Ltd.

Ed: Joe Castaldo. **Description:** Over half of 101 business leaders who were recently surveyed oppose Liberal leader Stephane Dion's carbon-tax proposal, saying that manufacturers in Canada are likely to suffer from the plan. Additional key results of the survey are presented.

45478 ■ *"House Committee on Small Business Calls for Sweeping Changes to SBIR Program"* in *Hispanic Business (Vol. 30, March 2008, No. 3)*
Pub: Hispanic Business

Description: Proposals suggested by the House Committee on small business to revamp the Small Business Innovation and Research Program (SBIR) are reported. These include allowing participating firms greater flexibility to use venture capital funds, increasing SBIR grants and faster processing of applications.

45479 ■ *"Housing Markets Still Struggling"* in *Montana Business Quarterly (Vol. 49, Spring 2011, No. 1, pp. 17)*
Pub: Bureau of Business & Economic Research

Ed: Scott Rickard. **Description:** Montana's economic conditions are a bit better than national averages. Data ranked by state, year-over-year price change, and total price peak is presented, along with statistical data for the entire nation.

45480 ■ *"How to Boost Your Super Bowl ROI"* in *Advertising Age (Vol. 80, December 7, 2009, No. 41, pp. 3)*
Pub: Crain's Communications

Ed: Abbey Klaassen. **Description:** Internet marketing is essential, even for the corporations that can afford to spend $3 million on a 30-second Super Bowl spot; last year, Super Bowl advertising reached an online viewership of 99.5 million while 98.7 million people watched the game on television validating the idea that public relations must go farther than a mere television ad campaign. Social media provides businesses with a longer shelf life for their ad campaigns. Advice is also given regarding ways in which to strategize a smart and well-thought plan for utilizing the online marketing options currently available.

45481 ▪ *"How Growers Buy"* in *Farm Industry News (Vol. 42, January 1, 2009, No. 1)*
Pub: Penton Media Inc.
Contact: John French, President
Ed: Karen McMahon. **Description:** According to a survey regarding the buying habits among large commercial growers, most prefer to purchase from local retailers, customer service is important concerning their decision on who to buy products from, and price and convenience seem to be more important then brand.

45482 ▪ *"How In the World?"* in *Business Strategy Review (Vol. 21, Spring 2010, No. 1, pp. 12)*
Pub: Wiley-Blackwell
Ed: Stuart Crainer. **Description:** We may think of management as a recent phenomenon, but its roots lie in the first organizing activities of our ancestors. The author looks a the emergence of management as a profession. He finds that the road to modern management leads to a paradox and questions ways to change that.

45483 ▪ *"How Marketers Can Tap the Web"* in *Sales and Marketing Management (November 12, 2009)*
Pub: Nielsen Business Media, Inc.
Description: Internet marketing strategies require careful planning and tools in order to track success. Businesses are utilizing this trend to attract new clients as well as keep customers they already have satisfied. Advice on website development and design is provided.

45484 ▪ *"How to Survive This Mess"* in *Crain's Chicago Business (Vol. 31, April 14, 2008, No. 15, pp. 18)*
Pub: Crain Communications, Inc.
Ed: Christina Le Beau. **Description:** Small business owners can make it through a possible recession with preparations such as reviewing their balance sheet and cash flow every week and spotting trends then reacting quickly to them.

45485 ▪ *"How To Get a Loan the Web 2.0 Way"* in *Black Enterprise (Vol. 41, December 2010, No. 5, pp. 23)*
Pub: Earl G. Graves Publishing Co. Inc.
Ed: John Simons. **Description:** People are turning to online peer-to-peer network for personal loans as banks are lending less money.

45486 ▪ *"How-To Workshops Teach Sewing, Styles"* in *St. Louis Post-Dispatch (September 14, 2010)*
Pub: St. Louis Post-Dispatch
Ed: Kalen Ponche. **Description:** Profile of DIY Style Workshop in St. Charles, Missouri, where sewing, designing and teaching is offered. The shop is home base for DIY Style, a Website created by mother and daughter to teach younger people how to sew.

45487 ▪ *"The Human Factor"* in *Canadian Business (Vol. 80, October 8, 2007, No. 20, pp. 22)*
Pub: Rogers Media
Ed: Alex Mynek. **Description:** David Foot, a demographer and an economics professor at the University of Toronto, talks about Canada's future, including economic and demographic trends. He discusses activities that should be done by businessmen in order to prepare for the future. He also addresses the role of the Canadian government in economic development.

45488 ▪ *"HVAC/R Evolution"* in *Indoor Comfort Marketing (Vol. 70, March 2011, No. 3, pp. 14)*
Pub: Industry Publications Inc.
Ed: Gene Bartholomew. **Description:** Tools and techniques for heating, ventilation, air conditioning and refrigeration are examined.

45489 ▪ *IBM on Demand Technology for the Growing Business: How to Optimize Your*

Computing Environment for Today and Tomorrow
Pub: Maximum Press
Ed: Jim Hoskins. **Released:** June 2005. **Price:** $29.95. **Description:** IBM is offering computer solutions to small companies entering the On Demand trend in business.

45490 ▪ *"ICC Works on Prescriptive Green Construction Code"* in *Contractor (Vol. 56, October 2009, No. 10, pp. 1)*
Pub: Penton Media, Inc.
Ed: Robert P. Mader. **Description:** International Code Council launched an initiative to create a green construction code that focuses on existing commercial buildings. The initiative's timeline will include public meetings leading up to a final draft that will be available in 2010.

45491 ▪ *"An Ill Wind: Icelandic Bank Failures Chill Atlantic Canada"* in *Canadian Business (Vol. 81, November 10, 2008, No. 19, pp. 10)*
Pub: Rogers Media Ltd.
Ed: Charles Mandel. **Description:** Bank failures in Iceland have put a stop to flights ferrying Icelanders to Newfoundland to purchase Christmas gifts, thereby threatening Newfoundland's tourism industry. The credit of Newfoundland's fisheries is also being squeezed since most of Atlantic Canadian seafood processors hold lines of credit from Icelandic banks.

45492 ▪ *"Illinois Bets On Recycling Program"* in *Chicago Tribune (November 29, 2008)*
Pub: McClatchy-Tribune Information Services
Ed: Joel Hood. **Description:** Traditionally the holiday gift-giving season is one of the most wasteful times of year and the state of Illinois is granting $760,000 to small businesses and cities in an attempt to expand curbside recycling programs and hire additional workers to address electronic waste.

45493 ▪ *"Imax Becomes Toast of Movie Industry"* in *Globe & Mail (January 10, 2006, pp. B2)*
Pub: CTVglobemedia Publishing Inc.
Ed: Grant Robertson. **Description:** The United States-based mainstream theatres company Imax Corp., has reported a 35 percent rise in its ticket sales, showing the growing interest of the American audience in the Imax formatted films. A complete focus on this trend is presented.

45494 ▪ *"Immigration Issues Frustrate Owners From Overseas"* in *The Business Journal-Serving Greater Tampa Bay (Vol. 28, August 15, 2008)*
Pub: American City Business Journals, Inc.
Ed: Margie Manning. **Description:** Investors who availed the E-2 visa program believe that the tightened restrictions on the visa program has trapped them in the United States. The E-2 investor visa program was designed to attract investors into the U.S., but restrictions were tightened after the September 11, 2001 attacks. Other views and information on E-2 and its impact on investors are presented.

45495 ▪ *Import/Export for Dummies*
Pub: John Wiley and Sons, Inc.
Ed: John J. Capela. **Released:** June 2008. **Price:** $19.99. **Description:** Provides entrepreneurs and small- to medium-size businesses with information required to start exporting products globally and importing goods to the U.S. Topics covered include the ins and outs of developing or expanding operations to gain market share, with details on the top ten countries in which America trades, from Canada to Germany to China.

45496 ▪ *"Incentives Debate Rages On Unabated"* in *The Business Journal-Serving Metropolitan Kansas City (Vol. 26, September 5, 2008, No. 52)*
Pub: American City Business Journals, Inc.
Ed: Rob Roberts. **Description:** Debate on the new economic development and incentives policy adopted by the Kansas City Council is still on. The city's Planned Industrial Expansion Authority has rejected

a standard property tax abatement proposal. The real estate development community has opposed the rejection of proposed the tax incentives policy.

45497 ▪ *"Inch by Inch, Employees Lose Ground"* in *Business Courier (Vol. 26, November 13, 2009, No. 29, pp. 1)*
Pub: American City Business Journals, Inc.
Ed: James Ritchie. **Description:** Employees in Ohio who retained their jobs have suffered losses in salary and other benefits, as companies exert efforts to save money. Thirty-four percent of employees experienced pay cuts. Statistical data included.

45498 ▪ *"Indigenous Tourism Operators"* in *International Journal of Entrepreneurship and Small Business (Vol. 10, July 6, 2010, No. 4)*
Pub: Publishers Communication Group
Ed: Andrews Cardow, Peter Wiltshier. **Description:** Emergent enthusiasm for tourism as a savior for economic development in the Chatham Islands of New Zealand is highlighted.

45499 ▪ *"Indoor Air Quality - a Tribute to Efficiency"* in *Indoor Comfort Marketing (Vol. 70, August 2011, No. 8, pp. 8)*
Pub: Industry Publications Inc.
Ed: Matthew Maleske. **Description:** Efficiency of new HVAC/R equipment has helped improve indoor air quality.

45500 ▪ *"Industry Escalates Lobbying Efforts For Loan Program"* in *Crain's Detroit Business (Vol. 24, September 22, 2008, No. 38, pp. 22)*
Pub: Crain Communications Inc.
Ed: Jay Greene; Ryan Beene; Harry Stoffer. **Description:** Auto suppliers such as Lear Corp., which is best known for vehicle seating, also supplies high-voltage wiring for Ford hybrids and is developing other hybrid components. These suppliers are joining automakers in lobbying for the loan program which would promote the accelerated development of fuel-efficient vehicles.

45501 ▪ *"The Influencers"* in *Entrepreneur (Vol. 36, March 2008, No. 3, pp. 66)*
Pub: Entrepreneur Media Inc.
Ed: Andrea Cooper. **Description:** Among the 25 people, events, and trends that will influence business in 2008 are: the 2008 U.S. presidential elections, climate change, China, weakening U.S. dollar, mortgage crisis, generational shift, Bill Drayton, and Bill Gates. Other 2008 influencers are presented.

45502 ▪ *"Innovation Can Be Imperative for Those in Hands-On Trades"* in *Crain's Cleveland Business (Vol. 28, November 12, 2007, No. 45)*
Pub: Crain Communications, Inc.
Ed: Harriet Tramer. **Description:** Discusses the importance of networking and innovative marketing concerning those in art and restoration trades.

45503 ▪ *"Insider"* in *Canadian Business (Vol. 81, Summer 2008, No. 9, pp. 170)*
Pub: Rogers Media Ltd.
Ed: Thomas Watson; Jeff Sanford. **Description:** Oil peak theory posits that the world has consumed half of the non-renewable resources is indicated by the surging oil prices. However, critics argued that the high oil prices are effects of market speculation and not the depletion of the supply. Ten reasons on why to buy and not buy peak oil are presented.

45504 ▪ *"Intel Joins Movement to Turn Cube Farms Into Wide-Open Spaces"* in *Sacramento Business Journal (Vol. 28, May 27, 2011, No. 13, pp. 1)*
Pub: Sacramento Business Journal
Ed: Melanie Turner. **Description:** Intel Corporation has remodeled its facility in Folsom, California. The renovation has required some workers to give up their cubicles. Comments from executives are included.

45505 ■ *"Interest in 'Encore Careers' is Growing"* in *HRMagazine* (Vol. 53, November 2008, No. 11, pp. 22)
Pub: Society for Human Resource Management
Contact: Henry G. Jackson, President
E-mail: hjackson@shrm.org
Description: Unexpectedly large numbers of baby boomers are looking for jobs that can provide them with 'means and meaning', according to a survey by MetLife and Civic Ventures. They can find those jobs in encore careers, an opportunity to do work that has a social impact and personal meaning.

45506 ■ *"Interested in 12 Billion Dollars?"* in *Indoor Comfort Marketing* (Vol. 70, March 2011, No. 3, pp. 18)
Pub: Industry Publications Inc.
Ed: Matthew Maleske. **Description:** Trends in the indoor quality industry are cited, with insight into expanding an existing indoor heating and cooling business.

45507 ■ *"Internet Marketing and Social Media Knowledge Vital for SMBs"* in *Internet Wire* (November 24, 2009)
Pub: Comtex News Network, Inc.
Description: Small and medium-size businesses must learn to market themselves over the Internet in order to succeed and grow in today's marketplace. Web Marketing Today offers the largest source of the most important information concerning doing business on the Internet including e-commerce, email marketing and social networking opportunities.

45508 ■ *"Investigation Hints at Workers' Comp Trouble"* in *Sacramento Business Journal* (Vol. 25, July 4, 2008, No. 18, pp. 1)
Pub: American City Business Journals, Inc.
Ed: Kelly Johnson. **Description:** In 500 California firms, a survey of worker compensation revealed that 38 percent of the companies had problems with required coverage. Government investigators are bothered that 107 companies did not respond to the official inquiry. Other views and information on the survey and on the expected economic implications of the findings are presented.

45509 ■ *"Is Business Ethics Getting Better? A Historical Perspective"* in *Business Ethics Quarterly* (Vol. 21, April 2011, No. 2, pp. 335)
Pub: Society for Business Ethics
Ed: Joanne B. Ciulla. **Description:** The question 'Is Business Ethics Getting Better?' as a heuristic for discussing the importance of history in understanding business and ethics is answered. The article uses a number of examples to illustrate how the same ethical problems in business have been around for a long time. It describes early attempts at the Harvard School of Business to use business history as a means of teaching students about moral and social values. In the end, the author suggests that history may be another way to teach ethics, enrich business ethics courses, and develop the perspective and vision in future business leaders.

45510 ■ *"Is this a Buying Opportunity?"* in *Canadian Business* (Vol. 82, April 27, 2009, No. 7, pp. 46)
Pub: Rogers Media
Ed: Andy Holloway. **Description:** Home prices in Canada are down by as much as 14.2 percent in 2009 compared to prices in 2008, making homes more affordable now. Some housing experts believe that homes are still good investments as prices of rent and properties always recover. Meanwhile, a survey found that Canadians under 35 plan to buy a home within two years.

45511 ■ *"Is Hawaii Ready for Universal Health Care?"* in *Hawaii Business* (Vol. 53, February 2008, No. 8, pp. 26)
Pub: Hawaii Business Publishing
Description: Representative Lyn Finnegan does not believe that a universal health is good for Hawaii as health insurance for everyone will be difficult to achieve. Representative John M. Mizuno says that House Bill 1008 introduced in the state was a landmark for Hawaii as it will provide the people with health care insurance. Other details about their opinion on the topic are presented.

45512 ■ *"Jobs Data Show Wild Card"* in *Barron's* (Vol. 90, September 6, 2010, No. 36, pp. M12)
Pub: Barron's Editorial & Corporate Headquarters
Ed: Gene Epstein. **Description:** August 2010 jobs report revealed a 54,000 decline in non-farm payrolls and that the unemployment rate remains unchanged at 9.6 percent. The report also shows a welcome rise of 848,999 in the household-data category. The unemployment rate shows a reversed trend where men's 10.6 percent unemployment is higher than women's 8.6 percent rate.

45513 ■ *"The Keeper of Records"* in *Black Enterprise* (Vol. 41, December 2010, No. 5, pp. 54)
Pub: Earl G. Graves Publishing Co. Inc.
Ed: Denise Campbell. **Description:** Medical billing and coding, submission of claims to health insurance companies and Medicare or Medicaid for payment is one of the fastest growing disciplines in healthcare.

45514 ■ *"Kenyans Embrace Moving Money By Text Message"* in *Chicago Tribune* (October 7, 2008)
Pub: McClatchy-Tribune Information Services
Ed: Laurie Goering. **Description:** Cell phone banking services are becoming more common, especially for foreign residents; customers are able to establish a virtual cell phone bank account through companies such as M-Pesa which allows their customers to pay bills, withdraw cash, pay merchants or text money to relatives.

45515 ■ *"Know the Facts About Natural Gas!"* in *Indoor Comfort Marketing* (Vol. 70, August 2011, No. 8, pp. 26)
Pub: Industry Publications Inc.
Description: AEC Activity Update is presented on the American Energy Coalition's Website.

45516 ■ *"LA Passes HET Ordinance, California Greens Code"* in *Contractor* (Vol. 56, September 2009, No. 9, pp. 1)
Pub: Penton Media, Inc.
Ed: Candace Ruolo. **Description:** Los Angeles City Council has passed a Water Efficiency Requirements ordinance. The law mandates lower low-flow plumbing requirements for plumbing fixtures installed in new buildings and retrofits. Under the ordinance, a toilet's maximum flush volume may not exceed 1.28-gpf.

45517 ■ *"A Late Night Run: After-Hours Pediatric Practice Fills Void for Affordable Urgent Care"* in *Black Enterprise* (February 2008)
Pub: Earl G. Graves Publishing Co. Inc.
Ed: Erinn R. Johnson. **Description:** Practicing pediatricians in Texas founded the Night Light After Hours Pediatrics facility in order to provide urgent care to children without the trauma witnessed in emergency rooms at hospitals.

45518 ■ *"Lawyers Lock Up Cops as Clients"* in *Sacramento Business Journal* (Vol. 28, April 8, 2011, No. 6, pp. 1)
Pub: Sacramento Business Journal
Ed: Kathy Robertson. **Description:** Sacramento-based law firm Mastagni, Holstedt and Chiurazzi has grown its client base by specializing in law enforcement labor issues. The firm represents 80,000 public sector correctional officers in the US. The firm has been experiencing an increase in new business as public sector employers face huge budget deficits.

45519 ■ *"Layoffs Continue to Be a Drag on Region's Recovery"* in *Philadelphia Business Journal* (Vol. 28, January 22, 2010, No. 49, pp. 1)
Pub: American City Business Journals
Ed: Athena D. Merritt. **Description:** Mass layoffs continue to hamper Pennsylvania's economic recovery. Job losses are predicted to decline in 2010.

45520 ■ *"Lead-Free Products must Meet Requirements"* in *Contractor* (Vol. 56, September 2009, No. 9, pp. 30)
Pub: Penton Media, Inc.
Ed: Robert Gottermeier. **Description:** United States Environmental Protection Agency's adoption of the Safe Drinking Water Act is aimed at lowering lead extraction levels from plumbing products. Manufacturers have since dealeaded brass and bronze potable water products. Meanwhile, California and Vermont have passed a law limiting lead content for potable water conveying plumbing products.

45521 ■ *"Legislation Introduced"* in *Indoor Comfort Marketing* (Vol. 70, July 2011, No. 7, pp. 6)
Pub: Industry Publications Inc.
Description: New industry legislation is examined by the National Oilheat Research Alliance.

45522 ■ *"Legislators Must Cut Cost of Government"* in *Crain's Detroit Business* (Vol. 24, October 6, 2008, No. 40, pp. 6)
Pub: Crain Communications, Inc.
Description: Southeast and West Michigan business leaders are setting aside their differences and have proposed clear agendas, ranging from eliminating the Michigan Business Tax to overhauling public employee and retiree benefits and pensions. Lawmakers must also come together to find solutions for the state's economy and discover an entirely new vision for the future of Michigan business.

45523 ■ *"Lending Act Touted by Michaud"* in *Morning Sentinel* (June 21, 2010)
Pub: Morning Sentinel
Ed: Doug Harlow. **Description:** If passed, the Small Business Jobs Tax Relief Act will leverage up to $300 billion in loans for small businesses through a $30 billion lending fund for small and medium-sized community banks, which focus on lending to small firms.

45524 ■ *"Lending Stays Down at Local Banks"* in *Business Courier* (Vol. 27, October 1, 2010, No. 22, pp. 1)
Pub: Business Courier
Ed: Steve Watkins. **Description:** Greater Cincinnati's largest banks have experienced decreases in loans in the past year due to weak economy and sagging loan demands. Analysis of mid-year data has shown that loans drop by a total of $3.6 billion or 4 percent at the ten largest banks as of June 30, 2010 compared to same period in 2009.

45525 ■ *"Let the Online Games Begin"* in *Canadian Business* (Vol. 80, January 29, 2007, No. 3, pp. 23)
Pub: Rogers Media
Ed: Andy Holloway. **Description:** The trends pertaining to the promotion of the products and services of different Canadian companies on the internet are discussed.

45526 ■ *"A Little Less Hot Air"* in *Canadian Business* (Vol. 81, March 17, 2008, No. 4, pp. 9)
Pub: Rogers Media
Description: British Columbia will levy an extra tax on all carbon-emitting fuels starting July 1, 2008. The tax will raise $1.8 billion in three years and in effect, the province will reduce general corporate income tax from 12 percent to 11 percent. The tax on small businesses and personal income will also be reduced.

45527 ■ *"Local Firms Will Feel Impact Of Wall St. Woes"* in *The Business Journal-Milwaukee* (Vol. 25, September 19, 2008, No. 52, pp. A1)
Pub: American City Business Journals, Inc.
Ed: Rich Kirchen. **Description:** Wall Street's crisis is expected to affect businesses in Wisconsin, in terms of decreased demand for services and products and increased financing costs. Businesses in Milwaukee area may face higher interest rates and tougher loan standards. The potential impacts of the Wall Street crisis on local businesses are examined further.

45528 ■ "Local Lending Tumbles $10 Billion Since '08" in Saint Louis Business Journal (Vol. 31, August 26, 2011, No. 53, pp. 1)
Pub: Saint Louis Business Journal
Ed: Greg Edwards. **Description:** St. Louis, Missouri-based banks lending fell by more than 30 percent in less than three years, from about $30 billion in third and fourth quarters 2008 to about $20 billion in the most recent quarter. However, community banks revealed that they want to lend but there is no loan demand.

45529 ■ "Location, Location" in Black Enterprise (Vol. 38, February 2008, No. 7, pp. 64)
Pub: Earl G. Graves Publishing Co. Inc.
Ed: Marcia Reed-Woodard. **Description:** Overseas work assignments are increasing, especially for workers in the U.S., Canada and Latin America.

45530 ■ "The Lost Opportunity for a Canadian Steel Giant" in Globe & Mail (April 23, 2007, pp. B1)
Pub: CTVglobemedia Publishing Inc.
Ed: Greg Keenan. **Description:** The efforts of Algoma Steel Inc. to create a Canadian steel manufacturer that could survive the global trends of consolidation in the steel industry are described. The company's efforts to acquire Stelco Inc., Ivaco Inc. and Slater Steel Inc. are discussed.

45531 ■ "A Love of Likes" in Boston Business Journal (Vol. 31, July 8, 2011, No. 24, pp. 1)
Pub: Boston Business Journal
Ed: Lisa van der Pool. **Description:** An increasing number of companies in Boston, Massachusetts have been keen on getting Facebook 'likes' from people. Business owners realize that Facebook 'likes' could generate sales and based on some studies, equate to specific dollar values.

45532 ■ "Lunch Box Maker Gives Back" in Marketing to Women (Vol. 23, November 2010, No. 11, pp. 5)
Pub: EPM Communications Inc.
Contact: Ira Mayer, President
E-mail: imayer@epmcom.com
Description: Female entrepreneurs launched a new program called, 'Share Your Lunch Project' that encourages mothers to give back and replace their child's lunchbox with their eco-friendly lunch boxes, which are available at select retailers. All proceeds from the project will benefit the World Food Program USA, which feeds children in developing countries.

45533 ■ "The Major Leagues: Have Front-Office Positions Opened Up for Blacks?" in Black Enterprise (Vol. 37, February 2007, No. 7, pp.)
Pub: Earl G. Graves Publishing Co. Inc.
Ed: Alexis McCombs. **Description:** Major leave sports teams are hiring more African Americans to manage and coach teams. Statistical data included.

45534 ■ "Make It Yourself: Home Sewing, Gender, and Culture, 1890-1930" in Business History Review (Vol. 84, Autumn 2010, No. 3, pp. 602)
Pub: Harvard Business School
Contact: Brian Kenny, Chief Marketing Officer
E-mail: bkenny@hbs.edu
Ed: Alexis McCrossen. **Description:** Review of the publication, 'Make It Yourself: Home Sewing, Gender, and Culture, 1890-1930, a nonfiction work.

45535 ■ "Managers as Visionaries: a Skill That Can Be Learned" in Strategy and Leadership (Vol. 39, September-October 2011, No. 5, pp. 56-58)
Pub: Emerald Group Publishing Inc.
Ed: Stephen M. Millett. **Description:** A study uses research findings to examine whether visionary management can be learned. Results conclude that managers can learn visionary management through intuitive pattern recognition of trends and by using scenarios for anticipating and planning for likely future occurrences.

45536 ■ "Managing the Older Worker: How to Prepare for the New Organizational Order
Pub: Harvard Business Press
Ed: Peter Cappelli, Bill Novelli. **Price:** $29.95. **Description:** Your organization needs older workers more than ever: They transfer knowledge between generations, transmit your company's values to new hires, make excellent mentors for younger employees, and provide a 'just in time' workforce for special projects.

45537 ■ "Manufacturing Jobs Go Begging in Downturn" in Puget Sound Business Journal (Vol. 29, December 26, 2008, No. 36, pp. 1)
Pub: American City Business Journals
Ed: Steve Wilhelm. **Description:** Trends show that skilled jobs in aerospace and other technology manufacturing industries are in a state of decline as layoffs hit broad sectors of the economy. Too few people are entering the field, prompting companies to try to maintain these skilled workers, thus creating problems that could affect the sector's vitality.

45538 ■ "A Manufacturing Revival" in Boston Business Journal (Vol. 31, May 27, 2011, No. 18, pp. 1)
Pub: Boston Business Journal
Ed: Kyle Alspach. **Description:** Massachusetts' manufacturing sector has grown despite the high cost of labor, real estate and electricity. Manufacturing jobs in the state have increased to 2,800 in April 2011.

45539 ■ "Many Retailers Soften Return Policies" in Austin Business JournalInc. (Vol. 28, December 26, 2008, No. 41, pp. 1)
Pub: American City Business Journals
Ed: Jean Kwon. **Description:** National Retail Federation reported the percentage of retailers saying their holiday return policy in 2008 will slacken compared to last season has increased from 3.4 percent to 11 percent. An increasing percentage of retailers are also getting stingier, as 17.1 percent revealed that their return policies will be stricter.

45540 ■ "Mapping Out a Career" in Occupational Outlook Quarterly (Vol. 54, Fall 2010, No. 3, pp. 12)
Pub: U.S. Bureau of Labor Statistics
Ed: Audrey Watson. **Description:** Geographic distribution of occupations is studied, along with lifestyle considerations when choosing a career.

45541 ■ "Market Squeezes Some Lawyers" in Austin Business JournalInc. (Vol. 28, December 12, 2008, No. 39, pp. 1)
Pub: American City Business Journals
Ed: Jean Kwon. **Description:** Austin, Texas-based lawyers have been adversely affected by the economic downturn. Fewer works for lawyers in mergers and acquisitions and other activities are being offered. Lawyers are refinancing debts and offering other services.

45542 ■ "Marketing in the Digital World: Here's How to Craft a Smart Online Strategy" in Black Enterprise (Vol. 40, July 2010, No. 12, pp. 47)
Pub: Earl G. Graves Publishing Co. Inc.
Ed: Sonya A. Donaldson. **Description:** Social media is an integral part of any small business plan in addressing marketing, sales, and branding strategies.

45543 ■ "Marketing Scholarship 2.0" in Journal of Marketing (Vol. 75, July 2011, No. 4, pp. 225)
Pub: American Marketing Association
Ed: Richard J. Lutz. **Description:** A study of the implications of changing environment and newer collaborative models for marketing knowledge production and dissemination is presented. Crowdsourcing has become a frequently employed strategy in industry. Academic researchers should collaborate more as well as the academe and industry, to make sure that important problems are being investigated.

45544 ■ "Maryland Hospitals Cope with Rare Drop in Patient Admissions" in Boston Business Journal (Vol. 29, September 23,

2011, No. 20, pp. 1)
Pub: American City Business Journals Inc.
Ed: Scott Dance. **Description:** Admissions to Maryland hospitals have dropped to less than 700,000 in fiscal year 2010 and initial figures for fiscal 2011 show in-patient admissions are now nearing 660,000. The decline can be partly attributed to new ways health insurers are paying hospitals for care and to the financial reward hospitals get for cutting back on admissions.

45545 ■ "Mass-Transit Backers: Change in State Funding Needed" in Crain's Detroit Business (Vol. 24, October 6, 2008, No. 40, pp. 19)
Pub: Crain Communications, Inc.
Ed: Bill Shea. **Description:** Options to reform transportation and infrastructure funding in the state of Michigan are examined. Transit revitalization investment zones are also discussed.

45546 ■ "MBT Add On: Gone by 2012?" in Crain's Detroit Business (Vol. 24, October 6, 2008, No. 40, pp. 1)
Pub: Crain Communications, Inc.
Ed: Amy Lane. **Description:** Discusses the Michigan Business Tax (MBT), which has angered many businesses in the state due to the addition of a 21.99 percent surcharge. Although the tax policy will cut taxes on 63 percent of businesses in the state and represent no tax liability change for another nine percent of firms, other businesses will see increases of 100 percent or more. This increase means that many business owners will be forced to relocate or close their establishment and others will have to eliminate jobs. Lawmakers are attempting to find a solution to this problem.

45547 ■ "McD's Dollar-Menu Fixation Sparks Revolt" in Advertising Age (Vol. 79, June 2, 2008, No. 22, pp. 1)
Pub: Crain Communications, Inc.
Ed: Emily Bryson York. **Description:** McDonald's franchisees say that low-cost dollar-menu offerings are impacting their bottom line and many have discontinued the dollar-menu altogether due to rising commodity costs, an increase in minimum wage and consumers trading down to the lower-price items.

45548 ■ "Medicaid Insurers See Growth in Small Business Market" in Boston Business Journal (Vol. 31, July 15, 2011, No. 25, pp. 1)
Pub: Boston Business Journal
Ed: Julie M. Donnelly. **Description:** BMC HealthNet Plan announced plans to launch small business products to serve small businesses that are priced out of rising premium rates at large Massachusetts insurers. BMC joined competitors CeltiCare Health Plan and Neighborhood Health Plan in augmenting its core business.

45549 ■ "The Medium 150" in Canadian Business (Vol. 81, Summer 2008, No. 9, pp. 129)
Pub: Rogers Media Ltd.
Description: Medium-sized companies are ranked based on market capitalization and stock performance. Timminico Ltd. topped the roster with 1,294.2 percent returns, while Petrominerales Ltd. ranked second with 325.4 percent. A table showing the 2008 rankings of the companies is presented.

45550 ■ "Meet Rebecca. She's Here to Fire You" in Inc. (November 2007, pp. 25-26)
Pub: Gruner & Jahr USA Publishing
Ed: Max Chafkin. **Description:** Amid liability concerns as well as CEO guilt, more and more firms are using consulting companies to fire workers. These outsourced firms help small companies structure severance and document information in order to limit legal liability when firing an employee.

45551 ■ "Meet the White-Label Cash Kings" in Globe & Mail (April 23, 2007, pp. B1)
Pub: CTVglobemedia Publishing Inc.
Ed: Tara Perkins; Tavia Grant. **Description:** The services provided by the independent Canadian companies managing automated banking machines are described. The trends of ownership of automated banking machines in Canada are discussed.

45552 ■ *"Michaud Touts Small-Business Credentials" in Bangor Daily News (September 10, 2010)*
Pub: Bangor Daily News
Ed: Nick Sambides Jr. **Description:** Mike Michaud, Democrat, is running against a Republican challenger in the 2nd District and states he will support the Small Business Jobs Tax Relief Act if reelected.

45553 ■ *"Micro-Cap Companies" in Canadian Business (Vol. 81, Summer 2008, No. 9, pp. 157)*
Pub: Rogers Media Ltd.
Description: Micro-cap companies have lower than $221 million in terms of market capitalization. Burnaby, British Columbia-based Fancamp Exploration Ltd. topped the roster with 1,116.7 percent in return. A table showing the 2008 rankings of the companies is presented.

45554 ■ *Microtrends*
Pub: Twelve Books/Hachette Book Group USA
Ed: Mark J. Pen with E. Kinney Zalesne. **Released:** September 2007. **Price:** $25.99. **Description:** Detecting small patterns the great impact they can have on business.

45555 ■ *Microtrends: The Small Forces Behind Tomorrow's Big Changes*
Pub: Business Plus
Ed: Mark J. Penn. **Released:** 2007. **Price:** $25.99. **Description:** Political pollster and lead presidential campaign strategist for Hillary Clinton, identifies seventy-five microtrends he believes are changing the social and cultural landscape in the U.S. and globally. The book covers the areas of health and wellness, technology, education and more.

45556 ■ *"Minimizing Import Risks" in Canadian Sailings (July 7, 2008)*
Pub: UBM Global Trade
Contact: Leonard J. Corallo, President
Ed: Jack Kohane. **Description:** New food and product safety laws may be enacted by Canada's Parliament; importers, retailers and manufacturers could face huge fines if the new laws are passed.

45557 ■ *"Misguided" in Canadian Business (Vol. 81, July 22, 2008, No. 12-13, pp. 30)*
Pub: Rogers Media Ltd.
Ed: Al Rosen. **Description:** Canada's securities regulations are discussed; differing views on using principles-based and rules-based securities regulations are also presented.

45558 ■ *The Missing Class: Portraits of the Near Poor in America*
Pub: Houghton Mifflin
Ed: Katherine S. Newman; Victor Tan Chen. **Released:** 2007. **Description:** Information regarding the 57 million Americans existing on the razor-thin margin between poverty and middle class.

45559 ■ *"More Ad Shops Link Payment to Results" in Boston Business Journal (Vol. 30, November 12, 2010, No. 42, pp. 1)*
Pub: Boston Business Journal
Ed: Lisa van der Pool. **Description:** A growing number of advertising firms are proposing a 'value-based' payment scheme where they are paid a base fee plus a bonus if certain sales goals or other targets are met. The proposed shift in payment scheme is seen as reminiscent of the dot-com boom about ten years ago. Advertising firms are traditionally paid by the hour.

45560 ■ *"More Brides, Grooms Say 'I Do' to Interracial Marriage" in Black Enterprise (Vol. 41, August 2010, No. 1, pp. 36)*
Pub: Earl G. Graves Publishing Co. Inc.
Description: According to a recent survey conducted by Pew Research Center, a record 14.6 percent of all new marriages in the U.S. in 2008 were interracial. Statistical data included.

45561 ■ *"More Businesses Will Shift Health Costs to Workers" in Business Review, Albany New York (Vol. 34, November 16,*

2007, No. 33, pp. 1)*
Pub: American City Business Journals, Inc.
Ed: Barbara Pinckney. **Description:** Survey conducted by consulting firm Benetech Inc. showed that sixty percent of employers are planning to increase payroll deductions to pay for health insurance premiums. More than ninety percent of the employers prefer HMO plans, followed by Preferred Provider Organizations. Other details of the survey are discussed.

45562 ■ *"More Callers Are Cutting Their Landlines" in Chicago Tribune (December 30, 2008)*
Pub: McClatchy-Tribune Information Services
Ed: Eric Benderoff. **Description:** Despite sporadic outages for cell phone users, the trend for consumers to cut out the expense of a landline does not appear to be slowing; experts believe that the recession will further increase the number of consumers who decide to go completely wireless.

45563 ■ *"More Law Partners Jumping Ship" in Boston Business Journal (Vol. 27, October 5, 2007, No. 36, pp. 1)*
Pub: American City Business Journals Inc.
Ed: Lisa van der Pool. **Description:** Boston lawyers are moving from one law firm to another, a practice becoming more prevalent than in recent times. Loss of revenue, clients and poor partner morale are some of the reasons for these actions. Details of this profound trend are discussed.

45564 ■ *"More Small Businesses Willing to Fund Employees' Benefits" in Baltimore Business Journal (Vol. 28, June 18, 2010, No. 6, pp. 1)*
Pub: Baltimore Business Journal
Ed: Scott Graham. **Description:** An increasing number of small businesses in Maryland are tapping into potentially cheaper self-funded health plans instead of providing fully insured benefits to employees through traditional health plans. Self-funded health plans charge employers for health care up to a specified level. Economic implications of self-funded plans to small businesses are discussed.

45565 ■ *"Mortgages Going Under" in Black Enterprise (Vol. 41, December 2010, No. 5, pp. 20)*
Pub: Earl G. Graves Publishing Co. Inc.
Description: Nearly one-fifth of the country's homeowners are underwater in their mortgages, which means they owe more on their home than the home's worth. Statistical data included.

45566 ■ *"Most Viewed Stories, Videos on farmindustrynews.com in 2010" in Farm Industry News (January 4, 2011)*
Pub: Penton Business Media Inc.
Description: The top ten most popularly viewed stories and videos presented on farmindustrynews.com Website are listed.

45567 ■ *"Move Over - Or Out" in Puget Sound Business Journal (Vol. 29, November 28, 2008, No. 32, pp. 1)*
Pub: American City Business Journals
Ed: Kirsten Grind. **Description:** Real estate agents in the state of Washington are either moving to smaller real estate firms or quitting the industry due to the weak housing market. Lesser-known firms are experiencing an influx of experienced real estate agents, while 2,800 agents in the state have left the industry.

45568 ■ *"Moving Into the Digital Space: How New Media Create Opportunities for Minorities" in Black Enterprise (February 2008)*
Pub: Earl G. Graves Publishing Co. Inc.
Ed: Sonia Alleyne. **Description:** The Internet is becoming an alternative to traditional sources of entertainment; nearly 16 percent of American households who use the Internet watch television online. One such Internet show features a variety of African American lifestyles.

45569 ■ *"Must Work for Food" in Pet Product News (Vol. 64, November 2010, No. 11, pp. 24)*
Pub: BowTie Inc.
Ed: Wendy Bedwell-Wilson. **Description:** Pet supply retailers can benefit from stocking foods and treats that address obesity, which according to the American Veterinary Medical Association, has become the most prevalent nutritional disorder in dogs. With the rise in dog obesity, products like work-for-their food toys have been sought by dog owners.

45570 ■ *"Myths of Deleveraging" in Barron's (Vol. 90, August 23, 2010, No. 34, pp. M14)*
Pub: Barron's Editorial & Corporate Headquarters
Ed: Gene Epstein. **Description:** The opposite is true against reports about deleveraging or the decrease in credit since inflation-adjusted-investment factories and equipment rose 7.8 percent in the first quarter of 2010. On consumer deleveraging, sales of homes through credit is weak but there is a trend towards more realistic homeownership and consumer spending on durable goods rose 8.8 percent.

45571 ■ *"NAWBO Takes the Stage at Press Conference for Small Business Jobs, Credit and Tax Relief Acts" in Internet Wire (June 17, 2010)*
Pub: Comtex
Description: A survey of the National Association of Women Business Owners reported optimism returning and women business owners are ready to invest in job creation. The Small Business Jobs Tax Relief Act will aid in their progress.

45572 ■ *"Need Fiber in Your Diet? Pour Some Milk" in Globe & Mail (April 10, 2007, pp. B7)*
Pub: CTVglobemedia Publishing Inc.
Ed: William Illsey Atkinson. **Description:** The growing market and demand for functional foods and neutraceuticals in Canada is discussed. The research being conducted by University of Manitoba's Richardson Centre for Functional Foods and Nutraceuticals to explore new health compounds in food is highlighted.

45573 ■ *"New Approach Could Boost Ivory Tower Innovation" in Business Journal-Portland (Vol. 24, November 16, 2007, No. 37, pp. 1)*
Pub: American City Business Journals, Inc.
Ed: Aliza Earnshaw. **Description:** New approach which aims to help universities move to a corporate structure, secure funds, and find professional managers is being explored. Accelerator Corporation was able to help six companies through its funding. Joe Tanous who is behind Oregon's State University's enhanced commercialization, would like to apply the same approach Accelerator used to help Oregon State University, the University of Oregon, Portland State University and Oregon Health and Science University.

45574 ■ *"A New Day is Dawning" in Indoor Comfort Marketing (Vol. 70, August 2011, No. 8, pp. 18)*
Pub: Industry Publications Inc.
Ed: Paul Nazzaro. **Description:** New trends in the HVAC/R industry regarding biofuels and bioheat are explored.

45575 ■ *"The New Face of Social Media" in Hispanic Business (December 2010)*
Pub: Hispanic Business
Ed: Gary D. Fackler. **Description:** Latina bloggers carve out a new niche in social media that helps preserve their unique cultural identities.

45576 ■ *"New Global Hot Spots: Look Beyond Shanghai for the Next Big Thing" in Inc. (October 2007, pp. 40-41)*
Pub: Gruner & Jahr USA Publishing
Description: The Chinese government is investing money to lure U.S. companies to start doing business in Chengdu, China. The government is upgrading Chengdu's infrastructure and establishing free trade zones in a less polluted environment. Other cities profiled in the article include: Yekaterinburg, Rus-

sia; Poznan, Poland; Ahmadabad and Kolkata, India; Suzhou, China; Belo Horizonte, Brazil; Ras Al Khaimah, United Arab Emirates; and Aguascalientes, Mexico.

45577 ■ "New Health Care Sector" in Hispanic Business (July-August 2009, pp. 10-12)
Pub: Hispanic Business
Ed: Rob Kuznia. **Description:** Despite the recession and reform, the health care sector continues to grow at a fast rate. The top ten health care organizations are outlined.

45578 ■ "New Jobless Claims Filed in December Soar" in Baltimore Business Journal (Vol. 27, January 29, 2010, No. 39, pp. 1)
Pub: American City Business Journals
Ed: Scott Dance. **Description:** Maryland received 48,693 new claims for unemployment benefits in December 2009, reaching its highest monthly total since 1974. The number of claims was up 49 percent from November and 13 percent from the same period in 2008. Labor officials and economists discuss this trend.

45579 ■ "A New Mix of Tenants Settles In" in Crain's New York Business (Vol. 24, January 14, 2008, No. 2, pp. 26)
Pub: Crain Communications, Inc.
Ed: Andrew Marks. **Description:** More and more nonfinancial firms are relocating downtown due to the new retailers and restaurants that are reshaping the look and feel of lower Manhattan.

45580 ■ "The New Nimble" in Barron's (Vol. 90, August 30, 2010, No. 35, pp. S12)
Pub: Barron's Editorial & Corporate Headquarters
Ed: Suzanne McGee. **Description:** Financial advisors are making investments based on short-lived market trends due to the uncertainty in the long-term market. This strategy can be demanding and advisors should only try it if they are confident about their skill in spotting short-term trends.

45581 ■ "New Recession-Proof Internet Marketing Package Allows Businesses to Ramp Up Web Traffic and Profits" in PR Newswire (Jan. 25, 2010)
Pub: PR Newswire Association, LLC
Description: Profile of Reel Web Design, a leading marketing firm in New York City that caters to small to medium sized businesses with smaller budgets that need substantial return on investment; Reel Web Design offers video production and submission, web design and maintenance and press release writing among additional services.

45582 ■ "New Recession-Proof Internet Marketing Package Allows Businesses to Ramp Up Web Traffic and Profits" in PR Newswire (Jan. 25, 2010)
Pub: PR Newswire Association, LLC
Description: Profile of Reel Web Design, a leading marketing firm in New York City that caters to small to medium sized businesses with smaller budgets that need substantial return on investment; Reel Web Design offers video production and submission, web design and maintenance and press release writing among additional services.

45583 ■ The New Role of Regional Management
Pub: Palgrave Macmillan
Ed: Bjorn Ambos, Bodo B. Schlegelmilch. **Released:** January 19, 2010. **Price:** $95.00. **Description:** Regional management is becoming more important to companies as they expand globally. This book explores the challenges of European, United States and Asian companies and outlines how regional headquarters can develop into Dynamic Competence Relay centers to master these issues.

45584 ■ "The New Schools" in Black Enterprise (February 2008)
Pub: Earl G. Graves Publishing Co. Inc.
Ed: Kinsley Kanu, Jr. **Description:** Ten educational programs to help top executives keep pace with the ever-changing market trends while gaining perspective on innovation and new ideas are examined.

45585 ■ "New Technology, Growing Fan Base Fuel Truck Trend" in Nation's Restaurant News (Vol. 45, June 13, 2001, No. 12, pp. 16)
Pub: Penton Media Inc.
Contact: John French, President
Ed: Ron Ruggless. **Description:** Food trucks drove more interest at this year's National Restaurant Association Restaurant Hotel-Motel Show in Chicago. The trend continues to show long-term growth.

45586 ■ The New Wellness Revolution: Make a Fortune in the Next Trillion Dollar Industry
Pub: John Wiley & Sons, Incorporated
Ed: Paul Zane Pilzer. **Released:** February 16, 2007. **Price:** $24.95. **Description:** Tips for starting and running a healthcare business.

45587 ■ "Nexstar Super Meeting Breaks Business Barriers" in Contractor (Vol. 56, November 2009, No. 11, pp. 3)
Pub: Penton Media, Inc.
Ed: Candace Roulo. **Description:** Around 400 Nexstar members met to discuss the trends in the HVAC industry and the economic outlook for 2010. Former lead solo pilot John Foley for the Blue Angels made a presentation on how a business can increase overall productivity based on the culture of the Blue Angels. Some breakout sessions tackled how to optimize workflow and marketing.

45588 ■ "The Next 20 Years: How Customer and Workforce Attitudes Will Evolve" in Harvard Business Review (Vol. 85, July-August 2007, No. 7-8)
Pub: Harvard Business School Publishing
Ed: Neil Howe, William Strauss. **Description:** Identification of social categories inhabited by age groups is used to calculate how consumer and employee opinions and behavior will change, and how this will impact economic development and corporate growth.

45589 ■ "No Matter the Workplace Size, Handbooks Can Play a Vital Role" in Crain's Cleveland Business (Vol. 28, November 12, 2007, No. 45)
Pub: Crain Communications, Inc.
Ed: David Prizinsky. **Description:** Employee handbooks are important for even small businesses that wish to remain relatively informal since that documentation can help a company with a defense when confronted by employee or government lawsuits; they also demonstrate a consistency in policy which is a vital way in which employees, managers and owners remain focused on the company's prime goals.

45590 ■ "No Place Like Home" in Small Business Opportunities (Winter 2010)
Pub: Harris Publications Inc.
Description: Five reasons to start a home-staging business in any economy are listed. Home staging is listed as the top emerging career on Website, Careerbuilder.com.

45591 ■ "No Shortage of Challenges for Cross-Border Trade" in Canadian Sailings (June 30, 2008)
Pub: UBM Global Trade
Contact: Leonard J. Corallo, President
Ed: Kathlyn Horibe. **Description:** Pros and cons of the North American Free Trade Agreement are examined. The agreement between the U.S. and Canada concerning trade was an essential step toward securing economic growth for Canadian citizens. Two-way trade between the counties has tripled since the agreement and accounts for 7.1 million American and 3 million Canadian jobs.

45592 ■ Non-Standard Employment under Globalization
Pub: Palgrave Macmillan
Ed: Koichi Usami. **Released:** January 19, 2010. **Price:** $100.00. **Description:** Expansion of non-standard employment under globalization is being recognized in all of the newly industrialized countries. The book examines deregulation of labor markets, social protection for nonstandard workers, and social security reforms in accordance with the transformation of employment.

45593 ■ "Nortel Makes Customers Stars in New Campaign" in Brandweek (Vol. 49, April 21, 2008, No. 16, pp. 8)
Pub: VNU Business Media, Inc.
Ed: Mike Beirne. **Description:** Nortel has launched a new television advertising campaign in which the business-to-business communications technology provider cast senior executives in 30-second TV case studies that show how Nortel's technology helped their businesses innovate.

45594 ■ "North American Pet Health Insurance Market Poised for Growth" in Pet Product News (Vol. 64, December 2010, No. 12, pp. 4)
Pub: BowTie Inc.
Ed: David Lummis. **Description:** The pet health insurance market is expected to further grow after posting about $350 million in sales in 2009, a gain of more than $40 million. Pet insurance firms have offered strategies such as product humanization in response to this growth forecast. Meanwhile, pet insurance shoppers have been provided more by insurance firms with wider choices.

45595 ■ "Not Your Dad's Business Card" in Small Business Opportunities (July 2008)
Pub: Entrepreneur Press
Contact: Perlman Neil, President
Ed: Rob Schlacter. **Description:** Provides tips on how to effectively design and use business cards.

45596 ■ "Now Entering A Secure Area" in Women Entrepreneur (January 14, 2009)
Pub: Entrepreneur Media Inc.
Ed: Aliza Sherman. **Description:** Despite the fact that the field of government intelligence and security is dominated by males, many women entrepreneurs are finding opportunities for their products and services in homeland security. Profiles of several women who have found such opportunities are included.

45597 ■ "Nowspeed and OneSource to Conduct Webinar" in Internet Wire (December 14, 2009)
Pub: Comtex News Network, Inc.
Description: OneSource, a leading provider of global business information, and Nowspeed, an Internet marketing agency, will conduct a webinar titled 'How to Develop Social Media Content That Gets Results' in order to provide marketers insight into how to develop and optimize effective social media content to get consumer results that translate into purchases and lead generation.

45598 ■ On the Make: Clerks and the Quest for Capital in Nineteenth-Century America
Pub: New York University Press
Contact: Steve Maikowski, Director
E-mail: steve.maikowski@nyu.edu
Ed: Brian Luskey. **Released:** January 1, 2010. **Price:** $48.00. **Description:** Through exploration into the diaries, newspapers, credit reports, census data, advice literature and fiction, the book presents the origins of the white collar culture, the antebellum clerk.

45599 ■ "On tap: More Could Get MEGA Credits; Need to Look Outside State May Be Cut" in Crain's Detroit Business (April 7, 2008)
Pub: Crain Communications, Inc.
Ed: Amy Lane. **Description:** In order to qualify for Michigan Economic Growth Authority tax credits Michigan businesses may no longer have to shop outside the state due to a new bill which has already passed the state Senate and will move on to the House; the bill, along with further changes to the MEGA program, is designed to provide incentives for investments that would add relevance and make Michigan more competitive.

45600 ■ "On Target" in Canadian Business (Vol. 81, July 22, 2008, No. 12-13, pp. 45)
Pub: Rogers Media Ltd.
Ed: Calvin Leung. **Description:** Companies such as LavalifePRIME, a dating website devoted to singles 45 and older, discuss the value of marketing and

services aimed at Canada's older consumers. One-third of Canada's 33 million people are 50-plus, controlling 77 percent of the countries wealth.

45601 ■ "On Their Own" in Crain's Cleveland Business (Vol. 28, November 12, 2007, No. 45, pp. 19)
Pub: Crain Communications, Inc.
Ed: Eileen Beal. **Description:** Discusses the reasons more physicians with entrepreneurial spirit are opening their own practices as well the added challenges and responsibilities that comes with owning one's own practice.

45602 ■ "One Hundred Years of Excellence in Business Education: What Have We Learned?" in Business Horizons (January-February 2008)
Pub: Elsevier Advanced Technology Publications
Ed: Frank Acito, Patricia M. McDougall, Daniel C. Smith. **Description:** Business schools have to be more innovative, efficient and nimble, so that the quality of the next generation of business leaders is improved. The Kelley School of Business, Indiana University ahs long been a leader in business education. The trends that influence the future of business education and useful success principles are discussed.

45603 ■ "One on One With SEIA's President, CEO" in Contractor (Vol. 57, January 2010, No. 1, pp. 40)
Pub: Penton Media, Inc.
Ed: Dave Yates. **Description:** Solar Energy Industries Association President and CEO Rhone Resch says that the deployment of solar systems in the U.S. has exploded since 2005 and that there is a need to make inroads for shaping the U.S. energy policy. Resch says one of the hurdles they face is that there are no universal standards.

45604 ■ "Online Book Sales Surpass Bookstores" in Information Today (Vol. 28, September 2011, No. 8, pp. 11)
Pub: Information Today, Inc.
Ed: Cindy Martine. **Description:** Online book sales outpaced bookstore purchases in the United States, signaling a shift in the US book industry. Statistical data included.

45605 ■ "Opportunity Knocks" in Small Business Opportunities (September 2008)
Pub: Entrepreneur Media Inc.
Description: Profile of YourOffice USA, a franchise that provides home-based and small businesses cost-effective and efficient support through 'virtual' offices that are available as much or as little as the client needs it; they also supply necessary tools such as a professional business address, private mailbox service, personalized telephone answering and more that supports clients who want to look, act and operate with an advanced business image.

45606 ■ "Optimism Index" in Black Enterprise (Vol. 41, September 2010, No. 2, pp. 24)
Pub: Earl G. Graves Publishing Co. Inc.
Description: According to a Pew Research Center report, 81 percent of African Americans expect to improve their finances in 2011. Blacks have carried a disproportionate share of job losses and housing foreclosures in the recession that began in 2007.

45607 ■ "Optimize.ca Supplies Free Online Financial Advice" in Entertainment Close-Up (October 9, 2010)
Pub: Close-Up Media Inc.
Description: Optimize.ca provides free online financial advice, focusing on instant savings for their mutual funds and other banking products while improving rates of return and overall financial health.

45608 ■ "Ordering Pizza Hut From Your Facebook Page?" in Advertising Age (Vol. 79, November 10, 2008, No. 42, pp. 50)
Pub: Crain Communications, Inc.
Ed: Emily Bryson York. **Description:** Fast-food chains are experimenting with delivery/takeout services via social networks such as Facebook and iPhone applications. This also allows the chains to build valuable databases of their customers.

45609 ■ "Organic Chain Scouting Tri-State Sites, Including Kenwood" in Business Courier (Vol. 27, December 3, 2010, No. 31, pp. 1)
Pub: Business Courier
Ed: Tom Demeropolis. **Description:** Asheville, North Carolina-based Earth Fare has been planning to add a total of six stores in 2011, including the potential opening of more than one store in the Greater Cincinnati area market. Earth Fare has not named specific locations but Kenwood area was reportedly being considered for its first location. Insights on growing trends toward health food stores are also given.

45610 ■ "Organic Dairy Farmers Wanted" in Canadian Business (Vol. 80, April 23, 2007, No. 9, pp. 11)
Pub: Rogers Media
Ed: Wendy Glauser. **Description:** The growth of the Harmony Organic due to demand for organic dairy products is presented.

45611 ■ "Our Hoarder Mentality: Blame the Hard Disk" in PC Magazine (Vol. 30, November 2011, No. 11, pp. 46)
Pub: Ziff-Davis Inc.
Contact: Vivek Shah, Chief Executive Officer
Ed: John C. Dvorak. **Description:** Computer programmers, once referred to as computer users, are slowly being replaced by passive consumers of products and content of tablets and handheld mobile phones and devices of the future. Understanding is garnered as this article examines this industry trend.

45612 ■ "Outpouring of Outreach" in Crain's Cleveland Business (Vol. 30, June 15, 2009, No. 23, pp. 3)
Pub: Crain Communications, Inc.
Ed: Shannon Mortland. **Description:** Nonprofit organizations are experiencing a higher number of volunteers than in the past. People are willing to donate their skills and services rather than contributing money.

45613 ■ Over the Counter
Pub: The Mercier Press, Ltd.
Ed: Keogh. **Released:** January 1, 2009. **Price:** $54.95. **Description:** An overview of the changing landscape of Cork, Ireland's retail stores is presented.

45614 ■ "Overheating Taking Place? Pay Attention to Details.." in Indoor Comfort Marketing (Vol. 70, March 2011, No. 3, pp.)
Pub: Industry Publications Inc.
Ed: George R. Carey. **Description:** Boiler facts are outlined to help the small HVAC company when servicing customers.

45615 ■ "Overview - Small Business Optimism" in Small Business Economic Trends (April 2008, pp. 4)
Pub: National Federation of Independent Business
Ed: William C. Dunkelberg, Holly Wade. **Description:** Graph and table representing the optimism index for small businesses in the U.S., based on ten survey indicators, are presented. The index values include data from 1986 to 2008.

45616 ■ "Overview - Small Business Optimism" in Small Business Economic Trends (March 2008, pp. 4)
Pub: National Federation of Independent Business
Ed: William C. Dunkelberg, Holly Wade. **Description:** A graph and a table representing the optimism index for small businesses in the U.S., based on ten survey indicators, are presented. The index values include data from 1986 to 2008.

45617 ■ "Overview - Small Business Optimism" in Small Business Economic Trends (February 2008, pp. 4)
Pub: National Federation of Independent Business
Ed: William C. Dunkelberg, Holly Wade. **Description:** A graph and a table representing the optimism index for small businesses in the U.S., based on ten survey indicators, are presented. The index values include data from 1975 to 2008.

45618 ■ "Overview - Small Business Optimism" in Small Business Economic Trends (January 2008, pp. 4)
Pub: National Federation of Independent Business
Description: Optimism index among small businesses surveyed in the U.S. from 1986 to 1007 is presented in a graph. A small business optimism index from January 2002 to June 2007 is also given in tabular form. The index value was seasonally adjusted at 1986=100.

45619 ■ "Overview - Small Business Optimism" in Small Business Economic Trends (July 2010, pp. 4)
Pub: National Federation of Independent Business
Description: An optimism index among small businesses surveyed in the U.S. from 1986 to 2010 is presented in graph form. A small business optimism index from January 2005 to June 2010 is also given in tabular form. The index value was seasonally adjusted at 1986=100.

45620 ■ "Paper Replaces PVC for Gift Cards" in American Printer (Vol. 128, June 1, 2011, No. 6)
Pub: Penton Media Inc.
Description: Monadnock Envi Card Stock replaces paper for gift cards, loyalty cards, membership cards, hotel keys and durable signage. This renewable wood fiber alternative to PVC card materials comes from Monadock Paper Mills.

45621 ■ "Part-Time Assignments" in Black Enterprise (Vol. 37, December 2006, No. 5, pp. 70)
Pub: Earl G. Graves Publishing Co. Inc.
Description: During critical change initiatives interim management, an employment model which uses senior-level executives to manage a special project or specific business function on a temporary basis, can have many benefits.

45622 ■ "Part-Time Office Space" in Hawaii Business (Vol. 53, December 2007, No. 6, pp. 132)
Pub: Hawaii Business Publishing
Ed: Ashley Hamershock. **Description:** My Office is one of the companies that are renting space office not only by the month, but by the hour. Such setup is beneficial to small businesses that do not need a whole office all to themselves, and are interested in cutting the cost of office space rental. The prices of office space in Hawaii are mentioned.

45623 ■ "Patients: Make Mine a Single" in Business Courier (Vol. 24, March 28, 2008, No. 51, pp. 1)
Pub: American City Business Journals, Inc.
Ed: James Ritchie. **Description:** Hospitals in the Tri-State area are switching from double to private rooms since patients heal better in private rooms and also they provide peace and quiet to patients. Private rooms also contribute to the reduction of medical errors and hospital acquired infection rates.

45624 ■ "Peak Show" in Canadian Business (Vol. 81, December 24, 2007, No. 1, pp. 28)
Pub: Rogers Media
Ed: Thomas Watson. **Description:** Factors affecting oil prices could include political instability and economic slowdown, but peak oil is not one of them as it is believed there is still plenty of oil in supply. Details on the oil supply and demand, trend for higher prices, and peak oil expert Matthew Simmons' prediction on the issue are discussed.

45625 ■ "Phoenix Conference Reveals Opportunities are Coming" in Indoor Comfort Marketing (Vol. 70, March 2011, No. 3, pp. 24)
Pub: Industry Publications Inc.
Ed: Paul J. Nazzaro. **Description:** Advanced liquid fuels were spotlighted at the Phoenix conference revealing the opportunities for using liquid fuels.

45626 ■ "Pioneers Get All The Perks" in Canadian Business (Vol. 81, March 3, 2008, No. 3, pp. 18)
Pub: Rogers Media
Description: Suncor Energy Inc. will face royalty payments from 25% to 30% of net profits as it signs a new deal with Alberta. Biovail Corp., meanwhile, is

under a U.S. grand jury investigation for supposed improprieties in Cardizem LA heart drug launch. The Conference Board of Canada's proposal to impose taxes on greenhouse gas emissions and other developments in the business community are discussed.

45627 ■ *"Point, Click, Buy" in Barron's (Vol. 90, September 6, 2010, No. 36, pp. 11)*
Pub: Barron's Editorial & Corporate Headquarters
Ed: Vito J. Racanelli. **Description:** Non-travel online retail sales from January to July 2010 increased nine percent which indicates that online shopping for the coming holidays will be good. Online sales are outpacing traditional shopping, but pricing is still critical.

45628 ■ *"Positive Transformational Change" in Indoor Comfort Marketing (Vol. 70, April 2011, No. 4, pp. 30)*
Pub: Industry Publications Inc.
Ed: Blaine Fox. **Description:** Management changes taking place at Shark Bites HVAC firm are discussed.

45629 ■ *The Post-American World*
Pub: W.W. Norton & Company
Ed: Fareed Zakaria. **Released:** 2009. **Price:** $25.95. **Description:** Analysis of the changes taking place as new countries are rising as status players challenging American dominance.

45630 ■ *"The Power of Innovation" in Canadian Business (Vol. 81, March 17, 2008, No. 4, pp. 57)*
Pub: Rogers Media
Ed: Andrew Wahl. **Description:** Canada ranks badly in terms innovation yardsticks that directly translate to economic growth such as business R&D as a percentage of GDP and R&D per capita. Canada's reliance on natural resources does not provide incentives to innovate unlike smaller countries with little natural resources. Canada could spur innovation through regulations that encourage industrial research.

45631 ■ *The Power of Social Innovation: How Civic Entrepreneurs Ignite Community Networks for Good*
Pub: John Wiley & Sons, Inc.
Ed: Stephen Goldsmith, Tim Burke, Gigi Georges. **Released:** March 10, 2010. **Price:** $35.00. **Description:** This seminal book provides tools for civic entrepreneurs to create healthier communities and promote innovative solutions to public and social problems. It shows how to effectively tackle the intractable issues facing the country.

45632 ■ *"PPC's Major Commitment to Biofuel Infrastructure" in Indoor Comfort Marketing (Vol. 70, April 2011, No. 4, pp. 6)*
Pub: Industry Publications Inc.
Description: Petroleum Products Corporation's commitment to the biofuel infrastructure is outlined.

45633 ■ *"Pre-K Pressure" in Hawaii Business (Vol. 53, October 2007, No. 4, pp. 32)*
Pub: Hawaii Business Publishing
Ed: David K. Choo. **Description:** Kindergarten admission in Hawaii is becoming more competitive. Parents, for example, prepare their children for the kindergarten admissions process by bringing them to the schools before the interview or by paying for tutorial services. The impacts of increased competition in school admissions on the life of Hawaiian children are discussed.

45634 ■ *"A Precious Resource: Investing In the Fate of Fresh Water" in Black Enterprise (Vol. 38, February 2008, No. 7, pp. 44)*
Pub: Earl G. Graves Publishing Co. Inc.
Ed: Charles Keenan. **Description:** Despite rising oil prices, water may become the most precious commodity in years to come because the world's supply of drinkable water is dwindling.

45635 ■ *Predictably Irrational: The Hidden Forces That Shape Our Decisions*
Pub: HarperCollins Publishers
Ed: Dan Ariely. **Released:** 2009. **Price:** $25.95. **Description:** Behaviorists are bringing the economics profession around to realizing that human beings are impulsive, shortsighted and procrastinating in behavior. Economists are using this information to market products to consumers.

45636 ■ *"Prescription for Health: Choosing the Best Healthcare Plan" in Black Enterprise (Vol. 38, July 2008, No. 12, pp. 48)*
Pub: Earl G. Graves Publishing Co. Inc.
Ed: Tamara E. Holmes. **Description:** According to a survey of small-business owners conducted by Sure-Payroll Inc., 20 percent of respondents have had a prospective employee refuse a job offer because healthcare benefits did not come with it. Cost is not the only reason many small-business owners do not offer these benefits. Guidelines to help take some of the confusion out of the guesswork that comes with trying to find the proper fit concerning healthcare benefits are outlined.

45637 ■ *"Price Data" in Montly Labor Review (Vol. 133, September 2010, No. 9, pp. 128)*
Pub: Bureau of Labor Statistics
Description: Consumer price indexes for all urban consumers and for urban wage earners and clerical workers is presented with U.S. city average, by expenditure category and commodity or service group.

45638 ■ *"Private Equity Firms Focus on Failing Banks" in Baltimore Business Journal (Vol. 28, July 16, 2010, No. 10, pp. 1)*
Pub: Baltimore Business Journal
Ed: Gary Haber. **Description:** Four deals in which assets of failed banks were acquired by private equity firms have been approved by the Federal Deposit Insurance Corporation in the past couple of years. Bay Bank FSK, for example, purchased Bay National Bank's assets in July 2010. Forecasts on more private equity acquisitions in the community banking industry are given.

45639 ■ *"Profit Predictions Look Too Plump" in Barron's (Vol. 88, March 31, 2008, No. 13, pp. 37)*
Pub: Dow Jones & Company, Inc.
Ed: Johanna Bennett. **Description:** Full-year forecast points to a 14 percent gain for 2008 but the second-half increases would have to grow at a fast rate and peak at 61 percent in the fourth quarter to achieve this. Trends in the U.S. economic conditions are also discussed.

45640 ■ *Profiting from Diversity: The Business Advantages and the Obstacles to Achieving Diversity*
Pub: Palgrave Macmillan
Ed: Gloria Moss. **Released:** January 5, 2010. **Price:** $95.00. **Description:** Although the benefits of diversity in small business are often discussed, specific ways in which organizations can profit from diversity and some of the obstacles faced are defined.

45641 ■ *"Protection, Flexibility Make Single-Member LLCs Attractive" in Crain's Cleveland Business (Vol. 28, November 12, 2007, No. 45)*
Pub: Crain Communications, Inc.
Ed: Peter DeMarco. **Description:** Discusses the reasons why single-member limited liability companies are gaining popularity; LLC structure allows a great deal of flexibility and protects the owner from liability.

45642 ■ *"Provinces Tackle E-Waste Problem" in Canadian Electronics (Vol. 23, June-July 2008, No. 4, pp. 1)*
Pub: Action Communication Inc.
Ed: Ken Manchen. **Description:** Canadian provinces are implementing measures concerning the safe and environmentally friendly disposal of electronic waste. Alberta, British Columbia, Nova Scotia, and Saskatchewan impose an e-waste recycling fee on electronic equipment purchases.

45643 ■ *"Psst..Spread the Word" in Boston Business Journal (Vol. 27, November 23, 2007, No. 43, pp. 1)*
Pub: American City Business Journals Inc.
Ed: Lisa van der Pool. **Description:** More and more Boston companies are using word-of-mouth marketing to boost sales, and spending on it rose to $981 million in 2006. It is projected that spending on word-of-mouth marketing will reach $1.4 billion in 2007, and marketing companies using this type of method are getting higher funding. Trends in word-of-mouth marketing are discussed.

45644 ■ *"Quality at Bargain Prices" in Black Enterprise (Vol. 41, December 2010, No. 5, pp. 30)*
Pub: Earl G. Graves Publishing Co. Inc.
Ed: James A. Anderson. **Description:** Monica L. Walker, CEO of Holland Capital Management, suggests investors to watch prevailing trends in the financial market and to focus on using bottom-up analysis to identify companies meeting their investment criteria.

45645 ■ *"Quits Versus Layoffs" in Occupational Outlook Quarterly (Vol. 55, Fall 2011, No. 3, pp. 36)*
Pub: U.S. Bureau of Labor Statistics
Description: Data from the U.S. Bureau of Labor Statistics provides data from the Job Openings and Labor Turnover Survey regarding quits and layoffs.

45646 ■ *"The Rabbi Trust" in Barron's (Vol. 88, March 24, 2008, No. 12, pp. 55)*
Pub: Dow Jones & Company, Inc.
Ed: Joseph F. Gelband. **Description:** Discusses a rabbi trust which is a method of deferring taxes on compensation allowed by the Internal Revenue Service. Funding of the trust is not considered taxable. Other regulations concerning tax deferment are also discussed.

45647 ■ *Race and Entrepreneurial Success: Black-, Asian-, and White-Owned Businesses in the United States*
Pub: The MIT Press
Contact: Ellen W. Faran, Director
E-mail: ewfaran@mit.edu
Ed: Robert W. Fairlie. **Released:** September 30, 2008. **Price:** $35.00. **Description:** Trends in minority small business ownership are explored, focusing on the importance of human capital, financial capital, and family business background in successful business ownership.

45648 ■ *"The Racial Divide and the Class Struggle in the United States" in WorkingUSA (Vol. 11, September 2008, No. 3, pp. 311)*
Pub: Blackwell Publishers Ltd.
Ed: Michael Goldfield. **Description:** An examination of questions of race that continue to play such a prominent role in contemporary society is presented, focusing on the undermining of potential solidarity and strength of the working class movement, what sustains racists attitudes, practices and institutions, especially in the face of trends in world economic development.

45649 ■ *"Radiant - the Hottest Topic in .. Cooling" in Indoor Comfort Marketing (Vol. 70, February 2011, No. 2, pp. 8)*
Pub: Industry Publications Inc.
Description: Examination of radiant cooling systems, a new trend in cooling homes and buildings.

45650 ■ *Reading Financial Reports for Dummies*
Pub: John Wiley and Sons, Inc.
Ed: Lita Epstein. **Released:** January 2009. **Price:** $21.99. **Description:** This second edition contains more new and updated information, including new information on the separate accounting and financial reporting standards for private/small businesses versus public/large businesses; updated information reflecting 2007 laws on international financial reporting standards; new content to match SEC and other governmental regulatory changes over the last three years; new information about how the analyst-corporate connection has changed the playing field; the impact of corporate communications and new technologies; new examples that reflect the current trends; and updated Websites and resources.

45651 ■ *"Real Estate Defaults Top $300M" in Business Courier (Vol. 26, January 15, 2010,*

No. 39, pp. 1)
Pub: American City Business Journals, Inc.
Ed: Dan Monk. **Description:** Cincinnati commercial real estate owners defaulting in securitized loans reached $306 million at the end of 2009. The trend has lifted the region's default rate to nearly 9 percent. National average for commercial real estate default is examined.

45652 ■ *"Real Estate Funds Swell Past $350M" in Business Journal Portland (Vol. 27, December 31, 2010, No. 44, pp. 1)*
Pub: Portland Business Journal
Ed: Wendy Culverwell. **Description:** Oregon-based real estate funds have raised around half of the $735 million that was raised by local companies. Investors have been purchasing distressed properties. Commercial real estate prices have declined since 2007.

45653 ■ *"Real Estate Market Still in a Slump" in Montana Business Quarterly (Vol. 49, Summer 2011, No. 2, pp. 15)*
Pub: Bureau of Business & Economic Research
Ed: Patrick M. Barkey. **Description:** Montana's housing market is still in decline with no sign of improving in the near future. Statistical data included.

45654 ■ *"The Reality of Fantasy Sports" in Entrepreneur (Vol. 37, September 2009, No. 9, pp. 52)*
Pub: Entrepreneur Media, Inc.
Ed: Jason Ankeny. **Description:** United States fantasy sports business has grown into a $1 billion industry. Fantasy gaming in the country remains affordable and accessible despite the increase in the prices of tickets to sports games. Comments from analysts are also presented.

45655 ■ *"Realtors Signing Out" in The Business Journal-Serving Metropolitan Kansas City (Vol. 27, November 21, 2008, No. 11, pp. 1)*
Pub: American City Business Journals, Inc.
Ed: Rob Roberts. **Description:** The Kansas City Regional Association of Realtors has lost 1,000 of its members due to the downturn in the housing market. Applications for realtor licenses have dropped by 159 percent. Changes in Missouri's licensing requirements are seen as additional reasons for the declines.

45656 ■ *"A Recipe for Change" in Canadian Business (Vol. 80, October 22, 2007, No. 21, pp. 25)*
Pub: Rogers Media
Ed: Erin Pooley. **Description:** Market conditions have changed and customers around the world are demanding low-fat alternatives. Labor costs have risen and so did the price of foodstuffs. The impacts of this on fast food restaurants as well as the measures they have taken to cope with the new demands are discussed.

45657 ■ *"Recruiting 2.0" in Entrepreneur (Vol. 35, November 2007, No. 11, pp. 100)*
Pub: Entrepreneur Media Inc.
Ed: Andrea Cooper. **Description:** Technology is becoming a tool to help small companies find the best employees. Firms can look into social networking sites to see recommendations from the applicants' colleagues. Tips on how to select the employees online are listed.

45658 ■ *"Red, Pink and More: Cause Marketing Surges as a Prime Tactic to Reach Female Customers" in Marketing to Women (April 2008)*
Pub: EPM Communications Inc.
Contact: Ira Mayer, President
E-mail: imayer@epmcom.com
Description: According to the American Marketing Association, forty percent of women say they are more likely to purchase a product or service if they know a certain amount of the price is being donated directly to a cause or campaign that they believe in supporting.

45659 ■ *"Research and Markets Adds: 2011 U.S. Women's & Children's Clothing Wholesale Report" in Health & Beauty*

Close-Up (October 16, 2010)
Pub: Close-Up Media Inc.
Description: The Women's & Children's Clothing Wholesale Report is an annual report containing timely and accurate industry statistics, forecasts and demographics.

45660 ■ *"Research and Markets Adds Report: Credit and Collection Practices 2009" in Wireless News (August 12, 2009)*
Pub: Close-Up Media
Description: Research and Markets announced the addition of the 'Credit and Collection Practices 2009' report which will highlight credit and collection industry practices and technologies. The report also includes an overview of the best practices in the field.

45661 ■ *"Research and Markets: Wedding Statistics and Industry Reports" in Benzinga.com (June 24, 2011)*
Pub: Benzinga.com
Ed: Benzinga Staff. **Description:** The latest trends and statistics regarding weddings and the wedding industry are spotlighted.

45662 ■ *"Resource Line" in Black Enterprise (Vol. 37, January 2007, No. 6, pp. 6)*
Pub: Earl G. Graves Publishing Co. Inc.
Description: Interactive Media Editor, Philana Patterson, writes a column for blackenterprise.com that offers advice and provides resources for entrepreneurs, corporate executives, business owners, and budding investors.

45663 ■ *"Rest Easy, Retailers" in Pet Product News (Vol. 64, December 2010, No. 12, pp. S1)*
Pub: BowTie Inc.
Ed: Wendy Bedwell-Wilson. **Description:** Pointers on how retailers can market all-natural beds and bedding products for pets are provided. The demand for these pet beds and bedding products has been increasing as customers become aware of the benefits of natural rest and relaxation products.

45664 ■ *"Restaurants Dish Up Meal Deals To Attract Customers" in Crain's Detroit Business (Vol. 24, October 6, 2008, No. 40, pp. 1)*
Pub: Crain Communications, Inc.
Ed: Nathan Skid. **Description:** Restaurateurs are devising many creative and rewarding incentives to get customers to frequent their establishments during this economic crisis. Innovative ways in which even higher-end establishments are drawing in business are discussed.

45665 ■ *"A Rise in Rental Units" in Philadelphia Business Journal (Vol. 30, October 7, 2011, No. 34, pp. 1)*
Pub: American City Business Journals Inc.
Ed: Natalie Kostelni. **Description:** Housing developers have been stepping up the construction of new apartment complexes throughout the suburbs of Pennsylvania in order to capture growing demand for rental properties. BPG Properties Ltd. has nearly 1,000 new apartments under construction.

45666 ■ *"Running On Empty" in The Business Journal-Milwaukee (Vol. 25, July 4, 2008, No. 41, pp. A1)*
Pub: American City Business Journals, Inc.
Ed: David Doege. **Description:** Employers are more engaged in offering incentives designed to offset commuting costs. Among the incentives offered are gas cards, parking reimbursement and midyear wage increases. The other efforts to help employees with the costs of going to work are discussed.

45667 ■ *"Safeway" in Ice Cream Reporter (Vol. 23, September 20, 2010, No. 10, pp. 8)*
Pub: Ice Cream Reporter
Description: Safeway supermarkets have upsized their private label ice cream to a full half gallon, thus reversing the trend where most brands were shrinking their containers.

45668 ■ *"Sales of Pension Income Targeted by Senator" in Wall Street Journal Eastern Edition (November 21 , 2011, pp. C7)*
Pub: Dow Jones & Company Inc.
Ed: Leslie Scism. **Description:** Senator Tom Harkin is concerned about a widening business in which retirees and veterans sell pension income to investors in the secondary market. The business provides major profits for middlemen. Harkin wants those who are considering such a sale to have adequate information provided and knowledge in order to avoid unscrupulous dealings.

45669 ■ *Sarbanes-Oxley for Dummies, 2nd Ed.*
Pub: John Wiley and Sons, Inc.
Ed: Jill Gilbert Welytok. **Released:** February 2008. **Price:** $21.99. **Description:** Provides the latest Sarbanes-Oxley (SOX) legislation with procedures to safely and effectively reduce compliance costs. Topics include way to: establish SOX standards for IT professionals, minimize compliances costs for every aspect of a business, survive a Section 404 audit, avoid litigation under SOX, anticipate future rules and trends, create a post-SOX paper trail, increase a company's standing and reputation, work with SOX in a small business, meet new SOX standards, build a board that can't be bought, and to comply with all SOX management mandates.

45670 ■ *Say Everything: How Blogging Began, What It's Becoming, and Why It Matters*
Pub: Crown Business
Ed: Scott Rosenberg. **Released:** 2009. **Price:** $26.00. **Description:** A history of Internet blogs that explains how they started and why they matter to any small business.

45671 ■ *"Scottsdale Bank Plans 4Q Opening" in The Business Journal - Serving Phoenix and the Valley of the Sun (Vol. 28, August 15, 2008, No. 50)*
Pub: American City Business Journals, Inc.
Ed: Chris Casacchia. **Description:** Arizona's Department of Financial Institutions has approved Scottsdale Business Bank, a community bank which plans to open in the fourth quarter of 2008. The bank, which is to be located near McCormick Ranch in Scottsdale, Arizona, will cater to small business owners in the professional sector, such as accountants and doctors.

45672 ■ *"SEC Report On Rating Agencies Falls Short" in Barron's (Vol. 88, July 14, 2008, No. 28, pp. 35)*
Pub: Dow Jones & Co., Inc.
Ed: Jack Willoughby. **Description:** The Securities and Exchange Commissions report on credit-rating firms should have drawn attention to the slipshod practices in the offerings of collateralized debt obligations. The report fell short of prescribing correctives for the flawed system of these agencies' relationship with their clients.

45673 ■ *"A Second Chance to Make a Living" in The Business Journal-Milwaukee (Vol. 25, September 19, 2008, No. 52, pp. A1)*
Pub: American City Business Journals, Inc.
Description: Unemployed workers and baby boomers are driving interest in purchasing small businesses. BizBuySell general manager Mike Handelsman reveals that the supply of small businesses for sale is decreasing due to the increased demand. The trends in the small business market are analyzed.

45674 ■ *"Seeing Green in Going Green" in The Business Journal-Serving Greater Tampa Bay (Vol. 28, July 4, 2008, No. 28, pp. 1)*
Pub: American City Business Journals, Inc.
Ed: Janet Leiser. **Description:** Atlanta, Georgia-based developer IDI Corp. is pushing for Leadership in Energy and Environmental Design certification for the warehouse that is currently under construction at Madison Business Center along Port Sutton and U.S. 41. The industrial building is the first in Tampa Bay to seek certification for LEED as set by the U.S. Green Building Council.

45675 ■ *"Self-Employment in the United States" in Montly Labor Review (Vol. 133, September 2010, No. 9, pp. 17)*
Pub: Bureau of Labor Statistics
Description: Self employment in 2009 in the U.S. continued to be more common among men, Whites, Asians, and older workers and in the agriculture, construction, and services industries.

45676 ■ *"Senate Bill Would Eliminate MBT Surcharge in 2011" in Crain's Detroit Business (Vol. 24, April 7, 2008, No. 14, pp. 33)*
Pub: Crain Communications, Inc.
Ed: Amy Lane. **Description:** Discusses possible changes to the new Michigan Business Tax, including a proposed bill which would phase out a 21.99 percent surcharge on the tax.

45677 ■ *"Senate OKs Funds for Promoting Tourism" in Crain's Detroit Business (Vol. 24, March 31, 2008, No. 13, pp. 6)*
Pub: Crain Communications, Inc.
Ed: Amy Lane. **Description:** Discusses the Senate proposal which allocates funds for Michigan tourism and business promotion as well as Michigan's No Worker Left Behind initiative, a program that provides free tuition at community colleges and other venues to train displaced workers for high-demand occupations.

45678 ■ *"Senators Predict Online School Changes" in Puget Sound Business Journal (Vol. 29, September 19, 2008, No. 22, pp. 1)*
Pub: American City Business Journals
Ed: Clay Holtzman. **Description:** State senators promise to create new legislation that would tighten the monitoring and oversight of online public schools. The officials are concerned about the lack of oversight of the programs as well as lack of knowledge about content of the lessons.

45679 ■ *"Setting Out on Your Own? Think Franchises" in Crain's Cleveland Business (Vol. 28, October 8, 2007, No. 40, pp. 20)*
Pub: Crain Communications, Inc.
Description: Franchisers are targeting baby boomers due to their willingness to put up some of their own money to open their own business. According to local franchising expert, Joel Libava, entrepreneurs should expect to pay about 15 to 30 percent of the total cost of starting the franchise out of their own pocket.

45680 ■ *"Sewing Resurgence" in Northeast Mississippi Daily Journal (June 11, 2010)*
Pub: Northeast Mississippi Daily Journal
Ed: Ginna Parsons. **Description:** Information about the growing trend in sewing is discussed.

45681 ■ *Shedworking: The Alternative Workplace Revolution*
Pub: Frances Lincoln Limited
Ed: Alex Johnson. **Released:** June 10, 2010. **Price:** $29.95. **Description:** Shedworking is an alternative office space for those working at home. The book features shedworkers and shedbuilders from around the world who are leading this alternative workplace revolution and why this trend is working.

45682 ■ *"Shoestring-Budget Marketing" in Women Entrepreneur (January 5, 2009)*
Pub: Entrepreneur Media Inc.
Ed: Maria Falconer. **Description:** Pay-per-click search engine advertising is the traditional type of e-marketing that may not only be too expensive for certain kinds of businesses but also may not attract the quality customer base a business looking to grow needs to find. Social networking websites have become a mandatory marketing tool for business owners who want to see growth in their sales; tips are provided for utilizing these networking websites in order to gain more visibility on the Internet which can, in turn, lead to the more sales.

45683 ■ *"Should I or Shouldn't I?" in Indoor Comfort Marketing (Vol. 70, February 2011, No. 2, pp. 30)*
Pub: Industry Publications Inc.
Ed: Philip J. Baratz. **Description:** Investment tips are shared for investing in futures options.

45684 ■ *"Sick of Trends? You Should Be" in Brandweek (Vol. 49, April 21, 2008, No. 16, pp. 22)*
Pub: VNU Business Media, Inc.
Ed: Eric Zeitoun. **Description:** Eric Zeitoun, the president of Dragon Rouge, a global brand consultancy, discusses the importance of macrotrends as opposed to microtrends which he feels are often irrelevant, create confusion and cause marketers to lose site of the larger picture of their industry. Macrotrends, on the other hand, create a fundamental, societal shift that influences consumer attitudes over a long period of time.

45685 ■ *"Sign of the Times: Temp-To-Perm Attorneys" in HRMagazine (Vol. 54, January 2009, No. 1, pp. 24)*
Pub: Society for Human Resource Management
Contact: Henry G. Jackson, President
E-mail: hjackson@shrm.org
Ed: Bill Leonard. **Description:** A growing number of law firms are hiring professional staff on a temp-to-perm basis according to the president of Professional Placement Services in Florida. Firms can save money while testing potential employees on a temporary basis.

45686 ■ *"Single Most Important Problem" in Small Business Economic Trends (March 2008, pp. 18)*
Pub: National Federation of Independent Business
Ed: William C. Dunkelberg, Holly Wade. **Description:** Two graphs and a table representing the economic problems encountered by small businesses in the U.S. are presented. The figures presented in the graphs include data from 1986 to 2008.

45687 ■ *"Single Most Important Problem" in Small Business Economic Trends (February 2008, pp. 18)*
Pub: National Federation of Independent Business
Ed: William C. Dunkelberg, Holly Wade. **Description:** Two graphs and a table representing the economic problems encountered by small businesses in the U.S. are presented. The figures presented in the graphs include data from 1974 to 2008.

45688 ■ *"Single Most Important Problem" in Small Business Economic Trends (January 2008, pp. 18)*
Pub: National Federation of Independent Business
Description: Table of the single most important problem among small businesses surveyed in the U.S. in December 2007 is presented. Taxes were selected by 21 percent of firms as the single most important problem, followed by cost and availability of insurance at 16 percent. Graphs comparing selected single most important problem from January 1986 to December 2007 are also given.

45689 ■ *"Single Most Important Problem" in Small Business Economic Trends (July 2010, pp. 18)*
Pub: National Federation of Independent Business
Description: A table showing the single most important problem among small businesses surveyed in the U.S. for June 2010 is presented. Poor sales was selected by 30 percent of firms as the single most important problem, followed by taxes and government requirements and red tape. Graphs comparing selected single most important problem from January 1986 to June 2010 are also given.

45690 ■ *"Skinny Jeans Sticking Around for Fall" in Charlotte Observer (February 5, 2007)*
Pub: Knight-Ridder/Tribune Business News
Ed: Crystal Dempsey. **Description:** Clothing designers were showing skinny jeans in the fall/winter fashion shows for 2007.

45691 ■ *"Slimmer Interiros Make Small Cars Seem Big" in Automotive News (Vol. 86, October 31, 2011, No. 6488, pp. 16)*
Pub: Crain Communications Inc.
Ed: David Sedgwick. **Description:** Cost-conscious buyers want luxury car amenities in their smaller vehicles, so automakers are rethinking interiors. Style, efficiency and value could be the next trend in vehicles.

45692 ■ *"The Small 300" in Canadian Business (Vol. 81, Summer 2008, No. 9, pp. 137)*
Pub: Rogers Media Ltd.
Description: Small cap-companies are ranked based on market capitalization and stock performance. Calgary-based Grande Cache Coal Corp. topped the roster with 1,000 percent of return resulting from strong sales. A table showing the 2008 rankings of the companies is presented.

45693 ■ *"Small Business Capital Outlays" in Small Business Economic Trends (March 2008, pp. 16)*
Pub: National Federation of Independent Business
Ed: William C. Dunkelberg, Holly Wade. **Description:** Graphs and tables that present the capital outlays of small businesses in the U.S. are provided. The tables include figures on planned and actual capital expenditures, and type and amount of capital expenditures.

45694 ■ *"Small Business Capital Outlays" in Small Business Economic Trends (February 2008, pp. 16)*
Pub: National Federation of Independent Business
Ed: William C. Dunkelberg, Holly Wade. **Description:** Graphs and tables that present the capital outlays of small businesses in the U.S. are provided. The tables include figures on planned and actual capital expenditures, and type and amount of capital expenditures.

45695 ■ *"Small Business Capital Outlays" in Small Business Economic Trends (January 2008, pp. 16)*
Pub: National Federation of Independent Business
Description: Graph representing actual and planned capital expenditures among small businesses surveyed in the U.S. from January 1986 to December 2007 is given. Tables showing actual capital expenditures, type of capital expenditures made, amount of capital expenditures made, and capital expenditure plans are also presented.

45696 ■ *"Small Business Capital Outlays" in Small Business Economic Trends (July 2010, pp. 16)*
Pub: National Federation of Independent Business
Description: A graph representing actual and planned capital expenditures among small businesses surveyed in the U.S. from January 1986 to June 2010 is given. Tables showing actual capital expenditures, type of capital expenditures made, amount of capital expenditures made, and capital expenditure plans are also presented.

45697 ■ *"Small Business Compensation" in Small Business Economic Trends (April 2008, pp. 10)*
Pub: National Federation of Independent Business
Ed: William C. Dunkelberg, Holly Wade. **Description:** Graphs and tables that present compensation plans and compensation changes of small businesses in the U.S. are provided. The figures include data from 1986 to 2008.

45698 ■ *"Small Business Compensation" in Small Business Economic Trends (March 2008, pp. 10)*
Pub: National Federation of Independent Business
Ed: William C. Dunkelberg, Holly Wade. **Description:** Graphs and tables that present compensation plans and compensation changes of small businesses in the U.S. are provided. The figures include data from 1968 to 2008.

45699 ■ *"Small Business Compensation" in Small Business Economic Trends (February 2008, pp. 10)*
Pub: National Federation of Independent Business
Ed: William C. Dunkelberg, Holly Wade. **Description:** Graphs and tables that present compensation plans and compensation changes of small businesses in the U.S. are provided. The figures include data from 1974 to 2008.

45700 ■ *"Small Business Compensation"* in *Small Business Economic Trends (January 2008, pp. 10)*
Pub: National Federation of Independent Business
Description: Graph from a survey of small businesses in the U.S. is given, representing small business compensation from January 1986 to December 2007. Tables showing actual compensation changes and compensation plans are also presented. A graph comparing small business prices and labor compensation is supplied.

45701 ■ *"Small Business Compensation"* in *Small Business Economic Trends (July 2010, pp. 10)*
Pub: National Federation of Independent Business
Description: A graph from a survey of small businesses in the U.S. is given representing small business compensation from January 1986 to June 2010. Tables showing actual compensation changes and compensation plans are also presented. A graph comparing small business prices and labor compensation is supplied.

45702 ■ *"Small Business Credit Conditions"* in *Small Business Economic Trends (July 2010, pp. 12)*
Pub: National Federation of Independent Business
Description: Graphs representing loan availability and interest rates among U.S. small businesses surveyed from January 1986 to June 2010 are given. Tables showing regular borrowers, availability of loans, satisfied borrowing needs, expected credit conditions, relative interest rate paid by regular borrowers, and actual interest rate paid on short-term loans by borrowers are also presented.

45703 ■ *"Small Business Earnings"* in *Small Business Economic Trends (April 2008, pp. 6)*
Pub: National Federation of Independent Business
Ed: William C. Dunkelberg, Holly Wade. **Description:** Two tables and a graph presenting the earnings of small businesses in the U.S. are provided. Statistics for actual earnings changes are provided. The figures in the graph include data from 1986 to 2008.

45704 ■ *"Small Business Earnings"* in *Small Business Economic Trends (July 2010, pp. 6)*
Pub: National Federation of Independent Business
Description: A graph from a survey of small businesses in the U.S. is given representing actual small business earnings from January 1986 to June 2010. Tables showing actual earnings changes and most important reason for lower earnings are also presented.

45705 ■ *"Small Business Employment"* in *Small Business Economic Trends (April 2008, pp. 9)*
Pub: National Federation of Independent Business
Ed: William C. Dunkelberg, Holly Wade. **Description:** Four tables and a graph representing employment rates of small businesses in the U.S. are presented. The tables include figures on employment changes, number of qualified applicants, job openings, and hiring plans.

45706 ■ *"Small Business Employment"* in *Small Business Economic Trends (March 2008, pp. 9)*
Pub: National Federation of Independent Business
Ed: William C. Dunkelberg, Holly Wade. **Description:** Four tables and a graph that present employment rates of small businesses in the U.S. are provided. The tables include figures on employment changes, number of qualified applicants, job openings and hiring plans.

45707 ■ *"Small Business Employment"* in *Small Business Economic Trends (February 2008, pp. 9)*
Pub: National Federation of Independent Business
Ed: William C. Dunkelberg, Holly Wade. **Description:** Four tables and a graph that present employment rates of small businesses in the U.S. are provided. The tables include figures on employment changes, number of qualified applicants, job openings and hiring plans.

45708 ■ *"Small Business Employment"* in *Small Business Economic Trends (January 2008, pp. 9)*
Pub: National Federation of Independent Business
Description: Table from a survey of small businesses in the U.S. is given, representing actual employment changes from January 2002 to December 2007. A graph comparing planned employment and current job openings from January 1986 to December 2007 is also supplied. Tables showing job opening, hiring plans, and qualified applicants for job openings are also presented.

45709 ■ *"Small Business Employment"* in *Small Business Economic Trends (July 2010, pp. 9)*
Pub: National Federation of Independent Business
Description: A table from a survey of small businesses in the U.S. is given representing actual employment changes from January 2005 to June 2010. A graph comparing planned employment and current job openings from January 1986 to June 2010 is also supplied. Tables showing job openings, hiring plans, and qualified applicants for job openings are also presented.

45710 ■ *The Small Business Guide to HSAs*
Pub: Brick Tower Press
Ed: JoAnn Mills Laing. **Released:** September 2004. **Price:** $14.95. **Description:** Government-assisted Health Savings Accounts (HSAs) offer employees a tax-free way to accumulate savings to be used for qualified medical expenses, they can be rolled over without penalty for future spending, or invested to accumulate savings to pay for health needs after retirement. Employers offering HSAs can save up to two-thirds of business expenses on health insurance costs.

45711 ■ *"Small Business Inventories"* in *Small Business Economic Trends (April 2008, pp. 14)*
Pub: National Federation of Independent Business
Ed: William C. Dunkelberg, Holly Wade. **Description:** Three tables and a graph presenting the inventories of small businesses in the U.S. are provided. The tables include figures on actual inventory changes, inventory satisfaction, and inventory plans.

45712 ■ *"Small Business Inventories"* in *Small Business Economic Trends (March 2008, pp. 14)*
Pub: National Federation of Independent Business
Ed: William C. Dunkelberg, Holly Wade. **Description:** Three tables and a graph presenting the inventories of small businesses in the U.S. are given. The tables include figures on actual inventory changes, inventory satisfaction, and inventory plans.

45713 ■ *"Small Business Inventories"* in *Small Business Economic Trends (February 2008, pp. 14)*
Pub: National Federation of Independent Business
Ed: William C. Dunkelberg, Holly Wade. **Description:** Three tables and a graph presenting the inventories of small businesses in the U.S. are given. The tables include figures on actual inventory changes, inventory satisfaction, and inventory plans.

45714 ■ *"Small Business Inventories"* in *Small Business Economic Trends (January 2008, pp. 14)*
Pub: National Federation of Independent Business
Description: Graph representing actual and planned inventories among small businesses surveyed in the U.S. from January 1986 to December 2007 is presented. A graph comparing inventory satisfaction and inventory plans over the same time period is also given. Tables showing actual inventory changes, inventory satisfaction, and inventory plans are also supplied.

45715 ■ *"Small Business Inventories"* in *Small Business Economic Trends (July 2010, pp. 14)*
Pub: National Federation of Independent Business
Description: A graph representing actual and planned inventories among small businesses surveyed in the U.S. from January 1986 to June 2010 is

presented. A graph comparing inventory satisfaction and inventory plans over the same time period is also given. Tables showing actual inventory changes, inventory satisfaction, and inventory plans are also supplied.

45716 ■ *"Small Business Outlook"* in *Small Business Economic Trends (April 2008, pp. 4)*
Pub: National Federation of Independent Business
Ed: William C. Dunkelberg, Holly Wade. **Description:** Three tables and a graph presenting forecasts in business expansions of small businesses in the U.S. are presented. The figures presented in the graph include data from 1986 to 2008.

45717 ■ *"Small Business Outlook"* in *Small Business Economic Trends (March 2008, pp. 4)*
Pub: National Federation of Independent Business
Ed: William C. Dunkelberg, Holly Wade. **Description:** Three tables and a graph representing forecasts in business expansions of small businesses in the U.S. are presented. The figures presented in the graph include data from 1986 to 2008.

45718 ■ *"Small Business Outlook"* in *Small Business Economic Trends (February 2008, pp. 4)*
Pub: National Federation of Independent Business
Ed: William C. Dunkelberg, Holly Wade. **Description:** Three tables and a graph representing forecasts in business expansions of small businesses in the U.S. are presented. The figures presented in the graph include data from 1974 to 2008.

45719 ■ *"Small Business Outlook"* in *Small Business Economic Trends (January 2008, pp. 4)*
Pub: National Federation of Independent Business
Description: Graph representing outlook among small businesses surveyed in the U.S. from January 1986 to December 2007 is presented. Tables showing small business outlook for expansion and outlook for general business conditions from January 2002 to December 2007 and the most important reasons for expansion outlook are also given.

45720 ■ *"Small Business Outlook"* in *Small Business Economic Trends (July 2010, pp. 4)*
Pub: National Federation of Independent Business
Description: A graph representing outlook among small businesses surveyed in the U.S. from January 1986 to June 2010 is presented. Tables showing small business outlook for expansion and outlook for general business conditions from January 2005 to June 2010, and most important reasons for expansion outlook are also given.

45721 ■ *"Small Business Prices"* in *Small Business Economic Trends (April 2008, pp. 8)*
Pub: National Federation of Independent Business
Ed: William C. Dunkelberg, Holly Wade. **Description:** Two tables and a graph presenting the price changes and price plans of small businesses in the U.S. are provided. The net percentage of planned and actual prices includes data from 1968 to 2008.

45722 ■ *"Small Business Prices"* in *Small Business Economic Trends (March 2008, pp. 8)*
Pub: National Federation of Independent Business
Ed: William C. Dunkelberg. **Description:** Two tables and a graph presenting the price changes and price plans of small businesses in the U.S. are provided. The net percentage of planned and actual prices includes data from 1986 to 2008.

45723 ■ *"Small Business Prices"* in *Small Business Economic Trends (February 2008, pp. 8)*
Pub: National Federation of Independent Business
Ed: William C. Dunkelberg. **Description:** Two tables and a graph presenting the price changes and price plans of small businesses in the U.S. are provided. The net percentage of planned and actual prices includes data from 1974 to 2008.

45724 ■ *"Small Business Prices" in Small Business Economic Trends (January 2008, pp. 8)*
Pub: National Federation of Independent Business

Description: Graph from a survey of small businesses in the U.S. is given representing business prices from January 1986 to December 2007. Actual prices (last three months) and planned prices (next three months) were compared in the graph. Tables of actual price changes and price plans from January 2002 to December 2007 are also supplied.

45725 ■ *"Small Business Prices" in Small Business Economic Trends (July 2010, pp. 8)*
Pub: National Federation of Independent Business

Description: A graph from a survey of small businesses in the U.S. is given representing business prices from January 1986 to June 2010. Actual prices (last three months) and planned prices (next three months) were compared in the graph. Tables of actual price changes and price plans from January 2005 to June 2010 are also supplied.

45726 ■ *"Small Business Sales" in Small Business Economic Trends (April 2008, pp. 7)*
Pub: National Federation of Independent Business

Ed: William C. Dunkelberg, Holly Wade. **Description:** Two tables and a graph resenting sales figures of small businesses in the U.S. is presented. Statistics for sales changes and sales expectations are provided. The figures in the graph include data from 1986 to 2008.

45727 ■ *"Small Business Sales" in Small Business Economic Trends (March 2008, pp. 7)*
Pub: National Federation of Independent Business

Ed: William C. Dunkelberg, Holly Wade. **Description:** Two tables and a graph that present sales figures for small businesses in the U.S. are given. Statistics for sales changes and sales expectations are provided. The figures in the graph include data from 1986 to 2008.

45728 ■ *"Small Business Sales" in Small Business Economic Trends (February, pp. 7)*
Pub: National Federation of Independent Business

Ed: William C. Dunkelberg, Holly Wade. **Description:** Two tables and a graph that present sales figures for small businesses in the U.S. are given. Statistics for sales changes and sales expectations are provided. The figures in the graph include data from 1974 to 2008.

45729 ■ *"Small Business Sales" in Small Business Economic Trends (January, pp. 7)*
Pub: National Federation of Independent Business

Description: Graph from a survey of small businesses in the U.S. is given, representing sales figures from January 1986 to December 2007. Actual sales (prior three months) and expected sales (next three months) were compared in the graph. Tables of actual sales changes and sales expectations from January 2002 to December 2007 are also given.

45730 ■ *"Small Business Sales" in Small Business Economic Trends (July 2010, pp. 7)*
Pub: National Federation of Independent Business

Description: A graph from a survey of small businesses in the U.S. is given representing sales from January 1986 to June 2010. Actual sales (prior three months) and expected sales (next three months) were compared in the graph. Tables of actual sales changes and sales expectations from January 2005 to June 2010 are also given.

45731 ■ *"Small Changes Can Mean Big Energy Savings" in Crain's Cleveland Business (Vol. 28, November 5, 2007, No. 44, pp. 21)*
Pub: Crain Communications, Inc.

Ed: Harriet Tramer. **Description:** Many Northeast Ohio businesses are taking their cues from the residential real estate market to draw and capitalize on interest in energy efficiency and is regularly taken into account by local architects.

45732 ■ *"Smaller Banks Could Face Tough 2008" in Austin Business JournalInc. (Vol. 28, January 2, 2009, No. 1, pp. 3)*
Pub: American City Business Journals

Ed: Christopher Calnan. **Description:** The turbulence in the banking industry is expected to reach Texas in 2009 and industry insiders believe there will be a shift in deposits from small, regional banks to larger banks due to low consumer confidence. One economist says that a large number of banks are going to go out of business in 2009.

45733 ■ *So You Want to Start a Business?*
Pub: Pearson Education, Limited
Contact: Steven A. Dowling, President

Ed: Edward D. Hess; Charles Goetz. **Released:** August 30, 2008. **Price:** $18.99. **Description:** Over sixty percent of Americans say they would like to own their own business and more than five million business startups are launched annually. However, fifty to seventy percent of new businesses fail. This book identifies the eight mistakes that cause these business failures and offers entrepreneurs the knowledge, tools, templates, strategies, and hands-on how-to advice needed to avoid these errors and succeed.

45734 ■ *Social Enterprise: Developing Sustainable Businesses*
Pub: Palgrave Macmillan

Ed: Frank Martin, Marcus Thompson. **Released:** January 1, 2010. **Price:** $106.00. **Description:** Social enterprises bring people and communities together for economic development and social gain and represent a growing sector of the business community.

45735 ■ *"Social Media By the Numbers: Social-Media Marketing Is All the Rage" in Inc. (Vol. 33, November 2011, No. 9, pp. 70)*
Pub: Inc. Magazine

Ed: J.J. McCorvey, Issie Lapowsky. **Description:** Six strategies to help small businesses use social media sites such as Facebook and Twitter to promote their companies are presented.

45736 ■ *"Social Networks in the Workplace" in Strategy & Leadership (Vol. 38, July-August 2010, No. 4, pp. 50-53)*
Pub: Emerald Inc.

Ed: Daniel Burrus. **Description:** The opinions of futurist Daniel Burrus on a novel trend called 'Business 2.0', which involves the use of social networking applications as business tools, are presented. His suggestion that personal social networking technology can be used by businesses to improve collaboration, problem solving, and leadership communications to achieve continuous value innovation is discussed.

45737 ■ *"Sole Proprietorship Returns, 2008" in SOI Bulletin (Vol. 30, Summer 2010, No. 1, pp. 6)*
Pub: Government Printing Office

Ed: Adrian Dungan. **Description:** Approximately 22.6 million individual income tax returns reported nonfarm sole proprietorship activity, a 2.2 percent decrease from 2007. Statistical data included.

45738 ■ *"Sole Proprietorship Returns, 2008 Part 2" in SOI Bulletin (Vol. 30, Summer 2010, No. 1, pp. 27)*
Pub: Government Printing Office

Description: Table of Nonfarm Sole Proprietorships is presented. Statistics are broken down by sector reporting all nonfarm industries as well as agriculture, forestry, hunting and fishing.

45739 ■ *"Solidarity UAW Forever" in Crain's Detroit Business (Vol. 25, June 1, 2009, No. 22, pp. M001)*
Pub: Crain Communications Inc. - Detroit

Ed: Ryan Beene. **Description:** United Auto Workers union has made it difficult for certain businesses to move to Michigan. Discussion is made about the issues involved and changes that need to be made in the way labor and management do business.

45740 ■ *"Solo, But Not Alone" in Entrepreneur (Vol. 37, October 2009, No. 10, pp. 99)*
Pub: Entrepreneur Media, Inc.

Ed: David Port. **Description:** Co-working spaces are emerging in different US cities, allowing entrepreneurs and other independent workers to co-exist. These work spaces, which can be availed for about $500 a month or $25 a day, also afford networking opportunities.

45741 ■ *"Some Big Biotechs Buying Own Stock" in Boston Business Journal (Vol. 30, November 5, 2010, No. 41, pp. 1)*
Pub: Boston Business Journal

Ed: Julie M. Donnelly. **Description:** Biotechnology companies such as Biogen Idec and Genzyme Corporation are conducting stock buybacks as they look to invest their cash holdings. Other analysts see the buybacks as reluctance in committing to longer-term investments.

45742 ■ *"Sorry: Good Defense for Mal Offense" in The Business Journal-Serving Metropolitan Kansas City (Vol. 26, July 4, 2008, No. 43, pp. 1)*
Pub: American City Business Journals, Inc.

Ed: Rob Roberts. **Description:** According to a survey conducted by the Kansas City Business Journal, ten hospitals in Kansas City showed that they have adopted disclosure policies that include prompt apologies and settlement offers. The policy is effective in minimizing medical malpractice lawsuits. Other details of the survey are presented.

45743 ■ *"Sprinkler Advocates Beat Builders Again" in Contractor (Vol. 56, November 2009, No. 11, pp. 58)*
Pub: Penton Media, Inc.

Ed: Bob Mader. **Description:** Proponents of residential fire sprinklers were able to fend off the attempt by the National Association of Home Builders to do away with mandated fire sprinklers on the International Residential Code by the International Code Council (ICC). The ICC's vote on the issue is good news for fire sprinkler contractors and plumbing contractors.

45744 ■ *"Staging a Martini-and-GQ Lifestyle; Faux Possessions Play to Buyer's Aspirations" in Crain's Chicago Business (April 21, 2008)*
Pub: Crain Communications, Inc.

Ed: Kevin Davis. **Description:** Due to the competition of the slumping housing market, home stagers are becoming more prominent and are using creative ways to make an impression beyond de-cluttering, painting and cleaning by using accents such as casually placed magazines, candles and table settings.

45745 ■ *"The Start of a Beautiful Friendship: Partnering with Your Customers on R&D" in Inc. (March 2008, pp. 37-38)*
Pub: Gruner & Jahr USA Publishing

Ed: Leigh Buchanan. **Description:** Joint research and development projects between customers and suppliers are a growing trend in the small business community; these ventures can help keep new product development costs lower. Four tips to maintain a good working relationship in these ventures are outlined.

45746 ■ *"Start Connecting Today" in Indoor Comfort Marketing (Vol. 70, May 2011, No. 5, pp. 34)*
Pub: Industry Publications Inc.

Ed: Paul Nazzaro. **Description:** An in-depth discussion regarding the use of biofuels on bioheat use and dealership.

45747 ■ *"Startup on Cusp of Trend" in Austin Business JournalInc. (Vol. 29, January 8, 2010, No. 44, pp. 1)*
Pub: American City Business Journals

Ed: Christopher Calnan. **Description:** Austin-based Socialware Inc. introduced a new business called social middleware, which is a software that is layered between the company network and social networking

Website used by workers. The software was designed to give employers a measure of control over content while allowing workers to continue using online social networks.

45748 ■ *"State Film Business Tops $1.3 Billion"* in *The Business Journal-Portland (Vol. 25, August 22, 2008, No. 24, pp. 1)*
Pub: American City Business Journals, Inc.
Ed: Andy Giegerich. **Description:** Oregon's film industry has generated $1.39 billion in direct and indirect economic impact in 2007, a 55 percent rise from 2005 levels. The growth of the industry is attributed to tax incentives issued in 2007, which attracted film production companies from other states.

45749 ■ *"The State of the Stores"* in *Playthings (Vol. 106, November 1, 2008, No. 10, pp. 8)*
Pub: Reed Business Information
Contact: Jeff Greisch, President
Ed: Dana French. **Description:** Investigation into the top twenty-five toy and game retailers shows that video games and related handheld and console systems as well as computer games were number one with America's children in 2007.

45750 ■ *"State Unemployment Fraud Rising Sharply"* in *Sacramento Business Journal (Vol. 28, October 21, 2011, No. 34, pp. 1)*
Pub: Sacramento Business Journal
Ed: Michael Shaw. **Description:** California's Employment Development Department has reported that overpayments, especially due to fraud or misrepresentation, have increased from $88 million in 2008 to more than $250 million in 2010. However, criminal prosecutions in 2010 were fewer than in 2008 as the agency struggles to recover the money.

45751 ■ *"Stimulating Fare at the SBA"* in *Barron's (Vol. 89, July 20, 2009, No. 29, pp. 12)*
Pub: Dow Jones & Co., Inc.
Ed: Jim McTague. **Description:** Internet access at the Small Business Administration slowed down on 7 July 2009, apparently caused by employees streaming videos of the Michael Jackson tribute. The agency claims that the event did not disrupt its operations.

45752 ■ *"Stop the Madness"* in *Hawaii Business (Vol. 53, October 2007, No. 4, pp. 10)*
Pub: Hawaii Business Publishing
Ed: Kelli Abe Trifonovitch. **Description:** Discusses the number of parents paying for kindergarten admissions tutorials for their kids which has increased, as parents want to improve their children's chances of being admitted at a prestigious school. Some schools in Hawaii are not in favor of this trend, and they actually rate an applicant negatively if his or her answers seem to be too rehearsed. Some of the lessons in the admissions tutorials are discussed.

45753 ■ *"Storm Takes Toll On Area Businesses"* in *The Business Journal - Serving Phoenix and the Valley of the Sun (Vol. 28, September 5, 2008, No. 52, pp. 1)*
Pub: American City Business Journals, Inc.
Ed: Chris Casacchia. **Description:** Many small businesses in Phoenix, Arizona have lost sales and goods from storms and power outages. Retailers were forced to dispose of spoiled products. Details of damages inflicted by the storm are also presented.

45754 ■ *"Struggling Community Banks Find Little Help In Wall Street Bailout"* in *Crain's Detroit Business (Vol. 24, September 29, 2008)*
Pub: Crain Communications Inc.
Ed: Tom Henderson. **Description:** Both public and private Michigan bands have been hit hard by poorly performing loan portfolios and although their problems were not caused by high-risk securities but by a longtime statewide recession and a housing slump, these community banks have little hope of seeing any of the bailout money that has been allotted for the larger institutions.

45755 ■ *"Succeed With the Right Equipment"* in *Pet Product News (Vol. 64, November 2010, No. 11, pp. 42)*
Pub: BowTie Inc.
Ed: Sandi Cain. **Description:** Grooming shop owners have been focusing on obtaining ergonomic, durable, and efficient products such as restraints, tables, and tubs. These products enhance the way grooming tasks are conducted. Ways pet supply manufacturers have responded to this trend are examined.

45756 ■ *"Sudden Shift Leaves Wells Vendor Scrambling"* in *Charlotte Business Journal (Vol. 25, July 9, 2010, No. 16, pp. 1)*
Pub: Charlotte Business Journal
Ed: Adam O'Daniel. **Description:** Rubber stamps vendor Carolina Marking Devices is facing a 30 percent drop in business after banking firm Wells Fargo & Company decided to buy its rubber stamps from another vendor. Carolina Marking Devices had provided rubber to First Union Corporation and its successor Wachovia Corporation, which was eventually acquired by Wells Fargo. Other reactions from Carolina Marking Device owners are given.

45757 ■ *"Suddenly, Sewing Is Hip Again for Kids, Moms and Crafters"* in *Atlanta Journal-Constitution (August 29, 2010)*
Pub: Atlanta Journal-Constitution
Ed: Rosalind Bentley. **Description:** Across Atlanta, Georgia, along with the entire nation, sewing classes are increasing in popularity.

45758 ■ *"Summary. Economic Trends for Small Business"* in *Small Business Economic Trends (March 2008, pp. 1)*
Pub: National Federation of Independent Business
Ed: William C. Dunkelberg, Holly Wade. **Description:** Summary of economic trends for small businesses in the U.S. is provided. Economic indicators such as capital spending, inventories and sales, inflation, and profits are given. Analysis of credit markets is also provided.

45759 ■ *"Summary. Economic Trends for Small Business"* in *Small Business Economic Trends (February 2008, pp. 1)*
Pub: National Federation of Independent Business
Ed: William C. Dunkelberg, Holly Wade. **Description:** Summary of economic trends for small businesses in the U.S. is provided. Economic indicators such as capital spending, inventories and sales, inflation, and profits are given. Analysis of credit markets is also provided.

45760 ■ *"Survey Finds State Execs Cool On Climate Change"* in *The Business Journal-Milwaukee (Vol. 25, August 8, 2008, No. 46, pp. A1)*
Pub: American City Business Journals, Inc.
Ed: David Doege. **Description:** According to a survey of business executives in Wisconsin, business leaders do not see climate change as a pressing concern, but businesses are moving toward more energy-efficient operations. The survey also revealed that executives believe that financial incentives can promote energy conservation. Other survey results are provided.

45761 ■ *"Survey Profile"* in *Small Business Economic Trends (March 2008, pp. 19)*
Pub: National Federation of Independent Business
Ed: William C. Dunkelberg, Holly Wade. **Description:** Two graphs and a table that present the profile of small businesses that participated in the National Federation of Independent Business (NFIB) survey are provided. The actual number of firms, their industry types, and the number of full and part-time employees are also given.

45762 ■ *"Survey Profile"* in *Small Business Economic Trends (February 2008, pp. 19)*
Pub: National Federation of Independent Business
Ed: William C. Dunkelberg, Holly Wade. **Description:** Two graphs and a table that present the profile of small businesses that participated in the National Federation of Independent Business (NFIB) survey are provided. The actual number of firms, their industry types, and the number of full and part-time employees are also given.

45763 ■ *"Sustaining Health"* in *Pet Product News (Vol. 64, November 2010, No. 11, pp. 28)*
Pub: BowTie Inc.
Ed: Angela Pham. **Description:** How pet supply retailers have responded to dog owners' interest in health supplements and their ingredients is discussed. Dog owners are showing interest in the ingredients inside the supplements and are reading labels. Retailers must now prove the beneficial effects of these ingredients in order to make the sale.

45764 ■ *"A Switch in the Kitchen"* in *Barron's (Vol. 88, March 24, 2008, No. 12, pp. 17)*
Pub: Dow Jones & Company, Inc.
Description: Men are doing more kitchen duties, with 18 percent of meals at home being made by men in 2007 compared to 11 percent four years previously. Young wives, however, choose to forgo work and stay at home.

45765 ■ *"Take the Right Approach to Concrete Polishing Rentals"* in *Rental Product News (Vol. 33, June 2011)*
Pub: Cygnus Business Media
Ed: Jenny Lescohier. **Description:** A recent trend in flooring is concrete polishing for a practical, beautiful and sustainable way to decorate homes and businesses. Things to keep in mind when assessing the value of adding concrete polishing equipment to an existing rental store are evaluated.

45766 ■ *"Tap Into Food Truck Trend to Rev Up Sales, Build Buzz"* in *Nation's Restaurant News (Vol. 45, February 7, 2011, No. 3, pp. 18)*
Pub: Penton Media, Inc.
Ed: Brian Sacks. **Description:** Food truck trend is growing, particularly in New York City, Philadelphia, Washington DC, and Los Angeles, California. Man entrepreneurs are using a mobile food component to market their food before opening a restaurant.

45767 ■ *"Tapping the 'Well' in Wellness"* in *Pet Product News (Vol. 64, November 2010, No. 11, pp. 1)*
Pub: BowTie Inc.
Ed: Wendy-Bedwell Wilson. **Description:** Healthy food and treats are among the leading wellness products being sought by customers from specialty retailers to keep their pets healthy. With this demand for pet wellness products, retailers suggest making sure that staff know key ingredients to emphasize to customers. Other insights into this trend and ways to engage customers are discussed.

45768 ■ *"Tax Talk; Usual Election-Year Obstacles to Income Tax May Not Apply This Time"* in *Crain's Chicago Business (March 24, 2008)*
Pub: Crain Communications, Inc.
Ed: Greg Hinz. **Description:** Discusses the possible raising of the state's income tax; The latest version of the income tax hike bill, sponsored by Senator James Meeks, D-Chicago, would boost individual rates to 5 percent from 3 percent, with the corporate rate rising to a total of 8 percent from 4.8 percent; about $3 billion of the projected $8 billion that would be brought in would be used to cut local property taxes and experts believe the business community overall would benefit.

45769 ■ *"Taxes, Right-To-Work Top West Michigan Concerns"* in *Crain's Detroit Business (Vol. 24, September 22, 2008, No. 38, pp. 6)*
Pub: Crain Communications Inc.
Ed: Amy Lane. **Description:** Two of the top priorities of business leaders in Western Michigan are the new business tax which they want to end as well as making the state a 'right-to-work' one through laws to prohibit unions from requiring workers to pay dues and membership as a condition of their employment.

45770 ■ *"Taxis Are Set to Go Hybrid"* in *Philadelphia Business Journal (Vol. 30,*

September 16, 2011, No. 31, pp. 1)
Pub: American City Business Journals Inc.

Ed: Natalie Kostelni. Description: Taxis are going hybrid in several major states such as New York, California and Maryland where it is mandated, but it is yet to happen in Philadelphia, Pennsylvania with the exception of one taxi company. Freedom Taxi is awaiting Philadelphia Parking Authority's sign off.

45771 ■ *"Tell Us What You Really Think Collecting Customer Feedback" in Inc. (Vol. 30, December 2008, No. 12, pp. 52)*
Pub: Mansueto Ventures LLC

Ed: Ryan Underwood. Description: According to a recent survey, nearly 77 percent of online shoppers review consumer-generated reviews of products before making a purchase.

45772 ■ *"Texas State Poised for Boom" in Austin Business JournalInc. (Vol. 29, January 29, 2010, No. 47, pp. 1)*
Pub: American City Business Journals

Ed: Sandra Zaragoza. Description: Texas State University, San Marcos has seen its student population grow to 30,800 and the university is set for $633 million in construction projects to address demand for student housing and building expansions and renovations. Details on the buildings and student housing plans for the projects are provided.

45773 ■ *"Tied to Home: Female Owned Businesses Export Less, And It's Not Just Because They're Smaller" in Canadian Business (April 14, 2008)*
Pub: Rogers Media

Ed: Lauren McKeon. Description: Only 12 percent of small and midsized enterprises that are run by women export their products and services. Government agencies can be more proactive in promoting the benefits of exporting by including women in case studies and recruiting women as mentors. Exporting provides great growth potential especially for the service sector where women have an advantage.

45774 ■ *"Time for State Tax Restructure?" in Crain's Detroit Business (Vol. 26, January 18, 2010, No. 3, pp. 3)*
Pub: Crain Communications Inc.

Ed: Amy Lane. Description: Business Leaders for Michigan, a statewide CEO group, launched a proposal to cut the Michigan Business Tax by about $1.1 billion and replace the revenue by taxing services. Statistical data included.

45775 ■ *The Tipping Point: How Little Things Can Make a Big Difference*
Pub: Little Brown & Company

Ed: Malcolm Gladwell. Released: January 2002. Price: $14.95. Description: Correlation between societal changes and marketing and business trends.

45776 ■ *"TiVo, Domino's Team to Offer Pizza Ordering by DVR" in Advertising Age (Vol. 79, November 17, 2008, No. 43, pp. 48)*
Pub: Crain Communications, Inc.

Ed: Brian Steinberg. Description: Domino's Pizza and TiVo are teaming up to make it possible for customers to order from the restaurant straight from their DVR. The companies see that this kind of interactive television and consumer experience will only serve to generate more sales as the customer can be exposed to a fuller range of menu selections and will not have to interrupt their viewing, while workers can spend more time making the product.

45777 ■ *"Tough Sell: Senior Projects Hustle to Keep Buyers" in Puget Sound Business Journal (Vol. 29, November 21, 2008, No. 31, pp.)*
Pub: American City Business Journals

Ed: Heidi Dietrich. Description: Plans to move to retirement communities are being postponed by seniors in Washington's Puget Sound area due to difficulty selling their current homes in the slow economy. Retirement communities are trying to lure clients by offering new finance programs and sales plans.

45778 ■ *"Toughen Up, Cupcake: You Know Who Plays for Keeps These Days? Cupcake Makers" in Inc (Vol. 33, May 2011, No. 4, pp. 100)*
Pub: Inc. Magazine

Ed: Burt Helm. Description: Cupcake shops are sprouting up everywhere across the nation and Washington, DC seems to be the epicenter for the trend. Profile of a new bakery called Sprinkles, that offers cupcake creations, is featured.

45779 ■ *"Tower City Hopes Restrictions on Minors Boost Retail Center" in Crain's Cleveland Business (Vol. 28, November 5, 2007, No. 44)*
Pub: Crain Communications, Inc.

Ed: John Booth. Description: Tower City Center, a shopping mall in downtown Cleveland, hopes to generate more business with their new rules restricting the access of unaccompanied minors after 2:30 p.m.

45780 ■ *"The Transparent Supply Chain" in Harvard Business Review (Vol. 88, October 2010, No. 10, pp. 76)*
Pub: Harvard Business School Publishing

Ed: Steve New. Description: Examination of the use of new technologies to create a transparent supply chain, such as next-generation 2D bar codes in clothing labels that can provide data on a garment's provenance.

45781 ■ *True Green at Work: 100 Ways You Can Make the Environment Your Business*
Pub: National Geographic

Ed: Kim McKay; Jenny Bonnin; Tim Wallace. Released: February 19, 2008. Price: $19.95 paperback. Description: Manual to help any small business minimize its carbon footprint by reducing waste.

45782 ■ *"Turbulent Skies" in The Business Journal-Portland (Vol. 25, August 29, 2008, No. 25, pp. 1)*
Pub: American City Business Journals, Inc.

Ed: Erik Siemers. Description: Small airlines are struggling to keep their commercial services amid the troubled commercial airline sector. Small communities, for example, were expected to pony up about $650,000 in revenue guarantees each in order to convince SkyWest Airlines to offer two direct flights to Portland daily beginning October 12, 2008. The trends in the commercial airline industry are analyzed.

45783 ■ *"Turfway Slowing its Gait" in Business Courier (Vol. 26, November 6, 2009, No. 28, pp. 1)*
Pub: American City Business Journals, Inc.

Ed: Jon Newberry. Description: Kentucky's Turfway Park will be decreasing its weekly race schedule from five days to three days in the first two months of 2010, and to four days in March 2010. The decision to make reductions in the schedule is attributed to the relocation of thoroughbred racing to states that allow casino gambling. As a result, Turfway Park's resources and purse money would be focused on less days.

45784 ■ *"Turmoil Means Changes For Retailers" in The Business Journal-Serving Metropolitan Kansas City (Vol. 27, October 10, 2008, No. 4)*
Pub: American City Business Journals, Inc.

Ed: Suzanna Stagemeyer. Description: Impacts of the financial crisis on Kansas Metropolitan Area retailers are varied. Rob Dalzell, for instance, found it difficult to secure a loan for his new self-serve yogurt store Yummo. The trends in retailing in the area are examined further as well as ways in which local businesses are changing in an attempt to stay solvent during the economic downturn.

45785 ■ *"Ultra Green Energy Services Opens NJ Biodiesel Transload Facility" in Indoor Comfort Marketing (Vol. 70, June 2011, No. 6, pp. 35)*
Pub: Industry Publications Inc.

Description: Profile of Ultra Green Energy Services and the opening of their new biodiesel facility in New Jersey is discussed.

45786 ■ *"Ultra Low Sulfur Diesel: The Promise and the Reality" in Indoor Comfort Marketing (Vol. 70, July 2011, No. 7, pp. 22)*
Pub: Industry Publications Inc.

Ed: Ed Kitchen. Description: Impacts of ultra low sulfur diesel are examined.

45787 ■ *"Unions and Upward Mobility for Low-Wage Workers" in WorkingUSA (Vol. 11, September 2008, No. 3, pp. 337)*
Pub: Blackwell Publishers Ltd.

Ed: John Schmitt, Margy Waller, Shawn Fremstad, Ben Zipperer. Description: Examination of the impact of unionization on the pay and benefits in fifteen important low-wage occupations is outlined. Even after controlling for important differences between union and nonunion workers, including such factors as age and education level, unionization improves the pay and benefits offered in what are otherwise low-paying occupations.

45788 ■ *"U.S. Recession Officially Over: Is Recovery Ever Going to Arrive?" in Montana Business Quarterly (Vol. 49, Spring 2011, No. 1, pp. 6)*
Pub: Bureau of Business & Economic Research

Ed: Patrick M. Barkey. Description: Ten predictions regarding American's economy for 2012 are listed.

45789 ■ *"Univest Charter Switch Signals Banking Trend" in Philadelphia Business Journal (Vol. 30, September 2, 2011, No. 29, pp. 1)*
Pub: American City Business Journals Inc.

Ed: Jeff Blumenthal. Description: Univest Corporation of Pennsylvania changed from a federal to state charter because of cost savings and state agency has greater understanding of the intricacies of the local economy. The Pennsylvania Department of Banking has also received inquiries from seven other banks about doing the same this year.

45790 ■ *Upstarts! How GenY Entrepreneurs Are Rocking the World of Business and 8 Ways You Can Profit from Their Success*
Pub: The McGraw-Hill Companies

Ed: Donna Fenn. Released: September 1, 2009. Price: $25.95. Description: An inside glance at the GenY startup companies that are changing the way the world conducts business.

45791 ■ *"USAmeriBank Deals for Growth" in The Business Journal-Serving Greater Tampa Bay (Vol. 28, September 26, 2008, No. 40, pp. 1)*
Pub: American City Business Journals, Inc.

Ed: Margie Manning. Description: It is believed that the pending $14.9 million purchase of Liberty Bank by USAmeriBank could be at the forefront of a trend. Executives of both companies expect the deal to close by the end of 2008. USAmeriBank will have $430 million in assets and five offices in Pinellas, Florida once the deal is completed.

45792 ■ *"Use Ink Presets to Minimize Makeready" in American Printer (Vol. 128, July 1, 2011, No. 7)*
Pub: Penton Media Inc.

Description: Automatic registration systems enable most printers to be in register very quickly after press startup. If the paper, ink and press time wasted during makeready can be reduced, these savings will flow directly to the bottom line. Ink presetting as an economical solution to set color quickly is a trend that continues to gain momentum.

45793 ■ *"Vacation, What Vacation?" in Black Enterprise (Vol. 41, August 2010, No. 1, pp. 36)*
Pub: Earl G. Graves Publishing Co. Inc.

Description: Nearly 50 percent of employers expect employees to check in with the office while they are away on vacation.

45794 ■ *"Valenti: Roots of Financial Crisis Go Back to 1998" in Crain's Detroit Business (Vol. 24, October 6, 2008, No. 40, pp. 25)*
Pub: Crain Communications, Inc.

Ed: Tom Henderson; Nathan Skid. Description: Interview with Sam Valenti III who is the chairman and CEO of Valenti Capital L.L.C., a wealth-management firm; Valenti discusses in detail the history that led up to the current economic crisis as well as his prediction for the future of the country.

45795 ■ *Values and Opportunities in Social Entrepreneurship*
Pub: Palgrave Macmillan
Ed: Kai Hockerts. **Released:** November 1, 2009. **Price:** $90.00. **Description:** Social entrepreneurship has grown as a research field. This book discusses social entrepreneurship as well as the identification and exploitation of social venturing opportunities.

45796 ■ *"Verdict: Few Legal Jobs" in Boston Business Journal (Vol. 31, June 17, 2011, No. 21, pp. 1)*
Pub: Boston Business Journal
Ed: Lisa van der Pool. **Description:** Law school graduates in Massachusetts are finding it harder to find work as the legal job market remains weak. The national employment rate for the 2010 law school class fell to 87.6 percent, while only 68.4 percent held jobs that require passing the bar examination.

45797 ■ *"Video Surveillance Enters Digital Era, Makes Giant Strides" in Arkansas Business (Vol. 26, September 28, 2009, No. 39, pp. 1)*
Pub: Journal Publishing Inc.
Ed: Jamie Walden. **Description:** Arkansas business owners are finding that the newest technology in video surveillance is leading to swift apprehension of thieves due to the high-quality digital imagery now being captured on surveillance equipment. Motion detection software for these systems is enhancing the capabilities of these systems and providing opportunities for businesses that would normally have problems integrating these systems.

45798 ■ *"Vistaprint Survey Indicates that Online Marketing Taking Hold Among Small Businesses" in Internet Wire (December 10, 2009)*
Pub: Comtex News Network, Inc.
Description: According to a comprehensive survey from Vistaprint N.V., small businesses are very likely to increase their use of Internet marketing strategies such as paid and organic search, email marketing, social media networking and custom websites over the next year. Trends continue to show that more small businesses are indeed adapting to the changing marketplace and are more willing to diversify their marketing strategies than ever before.

45799 ■ *"Vive La Resistance: Competing Logics and the Consolidation of U.S. Community Banking" in Academy of Management Journal (August 2007)*
Pub: Academy of Management
Contact: Ming-Jer Chen, President
Ed: Christopher Marquis, Michael Lounsbury. **Description:** Ways in which competing logics facilitate resistance to institutional change is presented, highlighting on banking professionals' resistance to large, national banks acquisitions of smaller, local banks.

45800 ■ *"Volunteers Needed" in Canadian Business (Vol. 81, October 27, 2008, No. 18, pp. 60)*
Pub: Rogers Media Ltd.
Ed: Megan Harman. **Description:** Emissions-targeting regulations focus on the biggest polluters, missing out on other companies that leave carbon footprints in things such as shipping and travel. Some companies in Canada have initiated programs to offset their carbon emissions. Critics claim that offsetting does not reduce emissions and the programs merely justify pollution.

45801 ■ *"The War for Talent" in Canadian Business (Vol. 80, January 29, 2007, No. 3, pp. 60)*
Pub: Rogers Media
Ed: Erin Pooley. **Description:** The recruitment policies of Canadian businesses are described. The trends pertaining to the growth of executive salaries in Canada are discussed.

45802 ■ *"Web-Based Marketing Excites, Challenges Small Business Use" in Colorado Springs Business Journal (January 20, 2010)*
Pub: Dolan Media Co.
Ed: Becky Hurley. **Description:** Business-to-business and consumer-direct firms alike are using the fast-changing Web technologies to increase sales, leads and track consumer behavior but once a company commits to an Online marketing plan, experts believe, they must be prepared to consistently tweak and overhaul content and distribution vehicles in order to keep up.

45803 ■ *"Welcome to a New Kind of Cubicle Culture" in Boston Business Journal (Vol. 29, August 19, 2011, No. 15, pp. 1)*
Pub: American City Business Journals Inc.
Ed: Alexander Jackson. **Description:** Beehive Baltimore offers a co-working space where independent freelancers and entrepreneurs can work. There are two other companies that provide the same service and the value of these services to these professional is that it provides them with an office that is both convenient and affordable aside from letting them network with peers.

45804 ■ *"What is the Future of Disk Drives, Death or Rebirth?" in ACM Computing Surveys (Vol. 43, Fall 2011, No. 3, pp. 23)*
Pub: Association for Computing Machinery
Ed: Yuhui Deng. **Description:** Disk drives have experienced dramatic development to meet performance requirements since the IBM 1301 disk drive was announced in 1961. However, the performance gap between memory and disk drives has widened to 6 orders of magnitude and continues to widen by about 50 percent per year. Challenges and opportunities facing these storage devices are explored.

45805 ■ *"What the Future Holds for Consumers" in Black Enterprise (Vol. 41, August 2010, No. 1, pp. 47)*
Pub: Earl G. Graves Publishing Co. Inc.
Ed: Sheiresa Ngo. **Description:** The way people purchase goods and service has changed with technology. With an increased focus on security (as well as privacy and fairness) the U.S. Congress began regulating the credit card industry with the Fair Credit Reporting Act of 1970 and the Credit Card Accountability, Responsibility, and Disclosure (CARD) Act of 2009.

45806 ■ *"What Is a Geothermal Heat Pump" in Indoor Comfort Marketing (Vol. 70, August 2011, No. 8, pp. 14)*
Pub: Industry Publications Inc.
Ed: George Carey. **Description:** Examination of geothermal heat pumps is provided, citing new trends in the industry.

45807 ■ *"What Moms Want" in Marketing to Women (Vol. 21, February 2008, No. 2, pp. 6)*
Pub: EPM Communications Inc.
Contact: Ira Mayer, President
E-mail: imayer@epmcom.com
Description: According to a survey conducted by Eureka's Spa, moms would rather have an experience gift than flowers or chocolate. The top five dream gifts include a spa day, a weekend getaway, maid service, a bathroom makeover or a getaway weekend with girlfriends.

45808 ■ *"What Will Green Power Cost? Surcharge, Spending Cap Considered" in Crain's Detroit Business (Vol. 24, March 10, 2008, No. 10, pp. 1)*
Pub: Crain Communications, Inc.
Ed: Amy Lane. **Description:** Due to a proposed mandate, which states that 10 percent of power will have to come from renewable sources by 2015 in the state of Michigan, concern is being raised about the higher electricity prices this legislation will undoubtedly cause to business and residential customers.

45809 ■ *"What You Should Know If Your Bank Fails" in Black Enterprise (Vol. 41,*

December 2010, No. 5, pp. 29)
Pub: Earl G. Graves Publishing Co. Inc.
Ed: John Simons. **Description:** The Federal Deposit Insurance Corporation announced that the number of banks in trouble has reached the highest level since March 1993. Advice from the FDIC is cited. Statistical data included.

45810 ■ *"What's Holding Down Small Business?" in Business Owner (Vol. 35, November-December 2011, No. 6, pp. 3)*
Pub: DL Perkins Company
Description: According to a recent survey conducted by the National Federation of Independent Business, demand is the number one reason for slow growth to any small business in today's economy.

45811 ■ *"Where the Future is Made" in Indoor Comfort Marketing (Vol. 70, May 2011, No. 5, pp. 48)*
Pub: Industry Publications Inc.
Description: Research being performed at Brookhaven National Laboratory, located in Upton, New York, is discussed, focusing on new energy sources for our nation.

45812 ■ *"Where Next?" in Business Strategy Review (Vol. 21, Summer 2010, No. 2, pp. 20)*
Pub: Wiley-Blackwell
Description: The emergence of large, vibrant and seemingly unstoppable new markets has been the good news story of the past decade. Brazil, Russia, India and China (BRIC) are among those who have emerged blinking into the new economy.

45813 ■ *"Where Women Work" in Marketing to Women (Vol. 21, April 2008, No. 4, pp. 8)*
Pub: EPM Communications Inc.
Contact: Ira Mayer, President
E-mail: imayer@epmcom.com
Description: According to the U.S. Census Bureau, 60 percent of America's professional tax preparers are women. Also features additional trends concerning women in the workplace. Statistical data included.

45814 ■ *"Which Direction are Herbicides Heading?" in Farm Industry News (October 11, 2011)*
Pub: Penton Business Media Inc.
Ed: Jennifer Shike. **Description:** Currently, one of the best solutions for growers fighting weed resistance may be 2,4-D or other auxin herbicides.

45815 ■ *"Wikinomics: The Sequel" in Business Strategy Review (Vol. 21, Summer 2010, No. 2, pp. 64)*
Pub: Wiley-Blackwell
Description: Ever-optimistic Don Tapscott and Anthony Williams, coauthors of Wikinomics and individually, of a number of other books that study the Internet and its relation to society, are now working on a new book, one for which they're using the Internet to determine its title.

45816 ■ *"Will Home Buyers Pay for Green Features?" in Contractor (Vol. 56, October 2009, No. 10, pp. 70)*
Pub: Penton Media, Inc.
Ed: Bob Mader. **Description:** National Association of Home Builders commissioned a survey which shows that homeowners are interested in green as long as they do no have to pay much for it. The association did not allow a board member to read the survey which raises questions about how the questions were phrased and how the sample was selected.

45817 ■ *"Will Small Business be Stimulated" in Entrepreneur (Vol. 37, July 2009, No. 7, pp. 18)*
Pub: Entrepreneur Media, Inc.
Ed: Jennifer Wang. **Description:** Steven Strauss, Alberto G. Alvarado, Jeff Rosenweig, Al Gordon, and Theresa Alfaro Daytner share their views on how the American Recovery and Reinvestment Act of 2009, also known as the economic stimulus, will affect small businesses. Their backgrounds are also provided.

45818 ■ *"Will Workers Be Left To Build It Here?" in Boston Business Journal (Vol. 31, June 3, 2011, No. 19, pp. 1)*
Pub: Boston Business Journal
Ed: Kyle Alspach. **Description:** Lack of skilled workers has resulted in delayed expansion of local manufacturing operations in Massachusetts. Acme Packet Inc. expects to add only 10 jobs by the end of 2011.

45819 ■ *Winner Take All: How Competitiveness Shapes the Fate of Nations*
Pub: Basic Books
Ed: Richard J. Elkus Jr. **Released:** 2009. **Price:** $27.00. **Description:** American government and misguided business practices has allowed the U.S. to fall behind other countries in various market sectors such as cameras and televisions, as well as information technologies. It will take a national strategy to for America to regain its lead in crucial industries.

45820 ■ *"Women Board Number Stagnates" in Boston Business Journal (Vol. 30, November 26, 2010, No. 44, pp. 1)*
Pub: Boston Business Journal
Ed: Mary Moore. **Description:** The 2010 data in 'Census of Women Directors and Executive Officers of Massachusetts Public Companies' showed little change in the number of executive officers and board members in the state's top 100 firms. The data was compiled by Bentley University, The Boston Club, and Mercer. Key information on 2010 Women on Boards is also provided.

45821 ■ *"Women Clicking to Earn Virtual Dollars" in Sales and Marketing Management (November 11, 2009)*
Pub: Nielsen Business Media, Inc.
Ed: Stacy Straczynski. **Description:** According to a new report from Internet marketing firm Q Interactive, women are increasingly playing social media games where they are able to click on an ad or sign up for a promotion to earn virtual currency. Research is showing that this kind of marketing may be a potent tool, especially for e-commerce and online stores.

45822 ■ *"Women Workers Spend Lunchtime on Fridays Shopping Online" in Marketing to Women (Vol. 23, November 2010, No. 11, pp. 8)*
Pub: EPM Communications Inc.
Contact: Ira Mayer, President
E-mail: imayer@epmcom.com
Description: Forty percent of women shop online during work hours, particularly on Fridays. The largest number of women make these purchases during their lunch break. Demographics are included.

45823 ■ *"Words at Work" in Information Today (Vol. 26, February 2009, No. 2, pp. 25)*
Pub: Information Today, Inc.
Description: Current new buzzwords include the following: digital amnesia, or overload by availability, speed and volume of digital information; maternal profiling, a form a discrimination against women; recipe malpractice, a reminder that just because you can turn on a stove it doesn't make you a chef; ringxiety, the act when everyone reaches for their cell phone when one rings; verbing, the practice of turning good nouns into verbs.

45824 ■ *"Work/Family Balance Boosts Business" in Marketing to Women (Vol. 21, February 2008, No. 2, pp. 8)*
Pub: EPM Communications Inc.
Contact: Ira Mayer, President
E-mail: imayer@epmcom.com
Description: Flexibility in the workplace is becoming a more important issue to both women and men. Statistical data included.

45825 ■ *"Workers' Comp System Cuts Through Paper" in Sacramento Business Journal (Vol. 25, July 11, 2008, No. 19, pp. 1)*
Pub: American City Business Journals, Inc.
Ed: Kelly Johnson. **Description:** California has started testing a new paperless system for handling disputed workers' compensation claims. It is believed that the shift will affect people both inside and outside

of the state Division of Workers' Compensation and the state Workers' Compensation Appeals Board. The other details of the planned system are also presented.

45826 ■ *"WQA's Leadership Conference Tackles Industry Issues" in Contractor (Vol. 56, October 2009, No. 10, pp. 3)*
Pub: Penton Media, Inc.
Ed: Candace Roulo. **Description:** Water Quality Association's Mid-Year Leadership Conference held in Bloomingdale, Illinois in September 2009 tackled lead regulation, water softeners, and product efficiency. The possibility of a WQA green seal was discussed by the Water Sciences Committee and the Government Relations Committee meeting.

45827 ■ *"Xbox 360 Excels as a Media Hub" in Hispanic Business (October 2009, pp. 40)*
Pub: Hispanic Business
Ed: Jeremy Nisen. **Description:** Xbox 360 video game console from Microsoft offers games, amazing graphics and state-of-the-art accessories. The trend towards purchase of the Xbox includes more than teenagers.

45828 ■ *"Yao Ming Courts China's Wine Boom" in Wall Street Journal Eastern Edition (November 28, 2011, pp. B4)*
Pub: Dow Jones & Company Inc. Enterprise Media Group
Contact: Clare Hart, President
Ed: Jason Chow. **Description:** Yao Ming, the former NBA 7-foot 6-inch Chinese basketball star, is set to cash in on the market potential for wine in China. He has created his own winery in California, Yao Family Wines, which will produce wines solely for the Chinese market.

45829 ■ *"Year-End Tax Tips" in Hawaii Business (Vol. 53, December 2007, No. 6, pp. 136)*
Pub: Hawaii Business Publishing
Ed: Kathleen Bryan. **Description:** Tax planning tips for the end of 2007, in relation to the tax breaks that are scheduled to expire, are presented. Among the tax breaks that will be expiring at the 2007 year-end are sales tax deduction in the state and local level, premiums on mortgage insurance, and deduction on tuition. The impacts of these changes are discussed.

45830 ■ *"Young Adults Choose to go Without Health Insurance" in Business Review, Albany New York (Vol. 34, November 30, 2007, No. 35, pp. 1)*
Pub: American City Business Journals, Inc.
Ed: Barbara Pinckney. **Description:** U.S. Census Bureau revealed that in 2006, 19 million people between the ages of 18 and 34 were without health insurance, or 40 percent of the uninsured individuals in the country. College graduation usually means the end of health coverage, since most fresh graduates opt to not get any health insurance plan. Solutions to this growing issue are also addressed.

45831 ■ *"Your Guide to Local Style Business" in Hawaii Business (Vol. 53, December 2007, No. 6, pp. 36)*
Pub: Hawaii Business Publishing
Ed: David K. Choo. **Description:** Discusses the importance of studying the Hawaiian culture when doing business locally. It was observed that geographical aspects increase emphasis on culture and lifestyle more than the need to rectify false imaging do. Details of how locals adhere to their culture are supplied.

45832 ■ *"Your Place: Housing Developers Try to Read Generation Y" in Philadelphia Inquirer (December 2, 2010)*
Pub: Philadelphia Media Network Inc.
Ed: Al Heavens. **Description:** Results of a survey conducted with Generation Y individuals are examined, focusing on housing developments and whether this particular generation prefers suburban or rural lifestyles. Generation Y encompasses people ages 18 to 32 years old. Statistical data included.

45833 ■ *YouTube and Video Marketing: An Hour a Day*
Pub: Sybex
Ed: Greg Jarboe. **Released:** August 10, 2009. **Price:** $29.99. **Description:** The importance of online video marketing for businesses is stressed. Tips for developing and implementing video marketing are outlined.

TRADE PERIODICALS

45834 ■ *Business Trends*
Pub: Quebecor Media
Contact: Pierre Peladeau, President
URL(s): www.sarniabusinesstrends.com/. **Ed:** Gord Bowes. **Released:** Monthly **Price:** $24, Individuals Canadian (GST included); $2, Single issue outside of our regular delivery area; $48, Individuals Canadian funds (surface mail only).

CONSULTANTS

45835 ■ Sklar and Associates Inc.
242 Laurel Bay Dr.
Murrells Inlet, SC 29576
Ph: (843)798-0412
Fax: (843)651-3090
Co. E-mail: sklarincdc@aol.com
URL: http://www.sklarinc.com
Contact: Tim Sklar, President
Scope: Provider of consulting services for business acquisitions, business development and project finance. Provides audit oversight services to listed corporations on Sarbanes-Oxley compliance. Services include: Due diligence analyses and corporate governance. Industries served: transportation sectors, energy sector and commercial real estate industries. **Seminars:** Financial Analysis in MBA; Emerging Company Finance; Due Diligence in Business Acquisition; Business Valuation.

COMPUTERIZED DATABASES

45836 ■ *Stern's Management Review*
11260 Overland Ave., Ste. 16A
Culver City, CA 90230
Ph: (310)838-0551
Free: 800-773-0029
Fax: (310)838-2344
Co. E-mail: info@hrconsultant.com
URL: http://www.hrconsultant.com
Contact: Charlotte Page, Chief Executive Officer
Availability: Online: Stern & Associates. **Type:** Full-text.

LIBRARIES

45837 ■ Colorado Mountain College - Alpine Campus Library
1330 Bob Adams Dr.
Steamboat Springs, CO 80487-5027
Ph: (970)870-4445
Co. E-mail: kwilliams@coloradomtn.edu
URL: http://library.coloradomtn.edu/steamboat
Contact: Kevin Williams, Director, Library Services
Scope: Small business, hotel and restaurant management, health and fitness, U.S. history and literature, American music, skiing. **Services:** Interlibrary loan; library open to the public; copying. **Founded:** 1982. **Holdings:** 30,000 books; 580 CDs; maps; state documents; CD-ROMs. **Subscriptions:** 225 journals and other serials; 15 newspapers.

45838 ■ Greater Oviedo Chamber of Commerce Business Library
PO Box 621236
Oviedo, FL 32765
Ph: (407)365-6500
Fax: (407)365-6587
Co. E-mail: cory@oviedowintersprings.org
URL: http://www.oviedowintersprings.org
Contact: Corydon G. Skeates, Executive Director
Scope: Small business; central Florida business. **Services:** Copying; library open to the public. **Founded:** 1995. **Holdings:** 3 books; 10 reports; periodicals. **Subscriptions:** 3 newspapers.

45839 ■ Indian River Area Library
PO Box 160
Indian River, MI 49749
Ph: (231)238-8581
Fax: (231)238-9494
Co. E-mail: indrivl@northland.lib.mi.us
URL: http://www.libnet.org/iriver/
Contact: Cindy Lou Poquette, Director
Scope: Small business, careers, fine arts, music, dance. **Services:** Interlibrary loan; copying; library open to the public (fee for non-residents to check out materials). **Founded:** 1976. **Holdings:** 52,000 books; 32,000 videocassettes and DVDs; 2000 microfiche; sound cassettes; DVDs; CDs; periodicals; large print books. **Subscriptions:** 80 journals and other serials; 3 newspapers.

45840 ■ Small Business Administration Reference Library
409 3rd St., SW
Washington, DC 20416
Ph: (202)205-7033
Fax: (202)481-5881
Co. E-mail: answerdesk@sba.gov
URL: http://www.sba.gov
Contact: Margaret Hickey, Librarian
Scope: Small business, finance, management, venture capital. **Services:** Interlibrary loan; Library open to the public for reference use only. **Founded:** 1958. **Holdings:** 8000 volumes. **Subscriptions:** 72 journals and other serials.

RESEARCH CENTERS

45841 ■ Alabama Law Institute (ALI)
PO Box 861425
Tuscaloosa, AL 35486-0013
Ph: (205)348-7411
Fax: (205)348-8411
Co. E-mail: rmccurley@ali.state.al.us
URL: http://ali.state.al.us
Contact: Robert L. (Bob) McCurley, Jr., Director
Founded: 1967. **Publications:** *ALI Annual Report.* **Educational Activities:** Basic and advanced law courses, for probate judges; Capital Intern Program, allowing three students to work at the State Legislature; ALI Conferences, for state officials.

45842 ■ Bradley University - Center for Business and Economic Research (CBER)
Foster College of Business Administration
1501 W Bradley Ave.
Peoria, IL 61625
Ph: (309)677-2262
Co. E-mail: bjg@bradley.edu
URL: http://www.bradley.edu/academic/colleges/fcba/
  centers/economic
Contact: Dr. Bernard Goitein, Director
Founded: 1979. **Publications:** *Peoria MSA Business Database Report* (Quarterly); *Peoria MSA Consumer Sentiment* (3/year). **Awards:** CBER Assistantships.

45843 ■ Central Connecticut State University - Connecticut Small Business Development Center (CSBDC)
Downtown Bldg.
185 Main St.
New Britain, CT 06051
Ph: (860)832-0650
Fax: (860)832-0656
Co. E-mail: csbdc@ccsu.edu
URL: http://www.ctsbdc.org
Contact: Ginne Rae Clay-Gilmore, Director
Services: Technical assistance and education for business owners and entrepreneurs. **Founded:** 1981. **Publications:** *CSBDC Reports* (Periodic). **Educational Activities:** Professional counseling; CSBDC Seminars. **Telecommunication Services:** g.clay@ccsu.edu.

45844 ■ East Tennessee State University - Tennessee Small Business Development Center (TSBDC)
College of Business & Technology
2109 W Market St.
Johnson City, TN 37604
Ph: (423)439-8505
Fax: (423)439-8506
Co. E-mail: bjustice@mail.tsbdc.org
URL: http://www.tsbdc.org
Contact: Dr. Robert A. Justice, Director
Services: Provides free Internet access to clients (Daily). **Founded:** 1983. **Educational Activities:** Consulting, technical assistance, and management assistance (Daily); Workshops, seminars and conferences (Weekly).

45845 ■ Michigan State University - Institute for Public Policy and Social Research (IPPSR)
321 Berkey Hall
East Lansing, MI 48824-1111
Ph: (517)355-6672
Fax: (517)432-1544
Co. E-mail: douglas.roberts@ssc.msu.edu
URL: http://www.ippsr.msu.edu
Contact: Douglas B. Roberts, Director
Services: Public policy forums (Quarterly). **Founded:** 1951. **Publications:** *Policy briefs*; *SOSS Bulletins.* **Educational Activities:** Conference, seminars, and special events; Political leadership program (Monthly); Public Policy Seminars (Monthly).

45846 ■ Pennsylvania Small Business Development Centers
3819-33 Chestnut St., Ste. 325
Philadelphia, PA 19104-3238
Ph: (215)898-1219
Fax: (215)573-2135
Co. E-mail: cconroy@wharton.upenn.edu
URL: http://pasbdc.org
Contact: Christian Conroy, Director
Services: Free management consulting to entrepreneurs and prospective business owners. **Educational Activities:** Training programs, workshops, and

seminars. **Telecommunication Services:** pasbdc@wharton.upenn.edu.

45847 ■ University of Mississippi - Small Business Development Center (SBDC)
122 Jeanette Phillips Dr.
University, MS 38677-1848
Ph: (662)915-5001
Free: 800-725-7232
Fax: (662)915-5650
Co. E-mail: msbdc@olemiss.edu
URL: http://mssbdc.org
Contact: James Carden, Director
Services: Management counseling and marketing assistance for entrepreneurs and small business owners and managers. **Founded:** 1981. **Educational Activities:** Seminars and training on small business development.

45848 ■ University of New Hampshire - New Hampshire Small Business Development Center (NHSBDC)
110 McConnell Hall
Whittemore School of Business & Economics
Durham, NH 03824
Ph: (603)862-2200
Fax: (603)862-4876
Co. E-mail: mary.collins@unh.edu
URL: http://www.nhsbdc.org
Contact: Mary E. Collins, Director
Services: Consulting and technical assistance. **Founded:** 1984. **Publications:** *NHSBDC Annual report.* **Educational Activities:** Conferences, workshops and seminars.

45849 ■ World Jurist Association (WJA)
7910 Woodmont Ave., Ste. 1440
Bethesda, MD 20814
Ph: (202)466-5428
Fax: (202)452-8540
Co. E-mail: wja@worldjurist.org
URL: http://www.worldjurist.org
Contact: Valeriy Yevdikyov, President
Description: Lawyers, judges, law professors, jurists, law students, and nonlegal professionals in 140 countries and territories. Seeks to build laws and legal institutions for international cooperation. Conducts Global Work Program to recommend research and voluntary action for development of international law as a basis for promoting the rule of law and the resolution of disputes by peaceful means. Sponsors biennial World Law Day. Maintains biographical archives. Contains 21 Sections, including Constitutional Law, Foreign Trade and Investment, Human Rights, and Litigation. **Founded:** 1963. **Publications:** *Directory of law and judicial systems of nations*; *Law/Technology* (Quarterly); *Pamphlets Series* (Occasionally); *Workpapers*; *The World Jurist* (Bimonthly); *Law/Technology* (Quarterly); *The World Jurist* (Bimonthly); *Report Series on Law-making Activities of International Organizations*; *Law and Judicial Systems of Nations* (Periodic). **Educational Activities:** Conference on the Law of the World (Biennial); World conferences (Biennial), in odd years.

START-UP INFORMATION

45850 ■ *"Making Social Ventures Work" in Harvard Business Review (Vol. 88, September 2010, No. 9, pp. 66)*
Pub: Harvard Business School Publishing
Ed: James D. Thompson, Ian C. MacMillan. **Description:** Five steps are to define, examine the political aspects, focus on discovery-driven planning, develop an appropriate exit strategy, and anticipate unexpected consequences when starting a new social venture.

ASSOCIATIONS AND OTHER ORGANIZATIONS

45851 ■ **As You Sow Foundation (AYS)**
1611 Telegraph Ave., Ste. 1450
Oakland, CA 94612
Ph: (510)735-8158
Fax: (510)735-8143
Co. E-mail: michael@asyousow.org
URL: http://www.asyousow.org
Description: Dedicated to promoting corporate social responsibility. **Founded:** 1992. **Publications:** *Proxy Season Preview* (Quarterly); *Unlocking the Power of the Proxy.*

45852 ■ **Business for Social Responsibility (BSR)**
88 Kearny St., 12th Fl.
San Francisco, CA 94108
Ph: (415)984-3200
Fax: (415)984-3201
Co. E-mail: connect@bsr.org
URL: http://www.bsr.org
Contact: Mats Lederhausen, Chairman
Description: Large, small, and medium-sized businesses. Promotes responsible business behavior and serves as a resource to companies striving to make ethical business decisions. **Founded:** 1992. **Publications:** *BSR Weekly* (Weekly). **Educational Activities:** Business for Social Responsibility Conference (Annual).

45853 ■ *Women and Environments*
215 Spadina Ave., Ste. 400
Toronto, ON, Canada M5T 2C7
Ph: (416)928-0880
Fax: (416)644-0116
Co. E-mail: office@womenshealthyenvironments.ca
URL: http://www.womenshealthyenvironments.ca
Contact: Marie Lorenzo, Chairperson
Released: Quarterly **Price:** C$8, /issue; C$21.97, /year.

45854 ■ **Women's Healthy Environments Network (WHEN)**
215 Spadina Ave., Ste. 400
Toronto, ON, Canada M5T 2C7
Ph: (416)928-0880

Fax: (416)644-0116
Co. E-mail: office@womenshealthyenvironments.ca
URL: http://www.womenshealthyenvironments.ca
Contact: Marie Lorenzo, Chairperson
Description: Women experts in environmental studies and issues. Works to implement community development projects to improve the environment. Provides a forum for discussion, information exchange, and the conducting of research related to women in the fields of planning, health, workplace, design, economy, urban and rural sociology, and community development. Initiates and organizes community projects. Advocates environmental protection, anti-discriminatory zoning practices, and the development of affordable housing. **Founded:** 1994. **Publications:** *Women and Environments* (Quarterly); *Whitewash.*

EDUCATIONAL PROGRAMS

45855 ■ **Social Media Overview**
EEI Communications
8945 Guilford Rd., Ste. 145
Columbia, MD 21046
Ph: (410)309-8200
Free: 888-253-2762
Fax: (410)630-3980
Co. E-mail: train@eeicom.com
URL: http://www.eeicom.com/eei-training-services
Price: $425.00. **Description:** Learn how to model your website and online initiatives to the new Web 2.0 movement, including working with Facebook and Twitter, pros and cons of MySpace, Wikis, working with blogs, and podcasting in a nutshell. **Dates and Locations:** Alexandria, VA.

REFERENCE WORKS

45856 ■ *"2008 Woman of the Year Gala" in Hispanic Business (Vol. 30, July-August 2008, No. 7-8, pp. 58)*
Pub: Hispanic Business, Inc.
Ed: Brynne Chappell. **Description:** Brief report on the sixth annual Women of the Year Awards gala which was held at JW Marriott Desert Ridge Resort and Spa is given; 20 women were honored with these awards for their professional contribution, commitment to the advancement of the Hispanic community and involvement with charitable organizations.

45857 ■ *"Active Duty" in Crain's Cleveland Business (Vol. 28, November 26, 2007, No. 47, pp. 3)*
Pub: Crain Communications, Inc.
Ed: David Bennett. **Description:** Discusses the Veteran Workforce Training Program, sponsored by the Volunteers of America - Greater Ohio; the program is meant to provide employment training for military veterans and to assist them in transitioning back into the work force.

45858 ■ *"Alliance to End Hunger to Hold Press Conference on Fasting, Prayer and Budget Cuts" in Food & Beverage Close-Up*

(March 28, 2011)
Pub: Close-Up Media
Description: A coalition of religious and other leaders are launching a new campaign to protect programs for vulnerable people. Partners include: Alliance to End Hunger, American Jewish World Service, Bread for the World, Congressional Hunger Center, Feeding America, Food for the Hungry, Islamic Relief USA, Meals on Wheels Association of America, New Manna Inc., ONE, Society of Saint Andrews, Sojourners, and World Food Program USA.

45859 ■ *"Alliance Offers to Help Italian Workers Settle In" in Crain's Detroit Business (Vol. 25, June 15, 2009, No. 24, pp. 21)*
Pub: Crain Communications Inc. - Detroit
Ed: Nancy Kaffer. **Description:** Italian American Alliance for Business and Technology will help workers arriving from Italy to transition to their new homes in the Detroit area.

45860 ■ *"Also Active in the Fight Against Cancer is Dreyer's Grand Ice Cream" in Ice Cream Reporter (Vol. 23, October 20, 2010, No. 11, pp. 8)*
Pub: Ice Cream Reporter
Description: Dreyer's Grand Ice Cream partnered with Experience Project's BroadCause.com to raise awareness around pediatric cancer research.

45861 ■ *"Are EO Programs Right for Your Business?" in Contractor (Vol. 56, October 2009, No. 10, pp. 49)*
Pub: Penton Media, Inc.
Ed: Susan Linden McGreevy. **Description:** Some of the laws regarding equal opportunity programs are discussed. Suggestions for mechanical contractors who are considering certification to qualify for these programs are presented.

45862 ■ *"Are There Material Benefits To Social Diversity?" in Hispanic Business (Vol. 30, September 2008, No. 9, pp. 10)*
Pub: Hispanic Business, Inc.
Ed: Brigida Benitez. **Description:** Diversity in American colleges and universities, where students view and appreciate their peers as individuals and do not judge them on the basis of race, gender, or ethnicity is discussed. The benefits of diversity in higher education are also acknowledged by the U.S. Supreme Court and by leading American corporations.

45863 ■ *"Are You a Young Canadian Entrepreneur Looking for Recognition?" in CNW Group (November 10, 2010)*
Pub: Comtex
Description: Business Development Bank of Canada is looking for young Canadian entrepreneurs ages 19 to 35 for its 2011 Young Entrepreneur Awards. The awards pay tribute to remarkable young Canadian entrepreneurs for their creativity, innovative spirit and community development, as well as business success.

45864 ■ *The Art of the Start*
Pub: Portfolio Publishing

Ed: Guy Kawasaki. **Price:** $26.95. **Description:** Apple's Guy Kawasaki offers information to help would-be entrepreneurs create new enterprises. As founder and CEO of Garage Technology Ventures, he has field-tested his ideas with newly hatched companies and he takes readers through every phase of creating a business, from the very basics of raising money and designing a business model through the many stages that eventually lead to success and thus giving back to society.

45865 ■ *"The Asian Decade" in Hawaii Business (Vol. 53, January 2008, No. 7, pp. 19)*
Pub: Hawaii Business Publishing

Ed: Cathy S. Cruz-George. **Description:** Chaney Brooks, a Hawaiian real estate company, has affiliated with commercial real estate network NAI Global. The NAI partnership will improve Hawaii's international business, particularly its Asian investments. Hawaii's diverse workforce is evaluated, with regards to being an asset for international businesses.

45866 ■ *"At This Bakery, Interns' Hope Rises Along With the Bread" in Chicago Tribune (October 31, 2008)*
Pub: McClatchy-Tribune Information Services

Ed: Mary Schmich. **Description:** Profile of Sweet Miss Givings Bakery and its diverse founder, interns and employees; the bakery was founded by Stan Sloan, an Episcopal priest who started the business to help fund his ministry; Sloan saw a need for jobs for those living with HIV and other disabilities and through the bakery the interns learn the skills needed to eventually find work elsewhere.

45867 ■ *"Athletes Face Wins and Losses After Pro Sport" in The Business Journal - Serving Phoenix and the Valley of the Sun (Vol. 29, September 19, 2008, No. 3, pp. 1)*
Pub: American City Business Journals, Inc.

Ed: Chris Casacchia. **Description:** Professional athletes like hockey star Jeremy Roenick start businesses, while others like Joel Adamson work to boost local communities. Former athletes were found to be particularly interested with real estate businesses. Other views and information on former athletes and their life after sports are presented.

45868 ■ *"Attracting Veteran-Franchisees To Your System" in Franchising World (Vol. 42, November 2010, No. 11, pp. 53)*
Pub: International Franchise Association

Ed: Mary Kennedy Thompson. **Description:** As military servicemen and women return home, the franchising industry expects an increase in veterans as franchise owners. The Veterans Transition Franchise Initiative, also known as VetFran, is described.

45869 ■ *"Automaker Foundations Run Leaner" in Crain's Detroit Business (Vol. 26, January 11, 2010, No. 2, pp. 1)*
Pub: Crain Communications Inc.

Ed: Sherri Welch. **Description:** Overview of the Detroit automobile industry includes restoring profitability, smarter marketing strategies and philanthropy. Each company comprising the Big 3 is examined, as is their vision for the future.

45870 ■ *"Back Talk With Terrie M. Williams" in Black Enterprise (Vol. 38, December 2007, No. 5, pp. 204)*
Pub: Earl G. Graves Publishing Co. Inc.

Ed: Tennille M. Robinson. **Description:** Profile of Terrie M. Williams, president of a public relations agency as well as founder of a youth empowerment organization called Stay Strong Foundation. Williams reflects on her bouts with depression and how the disease impacts sufferers and talks about her book that will inspire others dealing with depression.

45871 ■ *"Banking on Cord Blood" in Business Journal-Serving Phoenix & the Valley of the Sun (Vol. 31, September 10,*

2010, No. 1, pp. 1)
Pub: Phoenix Business Journal

Ed: Angela Gonzales. **Description:** Celebration Stem Cell Centre obtained contracts from Mercy Gilbert Medical Center and its two sister hospitals, St. Joseph Hospital and Medical Center in Phoenix, Arizona and Chandler Regional Medical Center. The contract will facilitate the donation of unused umbilical cord blood for research.

45872 ■ *"Become A Brand" in Women Entrepreneur (September 14, 2008)*
Pub: Entrepreneur Media Inc.

Ed: Suzy Girard-Ruttenberg. **Description:** Powerful brands are effective, innovative, exclusive or even socially conscious; it is important for small businesses to understand the power of becoming a brand since it is one of the best ways in which to position one's company and drive its growth.

45873 ■ *"The Believer" in Inc. (December 2007, pp. 130-138)*
Pub: Gruner & Jahr USA Publishing

Ed: Leigh Buchanan. **Description:** Profile of Selena Cuffe, wine importer and socially conscious woman entrepreneur, who is focusing her talents on helping South Africa get wine products to America.

45874 ■ *"The Best Advice I Ever Got" in Harvard Business Review (Vol. 86, September 2008, No. 9, pp. 29)*
Pub: Harvard Business School Press

Ed: Daisy Wademan Dowling. **Description:** Bright Horizons Family Solutions founder and chair Linda Mason illustrates how letting one's life passion direct entrepreneurship and business success. She describes how her humanitarian interests and efforts gave her the drive to launch a childcare service.

45875 ■ *"Bethesda Stepping Out" in Business Courier (Vol. 27, October 15, 2010, No. 24, pp. 1)*
Pub: Business Courier

Ed: James Ritchie. **Description:** Nonprofit organization Bethesda Inc. is planning to donate $5 million a year for the next three years to Greater Cincinnati health care reforms. Bethesda revealed that it announced its donations to pressure other organizations to help.

45876 ■ *Big-Box Swindle: The True Cost of Mega-Retailers and the Fight for America's Independent Businesses*
Pub: Beacon Press

Ed: Stacy Mitchell. **Released:** October 2007. **Price:** $15.00. **Description:** Examination of the economic, environmental, and social damage done by big-box retailers like Wal-Mart, Costco, and Home Depot. Labor policies of these retailers, particularly those enforced by Wal-Mart, are discussed at length.

45877 ■ *"Big Shoes to Fill for New United Way Chairman" in Business Courier (Vol. 27, June 25, 2010, No. 8, pp. 4)*
Pub: Business Courier

Ed: Lucy May. **Description:** David Dougherty, chairman of the nonprofit United Way of Greater Cincinnati, explains how he can surpass the nonprofit's 2009 campaign kickoff that raised $62 million. For 2010, Dougherty has prepared a $2 million matching grant from a group of local individuals, corporations, and foundations. Dougherty also discusses what he learned from participating in the 2009 campaign.

45878 ■ *"Billion-Dollar Impact" in Business First Buffalo (November 9, 2007, pp. 1)*
Pub: American City Business Journals, Inc.

Ed: Tracey Dury. **Description:** Western New York has thousands of nonprofit organizations, 240 of which have collective revenue of $1.74 billion based on federal tax returns for the 2005 and 2006 fiscal years. The nonprofit sector has a large impact on WNY's economy, but it is not highly recognized. The financial performance of notable nonprofit organizations is given.

45879 ■ *"Bits 'n' Pieces: Shelter Gives Out Pet Food to Keep Animals At Home" in Columbian (January 19, 2009)*
Pub: The Columbian

Ed: Elisa Williams. **Description:** Lend a Paw program gives surplus food to pet owners in need; since August 2008 they distributed over 7,000 pounds of dry and wet food to shelters and pet owners.

45880 ■ *"Blue Cross Confronts Baby Blues" in Marketing to Women (Vol. 21, March 2008, No. 3, pp. 3)*
Pub: EPM Communications Inc.
Contact: Ira Mayer, President
E-mail: imayer@epmcom.com

Description: Blue Cross of California has launched a Maternity Depression Program aimed at educating mothers suffering from postpartum depression.

45881 ■ *"Boxing, Tech Giants Team to Help Teens" in Hispanic Business (January-February 2009, pp. 44)*
Pub: Hispanic Business

Ed: Daniel Soussa. **Description:** Microsoft and Oscar de la Hoya are providing teens a head start for careers in the sciences by offering a competition in the categories of photography, short films or Web-based games.

45882 ■ *"Brewing a Love-Haiti Relationship" in The Business Journal - Serving Phoenix and the Valley of the Sun (Vol. 28, July 4, 2008, No. 44)*
Pub: American City Business Journals, Inc.

Ed: Yvonne Zusel. **Description:** Jean and Alicia Marseille have ventured into a coffee distribution company called Ka Bel LLC which markets Marabou brand of coffee imported from Haiti. Part of the proceeds of the business is donated to entrepreneurs from Jean's country, Haiti. Details of the Marseille's startup business and personal mission to help are discussed.

45883 ■ *"Bringing Charities More Bang for Their Buck" in Crain's Chicago Business (Vol. 34, May 23, 2011, No. 21, pp. 31)*
Pub: Crain Communications Inc.

Ed: Lisa Bertagnoli. **Description:** Marcy-Newberry Association connects charities with manufacturers in order to use excess items such as clothing, janitorial and office supplies.

45884 ■ *Business, Occupations, Professions and Vocations in the Bible*
Pub: ABC Book Publishing

Ed: Rich Brott. **Released:** 2008. **Price:** $19.99. **Description:** The important role small business has played in all societies and cultures throughout history is examined. The ingenuity of individuals and their ability to design, craft, manufacture and harvest has kept countries and kingdoms prosperous.

45885 ■ *"Business Through Hollywood's Lens" in Harvard Business Review (Vol. 88, October 2010, No. 10, pp. 146)*
Pub: Harvard Business School Publishing

Ed: Batia Wiesnefeld, Gino Cattani. **Description:** The authors contend that businesses are likely to be portrayed as villains in movies because corruption has higher entertainment draw. However, movies also depict popular opinion, which encourages businesses to be accountable and to help build communities.

45886 ■ *Business as Usual*
Pub: HarperBusiness

Ed: Anita Roddick. **Released:** 2005. **Price:** $12.95. **Description:** Founder of The Body Shop shares her story and gives her opinion on everything from cynical cosmetic companies to destructive consultants.

45887 ■ *"CBC and Chrysler Strike Deal" in Black Enterprise (Vol. 37, December 2006, No. 5, pp. 36)*
Pub: Earl G. Graves Publishing Co. Inc.

Ed: Kiara Ashanti. **Description:** Congressional Black Foundation and Chrysler Financial have partnered to provide financial education to students at historically black colleges and universities. The prime objective of the program is to reduce the number of college students that graduate with poor credit scores and high debt.

45888 ■ "Coming Up Short" in Boston Business Journal (Vol. 30, October 15, 2010, No. 36, pp. 1)
Pub: Boston Business Journal

Ed: Tim McLaughlin, Mary Moore. **Description:** Boston, Massachusetts-based nonprofits have been profiting less from charity golf tournaments. Nonprofits have been collecting less than 50 cents on the dollar from such events. But nonprofits have been restructuring golf tournaments in order to boost profits.

45889 ■ "Community Commitment Safeguards Franchising Industry" in Franchising World (Vol. 42, November 2010, No. 11, pp. 38)
Pub: International Franchise Association

Description: Individuals who are dedicated to committing time and resources to bring to the attention of legislators those laws and proposals affecting franchise small businesses are highlighted in a monthly format.

45890 ■ The Company We Keep: Reinventing Small Business for People, Community, and Place
Pub: Chelsea Green Publishing

Ed: John Abrams, William Grieder. **Released:** June 2006. **Price:** $18.00. **Description:** The new business trend in social entrepreneurship as a business plan enables small business owners to meet the triple bottom line of profits for people (employees and owners), community, and the environment.

45891 ■ The Complete Idiot's Guide to Starting and Running a Thrift Store
Pub: Alpha Publishing House

Ed: Ravel Buckley, Carol Costa. **Released:** January 5, 2010. **Price:** $18.95. **Description:** Thrift stores saw a 35 percent increase in sales during the falling economy in 2008. Despite the low startup costs, launching and running a thrift store is complicated. Two experts cover the entire process, including setting up a store on a nonprofit basis, choosing a location, funding, donations for saleable items, recruiting and managing staff, sorting items, pricing, and recycling donations.

45892 ■ "Conversation" in Harvard Business Review (Vol. 86, September 2008, No. 9, pp. 32)
Pub: Harvard Business School Press

Ed: Susan Donovan. **Description:** Danish software entrepreneur Thorkil Sonne has helped improve employment for individuals with autism after discovering the perception of detail and remarkable memory skills in his own son, who has autism. His company, Specialisterne, was built via focusing on these strengths.

45893 ■ "Corporate Diversity Driving Profits" in Hispanic Business (Vol. 30, September 2008, No. 9, pp. 12)
Pub: Hispanic Business, Inc.

Ed: Michael Bowker. **Description:** U.S. businesses are beginning to appreciate the importance of diversity and are developing strategies to introduce a diverse workforce that reflects the cultural composition of their customers. The realization that diversity increases profits and the use of professional networks to recruit and retain skilled minority employees are two other new trends impacting corporate diversity in the U.S.

45894 ■ "Corporate Responsibility" in Professional Services Close-Up (July 2, 2010)
Pub: Close-Up Media

Description: List of firms awarded the inaugural Best Corporate Citizens in Government Contracting by the Corporate Responsibility Magazine is presented. The list is based on the methodology of the Magazine's Best Corporate Citizen's List, with 324 data points of publicly-available information in seven categories

which include: environment, climate change, human rights, philanthropy, employee relations, financial performance, and governance.

45895 ■ "Corporate Social Responsibility: A Process Model of Sensemaking" in Academy of Management Review (January 2008, pp. 122)
Pub: ScholarOne, Inc.

Ed: Kunal Basu, Guido Palazzo. **Description:** A novel process model of corporate social responsibility is presented. It uses organizational sensemaking to educate managers about elements of appropriate relationships with stakeholders and others.

45896 ■ "Corporation, Be Good! The Story of Corporate Social Responsibility" in Business and Society (December 2007, pp. 479-485)
Pub: SAGE Publications USA

Contact: Blaise R. Simqu, President

Ed: David M. Wasieleski. **Description:** Review of the book, 'Corporation, Be Good! The Story of Corporate Social Responsibility' is presented. The book examines the importance of corporate responsibility and its economic impact.

45897 ■ "Could This Be Your Next Office Building?" in Austin Business Journal (Vol. 31, May 13, 2011, No. 10, pp. A1)
Pub: American City Business Journals Inc.

Ed: Cody Lyon. **Description:** Falcon Containers moved to a 51-acre site in Far East Austin, Texas and started construction of a 2,500-square-foot headquarters made from eight 40-foot shipping containers. Falcon's CEO Stephen Shang plans to use his headquarters building as a showroom to attract upscale, urban hipsters. Insights on the construction's environmental and social impact are shared.

45898 ■ "CR Magazine Taps ITT As a 'Best Corporate Citizen' in Government Contracting" in Profesisonal Services Close-Up (July 30, 2010)
Pub: Close-Up Media

Description: ITT Corporation was named by Corporate Responsibility Magazine as a Best Corporate Citizen in Government Contracting. The list recognizes publicly-traded companies that exemplify transparency and accountability while serving the U.S. government.

45899 ■ Creating a World without Poverty: Social Business and the Future of Capitalism
Pub: Basic Books

Released: April 26, 2009. **Price:** $26.00. **Description:** Explanation of how microcredit lending practices and more collaborative business strategies can be used to alleviate poverty worldwide.

45900 ■ "Diana Bonta: Keeping People Healthy and Thriving" in Hispanic Business (Vol. 30, April 2008, No. 4, pp. 30)
Pub: Hispanic Business

Ed: Leanndra Martinez. **Description:** Diana Bonta serves as vice president of public affairs for Kaiser Permanente and is a strong advocate for health reform and improving access to health care. In order to better serve the underinsured and uninsured, she directs Kaiser's Community Benefit division that devoted $369 million last year to this cause.

45901 ■ "Do-Gooder Finance: How a New Crop of Investors Is Helping Social Entrepreneurs" in Inc. (February 2008, pp. 29-30)
Pub: Gruner & Jahr USA Publishing

Ed: Nitasha Tiku. **Description:** Social venture firms are not seeking to sell companies as quickly as traditional venture companies. Four socially minded venture capital firms and banks profiled include, Underdog Venture, Island Pond, Vermont; Root Capital, Cambridge, Massachusetts; ShoreBank Pacific, Ilwaco, Washington; and TBL Capital, Sausalito, California.

45902 ■ "Doing Good: Cause and Effect" in Entrepreneur (Vol. 36, February 2008, No. 2, pp. 23)
Pub: Entrepreneur Media Inc.

Description: Lisa Knoppe established Art for a Cause LLC that employs people with mental and physical disabilities. The company makes hand-painted tools and furniture to be sold at gift retailers and hardware stores.

45903 ■ "Doing the Right Thing" in Black Enterprise (Vol. 38, July 2008, No. 12, pp. 50)
Pub: Earl G. Graves Publishing Co. Inc.

Ed: Tamara E. Holmes. **Description:** More business owners are trying to become more environmentally friendly, either due to their belief in social responsibility or for financial incentives or for both reasons. Tips for making one's business more environmentally responsible are included as well as a listing of resources that may be available to help owners in their efforts.

45904 ■ "Donated Sprinkler System Honors Fallen Firefighter" in Contractor (Vol. 56, July 2009, No. 7, pp. 3)
Pub: Penton Media, Inc.

Ed: Steve Spaulding. **Description:** Capital City District Habitat for Humanity has constructed a home with a residential fire sprinkler system in honor of Ted Abriel, a firefighter who died on the job. Albany Fire Protection donated the labor for the installation of the fire sprinkler system.

45905 ■ "Doubletree Finds a Niche for Giving Back" in Hotel and Motel Management (Vol. 225, July 2010, No. 8, pp. 6)
Pub: Questex Media Group Inc.

Ed: Paul J. Heney. **Description:** Profile of Doubletree Hotel's community outreach programs that help employee volunteers work to educate children and the public about issues important to the environment.

45906 ■ "Doubtful Donors" in Canadian Business (Vol. 81, December 8, 2008, No. 21, pp. 8)
Pub: Rogers Media Ltd.

Ed: Dennis Seguin. **Description:** Key information on fundraising consultancy Inspire, as well as views and information on charitable organizations in Canada is presented. Inspire designs the financial architecture of charitable foundations in Canada, which was affected by the current financial crisis. Inspire advises foundations to keep existing donors.

45907 ■ "Dragon, but.." in Canadian Business (Vol. 81, December 8, 2008, No. 21, pp. 45)
Pub: Rogers Media Ltd.

Ed: Matthew McLearn. **Description:** The greatest challenge in smooth trade relations between China and Canada is believed to be lukewarm relations with China over human rights issues. Australia on the other hand, has attracted huge Chinese outward direct investments because of strong trade relations.

45908 ■ The Dream Manager
Pub: Hyperion

Ed: Matthew Kelly. **Price:** $19.95. **Description:** A business fable about the virtues of helping those working for and with you to achieve their dreams. Managers can boost morale and control turnover by adopting this policy.

45909 ■ Ecopreneuring: Putting Purpose and the Planet Before Profits
Pub: New Society Publishers

Ed: John Ivanko; Lisa Kivirist. **Released:** July 1, 2008. **Price:** $17.95 paperback. **Description:** Ecopreneurs in America are shifting profits and market share towards green living. The book provides a guideline for ecopreneurs in the areas of eco-business basics, purposeful management, marketing in the green economy, and running a lifestyle business.

45910 ■ "Editor's Note" in Canadian Business (Vol. 81, March 17, 2008, No. 4, pp. 7)
Pub: Rogers Media

Ed: Joe Chidley. **Description:** Canadian Consolidated government expenditures increased by an average of 4.5 percent annually from 2003 to 2007.

Health care, housing, and the environment were some of the areas which experienced higher spending. However, government spending in labor, employment, and immigration dropped 6.6 percent.

45911 ■ *"Elder Care At Work" in HRMagazine (Vol. 53, September 2008, No. 9, pp. 111)*
Pub: Society for Human Resource Management
Contact: Henry G. Jackson, President
E-mail: hjackson@shrm.org
Ed: Pamela Babcock. **Description:** Many employers are helping workers who face sudden, short-term elder care needs.

45912 ■ *Entrepreneurship As Social Change: A Third New Movements in Entrepreneurship Book*
Pub: Edward Elgar Publishing, Incorporated
Ed: Steyaert. **Released:** February 2007. **Price:** $120.00. **Description:** Third book in a series, the edition examines entrepreneurship as a societal phenomenon.

45913 ■ *Entrepreneurship and Small Business*
Pub: Palgrave Macmillan
Ed: Paul Burns. **Released:** January 2007. **Price:** $74.95. **Description:** Entrepreneurial skills, focusing on good management practices are discussed. Topics include family businesses, corporate, international and social entrepreneurship.

45914 ■ *"Everybody Wants To Save the World: But When You Start a Charity Overseas, Good Intentions Often Go Awry" in Inc. (December 2007)*
Pub: Gruner & Jahr USA Publishing
Ed: Dalia Fahmy. **Description:** Unique set of challenges faced by small businesses wanting to create a charity overseas. Five key issues to explore before starting a charity overseas are examined.

45915 ■ *"The Evolution of Corporate Social Responsibility" in Business Horizons (November-December 2007, pp. 449)*
Pub: Elsevier Technology Publications
Ed: Philip L. Cochran. **Description:** Corporate social responsibility is now perceived as vital in enhancing the profitability of businesses while improving their reputation. It has changed business practices such as philanthropy, investment, and entrepreneurship.

45916 ■ *"Fairness First" in Canadian Business (Vol. 80, April 23, 2007, No. 9, pp. 45)*
Pub: Rogers Media
Ed: Erin Pooley. **Description:** The need for the fair treatment of employees from the perspective of employee compensation is discussed.

45917 ■ *"Family Matters: Founding Family Firms and Corporate Political Activity" in Business and Society (December 2007, pp. 395-428)*
Pub: SAGE Publications USA
Contact: Blaise R. Simqu, President
Ed: Michael Hadani. **Description:** The impact of publicly traded family founding firms and their inclination for corporate political activity is examined. Publicly traded family founding firms are more predisposed to engage in corporate political activity when the founder is in an executive position. Details of these findings are reported.

45918 ■ *"Festivals Press on Despite Loss of Sponsors" in Crain's Detroit Business (Vol. 25, June 22, 2009, No. 25, pp. 3)*
Pub: Crain Communications Inc. - Detroit
Ed: Sherri Begani Welch. **Description:** Organizers of local festivals are experiencing a decrease in sponsorship this summer due to the slow economy. These events help keep areas vibrant and stress the importance of community and cultural events.

45919 ■ *"Fire Destroys Veterans' Kiosk" in Houston Chronicle (November 24, 2010, pp. 14)*
Pub: Houston Chronicle
Description: A leaking propane heater is believed to have started a fire that destroyed a kiosk near the Vietnam Veterans Memorial in Washington DC. The

kiosk, manned by volunteers from the Rolling Thunder veterans group, provide education to the public about those individuals still missing from the Vietnam War.

45920 ■ *"FIS-Metavante Deal Paying Off for Many" in Business Journal-Milwaukee (Vol. 28, December 17, 2010, No. 11, pp. A1)*
Pub: Milwaukee Business Journal
Ed: Rich Kirchen. **Description:** Jacksonville, Florida-based Fidelity National Information Services Inc., also known as FIS, has remained committed to Milwaukee, Wisconsin more than a year after purchasing Metavante Technologies Inc. FIS has transferred several operations into Metropolitan Milwaukee and has continued its contribution to charitable organizations in the area.

45921 ■ *"Food Bank to Move, Double in Size" in Austin Business Journal (Vol. 31, July 8, 2011, No. 18, pp. 1)*
Pub: American City Business Journals Inc.
Ed: Sandra Zaragoza. **Description:** The Capital Area Food Bank (CAFB) of Texas intends to construct a 125,000-square-foot hub on the land it purchased in East Texas. The hub will accommodate administrative offices, warehouse and refrigeration space, and a production kitchen.

45922 ■ *"Give Until It Works" in Hispanic Business (March 2008, pp. 26-27)*
Pub: Hispanic Business
Ed: Rick Munarriz. **Description:** Ways to maximize a tax advantage from charitable contributions for small business owners are addressed.

45923 ■ *"Give Until It Works" in Hispanic Business (Vol. 30, March 2008, No. 3, pp. 26)*
Pub: Hispanic Business
Ed: Rick Munarriz. **Description:** Donating to qualified charities and non-profit organizations for maximizing tax advantage to be availed on the income tax bill is examined. The amount that can be deducted from the total taxable amount is usually less then the actual amount donated and must be made during that calendar year.

45924 ■ *Giving*
Pub: Knopf Publishing/Random House
Ed: Bill Clinton. **Price:** $24.95. **Description:** The former president describes people and projects that save lives and solve problems around the world.

45925 ■ *"The Global Talent Hunt" in Business Strategy Review (Vol. 21, Spring 2010, No. 1, pp. 78)*
Pub: Wiley-Blackwell
Ed: Richard Emerton. **Description:** Richard Emerton explains how the new 'triple context' of economy, environment and society will have profound implications for human resource practices. He suggests that viewing talent as abundant is the right perspective for a manager.

45926 ■ *"Gloria Christiansen: Tennessee's Unselfish Citizen" in Women In Business (Vol. 61, December 2009, No. 6, pp. 10)*
Pub: American Business Women's Association
Description: Gloria Christiansen, a Colombian-born secretary of the Knoxville Area American Business Women's Association (ABWA) Council, shares her experiences as an immigrant in Tennessee who has been provided with the opportunity to grow professionally through ABWA. Aside from participating in community development projects, she deems her American citizenship as an inspiring and honorable experience.

45927 ■ *The Go-Giver: A Little Story About a Powerful Business Idea*
Pub: Penguin Group
Ed: Bob Burg; John David Mann. **Released:** December 27, 2007. **Price:** $19.95. **Description:** Story of an ambitious young man named Joe who years for success. The book is a heartwarming tale that brings new relevance to the old proverb, 'Give and you shall receive'.

45928 ■ *"GoodNews.com and the Little Cupcake Shoppe Support Calgary Food Bank With Unique $1.00 Deal" in Marketwire*

Canada (March 9, 2011)
Pub: Marketwire Canada
Description: Socially-conscious group-buying Website, GoodNews.com has partnered with The Little Cupcake Shoppe in Calgary, to raise funds for the Inter-Faith Food Bank. The fundraiser will feature a half dozen, pre-packaged assorted miniature cupcakes for $1.00. The entire amount is donated to the Calgary Food Bank.

45929 ■ *Grassroots NGOs by Women for Women: The Driving Force of Development in India*
Pub: SAGE Publications USA
Contact: Blaise R. Simqu, President
Ed: Femida Handy; Meenaz Kassam; Suzanne Feeney; Bhagyashree Ranade. **Released:** July 2006. **Price:** $29.95. **Description:** Understanding the role of non-governmental organizations in women's development is offered through interviews with twenty women in India who have founded NGOs serving women.

45930 ■ *Groundswell: Winning in a World Transformed by Social Technologies*
Pub: Harvard Business School Press
Ed: Charlene Li; Josh Bernoff. **Released:** April 21, 2008. **Price:** $29.95. **Description:** Individuals are using online social technologies such as blogs, social networking sites, YouTube, and podcasts to discuss products and companies, write their own news, and find their own deals. When consumers you've never met are rating your company's products in public forums with which you have no experience or influence, your company is vulnerable. This book teaches the tools and data necessary to turn this treat into an opportunity.

45931 ■ *"Group Sewing for Area Charities" in Messenger-Inquirer (July 7, 2010)*
Pub: Messenger-Inquirer
Ed: Beth Wilberding. **Description:** Hobby Lobby in Owensboro, Kentucky features a weekly sewing group that made 656 pillowcases for area agencies.

45932 ■ *Growing Local Value: How to Build Business Partnerships That Strengthen Your Community*
Pub: Berrett-Koehler Publishers, Incorporated
Ed: Laury Hammel; Gun Denhart. **Released:** December 2006. **Price:** $15.00. **Description:** Advice and examples are provided for building socially responsible entrepreneurship.

45933 ■ *"Halls Give Hospital Drive $11 Million Infusion" in The Business Journal-Serving Metropolitan Kansas City (Vol. 26, July 18, 2008)*
Pub: American City Business Journals, Inc.
Ed: Rob Roberts. **Description:** Don Hall, chairman of Hallmark Cards Inc., and eight family members have announced that they will give $11 million to Children's Mercy Hospitals and Clinics for its $800 million expansion plan. Hall Family Foundation president Bill Hall that contributions such as that for Children's Mercy reflect the charitable interests of the foundation's board and founders. The possible impacts of the Hall's donation are analyzed.

45934 ■ *"Hansen Mechanical Performs Boiler Upgrade at Brookfield Zoo" in Contractor (Vol. 57, February 2010, No. 2, pp. 7)*
Pub: Penton Media, Inc.
Description: Hansen Mechanical installed a donated boiler in the Brookfield Zoo from Weil-McLain. The boilers were installed in the zoo's 'The Swamp' and 'The Living Coast' exhibits.

45935 ■ *"Help Employees Give Away Some Of That Bonus" in Harvard Business Review (Vol. 86, July-August 2008, No. 8, pp. 1)*
Pub: Harvard Business School Press
Ed: Michael I. Norton; Elizabeth W. Dunn. **Description:** Research indicates that how employees spend their bonuses is key to their resultant happiness, rather than simply receiving the bonus itself. Firms that offer donation options can thereby increase employee satisfaction.

45936 ■ *"Higher Thread Count for Metropole"* in *Business Courier* (Vol. 26, September 25, 2009, No. 22, pp. 1)

Pub: American City Business Journals, Inc.

Ed: Lisa Biank Fasig, Lucy May. **Description:** Cincinnati Center City Development Corporation is under contract to buy the 225-unit apartment building called Metropole Apartments and 21c Museum Hotel is the lead candidate for the space. Advocates of some residents of the low-income rental complex complain that this move could leave them homeless.

45937 ■ *"Hourly Payment and Volunteering"* in *Academy of Management Journal* (August 2007)

Pub: Academy of Management

Contact: Ming-Jer Chen, President

Ed: Sanford E. DeVoe, Jeffrey Pfeffer. **Description:** Brief description about theoretically important class of work, which is freely undertaken without remuneration, is presented.

45938 ■ *How Come That Idiot's Rich and I'm Not?*

Pub: Crown Publishing/Random House

Ed: Robert Shemin. **Released:** April 2009. **Price:** $13.95. **Description:** The book shows the average person not only how to get rich, but to create, connect and contribute greatly.

45939 ■ *How To Change the World*

Pub: Oxford University Press

Ed: David Bornstein. **Released:** September 2007. **Price:** $15.95. **Description:** Social entrepreneurs are individuals with powerful ideas that improve other people's lives and have implemented these ideas across cities, countries and in some cases, around the world. These are doctors, lawyers, engineers, teachers, journalists and parents who solve social problems on a large scale and have a profound effect on society.

45940 ■ *"Howl-o-ween"* in *Decatur Daily* (October 25, 2011)

Pub: Decatur Daily

Ed: Catherine Godbey. **Description:** Animal Friends Humane Society provides free pet food and cat litter to Meals on Wheels clients.

45941 ■ *"Innovating Globally"* in *Business Strategy Review* (Vol. 21, Spring 2010, No. 1, pp. 24)

Pub: Wiley-Blackwell

Ed: Costas Markides, Stuart Crainer. **Description:** Costas Markides has spent over two decades studying business strategy and innovation. Recently, he has been focusing on the bigger picture of how people can address major social problems. Can the techniques used by managers to create innovation inside organizations work with global change?.

45942 ■ *"The Innovator: Rob McEwen's Unique Vision of Philanthropy and Business"* in *Canadian Business* (Vol. 81, November 10, 2008, No. 19)

Pub: Rogers Media Ltd.

Ed: Alex Mlynek. **Description:** Rob McEwen says that his donation to the Schulich School of Business is his first large donation. He went to the University Health Network and was told about their pan for regenerative medicine, helping him make the decision. McEwan wants to be involved in philanthropy in the areas of leadership and education.

45943 ■ *"Institutional Logics in the Study of Organizations"* in *Business Ethics Quarterly* (Vol. 21, July 2011, No. 3, pp. 409)

Pub: Society for Business Ethics

Ed: Marc Orlitzky. **Description:** Examination into whether the empirical evidence on the relationship between corporate social performance (CSP) and corporate financial performance (CFP) differs depending on the publication outlet in which that evidence appears.

45944 ■ *"Interest in 'Encore Careers' is Growing"* in *HRMagazine* (Vol. 53, November 2008, No. 11, pp. 22)

Pub: Society for Human Resource Management

Contact: Henry G. Jackson, President

E-mail: hjackson@shrm.org

Description: Unexpectedly large numbers of baby boomers are looking for jobs that can provide them with 'means and meaning', according to a survey by MetLife and Civic Ventures. They can find those jobs in encore careers, an opportunity to do work that has a social impact and personal meaning.

45945 ■ *"Is Globalization Threatening U.S. Hispanic Progress?"* in *Hispanic Business* (Vol. 30, September 2008, No. 9, pp. 16)

Pub: Hispanic Business, Inc.

Ed: Jessica Haro. **Description:** Talented Hispanic employees are making progress within the increasingly diverse American corporate scenario. However, while some experts believe the induction of foreign professionals through globalization will not impact this progress, others feel it could hamper opportunities for American Hispanics.

45946 ■ *"Janet Froetscher, CEO, United Way of Metropolitan Chicago"* in *Crain's Chicago Business* (Vol. 31, May 5, 2008, No. 18, pp. 26)

Pub: Crain Communications, Inc.

Ed: Emily Stone. **Description:** Profile of Janet Froetscher who is the CEO of United Way of Metropolitan Chicago who organized the country's largest-ever merger of non-profits with 53 smaller suburban chapters consolidating with the Chicago one. The consolidation saves $4 million a year with departments such as finance, information technology and communications which allows that money be spent funding job training, after-school programs and aid for 7,000 Hurricane Katrina evacuees living in the Chicago area.

45947 ■ *"Kelvin Taketa"* in *Hawaii Business* (Vol. 53, October 2007, No. 4, pp. 30)

Pub: Hawaii Business Publishing

Ed: Scott Radway. **Description:** Hawaii Community Foundation chief executive officer Kelvin Taketa believes that the leadership shortage for nonprofit sector in Hawaii is a result of leaders retiring or switching to part-time work. Taketa adds that the duties of a nonprofit organization leader are very challenging, with the organizations being usually thinly staffed. His opinion on the prospects of young leadership in Hawaii is also given.

45948 ■ *The Leadership Challenge*

Pub: Jossey-Bass Publishers

Ed: James M. Kouzes, Barry Z. Posner. **Released:** June 30, 1995. **Price:** $22.00. **Description:** According to research by the authors, people can make extraordinary things happen by liberating the leader within everyone around them. This handbook gives practical tips to aspire leaders in retail, manufacturing, government, community, church and school settings.

45949 ■ *"Let It Shine: Organization Helps Disadvantaged Girls See Their Worth"* in *Black Enterprise* (Vol. 38, February 2008, No. 7, pp. 142)

Pub: Earl G. Graves Publishing Co. Inc.

Ed: George Alexander. **Description:** Wilson Mourning, founder of the clothing label Honey Child, attributes her success to her mother and other positive women who helped her through her adolescence. Mourning created a mentoring organization that helps young girls in the Miami, Florida area to develop life skills.

45950 ■ *"A Lifetime of Giving: Food Bank CEO Fights Hunger One Mouth At a Time"* in *Black Enterprise* (Vol. 41, November 2010, No. 4, pp. 86)

Pub: Earl G. Graves Publishing Co. Inc.

Ed: Tamara E. Holmes. **Description:** Profile of Valerie Traore, CEO of Food Bank of South Jersey. Traore stresses the importance of volunteerism that she learned from her grandparents. Hunger relief became her passion when she served as a temp office worker for the Maryland Food Bank in Baltimore. She earned her Bachelor's of Science in management and has dedicated herself to a career in nonprofit service.

45951 ■ *Living Above the Store: Building a Business That Creates Value, Inspires Change, and Restores Land and Community*

Pub: Chelsea Green Publishing

Ed: Martin Melaver. **Released:** May 1, 2009. **Price:** $27.95. **Description:** Martin Melaver shares insight into building a business plan that utilizes diversity, shared values, common purpose and land-community ethics that are restorative for humankind and nature.

45952 ■ *"The Loan Arranger"* in *Canadian Business* (Vol. 80, October 22, 2007, No. 21, pp. 15)

Pub: Rogers Media

Ed: Rachel Pulfer. **Description:** Muhammad Yunus received the Nobel Prize in 2006 for the organization that he founded, the Grameen Bank. The bank has helped women in developing countries and has also begun helping millions of individuals to make loans in the U.S. through the Grameen Bank. An evaluation of the Grameen model is provided.

45953 ■ *"Lunch Box Maker Gives Back"* in *Marketing to Women* (Vol. 23, November 2010, No. 11, pp. 5)

Pub: EPM Communications Inc.

Contact: Ira Mayer, President

E-mail: imayer@epmcom.com

Description: Female entrepreneurs launched a new program called, 'Share Your Lunch Project' that encourages mothers to give back and replace their child's lunchbox with their eco-friendly lunch boxes, which are available at select retailers. All proceeds from the project will benefit the World Food Program USA, which feeds children in developing countries.

45954 ■ *"Make a Resolution: ADA Training"* in *HRMagazine* (Vol. 54, January 2009, No. 1, pp. 81)

Pub: Society for Human Resource Management

Contact: Henry G. Jackson, President

E-mail: hjackson@shrm.org

Ed: Victoria Zellers. **Description:** Americans with Disabilities Act (ADA) Amendments Act took effect January 1, 2009. The ADA Amendments Act means that more applicants and employees are eligible for reasonable accommodations and that employers need to develop a new ADA compliance strategy.

45955 ■ *"McDonald's Founders Fund $80 Million Project"* in *The Business Journal - Serving Phoenix and the Valley of the Sun* (Vol. 28, September 12, 2008, No. 53, pp. 1)

Pub: American City Business Journals, Inc.

Ed: Jan Buchholz. **Description:** Construction will begin in early 2009 on an $80 million Ray and Joan Kroc Community Center in Phoenix, Arizona. It will be located adjacent to the Salvation Army, which received a $1.9 billion contribution from Joan Kroc after her death in 2003. This fund will be divided to construct 30 community centers across the country.

45956 ■ *Memos to the Prime Minister: What Canada Could Be in the 21st Century*

Pub: John Wiley & Sons, Incorporated

Ed: Harvey Schacter. **Released:** April 11, 2003. **Price:** $16.95. **Description:** A look into the business future of Canada. Topics include business, healthcare, think tanks, policy groups, education, the arts, economy, and social issues.

45957 ■ *Microfranchising: Creating Wealth at the Bottom of the Pyramid*

Pub: Edward Elgar Publishing, Incorporated

Ed: W. Gibb Dyer; Jason Fairbourne; Stephen W. Gibson. **Released:** July 2008. **Price:** $35.00. **Description:** Ideas from researchers and social entrepreneurs discusses the movement that moves microfranchising into a mechanism for sustainable poverty reduction on a scale to match microfinance.

45958 ■ *"Military Brides Can Get Free Wedding Gowns"* in *Virginian-Pilot* (November 10, 2010)

Pub: The Virginia-Pilot

Ed: Jamesetta Walker. **Description:** Seventy-five designer wedding gowns will be given to military brides on a first-come, first-served basis at Maya

Couture through the Brides Across America's wedding gown giveaway program. Gowns are valued between $500 to $3,000 and are donated by designers Maggie Sottero, Pronovias and Essense of Australia.

45959 ■ "Minority Entrepreneurs, Business Advocate of the Year Named" in Daily News (November 1, 2010)
Pub: Daily News
Ed: Aniesa Holmes. **Description:** Jacksonville-Onslow Chamber of Commerce Minority Enterprise Development Day honored outstanding entrepreneurs from the region. Candidates were chosen based on criteria such as business accomplishments, chamber involvement and dedication as well as their commitment to serving people in the community.

45960 ■ "Model Citizen" in Entrepreneur (Vol. 36, February 2008, No. 2, pp. 42)
Pub: Entrepreneur Media Inc.
Ed: Guy Kawasaki. **Description:** A mensch is a person of noble character, as defined by Leo Rosten. Tips on how to be a mensch and a better person, in relation to being an entrepreneur, are given. These include: helping others without expecting something in return, giving back to society, and knowing the line between right and wrong.

45961 ■ The Mom and Pop Store: How the Unsung Heroes of the American Economy Are Surviving and Thriving
Pub: Walker & Company
Ed: Robert Spector. **Released:** September 1, 2009. **Price:** $26.00. **Description:** The history of small independent retail enterprises and how mom and pop stores in the U.S. continue to thrive through customer service and renewed community support for local businesses.

45962 ■ "More Volunteers Needed to Make a Difference" in Times-News (October 18, 2011)
Pub: Times-News
Ed: Roselee Papandrea. **Description:** Meals on Wheels program in the Burlington, North Carolina area is seeking volunteers to deliver meals to senior citizens.

45963 ■ "New Economy Initiative Gains Partners" in Crain's Detroit Business (Vol. 25, June 1, 2009, No. 22, pp. M014)
Pub: Crain Communications Inc. - Detroit
Ed: Sherri Begin Welch. **Description:** New Economy Initiative is a $100 million philanthropic initiative that focuses on regional economic development. Recent grants awarded to Michigan companies are outlined.

45964 ■ The New Social Entrepreneurship What Awaits Social Entrepreneurship Ventures?
Pub: Edward Elgar Publishing, Incorporated
Ed: Perrini. **Released:** October 2006. **Price:** $120.00. **Description:** Social entrepreneurship seeks to improve societal well-being within entrepreneurial organizations.

45965 ■ "Nonprofit to Grow" in Austin Business JournalInc. (Vol. 29, January 22, 2010, No. 46, pp. 1)
Pub: American City Business Journals
Ed: Sandra Zaragoza. **Description:** Southwest Key Programs Inc. received a $2.1 million grant from the U.S. Economic Development Administration to help finance the building of a $3.6 million 'Social Enterprise Complex'. The complex is expected to create at least 100 jobs in East Austin, Texas. Details of the plan for the complex are presented.

45966 ■ "Nonprofit NAIC Acquires Software Developer as For-Profit Arm" in Crain's Detroit Business (Vol. 25, June 22, 2009, No. 25, pp. 10)
Pub: Crain Communications Inc. - Detroit
Ed: Sherri Begin Welch. **Description:** Details of National Association of Investors Corporation's acquisition of a Massachusetts investment software developer in order to offer more products to investment clubs and individual investors nationwide.

45967 ■ "Nonprofits Find Plenty of Optimism for the Future" in Business Courier (Vol. 26, January 1, 2010, No. 37, pp. 1)
Pub: American City Business Journals, Inc.
Ed: Lucy May. **Description:** Forecasts of various nonprofits in Cincinnati, Ohio such as the United Way of Greater Cincinnati, the Greater Cincinnati Foundation and The Fine Arts Fund for 2010 are presented.

45968 ■ "Nonprofits Hope Employees Dig Deep" in Austin Business JournalInc. (Vol. 28, December 5, 2008, No. 38, pp. A1)
Pub: American City Business Journals
Ed: Sandra Zaragoza. **Description:** Nonprofit organizations in Austin, Texas are stepping up workplace giving drives in the hope that workers will continue giving donations to them. Corporations are cutting costs due to the recession, reducing donations to nonprofit organizations in the process.

45969 ■ "Nonprofits Pressured to Rein in Fundraising Events" in Crain's Detroit Business (Vol. 25, June 15, 2009, No. 24, pp. 1)
Pub: Crain Communications Inc. - Detroit
Ed: Sherri Begin Welch. **Description:** Local corporations have asked nonprofit= s to limit fundraising events in order to cut costs during the recession.

45970 ■ "OHC Aids Long Island Family" in Indoor Comfort Marketing (Vol. 70, May 2011, No. 5, pp. 45)
Pub: Industry Publications Inc.
Ed: Judy Garber. **Description:** Ways Community Oil Heat helped a customer living in Long Island heat their home during desperate times.

45971 ■ "Oil Rich" in Canadian Business (Vol. 79, Winter 2006, No. 24, pp. 57)
Pub: Rogers Media
Ed: Calvin Leung. **Description:** The efforts of John Risley, the Chairman of the Candaian firm Clearwater Fine Foods Inc., to educate consumers about the health aspects of seafood, are described.

45972 ■ "On the Clock" in Canadian Business (Vol. 82, April 27, 2009, No. 7, pp. 28)
Pub: Rogers Media
Ed: Sarka Halas. **Description:** Survey of 100 Canadian executives found that senior managers can be out of a job for about nine months before their careers are adversely affected. The nine month mark can be avoided if job seekers build networks even before they lose their jobs. Job seekers should also take volunteer work and training opportunities to increase their changes of landing a job.

45973 ■ "On the Economic Dimensions of Corporate Social Responsibility" in Business and Society (December 2007, pp. 457-478)
Pub: SAGE Publications USA
Contact: Blaise R. Simqu, President
Ed: Fabienne Fortanier, Ans Kolk. **Description:** Economic impact of Fortune Global 250 firms analyzing concern for corporate social responsibility is discussed, focusing on an illustration of mechanisms by which multinational enterprises affect economic developed.

45974 ■ "One Laptop Per Child Weighs Going For-Profit" in Boston Business Journal (Vol. 31, May 20, 2011, No. 17, pp. 1)
Pub: Boston Business Journal
Ed: Mary Moore. **Description:** Nonprofit organization One Laptop Per Child is thinking of shifting into a for-profit structure in order to raise as much as $10 million in capital to achieve its goal of distributing more XO laptops to poor children worldwide. The organization has distributed 2 million computers since 2008 with Uruguay, Peru and Rwanda as its biggest markets.

45975 ■ "Online Pet Medication Store Supports Free Vaccinations for Cats" in Internet Wire (August 31, 2010)
Pub: Comtex
Description: Pethealth Inc., The Petango Store will help to support The Humane Society of Tampa Bay's efforts by offering free feline vaccinations for the cat's

entire lifetime that is adopted between September 1, 2010 and February 28, 2010. The cat must be one year or older at time of adoption.

45976 ■ "OPSEU: Developmental Service Workers Picketing Across Ontario to Raise Community Awareness" in Canadian Corporate News (May 16, 2007)
Pub: Comtex News Network Inc.
Description: Across Ontario staff who support people with developmental disabilities are picketing local MPP offices and other community hubs to highlight the Ontario government's inadequate response to the crisis in developmental services.

45977 ■ "Outpouring of Outreach" in Crain's Cleveland Business (Vol. 30, June 15, 2009, No. 23, pp. 3)
Pub: Crain Communications, Inc.
Ed: Shannon Mortland. **Description:** Nonprofit organizations are experiencing a higher number of volunteers than in the past. People are willing to donate their skills and services rather than contributing money.

45978 ■ "Pet Food Bank 'Shares the Love" in Pet Product News (Vol. 64, December 2010, No. 12, pp. 6)
Pub: BowTie Inc.
Description: Winston-Salem, North Carolina-based nonprofit Share the Love Pet Food Bank has donated 60,000 pounds of pet food since its establishment in 2009. It has been linking pet food manufacturers and rescue groups to supply unsold pet food to needy animals. The nonprofit intends to reach out to more animal welfare groups by building more warehouses.

45979 ■ "Pet Kiosk Offers Search Options" in Times-News (October 14, 2010)
Pub: Times-News Publishing Company
Ed: Roselee Papandrea. **Description:** Chameleon Pet Kiosk located at the Spay and Neuter Clinic of Alamance County in Burlington, North Carolina allows users to see and read about animals available for adoption at the center.

45980 ■ "Philanthropy Good For Business" in Crain's Detroit Business (Vol. 24, February 18, 2008, No. 7, pp. 14)
Pub: Crain Communications Inc. - Detroit
Ed: Sheena Harrison. **Description:** Profile of Burce McCully, founder of Dynamic Edge Inc., and his views on philanthropy as a key to any small company's success. The Ann Arbor, Michigan information technology firm has volunteered and raised funds for many causes since 1999 when the company was founded.

45981 ■ "A Place to Call Home" in Business Courier (Vol. 24, March 7, 2008, No. 48, pp. 1)
Pub: American City Business Journals, Inc.
Ed: Lucy May. **Description:** Discusses a new type of housing for Cincinnati's chronically homeless that will be developed by the Over-the-Rhine Community Housing Network and the Cincinnati Center City Development Corp. Advocates believe that it is the missing link in the community's efforts to eradicate homelessness. The details of the project are also presented.

45982 ■ "Planning Ahead" in Crain's Cleveland Business (Vol. 30, June 15, 2009, No. 23, pp. 12)
Pub: Crain Communications, Inc.
Ed: Shannon Mortland. **Description:** Cleveland area nonprofit organizations are developing new strategies for raising donations, while keeping costs down in the slow economy.

45983 ■ "Post-Prison Center Idea Rankles OTR" in Business Courier (Vol. 26, November 27, 2009, No. 31, pp. 1)
Pub: American City Business Journals, Inc.
Ed: Lucy May. **Description:** Cincinnati officials and community leaders oppose Firetree Ltd.'s plan to launch a residential program for federal offenders near the School for the Creative and Performing Arts in Over-the-Rhine. Firetree, a Pennsylvania-based reentry center services firm, proposed a five-year contract with the Federal Bureau of Prisons based on a letter to Cincinnati Police Chief Thomas Streicher.

45984 ■ *The Power of Social Innovation: How Civic Entrepreneurs Ignite Community Networks for Good*

Pub: John Wiley & Sons, Inc.

Ed: Stephen Goldsmith, Tim Burke, Gigi Georges. **Released:** March 10, 2010. **Price:** $35.00. **Description:** This seminal book provides tools for civic entrepreneurs to create healthier communities and promote innovative solutions to public and social problems. It shows how to effectively tackle the intractable issues facing the country.

45985 ■ *"Preserving a Nonprofit's Mission" in Boston Business Journal (Vol. 31, June 17, 2011, No. 21, pp. 3)*

Pub: Boston Business Journal

Ed: Mary Moore. **Description:** Young Women's Christian Association Boston (YWCA) agreed to absorb the LeadBoston social issues and youth programs operated by the Boston Center for Community Justice. The BCCJ is scheduled to close after failing to stabilize its finances.

45986 ■ *"Pride Lands Janitorial Work at New Terminal" in Sacramento Business Journal (Vol. 28, June 10, 2011, No. 15, pp. 1)*

Pub: Sacramento Business Journal

Ed: Kelly Johnson. **Description:** Pride Industries Inc. won the five-year $9.4 million contract to clean the Sacramento International Airport's new Terminal B, which will open in fall 2011. The nonprofit organization posts a revenue of $191 million for 2011 and currently employs more than 2,400 people with disabilities. The contract is expected to provide savings of over $3 million a year to the airport.

45987 ■ *"Priority: In Memoriam" in Inc. (December 2007, pp. 25-26, 28, 30)*

Pub: Gruner & Jahr USA Publishing

Ed: Ryan McCarthy. **Description:** Profiles of entrepreneurs who died in 2007; these individuals helped to create some major business trends in the last fifty years, from the advent of socially responsible business to development of quality manufacturing.

45988 ■ *"The Progressive Pet Shop: Showcasing Strays" in Animals' Agenda (March-April 1993, pp. 34)*

Pub: Animal Rights Network Inc.

Ed: Athena Rhiannon Schaffer. **Description:** Brothers Pets stopped selling cats and dogs in order to donate kennel space to the Aspen Hill, Maryland animal shelter. The events leading to this small business decision and its success are presented.

45989 ■ *"Proud Out Loud" in Canadian Business (Vol. 80, April 23, 2007, No. 9, pp. 52)*

Pub: Rogers Media

Description: The role of accomplishments of employees in improving workplace conditions is presented.

45990 ■ *"Readers Share How Sewing Shaped the Fabric of Their Lives" in Virginian-Pilot (September 14, 2010)*

Pub: Virginian-Pilot

Ed: Jamesetta Walker. **Description:** People discuss the ways sewing has help enrich their lives, from public service projects and conventions centered on sewing.

45991 ■ *"Religious Revival" in Canadian Business (Vol. 81, December 8, 2008, No. 21, pp. 57)*

Pub: Rogers Media Ltd.

Ed: Paul Webster. **Description:** Canada-based lawyer Cyndee Todgham Cherniak believes that Canadians wishing to do business in China should have professional competence, as well as cultural and spiritual sensitivity. Chinese government officials also acknowledge the role of religion in China's economy.

45992 ■ *"The Romance of Good Deeds: a Business With a Cause Can Do Good in the World" in Inc. (Volume 32, December 2010,*

No. 10, pp. 47)

Pub: Inc. Magazine

Ed: Meg Cadoux Hirshberg. **Description:** Entrepreneurship and family relationships are discussed. When a small business has a passion for philanthropy it can help any marriage by creating even greater passion for each other.

45993 ■ *"Sage Advice" in Canadian Business (Vol. 80, October 22, 2007, No. 21, pp. 70)*

Pub: Rogers Media

Ed: John Gray. **Description:** Seymour Schulich, one of Canada's richest men and generous philanthropist, wrote the book, 'Get Smarter: Life and Business Lessons'. The business book sold more than 50,000 copies and now sits on Canada's bestseller's list. Its popularity is attributed to the marketing efforts of the entrepreneur and author.

45994 ■ *"Second Chance Counselor" in Business Courier (Vol. 27, July 2, 2010, No. 9, pp. 1)*

Pub: Business Courier

Ed: Lucy May. **Description:** Stephen Tucker, director of workforce development for the Urban League of Greater Cincinnati, is an example of how ex-offenders can be given chances for employment after service jail sentences. How the Urban Leagues' Solid Opportunities for Advancement job training program helped Tucker and other ex-offenders is discussed.

45995 ■ *"Seymour Schulich" in Canadian Business (Vol. 79, Winter 2006, No. 24, pp. 144)*

Pub: Rogers Media

Ed: John Gray. **Description:** The views of the Canadian billionaire Seymour Schulich, on the evaluation of donations and gifts, are presented.

45996 ■ *"Silver Key Seeks Volunteer Drivers in Colorado Springs" in Colorado Springs Business Journal (October 21, 2011)*

Pub: Dolan Media

Ed: Amy Gillentine. **Description:** Silver Keyis look for drivers to use their own vehicles to deliver Meals on Wheels to area seniors. For many of these senior citizens, it is the only outside contact they have an entire day.

45997 ■ *"Small Is Best, Says Housing Officials" in Business First Buffalo (November 16, 2007, pp. 1)*

Pub: American City Business Journals, Inc.

Ed: Tracey Drury. **Description:** Nonprofit organizations in some parts of the U.S. are moving senior citizens from larger institutions into smaller housing. The benefits of smaller housing for the elderly are evaluated.

45998 ■ *Social Enterprise: Developing Sustainable Businesses*

Pub: Palgrave Macmillan

Ed: Frank Martin, Marcus Thompson. **Released:** January 1, 2010. **Price:** $106.00. **Description:** Social enterprises bring people and communities together for economic development and social gain and represent a growing sector of the business community.

45999 ■ *Social Entrepreneurship*

Pub: Palgrave Macmillan

Ed: Johanna Mair; Jeffrey Robinson; Kai Hockerts. **Released:** June 2006. **Price:** $80.00. **Description:** Social entrepreneurship is the process involving innovative approaches to solving social problems while creating economic value.

46000 ■ *Social Entrepreneurship For Dummies*

Pub: John Wiley & Sons

Ed: Mark Derieux, Robert Stebbins. **Released:** April 10, 2010. **Price:** $24.99. **Description:** Discover ways to bring social entrepreneurship to a small company in today's business environment. Today, a company is not measured by financial performance alone, but also on social entrepreneurship.

46001 ■ *Social Entrepreneurship: What Everyone Needs to Know*

Pub: Oxford University Press, Inc.

Ed: David Bornstein, Susan Davis. **Released:** April 10, 2010. **Price:** $16.95. **Description:** In development circles, there is now a widespread consensus that social entrepreneurs represent a far better mechanism to respond to needs than we have ever had before, a decentralized and emergent force that remains the best hope for solutions.

46002 ■ *The Spiritual Entrepreneur*

Pub: New Paradigm Media

Ed: Robert Morgen. **Released:** January 1, 2010. **Price:** $16.95. **Description:** Step-by-step guide to start a small business and then use that business to create various streams of passive income to support yourself and charities is presented.

46003 ■ *The Starbucks Experience*

Pub: McGraw-Hill

Ed: Joseph A. Michelli. **Released:** September 14, 2006. **Price:** $24.95. **Description:** Boardroom strategies, employee motivation tips, community involvement, and customer satisfaction are issues addressed, using Starbucks as a model.

46004 ■ *"Still on the Block" in Entrepreneur (Vol. 35, November 2007, No. 11, pp. 22)*

Pub: Entrepreneur Media Inc.

Ed: Laura Tiffany. **Description:** Neighborhoods where business enterprises are located sometimes go into decline, particularly in low-income communities with high crime rates. Some entrepreneurs share stories about getting involved to help revive the community and keep their businesses thriving.

46005 ■ *SuperCorp: How Vanguard Companies Create Innovation, Profits, Growth, and Social Good*

Pub: Crown Business

Ed: Rosabeth Moss Kanter. **Released:** 2009. **Price:** $27.50. **Description:** Harvard professor makes a persuasive case showing how social good is good for any company's bottom line.

46006 ■ *"Survey: Most Approve of Donating Used Pacemakers to Medically Underserved" in Crain's Detroit Business (Vol. 25, June 1, 2009)*

Pub: Crain Communications Inc. - Detroit

Description: According to a survey conducted by University of Michigan Cardiovascular Center, 87 percent of those with pacemakers and 71 percent of the general population would donate the device to patients in underserved nations.

46007 ■ *"The Tapestry of Life" in Women In Business (Vol. 61, December 2009, No. 6, pp. 8)*

Pub: American Business Women's Association

Ed: Kathleen Leighton. **Description:** Suzanne Fanch, co-owner of the Devil's Thumb Ranch, discusses the family and career-related influences that helped her to achieve success as a small business proprietor. She advises that opportunities should be treated as building blocks towards success. Fanch's involvement in advocacies that take care of the welfare of community, children, and environment is also discussed.

46008 ■ *"Taxpayer Says a Simple Thank-You Would Help" in Boston Business Journal (Vol. 27, November 16, 2007, No. 42, pp. 1)*

Pub: American City Business Journals Inc.

Ed: Jesse Noyes. **Description:** Bill Freza founded the ThankTheTaxpayer.org, a Website and incorporated organization. The non-partisan group aims to induce gratitude and civility as a tax reform and attitude among taxpayers, particularly those in the top wage category.

46009 ■ *"Tech Giving 2.0" in Boston Business Journal (Vol. 31, August 5, 2011, No. 28, pp. 1)*

Pub: Boston Business Journal

Ed: Mary Moore. **Description:** Entrepreneurs and venture capitalists in Boston have launched Technology Underwriting Greater Good, the tech industry's answer to the criticism that they are not charitable.

The foundation finances nonprofits that aid young people through entrepreneurship, education and life experience. Other tech firms in Boston doing charitable works are discussed.

46010 ■ *"Tenacious Trailblazer"* in Hispanic Business (Vol. 30, April 2008, No. 4, pp. 26)
Pub: Hispanic Business
Ed: Melinda Burns. **Description:** Dr. Sandra Hernandez has been named as Hispanic Business Woman of the Year for her pioneering work in health care reform. Dr. Hernandez is the first Hispanic and the first woman to serve as public health director for the city and county of San Francisco.

46011 ■ *"This Just In"* in Crain's Detroit Business (Vol. 25, June 1, 2009, No. 22, pp. 1)
Pub: Crain Communications Inc. - Detroit
Description: Three veterans of the auto industry have partnered to create, Revitalizing Michigan, a nonprofit dedicated to help manufacturers improve their processes. The firm is seeking federal, state and private grants to fund the mission.

46012 ■ *"To Help Maintain an Adequate Blood Supply During the Summer Months"* in Ice Cream Reporter (Vol. 21, August 20, 2008, No. 9, pp. 8)
Pub: Ice Cream Reporter
Description: Friendly's and the American Red Cross have partnered to offer blood donors a coupon for one free carton of Friendly's ice cream in order to maintain an adequate supply during summer months.

46013 ■ *"Toward a Political Conception of Corporate Responsibility"* in Academy of Management Review (October 2007, pp. 1096)
Pub: ScholarOne, Inc.
Ed: Andreas Georg Scherer, Guido Palazzo. **Description:** The limitations of studies on corporate social responsibility and a new theory based on Jurgen Habermas theory of democracy are highlighted. The key role played by the business firm in globalization of society is presented.

46014 ■ *"Tualatin Senior Center Under Construction"* in Daily Journal of Commerce (October 21, 2011)
Pub: Dolan Media
Ed: Angela Webber. **Description:** Juanita Pohl Center in Tualatin Community Park is the home to TualatinAEs Meals on Wheels program that delivers meals to seniors in the area.

46015 ■ *Values-Centered Entrepreneurship*
Pub: Routledge
Ed: David Y. Choi, Edmund Gray. **Released:** August 10, 2010. **Price:** $39.95. **Description:** A new brand of entrepreneurs has arrived on the business scene, carrying with them a new set of values. They possess a sense of social responsibility, the need to protect the planet, and to do the right thing for all stakeholders.

46016 ■ *Values and Opportunities in Social Entrepreneurship*
Pub: Palgrave Macmillan
Ed: Kai Hockerts. **Released:** November 1, 2009. **Price:** $90.00. **Description:** Social entrepreneurship has grown as a research field. This book discusses social entrepreneurship as well as the identification and exploitation of social venturing opportunities.

46017 ■ *Values Sell: Transforming Purpose into Profit through Creative Sales and Distribution Strategies*
Pub: Berrett-Koehler Publishers, Incorporated
Ed: Nadine A. Thompson; Angela E. Soper. **Released:** March 28, 2007. **Price:** $16.95. **Description:** Sales and distribution are the lifeblood of any business, socially responsible businesses are no different.

46018 ■ *"Wal-Mart Sharpens Focus on Roxbury"* in Boston Business Journal (Vol. 31, July 8, 2011, No. 24, pp. 1)
Pub: Boston Business Journal
Ed: Mary Moore. **Description:** Wal-Mart Stores is boosting its search for a possible location in the Roxbury section of Boston, Massachusetts. The search

is focused on underserved communities in terms of jobs and access to reasonably-priced merchandise. The extent Boston's African American community has clashed with Mayor Thomas M. Memino over the accommodations of the retailer in Roxbury is discussed.

46019 ■ *"Water Distiller"* in Canadian Business (Vol. 81, September 29, 2008, No. 16, pp. 52)
Pub: Rogers Media Ltd.
Ed: Matthew McClearn. **Description:** Les Fairn's invention of a water distiller called a Solarsphere was recognized in the Great Canadian Invention Competition. Fairn's invention resembles a buoy that uses the sun's energy to vaporize dirty water then leaves the impurities behind in a sump. The invention has an application for producing potable water in impoverished countries.

46020 ■ *The Way We'll Be: The Zogby Report on the Transformation of the American Dream*
Pub: Crown Business
Ed: John Zogby. **Released:** 2009. **Price:** $26.00. **Description:** According to a recent poll, the next generation of Americans are not as concerned about making money as they are about making a difference in the world.

46021 ■ *"Weaving a Stronger Fabric: Organizing a Global Sweat-Free Apparel Production Agreement"* in WorkingUSA (Vol. 11, June 2008, No. 2)
Pub: Blackwell Publishers Ltd.
Ed: Eric Dirnbach. **Description:** Tens of millions of workers working under terrible sweatshop conditions in the global apparel industry. Workers are employed at apparel contractors and have been largely unsuccessful in organizing and improving their working conditions. The major apparel manufacturers and retailers have the most power in this industry, and they have adopted corporate social responsibility programs as a false solution to the sweatshop problem. The major North American apparel unions dealt with similar sweatshop conditions a century ago by organizing the contractors and brands into joint association contracts that significantly raised standards. Taking inspiration from their example, workers and their anti-sweatshop allies need to work together to coordinate a global organizing effort that builds worker power and establishes a global production agreement that negotiates with both contractors and the brands for improved wages, benefits, and working conditions.

46022 ■ *"When Profit Is Not the Incentive"* in Business North Carolina (Vol. 28, February 2008, No. 2, pp. 42)
Pub: Business North Carolina
Ed: Amanda Parry. **Description:** Novant Health is North Carolina's fifth-largest private-sector employer and one of the largest nonprofit companies. Nonprofits grew 35 percent in North Carolina from 1995 to 2003.

46023 ■ *"Where New Economy Initiative Grants Have Gone"* in Crain's Detroit Business (Vol. 25, June 1, 2009, No. 22, pp. M014)
Pub: Crain Communications Inc. - Detroit
Description: Listing of grants totaling $20.5 million focusing on talent development, attraction and retention; innovation and entrepreneurship; and shifting to a culture that values learning, work and innovation, is presented.

46024 ■ *"Winner Nonprofit, Hospitals"* in Crain's Detroit Business (Vol. 25, June 22, 2009, No. 25, pp. E002)
Pub: Crain Communications Inc. - Detroit
Ed: Jay Greene. **Description:** James Connelly, CFO for Henry Ford Health System, discusses the financial status of the system. Statistical data included.

46025 ■ *"Winner: Nonprofit, Human Services"* in Crain's Detroit Business (Vol. 25, June 22,

2009, No. 25, pp. E002)
Pub: Crain Communications Inc. - Detroit
Ed: Sherri Begin Welch. **Description:** Profile of Lighthouse of Oakland County, located in Pontiac, Michigan. The nonprofit and its three subsidiaries are operating on a consolidated 2009 budget of $8.5 million.

46026 ■ *Women Count: A Guide to Changing the World*
Pub: Purdue University Press
Ed: Susan Bulkeley Butler, Bob Keefe. **Released:** August 26, 2010. **Price:** $24.95. **Description:** Throughout history, women have struggled to change the workplace, change government, change society. It's time for women to change the world! Whether on the job, in politics, or in their community, there has never been a better time for women to make a difference in the world.

46027 ■ *The Working Man and Woman's Guide to Becoming a Millionaire*
Pub: Prentiss Publishing
Ed: Al Herron. **Released:** November 2006. **Description:** President and CEO of a Century 21 office in Dallas, Texas shares insight into financial security and commitment to community.

46028 ■ *"Your Big Give"* in Small Business Opportunities (September 2008)
Pub: Entrepreneur Press
Contact: Perlman Neil, President
Ed: Michael Guld. **Description:** Cause related marketing is beneficial to businesses as well as the communities they inhabit; three small businesses that are elevating their standing in the community while at the same time increasing their customer base are profiled.

TRADE PERIODICALS

46029 ■ *Business Ethics: The Magazine of Corporate Responsibility*
Pub: Business Ethics
URL(s): business-ethics.com/. **Ed:** Michael Connor. **Released:** Quarterly

RESEARCH CENTERS

46030 ■ Bentley College - Center for Business Ethics (CBE)
175 Forest St., AAC 108
Waltham, MA 02452-4705
Ph: (781)891-2981
Fax: (781)891-2988
Co. E-mail: cbeinfo@bentley.edu
URL: http://www.bentley.edu/cbe
Contact: W. Michael Hoffman, Executive Director
Services: Consulting. **Founded:** 1976. **Publications:** *Bibliographies on business ethics topics; CBE Conference proceedings; CBE News/Books and surveys.* **Educational Activities:** Executive education and training programs. **Awards:** Hoffman Prize in Business Ethics; Executive Scholar and Research Fellow Programs. **Telecommunication Services:** mhoffman@bentley.edu.

46031 ■ Ethics Resource Center, Inc. (ERC)
2345 Crystal Dr., Ste. 201
Arlington, VA 22202
Ph: (703)647-2185
Fax: (703)647-2180
Co. E-mail: pat@ethics.org
URL: http://www.ethics.org
Contact: Patricia Harned, President
Founded: 1977. **Publications:** *National Business Ethics survey reports; Survey reports; ERC Annual report; Ethics for Life Video Series; Ethics Today* (10/year); *Ethics at Work Video Series.* **Educational Activities:** Produces films and other instructional materials, for use in public schools to help teachers develop and reinforce positive values and character traits in students; ERC Seminars, on business ethics and character education; Teacher training institutes; Workshops designed to assist in the development and implementation of corporate ethics programs.

Awards: Princeton Project Fellowships; Stanley C. Pace Distinguished Award to Lecture on Leadership in Ethics. **Telecommunication Services:** ethics@ethics.org.

46032 ■ Santa Clara University - Markkula Center for Applied Ethics
500 El Camino Real
Santa Clara, CA 95053-0633
Ph: (408)554-5319
Fax: (408)554-2373
Co. E-mail: ethics@scu.edu
URL: http://www.scu.edu/ethics
Contact: Kirk O. Hanson, Executive Director
Services: Consulting: for hospitals, businesses, schools, and nonprofit groups (Weekly); Curriculum Development in K-12 Character Education. **Founded:** 1986. **Publications:** *At the Center* (Annual). **Educational Activities:** Business and Organizational Ethics Partnership (Quarterly), between businesses and ethics scholars; Symposia, workshops, lectures (Weekly), on applied ethics; Public Sector Roundtable (Quarterly), public officials from city, county, and state government review emerging issues in government ethics. **Awards:** Hackworth Grants (Semiannual), for faculty and students. **Telecommunication Services:** kohanson@scu.edu.

46033 ■ University of Virginia - Olsson Center for Applied Ethics
Darden School of Business
100 Darden Blvd.
Charlottesville, VA 22906
Ph: (434)924-7247
Fax: (434)924-6378
Co. E-mail: wicksa@darden.virginia.edu
URL: http://www.darden.virginia.edu/web/Olsson-Center-for-Applied-Ethics
Contact: Prof. Andrew C. Wicks, Director

Founded: 1969. **Educational Activities:** Lectures and seminars, conducive to the exchange of ethical concepts among business executives, academia, and others. **Telecommunication Services:** acw2z@virginia.edu.

START-UP INFORMATION

46034 ■ *Corporation: Small Business Start-Up Kit*
Pub: Nova Publishing Company
Ed: Daniel Sitarz. **Released:** February 2005. **Price:** $29.95. **Description:** Guidebook to help entrepreneurs start up and run a small business corporation. Book includes state and federal forms with instructions.

46035 ■ *How to Form Your Own California Corporation*
Pub: NOLO
Ed: Anthony Mancuso. **Released:** March 2009. **Price:** $39.99. **Description:** Instructions and forms required to incorporate any business in the State of California.

46036 ■ *How to Start and Run Your Own Corporation: S-Corporations For Small Business Owners*
Pub: HCM Publishing
Ed: Peter I. Hupalo. **Released:** March 6, 2003. **Price:** $22.95. **Description:** Basics of corporate business structure are explained. Topics include discovering the best business structure for your company; how to decided between an S-Corporation and LLC; choosing the state in which to incorporate, how to form a corporation, angel investing, special issues for one-person corporations, the role of bylaws and corporate minutes, board of directors, taxes, workers' compensation issues, retirement plans, and more.

46037 ■ *The Small Business Start-Up Kit*
Pub: NOLO
Ed: Peri Pakroo. **Released:** January 2008. **Price:** $29.95. **Description:** Entrepreneurial advice for launching a new business. Topics include compliance with state regulations, sole proprietorships, partnerships, corporations, limited liability companies, as well as accounting and tax information.

46038 ■ *Structuring Your Business*
Pub: Adams Media Corporation
Contact: Gary Krebs, Director
E-mail: swatrous@adamsmedia.com
Ed: Michele Cagan. **Released:** 2004. **Price:** $19.95. **Description:** Accountant and author shares insight into starting a new company. The guide assists entrepreneurs through the process, whether it is a corporation, an LLC, a sole proprietorship, or a partnership. Tax codes, accounting practices and legislation affecting every business as well as tips on managing finances are among the topics covered.

ASSOCIATIONS AND OTHER ORGANIZATIONS

46039 ■ **National Association for the Self-Employed (NASE)**
PO Box 241
Annapolis Junction, MD 20701-0241
Free: 800-232-6273
Fax: (800)551-4446
Co. E-mail: advocacy@nase.org
URL: http://www.nase.org
Contact: Kristie Arslan, President
Description: Self-employed and small independent businesspersons. Acts as an advocate at the state and federal levels for self-employed people. Provides discounts on products and services important to self-employed and small business owners. **Founded:** 1981. **Publications:** *Self-Employed*; *Self-Employed America* (Bimonthly); *Washington Watch* (Weekly). **Awards:** Future Entrepreneur (Annual); NASE Future Entrepreneur Scholarships; National Association for the Self-Employed Scholarships.

REFERENCE WORKS

46040 ■ *Breaking Free: How to Work at Home with the Perfect Small Business Opportunity*
Pub: Lulu.com
Ed: Brian Armstrong. **Released:** June 2007. **Price:** $24.95. **Description:** Three ways to smooth the transition from working for someone else to starting your own business are outlined. Seven exercises to help discover the type of business you should start, how to incorporate, get important tax benefits, and start accepting payments immediately are examined.

46041 ■ *Choosing the Right Legal Form of Business: The Complete Guide to Becoming a Sole Proprietor, Partnership, LLC, or Corporation*
Pub: Atlantic Publishing Company
Ed: Pat Mitchell. **Released:** January 1, 2009. **Price:** $24.95. **Description:** According to the U.S. Small Business Administration, nearly 250,000 new businesses start up annually; currently there are over nine million small companies in the nation. The importance of choosing the proper legal form of business is stressed.

46042 ■ *Entrepreneurial Finance*
Pub: Pearson Education, Limited
Contact: Steven A. Dowling, President
Ed: Philip J. Adelman; Alan M. Marks. **Released:** July 2006. **Price:** $87.35. **Description:** Financial aspects of running a small business are covered; topics include sole proprietorships, partnerships, limited liability companies, and private corporations.

46043 ■ *Fast-Track Business Start-Up Kit: California*
Pub: DP Group, Incorporated
Ed: Carolyn Usinger. **Released:** September 2006. **Price:** $29.00. **Description:** Step-by-step guide for starting and running a business in California, including information on sole proprietors, partnerships, limited liability companies, S and C corporations, as well as details concerning business entities, sales taxes, environmental issues, human resources, and more.

46044 ■ *Getting Rich In Your Underwear: How To Start and Run a Profitable*

Home-Based Business
Pub: HCM Publishing
Ed: Peter I. Hupalo. **Released:** April 1, 2005. **Price:** $17.95. **Description:** Book offers insight into starting a home-based business. Entrepreneurs will learn about business models and the home business; distribution and fulfillment of product or service; marketing and sales; how to overcome the fear of starting a business; personal success characteristics; naming a business; zoning and insurance; intellectual capital; copyrights, trademarks, and patents; limited liability companies and S-corporations; business expenses and accounting; taxes; fifteen basic steps for starting a home-based business, state resources for starting a home company; and seven home-based business ideas.

46045 ■ *How to Form Your Own Corporation without a Lawyer for Under $75.00*
Pub: Dearborn Trade Publishing Inc.
Contact: Roy Lipner, President
Ed: Ted Nicholas; Sean P. Melvin. **Price:** $19.95.

46046 ■ *Own Your Own Corporation: Why the Rich Own Their Own Companies and Everyone Else Works for Them*
Pub: Business Plus
Ed: Garrett Sutton; Robert T. Kiyosaki; Ann Blackman. **Released:** June 2008. **Price:** $17.99 paperback. **Description:** Part of the Rich Dad Advisor's Series, this edition shows how individuals can incorporate themselves and their businesses to save thousands of dollars in taxes and protect against financial disaster.

46047 ■ *"Protect Your Assets" in Black Enterprise (Vol. 38, January 2008, No. 6, pp. 38)*
Pub: Earl G. Graves Publishing Co. Inc.
Ed: Trevor Delaney. **Description:** Owner of rental properties seeks advice for incorporating versus getting an LLC for the business.

46048 ■ *Small Business: An Entrepreneur's Plan*
Pub: Nelson Thomson Learning
Ed: Ronald A. Knowles. **Released:** December 2006. **Description:** Entrepreneur's guide to planning a small business.

46049 ■ *"Sole Proprietorship Returns, 2008" in SOI Bulletin (Vol. 30, Summer 2010, No. 1, pp. 6)*
Pub: Government Printing Office
Ed: Adrian Dungan. **Description:** Approximately 22.6 million individual income tax returns reported nonfarm sole proprietorship activity, a 2.2 percent decrease from 2007. Statistical data included.

46050 ■ *"Sole Proprietorship Returns, 2008 Part 2" in SOI Bulletin (Vol. 30, Summer 2010, No. 1, pp. 27)*
Pub: Government Printing Office
Description: Table of Nonfarm Sole Proprietorships is presented. Statistics are broken down by sector reporting all nonfarm industries as well as agriculture, forestry, hunting and fishing.

46051 ▪ *"Startup Makes Attempt to 'Reform' Health Insurance" in Austin Business JournalInc. (Vol. 29, January 15, 2010, No. 45, pp. 1)*
Pub: American City Business Journals
Ed: Sandra Zaragoza. **Description:** Health insurance provider ETMG LLC of Austin, Texas plans to act as a managing general agent and a third-party administrator that can facilitate customized plans for small businesses and sole proprietors. According to CEO Mark Adams, profitability is expected for ETMG, which have also clinched $1.5 million worth of investments. Entities that have agreed to do business with ETMG are presented.

46052 ▪ *"Symbility Solutions Joins Motion Computing Partner Program" in Canadian Corporate News (May 14, 2007)*
Pub: Comtex News Network Inc.
Description: Symbility Solutions Inc., a wholly owned subsidiary of Automated Benefits Corp., announced an agreement with Alliance Partner of Motion Computing, a leader in wireless communications and mobile computing, in which both companies will invest in a sales and marketing strategy that focuses specifically on the insurance market.

46053 ▪ *Working Solo: The Real Guide to Freedom & Financial Success with Your Own Business, 2nd Edition*
Pub: Portico Press
URL(s): wiley.com. **Price:** $21.95, Individuals paperback. **Covers:** Over 1,000 solo business opportunities, as well as a resource section on publications, organizations, and other essential contacts for solo professionals.

VIDEOCASSETTES/ AUDIOCASSETTES

46054 ▪ *Be Your Own Boss: Start a Business*
The Learning Seed
641 W. Lake St., Ste. 301
Chicago, IL 60661
Free: 800-634-4941
Fax: (800)998-0854
Co. E-mail: info@learningseed.com
URL: http://www.learningseed.com
Released: 1992. **Price:** $89.00. **Description:** Four Chicago-area entrepreneurs offer advice on starting your own business and cover topics such as market research, location selection, promotion, financial planning, legal requirements and more. **Availability:** VHS.

46055 ▪ *Doing Business*
The Cinema Guild
115 W 30th St., Ste. 800
New York, NY 10001
Ph: (212)685-6242
Free: 800-723-5522
Fax: (212)685-4717
Co. E-mail: info@cinemaguild.com
URL: http://www.cinemaguild.com
Released: 1981. **Description:** This documentary offers an insightful examination of self-managed businesses. The film is frank about the problems involved in going into business for oneself, including the delicacy of managing employees, arranging non-stressful working conditions, and balancing the desire for growth with a sense of family. **Availability:** 3/4 U; Special order formats.

46056 ▪ *How to Beat the Odds*
National Audiovisual Center
5301 Shawnee Rd.
Alexandria, VA 22312
Ph: (703)605-6000
Free: 800-553-6847
Fax: (703)321-8547
Co. E-mail: customerservice@ntis.gov
URL: http://www.ntis.gov/products/nac.aspx
Released: 1980. **Price:** $95.00. **Description:** This video is designed to be an aid to small business owners trying to get ahead, and includes many strategies and tips from those entrepreneurs in the government bureaucracy. **Availability:** VHS; 3/4 U.

46057 ▪ *How to Start Your Own Successful Business*
Instructional Video
2219 C St.
Lincoln, NE 68502
Ph: (402)475-6570
Free: 800-228-0164
Fax: (402)475-6500
Co. E-mail: feedback@insvideo.com
URL: http://www.insvideo.com
Released: 19??. **Price:** $29.95. **Description:** Illustrates correct procedures for establishing and maintaining an effective business. Covers marketing, managing, financing, business insurance, buying an existing business, franchising, home-based business, youth entrepreneurial business, negotiating deals, and projecting your ideas. **Availability:** VHS.

46058 ▪ *New or Used? Buying a Firm or Starting Your Own*
Instructional Video
2219 C St.
Lincoln, NE 68502
Ph: (402)475-6570
Free: 800-228-0164
Fax: (402)475-6500
Co. E-mail: feedback@insvideo.com
URL: http://www.insvideo.com
Released: 19??. **Price:** $99.00. **Description:** Details the different options open to anyone wanting to start or obtain their own business. Discusses the various factors to be considered when putting a value on a company, negotiating price and terms, and closing the deal. **Availability:** VHS.

ASSOCIATIONS AND OTHER ORGANIZATIONS

46059 ■ **Alcoholics Anonymous World Services, Inc.—A.A. World Services Inc.**
PO Box 459
New York, NY 10163
Ph: (212)870-3400
Free: 800-631-6025
Fax: (212)870-3023
Co. E-mail: publicinfo@aa.org
URL: http://www.aa.org
Description: Individuals recovering from alcoholism. Maintains that members can solve their common problem and help others achieve sobriety through a twelve step program that includes sharing their experience, strength, and hope with each other. Self-supported through members' contributions, not an allied with any sect, denomination, political organization, or institution and does not endorse nor oppose any cause. **Founded:** 1935. **Publications:** *Alcoholics Anonymous*.

46060 ■ **Institute for a Drug-Free Workplace (IDFW)**
10701 Parkridge Blvd., Ste. 300
Reston, VA 20191
Ph: (703)391-7222
Fax: (703)391-7223
Co. E-mail: institute@drugfreeworkplace.org
URL: http://www.drugfreeworkplace.org
Contact: Mark A. de Bernardo, Executive Director
Description: Businesses, organizations, and individuals united to preserve the rights of employers and employees involved in corporate drug abuse prevention programs. Seeks to influence public policy pertaining to drug-abuse prevention in the workplace. Conducts surveys. **Founded:** 1989.

46061 ■ **Institute on Global Drug Policy (IGDP)**
c/o Sylvia Raymond, Managing Director
Journal of Global Drug Policy and Practice
2600 9th St. N, Ste. 200
St. Petersburg, FL 33704-2744
Ph: (727)828-0211
Fax: (727)828-0210
Co. E-mail: info@globaldrugpolicy.org
URL: http://www.globaldrugpolicy.org
Contact: Lana Beck, Managing Editor
Description: Works to exchange information about drug policy and practice while sharing different cultural attitudes and perspective on the drug issue. Disseminates accurate scientific information on drugs. **Founded:** 2000. **Publications:** *Journal of Global Drug Policy and Practice* (Quarterly).

46062 ■ **NAADAC: The Association for Addiction Professionals (NAADAC)**
1001 N Fairfax St., Ste. 201
Alexandria, VA 22314
Ph: (703)741-7686
Free: 800-548-0497

Fax: (703)741-7698
Co. E-mail: naadac2@naadac.org
URL: http://www.naadac.org
Contact: Robert C. Richards, President
Description: Promotes excellence in care by promoting up-to-date and science-based services to clients, families, and communities. Provides education, clinical training and certification. Among the organization's national certification programs are the National Certified Addiction Counselor, Tobacco Addiction Credential and the Masters Addiction Counselor designations. **Founded:** 1972. **Publications:** *NAADAC News* (Bimonthly); *The Basics of Addiction Counseling: A Desk Reference and Study Guide* (Periodic); *Basics of Addiction Counseling Independent Study Course* (Periodic). **Awards:** Organizational Achievement Award; Lifetime Honorary Membership Award (Annual); Medical Professional of the Year (Annual); NAADAC Organizational Achievement Award (Annual); Lora Roe Memorial Alcoholism and Drug Abuse Counselor of the Year; Mel Schulstad Professional of the Year; William F. (Bill) Callahan Award; Lora Roe Memorial Alcoholism and Drug Abuse Counselor of the Year (Annual); Mel Schulstad Professional of the Year (Annual); William F. "Bill" Callahan Award (Annual).

46063 ■ **Narcotics Anonymous (NA)**
c/o World Service Office
PO Box 9999
Van Nuys, CA 91409
Ph: (818)773-9999
Fax: (818)700-0700
Co. E-mail: fsmail@na.org
URL: http://www.na.org
Contact: Jeff Gershoff, Coordinator
Description: Aims to recover addicts throughout the world, works to offer help to fellow addicts seeking recovery. Meets regularly to facilitate and stabilize their recovery. Uses 12-step program adapted from Alcoholics Anonymous to aid in the recovery process. **Founded:** 1953. **Publications:** *A Guide to Public Information*; *The NA Way Magazine: The International Journal of Narcotics Anonymous* (Quarterly); *Just For Today: Daily Meditations for Recovering Addicts*. **Educational Activities:** Narcotics Anonymous Convention (Annual).

46064 ■ **National Association of Addiction Treatment Providers (NAATP)**
313 W Liberty St., Ste. 129
Lancaster, PA 17603-2748
Ph: (717)392-8480
Fax: (717)392-8481
Co. E-mail: mwalsh@naatp.org
URL: http://www.naatp.org
Contact: Michael E. Walsh, President
Description: Corporate and private institutional alcohol and/or drug dependency treatment facilities. Promotes awareness of chemical dependency as a treatable disease; advocates high standards of health care in substance abuse treatment facilities. Encourages member education. Maintains contact with U.S. Congress and state and local governments. Serves in an advisory capacity to the Joint Commission on Accreditation of Healthcare Organizations and to the

Commission on Accreditation of Rehabilitation Facilities. Compiles statistics on chemical dependency treatment and recovery. **Founded:** 1978. **Publications:** *Benchmark Survey* (Annual). **Awards:** Outstanding Service Award (Annual); Nelson J. Bradley Life Time Achievement Award (Annual).

46065 ■ **National Association on Drug Abuse Problems (NADAP)**
355 Lexington Ave.
New York, NY 10017
Ph: (212)986-1170
Fax: (212)697-2939
Co. E-mail: info@nadap.org
URL: http://www.nadap.org
Contact: John A. Darin, President
Description: Serves as an information clearinghouse and referral bureau for corporations and local communities interested in prevention of substance abuse and treatment of substance abusers. Provides: resources to local communities seeking to combat drug and alcohol abuse; corporate services for employers interested in creating a drug-free workplace. Makes available vocational education services including training in job hunting, job interview workshops, training programs for substance abuse treatment professionals, and individual consultations for recovering substance abusers seeking to return to the job market. Provides placement services; has conducted surveys on the employability of rehabilitated drug users and found that former addicts perform comparably with others hired for similar jobs. Operates Neighborhood Prevention Network, through which local communities develop parent support groups and youth peer leadership groups dedicated to combating drug and alcohol abuse. Maintains speakers' bureau. **Founded:** 1971. **Publications:** *NADAP News/Report* (Quarterly).

46066 ■ **Substance Abuse Librarians and Information Specialists (SALIS)**
PO Box 9513
Berkeley, CA 94709-0513
Ph: (510)769-1831
Fax: (510)865-2467
Co. E-mail: salis@salis.org
URL: http://www.salis.org
Contact: Andrea Mitchell, Executive Director
Description: Individuals and organizations interested in the collection, organization, dissemination, exchange, and retrieval of materials concerning substance abuse, including alcohol, tobacco, and other drugs. Provides professional development and exchange of information and concerns about access to and dissemination of information on substance abuse. Offers information on films, books, articles, pamphlets, reports, government publications, libraries, clearinghouses, and information centers. **Founded:** 1978. **Publications:** *SALIS News* (Quarterly). **Educational Activities:** Substance Abuse Librarians and Information Specialists Conference (Annual). **Telecommunication Services:** amitchell@salis.org.

REFERENCE WORKS

46067 ■ *Case Management Resource Guide*
Pub: Phillips Business Information Inc. Access Intelligence L.L.C.
Contact: Heather Farley, President
E-mail: hfarley@accessintel.com
URL(s): www.cmrg.com. **Released:** Annual; latest edition 2005-2006. **Price:** $60, Individuals for additional copy, per volume. **Entries include:** Facility name, address, phone names and titles of key personnel; number of employees, geographical area served, type of service or programs provided branch office or parent organization name and phone, and credentials. **Database covers:** In four regional volumes, lists 110,000 health care facilities and support services, including homecare, rehabilitation, psychiatric, and addiction treatment program; hospices, adult day care, and burn and cancer centers. **Arrangement:** Classified by service provided and location. **Indexes:** Company name, advertiser.

TRADE PERIODICALS

46068 ■ *Forensic Drug Abuse Advisor*
Pub: Forensic Drug Abuse Advisor Inc.
Ed: Steven B. Karch, M.D., Editor. **Released:** 10/year. **Price:** $197, individuals. **Description:** Acts as a drug information source. Emphasizes the latest scientific discoveries in drug abuse, workplace drug testing, federal drug law, and forensic pathology. An absolute necessity in drug related litigation. Recurring features include letters to the editor, news of research, a calendar of events, reports of meetings, news of educational opportunities, book reviews, and notices of publications available. Continuing medical education available.

46069 ■ *Hazelden Voice*
Pub: Hazelden Foundation
Contact: Sharon Birnbaum, Director, Corporate Operations
Ed: Marty Duda, Editor, mduda@hazelden.org. **Released:** 2/year. **Price:** Free. **Description:** Reports on Hazelden activities and programs, and discusses developments and issues in chemical dependency treatment and prevention.

46070 ■ *ICPA Reporter*
Pub: International Commission for the Prevention of Alcoholism and Drug Dependency
Contact: Gary B. Swanson, Managing Editor
Ed: Peter H. Landless, Editor. **Released:** DependencySemiannual. **Price:** Free. **Description:** Reports on activities of the Commission worldwide, which seeks to prevent alcoholism and drug dependency. Recurring features include a calendar of events and notices of publications available.

46071 ■ *Journal of Drug Education*
Pub: Baywood Publishing Company Inc.
Contact: Stuart Cohen, President
URL(s): www.baywood.com/journals/PreviewJournals.asp?Id=0047-2379. **Released:** 4/yr. **Price:** $402, Institutions; $381, Institutions online.

46072 ■ *The Prevention Researcher*
Pub: Integrated Research Services Inc.
Ed: Steven Ungerleider, Ph.D., Editor, suinteg@attglobal.net. **Released:** Quarterly, 4/year. **Price:** $36, individuals; $48 libraries. **Description:** Specializes in prevention topics for at-risk youth.

VIDEOCASSETTES/ AUDIOCASSETTES

46073 ■ *Creating a Drug-Free Workplace*
Coastal Training Technologies Corp.
500 Studio Dr.
Virginia Beach, VA 23452
Ph: (757)498-9014
Free: 877-262-7825
Fax: (757)498-3657
Co. E-mail: info@training.dupont.com
URL: http://www.coastal.com
Released: 1993. **Price:** $395. **Description:** Two acted stories illustrate workers having problems with drug and alcohol problems and who create problems for their companies. **Availability:** VHS.

46074 ■ *Disease Concept of Alcoholism/EAP*
New Dimension Media, Inc.
307 N Michigan Ave., Ste. 500
Chicago, IL 60601
Ph: (312)642-9400
Free: 800-288-4456
Fax: (312)642-9805
Co. E-mail: Info@NDMquestar.com
URL: http://www.ndmquestar.com
Released: 1986. **Price:** $50.00. **Description:** Information designed for supervisory training that stresses communication and motivation. **Availability:** VHS; 3/4 U.

46075 ■ *The Drug-Free Workplace*
Learning Communications L.L.C.
5520 Trabuco Rd.
Irvine, CA 92620-5705
Free: 800-622-3610
Fax: (949)727-4323
Co. E-mail: sales@learncom.com
URL: http://www.learncom.com
Contact: Lloyd W. Singer, President
Released: 1991. **Price:** $175.00. **Description:** A two-part program designed to make employees and managers aware of the provisions of the Drug-Free Workplace Act. Includes a Compliance and Implementation Guide, as well as participants manuals. **Availability:** VHS; 3/4 U.

46076 ■ *Drug Testing in the Workplace*
American Bar Association (ABA)
321 N Clark St.
Chicago, IL 60654-7598
Ph: (312)988-5522
Free: 800-285-2221
Fax: (312)988-5177
Co. E-mail: service@americanbar.org
URL: http://www.americanbar.org
Contact: Carolyn Lamm, President
Released: 1987. **Price:** $295.00. **Description:** The story of what one company did about drug testing after a suspicious on-the-job accident. Urine and blood testing are demonstrated. **Availability:** VHS; 3/4 U.

46077 ■ *Drugs in the Workplace 2: What Every Manager and Supervisor Must Know*
Aspen Publishers, Inc.
7201 McKinney Cir.
Frederick, MD 21704
Ph: (301)698-7100
Free: 800-234-1660
Fax: (800)901-9075
Co. E-mail: customerservice@aspenpublisher.com
URL: http://www.aspenpublishers.com
Contact: Robert Becker, President
Released: 1987. **Price:** $495.00. **Description:** Supervisors see what must be done to stop drug abuse in the workplace, and they also learn what, legally, they can and can't do about the problem. **Availability:** VHS; 3/4 U.

46078 ■ *Managing a Drug-Free Work Environment*
Encyclopedia Britannica
331 N. LaSalle St.
Chicago, IL 60654
Ph: (312)347-7159
Free: 800-323-1229
Fax: (312)294-2104
URL: http://www.britannica.com
Released: 1989. **Price:** $495.00. **Description:** This film focuses on the role and responsibility of managers in counteracting drug abuse in the workplace. **Availability:** VHS; 3/4 U.

46079 ■ *The Physiological Effects of Cocaine*
Phoenix Learning Group
2349 Chaffee Dr.
Saint Louis, MO 63146-3306
Ph: (314)569-0211
Free: 800-221-1274

Fax: (314)569-2834
URL: http://www.phoenixlearninggroup.com
Released: 198?. **Description:** Provides the professional with information on the physiological effects of cocaine. Also includes information on the history and physical properties of cocaine. **Availability:** VHS; 3/4 U.

46080 ■ *Substance Abuse: Everyone's Problem*
AJN Video Library/Lippincott Williams & Wilkins
American Journal of Nursing
345 Hudson St., 16th Fl.
New York, NY 10014
Ph: (212)886-1200
Free: 800-256-4045
Fax: (212)886-1276
Co. E-mail: info@nursingcenter.com
URL: http://www.nursingcenter.com
Released: 19??. **Price:** $250.00. **Description:** Describes the signs of drug and alcohol abuse and the steps to take if a staff member is suspected of having these problems. Also discusses how to plan and conduct a management conference, what to do when immediate action is needed, and how to motivate the staff member to seek help. Emphasis is placed on getting the employee to acknowledge that they have a problem and need help. **Availability:** VHS.

46081 ■ *Taking Action: Substance Abuse in the Workplace*
Phoenix Learning Group
2349 Chaffee Dr.
Saint Louis, MO 63146-3306
Ph: (314)569-0211
Free: 800-221-1274
Fax: (314)569-2834
URL: http://www.phoenixlearninggroup.com
Released: 1989. **Price:** $600.00. **Description:** This video will help managers implement an effective substance abuse prevention program for the workplace. **Availability:** VHS; 8 mm; 3/4 U.

46082 ■ *Taking Action 2: Frontline Against Drugs*
Aspen Publishers, Inc.
7201 McKinney Cir.
Frederick, MD 21704
Ph: (301)698-7100
Free: 800-234-1660
Fax: (800)901-9075
Co. E-mail: customerservice@aspenpublisher.com
URL: http://www.aspenpublishers.com
Contact: Robert Becker, President
Released: 1991. **Price:** $600. **Description:** A follow-up video to "Taking Action," this program creates scenarios where workers at various levels are advised what to do when co-workers are abusing drugs or alcohol. **Availability:** VHS.

CONSULTANTS

46083 ■ Bensinger, Du Pont & Associates
134 N LaSalle St., Ste. 2200
Chicago, IL 60602
Ph: (312)726-8620
Free: 800-227-8620
Fax: (312)726-1061
Co. E-mail: marie.apke@bensingerdupont.com
URL: http://www.bensingerdupont.com
Contact: Peter B. Bensinger, President
Scope: Employee Assistance Program EAP provider, gambling help line provider, consultant on substance abuse, drug testing and gambling addiction. **Founded:** 1982. **Publications:** "Drug Testing in Treatment Settings, Drug Testing in Schools," 2005; "Drug Testing in Correctional Settings," 2005; "Getting Tough on Gateway Drugs: A Guide for the Family"; "A Bridge to Recovery: An Introduction to Twelve-Step Programs"; "The Selfish Brain: Learning from Addiction".

46084 ■ Birenbaum & Associates
906 Olive St., Ste. 1200
Saint Louis, MO 63101-1448
Ph: (314)241-1445

Fax: (314)241-1449
Contact: Mark S. Birenbaum, President
Scope: Multi-association management firm and industrial relations specialists offering consultation to management in public and private sectors. Specializes in meeting management. Clients include manufacturing, service industry, fire protection districts, and government. **Founded:** 1968. **Seminars:** Alcohol/Drug Abuse Policies for Employers.

46085 ■ Chris Frings & Associates
633 Winwood Dr.
Birmingham, AL 35226-2837
Ph: (205)823-5044
Fax: (205)823-4283
Co. E-mail: chris@chrisfrings.com
Contact: Christopher S. Frings, President
E-mail: cfrings@compuserve.com
Scope: Provider of expert testimony and consultation for court and arbitration regarding abused drug testing. Consultant to industry and labor relations attorneys with abused drug testing needs and problems. Also offers seminars and workshops and keynote speeches on management issues. **Founded:** 1978. **Publications:** "The Hitchhikers Guide to Effective Time Management: The Only Time Management Book You Will Ever Need," Aacc Press, 2004. **Seminars:** Workplace Drug Testing; Effective Time Management; Stress Management; Managing Change; Management and Leadership Strategies for Succeeding in the 21st Century; Increasing Productivity Through Effective Time &Information Management; Mastering Change; Management Q & A.

46086 ■ Richard Haynes & Associates L.L.C.
1021 Temple St.
Charleston, WV 25312-2153
Ph: (304)346-6228
Fax: (304)346-9135
Co. E-mail: captrah@citynet.net
Contact: Capt. Richard A. Haynes, President
E-mail: captrah@citynet.net
Scope: Security management consultant. Offers the following services: security surveys and audits; security readiness for labor disputes; investigations; security training and awareness programs; special projects. Industries served: mining, petroleum, law enforcement, private security companies and government agencies. **Founded:** 1980. **Publications:** "Let's Talk Security," Kanawha Valley Business Monthly; "The SWAT Cyclopedia" Aug, 1999. **Seminars:** Personal Protection Workshop: Workplace Violence.

46087 ■ Healy & Associates Inc.
3033 W Jefferson St., Ste. 205
Joliet, IL 60435-6449
Ph: (815)741-0102
Fax: (815)744-5412
Contact: Richard Kelling, President
Scope: Personal development consultant with experience in alcoholism and family treatment; employee assistance program consultation and implementation; health promotion programming on stress, smoking cessation, weight control; alcohol and drug related prevention and educational programming; and individual, group and family counseling. Serves private industries as wells government agencies. **Founded:** 1982. **Seminars:** Assertive Communication; Alcohol and Drug Problems in the Workplace; Chemical Dependency: Enabling vs. Intervention; Stress Management; Employee Assistance Programs; Smoking Cessation in the Workplace; Eating and Weight Issues; Cultural Diversity Training; Adapting to Change in the Workplace; Adapting to Shift Work.

46088 ■ Aantia Kersey & Associates
17716 Oak Park Ave.
Tinley Park, IL 60477-3936
Ph: (708)460-6060
Fax: (708)460-6060
Contact: Dr. Kersey H. Antia, Owner
E-mail: antia@juno.com
Scope: Human resources development consultants offering employee assistance programs in alcohol and substance abuse for employees with problems, psychological services to industry and public and private organizations and on-the-spot or by-mail psychological testing programs for selection, promotion and transfer of employees. Serves private

industries as well as government agencies. **Founded:** 1972. **Seminars:** Stress; Time Management; Smoking Cessation; Morale Improvement; Detection of Substance Abuse Among Employees.

46089 ■ National Scientific Services
3411 Philips Dr.
Baltimore, MD 21208-1827
Ph: (410)486-7486
Fax: (410)653-4824
Co. E-mail: fortox@aol.com
Contact: Yale H. Caplan, Director
Scope: Consultant in toxicology, drug and chemical analysis, workplace drug testing, and interpretation of toxicology information. Serves as expert witness in drunk driving and drug testing cases. **Founded:** 1974. **Publications:** "Garriott's Medicolegal Aspects of Alcohol," Lawyers & Judges Publishing Co.

46090 ■ Professional Alternative Inc.
1 State St., Ste. 300
Boston, MA 02109
Ph: (617)722-6020
Fax: (617)722-6029
Co. E-mail: info@profalt.com
URL: http://www.profalt.com
Contact: Michael Blecher, Director
E-mail: mblecher@profalt.com
Scope: Human resources consulting firm specializes in technical industries.

46091 ■ Recovery Communications Inc.—Getting Them Sober
PO Box 19910
Baltimore, MD 21211
Ph: (410)243-8352
Fax: (410)243-8558
Co. E-mail: tdrews3879@aol.com
URL: http://www.gettingthemsober.com
Contact: Toby Rice Drews, President
E-mail: tdrews3879@aol.com
Scope: Acts as expert witness and offers consultation in the field of substance abuse and addiction. Industries served: legal, health care and government. **Publications:** "Getting Them Sober, Volume One"; "Getting Them Sober: You Can Help," Recovery Communications, Apr, 1998; "Getting Your Children Sober"; "Sex and the Sober Alcoholic: A Healing Guide and Workbook"; "Get Rid of Anxiety and Stress". **Seminars:** Attachments and Excited Miseries in the Workplace; Getting Past Stuck-Points in Recovery; Replacing the Excitement of Sickness.

46092 ■ Safety & Loss Control Associates
PO Box 611
South Elgin, IL 60177
Ph: (847)622-1690
Fax: (847)622-1695
Co. E-mail: donneslund@aol.com
URL: http://www.safetyandlosscontrolassoc.com
Contact: Donald A. Neslund, Owner
Scope: Assists contractors and industrial operators in reducing worker injuries and illnesses. Safety and training consulting includes employee training, supervisor and management seminars, OSHA compliance audits, pre-job inspections, expert witness work, accident investigation and reconstruction. Also provides expertise in ladders and scaffolds, fall protection, drugs and alcohol in work place, confined space entry, blasting and man produced vibration, driving, trench safety, Hazcom and lockout and tag out. Serves the construction, insurance, legal profession and manufacturing industries. **Founded:** 1984. **Seminars:** Hazard Communication-Construction, Trench Safety, OSHA 30-hour Hazard Recognition Course; Communication and Interpersonal Skills Workshops.

46093 ■ DW Smothers and Associates
3137 Castro Valley Blvd., Ste. 215
Castro Valley, CA 94546
Ph: (510)728-9861
Free: 800-818-7654

Fax: (510)728-9802
Co. E-mail: dwsl@flash.net
Contact: David W. Smothers, President
E-mail: dws1@flash.net
Scope: Provider of investigative consulting regarding loss prevention in areas of personnel safety and physical security. Active in systems and procedures design as well as development of same. Serves private industries as well as government agencies. **Founded:** 1978.

46094 ■ VMC Consulting Service
8 S Division St.
Peekskill, NY 10566-3608
Ph: (914)737-1977
Fax: (914)838-2331
Contact: Vail M. Conn, Director
Scope: Social issues counseling offered on family problems, dysfunctional disorders, and drug and alcohol abuse. Also provides expertise to companies including EAP consulting and assessment-referral services. Training extended to human resource management and staff on substance abuse problems. **Founded:** 1986. **Seminars:** Substance Abuse Problems: How to Deal With Them; Alcoholism in the Family and Workplace; Drug Addiction and the Consequences; Recognizing and Dealing With Substance Abuse Problems.

46095 ■ Richard C. Webber Associates L.L.C.
3760 S Highland Dr., Ste. 431
Salt Lake City, UT 84106
Ph: (801)273-3322
Fax: (801)273-3321
Co. E-mail: rickcwebber@cs.com
Contact: Richard C. Webber, President
E-mail: rickcwebber@cs.com
Scope: Consulting firm that provides public safety, law enforcement and expert witness testimony services. Specializing in the development and presentation of drug and substance abuse programs, as well as executive and employee development programs. Specializes in instructor development (train-the-trainer), curriculum design and development, presentation skills and stage fright coping skills, and media relations. Leadership and motivation seminars are offered for both middle management and executives. Industries served include city, county, state, and federal law enforcement agencies; energy and oil; aerospace and aircraft; motion picture; and government agencies. **Founded:** 1981. **Publications:** "Drugs/Alcohol in the Workplace"; "Employment change and individual career marketing when looking to change careers". **Seminars:** Drugs/Alcohol in the Workplace; Instructor Development; Media Relations; Leadership; Stress Management; Time Management; Outplacement and Job Searching Skill Enhancement.

COMPUTERIZED DATABASES

46096 ■ *ETOH, the Alcohol and Alcohol Problems Science Database*
5635 Fishers Ln.
MSC 9304
Bethesda, MD 20892-9304
Ph: (301)443-3860
Fax: (301)443-6077
Co. E-mail: niaaweb-r@exchange.nih.gov
URL: http://www.niaaa.nih.gov
Availability: Online: U.S. National Institutes of Health - National Institute on Alcohol Abuse and Alcoholism. **Type:** Bibliographic.

LIBRARIES

46097 ■ Addictions Foundation of Manitoba - William Potoroka Memorial Library—AFM Library.
1031 Portage Ave.
Winnipeg, MB, Canada R3G 0R8
Ph: (204)944-6279
Free: 866-638-2568

Fax: (204)772-0225
Co. E-mail: library@afm.mb.ca
URL: http://www.afm.mb.ca
Scope: Alcohol and drug use and abuse, gambling, psychology, education, treatment, counseling, FASD. **Services:** Interlibrary loan; copying; Library open to the public. **Founded:** 1970. **Holdings:** Journals and other serials; 5500 books; 36 pamphlet titles; 1020 videocassettes/DVDs.

46098 ■ Akeela Library
4111 Minnesota Dr.
Anchorage, AK 99503
Ph: (907)565-1200
Fax: (907)258-6052
Co. E-mail: library@akeela.org
URL: http://www.akeela.org
Contact: Anjana Roy, Librarian
Scope: Alcohol and other drugs. **Services:** Library open to the public. **Founded:** 1979. **Holdings:** 1500 curriculum and training materials; 4000 books; 1000 videotapes. **Subscriptions:** 160 journals and other serials. **Telecommunication Services:** aroy@akeela.org.

46099 ■ Alcohol Research Group - Library
Public Health Inst.
6475 Christie Ave., Ste. 400
Emeryville, CA 94608-1010
Ph: (510)597-3440
Fax: (510)985-6459
Co. E-mail: library@arg.org
URL: http://www.arg.org/resources/library.php
Contact: Jeff Schiller, Librarian
Scope: Alcohol use and abuse, epidemiology of alcohol use and allied problems, drug use and abuse, tobacco and use. **Services:** Copying; SDI; library open to the public by appointment. **Founded:** 1959. **Holdings:** 6000 books; 60,000 reprints, reports, dissertations, working papers, government documents. **Subscriptions:** 300 journals and other serials.

46100 ■ Centre for Addiction and Mental Health Library
33 Russell St.
Toronto, ON, Canada M5S 2S1
Ph: (416)595-6144
Fax: (416)595-6601
Co. E-mail: library@camh.net
URL: http://www.camh.ca/en/education/about/services/camh_library/Pages/camh_library.aspx
Contact: Syd Jones, Director
Scope: Alcoholism, substance abuse, psychiatric disorders, mental illness, mental health. **Services:** Interlibrary loan (in Canada only); AV loan (Ontario only); copying; SDI; library open to the public. **Founded:** 1998. **Holdings:** 30,000 books; 11,000 reprints; 1250 audio/visual items. **Subscriptions:** 300 journals and other serials.

46101 ■ Drug & Alcohol Treatment Association of Rhode Island - In-Rhodes Library Library
102 Dupont Dr.
Providence, RI 02907
Ph: (401)521-5759
Fax: (401)751-7850
Co. E-mail: dcohen@dataofri.org
URL: http://www.dataofri.org/
Contact: Debra Cohen-Estes, Librarian
Scope: Alcohol, tobacco, drugs, HIV, sexually transmitted diseases, domestic violence, mental health, parenting, mentoring, other isms and disorders, self-esteem gambling. **Services:** Library open to the public. **Founded:** 1994. **Holdings:** 1700 books; 1400 videocassettes; 375 audiocassettes; 4100 reference materials. **Subscriptions:** 2 journals and other serials.

46102 ■ Hazelden Library - Library CO-4
15251 Pleasant Valley Rd.
Center City, MN 55012
Ph: (651)213-4200
Free: 800-257-7810

Fax: (651)213-4411
Co. E-mail: info@hazelden.org
URL: http://www.hazelden.org/web/go/library
Scope: Chemical dependency, alcoholism, treatment, chronic illness, spirituality, twelve steps, recovery, self-help, addictions, personal growth, family, counseling. **Services:** Library open to the public with restrictions. **Founded:** 1966. **Holdings:** 15,000 books; 600 cassette tapes; 700 videos. **Subscriptions:** 90 journals and other serials. **Telecommunication Services:** webmaster@hazelden.org.

46103 ■ Lakeview Center, Inc. Library
1221 W. Lakeview Ave.
Pensacola, FL 32501
Ph: (850)432-1222
URL: http://www.ebaptisthealthcare.org/Lakeview-Center/
Scope: Psychiatry, psychology, alcoholism, drug addiction, children's and young adults' problems, management. **Services:** Interlibrary loan; copying; library open to adult practitioners and interns. **Founded:** 1982. **Holdings:** 1921 books; 106 videocassettes; 75 kits; 227 government documents; 5 games. **Subscriptions:** 33 journals and other serials.

46104 ■ Maine State Office of Substance Abuse - Information and Resource Center
11 State House Station
41 Anthony Ave.
Augusta, ME 04333-0011
Ph: (207)287-8900
Free: 800-499-0027
Fax: (207)287-8910
Co. E-mail: osa.ircosa@maine.gov
URL: http://www.maine.gov/dhhs/samhs/osa/irc/index.htm
Contact: Jo McCaslin, Coordinator
Scope: Alcohol and drugs - use, abuse, dependency, education, prevention, and training; youth suicide prevention. **Services:** Center open to school systems, community organizations, agencies, and professionals. **Founded:** 1979. **Holdings:** 5800 books; 1600 videotapes and DVDs. **Subscriptions:** 20 journals and other serials. **Telecommunication Services:** jo.mccaslin@maine.gov.

46105 ■ National Clearinghouse for Alcohol and Drug Information Library
PO Box 2345
Rockville, MD 20847-2345
Ph: (301)468-2600
Free: 800-729-6686
Fax: (301)468-6433
Co. E-mail: info@health.org
URL: http://ncadi.samhsa.gov/
Contact: Lizabeth J. Foster, Librarian
Scope: Alcohol, tobacco, and other drug abuse. **Services:** Interlibrary loan; copying; SDI; Library open to the public for reference use only. **Founded:** 1987. **Holdings:** 3721 books; 80,000 cataloged items; 80,000 accessioned items; digitized documents; reports; manuscripts. **Subscriptions:** 141 journals and other serials; 8 newspapers. **Telecommunication Services:** lfoster@health.org.

46106 ■ North Conway Institute - Resource Center - Alcohol and Drugs
PO Box 2247
Austin, TX 78768-2247
Ph: (512)472-6816
Fax: (512)480-0437
Co. E-mail: research@episcopalarchives.org
URL: http://northconwayinstitute.weebly.com/resources.html
Contact: Rev. David A. Works, President
Scope: Alcohol, drugs. **Services:** Center open to the public. **Founded:** 1951. **Holdings:** 800 books. **Subscriptions:** 50 journals and other serials.

46107 ■ Nova Scotia Department of Education - Drug Dependency Services Division Library
Lord Nelson Bldg.
5675 Spring Garden Rd.
Halifax, NS, Canada B3J 1H1
Ph: (902)424-7214

Fax: (902)425-0550
Contact: Ruth Vaughan
Scope: Health. **Services:** Interlibrary loan; copying. **Holdings:** 5000 books. **Subscriptions:** 50 journals and other serials; 3 newspapers.

46108 ■ Ohio Center for Prevention Studies - Ohio Safe Schools Center
PO Box 210105
Cincinnati, OH 45221-0105
Free: 800-788-7254
Fax: (513)556-0782
Co. E-mail: robert.canning@uc.edu
URL: http://www.ebasedprevention.org
Contact: Bonnie Hedrick, Investigator
Scope: Safe School trainings, school climate, violence, drug abuse, alcohol, AIDS. **Telecommunication Services:** andie.barker@uc.edu.

46109 ■ Prevention Research Center Library and Information Services—Pacific Institute for Research and Evaluation.
1995 University Ave., Ste. 450
Berkeley, CA 94704
Ph: (510)486-1111
Fax: (510)644-0594
Co. E-mail: center@prev.org
URL: http://www.prev.org/
Contact: Julie Murphy
Scope: Alcohol and drug abuse prevention research. **Services:** Interlibrary loan; library not open to the public. **Founded:** 1984. **Holdings:** 1500 books; 4000 reprints; 2000 reports. **Subscriptions:** 35 journals and other serials. **Telecommunication Services:** jmurphy@prev.org.

46110 ■ Rebok Memorial Library
12501 Old Columbia Pike
Silver Spring, MD 20904
Ph: (301)680-6495
Fax: (301)680-6090
Co. E-mail: ahecht@capaccess.org
URL: http://www.loc.gov/rr/main/religion/sevadv.html
Contact: Alan Hecht, Director
Scope: Social problems - alcohol, tobacco, narcotics; health and temperance general, history, religion, women's studies, family life. **Services:** Interlibrary loan; copying; SDI; library open to the public with restrictions (appointment required for first visit). **Founded:** 1983. **Holdings:** 9700 books. **Subscriptions:** 50 journals and other serials; 6 newspapers.

46111 ■ Research Institute on Addictions Library
University at Buffalo
1021 Main St.
Buffalo, NY 14203-1016
Ph: (716)887-2511
Fax: (716)887-2490
Co. E-mail: sawusch@ria.buffalo.edu
URL: http://www.ria.buffalo.edu
Contact: Ann Mina Sawusch, Librarian
Scope: Alcoholism, drug dependence, and alcohol and drug abuse physiological, psychological, sociological, biochemical, pharmacological aspects. **Services:** Interlibrary loan; copying; reference; library open to the public for reference use only. **Founded:** 1974. **Holdings:** 4000 books; 400 periodical titles. **Subscriptions:** 130 journals and other serials. **Telecommunication Services:** mvenkata@ria.buffalo.edu.

46112 ■ Rutgers University - Rutgers Center of Alcohol Studies
Smithers Hall
607 Allison Rd.
Piscataway, NJ 08854-8001
Ph: (732)445-4442
Fax: (732)445-5944
Co. E-mail: alclib@rci.rutgers.edu
URL: http://alcoholstudies.rutgers.edu
Contact: Dr. Judit H. Ward, Director, Information Services
Scope: Alcohol and drug use (biomedical and psychosocial aspects), alcohol and drug education, substance abuse prevention and treatment. **Services:** Interlibrary loan; copying; Center and Library open to the public. **Founded:** 1940. **Holdings:**

15,000 books and pamphlets; 250 videos; 500 research instruments. **Subscriptions:** 220 journals and other serials.

46113 ■ South Carolina Department of Alcohol and Other Drug Abuse Services - The Drugstore Information Clearinghouse
2414 Bull St.
Columbia, SC 29201
Ph: (803)896-5555
Fax: (803)896-5557
Co. E-mail: lfrederick@daodas.sc.gov
URL: http://www.daodas.state.sc.us
Contact: Lachelle Frederick, Coordinator, Administration
Scope: Alcohol and other drug abuse - education, prevention, intervention, treatment. **Founded:** 1969.

46114 ■ South Carolina Department of Mental Health - Earle E. Morris, Jr. Alcohol & Drug Addiction Treatment Center Library
610 Faison Dr.
Columbia, SC 29203
Ph: (803)935-7791
Fax: (803)935-6222
Contact: Michael Blanck, Director, Library Services
Scope: Alcoholism, drug addiction, group and family therapy. **Services:** Interlibrary loan; Library not open to the public. **Founded:** 1975. **Holdings:** 2000 books. **Subscriptions:** 31 journals and other serials.

46115 ■ U.S. Drug Enforcement Administration Library
8701 Morrissette Dr.
Springfield, VA 22152
Ph: (202)307-7787
Free: 800-882-9539
Fax: (202)307-8939
URL: http://www.justice.gov/dea
Contact: Michele M. Leonhart, Administrator
Scope: Narcotic addiction, dangerous drug abuse, law and legislation, law enforcement, drug abuse education, International control. **Services:** Interlibrary loan; Library not open to the public. **Founded:** 1959. **Holdings:** 10,000 books; 40 VF drawers. **Subscriptions:** 225 journals and other serials.

46116 ■ University of Washington - Alcohol & Drug Abuse Institute Library
1107 NE 45th St., Ste. 120
Box 354805
Seattle, WA 98105-4631
Ph: (206)543-0937
Fax: (206)543-5473
Co. E-mail: adai@u.washington.edu
URL: http://lib.adai.washington.edu
Contact: Jennifer Velotta, Manager
Scope: Alcohol and drug abuse. **Services:** Interlibrary loan; Library open to the public. **Founded:** 1975. **Holdings:** 4000 books and monographs; 10,000 reprints; 200 videos; 90,000 articles, reprints, pamphlets, and unpublished documents. **Subscriptions:** 100 journals and other serials. **Telecommunication Services:** library@adai.uw.edu.

46117 ■ West Central Georgia Regional Hospital Library
PO Box 12435
Columbus, GA 31917-2435
Ph: (706)568-5204
Co. E-mail: wcgrh@dhr.state.ga.us
URL: http://www.wcgrh.org
Scope: Alcohol and drug abuse, bibliotherapy, brief and short-term therapy/counseling, consumer/patient education, forensic psychiatry, psychiatric nursing, psychiatric social work, psychology. **Services:** Library not open to public. **Founded:** 1976. **Holdings:** 4500 books; 246 bound periodical volumes; 325 AV programs.

46118 ■ Western State Psychiatric Center Library
Box 1
Fort Supply, OK 73841
Ph: (580)766-2311

Fax: (580)766-2168
Contact: Karen Connell, Library Technician
Scope: Substance abuse, psychiatry, psychology. **Services:** Interlibrary loan; copying; Library open to the public for reference use only. **Founded:** 1950. **Holdings:** 2778 books; 23 bound periodical volumes; 50 boxes of booklets, pamphlets, and reports; 59 audiotapes; 49 video recordings. **Subscriptions:** 20 journals and other serials; 10 newspapers.

RESEARCH CENTERS

46119 ■ Columbia University - Center for Social Policy and Practice in the Workplace—Columbia University - The Workplace Center
1255 Amsterdam Ave., 11th Fl.
New York, NY 10027
Ph: (212)851-2256
Fax: (212)851-2262
Co. E-mail: sa12@columbia.edu
URL: http://www.workplacecenter.org
Contact: Prof. Sheila H. Akabas, Director
Services: Counseling at the workplace on family and work related problems; Employment of people with disabilities; Regional Information Clearinghouses; Written training packages on new social service ideas. **Founded:** 1969. **Educational Activities:** Continuing education courses and workshops for social workers; Seminars on the organization and delivery of services to workers, open to human service, union, and personnel professionals; Training in the social management of employee benefits. **Telecommunication Services:** workplace@columbia.edu.

46120 ■ Indiana University Bloomington - Center for Studies of Law in Action
Sycamore Hall, Rm. 302
1033 E 3rd St.
Bloomington, IN 47405
Ph: (812)855-1783
Fax: (812)855-7542
Co. E-mail: slfreder@indiana.edu
URL: http://www.borkensteincourse.org
Contact: Dr. Barry Logan, Executive Director
Founded: 1970. **Educational Activities:** Scientific testing personnel training on alcohol and drug use, and highway safety (3/year), 1 week courses held at Indiana University usually in April, May and December, provided by international experts in toxicology.

46121 ■ North Charles Mental Health Research and Training Foundation, Inc.
955 Massachusetts Ave., Ste. 301
Cambridge, MA 02139
Ph: (617)864-0941
Fax: (617)876-9760
Co. E-mail: wmcauliffe@ntc.org
URL: http://www.northcharles.org
Contact: William McAuliffe, Director
Founded: 1971. **Telecommunication Services:** info@northcharles.org.

46122 ■ Oregon Research Institute (ORI)
1715 Franklin Blvd.
Eugene, OR 97403
Ph: (541)484-2123
Fax: (541)484-1108
Co. E-mail: cynthia@ori.org
URL: http://www.ori.org
Contact: Cynthia Guinn, Executive Director
Founded: 1960. **Publications:** *ORI Annual report* (Annual); *Research bulletin* (Periodic). **Educational Activities:** Colloquia (Occasionally), provides an opportunity ORI scientists and visiting colleagues to present findings to the research community; Research to Practice Annual Conference, one-day conference to share research-based practices with health and educational professionals and policy makers.

46123 ■ Rutgers University - Center of Alcohol Studies (CAS)
607 Allison Rd.
Piscataway, NJ 08854-8001
Ph: (732)445-2190

Fax: (732)445-3500
Co. E-mail: alclib@rci.rutgers.edu
URL: http://alcoholstudies.rutgers.edu
Contact: Robert J. Pandina, Director
Services: Consulting; Outpatient clinical services. **Founded:** 1941. **Publications:** *Journal of Studies on Alcohol* (Bimonthly); *Monographs of the Rutgers Center of Alcohol Studies*; *National Institute of Alcohol Abuse and Alcoholism-Rutgers University Center of Alcohol Studies (NIAAA-RUCAS) Treatment Series.* **Educational Activities:** Community and industrial workshops; Cooper Colloquium Series, during the academic year; Institute of Alcohol and Drug Studies (Annual), in July; Summer School of Alcohol and Drug Studies, in August. **Telecommunication Services:** rpandina@rci.rutgers.edu.

46124 ■ Stanford University - Stanford Prevention Research Center (SPRC)
Medical School Office Bldg., MC 5411
251 Campus Dr.
Stanford, CA 94305-5411
Ph: (650)723-6254
Fax: (650)723-6254
Co. E-mail: fortmann@stanford.edu
URL: http://prevention.stanford.edu
Contact: Stephen P. Fortmann, Director
Services: Health Improvement Classes: classes offered in exercise, smoking cessation, stress management, weight control, and nutrition for University faculty, staff, and families (Daily); Technical assistance, education, and training: for the public, educators, health professionals, and communities (Daily); Worksite-based strategic planning and research: in managed care (Daily). **Founded:** 1971. **Educational Activities:** Postdoctoral research training program; SPRC Research seminars (Weekly); Undergraduate and graduate level teaching activities at the University.

46125 ■ State University of New York at Buffalo - Research Institute on Addictions (RIA)
1021 Main St.
Buffalo, NY 14203-1014
Ph: (716)887-2566
Fax: (716)887-2252
Co. E-mail: connors@ria.buffalo.edu
URL: http://www.ria.buffalo.edu
Contact: Gerard J. Connors, Director
Services: RIA Clinical Research Center: outpatient facilities. **Founded:** 1970. **Publications:** *RIA Annual Report*; *RIA Report* (Quarterly). **Educational Activities:** RIA Seminars (10/year), for researchers, treatment professionals, and interested persons; Substance Abuse Research Seminars. **Awards:** RIA Postdoctoral Fellowships, six per year.

46126 ■ University of Kentucky - Center on Drug and Alcohol Research (CDAR)
643 Maxwelton Ct.
Lexington, KY 40506-0350
Ph: (859)257-6485
Fax: (859)257-5232
Co. E-mail: sharon.walsh@uky.edu
URL: http://cdar.uky.edu
Contact: Sharon Walsh, Director
Services: Consulting and technical assistance for the community. **Founded:** 1990. **Educational Activities:** Epidemiology Workgroup; Prevention Research Society Meeting; Rural/Urban Drug Use Continuum. **Awards:** Graduate student and post doctoral student scholarships; Grants for faculty members; Small Grants for Faculty.

46127 ■ University of Washington - Addictive Behaviors Research Center (ABRC)
Department of Psychology, Box 351629
Seattle, WA 98195-1629
Ph: (206)685-1200
Fax: (206)685-1310
Co. E-mail: abrc@u.washington.edu
URL: http://depts.washington.edu/abrc
Contact: Dr. Mary Larimer, Associate Director
Founded: 1985. **Educational Activities:** Postdoctoral program in addictive behaviors. **Telecommunication Services:** larimer@u.washington.edu.

Taxation

START-UP INFORMATION

46128 ■ *"His Record, Not Polls, Is What Matters"* in *Bangor Daily News (October 13, 2010)*
Pub: Bangor Daily News
Ed: Nick Sambides Jr. **Description:** The Small Business Jobs Tax Relief Act could spur investment in small businesses by increasing capital gains tax cuts for investors in small business in 2010 and increase to $20,000 from $5,000 the deduction for start-up businesses.

46129 ■ *The Small Business Start-Up Kit*
Pub: NOLO
Ed: Peri Pakroo. **Released:** January 2008. **Price:** $29.99. **Description:** Entrepreneurial advice for launching a new business. Topics include compliance with state regulations, sole proprietorships, partnerships, corporations, limited liability companies, as well as accounting and tax information.

46130 ■ *Structuring Your Business*
Pub: Adams Media Corporation
Contact: Gary Krebs, Director
E-mail: swatrous@adamsmedia.com
Ed: Michele Cagan. **Released:** 2004. **Price:** $19.95. **Description:** Accountant and author shares insight into starting a new company. The guide assists entrepreneurs through the process, whether it is a corporation, an LLC, a sole proprietorship, or a partnership. Tax codes, accounting practices and legislation affecting every business as well as tips on managing finances are among the topics covered.

46131 ■ *Working for Yourself: An Entrepreneur's Guide to the Basics*
Pub: Kogan Page, Limited
Contact: Ben Glover, Director of Marketing
Ed: Jonathan Reuvid. **Released:** September 2006. **Description:** Guide for starting a new business venture, focusing on raising financing, legal and tax issues, marketing, information technology, and site location.

ASSOCIATIONS AND OTHER ORGANIZATIONS

46132 ■ **American Taxation Association (ATA)**
9201 University City Blvd.
Charlotte, NC 28223
Ph: (704)687-7696
Co. E-mail: americantaxationassociation@aaahq.org
URL: http://aaahq.org/ata/index.htm
Contact: Sandy Callaghan, President
Description: Membership comprises primarily university professors teaching federal income tax, federal estate, and/or gift tax courses; other members are practitioners, including certified public accountants. Seeks to further taxation education. Researches the impact of the tax process, particularly tax code sections, on the social and economic structure of the U.S. Maintains speakers' bureau. **Founded:** 1974. **Awards:** Dissertation Award; Outstanding Service

Award (Annual); Ray M. Sommerfeld Outstanding Tax Educator Award (Annual); Tax Manuscript Award; Teaching Innovation Award (Annual).

46133 ■ **Tax Executives Institute (TEI)**
1200 G St. NW, Ste. 300
Washington, DC 20005-3814
Ph: (202)638-5601
Fax: (202)638-5607
URL: http://www.tei.org
Contact: Timothy J. McCormally, Executive Director
Description: Professional society of executives administering and directing tax affairs for corporations and businesses. Maintains TEI Education Fund. **Founded:** 1944. **Publications:** *The Tax Executive* (Bimonthly); *The Tax Executive*; *The Tax Executive* (Bimonthly); *Value-Added Taxes - A Comparative Analysis*. **Awards:** Distinguished Service Award (Annual).

REFERENCE WORKS

46134 ■ *"3CDC's Biggest Year"* in *Business Courier (Vol. 26, December 18, 2009, No. 34, pp. 1)*
Pub: American City Business Journals, Inc.
Ed: Lucy May. **Description:** Cincinnati Center City Development Corporation (3CDC) will make 2010 its biggest year with nearly $164 million projects in the works. Historic tax credits and continued help from the city have allowed the private nonprofit organization to finance mega projects such as the $43 million renovation and expansion of Washington Park. Other projects that 3CDC will start or complete in 2010 are presented.

46135 ■ *"$100 Million Plan for Jefferson Arms"* in *Saint Louis Business Journal (Vol. 32, October 14, 2011, No. 7, pp. 1)*
Pub: Saint Louis Business Journal
Ed: Evan Binns. **Description:** Teach for America is planning a $100 million renovation project of the former Jefferson Arms hotel in St. Louis, Missouri. The organization has signed a letter of intent to occupy the space. Financing of the project will be mainly through tax credits.

46136 ■ *"$100 Million in Projects Jeopardized"* in *Business Courier (Vol. 24, March 28, 2008, No. 51, pp. 1)*
Pub: American City Business Journals, Inc.
Ed: Dan Monk. **Description:** Ohio's historic preservation tax credit program may be reinstated after some companies planned to sue over its stoppage. The Ohio Department of Development said the program was halted because it exceeded the allocated budget for the credit. $34 million in credits are at stake for more than two dozen local projects if the program is reinstated.

46137 ■ *"100 Percent Equipment Tax Deduction Deadline Nears"* in *Farm Industry News (December 1, 2010)*
Pub: Penton Business Media Inc.
Description: Farmers and small business owners are warned that the first deadline for taking advantage

of the tax code provision that allows them to deduct the full purchase price of qualified capital expenditures up to $500,000 during the tax year is nearing.

46138 ■ *"2011 Tax Information of Interest"* in *Business Owner (Vol. 35, November-December 2011, No. 6, pp. 10)*
Pub: DL Perkins Company
Description: Compilation of 2011 tax information to help small business take advantage of all tax incentives.

46139 ■ *"Alberta Slashes Tax Rate to Ten Percent"* in *Globe & Mail (March 23, 2006, pp. B1)*
Pub: CTVglobemedia Publishing Inc.
Ed: Patrick Brethour. **Description:** Alberta province has slashed its corporate taxes from 11.5 to 10 percent to draw more business to the state. Details of the tax cut and its impact is analyzed.

46140 ■ *"Alberta Warns Ottawa On Taxes"* in *Globe & Mail (March 9, 2007, pp. B1)*
Pub: CTVglobemedia Publishing Inc.
Ed: Steven Chase. **Description:** Ottawa's proposal to remove the tax break for oil sands projects has been criticized by Alberta finance minister Lyle Oberg. The cancelling of tax breaks could hamper development in oil sands and thus hit Alberta's economy.

46141 ■ *"All-Star Advice 2010"* in *Black Enterprise (Vol. 41, October 2010, No. 3, pp. 97)*
Pub: Earl G. Graves Publishing Co. Inc.
Ed: Renita Burns, Sheiresa Ngo, Marcia Wade Talbert. **Description:** Financial experts share tips on real estate, investing, taxes, insurance and debt management.

46142 ■ *"Allowing Ethanol Tax Incentive to Expire Would Risk Jobs, RFAas Dinneen Says"* in *Farm Industry News (November 3, 2010)*
Pub: Penton Business Media Inc.
Description: Jobs would be at risk if the ethanol tax incentive expires.

46143 ■ *"The Annual Entitlement Lecture: Trustees of Medicare and Social Security Issue Another Dismal Report"* in *Barron's (March 31, 2008)*
Pub: Dow Jones & Company, Inc.
Ed: Thomas G. Donlan. **Description:** Expenditures on Medicare hospital insurance and the revenues available to pay for it have led to a gap of capital valued at $38.6 trillion. Slashing the benefits or raising taxes will not solve the gap which exists unless the government saves the money and invests it in private markets.

46144 ■ *"Another Baby Step"* in *Canadian Business (Vol. 81, March 31, 2008, No. 5, pp. 32)*
Pub: Rogers Media
Ed: Andrew Wahl. **Description:** Discusses the Canadian government's federal budget which makes it easier to tap into tax credits for corporate research

and development. However, these steps do not really go far enough to boost industrial research levels in Canada. Making these incentives at least partially refundable could help during tough economic times.

46145 ■ "As Capital Gains Tax Hike Looms, Merger Activity Percolates" in Baltimore Business Journal (Vol. 28, August 27, 2010, No. 16, pp. 1)
Pub: Baltimore Business Journal
Ed: Scott Dance. **Description:** Concerns for higher capital gains taxes in 2011 have been provoking buyers and sellers to engage in mergers and acquisitions activity, which is expected to gain momentum before the end of 2010. Companies that had saved cash during the recession have been taking advantage of the buyer's market. Other trends in local and national mergers and acquisitions activity are presented.

46146 ■ "Austin Ponders Annexing F1 Racetrack" in Austin Business Journal (Vol. 31, July 8, 2011, No. 18, pp. 1)
Pub: American City Business Journals Inc.
Ed: Vicky Garza. **Description:** City planners in Austin, Texas are studying the feasibility of annexing the land under and around the Circuit of the Americas Formula One Racetrack being constructed east of the city. The annexation could generate at least $13 million in financial gain over 25 years from property taxes alone.

46147 ■ "BABs in Bond Land" in Barron's (Vol. 89, July 6, 2009, No. 27, pp. 14)
Pub: Dow Jones & Co., Inc.
Ed: Jim McTague. **Description:** American Recovery and Reinvestment Act has created taxable Build America Bonds (BAB) to finance new construction projects. The issuance of the two varieties of taxable BABs is expected to benefit the municipal bond market.

46148 ■ "Bank on It" in Hawaii Business (Vol. 53, November 2007, No. 5, pp. 60)
Pub: Hawaii Business Publishing
Ed: Kathleen Bryan. **Description:** Many Baby Boomers that are preparing to retire would like to give back and make a difference. One way is to make gifts of Individual Retirement Assets (IRA). During 2007 people over 70 years can make withdrawals from an IRA and donate it without realizing the income as taxable.

46149 ■ Beat the Taxman 2006: Easy Ways to Save Tax in Your Small Business
Pub: John Wiley & Sons, Incorporated
Ed: Stephen Thompson. **Released:** May 2006. **Price:** $21.95. **Description:** Tax advice is given to help small businesses maximize returns for 2006.

46150 ■ Beat the Taxman 2007: Easy Ways to Save Tax in Your Small Business, 2007 Edition For the 2006 Tax Year
Pub: John Wiley & Sons, Incorporated
Ed: Stephen Thompson. **Released:** December 2006. **Price:** $26.99. **Description:** Year-round tax planner for entrepreneurs; the book is written in a question and answer format to help small business owners save money on annual taxes.

46151 ■ Beat the Taxman: Easy Ways to Tax Save in Your Small Business
Pub: John Wiley & Sons, Incorporated
Ed: Stephen Thompson. **Released:** May 2008. **Price:** $26.95. **Description:** Concise tax planner to help entrepreneurs take advantage of current tax laws.

46152 ■ Being Self-Employed: How to Run a Business Out of Your Home, Claim Travel and Depreciation and Earn a Good Income Well into Your 70s or 80s
Pub: Allyear Tax Guides
Ed: Holmes F. Crouch, Irma Jean Crouch, Barbara J. MacRae. **Released:** September 2004. **Price:** $24.95 (US), $37.95 (Canadian). **Description:** Guide for small business to keep accurate tax records.

46153 ■ "Best Income Trusts" in Canadian Business (Vol. 82, Summer 2009, No. 8, pp. 36)
Pub: Rogers Media
Ed: Calvin Leung. **Description:** Boardwalk REIT and Can. Apartment Properties REIT are among the income trusts in Canada that are found to have the potential as a good investment. Suggested income trusts also include the Yellow Pages Income Fund, which recently reported a 19.4 percent yield. The income trusts however, are expected to be affected by the Conservatives' tax that will take effect in 2011.

46154 ■ "BETC Backers Plot Future" in Business Journal Portland (Vol. 27, December 10, 2010, No. 41, pp. 1)
Pub: Portland Business Journal
Ed: Erik Siemers. **Description:** A coalition of clean energy groups and industrial manufacturers have spearheaded a campaign aimed at persuading Oregon legislators that the state's Business Energy Tax Credit (BETC) is vital in job creation. Oregon's BETC grants tax credits for 50 percent of an eligible renewable or clean energy project's cost. However, some legislators propose BETC's abolition.

46155 ■ "Big Trouble at Sony Ericsson" in Barron's (Vol. 88, March 24, 2008, No. 12, pp. M9)
Pub: Dow Jones & Company, Inc.
Ed: Angelo Franchini. **Description:** Sony Ericsson is facing trouble as it warned that its sales and net income before taxes will fall by nearly half for the first quarter of 2008. The joint venture of Sony and Ericsson has a global mobile phone market share of nine percent as of 2007, fourth largest in the world.

46156 ■ "Bigger TIF Makes Development Inroads" in The Business Journal-Serving Metropolitan Kansas City (Vol. 26, July 11, 2008, No. 44)
Pub: American City Business Journals, Inc.
Ed: Rob Roberts. **Description:** On July 9, 2008 the Tax Increment Financing Commission voted to expand a TIF district to Tiffany Springs Road. The plan for the TIF district close to Kansas City International Airport is to include a-half mile of the road. The impacts of the expansion on construction projects and on the road network are analyzed.

46157 ■ "Bills Raise Blues Debate; An Unfair Edge or Level Playing Field?" in Crain's Detroit Business (Vol. 24, January 21, 2008, No. 3)
Pub: Crain Communications Inc. - Detroit
Ed: Sherri Begin. **Description:** Changes in Michigan state law would change the way health insurance can be sold to individuals. Michigan Blue Cross Blue Shield is working to keep its tax-exempt status while staying competitive against for-profit insurers and nonprofit HMOs.

46158 ■ "Biodiesel Poised to Regain Growth" in Farm Industry News (January 21, 2011)
Pub: Penton Business Media Inc.
Description: According to Gary Haer, vice president of sales and marketing for Renewable Energy Group, the biodiesel industry is positioned to regain growth in 2011 with the reinstatement of the biodiesel blendersa tax credt of $1 per gallon.

46159 ■ "BK Franchisees Lose Sleep Over Late-Night Rule" in Advertising Age (Vol. 79, August 11, 2008, No. 31, pp. 1)
Pub: Crain Communications, Inc.
Ed: Emily Bryson York. **Description:** Burger King's corporate headquarters mandates that franchisees remain open until at least 2 a.m. Three Miami operators have filed a lawsuit that alleges the extended hours can be dangerous, do not make money and overtax the workforce.

46160 ■ Breaking Free: How to Work at Home with the Perfect Small Business Opportunity
Pub: Lulu.com
Ed: Brian Armstrong. **Released:** June 2007. **Price:** $24.95. **Description:** Three ways to smooth the transition from working for someone else to starting

your own business are outlined. Seven exercises to help discover the type of business you should start, how to incorporate, get important tax benefits, and start accepting payments immediately are examined.

46161 ■ "Business Execs Await Walker's Tax Cut Plan" in Business Journal-Milwaukee (Vol. 28, December 17, 2010, No. 11, pp. A1)
Pub: Milwaukee Business Journal
Ed: Rich Kirchen. **Description:** Wisconsin governor-elect Scott Walker has to tackle the state's projected $3.3 billion budget deficit, which became the subject of speculation among business groups and state politic watchers. Walker has pledged to reduce the state taxes without driving costs down to the local government and school district level.

46162 ■ "Business Must Stand Up And Be Counted" in Crain's Detroit Business (Vol. 24, October 6, 2008, No. 40, pp. 6)
Pub: Crain Communications, Inc.
Description: Discusses the challenges that the new mayor of Detroit faces concerning business, the state of the economy and the exceptionally tight budget the city is running on, which includes a lot of red ink. It is very likely that the city is going to see tax revenues fall substantially in the next few months and business leaders may find it in their favor to lend their support to the new mayor as well as provide him with the executive talent necessary to overcome some of these crucial issues.

46163 ■ "Business Owners Lien Trinity Project" in The Business Journal-Serving Greater Tampa Bay (Vol. 28, July 25, 2008, No. 31, pp. 1)
Pub: American City Business Journals, Inc.
Ed: Janet Leiser. **Description:** The Internal Revenue Service is trying to collect $2.9 million from the developer of the Trinity Town Center, William Plaines, due to the delays in the project. This is in addition to a $5.2 million lien by the project's subcontractors.

46164 ■ Business Owner's Toolkit Tax Guide
Pub: Toolkit Media Group
Released: January 2009. **Price:** $17.95. **Description:** Resource addresses the tax-filing process while helping to minimize bills. Discussions are focused on important issues pertaining to the small business owner. Topics cover include: personal and business expenses and how they are differentiated, how employee benefit plans are handled on tax returns, and what the IRS looks for when conducting audits. Free online information and support is also included.

46165 ■ "Business Stands Firm for Reform" in Crain's Detroit Business (Vol. 26, January 4, 2010, No. 1, pp. 3)
Pub: Crain Communications, Inc.
Ed: Amy Lane. **Description:** As Michigan faces a new year of budgetary problems, many business groups are preparing to hold firm against tax increases and instead push for enacting spending reforms.

46166 ■ "Business Tax Complaints Prompt Action" in Sacramento Business Journal (Vol. 28, July 29, 2011, No. 22, pp. 1)
Pub: Sacramento Business Journal
Ed: Michael Shaw. **Description:** California's Board of Equalization has amended a program to collect taxes from businesses for out-of-state purchases due to a flood of complaints from owners who find the paperwork costly and time consuming. The program was created in 2009 and fell short of expectations as it only brought in $56 million in the first two years against the projected $264 million.

46167 ■ "Business Warns Against Tax Hike" in Puget Sound Business Journal (Vol. 29, November 14, 2008, No. 30, pp. 1)
Pub: American City Business Journals
Ed: Deirdre Gregg. **Description:** Washington-based businesses have warned state lawmakers against imposing new taxes because of the economic decline. They suggest the government should focus on spending cuts to address the $3 billion shortfall.

46168 ■ *"Businesses Balk at 1099 Provision in Health Reform Law"* in *Baltimore Business Journal* (Vol. 28, August 13, 2010, No. 14, pp. 1)

Pub: Baltimore Business Journal

Ed: Scott Dance. **Description:** Small business advocates and accountants have criticized the Internal Revenue Service Form 1099 provision in the health care reform law as not worth the cost of time and money. Critics believe the policy would create a deluge of the documents that is too much for the companies or the IRS to handle. Details of the provision are also discussed.

46169 ■ *"Cabela's Repays Incentives as Sales Lag"* in *Business Journal-Milwaukee* (Vol. 28, November 19, 2010, No. 7, pp. A1)

Pub: Milwaukee Business Journal

Ed: Stacy Vogel Davis. **Description:** Cabela's has given back $266,000 to the government of Wisconsin owing to its failure to meet projected revenue goals for its Richfield, Wisconsin store. It has also failed to meet sales tax and hiring projection. The company received $4 million in incentives from Washington County.

46170 ■ *"Calendar"* in *Crain's Detroit Business* (Vol. 24, March 10, 2008, No. 10, pp. 21)

Pub: Crain Communications, Inc.

Description: Listing of events in the Detroit area include conferences addressing entrepreneurialism, economic development, and women business ownership.

46171 ■ *"Calendar"* in *Crain's Detroit Business* (Vol. 24, March 17, 2008, No. 11, pp. 20)

Pub: Crain Communications, Inc.

Description: Listing of events in the Detroit area include conferences addressing entrepreneurialism, economic development, and women business ownership.

46172 ■ *"Calendar"* in *Crain's Detroit Business* (Vol. 24, March 24, 2008, No. 12, pp. 25)

Pub: Crain Communications, Inc.

Description: Listing of events in the Detroit area include conferences addressing entrepreneurialism, economic development, and women business ownership.

46173 ■ *"Calendar"* in *Crain's Detroit Business* (Vol. 24, March 31, 2008, No. 13, pp. 1)

Pub: Crain Communications, Inc.

Description: Listing of events in the Detroit area include conferences addressing entrepreneurialism, economic development, and minority business ownership.

46174 ■ *"Calendar"* in *Crain's Detroit Business* (Vol. 24, April 7, 2008, No. 14, pp. 27)

Pub: Crain Communications, Inc.

Description: Listing of events in the Detroit area include conferences addressing entrepreneurialism, economic development, and minority business ownership.

46175 ■ *"Calendar"* in *Crain's Detroit Business* (Vol. 24, April 14, 2008, No. 15, pp. 25)

Pub: Crain Communications Inc.

Description: Listing of events in the Detroit area include conferences addressing entrepreneurialism, economic development, and ways in which to develop environmentally friendly buildings.

46176 ■ *"Calendar"* in *Crain's Detroit Business* (Vol. 24, September 22, 2008, No. 38, pp. 17)

Pub: Crain Communications Inc.

Description: Listing of events in the Detroit area include conferences addressing entrepreneurialism, economic development, and women business ownership.

46177 ■ *"Calendar"* in *Crain's Detroit Business* (Vol. 24, October 6, 2008, No. 40, pp. 22)

Pub: Crain Communications, Inc.

Description: Listing of events in the Detroit area include conferences addressing entrepreneurialism, economic development, manufacturing, marketing, the housing crisis and women business ownership.

46178 ■ *"Canada Wins Second NAFTA Decision on Softwood Tariffs"* in *Globe & Mail* (March 18, 2006, pp. B2)

Pub: CTVglobemedia Publishing Inc.

Ed: Steven Chase; Peter Kennedy. **Description:** Canada has won a second major North American Free Trade Agreement (NAFTA) victory in five years of legal battles over U.S. tariffs on softwood. Details of the controversy and ruling are presented.

46179 ■ *Canadian Small Business Kit for Dummies*

Pub: John Wiley & Sons, Incorporated

Ed: Margaret Kerr; JoAnn Kurtz. **Released:** May 2006. **Price:** $28.99. **Description:** Resources include information on changes to laws and taxes for small businesses in Canada.

46180 ■ *"Candidates Differ On State's Green Streak"* in *Business Journal Portland* (Vol. 27, October 22, 2010, No. 34, pp. 1)

Pub: Portland Business Journal

Ed: Andy Giegerich. **Description:** The views of Oregon gubernatorial candidates Chris Dudley and John Kitzhaber on the state's economy and on environmental policies are presented. Both Dudley, who is a Republican, and his Democratic challenger believe that biomass could help drive the state's economy. Both candidates also pledged changes in Oregon's business energy tax credit (BETC) program.

46181 ■ *"The Carbon Equation"* in *Canadian Business* (Vol. 81, October 27, 2008, No. 18, pp. 109)

Pub: Rogers Media Ltd.

Ed: Jack M. Mintz. **Description:** Economic and environmental impacts of the likely rejection of a carbon tax for the cap-and-trade system in Canada are discussed. The Conservative Party is expected tow in the 2008 elections and would likely pursue the cap-and-trade system.

46182 ■ *"Cashing in Before You Join: Negotiating a Signing Bonus"* in *Black Enterprise* (Vol. 37, October 2006, No. 3, pp. 90)

Pub: Earl G. Graves Publishing Co. Inc.

Ed: Chauntelle Folds. **Description:** Information on how to research and negotiate a signing deal, including how to avoid a tax hit.

46183 ■ *"Cautions On Loans With Your Business"* in *Business Owner* (Vol. 35, July-August 2011, No. 4, pp. 5)

Pub: DL Perkins Company

Description: Caution must be used when borrowing from or lending to any small business. Tax guidelines for the borrowing and lending practice are also included.

46184 ■ *CCH Toolkit Tax Guide 2007*

Pub: CCH Inc.

Contact: Mike Sabbatis, President

Ed: Paul Gada. **Released:** January 2007. **Price:** $17.95. **Description:** Guide for filing 2007 tax forms for both personal and small businesses with expert line-by-line explanations.

46185 ■ *"CEOs Decry Budget Taxation Change"* in *Globe & Mail* (April 2, 2007, pp. B1)

Pub: CTVglobemedia Publishing Inc.

Ed: Steven Chase. **Description:** The views of the chief executive officers of Canadian firms, on the changes in the country's policy governing the taxation of foreign deals, are presented.

46186 ■ *"Channeling for Growth"* in *The Business Journal-Serving Greater Tampa Bay* (Vol. 28, July 11, 2008, No. 29, pp. 1)

Pub: American City Business Journals, Inc.

Ed: Margie Manning. **Description:** HSN Inc., one of the largest employers in Tampa Bay, Florida, is expected to spend an additional $9.7 million annually as it plans to hire more accounting, internal audit, legal, treasury and tax personnel after its spin-off to a public company. Details on the company's sales growth are provided.

46187 ■ *"The China Tax"* in *Forbes* (Vol. 180, October 1, 2007, No. 6, pp. 35)

Pub: Forbes Inc.

Ed: Robyn Meredith. **Description:** U.S. consumers can see a rise in prices for goods made in China due to growing pressure from Congress to ensure safe products from that country. Taxing products imported from China could be levied in five different forms listed.

46188 ■ *"City, County May Kill VC Tax"* in *Business Journal-Portland* (Vol. 24, October 12, 2007, No. 33, pp. 1)

Pub: American City Business Journals, Inc.

Ed: Aliza Earnshaw. **Description:** City of Portland and Multnomah County in Oregon may soon kill taxes levied on venture capital (VC) firms, which is expected to take place in late October 2007. Capitalists have long been saying that taxation is driving them out of town, but this change is expected to generate more investments and persuade VC firms to relocate within city limits.

46189 ■ *"City Eyeing Tax Breaks for Arena"* in *Boston Business Journal* (Vol. 29, June 3, 2011, No. 4, pp. 1)

Pub: American City Business Journals Inc.

Ed: Daniel J. Sernovitz. **Description:** Baltimore City is opting to give millions of dollars in tax breaks and construction loans to a group of private investors led by William Hackerman who is proposing to build a new arena and hotel at the Baltimore Convention Center. The project will cost $500 million with the state putting up another $400 million for the center's expansion.

46190 ■ *"Clock Ticking for Hotel Berry"* in *Sacramento Business Journal* (Vol. 25, July 25, 2008, No. 21, pp. 1)

Pub: American City Business Journals, Inc.

Ed: Michael Shaw. **Description:** Federal tax credits worth $13.6 million have been awarded to boost the renovation project for the aging Hotel Berry in downtown Sacramento, California. The owners of the hotel have five months before the expiration of the tax credits to raise the remaining funding for the $20 million renovation.

46191 ■ *"Commentary: US Economic Recovery and Policy"* in *Small Business Economic Trends* (July 2010, pp. 3)

Pub: National Federation of Independent Business

Description: U.S. Government is making economic recovery difficult, with one of the largest tax increases in history arriving in six months. Meanwhile, Congress is looking into taxing successful businesses, which will potentially hamper growth and real investment. Other insights on the government's role in the country's economic growth are presented.

46192 ■ *"Commotion Pictures; Bill C-10: Is It Censorship or Merely Inept?"* in *Canadian Business* (Vol. 81, March 31, 2008, No. 5, pp. 10)

Pub: Rogers Media

Ed: Denis Seguin. **Description:** Filmmakers are claiming that Bill C-10 amounts to censorship as it could retract a production's eligibility for a tax credit if it is deemed offensive. However, the bill's backers say that the bill protects against tax dollars being directed at productions that run contrary to public policy.

46193 ■ *The Complete Guide to Buying a Business*

Pub: NOLO

Ed: Fred S. Steingold. **Released:** November 2007. **Price:** $24.99. **Description:** Key steps in buying a business are highlighted, focusing on legal issues, tax considerations, approaches for valuing a business, financing, structuring the deal, along with forms and documents for taking ownership are included.

46194 ■ "Confidence High, But Lenders More Cautious" in Farmer's Weekly (March 28, 2008, No. 320)
Pub: Reed Business Information
Contact: Jeff Greisch, President
Description: Discusses the effect of the global credit crunch on farmers as well as recent auctions which were timed to beat changes to capital gains tax.

46195 ■ "Congress Ponders Annuity Trusts" in National Underwriter Life & Health (Vol. 114, June 21, 2010, No. 12, pp. 10)
Pub: Summit Business Media
Ed: Arthur D. Postal. **Description:** Congress is looking over several bills, including the Small Business Jobs Tax Relief Act that would significantly narrow the advantages of using grantor-retained annuity trusts (GRATs) to avoid estate and gift taxes.

46196 ■ "Council Power Shift Could Benefit Business" in Business Courier (Vol. 26, November 6, 2009, No. 28, pp. 1)
Pub: American City Business Journals, Inc.
Ed: Lucy May. **Description:** A majority in the Cincinnati City Council, which is comprised of reelected members, might be created by Charlie Winburn's impending return to the council. It would be empowered to decide on public safety, stock options taxes, and environmental justice. How the presumed majority would affect the city's economic progress is discussed.

46197 ■ "Countywide Tax Could Fund Metro" in Business Courier (Vol. 26, January 15, 2010, No. 39, pp. 1)
Pub: American City Business Journals, Inc.
Ed: Lucy May, Dan Monk. **Description:** Cincinnati officials are considering a new countywide tax to fund the Metro bus system and extend healthcare to the poor.

46198 ■ Craft, Inc.
Pub: Chronicle Books LLC
Ed: Meg Mateo Ilasco. **Released:** August 2007. **Price:** $16.95. **Description:** Business primer for entrepreneurial crafters wishing to turn their hobbies into a small business, including tips for developing products, naming the company, writing a business plan, applying for licenses, and paying taxes.

46199 ■ "Daley's Efforts to Ease Traffic Woes Fall Short" in Crain's Chicago Business (Vol. 31, May 5, 2008, No. 18, pp. 18)
Pub: Crain Communications, Inc.
Description: Discusses some of the inherent problems of Mayor Daley's plan to reduce traffic congestion by creating a tax on drivers who park their cars downtown during peak traffic periods and putting articulated buses on new bus-only lanes on major arterial streets leading into the Loop.

46200 ■ "Datebook" in Crain's Chicago Business (Vol. 31, March 24, 2008, No. 12, pp. 18)
Pub: Crain Communications, Inc.
Description: Listing of events in the Detroit area include conferences addressing entrepreneurialism, economic development, secrets of getting hired, and women business ownership.

46201 ■ "Datebook" in Crain's Chicago Business (Vol. 31, March 31, 2008, No. 13, pp. 1)
Pub: Crain Communications, Inc.
Description: Listing of events in the Detroit area include conferences addressing entrepreneurialism, economic development, secrets of getting hired, and women business ownership.

46202 ■ "Datebook" in Crain's Chicago Business (Vol. 31, April 28, 2008, No. 17, pp. 18)
Pub: Crain Communications, Inc.
Description: Listing of events in the Detroit area include conferences addressing entrepreneurialism, economic development, and women business ownership.

46203 ■ Deduct It! Lower Your Small Business Taxes
Pub: NOLO
Ed: Stephen Fishman. **Released:** November 2006. **Price:** $34.99. **Description:** Information is provided to help small companies maximize taxable deductions.

46204 ■ Deduct It!: Lower Your Small Business Taxes
Pub: NOLO
Ed: Stephen Fishman. **Released:** November 2009. **Price:** $34.99. **Description:** Ways to make the most of tax deductions for any small business are covered. The book is organized into categories featuring common deductions, start-up expenses, health deductions, entertainment, travel, inventory, equipment and more. Current tax laws and numbers for 2008 are included.

46205 ■ "Defer Tax with Installment Sale Election" in Business Owner (Vol. 35, September-October 2011, No. 5, pp. 12)
Pub: DL Perkins Company
Description: It is critical to consult with a tax professional before selling any high-value asset in order to minimize taxes.

46206 ■ "The Design of Tax Policy in Canada" in Canadian Journal of Economics (Vol. 44, November 2011, No. 4, pp. 1184)
Pub: Blackwell Publishers Ltd.
Ed: Kevin Milligan. **Description:** Empirical evidence and tax policy design are presented by Richard Blundell.

46207 ■ "The Display Group Is Super-Sized" in Michigan Vue (Vol. 13, July-August 2008, No. 4, pp. 34)
Pub: Entrepreneur Media Inc.
Description: Profile of the Display Group, located in downtown Detroit, this company provides custom designed mobile marketing displays as well as special event production services for trade show displays. The rental house and design service is also beginning to see more business due to the film initiative, which provides incentives for films that are shooting in Michigan.

46208 ■ "Dodge Slashes Growth Estimate" in Globe & Mail (January 19, 2007, pp. B3)
Pub: CTVglobemedia Publishing Inc.
Ed: Heather Scoffield. **Description:** Bank of Canada Governor David Dodge decision to keep the interest rate 4.25 percent despite a slowdown in the economy is discussed.

46209 ■ "Does it Add Up?" in Canadian Business (Vol. 81, October 13, 2008, No. 17, pp. 18)
Pub: Rogers Media Ltd.
Ed: Jack Mintz. **Description:** Views on Canada's tax policy, as well as on tax reforms planned by major parties and their expected economic impact are discussed. The Tories' proposal to cut federal diesel fuel tax is seen as politically smart, but reforms on other taxes could help generate economic growth. High income tax rates are believed to discourage talented individuals from working in Canada.

46210 ■ "Down to the Wire for Your Taxes" in Women In Business (Vol. 63, Spring 2011, No. 1, pp. 22)
Pub: American Business Women's Association
Ed: Maureen Sullivan. **Description:** A look at a last-minute checklist to consult before filing annual corporate tax returns for a small business owner is presented. Enlisting professional help for small business taxes is always a good investment. However, small business owners have to make sure their records back up their filing when planning to go it alone.

46211 ■ "Duro Bag to Expand, Add 130 Jobs" in Business Courier (Vol. 27, August 6, 2010, No. 14, pp. 1)
Pub: Business Courier
Ed: Jon Newberry. **Description:** Duro Bag Manufacturing Company will expand capacity at its Florence, Kentucky plant and will add around 130 jobs over the

next few years. The state of Kentucky has given preliminary approval for up to $1 million in tax incentives over 10 years, tied to the creation of new jobs. The company's investment will include new production and packaging equipment and building improvements.

46212 ■ "Easy to be Queasy" in Canadian Business (Vol. 81, December 24, 2007, No. 1, pp. 25)
Pub: Rogers Media
Ed: Jack Mintz. **Description:** Canada could be facing a slowdown in economic growth for 2008 as the country's economy depends on the U.S. economy, which is still facing recession in the subprime market. Details on Canada's economic growth, the impact of the weak U.S. dollar, increase in the unemployment rate, and decline in tax revenue are explored.

46213 ■ EBay Income: How ANYONE of Any Age, Location, and/or Background Can Build a Highly Profitable Online Business with eBay
Pub: Atlantic Publishing Company
Released: December 1, 2010. **Price:** $24.95. **Description:** A complete overview of eBay is given and guides any small company through the entire process of creating the auction and auction strategies, photography, writing copy, text and formatting, multiple sales, programming tricks, PayPal, accounting, creating marketing, merchandising, managing email lists, advertising plans, taxes and sales tax, best time to list items and for how long, sniping programs, international customers, opening a storefront, electronic commerce, buy-it now pricing, keywords, Google marketing and eBay secrets.

46214 ■ The Ebay Seller's Tax and Legal Answer Book
Pub: AMACOM
Ed: Cliff Ennico. **Released:** April 30, 2007. **Price:** $19.95. **Description:** Helps sellers using Ebay to file taxes properly, while saving money.

46215 ■ Electronic Commerce: Technical, Business, and Legal Issues
Pub: Prentice Hall PTR
Ed: Oktay Dogramaci; Aryya Gangopadhyay; Yelena Yesha; Nabil R. Adam. **Released:** August 1998. **Description:** Provides insight into the goals of using the Internet to grow a business in the areas of networking and telecommunication, security, and storage and retrieval; business areas such as marketing, procurement and purchasing, billing and payment, and supply chain management; and legal aspects such as privacy, intellectual property, taxation, contractual and legal settlements.

46216 ■ "Eliminating All of Your Estate Tax Burden" in Contractor (Vol. 57, January 2010, No. 1, pp. 48)
Pub: Penton Media, Inc.
Ed: Irv Blackman. **Description:** Suggestions on how family owned businesses can minimize their estate tax burdens are discussed. One of these includes not using life insurance in a business succession plan to move stocks to the children and to never use Section 6166 as part of the overall estate tax plan.

46217 ■ "Employer Jobless Tax Could Rise" in Sacramento Business Journal (Vol. 28, May 27, 2011, No. 13, pp. 1)
Pub: Sacramento Business Journal
Ed: Kathy Robertson. **Description:** The government of California is facing an estimated $16 billion deficit in its unemployment insurance fund. Unemployment insurance spending has exceeded employer contributions to the fund. Statistics on unemployment insurance is included.

46218 ■ "Employers Tied in Knots" in Sacramento Business Journal (Vol. 25, August 15, 2008, No. 24, pp. 1)
Pub: American City Business Journals, Inc.
Ed: Kathy Robertson. **Description:** Conflicting laws on same sex marriage have been posing problems for companies, and insurers in California. The court ruling that allowed gay marriages has created differ-

ences between state and federal laws. Federal laws on same-sex spouse taxation are also seen to complicate the issue.

46219 ■ *"EPA Grants E15 Waiver for 2001-2006 Vehicles" in Farm Industry News (January 21, 2011)*
Pub: Penton Business Media Inc.
Description: U.S. Environmental Protection Agency waived a limitation on selling gasoline that contains more than 10 percent ethanol for model year 2001-2006 cars and light trucks, allowing fuel to contain up to 15 percent ethanol (E15) for these vehicles.

46220 ■ *"Escape the AMT Trap" in Entrepreneur (Vol. 36, February 2008, No. 2, pp. 64)*
Pub: Entrepreneur Media Inc.
Ed: Scott Bernard Nelson. **Description:** Alternative Minimum Tax (AMT), developed by the Internal Revenue Service for taxation of high-income people, has also affected other taxpayers regarding thresholds for inflation. The goal to escape the AMT trap is to defer payments and push off saving strategies into the next year. Details about deferring payments are discussed.

46221 ■ *"Estate Tax Problems may Soon Disappear" in Contractor (Vol. 56, September 2009, No. 9, pp. 60)*
Pub: Penton Media, Inc.
Ed: Irv Blackman. **Description:** Advice on how to effectively plan estate tax in the United States. Pending changes to US estate tax laws are seen to resolve inheritance problems. Captive insurance firms can lower property and casualty insurance costs to transfer businesses to children.

46222 ■ *"Expect Action on Health Care and the Economy" in Contractor (Vol. 57, January 2010, No. 1, pp. 30)*
Pub: Penton Media, Inc.
Ed: Kevin Schwalb. **Description:** The Plumbing-Heating-Cooling Contractors National Association is working to solidify its standing in the public policy arena as the legislative agenda will focus on health care reform, estate tax and immigration reform, all of which will impact the industries.

46223 ■ *"Expert Sees No Radical Reform of 401(K) System" in Workforce Management (Vol. 88, November 16, 2009, No. 12, pp. 12)*
Pub: Crain Communications Inc.
Ed: Ed Frauenheim. **Description:** Although many would like to see an overhaul of the 401(k) retirement system, it is unlikely to occur anytime soon; however, the drastic stock market drop of 2008 has raised pointed questions about the 401(k) system and if it enables a secure retirement for American workers.

46224 ■ *"Experts Discuss New Tax Rules in Webinar to Help Farmers With Year-End Tax Planning" in Farm Industry News (November 22, 2011)*
Pub: Penton Business Media Inc.
Description: Section 179 deductions and Bonus Depreciation tax rules for years 2011 and 2012 and how they impact farming operations are available at TractorLife.com. The Website helps farmers maintain and extend the operating lives of their tractors.

46225 ■ *"Exposed?" in Mergers & Acquisitions: The Dealmaker's Journal (March 1, 2008)*
Pub: SourceMedia, Inc.
Ed: Jerry Abejo. **Description:** State-run pension plans' contributions are declining due to a loss of tax revenue from plummeting home values.

46226 ■ *Facing Financial Dysfunction*
Pub: Infinity Publishing
Ed: Bert Whitehead. **Released:** April 2004. **Description:** Handbook to help individuals manage their finances, investments, taxes and retirement.

46227 ■ *"Fair Play? China Cheats, Carney Talks and Rankin Walks; Here's the Latest" in Canadian Business (Vol. 81, March 17, 2008, No. 4)*
Pub: Rogers Media
Description: Discusses the World Trade Organization which says that China is breaking trade rules by taxing imports of auto parts at the same rate as foreign-made finished cars. Mark Carney first speech as the governor of the Bank of Canada made economists suspect a rate cut on overnight loans. Andre Rankin was ordered by the Ontario Securities Commission to pay $250,000 in investigation costs.

46228 ■ *"Fair Tax Backers Hope MBT Anger Will Bring Votes" in Crain's Detroit Business (Vol. 24, March 31, 2008, No. 13, pp. 32)*
Pub: Crain Communications, Inc.
Description: Discusses the Michigan Fair Tax Proposal which would eliminate Michigan's business taxes and income tax, raise the state sales tax to 9.75 percent and expand it to services.

46229 ■ *Family Limited Partnership Deskbook*
Pub: American Bar Association
Contact: Carolyn Lamm, President
Ed: David T. Lewis; Andrea C. Chomakos. **Released:** March 25, 2008. **Price:** $169.95. **Description:** Forming and funding a family limited partnership or limited liability company is complicated. In-depth analysis of all facets of this business entity are examined using detailed guidance on the basic principles of drafting, forming, funding, and valuing an FLP or LLC and also covers tax concerns. Examples and extensive sample forms are included on a CD-ROM included with the book.

46230 ■ *Family Limited Partnerships Deskbook: Forming and Funding FLPs and Other Closely Held Business Entities*
Pub: American Bar Association
Contact: Carolyn Lamm, President
Ed: David T. Lewis. **Released:** March 2008. **Price:** $169.95. **Description:** Forming and funding a family limited partnership (FLP) or limited liability company (LLC) is common and complicated. This handbook offers in-depth analysis of issues facing these types of businesses. Guidance is given on the principles of drafting, forming, funding, and valuing an FLP or LLC as well as tax matters. Examples and sample forms are included on a CD-ROM.

46231 ■ *A Family Matter: A Guide to Operating Your Personal Estate*
Pub: Brown Books Publishing Group
Ed: William A. Verkest. **Released:** May 2003. **Price:** $22.95. **Description:** Guidebook to financial management of personal assets is presented. Important documents must be maintained in a safe, secure place for family members or attorneys to access when necessary. The author suggests that a personal diary be kept with important information regarding records of investment accounts and financial summaries for every year in order to calculate taxes and manage financial matters more efficiently.

46232 ■ *Fast-Track Business Start-Up Kit: California*
Pub: DP Group, Incorporated
Ed: Carolyn Usinger. **Released:** September 2006. **Price:** $29.00. **Description:** Step-by-step guide for starting and running a business in California, including information on sole proprietors, partnerships, limited liability companies, S and C corporations, as well as details concerning business entities, sales taxes, environmental issues, human resources, and more.

46233 ■ *"Feds to Pay University $20M" in Business Courier (Vol. 27, July 23, 2010, No. 12, pp. 3)*
Pub: Business Courier
Ed: James Ritchie. **Description:** The U.S. government is set to pay University Hospital and medical residents who trained there $20 million as part of a tax dispute settlement. Around 1,000 former residents are to receive tax refunds. But the hospital must provide the U.S. Internal Revenue Service with extensive documentation.

46234 ■ *"Film Incentives: A Hit or a Flop?" in Michigan Vue (Vol. 13, July-August 2008, No. 4, pp. 10)*
Pub: Entrepreneur Media Inc.
Description: Michigan's new film incentive legislation is fulfilling its core purpose, according to Lisa Dancsok of the Michigan Economic Development Corp. (MEDC), by kickstarting the state's entry into the multi-billion dollar industry; the initiative is considered to be very competitive with other states and countries and is thought to be a way in which to help revitalize Michigan's struggling economy.

46235 ■ *"Final State Budget Is a Mixed Bag of Key Industries" in The Business Journal - Serving Phoenix and the Valley of the Sun (Vol. 28, July 4, 2008, No. 44, pp. 3)*
Pub: American City Business Journals, Inc.
Ed: Mike Sunnucks; Patrick O'Grady. **Description:** Approved by Governor Janet Napolitano and passed by the Arizona Legislature, the $9.9 billion state budget is beneficial to some industries in the business community. The tax cap for on Arizona Lottery has been removed which is beneficial to the industry, while the solar energy industry and real estate developers stand to lose from the spending bill. Other details of the finance budget are presented.

46236 ■ *"Finding Room for Financing" in The Business Journal-Serving Metropolitan Kansas City (Vol. 26, August 1, 2008, No. 47, pp. 1)*
Pub: American City Business Journals, Inc.
Ed: Rob Roberts. **Description:** Kansas City officials are expecting to receive financing recommendations for a new 1,000-room convention headquarters hotel. The $300-million project could be financed either through private ownership with public subsidies, or through public ownership with tax-exempt bond financing. Other views and information on the project and its expected economic impact, are presented.

46237 ■ *"First-Time Homebuyer Credit May Add Some Momentum to Market" in Crain's Cleveland Business (Vol. 30, May 18, 2009, No. 20)*
Pub: Crain Communications, Inc.
Ed: Stan Bullard. **Description:** Federal tax credits for first-time homebuyers have increased the number of homes being sold. Details of the tax credit are defined.

46238 ■ *"Five Area Businesses Win State Tax Breaks" in Crain's Detroit Business (Vol. 25, June 22, 2009, No. 25, pp. 9)*
Pub: Crain Communications Inc. - Detroit
Ed: Amy Lane. **Description:** Michigan Economic Growth Authority approved tax breaks for five area businesses among 15 across the state. Details of the tax credits are provided.

46239 ■ *"For All It's Worth" in Entrepreneur (Vol. 36, April 2008, No. 4, pp. 46)*
Pub: Entrepreneur Media, Inc.
Ed: Farnoosh Torabi. **Description:** Discusses the federal estate tax system requires that 45 percent of the money beyond $2 million be given to the government. Ways on how to minimize the effects of estate tax on assets include: creating bypass trusts for married couples; setting up an irrevocable life insurance trust to avoid taxation of estate for insurance benefactors; and having annual gift tax exclusion.

46240 ■ *"Foreign (In)Direct Investment and Corporate Taxation" in Canadian Journal of Economics (Vol. 44, November 2011, No. 4, pp. 1497)*
Pub: Blackwell Publishers Ltd.
Ed: Georg Wamser. **Description:** Foreign investments of multinational firms are often complex in that they involve conduit entities. In particular, a multinational can pursue either a direct or an indirect investment strategy, where the latter involves an intermediate corporate entity and is associated with enhanced opportunities for international tax planning. As a consequence, in the case of indirect investments, the role of corporate taxation in destination countries may change. An investigation into the effects of corporation taxation on foreign investment decisions of German multinationals, taking explicitly into account that firms choose in a first stage the investment regime, (direct vs. indirect) is provided.

46241 ■ *"Formaspace Finds a Bigger Home" in Austin Business JournalInc. (Vol. 29,*

December 4, 2009, No. 39, pp. 1)
Pub: American City Business Journals

Ed: Kate Harrington. **Description:** Formaspace Technical Furniture has signed a lease for 56,700 square feet in Harris Ridge Business Center at Northeast Austin, Texas, which represents one of the area's largest leases for 2009. The new lease enables Formaspace to hire new employees, invest in new equipment, and take advantage of a taxing designation created for manufacturers.

46242 ■ *Free Lunch: How the Wealthiest Americans Enrich Themselves at Government Expense*
Pub: Portfolio

Description: Johnston uses the case of the Texas Rangers as an example to support his belief that the nation's monied elite bend the rules of capitalism for their own benefit.

46243 ■ *"Freshman Lawmaker Graves Keeping Busy"* in Atlanta *Journal-Constitution (June 20, 2010, pp. A6)*
Pub: Atlanta Journal Constitution

Ed: Bob Keefe. **Description:** Newly elected Republican Representative Tom Graves of Ranger supports the Small Business Jobs Tax Relief Act.

46244 ■ *"Fuel for Thought"* in Canadian Business (Vol. 81, April 14, 2008, No. 6, pp. 18)
Pub: Rogers Media

Ed: John Gray. **Description:** Discusses a web poll of 133 CEOs and other business leaders that shows that they predict oil prices to increase to US $113 per barrel over the 2008 to 2010 timeframe. Most of the respondents did not favor cutting gas taxes but this group wants the government to cut taxes on fuel-efficient vehicles and increase subsidies to local transit systems.

46245 ■ *"Getting More Out of Retirement"* in Agency Sales Magazine (Vol. 39, November 2009, No. 10, pp. 48)
Pub: MANA

Ed: Joshua D. Mosshart. **Description:** Overview of the Tax Increase Prevention and Reconciliation Act, which lets employees convert to a Roth IRA in 2010. The benefits of conversion depend on age and wealth and it is best to consult a tax advisor to determine the best strategy for retirement planners.

46246 ■ *"Getting Out of an IRS Mess"* in Black Enterprise (Vol. 37, December 2006, No. 5, pp. 53)
Pub: Earl G. Graves Publishing Co. Inc.

Ed: Carolyn M. Brown. **Description:** Owing back taxes to the IRS can lead to huge penalties and interest. Here are some tips on how to handle paying the IRS what you owe them.

46247 ■ *Getting Rich In Your Underwear: How To Start and Run a Profitable Home-Based Business*
Pub: HCM Publishing

Ed: Peter I. Hupalo. **Released:** April 1, 2005. **Price:** $17.95. **Description:** Book offers insight into starting a home-based business. Entrepreneurs will learn about business models and the home business; distribution and fulfillment of product or service; marketing and sales; how to overcome the fear of starting a business; personal success characteristics; naming a business; zoning and insurance; intellectual capital; copyrights, trademarks, and patents; limited liability companies and S-corporations; business expenses and accounting; taxes; fifteen basic steps for starting a home-based business, state resources for starting a home company; and seven home-based business ideas.

46248 ■ *"Give a Little Back"* in Canadian Business (Vol. 79, November 20, 2006, No. 23, pp. 17)
Pub: Rogers Media

Ed: Jack Mintz. **Description:** The plans of Jim Flaherty, Canada's minister of finance, to remove the corporate tax bias on income paid to pension plans are discussed.

46249 ■ *"Give Until It Works"* in Hispanic Business (March 2008, pp. 26-27)
Pub: Hispanic Business

Ed: Rick Munarriz. **Description:** Ways to maximize a tax advantage from charitable contributions for small business owners are addressed.

46250 ■ *"Give Until It Works"* in Hispanic Business (Vol. 30, March 2008, No. 3, pp. 26)
Pub: Hispanic Business

Ed: Rick Munarriz. **Description:** Donating to qualified charities and non-profit organizations for maximizing tax advantage to be availed on the income tax bill is examined. The amount that can be deducted from the total taxable amount is usually less then the actual amount donated and must be made during that calendar year.

46251 ■ *"Global-Preneuring: Tax Ramifications Can Make or Break a Worldwide Enterprise"* in Small Business Opportunities (May 2008)
Pub: Harris Publications Inc.

Description: It is imperative to consider the tax ramifications when starting or expanding a global enterprise.

46252 ■ *"Goodwill Haunts Local Companies; Bad Buyouts During Boom Times Producing Big Writedowns"* in Crain's Chicago Business (Apr. 28, 2008)
Pub: Crain Communications, Inc.

Ed: Ann Saphir. **Description:** Many companies are having to face the reality that they overpaid for acquisitions made in better economic times; investors often dismiss such one-time charges as mere accounting adjustments but writeoffs related to past acquisitions can signal future problems because they mean the expected profits that justified the purchase have not materialized. Writeoffs are particularly worrisome for firms with a lot of debt and whose banks require them to have enough assets to back up their borrowings.

46253 ■ *"Government Intervention"* in Canadian Business (Vol. 79, November 6, 2006, No. 22, pp. 116)
Pub: Rogers Media

Description: The effects of income trust tax on economic conditions and investment of Canada are presented.

46254 ■ *"Grave Concerns"* in Canadian Business (Vol. 81, July 21 2008, No. 11, pp. 25)
Pub: Rogers Media Ltd.

Ed: Andrew Nikiforuk. **Description:** Air pollution control regulations to reduce greenhouse gasses have been implemented by the Canadian government. The federal government is planning to construct a carbon funeral industry that will store the global warming gases, however the expenditure for the project will be shifted to the taxpayers. Details of the Bruce Peachy's initiative on how to reduce GHGs are presented.

46255 ■ *"Green Shift Sees Red"* in Canadian Business (Vol. 81, September 29, 2008, No. 16)
Pub: Rogers Media Ltd.

Ed: Jeff Sanford. **Description:** Green Shift Inc. is suing the Liberal Party of Canada in an $8.5 million lawsuit for using the phrase 'green shift' when they rolled out their carbon tax and climate change policy. The company has come to be recognized as a consultant and provider of green products such as non-toxic, biodegradable cups, plates, and utensils for events.

46256 ■ *"Have High-Tech Tax Credits Helped or Hurt Hawaii?"* in Hawaii Business (Vol. 53, December 2007, No. 6, pp. 28)
Pub: Hawaii Business Publishing

Description: Presents the opinons of Channel Capital LLC's Walter R. Roth and Hawaii Venture Capital Association's Bill Spencer concerning the impacts of tax credits. Roth thinks that Act 221 appeals to investors who can earn despite business

failure while Spencer thinks that the legislation promotes investments in innovative technology firms. The need to support tax credits is also discussed.

46257 ■ *"Helping Small Businesses Create Jobs"* in America's Intelligence Wire (August 27, 2010)
Pub: HighBeam Research

Ed: Ross Raihala. **Description:** Ways the Small Business Jobs Tax Relief Act will help small businesses create jobs are investigated.

46258 ■ *"The Hidden Tax"* in Canadian Business (Vol. 81, April 14, 2008, No. 6, pp. 28)
Pub: Rogers Media

Ed: Al Rosen. **Description:** Accounting fraud could take out a sizable sum from one's retirement fund when computed over a long period of time. The much bigger tax on savings is the collective impact of the smaller losses that do not attract the attention they deserve. Ensuring that investors are not unnecessarily taxed 2 percent of their total investments every year outweighs the benefit of a 2 percent reduction in personal tax rates.

46259 ■ *"High-Tech Job-Apalooza!"* in Orlando Business Journal (Vol. 26, January 15, 2010, No. 33, pp. 1)
Pub: American City Business Journals

Ed: Christopher Boyd. **Description:** Science Applications International Corporation, Saab Training USA LLC, CAE USA, and Pelliconi &C.SPA attempt to obtain $939,000 in tax incentives to generate 222 technology and defense-related jobs in Orange County, Florida. Each job will provide an average salary of $67,000. Future plans of each technology and defense firm are also presented.

46260 ■ *"Hike in Md.'s Alcohol Tax May Be Hard For Lawmakers to Swallow"* in Baltimore Business Journal (Vol. 28, November 19, 2010, No. 28)
Pub: Baltimore Business Journal

Ed: Emily Mullin. **Description:** Maryland's General Assembly has been reluctant to support a dime-per-drink increase in alcohol tax that was drafted in the 2009 bill if the tax revenue goes into a separate fund. The alcohol tax increase is considered unnecessary by some lawmakers and business leaders due to impending federal spending boosts.

46261 ■ *"Hilliard Scans Horizon, Finds Defense Contractor"* in Business First Columbus (Vol. 25, October 17, 2008, No. 8, pp. A1)
Pub: American City Business Journals

Ed: Brian R. Ball. **Description:** An incentive package being offered by Hilliard may prompt a Powell defense contractor to relocate in 2009. The package offered to Star Dynamics Corporation incorporates incentives that return a sizeable amount of income taxes to the company.

46262 ■ *"Historic Tax Credit Plan Gains Support"* in Baltimore Business Journal (Vol. 27, January 8, 2010, No. 36, pp. 1)
Pub: American City Business Journals

Ed: Heather Harlan Warnack. **Description:** Maryland Governor Martin O'Malley plans to push legislation in the General Assembly to extend for three more years the tax credit program for rehabilitation of obsolete buildings. The Maryland Heritage Structure Rehabilitation Tax Credit Program has declined from almost $75 million in expenses in 2001 to roughly $5 million in 2010 fiscal year. Details on the projects that benefited from the program are explored.

46263 ■ *Home Business Tax Deductions: Keep What You Earn*
Pub: NOLO

Ed: Stephen Fishman. **Released:** November 2006. **Price:** $34.99. **Description:** Home business tax deductions are outlined. Basic information on the ways various business structures are taxed and how deductions work is included.

46264 ■ *"Hospital Tax Could Be a Separate Bill"* in *Business Journal-Milwaukee (Vol. 25, October 26, 2007, No. 4, pp. A1)*
Pub: American City Business Journals, Inc.

Ed: Elizabeth Sanders. **Description:** Hospital officials are working on reintroducing a hospital tax proposal that would increase Medicaid reimbursement, thereby generating millions of dollars of revenue for the Milwaukee-area hospitals. The bill sponsored by Governor Jim Doyle was supported by the Wisconsin Hospital Association. Details of the proposed hospital tax are presented.

46265 ■ *"Hospitals Face Big Whammy From State Fees"* in *Business Courier (Vol. 26, October 2, 2009, No. 23, pp. 1)*
Pub: American City Business Journals, Inc.

Ed: James Ritchie. **Description:** Ohio hospitals are facing losses of nearly $145 million in franchise fees which are set to be levied by the state. Ohio hospitals will be responsible for a total of $718 million franchise fees as required by 2010-2011 state budget but will recover only 80 percent of the amount in increased Medicaid fees. Possible effects of anticipated losses to Ohio hospitals are examined.

46266 ■ *"Hot Air"* in *Canadian Business (Vol. 81, July 22, 2008, No. 12-13, pp. 16)*
Pub: Rogers Media Ltd.

Ed: Joe Castaldo. **Description:** Over half of 101 business leaders who were recently surveyed oppose Liberal leader Stephane Dion's carbon-tax proposal, saying that manufacturers in Canada are likely to suffer from the plan. Additional key results of the survey are presented.

46267 ■ *"Hot Air: On Global Warming and Carbon Tax"* in *Canadian Business (Vol. 81, October 13, 2008, No. 17, pp. 12)*
Pub: Rogers Media Ltd.

Ed: Joe Castaldo. **Description:** Survey of Canadian business leaders revealed that the environment is a key issue in Canada's federal elections. Respondents believe that Prime Minister Stephen Harper's views on global warming and climate change are closer to their own views. Other key information on the survey is presented.

46268 ■ *"Hotel Tax Eyed For Waukesha"* in *The Business Journal-Milwaukee (Vol. 25, August 29, 2008, No. 49, pp. A1)*
Pub: American City Business Journals, Inc.

Ed: Rich Kirchen. **Description:** Midwest Airlines Center chairman Frank Gimbel wants Waukesha County to help in the funding of the $200-million expansion of the convention center through a hotel room tax. The Waukesha hotel industry is expected to oppose the new room tax. Other views and information on the planned new room tax in Waukesha are presented.

46269 ■ *"Housing Hedge"* in *Canadian Business (Vol. 79, July 17, 2006, No. 14-15, pp. 66)*
Pub: Rogers Media

Ed: Jeff Sanford. **Description:** The idea of starting a hedge scheme for housing is presented using the advent of pension schemes as an example to follow.

46270 ■ *"How About Trying a Foreclosure Tax?"* in *Crain's Detroit Business (Vol. 24, January 28, 2008, No. 4, pp. 9)*
Pub: Crain Communications Inc. - Detroit

Ed: Mark Goodell. **Description:** According to a recent study, local communities could see a $100 million decrease in property tax revenues, and the state could lose as much as $12 million in lower sales tax proceeds. Experts discuss options for Michigan's government to institute a foreclosure tax.

46271 ■ *"How to Maximize Your Investment Income"* in *Contractor (Vol. 56, December 2009, No. 12, pp. 33)*
Pub: Penton Media, Inc.

Ed: Irv Blackman. **Description:** Private placement life insurance (PPLI) can minimize taxes and protect assets. PPLI is a form of variable universal insurance

that is offered privately. Risk of insurance company illiquidity is avoided as investments are placed in separate accounts.

46272 ■ *How to Start an Internet Sales Business*
Pub: Lulu.com

Ed: Dan Davis. **Released:** August 2005. **Price:** $19.95. **Description:** Small business guide for launching an Internet sales company. Topics include business structure, licenses, and taxes.

46273 ■ *How to Start and Run a Small Book Publishing Company: A Small Business Guide to Self-Publishing and Independent Publishing*
Pub: HCM Publishing

Ed: Peter I. Hupalo. **Released:** August 30, 2002. **Price:** $18.95. **Description:** The book teaches all aspects of starting and running a small book publishing company. Topics covered include: inventory accounting in the book trade, just-in-time inventory management, turnkey fulfillment solutions, tax deductible costs, basics of sales and use tax, book pricing, standards in terms of the book industry, working with distributors and wholesalers, cover design and book layout, book promotion and marketing, how to select profitable authors to publish, printing process, printing on demand, the power of a strong backlist, and how to value copyright.

46274 ■ *How to Start and Run Your Own Corporation: S-Corporations For Small Business Owners*
Pub: HCM Publishing

Ed: Peter I. Hupalo. **Released:** March 6, 2003. **Price:** $22.95. **Description:** Basics of corporate business structure are explained. Topics include discovering the best business structure for your company; how to decided between an S-Corporation and LLC; choosing the state in which to incorporate, how to form a corporation, angel investing, special issues for one-person corporations, the role of bylaws and corporate minutes, board of directors, taxes, workers' compensation issues, retirement plans, and more.

46275 ■ *"The HST Hornet's Nest"* in *Canadian Business (Vol. 83, September 14, 2010, No. 15, pp. 17)*
Pub: Rogers Media Ltd.

Ed: Michael McCullough. **Description:** Canadian Premier Gordon Campbell's Harmonized Sales Tax (HST) initiative has left British Columbia's economic and political future stuck in uncertainty. The petition of a coalition group forced a bill to abolish the HST through legislation or referendum. How the HST's abolition will affect British Columbia's revenues is also discussed.

46276 ■ *"Incentives Debate Rages On Unabated"* in *The Business Journal-Serving Metropolitan Kansas City (Vol. 26, September 5, 2008, No. 52)*
Pub: American City Business Journals, Inc.

Ed: Rob Roberts. **Description:** Debate on the new economic development and incentives policy adopted by the Kansas City Council is still on. The city's Planned Industrial Expansion Authority has rejected a standard property tax abatement proposal. The real estate development community has opposed the rejection of proposed the tax incentives policy.

46277 ■ *"An Insurance Roll-Up In Danger of Unraveling"* in *Barron's (Vol. 88, March 17, 2008, No. 11, pp. 51)*
Pub: Dow Jones & Company, Inc.

Ed: Bill Alpert. **Description:** Shares of National Financial Partners have fallen below their initial offering price as sputtering sales and management turnover leave many investors wondering. One of the company's star brokers is being sued for their 'life settlement' contracts while another broker is being pursued by the IRS for unpaid taxes.

46278 ■ *"Intel: Tax Breaks Key"* in *Business Journal Portland (Vol. 27, October 22, 2010, No. 34, pp. 1)*
Pub: Portland Business Journal

Ed: Erik Siemers. **Description:** Intel Corporation believes that state tax incentives will be critical, especially in the purchase of manufacturing equip-

ment, as they build a new chip factory in Hillsboro, Oregon. The tax breaks would help Intel avoid paying 10 times more in property taxes compared to average Washington County firms. Critics argue that Intel has about $15 billion in cash assets, and can afford the factory without the tax breaks.

46279 ■ *"International Benefits Roundup"* in *Employee Benefit News (Vol. 25, December 1, 2011, No. 15)*
Pub: SourceMedia Inc.

Description: Employee contributions to an employer-sponsored defined contribution plan in Japan will allowed on a tax-deductible basis; however, currently employee contributions are not allowed. The defined contribution plan is outlined for better understanding.

46280 ■ *"Investment Firms Unite: Coalition Fights New Tax Law"* in *Black Enterprise (Vol. 38, December 2007, No. 5, pp. 52)*
Pub: Earl G. Graves Publishing Co. Inc.

Ed: Joyce Jones. **Description:** Minorities working in private equity, real estate and investment management firms have united to form the Access to Capital Coalition to oppose legislation that they feel would adversely affect their ability to attract investments and executives. Details of the group are included.

46281 ■ *"Iowa Tax Case Could Cost Nation's Franchises"* in *Franchising World (Vol. 42, September 2010, No. 9, pp. 38)*
Pub: International Franchise Association

Ed: Bruce A. Ackerman, Adam B. Thimmesch. **Description:** Ruling by the Iowa Supreme Court could have a financial impact on franchisors across the U.S. Iowa asserted that Kentucky Fried Chicken is subject to Iowa corporate income tax based solely on the fact that it received royalties from franchises in the state.

46282 ■ *"It's Not Perfect; But Illinois a Good Home for Business"* in *Crain's Chicago Business (Vol. 34, October 24, 2011, No. 42, pp. 18)*
Pub: Crain Communications Inc.

Description: Focusing on all factors that encompass Illinois' business environment, findings show that Illinois is a good place to start and grow a business. The study focused on corporate income tax rates and the fact that talent, access to capital and customers along with transportation connections are among the important factors the state has for small businesses.

46283 ■ *J. K. Lasser's Small Business Taxes 2008: Your Complete Guide to a Better Bottom Line*
Pub: John Wiley and Sons, Inc.

Ed: Barbara Weltman. **Released:** November 2007. **Description:** Comprehensive guide providing tax strategies for any small business in the U.S. Sample forms and checklists are included.

46284 ■ *JK Lasser's Small Business Taxes 2077: Your Complete Guide to a Better Bottom Line*
Pub: John Wiley & Sons, Incorporated

Ed: Barbara Weltman. **Released:** November 2006. **Price:** $17.95. **Description:** J.K. Lasser's guide that offers tax facts and strategies for small businesses. The book helps to maximize deductions while learning tax planning strategies.

46285 ■ *"Know Your Numbers"* in *Inc. (Volume 32, December 2010, No. 10, pp. 39)*
Pub: Inc. Magazine

Ed: Norm Brodsky. **Description:** Ways to maximize profit and minimize tax burden are presented.

46286 ■ *"Lean on Me"* in *Entrepreneur (Vol. 36, February 2008, No. 2, pp. 40)*
Pub: Entrepreneur Media Inc.

Ed: Farnoosh Torabi. **Description:** Investing in tax liens is booming with the growth in the number of homeowners missing property tax payments. Details on how to bid for and when to redeem tax liens are outlined.

46287 ■ *"Legislators Must Cut Cost of Government"* in Crain's Detroit Business (Vol. 24, October 6, 2008, No. 40, pp. 6)

Pub: Crain Communications, Inc.

Description: Southeast and West Michigan business leaders are setting aside their differences and have proposed clear agendas, ranging from eliminating the Michigan Business Tax to overhauling public employee and retiree benefits and pensions. Lawmakers must also come together to find solutions for the state's economy and discover an entirely new vision for the future of Michigan business.

46288 ■ *"Legislature Passes Increased Tax Credit for Urban Brownfield Projects"* in Crain's Detroit Business (Vol. 24, March 31, 2008, No. 13)

Pub: Crain Communications, Inc.

Ed: Amy Lane. **Description:** Discusses the bill passed by the Legislature that creates a tax credit of up to 20 percent for projects in urban development areas.

46289 ■ *"Lending Act Touted by Michaud"* in Morning Sentinel (June 21, 2010)

Pub: Morning Sentinel

Ed: Doug Harlow. **Description:** If passed, the Small Business Jobs Tax Relief Act will leverage up to $300 billion in loans for small businesses through a $30 billion lending fund for small and medium-sized community banks, which focus on lending to small firms.

46290 ■ *"Lifetime Planning with a Twist"* in Contractor (Vol. 56, July 2009, No. 7, pp. 40)

Pub: Penton Media, Inc.

Ed: Irv Blackman. **Description:** Private Placement Life Insurance lets wealthy investors make their investment gains tax-free and can be set up so investors can make tax-free loans from the policy. This can be used on a younger member of the family as a wealth-building strategy if the investor is uninsurable.

46291 ■ *"Lights, Camera..Incentive"* in Austin Business JournalInc. (Vol. 28, October 10, 2008, No. 30, pp. 1)

Pub: American City Business Journals

Ed: Sandra Zaragoza. **Description:** Film industry insiders are saying that state level tax breaks are needed to boost the sector, together with the help of the $700 billion bailout bill, which is expected to provide $470 million in tax incentives to the movie industry. Other details on filmmakers' call for more tax incentives for Texas' film industry are discussed.

46292 ■ *"Like Mom and Apple Pie"* in Canadian Business (Vol. 79, October 9, 2006, No. 20, pp. 19)

Pub: Rogers Media

Ed: Peter Shawn Taylor. **Description:** Impact of paying huge tax bills on the social benefits of family income is discussed. Income splitting as an effective way to lower household's overall tax bill is presented.

46293 ■ *"A Little Less Hot Air"* in Canadian Business (Vol. 81, March 17, 2008, No. 4, pp. 9)

Pub: Rogers Media

Description: British Columbia will levy an extra tax on all carbon-emitting fuels starting July 1, 2008. The tax will raise $1.8 billion in three years and in effect, the province will reduce general corporate income tax from 12 percent to 11 percent. The tax on small businesses and personal income will also be reduced.

46294 ■ *"Local Manufacturers See Tax Proposal Hurting Global Operations"* in Crain's Cleveland Business (Vol. 30, May 18, 2009, No. 20)

Pub: Crain Communications, Inc.

Ed: Dan Shingler. **Description:** New tax laws proposed by the Obama Administration could hinder the efforts of some Northeast Ohio industrial companies from expanding their overseas markets. The law is designed to prevent companies from moving jobs overseas.

46295 ■ *"Looking for a Sales Tax Extension"* in Milwaukee Business Journal (Vol. 27, January 29, 2010, No. 18, pp. A1)

Pub: American City Business Journals

Ed: Mark Kass. **Description:** Milwaukee, Wisconsin-area business executives believe the extension of the Miller Park 0.1 percent sales tax could help fund a new basketball arena to replace the 21-year-old Bradley Center in downtown Milwaukee. However, any sales tax expansion that includes the new basketball arena would need approval by Wisconsin's legislature.

46296 ■ *"Major Advances in Heat Pump Technology"* in Contractor (Vol. 57, January 2010, No. 1, pp. 42)

Pub: Penton Media, Inc.

Ed: Mark Eatherton. **Description:** Tax credits make ground-source heat pump technology more economically feasible. Suggestions on how to choose the right ground-source heat pump technology to install in a house are discussed.

46297 ■ *Make Sure It's Deductible*

Pub: McGraw-Hill Companies Inc.

Contact: Deven Sharma, President

Ed: Evelyn Jacks. **Released:** November 2006. **Price:** $22.95. **Description:** Tax planning, strategies are provided to help small businesses maximize deductions.

46298 ■ *Make Your Life Tax Deductible: Easy Techniques to Reduce Your Taxes and Start Building Wealth Immediately*

Pub: McGraw-Hill Companies Inc.

Contact: Deven Sharma, President

Ed: David Meier. **Released:** December 2005. **Price:** $16.95 (US), $22.95 (Canadian). **Description:** Over 150 tax deductions are listed to help small business owners lower taxes and boost profits.

46299 ■ *"Maryland Senate Gets Read to Talk Taxes"* in Boston Business Journal (Vol. 29, July 1, 2011, No. 8, pp. 1)

Pub: American City Business Journals Inc.

Ed: Scott Dance. **Description:** Maryland Senate Budget and Taxation Committee will meet July 26, 2011 to discuss some of business community's concerns including sales tax expansion to cover services, a restructuring of the corporate income tax brackets and an answer to questions regarding transportation funding project.

46300 ■ *"Mayor Unveils Business Plan"* in Boston Business Journal (Vol. 29, September 16, 2011, No. 19, pp. 1)

Pub: American City Business Journals Inc.

Ed: Gary Haber. **Description:** Mayor Stephanie Rawlings-Blake of Baltimore, Maryland unveiled her plan to push the economy forward. Her key objectives include giving more support for the city's technology companies and refocusing the Baltimore Development Corporation on job creation and retention.

46301 ■ *"MBT 'Sticker Shock' Surprises Business; Reaction? 'You Can't Print It,' Owner Says"* in Crain's Detroit Business (March 17, 2008)

Pub: Crain Communications, Inc.

Ed: Amy Lane. **Description:** Overview of the new Michigan Business Tax which is raising many middle-sized businesses' taxes by up to 400 percent.

46302 ■ *"Medicaid Expansion Could Prompt New Taxes, Program Cuts"* in Baltimore Business Journal (Vol. 27, October 23, 2009, No. 24, pp. 1)

Pub: American City Business Journals

Ed: Julekha Dash. **Description:** Effects of the expected federal expansion of Medicaid under federal health care reform on Maryland tax policy are presented. Health care executives believe new taxes are necessary for the state to pay for an expansion that could cost over $400 million to $600 million.

46303 ■ *Mergers and Acquisitions from A to Z*

Pub: Amacom

Ed: Andrew J. Sherman, Milledge A. Hart. **Released:** January 2006. **Price:** $35.00. **Description:** Guide for the entire process of mergers and acquisitions, including taxes, accounting, laws, and projected financial gain.

46304 ■ *"Michaud Touts Small-Business Credentials"* in Bangor Daily News (September 10, 2010)

Pub: Bangor Daily News

Ed: Nick Sambides Jr. **Description:** Mike Michaud, Democrat, is running against a Republican challenger in the 2nd District and states he will support the Small Business Jobs Tax Relief Act if reelected.

46305 ■ *Minding Her Own Business, 4th Ed.*

Pub: Sphinx Publishing

Ed: Jan Zobel. **Released:** January 1, 2005. **Price:** $16.95. **Description:** A guide to taxes and financial records for women entrepreneurs is presented.

46306 ■ *"More Corporate Welfare?"* in Canadian Business (Vol. 80, February 12, 2007, No. 4, pp. 96)

Pub: Rogers Media

Description: The burden on Canadian taxpayers by governmental efforts to finance loss-making companies in the name of corporate welfare is discussed.

46307 ■ *"More Jobs Moving Out of City"* in Business Courier (Vol. 24, March 14, 2008, No. 49, pp. 1)

Pub: American City Business Journals, Inc.

Ed: Steve Watkins; Laura Baverman. **Description:** UBS Financial Services Inc. is moving Gradison to Kenwood Town Place in Sycamore Township a year after UBS acquired Gradison. The township does not have a tax on earnings so the move will save Gradison's employees the 2.1 percent Cincinnati tax.

46308 ■ *"NAWBO Takes the Stage at Press Conference for Small Business Jobs, Credit and Tax Relief Acts"* in Internet Wire (June 17, 2010)

Pub: Comtex

Description: A survey of the National Association of Women Business Owners reported optimism returning and women business owners are ready to invest in job creation. The Small Business Jobs Tax Relief Act will aid in their progress.

46309 ■ *"New Rule Rankles In Jersey"* in Philadelphia Business Journal (Vol. 30, September 16, 2011, No. 31, pp. 1)

Pub: American City Business Journals Inc.

Ed: Jeff Blumenthal. **Description:** A new rule in New Jersey which taxes out-of-state companies that conduct business in the state earned the ire of several banks, mortgage lenders and credit card companies and prompted opponents to threaten to file lawsuits. The new rule is an amendment to New Jersey Division of Taxation's corporate business tax regulation and is retroactive to 2002. Details are given.

46310 ■ *"New Tax Sends Biz Scrambling; Service Levy Will Affect 16,000 Businesses"* in Crain's Detroit Business (October 8, 2007)

Pub: Crain Communications Inc. - Detroit

Ed: Amy Lane. **Description:** Legislation that imposes a tax on services in Michigan has business leaders upset. The new law exerts a 6 percent tax on 57 categories of services that affects 16,000 businesses in the state.

46311 ■ *"New Year, New Estate Plan"* in Hawaii Business (Vol. 53, February 2008, No. 8, pp. 54)

Pub: Hawaii Business Publishing

Ed: Antony M. Orme. **Description:** Discusses the start of the new year which can be a time to revise wills and estate plans as failure to do so may create problems of unequal inheritance and increase in estate tax exemption, which could disinherit beneficiaries. Other circumstances that can prompt changes in wills and estate plans are presented.

46312 ■ "Now You See It.." in Canadian Business (Vol. 81, November 10, 2008, No. 19, pp. 20)
Pub: Rogers Media Ltd.

Ed: Sharda Prashad. **Description:** Total return swaps were offered by Deutsche Bank AG and UBS AG to foreign investors for them to avoid paying taxes on the proceeds of their shares of Fording Canadian Coal Trust when Teck Cominco offered to buy the company. This means that the Canadian government is losing tax revenue from foreigners and it is argued that a simpler tax system would avoid this practice.

46313 ■ "Ohio Business Incentives Lag Offerings By Other States" in Crain's Cleveland Business (Vol. 30, May 18, 2009, No. 20, pp. 1)
Pub: Crain Communications, Inc.

Ed: Jay Miller. **Description:** Incentives designed to attract business and promote business expansion in Ohio has not done their job. According to a new study, despite tax changes made four years ago, the state's ability to attract new business has gone unchanged.

46314 ■ "On tap: More Could Get MEGA Credits; Need to Look Outside State May Be Cut" in Crain's Detroit Business (April 7, 2008)
Pub: Crain Communications, Inc.

Ed: Amy Lane. **Description:** In order to qualify for Michigan Economic Growth Authority tax credits Michigan businesses may no longer have to shop outside the state due to a new bill which has already passed the state Senate and will move on to the House; the bill, along with further changes to the MEGA program, is designed to provide incentives for investments that would add relevance and make Michigan more competitive.

46315 ■ "Ottawa Advised to Underwrite Carbon Technology" in Globe & Mail (March 10, 2007, pp. B3)
Pub: CTVglobemedia Publishing Inc.

Ed: Shawn McCarthy. **Description:** A federal panel's suggestion that carbon tax in Canada was not adequate to encourage oil companies and utilities to take up costly technologies to reduce carbon emissions is discussed.

46316 ■ "Ottawa Attacks!" in Canadian Business (Vol. 79, November 6, 2006, No. 22, pp. 21)
Pub: Rogers Media

Ed: Jeff Sanford. **Description:** The effects of new tax policy developed by Jim Flaherty, Finance Minister of Canada, on income trusts are presented.

46317 ■ Overcoming Barriers to Entrepreneurship in the United States
Pub: Lexington Books

Ed: Diana Furchtgott-Roth. **Released:** March 28, 2008. **Price:** $24.95. **Description:** Real and perceived barriers to the founding and running of small businesses in America are discussed. Each chapter outlines how policy and economic environments can hinder business owners and offers tips to overcome these obstacles. Starting with venture capital access in Silicon Valley during the Internet bubble, the book goes on to question the link between personal wealth and entrepreneurship, examines how federal tax rates affect small business creation and destruction, explains the low rate of self-employment among Mexican immigrants, and suggests ways pension coverage can be increased in small businesses.

46318 ■ Own Your Own Corporation: Why the Rich Own Their Own Companies and Everyone Else Works for Them
Pub: Business Plus

Ed: Garrett Sutton; Robert T. Kiyosaki; Ann Blackman. **Released:** June 2008. **Price:** $17.99 paperback. **Description:** Part of the Rich Dad Advisor's Series, this edition shows how individuals and their businesses to save thousands of dollars in taxes and protect against financial disaster.

46319 ■ "PA Tax Reforms See Some Progress" in Philadelphia Business Journal (Vol. 28, October 16, 2009, No. 35, pp. 1)
Pub: American City Business Journals

Ed: Athena D. Merritt. **Description:** It was reported that Pennsylvania's $27.8 billion budget arrived 101 days late, but business groups are encouraged that progress continues to be made on long-called-for tax reforms. The Research and Development Tax Credit, currently at $40 million, will drop to $20 million in 2009-2010.

46320 ■ "Pain Ahead as Profit Pressure Increases" in Crain's Chicago Business (Vol. 31, May 5, 2008, No. 18, pp. 4)
Pub: Crain Communications, Inc.

Ed: Daniel Rome Levine. **Description:** Interview with David Klaskin, the chairman and chief investment officer at Oak Ridge Investments LLC, who discusses the outlook for the economy and corporate earnings, particularly in the housing and auto industries, the impact of economic stimulus checks, the weakness of the dollar and recommendations of stocks that individual investors may find helpful.

46321 ■ "P&G vs. IRS: Split Decision" in Business Courier (Vol. 27, July 16, 2010, No. 11, pp. 1)
Pub: Business Courier

Ed: Jon Newberry. **Description:** Implications of a court ruling in a $435 million legal dispute between Procter & Gamble Company (P&G) and the Internal Revenue Service (IRS) are discussed. A $21 million win has been realized for P&G for its interpretation of research and development tax credits. However, the said case might involve more than $700 million in P&G tax deductions from 2001 through 2004 that the IRS had disallowed.

46322 ■ "P&L Building Owner Nears Start of $157M Condo Plan" in Business Journal-Serving Metropolitan Kansas City (November 23, 2007)
Pub: American City Business Journals, Inc.

Ed: Jim Davis. **Description:** The owner of Power and Light Building is ready to begin a $157 million plan to refurbish the Kansas City landmark and redevelop a property right next to it after receiving tax increment refinancing for the project.

46323 ■ "Paperless Bookkeeping Program" in Fleet Owner Online (February 15, 2011)
Pub: Penton Business Media Inc.

Description: TruckTax launched its new paperless bookkeeping system to help manage bookkeeping tasks, accounting and business tax information and filings for truckers.

46324 ■ "Pick and Save" in Entrepreneur (Vol. 36, April 2008, No. 4, pp. 66)
Pub: Entrepreneur Media, Inc.

Ed: C.J. Prince. **Description:** Business owners can purchase the needed big equipment to offset this year's expected profit. They can also switch to annualized computing of quarterly income and estimated tax payments to pay less estimated taxes for the first half of the year. Other tips on tax planning are provided.

46325 ■ "Pinellas Leaders Want First Leg of Light Rail" in The Business Journal-Serving Greater Tampa Bay (Vol. 28, August 8, 2008, No. 33)
Pub: American City Business Journals, Inc.

Ed: Larry Halstead. **Description:** Proposed routes for the first leg of the planned light railway system in the Tampa Bay, Florida area are being presented as the Tampa Bay Area Regional Transportation Authority is about to make its master plan for the project. A sales tax for transit is being proposed to fund the project, as well as an expansion of the accompanying bus system.

46326 ■ "Pioneers Get All The Perks" in Canadian Business (Vol. 81, March 3, 2008, No. 3, pp. 18)
Pub: Rogers Media

Description: Suncor Energy Inc. will face royalty payments from 25% to 30% of net profits as it signs a new deal with Alberta. Biovail Corp., meanwhile, is

under a U.S. grand jury investigation for supposed improprieties in Cardizem LA heart drug launch. The Conference Board of Canada's proposal to impose taxes on greenhouse gas emissions and other developments in the business community are discussed.

46327 ■ "Poor Economy Inspires Rich Alternatives In a Modern, and Tax-Free, Twist on Bartering" in Houston Chronicle (June 7, 2010)
Pub: Houston Chronicle Publishing Company

Ed: Michael Rubinkam. **Description:** Time banking helps individuals and firms receive goods or services by depositing time dollars into a bank reserved for receipt of goods and services.

46328 ■ PPC's Small Business Tax Guide
Pub: Practitioners Publishing Company

Ed: Douglas L. Weinbrenner, Virginia R. Bergman, Toni M. Greenwall, James A. Keller, Scott Mayfield, Linda A. Markwood. **Released:** January 2005. **Price:** $189.00. **Description:** Business tax laws are covered in an easy to understand format.

46329 ■ PPC's Small Business Tax Guide, Vol. 2
Pub: Practitioners Publishing Company

Ed: Douglas L. Weinbrenner, Virginia R. Bergman, Toni M. Greenwall, James A. Keller, Scott Mayfield, Linda A. Markwood. **Released:** January 2005. **Price:** $189.00. **Description:** Second volume containing technical guide covering business tax laws.

46330 ■ "Praise for Tax Cuts" in Canadian Business (Vol. 80, November 19, 2007, No. 23, pp. 16)
Pub: Rogers Media

Ed: Joe Castaldo. **Description:** A Compas Inc. survey found that most of the 158 business leaders polled are in favor of federal tax cuts. The findings revealed that the respondents gave an average of 74 percent to the mini-budget, an unusual score for a government initiative. Other opinions on the government's tax relief are presented.

46331 ■ Principles of Private Firm Valuation
Pub: John Wiley & Sons, Incorporated

Ed: Stanley J. Feldman. **Released:** April 2005. **Price:** $85.00. **Description:** Tools and techniques to correctly perform private firm valuation, including value and how to measure it, valuing control, determining the size of the marketability discount, creating transparency and the implications for value, the value of tax pass-through entities versus a C corporation, etc.

46332 ■ "Private Pitfalls" in Canadian Business (Vol. 80, October 22, 2007, No. 21, pp. 34)
Pub: Rogers Media

Ed: Al Rosen. **Description:** Guidelines on how minority shareholders can avoid drawbacks at the time of purchase, during ownership, and when selling shares are discussed; contractual protection, sales taxation and share price are also presented. Investment in a private company entails knowing the party you are buying share from.

46333 ■ "Proposed Transit Legislation" in Crain's Detroit Business (Vol. 24, October 6, 2008, No. 40, pp. 19)
Pub: Crain Communications, Inc.

Description: Breakdown of state Representative Marie Donigan's proposed transit legislation includes tax increment financing. Other pieces of the proposed legislation are examined.

46334 ■ QuickBooks Simple Start for Dummies
Pub: John Wiley and Sons, Inc.

Ed: Stephen L. Nelson. **Released:** October 2004. **Price:** $21.99. **Description:** Profile of Intuits new accounting software geared to micro businesses. Advice is offered on daily, monthly, and yearly accounting activities covering records, sales tax, and reports.

46335 ■ *QuickBooks X for Dummies* ■
Pub: John Wiley & Sons, Incorporated

Ed: Stephen L. Nelson. **Released:** November 2006. **Price:** $21.99. **Description:** Key features of Quick-Books software for small business are introduced. Invoicing and credit memos, recoding sales receipts, accounting, budgeting, taxes, payroll, financial reports, job estimating, billing, tracking, data backup, are among the features.

46336 ■ *"Quicken Starter Edition 2008" in Black Enterprise (Vol. 38, March 2008, No. 8, pp. 54)*
Pub: Earl G. Graves Publishing Co. Inc.

Ed: Sonya A. Donaldson. **Description:** Profile of Quicken Starter Edition 2008 offering programs that track spending; it will also categorize tax deductible expenses.

46337 ■ *"The Rabbi Trust" in Barron's (Vol. 88, March 24, 2008, No. 12, pp. 55)*
Pub: Dow Jones & Company, Inc.

Ed: Joseph F. Gelband. **Description:** Discusses a rabbi trust which is a method of deferring taxes on compensation allowed by the Internal Revenue Service. Funding of the trust is not considered taxable. Other regulations concerning tax deferment are also discussed.

46338 ■ *"Raising Money: the Bond that Lasts" in Entrepreneur (Vol. 35, October 2007, No. 10, pp. 73)*
Pub: Entrepreneur Media Inc.

Ed: Crystal Detamore-Rodman. **Description:** Tax-exempt bonds can be the solution to long-term financing needs of entrepreneurs. However, high initial costs may discourage some entrepreneurs to apply for these bonds, with transactions usually costing $3 mor more. How tax-exempt bonds work, and how rules vary with different states are discussed.

46339 ■ *"Real Estate Wheeling and Dealing Picks Up" in Business Journal Portland (Vol. 27, October 29, 2010, No. 35, pp. 1)*
Pub: Portland Business Journal

Ed: Wendy Culverwell. **Description:** LoopNet has listed 33 prominent commercial properties for sale in Portland, Oregon's real estate market. However, reasons for the sales rush are not totally clear, but speculations point to the end of the Bush tax cuts in 2010 that prompted real estate investors to close the deals and avoid the increase in capital gains taxes.

46340 ■ *"Red Tape Ties Detroit Housing Rehab Plan" in Crain's Detroit Business (Vol. 24, September 22, 2008, No. 38, pp. 1)*
Pub: Crain Communications Inc.

Ed: Ryan Beene. **Description:** Venture-capital firm Wilherst Oxford LLC is a Florida-based company that has purchased 300 inner-city homes which were in foreclosure in Detroit. Wilherst Oxford is asking the city to forgive the existing tax and utility liens so the firm can utilize the money for home improvements. The city, however, is reluctant but has stated that they are willing to negotiate.

46341 ■ *"Retailers, Your Will, and More" in Agency Sales Magazine (Vol. 39, July 2009, No. 7, pp. 46)*
Pub: MANA

Ed: Melvin H. Daskal. **Description:** IRS audit guide for small retail businesses is presented. Tips on how to make a will with multiple beneficiaries are discussed together with medical expenses that can not be deducted.

46342 ■ *Retire Dollar Smart* ■
Pub: Trafford Publishing

Ed: Jim Miller. **Released:** July 2006. **Price:** $25.99. **Description:** The difference between savings and investments and their importance is examined, along with four rules for converting good investments into even greater ones. Contingency plans for healthcare costs as well as ways to manage taxes on investments are discussed. Five methods to control the costs of investing and saving include the use of smart strategies; getting independent, accurate, complete

information; investing passively; asking for a discount; and taking off your blinders. Ten steps for designing a foolproof retirement investment portfolio are also provided.

46343 ■ *"Revenue Shortfall Leads to Budget Uncertainty" in Crain's Detroit Business (Vol. 24, March 10, 2008, No. 10, pp. 26)*
Pub: Crain Communications, Inc.

Ed: Amy Lane. **Description:** Michigan's current-year budget may face a $134 million shortfall due to such issues as lower-than-anticipated payment from a 1999 national settlement with the U.S. tobacco industry, overestimated growth in property-tax revenue, the impact of the federal stimulus package and the potential settlement of a Midland property-tax dispute. The governor's proposed budget for fiscal year for 2009 may face a $249.6 million shortfall.

46344 ■ *"S3 Entertainment Group Partners with WFW International for Film Services in Michigan" in Michigan Vue (July-August 2008)*
Pub: Entrepreneur Media Inc.

Description: William F. White (WFW), one of North America's largest production equipment providers has partnered with S3 Entertainment Group (S3EG), a Michigan-based full-service film production services company due to the new incentives package which currently offers the highest incentives in the United States, up to 42 percent. S3EG will actively store, lease, manage, distribute and sell WFW's equipment to the growing number of production teams that are filming in the state.

46345 ■ *"SABMiller Deal Hit by Tax Ruling" in Wall Street Journal Eastern Edition (November 21 , 2011, pp. B9)*
Pub: Dow Jones & Company Inc.

Ed: David Fickling, Simon Zekaria. **Description:** SABMiller PLC, the giant brewer in the United Kingdom, is acquiring Australian beer icon Foster's Group Ltd. for US$9.9 billion, but will have to come up with another A$582 million following a tax ruling by the Australian Taxation Office in order that shareholders of Foster's don't lose.

46346 ■ *"Sales Tax Proposed to Revive KRM" in Business Journal-Milwaukee (Vol. 25, October 26, 2007, No. 4, pp. A1)*
Pub: American City Business Journals, Inc.

Ed: Rich Kirchen. **Description:** City and county officials are proposing a $13 increase in rental car fees to finance the Kenosha-Racine-Milwaukee line. The Alliance of Cities proposed sales tax are backed by Milwaukee-area business groups, however it failed to generate support from the public.

46347 ■ *"Samsung 'Holding Breath" in Austin Business JournalInc. (Vol. 29, January 29, 2010, No. 47, pp. 1)*
Pub: American City Business Journals

Ed: Jacob Dirr. **Description:** Samsung Austin Semiconductor LLC entered into an incentives agreement with the State of Texas in 2005, which involved $230 million in tax breaks and public financing. Terms of the agreement have been met, but some are questioning whether the company will be able to meet its goals for the Austin operations in 2010.

46348 ■ *"Saratoga Eagle Project Quenches Thirst To Grow" in Business Review, Albany New York (Vol. 34, November 30, 2007, No. 35, pp. 3)*
Pub: American City Business Journals, Inc.

Ed: Robin K. Cooper. **Description:** Saratoga Eagle Sales and Service will be searching for contractors for the construction of its new beverage distribution center at the WJ Grande Industrial Park in Saratoga Springs, New York. The $8 million, 107,000 square foot facility is part of Saratoga Eagle's expansion plan. The company's growth in the Capital Region market and $1.3 million tax break are discussed.

46349 ■ *Sarbanes-Oxley for Small Businesses: Leveraging Compliance for Maximum Advantage* ■
Pub: John Wiley & Sons, Incorporated

Ed: Peggy M. Jackson. **Released:** November 2006. **Price:** $39.95. **Description:** Book lists five ways the Sarbane Oxley Act helps small businesses.

46350 ■ *Save $2000 to $8000 in Taxes with a Home-Based Business* ■
Pub: TKG Publishing

Ed: Greco Garcia. **Released:** February 2007. **Price:** $16.99. **Description:** Tax advice for a home-based business is given.

46351 ■ *Schaum's Outline Financial Management, Third Edition* ■
Pub: McGraw-Hill

Ed: Jae K. Shim; Joel G. Siegel. **Released:** May 2007. **Price:** $22.95 (CND). **Description:** Rules and regulations governing corporate finance, including the Sarbanes-Oxley Act are discussed.

46352 ■ *"Seasonal Franchises" in Franchising World (Vol. 42, August 2010, No. 8, pp. 50)*
Pub: International Franchise Association

Ed: Jennifer Lemcke. **Description:** Seasonal franchises, such as tax businesses can be slow during the summer months. Restaurants are slow during the months of January and February. The various challenges faced by seasonal franchises are examined.

46353 ■ *"SEC Extends Small Business Deadline for SOX Audit Requirement" in HRMagazine (Vol. 53, August 2008, No. 8, pp. 20)*
Pub: Society for Human Resource Management
Contact: Henry G. Jackson, President
E-mail: hjackson@shrm.org

Description: Securities and Exchange Commission has approved a one-year extension of the compliance date for smaller public companies to meet the Section 404(b) auditor attestation requirement of the Sarbanes-Oxley Act.

46354 ■ *The Secret of Exiting Your Business Under Your Terms!* ■
Pub: Outskirts Press, Incorporated

Ed: Gene H. Irwin. **Released:** August 2005. **Price:** $29.95. **Description:** Topics include how to sell a business for the highest value, tax laws governing the sale of a business, finding the right buyer, mergers and acquisitions, negotiating the sale, and using a limited auction to increase future value of a business.

46355 ■ *Self-Employed Tax Solutions: Quick, Simple, Money-Saving, Audit-Proof Tax and Recordkeeping Basics* ■
Pub: The Globe Pequot Press

Ed: June Walker. **Released:** January 1, 2009. **Price:** $17.95. **Description:** A simple system for maintaining tax records and filing tax forms for any small business is explored.

46356 ■ *"Senate Bill Would Eliminate MBT Surcharge in 2011" in Crain's Detroit Business (Vol. 24, April 7, 2008, No. 14, pp. 33)*
Pub: Crain Communications, Inc.

Ed: Amy Lane. **Description:** Discusses possible changes to the new Michigan Business Tax, including a proposed bill which would phase out a 21.99 percent surcharge on the tax.

46357 ■ *"Several Studio Projects in Production" in Crain's Detroit Business (Vol. 26, January 18, 2010, No. 3, pp. 21)*
Pub: Crain Communications Inc.

Ed: Bill Shea. **Description:** Overview of several projects in development in the metro Detroit area due to Michigan's film industry incentives which include a 25 percent tax credit for infrastructure projects.

46358 ■ *"Shear Profit" in Crain's Cleveland Business (Vol. 28, October 29, 2007, No. 43, pp. 3)*
Pub: Crain Communications, Inc.

Ed: David Bennett. **Description:** Alpaca farms are becoming a very profitable business for a number of Northeast Ohio entrepreneurs due to the high return on initial investments, tax incentives and the rise in demand for the animals. Ohio leads the country in the number of alpaca farms with roughly one-third located in Northeast Ohio.

46359 ■ A Simplified Guide to Small Business Tax Deductions
Pub: Frontline Publishers, Incorporated
Ed: Gladson I. Nwanna. **Released:** December 2005. **Price:** $39.99. **Description:** An overview of federal tax deductions allowed for small businesses; also lists tax schedules and forms and the line to claim the deductions.

46360 ■ "Single Most Important Problem" in Small Business Economic Trends (September 2010, pp. 18)
Pub: National Federation of Independent Business
Ed: William C. Dunkelberg, Holly Wade. **Description:** A table of the single most important problem among small businesses surveyed in the U.S. in August 2010 is presented. 'Poor sales' was selected by 31 percent of firms as the single most important problem, followed by taxes at 21 percent. Graphs comparing selected single most important problem from January 1986 to August 2010 are also provided.

46361 ■ "Single Most Important Problem" in Small Business Economic Trends (July 2010, pp. 18)
Pub: National Federation of Independent Business
Description: A table showing the single most important problem among small businesses surveyed in the U.S. for June 2010 is presented. Poor sales was selected by 30 percent of firms as the single most important problem, followed by taxes and government requirements and red tape. Graphs comparing selected single most important problem from January 1986 to June 2010 are also given.

46362 ■ "Small-Business Agenda: Increase Capital, Education, Tax Breaks" in Crain's Detroit Business (Vol. 24, March 17, 2008)
Pub: Crain Communications, Inc.
Ed: Nancy Kaffer. **Description:** Discusses the policy suggestions detailed in the Small Business Association of Michigan's entrepreneurial agenda which include five main categories of focus: making entrepreneurial education a higher state priority; increasing capital available to entrepreneurs; using the state's tax structure as an incentive for entrepreneurial growth; getting university research from the lab to the market; and limiting government regulation that's burdensome to small businesses and getting legislative support of entrepreneurial assistance efforts.

46363 ■ Small Business Desk Reference
Pub: Penguin Books USA Inc.
Ed: Gene Marks. **Released:** December 2004. **Description:** Comprehensive guide for starting or running a successful small business, focusing on buying a business or franchise, writing a business plan, financial management, accounting, legal issues, human resources management, operations, marketing, sales, customer service, taxes, insurance, and ethics. Information for launching a restaurant, property management firm, retail outlet, consulting firm, and service business is included.

46364 ■ Small Business Legal Tool Kit
Pub: Entrepreneur Press
Ed: Ira Nottonson; Theresa A. Pickner. **Released:** May 2007. **Price:** $36.95. **Description:** Legal expertise is provided by two leading entrepreneurial attorneys. Issues covered include forming and operating a business: taxes, contracts, leases, bylaws, trademarks, small claims court, etc.

46365 ■ Small Business Management
Pub: John Wiley & Sons, Incorporated
Ed: Margaret Burlingame. **Released:** March 2007. **Price:** $44.95. **Description:** Advice for starting and running a small business as well as information on the value and appeal of small businesses, is given. Topics include budgets, taxes, inventory, ethics, e-commerce, and current laws.

46366 ■ The Small Business Start-Up Kit for California
Pub: NOLO
Ed: Peri Pakroo. **Released:** March 2008. **Price:** $29.99. **Description:** Handbook covering all aspects of starting a business in California, including information about necessary fees, forms, and taxes.

46367 ■ Small Business Survival Guide: Starting, Protecting, and Securing Your Business for Long-Term Success
Pub: Adams Media Corporation
Ed: Cliff Ennico. **Released:** September 2005. **Price:** $12.95 (US), $17.95 (Canadian). **Description:** Entrepreneurship in the new millennium. Topics include creditors, taxes, competition, business law, and accounting.

46368 ■ Small Business Tax Deductions 2006
Pub: Continuing Education of the Bar-California
Ed: Stephen Fishman. **Released:** June 2006. **Price:** $99.00. **Description:** Allowable tax deductions for small business in 2006 are explained.

46369 ■ Small Business Taxes 2006: Your Complete Guide to a Better Bottom Line
Pub: John Wiley & Sons, Incorporated
Ed: Barbara Weltman. **Released:** November 2008. **Price:** $18.95. **Description:** Detailed information on new tax laws and IRS rules for small businesses.

46370 ■ Small Business Taxes Made Easy: How to Increase Your Deductions, Reduce What You Owe, and Boost Your Profits
Pub: McGraw-Hill Companies Inc.
Contact: Deven Sharma, President
Ed: Eva Rosenberg. **Released:** December 2004. **Price:** $16.95. **Description:** Tax expert gives advice to small business owners regarding tax issues. TaxMamma.com, run by Eva Rosenberg, is one of the top seven tax advice Websites on the Internet.

46371 ■ "Small Business Unsure of Impact of New Tax Law" in Crain's Detroit Business (Vol. 23, October 15, 2007, No. 42, pp. 13)
Pub: Crain Communications Inc. - Detroit
Ed: Sheena Harrison. **Description:** Small business owners in Michigan are concerned with issues surrounding the proposed increases in state taxes geared at small business, which includes a 6 percent service tax.

46372 ■ "Small Businesses Benefiting from Movie-Struck Hub" in Boston Business Journal (Vol. 27, October 12, 2007, No. 37, pp. 1)
Pub: American City Business Journals Inc.
Ed: Naomi R. Kooker. **Description:** Revision of the Massachusetts' film tax credits has attracted filming of major motion pictures in the state and local businesses have benefited. A list of businesses that saw boosts from the movie-making industry's presence is presented.

46373 ■ Small Time Operator: How to Start Your Own Business, Keep Your Books, Pay Your Taxes, and Stay Out of Trouble
Pub: Bell Springs Publishing
Ed: Bernard B. Kamoroff. **Released:** January 2008. **Price:** $18.95. **Description:** Comprehensive guide for starting any kind of business.

46374 ■ Smart Tax Write-Offs, 5th Ed.
Pub: Rayve Productions, Inc.
Ed: Norm Ray. **Released:** February 2008. **Price:** $15.95. **Description:** Guidebook to help small business owners take advantage of legitimate tax deductions for home-based and other entrepreneurial businesses.

46375 ■ "Smart Year-End Tax Moves" in Business Owner (Vol. 35, November-December 2011, No. 6, pp. 8)
Pub: DL Perkins Company
Description: Managing small business and individual taxes is more important in a bad economy. It is imperative to seek all tax incentives that apply to your business.

46376 ■ "A Smarter Kind of Taxes" in Canadian Business (Vol. 80, October 8, 2007, No. 20, pp. 203)
Pub: Rogers Media
Ed: Jack Mintz. **Description:** Forecasts on Canada's tax system by 2020 are analyzed. It is expected that the country's aging society will place great demands on elderly-related spending such as pensions and healthcare. And, since the elderly pay fewer taxes,

the revenue available to the government will be reduced. Other trends also show that several factors will cause significant change to the country's tax system.

46377 ■ "A Socko Payout Menu: Rural Phone Carrier Plots to Supercharge Its Shares" in Barron's (Vol. 88, June 30, 2008, No. 26, pp. M5)
Pub: Dow Jones & Co., Inc.
Ed: Shirley A. Lazo. **Description:** CenturyTel boosted its quarterly common payout to 70 cents from 6.75 cents per share due to its strong cash flows and solid balance sheet. Eastman Kodak's plan for a buyback will be partially funded by its $581 million tax refund. CME Group will buyback stocks through 2009 worth $1.1 billion.

46378 ■ "Solace for the Freshly Flaherty'd" in Canadian Business (Vol. 79, November 6, 2006, No. 22, pp. 114)
Pub: Rogers Media
Ed: Ian McGugan. **Description:** Tips to manage investments with relation to cash distribution tax on income trusts are presented.

46379 ■ "Solar Credit Lapse Spur Late Demand" in The Business Journal - Serving Phoenix and the Valley of the Sun (Vol. 28, July 18, 2008)
Pub: American City Business Journals, Inc.
Ed: Patrick O'Grady. **Description:** Businesses looking to engage in the solar energy industry are facing the problems of taxation and limited solar panel supply. Solar panels manufacturers are focusing more on the European market. Political issues surrounding the federal tax credit policy on solar energy users are also discussed.

46380 ■ "Solutions to Family Business Problems" in Contractor (Vol. 56, October 2009, No. 10, pp. 51)
Pub: Penton Media, Inc.
Ed: Irv Blackman. **Description:** Several common business problems that family owned firms face are presented together with their solutions. These problems include giving the children stock bonus options while another discusses the tax burden when a father wants to transfer the business to his son.

46381 ■ "Something to Like" in Canadian Business (Vol. 81, April 14, 2008, No. 6, pp. 22)
Pub: Rogers Media
Ed: Jack Mintz. **Description:** Jim Flaherty's policy on tax-free savings account (TFSA) will allow Canadians to accumulate wealth at a much faster rate and these accounts could be especially good for people who are subject to high effective taxes on savings. Investors should put their money into a Registered Retirement Savings Plan (RRSP) when it comes to risky investments but the TFSA is better than an RRSP if investors expect very high taxes on withdrawals from their RRSP.

46382 ■ "Spending on Innovation Down Sharply in State" in Crain's Detroit Business (Vol. 24, March 10, 2008, No. 10, pp. 7)
Pub: Crain Communications, Inc.
Ed: Chad Halcom. **Description:** Due to such issues as Michigan's uncertain tax structure, a shaky national economy, the credit crunch and mortgage lending crisis, investments in innovation for the state have sharply declined.

46383 ■ "Stadium Developers Seek a Win With the State" in The Business Journal-Serving Metropolitan Kansas City (Vol. 26, August 22, 2008)
Pub: American City Business Journals, Inc.
Ed: Rob Roberts. **Description:** Three Trails Redevelopment LLC is hoping to win $30 million in state tax credits from the Missouri Development Finance Board for the construction of an 18,500-seat Wizards stadium. The project is contingent on state tax incentives and the company remains optimistic about their goal.

46384 ■ *Starting and Running Your Own Horse Business*
Pub: Storey Publishing, LLC
Ed: Mary Ashby McDonald. **Released:** November 1, 2009. **Price:** $19.95. **Description:** Insight into starting and running a successful equestrian business is given. The book covers safety, tips for operating a riding school or horse camp, strategies for launching a carriage business, along with tax and insurance advice.

46385 ■ *"State Aviation Fuel Tax Proposal Runs Into Turbulence" in Crain's Detroit Business (Vol. 25, June 15, 2009, No. 24, pp. 5)*
Pub: Crain Communications Inc. - Detroit
Ed: Amy Lane. **Description:** Delta Airlines Inc. is concerned about a proposal that would change the way Michigan taxes aviation fuel. The plan would go from the current cents-per-gallon tax to a percentage tax on the wholesale price of fuel, which would raise the taxes significantly.

46386 ■ *"State Expects Increase of $50 Million from Film Bills; Come Back, Al Roker" in Crain's Detroit Business (March 24, 2008)*
Pub: Crain Communications, Inc.
Ed: Bill Shea. **Description:** Overview of the new film initiative and its incentives designed to entice more film work to Michigan; the measures could bring $50 million to $100 million in movie production work for the rest of this year compared to the $4 million total the state saw last year. Also discusses the show 'DEA' which was filmed in Detroit and stars Al Roker.

46387 ■ *"State Film Business Tops $1.3 Billion" in The Business Journal-Portland (Vol. 25, August 22, 2008, No. 24, pp. 1)*
Pub: American City Business Journals, Inc.
Ed: Andy Giegerich. **Description:** Oregon's film industry has generated $1.39 billion in direct and indirect economic impact in 2007, a 55 percent rise from 2005 levels. The growth of the industry is attributed to tax incentives issued in 2007, which attracted film production companies from other states.

46388 ■ *"State Lawmakers Should Try Raising Jobs, Not Taxes" in Crain's Chicago Business (Vol. 31, March 24, 2008, No. 12, pp. 20)*
Pub: Crain Communications, Inc.
Ed: Diug Whitley. **Description:** According to U.S. Department of Labor figures through December 2007, Illinois has ranked 45th in the nation for job growth for seven straight months. Many feel that the state would not need to raise taxes if they spent more time working to keep and attract employers that create jobs.

46389 ■ *"State Reaps $440M with Small-Biz Tax Crackdown" in Boston Business Journal (Vol. 27, October 19, 2007, No. 38, pp. 1)*
Pub: American City Business Journals, Inc.
Ed: Lisa van der Pool. **Description:** Massachusetts Department of Revenue has generated $440 million from businesses who have not filed or paid enough taxes. Discover Tax is a database program that targets tax evaders. Small businesses are impacted by this system most.

46390 ■ *"Statistical Data of Interest" in Business Owner (Vol. 35, July-August 2011, No. 4, pp. 7)*
Pub: DL Perkins Company
Description: Sources of federal tax revenue are presented; payroll taxes, 36 percent; corporate income tax, 12 percent, other 4 percent, excise taxes, 3 percent, individual income tax, 45 percent.

46391 ■ *"Super Bowl Events Get Tax Breaks" in Business Journal-Serving Phoenix and the Valley of the Sun (Vol. 7, October 12, 2007, No. 28)*
Pub: American City Business Journals, Inc.
Ed: Mike Sunnucks. **Description:** Cities of Glendale and Phoenix, Arizona increased sales taxes in September 2007 and have issued tax exemptions for professional sporting events like the Super Bowl. Phoenix is planning to exempt events included in the

2009 NBA All-Star Game. National Football League's tax abatement requirement to cities hosting the Super Bowl is discussed.

46392 ■ *"Surviving an IRS Audit: Tips for Small Businesses" in Agency Sales Magazine (Vol. 39, July 2009, No. 7, pp. 52)*
Pub: MANA
Ed: Joshua D. Mosshart. **Description:** It is a good idea to enlist the services of a tax professional even if an audit is expected to go smoothly since the IRS is likely to scrutinize the unreported income and personal as well as business expenses of a small business during an audit.

46393 ■ *"Suspense Hangs Over Fledging Film Industry" in Crain's Detroit Business (Vol. 26, January 18, 2010, No. 3, pp. 3)*
Pub: Crain Communications, Inc.
Ed: Bill Shea. **Description:** Overview of the film incentive package which has fostered a growth in the industry with 52 productions completed in 2009, bringing in $223.6 million in gross in-state production expenditures of which the state will refund $87.2 million. Opposition to the incentives has been growing among legislatures who believe that the initiatives cost more than they ultimately bring into the state. Experts believe that the initiatives will remain since they have already fostered economic growth and are good for the state's image.

46394 ■ *"Sweet Harmony" in Canadian Business (Vol. 82, April 27, 2009, No. 7, pp. 6)*
Pub: Rogers Media
Description: Canada will harmonize its 5 percent federal goods and services tax wit the 8 percent provincial sales tax effective July 1, 2010. Meanwhile, provinces like Ontario and Quebec have switched the sales taxes that are charged in new investments into a value-added tax. The conversion has led to an 11 percent increase in investments in Quebec and the three other provinces that made the conversion.

46395 ■ *"Take the Wheel: the Pension Protection Act Doesn't Mean You Can Sit Back and Relax" in Black Enterprise (October 2007)*
Pub: Earl G. Graves Publishing Co. Inc.
Ed: Mellody Hobson. **Description:** Pension Protection Act provides multiple benefits and tax advantages for retirement, however the investment options and contribution rates are very conservative.

46396 ■ *"Tax Abatement Changes Seen as Home Run for Cleveland Condo Market" in Crain's Cleveland Business (Vol. 30, June 15, 2009, No. 23)*
Pub: Crain Communications, Inc.
Ed: Jay Miller. **Description:** Condominium ownership became a bit more affordable for Cleveland residents since changes in both state and local tax abatement policy changes. The tax credits are examined.

46397 ■ *"Tax Credit Crunch" in Miami Daily Business Review (March 26, 2008)*
Pub: ALM Media Inc.
Ed: Paula Iuspa-Abbott. **Description:** Uncertainty is growing over the future of the low-income housing project in South Florida and the tax credit program that helps fuel the projects.

46398 ■ *"Tax Deal Yields Polaris Offices" in Business First-Columbus (October 26, 2007, pp. A1)*
Pub: American City Business Journals, Inc.
Ed: Brian R. Ball. **Description:** Speculation on a possible office building construction is increasing with the expansion of tax incentives to build at the Polaris Centers of Commerce. Details of community reinvestment in the Columbus, Ohio area along with possible 15-year 100 percent tax abatements for Polaris office buildings are discussed.

46399 ■ *"Tax-Free Zones Need Shows; Out-of-State Shoppers Are Key To Success" in Crain's Detroit Business (Vol. 24, January*

28, 2008, No. 4)
Pub: Crain Communications Inc. - Detroit
Ed: Daniel Duggan. **Description:** Sales tax-free zones are being considered by Michigan's legislators in order to promote the state as a conference destination.

46400 ■ *"Tax Reform Analysis: Reforms Equal Smaller 401(k)s" in Employee Benefit News (Vol. 25, December 1, 2011, No. 15, pp. 19)*
Pub: SourceMedia Inc.
Ed: Lisa V. Gillespie. **Description:** According to a new analysis by the Employee Benefit Research Institute, two recent proposals to change existing tax treatment of 401(k) retirement plans could cost workers because they would lower their account balances towards retirement.

46401 ■ *Tax Savvy for Small Business*
Pub: NOLO
Ed: Frederick W. Daily. **Released:** November 2006. **Price:** $36.99. **Description:** Strategies to help small business owners claim all legitimate deductions and keep accurate records.

46402 ■ *Tax Savvy for Small Business: Year-Round Tax Strategies to Save You Money*
Pub: NOLO
Ed: Frederick W. Daily, Bethany K. Laurence. **Released:** September 2005. **Price:** $36.99. **Description:** Tax strategies for small business. Includes the latest tax numbers and laws as well as current Internal Revenue Service forms and publications.

46403 ■ *Tax Smarts for Small Business*
Pub: Sourcebooks, Inc.
Contact: Len Vlahos, President
E-mail: dominique@sourcebooks.com
Ed: James O. Parker. **Released:** December 2006. **Price:** $27.95. **Description:** Tax guide for small businesses.

46404 ■ *"Tax Talk; Usual Election-Year Obstacles to Income Tax May Not Apply This Time" in Crain's Chicago Business (March 24, 2008)*
Pub: Crain Communications, Inc.
Ed: Greg Hinz. **Description:** Discusses the possible raising of the state's income tax; The latest version of the income tax hike bill, sponsored by Senator James Meeks, D-Chicago, would boost individual rates to 5 percent from 3 percent, with the corporate rate rising to a total of 8 percent from 4.8 percent; about $3 billion of the projected $8 billion that would be brought in would be used to cut local property taxes and experts believe the business community overall would benefit.

46405 ■ *"Tax Thriller in D.C." in Barron's (Vol. 90, August 30, 2010, No. 35, pp. 17)*
Pub: Barron's Editorial & Corporate Headquarters
Ed: Jim McTague. **Description:** There are speculations on how Senator Harry Reid can push his bill to raise taxes on the wealthy while retaining the George W. Bush tax rates for the rest. Reid's challenge is to get the 60 votes needed to pass the bill.

46406 ■ *"Taxes, Right-To-Work Top West Michigan Concerns" in Crain's Detroit Business (Vol. 24, September 22, 2008, No. 38, pp. 6)*
Pub: Crain Communications Inc.
Ed: Amy Lane. **Description:** Two of the top priorities of business leaders in Western Michigan are the new business tax which they want to end as well as making the state a 'right-to-work' one through laws to prohibit unions from requiring workers to pay dues and membership as a condition of their employment.

46407 ■ *"Taxing Position: Yoga Studios Hit for Back Sales Tax" in Puget Sound Business Journal (Vol. 29, August 29, 2008, No. 19, pp. 1)*
Pub: American City Business Journals
Ed: Deirdre Gregg. **Description:** Several yoga studies were audited and told they owe several years worth of back taxes. A spokesman from the Washing-

ton Department of Revenue stated the yoga studies should be collecting the tax in general and that yoga classes given for the purpose of physical fitness are taxable.

46408 ■ *"A Taxing Proposition"* in *Black Enterprise* (Vol. 37, January 2007, No. 6, pp. 6)
Pub: Earl G. Graves Publishing Co. Inc.
Description: Learn how to avoid tax problems on Black Enterprise's website, blackenterprise.com.

46409 ■ *"Taxpayer Says a Simple Thank-You Would Help"* in *Boston Business Journal* (Vol. 27, November 16, 2007, No. 42, pp. 1)
Pub: American City Business Journals, Inc.
Ed: Jesse Noyes. **Description:** Bill Freza founded the ThankTheTaxpayer.org, a Website and incorporated organization. The non-partisan group aims to induce gratitude and civility as a tax reform and attitude among taxpayers, particularly those in the top wage category.

46410 ■ *"Taxpayers' Banks Share Even Higher"* in *Business Courier* (Vol. 24, October 26, 2008, No. 28, pp. 1)
Pub: American City Business Journals, Inc.
Ed: Dan Monk; Lucy May. **Description:** Banks Working Group originally announced that it needs $106 million in public funds to build the Banks riverfront development but then declared it needs $45 million more from Cincinnati and Hamilton County after it approved a deal for the project. It would not be easy for the city and the county to come up with the money but many decision-makers think it's worth it.

46411 ■ *"Tech Tax Heroes Go from Political Neophytes to Savvy Fundraisers"* in *Baltimore Business Journal* (Vol. 27, November 20, 2009, No. 28)
Pub: American City Business Journals
Ed: Scott Dance. **Description:** A group of computer services and information technology executives in Maryland have arranged a private dinner that will function as a fundraiser for Governor Martin O'Malley and Lieutenant Governor Anthony Brown. The event is seen as an effort to ensure the industry's involvement in the state after fighting for the repeal of the tech tax in 2007.

46412 ■ *"Tempel Steel To Expand Its Chicago Plant"* in *Chicago Tribune* (August 22, 2008)
Pub: McClatchy-Tribune Information Services
Ed: James P. Miller. **Description:** Tempel Steel Co. is no longer considering transferring a Libertyville factory's production to Mexico; the company has responded to government incentives and will instead shift that work to its plant on Chicago's North Side.

46413 ■ *"Test Your Structural Integrity"* in *Entrepreneur* (Vol. 37, August 2009, No. 8, pp. 60)
Pub: Entrepreneur Media, Inc.
Ed: Jennifer Lawler. **Description:** Tax considerations can be important when choosing a business structure. For example, profits are taxed to the corporation in a C corp while profits are taxed only once at an S corp or a limited liability company. Meeting a tax professional should be done prior to switching to a different structure.

46414 ■ *"That Vision Thing"* in *Canadian Business* (Vol. 80, December 25, 2006, No. 1, pp. 78)
Pub: Rogers Media
Description: Suggestions for better Canadian tax policy and making airspace competitive among other things, to improve the economy in 2007, are presented.

46415 ■ *"They're Hopping Mad"* in *Canadian Business* (Vol. 80, October 22, 2007, No. 21, pp. 20)
Pub: Rogers Media
Description: Alberta Review Panel is calling for a 20 percent increase in oil and gas development taxes. SABMiller and Molson Coors Brewing Company combined its U.S. and Puerto Rican operations,

though the deal is still subject to regulatory approvals. Montreal Exchange Inc. filed for approval of the trade of Montreal Climate Exchange futures contracts.

46416 ■ *"Three Trails Blazes Tax Credit Deal"* in *The Business Journal-Serving Metropolitan Kansas City* (Vol. 27, November 7, 2008, No. 9)
Pub: American City Business Journals, Inc.
Ed: Rob Roberts. **Description:** Three Trails Redevelopment LLC plans to redevelop the Bannister Mall area. The Missouri Development Finance Board is expected to approve $30 million in tax credits for the project. A verbal agreement on the terms and conditions has already been reached according to the agency's executive director.

46417 ■ *"Time to Engage Europe"* in *Canadian Business* (Vol. 79, June 19, 2006, No. 13, pp. 19)
Pub: Rogers Media
Ed: Jack Mintz. **Description:** European and Canadian governments improved their trade and investment relations with the March 18, 2004 frame work to develop a Trade and Investment Enhancement Agreement. Still there is lot of opportunities to solve tax and trade issues.

46418 ■ *"Time for State Tax Restructure?"* in *Crain's Detroit Business* (Vol. 26, January 18, 2010, No. 3, pp. 3)
Pub: Crain Communications Inc.
Ed: Amy Lane. **Description:** Business Leaders for Michigan, a statewide CEO group, launched a proposal to cut the Michigan Business Tax by about $1.1 billion and replace the revenue by taxing services. Statistical data included.

46419 ■ *"To Be or Not To Be an S Corporation"* in *Modern Machine Shop* (Vol. 84, September 2011, No. 4, pp. 38)
Pub: Gardner Business Media, Inc.
Contact: Richard G. Kline, President
E-mail: rkline@gardnerweb.com
Ed: Irving L. Blackman. **Description:** The definitions of both C corporations and S corporations are defined to help any machine shop discover which best suits the owner's business plan.

46420 ■ *Top Tax Savings Ideas: How to Survive in Today's Tough Tax Environment*
Pub: Entrepreneur Press
Ed: Thomas J. Stemmy. **Released:** March 2004.
Price: $18.95 (US), $26.95 (Canadian). **Description:** Tax deductions, fringe benefits, and tax deferrals for small businesses.

46421 ■ *"Tourism Bureau Seeks Hotel Tax Hike"* in *Baltimore Business Journal* (Vol. 27, December 18, 2009, No. 32, pp. 1)
Pub: American City Business Journals
Ed: Rachel Bernstein. **Description:** Baltimore, Maryland's tourism agency, Visit Baltimore, has proposed a new hotel tax that could produce $2 million annually for its marketing budget, fund improvements to the city's 30-year-old convention center and help it compete for World Cup soccer games. Baltimore hotel leaders discuss the new tax.

46422 ■ *"Tourism Push Rising in Fall"* in *Philadelphia Business Journal* (Vol. 30, August 26, 2011, No. 28, pp. 1)
Pub: American City Business Journals Inc.
Ed: Peter Van Allen. **Description:** Philadelphia is offering events for tourists this fall despite massive cuts for tourism promotion. Governor Tim Corbet slashed $5.5 million in funding for the state's tourism-promotion agencies which received $32 million in 2009. The agencies were forced to cooperate and fend for themselves using the hotel taxes that sustain them.

46423 ■ *"The Trader's Edge"* in *Barron's* (Vol. 88, March 31, 2008, No. 13, pp. 56)
Pub: Dow Jones & Company, Inc.
Ed: Dan McGuire. **Description:** There is a $3,000 a year annual limit to deducting investor's losses and normal investment expenses are purportedly deductible as miscellaneous expenses on Schedule A only to the extent that they exceed two percent of adjusted

gross income. Professional gamblers who can use Schedule C are unable deduct a net gaming loss against income from any other sources.

46424 ■ *"Tradeshow Attendance Incentives Add Up"* in *Pet Product News* (Vol. 64, December 2010, No. 12, pp. 14)
Pub: BowTie Inc.
Ed: Mark E. Battersby. **Description:** Pointers on how pet specialty retailers can claim business travel tax and income tax deductions for expenses paid or incurred in participation at tradeshows, conventions, and meetings are presented. Incentives in form of these deductions could allow pet specialty retailers to gain business benefits, aside from the education and enjoyment involved with the travel.

46425 ■ *"Traditional VS. Roth IRA"* in *Black Enterprise* (Vol. 37, October 2006, No. 3, pp. 58)
Pub: Earl G. Graves Publishing Co. Inc.
Ed: K. Parker; Carolyn M. Brown. **Description:** Government taxes the traditional IRAs different than it taxes Roth IRAs.

46426 ■ *"Transborder Short-Sea Shipping: Hurdles Remain"* in *Canadian Sailings* (June 30, 2008)
Pub: UBM Global Trade
Contact: Leonard J. Corallo, President
Ed: Kathlyn Horibe. **Description:** Legislation that would exempt non-bulk commercial cargo by water in the Great Lakes region from U.S. taxation is discussed.

46427 ■ *"Travel Tears"* in *Crain's Chicago Business* (Vol. 31, November 17, 2008, No. 46, pp. 3)
Pub: Crain Communications, Inc.
Ed: Bob Tita. **Description:** Hotels, restaurants and conventions are seeing a decline in profits due to corporate travel cutbacks and the sagging economy. City and state revenues derived from taxes on tourism-related industries are also suffering.

46428 ■ *"Trust Tax Under Fire as Drain on Revenue"* in *Globe & Mail* (April 9, 2007, pp. B1)
Pub: CTVglobemedia Publishing Inc.
Ed: Steven Chase. **Description:** The economic aspects of the implementation of the trust levy by the Canadian government are discussed. The acquisition of Canadian income trusts by Canadian and international financial institutions is described.

46429 ■ *Ultimate Small Business Advisor*
Pub: Entrepreneur Press
Ed: Andi Axman. **Released:** May 2007. **Price:** $30.95. **Description:** Tip for starting and running a small business, including new tax rulings and laws affecting small business, are shared.

46430 ■ *"Unemployment Tax Surge Could Hit Businesses Hard"* in *Orlando Business Journal* (Vol. 26, January 1, 2010, No. 31, pp. 1)
Pub: American City Business Journals
Ed: Christopher Boyd. **Description:** Consequences of the almost 1,100 percent increase in Florida's minimum unemployment compensation insurance tax to businesses in the state are discussed. Employers pay for the said tax, which is used to fund the state's unemployment claims.

46431 ■ *"U.S. Buyer Rescues KCP From Trust Tax Burden"* in *Globe & Mail* (April 3, 2007, pp. B1)
Pub: CTVglobemedia Publishing Inc.
Ed: Richard Blackwell. **Description:** The economic aspects of the buyout of KCP Income Fund by Caxton-Iseman Capital Inc. are discussed.

46432 ■ *United States Taxes and Tax Policy*
Pub: Cambridge University Press
Contact: Richard Ziemacki, President
E-mail: rziemacki@cambridge.org
Ed: David G. Davies. **Released:** January 22, 2010.
Price: $34.99. **Description:** This book expands the information on taxes found in public finance texts by

using a combination of institutional, factual, theoretical and empirical information. It also stresses the economic effects of taxes and tax policy.

46433 ■ "Up In the Air" in The Business Journal-Serving Greater Tampa Bay (Vol. 28, July 18, 2008, No. 30, pp. 1)
Pub: American City Business Journals, Inc.
Ed: Margie Manning. **Description:** Views and information on Busch Gardens and on its future, are presented. The park's 3,769 employees worry for their future, after tourism industry experts have expressed concerns on possible tax cuts and other cost reductions. The future of the park, which ranks number 19 as the most visited park in the world, is expected to have a major impact on the tourism industry.

46434 ■ "VC Tax Almost Gone" in Business Journal-Portland (Vol. 24, November 23, 2007, No. 38, pp. 1)
Pub: American City Business Journals, Inc.
Ed: Aliza Earnshaw. **Description:** Portland Revenue Bureau's proposal to repeal a business income tax is scheduled to be approved by the Portland City Council and Multnomah County Council. Despite the good decision on the part of the city, the removal of the tax policy is not a guarantee that venture capital firms will relocate to the city.

46435 ■ "Venture Gap" in Canadian Business (Vol. 81, March 17, 2008, No. 4, pp. 82)
Pub: Rogers Media
Ed: Joe Castaldo. **Description:** Money raised by Canadian venture capitalist firms has been declining since 2001. A strong venture capital market is important if Canada is to build innovative companies. Fixing Canada's tax policy on foreign investments is a start in reviving the industry.

46436 ■ "Verizon Comes Calling With 500 Jobs" in Business First Columbus (Vol. 25, September 15, 2008, No. 4, pp. 1)
Pub: American City Business Journals
Ed: Brian R. Ball. **Description:** Hilliard, Ohio offered Verizon Wireless a 15-year incentive package worth $3.4 million for the company to move 300 customer financial services jobs to the city in addition to the 200 jobs from their facility in Dublin, Ohio. The incentives include a return of 15 percent of the income tax generated by the jobs.

46437 ■ "Wanted: Angels in the Country" in Austin Business JournalInc. (Vol. 28, July 18, 2008, No. 18, pp. 1)
Pub: American City Business Journals
Ed: Laura Hipp. **Description:** A proposal is being pushed forward by managers of Texas' Emerging Technology Fund to create an angel investors' network. The proposal is asking that tax credits for those who invest in research and development projects be granted in order to boost the number of technology companies in the state.

46438 ■ "Was Mandating Solar Power Water Heaters For New Homes Good Policy?" in Hawaii Business (Vol. 54, August 2008, No. 2, pp. 28)
Pub: Hawaii Business Publishing
Description: Senator Gary L. Kooser of District 7 Kauai-Niihau believes that the mandating of energy-efficient water heaters for new single-family homes starting in 2010 will help cut Hawaii's oil consumption. Ron Richmond of the Hawaii Solar Energy Association says that the content of SB 644 has negative consequences as it allows for choice of energy and not just solar, and it also eliminates tax credits for new homebuyers.

46439 ■ "Water Efficiency Bill Move Through Congress" in Contractor (Vol. 56, July 2009, No. 7, pp. 20)
Pub: Penton Media, Inc.
Ed: Kevin Schwalb. **Description:** National Association, a plumbing-heating-cooling contractor, was instrumental in drafting the Water Advanced Technologies for Efficient Resource Use Act of 2009 and they are also backing the Water Accountability Tax Ef-

ficiency Reinvestment Act. The first bill promotes WaterSense-labeled products while the other promotes water conservation through tax credits.

46440 ■ "The Weeks Ahead" in Crain's New York Business (Vol. 24, January 7, 2008, No. 1, pp. 26)
Pub: Crain Communications, Inc.
Description: Listing of events in the Detroit area include conferences addressing entrepreneurialism, economic development, and women business ownership.

46441 ■ "The Weeks Ahead" in Crain's New York Business (Vol. 24, January 14, 2008, No. 2, pp. 20)
Pub: Crain Communications, Inc.
Description: Listing of events in the Detroit area include conferences addressing entrepreneurialism, economic development, and women business ownership.

46442 ■ "Weighing the Write-Off" in Baltimore Business Journal (Vol. 28, September 10, 2010, No. 18, pp. 1)
Pub: Baltimore Business Journal
Ed: Daniel J. Sernovitz. **Description:** President Barrack Obama has proposed to let business write off their investments in plant and equipment upgrades under a plan aimed at getting the economy going. The plan would allow a company to write off 100 percent of the depreciation for their new investments at one time instead of over several years.

46443 ■ "Weyerhaeuser's REIT Decision Shouldn't Scare Investors Away" in Barron's (Vol. 88, June 30, 2008, No. 26, pp. 18)
Pub: Dow Jones & Co., Inc.
Ed: Christopher Williams. **Description:** Weyerhaeuser Co.'s management said that a conversion to a real estate investment trust was not likely in 2009 since the move is not tax-efficient as of the moment and would overload its non-timber assets with debt. The company's shares have fallen by 19.5 percent. However, the company remains an asset-rich outfit and its activist shareholder is pushing for change.

46444 ■ Working for Yourself: Law and Taxes for Independent Contractors, Freelancers and Consultants
Pub: NOLO Publications
Ed: Stephen Fishman. **Released:** March 2008. **Price:** $39.99 paperback. **Description:** In-depth information is shared for contractors, freelancers and consultants involving business law and small business taxes.

46445 ■ "Year-End Tax Tips" in Hawaii Business (Vol. 53, December 2007, No. 6, pp. 136)
Pub: Hawaii Business Publishing
Ed: Kathleen Bryan. **Description:** Tax planning tips for the end of 2007, in relation to the tax breaks that are scheduled to expire, are presented. Among the tax breaks that will be expiring at the 2007 year-end are sales tax deduction in the state and local level, premiums on mortgage insurance, and deduction on tuition. The impacts of these changes are discussed.

TRADE PERIODICALS

46446 ■ Corporate Directions
Pub: CCH Inc.
Contact: Mike Sabbatis, President
Ed: Charles W. Edwards, Editor. **Released:** Biweekly. **Price:** $213. **Description:** Discusses coverage of SEC news and regulations affecting publicly-traded companies and their officers and directors. Follows trends in corporate goverance and investor relations. Recurring features include interviews, news of research, reports of meetings, news of educational opportunities, notices of publications available, analyses of SEC regulations and court opinions, industry surveys, and columns titled Litigation Update and News from the States.

46447 ■ Intertax
Pub: Kluwer Academic/Plenum Publishing Corp.
Contact: Martin E. Tash, President
URL(s): www.kluwerlawonline.com/productinfo. php?pubcode=TAXI. **Ed:** Otmar Thommes. **Re-**

leased: Monthly **Price:** €1031, Individuals print or online; $1376, Individuals print or online; £758, Individuals print or online.

46448 ■ Small Business Council of America--Alert
Pub: Small Business Council of America Inc.
Released: Quarterly. **Price:** Included in membership. **Description:** Monitors federal tax legislation affecting small business. Reports on the Council's advocacy in support of legislation creating economic incentives for small businesses. Encourages members to participate in the legislative process. Recurring features include Council news and a calendar of events.

46449 ■ Small Business Taxes and Management
Pub: A/N Group Inc.
Contact: Steven A. Hopfenmuller, President
Released: Semimonthly, Daily (Mon. thru Fri.). **Price:** $49.95. **Description:** Offers current tax news, reviews of recent cases, tax saving tips, and personal financial planning for small business owners. Includes articles on issues such as finance and management. Remarks: Available online only.

VIDEOCASSETTES/ AUDIOCASSETTES

46450 ■ CPE Network: Tax & Accounting Report
Bisk Education
9417 Princess Palm Ave.
Tampa, FL 33619
Free: 800-874-7877
Co. E-mail: info@bisk.com
URL: http://www.bisk.com
Released: 19??. **Price:** $1200.00. **Description:** Provides information on current tax regulations and current accounting and auditing changes. Video newsletter published 11 times per year. **Availability:** VHS.

46451 ■ Tax Season Update: Small Businesses and Their Owners
Bisk Education
9417 Princess Palm Ave.
Tampa, FL 33619
Free: 800-874-7877
Co. E-mail: info@bisk.com
URL: http://www.bisk.com
Released: 19??. **Price:** $199.00. **Description:** Discusses year-end tax tips and the upcoming tax legislation affecting small businesses and their owners. Furnishes information on choice of entity, new tax rates, private pension plans, trusts, planning and strategies for small business, bankruptcy law, tax planning issues, and new penalty and compliance provisions. Includes workbook and quizzer. **Availability:** VHS.

CONSULTANTS

46452 ■ General Business Services Corp.
1020 N University Parks Dr.
Waco, TX 76707
Ph: (817)745-2525
Free: 800-583-6181
Fax: (817)745-2544
Contact: Gary Mattson, Principal
Scope: Provider of financial management, business counseling, and tax-related products and services to business owners and professionals. Additional services include proper record-keeping systems, accurate tax return preparation, computer software services, and financial planning services. Initial and continuous training is available to franchisees in all areas: Business and tax counseling, client acquisition and business operations. **Founded:** 1962. **Publications:** "Tax Tips for the Small Business Owner and Professional," 1993.

46453 ■ Gordian Concepts & Solutions
16 Blueberry Ln.
Lincoln, MA 01773

Ph: (617)259-8341
Contact: Stephen R. Low, President
Scope: Engineering and management consultancy offering general, financial, and valuation services, civil and tax litigation support. Assists clients in entering new businesses, planning new products and services, and evaluating feasibility. Targets industrial concerns engaged in manufacturing, assembly, warehousing, energy production, process systems and biotechnology, steel, paper, and electronics. Serves businesses such as retailing, financial services, health care, satellite broadcasting and cable television, outdoor advertising and professional practices. **Founded:** 1990. **Publications:** "Establishing Rural Cellular Company Values," Cellular Business.

46454 ■ Horwath International Association—Crowe Horwath International
420 Lexington Ave., Ste. 526
New York, NY 10170-0526
Ph: (212)808-2000
Fax: (212)808-2020
Co. E-mail: contactus@horwath.com
URL: http://www.horwath.com
Contact: Mark Hildebrand, Chief Executive Officer
E-mail: mhildebrand@horwath.com
Scope: Services include: Accounting, auditing, tax and management consulting. Provides innovative business solutions in the area of assurance, business services, consulting, corporate finance, risk management, tax and technology. **Founded:** 1991. **Publications:** "Does Your Business Have an E-Commerce Strategy"; "Americas Tax Facts," 2007; "Caring Sharing Investing Growing: The Story of Horwath International," Nov. 2006; "How To Franchise Internationally"; "International Tax Planning Manual: Expatriates and Migrants"; "Americas Tax Facts 2007"; "European and Middle East Tax Facts 2008"; "International Offshore Financial Services"; "International Tax Planning Manual: Corporations"; "Asia or Pacific Tax News 2008: Issue 2"; "FOMB: A Quiz for Business Owners". **Seminars:** Demand Creation Training, Dec, 2006; Marketing, Dec, 2006.

46455 ■ Pioneer Business Consultants
9042 Garfield Ave., Ste. 211
Huntington Beach, CA 92646
Ph: (714)964-7600
Fax: (714)962-6585
Contact: John J. Collins, President
Scope: Offers general management consulting specializing in business acquisitions, tax and business planning, cash flow analyses, business valuations and business sales and expert witness court testimony regarding business sales, valuations and accounting. **Founded:** 1980.

46456 ■ Marion S. Rice
5281 Pinnacle Rd.
Dayton, OH 45417-6442
Ph: (937)859-7763
Fax: (937)847-0046
Contact: Marion Rice, Owner
Scope: Provider of consultation to individuals and small businesses on tax management and bookkeeping activities.

46457 ■ Harvey C. Skoog
7151 E Addis Ave.
Prescott Valley, AZ 86314
Ph: (928)772-1448
Scope: Firm has expertise in taxes, payroll, financial planning, budgeting, buy/sell planning, business start-up, fraud detection, troubled business consulting, acquisition, and marketing. Serves the manufacturing, construction, and retailing industries in Arizona. **Founded:** 1977.

46458 ■ Donald C. Wright CPA
3906 Lawndale Ln. N
Plymouth, MN 55446-2940
Ph: (763)478-6999
Co. E-mail: donaldwright@compuserve.com
URL: http://www.donaldwrightcpa.com
Contact: Donald C. Wright, President
E-mail: donaldwright@compuserve.com
Scope: Offers accounting, tax, and small business consulting services. Services include cash flow and budgeting analysis; financial forecast and projections;

financial statements; reviews and compilations; tax planning, tax preparation; IRS and state/local representation; international taxation; estate, gift and trust tax return preparation; benefit plan services; business succession planning; estate planning; financial planning; management advisory services, pension and profit sharing plans, retirement planning, expert witness services and employee benefits plans. Serves individuals, corporations, partnerships, and non-profit organizations. **Founded:** 1968. **Seminars:** Qualified pension plans and employee welfare benefit plans.

FRANCHISES AND BUSINESS OPPORTUNITIES

46459 ■ Cash Plus
Cash Plus, Inc.
3002 Dow Ave., Ste, 120
Tustin, CA 92780
Ph: (714)731-2274
Free: 888-707-2274
Fax: (714)731-2099
Description: Check cashing service and related services, including money orders, wire transfers, cash advances, mailboxes, notary, UPS, fax, snacks, tax filing and other items. **No. of Franchise Units:** 91. **No. of Company-Owned Units:** 2. **Founded:** 1984.. **Franchised:** 1988. **Equity Capital Needed:** $190,200-$269,700. **Franchise Fee:** $35,000. **Financial Assistance:** Yes. **Training:** Provides training including easy-to-run computerized operating system, promotions and check verification and payday advance process.

COMPUTERIZED DATABASES

46460 ■ CCH Tax Protos™
90 Sheppard Ave. E, Ste. 300
Toronto, ON, Canada M2N 6X1
Ph: (416)224-2224
Free: 800-268-4522
Fax: (416)224-2243
Co. E-mail: cservice@cch.ca
URL: http://www.cch.ca
Availability: Online: Wolters Kluwer - CCH Canadian Ltd. **Type:** Bulletin board.

46461 ■ e-JEP
2014 Broadway, Ste. 305
Nashville, TN 37203
Ph: (615)322-2595
Fax: (615)343-7590
Co. E-mail: aeainfo@vanderbilt.edu
URL: http://www.vanderbilt.edu/AEA
Contact: Angus Deaton, President
Availability: Online: American Economic Association; Thomson Reuters - Westlaw. CD-ROM: American Economic Association. **Type:** Full-text.

46462 ■ Federal Income Taxation of Corporations and Shareholders
2395 Midway Rd.
Carrollton, TX 75006
Free: 800-431-9025
Co. E-mail: ria@thomson.com
URL: http://ria.thomsonreuters.com
Availability: Online: Thomson Reuters - RIA Tax & Accounting Unit. **Type:** Full-text.

46463 ■ Federal Income Taxation of S Corporations
2395 Midway Rd.
Carrollton, TX 75006
Free: 800-431-9025
Co. E-mail: ria@thomson.com
URL: http://ria.thomsonreuters.com
Availability: Online: Thomson Reuters - RIA Tax & Accounting Unit. **Type:** Full-text.

46464 ■ Federal Taxes Weekly Alert
2395 Midway Rd.
Carrollton, TX 75006

Free: 800-431-9025
Co. E-mail: ria@thomson.com
URL: http://ria.thomsonreuters.com
Availability: Online: Thomson Reuters - RIA Tax & Accounting Unit. **Type:** Full-text.

46465 ■ IRS Practice and Procedure
2395 Midway Rd.
Carrollton, TX 75006
Free: 800-431-9025
Co. E-mail: ria@thomson.com
URL: http://ria.thomsonreuters.com
Availability: Online: Thomson Reuters - RIA Tax & Accounting Unit. **Type:** Full-text.

46466 ■ Limited Liability Companies: Tax & Business Law
2395 Midway Rd.
Carrollton, TX 75006
Free: 800-431-9025
Co. E-mail: ria@thomson.com
URL: http://ria.thomsonreuters.com
Availability: Online: Thomson Reuters - RIA Tax & Accounting Unit. **Type:** Full-text.

46467 ■ State Tax Notes®
400 S Maple Ave., Ste. 400
Falls Church, VA 22046
Ph: (703)533-4400
Free: 800-955-2444
Co. E-mail: cservice@tax.org
URL: http://www.taxanalysts.com
Availability: Online: LexisNexis Group. **Type:** Full-text.

46468 ■ State Tax Today®
400 S Maple Ave., Ste. 400
Falls Church, VA 22046
Ph: (703)533-4400
Free: 800-955-2444
Co. E-mail: cservice@tax.org
URL: http://www.taxanalysts.com
Availability: Online: Tax Analysts. **Type:** Full-text.

46469 ■ The Tax Directory®
400 S Maple Ave., Ste. 400
Falls Church, VA 22046
Ph: (703)533-4400
Free: 800-955-2444
Co. E-mail: cservice@tax.org
URL: http://www.taxanalysts.com
Availability: Online: LexisNexis Group. CD-ROM: Tax Analysts. **Type:** Directory.

LIBRARIES

46470 ■ Arnold & Porter LLP Library
399 Park Ave.
New York, NY 10022-4690
Ph: (212)715-1000
Fax: (212)715-1399
Co. E-mail: kim.fenty@aporter.com
URL: http://www.arnoldporter.com
Contact: Kim R. Fenty, Director, Library Services
Scope: Litigation; law - tax, corporate, and environmental. **Services:** Interlibrary loan; Library not open to the public. **Founded:** 1988. **Holdings:** 20,000 books; 400 bound periodical volumes. **Subscriptions:** 205 journals and other serials; 15 newspapers. **Telecommunication Services:** angel.cancela@aporter.com.

46471 ■ Gardiner Roberts LLP Library
Scotia Plaza, Ste. 3100
40 King St., W.
Toronto, ON, Canada M5H 3Y2
Ph: (416)865-6600
Fax: (416)865-6636
URL: http://www.gardiner-roberts.com
Scope: Law - administrative, civil, commercial, insurance, municipal, real estate, tax; intellectual property; information technology. **Services:** Interlibrary loan; copying; library not open to public. **Founded:** 1920. **Holdings:** 2000 books; 300 bound periodical volumes; 500 reports; CD-ROMs. **Subscriptions:** 200 journals and other serials; 6 newspapers.

46472 ■ Greene Radovsky Maloney Share Library
4 Embarcadero Ctr., Ste. 4000
San Francisco, CA 94111
Ph: (415)981-1400
Fax: (415)777-4961
Co. E-mail: info@greeneradovsky.com
URL: http://www.greeneradovsky.com
Scope: Taxation. **Services:** Interlibrary loan; copying; library not open to the public. **Founded:** 1984.
Holdings: 1200 books; 75 bound periodical volumes.
Subscriptions: 150 journals and other serials; 10 newspapers.

46473 ■ Ross & McBride Library
PO Box 907
Hamilton, ON, Canada L8N 3P6
Ph: (905)526-9800
Fax: (905)526-0732
Co. E-mail: contact@rossmcbride.com
URL: http://www.rossmcbride.com/
Scope: Law, taxation. **Services:** Library not open to public. **Holdings:** Figures not available.

46474 ■ Southeastern University Library
501 I St., SW
Washington, DC 20024
Ph: (202)478-8225
Fax: (202)488-8093
Co. E-mail: library@seu.edu
URL: http://www.seuniversity.edu/library

Scope: Science, technology, humanities, health, social sciences. **Services:** Interlibrary loan; library open to the public. **Founded:** 1879. **Holdings:** 50,000 books.

Time Management

ASSOCIATIONS AND OTHER ORGANIZATIONS

46475 ■ APQC (APQC)
123 N Post Oak Ln., 3rd Fl.
Houston, TX 77024-7718
Ph: (713)681-4020
Free: 800-776-9676
Fax: (713)681-8578
Co. E-mail: apqcinfo@apqc.org
URL: http://www.apqc.org
Contact: Carla O'Dell, President
E-mail: codell@apqc.org
Description: Resource for process and performance improvement. Helps organizations adapt to rapidly changing environments, build new and better ways to work, and succeed in a competitive marketplace. Focuses on productivity, knowledge management, benchmarking, and quality improvement initiatives. Works with member organizations to identify best practices, discover effective methods of improvement, broadly disseminate findings, and connect individuals with one another and the knowledge and tools they need to succeed. Serves approximately 500 organizations worldwide in all sectors of business, education, and government. **Scope:** productivity, quality, quality of work life, benchmarking, measurement, reengineering, human resources, knowledge management, customer relationships. **Services:** Consulting services. **Founded:** 1977. **Subscriptions:** 1800 books. **Publications:** *CenterView Newsletter* (Monthly); *Practice case studies* (Quarterly); *APQC Center View* (Monthly); *Best Practice.* **Educational Activities:** APQC Conference (Semiannual); APQC Seminars; Training conferences; APQC Workshops. **Awards:** Best-Practice Partner Award; Grayson Medal (Annual).

46476 ■ Center For Creative Leadership (CCL)
1 Leadership Pl.
Greensboro, NC 27410-9427
Ph: (336)288-7210
Fax: (336)286-4087
Co. E-mail: info@leaders.cel.org
URL: http://www.ccl.org
Contact: John Ryan, President
Description: Promotes behavioral science research and leadership education. **Scope:** management development, industrial and organizational psychology. **Founded:** 1970. **Subscriptions:** 6000; 6000; 6000. **Publications:** *Center for Creative Leadership Catalog* (Annual); *Leadership in Action* (Bimonthly); *Research Reports* (Periodic); *Leadership in Action; Leadership Resources--A Guide to Training and Development Tools* (Biennial); *Leadership Education: A Source Book of Courses and Programs.* **Educational Activities:** Friends of the Century Leadership (Annual); CCL Conferences; Friends of the Center Annual Conference; CCL Training programs, including assessment, feedback, and practice of new behaviors. **Awards:** Best Paper Award for the Leadership Quarterly; Scholarships for women, people of color, nonprofit managers, to leadership development programs; Distinguished Alumni Award (Annual); Kenneth Clark Award; Kenneth E. Clark Research Paper Award; Walter F. Ulmer, Jr. Award for Applied Research; Walter Ulmer Award, Jr. Applied Research Award; Kenneth E. Clark Student Research Award; Walter F. Ulmer, Jr. Applied Research Award. **Telecommunication Services:** info@ccl.org.

46477 ■ Employers Group (EG)
1150 S Olive St., Ste. 2300
Los Angeles, CA 90015
Ph: (213)765-3920
Free: 800-748-8484
Fax: (213)742-0301
Co. E-mail: serviceone@employersgroup.com
URL: http://www.employersgroup.com
Contact: Mark Wilbur, President
Description: Provides human resources management services including wage, salary, and benefit surveys; personnel practices surveys; management counseling; management education programs; litigation surveillance; government relations; and research library service. Provides customized human resources services including employee opinion surveys and employee communications programs through its subsidiary, The Employers Group Service Corp. Offers unemployment insurance services, workers' compensation programs, and in-house management training programs. Conducts research and educational programs; maintains speakers' bureau. **Scope:** Human resources employers' association for California. **Founded:** 1896. **Publications:** *California Wage and Hour GuideAL* (Annual). **Seminars:** OC - First Time & Frontline Supervisors Boot Camp, 2012; NC - Leadership Essentials & Supervisory Laws, 2012.

46478 ■ HR People and Strategy (HRPS)
401 N Michigan Ave., Ste. 2200
Chicago, IL 60611
Ph: (312)321-6805
Fax: (312)673-6944
Co. E-mail: info@hrps.org
URL: http://www.hrps.org
Contact: Kevin Rubens, Chairperson
Description: Human resource planning professionals representing 160 corporations and 3,000 individual members, including strategic human resources planning and development specialists, staffing analysts, business planners, line managers, and others who function as business partners in the application of strategic human resource management practices. Seeks to increase the impact of human resource planning and management on business and organizational performance. Sponsors program of professional development in human resource planning concepts, techniques, and practices. Offers networking opportunities. **Founded:** 1977. **Publications:** *People and Strategy* (Quarterly); *People & Strategy* (Quarterly); *Human Resource Planning Society--Membership Directory* (Annual).

46479 ■ Institute of Management Accountants, Cost Management Group (CMG)
10 Paragon Dr.
Montvale, NJ 07645-1773
Ph: (201)573-9000
Free: 800-638-4427
Fax: (201)474-1600
Co. E-mail: ima@imanet.org
URL: http://www.imanet.org
Contact: Paul A. Sharman, President
Description: A group within the Institute of Management Accountants. Seeks to improve the quality of corporate cost management systems. Educates business professionals about decision-making and productivity improvement. Provides a means of exchanging opinions and experiences about cost management systems. Conducts surveys; compiles statistics. **Founded:** 1991.

46480 ■ Institute for Operations Research and the Management Sciences (INFORMS)
7240 Parkway. Dr., Ste. 300
Hanover, MD 21076-1310
Ph: (443)757-3500
Free: 800-446-3676
Fax: (443)757-3515
Co. E-mail: informs@informs.org
URL: http://www.informs.org
Contact: Terry P. Harrison, President
Description: International scientific society dedicated to improving operational processes, decision-making and management through the application of methods from science and mathematics. Represents operations researchers, management scientists and those working in related fields within engineering and the information, decision, mathematical and social sciences. **Founded:** 1995. **Publications:** *Interfaces* (Bimonthly); *Management Science* (Monthly); *Information Systems Research* (Quarterly); *Informs Transactions on Education* (Periodic); *Manufacturing and Service Operations Management* (Quarterly); *Marketing Science* (Quarterly); *Mathematics of Operations Research* (Quarterly); *Organization Science* (Bimonthly); *Transportation Science* (Quarterly). **Educational Activities:** Business Analytics and Operations Research (Annual); Institute for Operations Research and the Management Sciences Meeting (Annual). **Awards:** Franz Edelman Award for Achievement in Operations Research and the Management Science; George B. Dantzig Dissertation Award (Annual); George E. Kimball Medal; George Nicholson Student Paper Competition (Annual); INFORMS Expository Writing Award (Annual); INFORMS President's Award (Annual); INFORMS Prize (Annual); INFORMS Prize for the Teaching of OR/MS Practice (Annual); John von Neumann Theory Prize (Annual); Judith Liebman Award (Annual); Lanchester Prize (Annual); Philip McCord Morse Lectureship Award; Franz Edelman Award for Achievement in Operations Research and the Management Sciences; George E. Kimball Medal; Frederick W. Lanchester Prize; Philip McCord Morse Lectureship Award; George Nicholson Student Paper Competition; John von Neumann Theory Prize; INFORMS Prize; George B. Dantzig Dissertation Award; Expository Writing Award; President's Award; Prize for the Teaching of OR/MS Practice; INFORMS Fellow Award; Seth Bonder Scholarship for Applied Operations Research in Military Applications; Seth Bonder Scholarship for Applied Operations Research in Health Services.

46481 ■ **International Production Planning and Scheduling Association (IPPSA)**
PO Box 5031
Incline Village, NV 89450
Ph: (775)833-3922
Co. E-mail: billk@ippsa.org
URL: http://www.ippsa.org
Description: Seeks to expand the knowledge of advanced planning and scheduling technology among manufacturing companies. Conducts educational planning and scheduling seminars and integrates Material and Capacity Management in its workshops. **Publications:** *Evaluating Scheduling Performance*; *FCS Book Description*; *Scheduling Methods that Work*; *Seminar Presenters Biography*.

46482 ■ **International Society for the Study of Time (ISST)**
St. Joseph Univ.
English Dept.
5600 City Ave.
Philadelphia, PA 19131-1308
Co. E-mail: membership@studyoftime.org
URL: http://www.studyoftime.org
Contact: Paul Harris, President
Description: Scientists and humanists. Explores the idea and experience of time and the role time plays in the physical, organic, intellectual, and social worlds. Encourages interdisciplinary study; provides a forum for exchange of ideas among members. **Founded:** 1966. **Publications:** *KronoScope* (Semi-annual); *Time's News* (Annual). **Awards:** J.T. Fraser Prize (Triennial).

46483 ■ **Project Management Institute (PMI)**
14 Campus Blvd.
Newtown Square, PA 19073-3299
Ph: (610)356-4600
Free: 855-746-4849
Fax: (610)482-9971
Co. E-mail: customercare@pmi.org
URL: http://www.pmi.org
Contact: Peter Monkhouse, Chairman
Description: Corporations and individuals engaged in the practice of project management; project management students and educators. Seeks to advance the study, teaching and practice of project management. Establishes project management standards; conducts educational and professional certification courses; bestows Project Management Professional credential upon qualified individuals. Offers educational seminars and global congresses. **Scope:** project management. **Founded:** 1969. **Subscriptions:** 3800 archival material articles audiovisuals books monographs periodicals. **Publications:** *Project Management Salary Survey*; *Bibliography on the Project Manager and Project Oragnization*; *Project Management Journal*; *PM Network* (Monthly); *PMI Today* (Monthly); *Project Management Journal* (Quarterly). **Educational Activities:** Global Congress - Europe (Annual); Global Congress North America (Annual); Project Management Institute Annual Seminars and Symposium. **Awards:** PMI Professional Awards (Annual); PMI Project of the Year Award (Annual); Distinguished Contribution Award; Fellow Award; Project of the Year Award; Student Paper of the Year Award; Linn Stuckenbruck Person of the Year Award. **Telecommunication Services:** pmihq@pmi.org.

46484 ■ **Society for Advancement of Management (SAM)**
6300 Ocean Dr.
OCNR 330, Unit 5807
Corpus Christi, TX 78412
Ph: (361)825-6045
Free: 888-827-6077
Fax: (361)825-2725
Co. E-mail: sam@samnational.org
URL: http://www.samnational.org
Contact: Dr. Moustafa H. Abdelsamad, President
URL(s): www.cob.tamucc.edu/sam/, www.enterprise.tamucc.edu/sam. **Description:** Represents management executives in industry commerce, government, and education. Fields of interest include management education, policy and strategy, MIS, international management, administration, budgeting, collective bargaining, distribution, incentives, materials handling, quality control, and training. **Founded:** 1912. **Publications:** *Advanced Management Journal* (Quarterly); *SAM Advanced Management Journal* (Quarterly); *SAM Management In Practice* (Quarterly); *The SAM News International* (Quarterly); *Society for Advancement of Management--International Business Conference Proceedings* (Annual). **Educational Activities:** Society for Advancement of Management Meeting (Annual); Business Conference (Annual).

EDUCATIONAL PROGRAMS

46485 ■ **Basics of Time Management Workshop (Onsite)**
Seminar Information Service, Inc.
20 Executive Park, Ste. 120
Irvine, CA 92614
Ph: (949)261-9104
Free: 877-SEM-INFO
Fax: (949)261-1963
Co. E-mail: info@seminarinformation.com
URL: http://www.seminarinformation.com
Price: $895.00. **Description:** Identify and overcome barriers to effective time management issues, including proven time management and prioritizing skills to help you concentrate on how to determine how much time, energy and resources is needed.

46486 ■ **Brain-Based Time Management**
Seminar Information Service, Inc.
20 Executive Park, Ste. 120
Irvine, CA 92614
Ph: (949)261-9104
Free: 877-SEM-INFO
Fax: (949)261-1963
Co. E-mail: info@seminarinformation.com
URL: http://www.seminarinformation.com
Price: $795.00. **Description:** Determine your Time Type; understand how you accomplish your work; develop strategies to maximize your Time Type; apply Time Type strategies to daily tasks and activities. **Dates and Locations:** New York, NY.

46487 ■ **Effective Time Management: Prioritizing for Success (Onsite)**
Seminar Information Service, Inc.
20 Executive Park, Ste. 120
Irvine, CA 92614
Ph: (949)261-9104
Free: 877-SEM-INFO
Fax: (949)261-1963
Co. E-mail: info@seminarinformation.com
URL: http://www.seminarinformation.com
Price: $1,890.00. **Description:** Learn how to: Set goals and priorities that enable you to effectively manage your time; Monitor daily work habits and determine areas for improvement; Plan daily tasks and goals that align with your mission statement; Identify, evaluate and select tools that help with time and priority management; Avoid over-committing yourself and combat procrastination; Balance your professional and personal lives; Implement a personal time-management action plan. **Dates and Locations:** Ottawa, CN; Reston, VA; New York, NY; Alexandria, VA; and Rockville, MD.

46488 ■ **Essential Time Management & Organizational Skills (Onsite)**
Seminar Information Service, Inc.
20 Executive Park, Ste. 120
Irvine, CA 92614
Ph: (949)261-9104
Free: 877-SEM-INFO
Fax: (949)261-1963
Co. E-mail: info@seminarinformation.com
URL: http://www.seminarinformation.com
Price: $179.00. **Description:** Time management plan that you will design for yourself; allowing you to build in the flexibility you need to meet work and home commitments. **Dates and Locations:** Cities throughout the United States.

46489 ■ **How to Manage Inventories and Cycle Counts**
Fred Pryor Seminars & CareerTrack
5700 Broadmoor St., Ste. 300
Mission, KS 66202
Free: 800-780-8476
Fax: (913)967-8849
Co. E-mail: customerservice@pryor.com
URL: http://www.pryor.com
Price: $199.00; $189.00 for groups of 5 or more. **Description:** Cost saving methods and time saving techniques to ensure accurate counts and inventories. **Dates and Locations:** Cities throughout the United States.

46490 ■ **The Indispensable Assistant (Onsite)**
Seminar Information Service, Inc.
20 Executive Park, Ste. 120
Irvine, CA 92614
Ph: (949)261-9104
Free: 877-SEM-INFO
Fax: (949)261-1963
Co. E-mail: info@seminarinformation.com
URL: http://www.seminarinformation.com
Price: $149.00; $139.00 each for 4 or more. **Description:** Learn how to juggle multiple projects and priorities; how to keep things running smoothly when the boss is away; how to save time by delegating; and how to identify and overcome personal productivity roadblocks. **Dates and Locations:** Cities throughout the United States.

46491 ■ **Managing Information Overload: Techniques for Working Smarter (Onsite)**
Seminar Information Service, Inc.
20 Executive Park, Ste. 120
Irvine, CA 92614
Ph: (949)261-9104
Free: 877-SEM-INFO
Fax: (949)261-1963
Co. E-mail: info@seminarinformation.com
URL: http://www.seminarinformation.com
Price: $1,890.00. **Description:** Learn how to increase your productivity with effective information management skills, apply creative strategies, including mind maps, for processing information, adopt speed-reading techniques to quickly digest reports, and develop advanced memory skills to retain important information. **Dates and Locations:** Reston, VA; and Rockland MD.

46492 ■ **Managing Multiple Priorities (Onsite)**
Seminar Information Service, Inc.
20 Executive Park, Ste. 120
Irvine, CA 92614
Ph: (949)261-9104
Free: 877-SEM-INFO
Fax: (949)261-1963
Co. E-mail: info@seminarinformation.com
URL: http://www.seminarinformation.com
Price: $1,495.00. **Description:** Focus on practical techniques for setting priorities and goals and on how to manage ongoing projects from start to finish. Topics include: handling paperwork systematically, realistic ways to decrease interruptions, and learning to say no.

46493 ■ **Managing Multiple Priorities, Projects, and Deadlines (Onsite)**
Fred Pryor Seminars & CareerTrack
5700 Broadmoor St., Ste. 300
Mission, KS 66202
Free: 800-780-8476
Fax: (913)967-8849
Co. E-mail: customerservice@pryor.com
URL: http://www.pryor.com
Price: $99.00; $89.00 for groups of 5 or more. **Description:** Learn to manage multiple demands and priorities, get more done in less time, keep on top of numerous deadlines, and eliminate pressure and stress from your work day. **Dates and Locations:** Cities throughout the United States.

46494 ■ **Managing Multiple Priorities, Projects and Deadlines (Onsite)**
Seminar Information Service, Inc.
20 Executive Park, Ste. 120
Irvine, CA 92614
Ph: (949)261-9104
Free: 877-SEM-INFO

Fax: (949)261-1963
Co. E-mail: info@seminarinformation.com
URL: http://www.seminarinformation.com
Price: $99.00; $89.00 for five or more. **Description:** An intensive one-day seminar that helps participants gain more control over their time, tasks, and priorities. **Dates and Locations:** Cities throughout the United States.

46495 ■ Managing Multiple Projects, Competing Priorities & Tight Deadlines (Onsite)
Seminar Information Service, Inc.
20 Executive Park, Ste. 120
Irvine, CA 92614
Ph: (949)261-9104
Free: 877-SEM-INFO
Fax: (949)261-1963
Co. E-mail: info@seminarinformation.com
URL: http://www.seminarinformation.com
Price: $199.00. **Description:** Skills you need to immediately and effectively deal with multiple projects, expectations, and deadlines without backlog, burnout, and stress. **Dates and Locations:** Cities throughout the United States.

46496 ■ Managing Multiple Projects, Objectives and Deadlines (Onsite)
Seminar Information Service, Inc.
20 Executive Park, Ste. 120
Irvine, CA 92614
Ph: (949)261-9104
Free: 877-SEM-INFO
Fax: (949)261-1963
Co. E-mail: info@seminarinformation.com
URL: http://www.seminarinformation.com
Price: $149.00; $139.00 for four or more. **Description:** Learn organizational skills to help you get more accomplished. **Dates and Locations:** Cities throughout the United States.

46497 ■ The Strategic Speed-Reading Advantage for Executives & Legal Professionals (Onsite)
Fred Pryor Seminars & CareerTrack
5700 Broadmoor St., Ste. 300
Mission, KS 66202
Free: 800-780-8476
Fax: (913)967-8849
Co. E-mail: customerservice@pryor.com
URL: http://www.pryor.com
Price: $149.00; $139.00 for groups of 5 or more. **Description:** Learn to organize, prioritize, and absorb volumes of information for effortlessly making critical decisions. **Dates and Locations:** Cities throughout the United States.

46498 ■ Superior Time Planning: The Organizer (Onsite)
Seminar Information Service, Inc.
20 Executive Park, Ste. 120
Irvine, CA 92614
Ph: (949)261-9104
Free: 877-SEM-INFO
Fax: (949)261-1963
Co. E-mail: info@seminarinformation.com
URL: http://www.seminarinformation.com
Price: Contact for fees. **Description:** Participants learn to organize information to increase overall effectiveness through comprehensive long range planning and documentation, including how to monitor activities and track results.

46499 ■ Time Management (Onsite)
Seminar Information Service, Inc.
20 Executive Park, Ste. 120
Irvine, CA 92614
Ph: (949)261-9104
Free: 877-SEM-INFO
Fax: (949)261-1963
Co. E-mail: info@seminarinformation.com
URL: http://www.seminarinformation.com
Price: $1,995.00. **Description:** Learn to determine how your time is being spent, develop strategies for time allocation, create a structure to control time spent on tasks and activities, and prioritize what mat-

ters most in your life. **Dates and Locations:** Chicago, IL; Arlington, VA; New York, NY; Indianapolis, IN; Melville, NY; San Francisco, CA; and Philadelphia , PA.

46500 ■ Time Management Survival Skills (Onsite)
Seminar Information Service, Inc.
20 Executive Park, Ste. 120
Irvine, CA 92614
Ph: (949)261-9104
Free: 877-SEM-INFO
Fax: (949)261-1963
Co. E-mail: info@seminarinformation.com
URL: http://www.seminarinformation.com
Price: $845.00. **Description:** Develop a step-by-step action plan and use the latest tools for accomplishing your important goals, objectives, and activities. **Dates and Locations:** Framingham, MA; and Boston, MA.

REFERENCE WORKS

46501 ■ 10 Steps to Successful Social Networking for Business
Pub: ASTD
Contact: Tony Bingham, President
E-mail: tbingham@astd.org
Ed: Darin Hartley. **Released:** July 1, 2010. **Price:** $19.95. **Description:** Designed for today's fast-paced, need-it-yesterday business environment and for the thousands of workers who find themselves faced with new assignments, responsibilities, and requirements and too little time to learn what they must know.

46502 ■ "2007 Fittest CEOs" in Hawaii Business (Vol. 53, October 2007, No. 4, pp. 40)
Pub: Hawaii Business Publishing
Description: Discusses the outcome of the fittest chief executive officers in Hawaii competition for 2007. Hawaii Capital Management's David Low leads the list while Group Pacific (Hawaii) Inc.'s Chip Doyle and Greater Good Inc.'s Kari Leong placed second and third, respectively. The CEO's routines, eating habits, and inspirations for staying fit are provided.

46503 ■ "The Balancing Act: How Busy Executives Make Their Lives Work" in Black Enterprise (Vol. 37, February 2007, No. 7, pp. 118)
Pub: Earl G. Graves Publishing Co. Inc.
Ed: Marcia A. Reed-Woodard. **Description:** More than 70 percent of women with children work outside the home, according to a 2005 survey conducted by the U.S. Department of Labor Bureau. One of the biggest struggles these women face is balancing family with career aspirations and climbing the corporate ranks.

46504 ■ "Cyberwise" in Black Enterprise (Vol. 40, July 2010, No. 12, pp. 48)
Pub: Earl G. Graves Publishing Co. Inc.
Description: Tools to effectively manage time are explored.

46505 ■ "Desk-Bound No More" in Charlotte Business Journal (Vol. 25, August 13, 2010, No. 21, pp. 1)
Pub: Charlotte Business Journal
Ed: Adam O' Daniel. **Description:** Bank of America has launched a program that encourages employees to work on their own schedules. The program encourages productivity and health work-life balance. A survey has also revealed that employees feel more productive under the program.

46506 ■ "Dick Haskayne" in Canadian Business (Vol. 81, March 31, 2008, No. 5, pp. 72)
Pub: Rogers Media
Ed: Andy Holloway. **Description:** Dick Haskayne says that he learned a lot about business from his dad who ran a butcher shop where they had to make a decision on buying cattle and getting credit. Haskayne says that family, friends, finances, career, health, and infrastructure are benchmarks that have to be balanced.

46507 ■ "The Early Bird Really Does Get the Worm" in Harvard Business Review (Vol. 88, July-August 2010, No. 7-8, pp. 30)
Pub: Harvard Business School Publishing
Ed: Christoph Randler. **Description:** Research indicates that those who identify themselves as 'morning people' tend to be more proactive, and thus have a career-development advantage over those who identify themselves as 'night people'. Implications of the research are also discussed.

46508 ■ "The End of Clock-Punching" in Canadian Business (Vol. 83, September 14, 2010, No. 15, pp. 96)
Pub: Rogers Media Ltd.
Ed: Lyndsie Bourgon. **Description:** Workplace consultant Peter Hadwen is pushing for the transformation of Canada's government departments into results-only work environments (ROWE). ROWE does not require employees to show up to work at a certain time as long as they are meeting goals and achieving results in their jobs. Details of studies regarding ROWE in US companies are examined.

46509 ■ Enlightened Leadership: Best Practice Guidelines and Time Tools for Easily Implementing Learning Organizations
Pub: Learning House Publishing, Inc.
Ed: Ralph LoVuolo; Alan G. Thomas. **Released:** May 2006. **Price:** $79.99. **Description:** Innovation and creativity are essential for any successful small business. The book provides owners, managers, and team leaders with the tools necessary to produce 'disciplined innovation'.

46510 ■ Enlightened Leadership: Best Practice Guidelines and Timesaving Tools for Easily Implementing Learning Organizations
Pub: Learning House Publishing, Incorporated
Ed: Alan G. Thomas; Ralph L. LoVuolo; Jeanne C. Hillson. **Released:** September 2006, printable 3 times/year. **Price:** $21.00. **Description:** Book provides the tools required to create a learning organization management model along with a step-by-step guide for team planning and learning. The strategy works as a manager's self-help guide as well as offering continuous learning and improvement for company-wide success.

46511 ■ Getting Things Done: The Art of Stress-Free Productivity
Pub: Penguin Books USA Inc.
Ed: David Allen. **Released:** December 2002. **Price:** $16.00. **Description:** Coach and management consultant recommends methods for stress-free performance under the premise that productivity is directly related to our ability to relax.

46512 ■ "Heavy Duty: The Case Against Packing Lightly" in Crain's Chicago Business (Vol. 31, April 21, 2008, No. 16, pp. 29)
Pub: Crain Communications, Inc.
Ed: Sarah A. Klein. **Description:** Penelope Biggs, a Northern Trust executive who manages sales teams in North America, Europe and Asia gives advice on traveling abroad for business including time management skills, handling time-zone hops and avoiding jet-lag.

46513 ■ Home-Based Business for Dummies
Pub: John Wiley and Sons, Inc.
Ed: Paul Edwards, Sarah Edwards, Peter Economy. **Released:** February 25, 2005. **Price:** $19.99. **Description:** Provides all the information needed to start and run a home-based business. Topics include: selecting the right business; setting up a home office; managing money, credit, and financing; marketing; and ways to avoid distractions while working at home.

46514 ■ "How To Turn Your Efforts Into Results" in Green Industry Pro (Vol. 23, September 2011)
Pub: Cygnus Business Media
Ed: Bob Coulter. **Description:** Working Smarter Training Challenge teaches that leaders are able to carry out solutions directly into their organization, develop skills and drive business results in key areas

by creating a culture of energized workers who are able to take ownership of their performance as well as the performance of the company as a whole.

46515 ■ *"Ian Delaney" in Canadian Business (Vol. 81, Summer 2008, No. 9, pp. 168)*
Pub: Rogers Media Ltd.
Ed: Joe Castaldo. **Description:** Interview with Ian Delaney who is the executive chairman of chemical company Sherritt International Corp.; Delaney previously worked as chief executive for a holding company owned by Peter Munk. Details of his beliefs, profession and family life are discussed.

46516 ■ *"Integrating Business Core Knowledge through Upper Division Report Composition" in Business Communication Quarterly (December 2007)*
Pub: SAGE Publications USA
Contact: Blaise R. Simqu, President
Ed: Joy Roach, Daniel Tracy, Kay Durden. **Description:** An assignment that integrates subjects and encourages the use of business communication report-writing skills is presented. This assignment is designed to complement business school curricula and help develop critical thinking and organizational skills.

46517 ■ *"Interview Advisory; Warning! Do YOU Have VD?" in Canadian Corporate News (May 18, 2007)*
Pub: Comtex News Network Inc.
Description: Interview with Beverly Beuermann-King, a stress and wellness specialist, who provides insights on the problems associated with Vacation Deprivation.

46518 ■ *Lean Six Sigmas That Works: A Powerful Action Plan for Dramatically Improving Quality, Increasing Speed, and Reducing Waste*
Pub: American Management Association
Contact: Charles R. Craig, Chairman
Ed: Bill Carreira; Bill Trudell. **Released:** 2006. **Price:** $21.95.

46519 ■ *"Leave It Behind; Novel Packing Strategy" in Crain's Chicago Business (Vol. 31, April 21, 2008, No. 16, pp. 32)*
Pub: Crain Communications, Inc.
Ed: Sarah A. Klein. **Description:** Patrick Brady who investigates possible violations of the Foreign Corrupt Practices Act has a novel approach when traveling to frequent destinations which allows him to travel with only a carry-on piece of luggage: he leaves suits at dry cleaners in the places he visits most often and since he mainly stays at the same hotels, he also leaves sets of workout clothes and running shoes with hotel staff.

46520 ■ *"Madeleine Paquin" in Canadian Business (Vol. 81, March 3, 2008, No. 3, pp. 92)*
Pub: Rogers Media
Ed: Regan Ray. **Description:** Madeleine Paquin, chief executive officer and president of Logistec Corp., talks about how she balanced her career and her life as a mother to two girls. Paquin thinks that working mothers need to focus on some things instead of trying to do everything. Her career in the marine cargo handling industry is also discussed.

46521 ■ *"Make It Easier On Yourself" in Women In Business (Vol. 63, Fall 2011, No. 3, pp. 28)*
Pub: American Business Women's Association
Ed: Maureen Sullivan. **Description:** Getting and staying organized helps avoid wasting time on deciding which priorities to address first. Taking help and avoiding hoarding are examples of how to become organized. The use of technology for organizing priorities is also explained.

46522 ■ *"Make It Easy" in Entrepreneur (Vol. 36, May 2008, No. 5, pp. 49)*
Pub: Entrepreneur Media, Inc.
Ed: Mike Hogan. **Description:** Zoho has a Planner that keep contacts, notes and reminders and a DB & Reports feature for reports, data analysis and pricing

comparisons. WebEx WebOffice Workgroup supports document management and templates for contacts lists, time sheets and sales tracking. Other online data manages are presented.

46523 ■ *"The Middle Ages" in Hawaii Business (Vol. 53, October 2007, No. 4, pp. 42)*
Pub: Hawaii Business Publishing
Ed: Cathy S. Cruz-George. **Description:** Starcom Builders Inc.'s Theodore 'Ted' Taketa, School Kine Cookies' Steven Gold And Sharon Serene of Sharon Serene Creative are among the participants in Hawaii's Fittest CEO competition for executives over 50 years old. Taketa takes yoga classes, and also goes to the gym while Serne has Mike Hann as her professional trainer. Eating habits of the aforementioned executives are also described.

46524 ■ *"Mobility: So Happy Together" in Entrepreneur (Vol. 35, October 2007, No. 10, pp. 64)*
Pub: Entrepreneur Media Inc.
Ed: Heather Clancy. **Description:** Joshua Burnett, CEO and founder of 9ci, uses index cards to keep track of what he needs to do despite the fact that he has a notebook computer, cell phone and PDA. Kim Hahn, a media entrepreneur, prefers jotting her ideas down in a spiral notebook, has a team that would organize her records for her, and a personal assistant that would keep track of changes to her schedule. Reasons why these entrepreneurs use old-fashioned methods along with new technology are given.

46525 ■ *"Monday Organizer: Clean and De-Clutter in 15 Minutes" in Tulsa World (June 13, 2011)*
Pub: McClatchy Company
Ed: Kim Brown. **Description:** New weekly series highlights practical tips and helpful ideas to simply life by taking 15 minutes to de-clutter your home or office. Paper clutter can be eliminated in 15 minutes by gathering up newspapers and magazines to recycle; sort mail as soon as you receive it and throw away any junk mail at that time. If watching TV, use commercial time to accomplish small tasks.

46526 ■ *"Our Gadget of the Week" in Barron's (Vol. 89, July 27, 2009, No. 30, pp. 26)*
Pub: Dow Jones & Co., Inc.
Ed: Jay Palmer. **Description:** Zeo Sleep Coach has a lightweight headband with built-in sensors which measures the user's brain waves and records their sleep patterns. The device details the time the users spends in deep sleep, light sleep and the restorative REM (rapid eye movement) sleep mode. Users can get lifestyle change recommendations from a website to improve their sleep.

46527 ■ *"Pack Mentality" in Crain's Chicago Business (Vol. 31, April 21, 2008, No. 16, pp. 31)*
Pub: Crain Communications, Inc.
Ed: Sarah A. Klein. **Description:** Jill Smart, the head of human resources for a company with 170,000 employees worldwide, frequently travels to India, London and Singapore; Ms. Smart provides advice concerning efficiency, time management and avoiding jet-lag.

46528 ■ *"Pau Hana" in Hawaii Business (Vol. 53, December 2007, No. 6, pp. 118)*
Pub: Hawaii Business Publishing
Ed: Cathy Cruz-George. **Description:** Presented are the hobbies of four Hawaii executives as well as the reason these hobbies are an important part of their lives and add to their ability to manage effectively. Mike Wilkins, for example, is not only Turtle Bay Resort's director of sales and marketing, but is also a glider pilot, while Aubrey Hawk Public Relations president Aubrey Hawk loves baking. The interests of Queen Liliuokalani Trust's Thomas K. Kaulukukui Jr., Reyn Spooner's Tim McCullough, and Heide and Cook Ltd.'s Dexter S. Kekua, are discussed.

46529 ■ *The Power of Full Engagement: Managing Energy, Not Time, is the Key to*

High Performance and Personal Renewal
Pub: Free Press/Simon & Schuster
Ed: Jim Loehr; Tony Schwartz. **Released:** December 21, 2004. **Price:** $15.95 paperback. **Description:** The book presents a program to help stressed individuals find more purpose in their work and ways to better handle overburdened relationships.

46530 ■ *"Power Play" in Harvard Business Review (Vol. 88, July-August 2010, No. 7-8, pp. 84)*
Pub: Harvard Business School Publishing
Ed: Jeffrey Pfeffer. **Description:** Guidelines include in-depth understanding of resources at one's disposal, relentlessness that still provides opponents with opportunities to save face, and a determination not to be put off by the processes of politics.

46531 ■ *"Pressed for Time" in Marketing to Women (Vol. 21, March 2008, No. 3, pp. 1)*
Pub: EPM Communications Inc.
Contact: Ira Mayer, President
E-mail: imayer@epmcom.com
Description: Statistical data concerning the tools women use for time management which include gadgets as well as traditional media such as calendars.

46532 ■ *"Professional Help: Cross That Off Your To-Do List" in Inc. (November 2007, pp. 89-90, 92)*
Pub: Gruner & Jahr USA Publishing
Ed: Alison Stein Wellner. **Description:** Small business owners are finding that it pays to hire someone to takeover the personal tasks of daily living, including hiring a personal assistant, chauffeur, chef, stylist, pet caregiver, or concierge service.

46533 ■ *"The Sweet Spot: A Sugar-Coated Pitch Paid Off Big Time" in Black Enterprise (Vol. 37, November 2006, No. 4, pp. 71)*
Pub: Earl G. Graves Publishing Co. Inc.
Ed: Laura Egodigwe. **Description:** In an interview with Debra Sandler, president of McNeil Nutritionals L.L.C., Sandler talks about the challenges of bringing a new product to the marketplace, how her personal experiences effect her business decisions, and the difficulties of re-entering the workforce.

46534 ■ *Table Talk: The Savvy Girl's Alternative to Networking*
Pub: AuthorHouse
Ed: Diane Danielson. **Released:** April 1, 2003. **Price:** $17.50. **Description:** Let's face it. Women and men are different. So why should we all have to network in the same way? And, why should women have to 'network' at all? Between family and work responsibilities, the idea of pressing flesh at some not-very-festive cocktail party is right up there in appeal with a root canal. But what if women could find a way to make career boosting connections that are actually fun? Enter 'table talk', a new way to network for time-pressed, professional women.

46535 ■ *Take Back Your Time: How to Regain Control of Work, Information and Technology*
Pub: St. Martin's Press LLC
Ed: Jan Jasper. **Released:** November 1999. **Price:** $16.99. **Description:** Strategies to become more organized and productive.

46536 ■ *"Time Value of Money Rate of Return" in Business Owner (Vol. 35, September-October 2011, No. 5, pp. 8)*
Pub: DL Perkins Company
Description: Estimating value of an income-generating asset or group of assets requires the small business owner to consider concepts such as the time value of money, risk and required rate of return. A brief summary explaining this theory is presented.

46537 ■ *"Transform Your Life" in Black Enterprise (Vol. 37, January 2007, No. 6, pp. 14)*
Pub: Earl G. Graves Publishing Co. Inc.
Description: Through the magazine, television and radio programs, events, and the website, the various platforms of Black Enterprise will provide the tools necessary to achieve success in business ventures, career aspirations, and personal goals.

46538 ■ *"Use Ink Presets to Minimize Makeready" in American Printer (Vol. 128, July 1, 2011, No. 7)*
Pub: Penton Media Inc.
Description: Automatic registration systems enable most printers to be in register very quickly after press startup. If the paper, ink and press time wasted during makeready can be reduced, these savings will flow directly to the bottom line. Ink presetting as an economical solution to set color quickly is a trend that continues to gain momentum.

46539 ■ *"What Are You Afraid Of?" in Entrepreneur (Vol. 37, July 2009, No. 7, pp. 79)*
Pub: Entrepreneur Media, Inc.
Ed: Lindsay Holloway. **Description:** According to a survey of entrepreneurs in the US, failure, economic uncertainty, not having enough personal time, being their own boss, and staying afloat are the biggest fears when starting a business. Advice on how to deal with these fears is also given.

46540 ■ *"What Brain Science Tells Us About How to Excel" in Harvard Business Review (Vol. 88, December 2010, No. 12, pp. 123)*
Pub: Harvard Business School Publishing
Ed: Edward M. Hallowell. **Description:** Relevant discoveries in brain research as they apply to boosting employee motivation and organizational effectiveness are explained. Included is a checklist of 15 items for use in assessing the fitness of a person for a particular job, focusing on the intersection of what one likes to do, what one does best, and what increases organizational value.

46541 ■ *"What Moms Want" in Marketing to Women (Vol. 21, February 2008, No. 2, pp. 6)*
Pub: EPM Communications Inc.
Contact: Ira Mayer, President
E-mail: imayer@epmcom.com
Description: According to a survey conducted by Eureka's Spa, moms would rather have an experience gift than flowers or chocolate. The top five dream gifts include a spa day, a weekend getaway, maid service, a bathroom makeover or a getaway weekend with girlfriends.

46542 ■ *What Self-Made Millionaires Really Think, Know and Do: A Straight-Talking Guide to Business Success and Personal Riches*
Pub: John Wiley & Sons, Incorporated
Ed: Richard Dobbins; Barrie Pettman. **Released:** September 2006. **Price:** $24.95. **Description:** Guide for understanding the concepts of entrepreneurial success; the book offers insight into bringing an idea into reality, marketing, time management, leadership skills, and setting clear goals.

46543 ■ *"When Virtue Is A Vice" in Harvard Business Review (Vol. 86, July-August 2008, No. 8, pp. 22)*
Pub: Harvard Business School Press
Ed: Anat Keinan; Ran Kivetz. **Description:** Negative consequences of habitually denying self-indulgence, from work and life balance to consumer shopping behaviors are discussed.

46544 ■ *"Why Mumbai at 1PM is the Center of the Business World" in Harvard Business Review (Vol. 88, October 2010, No. 10, pp. 38)*
Pub: Harvard Business School Publishing
Ed: Michael Segalla. **Description:** A time zone chart is presented for assisting in the planning of international conference calls.

46545 ■ *"Work/Family Balance Boosts Business" in Marketing to Women (Vol. 21, February 2008, No. 2, pp. 8)*
Pub: EPM Communications Inc.
Contact: Ira Mayer, President
E-mail: imayer@epmcom.com
Description: Flexibility in the workplace is becoming a more important issue to both women and men. Statistical data included.

VIDEOCASSETTES/ AUDIOCASSETTES

46546 ■ *Analyzing Our Time Usage*
Resources for Education & Management, Inc.
1804 Montreal Ct., Ste. A
Tucker, GA 30084
Released: 1972. **Description:** Two methods for managing time-breaking down the types of work we do and setting priorities-are discussed. **Availability:** VHS; 3/4 U.

46547 ■ *Another Meeting*
Exec-U-Service Associates
4326 US Highway 1
Princeton, NJ 08540
Released: 1978. **Description:** Gives practical ideas on how to improve the results and time efficiency of meetings. A solid basis for analyzing the meeting process is explored. **Availability:** 3/4 U.

46548 ■ *Do It Now!*
Aspen Publishers, Inc.
7201 McKinney Cir.
Frederick, MD 21704
Ph: (301)698-7100
Free: 800-234-1660
Fax: (800)901-9075
Co. E-mail: customerservice@aspenpublisher.com
URL: http://www.aspenpublishers.com
Contact: Robert Becker, President
Released: 197?. **Description:** This program examines what procrastination is, what causes it, and suggests techniques for breaking the habit. **Availability:** VHS; 3/4 U.

46549 ■ *Don't Agonize—Organize Series with Dr. John Wayne Lee*
Instructional Video
2219 C St.
Lincoln, NE 68502
Ph: (402)475-6570
Free: 800-228-0164
Fax: (402)475-6500
Co. E-mail: feedback@insvideo.com
URL: http://www.insvideo.com
Released: 19??. **Price:** $179.10. **Description:** Dr. John Wayne Lee teaches his techniques on time and self management. Only available in the U.S. **Availability:** VHS.

46550 ■ *The Effective Manager*
Nightingale-Conant Corp.
6245 W. Howard St.
Niles, IL 60714
Ph: (847)647-0300
Free: 800-560-6081
URL: http://www.nightingale.com
Released: 19??. **Price:** $95.00. **Description:** A series of award-winning programs designed to promote effective management and help increase sales. Audio tapes and booklets are included, and the series can be purchased individually or as a set. **Availability:** VHS.

46551 ■ *Empowerment: Managing Your Time*
International Training Consultants, Inc.
1838 Park Oaks
Kemah, TX 77565
Free: 800-998-8764
Co. E-mail: itc@trainingitc.com
URL: http://www.trainingitc.com
Released: 19??. **Price:** $495.00. **Description:** Part of the "Empowerment: The Employee Development Series." Teaches employees to become aware of how they manage their time and offers advice on how they can manage it better. Also discusses priority setting, daily planning, long-range planning, scheduling, and other time management functions. **Availability:** VHS.

46552 ■ *Empowerment: The Employee Development Series*
International Training Consultants, Inc.
1838 Park Oaks
Kemah, TX 77565
Free: 800-998-8764
Co. E-mail: itc@trainingitc.com
URL: http://www.trainingitc.com
Released: 19??. **Price:** $10350.00. **Description:** Employee development series which prepares employees to meet the demands of today's workplace with skill and confidence. Covers such topics as time management, team work, communication, career advancement, working together, and problem solving. Comes with leader's guide, overhead transparencies, five participant booklets, and a complete participant's manual. **Availability:** VHS.

46553 ■ *Get the Edge with Time Management/Rick Barrera*
Instructional Video
2219 C St.
Lincoln, NE 68502
Ph: (402)475-6570
Free: 800-228-0164
Fax: (402)475-6500
Co. E-mail: feedback@insvideo.com
URL: http://www.insvideo.com
Released: 19??. **Price:** $95.00. **Description:** Rick Barrera discusses time management skills. Points out how time management team affect success. Only available in the U.S. **Availability:** VHS.

46554 ■ *Getting Things Done: An Achiever's Guide to Better Time-Management*
Instructional Video
2219 C St.
Lincoln, NE 68502
Ph: (402)475-6570
Free: 800-228-0164
Fax: (402)475-6500
Co. E-mail: feedback@insvideo.com
URL: http://www.insvideo.com
Released: 19??. **Price:** $79.95. **Description:** Offers a systematic approach to achieving goals through the use of time management, stressing the importance of proper prioritization. **Availability:** VHS.

46555 ■ *How to Get Control of Your Time and Your Job*
Aspen Publishers, Inc.
7201 McKinney Cir.
Frederick, MD 21704
Ph: (301)698-7100
Free: 800-234-1660
Fax: (800)901-9075
Co. E-mail: customerservice@aspenpublisher.com
URL: http://www.aspenpublishers.com
Contact: Robert Becker, President
Released: 1983. **Description:** This is a complete program designed by time management expert Alan La Kein to help you learn to use your time effectively. **Availability:** VHS.

46556 ■ *How to Get Things Done*
Nightingale-Conant Corp.
6245 W. Howard St.
Niles, IL 60714
Ph: (847)647-0300
Free: 800-560-6081
URL: http://www.nightingale.com
Released: 19??. **Price:** $95.00. **Description:** Time-management and time-allocation skills are presented, to help workers accomplish more in less time. Includes an audio cassette and book. **Availability:** VHS.

46557 ■ *Manage Your Time to Build Your Territory*
Dartnell Corp.
2222 Sedwick Dr.
Durham, NC 34112
Ph: (239)417-2079
Free: 800-223-8720
Fax: (800)508-2592
Co. E-mail: customerservice@dartnellcorp.com
URL: http://www.dartnellcorp.com
Contact: Kenneth F. Kahn, Publisher
Released: 1974. **Description:** An examination of time thieves that rob salespeople of both hours and sales volume. From the "Tough-Minded Salesmanship" series. **Availability:** VHS; 3/4 U; Special order formats.

46558 ■ *Management of Time*
Resources for Education & Management, Inc.
1804 Montreal Ct., Ste. A
Tucker, GA 30084
Released: 1972. **Description:** Teaches supervisors how to manage time effectively. It consists of four modules: The Time of Our Lives; Analyzing Our Time Usage; Using Others to Save Time; and Our Time Is Our Time. **Availability:** VHS; 3/4 U.

46559 ■ *Managing Time*
Learning Communications L.L.C.
5520 Trabuco Rd.
Irvine, CA 92620-5705
Free: 800-622-3610
Fax: (949)727-4323
Co. E-mail: sales@learncom.com
URL: http://www.learncom.com
Contact: Lloyd W. Singer, President
Released: 1968. **Description:** Stimulates the day-to-day planning of work, use of personnel, staff, and use of time. **Availability:** VHS; 3/4 U.

46560 ■ *Managing Your Time*
Resources for Education & Management, Inc.
1804 Montreal Ct., Ste. A
Tucker, GA 30084
Released: 1970. **Description:** Shows office workers more than 20 ways to manage their time more effectively. Time-saving suggestions are given for typing, filing, and dictation that pay off in increased productivity and efficiency. **Availability:** VHS; 3/4 U.

46561 ■ *A Perfectly Normal Day*
Aspen Publishers, Inc.
7201 McKinney Cir.
Frederick, MD 21704
Ph: (301)698-7100
Free: 800-234-1660
Fax: (800)901-9075
Co. E-mail: customerservice@aspenpublisher.com
URL: http://www.aspenpublishers.com
Contact: Robert Becker, President
Released: 197?. **Description:** Helps develop a new attitude toward interruptions and crises-and teaches us how to reduce and manage them. **Availability:** VHS; 3/4 U.

46562 ■ *Personal Achievement Series—Time Management: How to Increase Your Productivity and Get the Results You Want*
Instructional Video
2219 C St.
Lincoln, NE 68502
Ph: (402)475-6570
Free: 800-228-0164
Fax: (402)475-6500
Co. E-mail: feedback@insvideo.com
URL: http://www.insvideo.com
Released: 19??. **Price:** $69.95. **Description:** Outlines ways to eliminate time-wasting elements of daily life. Includes guidebook. **Availability:** VHS.

46563 ■ *Personal Time Management Video*
Instructional Video
2219 C St.
Lincoln, NE 68502
Ph: (402)475-6570
Free: 800-228-0164
Fax: (402)475-6500
Co. E-mail: feedback@insvideo.com
URL: http://www.insvideo.com
Released: 19??. **Price:** $59.95. **Description:** Brian Tracy illustrates techniques to help put short-term goals in focus to gain long-term aspirations, overcome anxieties related to time restraints, and move on to complete any task. **Availability:** VHS.

46564 ■ *Time Is Money!*
Aspen Publishers, Inc.
7201 McKinney Cir.
Frederick, MD 21704
Ph: (301)698-7100
Free: 800-234-1660

Fax: (800)901-9075
Co. E-mail: customerservice@aspenpublisher.com
URL: http://www.aspenpublishers.com
Contact: Robert Becker, President
Released: 197?. **Description:** Helps solve salespeople's time problems by teaching them good habits, and provides them with timesaving techniques so they'll spend their time more profitably. **Availability:** VHS; 3/4 U.

46565 ■ *Time Management: Keeping the Monkey off Your Back*
Excellence in Training Corp.
c/o ICON Training
804 Roosevelt St.
Polk City, IA 50226
Free: 800-609-0479
Co. E-mail: info@icontraining.com
URL: http://www.icontraining.com
Released: 1991. **Price:** $595.00. **Description:** A discussion of ways to manage events, rather than being managed by events. **Availability:** VHS; 3/4 U; Special order formats.

46566 ■ *Time Management for Managers*
Time-Life Video and Television
1450 Palmyra Ave.
Richmond, VA 23227-4420
Ph: (804)266-6330
Free: 800-950-7887
Fax: (757)427-7905
URL: http://www.timelife.com
Released: 1980. **Description:** This six-part series of untitled programs covers the principles of time management, including decision-making, delegating, scheduling, and managing interruptions. It is designed to help managers become more productive in both personal and professional time. Available only as a set. **Availability:** VHS; 3/4 U; Special order formats.

46567 ■ *Time Management for Managers and Professionals: 41-1XX*
SkillSoft
107 Northeastern Blvd.
Nashua, NH 03062
Ph: (603)324-3000
Free: 877-545-5763
Fax: (603)324-3009
Co. E-mail: information@skillsoft.com
URL: http://www.skillsoft.com
Contact: Chuck Moran, President
Released: 1979. **Description:** Part of an integrated course aimed at teaching a strategy for time management which will enable participants to make better contributions to their organization. **Availability:** 3/4 U.

46568 ■ *Time Management for Women*
Instructional Video
2219 C St.
Lincoln, NE 68502
Ph: (402)475-6570
Free: 800-228-0164
Fax: (402)475-6500
Co. E-mail: feedback@insvideo.com
URL: http://www.insvideo.com
Released: 19??. **Price:** $79.95. **Description:** Kay Cronkite Waldo offers time management training for women, focusing on behavior patterns, energy cycles, efficiency vs. effectiveness, time wasters, decision-making factors, and the superwoman theory. **Availability:** VHS.

46569 ■ *The Time of Our Lives*
Resources for Education & Management, Inc.
1804 Montreal Ct., Ste. A
Tucker, GA 30084
Released: 1972. **Description:** Good planning is necessary if work is to fit into the time available. The keys of proper time management are introduced. **Availability:** VHS; 3/4 U.

46570 ■ *The Time Trap*
American Media, Inc.
4621 121st St.
Urbandale, IA 50323-2311
Ph: (515)224-0919
Free: 888-776-8268

Fax: (515)327-2555
Co. E-mail: custsvc@ammedia.com
URL: http://www.ammedia.com
Released: 1982. **Description:** This program dramatically demonstrates techniques that can help individuals to manage their time better, avoiding those everyday time-wasting problems at the office. **Availability:** VHS; 3/4 U.

46571 ■ *The Time of Your Life*
Aspen Publishers, Inc.
7201 McKinney Cir.
Frederick, MD 21704
Ph: (301)698-7100
Free: 800-234-1660
Fax: (800)901-9075
Co. E-mail: customerservice@aspenpublisher.com
URL: http://www.aspenpublishers.com
Contact: Robert Becker, President
Released: 1985. **Price:** $570.00. **Description:** Based on Alan Lakein's bestseller, outlines 60 simple ideas on how to make more effective use of your time. A meeting guide and optional support materials are available. Revised and updated in 1991. **Availability:** VHS; 3/4 U.

46572 ■ *Using Others to Save Time*
Resources for Education & Management, Inc.
1804 Montreal Ct., Ste. A
Tucker, GA 30084
Released: 1972. **Description:** Delegation is defined as more than giving other people more work to do. It is shown to save time, and in the process, develop others' abilities. **Availability:** VHS; 3/4 U.

CONSULTANTS

46573 ■ Associations Plus
50 Laurelton Rd.
Mount Kisco, NY 10549-4218
Ph: (914)241-3917
Fax: (914)946-2674
Contact: Marie T. Rossi, President
Scope: Offers human resource development services specializing in sales training, support staff training, trade show selling, time management skills and stress management training. **Founded:** 1979. **Seminars:** Non-verbal Communications; Time/Stress Management; Better Selling Techniques; Trade Show Sales Techniques.

46574 ■ Carson Research Center
2957 Flamingo Dr.
Miami Beach, FL 33140-3916
Ph: (305)534-8846
Free: 800-541-8846
Fax: (305)532-8826
Co. E-mail: gayle@gaylecarson.com
URL: http://www.spunkyoldbroad.com
Contact: Dr. Gayle Carson, President
E-mail: gayle@gaylecarson.com
Scope: Human performance improvement consultants offering a wide variety of training opportunities for personnel of businesses of all kinds, state and national association and government agencies. General areas of training include management training, assertiveness, time management, change management, sales training, supervisory skills, coping with difficult people, stress management and strategic quality management and customer service, negotiation and shoe string marketing. Serves clients worldwide. Facilitation of board retreats, web-based programs available 24/7. **Founded:** 1980. **Publications:** "Creating a Winning Image"; "Making Meetings Work"; "How to Turn Customer Service Into an Ongoing Profit Center"; "Business 2005-Six Traits of Success"; "The Leading Edge"; "Communication Cash: How to Earn Fame & Fortune As a Professional Speaker"; "Winning Ways"; "How To Energize Your Life And Make The Difference You Want". **Seminars:** Dynamic Leadership; Business 2005; Negotiating to Win; How to Energize Your Life and Make the Difference You Want; Dealing with Difficult People; How to be A Great Coach; How To Turn Customer Service Into An Ongoing Profit Center; The Virtual Classroom.

46575 ■ Dr. Donald Kirkpatrick
842 Kirkland Ct.
Pewaukee, WI 53072-1822
Ph: (262)695-5851
Fax: (262)784-7994
Co. E-mail: dleekirk@aol.com
Contact: Dr. Donald L. Kirkpatrick, Owner
Scope: Gives presentations for professional societies including ASTD, IQPC, Training and linkage, and conducts in-house seminars for all levels of management on various subjects including: leadership and motivation, communications, managing change, time management, supervisory/management selection, training and development, performance appraisal, coaching, managing conflict, decision making, how to conduct productive meetings, and Evaluating Training Programs: The Four Levels. Serves private industries as well as government agencies. **Founded:** 1950. **Publications:** "Evaluating Training Programs; the Four Levels," Bennett-Koehler Publishers, 2006; "Developing Supervisors and Team Leaders," Butterworth-Heinemann, Jun, 2006. **Seminars:** Effective Communication; Leadership and Motivation; Teambuilding; Decision Making and Empowerment; Performance Appraisal and Coaching; How to Conduct Productive Meetings; How to Manage Change; Time Management; Orienting and Training Employees; Evaluating Training Programs; Training Tools/Supervisory; Management Inventories on Human Relations; Communications; Managing Change; Time Management; Performance Approval and Coaching; Modern Management; Leadership Motivation and Decision Making, Evaluating Training Programs: The Four Levels. **Telecommunication Services:** dleekirk1@aol.com.

46576 ■ Organization Plus
14 Palmer Rd.
Beverly, MA 01915
Ph: (978)922-6136
Fax: (978)922-0143
Co. E-mail: information@organizationplus.com
URL: http://www.organizationplus.com
Contact: Nancy G. Black, Chief Executive Officer
E-mail: nancy@organizationplus.com
Scope: Organizing consultant specializing in time management, clutter control, office organization and as a business consultant. Serves individuals and small businesses (including home based). **Founded:** 1983. **Seminars:** Get Organized, Get Energized!; Triumph Over Time; The 3 Hour Transformation; The National Association of Professional Organizers (NAPO); The National Association of Women Business Owners; Wellspring Working Capital; Home Based Businesswomen's Network; Cape Ann Chamber of Commerce; Small Business Administration.

46577 ■ Quma Learning Systems Inc.
505 S Val Vista Dr., Ste. 4
Mesa, AZ 85204-3215
Ph: (480)545-8311
Free: 800-622-6463
Fax: (480)545-8233
Co. E-mail: info@quma.net
URL: http://www.quma.net
Contact: Dr. Dennis R. Deaton, Chief Executive Officer
E-mail: dennis@quma.net
Scope: Business management firm that works with corporations in developing empowering cultures by laying the foundation of ownership spirit. Specializes in providing principles and tools for maximizing full potential in one's self by becoming more accountable, responsible and committed. **Founded:** 1985. **Publications:** "The Book On Mind Management Discussion Guide"; "The Ownership Spirit Handbook"; "The Book on Mind Management"; "Money: An Owner's Manual". **Seminars:** The Ownership Spirit; Visioneering; Life Management; Money: An Owner's Manual; Communicating For Success; Sustaining Peak Performance.

46578 ■ Smart Ways to Work
1441 Franklin St., Ste. 301
Oakland, CA 94612-3219
Ph: (510)763-8482
Free: 800-599-8463
Fax: (510)763-0790
Co. E-mail: odette@smartwaystowork.com
URL: http://www.smartwaystowork.com
Contact: Odette Pollar, Owner
E-mail: odette@smartwaystowork.com
Scope: A management consulting firm specializing in the training of supervisors, managers and professional staff in the area of time management, problem solving, decision making and strategic planning. Assists businesses and corporations in developing and implementing programs for increased productivity, greater profit and improved employee morale. Serves private industries as well as government agencies. **Founded:** 1979. **Publications:** "Surviving Information Overload driving Information Overload: How to Find, Filter, and Focus on What's Important," Crisp Publications, Sep, 2003; "Take Back Your Life: Smart Ways to Simplify Daily Living," Conari Press, Apr, 1999; "365 Ways to Simplify Your Work Life," Kaplan Business, Aug, 1996; "Dynamics of Diversity: Strategic Programs for Your Organization," Crisp Publications, 1994; "Organizing Your Workspace: A Guide to Personal Productivity," Crisp Publications, May, 1992. **Seminars:** Managing Multiple Demands: Surviving Ground Zero; Defending Your Life: Balancing Work And Home; Desktop Sprawl: Conquer Your Paper Pile-Up; Getting It All Done: Breaking The Time Bind; To Give or Not To Give: The Delegation Dilemma; Information Happens: Don't Let It Happen On You; Take The Terror Out Of Talk: Secrets To Successful Speaking; To Give or Not To Give: The Delegation Dilemma; Managing Meetings.

46579 ■ SunCoach Inc.—Schlenger Organizational Systems Inc.
6 Aberdeen Pl.
Fair Lawn, NJ 07410
Ph: (201)791-2396
Free: 800-764-3047
Fax: (201)796-5490
Co. E-mail: sunny@suncoach.com
Contact: Sunny Schlenger, President
E-mail: sunny@suncoach.com
Scope: Consults with corporate and individual clients in the areas of time management and office space organization. Offers group seminars and personal counseling in time management and related topics. **Founded:** 1978. **Publications:** "Organizing for the Spirit," Jossey-Bass J.Wiley & Sons, Apr, 2004; "How To Be Organized In Spite Of Yourself," Penguin Putnam, 1999; "Connections "; "What Are You Afraid Of"; "Redefining Yourself "; "When Old Dreams Change "; "What Do You Do When You've Run Out of Room"; "Get Organized: Heal the World"; "Reframing the Past "; "Giving Through Hospice"; "The Day The Ceiling Fell In". **Seminars:** Organizing as Self-Discovery: Preserving Your Legacy, Oct, 2009.

46580 ■ Harold Taylor Time Consultants Inc.
1176 N Shore Dr.
Dunnville, ON, Canada N1A 2W5
Ph: (905)296-4932
Free: 800-361-8463
Fax: (905)701-0970
Co. E-mail: info@taylorintime.com
URL: http://www.taylorintime.com
Contact: Harold L. Taylor, Chief Executive Officer
E-mail: harold@taylorintime.com
Scope: Offers time management seminars or workshops for managers, salespeople and support staff in all industries and organizations. Also available for keynote addresses. **Founded:** 1981. **Publications:** "Benefits of Time Management"; "The Truth About Multitasking"; "Schedule, Don't List"; "Put Off Procrastination"; "Am I a Workaholic?"; "Don't Be a Perfectionist"; "Shortcuts Through Life"; "Ten Principles of Scheduling"; "The Road to Success is Paved with Goals"; "Time Management for Creative People"; "The High Cost of Complexity"; "Scheduling is the Key to Goal Achievement"; "Sleep Deprivation, the Latest Time Waster"; "Pareto Visits a Retail Store". **Seminars:** Making Time Work For You, May, 2007; Time Management Tele class for Professional Organizers, Mar, 2007; Time management with the Palm; Managing Paperwork; Time Management for Students. **Telecommunication Services:** jason@taylorintime.com.

46581 ■ Time Masters - The Institute for Personal Excellence
776 South 980 East
Pleasant Grove, UT 84062-9531
Ph: (801)785-1105
Fax: (801)785-5035
Contact: Todd L. Pearson, President
Scope: Employs a telephone coaching approach to teaching personal productivity, one-on-one, to any location in the world. Focuses on implementation and application of success principles over four months. Training course focuses on motivation, personal leadership, time management, sales, and entrepreneurship. **Founded:** 1988. **Seminars:** The Time Masters Personal Productivity Seminars; Personal Skills One-on-One Coaching.

46582 ■ TWD & Associates—Thomas W. Dooley & Associates
431 S Patton Ave.
Arlington Heights, IL 60005-2253
Ph: (847)398-6410
Fax: (847)255-5095
Co. E-mail: tdoo@aol.com
Contact: Thomas W. Dooley, President
E-mail: twhdoo@yahoo.com
Scope: Consulting specialists in small business management particularly in the areas of personnel, training, marketing, franchising, sales, time management, budgeting, raising capital, and long-range planning. **Founded:** 1976. **Seminars:** Alternative Methods of Financing for Franchising; Effectiveness of Organizational Development Training Programs for Hourly-Hire Workers in Manufacturing Plants. **Special Services:** ABR®.

46583 ■ David L. Ward and Associates Inc.—Ward Mosaic Glass
1951 - 47th St., Ste. 179
San Diego, CA 92102
Ph: (619)266-2701
Fax: (773)935-3779
Co. E-mail: dward@wardmosaic.com
URL: http://www.wardmosaic.com
Contact: David L. Ward, President
E-mail: dward@wardmosaic.com
Scope: Specializes in mosaic glass art consulting. The firm provides various seminars on mosaic glass art. **Founded:** 1974. **Publications:** "Mosaic Glue Comparison Testing". **Seminars:** Mosaic Glass Art Workshop; How to Turn Your Glass Hobby Into a Money-Making Business.

ASSOCIATIONS AND OTHER ORGANIZATIONS

46584 ■ Exhibit Designers and Producers Association (EDPA)
10 Norden Pl.
Norwalk, CT 06855
Ph: (203)852-5698
Fax: (203)854-6735
Co. E-mail: jprovost@edpa.com
URL: http://www.edpa.com
Contact: Cam Stevens, President
Description: Firms designing and building exhibits for trade shows and museums. Conducts educational and research programs. **Founded:** 1954. **Publications:** *EDP Action News* (Bimonthly); *EDPA.COMmunications* (Monthly); *EDPA Today* (Quarterly). **Educational Activities:** Exhibit Designers and Producers Association Convention (Annual). **Awards:** Hazel Hays Award; Ambassador Award; EDDIE Award; Designer of the Year Award; Ambassador Award (Annual); Chapter of the Year (Annual); Hazel Hays Award (Annual).

46585 ■ Trade Show Exhibitors Association (TSEA)
2301 S Lake Shore Dr., Ste. 1005
Chicago, IL 60616
Ph: (312)842-8732
Fax: (312)842-8744
Co. E-mail: tsea@tsea.org
URL: http://www.tsea.org
Contact: Margit B. Weisgal, President
Description: Exhibitors working to improve the effectiveness of trade shows as a marketing tool. Purposes are to promote the progress and development of trade show exhibiting; to collect and disseminate trade show information; conduct studies, surveys, and stated projects designed to improve trade shows; to foster good relations and communications with organizations representing others in the industry; to undertake other activities necessary to promote the welfare of member companies. Sponsors Exhibit Industry Education Foundation and professional exhibiting seminars; the forum series of educational programs on key issues affecting the industry. Maintains placement services; compiles statistics. **Publications:** *Trade Show Ideas Magazine* (Monthly); *Trade Show Ideas*; *Trade Show Exhibitors Association--Membership Directory and Industry Buyer's Guide* (Continuous). **Awards:** Focus Awards; President's Award (Annual); Chairman's Award (Annual); Distinguished Service Award (Annual).

REFERENCE WORKS

46586 ■ "$3 Million in Repairs Prep Cobo for Auto Show" in Crain's Detroit Business (Vol. 26, January 4, 2010, No. 1, pp. 1)
Pub: Crain Communications Inc.
Ed: Nancy Kaffer. **Description:** Overview of the six projects priced roughly at $3 million which were needed in order to host the North American International Auto Show; show organizers stated that the work was absolutely necessary to keep the show in the city of Detroit.

46587 ■ "2008 Woman of the Year Gala" in Hispanic Business (Vol. 30, July-August 2008, No. 7-8, pp. 58)
Pub: Hispanic Business, Inc.
Ed: Brynne Chappell. **Description:** Brief report on the sixth annual Women of the Year Awards gala which was held at JW Marriott Desert Ridge Resort and Spa is given; 20 women were honored with these awards for their professional contribution, commitment to the advancement of the Hispanic community and involvement with charitable organizations.

46588 ■ "ALA: Hot Topics for Librarianship" in Information Today (Vol. 28, September 2011, No. 8, pp. 17)
Pub: Information Today, Inc.
Ed: Barbara Brynko. **Description:** Highlights from the American Library Association Annual Conference and Exhibition are listed. Thousands of attendees sought out services, displays, demos, new product rollouts, and freebies. Emerging technology for librarians, staff development, gray literature, interlibrary loans, and next-generation interfaces were among the topics discussed.

46589 ■ "And In This Briefcase" in Mergers & Acquisitions: The Dealmaker's Journal (March 1, 2008)
Pub: SourceMedia, Inc.
Description: ACG San Diego decided to address the impact the changes in the economy will have on potential private equity transactions as well as what criteria private equity firms are looking for when assessing a company. At the opening of the chapter's 2008 breakfast meeting, real-world case studies were utilized with the audiences' participation in order to assess pre-deal risk scenarios.

46590 ■ Annual Trade Show Directory
Pub: Forum Publishing Co.
Contact: Justo Rey, President
URL(s): www.forum123.com/inc/sdetail/214. **Released:** Annual; Latest edition 2011. **Price:** $39.95, Individuals. **Covers:** over 2,400 merchandise trade shows throughout the United States and Canada. **Entries include:** Company name, address, phone, estimated attendance and number of exhibitors, show description. **Arrangement:** Classified by product, then chronological. **Indexes:** Product, type of show.

46591 ■ "AREE Meets in Atlantic City" in Indoor Comfort Marketing (Vol. 70, June 2011, No. 6, pp. 28)
Pub: Industry Publications Inc.
Description: Highlights of the Atlantic Region Energy Expo are provided.

46592 ■ "Around the World in a Day" in Agency Sales Magazine (Vol. 39, August 2009, No. 8, pp. 36)
Pub: MANA
Ed: Jack Foster. **Description:** Highlights of Manufacturer's Agents National Association (MANA) member Les Rapchak one-day visit to Basra, Iraq are presented. Rapchak completed the trip via Frankfurt, Germany and Kuwait with a stop afterwards in Istanbul, Turkey. His purpose for the trip was to take part in a seminar at the State Company for Petrochemical Industries.

46593 ■ "Art Attack 2007 Comes to Minneapolis" in Art Business News (Vol. 34, November 2007, No. 11, pp. 11)
Pub: Pfingsten Publishing, LLC
Description: Overview of Art Attack 2007, an open studio and gallery crawl in the Northeast Minneapolis Arts District which featured artists working in glass, ceramics, jewelry, mosaics, mixed media, photography, painting, pottery, sculpture, textiles and wood.

46594 ■ "Art Miami Comes to Miami's Wynwood Art District" in Art Business News (Vol. 34, November 2007, No. 11, pp. 18)
Pub: Pfingsten Publishing, LLC
Description: In December, The Art Group will hold its Art Miami fair in the Wynwood Art District; the exhibitors range from painting, sculpture, video and works on paper.

46595 ■ "The Art of War for Women" in Hawaii Business (Vol. 54, July 2008, No. 1, pp. 23)
Pub: Hawaii Business Publishing
Description: Business consultant Chi-Ning Chu talks about her new book 'The Art of War for Women: Sun Tzu's Ancient Strategies and Wisdom for Winning at Work', which discusses how women can more effectively win in business. She also shares her thoughts about the advantages that women have, which they can use in businesses decisions.

46596 ■ "Artexpo Celebrates 30th Anniversary" in Art Business News (Vol. 34, November 2007, No. 11, pp. 18)
Pub: Pfingsten Publishing, LLC
Description: In honor of its 30th anniversary Artexpo New York 2008 will be an unforgettable show offering a collection of fine-art education courses for both trade and consumer attendees and featuring a variety of artists working in all mediums.

46597 ■ "An Artwork in Progress" in Hawaii Business (Vol. 53, March 2008, No. 9, pp. 45)
Pub: Hawaii Business Publishing
Ed: Jolyn Okimoto Rosa. **Description:** Art galleries in Honolulu, Hawaii holds the First Friday Gallery Walk and other special events, which draw crowd to and increase sales activities in the city's downtown. The district also advocates for the reintroduction of Honolulu's Chinatown to the people. Details regarding the art galleries' Chinatown revival and its local economic impact are discussed.

46598 ■ "Attorney Panel Tackles Contract Questions" in Agency Sales Magazine (Vol. 39, September-October 2009, No. 9, pp. 8)
Pub: MANA
Ed: Jack Foster. **Description:** MANAfest conference tackled issues regarding a sales representative's contract. One attorney from the panel advised reps

to go through proposed agreements with attorneys who are knowledgeable concerning rep laws. Another attorney advised reps to communicate with a company to ask about their responsibilities if that company is facing financial difficulty.

46599 ■ "Auto Show Aims to Electrify" in Crain's Detroit Business (Vol. 26, January 11, 2010, No. 2, pp. 1)
Pub: Crain Communications, Inc.

Ed: Ryan Beene. **Description:** Overview of the North American International Auto show include sixteen production and concept vehicles including eight from the Detroit 3. High-tech battery suppliers as well as hybrid and electric vehicles will highlight the show.

46600 ■ "Avanti Hosts Users Conference" in American Printer (Vol. 128, July 1, 2011, No. 7)
Pub: Penton Media Inc.

Description: Avanti Computer Systems Ltd. hosted its 19th annual users conference in Washington DC. In-plant and commercial printers were in attendance.

46601 ■ "BBB Hires Marketing Firm to Attract More Businesses" in Baltimore Business Journal (Vol. 27, January 1, 2010, No. 35, pp. 1)
Pub: American City Business Journals

Ed: Julekha Dash. **Description:** Better Business Bureau (BBB) of Greater Maryland hired Bystry Carson & Associates Ltd. to assist in its rebranding efforts in order to entice more businesses. Bystry Carson will promote BBB's new mission at lectures, seminars, and networking events, as well as educate businesses about the agency through blogs and Twitter. BBB's services are also outlined.

46602 ■ "Biz Assesses 'Textgate' Fallout; Conventions, Smaller Deals Affected" in Crain's Detroit Business (Vol. 24, March 31, 2008)
Pub: Crain Communications, Inc.

Ed: Tom Henderson. **Description:** Businesspeople who were trying to measure the amount of economic damage is likely to be caused due to Mayor Kwame Kilpatrick's indictment on eight charges and found that: automotive and other large global deals are less likely to be affected than location decisions by smaller companies and convention site decisions. Also being affected are negotiations in which Mexican startup companies were planning a partnership with the TechTown incubator to pursue opportunities in the auto sector; those plans are being put on hold while they look at other sites.

46603 ■ "Bottom-Fishing and Speed-Dating in India" in Barron's (Vol. 88, March 24, 2008, No. 12, pp. M12)
Pub: Dow Jones & Company, Inc.

Ed: Elliot Wilson. **Description:** Indian stocks have fallen hard in 2008, with Mumbai's Sensex 30 down 30 percent from its January 2008 peak of 21,000 to 14,995 in March. The India Private Equity Fair 2008 attracted 140 of the world's largest private equity firms and about 24 of India's fastest-growing corporations. Statistical data included.

46604 ■ "The British Aren't Coming" in Crain's Chicago Business (Vol. 34, October 24, 2011, No. 42, pp. 3)
Pub: Crain Communications Inc.

Ed: Brigid Sweeney. **Description:** In a move to attract tourists back to Chicago, its Convention and Tourism Bureau is marketing in London, England, Mexico, and Canada, but not Germany or France because of budget constraints.

46605 ■ "Calendar" in Crain's Detroit Business (Vol. 24, March 10, 2008, No. 10, pp. 21)
Pub: Crain Communications, Inc.

Description: Listing of events in the Detroit area include conferences addressing entrepreneurialism, economic development, and women business ownership.

46606 ■ "Calendar" in Crain's Detroit Business (Vol. 24, March 17, 2008, No. 11, pp. 20)
Pub: Crain Communications, Inc.

Description: Listing of events in the Detroit area include conferences addressing entrepreneurialism, economic development, and women business ownership.

46607 ■ "Calendar" in Crain's Detroit Business (Vol. 24, March 24, 2008, No. 12, pp. 25)
Pub: Crain Communications, Inc.

Description: Listing of events in the Detroit area include conferences addressing entrepreneurialism, economic development, and women business ownership.

46608 ■ "Calendar" in Crain's Detroit Business (Vol. 24, March 31, 2008, No. 13, pp. 1)
Pub: Crain Communications, Inc.

Description: Listing of events in the Detroit area include conferences addressing entrepreneurialism, economic development, and minority business ownership.

46609 ■ "Calendar" in Crain's Detroit Business (Vol. 24, April 7, 2008, No. 14, pp. 27)
Pub: Crain Communications, Inc.

Description: Listing of events in the Detroit area include conferences addressing entrepreneurialism, economic development, and minority business ownership.

46610 ■ "Calendar" in Crain's Detroit Business (Vol. 24, April 14, 2008, No. 15, pp. 25)
Pub: Crain Communications Inc.

Description: Listing of events in the Detroit area include conferences addressing entrepreneurialism, economic development, and ways in which to develop environmentally friendly buildings.

46611 ■ "Calendar" in Crain's Detroit Business (Vol. 24, September 22, 2008, No. 38, pp. 17)
Pub: Crain Communications Inc.

Description: Listing of events in the Detroit area include conferences addressing entrepreneurialism, economic development, and women business ownership.

46612 ■ "Calendar" in Crain's Detroit Business (Vol. 24, October 6, 2008, No. 40, pp. 22)
Pub: Crain Communications, Inc.

Description: Listing of events in the Detroit area include conferences addressing entrepreneurialism, economic development, manufacturing, marketing, the housing crisis and women business ownership.

46613 ■ "Calendar" in Crain's Detroit Business (Vol. 26, January 11, 2010, No. 2, pp. 16)
Pub: Crain Communications Inc.

Description: Listing of events includes seminars sponsored by the Detroit Economic Club as well as conferences dealing with globalization and graphic design.

46614 ■ "Calendar" in Crain's Detroit Business (Vol. 26, January 18, 2010, No. 3, pp. 16)
Pub: Crain Communications Inc.

Description: Listing of events includes seminars sponsored by the Detroit Economic Club as well as conferences dealing with globalization and marketing.

46615 ■ "CarBiz Inc. Speaking At NABD" in Canadian Corporate News (May 14, 2007)
Pub: Comtex News Network Inc.

Description: CarBiz Inc., a leading provider of software, consulting, and training solutions to the United States' automotive industry, had two of its executive officers speak at the National Alliance of Buy Here - Pay Here Dealers (NABD), a conference that draws over 2,000 dealers, service providers, and experts from across the United States.

46616 ■ "Celebrate Success. Embrace Innovation" in Black Enterprise (Vol. 37, February 2007, No. 7, pp. 145)
Pub: Earl G. Graves Publishing Co. Inc.

Description: 2007 Women of Power Summit provides networking opportunities, empowerment sessions, and nightly entertainment. More than 500 executive women of color are expected to attend this inspiring summit in Phoenix, February 7-10.

46617 ■ "Change Is in the Air" in Agency Sales Magazine (Vol. 39, August 2009, No. 8, pp. 30)
Pub: MANA

Ed: Jack Foster. **Description:** Highlights of the Power-Motion Technology Representatives Association (PTRA) 37th Annual Conference, which projected an economic upturn, are presented. Allan Bealulieu of the Institute for Trend Research gave the positive news while Manufacturer's Agents National Association (MANA) president Brain Shirley emphasized the need to take advantage of a turnaround.

46618 ■ "Chattanooga at a Glance" in Women In Business (Vol. 62, June 2010, No. 2, pp. 29)
Pub: American Business Women's Association

Ed: Jill Yates Bagby. **Description:** City of Chattanooga, Tennessee is the location of the 2010 American Business Women's Association (ABWA) National Women's Leadership Conference. The city offers historical sites, parks and tourist attractions, as well as dining options.

46619 ■ "City's Hilton Hotel Still Losing Money" in Baltimore Business Journal (Vol. 28, October 15, 2010, No. 23, pp. 1)
Pub: Baltimore Business Journal

Ed: Danile J. Sernovitz. **Description:** Baltimore, Maryland-owned Hilton Baltimore Convention Center Hotel has been expected by Baltimore Hotel Corporation to wrap up 2010 with a $9.8 million deficit after completing its first year in operation in the red. The forecast would mark the controversial project's third-straight year of losses.

46620 ■ "Clinic to Use Medical Summit to Pump Up Cardiology Center" in Crain's Cleveland Business (Vol. 28, October 1, 2007, No. 39, pp. 6)
Pub: Crain Communications, Inc.

Ed: Chuck Soder. **Description:** Overview of the Medical Innovation Summit, sponsored by the Cleveland Clinic and regional business recruitment group Team NEO, whose theme was cardiology. The goal for this year's summit went beyond finding companies for the cardiovascular center, it also looked to market the region to other industries with growth potential.

46621 ■ "Clusters Last Stand?" in Canadian Electronics (Vol. 23, February 2008, No. 1, pp. 6)
Pub: CLB Media Inc.

Description: Survival of technology clusters was the focus of Strategic Microelectronics Council's conference entitled, 'The Power of Community: Building Technology Clusters in Canada'. Clusters can help foster growth in the microelectronics sector, and it was recognized that government intervention is needed to maintain these clusters.

46622 ■ "Conference Calendar" in Marketing to Women (Vol. 21, April 2008, No. 4, pp. 7)
Pub: EPM Communications Inc.
Contact: Ira Mayer, President
E-mail: imayer@epmcom.com

Description: Listing of current conferences and events concerning women, marketing and business.

46623 ■ "Conference Calendar" in Marketing to Women (Vol. 21, March 2008, No. 3, pp. 7)
Pub: EPM Communications Inc.
Contact: Ira Mayer, President
E-mail: imayer@epmcom.com

Description: Listing of current conferences and events aimed at women entrepreneurs and leaders.

46624 ■ *"Conference Calendar" in Marketing to Women (Vol. 21, February 2008, No. 2, pp. 1)*
Pub: EPM Communications Inc.
Contact: Ira Mayer, President
E-mail: imayer@epmcom.com
Description: Listing of current conferences and events concerning women, marketing and business.

46625 ■ *"Conference Calendar" in Marketing to Women (Vol. 22, July 2009, No. 7, pp. 7)*
Pub: EPM Communications Inc.
Contact: Ira Mayer, President
E-mail: imayer@epmcom.com
Description: Listing of conferences and seminars targeting female entrepreneurs.

46626 ■ *"Conference Calendar" in Marketing to Women (Vol. 22, August 2009, No. 8, pp. 7)*
Pub: EPM Communications Inc.
Contact: Ira Mayer, President
E-mail: imayer@epmcom.com
Description: Listing of conferences and seminars targeting female entrepreneurs.

46627 ■ *"Convention Budgeting Best Practice" in Franchising World (Vol. 42, November 2010, No. 11, pp. 11)*
Pub: International Franchise Association
Contact: Stephen J. Caldeira, Chief Executive Officer
E-mail: scaldeira@franchise.org
Ed: Steve Friedman. **Description:** Franchise conventions can offer benefits to both franchisor and franchisee in terms of culture-building, professional education and networking. However, these conventions can be costly. Tips for planning a successful franchising convention on a budget are outlined.

46628 ■ *"Convention Calendar" in Black Enterprise (Vol. 37, December 2006, No. 5, pp. 74)*
Pub: Earl G. Graves Publishing Co. Inc.
Description: Listing of conferences and summits targeting African American business owners and executives.

46629 ■ *Craft Inc: Turn Your Creative Hobby into a Business*
Pub: Chronicle Books LLC
Ed: Meg Mateo Ilasco. **Released:** September 2007. **Price:** $16.95. **Description:** Guide to help any crafter turn their hobby into a successful business. The book covers all aspects including pricing, sales and marketing, trade shows, as well as interviews with successful craft artisans Jonathan Adler, Lotta Jansdotter, Denyse Schmidt and Jill Bliss.

46630 ■ *"Datebook" in Crain's Chicago Business (Vol. 31, March 24, 2008, No. 12, pp. 18)*
Pub: Crain Communications, Inc.
Description: Listing of events in the Detroit area include conferences addressing entrepreneurialism, economic development, secrets of getting hired, and women business ownership.

46631 ■ *"Datebook" in Crain's Chicago Business (Vol. 31, March 31, 2008, No. 13, pp. 1)*
Pub: Crain Communications, Inc.
Description: Listing of events in the Detroit area include conferences addressing entrepreneurialism, economic development, secrets of getting hired, and women business ownership.

46632 ■ *"Datebook" in Crain's Chicago Business (Vol. 31, April 28, 2008, No. 17, pp. 18)*
Pub: Crain Communications, Inc.
Description: Listing of events in the Detroit area include conferences addressing entrepreneurialism, economic development, and women business ownership.

46633 ■ *"Datran Media Executives to Lead Industry Debates Across Q1 Conferences" in Internet Wire (January 22, 2010)*
Pub: Comtex News Network, Inc.
Description: Datran Media, an industry-leading digital marketing technology company, will be sending members of its management team to several conferences in the early part of the first quarter of 2010; discussions will include Internet marketing innovations, e-commerce and media distribution.

46634 ■ *"Designing Events Updates Online Suite" in Wireless News (October 25, 2009)*
Pub: Close-Up Media
Description: Designing Events, an outsourcing and consulting firm for conferences and meetings, announced the release of an update to its Designing Events Online suite of web-based management and marketing tools; features include enhanced versions of online registration and collaboration, content management, session development, social media and conference websites.

46635 ■ *"Detroit Hosts Conferences on Green Building, IT, Finance" in Crain's Detroit Business (Vol. 25, June 1, 2009, No. 22, pp. 9)*
Pub: Crain Communications Inc. - Detroit
Ed: Tom Henderson. **Description:** Detroit will host three conferences in June 2009, one features green technology, one information technology and the third will gather black bankers and financial experts from across the nation.

46636 ■ *"Developer Banks On East Submarket, Slowdown Not a Hinderance" in The Business Journal-Serving Greater Tampa Bay (August 1, 2008)*
Pub: American City Business Journals, Inc.
Ed: Janet Leiser. **Description:** CLW Industrial Group and Cobalt Industrial REIT II have teamed up to develop a 14-acre area in northeast Hillsborough County, Florida. The $15 million industrial park project includes the 175,000-square-foot New Tampa Commerce Center, scheduled for completion in the first quarter of 2009.

46637 ■ *"Developers Await Hotel" in The Business Journal-Portland (Vol. 25, July 11, 2008, No. 18, pp. 1)*
Pub: American City Business Journals, Inc.
Ed: Wendy Culverwell. **Description:** Developers are eager to start the construction of a new hotel at the Oregon Convention Center in Portland, Oregon as hey say that the project will help boost the convention center neighborhood. The project, called The Westin Portland at the Convention Center, is partly handled by Ashforth Pacific Inc.

46638 ■ *"The Display Group Is Super-Sized" in Michigan Vue (Vol. 13, July-August 2008, No. 4, pp. 34)*
Pub: Entrepreneur Media Inc.
Description: Profile of the Display Group, located in downtown Detroit, this company provides custom designed mobile marketing displays as well as special event production services for trade show displays. The rental house and design service is also beginning to see more business due to the film initiative, which provides incentives for films that are shooting in Michigan.

46639 ■ *"Dow Champions Innovative Energy Solutions for Auto Industry at NAIAS" in Business of Global Warming (January 25, 2010, pp. 7)*
Pub: Investment Weekly News
Description: This year's North American International Auto Show in Detroit will host the 'Electric Avenue' exhibit sponsored by the Dow Chemical Company. The display will showcase the latest in innovative energy solutions from Dow as well as electric vehicles and the technology supporting them. This marks the first time a non-automotive manufacturer is part of the main floor of the show.

46640 ■ *"Downtowns Must Court Young, CEOs for Cities President Says" in Crain's Detroit Business (Vol. 24, October 6, 2008,*
No. 40, pp. 18)
Pub: Crain Communications, Inc.
Ed: Amy Lane. **Description:** It is important to produce more college graduates, and keep them in Michigan, according to CEOs for Cities President Carol Coletta when she spoke to a session at the West Michigan Regional Policy Conference which was held in September in Grand Rapids. Ways in which city leaders can connect students to communities, resulting in employees who have vested interest in the region, are also discussed.

46641 ■ *"The Early Bird Gets the Worm" in Black Enterprise (Vol. 37, January 2007, No. 6, pp. 111)*
Pub: Earl G. Graves Publishing Co. Inc.
Ed: Tykisha N. Lundy. **Description:** General Motors hosts the Black Enterprise Conference And Expo: Where Deals Are Made at Walt Disney World's Swan and Dolphin Resort, May 9-12. The conference will offer great information to entrepreneurs.

46642 ■ *"East-Side Real Estate Forum Detours To Grand Rapids" in Crain's Detroit Business (Vol. 24, October 6, 2008, No. 40, pp. 17)*
Pub: Crain Communications, Inc.
Ed: Daniel Duggan. **Description:** Tom Wackerman was elected chairman of the University of Michigan-Urban Land Institute Real Estate Forum and proposed that the annual conference be held in Grand Rapids due to the brisk economic activity he was finding there; although the idea was initially met with resistance, the plan to introduce East-siders to the West side began receiving more enthusiasm due to the revitalization of the area, which was once considered to have a bleak outlook. Many are hoping to learn the lessons of those who were able to change a negative economic climate into a positive one in which the cooperation of private business and government can work together to accomplish goals.

46643 ■ *"Economy Forcing Meeting Planners to Think Fast" in Crain's Cleveland Business (Vol. 30, June 15, 2009, No. 23, pp. 15)*
Pub: Crain Communications, Inc.
Ed: Amy Ann Stoessel. **Description:** Meeting planners are working hard to meet lower corporate budgets when planning events.

46644 ■ *"Entrepreneurs Conference" in Black Enterprise (Vol. 38, February 2008, No. 7, pp. 163)*
Pub: Earl G. Graves Publishing Co. Inc.
Description: Black Enterprise Entrepreneurs Conference and Expo will be held May 14-17, 2008 at the Charlotte Westin Hotel and Charlotte Convention Center in North Carolina. Entrepreneurs are given the opportunity to present their business ideas in the Bevator Pitch Competition for a chance to win products and services.

46645 ■ *"Events Struggling with Fees" in Philadelphia Business Journal (Vol. 28, November 20, 2009, No. 40, pp. 1)*
Pub: American City Business Journals
Ed: Peter van Allen. **Description:** Dad Vail Regatta organizers told Philadelphia officials their plans to move the rowing event out of Philadelphia into Rumson, New Jersey was due to rising fees from the city and the loss of corporate sponsorship. Smaller events have been left out of funding or transferred to other locations due, in part, to higher fees also.

46646 ■ *"Facebook, Adobe, Kenshoo, Outright and Cignex Datamatics Sign On to X.commerce" in Entertainment Close-Up (October 24, 2011)*
Pub: Close-Up Media
Description: Facebook, Adobe, Kenshoo, Outright and Cignex Datamatics have all partnered with X.commerce's ecosystem, where developers build and merchants can come to shop for new technologies and services.

46647 ■ *"Finding Room for Financing" in The Business Journal-Serving Metropolitan*

***Kansas City** (Vol. 26, August 1, 2008, No. 47, pp. 1)*
Pub: American City Business Journals, Inc.
Ed: Rob Roberts. **Description:** Kansas City officials are expecting to receive financing recommendations for a new 1,000-room convention headquarters hotel. The $300-million project could be financed either through private ownership with public subsidies, or through public ownership with tax-exempt bond financing. Other views and information on the project and its expected economic impact, are presented.

46648 ■ *"Four Exhibition Considerations"* in *American Printer* (Vol. 128, August 1, 2011, No. 8)*
Pub: Penton Media Inc.
Description: Four questions to ask at the Graph Expo will help printers improve their own business.

46649 ■ *"Grainger Show Highlights Building Green, Economy"* in *Contractor* (Vol. 57, February 2010, No. 2, pp. 3)*
Pub: Penton Media, Inc.
Ed: Candace Roulo. **Description:** chief U.S. economist told attendees of the Grainger's 2010 Total MRO Solutions National Customer Show that the economic recovery would be subdued. Mechanical contractors who attended the event also learned about building sustainable, green products, and technologies, and economic and business challenges.

46650 ■ *"Grand Action Makes Grand Changes in Grand Rapids"* in *Crain's Detroit Business* (Vol. 25, June 1, 2009, No. 22, pp. M012)*
Pub: Crain Communications Inc. - Detroit
Ed: Amy Lane. **Description:** Businessman Dick De-Vos believes that governments are not always the best to lead certain initiatives. That's why, in 1991, he gathered 50 west Michigan community leaders and volunteers to look consider the construction of an arena and expanding or renovating local convention operations. Grand Action has undertaken four major projects in the city.

46651 ■ *"Half a World Away"* in *Tampa Bay Business Journal* (Vol. 30, December 4, 2009, No. 50, pp. 1)*
Pub: American City Business Journals
Ed: Jane Meinhardt. **Description:** Enterprise Florida has offered four trade grants for Florida's marine industry businesses to give them a chance to tap into the Middle East market at the Dubai International Boat Show on March 9 to 13, 2010. The grants pay for 50 percent of the exhibition costs for the qualifying business.

46652 ■ *"Here's the Deal"* in *Crain's Cleveland Business* (Vol. 30, June 15, 2009, No. 23, pp. 14)*
Pub: Crain Communications, Inc.
Description: Incentives being offered by hotels, restaurants, golf courses and major chains in order to promote bookings for meetings or conferences in the Cleveland area are listed.

46653 ■ *"Herrell's Launches New Corporate Identity at Fancy Food Show"* in *Ice Cream Reporter* (Vol. 23, July 20, 2010, No. 8, pp. 3)*
Pub: Ice Cream Reporter
Description: Herrell's ice cream introduced a new corporate branding at the Summer 2010 Fancy Food Show last summer. Slightly Mad Communications advertising agency developed the new brand to reflect the era of the early 1970s.

46654 ■ *"Hotel Tax Eyed For Waukesha"* in *The Business Journal-Milwaukee* (Vol. 25, August 29, 2008, No. 49, pp. A1)*
Pub: American City Business Journals, Inc.
Ed: Rich Kirchen. **Description:** Midwest Airlines Center chairman Frank Gimbel wants Waukesha County to help in the funding of the $200-million expansion of the convention center through a hotel room tax. The Waukesha hotel industry is expected to oppose the new room tax. Other views and information on the planned new room tax in Waukesha are presented.

46655 ■ *"How to Declutter Your Life Closet Cleanup: Putting a Lid on Clutter"* in *Atlanta Journal-Constitution* (May 1, 2011)*
Pub: Atlanta Journal-Constitution
Ed: Felicia Feaster. **Description:** The annual Closets and Home Organization Convention and Expo spotlights new products and services designed to help people get organized at home or the workplace. The organization sector is holding steady despite the recession and is expected to expand into garage organization.

46656 ■ *"IFA-AAG Professional Athlete Franchise Summit Scores"* in *Franchising World* (Vol. 42, August 2010, No. 8, pp. 56)*
Pub: International Franchise Association
Ed: Miriam L. Brewer. **Description:** The first International Franchise Association-Allied Athlete Group Franchise summit spotlighted athletes turned business owners addressing peers on franchising. The summit is expected to become an annual event.

46657 ■ *"Industry Events 2011"* in *American Printer* (Vol. 128, August 1, 2011, No. 8)*
Pub: Penton Media Inc.
Description: Listing of events of interest to graphic arts and printing businesses in presented.

46658 ■ *"Industry/Events 2011"* in *American Printer* (Vol. 128, July 1, 2011, No. 7)*
Pub: Penton Media Inc.
Description: PMA, the Worldwide Community of Imaging Association launched its new CliQ with how-to tips, product reviews and monthly photo contests. PMA formed a partnership with the Consumer Electronics Association to make changes to this year's annual convention.

46659 ■ *"IPEX Moves to London Venue"* in *American Printer* (Vol. 128, July 1, 2011, No. 7)*
Pub: Penton Media Inc.
Description: IPES 2014 is being relocated to London's ExCeL International Exhibition and Conference Centre from March 26 to April 2, 2014.

46660 ■ *"Javo Beverage to Feature On-Demand Coffee System"* in *GlobeNewswire* (October 20, 2009)*
Pub: Comtex News Network, Inc.
Description: During the National Association of Convenience Store Show (NACS) at the Las Vegas Convention Center, Javo Beverage Company, Inc., a leading provider of premium dispensable coffee and tea-based beverages to the foodservice industry, will introduce its on-demand hot coffee system as well as a new line of products for the convenience store industry.

46661 ■ *"Jay Berkowitz to Present Making Social Media Money Seminar at Affiliate Summit West"* in *Entertainment Close-Up* (January 15, 2010)*
Pub: Close-Up Media
Description: Highlights of Jay Berkowitz's conference, 'Making Social Media Make Money' include ways in which to develop Internet marketing strategies that will maximize Website traffic and convert that traffic to sales.

46662 ■ *"Kent Officials Seek Further KSU, City Unity"* in *Crain's Cleveland Business* (Vol. 28, December 3, 2007, No. 48, pp. 3)*
Pub: Crain Communications, Inc.
Ed: Jay Miller. **Description:** Kent State University and Portage County are searching for a developer who will use a three-acre parcel to bring new life to the city's sagging downtown and create an area that will better link the town and the Kent State campus. The project will include a hotel and conference center as well as retail and restaurant space.

46663 ■ *"Kuno Creative to Present B2B Social Media Campaign Webinar"* in *Entertainment Close-Up* (August 25, 2011)*
Pub: Close-Up Media
Description: Kuno Creative, an inbound marketing agency, will host Three Steps of a Successful B2B Social Media Campaign. The firm is a provider of Website development, branding, marketing strategy, public relations, Internet marketing, and inbound marketing.

46664 ■ *"Let's Put On a Show"* in *Inc.* (November 2007, pp. 127)*
Pub: Gruner & Jahr USA Publishing
Ed: Elaine Appleton Grant. **Description:** Profile of Jeff Baker, CEO of Image 4, designer of trade show exhibits. Baker shares details of the firm's commitment to being green.

46665 ■ *"Local Green Technology on Display"* in *Crain's Detroit Business* (Vol. 26, January 18, 2010, No. 3, pp. 1)*
Pub: Crain Communications Inc.
Ed: Ryan Beene. **Description:** Detroit's 2010 North American International Auto Show put the newest, most innovative green technologies on display showing that the Southeast Michigan automobile industry is gaining traction with its burgeoning e-vehicle infrastructure. Think, a Norwegian electric city-car manufacturer is eyeing sites in Southeast Michigan in which to locate its corporate headquarters and technical center for its North American branch.

46666 ■ *"Look, Leap, and License"* in *Retail Merchandiser* (Vol. 51, July-August 2011, No. 4, pp. 16)*
Pub: Phoenix Media Corporation
Description: Toys highlighting the Licensing International Expo 2011 included a life-sized Cookie Monster, Papa Smurf, Power Rangers, Transformer, and margarita wrestlers. Taking licensed properties international was a common theme at this year's show.

46667 ■ *Mail Order in the Internet Age*
Pub: Morgan James Publishing, LLC
Ed: Ted Ciuba. **Released:** May 2004. **Price:** $19.95.
Description: Direct response market, or mail order, for marketing and selling a product or service is discussed, with emphasis on how direct marketing compares favorably to other methods in terms of speed, ease, profitability, and affordability. Advice is given for writing ads; seminars to attend; and newsletters, mailing lists and magazines in which to subscribe.

46668 ■ *"Major Golf Retail Show in the Rough for 2010"* in *Orlando Business Journal* (Vol. 26, January 15, 2010, No. 33, pp. 1)*
Pub: American City Business Journals
Ed: Anjali Fluker. **Description:** The 57th Annual PGA Merchandise Show in Orlando, Florida is projected to attract 39,000 attendees in 2010, compared with 41,000 in 2009. According to the Orange County Convention Center, economic benefits that could be obtained from the 2010 edition of the golf retail show might reach only $77 million, compared with $78 million generated last year.

46669 ■ *"MANAfest Provides Reps with Tools for the Future"* in *Agency Sales Magazine* (Vol. 39, September-October 2009, No. 9, pp. 36)*
Pub: MANA
Ed: Jack Foster. **Description:** Former Harley Davidson director of communications Ken Schmidt was the keynote speaker at the MANAfest conference; he discussed how the company delivered itself from bankruptcy. Selling Power magazine publisher Gerhard Gschwandtner also made a presentation; he believes that there will be opportunities for sales people involved in relationship selling.

46670 ■ *"Minnesota ABC Event Looks at Government Contracting"* in *Finance and Commerce Daily Newspaper* (November 23, 2010)*
Pub: Dolan Media Newswires
Ed: Brian Johnson. **Description:** Minnesota Associated Builders and Contractors hosted an event focusing on doing business with government agencies. Topics included bidding work, awarding jobs, paperwork, guidelines, certifications and upcoming projects.

46671 ■ *"More Than 1,000 Attend Second WaterSmart"* in *Contractor* (Vol. 56, November 2009, No. 11, pp. 3)*
Pub: Penton Media, Inc.
Description: Over 1,000 plumbing and water conservation professionals attended the second WaterSmart Innovations Conference and Exposition in Las

Vegas. Plumbing industry personalities made presentations during the conference and several innovative products were displayed at the trade show.

46672 ■ "Nobody Knows What To Do" in Barron's (Vol. 88, March 17, 2008, No. 11, pp. 40)
Pub: Dow Jones & Company, Inc.
Ed: Mark Veverka. Description: Attendees of the South by Southwest Interactive conference failed to get an insight on how to make money on the Web from former Walt Disney CEO Michael Eisner when Eisner said there's no proven business model for financing projects. Eisner said he finances his projects with the help of his connections to get product-placement deals.

46673 ■ "Norvax University Health Insurance Sales Training and Online Marketing Conference" in Internet Wire (January 27, 2010)
Pub: Comtex News Network, Inc.
Description: Overview of the Norvax University Marketing and Sales Success Conference Tour which includes insurance sales training seminars, proven and innovative online marketing techniques and a host of additional information and networking opportunities.

46674 ■ "Not Enough Room" in Austin Business JournalInc. (Vol. 29, November 13, 2009, No. 36, pp. A1)
Pub: American City Business Journals
Ed: Jacob Dirr. Description: Hotel and convention business in downtown Austin, Texas lost nearly $5.3 million when Dell Inc. relocated its annual convention to Las Vegas. However, lack of capital caused the postponement of various hotel projects which need to be finished in order to attract well-attended conventions. Makeover projects on Austin's Waller Creek and Sixth Street are discussed.

46675 ■ "Now See This" in Entrepreneur (Vol. 36, April 2008, No. 4, pp. 53)
Pub: Entrepreneur Media, Inc.
Ed: Mike Hogan. Description: New high definition (HD) products are to be introduced in 2008 at the Consumer Electronics Show and the Macworld Conference & Expo. HD lineup from companies such as Dell Inc. and Hewlett-Packard Co. are discussed.

46676 ■ "Nowspeed and OneSource to Conduct Webinar" in Internet Wire (December 14, 2009)
Pub: Comtex News Network, Inc.
Description: OneSource, a leading provider of global business information, and Nowspeed, an Internet marketing agency, will conduct a webinar titled 'How to Develop Social Media Content That Gets Results' in order to provide marketers insight into how to develop and optimize effective social media content to get consumer results that translate into purchases and lead generation.

46677 ■ "Nowspeed's David Reske to Speak at SolidWorks World 2010 in Anaheim" in Internet Wire (January 7, 2010)
Pub: Comtex News Network, Inc.
Description: David Reske, managing director at Nowspeed, an Internet marketing agency based in the Boston area, will be presenting at SolidWorks World 2010; the convention's presentation will focus on proven methodologies, practical tips and real-world case studies in order to help attendees leverage the powerful Internet marketing innovations that are proving effective for businesses.

46678 ■ "O'Loughlin Cuts $6 Million for Chesterfield Doubletree" in Saint Louis Business Journal (Vol. 32, September 2, 2011, No. 1, pp. 1)
Pub: Saint Louis Business Journal
Ed: Angela Mueller. Description: Lodging Hospitality Management (LHM) acquired the Doubletree Hotel and Conference Center in Chesterfield, Missouri and added it as the 18th hotel in its portfolio. LHM chairman and CEO Bob O'Loughlin plans to invest nearly $15 million in the hotel, including $9 for renovation.

46679 ■ "One World" in American Printer (Vol. 128, August 1, 2011, No. 8)
Pub: Penton Media Inc.
Description: Graph Expo will highlight entrepreneurs focused on the connection between content, technology and business models.

46680 ■ "The Open Mobile Summit Opens in San Francisco Today: John Donahoe CEO eBay to Keynote" in Benzinga.com (November 2, 2011)
Pub: Benzinga.com
Ed: Benzinga Staff. Description: eBay's CEO, John Donahoe was keynote speaker at the 4th Annual Open Mobile Summit held in San Francisco, California. eBay is one of the 130 companies participating as speakers at the event.

46681 ■ "Other First Place Winners From the Expo" in Ice Cream Reporter (Vol. 23, September 20, 2010, No. 10, pp. 8)
Pub: Ice Cream Reporter
Description: Sassy Cow Creamery, Columbus, Wisconsin; Stewarts, Saratoga Springs, New York; Purity Dairies, Nashville, Tennessee; Kemps, Cedarburg, Wisconsin, and Kelly Country Creamery also won first place awards for various categories at the 2010 World Dairy Expo.

46682 ■ "People/Calendar" in Brandweek (Vol. 49, April 21, 2008, No. 16, pp. 30)
Pub: VNU Business Media, Inc.
Description: Listing of current conferences, tradeshows and events concerning the marketing industry.

46683 ■ "People and Places" in Entrepreneur (Vol. 36, February 2008, No. 2, pp. 12)
Pub: Entrepreneur Media Inc.
Ed: Rieva Lesonsky. Description: Websites of different organizations that can provide entrepreneurs with business help are presented. Business-related events such as the Women in Charge conference and Xerox Smart Business Symposium are mentioned.

46684 ■ "PHCC Convention, Show Gets High Marks" in Contractor (Vol. 56, December 2009, No. 12, pp. 1)
Pub: Penton Media, Inc.
Ed: Robert P. Mader. Description: Plumbing-Heating-Cooling Contractors National Association has held its first convention and trade show in New Orleans, Louisiana. Attendees were treated to a variety of seminars and exhibitors during the event. Comments from event organizers are also given.

46685 ■ "Pipe Show Finds a Way for Smokers to Light Up" in Crain's Chicago Business (Vol. 31, April 28, 2008, No. 17, pp. 57)
Pub: Crain Communications, Inc.
Ed: H. Lee Murphy. Description: With the help of attorneys within its local membership of 150 pipe collectors, the Chicagoland Pipe Collectors Club will be allowed to smoke at its 13th International Pipe & Tobacciana Show at Pheasant Run Resort. The event is expected to draw 4,000 pipe enthusiasts from as far as China and Russia.

46686 ■ "Plan Your Next Event at Newport News Marriott at City Center" in Benzinga.com (July 29, 2011)
Pub: Benzinga.com
Ed: Benzinga Staff. Description: Newport News Marriott at City Center is promoting itself as the premier venue for business meetings, conventions and weddings.

46687 ■ "Plumbing, Heating Products Shine at Greenbuild" in Contractor (Vol. 57, January 2010, No. 1, pp. 3)
Pub: Penton Media, Inc.
Ed: Robert P. Mader. Description: Among the many exhibitors at Greenbuild 2009 was T&S Brass which showcased their low-flow pre-rinse spray valves and Watts Water Technologies which showed off their hot water recirculating system. Aquatherm and Acorn Engineering were also at the show.

46688 ■ "Plumbing, Heating Products Shine at Greenbuild Expo" in Contractor (Vol. 56, December 2009, No. 12, pp. 1)
Pub: Penton Media, Inc.
Ed: Robert P. Mader. Description: Greenbuild Show held in Phoenix, Arizona has showcased the latest in plumbing and heating products. Zurn displayed its EcoVantage line of fixtures and valves during the event. Meanwhile, Sloan Valve offered its washdown 1-pint/flush Alphine urinal.

46689 ■ "Polite Conversation" in Mergers & Acquisitions: The Dealmaker's Journal (March 1, 2008)
Pub: SourceMedia, Inc.
Description: In January, industry leaders and dealmakers met at Davos to discuss topics ranging from the possibility of a recession to what lies ahead in the deal market.

46690 ■ "Prepping for the Unpredictable" in Crain's Cleveland Business (Vol. 30, June 15, 2009, No. 23, pp. 16)
Pub: Crain Communications, Inc.
Ed: Joel Hammond. Description: Michael Ferrara, event planner and designer for Executive Caterers discusses the many events he has planned.

46691 ■ "Proposal for a Macomb County Visitors Bureau Draws Mixed Reaction" in Crain's Detroit Business (Vol. 24, March 31, 2008, No. 13)
Pub: Crain Communications, Inc.
Ed: Chad Halcom. Description: Discusses the newly formed M-59 Corridor Business Association and its proposal to create a convention and visitors bureau dedicated to the county's interests.

46692 ■ "Real-Life Coursework for Real-Life Business People" in Women In Business (Vol. 63, Summer 2011, No. 2, pp. 22)
Pub: American Business Women's Association
Ed: Leigh Elmore. Description: American Business Women's Association National Women's Leadership Conference provides members with academic business training courses. Members can take a variety of MBA-level courses that are taught by University of Kansas School of Business professors. Courses include marketing, management, leadership and communication and decision making.

46693 ■ "Renren Partners With Recruit to Launch Social Wedding Services" in Benzinga.com (June 7, 2011)
Pub: Benzinga.com
Ed: Benzinga Staff. Description: Renren Inc. and Recruit Company Ltd. partnered to build a wedding social media catering to engaged couples and newlyweds in China. The platform will integrate online wedding related social content and offline media such as magazine and wedding exhibitions.

46694 ■ "Rock Festival: High Spirited Conventioneers Celebrate Their Good Fortune" in Canadian Business (Vol. 81, March 31, 2008, No. 5)
Pub: Rogers Media
Ed: Jeff Sanford. Description: Soaring prices of commodities in the mining industry have been very good for the attendees of the 76th annual conference of the Prospectors & Developers Association of Canada. A speaker at the conference expects commodity prices to come off a bit but not fall dramatically as it did in the 1980's.

46695 ■ "RPA Preps for Building Radiant Conference, Show" in Contractor (Vol. 57, January 2010, No. 1, pp. 5)
Pub: Penton Media, Inc.
Description: Radiant Panel Association is accepting registrations for its Building Radiant 2010 Conference and Trade Show. The conference will discuss radiant heating as well as insurance and other legal matters for mechanical contractors.

46696 ■ "A Safe Bet" in Entrepreneur (Vol. 35, October 2007, No. 10, pp. 26)
Pub: Entrepreneur Media Inc.
Ed: Carol Tice. Description: U.S. Department of Defense has developed a program, called the Defense Venture Catalyst Initiative or DeVenCI, that will

match defense officials to the products that they need. DeVenCI uses conferences to showcase the defense contractors and their technologies to defense managers. Details of how this program helps both contractors and defense officials are overviewed.

46697 ■ *"Save the Date"* in *Mergers & Acquisitions: The Dealmaker's Journal (March 1, 2008)*
Pub: SourceMedia, Inc.
Description: Listing of conferences and forums that deal with business and investing, particularly with mergers and acquisitions. Includes dates, locations and Internet addresses.

46698 ■ *"Save the Date"* in *Barron's (Vol. 90, September 13, 2010, No. 37, pp. 35)*
Pub: Barron's Editorial & Corporate Headquarters
Ed: Mark Veverka. **Description:** Mark Hurd is the new Co-President of Oracle after being forced out at Hewlett-Packard where he faced a harassment complaint. HP fired Hurd due to expense account malfeasance. Hurd is also set to speak at an Oracle trade show in San Francisco on September 20, 2010.

46699 ■ *"Secrets To Trade Show Success"* in *Women Entrepreneur (September 12, 2008)*
Pub: Entrepreneur Media Inc.
Ed: Lesley Spencer Pyle. **Description:** Trade shows require an enormous amount of work, but they are an investment that can pay off handsomely because they allow a business to get their product or service in front of their target market. Advice regarding trade shows is given including selecting the correct venue, researching the affair and following up on leads obtained at the event.

46700 ■ *"Sherwin-Williams Workers Forgo Travel for Virtual Trade Show"* in *Crain's Cleveland Business (Vol. 28, October 15, 2007, No. 41)*
Pub: Crain Communications, Inc.
Ed: John Booth. **Description:** Overview of Cyber-Coating 2007, a cutting-edge virtual three-dimensional trade show that exhibitors such as Sherwin-Williams Co.'s Chemical Coatings Division will take part in by chatting verbally or via text messages in order to exchange information and listen to pitches just like they would on an actual trade show floor.

46701 ■ *"Show Dates"* in *Art Business News (Vol. 34, November 2007, No. 11, pp. 18)*
Pub: Pfingsten Publishing, LLC
Description: Listing of conferences, trade shows and gallery openings for artists and those in the art industry.

46702 ■ *"Silverdome Bidders Bring New Proposals"* in *Crain's Detroit Business (Vol. 24, March 17, 2008, No. 11, pp. 23)*
Pub: Crain Communications, Inc.
Ed: Daniel Duggan. **Description:** Discusses the seven plans which have been proposed as part of the third round of bidding for the Pontiac Silverdome; proposals range from Global Baseball Inc., a baseball league that would pit a team from every country against one another, to an Indian casino, a musical 'hall of fame', a convention center, a horse track, a hotel and an indoor water park.

46703 ■ *"Six Tips To Maximize Networking Opportunities"* in *Women Entrepreneur (November 3, 2008)*
Pub: Entrepreneur Media Inc.
Ed: Tamara Monosoff. **Description:** Networking events fall into the realm of business development as opposed to immediate sales opportunities. It is important to remember that these events provide a chance to build relationships that may someday help one's business. Tips to help make the most out of networking events are provided.

46704 ■ *"Social Media Event Slated for March 25"* in *Bellingham Business Journal (Vol. February 2010, pp. 3)*
Pub: Sound Publishing Inc.
Description: Center for Economic Vitality (CEV) and the Technology Alliance Group (TAG) will host the 2010 Social Media Conference at the McIntyre Hall

Performing Arts & Conference Center in Mt. Vernon, Washington. The event will provide networking opportunities for attendees.

46705 ■ *"Speak Better: Five Tips for Polished Presentations"* in *Women Entrepreneur (September 19, 2008)*
Pub: Entrepreneur Media Inc.
Ed: Suzannah Baum. **Description:** Successful entrepreneurs agree that exemplary public speaking skills are among the core techniques needed to propel their business forward. A well-delivered presentation can result in securing a new distribution channel, gaining new customers, locking into a new referral stream or receiving extra funding.

46706 ■ *"Sponsorship, Booths Available for Spring Business Showcase"* in *Bellingham Business Journal (Vol. February 2010, pp. 3)*
Pub: Sound Publishing Inc.
Description: Third Annual Spring Business Showcase still have space available for vendors and sponsors. The event gives local businesses the opportunity to increase their visibility and provides a means to increase sales and build relationships.

46707 ■ *"State of a Fair!"* in *Small Business Opportunities (March 2008)*
Pub: Harris Publications Inc.
Ed: Shelly Buss. **Description:** State fairs are money-making venues; one company made $2 million in 12 days at the Minnesota State Fair.

46708 ■ *"State Fairgrounds Adding Year-Round Attractions"* in *Crain's Detroit Business (Vol. 24, February 18, 2008, No. 7, pp. 17)*
Pub: Crain Communications Inc. - Detroit
Ed: Robert Ankeny. **Description:** Michigan State Fairgrounds and Exposition Center shares its plans to become a year-round recreation, entertainment and education center.

46709 ■ *"Success Products"* in *Black Enterprise (Vol. 37, February 2007, No. 7, pp. 135)*
Pub: Earl G. Graves Publishing Co. Inc.
Ed: Tanisha A. Sykes. **Description:** Using innovative resources that are already at your fingertips instead of trying to reach out to companies first is a great way to discover whether you have a viable idea or product. Be motivated to start an e-newsletter letting people know about your products and attend conferences like The Motivation Show, the world's largest exhibition of motivational products and services related to performance in business.

46710 ■ *"Tax-Free Zones Need Shows; Out-of-State Shoppers Are Key To Success"* in *Crain's Detroit Business (Vol. 24, January 28, 2008, No. 4)*
Pub: Crain Communications Inc. - Detroit
Ed: Daniel Duggan. **Description:** Sales tax-free zones are being considered by Michigan's legislators in order to promote the state as a conference destination.

46711 ■ *"Teachable Moments: Worth Every Penny"* in *Pet Product News (Vol. 64, December 2010, No. 12, pp. 34)*
Pub: BowTie Inc.
Ed: Cheryl Reeves. **Description:** Pet bird retailers can attain both outreach to customers and enhanced profitability by staging educational events such as the annual Parrot Palooza event of Burlington, New Jersey-based Bird Paradise. Aside from attracting a global audience, Parrot Palooza features seminars, workshops, classes, and bird-related contests.

46712 ■ *"Tic-Tac-Show"* in *American Printer (Vol. 128, August 1, 2011, No. 8)*
Pub: Penton Media Inc.
Description: Graph Expo has become the US print industry's main event. There will be as many as 500 exhibitors at this year's event and the Graphic Arts Show Company lists over 30 co-located events as well as 53 new sessions in the seminar program's 28 education categories.

46713 ■ *"Tightening Economy Squeezes Business Travel"* in *HRMagazine (Vol. 53, August 2008, No. 8, pp. 19)*
Pub: Society for Human Resource Management
Contact: Henry G. Jackson, President
E-mail: hjackson@shrm.org
Ed: Kathy Gurchiek. **Description:** New surveys show that some companies are not cutting out business travel, they are using cheaper hotels and cutting back on trade shows and conference travel. Statistical data included.

46714 ■ *"Tool Time"* in *Entrepreneur (Vol. 36, March 2008, No. 3, pp. 90)*
Pub: Entrepreneur Media Inc.
Ed: Nichole A. Torres. **Description:** DaVinci Institute holds an annual event in Colorado to display new products and inventions. Innovative Design Engineering Animation is a consulting company that helps inventors develop product through various stages. NineSigma Inc. has an online marketplace where inventors can post ideas for clients needing new products.

46715 ■ *"Tourism Bureau Seeks Hotel Tax Hike"* in *Baltimore Business Journal (Vol. 27, December 18, 2009, No. 32, pp. 1)*
Pub: American City Business Journals
Ed: Rachel Bernstein. **Description:** Baltimore, Maryland's tourism agency, Visit Baltimore, has proposed a new hotel tax that could produce $2 million annually for its marketing budget, fund improvements to the city's 30-year-old convention center and help it compete for World Cup soccer games. Baltimore hotel leaders discuss the new tax.

46716 ■ *Trade Shows Worldwide: An International Directory of Events, Facilities, and Suppliers*
Pub: Cengage Learning Inc.
Contact: Ronald Dunn, President
URL(s): www.gale.cengage.com. **Released:** Annual; Latest edition 30th, April 2012. **Price:** $645, Individuals. **Covers:** Over 10,000 trade shows and exhibitions, including those held at conferences, conventions, meetings, trade and industrial events, merchandise marts, and national expositions; 6,000 trade show sponsors and organizers; of trade show facilities, services, and information sources, approximately 5,900 conference and convention centers, about 600 visitor and convention bureaus, 400 World Trade Centers; sources of information for the trade show industry, including professional associations, consulting organizations, and publications; and 1,900 trade show industry service suppliers. **Entries include:** name, address, phone, fax, e-mail, website, toll-free, phone, fax, name and title of contact; show frequency; founding date; audience; number of attendees; price for display space; description of exhibits; registration fees; industry programs; social events; square feet/meters of exhibition space; number of meeting rooms needed; number of hotel rooms and nights needed; publications, dates and locations of future shows. **Database includes:** Ranked lists of events by amount of exhibit space needed and by number of hotel rooms needed. **Arrangement:** Separate sections for shows and exhibitions, for sponsors/organizers, and for trade show facilities, services, and information sources. **Indexes:** Chronological (show date), geographical (show location), subject, name and keyword.

46717 ■ *"Tradeshow Attendance Incentives Add Up"* in *Pet Product News (Vol. 64, December 2010, No. 12, pp. 14)*
Pub: BowTie Inc.
Ed: Mark E. Battersby. **Description:** Pointers on how pet specialty retailers can claim business travel tax and income tax deductions for expenses paid or incurred in participation at tradeshows, conventions, and meetings are presented. Information in form of these deductions could allow pet specialty retailers to gain business benefits, aside from the education and enjoyment involved with the travel.

46718 ■ *The Tradeshow Week Calendar*
Pub: Tradeshow Week Inc.
Contact: Maggie Moe, Manager
E-mail: maggie.moe@reedbusiness.com
URL(s): www.tradeshowweek.comwww.tradeshowweek.com/article/CA388902.html?q=CALENDAR.

Ed: Carri Jensen. **Released:** Annual; Latest edition December, 2003. **Price:** $10; Free with subscription to Tradeshow Week magazine. **Publication includes:** About 100 major North American trade shows and expositions for a one-week period six months from the date of the issue and one year from date of the issue; overseas trade shows and expositions for a one-week period eight months from the date of the issue. **Entries include:** Exposition name, dates, location, frequency of meeting, number of booths, number of companies exhibiting in show, expected attendance, name, address, phone and fax of show management. Principal content of publication is news and statistics on the tradeshow industry. **Arrangement:** Chronological.

46719 ■ *Tradeshow Week Data Book*
Pub: Tradeshow Week Inc.
Contact: Maggie Moe, Manager
E-mail: maggie.moe@reedbusiness.com
URL(s): www.tradeshowweek.comwww.reedbusiness.com, databook.tradeshowweek.com/aspx/TradeshowSearch.aspx. **Released:** Annual; Latest edition 2010. **Price:** $305, Individuals plus $25 shipping and handling. **Covers:** Nearly 5,300 trade and public shows with at least 5,000 net square feet of exhibit space scheduled in the United States and Canada up to five years from publication date. **Entries include:** Show title, show management and sponsor, show description, location, dates, general contractor, estimated net square feet of exhibit space, number and profile of exhibitors and participants, fees, associated seminars, meetings and conferences, show history, future dates and sites. **Arrangement:** Classified by industry category. **Indexes:** Geographical, alphabetical, chronological, show management, show size, rotation pattern, new shows.

46720 ■ *"Travel Tears" in Crain's Chicago Business (Vol. 31, November 17, 2008, No. 46, pp. 3)*
Pub: Crain Communications, Inc.
Ed: Bob Tita. **Description:** Hotels, restaurants and conventions are seeing a decline in profits due to corporate travel cutbacks and the sagging economy. City and state revenues derived from taxes on tourism-related industries are also suffering.

46721 ■ *"A Vegas Sensation Inaugural Artexpo Las Vegas" in Art Business News (Vol. 34, November 2007, No. 11, pp. 1)*
Pub: Pfingsten Publishing, LLC
Ed: Jennifer Dulin. **Description:** Overview of the first Artexpo Las Vegas which featured exhibitors, artists and buyers and was a wonderful place for networking.

46722 ■ *"Wal-Mart Doesn't Sell Council" in The Business Journal-Serving Metropolitan Kansas City (Vol. 26, July 4, 2008, No. 43, pp. 1)*
Pub: American City Business Journals, Inc.
Ed: Steve Vockrodt. **Description:** Wal-Mart Stores Inc. announced that it will move the location of its annual convention from Kansas City, Missouri to Orlando, Florida. The change of venue came after Rick Hughes, Kansas City Convention and Visitors Association president rejected Wal-Mart's proposal to subsidize a new hotel in the downtown area that is needed for the event.

46723 ■ *"The Weeks Ahead" in Crain's New York Business (Vol. 24, January 7, 2008, No. 1, pp. 26)*
Pub: Crain Communications, Inc.
Description: Listing of events in the Detroit area include conferences addressing entrepreneurialism, economic development, and women business ownership.

46724 ■ *"The Weeks Ahead" in Crain's New York Business (Vol. 24, January 14, 2008, No. 2, pp. 20)*
Pub: Crain Communications, Inc.
Description: Listing of events in the Detroit area include conferences addressing entrepreneurialism, economic development, and women business ownership.

46725 ■ *"Welcome to Babesland" in Women In Business (Vol. 62, June 2010, No. 2, pp. 33)*
Pub: American Business Women's Association
Ed: Leigh Elmore. **Description:** Music group, Four Bitchin' Babes will be performing at the 2010 American Business Women's Association's National Women's Leadership Conference. The group has been in the industry for 20 years and has released nine albums. The Four Bitchin' Babes consist of Sally Fingerett, Nancy Moran, Deirdre Flint, and Debi Smith.

46726 ■ *"Women of Power" in Black Enterprise (Vol. 41, November 2010, No. 4, pp. 94)*
Pub: Earl G. Graves Publishing Co. Inc.
Description: Black Enterprise Women of Power Summit will be held February 23-26, 2011 at the Ritz Carlton in Orlando, Florida. Speakers will offer insight into career, household, and life in general.

46727 ■ *"Women of Power Summit" in Black Enterprise (Vol. 38, February 2008, No. 7, pp. 163)*
Pub: Earl G. Graves Publishing Co. Inc.
Description: Third annual Women of Power Summit, hosted by State Farm, will host over 700 executive women of color offering empowerment sessions, tips for networking, along with entertainment.

46728 ■ *"Worry No. 1 at Auto Show" in Crain's Detroit Business (Vol. 24, January 21, 2008, No. 3, pp. 1)*
Pub: Crain Communications Inc. - Detroit
Ed: Brent Snavely. **Description:** Recession fears clouded activity at the 2008 Annual North American International Auto Show. Automakers are expecting to see a drop in sales due to slow holiday retail spending as well as fallout from the subprime lending crisis.

46729 ■ *"WQA's Leadership Conference Tackles Industry Issues" in Contractor (Vol. 56, October 2009, No. 10, pp. 3)*
Pub: Penton Media, Inc.
Ed: Candace Roulo. **Description:** Water Quality Association's Mid-Year Leadership Conference held in Bloomingdale, Illinois in September 2009 tackled lead regulation, water softeners, and product efficiency. The possibility of a WQA green seal was discussed by the Water Sciences Committee and the Government Relations Committee meeting.

46730 ■ *"Your Turn in the Spotlight" in Inc. (March 2008, pp. 30)*
Pub: Gruner & Jahr USA Publishing
Ed: Elaine Appleton Grant. **Description:** Profile of a Tennessee business that produces events and concerts. The company offers a complete package of services handling staging, lighting, video, musical instrument rentals, and audio support. The founder has decided to sell the business and details of the asking price, price rationale, the pros and cons of buying the firm and its bottom line are examined.

TRADE PERIODICALS

46731 ■ *Exhibit Builder*
Pub: Exhibit Builder Magazine
Contact: Jollen Ryan, Manager
URL(s): www.exhibitbuilder.net. **Released:** Periodic; 7/yr. **Price:** $45, Individuals; $50, Canada; $70, Other countries; $90, Other countries 2 years.

46732 ■ *Expo*
Pub: EXPO Magazine Inc.
URL(s): www.expoweb.com. **Ed:** Danica Tormohlen. **Released:** Monthly **Price:** Free U.S. residents only.

46733 ■ *Successful Meetings: The Authority on Meetings and Incentive Travel Management*
Pub: Successful Meetings
URL(s): www.mimegasite.com/mimegasite/index.jsp. **Released:** Monthly **Price:** $79, Individuals; $95, Canada; $195, Other countries.

VIDEOCASSETTES/ AUDIOCASSETTES

46734 ■ *It'll Be O.K. on the Day*
Video Arts, Inc.
c/o Aim Learning Group
8238-40 Lehigh
Morton Grove, IL 60053-2615
Free: 877-444-2230
Fax: (416)252-2155
Co. E-mail: service@aimlearninggroup.com
URL: http://www.aimlearninggroup.com
Released: 1989. **Price:** $695.00. **Description:** Understand the best way to set up an exhibition booth so that it will be most efficient. **Availability:** VHS; 3/4 U.

46735 ■ *That's Show Business: The Rules of Exhibiting*
Video Arts, Inc.
c/o Aim Learning Group
8238-40 Lehigh
Morton Grove, IL 60053-2615
Free: 877-444-2230
Fax: (416)252-2155
Co. E-mail: service@aimlearninggroup.com
URL: http://www.aimlearninggroup.com
Released: 1991. **Price:** $790.00. **Description:** A sensible yet humorous approach to business exhibitions show the most common mistakes and how to avoid them. **Availability:** VHS; 8 mm; 3/4 U; Special order formats.

46736 ■ *The Trade Show Advantage*
Creative Training Solutions
5 Timberline Dr.
Voorhees, NJ 08043
Ph: (856)784-3468
Free: 800-515-4114
Fax: (856)784-7087
Co. E-mail: mail@creativetraining.com
URL: http://www.creativetraining.com
Released: 19??. **Price:** $395.00. **Description:** Shows how to set up a booth at a trade show. Includes everything from personal comportment to information on the typical trade show environment. Includes planning guide, handout, and audiocassette. **Availability:** VHS.

46737 ■ *Working the Booth: Trade Show Success*
American Media, Inc.
4621 121st St.
Urbandale, IA 50323-2311
Ph: (515)224-0919
Free: 888-776-8268
Fax: (515)327-2555
Co. E-mail: custsvc@ammedia.com
URL: http://www.ammedia.com
Released: 1992. **Price:** $395.00. **Description:** Details techniques on successfully setting up and maintaining a booth at a trade show. Stresses etiquette, professionalism, positivity, correct prospect handling, and salesmanship. **Availability:** VHS; 3/4 U; 8 mm.

TRADE SHOWS AND CONVENTIONS

46738 ■ ABA/BMA National Conference for Community Bankers
American Bankers Association (ABA)
1120 Connecticut Ave. NW
Washington, DC 20036
Ph: (202)663-5564
Free: 800-226-5377
Fax: (202)663-7543
Co. E-mail: custserv@aba.com
URL: http://www.aba.com
Contact: Edward L. Yingling, President
Frequency: Annual. **Audience:** Chairmen and presidents, mainly of banks with less than $500 million in assets, community bank CEOs, bank directors, and other community bank executives. **Principal Exhibits:** Products and services related to investment management, customer service improvements,

advertising, asset/liability management, bank management, electronic data interchange, employee recruitment/training, insurance, strategic planning models, including preparation for the 21st century, new revenue sources, cost control techniques, mainframe computers, market research, MCIF technology, minicomputers in community banking applications, software: platform, optical disk, and loan pricing, sweep accounts, and relationship banking for community bankers.

46739 ■ American Public Health Association Public Health Expo
American Public Health Association (APHA)
800 I St. NW
Washington, DC 20001-3710
Ph: (202)777-2742
Fax: (202)777-2534
Co. E-mail: comments@apha.org
URL: http://www.apha.org
Contact: Melvin D. Shipp, President
E-mail: mshipp@optometry.osu.edu
URL(s): www.apha.org. **Frequency:** Annual. **Audience:** Public health professionals, physicians, nurses, and health administrators. **Principal Exhibits:** Medical, products-related and pharmaceutical, health services, publishers, computer/software, educational, government, schools of public health. **Telecommunication Services:** comments@apha.org.

46740 ■ American Quilt Study Group Seminar
American Quilt Study Group (AQSG)
1610 L St.
Lincoln, NE 68508-2509
Ph: (402)477-1181
Fax: (402)477-1181
Co. E-mail: aqsg2@americanquiltstudygroup.org
URL: http://www.americanquiltstudygroup.org
Contact: Mary G. Persyn, President
URL(s): www.americanquiltstudygroup.org. **Frequency:** Annual. **Principal Exhibits:** Quilt-related articles.

46741 ■ American Real Estate Society Annual Meeting
American Real Estate Society
5353 Parkside Dr.
Cleveland State Univ.
Coll. of Bus.
Dept. of Finance, UC513
Jupiter, FL 33458
Ph: (561)799-8664
Fax: (561)799-8535
Co. E-mail: dcooper@fau.edu
URL: http://www.aresnet.org
Contact: Stephen A. Pyhrr, Executive Director
E-mail: spyhrr@kennedywilson.com
URL(s): www.aresnet.org. **Frequency:** Annual. **Audience:** College and university professors; high-level practicing professionals involved in all aspects real estate. **Principal Exhibits:** Exhibits relating to decision-making within real estate finance, real estate market analysis, investment, valuation, development, and other areas related to real estate in the private sector. Data providers, book publishers, etc. **Dates and Locations:** , Mauna Lani Bay Hotel.

46742 ■ American School Health Association National School Health Conference
American School Health Association (ASHA)
4340 East West Hwy., Ste. 403
Bethesda, MD 20814
Ph: (301)652-8072
Free: 800-445-2742
Fax: (301)652-8077
Co. E-mail: info@ashaweb.org
URL: http://www.ashaweb.org
Contact: Stephen Conley, Executive Director
URL(s): www.ashaweb.org. **Price:** $195, Members; $290, Non-members; $215, Onsite registered, members; $310, Onsite registered, non-members. **Frequency:** Annual. **Audience:** School nurses, health educators, physicians, teachers, school administrators, dentists, school counselors, physical educators, and school health coordinators. **Principal Exhibits:** Publications, pharmaceuticals, clinical and medical equipment and supplies, information on health

organizations, and health education methods and materials. **Telecommunication Services:** mbramsier@ashaweb.org.

46743 ■ American Technical Education Association National Conference on Technical Education
American Technical Education Association
c/o North Dakota State College of Science
800 N. 6th St.
Wahpeton, ND 58076-0002
Ph: (701)671-2301
Fax: (701)671-2260
URL: http://www.ateaonline.org
Contact: Betty M. Krump, Executive Director
E-mail: betty.krump@ndscs.edu
URL(s): www.ateaonline.org. **Frequency:** Annual. **Audience:** Technical educators and administrators of post-secondary technical education. **Principal Exhibits:** Supplies and services related to post secondary technical education. **Telecommunication Services:** deeann.bilben@ndscs.edu.

46744 ■ ApEx
Canadian Restaurant and Foodservices Association (CRFA)
316 Bloor St. W
Toronto, ON, Canada M5S 1W5
Ph: (416)923-8416
Free: 800-387-5649
Fax: (416)923-1450
Co. E-mail: info@crfa.ca
URL: http://www.crfa.ca
Contact: Garth Whyte, President
URL(s): www.crfa.ca/tradeshows/apex. **Audience:** Trade. **Principal Exhibits:** Products and services for the restaurant and hospitality industry, as well as institutions, convenience stores, delis and bakeries. **Telecommunication Services:** escanlan@crfa.ca.

46745 ■ Association for Research on Nonprofit Organizations and Voluntary Action Conference (ACNOVA)
Association for Research on Nonprofit Organizations and Voluntary Action
550 W. North St., Ste. 301
Indianapolis, IN 46202
Ph: (317)684-2120
Fax: (317)684-2128
URL: http://www.arnova.org
Contact: Roseanne Mirabella, President
E-mail: roseanne.mirabella@shu.edu
URL(s): www.arnova.org. **Frequency:** Annual. **Audience:** Scholars and non-profit organization professionals. **Principal Exhibits:** Exhibits for citizen participation and voluntary action, including social movements, interest groups, consumer groups, political participation, community development, and religious organizations. **Telecommunication Services:** conference@arnova.org.

46746 ■ Baltimore Women's Show
S & L Productions, Inc.
1916 Crain Hwy., Ste. 16
Glen Burnie, MD 21061
Ph: (410)863-1180
Fax: (410)863-1187
URL: http://www.mdhomeandgarden.com
URL(s): www.spoilyourself.com. **Frequency:** Annual. **Audience:** Women 25-65 yrs. **Principal Exhibits:** Products and services for women.

46747 ■ BMA Annual Marketing Forum
American Bankers Association (ABA)
1120 Connecticut Ave. NW
Washington, DC 20036
Ph: (202)663-5564
Free: 800-226-5377
Fax: (202)663-7543
Co. E-mail: custserv@aba.com
URL: http://www.aba.com
Contact: Edward L. Yingling, President
Frequency: Annual. **Audience:** Bankers including community bank CEOs, marketing directors, sales managers, advertising directors, public relations managers. **Principal Exhibits:** Financial services marketing offering banking solutions in advertising services, bank equipment/systems, computer soft-

ware, database marketing, direct marketing/sales, incentive/premium programs, insurance services, investment services, marketing consulting, merchandising, publishing, research, retail delivery, sales training, service quality, signage, and telemarketing.

46748 ■ BMA Private Wealth Sales Management Workshop, an ABA Program
American Bankers Association (ABA)
1120 Connecticut Ave. NW
Washington, DC 20036
Ph: (202)663-5564
Free: 800-226-5377
Fax: (202)663-7543
Co. E-mail: custserv@aba.com
URL: http://www.aba.com
Contact: Edward L. Yingling, President
Frequency: Annual. **Audience:** Trust, private banking and asset management officers, bank brokerage managers, sales managers, business development managers, and regional department managers. **Principal Exhibits:** Provides marketing education and information, professional growth and networking resources to marketing professionals in the financial services industry.

46749 ■ Broadcast Cable Financial Management Association Conference
Broadcast Cable Financial Management Association
550 Frontage Rd., Ste. 3600
Northfield, IL 60093
Ph: (847)716-7000
Fax: (847)716-7004
Co. E-mail: info@bcfm.com
URL: http://www.bcfm.com
Contact: Joe Barlek, Chairman of the Board
E-mail: jbarlek@suscom.com
URL(s): www.bcfm.com. **Price:** $895, Pre-registered, members; $795, Pre-registered, members corporate member advance registration; $695, Members past MFM/BCCA Chairpersons; $1095, Non-members. **Frequency:** Annual. **Audience:** Business managers, CFOs. **Principal Exhibits:** Exhibits relating to the financial management of radio, television, and cable television operations, including issues such as industry - specific software, collection agencies, insurance, investments, banking, accounting firms and music licensing.

46750 ■ Cabletelevision Advertising Bureau - Cable Advertising Conference
Cabletelevision Advertising Bureau
830 3rd Ave., 2nd Fl.
New York, NY 10022
Ph: (212)508-1200
Fax: (212)832-3268
URL: http://www.thecab.tv/
URL(s): www.thecab.tv/. **Price:** $800, Members. **Frequency:** Annual. **Audience:** Cable television and advertising trade. **Principal Exhibits:** Cable television and advertising equipment, supplies, and services.

46751 ■ Canadian Real Estate Association Annual Conference and Trade Show
Canadian Real Estate Association
Canada Bldg.
200 Catherine St., 6th Fl.
Ottawa, ON, Canada K2P 2K9
Ph: (613)237-7111
Free: 800-842-2732
Fax: (613)234-2567
Co. E-mail: info@crea.ca
URL: http://www.crea.ca
URL(s): crea.ca. **Price:** $425, Pre-registered, members. **Frequency:** Annual. **Audience:** Real estate professionals, brokers, managers, corporate representatives from real estate boards across the country. **Principal Exhibits:** Real Estate, financial, printing, and computer business equipment.

46752 ■ Computer Game Developers' Conference
UBM LLC
240 West 35th Street
New York, CA 94403
Ph: (650)513-4300
Free: 800-842-0798

Fax: (650)513-4618
URL: http://www.cmp.com
URL(s): www.gdconf.com. **Frequency:** Annual. **Principal Exhibits:** Equipment, supplies, and services for developers and producers of computer games. **Telecommunication Services:** pchapnick@cmp.com.

46753 ■ Estuarine Research Federation Conference
Estuarine Research Federation
University of Southwest Louisiana
Dept. of Biology
Port Republic, MD 20676
Ph: (410)326-7467
Fax: (410)326-7466
Co. E-mail: info@erf.org
URL: http://www.erf.org
Contact: Linda Schaffner, President
E-mail: Linda@vims.edu
URL(s): www.sgmeet.com. **Frequency:** Biennial. **Principal Exhibits:** Exhibits for persons actively engaged in biological, hydrographic, or related investigations of estuarine problems.

46754 ■ Expo Comm Wireless Korea
E.J. Krause & Associates, Inc.
6550 Rock Spring Dr., Ste. 500
Bethesda, MD 20817
Ph: (301)493-5500
Fax: (301)493-5705
Co. E-mail: info@ejkrause.com
URL: http://www.ejkrause.com
Contact: Sharon Deutch, Director
E-mail: deutch@ejkrause.com
Frequency: Annual. **Principal Exhibits:** Equipment, supplies, and services for computers. **Telecommunication Services:** owens@ejkrause.com.

46755 ■ Florida RV Supershow
Florida RV Trade Association
10510 Gibsonton Dr.
Riverview, FL 33578
Ph: (813)741-0488
Fax: (813)741-0688
Co. E-mail: info@frvta.org
URL: http://www.frvta.org
Contact: Lance Wilson, Executive Director
E-mail: lancewilson@frvta.org
URL(s): www.frvta.org/supershow.asp. **Price:** $10, adults; kids ages 16 and under. **Frequency:** Annual. **Audience:** First time buyers as well as current owners. **Principal Exhibits:** Recreational vehicle supplies and accessories.

46756 ■ Handmade - A Division of the San Francisco International Gift Fair
George Little Management, LLC
1133 Westchester Ave., Ste. N136
White Plains, NY 10606
Ph: (914)421-3200
Free: 800-272-SHOW
Co. E-mail: cathy_steel@glmshows.com
URL: http://www.glmshows.com
URL(s): www.sfigf.com. **Frequency:** Semiannual. **Audience:** Specialty, department, stationery, juvenile, and jewelry stores, interior designers, gift shops, mail order catalogs, importers/distributors of home products. **Principal Exhibits:** Handmade merchandise, including functional and decorative home furnishings, fashion accessories, jewelry plus an array of other unique craft objects. All merchandise is selected by a panel of craft professionals for uniqueness, originality and marketability.

46757 ■ Home Entertainment Show
Trigger Agency
3539 Clipper Mill Rd.
Baltimore, MD 21211
Free: 800-830-3976
Fax: (410)878-9911
Co. E-mail: info@triggeragency.com
URL: http://www.triggeragency.com/
Contact: Greg Nivens, President
E-mail: gnivens@triggeragency.com
URL(s): www.mooreamarketing.com. **Price:** $32, Pre-registered 3-day pass; $37, Onsite 3-day pass; $22, Pre-registered 1-day pass; $27, Onsite 1-day

pass. **Frequency:** Biennial. **Audience:** Consumers, trade and press. **Principal Exhibits:** Home theater and high-fidelity audio equipment, supplies, and services. **Telecommunication Services:** gnivens@mooreamarketing.com.

46758 ■ HSMAI - Affordable Meetings West
Hospitality Sales and Marketing Association International (HSMAI)
1760 Old Meadow Rd., Ste. 500
McLean, VA 22102
Ph: (703)506-3280
Free: 877-643-3511
Fax: (703)506-3266
Co. E-mail: info@hsmai.org
URL: http://www.hsmai.org
Contact: Robert A. Gilbert, President
E-mail: bgilbert@hsmai.org
URL(s): events.jspargo.com/AMW09/public/enter. aspx. **Frequency:** Annual. **Audience:** Trade professionals. **Principal Exhibits:** Equipment, supplies, and services for the hospitality and marketing industry. **Telecommunication Services:** affordable-meetings@jspargo.com.

46759 ■ The Imprinted Sportswear Show, Atlantic City
Nielsen Business Media
770 Broadway
New York, NY 10003-9595
Ph: (646)654-4500
Co. E-mail: bmcomm@nielsen.com
URL: http://www.nielsenbusinessmedia.com/
URL(s): www.issshows.com/atlantic_city/. **Price:** $99, Non-members full seminar, advanced registration; $225, Onsite full seminar. **Frequency:** Annual. **Audience:** Trade only. **Principal Exhibits:** Trade show source for the imprinted sportswear/textile screen printing/embroidery industry; t-shirts, pre-prints, and other apparel; design software; screen printing supplies and equipment; transfers, lettering embroidery equipment and supplies.

46760 ■ International Conference on Fundraising
Association of Fundraising Professionals (AFP)
4300 Wilson Blvd., Ste. 300
Arlington, VA 22203
Ph: (703)684-0410
Free: 800-666-3863
Fax: (703)684-0540
Co. E-mail: afp@afpnet.org
URL: http://www.afpnet.org
Contact: Tom Clark, Chief Operating Officer
URL(s): www.afpnet.org. **Price:** $595, Pre-registered, members; $695, Onsite registered, members; $945, Pre-registered, non-members; $1250, Onsite registered, non-members. **Frequency:** Annual. **Audience:** Decision makers for development offices for nonprofits. **Principal Exhibits:** Fundraising tools. **Telecommunication Services:** conference@afpnet.org.

46761 ■ International Restaurant & Foodservice Show of New York
Reed Exhibitions North American Headquarters
383 Main Ave.
Norwalk, CT 06851
Ph: (203)840-4800
Fax: (203)840-5805
Co. E-mail: inquiry@reedexpo.com
URL: http://www.reedexpo.com
URL(s): www.internationalrestaurantny.com/. **Frequency:** Annual. **Principal Exhibits:** Equipment, supplies, and services for the food products, foodservice, restaurant, and institutional food service industries. **Dates and Locations:** , Jacob K. Javits Convention Center.

46762 ■ International Sport Summit
E.J. Krause & Associates, Inc.
6550 Rock Spring Dr., Ste. 500
Bethesda, MD 20817
Ph: (301)493-5500

Fax: (301)493-5705
Co. E-mail: info@ejkrause.com
URL: http://www.ejkrause.com
Contact: Sharon Deutch, Director
E-mail: info@ejkrause.com
URL(s): www.ejkrause.com. **Frequency:** Annual. **Audience:** Trade professionals. **Principal Exhibits:** Equipment, supplies, and services for sports facilities and events. **Telecommunication Services:** lecker@ejkrause.com.

46763 ■ JAGEN UND FISCHEN - International Exhibition for Hunters, Fishermen and Marksmen
Kallman Worldwide, Inc.
4 North St., Ste. 800
Waldwick, NJ 07463-1842
Ph: (201)251-2600
Fax: (201)251-2760
Co. E-mail: info@kallman.com
URL: http://www.kallman.com
URL(s): www.jagenundfischen.deComment2. **Principal Exhibits:** Equipment, supplies, and services for hunters, fishermen, and marksmen. **Telecommunication Services:** newsline@messe-muenchen.de.

46764 ■ Maryland Municipal League Convention
Maryland Municipal League (MML)
1212 W St.
Annapolis, MD 21401
Ph: (410)268-5514
Free: 800-492-7121
Fax: (410)268-7004
Co. E-mail: mml@mdmunicipal.org
URL: http://www.mdmunicipal.org
Contact: Michael E. Bennett, President
URL(s): www.mdmunicipal.org. **Frequency:** Annual. **Audience:** Municipal officials and other county and state officials. **Principal Exhibits:** Office equipment, public works equipment, insurance companies, consulting firms, recreation equipment, computers, engineering firms, police equipment, and code publishers. **Dates and Locations:** , Princess Royale Hotel. **Telecommunication Services:** mml@mdmunicipal.org.

46765 ■ Memories Expo
Offinger Management Co.
1100-H Brandywine Blvd.
Zanesville, OH 43701-7303
Ph: (740)452-4541
Free: 888-878-6334
Fax: (740)452-2552
Co. E-mail: omc.info@offinger.com
URL: http://www.offinger.com
URL(s): www.memoriesexpo.com. **Price:** $10, Non-members one day; $15, Non-members. **Frequency:** 5/year. **Audience:** Trade and public. **Principal Exhibits:** Scrapbook supplies. **Telecommunication Services:** memories@offinger.com.

46766 ■ Michigan Association for Computer Users in Learning Conference
Michigan Association for Computer Users in Learning
3410 Belle Chase Way, Ste. 100
Lansing, MI 48911
Ph: (517)882-1403
Fax: (517)882-2362
Co. E-mail: macul@macul.org
URL: http://www.macul.org
Contact: Ric Wiltse, Executive Director
URL(s): www.macul.org. **Frequency:** Annual. **Audience:** Educational technology professionals. **Principal Exhibits:** Computer and educational equipment, supplies, and services.

46767 ■ Michigan Interscholastic Athletic Administrators Mid-Winter Conference
Michigan Interscholastic Athletic Administrator Association
35445 Hathaway
Livonia, MI 48150-2513
Ph: (734)422-3569

Fax: (734)762-9957
URL: http://www.miaaa.com
Contact: Jack Johnson, Convention Manager
E-mail: jakdoljohn@aol.com
URL(s): www.miaaa.com. **Frequency:** Annual. **Audience:** Educators in the field of secondary interscholastic athletic administration. **Principal Exhibits:** Sports supplies, athletic equipment, clothing, publications, fund raisers, and athletic training supplies, and awards companies. **Dates and Locations:** , Grand Traverse Resort.

46768 ■ Michigan Restaurant Show
Michigan Restaurant Association (MRA)
c/o Robert A. Gifford, Pres./CEO
225 W Washtenaw St.
Lansing, MI 48933-1506
Ph: (517)482-5244
Free: 800-968-9668
Fax: (517)482-7663
Co. E-mail: rgifford@mramail.org
URL: http://www.michiganrestaurant.org
Contact: Robert A. Gifford, President
URL(s): www.michiganrestaurant.org. **Price:** $5, Pre-registered restaurant non-member (per attendee). **Frequency:** Annual. **Audience:** Food service industry professionals. **Principal Exhibits:** Equipment, supplies, and services for the food service industry.

46769 ■ Minneapolis International Motorcycle Show
Advanstar Communications
641 Lexington Ave., 8th Fl.
New York, NY 10022
Ph: (212)951-6600
Free: 800-346-0085
Fax: (212)951-6793
Co. E-mail: info@advanstar.com
URL: http://www.advanstar.com
Contact: Robert Krakoff, President
URL(s): www.motorcycleshows.com. **Audience:** Public: Motorcycle, watercraft and ATV enthusiasts. **Principal Exhibits:** A marketplace where manufacturers and retailers can display and sell their products such as motorcycles, all-terrain vehicles (ATV), scooters, watercraft, apparel, parts and accessories.

46770 ■ National Agricultural Bankers Conference
American Bankers Association (ABA)
1120 Connecticut Ave. NW
Washington, DC 20036
Ph: (202)663-5564
Free: 800-226-5377
Fax: (202)663-7543
Co. E-mail: custserv@aba.com
URL: http://www.aba.com
Contact: Edward L. Yingling, President
URL(s): www.aba.com. **Price:** $830, Pre-registered, members; $900, Pre-registered, members; $830, Pre-registered, members; $900, Pre-registered, members. **Frequency:** Annual. **Audience:** Bank CEOs, mainly from community banks in rural areas, executive vice presidents, senior vice presidents, economists, analysts. **Principal Exhibits:** The latest developments in the agricultural lending business, as well as strategies for better market share, profitability and customer service. **Telecommunication Services:** jblanchf@aba.com.

46771 ■ Natural Products Expo East
Delicious Living
New Hope Natural Media
1401 Pearl St.
Boulder, CO 80302
Ph: (303)939-8440
Fax: (303)998-9020
Co. E-mail: info@newhope.com
URL: http://www.deliciouslivingmag.com
URL(s): www.expoeast.com. **Frequency:** Annual. **Audience:** Retailers, wholesalers, distributors, and brokers from the natural products industry. **Principal Exhibits:** Natural, organic and environmentally sound products, including: alternative health care, vegetarian and allergy-free personal care recycled/recyclable

products, biodegradable products, and organic meats. **Dates and Locations:** , Convention Center. **Telecommunication Services:** tradeshows@newhope.com.

46772 ■ New Jersey League of Municipalities Annual Conference
New Jersey League of Municipalities
222 W. State St.
Trenton, NJ 08608
Ph: (609)695-3481
Fax: (609)695-0151
Co. E-mail: league@njslom.com
URL: http://www.njslom.com
Contact: William G. Dressel, Executive Director
E-mail: bdressel@njslom.com
URL(s): www.njslom.org. **Price:** $50, Pre-registered; $100, Pre-registered non-municipal. **Frequency:** Annual. **Audience:** Municipal officials. **Principal Exhibits:** Municipal products and services.

46773 ■ North American Association of State and Provincial Lotteries Conference and Trade Show
North American Association of State and Provincial Lotteries
6 N. Broadway
Geneva, OH 44041
Ph: (440)466-5630
Fax: (440)466-5649
Co. E-mail: info@nasplhq.org
URL: http://www.naspl.org
URL(s): www.naspl.org. **Price:** $925, lottery vendor; $825, lottery/government employee. **Frequency:** Annual. **Audience:** Lottery industry professionals. **Principal Exhibits:** Lottery equipment, supplies, and services. **Telecommunication Services:** nasplhq@aol.com.

46774 ■ Old House/New House Home Show
Kennedy Productions, Inc.
1208 Lisle Pl.
Lisle, IL 60532-2262
Ph: (630)515-1160
Fax: (630)515-1165
Co. E-mail: kp@core.com
URL: http://www.kennedyproductions.com
Contact: Joanne Kennedy, Manager
URL(s): www.kennedyproductions.com. **Frequency:** Semiannual. **Audience:** Trade professionals and general public. **Principal Exhibits:** Products and services for home remodeling, improvement, enhancement, decorating, landscaping and more. Hundreds of ideas to improve and beautify every home. **Dates and Locations:** Pleasant Run Resorts Mega Center.

46775 ■ ON DEMAND Digital Printing & Publishing Strategy Conference and Exposition
Advanstar Communications
641 Lexington Ave., 8th Fl.
New York, NY 10022
Ph: (212)951-6600
Free: 800-346-0085
Fax: (212)951-6793
Co. E-mail: info@advanstar.com
URL: http://www.advanstar.com
Contact: Robert Krakoff, President
URL(s): www.ondemandexpo.com. **Frequency:** Annual. **Audience:** Corporate executives, print providers, government users. **Principal Exhibits:** Addresses the digitalization of workflow in the printing and publishing marketplace. **Telecommunication Services:** sfrank@advanstar.com.

46776 ■ Outdoor Retailer Summer Market
VNU Expo
310 Broadway
Laguna Beach, CA 92651
Ph: (946)376-6200
Free: 800-486-2701
Fax: (949)497-5290
Co. E-mail: interbike@wyoming.com
URL: http://www.vnuexpo.com
URL(s): www.outdoorretailer.com. **Price:** $30, Onsite late retailers; $375, Onsite industry affiliate. **Frequency:** Annual. **Audience:** Owners and managers

of the specialty sports retail stores. **Principal Exhibits:** Human-powered outdoor sports goods. **Telecommunication Services:** kenji.haroutunian@nielsen.com.

46777 ■ Outdoor Retailer Winter Market
VNU Expo
310 Broadway
Laguna Beach, CA 92651
Ph: (946)376-6200
Free: 800-486-2701
Fax: (949)497-5290
Co. E-mail: interbike@wyoming.com
URL: http://www.vnuexpo.com
URL(s): www.outdoorretailer.com. **Price:** $30, Onsite late retailers; $375, industry affiliate. **Frequency:** Annual. **Audience:** Owners and managers of specialty sports retail stores. **Principal Exhibits:** Human-powered outdoor sports goods. **Telecommunication Services:** kenji.haroutunian@nielsen.com.

46778 ■ Philadelphia Home Show
dmg world media inc.
200 Haddonfield-Berlin Rd., Ste. 302
High Ridge Commons
Gibbsboro, NJ 08026
Ph: (856)784-4774
Free: 800-756-5692
Fax: (856)435-5920
URL: http://www.dmgworldmedia.com
URL(s): www.phillyhomeshow.com. **Frequency:** Annual. **Audience:** Home owners and apartment dwellers. **Principal Exhibits:** House and apartment products, supplies, and services.

46779 ■ Pittsburgh Women's Show
Trigger Agency
3539 Clipper Mill Rd.
Baltimore, MD 21211
Free: 800-830-3976
Fax: (410)878-9911
Co. E-mail: info@triggeragency.com
URL: http://www.triggeragency.com/
Contact: Greg Nivens, President
E-mail: gnivens@triggeragency.com
URL(s): www.pittsburghwomensshow.com. **Price:** $7, free for children 15 and under. **Frequency:** Annual. **Audience:** Trade and public. **Principal Exhibits:** Products and services for women relating to health, fitness, business, careers, and finance.

46780 ■ Rocky Mountain Snowmobile Expo
Industrial Expositions, Inc.
1675 Larimer St., No. 700
Denver, CO 80248-0084
Ph: (303)892-6800
Free: 800-457-2434
Fax: (303)892-6322
Co. E-mail: info@iei-expos.com
URL: http://www.iei-expos.com
URL(s): www.gsevents.com/shows/display.cfm?showID=57&action=exhibitors. **Price:** $6, Onsite. **Frequency:** Annual. **Audience:** Snowmobilers. **Principal Exhibits:** Snowmobiles, clothing and accessories, recreational vehicles, travel and accommodations. **Telecommunication Services:** dseymour@agievents.com.

46781 ■ Scuba ExtaSea Expo
Industrial Expositions, Inc.
1675 Larimer St., No. 700
Denver, CO 80248-0084
Ph: (303)892-6800
Free: 800-457-2434
Fax: (303)892-6322
Co. E-mail: info@iei-expos.com
URL: http://www.iei-expos.com/
URL(s): www.bigasalloutdoors.com/scuba. **Price:** $7, Onsite. **Frequency:** Annual. **Audience:** General public. **Principal Exhibits:** Scuba diving, snorkeling, travel and accessories. **Telecommunication Services:** info@iei-expos.com.

46782 ■ Society of Craft Designers Educational Seminar (SCD)
Offinger Management Co.
1100-H Brandywine Blvd.
Zanesville, OH 43701-7303
Ph: (740)452-4541

Free: 888-878-6334
Fax: (740)452-2552
Co. E-mail: omc.info@offinger.com
URL: http://www.offinger.com
URL(s): www.craftdesigners.org. **Frequency:** Annual. **Audience:** Designers, manufacturers, editors, and publishers. **Principal Exhibits:** Craft designer showcases and education. **Telecommunication Services:** scd@offinger.com.

46783 ■ Society for Human Resource Management Exposition (SHRM)
Society for Human Resource Management (SHRM)
1800 Duke St.
Alexandria, VA 22314
Ph: (703)548-3440
Free: 800-283-7476
Fax: (703)535-6490
Co. E-mail: shrm@shrm.org
URL: http://www.shrm.org
Contact: Henry G. Jackson, President
E-mail: hjackson@shrm.org
URL(s): www.shrm.org. **Frequency:** Annual. **Audience:** Human resource management and related professionals. **Principal Exhibits:** Human resource management products and services; including relocation human resource information systems, recruitment, executive search, temporary/contact personnel employee compensation and benefits, incentive program information, childcare/eldercare, and drug testing information.

46784 ■ South Dakota Association of Realtors Convention
South Dakota Association of Realtors
204 N. Euclid Ave.
Pierre, SD 57501
Ph: (605)224-0554
Free: 800-227-5877
Fax: (605)224-8975
Co. E-mail: sdar@sdrealtor.org
URL: http://www.sdrealtor.org
Contact: Cartor Carlson, President
URL(s): www.sdrealtor.org/realtorconventionofthedakotas. **Price:** $190, REALTOR members, state/board AE and staff; $150, affiliate or board association. **Frequency:** Annual. **Audience:** Industry professionals. **Principal Exhibits:** Real estate. **Telecommunication Services:** convention@2013blackhills.com.

46785 ■ Texas Apartment Association Annual Education Conference and Lone Star Expo
Texas Apartment Association, Inc.
1011 San Jacinto Blvd., Ste. 600
Austin, TX 78701-1951
Ph: (512)479-6252
Fax: (512)479-6291
Co. E-mail: communications@taa.org
URL: http://www.taa.org
URL(s): www.taa.org/member/eduandconf. **Frequency:** Annual. **Audience:** Owners and management company reps of multi-housing communities from Texas. **Principal Exhibits:** Goods and services geared to multi-housing professionals, including software, soft goods, and property supplies.

46786 ■ TS2 - The Trade Show About Trade Shows
National Trade Productions, Inc.
313 S. Patrick St.
Alexandria, VA 22314
Free: 800-687-7469
Fax: (703)836-4486
Co. E-mail: ntpinfo@ntpshow.com
URL: http://www.ntpshow.com
Contact: Glenn Feder, President
URL(s): www.ts2show.com/. **Frequency:** Annual. **Audience:** Exhibit managers. **Principal Exhibits:** Equipment, supplies, and services for the trade show industry, including moving companies, booths and

other structures, publications, audiovisual equipment, and related items. **Telecommunication Services:** ntpinfo@ntpshow.com.

46787 ■ Virginia Health Care Association Annual Convention and Trade Show
Virginia Health Care Association
2112 W. Laburnum Ave., Ste. 206
Richmond, VA 23227
Ph: (804)353-9101
Fax: (804)353-3098
Co. E-mail: kathy.robertson@vhca.org
URL: http://www.vhca.org
Contact: Stephen Morrisette, President
E-mail: steve.morrisette@vhca.org
URL(s): www.vhca.org. **Price:** $495, Members. **Frequency:** Annual. **Audience:** Nursing homeowners, administrators, purchasing agents, and nurses; dietary, housekeeping, social services, and activities departments' heads. **Principal Exhibits:** Equipment, supplies, and services for nursing home operations, including food, medical supplies, furniture, computer systems, linen, medical equipment, insurance, pharmaceuticals, optometrists, psychologists, and transportation.

46788 ■ West Ex: The Rocky Mountain Regional Hospitality Exposition
Colorado Restaurant Association
430 E. 7th Ave.
Denver, CO 80203
Ph: (303)830-2972
Free: 800-522-2972
Fax: (303)830-2973
Co. E-mail: info@coloradorestaurant.com
URL: http://www.coloradorestaurant.com
Contact: Pete Meersman, President
E-mail: meersman@coloradorestaurant.com
URL(s): www.coloradorestaurant.com. **Frequency:** Annual. **Audience:** Food service and restaurant industry personnel. **Principal Exhibits:** Food service and lodging products, equipment, and services.

46789 ■ Western Food Service & Hospitality Expo Los Angeles
California Restaurant Association
621 Capitol Mall, Ste. 2000
Sacramento, CA 95814
Ph: (916)447-5793
Free: 800-765-4842
Fax: (916)447-6182
Co. E-mail: membership@calrest.org
URL: http://www.calrest.org
URL(s): www.westernfoodexpo.com. **Audience:** Food service hospitality and lodging industry professionals. **Principal Exhibits:** Food, equipment, supplies, and services for food service and lodging industries.

CONSULTANTS

46790 ■ Featherlite Exhibits
7300 32nd Ave. N
Minneapolis, MN 55427
Ph: (763)537-5533
Free: 800-229-5533
Fax: (763)923-6041
Co. E-mail: marketing@featherlite.com
URL: http://www.featherlite.com
Contact: Graeme Nelson, President
Scope: Trade show consultancy includes full-service rentals, installation and dismantling, accessories and complete graphic design services. **Founded:** 1964. **Special Services:** Computer-aided drafting and design service; Featherlite?.

46791 ■ International Training and Management Co. (ITMC)
60 Prue Ave.
Toronto, ON, Canada M6B 1R5
Ph: (416)783-5200

Free: 800-358-6079
Fax: (416)783-6200
Co. E-mail: info@siskindtraining.com
URL: http://www.siskindtraining.com
Contact: Barry Siskind, President
E-mail: barry@siskindtraining.com
Scope: Provider of both exhibitor training products as well as consulting services. Industries served: private and public companies who exhibit at trade or consumer shows. **Founded:** 1983. **Publications:** "A Strategic Approach to Trade Show Staffing"; "Approach Your Show Selection Strategically"; "Approaching Prospects on the Show Floor"; "Powerful exhibit marketing: the complete guide to successful trade shows, conferences and consumer shows," J. Wiley and Sons Canada, 2005; "Bumblebees can't fly: 7 simple strategies for making the impossible pos,"Wiley and Sons Canada, 2004; "Eagles must soar: 7 strategies for living alife with certainty," Wiley and Sons Canada, 2004; "Bumblebees Can't Fly, a Practical Guide to Making Everyday Work," Stoddart, 2001; "Take the stress out of show planning"; "Avoid convention overload"; "Making Contact"; "Seminars to Build Your Business"; "Making Trade Shows Work". **Seminars:** The Successful Exhibitor.

46792 ■ Intex Exhibit Systems L.L.C.
1846 Sequoia Ave.
Orange, CA 92868
Ph: (714)940-0369
Free: 800-331-6633
Fax: (714)935-0223
Co. E-mail: info@intexexhibits.com
URL: http://www.intexexhibits.com
Contact: Matthias D. Kemeny, President
E-mail: mdk@intexexhibits.com
Scope: Specializes in the design and production of exhibits, displays and pavilions for world fairs, tradeshows and similar events. Services include product design, industrial and engineering design for educational exhibits, museum exhibits and science and technology museology. Serves private industry as well as government agencies. **Founded:** 1979. **Publications:** "Trade Show Marketing," Sep, 2000; "Exhibitor Times," 1998. **Special Services:** Fastpack™; Panelflo™; affordable-1™; thegraphic arm™; Expression™; TigerMark™.

46793 ■ Reed - Sendecke - Krebsbach Inc.
701 Deming Way
Madison, WI 53717-1937
Ph: (608)827-0701
Free: 800-373-0043
Fax: (608)827-0702
Co. E-mail: info@rsandk.com
URL: http://www.rsandk.com
Contact: Kay Krebsbach, President
Scope: Provider of marketing, advertising and design. Communications agency that specializes in creating image and awareness programs for business-to-business clients in the life sciences, computer technology, power quality, filtration, medical equipment, financial services and telecommunications industries. **Founded:** 1978.

46794 ■ Together Inc.
802 E 6th St.
Tulsa, OK 74120-3610
Ph: (918)587-2405
Free: 800-282-0085
Fax: (866)337-4644
Co. E-mail: pinrus@aol.com
URL: http://www.positivepins.com
Contact: Bern L. Gentry, Sr., Chief Executive Officer
Scope: Offers services in employee and client self development training, logo development, lapel pin design, fund raising, public relations, conference and exhibit planning, direct marketing, association management, human resource development, and photography. Industries served: Government agencies, education, association and business, public and private schools. **Founded:** 1973. **Seminars:** Adventures in Attitudes; Diversity and Board Training for non-profits. **Telecommunication Services:** pnlady@aol.com. **Special Services:** The Pin Man®.

ASSOCIATIONS AND OTHER ORGANIZATIONS

46795 ■ *Active Voice*
505-27 Carlton St.
Toronto, ON, Canada M5B 1L2
Ph: (416)975-1379
Free: 866-226-3348
Fax: (416)975-1637
Co. E-mail: info@editors.ca
URL: http://www.editors.ca
Contact: Greg Ioannou, President
Released: Bimonthly

46796 ■ Association des Aides Familiales du Quebec (AAFQ)
2348, Jean talon est, Local 407
Montreal, QC, Canada H2E 1V7
Ph: (514)272-2670
Fax: (514)272-8338
Co. E-mail: info@aafq.ca
URL: http://www.aafq.ca
Description: Domestic workers. Seeks to obtain optimal conditions of employment for members. Advocates for increased recognition of the rights of domestic workers; represents members in negotiations with employers. **Founded:** 1975. **Publications:** *Standing Tall* (Bimonthly). **Awards:** Standing Tall (Annual).

46797 ■ Building and Construction Trades Department - Canadian Office—Departement des Metiers de la Construction - Bureau Canadien
c/o Robert Blakely, Dir.
130 Albert St., Ste. 1902
Ottawa, ON, Canada K1P 5G4
Ph: (613)236-0653
Fax: (613)230-5138
URL: http://www.buildingtrades.ca
Contact: Sean McGarvey, President
Description: Individuals working in the building trades. Seeks to obtain optimal conditions of employment for members. Represents members in negotiations with employers.

46798 ■ *CALMideas*
PO Box 643
Toronto, ON, Canada M4T 1L0
Ph: (416)656-2256
Free: 888-290-CALM
Co. E-mail: editor@calm.ca
URL: http://www.calm.ca
Contact: Chris Lawson, President
Released: Annual

46799 ■ Canadian Association of Labour Media (CALM)
PO Box 643
Toronto, ON, Canada M4T 1L0
Ph: (416)656-2256
Free: 888-290-CALM
Co. E-mail: editor@calm.ca
URL: http://www.calm.ca
Contact: Chris Lawson, President
Description: Media organizations operated by labor unions. Promotes increased awareness of the trade union movement and issues affecting workers. Serves as a clearinghouse on trade unionism and labor issues. **Founded:** 1976. **Publications:** *CALMideas* (Annual).

46800 ■ Canadian Association of Professional Employees (CAPE)—Association Canadienne des employes professionels
100 Queen St., 4th Fl.
Ottawa, ON, Canada K1P 1J9
Ph: (613)236-9181
Free: 800-265-9181
Fax: (613)236-6017
Co. E-mail: general@acep-cape.ca
URL: http://www.acep-cape.ca
Contact: Claude Poirier, President
Description: Professional and technical employees. Seeks to obtain optimal conditions of employment for members. Represents members in negotiations with employers. **Founded:** 1979.

46801 ■ Canadian Auto Workers (CAW)
205 Placer Ct.
Toronto, ON, Canada M2H 3H9
Ph: (416)497-4110
Free: 800-268-5763
Fax: (416)495-6552
Co. E-mail: cawpres@caw.ca
URL: http://www.caw.ca
Contact: Ken Lewenza, President
Description: Represents the economic and workplace safety interests of Canadian automobile workers. Conducts economic and social action activities; maintains educational, charitable and research programs. Operates speakers' bureau. **Founded:** 1985. **Publications:** *CAW Contact* (Weekly).

46802 ■ Canadian Industrial Relations Association (CIRA)—Association Canadienne des Relations Industrielles
Dept. des Relations Industrielles
Universite de Laval, Pavillon J.-A.-DeSeve
Quebec, QC, Canada G1V 0A6
Ph: (418)656-2468
Fax: (418)656-7688
Co. E-mail: acri-cira@rlt.ulaval.ca
URL: http://www.cira-acri.ca
Contact: Kelly Williams Whitt, President
Description: Industrial relations' professionals. Seeks to advance the study and practice of industrial relations. Serves as a forum for the exchange of ideas and information among members; sponsors research. **Awards:** Gerard Dion Award (Annual).

46803 ■ Canadian Labour Congress (CLC)—Congres du travail du Canada
2841 Riverside Dr.
Ottawa, ON, Canada K1V 8X7
Ph: (613)521-3400
Fax: (613)521-4655
URL: http://www.canadianlabour.ca/home
Contact: Ken Georgetti, President
Description: Works to ensure that all Canadians are able to find employment at fair wages, with union representation and the right to collective bargaining, in a safe environment. Seeks to create a just and equitable society. Joins with other organizations for advocacy and action on behalf of working Canadians. Facilitates establishment of grass roots organizations. Conducts research and educational programs; maintains speakers' bureau; compiles statistics. **Founded:** 1956. **Publications:** *C.L.C. Fax-Press* (Weekly); *Sweatshop Alert*; *UI Bulletin* (Periodic).

46804 ■ Canadian Media Guild (CMG)—Guilde Canadienne des Medias
310 Front St. W, Ste. 810
Toronto, ON, Canada M5V 3B5
Ph: (416)591-5333
Free: 800-465-4149
Fax: (416)591-7278
Co. E-mail: info@cmg.ca
URL: http://www.cmg.ca
Contact: Carmel Smyth, President
Description: Employees of press and broadcasting companies and other media outlets. Seeks to secure optimal conditions of employment for members. Represents members in negotiations with employers. **Founded:** 1994. **Publications:** *G-Force* (Quarterly). **Awards:** President's Award (Biennial).

46805 ■ Canadian Teachers' Federation (CTF)—Federation canadienne des enseignantes et des enseignants (FCE)
2490 Don Reid Dr.
Ottawa, ON, Canada K1H 1E1
Ph: (613)232-1505
Free: 866-283-1505
Fax: (613)232-1886
Co. E-mail: info@ctf-fce.ca
URL: http://www.ctf-fce.ca
Contact: Dr. Calvin Fraser, Secretary General
Description: Provincial and territorial teachers' organizations. Works to ensure that teachers' opinions are considered when national government bodies debate educational legislation. Facilitates communication and cooperation among members. Conducts research, educational, and lobbying activities. **Founded:** 1920.

46806 ■ Canadian Union of Public Employees (CUPE)—Le Syndicat Canadien de la Fonction Publique
1375 St. Lauren Blvd.
Ottawa, ON, Canada K1G 0Z7
Ph: (613)237-1590
Fax: (613)237-5508
URL: http://cupe.ca
Contact: Paul Moist, President
Description: Seeks to protect the rights and improve the conditions of employment of members. Promotes fairness in hiring and promotion without regard to race or gender. Represents members in collective bargaining; makes available legal, educational,

research, job evaluation, and communications services. **Founded:** 1963. **Publications:** *CUPE: It's Your Union*; *Organize* (Periodic).

46807 ■ *CAW Contact*
205 Placer Ct.
Toronto, ON, Canada M2H 3H9
Ph: (416)497-4110
Free: 800-268-5763
Fax: (416)495-6552
Co. E-mail: cawpres@caw.ca
URL: http://www.caw.ca
Contact: Ken Lewenza, President
Released: Weekly

46808 ■ *C.L.C. Fax-Press*
2841 Riverside Dr.
Ottawa, ON, Canada K1V 8X7
Ph: (613)521-3400
Fax: (613)521-4655
URL: http://www.canadianlabour.ca/home
Contact: Ken Georgetti, President
Released: Weekly

46809 ■ Communications, Energy and Paperworkers Union of Canada (CEP)—Syndicat Canadien des Communications, de l'Energie et du Papier
301 Laurier Ave. W
Ottawa, ON, Canada K1P 6M6
Ph: (613)230-5200
Free: 877-230-5201
Fax: (613)230-5801
Co. E-mail: info@cep.ca
URL: http://www.cep.ca
Contact: Dave Coles, President
Description: Trade union. Organizes and conducts collective bargaining for individuals employed in the telecommunications, electrical, electronics, pulp and paper, energy, print and broadcast media, and chemical industries in Canada. **Founded:** 1992. **Awards:** CEP Scholarship (Annual). **Telecommunication Services:** dcoles@cep.ca.

46810 ■ Communications Workers of America/Canada (CWA)—Syndicat des Communications d'Amerique (SCA)
7B-1050 Baxter Rd.
Ottawa, ON, Canada K2C 3P1
Ph: (613)820-9777
Free: 877-486-4292
Fax: (613)820-8188
Co. E-mail: info@cwa-scacanada.ca
URL: http://www.cwa-scacanada.ca
Contact: Arnold Amber, Chairman
Description: Primarily union of journalists and media workers in Canada, as well as social workers and employees in the manufacturing industry. **Founded:** 1995. **Publications:** *TNG Canada Today* (Monthly).

46811 ■ Confederation of National Trade Unions (CNTU)—Confederation des Syndicats Nationaux (CSN)
1601 Ave. de Lorimier
Montreal, QC, Canada H2K 4M5
Ph: (514)598-2283
Free: 866-646-7760
Fax: (514)598-2476
Co. E-mail: csnexecutif@csn.qc.ca
URL: http://www.csn.qc.ca
Contact: Louis Roy, President
Description: National trade unions representing 235,000 workers. Promotes advancement of the Canadian labor movement. Represents workers in collective bargaining. **Founded:** 1921. **Publications:** *Nouvelles CSN* (Biweekly).

46812 ■ *CUPE: It's Your Union*
1375 St. Lauren Blvd.
Ottawa, ON, Canada K1G 0Z7
Ph: (613)237-1590
Fax: (613)237-5508
URL: http://cupe.ca
Contact: Paul Moist, President

46813 ■ Editors' Association of Canada (EAC)—Association canadienne des reviseurs
505-27 Carlton St.
Toronto, ON, Canada M5B 1L2
Ph: (416)975-1379
Free: 866-226-3348
Fax: (416)975-1637
Co. E-mail: info@editors.ca
URL: http://www.editors.ca
Contact: Greg Ioannou, President
Description: Editors, proofreaders, copy editors, and researchers working on both English and French language printed materials. Promotes advancement of the profession of editing, and of members' capabilities. Conducts professional development courses for members; makes available to members job hotline services and discount long-term disability, extended health, and dental and life insurance. Sets and enforces editorial standards of practice; establishes payment levels and conditions of employment for editorial work. Cooperates with other organizations pursuing similar goals. **Founded:** 1978. **Publications:** *Active Voice* (Bimonthly). **Awards:** Claudette Upton Scholarship (Annual); President's Award for Volunteer Service (Annual); Tom Fairley Award for Editorial Excellence (Annual); Lee d'Anjou Volunteer of the Year (Annual); Tom Fairley Award for Editorial Excellence.

46814 ■ *G-Force*
310 Front St. W, Ste. 810
Toronto, ON, Canada M5V 3B5
Ph: (416)591-5333
Free: 800-465-4149
Fax: (416)591-7278
Co. E-mail: info@cmg.ca
URL: http://www.cmg.ca
Contact: Carmel Smyth, President
Released: Quarterly

46815 ■ Labor Union Congress of Quebec—Centrale des Syndicats du Quebec
9405 rue Sherbrooke E
Montreal, QC, Canada H1L 6P3
Ph: (514)356-8888
Free: 800-465-0897
Fax: (514)356-9999
Co. E-mail: organisation_syndicale@csq.qc.net
URL: http://lacsq.org
Contact: Louise Chabot, President
Description: Professional unions representing teachers and other educational personnel. Represents members in collective bargaining negotiations; promotes members' professional interests. Conducts union education, political action, and research activities. Serves as liaison between French-speaking educational organizations in the world through the Comite Syndical Francophone de L'Education et de la Formation. **Publications:** *Nouvelles CSQ* (Bimonthly). **Awards:** Bourse Laure Geaudreault (Annual).

46816 ■ *Nouvelles CSN*
1601 Ave. de Lorimier
Montreal, QC, Canada H2K 4M5
Ph: (514)598-2283
Free: 866-646-7760
Fax: (514)598-2476
Co. E-mail: csnexecutif@csn.qc.ca
URL: http://www.csn.qc.ca
Contact: Louis Roy, President
Released: Biweekly

46817 ■ *Nouvelles CSQ*
9405 rue Sherbrooke E
Montreal, QC, Canada H1L 6P3
Ph: (514)356-8888
Free: 800-465-0897
Fax: (514)356-9999
Co. E-mail: organisation_syndicale@csq.qc.net
URL: http://lacsq.org
Contact: Louise Chabot, President
Released: Bimonthly **Price:** free.

46818 ■ *Organize*
1375 St. Lauren Blvd.
Ottawa, ON, Canada K1G 0Z7

Ph: (613)237-1590
Fax: (613)237-5508
URL: http://cupe.ca
Contact: Paul Moist, President
Released: Periodic

46819 ■ *Standing Tall*
2348, Jean talon est, Local 407
Montreal, QC, Canada H2E 1V7
Ph: (514)272-2670
Fax: (514)272-8338
Co. E-mail: info@aafq.ca
URL: http://www.aafq.ca
Released: Bimonthly **Price:** included in membership dues.

46820 ■ *Steelabor - Canadian Edition*
234 Eglinton Ave. E, 8th Fl.
Toronto, ON, Canada M4P 1K7
Ph: (416)487-1571
Free: 877-669-8792
Fax: (416)482-5548
Co. E-mail: info@usw.ca
URL: http://www.usw.ca
Contact: Ken Neumann, Director
Released: Monthly

46821 ■ *Steeleader*
234 Eglinton Ave. E, 8th Fl.
Toronto, ON, Canada M4P 1K7
Ph: (416)487-1571
Free: 877-669-8792
Fax: (416)482-5548
Co. E-mail: info@usw.ca
URL: http://www.usw.ca
Contact: Ken Neumann, Director
Released: Periodic

46822 ■ *Sweatshop Alert*
2841 Riverside Dr.
Ottawa, ON, Canada K1V 8X7
Ph: (613)521-3400
Fax: (613)521-4655
URL: http://www.canadianlabour.ca/home
Contact: Ken Georgetti, President

46823 ■ *Terre de Chez Nous*
555, Blvd. Roland Therrien
Longueuil, QC, Canada J4H 3Y9
Ph: (450)679-0530
Fax: (450)674-4415
Co. E-mail: upa@upa.qc.ca
URL: http://www.upa.qc.ca
Contact: Marcel Groleau, President
Released: Weekly **Price:** C$31.91, /year.

46824 ■ *TNG Canada Today*
7B-1050 Baxter Rd.
Ottawa, ON, Canada K2C 3P1
Ph: (613)820-9777
Free: 877-486-4292
Fax: (613)820-8188
Co. E-mail: info@cwa-scacanada.ca
URL: http://www.cwa-scacanada.ca
Contact: Arnold Amber, Chairman
Released: Monthly

46825 ■ *UI Bulletin*
2841 Riverside Dr.
Ottawa, ON, Canada K1V 8X7
Ph: (613)521-3400
Fax: (613)521-4655
URL: http://www.canadianlabour.ca/home
Contact: Ken Georgetti, President
Released: Periodic

46826 ■ Union of Canadian Transportation Employees (UCTE)
233 Gilmour St., Ste. 702
Ottawa, ON, Canada K2P 0P2
Ph: (613)238-4003
Fax: (613)236-0379
Co. E-mail: buschml@psac-afpc.com
URL: http://www.ucte.com
Contact: Christine Collins, President
Description: Individuals employed in the transportation industries. Seeks to obtain optimal conditions of employment for members. Represents members in

negotiations with employers. **Founded:** 1966. **Awards:** W. Weaver Memorial Scholarship (Annual). **Telecommunication Services:** collinc@psac-afpc.com.

46827 ■ Union des Producteurs Agricoles
555, Blvd. Roland Therrien
Longueuil, QC, Canada J4H 3Y9
Ph: (450)679-0530
Fax: (450)674-4415
Co. E-mail: upa@upa.qc.ca
URL: http://www.upa.qc.ca
Contact: Marcel Groleau, President
Description: Promotes and supports the interests of agricultural producers throughout Canada. Provides information on updated developments on the farming industry. Works as a communications network among Quebec farmers. Protects the rights of individuals within the agricultural producing community. **Publications:** *Terre de Chez Nous* (Weekly); *La Terre de Chez Nous* (Weekly (Thurs.)).

46828 ■ Unionbuilder
234 Eglinton Ave. E, 8th Fl.
Toronto, ON, Canada M4P 1K7
Ph: (416)487-1571
Free: 877-669-8792
Fax: (416)482-5548
Co. E-mail: info@usw.ca
URL: http://www.usw.ca
Contact: Ken Neumann, Director
Released: Periodic

46829 ■ United Steelworkers of America - Canadian Branch (USWA)—Metallurgistes Unis d'Amerique
234 Eglinton Ave. E, 8th Fl.
Toronto, ON, Canada M4P 1K7
Ph: (416)487-1571
Free: 877-669-8792
Fax: (416)482-5548
Co. E-mail: info@usw.ca
URL: http://www.usw.ca
Contact: Ken Neumann, Director
Description: Represents the interests of workers in a variety of sectors in Canada. Maintains charitable program. **Founded:** 1942. **Publications:** *Steelabor - Canadian Edition* (Monthly); *Steeleader* (Periodic); *Unionbuilder* (Periodic).

EDUCATIONAL PROGRAMS

46830 ■ Investigation Tools and Techniques: Developing Facts and Evidence (Onsite)
Seminar Information Service, Inc.
20 Executive Park, Ste. 120
Irvine, CA 92614
Ph: (949)261-9104
Free: 877-SEM-INFO
Fax: (949)261-1963
Co. E-mail: info@seminarinformation.com
URL: http://www.seminarinformation.com
Price: $895.00. **Description:** Interactive workshop provides valuable information and tools on how to conduct an investigation of major workplace offenses that may result in immediate termination and that may be the subject of employment litigation. **Dates and Locations:** New York, NY.

46831 ■ The Law of Equal Employment Opportunity (Onsite)
Seminar Information Service, Inc.
20 Executive Park, Ste. 120
Irvine, CA 92614
Ph: (949)261-9104
Free: 877-SEM-INFO
Fax: (949)261-1963
Co. E-mail: info@seminarinformation.com
URL: http://www.seminarinformation.com
Price: $1,995.00. **Description:** Participants examine Equal Employment Opportunity/affirmative action laws and obligations of employers, recent legislation, guidelines, compliance agencies' interpretations, and court decisions and the impact of Equal Employment laws on policies, procedures, and day-to-day operations. **Dates and Locations:** New York, NY.

46832 ■ Legal Issues for Managers (Onsite)
Seminar Information Service, Inc.
20 Executive Park, Ste. 120
Irvine, CA 92614
Ph: (949)261-9104
Free: 877-SEM-INFO
Fax: (949)261-1963
Co. E-mail: info@seminarinformation.com
URL: http://www.seminarinformation.com
Price: $1,990.00. **Description:** Using a case study, practical examples, and discussions participants will explore the law as it relates to making nondiscriminatory employment decisions, compliance with wage and hour laws, safety and health rights and responsibilities, required versus discretionary leaves of absence, managing employees covered by labor agreements, and individual rights and wrongful discharge.

46833 ■ The Service Contract Act (Onsite)
Seminar Information Service, Inc.
20 Executive Park, Ste. 120
Irvine, CA 92614
Ph: (949)261-9104
Free: 877-SEM-INFO
Fax: (949)261-1963
Co. E-mail: info@seminarinformation.com
URL: http://www.seminarinformation.com
Price: $995.00. **Description:** This course covers the applicable labor requirements, how they are enforced, and how to efficiently incorporate them into contract activities. **Dates and Locations:** Arlington, VA; and Las Vegas, NV.

46834 ■ Wage and Hour Law Compliance (Onsite)
Seminar Information Service, Inc.
20 Executive Park, Ste. 120
Irvine, CA 92614
Ph: (949)261-9104
Free: 877-SEM-INFO
Fax: (949)261-1963
Co. E-mail: info@seminarinformation.com
URL: http://www.seminarinformation.com
Price: $199.00. **Description:** Learn the latest decisions and applications of the Fair Labor Standards Act. **Dates and Locations:** Pasco, WA; Spokane, WA; Everett, WA; Seattle, WA; and Tacoma, WA.

REFERENCE WORKS

46835 ■ "ACTRA Phones It In" in Canadian Business (Vol. 80, January 15, 2007, No. 2, pp. 8)
Pub: Rogers Media
Ed: Denis Seguin. **Description:** The strike held by the members of the ACTRA or Canadian Cinema, Television and Radio Artists from January 8 2007, due to the contract dispute with the trade association representing Canadian producers, is discussed.

46836 ■ "Air Canada to Slash 600 Non-Union Jobs" in Globe & Mail (February 11, 2006, pp. B3)
Pub: CTVglobemedia Publishing Inc.
Ed: Brent Jang. **Description:** The reasons behind workforce reduction by ACE Aviation Holdings Inc. at Air Canada are presented.

46837 ■ "Airline Mergers: United Next?" in Crain's Chicago Business (Vol. 31, April 21, 2008, No. 16, pp. 12)
Pub: Crain Communications, Inc.
Description: Discusses a potential merger between United and Continental airlines. Unions representing 48,900 pilots, mechanics, flight attendants, ticket agents and ramp workers at United have put the management on notice that they expect to be a factor in any merger discussions if the company wants their cooperation.

46838 ■ "An Analysis of Three Labor Unions' Outreach to Brazilian Immigrant Workers in Boston" in WorkingUSA (Vol. 11, June 2008, No. 2)
Pub: Blackwell Publishers Ltd.
Ed: Joshua Kirshner. **Description:** Author seeks to shed light on the conditions under which labor unions can include immigrants in their ranks as a means to

regain their strength. It does so by focusing on the example of Brazilian immigrants in Boston and compares the approaches of three union locals in Boston toward organizing Brazilian workers, the Painters, the Teamsters, and the United Food and Commercial Workers Union. While previous studies argue that ethnicity and social networks can account for immigrants' receptivity to unions, this article highlights strategic choice on the part of union officials as an important factor in facilitating unionization of Brazilian workers.

46839 ■ "Apprenticeship: Earn While You Learn" in Occupational Outlook Quarterly (Vol. 54, Fall 2010, No. 3, pp. 24)
Pub: U.S. Bureau of Labor Statistics
Description: Paid training, or apprenticeships, are examined. Registered apprenticeship programs conform to certain guidelines and industry-established training standards and may be run by businesses, trade or professional associations, or partnerships with business and unions.

46840 ■ "As Tradesmen Age, New Workers In Short Supply" in Boston Business Journal (Vol. 27, November 9, 2007, No. 41, pp. 1)
Pub: American City Business Journals Inc.
Ed: Jackie Noblett. **Description:** It is becoming more difficult to find young people who have the skills for installation and maintenance businesses. Some businesses are unable to complete contracts on time due to lack of staff. Unions are making efforts to address the expected shortfall of laborers in the coming years through apprenticeship programs.

46841 ■ "Back to Business" in Retail Merchandiser (Vol. 51, September-October 2011, No. 5, pp. 18)
Pub: Phoenix Media Corporation
Ed: Eric Slack. **Description:** National Football League owners and players have reached a labor agreement for the next ten years. America's football league can once again focus on providing fans with a great product both on and off the field.

46842 ■ Big-Box Swindle: The True Cost of Mega-Retailers and the Fight for America's Independent Businesses
Pub: Beacon Press
Ed: Stacy Mitchell. **Released:** October 2007. **Price:** $15.00. **Description:** Examination of the economic, environmental, and social damage done by big-box retailers like Wal-Mart, Costco, and Home Depot. Labor policies of these retailers, particularly those enforced by Wal-Mart, are discussed at length.

46843 ■ "Boeing's Next Flight May Well Be to the South" in Puget Sound Business Journal (Vol. 29, November 21, 2008, No. 31, pp.)
Pub: American City Business Journals
Ed: Steve Wilhelm. **Description:** Southern states in the U.S. are luring Boeing Company to locate a new plant in their region which is experiencing a growing industrial base while offering permissive labor laws as selling points.

46844 ■ "The Bottom Line: Did CN Push Too Hard?" in Globe & Mail (February 23, 2007, pp. B1)
Pub: CTVglobemedia Publishing Inc.
Ed: Brett Jang. **Description:** The effect of the efficiency drive started by Hunter Harrison at Canadian National Railway Company on the company's labor relations is discussed.

46845 ■ "Brief: Janitorial Company Must Pay Back Wages" in Buffalo News (September 24, 2011)
Pub: The Buffalo News
Ed: Jonathan D. Epstein. **Description:** Knights Facilities Management, located in Michigan, provides grounds maintenance and janitorial services at the Ralph Wilson Stadium in Buffalo, New York. The US Department of Labor ordered the firm to pay $22,000 in back wages and damages to 26 employees for overtime and minimum wage compensation. Details of the company's violation of the Fair Labor Standards Act are included.

46846 ■ *"Builders, Unions Aim to Cut Costs; Pushing Changes to Regain Share of Residential Market; Seek Council's Help"* in *Crain's New York Business*

Pub: Crain Communications, Inc.

Ed: Erik Engquist. **Description:** Union contractors and workers are worried about a decline in their market share for housing so they intend to ask the City Council to impose new safety and benefit standards on all contractors to avoid being undercut by nonunion competitors.

46847 ■ *"Businesses Keep a Watchful Eye on Worker's Comp"* in *The Business Journal-Serving Greater Tampa Bay (September 5, 2008)*

Pub: American City Business Journals, Inc.

Ed: Jane Meinhardt. **Description:** Pending a ruling from the Florida Supreme Court that could uphold the 2003 changes on workers' compensation law, the outcome would include restrictions on claimant attorneys' fees and allow the competitive workers' compensation insurance rates to remain low. However, insurance rates are expected to go up if the court overturns the changes.

46848 ■ *"Car Trouble"* in *Canadian Business (Vol. 80, October 22, 2007, No. 21, pp. 27)*

Pub: Rogers Media

Ed: Thomas Watson. **Description:** Contract between General Motors Corporation and the United Auto Workers Union has created a competitive arm for the U.S. Big Three automakers. Data on the market and production data of car companies are presented.

46849 ■ *"CAW Boss Troubled Over 'Vulnerable' Ford Plants"* in *Globe & Mail (January 19, 2006, pp. B6)*

Pub: CTVglobemedia Publishing Inc.

Ed: Greg Keenan. **Description:** The concerns of president Buzz Hargrove of Canadian Auto Workers on the impact of Ford Motor Co.'s restructuring efforts on closure of automotive plants in Canada, are presented.

46850 ■ *"CAW Hopes to Beat Xstrata Deadline"* in *Globe & Mail (January 30, 2007, pp. B3)*

Pub: CTVglobemedia Publishing Inc.

Ed: Andy Hoffman. **Description:** The decision of Canadian Auto Workers to strike work at Xstrata PLC over wage increase is discussed.

46851 ■ *"Centerpoint Nurses Unionize Despite Change In Hospital CEO"* in *Business Journal-Serving Metropolitan Kansas City (November 16, 2007)*

Pub: American City Business Journals, Inc.

Ed: Rob Roberts. **Description:** The change in Centerpoint Medical Center's CEO did not stop the hospital's 336 registered nurses from joining Nurses United for Improved Patient Care. Carolyn Caldwell was named CEO of Centerpoint on October 8, 2007, one week after Dan Jones announced his resignation. Poor communications are pointed out as the reason why the nurses joined the union.

46852 ■ *Change in SMEs: The New European Capitalism*

Pub: Palgrave Macmillan

Ed: Katharina Bluhm; Rudi Schmidt. **Released:** October 2008. **Price:** $95.00. **Description:** Effects of global change on corporate governance, management, competitive strategies and labor relations in small-to-medium sized enterprises in various European countries are discussed.

46853 ■ *"Chrysler Unions Set Up Roadblocks to Private Equity"* in *Globe & Mail (March 20, 2007, pp. B3)*

Pub: CTVglobemedia Publishing Inc.

Ed: Greg Keenan. **Description:** The opposition of the Canadian Auto Workers union and the United Auto Workers to any proposal to sell Chrysler Group is discussed.

46854 ■ *"CN Aims for Regional Pacts to Halt Labor Row"* in *Globe & Mail (April 17, 2007, pp. B2)*

Pub: CTVglobemedia Publishing Inc.

Ed: Brent Jang. **Description:** The decision of Canadian National Railway Co. to settle labor dispute with regional unions is discussed.

46855 ■ *"CN Rail Strike Ends With Fragile Truce"* in *Globe & Mail (February 26, 2007, pp. B1)*

Pub: CTVglobemedia Publishing Inc.

Ed: Brent Jang. **Description:** The agreement between Canadian National Railway Co. and the United Transportation Union on wage increase that ended employee strike is discussed.

46856 ■ *"Coherent Laying Off 144 As It Prepares To Shut Auburn Plant"* in *Sacramento Business Journal (Vol. 25, August 1, 2008, No. 22, pp. 1)*

Pub: American City Business Journals, Inc.

Ed: Melanie Turner. **Description:** Sacramento, California-based Coherent Inc. is planning to lay off 144 workers at its Auburn facility. Coherent has been cutting payroll and its real estate holdings. Statistics on the company's earnings are also provided.

46857 ■ *"Collateral Damage"* in *Business Courier (Vol. 26, October 16, 2009, No. 25, pp. 1)*

Pub: American City Business Journals, Inc.

Ed: Jon Newberry. **Description:** Non-union construction firms representing Ohio Valley Associated Builders and Contractors Inc. have filed cases against unionized shops claiming violations of wage law in Ohio. Defendants say the violations are minor, however, they believe they are caught in the middle of the group's campaign to change the state's wage law.

46858 ■ *"Companies Must Set Goals for Diversity"* in *Crain's Detroit Business (Vol. 24, April 14, 2008, No. 15, pp. 16)*

Pub: Crain Communications Inc.

Ed: Laura Weiner. **Description:** Diversity programs should start with a plan that takes into account exactly what the company wants to accomplish; this may include wanting to increase the bottom line with new contracts or wanting a staff that is more innovative in their ideas due to their varied backgrounds.

46859 ■ *"Companies Press Ottawa to End CN Labor Dispute"* in *Globe & Mail (April 16, 2007, pp. B1)*

Pub: CTVglobemedia Publishing Inc.

Ed: Brent Jang. **Description:** The plea of several industries to the Canadian parliament to end the labor dispute at the Canadian National Railway Co. is discussed.

46860 ■ *"Compulsory Proportional Representation: Allaying Potential Concerns"* in *WorkingUSA (Vol. 11, September 2008, No. 3, pp. 349)*

Pub: Blackwell Publishers Ltd.

Ed: Mark Harcourt, Helen Lam. **Description:** Present union certification system has many faults, the most important of which is its failure to deliver employee representation to all but a small and declining minority of workers. As an alternative, compulsory proportional representation (CPR) would have many advantages, particularly when compared with other reform proposals, most of which are designed to only reinvigorate, modify, or supplement the existing system.

46861 ■ *"Contractors Can't Do It Alone, PHCC's Pfeffer Says"* in *Contractor (Vol. 56, October 2009, No. 10, pp. 3)*

Pub: Penton Media, Inc.

Ed: Robert P. Mader. **Description:** President Herbert 'Skip' Pfeffer of the Plumbing-Heating-Cooling Contractors National Association says lobbying and education are the services that the association offers that a contractor cannot do individually. Pfeffer says the dues for the association are set up in a manner that allows members to pay monthly.

46862 ■ *"Councilman May Revive Labor Bill"* in *Baltimore Business Journal (Vol. 28, August 13, 2010, No. 14, pp. 1)*

Pub: Baltimore Business Journal

Ed: Daniel J. Sernovitz. **Description:** Baltimore, Maryland Councilman Bill Henry has started reviving controversial legislation that would force developers and contractors to give preference to union labor. The legislation requires contractors to give preference to city workers in order to lower Baltimore's unemployment rate.

46863 ■ *"Counting on Engagement at Ernst and Young"* in *Workforce Management (Vol. 88, November 16, 2009, No. 12, pp. 25)*

Pub: Crain Communications Inc.

Ed: Ed Frauenheim. **Description:** Employee engagement has been difficult to maintain through the recession but firms such as Ernst & Young have found that the effort to keep their employees loyal has paid off.

46864 ■ *"Cultural Due Diligence"* in *Canadian Business (Vol. 80, April 23, 2007, No. 9, pp. 60)*

Pub: Rogers Media

Ed: Graham Lowe. **Description:** The factors to be considered by job seekers during judging good workplace with relation to corporate culture are presented.

46865 ■ *"CVRD Inco Strike Shuts Sudbury Mines"* in *Globe & Mail (April 2, 2007, pp. B1)*

Pub: CTVglobemedia Publishing Inc.

Ed: Andy Hoffman. **Description:** The closure of nickel mining operations at the Sudbury mines due to the strike by employees of CVRD Inco Ltd. is described. The prospects of a rise in the prices of nickel are discussed, besides the production of metals in Canada.

46866 ■ *"Defensive Training"* in *Crain's Detroit Business (Vol. 24, September 22, 2008, No. 38, pp. 11)*

Pub: Crain Communications Inc.

Ed: Robert Ankeny. **Description:** Rising retaliation claims in regards to discrimination complaints are creating an atmosphere in which managers must learn how to avoid or deal with these lawsuits as well as the retaliation that often follows. Examples of cases are given as well as advice for dealing with such problems that may arise in the workplace.

46867 ■ *"Dirty Work Required"* in *Workforce Management (Vol. 88, November 16, 2009, No. 12, pp. 34)*

Pub: Crain Communications Inc.

Ed: John Hollon. **Description:** Due to salary freezes, pay cuts, layoffs, buyouts and a number of other stress factors brought about by the recession, employee engagement has been difficult to maintain by managers.

46868 ■ *"Downturn Tests HCL's Pledge to Employees"* in *Workforce Management (Vol. 88, November 16, 2009, No. 12, pp. 23)*

Pub: Crain Communications Inc.

Ed: Ed Frauenheim. **Description:** HCL Technologies has kept its promise to keep from laying any employees off during the recession which served as a test for the tech firm's Employee First program, which seeks to give workers greater income security as well as a stronger voice in the firm.

46869 ■ *"Empathy: An Entrepreneur's Killer App"* in *Women Entrepreneur (February 3, 2009)*

Pub: Entrepreneur Media Inc.

Ed: Kristi Hedges. **Description:** It is just as important to treat employees with courtesy and respect during bad economic times as it is in a good economy. Employers sometimes take advantage of such bad economic times since they realize that employees are grateful to have a job and cannot just quit and easily find work elsewhere. The importance of empathy in a company's leadership personnel is discussed.

46870 ■ "Energy Sparks Job Growth" in The Business Journal-Serving Greater Tampa Bay (Vol. 28, August 8, 2008, No. 33, pp. 1)
Pub: American City Business Journals, Inc.
Ed: Margie Manning. **Description:** Energy infrastructure projects in Tampa Bay, Florida, are increasing the demand for labor in the area. Energy projects requiring an increase in labor include TECO Energy Inc.'s plan for a natural gas pipeline in the area and the installation of energy management system in Bank of America's branches in the area.

46871 ■ "Fairness First" in Canadian Business (Vol. 80, April 23, 2007, No. 9, pp. 45)
Pub: Rogers Media
Ed: Erin Pooley. **Description:** The need for the fair treatment of employees from the perspective of employee compensation is discussed.

46872 ■ "For Yung, Lady Luck a Fickle Mistress" in Business Courier (Vol. 24, November 30, 2008, No. 33, pp. 1)
Pub: American City Business Journals, Inc.
Ed: Dan Monk. **Description:** Bill Yung's Columbia Sussex Corp. won the bid for the parent company of Tropicana casinos in November 2006, and a year after, the company is facing regulatory and labor issues.

46873 ■ "Ford Executive Pay Could Fuel Tensions" in Globe & Mail (April 6, 2007, pp. B7)
Pub: CTVglobemedia Publishing Inc.
Ed: John D. Stoll; Terry Kosdrosky; Chad Clinton. **Description:** The likely tension between workers and management over the $62 million offer of Ford Motor Co. to its top executives is discussed.

46874 ■ "Fresh Direct's Crisis" in Crain's New York Business (Vol. 24, January 14, 2008, No. 2, pp. 3)
Pub: Crain Communications, Inc.
Ed: Lisa Fickenscher. **Description:** Freshdirect, an Internet grocery delivery service, finds itself under siege from federal immigration authorities, customers and labor organizations due to its employment practice of hiring illegals. At stake is the grocer's reputation as well as its ambitious growth plans, including an initial public offering of its stock.

46875 ■ "Generation Y Goes To Work; Management" in The Economist (Vol. 390, January 3, 2009, No. 8612, pp. 48)
Pub: The Economist Newspaper Inc.
Description: Unemployment rates among people in their 20s has increased significantly and there is a lower turnover in crisis-hit firms, which has made it more difficult to simply find another job if one is unsatisfied with the management style of his or her company. Managers are adopting a more command-and-control approach which is the antithesis of the open, collaborative style that younger employees prefer.

46876 ■ "Get Back To Business Planning Fundamentals" in Entrepreneur (October 24, 2008)
Pub: Entrepreneur Media Inc.
Ed: Tim Berry. **Description:** During a recession it is important to know what adjustment to make to your business plan. Some fundamentals to remember include: watching things more closely by tracking progress on cash, sales, new projects, customer satisfaction, ad spending and expenses; looking for built-in indicators such as what drives sales or expenses; watching what drives cash flow; and do not make mistakes such as laying off experienced employees too soon.

46877 ■ "Get Prepared for New Employee Free Choice Act" in HRMagazine (Vol. 53, December 2008, No. 12, pp. 22)
Pub: Society for Human Resource Management
Contact: Henry G. Jackson, President
E-mail: hjackson@shrm.org
Ed: Allen Smith. **Description:** According to the director of global labor and employee relations with Ingersoll Rand Company, unions may have started having

employees signing authorization cards in anticipation of the Employee Free Choice Act. Once signed, the cards are good for one year and employers would have only ten days in which to prepare for bargaining with unions over the first labor contract. The Act also requires these negotiations be subject to mandatory arbitration if a contract is not reached within 120 days of negotiations with unions, resulting in employers' wage rates, health insurance, retirement benefits and key language about flexibility would be determined by an arbitrator with no vested interest in the success of the company.

46878 ■ "Hot-Button Ordinances May Go Up for Review" in Crain's Detroit Business (Vol. 26, January 18, 2010, No. 3, pp. 1)
Pub: Crain Communications Inc.
Ed: Nancy Kaffer. **Description:** Detroit's economic fate may be tied to the city's anti-privatization ordinance and its policy of giving contract preference to Detroit-based businesses. The new administration feels that it is time to put everything on the table in an attempt to look for ways in which to save the city money.

46879 ■ "How Much Profit is Enough?" in Automotive News (Vol. 86, October 31, 2011, No. 6488, pp. 12)
Pub: Crain Communications Inc.
Ed: Keith Crain. **Description:** Workers at the big three automobile companies are unhappy about the issues of class wealth, like the high compensations offered to CEOs.

46880 ■ "How to Protect Your Job in a Recession" in Harvard Business Review (Vol. 86, September 2008, No. 9, pp. 113)
Pub: Harvard Business School Press
Ed: Janet Banks; Diane Coutu. **Description:** Strategies are presented for enhancing one's job security. These include being a team player, empathizing with management, preserving optimism, and concentrating on the customer.

46881 ■ "In Everyone's Interests" in Canadian Business (Vol. 80, April 23, 2007, No. 9, pp. 62)
Pub: Rogers Media
Ed: Rachel Pulfer. **Description:** The need of strategic negotiations during a labor contract to prevent disputes with employer is emphasized.

46882 ■ "Investigation Hints at Workers' Comp Trouble" in Sacramento Business Journal (Vol. 25, July 4, 2008, No. 18, pp. 1)
Pub: American City Business Journals, Inc.
Ed: Kelly Johnson. **Description:** In 500 California firms, a survey of worker compensation revealed that 38 percent of the companies had problems with required coverage. Government investigators are bothered that 107 companies did not respond to the official inquiry. Other views and information on the survey and on the expected economic implications of the findings are presented.

46883 ■ "Is Raising CPP Premiums a Good Idea?" in Canadian Business (Vol. 83, July 20, 2010, No. 11-12, pp. 37)
Pub: Rogers Media Ltd.
Description: Big labor is pushing for an increase in Canada Pension Plan premiums but pension consultants believe this system is not broken and that the government needs to focus on addressing the low rate of personal retirement savings. If the premiums go up, even those with high savings will be forced to pay more and it could block other plans that really address the real issue.

46884 ■ "It's All in the Details" in Canadian Business (Vol. 80, December 25, 2006, No. 1, pp. 11)
Pub: Rogers Media
Description: The failure of several Canadian clothing retailers to disclose their labor practices is discussed.

46885 ■ "Just Shut The Hell Up" in Canadian Business (Vol. 81, July 22, 2008, No. 12-13, pp. 33)
Pub: Rogers Media Ltd.
Ed: Jane Bao. **Description:** Employees desire better communication as opposed to more communication

from their managers. Advice regarding managing communication in the workplace is given including ways in which speakers can say more with fewer words.

46886 ■ "KC Plants Downshift" in The Business Journal-Serving Metropolitan Kansas City (Vol. 27, November 7, 2008, No. 9, pp. 1)
Pub: American City Business Journals, Inc.
Ed: James Dornbrook. **Description:** Discusses Ford Motor Co. and General Motors' factories in the region; Ford Motor Co. removed the second shift on the F-150 line at the Kansas City Assembly Plant but added a shift to the production of the Ford Escape and Mercury Mariner in an attempt to avoid layoffs. One spokesman for General Motors, however, states that they cannot guarantee that they won't make any production cuts and layoffs in the future.

46887 ■ "Labor Compensation and Collective Bargaining Data" in Montly Labor Review (Vol. 133, September 2010, No. 9, pp. 116)
Pub: Bureau of Labor Statistics
Description: Employment cost index is presented, citing compensation by occupation and industry group.

46888 ■ "Labor and Management: Working Together for a Stable Future" in Alaska Business Monthly (Vol. 27, October 2011, No. 10, pp. 130)
Pub: Alaska Business Publishing Company
Ed: Nicole A. Bonham Colby. **Description:** Alaska unions and employers are working to ensure a consistent flow of skilled Alaska workers as current the current workforce reaches retirement age.

46889 ■ "LaSalle Street Firms Cherry-Pick Talent As Wall Street Tanks" in Crain's Chicago Business (Vol. 31, November 17, 2008, No. 46)
Pub: Crain Communications, Inc.
Ed: H. Lee Murphy. **Description:** Many local businesses are taking advantage of the lay offs that many major Wall Street firms are undergoing in their workforces; these companies see the opportunity to woo talent and expand their staff with quality executives.

46890 ■ "Law Firms Troll for Complaints Among Disgruntled Workers" in The Business Journal-Serving Greater Tampa Bay (Vol. 28, July 11, 2008)
Pub: American City Business Journals, Inc.
Ed: Jane Meinhardt. **Description:** Economic slowdown has affected businesses as they downsize, seeing an increase in wage and hour complaints using loopholes in the Fair Labor Standards Act, from which several law firms are recently generating revenue. Federal judges notice the increase in lawsuits and ordered that law firms show cause for non-compliance.

46891 ■ "Law Reform, Collective Bargaining, and the Balance of Power: Results of an Empirical Study" in WorkingUSA (June 2008)
Pub: Blackwell Publishers Ltd.
Ed: Ellen Dannin, Michelle Dean, Gangaram Singh. **Description:** Despite Congress' having made clear policy statements in the National Labor Relations Act that the law was intended to promote equality of bargaining power between employers and employees, to promote the practice and procedure of collective bargaining as the method of setting workplace terms and conditions of employment, and forbidding construing the law 'so as to either interfere with or impede or diminish in any way the right to strike,' by early 1940, the courts had given employers the right to permanently replace strikers and implement their final offer at impasse. Judges have often justified these doctrines as promoting balance in bargaining. Critics contend that the doctrines have the capacity to destroy the right to strike, unbalance bargaining power, and divert parties from the process of bargaining collectively. Some have proposed allowing temporary but not permanent striker replacement. The article uses a bargaining simulation followed by a survey and debriefing comments to test these opposing claims.

46892 ■ *"Lawyers Lock Up Cops as Clients"* in Sacramento Business Journal (Vol. 28, April 8, 2011, No. 6, pp. 1)
Pub: Sacramento Business Journal
Ed: Kathy Robertson. **Description:** Sacramento-based law firm Mastagni, Holstedt and Chiurazzi has grown its client base by specializing in law enforcement labor issues. The firm represents 80,000 public sector correctional officers in the US. The firm has been experiencing an increase in new business as public sector employers face huge budget deficits.

46893 ■ *"Legislators Must Cut Cost of Government"* in Crain's Detroit Business (Vol. 24, October 6, 2008, No. 40, pp. 6)
Pub: Crain Communications, Inc.
Description: Southeast and West Michigan business leaders are setting aside their differences and have proposed clear agendas, ranging from eliminating the Michigan Business Tax to overhauling public employee and retiree benefits and pensions. Lawmakers must also come together to find solutions for the state's economy and discover an entirely new vision for the future of Michigan business.

46894 ■ *"Living in a 'Goldfish Bowl'"* in WorkingUSA (Vol. 11, June 2008, No. 2, pp. 277)
Pub: Blackwell Publishers Ltd.
Ed: John Lund. **Description:** Recent changes in laws, regulations and even the reporting format of labor organization annual financial reports in both the U.S. and Australia have received surprisingly little attention, yet they have significantly increased the amount of information available both to union members and the public in general, as reports in both countries are available via government Websites. While such financial reporting laws are extremely rare in European countries, with the exception of the UK and Ireland, the U.S. and Australian reporting systems have become among the most detailed in the world. After reviewing these changes in financial reporting, as well as the availability of these reports, as well as comparing and contrasting the specific reporting requirements of each country, this paper then examines the cost-benefit impact of more detailed financial reporting.

46895 ■ *"Making Diverse Teams Click"* in Harvard Business Review (Vol. 86, July-August 2008, No. 8, pp. 20)
Pub: Harvard Business School Press
Ed: Jeffrey T. Polzer. **Description:** 360-degree feedback to increase the efficacy of diverse-member workplace teams, which involves each member providing feedback to the others on the team is discussed.

46896 ■ *"Managing the Facebookers; Business"* in The Economist (Vol. 390, January 3, 2009, No. 8612, pp. 10)
Pub: Economist Newspaper Ltd.
Description: According to a report from PricewaterhouseCoopers, a business consultancy, workers from Generation Y, also known as the Net Generation, are more difficult to recruit and integrate into companies that practice traditional business acumen. 61 percent of chief executive managers say that they have trouble with younger employees who tend to be more narcissistic and more interested in personal fulfillment with a need for frequent feedback and an over-precise set of objectives on the path to promotion which can be hard for managers who are used to a different relationship with their subordinates. Older bosses should prepare to make some concessions to their younger talent since some of the issues that make them happy include cheaper online ways to communicate and additional coaching, both of which are good for business.

46897 ■ *"Mentoring Support"* in Black Enterprise (Vol. 38, July 2008, No. 12, pp. 64)
Pub: Earl G. Graves Publishing Co. Inc.
Description: With his relocation from his multicultural team in New York to the less diverse Scripps Networks' headquarters in Knoxville, Earl Cokley has made it a top priority to push for more diversity and mentoring opportunities within the management of the media and marketing company.

46898 ■ *"The Mobile Workforce Revolution"* in Canadian Business (Vol. 81, March 31, 2008, No. 5, pp. 28)
Pub: Rogers Media
Ed: Diane Horton. **Description:** Diane Horton explains how a mobile workforce helps companies cut costs, increase productivity, and boost employee motivation. Horton says that employees believe they usually become more productive by 15 to 30 percent after their companies go mobile.

46899 ■ *"New Jobless Claims Filed in December Soar"* in Baltimore Business Journal (Vol. 27, January 29, 2010, No. 39, pp. 1)
Pub: American City Business Journals
Ed: Scott Dance. **Description:** Maryland received 48,693 new claims for unemployment benefits in December 2009, reaching its highest monthly total since 1974. The number of claims was up 49 percent from November and 13 percent from the same period in 2008. Labor officials and economists discuss this trend.

46900 ■ *"New Race Suit at Local Coke Plant"* in Business Courier (Vol. 24, February 1, 2008, No. 43, pp. 1)
Pub: American City Business Journals, Inc.
Ed: Jon Newberry. **Description:** Another racial harassment lawsuit has been filed against the Coca-Cola Enterprises Inc. plant in Madisonville by its 23 black workers. The lawsuit alleges that the working environment at the plant continues to be offensive, abusive, intimidating and hostile. Details of the class-action suit are provided.

46901 ■ *"NFL Labor, Legal Issues Hang Over Detroit Lions' Rebuilding Efforts"* in Crain's Detroit Business (Vol. 26, January 11, 2010, No. 2)
Pub: Crain Communications Inc.
Ed: Bill Shea. **Description:** Overview of the possible outcomes regarding labor talks with Detroit Lion's players as well as the outcome of a U.S. Supreme Court decision that could boost franchise values but at the expense of fans and corporate sponsors.

46902 ■ *"Nine Sectors to Watch: Automotive"* in Canadian Business (Vol. 81, December 24, 2007, No. 1, pp. 47)
Pub: Rogers Media
Ed: Thomas Watson. **Description:** Forecasts on the Canadian automotive sector for 2008 are presented. Details on contract concessions made by American unions, the industry's Big Three (General Motors, Chrysler, and Ford) operations in Canada, and Canadian Auto Workers demand for higher wages are also discussed.

46903 ■ *"No End to the Nightmare; America's Car Industry"* in The Economist (Vol. 390, January 3, 2009, No. 8612, pp. 46)
Pub: The Economist Newspaper Inc.
Description: Detroit's struggling auto industry and the government loan package is discussed as well as the United Auto Worker union, which is loathed by Senate Republicans.

46904 ■ *No Place Like Home: Organizing Home-Based Labor in the Era of Structural Adjustment*
Pub: Routledge Inc.
Ed: David Staples. **Released:** November 2006. **Price:** $70.00. **Description:** The book examines the role of home-based women workers in contemporary capitalism.

46905 ■ *"OPSEU: Developmental Service Workers Picketing Across Ontario to Raise Community Awareness"* in Canadian Corporate News (May 16, 2007)
Pub: Comtex News Network Inc.
Description: Across Ontario staff who support people with developmental disabilities are picketing local MPP offices and other community hubs to highlight the Ontario government's inadequate response to the crisis in developmental services.

46906 ■ *"Randy Perreira"* in Hawaii Business (Vol. 53, February 2008, No. 8, pp. 28)
Pub: Hawaii Business Publishing
Ed: David K. Choo. **Description:** Randy Perreira is recently named executive director of Hawaii Government Employees Association. He talks about how he was shaped growing up with a father who was a labor leader and how the challenges in 2008 compare with those in the time of his father. He also shares his thoughts about the importance of employees fighting for their rights.

46907 ■ *"Recession Survival Tip: Less Is More"* in Women Entrepreneur (December 31, 2008)
Pub: Entrepreneur Media Inc.
Ed: Suzy Girard-Ruttenberg. **Description:** These trying economic times can be an opportunity to make bold changes in one's business that may yield lasting results, not just short-term survival; simplification, accountability and shoring up one's margins are things to look at when determining the goals of the company.

46908 ■ *"Ronald Taketa"* in Hawaii Business (Vol. 54, September 2008, No. 3, pp. 28)
Pub: Hawaii Business Publishing
Ed: Shara Enay. **Description:** Interview with Ronald Taketa of the Hawaii Carpenters Union who states that the economic downturn has affected the construction industry as 20 percent of the union's 7,800 members are unemployed. He shares his thoughts about the industry's economic situation, the union's advertisements, and his role as a leader of the union.

46909 ■ *"Running On Empty"* in The Business Journal-Milwaukee (Vol. 25, July 4, 2008, No. 41, pp. A1)
Pub: American City Business Journals, Inc.
Ed: David Doege. **Description:** Employers are more engaged in offering incentives designed to offset commuting costs. Among the incentives offered are gas cards, parking reimbursement and midyear wage increases. The other efforts to help employees with the costs of going to work are discussed.

46910 ■ *"The Rypple Effect; Performance Management"* in The Economist (Vol. 390, January 3, 2009, No. 8612, pp. 48)
Pub: The Economist Newspaper Inc.
Description: New companies such as Rypple, a new, web-based service, claim that they can satisfy the Net Generation's need for frequent assessments while easing the burden this creates for management.

46911 ■ *"Scouting and Keeping Good Talent in the Workplace"* in Hawaii Business (Vol. 53, January 2008, No. 7, pp. 50)
Pub: Hawaii Business Publishing
Ed: Christie Dermegian. **Description:** Tips on improving employee selection and retention are presented. The strategies in choosing and keeping the right employees include identifying which type of people the company needs and improving the workplace environment.

46912 ■ *"Solidarity UAW Forever"* in Crain's Detroit Business (Vol. 25, June 1, 2009, No. 22, pp. M001)
Pub: Crain Communications Inc. - Detroit
Ed: Ryan Beene. **Description:** United Auto Workers union has made it difficult for certain businesses to move to Michigan. Discussion is made about the issues involved and changes that need to be made in the way labor and management do business.

46913 ■ *"Sorry: Good Defense for Mal Offense"* in The Business Journal-Serving Metropolitan Kansas City (Vol. 26, July 4, 2008, No. 43, pp. 1)
Pub: American City Business Journals, Inc.
Ed: Rob Roberts. **Description:** According to a survey conducted by the Kansas City Business Journal, ten hospitals in Kansas City showed that they have adopted disclosure policies that include prompt apologies and settlement offers. The policy is effective in minimizing medical malpractice lawsuits. Other details of the survey are presented.

46914 ■ "A Stalled Culture Change?" in Workforce Management (Vol. 88, December 14, 2009, No. 13, pp. 1)
Pub: Crain Communications Inc.
Ed: Jeremy Smerd. Description: General Motors CEO Fritz Henderson's abrupt resignation shocked employees and signaled that Henderson had not done enough to change the company's culture, especially in dealing with its top management.

46915 ■ "Star Power" in Small Business Opportunities (September 2008)
Pub: Entrepreneur Press
Contact: Perlman Neil, President
Description: Employee retention is an important factor for corporate executives to consider because the impact of excessive turnovers can be devastating to a company causing poor morale, unemployment claims, hiring costs, lost production and customer loss. Although there is no specific formula for retaining employees, there are several things every organization can do to keep their workers happy and increase the chances that they will stay loyal and keep working for the company for years to come; tips aimed at management regarding good employee relationships are included.

46916 ■ "Steeling for Battle" in Crain's Chicago Business (Vol. 31, April 21, 2008, No. 16, pp. 3)
Pub: Crain Communications, Inc.
Ed: Bob Tita. Description: Discusses contract negotiations between the United Steelworkers union and ArcelorMittal USA Inc., the nation's largest steelmaker, and U.S. Steel Corp., the third-largest; the union sees these negotiations as the best chance in two decades to regain lost ground but industry experts predict the companies will try to reduce benefits, demand a separate, lower wage scale for new hires and look for relief from the rising costs for retirees' health insurance coverage.

46917 ■ "The Story Of Diane Greene" in Barron's (Vol. 88, July 14, 2008, No. 28, pp. 31)
Pub: Dow Jones & Co., Inc.
Ed: Mark Veverka. Description: Discusses the ousting of Diane Greene as a chief executive of VMWare, a developer of virtualization software, after the firm went public; in this case Greene, a brilliant engineer, should not be negatively impacted by the decision because it is common for companies to bring in new executive leadership that is more operations oriented after the company goes public.

46918 ■ "Taxes, Right-To-Work Top West Michigan Concerns" in Crain's Detroit Business (Vol. 24, September 22, 2008, No. 38, pp. 6)
Pub: Crain Communications Inc.
Ed: Amy Lane. Description: Two of the top priorities of business leaders in Western Michigan are the new business tax which they want to end as well as making the state a 'right-to-work' one through laws to prohibit unions from requiring workers to pay dues and membership as a condition of their employment.

46919 ■ "Truckers Walk Strike Line" in Puget Sound Business Journal (Vol. 29, October 24, 2008, No. 27, pp. 1)
Pub: American City Business Journals
Ed: Steve Wilhelm. Description: Teamsters Local 174 went on strike against Oak Harbor Freight Lines Inc. over alleged company violations of federal labor laws. The union also accuses the company of engaging directly with employees and holding mandatory meetings about contract negotiations.

46920 ■ "U Overhauling Its Janitorial Program, but Custodians Taking Exception" in Saint Paul Pioneer Press (August 20, 2011)
Pub: McClatchy-Tribune Regional News
Ed: Mila Koumpilova. Description: University of Minnesota developed a new team cleaning approach for its campus. The new custodian program will save $3.1 million annually while providing a cleaner campus. The union representing the custodians questions both claims.

46921 ■ "Union Ethics Training: Building the Legitimacy and Effectiveness of Organized Labor" in WorkingUSA (Vol. 11, September 2008, No. 3)
Pub: Blackwell Publishers Ltd.
Ed: Maggie Cohen. Description: Arguments are presented for the implementation of serious ethics training at all levels of labor unions and their contribution to union effectiveness by enhancing union legitimacy-understood as an amalgam of legal, pragmatic, and moral legitimacy and by paving the way to stable recognition of the labor movement as an integral part of American society, necessary to economic prosperity and the realization of fundamental American moral and social values.

46922 ■ "Union, Heal Thyself" in Canadian Business (Vol. 81, July 21, 2008, No. 11, pp. 9)
Pub: Rogers Media Ltd.
Description: General Motors Corp. was offered by the federal government a $250 million fund after the company declared plans to close its facility in Ontario. The government move is geared towards supporting the workers who have refused to support the automotive company. Details of the labor contract between General Motors and the Canadian Auto Workers are presented.

46923 ■ "Union Questions Patrick Cudahy Layoffs" in Business Journal-Milwaukee (Vol. 28, December 3, 2010, No. 9, pp. A1)
Pub: Milwaukee Business Journal
Ed: Rich Ravito. Description: United Food and Commercial Workers Local 1473 is investigating Patrick Cudahy Inc.'s termination of 340 jobs. The union said the company has violated the law for failing to issue proper notice of a mass layoff.

46924 ■ "Unions Pony Up $1 Million for McBride Stimulus" in Saint Louis Business Journal (Vol. 31, July 29, 2011, No. 49, pp. 1)
Pub: Saint Louis Business Journal
Ed: Evan Binns. Description: Carpenters District Council of Greater St. Louis and International Brotherhood of Electrical Workers Local 1 are among the nine unions that agreed to split the cost of nearly $1 million in incentives for homebuyers who purchase homes in McBride communities. McBride & Son has spent over $100,000 to promote the incentive program.

46925 ■ "Unions and Upward Mobility for Low-Wage Workers" in WorkingUSA (Vol. 11, September 2008, No. 3, pp. 337)
Pub: Blackwell Publishers Ltd.
Ed: John Schmitt, Margy Waller, Shawn Fremstad, Ben Zipperer. Description: Examination of the impact of unionization on the pay and benefits in fifteen important low-wage occupations is outlined. Even after controlling for important differences between union and nonunion workers, including such factors as age and education level, unionization improves the pay and benefits offered in what are otherwise low-paying occupations.

46926 ■ "UnitedHealthcare Resists Prognosis" in The Business Journal-Serving Metropolitan Kansas City (Vol. 26, August 29, 2008, No. 51)
Pub: American City Business Journals, Inc.
Ed: Rob Roberts. Description: Saint Luke's Hospital Systems terminated UnitedHealthcare from its insurance provider network on July 25, 2008. Negotiators with both parties have stopped speaking, and employees under UnitedHealthcare plans will have to pay higher bills unless Saint Luke's reconsiders its decision. The parties' previous negotiations are discussed.

46927 ■ "Unmasking Manly Men" in Harvard Business Review (Vol. 86, July-August 2008, No. 8, pp. 20)
Pub: Harvard Business School Press
Ed: Robin J. Ely; Debra Meyerson. Description: Oil rig work is used to explore how focusing on job requirements and performance successfully challenged stereotypical views of masculinity and competence.

46928 ■ "Verizon, Union Dispute is a Vestige of the Past" in Philadelphia Business Journal (Vol. 30, August 26, 2011, No. 28, pp. 1)
Pub: American City Business Journals Inc.
Ed: Peter Key. Description: Verizon is arguing that some of the provisions of its unionized workers' contracts date back to the days before AT&T were forced to spin off its local phone-service providers in 1984. The evolution of Verizon through the years and its relations with its unions are discussed.

46929 ■ "Vicki Avril; Senior Vice-President of Tubular Division, Ipsco Inc." in Crain's Chicago Business (Vol. 31, May 5, 2008, No. 18)
Pub: Crain Communications, Inc.
Ed: Miriam Gottfried. Description: Profile of Vicki Avril who is the senior vice-president of the tubular division at Ipsco Inc. where she supervises 2,800 employees and 13 mills throughout the United States and Canada.

46930 ■ "Wal-Mart Expansion Plans Hit Roadblock" in Crain's Chicago Business (Vol. 31, March 24, 2008, No. 12, pp. 2)
Pub: Crain Communications, Inc.
Ed: Monee Fields-White. Description: Wal-Mart Stores Inc.'s expansion plans in Chicago have suffered a series of setbacks due to a shifting political landscape in which may require the company to pay higher wages. Wal-Mart claims that its hourly pay and benefits are fair; however, the labor force does not agree.

46931 ■ "Weaving a Stronger Fabric: Organizing a Global Sweat-Free Apparel Production Agreement" in WorkingUSA (Vol. 11, June 2008, No. 2)
Pub: Blackwell Publishers Ltd.
Ed: Eric Dirnbach. Description: Tens of millions of workers working under terrible sweatshop conditions in the global apparel industry. Workers are employed at apparel contractors and have been largely unsuccessful in organizing and improving their working conditions. The major apparel manufacturers and retailers have the most power in this industry, and they have adopted corporate social responsibility programs as a false solution to the sweatshop problem. The major North American apparel unions dealt with similar sweatshop conditions a century ago by organizing the contractors and brands into joint association contracts that significantly raised standards. Taking inspiration from their example, workers and their anti-sweatshop allies need to work together to coordinate a global organizing effort that builds worker power and establishes a global production agreement that negotiates with both contractors and the brands for improved wages, benefits, and working conditions.

46932 ■ "Whistleblower or Manipulator?" in Canadian Business (Vol. 81, July 22, 2008, No. 12-13, pp. 11)
Pub: Rogers Media Ltd.
Ed: John Gray. Description: Discusses Maria Messina who is portrayed by prosecutors of the Livent Inc. trial as a whistleblower, while defense lawyers insist that she is a manipulator. Defense lawyers allege that Messina, who was Livent's chief financial officer, is a character assassin that made money out of Livent's bankruptcy. Other views on Messina, as well as information on the case, are presented.

46933 ■ "Will Call Center Servicing Solve Labor's Customer Satisfaction Problems?" in WorkingUSA (Vol. 11, September 2008, No. 3, pp. 383)
Pub: Blackwell Publishers Ltd.
Ed: Steve Early. Description: Service Employees International Union (SEIU) has launched an ambitious plan to service hundreds of thousands of members through a network of Member Resource Centers (MRCs). This call center servicing strategy draws on the experience of unions in Australia and the customer service centers operated by major corporations. Call center critics fear the role of union stewards and shop floor activity will be undermined by the introduction of this system in SEIU workplaces in the U.S.

46934 ■ *"Women's Union Leadership: Closing the Gender Gap" in WorkingUSA (Vol. 11, December 2008, No. 4, pp. 459)*
Pub: Blackwell Publishers Ltd.
Ed: Michelle Kaminski, Elaine K. Yakura. **Description:** Women make up 44 percent of the labor movement, but a smaller percentage of union leaders. The importance of having a leadership representative of membership, some differences between male and female leadership, and why the labor movement needs more women leaders is discussed.

46935 ■ *"Worth His Salt" in Hawaii Business (Vol. 53, January 2008, No. 7, pp. 45)*
Pub: Hawaii Business Publishing
Ed: Jolyn Okimoto Rosa. **Description:** Bryan Zada owns three PretzelMaker franchises, whose total loss amounted to $40,000 in 2003. Zada believes that listening to employees was one of the key steps in turning the business around. The efforts made to improve the franchises' products are also given.

46936 ■ *"Xstrata and CAW Get Tentative Deal" in Globe & Mail (February 2, 2007, pp. B3)*
Pub: CTVglobemedia Publishing Inc.
Ed: Andy Hoffman. **Description:** The agreement between Xstrata PLC and Canadian Auto Workers union over wage hike is discussed.

TRADE PERIODICALS

46937 ■ *Collective Bargaining Negotiations and Contracts*
Pub: Bureau of National Affairs Inc.
Contact: Leslie Goldman, Managing Editor
Released: Biweekly. **Price:** $246. **Description:** Presents news of developments in collective bargaining, including contract settlements, bargaining techniques and trends, and contract interpretations by the courts. Recurring features include columns titled Clause Talk, Arbitrating the Contract, Facts & Figures, and Perspective.

46938 ■ *Daily Labor Report*
Pub: Bureau of National Affairs Inc.
Contact: Susan Sala, Managing Editor
Released: Daily. **Price:** $6,160. **Description:** Covers labor developments in Congress, the courts, federal agencies, unions, management, and the National Labor Relations Board.

46939 ■ *Human Resources Report*
Pub: Bureau of National Affairs Inc.
Contact: Gail Moorstein, Managing Editor
Released: Weekly. **Price:** $875. **Description:** Monitors employee and labor relations in the United States. Follows private sector developments in compensation, health benefits, Equal Employment Opportunity (EEO), labor economics, legislation, and regulatory issues. Recurring features include a calendar of events, and weekly analysis.

46940 ■ *IRC Newsletter*
Pub: Industrial Relations Center
Released: Bimonthly. **Description:** Focuses on industrial relations and collective bargaining, with summaries of court decisions in the field and of decisions of the National Labor Relations Board and other boards and commissions. Covers pending legislation pertaining to work, labor-management relations, and similar subjects. Recurring features include bibliographic information, statistics, announcements of appointments, and synopses of significant reports and studies.

46941 ■ *Labor Center Reporter*
Pub: Center for Labor Research and Education
Released: Quarterly. **Price:** $20 (Donation). **Description:** Supplies economic and social analysis of issues of concern to the trade union community.

46942 ■ *Labor Relations Week*
Pub: Bureau of National Affairs Inc.
Contact: Susan Sala, Managing Editor
Released: Weekly. **Price:** $944. **Description:** Provides a comprehensive overview of developments influencing labor relations in the private sector.

46943 ■ *School of Labor and Industrial Relations eNewsletter*
Pub: School of Labor and Industrial Relations
Released: Semiannual. **Price:** Free. **Description:** Reports news of the School, including the status of various programs and services and statistics on growth. Contains articles on manpower, organizational behavior and personnel management, international and comparative labor and industrial relations, social structure and community organization, and social and industrial psychology. Recurring features include notices of job opportunities for graduates, courses offered, activities of the faculty, and meetings; book reviews; and recent reprints.

46944 ■ *Union Labor Report Weekly Newsletter*
Pub: Bureau of National Affairs Inc.
Contact: Jeff Day, Managing Editor
Released: Weekly. **Price:** $162. **Description:** Provides a roundup of developments of concern to organized labor. Includes summaries of arbitration awards and court cases. Recurring features include sections titled Special Report, Labor Facts, and Grievance Guide. Included with subscription to Union Labor Report or available separately. Subscription price includes Union Labor Report's On The Line newsletter.

VIDEOCASSETTES/ AUDIOCASSETTES

46945 ■ *Labor Management*
New Dimension Media, Inc.
307 N Michigan Ave., Ste. 500
Chicago, IL 60601
Ph: (312)642-9400
Free: 800-288-4456
Fax: (312)642-9805
Co. E-mail: Info@NDMquestar.com
URL: http://www.ndmquestar.com
Released: 1987. **Price:** $50.00. **Description:** Shows the importance of cooperation between union workers and management. Because it supplies solutions for handling employee situations, it is aimed towards management. **Availability:** VHS; 3/4 U.

COMPUTERIZED DATABASES

46946 ■ *Construction Labor Report™*
1801 S Bell St.
Arlington, VA 22202
Free: 800-372-1033
Co. E-mail: customercare@bna.com
URL: http://www.bna.com
Availability: Online: Bloomberg LP-Bloomberg BNA; Thomson Reuters - Westlaw. **Type:** Full-text.

46947 ■ *Human Resources Report*
1801 S Bell St.
Arlington, VA 22202
Free: 800-372-1033
Co. E-mail: customercare@bna.com
URL: http://www.bna.com
Availability: Online: Bloomberg LP-Bloomberg BNA. **Type:** Full-text.

46948 ■ *Labor Relations Week™ (LRW)*
1801 S Bell St.
Arlington, VA 22202
Free: 800-372-1033
Co. E-mail: customercare@bna.com
URL: http://www.bna.com
Availability: Online: Bloomberg LP-Bloomberg BNA. **Type:** Full-text; Numeric.

LIBRARIES

46949 ■ *Canadian Labour Congress Library*
2841 Riverside Dr.
Ottawa, ON, Canada K1V 8X7
Ph: (613)521-3400

Fax: (613)521-4655
URL: http://www.canadianlabour.ca/home
Contact: Ken Georgetti, President
Scope: Labor, labor history, industrial relations, trade unions, economics. **Services:** Interlibrary loan; copying; library open to public by appointment. **Founded:** 1956. **Holdings:** 4000 books; CLC Convention documents. **Subscriptions:** 36 journals and other serials.

46950 ■ *Federation des Travailleurs et Travailleuses du Quebec - Centre de Documentation*
565 boul Cremazie E. Bureau 12100
Montreal, QC, Canada H2M 2W3
Ph: (514)383-8025
Fax: (514)383-8001
Co. E-mail: ireny@ftq.qc.ca
URL: http://www.ftq.qc.ca
Contact: Isabelle Reny, Specialist, Document Delivery
Scope: Work, unions, sociology, economy. **Services:** Copying; library open to the public. **Founded:** 1957. **Holdings:** 10,200 books. **Subscriptions:** 150 journals and other serials; 3 newspapers.

46951 ■ *Manitoba Department of Labour - Manitoba Labour Board Library*
500-175 Hargrave St.
Winnipeg, MB, Canada R3C 3R8
Ph: (204)945-5046
Fax: (204)945-1296
Co. E-mail: mlb@gov.mb.ca
URL: http://www.gov.mb.ca/labour/labbrd/
Contact: Jodi Gilmore, Researcher
Scope: Labor. **Services:** Library open to the public. **Founded:** 1985. **Holdings:** 100 books; 1080 bound periodical volumes. **Subscriptions:** 5 journals and other serials.

46952 ■ *York University - Centre for Research in Work and Society*
York Res. Tower, 6th Fl.
4700 Keele St.
Toronto, ON, Canada M3J 1P3
Ph: (416)736-5612
Fax: (416)736-5916
Co. E-mail: crws@yorku.ca
URL: http://www.yorku.ca/crws
Contact: Stephanie Ross, Director
Scope: Work and society, unions, arbitration. **Services:** Library open to students, faculty and staff; open by appointment only from May to August. **Holdings:** 500 books; journals; primary and secondary documents and sources.

RESEARCH CENTERS

46953 ■ *International Labor Rights Forum (ILRF)*
1634 I St. NW, No. 1001
Washington, DC 20006
Ph: (202)347-4100
Fax: (202)347-4885
Co. E-mail: laborrights@ilrf.org
URL: http://www.laborrights.org
Contact: Judy Gearhart, Executive Director
Services: Information and analyses regarding labor rights conditions internationally. **Founded:** 1986. **Publications:** *Books and papers* (Quarterly). **Educational Activities:** ILRF Conferences (Periodic). **Awards:** Award for leadership in defending labor rights (Occasionally). **Telecommunication Services:** judy@ilrf.org.

46954 ■ *Labor and Employment Relations Association (LERA)*
University of Illinois at Urbana-Champaign
Champaign, IL 61820
Ph: (217)333-0072
Fax: (217)265-5130
Co. E-mail: leraoffice@uiuc.edu
URL: http://www.leraweb.org
Contact: David Lewin, President
Description: Business persons, union leaders, government officials, lawyers, arbitrators, academics, and others interested in research and exchange of ideas on social, political, economic, legal, and psychological aspects of labor and employment rela-

tions. **Founded:** 1947. **Publications:** *IRRA Newsletter; LERA Newsletter* (Quarterly); *IRRA Newsletter* (Quarterly); *Perspectives on Work* (Semiannual); *LERA proceedings of the annual meeting* (Annual); *LERA Newsletter* (Quarterly); *Perspectives on Work magazine* (Annual); *Research Volume* (Annual); *Industrial Relations Research Association--Membership Directory; IRRA Proceedings of the Annual Meeting* (Annual). **Educational Activities:** LERA jobs announcement service (Weekly); LERA PhD Student Consortium (Annual); LERA Annual Meeting (Annual), in January; LERA National Policy Forum (Annual); Executive Board Meeting (Semiannual); Labor and Employment Relations Association Meeting (Annual); IRRA National Policy Forum (Annual). **Awards:** Best Dissertation (Annual); Excellence in Education (Annual); Lifetime Achievement (Annual); Young Practitioner (Annual); Young Scholar (Annual); LERA Best Dissertation Award (Annual); LERA Lifetime Achievement Award (Annual); LERA Outstanding Young Practitioner Award (Annual); LERA Outstanding Young Scholar Awards (Annual); Susan C. Eaton Scholar-Practitioner Award (Annual). **Telecommunication Services:** leraoffice@illinois.edu; pdwells@illinois.edu; irra@uiuc.edu.

46955 ■ Labor Research Association (LRA)
330 W 42nd St., 13th Fl.
New York, NY 10001
Ph: (212)714-1677
Fax: (212)714-1674
Co. E-mail: info@lra-ny.com
URL: http://www.laborresearch.org/about.php
Contact: Jonathan Tasini, Executive Director
Founded: 1927.

46956 ■ University of Louisville - Labor-Management Center (LMC)
Patterson Hall, Rm. 113
Louisville, KY 40292
Ph: (502)852-6482
Fax: (502)852-6453
Co. E-mail: carrie.donald@louisville.edu
URL: http://louisville.edu/labormanagement
Contact: Prof. Carrie G. Donald, Director

Services: Arbitration Advocacy Institute; Institute for ADA Medication; Planning and consulting services. **Founded:** 1986. **Publications:** *LMC Newsletter* (Quarterly); *Research publications series.* **Educational Activities:** Symposia and seminars. **Awards:** Labor-Management Annual Award, honors a workplace where management and the union(s) have promoted and demonstrated positive labor-management relations. **Telecommunication Services:** lmcenter@louisville.edu.

START-UP INFORMATION

46957 ■ *Angel Financing: How to Find and Invest in Private Equity*
Pub: John Wiley and Sons, Inc.
Ed: Gerald A. Benjamin; Joel B. Margulis. **Price:** $65.00. **Description:** The book provides a proven strategy to help entrepreneurs find angel investors. Interviews with angel investors as well as information about investors' hedging strategies, risk assessments, syndication orientation, financial return expectations, deal structuring preferences, monitoring investments, harvesting returns, and realist exit strategies are covered.

46958 ■ *"ATI Now Ready to Pounce on Biotech" in Austin Business JournalInc. (Vol. 28, August 22, 2008, No. 23, pp. 1)*
Pub: American City Business Journals
Ed: Laura Hipp. **Description:** Austin Technology Incubator has entered the biotechnology sector through a program of the University of Texas incubator. The company's bioscience program was set off by a grant from the City of Austin worth $125,000. The growth of Austin's biotechnology sector is examined.

46959 ■ *"EDCO Doling Out Capital Along Border" in Austin Business JournalInc. (Vol. 28, August 1, 2008, No. 20, pp. 1)*
Pub: American City Business Journals
Ed: Sandra Zaragoza. **Description:** Non-profit business incubator Economic Development Catalyst Organization Ventures is searching for promising startup companies. The company is targeting startups in green energy, technology and consumer markets. EDCO has partnered with consumer electronics repair company CherryFusion and technology firm MiniDonations.

46960 ■ *"EMU, Spark Plan Business Incubator for Ypsilanti" in Crain's Detroit Business (Vol. 23, October 15, 2007, No. 42, pp. 3)*
Pub: Crain Communications Inc. - Detroit
Ed: Chad Halcom. **Description:** Eastern Michigan University is seeking federal grants and other funding for a new business incubator program that would be in cooperation with Ann Arbor Spark. The site would become a part of a network of three Spark incubator programs with a focus on innovation in biotechnology and pharmaceuticals.

46961 ■ *"Friends With Money" in Entrepreneur (Vol. 37, August 2009, No. 8, pp. 74)*
Pub: Entrepreneur Media, Inc.
Ed: Asheesh Advani. **Description:** Providing a strong introduction to an investor will maximize a startup's chances of getting a second meeting. Startups should also pick an achievable fund raising goal and to keep track of their labor-adjusted net capital when fund raising.

46962 ■ *"Macomb County, OU Eye Business Incubator" in Crain's Detroit Business (Vol. 24, February 11, 2008, No. 6, pp. 1)*
Pub: Crain Communications Inc. - Detroit
Ed: Chad Halcom. **Description:** Officials in Macomb County, Michigan are discussing plans to create a defense-themed business incubator in the county. Macomb County was awarded $282,000 in federal budget appropriation for the project.

46963 ■ *Mommy Millionaire: How I Turned My Kitchen Table Idea Into a Million Dollars and How You Can, Too!*
Pub: St. Martin's Press LLC
Ed: Kim Lavine. **Released:** February 19, 2008. **Price:** $14.95. **Description:** Advice, secrets and lessons for making a million dollars from a mom who turned her kitchen into a successful business; tools cover developing and patenting an idea, cold calling, trade shows, QVC, big retailers, manufacturing, and raising venture capital.

46964 ■ *"New Program for Entrepreneurs" in Austin Business JournalInc. (Vol. 29, February 12, 2010, No. 29, pp. 1)*
Pub: American City Business Journals
Ed: Christopher Calnan. **Description:** Nonprofit group Economic Development Catalyst Organization (ECDO) is formalizing its BizLaunch mentoring program, which was stated in 2009. The program aims to offer support networks to entrepreneurs and assistance regarding early-stage venture capital.

46965 ■ *"Oversubscribed: Startup Funds Pour In" in Boston Business Journal (Vol. 31, July 22, 2011, No. 26, pp. 1)*
Pub: Boston Business Journal
Ed: Kyle Alspach. **Description:** Companies in Boston, Massachusetts are attracting strong interest from venture capital companies, resulting in increased venture capital funding. About $1.14 billion was invested in local companies during second quarter 2011.

46966 ■ *Raising Capital*
Pub: Kiplinger Books and Tapes
Ed: Andrew J. Sherman. **Price:** $34.95. **Description:** Corporate attorney provides a comprehensive guide using in-depth, practical advice on raising money to start and grow a business. A 115-page appendix contains samples of financing agreements, forms and questionnaires.

46967 ■ *Seed-Stage Venture Investing: The Ins and Outs for Entrepreneurs, Start-Ups, and Investors on Successfully Starting a New Business*
Pub: Aspatore Books, Incorporated
Ed: William J. Robbins. **Released:** July 2006. **Price:** $199.95. **Description:** Ideas for starting, funding, and managing technology-based firms, also known as, venture capitalists, are featured.

46968 ■ *"Spread Your Wings" in Canadian Business (Vol. 81, March 17, 2008, No. 4, pp. 31)*
Pub: Rogers Media
Ed: Megan Harman. **Description:** Financing from angel investors is one avenue that should be explored by startups. Angel investors are typically affluent individuals who invest their own money. Angel investors usually want at least 10 times their initial investment within eight years but they benefit the businesses through their help in decision-making and the industry expertise they provide.

46969 ■ *"State Fund That Aids New Companies Likely To Wither" in Crain's Detroit Business (Vol. 24, February 25, 2008, No. 8, pp. 16)*
Pub: Crain Communications Inc. - Detroit
Ed: Tom Henderson. **Description:** Officials are committed to fighting to save funding for the statewide Strategic Economic Investment and Commercialization Board which provides pre-seed money to start-up firms.

46970 ■ *"UM-Dearborn to Launch Program for Entrepreneurs" in Crain's Detroit Business (Vol. 24, April 14, 2008, No. 15, pp. 7)*
Pub: Crain Communications Inc.
Ed: Chad Halcom. **Description:** Starting this fall the University of Michigan-Dearborn will begin its Product Realization and Technology Commercialization Program for entrepreneurs and innovators with lab-tested, high-technology products. Ultimately, 20 businesses will each work with the university in creating a customer base, commercializing a new high-tech product or process and connecting with venture capitalists who may invest in the new companies.

46971 ■ *"The Y Factor" in Entrepreneur (Vol. 35, November 2007, No. 11, pp. 58)*
Pub: Entrepreneur Media Inc.
Ed: Sara Wilson. **Description:** Venture capital company Y Cominbator hosts a three-month program wherein the firm's founders select technology entrepreneurs from across the U.S. to help and to mentor them on starting a business.

ASSOCIATIONS AND OTHER ORGANIZATIONS

46972 ■ **Canada's Venture Capital and Private Equity Association (CVCA)—Association Canadienne du Capital de Risque et d'Investissement**
MaRS Centre
Heritage Bldg.
101 College St., Ste. 120 J
Toronto, ON, Canada M5G 1L7
Ph: (416)487-0519
Fax: (416)487-5899
Co. E-mail: cvca@cvca.ca
URL: http://www.cvca.ca
Contact: Rick Nathan, Chairman
Description: Ventures and risks capital companies. Promotes economic growth through provision of capital to emerging businesses. Conducts research; facilitates exchange of information among members; represents the venture capital industry before government agencies, industrial and financial organizations, and the public. **Founded:** 1974. **Publications:** *Enter-*

prise (Quarterly). **Awards:** Deal of the Year (Annual); Entrepreneur of the Year (Annual); Deal of the Year Award; Entrepreneur of the Year Award.

46973 ■ Center for Venture Research (CVR)
University of New Hampshire
Whittemore School of Business and Economics
15 Academic Way, McConnell Hall
Durham, NH 03824
Ph: (603)862-0017
Fax: (603)862-4468
Co. E-mail: cnmc@cisunix.unh.edu
URL: http://wsbe.unh.edu/cvr
Contact: Cynthia Nizzari-McClain, Coordinator
Description: Encourages and conducts research into methods of financing new technology-based industries and firms. **Founded:** 1986.

46974 ■ Coleman Foundation
651 W Washington Blvd., Ste. 306
Chicago, IL 60661
Ph: (312)902-7120
Fax: (312)902-7124
Co. E-mail: info@colemanfoundation.org
URL: http://www.colemanfoundation.org
Contact: Michael W. Hennessy, President
Description: Strives to support entrepreneurship, cancer research, housing and education for the handicapped, and diverse educational programs. **Founded:** 1951. **Awards:** Entrepreneur Excellence in Teaching (Annual).

46975 ■ Commercial Finance Association (CFA)
370 7th Ave., Ste. 1801
New York, NY 10001-3979
Ph: (212)792-9390
Fax: (212)564-6053
Co. E-mail: info@cfa.com
URL: http://www.cfa.com
Contact: John Fox, Chairman
Description: Organizations engaged in asset-based financial services including commercial financing and factoring and lending money on a secured basis to small- and medium-sized business firms. Acts as a forum for information and consideration about ideas, opportunities and legislation concerning asset-based financial services. Seeks to improve the industry's legal and operational procedures. Offers job placement and reference services for members. Sponsors School for Field Examiners and other educational programs. Compiles statistics; conducts seminars and surveys; maintains speakers' bureau and 21 committees. **Founded:** 1944. **Publications:** *The Secured Lender* (Bimonthly). **Educational Activities:** Commercial Finance Association Convention (Annual).

46976 ■ Council of Development Finance Agencies (CDFA)
85 E Gay St., Ste. 700
Columbus, OH 43215
Ph: (614)224-1300
Fax: (614)224-1343
Co. E-mail: info@cdfa.net
URL: http://www.cdfa.net
Contact: Toby Rittner, President
Description: Works for the advancement of development finance concerns and interests. Represents members of the development finance community from the public, private and non-profit sectors. **Founded:** 1982. **Publications:** *Development Finance Review Weekly* (Weekly). **Educational Activities:** Development Finance Summit (Annual). **Awards:** Practitioners Showcase.

46977 ■ Enterprise
MaRS Centre
Heritage Bldg.
101 College St., Ste. 120 J
Toronto, ON, Canada M5G 1L7
Ph: (416)487-0519
Fax: (416)487-5899
Co. E-mail: cvca@cvca.ca
URL: http://www.cvca.ca
Contact: Rick Nathan, Chairman
Released: Quarterly

46978 ■ National Association of Development Companies (NADCO)
6764 Old McLean Village Dr.
McLean, VA 22101
Ph: (703)748-2575
Fax: (703)748-2582
Co. E-mail: chris@nadco.org
URL: http://www.nadco.org
Contact: Christopher L. Crawford, President
Description: Small Business Administration Section 504 certified development companies. Provides long-term financing to small and medium-sized businesses. Represents membership in negotiations with the SBA, Congress, and congressional staff members; negotiates changes in legislation, regulations, operation procedures, and other matters such as prepayments problems, reporting requirements, and loan servicing procedures. Provides technical assistance and information regarding special training programs, marketing techniques, audit checklists, and loan closing and processing procedures. Compiles statistics. **Founded:** 1981. **Publications:** *NADCO News* (Monthly). **Educational Activities:** Winter Board Meeting (Annual).

46979 ■ National Association of Equity Source Banks (NAESB)
5432 Price Ave.
Baltimore, MD 21215
Ph: (410)367-5309
Co. E-mail: nahbb@msn.com
Contact: Rudolph Lewis, President
Description: Private investors and venture capital firms. Promotes investments in micro-economic enterprises from urban and rural areas with certified business models and franchises (these models must be third party verified from a business development institution authorized by the Association). **Founded:** 2000.

46980 ■ National Association of Investment Companies (NAIC)
1300 Pennsylvania Ave. NW, Ste. 700
Washington, DC 20004
Ph: (202)289-4336
Fax: (202)289-4329
Co. E-mail: info@naicpe.com
URL: http://www.naicvc.com
Contact: Ed Dandridge, President
Description: Aims to: represent the minority small business investment company industry in the public sector; provide industry education and develop research material on the activities of the industry. Collects and disseminates relevant business and trade information to members; facilitates the exchange of new ideas and financing strategies; assists organizing groups attempting to form or acquire minority enterprise small business investment companies; provide management and technical assistance to members. **Founded:** 1971. **Publications:** *NAIC Membership Directory* (Annual); *National Association of Investment Companies--Membership Directory* (Annual). **Telecommunication Services:** admin@naicvc.com.

46981 ■ National Association of Small Business Investment Companies (NASBIC)
1100 H St. NW, Ste. 610
Washington, DC 20005
Ph: (202)628-5055
Fax: (202)628-5080
Co. E-mail: bpalmer@nasbic.org
URL: http://www.nasbic.org
Contact: Brett Palmer, President
E-mail: bpalmer@nasbic.org
URL(s): www.nasbic.com/. **Description:** Firms licensed as Small Business Investment Companies (SBICs) under the Small Business Investment Act of 1958. **Founded:** 1958. **Publications:** *NASBIC News* (Quarterly); *NASBIC Membership Directory* (Annual); *NASBIC Membership Directory* (Annual); *Today's SBICs: Investing in America's Future*; *Venture Capital: Where to Find It* (Annual). **Educational Activities:** Venture Capital Institute for Entrepreneurs (Annual); Venture Capital Institute for Entrepreneurs (Annual); National Association of Small Business Investment Companies Annual Convention (Annual).

Awards: Portfolio Company of the Year Award (Annual). **Telecommunication Services:** info@sbia.org; nasbic@nasbic.org.

46982 ■ National Venture Capital Association (NVCA)
1655 N Ft. Myer Dr., Ste. 850
Arlington, VA 22209
Ph: (703)524-2549
Fax: (703)524-3940
Co. E-mail: mheesen@nvca.org
URL: http://www.nvca.org
Contact: Ray Rothrock, Chairman
Description: Venture capital organizations, corporate financiers, and individual venture capitalists who are responsible for investing private capital in young companies on a professional basis. Fosters a broader understanding of the importance of venture capital to the vitality of the U.S. economy and to stimulate the free flow of capital to young companies. Seeks to improve communications among venture capitalists throughout the country and to improve the general level of knowledge of the venturing process in government, universities, and the business community. **Founded:** 1973. **Publications:** *National Venture Capital Association--Annual Membership Directory* (Annual); *The Venture Capital Review* (Semi-annual); *National Venture Capital Association--Membership Directory* (Annual). **Awards:** Steiger Award (Annual).

REFERENCE WORKS

46983 ■ "75 Most Powerful Blacks on Wall Street" in Black Enterprise (Vol. 37, October 2006, No. 3, pp. 136)
Pub: Earl G. Graves Publishing Co. Inc.

Ed: Carolyn M. Brown. **Description:** Profiles of seventy-five African American top executives. The listing is a compilation of the brightest and best venture capitalists, asset managers, CEOs, traders, and investment bankers.

46984 ■ "AIC To Buy $350M of Real Estate" in Austin Business JournalInc. (Vol. 28, November 14, 2008, No. 35, pp. 1)
Pub: American City Business Journals

Ed: Kate Harrington. **Description:** Austin-based AIC Ventures LP is planning to buy $350 million worth of commercial real estate. The company's move will double its acquisitions. It is also planning to acquire 30 assets for its eight fun in 2009 from middle-market companies.

46985 ■ "Alberta Star Begins Phase 2 Drilling On Its Eldorado & Contact Lake IOCG & Uranium Projects" in Canadian Corporate News (May 16, 2007)
Pub: Comtex News Network Inc.

Description: Profile of Alberta Star Development Corp., a Canadian mineral exploration company that identifies, acquires, and finances advanced stage exploration projects in Canada, and its current undertaking of its 2007 drill program in which the company intends to begin accelerating its uranium and poly-metallic exploration and drilling activities on all of its drill targets for 2007 now that it has been granted its permits.

46986 ■ "All Indicators in Michigan Innovation Index Drop in 4Q" in Crain's Detroit Business (Vol. 25, June 22, 2009, No. 25, pp. 9)
Pub: Crain Communications Inc. - Detroit

Ed: Ryan Beene. **Description:** Economic indicators that rate Michigan's innovation fell in the fourth quarter of 2008. The index of trademark applications, SBA loans, venture capital funding, new incorporations and other indicators traced dropped 12.6 points.

46987 ■ "Angel Investing 2009" in Inc. (Vol. 31, January-February 2009, No. 1, pp. 83)
Pub: Mansueto Ventures LLC

Ed: Kasey Wehrum. **Description:** Tips for finding funding in tough economic times are presented, including secrets for closing second-round deals.

46988 ■ *"Angel Investments Tripled in 2009"* in Austin Business JournalInc. (Vol. 29, January 8, 2010, No. 44, pp. 1)
Pub: American City Business Journals
Ed: Christopher Calnan. **Description:** Central Texas Angel Network (CTAN) has invested $3.5 million in 12 ventures, which include 10 in Austin, Texas in 2009 to triple the amount it invested during 2008. The largest recipient of CTAN's investments is life sciences, which attracted 20 percent of the capital, while software investments fell to 18 percent. The new screening process that helps startups secure CTAN capital is explored.

46989 ■ *"Aptitudes for Apps"* in Boston Business Journal (Vol. 31, July 1, 2011, No. 23, pp. 3)
Pub: Boston Business Journal
Ed: Kyle Alspach. **Description:** Startups Apperian Inc. and Kinvey Inc. are aiming to accelerate the development and deployment of mobile applications and have received fund pledges from Boston-area venture capital firms.

46990 ■ *"Ardesta Venture-Capital Fund Folds"* in Crain's Detroit Business (Vol. 24, September 22, 2008, No. 38, pp. 24)
Pub: Crain Communications Inc.
Ed: Tom Henderson. **Description:** Due to the down-turn in the local economy, Ann Arbor-based Ardesta LLC, a venture-capital firm specializing in micro- and nanotechnology research, has pulled the plug on its planned fund of $100 million and said no to an investment of up to $15 million from the state.

46991 ■ *"Area VCs Take Praise, Lumps, on Web site"* in Boston Business Journal (Vol. 27, October 26, 2007, No. 39, pp. 1)
Pub: American City Business Journals Inc.
Ed: Jesse Noyes. **Description:** TheFunded.com is a social networking site that allows entrepreneurs to rate venture capitalists and post their comments. Information about venture capitalist firms such as size and the partners behind it are also provided.

46992 ■ *The Art of the Start*
Pub: Portfolio Publishing
Ed: Guy Kawasaki. **Price:** $26.95. **Description:** Apple's Guy Kawasaki offers information to help would-be entrepreneurs create new enterprises. As founder and CEO of Garage Technology Ventures, he has field-tested his ideas with newly hatched companies and he takes readers through every phase of creating a business, from the very basics of raising money and designing a business model through the many stages that eventually lead to success and thus giving back to society.

46993 ■ *"ATS Secures Investment From Goldman Sachs"* in The Business Journal - Serving Phoenix and the Valley of the Sun (Vol. 29, September 26, 2008, No. 4, pp. 1)
Pub: American City Business Journals, Inc.
Ed: Patrick O'Grady. **Description:** Goldman Sachs made an investment to American Traffic Solutions Inc. (ATS) which will allow it to gain two seats on the board of the red-light and speed cameras maker. The investment will help ATS maintain its rapid growth which is at 83 percent over the past 18 months leading up to September 2008.

46994 ■ *"Attorney Guides Biotech Company in $6 Million Initial Public Offering"* in Miami Daily Business Review (March 26, 2008)
Pub: ALM Media Inc.
Description: In order to raise capital to engage in a full-scale trial of MyoCell to receive clinical approval, Bioheart Inc., launched an initial public offering. Bioheart researches and develops cell therapies to treat heart damage.

46995 ■ *Attracting Investors: A Marketing Approach to Finding Funds for Your Business*
Pub: John Wiley and Sons, Inc.
Ed: Philip Kotler, Hermawan Kartajaya, S. David Young. **Released:** August 2004. **Price:** $29.95 (US), $42.99 (Canadian). **Description:** Marketing experts advise entrepreneurs in ways to find investors in order to raise capital for their companies.

46996 ■ *"Austin Ventures: Is It a VC Firm?"* in Austin Business Journal (Vol. 31, June 17, 2011, No. 15, pp. 1)
Pub: American City Business Journals Inc.
Ed: Christopher Calnan. **Description:** Investment firm Austin Ventures could lose its classification as a venture capital firm under a new definition of venture capital by the Securities and Exchange Commission. The reclassification could result in additional expenses for Austin Ventures, which has two-thirds of its investments in growth equity transactions.

46997 ■ *"Bigger TIF Makes Development Inroads"* in The Business Journal-Serving Metropolitan Kansas City (Vol. 26, July 11, 2008, No. 44)
Pub: American City Business Journals, Inc.
Ed: Rob Roberts. **Description:** On July 9, 2008 the Tax Increment Financing Commission voted to expand a TIF district to Tiffany Springs Road. The plan for the TIF district close to Kansas City International Airport is to include a-half mile of the road. The impacts of the expansion on construction projects and on the road network are analyzed.

46998 ■ *"Boise-based Highway 12 Invests in Crowdsourcing Platform"* in Idaho Business Review (September 24, 2010)
Pub: Dolan Media Newswires
Ed: Simon Shifrin. **Description:** The only venture capital fund in Idaho, Highway 12 Ventures, is funding Kapost a new company that helps news Websites, blogs and other online venues to pull content from a larger network of writers.

46999 ■ *"Catching Creatives; Detroit Group Gets Grant to Attract 1,000 Design Pros"* in Crain's Detroit Business (March 24, 2008)
Pub: Crain Communications, Inc.
Ed: Sherri Begin. **Description:** Design Detroit was given a $200,000 planning grant by the Knight Foundation, an organization that strives to back initiatives that leverage talent and resources in each of the 26 U.S. cities it funds, to inspire strategies to attract up to 1,000 creative professionals to live in Detroit.

47000 ■ *"Centerpoint Funding In Limbo"* in The Business Journal - Serving Phoenix and the Valley of the Sun (Vol. 28, August 1, 2008, No. 48)
Pub: American City Business Journals, Inc.
Ed: Jan Buchholz. **Description:** Avenue Communities LLC has threatened to file a case against Mortgages Ltd. over the finance of the Centerpoint development project in Tempe, Arizona. Avenue Communities want Mortgages Ltd. to file a motion with the U.S. Bankruptcy Court so that it can secure financing for the project. Other views and information on the finance of Centerpoint, are presented.

47001 ■ *"The Chips Are In"* in Business Journal-Portland (Vol. 24, November 2, 2007, No. 35, pp. 1)
Pub: American City Business Journals, Inc.
Ed: Aliza Earnshaw. **Description:** The $30 million funding round of Ambric Inc., which brings a total investment of $51 million, is about to close, and its clients are releasing over half-dozen products containing Ambric chips in January 2008. The features of Ambric's semiconductors, its market sectors and market positioning, as well as its investor relations, are discussed.

47002 ■ *"City, County May Kill VC Tax"* in Business Journal-Portland (Vol. 24, October 12, 2007, No. 33, pp. 1)
Pub: American City Business Journals, Inc.
Ed: Aliza Earnshaw. **Description:** City of Portland and Multnomah County in Oregon may soon kill taxes levied on venture capital (VC) firms, which is expected to take place in late October 2007. Capitalists have long been saying that taxation is driving them out of town, but this change is expected to generate more investments and persuade VC firms to relocate within city limits.

47003 ■ *"ClearEdge Hums Along"* in Business Journal Portland (Vol. 26, December 18, 2009, No. 41, pp. 1)
Pub: American City Business Journals Inc.
Ed: Erik Siemers. **Description:** Hillsboro-based ClearEdge Power Inc. expanded its workforce and facilities with $15M capital from investors. Since May 2009, the number of employees increased from 40 to 150 and headquarters expanded from 5,000 to 80,000 square feet.

47004 ■ *"Columbia's JPB Raising $175M to Acquire Companies, Real Estate"* in Boston Business Journal (Vol. 29, May 27, 2011, No. 3, pp. 1)
Pub: American City Business Journals Inc.
Ed: Gary Haber. **Description:** JPB Enterprises is preparing to raise $175 million in its goal of acquiring companies and real estate that are major names in America. The $75 million will be raised for a buyout fund that will target wide range of industries while the $100 million will be used for land investment projects in the Florida Panhandle. Baltimore firms are expected to benefit from this deal.

47005 ■ *"Commensurate with Experience"* in Entrepreneur (Vol. 37, October 2009, No. 10, pp. 84)
Pub: Entrepreneur Media, Inc.
Ed: Carol Tice. **Description:** RingRevenue, a firm that specializes in pay-per-call technology that allows affiliate networks and advertising agencies to track purchases, began a funding round in June 2009 which it closed quickly after obtaining $3.5 million in venture capital. The round was closed earlier than the projections of its owners due to their track record.

47006 ■ *"Company Goes High-Tech To Attack Some Sore Spots"* in Boston Business Journal (Vol. 27, December 7, 2007, No. 45, pp. 10)
Pub: American City Business Journals Inc.
Ed: Mark Hollmer. **Description:** Transport Pharmaceuticals Inc. hopes to raise $35 million to fund a drug and a treatment device for treating cold sores, and seek federal regulatory approval. Dennis Goldberg, the company's CEO, believes that existing treatments that use acyclovir cream are relatively weak. Transport's drug uses a soluble gel cartridge with a higher concentration of acyclovir.

47007 ■ *Directory of Operating Small Business Investment Companies*
Pub: Investment Div. Small Business Administration
Contact: Dennis Chrisbaum, Manager
E-mail: dennis.chrisbaum@sba.gov
URL(s): www.sba.gov/content/all-sbic-licensees-state. **Released:** Semiannual; April and October. **Covers:** About 300 operating small business investment companies holding regular licenses and licenses under the section 301(d) of the Small Business Investment Act covering minority enterprise SBICs. **Entries include:** Company name, address, phone, branch offices, type of ownership, date licensed by SBA, license number, amount of obligation to the Small Business Administration, amount of private capital held, and type of investments made. **Arrangement:** Separate geographical sections for each type of license.

47008 ■ *Directory of Venture Capital: 2nd Edition*
Pub: John Wiley & Sons Inc.
Contact: Stephen M. Smith, President
URL(s): www.wiley.com/WileyCDA/WileyTitle/productCd-0471361046.html. **Released:** Latest edition April 2000. **Price:** $59.95, Individuals paperback. **Covers:** More than 600 actively investing venture capital firms and funding sources. **Entries include:** Company name, address, phone, types of investments, geographic preference. **Database includes:** Samples of standard agreements and contracts.

47009 ■ *The Directory of Venture Capital and Private Equity Firms: 2009*
Pub: Grey House Publishing
Contact: Richard Gottlieb, President
E-mail: rhg2@greyhouse.com
Ed: Laura Mars-Proietti. **Released:** April 1, 2009. **Price:** $450.00. **Description:** Updated and expanded edition that includes new entries offering access to

more than 3,500 domestic and international venture capital and private equity firms; detailed contact information and extensive data on investments and funds is included.

47010 ■ "Do-Gooder Finance: How a New Crop of Investors Is Helping Social Entrepreneurs" in Inc. (February 2008, pp. 29-30)
Pub: Gruner & Jahr USA Publishing
Ed: Nitasha Tiku. **Description:** Social venture firms are not seeking to sell companies as quickly as traditional venture companies. Four socially minded venture capital firms and banks profiled include, Underdog Venture, Island Pond, Vermont; Root Capital, Cambridge, Massachusetts; ShoreBank Pacific, Ilwaco, Washington; and TBL Capital, Sausalito, California.

47011 ■ Doing Business with Beauty: Black Women, Hair Salons, and the Racial Enclave Economy
Pub: Rowman & Littlefield Publishers Inc.
Contact: Jason Aronson, President
Ed: Adia Harvey Wingfield. **Released:** June 28, 2008. **Price:** $19.95. **Description:** Factors that draw black women into the hair industry are examined. Interviews with hair salon owners explore aspects of owning a salon, owner-employee relationships, and the black female owner's struggle for autonomy and success in entrepreneurship.

47012 ■ "EDF Ventures Dissolves Fund, Begins Anew On Investment" in Crain's Detroit Business (Vol. 24, February 25, 2008, No. 8, pp. 14)
Pub: Crain Communications Inc. - Detroit
Ed: Tom Henderson. **Description:** EDF Ventures is Michigan's oldest venture capital firm and was part of the second round of investments by the state's 21st Century Investment Fund and the Venture Michigan Fund.

47013 ■ "Elemental Nabs $5.5 Million" in The Business Journal-Portland (Vol. 25, July 18, 2008, No. 19, pp. 1)
Pub: American City Business Journals, Inc.
Ed: Aliza Earnshaw. **Description:** Elemental Technologies Inc., a Portland, Oregon-based software company got $5.5 million in new funding, bringing its total invested capital to $7.1 million in nine months since October 2008. The company plans to launch Badaboom, software for converting video into various formats, later in 2008.

47014 ■ "The Emerging Capital Market for Nonprofits" in Harvard Business Review (Vol. 88, October 2010, No. 10, pp. 110)
Pub: Harvard Business School Publishing
Ed: Robert S. Kaplan, Allen S. Grossman. **Description:** Demonstration of how nonprofits can use intermediaries to grow their organizational structures, giving them improved scale and impact is offered. Some intermediaries play a mutual-fund role and conduct due diligence, while others act as venture capital funds and implement strategy.

47015 ■ "Emerging Tech Fund Strong in 2009" in Austin Business JournalInc. (Vol. 29, December 25, 2009, No. 42, pp. 1)
Pub: American City Business Journals
Ed: Christopher Calnan. **Description:** Texas' Emerging Technology Fund (ETF) has seen an increase in applications from the state's technology companies in 2009. ETF received 87 applications in 2009 from Central Texas companies versus 50 during 2008 while $10.5 million was given to seven Texas companies compared with $10.6 million to ten companies in 2008.

47016 ■ "Fight Ensues Over Irreplaceable Gowns" in Tampa Bay Business Journal (Vol. 30, January 15, 2010, No. 4, pp. 1)
Pub: American City Business Journals
Ed: Janet Leiser. **Description:** People's Princess Charitable Foundation Inc. founder Maureen Rorech Dunkel has sought Chapter 11 bankruptcy protection before a state court decides on the fate of the five of

13 Princess Diana Gowns. Dunkel and the nonprofit were sued by Patricia Sullivan of HRH Venture LLC who claimed they defaulted on $1.5 million in loans.

47017 ■ "Financing Your Small Business
Pub: Barron's Educational Series Inc.
Contact: Alex Holtz, President
E-mail: aholtz@berronseduc.com
Ed: Robert Walter. **Released:** December 2003. **Description:** Tips for raising venture capital, dealing with bank officials, and initiating public offerings of stock shares for small business.

47018 ■ "Finding Room for Financing" in The Business Journal-Serving Metropolitan Kansas City (Vol. 26, August 1, 2008, No. 47, pp. 1)
Pub: American City Business Journals, Inc.
Ed: Rob Roberts. **Description:** Kansas City officials are expecting to receive financing recommendations for a new 1,000-room convention headquarters hotel. The $300-million project could be financed either through private ownership with public subsidies, or through public ownership with tax-exempt bond financing. Other views and information on the project and its expected economic impact, are presented.

47019 ■ "Former Mayor Driving $500 Million Real Estate Equity Fund" in The Business Journal - Serving Phoenix and the Valley of the Sun (Vol. 28, August 15, 2008, No. 50, pp. 1)
Pub: American City Business Journals, Inc.
Ed: Jan Buchholz. **Description:** Paul John, the former mayor of Phoenix, is establishing a $500 million real estate asset management fund. The fund is dubbed Southwest Next Capital Management and has attracted three local partners, namely Joseph Meyer, Jay Michalowski, and James Mullany, who all have background in finance and construction.

47020 ■ "Friends With Money" in Canadian Business (Vol. 81, Summer 2008, No. 9, pp. 22)
Pub: Rogers Media Ltd.
Description: Two of the most well connected managers in Canadian capital markets Rob Farquharson and Brian Gibson will launch Panoply Capital Asset Management in June. The investment management company aims to raise a billion dollars from institutions and high-net worth individuals.

47021 ■ "Funding Drought Stalls Biotech Incubators" in Saint Louis Business Journal (Vol. 31, July 29, 2011, No. 49, pp. 1)
Pub: Saint Louis Business Journal
Ed: Angela Mueller. **Description:** Economic slowdown took its toll on cash-strapped startups that fill incubators such as the Bio-Research and Development Growth (BRDG) Park in Creve Coeur, Missouri and the Center for Emerging Technologies in Midtown St. Louis. BRDG put a hold on construction of of its two buildings.

47022 ■ "Get With the Program" in Entrepreneur (Vol. 36, April 2008, No. 4, pp. 130)
Pub: Entrepreneur Media, Inc.
Ed: Nichole L. Torres. **Description:** Entrepreneurship initiatives help college students get connected with other students, teach them about how to start their own business while still in school, and help with funding. Some of these programs are the Harold Grinspoon Charitable Foundation's Entrepreneurship Initiative and the Syracuse Campus-Community Entrepreneurship Initiative.

47023 ■ "Graduates to the TSX in 2008" in Canadian Business (Vol. 81, Summer 2008, No. 9, pp. 79)
Pub: Rogers Media Ltd.
Ed: Calvin Leung. **Description:** Table showing the market capitalization and stock performance of the companies that jumped to the TSX Venture Exchange is presented. The 17 companies that made the leap to the list will have an easier time raising capital, although leeway must be made in investing since they are still new businesses.

47024 ■ "Greener Pastures" in Canadian Business (Vol. 80, February 12, 2007, No. 4, pp. 69)
Pub: Rogers Media
Ed: Thomas Watson. **Description:** The effort of venture capitalists, including chief executive officer of Fun Technologies Lorne Abony, in successful running of several ventures in diverse fields is discussed.

47025 ■ "Growing Field" in Crain's Detroit Business (Vol. 26, January 11, 2010, No. 2, pp. 3)
Pub: Crain Communications Inc.
Description: Detroit's TechTown was awarded a combination loan and grant of $4.1 million from the U.S. Department of Housing and Urban Development to build a 15,000-square-foot stem cell center, a collection of laboratories that will be available to both for-profit companies and university researchers.

47026 ■ "Health Care Leads Sectors Attracting Capital" in Hispanic Business (March 2008, pp. 14-16, 18)
Pub: Hispanic Business
Ed: Scott Williams. **Description:** U. S. Hispanic healthcare, media, and food were the key industries in the U.S. gaining investors in 2007.

47027 ■ "House Committee on Small Business Calls for Sweeping Changes to SBIR Program" in Hispanic Business (March 2008, pp. 44)
Pub: Hispanic Business
Description: Changes in the Small Business Innovation and Research Program would allow greater flexibility for firms participating in the program to leverage venture capital funds.

47028 ■ "House Committee on Small Business Calls for Sweeping Changes to SBIR Program" in Hispanic Business (Vol. 30, March 2008, No. 3)
Pub: Hispanic Business
Description: Proposals suggested by the House Committee on small business to revamp the Small Business Innovation and Research Program (SBIR) are reported. These include allowing participating firms greater flexibility to use venture capital funds, increasing SBIR grants and faster processing of applications.

47029 ■ "How to Not Get Fired" in Entrepreneur (Vol. 37, September 2009, No. 9, pp. 62)
Pub: Entrepreneur Media, Inc.
Ed: Brad Feld. **Description:** Advice on how chief executive officers (CEO) of venture capital funded firms can avoid being replaced is presented. A CEO should not be defensive of the prospect of being replaced. The CEO may also work with the investors and the board for a smooth transition.

47030 ■ How to Start and Run Your Own Corporation: S-Corporations For Small Business Owners
Pub: HCM Publishing
Ed: Peter I. Hupalo. **Released:** March 6, 2003. **Price:** $22.95. **Description:** Basics of corporate business structure are explained. Topics include discovering the best business structure for your company; how to decided between an S-Corporation and LLC; choosing the state in which to incorporate, how to form a corporation, angel investing, special issues for one-person corporations, the role of bylaws and corporate minutes, board of directors, taxes, workers' compensation issues, retirement plans, and more.

47031 ■ "Human Bone Breakthrough" in Houston Business Journal (Vol. 40, January 8, 2010, No. 35, pp. 1)
Pub: American City Business Journals
Ed: Casey Wooten. **Description:** Biotech startup company Osteosphere in Houston, Texas aims to market a technology in which laboratory-grown bone tissues can be processed to appear like a real human bone tissue. The technology was developed by a co-founder of the startup and it can be applied to

bone disease and injury treatment. Osteophere's future plans, such as the search for possible investors, is also outlined.

47032 ■ *"I-5 Bridge Funding Unclear"* in *The Business Journal-Portland (Vol. 25, July 11, 2008, No. 18, pp. 1)*

Pub: American City Business Journals, Inc.

Ed: Andy Giegerich. **Description:** Financing for a new Interstate 5 bridge is unclear as Washington lawmakers identify two priority projects other than the planned bridge, which is shared with Oregon. An estimate says that the two states could pay between $487.6 million and $1.5 billion for the new bridge. Other details on the financing of the project are discussed.

47033 ■ *"In China, Railways to Riches"* in *Barron's (Vol. 88, July 7, 2008, No. 27, pp. M9)*

Pub: Dow Jones & Co., Inc.

Ed: Assif Shameen. **Description:** Shares of Chinese railway companies look to benefit from multimillion-dollar investments aimed at upgrading the Chinese railway network. Investment in the sector is expected to reach $210 billion for the 2006-2010 period.

47034 ■ *"In the Know?"* in *Entrepreneur (Vol. 37, July 2009, No. 7, pp. 30)*

Pub: Entrepreneur Media, Inc.

Ed: Brad Feld. **Description:** Tips on what entrepreneurs should and should not share with their venture capitalists (VCs) are given. Entrepreneurs must be transparent with their VCs, but they should not bombard VCs with too many details. The aspect of a business that a VC is concerned with varies from one VC to another, and it is important that entrepreneurs understand the best way to communicate with their VC.

47035 ■ *"Inside the Mind of an Investor: Lessons from Bill Draper"* in *Inc. (Volume 32, December 2010, No. 10, pp. 140)*

Pub: Inc. Magazine

Ed: Leigh Buchanan. **Description:** Profile of the three-generation Draper family, the first venture capital firm west of the Mississippi.

47036 ■ *"Inventive Doctor New Venture Partner"* in *Houston Business Journal (Vol. 40, January 29, 2010, No. 38, pp. A2)*

Pub: American City Business Journals

Ed: Ford Gunter. **Description:** Dr. Billy Cohn, a surgeon from Houston, Texas has been named as venture partner for venture firm Sante Ventures LLC of Austin, Texas. Cohn will be responsible for seeing marketable developing technologies in the medical industry. The motivation for Cohn's naming as venture partner is his development of a minimally invasive therapy for end-stage renal disease.

47037 ■ *"Investors Sue Jackson Properties for Fraud, Breach of Contract"* in *The Business Journal - Serving Phoenix and the Valley of the Sun (Vol. 28, July 18, 2008, No. 46, pp. 1)*

Pub: American City Business Journals, Inc.

Ed: Jan Buchholz. **Description:** Investors sued Jackson Properties EVB Inc. and Jackson Properties EVB LLC for fraud and breach of contract over a botched housing development deal. The investors also filed a complaint before the Arizona Corporation Commission. The investors stand to lose $8 million from the halted development deal.

47038 ■ *"It's Not Easy Investing Green"* in *Entrepreneur (Vol. 37, August 2009, No. 8, pp. 64)*

Pub: Entrepreneur Media, Inc.

Ed: Rosalind Resnick. **Description:** Some venture capitalists remain bullish on green investing despite signs of stagnation. One way for an investor to cash in on green investing is to invest in large public companies that are investing big in green initiatives. Being an angel investor to a local clean-tech company is another avenue.

47039 ■ *"A Knack for Entrepreneurship"* in *Hispanic Business (January-February 2008, pp. 42, 44-45)*

Pub: Hispanic Business

Ed: Hildy Medina. **Description:** Profile of Carlos Antonio Garcia, CEO of Kira, is investing in young companies.

47040 ■ *"Lack of Support Drives Scientists Away from Valley"* in *The Business Journal - Serving Phoenix and the Valley of the Sun (Vol. 28, August 1, 2008, No. 48, pp. 1)*

Pub: American City Business Journals, Inc.

Ed: Angela Gonzales. **Description:** Lack of support for scientists has caused scientists like Dietrich Stephan to depart from the city. Stephan is expected to relocate to California where he has found funding for his company Navigenics. Other views and information on the rising rate of the departure of scientists are presented.

47041 ■ *"Lenders"* in *The Business Journal - Serving Phoenix and the Valley of the Sun (Vol. 28, July 25, 2008, No. 47, pp. 1)*

Pub: American City Business Journals, Inc.

Ed: Jan Buchholz. **Description:** Private equity lender Investor Mortgage Holdings Inc. has continued growing despite the crisis surrounding the real estate and financial industries and has accumulated a $700 million loan portfolio. Private lending has become increasingly important in financing real estate deals as commercial credit has dried up.

47042 ■ *"Lines of Communication"* in *Entrepreneur (Vol. 37, October 2009, No. 10, pp. 80)*

Pub: Entrepreneur Media, Inc.

Ed: Brad Feld. **Description:** Entrepreneurial companies should establish a clear and open communication culture between their management teams and their venture capital backers. Chief executive officers should trust their leadership teams when it comes to communicating with venture capitalists.

47043 ■ *"Looking For Financing?"* in *Hispanic Business (Vol. 30, July-August 2008, No. 7-8, pp. 16)*

Pub: Hispanic Business, Inc.

Ed: Frank Nelson. **Description:** Investment firms want to know about businesses that need funding for either expansion or acquisition; companies fitting this profile are interviewed and their perceptions are discussed. Investment firms need businesses to be realistic in their expectations and business plans which show spending of funds and expected benefits, long term goals, track record and strong management teams.

47044 ■ *"Losses Threaten Comp Care's Future Viability"* in *The Business Journal-Serving Greater Tampa Bay (Vol. 28, August 15, 2008, No. 34)*

Pub: American City Business Journals, Inc.

Ed: Margie Manning. **Description:** Comprehensive Care Corp. expressed that it may have to cease or drastically curtail its operations if it won't be able to raise additional funding in the next two or three months. The firm, which provides managed behavioral health care services, is also believed to be exploring a sale. Other views and information on Comprehensive Care's finances and plans are presented.

47045 ■ *"Making Waves"* in *Business Journal Portland (Vol. 27, November 26, 2010, No. 39, pp. 1)*

Pub: Portland Business Journal

Ed: Erik Siemers. **Description:** Corvallis, Oregon-based Columbia Power Technologies LLC is about to close a $2 million Series A round of investment initiated by $750,000 from Oregon Angel Fund. The wave energy startup company was formed to commercialize the wave buoy technology developed by Oregon State University researchers.

47046 ■ *"The Marathon Club: Building a Bridge to Wealth"* in *Hispanic Business*

(March 2008, pp. 24)

Pub: Hispanic Business

Ed: Hildy Median. **Description:** Minority businesses find it more difficult to secure venture capital for entrepreneurial pursuits. Joe Watson, CEO of Without Excuses and Strategic Hire, suggests Hispanics and African Americans collaborate on issues of importance to minority entrepreneurs.

47047 ■ *"McMafia: A Journey Through the Global Criminal Underworld"*

Pub: Pantheon Books

Ed: Misha Glenny. **Released:** 2009. **Price:** $27.95. **Description:** Criminal entrepreneurs are using well-organized cosmopolitan networks to capitalize on globalization. Money from wars and illegal activities are being used to raise venture capital to finance criminal enterprises.

47048 ■ *"MEDC: Put Venture Funds to Work"* in *Crain's Detroit Business (Vol. 25, June 22, 2009, No. 25, pp. 1)*

Pub: Crain Communications Inc. - Detroit

Ed: Tom Henderson. **Description:** Michigan Strategic Fund board will finalize approval for ESP Holdings II LLC, Peninsula Capital Partners LLC, Triathlon Medical Ventures LLC and Arsenal Venture Partners Inc. are expected to share $35.5 million from the fund.

47049 ■ *"Meet the Dropouts: the Students Who Chose Start-Ups Over College"* in *Inc. (Vol. 33, September 2011, No. 7, pp. 32)*

Pub: Inc. Magazine

Ed: Eric Markowitz. **Description:** Profiles of 24 college students who left school in order to work on their own startup companies. Each new company is receiving $100,000 from Peter Thiel, cofounder of PayPal and an angel investor.

47050 ■ *"Meet UT's New Business Mind"* in *Austin Business Journal (Vol. 31, May 13, 2011, No. 10, pp. A1)*

Pub: American City Business Journals Inc.

Ed: Sandra Zaragoza. **Description:** University of Texas (UT) chief commercialization officer, Dr. Richard Miller, has opened a satellite office in Silicon Valley, California in the hopes of luring Californian investors to the science and technology at UT. The satellite office is just one of Miller's efforts to reshape and widen the commercialization of UT-Austin. Insights into Miller's long-term view approach to commercialization are also covered.

47051 ■ *"Merkle Lands $75M"* in *Baltimore Business Journal (Vol. 28, October 15, 2010, No. 23, pp. 1)*

Pub: Baltimore Business Journal

Ed: Gary Haber. **Description:** Baltimore, Maryland-based Merkle has received a $75 million investment from Silicon Valley-based Technology Crossover Ventures. The private equity firm's cash infusion was considered the biggest stake made in a company in the region and provides a healthy sign for Greater Baltimore's company.

47052 ■ *"Microsoft Goes Macrosoft"* in *Barron's (Vol. 89, July 27, 2009, No. 30, pp. 25)*

Pub: Dow Jones & Co., Inc.

Ed: Mark Veverka. **Description:** Microsoft reported a weak quarter on the heels of a tech rally which suggests the economy has not turned around. Marc Andreesen describes his new venture-capital fund as focused on 'classic tech' and that historical reference places him in the annals of the last millennium.

47053 ■ *"Millions Needed To Finish First Place"* in *The Business Journal-Milwaukee (Vol. 25, August 15, 2008, No. 47, pp. A1)*

Pub: American City Business Journals, Inc.

Ed: Rich Kirchen. **Description:** First Place on the River condominium project in Milwaukee, Wisconsin, needs $18.2 million before it can be completed. A total of $6.8 million have already been spent since the project went into receivership on 31 January 2008.

47054 ■ "Molycorp Funds Wind Energy Technology Company" in Manufacturing Close-Up (September 19, 2011)
Pub: Close-Up Media

Description: Molycorp Inc., producer of rare earth oxides (REO) and a REO producer outside of China, announced it will invest in Boulder Wind Power, which has designed a rare earth magnet powered wind turbine generator. This new generator can produce electricity as low as $0.04 per Kilowatt Hour. Boulder Wind Power's patented wind turbine technology allows for use of rare earth permanent magnets that do not require dysprosium, which is relatively scarce.

47055 ■ "Mr. Clean" in Canadian Business (Vol. 81, October 27, 2008, No. 18, pp. 74)
Pub: Rogers Media Ltd.

Ed: Rachel Pulfer. **Description:** Profile of Nicholas Parker, co-founder of Cleantech Group LLC, a pioneer in clean technology investing. Cleantech, now a global industry, accounts for 10 percent of all venture capital investments made by U.S. companies in 2007.

47056 ■ "Nanoready?" in Entrepreneur (Vol. 36, May 2008, No. 5, pp. 20)
Pub: Entrepreneur Media, Inc.

Ed: Andrea Cooper. **Description:** Experts predict that the medicine and energy sectors are among those that will see nanotechnology innovations in the coming years, and that nanotechnology will produce significant commercial value in new products. Some entrepreneurs are investing in nanotech and are partnering with universities. Details on nanotech funding concerns are discussed.

47057 ■ National Venture Capital Association--Membership Directory
Pub: National Venture Capital Association
Contact: Ray Rothrock, Chairman

URL(s): www.nvca.org/index.php?option=com_content&view=article&id=252&Itemid=624. **Released:** Annual; Latest edition 2009. **Price:** $195, hard copy; $325, CD-ROM one-user license (additional license $75). **Covers:** 480 venture capital firms, including subsidiaries of banks and insurance companies. **Entries include:** Firm name, address, phone, contact names, fax number, investment preferences. **Arrangement:** Alphabetical. **Indexes:** Contact name.

47058 ■ "The New Face of Detroit" in Inc. (Vol. 33, October 2011, No. 8, pp. 6)
Pub: Inc. Magazine

Ed: Elizabeth Sile. **Description:** Basketball legend Magic Johnson has joined Detroit Venture Partners and Detroit will be one of the firm's three inaugural cities to host fellows from Venture for America, a new organization that places recent college graduates in start-up companies.

47059 ■ "Nobody Knows What To Do" in Barron's (Vol. 88, March 17, 2008, No. 11, pp. 40)
Pub: Dow Jones & Company, Inc.

Ed: Mark Veverka. **Description:** Attendees of the South by Southwest Interactive conference failed to get an insight on how to make money on the Web from former Walt Disney CEO Michael Eisner when Eisner said there's no proven business model for financing projects. Eisner said he finances his projects with the help of his connections to get product-placement deals.

47060 ■ "NYC Tops Hub in Tech VC Dollars" in Boston Business Journal (Vol. 31, August 5, 2011, No. 28, pp. 1)
Pub: Boston Business Journal

Ed: Kyle Alspach. **Description:** New York City has been outdoing Boston in terms of venture capital for technology firms since second quarter 2010. New York tech firms raised $865 million during the first two quarters of 2011 against Boston techs' $682 million. Boston has the edge, though, when it comes to hiring engineering talent as it is home to the Massachusetts Institute of Technology.

47061 ■ Overcoming Barriers to Entrepreneurship in the United States
Pub: Lexington Books

Ed: Diana Furchtgott-Roth. **Released:** March 28, 2008. **Price:** $24.95. **Description:** Real and perceived barriers to the founding and running of small businesses in America are discussed. Each chapter outlines how policy and economic environments can hinder business owners and offers tips to overcome these obstacles. Starting with venture capital access in Silicon Valley during the Internet bubble, the book goes on to question the link between personal wealth and entrepreneurship, examines how federal tax rates affect small business creation and destruction, explains the low rate of self-employment among Mexican immigrants, and suggests ways pension coverage can be increased in small businesses.

47062 ■ "The Perks of Going Public" in Austin Business Journal (Vol. 31, July 15, 2011, No. 19, pp. A17)
Pub: American City Business Journals Inc.

Ed: Christopher Calnan. **Description:** HomeAway Inc. launched a $216 million initial public offering. Austin Ventures has generated more than $32 million from the IPO.

47063 ■ "Phoenix Company Realizing Dream of Global Growth" in The Business Journal - Serving Phoenix and the Valley of the Sun (Vol. 28, July 18, 2008, No. 46, pp. 1)
Pub: American City Business Journals, Inc.

Ed: Chris Casacchia. **Description:** Phoenix, Arizona-based lubricant maker DreamBrands Inc. is realizing global growth. The company, which has been generating interest from institutional investors, is seeking a second round of funding. Details of the company's products and marketing plans are also discussed.

47064 ■ "Private Equity Firm Links First Arizona Deal" in Business Journal-Serving Phoenix and the Valley of the Sun (November 2, 2007)
Pub: American City Business Journals, Inc.

Ed: Chris Casacchia. **Description:** Pacific Investment Partners and Your Source Financial launched a $10 million fund and signed their first deal. The two companies acquire a minority stake in Dreambrands Inc. for $3 million. Dreambrands is using the capital to market its personal lubricant product Carrageenana.

47065 ■ "Private Equity Party Fuelled by Cheap Debt" in Globe & Mail (February 27, 2007, pp. B1)
Pub: CTVglobemedia Publishing Inc.

Ed: Sinclair Stewart. **Description:** The funding of private equity fund Kohlberg Kravis through cheap debt, during the buyout of the TXU Corp. is discussed.

47066 ■ "PSU Launches $90 Million Project" in The Business Journal-Portland (Vol. 25, July 18, 2008, No. 19, pp. 1)
Pub: American City Business Journals, Inc.

Ed: Aliza Earnshaw. **Description:** Portland State University (PSU) has launched a $90-million project for a new business school building, which is to be located at Southwest Market and Southwest Park. The business school is expected to move in to its new 130,000-suqare-foot building by 2013. PSU business school needs to raise $30 million for the project.

47067 ■ Raising Capital
Pub: Raising Capital
Ed: Andrew J. Sherman. Price: $34.95.

47068 ■ Raising Capital
Pub: Greenwood Publishing Group, Inc.

Ed: David Nour. **Released:** March 1, 2009. **Price:** $39.95. **Description:** An overview to help entrepreneurs find capital for starting and maintaining a small business is presented. The author shows how to develop long-term relationships with financial partners and ways to attract financing to fund the startup and growth phases of any business. Entrepreneurs tell how they raised money from friends, family, angel investors, banks and venture capitalists and private equity firms.

47069 ■ Raising Venture Capital for the Serious Entrepreneur
Pub: McGraw-Hill Inc.

Ed: Dermot Berkery. **Released:** September 2007. **Price:** $49.95. **Description:** Sourcebook to help entrepreneurs secure venture capital from investors.

47070 ■ "Raptor Opens Consultancy" in Austin Business Journal (Vol. 31, July 8, 2011, No. 18, pp. 1)
Pub: American City Business Journals Inc.

Ed: Christopher Calnan. **Description:** Boston hedge fund operator Raptor Group launched Raptor Accelerator, a consulting business providing sales and advisory services to early-stage companies in Central Texas. Aside from getting involved with the startups in which the Raptor Group invests, Raptor Accelerator will target firms operating in the sports, media, entertainment, and content technology sectors.

47071 ■ "Rebels' Cause: Adult Stem Cell" in Austin Business Journal (Vol. 31, June 3, 2011, No. 13, pp. 1)
Pub: American City Business Journals Inc.

Ed: Sandra Zaragoza. **Description:** MedRebels Foundation was launched in February 2011 with the goal of providing millions of dollars for research funding, education and advocacy for adult stem cell-focused medicine. The foundation, whose major contributor is SpineSmith LP, is a collaboration of other adult stem cell-related companies and nonprofit partners. It hopes to raise $200,000 by the end of 2011.

47072 ■ "Recession-Proof Your Startup" in Crain's Chicago Business (Vol. 31, November 10, 2008, No. 45, pp. 24)
Pub: Crain Communications, Inc.

Description: Detailed information concerning ways in which to start a business during an economic crisis is provided. Ways in which to find financing, the importance of a solid business plan, customer service, problem-solving and finding the right niche for the region are also discussed.

47073 ■ "Red Tape Ties Detroit Housing Rehab Plan" in Crain's Detroit Business (Vol. 24, September 22, 2008, No. 38, pp. 1)
Pub: Crain Communications Inc.

Ed: Ryan Beene. **Description:** Venture-capital firm Wilherst Oxford LLC is a Florida-based company that has purchased 300 inner-city homes which were in foreclosure in Detroit. Wilherst Oxford is asking the city to forgive the existing tax and utility liens so the firm can utilize the money for home improvements. The city, however, is reluctant but has stated that they are willing to negotiate.

47074 ■ "Running the Numbers" in Entrepreneur (Vol. 37, July 2009, No. 7, pp. 87)
Pub: Entrepreneur Media, Inc.

Ed: Carol Tice. **Description:** Ways in which entrepreneurs can assess if they are ready to be a multi-unit franchisee are presented. Choosing the right locations, knowing how much assistance they can get from the franchisor, and financing are the key considerations when planning additional franchise units. Examples of success in multi-unit operations and multi-unit terms are also presented.

47075 ■ "A Safe Bet" in Entrepreneur (Vol. 35, October 2007, No. 10, pp. 26)
Pub: Entrepreneur Media Inc.

Ed: Carol Tice. **Description:** U.S. Department of Defense has developed a program, called the Defense Venture Catalyst Initiative or DeVenCI, that will match defense officials to the products that they need. DeVenCI uses conferences to showcase the defense contractors and their technologies to defense managers. Details of how this program helps both contractors and defense officials are overviewed.

47076 ■ "Seed Funding" in Saint Louis Business Journal (Vol. 31, July 29, 2011, No. 49, pp. 1)
Pub: Saint Louis Business Journal

Ed: Kelsey Volkmann. **Description:** Monsanto kicked off a new campaign, 'St. Louis Grown' to show its commitment to the St. Louis, Missouri region after spending millions of dollars in recent years on national advertising campaigns. Monsanto had a marketing budget totaling $839 million in 2010 for both brand and corporate marketing.

47077 ■ "Small-Business Agenda: Increase Capital, Education, Tax Breaks" in Crain's Detroit Business (Vol. 24, March 17, 2008)
Pub: Crain Communications, Inc.
Ed: Nancy Kaffer. **Description:** Discusses the policy suggestions detailed in the Small Business Association of Michigan's entrepreneurial agenda which include five main categories of focus: making entrepreneurial education a higher state priority; increasing capital available to entrepreneurs; using the state's tax structure as an incentive for entrepreneurial growth; getting university research from the lab to the market; and limiting government regulation that's burdensome to small businesses and getting legislative support of entrepreneurial assistance efforts.

47078 ■ "Speak Better: Five Tips for Polished Presentations" in Women Entrepreneur (September 19, 2008)
Pub: Entrepreneur Media Inc.
Ed: Suzannah Baum. **Description:** Successful entrepreneurs agree that exemplary public speaking skills are among the core techniques needed to propel their business forward. A well-delivered presentation can result in securing a new distribution channel, gaining new customers, locking into a new referral stream or receiving extra funding.

47079 ■ "Spending on Innovation Down Sharply in State" in Crain's Detroit Business (Vol. 24, March 10, 2008, No. 10, pp. 7)
Pub: Crain Communications, Inc.
Ed: Chad Halcom. **Description:** Due to such issues as Michigan's uncertain tax structure, a shaky national economy, the credit crunch and mortgage lending crisis, investments in innovation for the state have sharply declined.

47080 ■ "State VC Fund To Get At Least $7.5 Million" in Crain's Detroit Business (Vol. 24, February 25, 2008, No. 8, pp. 14)
Pub: Crain Communications Inc. - Detroit
Description: Michigan's 21st Century Investment Fund is expected to receive $7.5 million, financed by tobacco-settlement money. The Michigan Strategic Fund Board will determine which firms will receive venture capital, which is mandated by legislation to invest the fund within three years.

47081 ■ "Study Puts Hub On Top of the Tech Heap" in Boston Business Journal (Vol. 30, November 26, 2010, No. 44, pp. 1)
Pub: Boston Business Journal
Ed: Galen Moore. **Description:** The Ewing Marion Kauffman Foundation ranked Massachusetts at the top in its evaluations of states' innovative industries, government leadership, and education. Meanwhile, research blog formDs.com also ranked Massachusetts number one in terms of venture-capital financings per capita.

47082 ■ "Tech Giving 2.0" in Boston Business Journal (Vol. 31, August 5, 2011, No. 28, pp. 1)
Pub: Boston Business Journal
Ed: Mary Moore. **Description:** Entrepreneurs and venture capitalists in Boston have launched Technology Underwriting Greater Good, the tech industry's answer to the criticism that they are not charitable. The foundation finances nonprofits that aid young people through entrepreneurship, education and life experience. Other tech firms in Boston doing charitable works are discussed.

47083 ■ "Tech Godfather Steve Walker Winding Down Howard Venture Fund" in Baltimore Business Journal (Vol. 27, December 11, 2009, No. 31)
Pub: American City Business Journals
Ed: Scott Dance. **Description:** Steve Walker, president of venture capital fund firm Walker Ventures, will be closing the Howard County, Maryland-based firm as the economic situation is finding it difficult to recover investor's money. According to Walker, the

economy also constrained investors from financing venture funds. Despite the closure, Walker will continue his work in the local angel investing community.

47084 ■ "TechLift Strives to Fill in Gaps in Entrepreneurial Support Efforts" in Crain's Cleveland Business (November 12, 2007)
Pub: Crain Communications, Inc.
Ed: Marsha Powers. **Description:** Profile of the program, TechLift, a new business model launched by NorTech, that is aiming to provide assistance to technology-based companies that may not be a good fit for other entrepreneurial support venues.

47085 ■ Technological Entrepreneurship
Pub: Edward Elgar Publishing, Incorporated
Ed: Donald Siegel. **Released:** October 2006. **Price:** $230.00. **Description:** Technological entrepreneurship at universities is discussed. The book covers four related topics: university licensing and patenting; science parks and incubators; university-based startups; and the role of academic science in entrepreneurship.

47086 ■ "TELUS Says No Thanks to Joining BCE Fray" in Globe & Mail (April 24, 2007, pp. B1)
Pub: CTVglobemedia Publishing Inc.
Ed: Eric Reguly; Catherine McLean. **Description:** The causes of the refusal of TELUS Corp. to try and acquire BCE Inc. are discussed. The prospects of the acquisition of TELUS Corp. by private equity funds are discussed, besides the availability of cash with private equity funds.

47087 ■ They Made America
Pub: Little Brown Company/Time Warner Book Group
Ed: Harold Evans, Gail Buckland, David Lefer. **Released:** 2006. **Price:** $18.95. **Description:** Coffee table book highlighting entrepreneurship; this book is filled with interesting illustrated portraits of entrepreneurs and innovators like Thomas Edison, George Doriot (a venture capital pioneer), and Ida Rosenthal (inventor of the Maidenform bra).

47088 ■ "Top of the Food Chain" in Entrepreneur (Vol. 37, October 2009, No. 10, pp. 19)
Pub: Entrepreneur Media Inc.
Ed: Jennifer Wang. **Description:** Television producer Mark Burnett discusses his latest reality television production, Shark Tank. The show pits venture capitalists against entrepreneurs in a contest to obtain business funding.

47089 ■ "Troubled Project In Court" in The Business Journal-Portland (Vol. 25, July 25, 2008, No. 20, pp. 1)
Pub: American City Business Journals, Inc.
Ed: Wendy Culverwell. **Description:** Views and information on Salpare Bay's Hayden Island project, as well as on financing problems and cases associated with the project, are presented. Construction of luxurious waterside condominiums stopped last fall, after the discovery of financing problems and subcontractors and other parties started filing claims and counterclaims.

47090 ■ "Unbound ID Raises $2 Million" in Austin Business JournalInc. (Vol. 28, December 12, 2008, No. 39, pp. 1)
Pub: American City Business Journals
Ed: Christopher Calnan. **Description:** Austin, Texas-based Unbound ID Corporation has secured $2 million in funding from venture capital firm Silverton Partners. The company has developed identity management software for network directories. The market for identity management technology is expected to grow to more than $12.3 billion by 2014.

47091 ■ Values and Opportunities in Social Entrepreneurship
Pub: Palgrave Macmillan
Ed: Kai Hockerts. **Released:** November 1, 2009. **Price:** $90.00. **Description:** Social entrepreneurship has grown as a research field. This book discusses social entrepreneurship as well as the identification and exploitation of social venturing opportunities.

47092 ■ Valuing Early Stage and Venture Backed Companies
Pub: John Wiley & Sons, Inc.
Ed: Neil J. Beaton. **Released:** December 1, 2009. **Price:** $110.00. **Description:** Valuation techniques that can be used to value early stage companies with complex capital structures are examined.

47093 ■ "VC Boosts WorkForce; Livonia Software Company to Add Sales, Marketing Staff" in Crain's Detroit Business (March 24, 2008)
Pub: Crain Communications, Inc.
Ed: Tom Henderson. **Description:** WorkForce Software Inc., a company that provides software to manage payroll processes and oversee compliance with state and federal regulations and with union rules, plans to use an investment of $5.5 million in venture capital to hire more sales and marketing staff.

47094 ■ "VC-Heavy, Revenue-Light Sensicore Sold to GE Division" in Crain's Detroit Business (Vol. 24, April 14, 2008, No. 15, pp. 28)
Pub: Crain Communications Inc.
Ed: Tom Henderson. **Description:** General Electric has acquired Sensicore Inc., which although one of Michigan's most successful companies in raising venture capital was unable to generate significant revenue from its handheld water-testing devices. GE is capable of penetrating a larger market than a private company and will be able to take the devices to the municipal marketplace.

47095 ■ "VC Investing Down 63 Percent" in Austin Business JournalInc. (Vol. 29, January 29, 2010, No. 47, pp. 1)
Pub: American City Business Journals
Ed: Christopher Calnan. **Description:** Venture capital investments in the Austin, Texas area have declined by about 63 percent from $590.1 million in 2008 to $219.2 million in 2009. Deal volume remained steady at 53 local company fundings, but the median deal value declined from $6.5 million in 2008 to $3 million in 2009. Details on several local deals are presented.

47096 ■ "VC Money Down In State, Number of Deals Up" in Crain's Detroit Business (Vol. 24, January 28, 2008, No. 4, pp. 18)
Pub: Crain Communications Inc. - Detroit
Ed: Tom Henderson. **Description:** Despite the amount of money invested by venture capitalists in Michigan is down, the number of deals rose according to the annual Money Tree report. Venture capital firms invested a combined $105.4 million in 22 deals that involved 19 companies in the state.

47097 ■ "The VC Shakeout" in Harvard Business Review (Vol. 88, July-August 2010, No. 7-8, pp. 21)
Pub: Harvard Business School Publishing
Ed: Joseph Ghalbouni, Dominque Rouzies. **Description:** Authors argue that in order to be successful, venture capital needs to focus less on how to sell a newly acquired investment and more on ways to grow a good company.

47098 ■ "VC Tax Almost Gone" in Business Journal-Portland (Vol. 24, November 23, 2007, No. 38, pp. 1)
Pub: American City Business Journals, Inc.
Ed: Aliza Earnshaw. **Description:** Portland Revenue Bureau's proposal to repeal a business income tax is scheduled to be approved by the Portland City Council and Multnomah County Council. Despite the good decision on the part of the city, the removal of the tax policy is not a guarantee that venture capital firms will relocate to the city.

47099 ■ "Venture Capital's Capital Infusion: Federal Incentives Mean More Money for VC Firms" in Entrepreneur (August 2009)
Pub: Entrepreneur Media, Inc.
Ed: Carol Tice. **Description:** American Recovery and Reinvestment Act of 2009 changed the rules for the Small Business Investment Corporations (SBIC) program under the Small Business Authority. The

rule changes are meant to put more money from the program into circulation and it increases funding to existing SBICs.

47100 ■ *"Venture Capital's Capital Infusion: Federal Incentives Mean More Money for VC Firms"* in *Entrepreneur (Vol. 37, August 2009)*
Pub: Entrepreneur Media, Inc.
Ed: Carol Tice. **Description:** American Recovery and Reinvestment Act of 2009 changed the rules for the Small Business Investment Corporations (SBIC) program under the Small Business Authority. The rule changes are meant to put more money from the program into circulation and it increases funding to existing SBICs.

47101 ■ *"Venture Gap"* in *Canadian Business (Vol. 81, March 17, 2008, No. 4, pp. 82)*
Pub: Rogers Media
Ed: Joe Castaldo. **Description:** Money raised by Canadian venture capitalist firms has been declining since 2001. A strong venture capital market is important if Canada is to build innovative companies. Fixing Canada's tax policy on foreign investments is a start in reviving the industry.

47102 ■ *"Wait a Minute!"* in *Entrepreneur (Vol. 37, September 2009, No. 9, pp. 76)*
Pub: Entrepreneur Media, Inc.
Ed: Jennifer Wang. **Description:** Advice on how entrepreneurs in the United States should secure funding in view of the economic crisis is presented. Enough interest should be stimulated so as to secure a follow-up meeting. Investors should be asked questions that would encourage them to tell stories related to the downturn.

47103 ■ *The Wall Street Journal. Complete Small Business Guidebook*
Pub: Three Rivers Press
Ed: Colleen DeBaise. **Released:** December 29, 2009. **Price:** $15.00. **Description:** The mechanics of building, running and growing a profitable business are outlined, teaching how to write a business plan, ways to finding money during lean years, how to keep stress in check, time management, investment in technology, hiring, marketing, management basics, angel investing and venture capital, as well as an exit strategy.

47104 ■ *"Wanted: Angels in the Country"* in *Austin Business JournalInc. (Vol. 28, July 18, 2008, No. 18, pp. 1)*
Pub: American City Business Journals
Ed: Laura Hipp. **Description:** A proposal is being pushed forward by managers of Texas' Emerging Technology Fund to create an angel investors' network. The proposal is asking that tax credits for those who invest in research and development projects be granted in order to boost the number of technology companies in the state.

47105 ■ *"Well-Heeled Startup"* in *Business Journal Portland (Vol. 27, November 12, 2010, No. 37, pp. 1)*
Pub: Portland Business Journal
Ed: Erik Siemers. **Description:** Oh! Shoes LLC expects to receive about $1.5 million in funding from angel investors, while marketing a new line of high heel shoes that are comfortable, healthy, and attractive. The new line of shoes will use the technology of athletic footwear while having the look of an Italian designer. Oh! Shoes hopes to generate $35 million in sales by 2014.

47106 ■ *Western Association of Venture Capitalists--Directory of Members*
Pub: Western Association of Venture Capitalists
Contact: Greg Sands, President
URL(s): www.wavc.net/memberdirectory.cfm. **Released:** Annual; February; Latest edition 2008. **Price:** $300, Nonmembers. **Covers:** About 169 venture capital firms; coverage limited to the western United States. **Entries include:** Company name, address, phone, name and title of contact; years experienced in venture capital field; description of investment preferences, desired maturity of company, desired investment position. **Arrangement:** Alphabetical.

47107 ■ *"White Cat Media Tells You Where to Get a Bargain. Now It's Shopping for $1.5 Million"* in *Inc. (March 2008, pp. 48)*
Pub: Gruner & Jahr USA Publishing
Ed: Athena Schindelheim. **Description:** Profile of White Cat Media which runs two shopping Websites: SheFinds.com for fashion and beauty items, and MomFinds.com for mothers. The New York City firm reported revenues for 2007 at $400,000 and is looking for funding capital in the amount of $1.7 million.

47108 ■ *"Will Work for Equity"* in *Inc. (March 2008, pp. 50, 52)*
Pub: Gruner & Jahr USA Publishing
Ed: Ryan McCarthy. **Description:** Profile of Dave Graham and his information technology company; Graham built his business by taking equity in client firms rather than charging fees. Four tips to consider before signing a work-for-equity business deal are outlined.

47109 ■ *"Women: Send Me An Angel"* in *Entrepreneur (Vol. 35, October 2007, No. 10, pp. 38)*
Pub: Entrepreneur Media Inc.
Ed: Aliza Sherman. **Description:** Golden Seeds has invested in Enter Artemis Woman LLC when the latter decided to put its products into Wal-Mart. Golden Seeds was formed by angel investors who aim to help women build their own businesses. Tips on how to approach angel investors and getting angel funding are given.

47110 ■ *"A World of Investors"* in *Entrepreneur (Vol. 35, November 2007, No. 11, pp. 72)*
Pub: Entrepreneur Media Inc.
Ed: Gail Dutton. **Description:** Information technology services company mPortal Inc. raised nearly $15 million in financing from venture capital company Friedli Corporate Finance. The biggest international investors are European companies, while the venture capital market is growing in Asia.

47111 ■ *"Xtium Has Its Head in the Clouds"* in *Philadelphia Business Journal (Vol. 30, September 23, 2011, No. 32, pp. 1)*
Pub: American City Business Journals Inc.
Ed: Peter Key. **Description:** Philadelphia-based cloud computing firm Xtium LLC received an $11.5 million first-round investment from Boston-Massachusetts-based OpenView Venture Partners. Catering to midsize businesses and unit of bigger firms, Xtium offers disaster-recovery, hosting, and managed-information-technology-infrastructure services.

47112 ■ *"Your Startup may be Worth Less than You Think"* in *Entrepreneur (Vol. 37, October 2009, No. 10, pp. 96)*
Pub: Entrepreneur Media, Inc.
Ed: Asheesh Advani. **Description:** Valuations of startups at the idea stage are dropping due to the effects of the recession. This drop is due to the decreasing availability of investment capital, the reduction in portfolio values of investors, and the increase in early stage startups.

47113 ■ *"Zit Zapper Lands New Funding"* in *Houston Business Journal (Vol. 40, November 27, 2009, No. 29, pp. 1)*
Pub: American City Business Journals
Ed: Mary Ann Azevedo. **Description:** Tyrell Inc. of Houston, Texas generated $20 million in funds for making a cheaper version of its acne-removing Zeno device. The upcoming product, Zeno Mini, will be targeted to a mass market with a price tag of about $89. In 2005, the original Zeno acne treatment device could only be bought through medical offices and spas at about $225.

TRADE PERIODICALS

47114 ■ *Venture Capital Journal*
Pub: Venture Economics Inc.
Contact: Kathleen Devlin, Editor-in-Chief
E-mail: Lawrence.Aragon@thomson.com
Released: Monthly. **Price:** $960, U.S. first year; $1650, elsewhere for combination of print and. **Description:** Hard news, analysis and data on the North American private equity market.

CONSULTANTS

47115 ■ Abrams Valuation Group Inc. (AVGI)
4605 Lankershim Blvd., Ste. 716
North Hollywood, CA 91602-1818
Ph: (818)505-6008
Fax: (818)761-2148
Co. E-mail: ask.avg@abramsvaluation.com
URL: http://www.abramsvaluation.com
Contact: Jay B. Abrams, President
E-mail: jay@abramsvaluation.com
Scope: Valuators of businesses and intangible assets, providing expert analysis of difficult-to-resolve valuation issues for litigation, tax planning and business transactions. **Publications:** "Lost Inventory and Lost Profits Damage Formulas in Litigation," Sep, 2004; "The Bias in Annual (vs. Monthly) Discounting is Immaterial," Sep, 2003; "Forecasting Cash Flow: Mathematics of the Payout Ratio," Jun, 2003; "Problems in the QMDM and Comparison to Economic Components Model: A Response to Chris Mercer," Jun, 2002; "Discount Rates as a Function of Log Size and Valuation Error Measurement".

47116 ■ Alimansky Capital Group Inc.
12 E 44th St., Penthouse
New York, NY 10017-3606
Ph: (212)832-7300
Fax: (212)832-7338
Co. E-mail: info@alimansky.com
URL: http://www.alimansky.com
Contact: Arlene P. West, President
E-mail: awest@capitalroundtable.com
Scope: A private investment banking and advisory firm specializing in advising smaller middle market companies on raising equity and debt for acquisitions, expansion, and restructurings, and in sponsoring such businesses to appropriate sources of capital. Also works with management teams that seeking leveraged buyout or acquisition financing, and with private and institutional investors. Helps formulate investment strategies and evaluate venture capital and buyout opportunities. Serves companies in a broad range of industries, from leading edge technologies to consumer products and services. **Founded:** 1981.

47117 ■ Alpha Capital Partners Ltd.
122 S Michigan Ave., Ste. 1700
Chicago, IL 60603-6142
Ph: (312)322-9800
Fax: (312)322-9808
Co. E-mail: info@alphacapital.com
URL: http://www.alphacapital.com
Contact: Andrew H. Kalnow, President
E-mail: ahkalnow@alphacapital.com
Scope: A venture capital management organization that provides equity financing for promising growth businesses and buyouts or recapitalization of established companies. **Founded:** 1984.

47118 ■ Antares Capital Corp.
9999 NE 2nd Ave., Ste. 306
Miami Shores, FL 33138-2346
Ph: (305)894-2888
Fax: (305)894-3227
Co. E-mail: info@antarescapital.com
URL: http://www.antarescapital.com
Contact: Thomas Domencich, Partner
Scope: Invests equity capital in developmental and expansion stage companies and in management buyout opportunities. Looks for firms that have an opportunity to deploy capital on an efficient basis to significantly alter their growth trajectory and create value for the founders, managers, and owners of the businesses. **Founded:** 1993.

47119 ■ Avery Business Development Services
2506 St. Michel Ct.
Ponte Vedra Beach, FL 32082-2944
Ph: (904)285-6033
Fax: (904)280-8840
Contact: Henry Avery, Owner
Scope: Offers general business and management consulting of business development from project conception to full commercialization. Scope of activities includes new venture development, business

strategy planning, corporate development, licensing, and merger/acquisitions. Industries served: Chemical, plastics, and biotechnology coatings. **Founded:** 1981. **Seminars:** Constructing the Business Plan and Obtaining Financing For a New Business Venture; Business Strategy Planning.

47120 ■ Andrew Barile Consulting Corporation Inc.
2424B Badajoz Pl.
Carlsbad, CA 92009
Ph: (858)759-5039
Fax: (858)759-8436
Co. E-mail: abarile@abarileconsult.com
URL: http://www.abarileconsult.com
Contact: Andrew J. Barile, Principal
E-mail: abarile@abarileconsult.com

Scope: A strategic insurance and reinsurance consulting firm providing unique and creative insurance solutions to members of the insurance industry. **Publications:** "Private Power," Apr, 2012; "A Practical Guide to Finite Risk Insurance and Reinsurance," 1995; "A Practical Guide to Financial Reinsurance," 1991; "Reinsurance and Reinsurance Management," 1981; "The Captive Insurance Company," 1978; "Reinsurance, A Practical Guide," 1978.

47121 ■ Burt Bernstein Insurance Litigation Consultants
626 Carlo Dr.
Goleta, CA 93117
Ph: (805)692-1978
Fax: (805)964-8041
Co. E-mail: burtins@cox.net
URL: http://www.burtbernstein.com
Contact: Burt Bernstein, Principal
E-mail: burtins@cox.net

Scope: An insurance litigation consultant offering services for disputes involving life, disability, and health insurance. **Founded:** 1990.

47122 ■ Blueprint Fundraising and Communications
54 - 1101 Nicola St.
Vancouver, ON, Canada V6G 2E3
Ph: (604)682-6582
Free: 877-682-6582
Fax: (604)682-6580
Co. E-mail: andrea@blueprintfundraising.com
URL: http://www.blueprintfundraising.com
Contact: Marc Smith, President

Scope: Firm provides fund raising-related consulting, coaching and workshops for nonprofits. Services include fund raising audits and plans; major gift, membership and planned giving programs; communications strategies and writing projects; campaign feasibility studies; hands-on campaign management; fund raising training and coaching for staff and boards; case statements, proposals, direct mail and other materials; donor stewardship program development; sponsorship development; and prospect research. **Founded:** 2000. **Seminars:** Your Major Gifts Campaign, Vancouver, Sep, 2010.

47123 ■ Samuel E. Bodily Associates
Office:172, 100 Darden Blvd.
Charlottesville, VA 22903
Ph: (434)924-4813
Fax: (434)243-7677
Contact: Samuel E. Bodily, Principal
E-mail: bodilys@virginia.edu

Scope: Consultant specializes in financial analysis, capital investment, business/product/market planners, financial risk analysis and decision sciences. **Founded:** 1977. **Publications:** "I Can't Get No Satisfaction: How Bundling and Multi-Part Pricing Can Satisfy Consumers and Suppliers," Feb, 2006; "Organizational Use of Decision Analysis," Oct, 2004; "Real Options," Oct, 2004.

47124 ■ Bridge Consulting Group
3235 Ella Lee Ln.
Houston, TX 77019-5923
Ph: (713)521-1352

Fax: (713)521-0025
Co. E-mail: dgehrman@bridgecons.com
Contact: Douglas B. Gehrman, Managing Director

Scope: Consulting practice delivers strategic solutions for managing mergers, acquisitions and business transformations and developing leaders. Focuses on the human, organizational and cultural factors vital to corporate change and on programs for developing the leadership. **Publications:** "Navigating the Whitewater of a Merger Strategies for Success"; "The Leadership Promise Guideposts for Aspiring Leaders"; "The Rise of Intellectual Capitalism".

47125 ■ Bridgewood Consultants
20793 Farmington Rd., Ste. 21
Farmington, MI 48336
Ph: (248)426-0079
Contact: Dorothy Zynda Snyder, Principal

Scope: Firm specializes in assisting service-oriented businesses develop a professional image, organizational skills and a structural foundation. **Publications:** "Don't Give Up Before You've Begun!"; "Invest in Your Success"; "Marketing Our Way"; "Marketing - Sorting Fact from Option; and Times, They are a Chang'in - What About You?". **Seminars:** Make Your Waiting Room Standing Room Only, Sep, 2007; Marketing 101, Sep, 2007; Creating a Lucrative Practice.

47126 ■ BSpudly Enterprises Inc.
524 W Portland St.
Phoenix, AZ 85003
Ph: (602)293-3474
Fax: (602)296-7270
Co. E-mail: kurtbloeser@gmail.com
URL: http://www.bspudly.com
Contact: Kurt Bloeser, President

Scope: Consultant provides financial consulting, bank training and expert testimony.

47127 ■ Burns Innovation Group Inc.
Landmark Sq. II, 1708 Dolphin Ave., Ste. 806
Kelowna, BC, Canada V1Y 9S4
Ph: (250)763-4716
Free: 877-763-4022
Fax: (877)353-8608
Contact: Steve Burns, President
E-mail: steve@burnsinnovation.com

Scope: A full-service consulting firm dedicated to helping entrepreneurs build their businesses by providing hands-on consulting services. Provides services in finance, marketing and sales, and human resources. Business strategy services include evaluating the strategy of a business, conducting strategic planning sessions, development of strategic performance indicators, development of full business plans, and facilitation of planning sessions/business builder system. Financial services include mergers and acquisitions, cash flow management, profit improvement analysis, financial statement analysis, financial ratio analysis assistance in obtaining financing, and negotiation of new business arrangements including sales or purchase of a business, joint ventures, and partnerships and strategic alliances. Marketing and sales services include development and execution of marketing plans, development and execution of sales strategies, marketing mix, product and pricing strategies, and providing focus groups and customer advisory boards. Human resource services include recruitment and selection of key personnel, recruitment strategies, online recruitment, establishing compensation strategies, assistance in hiring and selection, assistance in developing and executing employee retention strategies, employee satisfaction surveys, and customized training programs. Process and technology services include review and improvement of key processes in the business, development of key indicators to better manage key business processes, utilization of technology to improve process management, and development and execution of e-commerce strategies.

47128 ■ The Business Continuity Group Inc.
101 Federal St., Ste. 1900
Boston, MA 02110
Ph: (617)342-7260

Free: 888-438-0224
URL: http://www.continuityhost.com
Contact: Roy T. Weston, Chief Executive Officer
E-mail: rweston@bcgit.com

Scope: Provides expertise in international business contingency. Offers technical consulting and training services as well as specialized consulting services in the areas of continuity, such as security and regulatory compliance, storage and networking, and contract negotiations. Also provides support services in site hosting, monitoring services. Typical services cover continuity planning, security issues, compliance and litigation, vendor due diligence, disaster recovery, integration issues and research and training. **Founded:** 1988.

47129 ■ The Business Place Ltd.
10 Kingsbridge Garden Cir., Ste. 506
Mississauga, ON, Canada L5R 3K6
Ph: (905)890-9245
Fax: (905)890-3229
Co. E-mail: gary.landa@thebusinessplace.com
URL: http://www.thebusinessplace.com
Contact: Gary R. Landa, President
E-mail: gary.landa@thebusinessplace.com

Scope: Assists in the buying and selling of businesses, arranging bank financing, venture capital loans/investments, mergers and acquisitions. **Founded:** 1986. **Publications:** "Did you find the right business for sale Part II," Feb, 2009; "Did you find the right business," Feb, 2009; "Buying a business what do you look for when looking at financial statements," Feb, 2009; "Business brokers how do you know if you found the right business broker," Feb, 2009; "Businesses how do you determine if you found the right one," Feb, 2009; "Start up businesses how do you value them when you are looking for equity," Feb, 2009; "Business locations time to move intone space, " Feb, 2009; Business brokers are they helpful," Feb, 2009.

47130 ■ Business Systems Consulting (BSC)
15 Lincoln St.
Wakefield, MA 01880
Ph: (781)683-4040
Co. E-mail: info@bizsysconsulting.com
URL: http://www.bizsysconsulting.com
Contact: Len Levin, Principal
E-mail: len@bizsysconsulting.com

Scope: IT consultancy providing a range of services to companies. Services include analysis, planning and implementation; procurement management; outsourcing services; ongoing support; process and work flow development and training. **Founded:** 1993.

47131 ■ Butterflies in Progress L.L.C. (BiP)
9352 Rockfish Gap Tpke.
Afton, VA 22920
Ph: (540)447-6823
Fax: (540)456-6758
Co. E-mail: cynthia@butterfliesinprogress.com
URL: http://www.butterfliesinprogress.com
Contact: Cynthia Hurst, Owner
E-mail: cynthia@butterfliesinprogress.com

Scope: Consultant specializes in raising corporate and foundation funds, the development of annual fundraising campaigns and overseeing special fund raising. **Founded:** 2006.

47132 ■ Canadian Association of Professional Speakers (CAPS)
1370 Don Mills Rd., Ste. 300
Toronto, ON, Canada M3B 3N7
Ph: (416)847-3355
Free: 877-847-3350
Fax: (416)441-0591
Co. E-mail: info@canadianspeakers.org
URL: http://www.canadianspeakers.org
Contact: Shelle Rose Charvet, President

Scope: Canadian speakers, trainers, consultants and facilitators. Specialists in a range of topics and responsive to media. Seeks to raise the profile and professionalism of members. Helps members hone their skills at securing more business and in delivering their expertise through education, focused programming and networking. **Founded:** 1997.

47133 ■ Concept Development Associates Inc.
PO Box 15245
Evansville, IN 47716-0245
Ph: (812)471-3334
Fax: (812)477-6499
Contact: Steve Brackmann, Principal
Scope: A globally-connected venture capital group. **Founded:** 1985.

47134 ■ Crosslink Capital
Two Embarcadero Ctr., Ste. 2200
San Francisco, CA 94111
Ph: (415)617-1800
Fax: (415)617-1801
Co. E-mail: ewinterhalter@crosslinkcapital.com
URL: http://www.crosslinkcapital.com
Contact: Peter Van Camp, Chief Executive Officer
Scope: An independent venture capital and investment firm. Firm focuses on strategic business and technology questions as well as to discuss tactical approaches to addressing these challenges. **Founded:** 1989. **Preferred Investment Size:** $8,000,000 to $20,000,000. **Industry Preferences:** Internet specific, computer software and services, semiconductors and other electronics, communications and media, biotechnology, computer hardware, other products, consumer related, medical and health, industrial and energy. **Geographic Preference:** California and U.S. **Telecommunication Services:** info@crosslinkcapital.com.

47135 ■ Design Financial Inc.
5 Belleview St., Ste. 100
Mount Clemens, MI 48043-2238
Ph: (586)469-7788
Fax: (586)469-4700
Contact: Anthony G. Forlini, President
E-mail: anthony.forlini@designfinancial.com
Scope: Firm provides individual and business financial planning services. Services offered include business succession strategies, charitable donation strategies, estate analysis, and retirement strategies. **Publications:** "Estates & Trusts"; "Tax Planning"; "Cash Management"; "Retirement"; "Investing"; "Risk Management". **Seminars:** Retirement; Estate Planning; Tax Strategies; Long Term Care; Financial Management.

47136 ■ Disability Income Concepts Inc. (DIC)
1433 Camellia Cir.
Weston, FL 33326-3616
Ph: (954)217-8260
Free: 877-776-3948
Fax: (954)217-8241
Co. E-mail: disability@disabilityconcepts.com
URL: http://www.disabilityconcepts.com
Contact: Gerald Katz, President
Scope: It specializes in disabled insured claims and consulting services. Services include expert witness testimony for disability insurance claim disputes; independent and comprehensive review, analysis and summary of current disability and/or long term care insurance coverage; consultation on how to complete initial disability claim forms and ongoing progress reports; coordination of disability policy information and claims status with personal attorneys; and review and coordination of financial claims information with accountants. **Founded:** 1980.

47137 ■ Antoinette Doyle Consulting
695 42nd Ave.
San Francisco, CA 94121-2532
Ph: (415)752-2413
Fax: (415)752-2440
Co. E-mail: tdoyle@planeteria.net
Contact: Toni Doyle, Owner
E-mail: tdoyle@planeteria.net
Scope: Provides fundraising consulting services to non-profit organizations. Services include annual campaigns, capital and major gift campaigns, and foundation and corporate relations.

47138 ■ ECG Advisors L.L.C.
1458 Bienveneda Ave.
Pacific Palisades, CA 90272
Ph: (310)251-0860

Fax: (310)459-0615
Contact: Randolph O. Ramirez, Owner
Scope: Firm advises boards of directors and their compensation committees, large share holders/investors and other stake holders on executive compensation, directors pay, corporate governance and other compensation issues such as linking compensation strategy with corporate strategy, equity and pseudo-equity pay, competitive bench marking, pay systems, regulatory compliance and performance measurement. Firm also provides litigation and arbitration support, assisting clients in IRS proceedings, divorce and asset division disputes, defense contract audit agency (DCAA) action, expert testimony and corporate and individual bankruptcy proceedings. **Founded:** 2004.

47139 ■ ECnow.com Inc.
20660 Stevens Creek Blvd., Ste. 210
Cupertino, CA 95014
Ph: (408)257-3000
Fax: (408)843-0769
Co. E-mail: info@ecnow.com
URL: http://www.ecnow.com
Contact: Mitchell Levy, President
E-mail: mitchell.levy.sjsupd@ecnow.com
Scope: A management consulting firm specializing in strategic consulting and targeted business education. **Publications:** "E-Volve-or-Die.com"; "Happy About Outsourcing"; "Happy About Knowing What to Expect in 2005, 2006, 2007 & 2008"; "Business Models for the 21st century," 2002. **Seminars:** Business and Management Issues. **Special Services:** Value Framework®; Happy About®.

47140 ■ Elliott Appraisers L.L.C.—Appraiser 4 Jewelry
3000 Richmond Ave., Ste. 240
Houston, TX 77098-3188
Ph: (713)530-9919
Fax: (713)337-0919
Contact: Quenton T. Elliott, Jr., Principal
E-mail: quenton@appraiser4jewelry.com
Scope: Provides independent valuation of gems and fine jewelry, forensic gemology services, and consulting. **Founded:** 2003.

47141 ■ The Hotel Experts L.L.C.
126 Tierra Ln., Ste. 104
Jupiter, FL 33477
Ph: (561)775-4990
Fax: (561)622-9223
Co. E-mail: stevest50@aol.com
URL: http://member.expertpages.com/thehotelexperts
Contact: Steve Stearns, Partner
E-mail: stevest50@aol.com
Scope: Attorney case consultants and expert witnesses in hotel litigation. Guides through discovery, depositions and case strategy, submitting detailed opinions, and offering trial testimony both for and against hotel properties, owners, operators, franchisers and individual litigants. **Seminars:** Operating standards and quality practices in hospitality.

47142 ■ Integrated Development Consulting (IDC)
1115 W Mead Ave.
Salt Lake City, UT 84104
Ph: (801)533-8375
URL: http://www.integrated-development.biz
Contact: Amy O'Connor, President
E-mail: amyoconnor@earthlink.net
Scope: Provides organizational development consulting to nonprofits through training, coaching and facilitation. Areas include strategic planning, organizational assessments, board development, membership acquisition, message development, and communication.

47143 ■ Jewels by Stacy Appraisals
712 Bancroft Rd., Ste. 436
Walnut Creek, CA 94598
Ph: (925)939-4367

Fax: (925)939-4567
Co. E-mail: nancy@appraiser.net
URL: http://www.jewelry-appraisal.com
Contact: Randy Trahan, Manager
Scope: An independent jewelry appraiser specializing in appraisal of modern and antique fine jewelry, diamonds, gemstones and watches. **Founded:** 1980. **Publications:** "Gem print Goes Hollywood"; "Some Good Advice on Buying Diamonds"; "Gold Buying Scams"; "Cruise Purchases of Jewelry"; "Buying Gemstones in Afghanistan"; "Red Labradorite Scams"; "Tanzanite Scams"; "Shipping jewelry". **Seminars:** Conquering Comps workshop, San Francisco, Oct, 2009.

47144 ■ Mara Perez, Ph.D. Fund Development and Planning Services—Mara Perez, Ph.D. Development and Planning Services
320 Via Casitas, Ste. 107
Greenbrae, CA 94904
Ph: (415)461-0141
Fax: (415)461-7741
Co. E-mail: mperez@svn.net
URL: http://www.svn.net/mperez
Contact: Mara Perez, Owner
E-mail: mperez@svn.net
Scope: Consultant works with boards and staff leadership of non profit organizations and educational institutions. Areas include Latino affairs, diversity, health, the arts, education, spirituality, the environment and international affairs. Services in fund development, strategic planning, and coalition development. **Founded:** 1995. **Publications:** "Democratization's: Comparisons, Confrontations, and Contrasts," MIT Press, 2009; "International migration and the Latino population in the U.S". **Seminars:** International migration; Wednesday Morning Dialogue; National Association of Hispanic Realtors.

47145 ■ Micro Cap et Al
470 Granville St., Ste. 1120
Vancouver, BC, Canada V6C 1V5
Ph: (604)713-8010
Free: 877-642-7622
Fax: (604)713-8018
Co. E-mail: info@microcapetal.com
URL: http://www.microcapetal.com
Contact: Robert Bell, President
E-mail: bbell@microcapetal.com
Scope: Strategic business solutions partners specializing in investor relations (lead generation programs, pro-active IR programs, maintenance IR Programs, and shareholder audits); capital placement (private placements, debt placements, and seed stock offerings); and consulting (corporate structure, syndication strategies, and merger and acquisition advice). **Founded:** 1985.

47146 ■ New York Grant Co.
29 Broadway, Ste. 2222
New York, NY 10006
Ph: (212)227-8283
Fax: (212)214-0814
Co. E-mail: marsha@nygrants.com
URL: http://www.nygrants.com
Contact: Ann Kayman, Chief Executive Officer
E-mail: ann@nygrants.com
Scope: Consultants in economic development to assist clients in navigating the maze of economic incentives in New York, such as tax breaks, wage tax credits, energy discounts, real estate tax exemptions, investment tax credits and other benefits from local, state, and federal agencies. **Founded:** 2002.

47147 ■ Pacific Century Group Ventures Ltd.
105-150 Crowfoot Cres. NW, Ste. 700
Calgary, AB, Canada T3G 3T2
Ph: (604)871-0452
Fax: (604)871-0451
Contact: Harish C. Consul, President
E-mail: hconsul@pcentury.com
Scope: Experienced in fund management, venture capital and corporate finance. Specializes in information technology and real estate sectors. **Founded:** 1994.

47148 ■ Predictable Futures Inc.—The Business Family Centre
10104 103 Ave., Ste. 1211
Edmonton, AB, Canada T5J 0H8
Ph: (780)702-2499
Free: 866-241-2221
Fax: (780)428-1410
Co. E-mail: solutions@predictablefutures.com
URL: http://www.predictablefutures.com
Contact: Dianne Young, Manager
Scope: Firm partners with clients to design and coordinate succession, estate and wealth management strategies. Specialists in the fields of strategic planning, governance, mediation, facilitation, law, taxation, and business and insurance planning. **Publications:** "Beyond Survival: A Guide for Business Owners and their Families"; "Achieving Authentic Success"; "Halftime"; "Game Plan"; "How to RETIRE Happy, Wild & Free". **Seminars:** Family Business Succession-It's All About Planning, Hawaii, Mar, 2006.

47149 ■ Seacoast Capital
55 Ferncroft Rd., Ste. 110
Danvers, MA 01923
Ph: (978)750-1300
Fax: (978)750-1301
Co. E-mail: gdeli@seacoastcapital.com
URL: http://www.seacoastcapital.com
Contact: Matthew J. Mitchell, Manager
E-mail: mmitchell@seacoastcapital.com
Scope: Invests growth capital in small companies led by strong, entrepreneurial management teams. Provides follow-on financing for acquisitions, internal growth or the execution of roll-out strategies. Assists portfolio companies develop and refine strategic plans, recruit additional management or board talent, access debt or equity capital markets, identify and negotiate acquisitions, develop compensation and incentive programs, and maximize value for all stakeholders upon exit. **Founded:** 1994.

47150 ■ Spherix Inc.
6430 Rockledge Dr., Ste. 503
Bethesda, MD 20817-1886
Ph: (301)897-2540
Fax: (301)897-2567
Co. E-mail: info@spherix.com
URL: http://www.spherix.com
Contact: Robert Lodder, President
URL(s): www.biospherics.com. **Scope:** Provides health sciences consulting services that provides scientific and strategic support for suppliers, manufacturers, distributors and retailers of: Conventional foods, biotechnology-derived foods, medical foods, infant formulas, food ingredients, dietary supplements, food contact substances, pharmaceuticals, medical devices, consumer products and industrial chemicals and pesticides. Provides teleservices, ebusinesses, and IT solutions for the health and information industries. **Founded:** 1967. **Publications:** "Viking found no life on Mars, and, just as important, it found why there can be no life". **Special Services:** Naturlose®.

47151 ■ Sprout Group (New York, New York)
11 Madison Ave., 13th Fl.
New York, NY 10010-3698
Ph: (212)538-3600
Fax: (212)538-8245
Co. E-mail: info@sproutgroup.com
URL: http://www.sproutgroup.com
Contact: Stephen M. Diamond, Partner
E-mail: steve.diamond@sproutgroup.com
Scope: The firm invests in stages from start-ups through buyouts in high growth areas such as information technology, medical products and services, business services and retail. **Founded:** 1969.

47152 ■ Strategies for Social Change L.L.C.
50 Broad St., Ste. 1937
New York, NY 10004
Ph: (212)785-0544

Fax: (212)785-0669
Co. E-mail: info@communityimpactconsulting.com
URL: http://www.strategiesforsocialchange.com
Contact: Elsa A. Rios, President
Scope: Culture-minded firm develops capacity building services, strategies and solutions to help nonprofits increase their resources, maximize strategic impact and achieve their mission. Services include strategic planning, board development, executive coaching, fund development and grant writing, executive transition planning, leadership skills training, needs assessment and program evaluation, program planning, outcomes management, retreat facilitation, financial management consultation, and website development. **Publications:** "The Do's and Don'ts of Hiring a Consultant"; "Executive Coaching Works!"; "Characteristics of Highly Effective Organizations". **Seminars:** Grant Writing and Fund Development Training; Board Governance and Training Retreat Facilitation; Strategic Planning Training; Cultural Competency Training and Retreat Facilitation; Leadership Training and Retreat Facilitation.

47153 ■ Thomson Venture Economics Inc.—Thomson Financial Inc.Thomson Financial Services Inc.;
395 Hudson St., Ste. 3
New York, NY 10014
Ph: (212)807-5000
Fax: (212)807-5122
Contact: Ted Weissberg, President
E-mail: edward.weissberg@tfn.com
Scope: Venture capital and business development specialists providing customized research for industrial and financial corporations. Services include: identification of high-potential companies for investment, alliance or acquisition; assistance in establishing venture capital or strategic alliance programs; and assistance with specific acquisition searches. Services for institutional investors in venture capital include: Basic education and due diligence evaluation of venture capital as an investment; development of venture capital investment strategy; and identification of investment opportunities, portfolio monitoring, analysis, performance; and benchmarking for the venture capital asset class. Serves private industries as well as government agencies. **Founded:** 1961. **Seminars:** Performance Monitoring Workshop.

47154 ■ Venture Planning Associates Inc.
2515 Glen Eagles Dr.
Reno, NV 89533
Ph: (775)747-8829
Free: 888-404-1212
URL: http://www.ventureplan.com
Contact: William McCready, Chief Executive Officer
Scope: Provides venture capital consulting services for all phases of business development, from start-ups to IPOs. Investment criteria and participation in projects include: the ability to purchase founders stock convertible preferred or warrants; direct participation in management either on the board of directors or as an officer business market large enough to go national; exit strategy via buyout or acquisition by larger firms; fee for services paid following seed capital funding. Provides entrepreneurial training, consulting, executive search, marketing assistance and referral services to other professionals. **Founded:** 1989.

47155 ■ Wall Street Services Inc.
11 Broadway, Ste. 632
New York, NY 10004
Ph: (212)509-7200
Fax: (212)943-1597
Co. E-mail: info@wallstreetservices.com
URL: http://www.wallstreetservices.com
Contact: Peter Laughter, Chief Executive Officer
E-mail: pjlaughter@wallstreetservices.com
Scope: A staffing agency catering to top tier Manhattan investment banks and legal firms. Specializes in personnel placement and executive search. Proprietary systems include an instrument for measuring key work place attributes, a method for determining what position will inspire and challenge the best available workers, and tools for rapidly matching the right candidate to the job. **Founded:** 1983. **Publications:** "Wall Street Services Editorial".

47156 ■ Western Capital Financial Services Inc.—Western Capital Financial Corporate
11075 S State St., Ste. 12B
Sandy, UT 84070
Ph: (801)619-4700
Free: 877-517-9555
Fax: (408)889-2415
Co. E-mail: support@mycollector.com
URL: http://www.mycollector.com
Contact: Robert Paisola, President
E-mail: robert@mycollector.com
Scope: Firm specializes in debt collection and portfolio recovery business. **Founded:** 1992. **Publications:** "Careers and Opportunities in the Collection Industry"; "Starting and Managing a Collection Service"; "Selecting a Professional Collection Service"; "Collectors and Technology"; "Collection Tips for Credit Grantors"; "What to Do When You Can't Pay Your Bills"; "What to Do When a Collector Calls"; "The art of getting paid". **Telecommunication Services:** training@westerncapitalcredit.com; support@westerncapitalcredit.com.

47157 ■ Western Capital Holdings Inc.
10050 E Applewood Dr.
Parker, CO 80138
Ph: (303)841-1022
Contact: Patrick T. Frasco, President
Scope: Specialists in all phases of financial and management consulting. Provide strong emphasis in strategic planning and corporate development, financial analysis, acquisitions, investment banking and corporate finance. Projects range in size and duration to fit clients needs. Services can be applied to many diverse financial projects that may include the following: Business plan development, budgeting and forecasting, strategic planning, cash flow analysis, cash flow management, corporate development, banking relations, asset management, and financial analysis. Industries served: Food industry, manufacturing, distribution, retailing, computer services, agribusiness, financial services, insurance, and government agencies. **Founded:** 1986. **Seminars:** Buy Low, Sell High, Collect Early and Pay Late; Preparing Your Company for Sale; Venture Capital - Finding an Angel.

FRANCHISES AND BUSINESS OPPORTUNITIES

47158 ■ The Entrust Group
Entrust
555 12th St., Ste. 1250
Oakland, CA 94607
Free: 888-340-8977
Fax: (510)251-2847
Description: Administrators of self directed IRAs. **Training:** Yes.

47159 ■ Innovative Lease Services, Inc.
5931 Priestly Dr., Ste. 102
Carlsbad, CA 92008
Ph: (760)438-1470
Fax: (760)438-2046
Description: Equipment financing for franchises. **Founded:** 1987..

47160 ■ Wirth Business Credit
Winmark Corp.
605 Hwy. 169 N, Ste. 400
Minneapolis, MN 55441-6536
Ph: (763)520-8500
Free: 800-433-2540
Fax: (763)520-8410
Co. E-mail: winmark.information@winmarkcorporation.com
URL: http://www.winmarkcorporation.com
Description: Equipment leasing and financing. **No. of Franchise Units:** 56. **Founded:** 2005.. **Franchised:** 2005. **Equity Capital Needed:** $39,630-$74,510. **Franchise Fee:** $35,000. **Training:** Yes.

COMPUTER SYSTEMS/ SOFTWARE

47161 ■ Loan Express
Entrepreneur, Inc.
2445 McCabe Way
Irvine, CA 92614

Ph: (949)261-2325
Free: 800-421-2300
Fax: (949)261-7729
URL: http://www.entrepreneur.com
Price: $99.95. **Description:** Software program providing step-by-step information for writing a loan proposal.

LIBRARIES

47162 ■ Innovation Ontario Corporation Information Centre
56 Wellesley St. W, 7th Fl.
Toronto, ON, Canada M7A 2E7
Ph: (416)326-1041
Fax: (416)326-1109
Scope: Venture capital, innovation, new technology licensing. **Services:** Copying; Library not open to the public. **Holdings:** Figures not available.

47163 ■ Loan Brokers Association Information Services
917 S. Park St.
Owosso, MI 48867-4422
Contact: Ben Campbell, Director
Scope: Loan brokers, loan consulting, credit repair, lending, credit cards, venture capital. **Services:** Copying; SDI; library to members or by permission.

47164 ■ Sentron Medical Inc. - Senmed Medical Ventures Library
4445 Lake Forest Dr., No. 600
Cincinnati, OH 45242-3798
Ph: (513)563-3240
Fax: (513)563-3261
URL: http://www.senmed.com/organization.htm
Contact: Rosanne Wohlwender
Scope: Biotechnology, medical devices and diagnostics, technology transfer, pharmaceuticals, venture capital, licensing. **Services:** Library not open to the public. **Founded:** 1987. **Holdings:** 800 books; 50 reports. **Subscriptions:** 100 journals and other serials; 2 newspapers.

RESEARCH CENTERS

47165 ■ St. Louis University - Smurfit-Stone Center for Entrepreneurship (SSCE)
John Cook School of Business
3674 Lindell Blvd.
Saint Louis, MO 63108
Ph: (314)977-3850
Fax: (314)977-3627
Co. E-mail: rhodesja@slu.edu
URL: http://www.slu.edu/ssce.xml
Contact: Jeanne Rhodes, Administrative Assistant
Founded: 1987. **Educational Activities:** Billiken Angel Network; Collegiate Entrepreneurship Organizations; Gateway Series for Entrepreneurship Research for faculty (Annual), in spring; Habitat for Neighborhood Business; Idea to Product Competition for Missouri and Illinois universities; Summer Entrepreneurship Academy for high school students. **Awards:** Smurfit-Stone Entrepreneurial Alumni Hall of Fame. **Telecommunication Services:** ecenter@slu.edu.

START-UP INFORMATION

47166 ■ *Scrapbooking for Profit: Cashing in on Retail, Home-Based and Internet Opportunities*
Pub: Allworth Press
Ed: Rebecca Pittman. **Released:** June 2005. **Price:** $19.95 (US), $22.95 (Canadian). **Description:** Eleven strategies for starting a scrapbooking business, including brick-and-mortar stores, home-based businesses, and online retail and wholesale outlets.

ASSOCIATIONS AND OTHER ORGANIZATIONS

47167 ■ **International Federation of Pharmaceutical Wholesalers (IFPW)**
10569 Crestwood Dr.
Manassas, VA 20109
Ph: (703)331-3714
Fax: (703)331-3715
Co. E-mail: info@ifpw.com
URL: http://www.ifpw.com
Contact: Eric V. Zwisler, Vice Chairman
Description: Wholesalers and distributors of pharmaceutical products. Promotes efficient delivery of pharmaceuticals to hospitals, physicians, and pharmacists; seeks to increase public awareness of the role played by members in the health care system. Facilitates cooperation and exchange of information among members; represents members' commercial and regulatory interests; sponsors educational and promotional programs.

47168 ■ **National Association of Wholesaler-Distributors (NAW)**
1325 G St. NW, Ste. 1000
Washington, DC 20005
Ph: (202)872-0885
Fax: (202)785-0586
Co. E-mail: naw@naw.org
URL: http://www.naw.org
Contact: Dirk Van Dongen, President
Description: Federation of national, state, and regional associations, and individual wholesaler-distributor firms. Represents industry's views to the federal government. Analyzes current and proposed legislation and government regulations affecting the industry. Maintains public relations and media programs and a research foundation. Conducts wholesale executive management courses. **Founded:** 1946. **Publications:** *NAW Report*; *NAW Report* (Bimonthly); *SmartBrief*. **Telecommunication Services:** naw@nawd.org.

47169 ■ **NAW Institute for Distribution Excellence**
1325 G St. NW, Ste. 1000
Washington, DC 20005
Ph: (202)872-0885
Fax: (202)785-0586
Co. E-mail: naw@naw.org
URL: http://www.naw.org/institute/iindex.php
Contact: Ruth Stadius, President
Description: Firms that are members of the National Association of Wholesaler-Distributors, wholesalers, and trade associations. Seeks to advance knowledge in the field of wholesale distribution by means of long-range research projects. **Founded:** 1967. **Publications:** *Facing the Forces of Change: The Road to Opportunity* (Triennial); *Connect with Your Suppliers: A Wholesaler-Distributor's Guide to Electronic Communications Systems*; *Price for Success: A Practical Guide for Improving Margins in Wholesale Distribution.*

REFERENCE WORKS

47170 ■ **American Wholesalers and Distributors Directory**
Pub: Cengage Learning Inc.
Contact: Ronald Dunn, President
URL(s): www.gale.cengage.com. **Released:** Annual; Latest edition 22nd; April, 2011. **Price:** $410, Individuals. **Covers:** Name and address, fax number, SIC code, principal product lines, total number of employees, estimated annual sales volume and principal officers' information of 27,000 large and small wholesalers and distributors in the U.S. and Puerto Rico. **Arrangement:** By broad subject from principal product line, by Standard Industrial Classification code (SIC index), by state and city (geographical index), and by company name (alphabetic index). **Indexes:** SIC, geographical, alphabetical. **Availability:** Online: Cengage Learning Inc. **Type:** Directory.

47171 ■ *The Big Payback: The History of the Business of Hip-Hop*
Pub: New American Library/Penguin Group
Ed: Dan Charnas. **Price:** $24.95. **Description:** The complete history of hip-hop music is presented, by following the money and the relationship between artist and merchant. In its promise of economic security and creative control for black artist-entrepreneurs, it is the culmination of dreams of black nationalists and civil rights leaders.

47172 ■ *"From Craft Biz To Wholesale Giant"* in Women Entrepreneur (January 19, 2009)
Pub: Entrepreneur Media Inc.
Ed: Maria Falconer. **Description:** Advice is given on how to turn a small craft business into a full-time venture; tips to help one transition from a part-time designer to a full-time wholesaler and brand are also included.

47173 ■ *"Ground Floor Opportunity"* in Small Business Opportunities (July 2008)
Pub: Entrepreneur Press
Contact: Perlman Neil, President
Description: Profile of Doug Disney, the founder of the booming franchise Tile Outlet Always in Stock, which sells ceramic and porcelain tile and stone products at wholesale prices; Disney found inspiration in a book he read in two days and that motivated him to expand his venture into a huge franchise opportunity.

47174 ■ *"Home Depot Eyes Wholesale Spinoff"* in Globe & Mail (February 13, 2007, pp. B13)
Pub: CTVglobemedia Publishing Inc.
Description: Home Depot Inc. is planning to sell or spinoff its professional supply business to focus on retail stores. The weakening sales and profits are the main driving force behind the company's decision.

47175 ■ *"How to Start and Run a Small Book Publishing Company: A Small Business Guide to Self-Publishing and Independent Publishing*
Pub: HCM Publishing
Ed: Peter I. Hupalo. **Released:** August 30, 2002. **Price:** $18.95. **Description:** The book teaches all aspects of starting and running a small book publishing company. Topics covered include: inventory accounting in the book trade, just-in-time inventory management, turnkey fulfillment solutions, tax deductible costs, basics of sales and use tax, book pricing, standards in terms of the book industry, working with distributors and wholesalers, cover design and book layout, book promotion and marketing, how to select profitable authors to publish, printing process, printing on demand, the power of a strong backlist, and how to value copyright.

47176 ■ *"Identify and Conquer"* in Black Enterprise (Vol. 38, December 2007, No. 5, pp. 76)
Pub: Earl G. Graves Publishing Co. Inc.
Ed: Tennille M. Robinson. **Description:** Twenty-two-year-old entrepreneur wants to expand her wholesale body oil and skincare products business.

47177 ■ *"Merchants Association Working on Deal for Large Wholesale Warehouse"* in Austin Business JournalInc. (September 19, 2008)
Pub: American City Business Journals
Ed: Jean Kwon. **Description:** Greater Austin Merchants Association planning to buy a former Dell Outlet Factory in Austin, Texas and convert it into a warehouse for convenience stores and gas stations.

47178 ■ *"Printers to the Trade"* in American Printer (Vol. 128, July 1, 2011, No. 7)
Pub: Penton Media Inc.
Description: Wholesale printing is discussed. Two wholesale printers share insight into their success, from business philosophies in general to practices that build strong relationships.

47179 ■ *"Research and Market Adds: 2010 US Women's and Children's Clothing Wholesale Report"* in Wireless News (November 8, 2009)
Pub: Close-Up Media
Description: Highlights of the annual Research and Markets '2010 U.S. Women's and Children's Clothing Wholesale Report' include industry statistics, demographics and forecasts.

47180 ■ *"Research and Markets Adds: 2011 U.S. Women's & Children's Clothing Wholesale Report"* in Health & Beauty Close-Up (October 16, 2010)
Pub: Close-Up Media Inc.
Description: The Women's & Children's Clothing Wholesale Report is an annual report containing timely and accurate industry statistics, forecasts and demographics.

STATISTICAL SOURCES

47181 ■ *RMA Annual Statement Studies*
Pub: Risk Management Association
Contact: Kevin M. Blakey, President
Released: Annual. **Price:** $175.00 2006-07 edition,
$105.00. **Description:** Contains composite balance
sheets and income statements for more than 360
industries, including the accounting, auditing, and
bookkeeping industries. Also contains five years of
comparative historical data for discerning trends.
Includes 16 commonly used ratios, computed for
most of the size groupings for nearly every industry.

TRADE PERIODICALS

47182 ■ *NAW Report*
Pub: National Association of Wholesaler-Distributors
Contact: Dirk Van Dongen, President
Ed: Ruth Stadius, Editor. **Released:** Bimonthly. **De-
scription:** Publishes information on government is-
sues and actions affecting wholesaler-distributors

specifically and the business community generally.
Recurring features include reports on federal legislative and regulatory developments; legal and insurance trends; industry research and statistics; and
business services offered through the association's
group purchasing program. Remarks: Available online only.

FRANCHISES AND BUSINESS OPPORTUNITIES

47183 ■ Business Cards Tomorrow
Business Cards Tomorrow, Inc.
3000 NE 30th Pl., 5th Fl.
Ft. Lauderdale, FL 33306
Ph: (954)563-1224
Free: 800-627-9998
Fax: (954)565-0742
Description: Professional, niche wholesale service
business. **No. of Franchise Units:** 64. **No. of
Company-Owned Units:** 5. **Founded:** 1975.. **Fran-**

chised: 1977. **Equity Capital Needed:** $991,700-
$1,100,000. **Franchise Fee:** $35,000. **Royalty Fee:**
6%. **Financial Assistance:** Third party financing
available. **Training:** Provides 2 weeks at headquarters, 4 weeks onsite and ongoing support.

47184 ■ Prosource Wholesale Floorcoverings
CCA Global Partners
4301 Earth City Expy.
Earth City, MO 63045
Free: 800-466-6984
Fax: (314)506-0953
Co. E-mail: mjameson@pswwholesale.com
URL: http://www.prosourcefloors.com
Description: Members-only wholesale flooring
showroom. **No. of Franchise Units:** 138. **No. of
Company-Owned Units:** 3. **Founded:** 1990.. **Fran-
chised:** 1991. **Equity Capital Needed:** $750,000 net
worth; $375,000 minimum investment. **Franchise
Fee:** $46,450. **Financial Assistance:** Yes. **Training:**
Initial training provided at headquarters in St. Louis
and ongoing support.

START-UP INFORMATION

47185 ■ *Birthing the Elephant: A Woman's Go-For-It Guide to Overcoming the Big Challenges of Launching a Business*
Pub: Celestial Arts Publishing Co.
Contact: Patricia Kelly, Manager
Ed: Karin Abarbanel; Bruce Freeman. **Released:** 2008. **Price:** $15.95. **Description:** Consultants help women think like an entrepreneur in order to successfully launch any new business.

47186 ■ *Birthing the Elephant: The Woman's Go-for-It! Guide to Overcoming the Big Challenges of Launching a Business*
Pub: Celestial Arts Publishing Co.
Contact: Patricia Kelly, Manager
Ed: Karin Abarbanel; Bruce Freeman. **Released:** March 2008. **Price:** $15.95. **Description:** Advice for women entrepreneurs is given. The book explores the emotional challenges faced by women starting businesses, along with advice for reshaping image. This handbook helps women survive and succeed in business.

47187 ■ *"Find the Upside to a Down Economy" in Women Entrepreneur (September 30, 2008)*
Pub: Entrepreneur Media Inc.
Ed: Tamara Monosoff. **Description:** Starting a new business in this economic crisis may not be as daunting of a pursuit as one might think. Aspiring entrepreneurs may find success by looking for opportunities in unusual places and relying on what they do best.

47188 ■ *"Getting Others To Take Your Startup Seriously" in Women Entrepreneur (August 1, 2008)*
Pub: Entrepreneur Media Inc.
Ed: Tamara Monosoff. **Description:** Writing a serious business plan is essential if you want others to take your startup endeavor seriously. As friends, family and acquaintances see you taking positive steps toward your goal they will begin to lend their support and may even help get the business off the ground.

47189 ■ *The Girl's Guide to Starting Your Own Business: Candid Advice, Frank Talk, and True Stories*
Pub: Collins Publications
Contact: Rachel Anderson, Director
Ed: Caitlin Friedman; Kimberly Yorio. **Released:** January 1, 2005. **Price:** $14.95. **Description:** Advice is given to help any woman start her own company. Every chapter includes interviews, charts, quizzes and witty directives about self-employment. Topics include, choosing a name and logo, business law, communication and information about business associations.

47190 ■ *"I Have A Business Idea. What Now?" in Women Entrepreneur (October 15, 2008)*
Pub: Entrepreneur Media Inc.
Ed: Cheryl Isaac. **Description:** Four pre-planning steps to take before launching a new business are discussed in detail.

47191 ■ *Mommy Millionaire: How I Turned My Kitchen Table Idea Into a Million Dollars and How You Can, Too!*
Pub: St. Martin's Press LLC
Ed: Kim Lavine. **Released:** February 19, 2008. **Price:** $14.95. **Description:** Advice, secrets and lessons for making a million dollars from a mom who turned her kitchen into a successful business; tools cover developing and patenting an idea, cold calling, trade shows, QVC, big retailers, manufacturing, and raising venture capital.

47192 ■ *"Mount Laurel Woman Launches Venture Into Children's Used Clothing" in Philadelphia Inquirer (September 17, 2010)*
Pub: Philadelphia Media Network
Ed: Maria Panaritis. **Description:** Profile of Jennifer Frisch, stay-at-home mom turned entrepreneur. Frisch started a used-clothing store Once Upon a Child after opening her franchised Plato's Closet, selling unwanted and used baby clothing and accessories at her new shop, while offering used merchandise to teens at Plato's Closet.

47193 ■ *"Secure Future" in Small Business Opportunities (November 2010)*
Pub: Harris Publications Inc.
Ed: Stan Roberts. **Description:** Fed up with the corporate world, this first-time business owner sells security equipment over the phone. Last year, sales hit $4 million. Profile of the founder of SmartWatch Security & Sound, Madelaine Lock is included.

47194 ■ *Small Business Savvy*
Pub: Adams Media Corporation
Contact: Gary Krebs, Director
E-mail: swatrous@adamsmedia.com
Ed: Norma J. Rist; Katina Z. Jones. **Released:** 2002. **Description:** Advice is given to women wishing to start their own companies using guidance and real-world examples to help position themselves for future growth. Tips to survive through a bad economic environment, breaking into a market, working with less money, accepting change, and ways to balance success with personal life are explored.

47195 ■ *There's a Business In Every Woman: A 7-Step Guide to Discovering, Starting, and Building the Business of Your Dreams*
Pub: Ballantine/Random House
Ed: Ann M. Holmes. **Released:** 2008. **Price:** $15.00 paperback. **Description:** Economist and workplace expert provides a no-nonsense guide detailing seven steps to creating a successful business, based on her own experiences and on those of her employees. She highlights the importance of understanding and using your core competencies, building an organized infrastructure from the start, and planning for and managing your growth.

47196 ■ *"Time for a Leap Of Faith?" in Women Entrepreneur (November 18, 2008)*
Pub: Entrepreneur Media Inc.
Ed: Cynthia McKay. **Description:** Starting a new business, despite the downturn in the economy, can prove to be a successful endeavor if one has the time, energy and most importantly a good idea.

47197 ■ *"Try a Little Piece of Heaven at this Suffolk Cupcakery" in Virginia-Pilot (February 13, 2011)*
Pub: McClatchy Company
Ed: Hattie Brown Garrow. **Description:** Profile of Tanya West, owner of the new startup called Divine Creations Cupcakery and Desserts located in Suffolk, Virginia. West is a full-time baker and mother of three children.

47198 ■ *"Victoria Colligan; Co-Founder, Ladies Who Launch Inc., 38" in Crain's Cleveland Business (Vol. 28, November 19, 2007, No. 46)*
Pub: Crain Communications, Inc.
Ed: Jay Miller. **Description:** Profile of Victoria Colligan who is the co-founder of Ladies Who Launch Inc., an organization with franchises in nearly 50 cities; the company offers women entrepreneurs workshops and a newsletter to help women balance their businesses with other aspects of their lives. Ms. Colligan found that women were learning about being business owners differently than men and she felt that there was a need to create opportunities for networking for women launching businesses that had more of a lifestyle purpose.

47199 ■ *Work@home: A Practical Guide for Women Who Want to Work from Home*
Pub: Woman's Missionary Union
Contact: Debby Akerman, President
Ed: Glynnis Whitwer. **Released:** March 2007. **Price:** $15.99. **Description:** Fifty-three percent of all small business are home-based. The book provides tips to women for starting a home-based business.

ASSOCIATIONS AND OTHER ORGANIZATIONS

47200 ■ *Acclaim*
401 Bay St., Ste. 1600
Toronto, ON, Canada M5K 2Y4
Ph: (416)756-0000
Fax: (416)756-0000
Co. E-mail: contact@cawee.net
URL: http://www.cawee.net
Contact: Helga Teitson, President
Released: Quarterly **Price:** available to members only.

47201 ■ *American Academy of Professional Coders (AAPC)*
2480 S 3850 W, Ste. B
Salt Lake City, UT 84120
Ph: (801)236-2200
Free: 800-626-2633
Fax: (801)236-2258
Co. E-mail: info@aapc.com
URL: http://www.aapc.com
Contact: Reed Pew, Chairman
Description: Works to elevate the standards of medical coding by providing ongoing education, certification, networking and recognition. Promotes high standards of physician and outpatient facility coding

through education and certification. **Scope:** medical coding. **Founded:** 1988. **Subscriptions:** archival material articles books clippings periodicals. **Publications:** *Physician Coding Book Bundle 1.* **Educational Activities:** Coding Conference (Annual). **Awards:** Coder of the Year (Annual); Networker of the Year (Annual).

47202 ■ American Business Women's Association (ABWA)

11050 Roe Ave., Ste. 200
Overland Park, KS 66211
Free: 800-228-0007
Fax: (913)732-5100
Co. E-mail: abwa@abwa.org
URL: http://www.abwa.org
Contact: Tina Gandy, President

Description: Women in business, including women owning or operating their own businesses, women in professions and women employed in any level of government, education, or retailing, manufacturing and service companies. Provides opportunities for businesswomen to help themselves and others grow personally and professionally through leadership, education, networking support and national recognition. Offers leadership training, business skills training and business education; special membership options for retired businesswomen and the Company Connection for business owners, a resume service, credit card and programs, various travel and insurance benefits. Sponsors American Business Women's Day and National Convention and regional conferences held annually. **Founded:** 1949. **Publications:** *The Leadership Edge* (Quarterly); *Women in Business* (Bimonthly). **Awards:** Stephen Bufton Memorial Educational Fund (Annual); Top Ten Business Women of ABWA (Annual); Woman of the Year (Annual); Top Ten Business Women of ABWA.

47203 ■ Asian Women in Business (AWIB)

42 Broadway, Ste. 1748
New York, NY 10004
Ph: (212)868-1368
Fax: (212)868-1373
Co. E-mail: info@awib.org
URL: http://www.awib.org
Contact: Bonnie Wong, President

Description: Asian-American women in business. Seeks to enable Asian-American women to achieve their entrepreneurial potential. Serves as a clearinghouse on issues affecting small business owners; provides technical assistance and other support to members; sponsors business and entrepreneurial education courses. **Scope:** women, business, Asian American. **Founded:** 1995. **Awards:** Entrepreneurial Leadership Award (Annual).

47204 ■ *Business and Professional Women*

718C Circle Dr. E
Saskatoon, SK, Canada S7K 3T7
Ph: (519)473-3505
Co. E-mail: bpwcanada@bpwcanada.com
URL: http://www.bpwcanada.com
Contact: Cara Cote, President
Released: Quarterly **Price:** C$4, for nonmembers.

47205 ■ Canadian Association of Women Executives and Entrepreneurs (CAWEE)—Association Canadienne des Femmes Cadres et Entrepreneurs

401 Bay St., Ste. 1600
Toronto, ON, Canada M5K 2Y4
Ph: (416)756-0000
Fax: (416)756-0000
Co. E-mail: contact@cawee.net
URL: http://www.cawee.net
Contact: Helga Teitson, President

Description: Seeks to provide opportunities for women to empower other women in the development and advancement of their business and professional lives; which fosters financial independence, professional development and personal satisfaction. **Founded:** 1976. **Publications:** *Acclaim* (Quarterly). **Educational Activities:** Leaders of Distinction (Monthly). **Awards:** Charity of the Year (Annual); MBA Scholarship (Annual).

47206 ■ Canadian Federation of Business and Professional Women's Clubs (CFBPWC)—BPW Canada

718C Circle Dr. E
Saskatoon, SK, Canada S7K 3T7
Ph: (519)473-3505
Co. E-mail: bpwcanada@bpwcanada.com
URL: http://www.bpwcanada.com
Contact: Cara Cote, President

Description: Canadian women engaged in business, the professions, or industry. Works to enhance the economic, social, and employment status of women. Encourages women to become active in government at every level. Strives to improve business service standards. Networks with related organizations to promote common concerns. **Scope:** women's history. **Founded:** 1930. **Publications:** *Business and Professional Women* (Quarterly). **Educational Activities:** Canadian Federation of Business and Professional Women's Clubs Convention (Biennial). **Awards:** Leadership Award (Annual).

47207 ■ Center for Economic Options (CEO)

910 Quarrier St., Ste. 206
Charleston, WV 25301
Ph: (304)345-1298
Fax: (304)342-0641
Co. E-mail: info@economicoptions.org
URL: http://www.centerforeconomicoptions.org
Contact: Pam Curry, Executive Director

Description: Seeks to improve the economic position and quality of life for women, especially low-income and minority women. Works to provide access to job training and employment options to women. Supports self-employed women and small business owners by offering training and technical assistance and information. Advocates women's legal right to employment, training, education, and credit. Seeks to inform the public on economic issues related to women; while activities are conducted on local and state levels, group cooperates with national and international organizations on issues relating to employment and economic justice for women. Maintains speakers' bureau and library. Compiles statistics; conducts research. **Founded:** 1979. **Publications:** *Women and Employment News.*

47208 ■ Center for Women's Business Research

1760 Old Meadow Rd., Ste. 500
McLean, VA 22102
Ph: (703)556-7162
Fax: (703)506-3266
Co. E-mail: info@womensbusinessresearch.org
URL: http://www.cfwbr.org
Contact: Dr. Patricia G. Greene, Chairperson
URL(s): www.nfwbo.org, www.womensbusinessresearch.org, www.womensbusinessresearchcenter.org. **Description:** Women business owners. Supports the growth of women business owners and their enterprises by conducting research, sharing information and increasing knowledge. Offers marketing consulting and seminars. **Scope:** High visibility research projects on ground breaking topics. Customized research for corporations to gain marketing intelligence. Consulting with corporations on marketing to women-owned businesses. Public relations consulting on media campaigns relating to women-owned firms. **Services:** Speaking engagements (Occasionally). **Founded:** 1989. **Publications:** *Center for Women's Business Research Newsletters; Center for Women's Business Research Reports; Key Facts about Women-Owned Businesses.* **Educational Activities:** Center for Women's Business Research Seminars (Occasionally).

47209 ■ Educational Foundation for Women in Accounting (EFWA)

136 S Keowee St.
Dayton, OH 45402
Ph: (937)424-3391
Fax: (937)222-5794
Co. E-mail: info@efwa.org
URL: http://www.efwa.org
Contact: Laurie Burney, President

Description: Women in the accounting field. Supports the advancement of women in the accounting profession through funding of education, research, career literature, publications, and other projects. **Founded:** 1966. **Publications:** *The Educator* (Semiannual). **Awards:** Laurels (Periodic); Women in Need (Periodic); Women in Transition (Periodic); Michele L. McDonald Scholarships; Seattle Chapter ASWA Scholarships; Women In Need Scholarships; Women In Transition Scholarships; EFWA Moss Adams Foundation Scholarships.

47210 ■ National Association for Female Executives (NAFE)

2 Park Ave.
New York, NY 10016
Ph: (212)477-2200
Fax: (212)477-8125
Co. E-mail: roxanne.natale@nafe.com
URL: http://www.nafe.com
Contact: Dr. Betty Spence, President

Description: Represents and supports professional women and women business owners; provides resources and services through education, networking and public advocacy to empower members to achieve career success and financial security. **Founded:** 1972. **Publications:** *NAFE E-Newsletter* (Biweekly); *Executive Female* (Bimonthly). **Awards:** Women of Achievement Awards (Annual). **Telecommunication Services:** nafe@nafe.com.

47211 ■ National Association of Women Business Owners (NAWBO)

601 Pennsylvania Ave. NW
South Bldg., Ste. 900
Washington, DC 20004
Ph: (301)608-2590
Free: 800-556-2926
Fax: (202)403-3788
Co. E-mail: national@nawbo.org
URL: http://www.nawbo.org
Contact: Diane Leneghan Tomb, President

Description: Represents and promotes women-owned businesses to shape economic and public policy. **Founded:** 1975. **Educational Activities:** Public Policy Days (Annual); Women's Business Conference (Annual). **Awards:** Susan Hager Legacy Award (Annual); Member of the Year; Gillian Rudd Business Leadership Award (Annual); NAWBO/Wells Fargo Trailblazer Award (Annual); Woman Business Owner of the Year; Chapter Corporate Partner of the Year; NAWBO/Wells Fargo Trailblazer Award.

47212 ■ National Association of Women MBAs (NAWMBA)

Rice University
PO Box 2932
Houston, TX 77251-2932
Co. E-mail: director@mbawomen.org
URL: http://www.mbawomen.org
Contact: Stacey A. Gordon, Managing Director

Description: Provides networking opportunities for its members. Increases communication among graduate business schools regarding their initiatives to educate and support women in business. **Founded:** 1982.

47213 ■ National Women's Business Council (NWBC)

409 3rd St. SW, Ste. 210
Washington, DC 20024
Ph: (202)205-3850
Fax: (202)205-6825
Co. E-mail: info@nwbc.gov
URL: http://www.nwbc.gov
Contact: Anie Borja, Executive Director

Description: Women business owners. Strives to promote initiatives, policies, and programs designed to support women's business enterprises. **Founded:** 1988. **Publications:** *Engage* (Bimonthly); *Study of Women-Owned and Led Businesses; Support for Women's Enterprise Development in the United States: Lessons Learned,* by the Council's Executive Director, Julie Weeks.

47214 ■ United Nations - Commission on the Status of Women (CSW)

Division for the Advancement of Women
2 United Nations Plz., 12th Fl., Rm. DC2
New York, NY 10017

Fax: (212)963-3463
Co. E-mail: daw@un.org
URL: http://www.un.org/womenwatch/daw/csw/index.
html
Contact: Mr. Olivier Belle, Chairman
URL(s): www.un.org/womenwatch/daw/csw. **Description:** Intergovernmental body focused on the social, economic, and legal status of women worldwide. Facilitates exchange on local, national, and global issues affecting women; gathers and disseminates information; adopts policy recommendations on gender equality and advancement by women. **Founded:** 1946.

47215 ■ Women in Franchising (WIF)

53 W Jackson Blvd., Ste. 1157
Chicago, IL 60604
Ph: (312)431-1467
Fax: (312)431-1469
Co. E-mail: spkezios@womeninfranchising.com
URL: http://www.womeninfranchising.com
Contact: Susan P. Kezios, President
Description: Assists women interested in all aspects of franchise business development including those buying a franchised business and those expanding their businesses via franchising. Provides franchise technical assistance in both of these areas. Surveys the industry on the status of women. **Scope:** The firm offers franchise consulting services for women and minorities interested in becoming franchisees or franchisors. Also offers a number of consulting services including presenting workshops and seminars that teach prospective franchisees the skills and knowledge needed to evaluate, finance and purchase a franchise, providing one-on-one assistance to persons considering buying a franchise by conducting a UFOC (Uniform Franchise Offering Circular) Review and feasibility studies. Provides a variety of tools and one-on-one assistance to prospective franchisees and franchisors including audio seminars, a detailed Operations Manual and sales guidance and national public relations contracts for recruiting franchisees. **Founded:** 1987. **Seminars:** Buying a Franchise: How To Make The Right Choice; Growing Your Business: The Franchise Option.

47216 ■ Women in Packaging (WMPKG)

4290 Bells Ferry Rd., Ste. 106-17
Kennesaw, GA 30144-1300
Ph: (678)594-6872
Co. E-mail: joann@womeninpackaging.org
URL: http://womeninpackaging.org
Contact: JoAnn R. Hines, Founder
URL(s): www.womeninpackaging.org/. **Description:** Works to promote and encourage women in the packaging industry. Educates the packaging industry about the contributions of women to the industry; helps to eliminate stereotypes and discrimination in the profession; offers networking opportunities; conducts career enhancement programs; compiles statistics; maintains speakers' bureau. **Founded:** 1993. **Publications:** *Packaging Horizons Online* (Weekly); *Packaging Horizons*.

47217 ■ Women's Regional Publications of America (WRPA)

c/o Jill Duval, VP/Membership Chair
PO Box 12955
Albuquerque, NM 87195
Ph: (505)247-9195
Free: 800-282-8749
Co. E-mail: kgreen@womsdigest.net
URL: http://www.womensyellowpages.org
Contact: Karen Green, President
Description: Provides a forum where publishers of women's publications and business directories share information and resources. Increases the visibility, authority, influence and status of women's business for the purpose of promoting growth and support of women. Educates the general public about the need to support women-owned businesses, including equal opportunity employers and contractors. **Founded:** 1986.

REFERENCE WORKS

47218 ■ *"2008 Woman of the Year Gala"* in *Hispanic Business* (Vol. 30, July-August 2008,

No. 7-8, pp. 58)
Pub: Hispanic Business, Inc.
Ed: Brynne Chappell. **Description:** Brief report on the sixth annual Women of the Year Awards gala which was held at JW Marriott Desert Ridge Resort and Spa is given; 20 women were honored with these awards for their professional contribution, commitment to the advancement of the Hispanic community and involvement with charitable organizations.

47219 ■ *"ABWA Through the Years: Extending the Hand of Friendship"* in *Women In Business* (Vol. 63, Spring 2011, No. 1, pp. 8)

Pub: American Business Women's Association
Ed: Rene Street, Leigh Elmore. **Description:** A look back at the history of the American Business Women's Association (ABWA) as they celebrate March as Women's History month is presented. Looking back at the archives has revealed how several veteran ABWA members came to join the sisterhood of ABWA through the Hand of Friendship Tea.

47220 ■ *"Ace Every Introduction"* in *Women Entrepreneur* (September 10, 2008)

Pub: Entrepreneur Media Inc.
Ed: Cynthia McKay. **Description:** Making a powerful first impression is one of the most important marketing tools a business owner can possess. Advice about meeting new business contacts is given.

47221 ■ *"AG Warns Slots MBE Plan Risky"* in *Boston Business Journal* (Vol. 29, May 27, 2011, No. 3, pp. 1)

Pub: American City Business Journals Inc.
Ed: Scott Dance. **Description:** Attorney General Doug Gansler states that the law extending the minority business program on slots parlors contracting through 2018 could be open to lawsuits. He recommended that the state should conduct a study proving that minority- and women-owned businesses do not get a fair share in the gaming industry before it signs the bill to avoid lawsuits from majority-owned firms.

47222 ■ *"The AHA Moment"* in *Hispanic Business* (December 2010)

Pub: Hispanic Business
Ed: Rebecca Vallaneda. **Description:** An interview with Gisela Girard on how competitive market conditions push buttons. Girard stepped down from her 18-month position as chairwoman the Association of Hispanic Advertising Agencies. She has more than 20 years of experience in advertising and research marketing.

47223 ■ *"Are You Ready for a Transformation?"* in *Women Entrepreneur* (November 28, 2008)

Pub: Entrepreneur Media Inc.
Ed: Aliza Sherman. **Description:** Marlene J. Waldock, an expert in women's empowerment and reinvention, discusses brand modification and what a business owner should consider before attempting to change or modify their brand.

47224 ■ *The Art of War for Women*

Pub: Doubleday
Ed: Chin-ning Chu. **Released:** April 10, 2007. **Price:** $21.95. **Description:** According to the author, the workplace is a battlefield for women. She offers a strategy for women to succeed in business.

47225 ■ *Avon: Building the World's Premier Company for Women*

Pub: John Wiley & Sons, Incorporated
Ed: Laura Klepacki. **Released:** May 2006. **Price:** $16.95. **Description:** Profile of Avon and how it grew from a small business selling door-to-door to one of the largest cosmetics companies in the world.

47226 ■ *Back on the Career Track: A Guide for Stay-At-Home Moms Who Want to Return to Work*

Pub: Warner Books Inc.
Ed: Carol Fishman Cohen; Vivian Steir Rabin. **Released:** 2008. **Price:** $14.99 paperback. **Description:** For women like themselves who have rejoined the workforce after a prolonged absence, the authors

detail seven main steps for reentry; profiles of six women who have successfully re-launched their careers are included.

47227 ■ *"Back Talk With Terrie M. Williams"* in *Black Enterprise* (Vol. 38, December 2007, No. 5, pp. 204)

Pub: Earl G. Graves Publishing Co. Inc.
Ed: Tennille M. Robinson. **Description:** Profile of Terrie M. Williams, president of a public relations agency as well as founder of a youth empowerment organization called Stay Strong Foundation. Williams reflects on her bouts with depression and how the disease impacts sufferers and talks about her book that will inspire others dealing with depression.

47228 ■ *"Barbara West"* in *Crain's Cleveland Business* (Vol. 30, June 29, 2009, No. 25, pp. 14)

Pub: Crain Communications, Inc.
Ed: Shannon Mortland. **Description:** Profile of Barbara West, administrative director of emergency medicine at MetroHealth Medical Center in Ohio. Ms. West manages Metro Life Flight that uses helicopters to transport patients to MetroHealth. She discusses the challenges of taking care of patients when big emergencies occur.

47229 ■ *"Baxter Baker Wins in Hot Finale of 'Cupcake Wars"* in *Fort Mill Times* (September 13, 2011)

Pub: McClatchy Company
Ed: Jenny Overmann. **Description:** Heather McDonnell, owner of Cupcrazed Cakery, and her assistant Debbie McDonnell, vied for a chance to win $10,000 on the cable network show called 'Cupcake Wars', and to serve cupcakes at the album release party for country singer Jennette McCurdy. At the end of the show, the sisters-in-law won the top prize.

47230 ■ *"Because Kids Need To Be Heard: Tina Wells: Buzz Marketing Group: Voorhees, New Jersey"* in *Inc.* (Volume 32, December 2010)

Pub: Inc. Magazine
Ed: Tamara Schweitzer. **Description:** Profile of Tina Wells, founder and CEO of Buzz Marketing Group, who writes a tween book series called Mackenzie Blue to reach young girls.

47231 ■ *"Become A Brand"* in *Women Entrepreneur* (September 14, 2008)

Pub: Entrepreneur Media Inc.
Ed: Suzy Girard-Ruttenberg. **Description:** Powerful brands are effective, innovative, exclusive or even socially conscious; it is important for small businesses to understand the power of becoming a brand since it is one of the best ways in which to position one's company and drive its growth.

47232 ■ *"The Believer"* in *Inc.* (December 2007, pp. 130-138)

Pub: Gruner & Jahr USA Publishing
Ed: Leigh Buchanan. **Description:** Profile of Selena Cuffe, wine importer and socially conscious woman entrepreneur, who is focusing her talents on helping South Africa get wine products to America.

47233 ■ *"Best Practices Award-Winning Teams 2010-2011"* in *Women In Business* (Vol. 63, Fall 2011, No. 3, pp. 19)

Pub: American Business Women's Association
Description: List of American Business Women's Association's best practices award winning teams for 2010-2011 is given. Coral Springs Charter Chapter, Emerald Coast Chapter, and Golden Dome Chapter are some of the winners for level one. Level two and level three winners are also presented.

47234 ■ *Big Vision, Small Business*

Pub: Ivy Sea, Inc.
Ed: Jamie S. Walters. **Released:** October 10, 2002. **Price:** $17.95. **Description:** The power of the small enterprise is examined. The author shares her expertise as an entrepreneur and founder of a business consulting firm to help small business owners successfully run their companies. Interviews with more than seventy small business owners provide

insight into visioning, planning, and establishing a small company, as well as strategies for good employee and customer relationships.

47235 ■ *Boss of You: Everything a Woman Needs to Know to Start, Run, and Maintain Her Own Business*
Pub: Seal Press
Contact: Charlie Winton, Manager
Ed: Lauren Bacon; Emira Mears. **Released:** June 2008. **Price:** $15.95. **Description:** Women entrepreneurs start businesses at twice the rate of male counterparts. Information is shared to help a woman start, run and maintain a successful company.

47236 ■ *"Business Forecast: Stormy and Successful"* in *Women In Business* (Vol. 62, June 2010, No. 2, pp. 12)
Pub: American Business Women's Association
Ed: Kathleen Leighton. **Description:** Stormy Simon, vice president of customer service at Overstock.com is a self-made career woman who started out as a temporary employee in the company in 2001. She was not able to attend college because she had two sons to care for after her divorce. Simon got involved in advertising and media buying and shares her love for business.

47237 ■ *Business as Usual*
Pub: HarperBusiness
Ed: Anita Roddick. **Released:** 2005. **Price:** $12.95. **Description:** Founder of The Body Shop shares her story and gives her opinion on everything from cynical cosmetic companies to destructive consultants.

47238 ■ *"Calendar"* in *Crain's Detroit Business* (Vol. 24, March 10, 2008, No. 10, pp. 21)
Pub: Crain Communications, Inc.
Description: Listing of events in the Detroit area include conferences addressing entrepreneurialism, economic development, and women business ownership.

47239 ■ *"Calendar"* in *Crain's Detroit Business* (Vol. 24, March 17, 2008, No. 11, pp. 20)
Pub: Crain Communications, Inc.
Description: Listing of events in the Detroit area include conferences addressing entrepreneurialism, economic development, and women business ownership.

47240 ■ *"Calendar"* in *Crain's Detroit Business* (Vol. 24, March 24, 2008, No. 12, pp. 25)
Pub: Crain Communications, Inc.
Description: Listing of events in the Detroit area include conferences addressing entrepreneurialism, economic development, and women business ownership.

47241 ■ *"Calendar"* in *Crain's Detroit Business* (Vol. 24, September 22, 2008, No. 38, pp. 17)
Pub: Crain Communications Inc.
Description: Listing of events in the Detroit area include conferences addressing entrepreneurialism, economic development, and women business ownership.

47242 ■ *"Calendar"* in *Crain's Detroit Business* (Vol. 24, October 6, 2008, No. 40, pp. 22)
Pub: Crain Communications, Inc.
Description: Listing of events in the Detroit area include conferences addressing entrepreneurialism, economic development, manufacturing, marketing, the housing crisis and women business ownership.

47243 ■ *"Car Dealer Closings: Immoral, Slow-Death"* in *Crain's Detroit Business* (Vol. 25, June 8, 2009, No. 23)
Pub: Crain Communications Inc. - Detroit
Ed: Daniel Duggan. **Description:** Colleen McDonald discusses the closing of her two Chrysler dealerships located in Taylor and Livonia, Michigan, along with her Farmington Hills store, Holiday Chevrolet.

47244 ■ *"Celebrate Success. Embrace Innovation"* in *Black Enterprise* (Vol. 37, February 2007, No. 7, pp. 145)
Pub: Earl G. Graves Publishing Co. Inc.
Description: 2007 Women of Power Summit provides networking opportunities, empowerment sessions, and nightly entertainment. More than 500 executive women of color are expected to attend this inspiring summit in Phoenix, February 7-10.

47245 ■ *"Chattanooga at a Glance"* in *Women In Business* (Vol. 62, June 2010, No. 2, pp. 29)
Pub: American Business Women's Association
Ed: Jill Yates Bagby. **Description:** City of Chattanooga, Tennessee is the location of the 2010 American Business Women's Association (ABWA) National Women's Leadership Conference. The city offers historical sites, parks and tourist attractions, as well as dining options.

47246 ■ *"City Seeks More Minorities"* in *Austin Business JournalInc.* (Vol. 28, November 7, 2008, No. 34, pp. A1)
Pub: American City Business Journals
Ed: Jean Kwon. **Description:** Austin, Texas is planning to increase the participation of minority- and women-owned businesses in government contracts. Contractors are required to show 'good faith' to comply with the specified goals. The city is planning to effect the changes in the construction and professional services sector.

47247 ■ *"Common Thread"* in *Entrepreneur* (Vol. 36, March 2008, No. 3, pp. 144)
Pub: Entrepreneur Media Inc.
Ed: Sara Wilson. **Description:** Profile of Stacey Benet and her business, Alice and Olivia, and how she jumpstarted her career in the clothing industry after she wore a self-designed pair of pants that caught the attention of a Barney's New York representative is presented.

47248 ■ *"Conference Calendar"* in *Marketing to Women* (Vol. 21, April 2008, No. 4, pp. 7)
Pub: EPM Communications Inc.
Contact: Ira Mayer, President
E-mail: imayer@epmcom.com
Description: Listing of current conferences and events concerning women, marketing and business.

47249 ■ *"Conference Calendar"* in *Marketing to Women* (Vol. 21, March 2008, No. 3, pp. 7)
Pub: EPM Communications Inc.
Contact: Ira Mayer, President
E-mail: imayer@epmcom.com
Description: Listing of current conferences and events aimed at women entrepreneurs and leaders.

47250 ■ *"Conference Calendar"* in *Marketing to Women* (Vol. 21, February 2008, No. 2, pp. 1)
Pub: EPM Communications Inc.
Contact: Ira Mayer, President
E-mail: imayer@epmcom.com
Description: Listing of current conferences and events concerning women, marketing and business.

47251 ■ *"Congratulations to the 2010 Top Ten Business Women of ABWA"* in *Women In Business* (Vol. 61, August-September 2009, No. 4, pp. 12)
Pub: American Business Women's Association
Description: Listing of the top 10 members of the American Business Women's Association (ABWA) for 2010 is presented. The lists of the top ten 2010 members selected by each of the six ABWA chapters are also provided.

47252 ■ *"Congratulations to the 2012 Top Ten Business Women of ABWA"* in *Women In Business* (Vol. 63, Fall 2011, No. 3, pp. 14)
Pub: American Business Women's Association
Description: Geri Bertram, Patti Bigger, and Susan Crowther are among the top ten businesswomen of the American Business Women's Association recognized for their contribution to the group, community involvement, and career achievements. Bertram is the manager for procurement planning control in In-

galls Shipbuilding while Bigger is Specialty Screw Corporation's corporate relations manager. Also on the list are Virginia DeGiorgi and Geanna Kincanon.

47253 ■ *"Convention Calendar"* in *Black Enterprise* (Vol. 37, February 2007, No. 7, pp. 68)
Pub: Earl G. Graves Publishing Co. Inc.
Description: Listing of conventions and trade show of interest to minority and women business leaders.

47254 ■ *"A Conversation with; Renea Butler, Real Estate One Inc."* in *Crain's Detroit Business* (Vol. 25, June 8, 2009, No. 23, pp. 12)
Pub: Crain Communications Inc. - Detroit
Ed: Ryan Beene. **Description:** Renea Butler, vice president of administration and human resources for Real Estate One Inc. in Southfield as well as vice president for public relations for the Human Resource Association of Greater Detroit, talks about how the economy has affected human resource services.

47255 ■ *"Crafting Kinship at Home and Work: Women Miners in Wyoming"* in *WorkingUSA* (Vol. 11, December 2008, No. 4, pp. 439)
Pub: Blackwell Publishers Ltd.
Ed: Jessica M. Smith. **Description:** Institutional policies and social dynamics shaping women working in the northeastern Wyoming mining industry are examined. Ethnographic research suggests that the women's successful integration into this nontraditional workplace is predicated on their ability to craft and maintain kin-like social relationships in two spheres. First, women miners have addressed the challenges of managing their home and work responsibilities by cultivating networks of friends and family to care for their children while they are at work. Second, women miners craft close relationships with coworkers in what are called 'crew families'. These relationships make their work more enjoyable and the ways in which they create camaraderie prompt a reconsideration of conventional accounts of sexual harassment in the mining industry.

47256 ■ *"Cupcake Maker Explains Tricks of the Trade"* in *Chattanooga Times/Free Press* (September 6, 2011)
Pub: Chattanooga Publishing Company
Ed: Holly Leber. **Description:** Sunny Burden, head baker at Whipped Cupcakes in Chattanooga, Tennessee creates themed cupcakes as well as traditional ones. Burden finds baking therapeutic.

47257 ■ *"Cupcake Maker Grabs Outpost"* in *Crain's New York Business* (Vol. 27, August 15, 2011, No. 33, pp. 16)
Pub: Crain Communications, Inc.
Ed: Jermaine Taylor. **Description:** Family-owned miniature cupcake maker, Baked by Melissa, singed a ten-year lease, expanding their stores to five. The business was started three years ago by advertising executive Melissa Bushell.

47258 ■ *"'Cupcake Wars' TV Show Returns to Hampton Roads"* in *Virginian-Pilot* (September 11, 2011)
Pub: McClatchy Company
Ed: Carolyn Shapiro. **Description:** Virginia Beach, Virginia sweet shop called Just Cupcakes and Carolina Cupcakery will compete for prizes on cable TV's Food Network Channel. Carla Hesseltine, owner of Just Cupcakes made it to the final rounds.

47259 ■ *"Datebook"* in *Crain's Chicago Business* (Vol. 31, March 24, 2008, No. 12, pp. 18)
Pub: Crain Communications, Inc.
Description: Listing of events in the Detroit area include conferences addressing entrepreneurialism, economic development, secrets of getting hired, and women business ownership.

47260 ■ *"Datebook"* in *Crain's Chicago Business* (Vol. 31, March 31, 2008, No. 13, pp. 1)
Pub: Crain Communications, Inc.
Description: Listing of events in the Detroit area include conferences addressing entrepreneurialism, economic development, secrets of getting hired, and women business ownership.

47261 ■ *"Datebook" in Crain's Chicago Business (Vol. 31, April 28, 2008, No. 17, pp. 18)*
Pub: Crain Communications, Inc.
Description: Listing of events in the Detroit area include conferences addressing entrepreneurialism, economic development, and women business ownership.

47262 ■ *"Developing the Next Generation of Rosies" in Employee Benefit News (Vol. 25, November 1, 2011, No. 14, pp. 36)*
Pub: SourceMedia Inc.
Ed: Kathleen Koster. **Description:** According to the research group Catalyst, women made up 46.7 percent of the American workforce in 2010, however only 14.4 percent was Fortune 500 executive officers and 15.7 percent held Fortune 500 board seats. Statistical data included.

47263 ■ *Divas Doing Business: What the Guidebooks Don't Tell You About Being A Woman Entrepreneur*
Pub: Nouveau Connoisseurs Corporation
Ed: Monique Hayward. **Released:** February 14, 2009. **Price:** $19.95. **Description:** A must-read for any woman who's currently running a business or is thinking of starting one.

47264 ■ *Doing Business with Beauty: Black Women, Hair Salons, and the Racial Enclave Economy*
Pub: Rowman & Littlefield Publishers Inc.
Contact: Jason Aronson, President
Ed: Adia Harvey Wingfield. **Released:** June 28, 2008. **Price:** $19.95. **Description:** Factors that draw black women into the hair industry are examined. Interviews with hair salon owners explore aspects of owning a salon, owner-employee relationships, and the black female owner's struggle for autonomy and success in entrepreneurship.

47265 ■ *"Doing Good: Cause and Effect" in Entrepreneur (Vol. 36, February 2008, No. 2, pp. 23)*
Pub: Entrepreneur Media Inc.
Description: Lisa Knoppe established Art for a Cause LLC that employs people with mental and physical disabilities. The company makes hand-painted tools and furniture to be sold at gift retailers and hardware stores.

47266 ■ *"Don't Quit When The Road Gets Bumpy" in Women Entrepreneur (November 25, 2008)*
Pub: Entrepreneur Media Inc.
Ed: Bonnie Price. **Description:** Discusses techniques four women entrepreneurs are utilizing to keep their businesses successful despite the credit crunch and the economic downturn.

47267 ■ *"Dress Professionally Cool for Summer" in Women In Business (Vol. 62, June 2010, No. 2, pp. 38)*
Pub: American Business Women's Association
Ed: Maureen Sullivan. **Description:** Summer clothing for business and career women is discussed with regard to traditional and relaxed work places. Fabric considerations, tips on choosing blazers and a list of clothes and other items that are not appropriate for the workplace are presented.

47268 ■ *"Edible Endeavors" in Black Enterprise (March 2008)*
Pub: Earl G. Graves Publishing Co. Inc.
Ed: Carolyn M. Brown. **Description:** Profile of Jacqueline Frazer, woman entrepreneur who turned her love for cooking into a catering business. She is chef and owner of Command Performance in New York City. The firm works with more than 50 clients annually and generates annual revenues of about $350,000.

47269 ■ *Enterprising Women in Urban Zimbabwe: Gender, Microbusiness, and Globalization*
Pub: Indiana University Press
Contact: Janet Rabinowitch, Director
E-mail: jrabinow@indiana.edu
Ed: Mary Johnson Osirim. **Released:** April 1, 2009. **Price:** $39.95. **Description:** An investigation into the business and personal experiences of women entrepreneurs in the microenterprise sector in Zimbabwe. Many of these women work as market traders, crocheters, seamstresses, and hairdressers.

47270 ■ *"Entrepreneur Says Spirituality Has Been a Key to Her Success" in Business First Columbus (Vol. 25, October 17, 2008, No. 8, pp. 1)*
Pub: American City Business Journals
Ed: Scott Rawdon. **Description:** Profile of Carolyn Williams Francis, CEO of Williams Interior Designs Inc. She outlines her mantra for success in her furniture design business, but emphasizes that faith has taken her business to greater heights.

47271 ■ *"Every Resume Tells a Story" in Women In Business (Vol. 62, September 2010, No. 3, pp. 26)*
Pub: American Business Women's Association
Ed: Kathleen Leighton. **Description:** Ways in which job applicants can write a good resume and promote themselves are discussed. It is believed that applicants should be proud of their accomplishments and they need to add details that will make them stand out. The importance of including a professional narrative in the resume is also explained.

47272 ■ *"The Evolution of Carolyn Elman" in Women In Business (Vol. 62, September 2010, No. 3, pp. 11)*
Pub: American Business Women's Association
Ed: Leigh Elmore. **Description:** Carolyn Elman, former executive director of the American Business Women's Association (ABWA), provides an overview of her career. Elman grew up with the Association, and it was part of her family's existence. She believes that the ABWA provides women the opportunity to learn and improve their skills in business.

47273 ■ *"Fall Wardrobe on a Budget" in Women In Business (Vol. 62, September 2010, No. 3, pp. 38)*
Pub: American Business Women's Association
Ed: Kathleen Leighton. **Description:** Things women should keep in mind when putting together a fall wardrobe are discussed. Women should aim for at least two jackets, five tops, four pants or skirts, two twin sets, five pairs of pantyhose, and two pair of shoes. They should also be ruthless when it comes to quality and practicality.

47274 ■ *Female Enterprise in the New Economy*
Pub: University of Toronto Press
Ed: Karen D. Hughes. **Released:** January 2006. **Price:** $67.00, paperback $27.50. **Description:** Examination of whether the increasingly entrepreneurial economy is offering women more opportunity or increases their risk for poverty and economic insecurity.

47275 ■ *Female Entrepreneurship in East and South-East Asia: Opportunities and Challenges*
Pub: Woodhead Publishing Ltd.
Ed: Philippe Debroux. **Released:** February 10, 2010. **Description:** A detailed study of female entrepreneurship in Asia, where public authorities are slowly realizing the importance of women as workers and entrepreneurs.

47276 ■ *Female Hispanic Professionals by the Number" in Hispanic Business (Vol. 30, April 2008, No. 4, pp. 8)*
Pub: Hispanic Business
Description: More executive opportunities are presenting themselves for future generations of Hispanic women who are more frequently being found in high-level positions. Statistical data included.

47277 ■ *"Filling the Business Gap" in Hispanic Business (December 2010)*
Pub: Hispanic Business
Ed: Richard Larsen. **Description:** New York group seeks to increase state diversity supplier spending to help create jobs and boost the economy. According to a recent study, six out of 10 small business owners will increase capital spending but delay hiring in 2011. However, potential job creation is good among businesses owned by women and minorities.

47278 ■ *"The Final Say" in Hispanic Business (Vol. 30, March 2008, No. 3, pp. 52)*
Pub: Hispanic Business
Ed: Hildy Medina. **Description:** Vice-Chairwoman of the pensions and investments committee and Illinois State Senator Iris Martinez is the first Hispanic woman to be elected Senator and is advocating for pension funds to include Hispanic money managers and minority- and female-owned businesses in the investment plans.

47279 ■ *"Fitter from Twitter" in Boston Business Journal (Vol. 30, December 17, 2010, No. 47, pp. 1)*
Pub: Boston Business Journal
Ed: Lisa van der Pool. **Description:** Small businesses are increasing their use of the Twitter microblogging platform to attract and retain customers. Lisa Johnson, who owns Modern Pilates studios, managed to raise awareness of her personal brand nationally through the social media platform.

47280 ■ *"Five Low-Cost Home Based Startups" in Women Entrepreneur (December 16, 2008)*
Pub: Entrepreneur Media Inc.
Ed: Lesley Spencer Pyle. **Description:** During tough economic times, small businesses have an advantage over large companies because they can adjust to economic conditions more easily and without having to go through corporate red tape that can slow the implementation process. A budding entrepreneur may find success by taking inventory of his or her skills, experience, expertise and passions and utilizing those qualities to start a business. Five low-cost home-based startups are profiled. These include starting an online store, a virtual assistant service, web designer, sales representative and a home staging counselor.

47281 ■ *"Floral-Design Kiosk Business in Colorado Springs Blossoming" in Colorado Springs Business Journal (September 24, 2010)*
Pub: Dolan Media Newswires
Ed: Monica Mendoza. **Description:** Profile of Shellie Greto and her mother Jackie Martin who started a wholesale flower business in their garage. The do-it-yourself floral arrangement firm started a kiosk business in supermarkets called Complete Design.

47282 ■ *"For Giving Us a Way To Say Yes To Solar: Lynn Jurich and Edward Fenster" in Inc. (Volume 32, December 2010, No. 10, pp. 110)*
Pub: Inc. Magazine
Description: Profile of entrepreneurs Lynn Jurich and Edward Fenster, cofounders of SunRun. The firm installs solar panels at little or no cost and homeowners sign 20-year contracts to buy power at a fixed price.

47283 ■ *"For Putting Down Roots in Business: Amy Norquist: Greensulate, New York City" in Inc. (Volume 32, December 2010, No. 10, pp. 106)*
Pub: Inc. Magazine
Ed: Christine Lagorio. **Description:** Profile of Amy Norquist who left her position at an environmental nonprofit organization to found Greensulate. Her firm insulates rooftops with lavender, native grasses and succulents called sedum in order to eliminate carbon from the atmosphere.

47284 ■ *The Foundations of Female Entrepreneurship: Women in Business in Mid-Victorian London*
Pub: Routledge
Ed: Alison Kay. **Released:** April 1, 2009. **Price:** $130.00. **Description:** This book argues that active business did not exclude women from 1747 to 1880, although careful representation was necessary and this has obscured the similarities of women's businesses to those of many male business owners.

47285 ■ *"From Craft Biz To Wholesale Giant" in Women Entrepreneur (January 19, 2009)*
Pub: Entrepreneur Media Inc.
Ed: Maria Falconer. **Description:** Advice is given on how to turn a small craft business into a full-time

venture; tips to help one transition from a part-time designer to a full-time wholesaler and brand are also included.

47286 ■ *"Game Changer"* in Canadian Business (Vol. 83, June 15, 2010, No. 10, pp. 52)

Pub: Rogers Media Ltd.

Ed: Jordan Timm. **Description:** Ubisoft chose Ontario to be the site for its new development studio and it has appointed Jade Raymond as its managing director. Raymond was born in Montreal in 1975 and studied computer science at McGill. Raymond is said to possess the understanding of the game industry's technical, art, and business components.

47287 ■ The Girl's Guide to Being a Boss (Without Being a Bitch): Valuable Lessons, Smart Suggestions, and True Stories for Succeeding

Pub: Random Housing Publishing Group

Ed: Caitlin Friedman; Kimberly Yorio. **Released:** April 2006.

47288 ■ The Girl's Guide to Building a Million-Dollar Business

Pub: AMACOM

Ed: Susan Wilson Solovic. **Released:** 2008. **Price:** $21.95. **Description:** Success plan for women business owners; the book includes tips for determination, managing changing relationships, keeping employees and customers happy, getting and maintaining credit, overcoming gender bias, and creating a good business plan and solid brand.

47289 ■ *"Going for the APEX"* in Women In Business (Vol. 62, September 2010, No. 3, pp. 28)

Pub: American Business Women's Association

Description: Information about the American Business Women's Association (ABWA) professional development tools, which keep members focused on personal excellence, is presented. The organization recently launched the APEX (Achieving Personal Excellence) Award to honor women who are making a commitment to themselves.

47290 ■ *"The Good Guys of ABWA"* in Women In Business (Vol. 63, Fall 2011, No. 3, pp. 9)

Pub: American Business Women's Association

Ed: Rene Street. **Description:** The American Business Women's Association (ABWA) was an all-woman group since its founding in 1949. However, a Supreme Court ruling in 1987 opened all-male and all-female organizations of the opposite sex. Some of the male members of the ABWA are Bill Hense, James Drager, and John Lester.

47291 ■ Grassroots NGOs by Women for Women: The Driving Force of Development in India

Pub: SAGE Publications USA

Contact: Blaise R. Simqu, President

Ed: Femida Handy; Meenaz Kassam; Suzanne Feeney; Bhagyashree Ranade. **Released:** July 2006. **Price:** $29.95. **Description:** Understanding the role of non-governmental organizations in women's development is offered through interviews with twenty women in India who have founded NGOs serving women.

47292 ■ *"Grooming Your Online Persona"* in Women In Business (Vol. 62, June 2010, No. 2, pp. 36)

Pub: American Business Women's Association

Ed: Diane Stafford. **Description:** Employees' use of online social networks could become a basis on how their employers, clients, or business partners would judge them. Personal details, pictures and other online data should be filtered to avoid inappropriate or uncomfortable situations and distinguish personal from professional or work life.

47293 ■ *"Growing Strong"* in Entrepreneur (Vol. 35, November 2007, No. 11, pp. 36)

Pub: Entrepreneur Media Inc.

Ed: Nichole L. Torres. **Description:** Amy Langer founded Salo LL with partner John Folkestad. The company is growing fast since its 2002 launch, with over $40 million in projections for 2007. The finance and accounting staffing company tops the list of the fastest-growing women-led companies in North America.

47294 ■ Growth Oriented Women Entrepreneurs and Their Businesses: A Global Research Perspective

Pub: Edward Elgar Publishing, Incorporated

Ed: Candida G. Brush. **Released:** June 2006. **Price:** $135.00. **Description:** Roles women play in entrepreneurship globally and their economic impact are examined.

47295 ■ *"Helping Women Grow Their Businesses One Entrepreneur at a Time"* in Hispanic Business (July-August 2007, pp. 56-57)

Pub: Hispanic Business

Ed: Hildy Medina. **Description:** American Express OPEN is a program focusing on women business owners whose companies report revenues of $200,000 or more. The program offers the chance to win a free year of mentoring, marketing and technology assistance along with a $50,000 line of credit.

47296 ■ *"The Hispanic Business 100 Most Influential Hispanics"* in Hispanic Business (October 2007, pp. 30)

Pub: Hispanic Business

Description: Profiles of the one hundred Hispanic business leaders are presented.

47297 ■ *"Honoring Creativity"* in Playthings (Vol. 107, January 1, 2009, No. 1, pp. 28)

Pub: Reed Business Information

Contact: Jeff Greisch, President

Ed: Cliff Annicelli. **Description:** Toy & Game Inventors Expo is held annually in conjunction with the Chicago Toy & Game Fair. The event honors toy inventors in the categories of Game Design, Toy Design and Rising Stars, plus a lifetime achievement award. Profile of the company, Toying With Games, founded by Joyce Johnson and Colleen McCarthy-Evans are included in the article.

47298 ■ *"How I Did It: It Just Came Naturally"* in Inc. (November 2007, pp. 110-112)

Pub: Gruner & Jahr USA Publishing

Ed: Athena Schindelheim. **Description:** Profile of Bobbi Brown, CEO and founder of Bobbi Brown Cosmetics, designed to highlight a woman's natural look. Brown opened her first freestanding retail store recently that houses a makeup artistry school in the back.

47299 ■ *"How I Did It: Laurel Touby Mediabistro"* in Inc. (March 2008, pp. 124-126)

Pub: Gruner & Jahr USA Publishing

Ed: Eric Schine. **Description:** Profile of Laurel Touby and her business plan; Touby started Mediabistro as a series of parties that turned into an influential job listing and training Website for journalists. Last year she sold it for $23 million.

47300 ■ *"How Investors React When Women Join Boards"* in Harvard Business Review (Vol. 88, July-August 2010, No. 7-8, pp. 24)

Pub: Harvard Business School Publishing

Ed: Andrew O'Connell. **Description:** Research reveals a cognitive bias in blockholders regarding the presence of women on boards of directors despite evidence showing that diversity improves results.

47301 ■ *"How Not to Build a Website"* in Women Entrepreneur (December 24, 2008)

Pub: Entrepreneur Media Inc.

Ed: Erica Ruback; Joanie Reisen. **Description:** Tips for producing a unique and functional Website are given as well as a number of lessons a pair of entrepreneurs learned while trying to launch their networking website, MomSpace.com.

47302 ■ How Remarkable Women Lead: A Breakthrough Model for Work and Life

Pub: Crown Business

Ed: Joanna Barsh; Susie Cranston. **Released:** September 24, 2009. **Price:** $27.50. **Description:** An introduction to remarkable women, from Time Inc.'s Ann Moore to Xerox's Anne Mulcahy, who recount their inspiring struggles.

47303 ■ *How to Run Your Business Like a Girl: Successful Strategies from Entrepreneurial Women Who Made It Happen*

Pub: Adams Media Corporation

Contact: Gary Krebs, Director

E-mail: swatrous@adamsmedia.com

Ed: Elizabeth Cogswell Baskin. **Released:** September 2005. **Description:** Tour of three women entrepreneurs and their successful companies.

47304 ■ *"How to Set Up an Effective Home Office"* in Women Entrepreneur (August 22, 2008)

Pub: Entrepreneur Media Inc.

Ed: Laura Stack. **Description:** Checklist provides ways in which one can arrange their home office to provide the greatest efficiency which will allow maximum productivity and as a result the greater the chance of success.

47305 ■ *"How Sweet It Is: a Health Hardship Leads to Cupcake Commerce"* in Black Enterprise (Vol. 41, August 2010, No. 1, pp. 56)

Pub: Earl G. Graves Publishing Co. Inc.

Ed: Tamara E. Holmes. **Description:** Profile of Andra Hall, entrepreneur who started her cupcake business when her one-year-old daughter suffered from sleep apnea and wanted the flexibility to be with her baby. Hall and her husband refinanced their home in order to start the bakery.

47306 ■ How Women Make Money: Inspirational Stories and Practical Advice from Successful Canadian Entrepreneurs

Pub: Dundurn Press

Ed: Julie V. Watson. **Released:** April 1, 2004. **Price:** $24.99. **Description:** Collection of profiles, anecdotes, and practical advice and guides to help women take control of their lives, start a new business, and reach financial goals.

47307 ■ If You Have to Cry, Go Outside: And Other Things Your Mother Never Told You

Pub: HarperOne

Ed: Kelly Cutrone. **Released:** February 2, 2010. **Price:** $22.99. **Description:** Women's mentor advices on how to make it in one of the most competitive industries in the world, fashion. She has kicked people out of fashion shows, forced some of reality television's shiny start to fire their friends, and built her own company which is one of the most powerful public relations firms in the fashion business.

47308 ■ In the Company of Women: Canadian Women Talk About What It Takes to Start and Manage a Successful Business

Pub: HarperCollins Publishers Inc.

Ed: Katherine Gay. **Released:** 1998. **Description:** Information to help women start and run a small business in Canada.

47309 ■ *"In It For the Long Run"* in Business Journal-Serving Phoenix & the Valley of the Sun (Vol. 30, August 20, 2010, No. 50, pp. 1)

Pub: Phoenix Business Journal

Ed: Angela Gonzales. **Description:** Cancer survivor Helene Neville has finished a record-breaking 2,520-mile run in 93 days and then celebrated her 50th birthday despite being diagnosed with Hodgkins' lymphoma in 1991. Neveille, who is also a Phoenix area registered nurse, made stops along the way to promote her book, 'Nurses in Shape'. Neville also discusses how she fought her cancer through running.

47310 ■ *"In the Raw: Karyn Calabrese Brings Healthy Dining to a New Sophisticated Level"* in Black Enterprise (Vol. 41, September 2010)

Pub: Earl G. Graves Publishing Co. Inc.

Ed: Sonia Alleyne. **Description:** Profile of Karyn Calabrese whose businesses are based in Chicago, Illinois. Calabrese has launched a complete line of products (vitamins and beauty items), services (spa, chiropractic, and acupuncture treatments), and restaurants to bring health dining and lifestyles to a better level.

47311 ■ *International Handbook of Women and Small Business Entrepreneurship*
Pub: Edward Elgar Publishing, Incorporated
Ed: Fielden. **Released:** December 2006. **Price:** $50.00. **Description:** Practical initiatives and strategies for women entering small business entrepreneurial ventures are examined.

47312 ■ *"The Interview" in Crain's Cleveland Business (Vol. 30, June 22, 2009, No. 24, pp. 9)*
Pub: Crain Communications, Inc.
Description: In an interview with Mary K. Whitmer, partner at Kohrman Jackson & Krantz, she addresses issues facing the Northeast Ohio legal community. Ms. Whitmer is the new president of the Cleveland Metropolitan Bar Association.

47313 ■ *"Is It Time to Move to a Real Office?" in Women Entrepreneur (December 30, 2008)*
Pub: Entrepreneur Media Inc.
Ed: Aliza Sherman. **Description:** Before moving a company from a home-office to a real office it is important to make sure that the additional overhead that will be incurred by the move is comfortably covered and that the move is being done for the right reasons. Several women entrepreneurs who have moved their businesses from their homes to an actual rental space are profiled.

47314 ■ *"It's Not Rocket Science" in Hispanic Business (September 2007, pp. 30, 32)*
Pub: Hispanic Business
Ed: Hildy Medina. **Description:** Profile of France Cordova, president of Purdue University. Cordova has established many diversity programs at the school.

47315 ■ *"Kaminsky Back in the Business of Selling Her Chocolate Treats" in Business First Buffalo (October 5, 2007, pp. 4)*
Pub: American City Business Journals, Inc.
Ed: Tracey Drury. **Description:** Loretta Kaminsky, the original owner of Lou-Retta's Custom Chocolates brand, has decided to bring her products back into the market after winning a breach of contract lawsuit against Art Coco. Kaminsky sold her business to Art Coco in 2003, agreeing to the deal that Kaminsky will promote the products for two years in exchange for royalties and Art Coco's maintaining of product quality. Details of the distribution agreement with Wegmans, which will reintroduce Kaminsky's products are presented.

47316 ■ *"Katie's Cupcakes to Celebrate One-Year Anniversary" in Bellingham Business Journal (Vol. March 2010, pp. 3)*
Pub: Sound Publishing Inc.
Description: Katie Swanson, owner of Katie's Cupcakes, celebrated her firm's one-year anniversary with a fundraiser for the Whatcom Humane Society by offering free specialty cupcakes and other special events to the public. The specialty cupcakes will feature either a paw or bone and will be available throughout the month of March.

47317 ■ *Kitchen Table Entrepreneurs: How Eleven Women Escaped Poverty and Became Their Own Bosses*
Pub: Westview Press
Ed: Martha Shirk, Anna S. Wadia. **Released:** October 2008. **Price:** $16.95. **Description:** Profile of eleven successful women entrepreneurs.

47318 ■ *"Know Your Bones: Take Your Bone Health Seriously" in Women In Business (Vol. 62, June 2010, No. 2, pp. 40)*
Pub: American Business Women's Association
Description: Bone health for women with postmenopausal osteoporosis is encouraged to help create an appropriate health plan that includes exercise, diet and medication. Questions to consider when discussing possible plans with health care providers are presented.

47319 ■ *Lessons of a Lipstick Queen: Finding and Developing the Great Idea That*

Can Change Your Life
Pub: Simon and Schuster Inc.
Contact: Carolyn Reidy, President
E-mail: carolyn.reidy@simonandschuster.com
Ed: Poppy King. **Released:** May 1, 2009. **Price:** $14.00. **Description:** Poppy King tells how she started her lipstick brand at age eighteen. She reveals how she managed to launch her business using a good idea and finding financing, marketing the product and how she became successful.

47320 ■ *"Let It Shine: Organization Helps Disadvantaged Girls See Their Worth" in Black Enterprise (Vol. 38, February 2008, No. 7, pp. 142)*
Pub: Earl G. Graves Publishing Co. Inc.
Ed: George Alexander. **Description:** Wilson Mourning, founder of the clothing label Honey Child, attributes her success to her mother and other positive women who helped her through her adolescence. Mourning created a mentoring organization that helps young girls in the Miami, Florida area to develop life skills.

47321 ■ *"A Lifetime of Giving: Food Bank CEO Fights Hunger One Mouth At a Time" in Black Enterprise (Vol. 41, November 2010, No. 4, pp. 86)*
Pub: Earl G. Graves Publishing Co. Inc.
Ed: Tamara E. Holmes. **Description:** Profile of Valerie Traore, CEO of Food Bank of South Jersey. Traore stresses the importance of volunteerism that she learned from her grandparents. Hunger relief became her passion when she served as a temp office worker for the Maryland Food Bank in Baltimore. She earned her Bachelor's of Science in management and has dedicated herself to a career in nonprofit service.

47322 ■ *"Lunch Box Maker Gives Back" in Marketing to Women (Vol. 23, November 2010, No. 11, pp. 5)*
Pub: EPM Communications Inc.
Contact: Ira Mayer, President
E-mail: imayer@epmcom.com
Description: Female entrepreneurs launched a new program called, 'Share Your Lunch Project' that encourages mothers to give back and replace their child's lunchbox with their eco-friendly lunch boxes, which are available at select retailers. All proceeds from the project will benefit the World Food Program USA, which feeds children in developing countries.

47323 ■ *Martha, Inc.*
Pub: John Wiley and Sons, Inc.
Ed: Christopher Byron. **Released:** 2002. **Price:** $28.00. **Description:** Profile of Martha Stewart's rise from working class to a billionaire businesswoman is presented. The book covers Stewart's power struggles and personal conflicts as well as her triumphs.

47324 ■ *Minding Her Own Business, 4th Ed.*
Pub: Sphinx Publishing
Ed: Jan Zobel. **Released:** January 1, 2005. **Price:** $16.95. **Description:** A guide to taxes and financial records for women entrepreneurs is presented.

47325 ■ *"Mixing Business and Pleasure On the Green" in Black Enterprise (Vol. 41, October 2010, No. 3, pp. 65)*
Pub: Earl G. Graves Publishing Co. Inc.
Ed: Annya M. Lott. **Description:** Glow Golf, sponsored by Glow Sports, will offer instruction to 150 female corporate executives and entrepreneurs to learn the fundamentals of the game of golf.

47326 ■ *"Mom of Eight Named Regional Minority Small Business Person of the Year" in Daily News (November 8, 2010)*
Pub: Daily News
Ed: Suzanne Ulbrich. **Description:** Profile of Melissa Leifheit, mother of eight and named Regional Minority Small Business Person of the Year by the North Carolina Small Business Administration.

47327 ■ *The Mommy Manifesto: How to Use Our Power to Think Big, Break Limitations and Achieve Success*
Pub: John Wiley & Sons, Inc.
Ed: Kim Lavine. **Released:** September 1, 2009. **Price:** $24.95. **Description:** A new women's revolution will help women take control of their careers,

their lives, and their economic future. The book shows how mom's control the economy and have the power to become successful entrepreneurs.

47328 ■ *More Than a Pink Cadillac*
Pub: McGraw-Hill
Ed: Jim Underwood. **Released:** 2002. **Price:** $23.95. **Description:** Profile of Mary Kay Ash who turned her $5,000 investment into a billion-dollar corporation. Ash's nine principles that form the foundation of her company's global success are outlined. Stories from her sales force leaders share ideas for motivating employees, impressing customers and building a successful company. The book emphasizes the leadership skills required to drive performance in any successful enterprise.

47329 ■ *"My Day" in Business Strategy Review (Vol. 21, Autumn 2010, No. 3, pp. 77)*
Pub: Blackwell Publishers Ltd.
Ed: Julie Meyer. **Description:** Profile of Julie Meyer, who rose to prominence as cofounder of the entrepreneurial network, First Tuesday; Meyer sold the firm for $50 million in 2000.

47330 ■ *"My Day" in Business Strategy Review (Vol. 21, Autumn 2010, No. 3, pp. 77)*
Pub: Wiley-Blackwell
Ed: Julie Meyer. **Description:** Julie Meyer shot to prominence as cofounder of the entrepreneurial network, First Tuesday. The firm was sold for $50 million in 2000.

47331 ■ *My Life From Scratch: A Sweet Journey of Starting Over, One Cake at a Time*
Pub: Broadway Books
Contact: David Drake, Manager
E-mail: ddrake@randomhouse.com
Released: June 8, 2010. **Price:** $14.00. **Description:** Lively account of Old World recipes, Bullock-Prado, a former Hollywood film developer and sister to actress Sandra Bullock, recounts the joys and heartbreak of running her own patisserie in Montpelier, Vermont. Having fled Los Angeles with her husband, Ray for the simpler pleasures of a small town near the Green Mountains, she opened her own bake shop, Gesine Confectionary in 2004, mostly on the fame of the macaroons she refashioned from her German mother's favorite almond treat, mandelhoernchen (and the casual mention of her sister in an interview). Her memoir follows one day in a busy baker's life, from waking at 3 a.m. to prepare the batter and bake her croissants, scones, and sticky buns, before opening her shop at 7 a.m., through the hectic lunch, and 3 p.m. tea time.

47332 ■ *My So-Called Freelance Life: How to Survive and Thrive as a Creative Professional for Hire*
Pub: Seal Press
Contact: Charlie Winton, Manager
Ed: Michelle Goodman. **Released:** October 1, 2008. **Price:** $15.95. **Description:** Guidebook for women wishing to start a freelancing business; tips, advice, how-to's and all the information needed to survive working from home are included.

47333 ■ *"Nancy Hughes Anthony" in Canadian Business (Vol. 81, October 13, 2008, No. 17, pp. 104)*
Pub: Rogers Media Ltd.
Ed: Andy Holloway. **Description:** Profile of Nancy Hughes Anthony, who believes her experience operating large enterprises as a public servant helped her earn positions that ultimately brought her to her current position as chief executive and president of the Canadian Bankers Association. She also thinks there should be more public-private sector coordination within industries.

47334 ■ *National Directory of Woman-Owned Business Firms*
Pub: Business Research Services Inc.
Contact: Thomas D. Johnson, President
URL(s): www.sba8a.com. **Released:** Annual; Latest edition 13th. **Price:** $295, Individuals paperback. **Covers:** 30,000 woman-owned businesses. **Entries include:** Company name, address, phone, name and title of contact, minority group, certification status, date founded, number of employees, description of

products or services, sales volume, government contracting experience, references. **Arrangement:** Standard Industrial Classification (SIC) code, geographical. **Indexes:** Alphabetical by company.

47335 ■ "Natural Attraction: Bath and Body Products Maker Delivers Wholesome Goodness" in Black Enterprise (Vol. 38, November 2007, No. 4)
Pub: Earl G. Graves Publishing Co. Inc.
Ed: Kaylyn Kendall Dines. **Description:** Profile of Dawn Fitch, creator of Pooka Inc., manufacturer of handmade bath and body products that contain no preservatives. Sales are expected to reach $750,000 for 2007.

47336 ■ "NAWBO Takes the Stage at Press Conference for Small Business Jobs, Credit and Tax Relief Acts" in Internet Wire (June 17, 2010)
Pub: Comtex
Description: A survey of the National Association of Women Business Owners reported optimism returning and women business owners are ready to invest in job creation. The Small Business Jobs Tax Relief Act will aid in their progress.

47337 ■ "Need a Course Correction? Let ABWA Be Your Navigator" in Women In Business (Vol. 62, September 2010, No. 3, pp. 6)
Pub: American Business Women's Association
Ed: Rene Street. **Description:** It is believed that the American Business Women's Association (ABWA) has the ability to help women in their quest for greater success. The organization also has the energy needed to move on to the next stage for women in business. ABWA's members have taken the initiative to embrace the group's potential.

47338 ■ "Negotiating Muscle" in Black Enterprise (Vol. 38, February 2008, No. 7, pp. 70)
Pub: Earl G. Graves Publishing Co. Inc.
Ed: Sonia Alleyne. **Description:** Negotiating historically has been a barrier for women in business, the book, 'Ask For It: How Women Can Use the Power of Negotiation to Get What They Really Want' helps professional females identify and create great business opportunities.

47339 ■ "New York Collection Agency's Bribery Case Resolved" in Collections & Credit Risk (Vol. 15, August 1, 2010, No. 7, pp. 19)
Pub: SourceMedia Inc.
Description: Criminal conviction and civil settlement in a bribery scam and Medicaid scam involving H.I.S. Holdings Inc. and owner Deborah Kantor is examined.

47340 ■ "NJ Tries to Push Stimulus Funds to Minorities" in Philadelphia Business Journal (Vol. 28, September 25, 2009, No. 32, pp. 1)
Pub: American City Business Journals
Ed: Athena D. Merritt. **Description:** New Jersey Governor Jon S. Corzine signed an executive order that seeks to ease the way for minority and women-owned business to take on federal stimulus-funded work. New Jersey has also forged new relations with different organizations to reduce the time and cost of certifications for businesses.

47341 ■ "Nonprofit Ready to Get More Girls into 'STEM' Jobs" in Austin Business JournalInc. (Vol. 29, December 25, 2009, No. 42, pp. 1)
Pub: American City Business Journals
Ed: Sandra Zaragoza. **Description:** Girlstart has completed its $1.5 million capital campaign to buy the building it will care the Girlstart Tech Center. Girlstart is a nonprofit organization that prepares girls for science, technology, engineering and mathematics or STEM careers. Details of the program are highlighted.

47342 ■ "Nonprofits May Lose MBE Status in MD" in Boston Business Journal (Vol. 29, September 2, 2011, No. 17, pp. 1)
Pub: American City Business Journals Inc.
Ed: Scott Dance. **Description:** A business group has been pushing to bar nonprofits from Maryland's Minority Business program. Nonprofits have been

found to take a large portion of state contracts intended for women- and minority-owned businesses. The group is also crafting proposed legislation to remove nonprofits from the program.

47343 ■ "Now Entering A Secure Area" in Women Entrepreneur (January 14, 2009)
Pub: Entrepreneur Media Inc.
Ed: Aliza Sherman. **Description:** Despite the fact that the field of government intelligence and security is dominated by males, many women entrepreneurs are finding opportunities for their products and services in homeland security. Profiles of several women who have found such opportunities are included.

47344 ■ Off-Ramps and On-Ramps: Keeping Talented Women on the Road to Success
Pub: Harvard Business School Press
Ed: Sylvia Ann Hewlett. **Price:** $29.95. **Description:** Hewlett (founding president for the Center for Work-Life Policy) examines why many women exit their careers, taking 'off-ramps' (leaving altogether) or 'scenic routes' (opting to work part-time), often during critical, competitive times. She also provides valuable suggestions for companies hoping to retain talented employees of any gender.

47345 ■ "On the Green: Sheila Johnson Adds $35 Million Golf Resort To Her Expanding Portfolio" in Black Enterprise (January 2008)
Pub: Earl G. Graves Publishing Co. Inc.
Ed: Donna M. Owens. **Description:** Profile of Sheila Johnson, CEO of Salamander Hospitality LLC, made history when she purchased the Innisbrook Resort and Golf Club, making her the first African American woman to own this type of property. The resort includes four championship golf courses, six swimming pools, four restaurants, eleven tennis courts, three conference halls, and a nature preserve.

47346 ■ "On Your Marks, American Airlines, Now Vote!" in Benzinga.com (, 2011)
Pub: Benzinga.com
Ed: Benzinga Staff. **Description:** Wedding planner, Aviva Samuels, owner of Kiss the Planner boutique wedding and event planning agency in Florida, says that winning this contest would help her increase her knowledge base and provide in-depth, personal experience offering more destination wedding destinations.

47347 ■ "The One Thing That's Holding Back Your Wellness Program" in Employee Benefit News (Vol. 25, December 1, 2011, No. 15, pp. 8)
Pub: SourceMedia Inc.
Ed: Kelley M. Butler. **Description:** A 13-year study shows that women who sat for more than six hours a day were 94 percent more likely to die during the study period. Most women sit at their desks an average of 7.7 hours while at work.

47348 ■ "Out Front and Strong" in WorkingUSA (Vol. 11, December 2008, No. 4, pp. 477)
Pub: Blackwell Publishers Ltd.
Ed: Jessica Wilkerson. **Description:** History of the Tennessee Committee on Occupational Safety and Health that formed in East Tennessee in 1979 is explored. The article addresses how local women contributed to the organization at the grassroots.

47349 ■ "Packing Chic" in Black Enterprise (Vol. 38, February 2008, No. 7, pp. 154)
Pub: Earl G. Graves Publishing Co. Inc.
Ed: Sonai Alleyne. **Description:** Profile of Angela Theodora's leather overnight bags that offer a variety of smart compartments for the business traveler.

47350 ■ The Pampered Chef
Pub: Doubleday Broadway Publishing Group
Ed: Doris Christopher. **Description:** The Pampered Chef has been selling high quality kitchen tools through in-home cooking demonstration for twenty-five years. CEO and founder explains how she turned her one woman company into a a business with sales approaching $1 billion. Christopher shares her story

by providing the foundation, strategies for entrepreneurs, setting priorities, knowing when to expand and when to slow growth, and dealing with adversity.

47351 ■ "Passionate About Empowering Women" in Women In Business (Vol. 63, Spring 2011, No. 1, pp. 24)
Pub: American Business Women's Association
Ed: Leigh Elmore. **Description:** Krazy Coupon Ladies cofounder Joanie Demer shares her views about her book, 'Pick Another Checkout Lane, Honey', which she coauthored with Heather Wheeler. Demer believes using coupons is for everyone who wants to save money. She also believes that extreme couponing is not an exercise for those who lack organizational ability since it requires planning and discipline.

47352 ■ "Pedal to the Medal" in Small Business Opportunities (Summer 2010)
Pub: Harris Publications Inc.
Ed: Chuck Green. **Description:** Profile of Darlene Miller who became and partner and eventually took over Permac Industries, a firm that specializes in precision machine products.

47353 ■ "People and Places" in Entrepreneur (Vol. 36, February 2008, No. 2, pp. 12)
Pub: Entrepreneur Media Inc.
Ed: Rieva Lesonsky. **Description:** Websites of different organizations that can provide entrepreneurs with business help are presented. Business-related events such as the Women in Charge conference and Xerox Smart Business Symposium are mentioned.

47354 ■ "The People Who Influence You the Most - Believe In You" in Women In Business (Vol. 62, September 2010, No. 3, pp. 9)
Pub: American Business Women's Association
Description: The president of the American Business Women's Association (ABWA) talks about her experiences in the organization. She believes that the dynamic women with whom she worked with helped her shape the organization into one that her predecessors believed it could become. The importance of dealing with challenges while making each experience an opportunity to learn is also discussed.

47355 ■ "Physics for Females" in Occupational Outlook Quarterly (Vol. 55, Summer 2011, No. 2, pp. 22)
Pub: U.S. Bureau of Labor Statistics
Description: Free resources to help females investigate careers in medical physics and health physics are available from the American Physical Society. The booklet is designed for girls in middle and high school and describes the work of 15 women who use physics to solve medical mysteries, discover planets, research new materials, and more.

47356 ■ "Pick A Trademark You Can Protect" in Women Entrepreneur (November 3, 2008)
Pub: Entrepreneur Media Inc.
Ed: Nina L. Kaufman. **Description:** Provides information regarding trademarks, how to choose a name that will win approval from the U.S. Patent and Trademark Office, and how to choose a trademark that one can protect.

47357 ■ "Play It Safe or Take a Stand?" in Harvard Business Review (Vol. 88, November 2010, No. 11, pp. 139)
Pub: Harvard Business School Publishing
Ed: Trish Gorman Clifford, Jay Barney. **Description:** A fictitious leadership scenario is presented, with contributors providing comments and recommendations. A female executive ponders whether to assert a point of view on a new venture. Both experts agree that after providing careful analysis of pros and cons, the executive should come to a well-informed conclusion.

47358 ■ "The Power of ABWA" in Women In Business (Vol. 62, September 2010, No. 3, pp. 36)
Pub: American Business Women's Association
Ed: Leigh Elmore. **Description:** Information about the internship received by Erica Rockley at American Business Women's Association (ABWA) headquarters

is presented. Rockley received heartfelt professional advice the days she spent at the office. She also learned the importance of networking.

47359 ■ *"The Power of Commitment: Mere Motivation Is Often Not Enough To Achieve Your Goals" in Black Enterprise (November 2007)*
Pub: Earl G. Graves Publishing Co. Inc.
Ed: Tamara E. Holmes. **Description:** Profile of Michelle Tucker Kirk who opened her bridal shop in 2006. Kirk explains how her commitment and determination were keys to the company's success. Five signs to help any would-be entrepreneur discover if they are truly committed to a business idea are listed.

47360 ■ *Prepare to Be a Teen Millionaire*
Pub: Health Communications, Inc.
Contact: Peter Vegso, President
Ed: Robyn Collins; Kimberly Spinks Burleson. **Released:** April 1, 2008. **Price:** $16.95. **Description:** Business reference for any teenager wishing to become a successful entrepreneur; advice is given from successful teenage millionaires. Topics covered include: choosing a business name, type, and location; use of the Internet; legal issues; branding, sales, and marketing; funding and financial management; return on investment; retirement; development of a sound business plan; and certification for minority or women-owned companies.

47361 ■ *"Profile: Lynda Gratton" in Business Strategy Review (Vol. 21, Autumn 2010, No. 3, pp. 74)*
Pub: Wiley-Blackwell
Ed: Stuart Crainer. **Description:** The early 20th Century marked the dawn of modern enterprise management, and no one influenced its practice more than Frederick W. Taylor, inventor of 'scientific management'. This radical transformation of management and among the few thinkers most influencing this transformation is Lynda Gratton, London Business School Professor of Management Practice.

47362 ■ *"Program for Women Entrepreneurs: Tips for Surviving this Economy" in Crain's Detroit Business (Vol. 25, June 22, 2009, No. 25)*
Pub: Crain Communications Inc. - Detroit
Description: Michigan Leadership Institute for Women Entrepreneurs will hold its third and final program, 'Tough Times are Temporary, but Tough People are Permanent' at the Davenport University in Livonia, Michigan.

47363 ■ *"Public Opinion" in Entrepreneur (Vol. 36, April 2008, No. 4, pp. 28)*
Pub: Entrepreneur Media, Inc.
Ed: Aliza Sherman. **Description:** According to a 2007 report from Group and Organization Management, women in top positions can lead publicly traded companies to stock price and earnings growth. Some women business owners say that going public has provided them with the capital to grow. Details on the potential of women-managed publicly traded companies are discussed.

47364 ■ *"Queen Bees: All Sting, No Honey" in Business Horizons (September-October 2007, pp. 348)*
Pub: Elsevier Technology Publications
Ed: Catherine M. Dalton. **Description:** Female rivalry or competition in the workplace and other domains are explained and compared to the behavior of honeybees. Novels and other works on the topic of competition among women are discussed.

47365 ■ *"Real-Life Coursework for Real-Life Business People" in Women In Business (Vol. 63, Summer 2011, No. 2, pp. 22)*
Pub: American Business Women's Association
Ed: Leigh Elmore. **Description:** American Business Women's Association National Women's Leadership Conference provides members with academic business training courses. Members can take a variety of MBA-level courses that are taught by University of Kansas School of Business professors. Courses include marketing, management, leadership and communication and decision making.

47366 ■ *"The Right Remedy: Entrepreneur's Success Is a Matter of Life and Death" in Black Enterprise (Vol. 38, February 2008, No. 7, pp. 46)*
Pub: Earl G. Graves Publishing Co. Inc.
Ed: Tamara E. Holmes. **Description:** Profile of Leah Brown, whose company conducts clinical trials to determine if specific drugs will relieve particular symptoms. Her company will also visit physician's offices to make certain doctors are following proper protocol for a clinical trial or will collect data from patients.

47367 ■ *"The Role of Human and Financial Capital in the Profitability and Growth of Women-Owned Small Firms" in Journal of Small Business Management*
Pub: Blackwell Publishing Inc.
Contact: Gordon Tibbitts, President
Ed: Susan Coleman. **Description:** Examines the relationship between the human and financial capital in both men and women-owned businesses and firm performance in the service and retail sectors.

47368 ■ *The Savvy Gal's Guide to Online Networking*
Pub: Booklocker.com Inc.
Ed: Diane K. Daneilson, Lindsey Pollak. **Released:** August 10, 2007. **Price:** $14.95. **Description:** It is a truth universally acknowledged that a woman in search of a fabulous career must be in want of networking opportunities. Or so Jane Austen would say if she were writing, or more likely, blogging today. So begins the must-read guide to networking in the 21st Century. Authors and networking experts share the nuts, bolts and savvy secrets that businesswomen need in order to use technology to build professional relationships.

47369 ■ *The Savvy Girl's Guide to Online Networking*
Pub: Booklocker.com Inc.
Ed: Diane K. Danielson; Lindsey Pollak. **Released:** August 10, 2007. **Price:** $14.95. **Description:** The book offers tips, tactics and etiquette for businesswomen wishing to build professional relationships via email, online networks, blogs, and message boards.

47370 ■ *Secrets of Millionaire Moms*
Pub: McGraw-Hill
Ed: Tamara Monosoff. **Released:** March 2007. **Price:** $16.95. **Description:** Profiles of successful women/mother entrepreneurs are presented, including Julie Clark, Lane Nemeth, Lillian Vernon, Victoria Knight, Rachel Ashwell and other powerful businesswomen.

47371 ■ *"The Secret's Out About Kansas City" in Women In Business (Vol. 61, August-September 2009, No. 4, pp. 26)*
Pub: American Business Women's Association
Ed: Leigh Elmore. **Description:** Missouri's Kansas City offers various attractions, such as public fountains, the 18th and Vine Historic Districts for jazz enthusiasts, and the Crossroads Arts District with a variety of art galleries. Details on other cultural attractions and neighborhoods in the city are presented.

47372 ■ *"Secrets To Trade Show Success" in Women Entrepreneur (September 12, 2008)*
Pub: Entrepreneur Media Inc.
Ed: Lesley Spencer Pyle. **Description:** Trade shows require an enormous amount of work, but they are an investment that can pay off handsomely because they allow a business to get their product or service in front of their target market. Advice regarding trade shows is given including selecting the correct venue, researching the affair and following up on leads obtained at the event.

47373 ■ *"Shari's Berries Founder Shuts Last of Her Stores" in Sacramento Business Journal (Vol. 28, September 2, 2011, No. 27, pp. 1)*
Pub: Sacramento Business Journal
Ed: Kelly Johnson. **Description:** Sacramento, California-based Shari's Berries owner Shari Fitzpatrick closed the company's last three stores called

The Berry Factory. Fitzpatrick also filed for business bankruptcy protection. The weak economy is blamed for the company's failure.

47374 ■ *"Shop Around" in Houston Chronicle (December 7, 2010, pp. 3)*
Pub: Houston Chronicle
Ed: Tara Dooley. **Description:** Profile of Diana Candida and Maria Martinez who partnered to open Beatniks, a shop carrying vintage clothing, art from various artists, dance shoes, and jewelry.

47375 ■ *"Sign Up To Grow Your Business, Generate Jobs" in Women Entrepreneur (November 25, 2008)*
Pub: Entrepreneur Media Inc.
Ed: Eve Gumpel. **Description:** Nell Merlino has announced the new Make Mine A Million-Dollar Race, which aims to encourage hundreds of thousands of women entrepreneurs to grow their business to revenue goals of $250,00, $500,000 or $1 million and more as well as create 800,000 new jobs in an attempt to stimulate the nation's economy.

47376 ■ *"Six Tips To Maximize Networking Opportunities" in Women Entrepreneur (November 3, 2008)*
Pub: Entrepreneur Media Inc.
Ed: Tamara Monosoff. **Description:** Networking events fall into the realm of business development as opposed to immediate sales opportunities. It is important to remember that these events provide a chance to build relationships that may someday help one's business. Tips to help make the most out of networking events are provided.

47377 ■ *"So You Want to Start a Business?" in Women Entrepreneur (August 5, 2008)*
Pub: Entrepreneur Media Inc.
Ed: Cynthia McKay. **Description:** Advice for taking an idea and turning it into a legitimate business is given.

47378 ■ *"Some Women Warming Up to Economy's Prospects" in Crain's Cleveland Business (Vol. 30, June 1, 2009, No. 21, pp. 9)*
Pub: Crain Communications, Inc.
Ed: Mark Dodosh. **Description:** According to a recent survey conducted by the Center for Women's Business Research and KeyBank focusing on the experience and opinions of women business owners, 48 percent of respondents believe the economy will improve over the next six months. Statistical data included.

47379 ■ *"Speak Better: Five Tips for Polished Presentations" in Women Entrepreneur (September 19, 2008)*
Pub: Entrepreneur Media Inc.
Ed: Suzannah Baum. **Description:** Successful entrepreneurs agree that exemplary public speaking skills are among the core techniques needed to propel their business forward. A well-delivered presentation can result in securing a new distribution channel, gaining new customers, locking into a new referral stream or receiving extra funding.

47380 ■ *"The Stars Align: Trail Blazers, Headline Makers on 2007 List Set Example for Others" in Hispanic Business (October 2007, pp. 22)*
Pub: Hispanic Business
Description: Top one hundred most influential Hispanic business leaders comprise of 66 percent men and 34 percent women, distributed by 27 percent in government, 42 percent corporate, 11 percent education, five percent art and entertainment, and 15 percent in other sectors. Statistical data included.

47381 ■ *"State's Glass Ceiling Gets Higher" in Business Journal-Milwaukee (Vol. 25, October 5, 2007, No. 1, pp. A1)*
Pub: American City Business Journals, Inc.
Ed: Jennifer Batog. **Description:** Report showed that more than a third of Wisconsin's fifty largest companies have no female executive officers, and the number of companies with at least one woman at top departments has also decreased since 2005. Companies lacking women at upper management levels risk

jeopardizing their firms' vitality as diversity in executive offices leads to diverse ideas that can help in relating better to customers and clients.

47382 ■ *"A Step Up" in Black Enterprise (Vol. 38, January 2008, No. 6, pp. 53)*
Pub: Earl G. Graves Publishing Co. Inc.
Description: Professional black women can get advice from a nonprofit program called ASCENT: Leading Multicultural Women to the Top. ASCENT's sessions last six months and are held at both Tuck School of Business at Dartmouth and UCLA Anderson School of Management.

47383 ■ *"Stylish Successes" in Women In Business (Vol. 61, October-November 2009, No. 5, pp. 12)*
Pub: American Business Women's Association
Ed: Leigh Elmore; Megan L. Reese. **Description:** Amanda Horan Kennedy, Angela Samuels, Barbara Nast Saletan, and Patty Nast Canton are career women who ventured into entrepreneurship. They are deemed to possess networking and teamwork skills that ensured their success in the garment industry.

47384 ■ *"Susan Leger Ferraro Built a $7.2 Million Day Care Business. Now She Wants To Expand-And Cash Out" in Inc. (January 2008, pp. 50-53)*
Pub: Gruner & Jahr USA Publishing
Ed: Dalia Fahmy. **Description:** Profile of Susan Leger Ferraro who wants to expand her chain of day care centers into Florida and California and sell part of her 87 percent stake to reduce financial risk.

47385 ■ *"Sylvie Collection Offers a Feminine Perspective and Voice in Male Dominated Bridal Industry" in Benzinga.com (October 29, 2011)*
Pub: Benzinga.com
Ed: Benzinga Staff. **Description:** Bridal jewelry designer Sylvie Levine has created over 1,000 customizable styles of engagement rings and wedding bands and is reaching out to prospective new brides through a new Website, interactive social media campaign and monthly trunk show appearances.

47386 ■ *Table Talk: The Savvy Girl's Alternative to Networking*
Pub: AuthorHouse
Ed: Diane Danielson. **Released:** April 1, 2003. **Price:** $17.50. **Description:** Let's face it. Women and men are different. So why should we all have to network in the same way? And, why should women have to 'network' at all? Between family and work responsibilities, the idea of pressing flesh at some not-very-festive cocktail party is right up there in appeal with a root canal. But what if women could find a way to make career boosting connections that are actually fun? Enter 'talk talk', a new way to network for time-pressed, professional women.

47387 ■ *"Tamara Vrooman" in Canadian Business (Vol. 80, November 19, 2007, No. 23, pp. 9)*
Pub: Rogers Media
Ed: Regan Ray. **Description:** Profile of Tamara Vrooman, newly appointed CEO of Canada's largest credit union, Vancity. Vrooman believes that Vancity has an advantage over big bank when it comes to the flexibility of products the company offers. The role of Vancity and credit unions in the banking sector of Canada is discussed.

47388 ■ *"The Tapestry of Life" in Women In Business (Vol. 61, December 2009, No. 6, pp. 8)*
Pub: American Business Women's Association
Ed: Kathleen Leighton. **Description:** Suzanne Fanch, co-owner of the Devil's Thumb Ranch, discusses the family and career-related influences that helped her to achieve success as a small business proprietor. She advises that opportunities should be treated as building blocks towards success. Fanch's involvement in advocacies that take care of the welfare of community, children, and environment is also discussed.

47389 ■ *"Teaneck Resident Chairs National Minority Business Group" in Record (January 5, 2011)*
Pub: Record
Ed: Andrew Tangel. **Description:** National Minority Business Council Inc. is a trade group for minority women- and veteran-owned small businesses. Ben Jones began his term as chairman of the group in January 2011.

47390 ■ *"Ten Ways to Save on Business Travel" in Women Entrepreneur (November 21, 2008)*
Pub: Entrepreneur Media Inc.
Ed: Julie Moline. **Description:** Advice regarding ways in which to save money when traveling for business is given.

47391 ■ *"Tied to Home: Female Owned Businesses Export Less, And It's Not Just Because They're Smaller" in Canadian Business (April 14, 2008)*
Pub: Rogers Media
Ed: Lauren McKeon. **Description:** Only 12 percent of small and midsized enterprises that are run by women export their products and services. Government agencies can be more proactive in promoting the benefits of exporting by including women in case studies and recruiting women as mentors. Exporting provides great growth potential especially for the service sector where women have an advantage.

47392 ■ *"To Live and Thrive in L.A." in Canadian Business (Vol. 81, October 13, 2008, No. 17, pp. 78)*
Pub: Rogers Media Ltd.
Ed: Rachel Pulfer. **Description:** Toronto entrepreneur Shereen Arazm thrived in Los Angeles, California as the queen of nightlife. Arazm holds or has held ownership stakes in bars, nightspots and restaurants that include the Geisha House, Concorde, Shag, Parc and Central, and Terroni L.A.

47393 ■ *"Toes for Business" in Hispanic Business (October 2007, pp. 10, 12)*
Pub: Hispanic Business
Ed: Gabriel Rodriguez. **Description:** Prima ballerinas, Lorena and Lorna Feijoo, have increased box office sales by at least 30 to 40 percent. A discussion with Pedro Pablo Pena, artistic director of the Miami Hispanic Ballet Corps and founder of the first Choreographic Workshop of Havana is included.

47394 ■ *"Too Much Information?" in Black Enterprise (Vol. 37, December 2006, No. 5, pp. 59)*
Pub: Earl G. Graves Publishing Co. Inc.
Ed: James C. Johnson. **Description:** African American business owners often face the dilemma of whether or not to divulge their minority status when soliciting new customers and financial institutions. The quality of the products or services is always the key factor and race should never define one's business; however, it is appropriate to market oneself as a minority or women-owned business, especially if the company is in an industry where those clients are offered top-tier contracts.

47395 ■ *"Top 50" in Entrepreneur (Vol. 35, November 2007, No. 11, pp. 38)*
Pub: Entrepreneur Media Inc.
Description: List of the 50 fastest-growing women-led businesses in North America is presented.

47396 ■ *Tough Choices: A Memoir*
Pub: Penguin Group
Ed: Carly Florina. **Released:** October 2006. **Price:** $24.95. **Description:** Former woman CEO at Hewlett-Packard is profiled.

47397 ■ *"Transform Your Life" in Black Enterprise (Vol. 37, January 2007, No. 6, pp. 14)*
Pub: Earl G. Graves Publishing Co. Inc.
Description: Through the magazine, television and radio programs, events, and the website, the various platforms of Black Enterprise will provide the tools necessary to achieve success in business ventures, career aspirations, and personal goals.

47398 ■ *The Trump Card: Playing to Win in Work and Life*
Pub: Touchstone/Simon & Schuster Inc.
Ed: Ivanka Trump. **Released:** October 12, 2009. **Price:** $24.99. **Description:** Profile of Ivanka Trump, the daughter of Donald and Ivana Trump; she shares the life lessons and hard-won insights that have made her successful in the business world.

47399 ■ *"Turning Bright Ideas Into Profitable Businesses" in Inside Business (Vol. 13, September-October 2011, No. 5, pp. SS6)*
Pub: Great Lakes Publishing Co.
Ed: Susan Keen Flynn. **Description:** Startup Lakewood was launched by Mickie Rinehart. She provides free resources to entrepreneurs in the city in order to help them turn their small business vision into reality.

47400 ■ *"Twenty Years of Advocacy and Education" in Women Entrepreneur (January 18, 2009)*
Pub: Entrepreneur Media Inc.
Ed: Eve Gumpel. **Description:** Profile of Sharon Hadary who served as executive director of the Center for Women's Business Research for two decades; Hadary discusses what she has learned about women business owners, their impact on the economy and what successful business owners share in common.

47401 ■ *"Two Local Bakers Winners of TV's 'Cupcake Wars'" in Toledo Blade (July 6, 2011)*
Pub: Toledo Times
Description: Winners of cable network Food Channel's Cupcake Wars, Lori Jacobs and Dana Iliev own Cake in a Cup in Toledo, Ohio. The partners shop features creative cupcakes with names such as Monkey Business, Pretty in Pink, and Tropical Getaway.

47402 ■ *Use What You've Got*
Pub: Portfolio Publishing
Ed: Barbara Corcoran, Bruce Littlefield. **Released:** 2003. **Price:** $24.95. **Description:** Founder and chairman of New York's premier real estate company, the Corcoran Group, shares her successes in the real estate industry. The book offers tips and pointers to salespeople, entrepreneurs and business people alike. Corcoran explains how she went from waiting tables and borrowed $1,000 from a boyfriend to build her real estate company into the industry's powerhouse.

47403 ■ *"Virginia Albanese: President and CEO" in Inside Business (Vol. 13, September-October 2011, No. 5, pp. NC4)*
Pub: Great Lakes Publishing Co.
Ed: Jeannie Roberts. **Description:** Profile of Virginia Albanese, CEO of FedEx's Custom Critical Division in Akron, Ohio. Albanese discusses her philosophy on business leadership.

47404 ■ *"Want a Facial With That Steak?" in Charlotte Observer (February 5, 2007)*
Pub: Knight-Ridder/Tribune Business News
Ed: Jen Aronoff. **Description:** Profile of Burke Myotherapy Massage & Spa and Schell's Bistro. Lynn Shell moved her massage therapy business into a 106-year old home that had been used as a restaurant. She opened her own eatery on the first floor and offers massage therapy upstairs.

47405 ■ *"The Way I Work: Kim Kleeman" in Inc. (October 2007, pp. 110-112, 114)*
Pub: Gruner & Jahr USA Publishing
Ed: Leigh Buchanan. **Description:** Profile of Kim Kleemna, founder and president of ShakespeareSquared, a firm that develops educational materials, including lesson plans, teacher guides, activity workbooks, and discussion guides for large publishers. Kleeman talks about the challenges she faces running her nearly all-women company while maintaining a balance with her family.

47406 ■ *"We Were Strutting Our Stuff" in Women In Business (Vol. 63, Summer 2011, No. 2, pp. 10)*
Pub: American Business Women's Association
Ed: Rene Street, Leigh Elmore. **Description:** American Business Women's Association's STRUT relay race event helped raise awareness of the group in

the United States. The event also provided excellent team-building exercises for ABWA chapters. It also helped participants boost their leadership and business skills.

47407 ▪ *"The Weeks Ahead' in Crain's New York Business (Vol. 24, January 7, 2008, No. 1, pp. 26)*
Pub: Crain Communications, Inc.
Description: Listing of events in the Detroit area include conferences addressing entrepreneurialism, economic development, and women business ownership.

47408 ▪ *"The Weeks Ahead' in Crain's New York Business (Vol. 24, January 14, 2008, No. 2, pp. 20)*
Pub: Crain Communications, Inc.
Description: Listing of events in the Detroit area include conferences addressing entrepreneurialism, economic development, and women business ownership.

47409 ▪ *"Welcome to Babesland' in Women In Business (Vol. 62, June 2010, No. 2, pp. 33)*
Pub: American Business Women's Association
Ed: Leigh Elmore. **Description:** Music group, Four Bitchin' Babes will be performing at the 2010 American Business Women's Association's National Women's Leadership Conference. The group has been in the industry for 20 years and has released nine albums. The Four Bitchin' Babes consist of Sally Fingerett, Nancy Moran, Deirdre Flint, and Debi Smith.

47410 ▪ *What Men Don't Tell Woman about Business: Opening Up the Heavily Guarded Alpha Male Playbook*
Pub: John Wiley and Sons, Inc.
Ed: Christopher V. Fleet. **Released:** October 26, 2007. **Description:** Valuable guide for any woman in business, this book helps reveal everything a woman needs to know in order to understand, communicate, and compete with men in business.

47411 ▪ *"The Whole Package' in Entrepreneur (Vol. 36, February 2008, No. 2, pp. 24)*
Pub: Entrepreneur Media Inc.
Description: Holy Bohn, owner of The Honest Statute, developed an environmentally-friendly packaging for her pet food products. The company hired a packaging consultant and spent $175,000. Big corporations also spend money and plunge into the latest trends in packaging ranging from lighter and flexible to temperature-sensitive labels.

47412 ▪ *"Why Men Still Get More Promotions Than Women" in Harvard Business Review (Vol. 88, September 2010, No. 9, pp. 80)*
Pub: Harvard Business School Publishing
Ed: Herminia Ibarra, Nancy M. Carter, Christine Silva. **Description:** Sponsorship, rather than mentoring, is identified as the main difference in why men still receive more promotions than women. Active executive sponsorship is key to fostering career advancement.

47413 ▪ *"The WIN Library" in Women In Business (Vol. 61, August-September 2009, No. 4, pp. 36)*
Pub: American Business Women's Association
Ed: Leigh Elmore. **Description:** Women's Instructional Network (WIN) offers members of the American Business Women's Association with information about the organization and 15 Team Tools learning modules to help further the learning of business women. Other training programs and services offered by WIN are presented.

47414 ▪ *"Women as 21st Century Leaders" in Women In Business (Vol. 63, Summer 2011, No. 2, pp. 26)*
Pub: American Business Women's Association
Ed: Leigh Elmore. **Description:** American Business Women's Association and Park University have partnered to provide a leadership training program to attendees of the 2011 National Women's Leadership Conference. The courses will incorporate introduction

to concepts, development of critical thinking skills and direct application through exercises. Comments from executives are also included.

47415 ▪ *"Women: the Alpha Advantage" in Entrepreneur (Vol. 36, February 2008, No. 2, pp. 34)*
Pub: Entrepreneur Media Inc.
Ed: Aliza Sherman. **Description:** Women entrepreneurs are said to be mistaken with the belief that they need to display aggression and compete with other women to gain power. Workshops and books address this issue and discuss how women could be alpha entrepreneurs. Recommendations with regard to the topic are explored.

47416 ▪ *"Women Board Number Stagnates" in Boston Business Journal (Vol. 30, November 26, 2010, No. 44, pp. 1)*
Pub: Boston Business Journal
Ed: Mary Moore. **Description:** The 2010 data in 'Census of Women Directors and Executive Officers of Massachusetts Public Companies' showed little change in the number of executive officers and board members in the state's top 100 firms. The data was compiled by Bentley University, The Boston Club, and Mercer. Key information on 2010 Women on Boards is also provided.

47417 ▪ *Women Count: A Guide to Changing the World*
Pub: Purdue University Press
Ed: Susan Bulkeley Butler, Bob Keefe. **Released:** August 26, 2010. **Price:** $24.95. **Description:** Throughout history, women have struggled to change the workplace, change government, change society. It's time for women to change the world! Whether on the job, in politics, or in their community, there has never been a better time for women to make a difference in the world.

47418 ▪ *Women Entrepreneurs*
Pub: Edward Elgar Publishing, Incorporated
Ed: Andrea Smith-Hunter. **Released:** October 2006. **Price:** $120.00. **Description:** Focus is on women entrepreneurs; information includes human capital, network structures and financial capital, with comparative analysis across racial lines.

47419 ▪ *"Women and Higher Education" in Montly Labor Review (Vol. 133, September 2010, No. 9, pp. 70)*
Pub: Bureau of Labor Statistics
Description: The increase in people going to college has been mostly among women. Statistical data included.

47420 ▪ *Women-Owned & Home-Based Businesses*
Pub: DIANE Publishing Co.
Ed: Christopher S. Bond. **Released:** 1999. **Price:** $40.00.

47421 ▪ *"Women of Power" in Black Enterprise (Vol. 41, November 2010, No. 4, pp. 94)*
Pub: Earl G. Graves Publishing Co. Inc.
Description: Black Enterprise Women of Power Summit will be held February 23-26, 2011 at the Ritz Carlton in Orlando, Florida. Speakers will offer insight into career, household, and life in general.

47422 ▪ *"Women of Power Summit" in Black Enterprise (Vol. 38, February 2008, No. 7, pp. 163)*
Pub: Earl G. Graves Publishing Co. Inc.
Description: Third annual Women of Power Summit, hosted by State Farm, will host over 700 executive women of color offering empowerment sessions, tips for networking, along with entertainment.

47423 ▪ *"Women: Send Me An Angel' in Entrepreneur (Vol. 35, October 2007, No. 10, pp. 38)*
Pub: Entrepreneur Media Inc.
Ed: Aliza Sherman. **Description:** Golden Seeds has invested in Enter Artemis Woman LLC when the latter decided to put its products into Wal-Mart. Golden Seeds was formed by angel investors who aim to

help women build their own businesses. Tips on how to approach angel investors and getting angel funding are given.

47424 ▪ *"Women's Union Leadership: Closing the Gender Gap' in WorkingUSA (Vol. 11, December 2008, No. 4, pp. 459)*
Pub: Blackwell Publishers Ltd.
Ed: Michelle Kaminski, Elaine K. Yakura. **Description:** Women make up 44 percent of the labor movement, but a smaller percentage of union leaders. The importance of having a leadership representative of membership, some differences between male and female leadership, and why the labor movement needs more women leaders is discussed.

47425 ▪ *"Work Together" in Entrepreneur (Vol. 35, November 2007, No. 11, pp. 34)*
Pub: Entrepreneur Media Inc.
Ed: Aliza Sherman. **Description:** Marsha Firestone founded Women Presidents' Organization, creating small groups of women who head their own businesses. The idea was for each chapter of the organization to have businesswomen share experiences to help others learn from running their own business.

47426 ▪ *"The Workplace Generation Gaps" in Women In Business (Vol. 62, June 2010, No. 2, pp. 8)*
Pub: American Business Women's Association
Ed: Leigh Elmore. **Description:** Generation gaps among baby boomers, Generation X and Generation Y in the workplace are attributed to technological divides and differences in opinions. These factors could lead to workplace misunderstandings, employee turnover and communication difficulties. Details on managing such workplace gaps are discussed.

47427 ▪ *"Wowing Her Customers" in Women In Business (Vol. 61, August-September 2009, No. 4, pp. 34)*
Pub: American Business Women's Association
Ed: Kathleen Leighton. **Description:** Gail Worth, together with her brother, bought her parents' Harley-Davidson motorcycle dealership in Grandview, Missouri. She eventually had the dealership to herself when her brother broke out of the partnership. Gail says she is comfortable in a man's world kind of business and has expanded the business with a 10-acre site.

TRADE PERIODICALS

47428 ▪ *Business Woman Magazine*
Pub: Business and Professional Women/USA
Contact: Deborah L. Frett, Chief Executive Officer
E-mail: dfrett@bpwusa.org
URL(s): www.bpwusa.org. **Released:** 3/yr. **Price:** $30, Individuals; $35, Two years.

47429 ▪ *CWC Communicator*
Pub: California Women's Caucus
Ed: Dr. Pat Nellor Wickwire, Editor. **Released:** 2-4/ year. **Price:** $15, Included in membership. **Description:** Discusses issues affecting women, particularly regarding careers and especially women in counseling careers. Recurring features include news of research, a calendar of events, news of educational opportunities, and notices of publications available.

47430 ▪ *The Facilitator*
Pub: Nurre Ink
Contact: Susan M. Nurre, Editor
E-mail: snurre@thefacilitator.com
Released: Quarterly. **Price:** $35, U.S.; $35, institutions; $40, out of country. **Description:** Provides articles written by facilitators that are designed to link facilitators from around the world in a forum of sharing, networking, and communicating. Includes updates on training, automated meeting tools, and resources. Recurring features include tips and techniques, a calendar of events, reports of meetings, news of educational opportunities, book reviews, and notices of publications available.

47431 ■ *Multicultural Marketing News*
Pub: Multicultural Marketing Resources Inc.
Contact: Lisa Skriloff, Editor-in-Chief
Released: Bimonthly. **Price:** $1050 for Multicultural Marketing News only; $250 for MMN Online only. **Description:** Covers minority- and women-owned businesses and corporations that sell to them. Provides story ideas, diverse resources for journalists, and contacts for marketing executives. Recurring features include a calendar of events, business profiles, and a feature on a trend in multicultural marketing.

47432 ■ *Women in Business*
Pub: The ABWA Company Inc.
URL(s): www.abwa.org. **Released:** Bimonthly **Price:** $32, Nonmembers.

47433 ■ *Women Chemists*
Pub: American Chemical Society
Contact: Thomas H. Lane, President
Ed: Teri Quinn Gray, Editor. **Released:** Semiannual. **Description:** Aims "to be leaders in attracting, developing, and promoting women in the chemical sciences." Reports on women's achievements in the chemical sciences, as well as grants available, symposiums, and current events.

VIDEOCASSETTES/ AUDIOCASSETTES

47434 ■ *American Institute of Small Business: Women in Business*
American Institute of Small Business
23075 Highway 7, Ste. 200
Shorewood, MN 55331
Ph: (952)545-7001
Free: 800-328-2906
Fax: (952)545-7020
Co. E-mail: judy@aisb.biz
URL: http://www.pfa.com/AISB.htm
Released: 199?. **Price:** $69.95. **Description:** Female small business owners discuss success, overcoming stereotypes, obtaining financing, and other issues. **Availability:** VHS.

47435 ■ *Inc. Magazine Business Success Programs*
Cambridge Educational
c/o Films Media Group
132 West 31st Street, 17th Floor
Ste. 124
New York, NY 10001
Free: 800-257-5126
Fax: (609)671-0266
Co. E-mail: custserve@films.com
URL: http://www.cambridgeol.com
Released: 1987. **Price:** $99.95. **Description:** These four programs contain a step-by-step explanation of what must be done to succeed in business. **Availability:** VHS; CC.

47436 ■ *Special Issues for Women Entrepreneurs*
Instructional Video
2219 C St.
Lincoln, NE 68502
Ph: (402)475-6570
Free: 800-228-0164
Fax: (402)475-6500
Co. E-mail: feedback@insvideo.com
URL: http://www.insvideo.com
Released: 19??. **Price:** $89.95. **Description:** Contains panel discussion on the problems women face when starting and running their own business. Includes insight from honored women entrepreneurs. **Availability:** VHS.

47437 ■ *Time Management for Women*
Instructional Video
2219 C St.
Lincoln, NE 68502
Ph: (402)475-6570
Free: 800-228-0164
Fax: (402)475-6500
Co. E-mail: feedback@insvideo.com
URL: http://www.insvideo.com
Released: 19??. **Price:** $79.95. **Description:** Kay Cronkite Waldo offers time management training for women, focusing on behavior patterns, energy cycles, efficiency vs. effectiveness, time wasters, decision-making factors, and the superwoman theory. **Availability:** VHS.

47438 ■ *Woman Entrepreneur: Do You Have What it Takes?*
Cambridge Educational
c/o Films Media Group
132 West 31st Street, 17th Floor
Ste. 124
New York, NY 10001
Free: 800-257-5126
Fax: (609)671-0266
Co. E-mail: custserve@films.com
URL: http://www.cambridgeol.com
Released: 1987. **Price:** $29.95. **Description:** A motivational look at starting a business for women, featuring interviews with a half-dozen women who have made it. **Availability:** VHS.

TRADE SHOWS AND CONVENTIONS

47439 ■ Annual NAIW Convention - National Association of Insurance Women International
National Association of Insurance Women International (NAIW)
9343 E 95th Ct. S
Tulsa, OK 74133
Ph: (918)294-3700
Free: 800-766-6249
Fax: (918)294-3711
Co. E-mail: joinnaiw@naiw.org
URL: http://www.naiw.org
Contact: Linda Wilson, President
URL(s): www.naiw.org. **Frequency:** Annual. **Principal Exhibits:** Equipment, supplies, and services for insurance industry professionals.

CONSULTANTS

47440 ■ Association of Home-Based Women Entrepreneurs (HBWE)
PO Box 31561
Saint Louis, MO 63131-1561
Ph: (314)805-9519
Fax: (314)909-8179
Co. E-mail: aschaefer@advbizsol.com
URL: http://www.hbwe.org
Contact: Louise Wiedermann, President
E-mail: lw@projektek.com
Scope: Organization dedicated to women working from home-based offices. Focuses on the needs and interests of women doing their own business. It also focuses on business-related programs and issues, networking, leads and mentoring for professional growth in a dynamic and friendly atmosphere. **Founded:** 1998. **Publications:** "Taking Your Business International"; "Dressing For Success"; "Web 2.0 The Future of the Internet"; "Assertiveness Skills for Women in Business". **Seminars:** Making Connec-

tions, Jul, 2008; One Inch Wide, One Mile Deep, Jun, 2008; Accelerating Your Business, May, 2008; Change is Good, Apr, 2008; Pyro Marketing, Jan, 2007; Twenty Five Key Steps To Maintaining A Successful Home-Based Business, Nov, 2006.

47441 ■ Donna Cornell Enterprises Inc.—Cornell Career Center
68 N Plank Rd., Ste. 204
Newburgh, NY 12550-2122
Ph: (845)565-0088
Free: 888-769-3792
Fax: (845)565-0084
Co. E-mail: rc@cornellcareercenter.com
Contact: Donna Cornell, President
E-mail: rc@cornellcareercenter.com
Scope: Offers services in career consultant, professional search, job placement and national professional search. **Founded:** 1996. **Publications:** "The Power of the Woman Within"; "Juggling it All!"; "Journey: A Woman's Guide to Success"; "Shatter the Traditions".

47442 ■ Joel Greenstein & Associates (JGA)
6212 Nethercombe Ct.
McLean, VA 22101
Ph: (703)893-1888
Co. E-mail: jgreenstein@contractmasters.com
Contact: Joel Greenstein, Principal
E-mail: jgreenstein@contractmasters.com
Scope: Provides services to minority and women-owned businesses and government agencies. Specializes in interpreting federal, agency-specific acquisition regulations and contract terms and conditions. Offers assistance with preparing technical, cost proposals and sealed bids.

COMPUTERIZED DATABASES

47443 ■ *National Directory of Woman-Owned Business Firms*
7720 Wisconsin Ave., Ste. 213
Bethesda, MD 20814
Ph: (301)229-5561
Free: 800-845-8420
Fax: (301)229-6133
Co. E-mail: brspubs@sba8a.com
URL: http://www.sba8a.com
Availability: CD-ROM: Business Research Services Inc. **Type:** Directory.

RESEARCH CENTERS

47444 ■ HEC Montreal - Group for Women, Management and Organizations—HEC Montreal - Groupe Femmes, Gestion et Entreprises
3000 Chemin de la Cote-Sainte-Catherine
Montreal, QC, Canada H3T 2A7
Ph: (514)340-6015
Fax: (514)340-3825
Co. E-mail: louise.st-cyr@hec.ca
URL: http://neumann.hec.ca/groupefge/
Contact: Louise St-Cyr, Director
Founded: 1981. **Publications:** *Research.* **Educational Activities:** Group for Women, Management and Organizations Conference. **Telecommunication Services:** groupe.fge@hec.ca.

ASSOCIATIONS AND OTHER ORGANIZATIONS

47445 ■ National Safety Council (NSC)
1121 Spring Lake Dr.
Itasca, IL 60143-3201
Ph: (630)285-1121
Free: 800-621-7615
Fax: (630)285-1315
Co. E-mail: info@nsc.org
URL: http://www.nsc.org/Pages/Home.aspx
Contact: Janet P. Froetscher, President
URL(s): www.nsc.org, www.nsc.org/gen/nscinfo.htm.
Description: Promotes injury reduction by providing a forum for the exchange of safety and health ideas, techniques, and experiences and the discussion of injury prevention methods. Offers courses in first aid, occupational safety and traffic safety. Maintains extensive library on health and safety subjects. **Founded:** 1913. **Publications:** *Family Safety & Health* (Quarterly); *NSC Journal of Safety Research*; *Accident Facts*; *Family Safety and Health* (Quarterly); *Safety and Health* (Monthly); *Industrial Safety Chronicle* (Quarterly); *Safety and Health*; *Safety-Health* (Monthly). **Educational Activities:** National Safety Council Congress and Expo (Annual); National Safety Congress and Exposition (Annual). **Awards:** Occupational Awards (Periodic); Safe Driver Award Program. **Telecommunication Services:** customer-service@nsc.org.

47446 ■ National Safety Management Society
PO Box 4460
Walnut Creek, CA 94596-0460
Free: 800-321-2910
Co. E-mail: nsms@isa.com
URL: http://www.nsms.us
Contact: Jeffrey Chung, Executive Director
Description: Individuals with managerial responsibilities related to safety/loss control management, including professionals in the fields of education, medicine, computer technology, security, personnel, law, and other disciplines. Advances new concepts of accident prevention and loss control and promotes the role of safety management in the total management effort. Advises concentration in areas where a favorable cost/benefit return can be achieved with these new concepts while being cognizant of humanitarian considerations. Participates in local, state, and regional safety conferences; conducts regional management improvement and executive safety training seminars. **Publications:** *Journal of Safety Management* (Quarterly); *Journal of Safety Management* (Quarterly); *NSMS Digest* (Monthly); *Journal of Safety Management* (Quarterly). **Educational Activities:** National Safety Management Society Meeting (Annual). **Awards:** Frank Bird Award (Periodic).

47447 ■ Voluntary Protection Programs Participants' Association (VPPPA)
7600-E Leesburg Pike, Ste. 100
Falls Church, VA 22043
Ph: (703)761-1146
Fax: (703)761-1148
Co. E-mail: administration@vpppa.org
URL: http://www.vpppa.org
Contact: Susan Jordan Sikes, Executive Director
Description: Companies participating in Voluntary Protection Programs and other workplace environmental protection, health, and safety programs. Promotes cooperation between labor, management, and government agencies to insure safe and environmentally sustainable workplaces. Works closely with federal environmental and safety agencies to develop and implement cooperative programs; provides information on environmental health and workplace safety to congressional committees considering legislation. **Publications:** *VPPPA On the Wire* (Bimonthly); *Safety News Network* (Biweekly); *VPPPA Washington Update* (Monthly). **Awards:** VPPPA Stephen Brown Scholarships; VPPPA William Sullivan Scholarships; VPPPA June Brothers Scholarships; Safety and Health Achievement Award (Annual); Safety and Health Outreach Award (Annual); VPP Innovation Award (Annual); VPP Outreach Award (Annual); VPPPA June Brothers Scholarship (Annual); VPPPA Stephen Brown Scholarship (Annual); Innovation Award; Outreach Award; Delta/VPPPA Safety, Health and Environmental Scholarships; Safety and Health Achievement Award; Safety and Health Outreach Award; VPPPA June Brothers Scholarships; VPPPA Stephen Brown Scholarships.

EDUCATIONAL PROGRAMS

47448 ■ The Essentials of OSHA Compliance (Onsite)
Seminar Information Service, Inc.
20 Executive Park, Ste. 120
Irvine, CA 92614
Ph: (949)261-9104
Free: 877-SEM-INFO
Fax: (949)261-1963
Co. E-mail: info@seminarinformation.com
URL: http://www.seminarinformation.com
Price: $299.00. **Description:** A comprehensive update on changes in OSHA rules and guidelines and more. **Dates and Locations:** Concord, CA; Sacramento, CA; Little Rock, AR; and Dallas, TX.

47449 ■ OSHA 30-Hour Compliance Course (Onsite)
Fred Pryor Seminars & CareerTrack
5700 Broadmoor St., Ste. 300
Mission, KS 66202
Free: 800-780-8476
Fax: (913)967-8849
Co. E-mail: customerservice@pryor.com
URL: http://www.pryor.com
Price: $999.00; $979.00 for groups of 3 or more. **Description:** A practical, handson experience you need to pinpoint hidden or overlooked safety and health issues, address them, and become fully compliant with OSHA's general industry standards. **Dates and Locations:** Cities throughout the United States.

47450 ■ OSHA Compliance (Onsite)
Fred Pryor Seminars & CareerTrack
5700 Broadmoor St., Ste. 300
Mission, KS 66202
Free: 800-780-8476
Fax: (913)967-8849
Co. E-mail: customerservice@pryor.com
URL: http://www.pryor.com
Price: $179.00; $169.00 for groups of 5 or more. **Description:** Learn cost effective methods for getting your organization into compliance, how to expand the effectiveness of your safety training program, learn how to keep records required by OSHA, and how to assess your organization for a variety of hazards. **Dates and Locations:** Cities throughout the United States.

47451 ■ OSHA Compliance and Training for Medical and Dental (Onsite)
Seminar Information Service, Inc.
20 Executive Park, Ste. 120
Irvine, CA 92614
Ph: (949)261-9104
Free: 877-SEM-INFO
Fax: (949)261-1963
Co. E-mail: info@seminarinformation.com
URL: http://www.seminarinformation.com
Price: $319.00. **Description:** Covers everything you need to ensure compliance with all OSHA standards and requirements. **Dates and Locations:** Cities throughout the United States.

47452 ■ OSHA Compliance & Workplace Safety (Onsite)
Seminar Information Service, Inc.
20 Executive Park, Ste. 120
Irvine, CA 92614
Ph: (949)261-9104
Free: 877-SEM-INFO
Fax: (949)261-1963
Co. E-mail: info@seminarinformation.com
URL: http://www.seminarinformation.com
Price: $199.00. **Description:** Comprehensive update in OSHA's ever-changing requirements and innovative methods other organizations are successfully using to meet these stringent standards. **Dates and Locations:** Cities throughout the United States.

REFERENCE WORKS

47453 ■ "BC Forest Safety Council Unveils Supervisor Course to Respond to Industry Demands" in Canadian Corporate News (May 14, 2007)
Pub: Comtex News Network Inc.
Description: BC Forest Safety Council launched the sector's first supervisor training program that will lead to certification of forest supervisors in response to an industry-wide demand for standardized safety training for supervisors.

47454 ■ "Be Safe: CSE Requires a Series of Steps" in Contractor (Vol. 56, October 2009, No. 10, pp. 40)
Pub: Penton Media, Inc.
Ed: Dave Yates. Description: Confined Space Entry claims 91 lives each year and plumbers can prevent this by following several steps starting with the use of a four-gas analyzer which costs $1,262. It measures oxygen levels, as well as combustible gases, carbon monoxide, and hydrogen sulfide.

47455 ■ "Blast Blame" in The Business Journal-Milwaukee (Vol. 25, September 5, 2008, No. 50, pp. 1)
Pub: American City Business Journals, Inc.
Description: Rexnord Industries LLC and J.M. Brennan Inc.'s property damage trial in connection with the explosion at the Falk Corp. plant in Menomonee Valley, Wisconsin is set to begin. Lawyers for the two companies have failed to reach a settlement. A leaking propane line was seen as the cause of the blast.

47456 ■ "Businesses Keep a Watchful Eye on Worker's Comp" in The Business Journal-Serving Greater Tampa Bay (September 5, 2008)
Pub: American City Business Journals, Inc.
Ed: Jane Meinhardt. Description: Pending a ruling from the Florida Supreme Court that could uphold the 2003 changes on workers' compensation law, the outcome would include restrictions on claimant attorneys' fees and allow the competitive workers' compensation insurance rates to remain low. However, insurance rates are expected to go up if the court overturns the changes.

47457 ■ "Connectors for Space, Mil/Aero and Medical Applications" in Canadian Electronics (Vol. 23, June-July 2008, No. 4, pp. 13)
Pub: Action Communication Inc.
Ed: Gilles Parguey. Description: Product information on electrical connectors for use in space, military, aeronautics, and medical applications is provided. These connectors are built to withstand the extreme conditions offered by the harsh working environments in those applications.

47458 ■ "CSE: Contractors Are Always Responsible" in Contractor (Vol. 56, November 2009, No. 11, pp. 34)
Pub: Penton Media, Inc.
Ed: Dave Yates. Description: Plumbing contractors should purchase a long snorkel hose, a tripod with manual-crank hoist, and a sump pump in order to prevent accidents associated with Confined Space Entry. Liability issues surrounding confined space entry prevention and accidents are discussed.

47459 ■ "Don't Fall Foul of Farming's Workplace Killer" in Farmer's Weekly (March 28, 2008, No. 320)
Pub: Reed Business Information
Contact: Jeff Greisch, President
Description: Discusses the Work at Height Regulations that were introduced to reduce the risk of injury and death caused by accidental falls in the workplace.

47460 ■ "Employers See Workers' Comp Rates Rising" in Sacramento Business Journal (Vol. 28, April 8, 2011, No. 6, pp. 1)
Pub: Sacramento Business Journal
Ed: Kelly Johnson. Description: Employers in California are facing higher workers compensation costs. Increased medical costs and litigation are seen to drive the trend.

47461 ■ "Employers Waking Up to Effects of Workers' Sleep Problems" in Crain's Cleveland Business (Vol. 28, December 3, 2007, No. 48, pp. 18)
Pub: Crain Communications, Inc.
Ed: Jennifer Keirn. Description: Employers are beginning to realize that poor sleep quality can impact their bottom lines with higher health care costs and more lost-time accidents. The National Institutes of Health estimates that sleep deprivation, sleep disorders and excessive daytime sleepiness add about $15 billion to our national health care bill and cost employers $50 billion in lost productivity.

47462 ■ Enabling Environments for Jobs and Entrepreneurship: The Role of Policy and Law in Small Enterprise Employment
Pub: International Labour Office
Ed: Gerhard Reinecke. Released: February 2004. Price: $83.25. Description: National policies, laws and regulations governing workplace safety.

47463 ■ "Fewer People Dying At Work" in Sacramento Business Journal (Vol. 25, August 29, 2008, No. 26, pp. 1)
Pub: American City Business Journals, Inc.
Ed: Kathy Robertson. Description: Statistics show that workplace deaths in California dropped by 24 percent in 2007 compared with the previous year. Much of the decline was observed in the construction industry, where a slowing economy affected employment and dangerous work. The number of workplace deaths in the state also declined in all major categories except fires and explosions.

47464 ■ "Grace Puma; Senior Vice-President of Strategic Sourcing, United Airlines" in Crain's Chicago Business (May 5, 2008)
Pub: Crain Communications, Inc.
Ed: John Rosenthal. Description: Profile of Grace Puma who is the senior vice-president of strategic sourcing at United Airlines and is responsible for cutting costs at the company in a number of ways including scheduling safety inspections at the same time as routine maintenance, thereby reducing the downtime of each aircraft by five days as well as replacing a third of her staff with outside talent.

47465 ■ "Hot For All The Wrong Reasons" in Canadian Business (Vol. 81, March 31, 2008, No. 5, pp. 19)
Pub: Rogers Media
Ed: Andrea Jezovit. Description: Soaring platinum prices are due to South Africa's platinum mining industry's safety issues and power supply disruptions that exacerbate the metal's supply problems. South Africa supplies 80 percent of the world's platinum. South Africa's power utility has said that it cannot guarantee the industry's power needs until 2013.

47466 ■ "Huberman Failing to Keep CTA on Track" in Crain's Chicago Business (Vol. 31, April 21, 2008, No. 16, pp. 22)
Pub: Crain Communications, Inc.
Description: Discusses the deplorable service of CTA, the Chicago Transit Authority, as well as CTA President Ron Huberman who, up until last week had riders hoping he had the management skills necessary to fix the system's problems; Tuesday's event left hundreds of riders trapped for hours and thousands standing on train platforms along the Blue Line waiting for trains that never came.

47467 ■ "Injured Workers Caught in the Middle" in Sacramento Business Journal (Vol. 28, June 10, 2011, No. 15, pp. 1)
Pub: Sacramento Business Journal
Ed: Kelly Johnson. Description: A bill that would extend the cap on disability payments to nearly five years is in the works, but employers and insurance companies fear it would increase their costs. Proponents of the bill say, however, that it would correct unfairness suffered by the employees. Features of the bill are discussed as well as its effects on both parties and the State of California.

47468 ■ Law for the Small and Growing Business
Pub: Jordans Publishing Limited
Ed: P. Bohm. Released: February 2007. Price: $59.98. Description: Legal and regulatory issues facing small businesses, including employment law, health and safety, commercial property, company law and finance are covered.

47469 ■ "Marine Act Amendments Gain Parliamentary Approval" in Canadian Sailings (July 7, 2008)
Pub: UBM Global Trade
Contact: Leonard J. Corallo, President
Ed: Alex Binkley. Description: Changes to the Canada Marine Act provides better borrowing deals as well as an ability to tap into federal infrastructure funding for environmental protection measures, security improvements and other site enhancements.

47470 ■ National Directory of Safety Consultants
Pub: American Society of Safety Engineers
Contact: Darryl C. Hill, President
URL(s): www.asse.org. Released: latest edition 18th ed. Price: Free. Covers: Over 2,000 occupational health and safety consultants who are members of the society's consultants division. Entries include: Name, office address and phone, highest degree held, areas of occupational specialization, memberships, licenses and registrations held. Arrangement: Alphabetical. Indexes: Geographical, area of expertise.

47471 ■ "Omniplex on the Case" in Black Enterprise (Vol. 37, December 2006, No. 5, pp. 38)
Pub: Earl G. Graves Publishing Co. Inc.
Ed: Glenn Townes. Description: Office of Personnel Management in Washington D.C. recently awarded a service contract to Omniplex World Services Corp. Virginia-based, The Chantilly, will perform security investigations and background checks on current and prospective federal employees and military personnel and contractors.

47472 ■ "The One Thing That's Holding Back Your Wellness Program" in Employee Benefit News (Vol. 25, December 1, 2011, No. 15, pp. 8)
Pub: SourceMedia Inc.
Ed: Kelley M. Butler. Description: A 13-year study shows that women who sat for more than six hours a day were 94 percent more likely to die during the study period. Most women sit at their desks an average of 7.7 hours while at work.

47473 ■ "OSHA Proposes Historic Safety Penalty on BP" in Workforce Management (Vol. 88, November 16, 2009, No. 12, pp. 8)
Pub: Crain Communications Inc.
Ed: Mark Schoeff Jr. Description: Labor Secretary Hilda Solis has warned that she aims to toughen the enforcement of workplace laws; OSHA, the Occupational Safety and Health Administration, an agency within the Department of Labor, is penalizing BP Products North America Inc. for their failure to improve workplace safety.

47474 ■ "The Price of Citizenship" in Canadian Business (Vol. 79, August 14, 2006, No. 16-17, pp. 13)
Pub: Rogers Media
Ed: Jack Mintz. Description: Safety and insurance benefits provided by the Canadian government to Canadian passport holders returning from Lebanon, is discussed.

47475 ■ "Project Managers' Creed: Learn It, Live It" in Contractor (Vol. 56, November 2009, No. 11, pp. 46)
Pub: Penton Media, Inc.
Ed: Kent Craig. Description: Project managers should take the health and safety of their subordinates above all else. A manager should deal with the things that distract him from his job before starting a day on the site. The manager should maintain a comfortable and relaxed attitude with his employees.

47476 ■ Small Businesses and Workplace Fatality Risk: An Exploratory Analysis
Pub: RAND Corp.
Contact: Michael D. Rich, President
E-mail: michael_rich@rand.org
Ed: John F. Mendelhoff; Christopher Nelson; Kilkon Ko. Released: June 2006. Price: $20.00. Description: According to previous research, small business worksites report higher rates of deaths or serious injuries than larger corporations. Statistical data included.

47477 ■ "Solar Hot Water Sales Are Hot, Hot, Hot" in Contractor (Vol. 56, December 2009, No. 12, pp. 22)
Pub: Penton Media, Inc.
Ed: Dave Yates. Description: Plumbing contractors in the United States can benefit from the increased sales of solar thermal water systems. Licensed

plumbers have the base knowledge on the risks associated from heating and storing water. Safety issues associated with solar water heaters are also included.

47478 ■ *"United's Next Hurdle: Costly Repairs"* in Crain's Chicago Business (Vol. 31, April 14, 2008, No. 15, pp. 1)
Pub: Crain Communications, Inc.

Ed: John Pletz. **Description:** Discusses the recent crackdown by aviation regulators concerning airline safety at United Airlines as well as other carriers. Maintenance costs at United for the upkeep on the company's older planes is severely affecting its bottom line which is already sagging under heavy fuel costs.

TRADE PERIODICALS

47479 ■ *EHS Today: The Magazine of Safety, Health and Loss Prevention*
Pub: Penton Media Inc.

URL(s): ehstoday.com/. **Ed:** Sandy Smith. **Released:** Monthly

47480 ■ *Inside OSHA*
Pub: Inside Washington Publishers
Contact: Korila Malecha, Manager

Released: Biweekly, every other Monday. **Price:** $725, U.S. and Canada; $775, elsewhere. **Description:** Reports on news of the Occupational Safety and Health Administration.

47481 ■ *Occupational Health & Safety*
Pub: 1105 Media, Inc.

URL(s): ohsonline.com/Home.aspx. **Ed:** Jerry Laws. **Released:** Monthly **Price:** $99, Individuals.

47482 ■ *OSHA Compliance Advisor*
Pub: Business & Legal Resources, Inc.
Contact: Robert Brady, President

Released: Semimonthly, 24/year. **Price:** $299.95, individuals. **Description:** Provides information on employee safety issues, Occupational Safety and Health Act (OSHA), programs, accident incidents, and job hazards. Recurring features include columns titled Compliance Report, Federal Register Digest, From the States, Washington Watch, News Roundup.

47483 ■ *OSHAWeek*
Pub: Stevens Publishing Corp.
Contact: Ralph Jensen, Editor-in-Chief

Ed: Katie Hooten, Editor. **Released:** Weekly, 48/year. **Price:** $399. **Description:** Reports on news and updates on safety issues. Recurring features include news of research and a calendar of events.

47484 ■ *Safety Compliance Alert*
Pub: Progressive Business Publications

Ed: Rebecca Cavanaugh, Editor, cavanaugh@pbp.com. **Released:** Semimonthly. **Price:** $299, individuals. **Description:** Presents real world examples to help safety professionals avoid accidents and fires, reduce costs, and comply with changing OSHA rules. Recurring features include news of research, a calendar of events, news of educational opportunities, and a column titled Sharpen Your Judgment.

47485 ■ *Safety Update*
Pub: Ontario Safety League
Contact: Wendy Williams, Coordinator

Ed: Kira Vermond, Editor. **Released:** Quarterly. **Price:** $30. **Description:** Newsletter on the Ontario Safety League's activities and news related to transportation and safety education.

47486 ■ *Work & Stress*
Pub: Routledge, Taylor & Francis Group
Contact: David Smith, Chief Executive Officer

URL(s): www.tandf.co.uk/journals/titles/02678373.asp. **Ed:** Frank Bond, Bonita Long, Toon Taris. **Released:** Quarterly **Price:** $601, Institutions print and online; $541, Institutions online only; $288, Individuals print only; $82, Individuals society; £363, Institutions print and online; £327, Institutions online only; £50, Individuals society.

VIDEOCASSETTES/ AUDIOCASSETTES

47487 ■ *Accident Investigation: A Tool for Effective Prevention*
Learning Communications L.L.C.
5520 Trabuco Rd.
Irvine, CA 92620-5705
Free: 800-622-3610
Fax: (949)727-4323
Co. E-mail: sales@learncom.com
URL: http://www.learncom.com
Contact: Lloyd W. Singer, President
Released: 1992. **Description:** Provides accident investigation techniques for supervisors and managers. Includes Leader's Guide. **Availability:** VHS; 3/4 U.

47488 ■ *Back Injury Prevention Through Ergonomics*
Film Library/National Safety Council California Chapter
4553 Glencoe Ave., Ste. 150
Marina Del Rey, CA 90292
Ph: (310)827-9781
Free: 800-421-9585
Fax: (310)827-9861
Co. E-mail: California@nsc.org
URL: http://www.nsc.org/nsc_near_you/FindYourLocalChapter/Pages/California.aspx
Released: 198?. **Description:** This is a demonstration of how a total ergonomics program can reduce workers' on-the-job injuries. **Availability:** VHS; 3/4 U.

47489 ■ *CHEMSAFE*
Learning Communications L.L.C.
5520 Trabuco Rd.
Irvine, CA 92620-5705
Free: 800-622-3610
Fax: (949)727-4323
Co. E-mail: sales@learncom.com
URL: http://www.learncom.com
Contact: Lloyd W. Singer, President
Released: 1991. **Price:** $175.00. **Description:** A nine-module program designed to help companies comply with OSHA's Hazard Communication Standard. Each module covers a different type of chemical hazard. A leader's guide and participants' handouts are included. **Availability:** VHS; 3/4 U.

47490 ■ *80% Preventable: Burn Injury Prevention*
Bergwall Productions, Inc.
1 DIckinson Drive, Brandywine BUilding 5, Ste. 105
Chadds Ford, PA 19317
Ph: (610)361-0334
Free: 800-934-8696
Fax: (610)361-0092
URL: http://www.bergwall.com
Released: 1992. **Price:** $99.00. **Description:** Dramatizes what can happen when a lazy and careless worker goofs around once too often. Testimony from a nurse reaffirms the message of the title--that 80% of burn accidents are preventable. **Availability:** VHS.

47491 ■ *Electrical Safety in the Lab*
Film Library/National Safety Council California Chapter
4553 Glencoe Ave., Ste. 150
Marina Del Rey, CA 90292
Ph: (310)827-9781
Free: 800-421-9585
Fax: (310)827-9861
Co. E-mail: California@nsc.org
URL: http://www.nsc.org/nsc_near_you/FindYourLocalChapter/Pages/California.aspx
Released: 1995. **Price:** $99.95. **Description:** Explains how electricity works and its potential hazards. **Availability:** VHS.

47492 ■ *Electrical Safety Related Work Practices*
Gulf Publishing Co.
2 Greenway Plz., Ste. 1020
Houston, TX 77046-0208
Ph: (713)529-4301
Free: 800-231-6275

Fax: (713)520-4433
Co. E-mail: advertising@gulfpub.com
URL: http://www.gulfpub.com
Contact: John Royall, President
Released: 1992. **Price:** $1495.00. **Description:** Six-part training program that offers educational material on electrical safety. Centers on the new OSHA requirements for work performed on or near exposed energized and de-energized parts of electrical equipment, the use of electrical protective equipment, and the safe use of electrical equipment. **Availability:** VHS; 3/4 U; Special order formats.

47493 ■ *Emergency Planning and Crisis Management Series*
Gulf Publishing Co.
2 Greenway Plz., Ste. 1020
Houston, TX 77046-0208
Ph: (713)529-4301
Free: 800-231-6275
Fax: (713)520-4433
Co. E-mail: advertising@gulfpub.com
URL: http://www.gulfpub.com
Contact: John Royall, President
Released: 1992. **Price:** $995.00. **Description:** Three-part vocational series that helps facilities develop an emergency plan and provide for employee training regarding this plan. Comes with detailed leader's guide. **Availability:** VHS; 3/4 U.

47494 ■ *ErgoKinetics: Safety in Motion*
Aspen Publishers, Inc.
7201 McKinney Cir.
Frederick, MD 21704
Ph: (301)698-7100
Free: 800-234-1660
Fax: (800)901-9075
Co. E-mail: customerservice@aspenpublisher.com
URL: http://www.aspenpublishers.com
Contact: Robert Becker, President
Released: 1994. **Description:** Training program that offers ergonomic solutions for preventing three of the most common types of complaints in the workplace: back and neck injuries; hand, wrist, and arm injuries; and VDT-related visual problems. Contains two separate modules: one for the plant and one for the office. Comes with leader's guide and participants' workbooks. **Availability:** VHS.

47495 ■ *Ergonomics: Low-Cost, Common-Sense Training Solutions*
Learning Communications L.L.C.
5520 Trabuco Rd.
Irvine, CA 92620-5705
Free: 800-622-3610
Fax: (949)727-4323
Co. E-mail: sales@learncom.com
URL: http://www.learncom.com
Contact: Lloyd W. Singer, President
Released: 1991. **Description:** A 3-tape guide to reducing cumulative trauma disorders (also known as repetitive motion illnesses), reduce stress, and increase productivity--all without costly engineering controls or job redesigns. A set of three tapes, complete with Leader's Guides and Participant Workbooks. **Availability:** VHS; 3/4 U.

47496 ■ *Ergonomics at Work*
Film Library/National Safety Council California Chapter
4553 Glencoe Ave., Ste. 150
Marina Del Rey, CA 90292
Ph: (310)827-9781
Free: 800-421-9585
Fax: (310)827-9861
Co. E-mail: California@nsc.org
URL: http://www.nsc.org/nsc_near_you/FindYourLocalChapter/Pages/California.aspx
Released: 198?. **Description:** This tape looks at how ergonomics can aid in creating safer working conditions. **Availability:** VHS; 3/4 U.

47497 ■ *Facts about OSHA Inspections*
Film Library/National Safety Council California Chapter
4553 Glencoe Ave., Ste. 150
Marina Del Rey, CA 90292
Ph: (310)827-9781

Free: 800-421-9585
Fax: (310)827-9861
Co. E-mail: California@nsc.org
URL: http://www.nsc.org/nsc_near_you/FindYourLo-
calChapter/Pages/California.aspx
Released: 1995. **Price:** $195.00. **Description:**
Explains compliance procedures for conducting
OSHA inspections. Aids workers, supervisors and
managers to improve the workplace in order to avoid
fines, penalties and citations. **Availability:** VHS.

47498 ■ *First Aid on the Job*
Audio Graphics Training Systems
301 West Broome St., Suite 100
Lagrange, GA 30240
Ph: (404)507-2487
Free: 800-814-9792
Fax: (706)883-7136
Co. E-mail: customerservice@agts-web.com
URL: http://www.agts-web.com
Released: 199?. **Price:** $395.00. **Description:** Cov-
ers when and how to move a victim, stopping bleed-
ing, symptoms of shock and prevention, and blood-
borne precautions. **Availability:** VHS.

**47499 ■ *Foreman's Accident Protection
Series***
Gulf Publishing Co.
2 Greenway Plz., Ste. 1020
Houston, TX 77046-0208
Ph: (713)529-4301
Free: 800-231-6275
Fax: (713)520-4433
Co. E-mail: advertising@gulfpub.com
URL: http://www.gulfpub.com
Contact: John Royall, President
Released: 1988. **Price:** $375.00. **Description:** An
11-tape series on setting up an effective industrial
safety program. **Availability:** VHS; 3/4 U.

47500 ■ *Handle with Care*
Bergwall Productions, Inc.
1 DIckinson Drive, Brandywine BUilding 5, Ste. 105
Chadds Ford, PA 19317
Ph: (610)361-0334
Free: 800-934-8696
Fax: (610)361-0092
URL: http://www.bergwall.com
Released: 1992. **Price:** $99.00. **Description:** Short
story segments dramatize dangerous situations a
variety of people can find themselves in on any given
day. Impacts viewers in a more direct way than many
lectures devoted to safety. **Availability:** VHS.

**47501 ■ *The Hazard Awareness Training
Series***
Genium Group Inc.
79 The Mall
Amsterdam, NY 12010
Ph: (518)842-4111
Free: 877-284-1963
Fax: (518)842-1843
Co. E-mail: info@genium.com
URL: http://www.genium.com
Released: 1989. **Price:** $534.00. **Description:**
OSHA laws, how to read and label material safety
data sheets, and other industrial health threats are
covered in this series. **Availability:** VHS; 3/4 U.

47502 ■ *Industrial Safety*
Agency for Instructional Technology (AIT)
1800 N Stonelake Dr., Box A
Bloomington, IN 47404-1517
Ph: (812)339-2203
Free: 800-457-4509
Fax: (812)333-4218
Co. E-mail: info@ait.net
URL: http://www.ait.net
Contact: Sandra L. McBrayer, Chief Executive Of-
ficer
Released: 1986. **Price:** $1095.00. **Description:** A
series of ten programs about things that can be done
to make the workplace safer. **Availability:** VHS; 3/4
U.

**47503 ■ *Making It Better: How Everyone Can
Create a Safer Workplace***
Learning Communications L.L.C.
5520 Trabuco Rd.
Irvine, CA 92620-5705
Free: 800-622-3610
Fax: (949)727-4323
Co. E-mail: sales@learncom.com
URL: http://www.learncom.com
Contact: Lloyd W. Singer, President
Released: 19??. **Price:** $295.00. **Description:**
Shows examples of safety measures created and
implemented by employees. Encourages employees
to take an active role in workplace safety. Includes
leader guide and 10 workbooks. **Availability:** VHS;
3/4 U; 8 mm.

47504 ■ *The Man from OSHA*
Film Library/National Safety Council California
Chapter
4553 Glencoe Ave., Ste. 150
Marina Del Rey, CA 90292
Ph: (310)827-9781
Free: 800-421-9585
Fax: (310)827-9861
Co. E-mail: California@nsc.org
URL: http://www.nsc.org/nsc_near_you/FindYourLo-
calChapter/Pages/California.aspx
Released: 198?. **Description:** This is an explanation
of the OSHA program and what an OSHA inspector
does. **Availability:** VHS; 3/4 U.

**47505 ■ *Office Safety and Workplace
Ergonomics***
Gulf Publishing Co.
2 Greenway Plz., Ste. 1020
Houston, TX 77046-0208
Ph: (713)529-4301
Free: 800-231-6275
Fax: (713)520-4433
Co. E-mail: advertising@gulfpub.com
URL: http://www.gulfpub.com
Contact: John Royall, President
Released: 1992. **Price:** $495.00. **Description:** Train-
ing program that centers on ways of fostering aware-
ness among office employees regarding safety in the
office. **Availability:** VHS; 3/4 U.

47506 ■ *OSHA Confined Space Entry*
Williams Learning Network
15400 Calhoun Dr.
Rockville, MD 20855-2762
Fax: (301)315-6880
Co. E-mail: mait@willearn.com
URL: http://www.willearn.com
Released: 1993. **Description:** Outlines OSHA
regulations for permit required confined spaces
covering such topics as isolating, testing, and prepar-
ing permit spaces; properly equipping workers;
maintaining entry conditions and employee duties.
Includes Leader's Guide and 25 Program Guides.
Availability: VHS; 3/4 U.

**47507 ■ *OSHA Electrical Safety for
Non-Electrical Workers***
Williams Learning Network
15400 Calhoun Dr.
Rockville, MD 20855-2762
Fax: (301)315-6880
Co. E-mail: mait@willearn.com
URL: http://www.willearn.com
Released: 19??. **Description:** Describes basic
electrical safety for employees with little or no training. Explains basic properties of electricity, avoidance
of electrical hazards, and steps to take in an electrical emergency. Helps meet OSHA 29 CFR 1910.331-
335 training requirements. Includes Leader's Guide
and 25 Program Guides. **Availability:** VHS; 3/4 U.

**47508 ■ *Right-to-Know: Working Around
Hazardous Substances***
Learning Communications L.L.C.
5520 Trabuco Rd.
Irvine, CA 92620-5705
Free: 800-622-3610

Fax: (949)727-4323
Co. E-mail: sales@learncom.com
URL: http://www.learncom.com
Contact: Lloyd W. Singer, President
Released: 19??. **Price:** $295.00. **Description:**
Employees learn how to properly handle hazardous
chemicals to eliminate or minimize accidents. In-
cludes a leader's guide and 10 workbooks. **Avail-
ability:** VHS; 8 mm; 3/4 U.

47509 ■ *Take Two . . . for Safety*
DuPont Safety Resources
PO Box 80013
Wilmington, DE 19880-0013
Free: 800-532-7233
Fax: (888)644-7233
URL: http://www2.dupont.com/Sustainable_
Solutions/en_US/practice_areas/safety_consultan
ts/index.html
Released: 1993. **Description:** A series about indus-
trial safety precautions. **Availability:** VHS; 3/4 U.

47510 ■ *What's Your Risk?*
Gulf Publishing Co.
2 Greenway Plz., Ste. 1020
Houston, TX 77046-0208
Ph: (713)529-4301
Free: 800-231-6275
Fax: (713)520-4433
Co. E-mail: advertising@gulfpub.com
URL: http://www.gulfpub.com
Contact: John Royall, President
Released: 1991. **Price:** $395.00. **Description:** A look
at the three categories of risk infection as defined by
OSHA, and the safe work practices and protective
equipment necessary to minimize exposure. **Avail-
ability:** VHS; 3/4 U.

TRADE SHOWS AND CONVENTIONS

47511 ■ Ohio Safety Congress and Expo
Bureau of Workers Compensation
30 W Spring St.
Columbus, OH 43215-2256
Fax: (877)520-6446
Co. E-mail: ombudsperson@bwc.state.oh.us
URL: http://www.ohiobwc.com
URL(s): www.ohiobwc.com. **Frequency:** Annual. **Audience:** Occupational safety and health professionals. **Principal Exhibits:** Occupational safety and
health equipment, supplies, and services. **Telecommunication Services:** safetycongress@ohiobwc.
com.

**47512 ■ Wisconsin Safety and Health
Congress/Exposition**
Wisconsin Council of Safety, Division WMC Founda-
tion
501 E Washington Ave.
Madison, WI 53701-0352
Ph: (608)258-3400
Fax: (608)258-3413
URL: http://www.wmc.org
Frequency: Annual. **Audience:** Safety professionals;
executives; local representatives; occupational health
and industrial hygiene personnel. **Principal Exhibits:**
Safety, health and compliance products/services for
industry. **Dates and Locations:** , Holiday Inn.

CONSULTANTS

47513 ■ American Forensic Engineers
34 Sammis Ln.
White Plains, NY 10605
Ph: (914)949-5978
Fax: (914)949-0350
Co. E-mail: gusmundel@aol.com
Contact: August B. Mundel, President
E-mail: gusmundel@aol.com
Scope: Provider of industrial, safety, and forensic
consulting services. Services include relevant engineering studies, sampling, statistical studies, quality
and reliability efforts, industrial hygiene, human factors analysis, industrial experimentation, product
safety analysis and product liability causes in the
electrical, electronic, electro-chemical, chemical,

mechanical, and battery industrial areas. Also offers building inspection services. Serves private industries as well as government agencies in the U.S. **Founded:** 1975. **Publications:** "Ethics in Quality," Marcell Dekker.

47514 ■ Caliche Ltd.
200 Brantley Ln.
Magnolia, TX 77353-0107
Ph: (281)356-6038
Free: 800-683-1046
Fax: (281)356-6224
Co. E-mail: calicheltd@calicheltd.com
URL: http://www.calicheltd.com
Contact: Marceile C. Parker, President
Scope: Safety, health and environmental management consulting company. Provides comprehensive environmental services including air, soil and water monitoring and analysis, emission and ventilation studies, asbestos and lead-based paint consulting, environmental site assessments, industrial hygiene and safety audits, indoor air quality and underground storage tank closures. Industries served: all. **Founded:** 1980. **Seminars:** How You Can Get the Most of Your Industrial Hygiene Assessment: A Systematic and Comprehensive Approach to Exposure Assessment, Aug, 2007.

47515 ■ Charp Associates Inc.
39 Maple Ave.
Upper Darby, PA 19082-1902
Contact: Solomon Charp, President
Scope: Provider of consulting, analysis, and design services. It serves the manufacturing and industrial, transportation, occupational safety, legal, and insurance industries. **Founded:** 1969. **Publications:** "Technological Horizons in Education".

47516 ■ Claymore Engineering
1308 Valle Vista Dr.
Fullerton, CA 92831-1944
Ph: (714)870-4521
Fax: (714)870-7051
Co. E-mail: claymoreengr@cs.com
Contact: Denison W. York, President
Scope: Practice limited to solving air pollution and industrial safety compliance problems. Serves private industries as well as government agencies. **Founded:** 1982.

47517 ■ Cocciardi & Associates Inc.
4 Kacey Ct.
Mechanicsburg, PA 17055-5596
Ph: (717)766-4500
Free: 800-377-3024
Fax: (717)766-3999
Co. E-mail: jcocciardi@cocciardi.com
URL: http://www.cocciardi.com
Contact: Rocco DiPietro, Manager
E-mail: rdipietro@cocciardi.com
Scope: Provider of safety, health and environmental consulting and training. It handles such issues as Hazardous Waste Operations and Emergency Response Regulation (HAZWOPER), asbestos and lead training (for licensing requirements), environmental auditing, and health and safety investigations. It serves all industries worldwide. **Founded:** 1988. **Publications:** "Guidebook on Pennsylvania Environmental Laws & Regulations; Storage Tank Compliance: Above Ground and Underground," The Pennsylvania Chamber of Business and Industry, 2009; "Briefing's on Hospital Safety," Health Care Pro, 2009; "Flammable and Combustible Liquids Hazards in the Workplace: OSHA Requirements Put Focus on Safe Storage," 2008; "Creating Isolation Surge Capacity," Rusting Publications, 2008; "Arc Flash Hazards and Protecting Your Employees," Nov, 2008; "United States Department of Homeland Security (DHS) Chemical Facility AntiTerrorism Rule," Sep, 2008; "Mold Contamination and Its Regulatory Status in Pennsylvania," Aug, 2006; "Arc Flash Hazards and How to Protect Your Employees," Feb, 2006; "Hidden Benefits of Training," Jun, 2005; "Terrorism Response Field Guide," Jones and Bartlett, 2003; "Terrorism Response Training Manual," Jones and Bartlett, 2003; "Emergency Response Team Manual," National Fire Protection Association, 2004.

47518 ■ Roy C. Craft
1707 Pecan St.
Bay City, TX 77414-4648
Ph: (409)245-9991
Fax: (409)245-9991
Co. E-mail: rcraft@tgn.net
Contact: Roy Craft, President
Scope: Consultant in health physics concerning control, protection, contamination, regulation and environmental impact. **Founded:** 1991.

47519 ■ donphin.com Inc.
1001 B Ave., Ste. 200
Coronado, CA 92118
Ph: (619)550-3533
Free: 800-234-3304
Fax: (619)600-0096
Co. E-mail: inquiry@donphin.com
URL: http://www.donphin.com
Contact: Vito Tanzi, President
Scope: Offers a comprehensive approach to understanding and applying a broad range of business principles: legal compliance issues, management concerns, health and safety, customer service, marketing, information management. Industries served: All developing small businesses. **Publications:** "Doing Business Right!"; "HR That Works!"; "Lawsuit Free! How to Prevent Employee Lawsuits"; "Building Powerful Employment Relationships!"; "Victims, Villains and Heroes: Managing Emotions in The Workplace". **Seminars:** Doing Business Right!; HR That Works!; Building Powerful Employment Relationships; Lawsuit Free!.

47520 ■ Environmental Assessment Services Inc.
124 S Main St.
Middletown, OH 45044-4002
Ph: (513)424-3400
Fax: (513)424-2020
Contact: David W. Armentrout, Owner
Scope: Offers environmental and health and safety services in compliance auditing, program management and implementation, field services (monitoring/testing) and real estate assessment. **Founded:** 1988.

47521 ■ Environmental Support Network Inc.
5376 Fulton Dr. NW
Canton, OH 44718-1808
Ph: (330)494-0905
Fax: (330)494-1650
Co. E-mail: esn@sssnet.com
URL: http://www.environmental-support.com
Contact: William P. Racine, President
Scope: Provides environmental, health, and safety consulting and project management services. These include compliance auditing and remediation specifications concerning air, groundwater, and soil quality. Also offers health and safety reviews, asbestos and lead-based paint handling, noise sampling, industrial permitting, and UST management. Industries served: education, finance, industry and government. **Founded:** 1989. **Seminars:** Environmental Health and Safety Management in Ohio; Managing Compliance in Ohio; Environmental Site Remediation in Ohio and Surrounding States; Conducting ESAs by ASTM Standards; Health and Safety Management in the Medical Setting; Exposure Monitoring in Schools and Public Buildings.

47522 ■ Error Analysis Inc. (EAI)
5173 Waring Rd., Ste. 157
San Diego, CA 92120-2705
Ph: (619)464-4427
Fax: (619)464-4992
Co. E-mail: info@erroranalysis.com
URL: http://www.erroranalysis.com
Contact: Kristy Norris, Manager
Scope: Research and consulting in the fields of human factors, safety and accident reconstruction. Provides consulting and expert witness services to attorneys, the insurance industry and businesses throughout the world. **Founded:** 1988. **Publications:** "Participation on voluntary committees for standards and codes by forensic practitioners: A win-win combination,"2011; "Ergonomics in Design,"2011; "Stairway falls: An ergonomics analysis of 80 cases," Professional Safety, 2009; "The practice of forensic human factors/ergonomics and related safety profes-

sions," Lawyers & Judges Publishing Company, 2009. **Seminars:** The role of a just culture, American Society of Safety Engineers, Costa Mesa, TCA, Jan, 2009; Common trends in slip and falls, Las Vegas, NV, Sep, 2008; Safety; Risk Management; Premises and Product Liability.

47523 ■ Fox Fire Safety Inc.
4605 Lincoln Way E
Mishawaka, IN 46544
Ph: (574)258-5479
Free: 800-919-0410
Fax: (574)674-0911
Co. E-mail: ffsinfo@foxfiresafety.com
URL: http://www.foxfiresafety.com
Contact: Robert E. Murray, Owner
Scope: Provider of fire protection and fire suppression needs in a range of systems. Also offers service and installation of fire protection equipment. Serves all industries. **Founded:** 1986.

47524 ■ Leonard R. Friedman Risk Management Inc. (LRF/RM)
170 Great Neck Rd., Ste. 140
Great Neck, NY 11021-3337
Ph: (516)466-0750
Fax: (516)466-0997
Co. E-mail: info@lrfrm.com
URL: http://www.lrfrm.com
Contact: Rachel L. Efrati, Vice President
E-mail: refrati@lrfrm.com
Scope: Provider of risk and insurance management and safety and claims managements services to corporations across the country. Analyzes exposure to loss, audits insurance contracts, structures competitive bidding, reviews contracts and leases, implements and monitors safety and claims management programs and recommends risk transfer programs to reduce exposure to loss. Industries served: profit and nonprofit companies engaged in retail, manufacturing, distributing, hospitality, real estate and service. **Founded:** 1974.

47525 ■ Humanics ErgoSystems Inc.—Humanics Ergonomics
22287 Mulholland Hwy., Ste. 273
Calabasas, CA 91302-5190
Ph: (818)345-3746
Fax: (818)705-3903
Co. E-mail: ergonomics@humanics-es.com
URL: http://www.humanics-es.com
Contact: Rani Lueder, Principal
E-mail: rani@humanics-es.com
Scope: Specializes in occupational ergonomics; ergonomic workplace evaluations; ergonomics research; ergonomic seminars and training; psychological and biomechanics testing (EMG, dynamic lumbar motion, strength assessment, nerve conduction); product evaluations; compliance with ergonomic standards; and expert witnessing. **Founded:** 1982. **Publications:** "The Future of Ergonomics in Children's Education," IEA 2009; "Ergonomics for Children; designing products and places for toddlers to teens," 2007; "Are Children just Little Adults? Child growth, development and age-related risk," Dec, 2003; "Rethinking Sitting," Oct, 2003; "Revisiting Ergonomics," May, 2003. **Seminars:** Teaching elder design, Las Vegas, Jul, 2008; Ergonomic considerations in seated work activities, University of California, Los Angeles, Jun, 2008; Rethinking back support: Sacral, lumbar or live backs, Dec, 2007; Adjunct Faculty, Human Factors and Design, 2006; Zen sitting and Western seating, 2005; Behavioral ergonomics, Oct, 2005; Sitting & seating in Zenmonasteries, Sep, 2005; Walking in their shoe. **Telecommunication Services:** ergoquestions@gmail.com.

47526 ■ Retail Safety Consortium
640 N Main St., Ste. 1256
Bountiful, UT 84010
Ph: (801)951-2566
Free: 800-370-9168
Contact: Michael E. Howell, President
Scope: Specializes in safety and human factors for retail industries. **Founded:** 2000.

47527 ■ Safety Management Services
4012 Santa Nella Pl.
San Diego, CA 92130-2291

Ph: (858)259-0591
Fax: (858)792-2350
Contact: Bob Harrell, President
Scope: Offers safety consulting services: Evaluates safety policies and procedures to determine degree of effectiveness; advises on compliance with OSHA standards; and provides safety programs for managers, supervisors, and workers. Industries served: general contractors in new construction, renovation, and demolition; and tenant improvement companies which hire general contractors to perform construction activities on their premises. Also assists litigation as construction safety expert witness. Safety training programs customized to meet clients needs. **Founded:** 1978. **Publications:** "What Can Go Wrong?," International Cranes magazine, Apr, 1994. **Seminars:** Federal OSHA Construction Safety and Health Course for Trainers, University of California, San Diego; OSHA 10-Hour Construction Safety Course; 90-Hour Construction Safety Management Certificate Course - 1991 to 1993; Fall Protection; Confined Space Standards; Cranes and Rigging; Scaffold or Trenching and Excavation; and Safe Construction Work Practices.

47528 ■ John Smithkey, III, RN
1271 Overland Ave. NE
North Canton, OH 44720-1731
Ph: (330)494-3729
Co. E-mail: schoolnurse007@aol.com
Scope: Specializes in public and occupational health, HIV/AIDS education and prevention programs, grant and proposal writing, and programs for businesses and employees. **Publications:** "The Strange World of Head Lice Information," Jun, 2003. **Seminars:** CPR; Communicable Diseases; Bloodborne Pathogen Training; Delegation of Nursing Tasks and Medication Administration Certification; Anaphylactic Shock and EpiPen Training.

47529 ■ Vaccari & Associates Inc.
17 Cypress St. 1
Marblehead, MA 01945-1925
Ph: (781)639-0946
Fax: (781)639-0946
Co. E-mail: rvaccari1@verizon.net
Contact: Ralph J. Vaccari, President
E-mail: rvaccari@rcn.com
Scope: A provider of appraisals for primary and secondary mortgages, mortgage refinancing, employee relocation, private mortgage insurance removal, estate planning and divorce settlement. **Founded:** 1996.

COMPUTERIZED DATABASES

47530 ■ *Environment & Safety Library™*
1801 S Bell St.
Arlington, VA 22202
Free: 800-372-1033
Co. E-mail: customercare@bna.com
URL: http://www.bna.com
Availability: Online: Bloomberg LP-Bloomberg BNA. CD-ROM: Bloomberg LP-Bloomberg BNA. **Type:** Full-text.

47531 ■ *Health and Safety Science Abstracts (HSSA)*
789 E Eisenhower Pky.
Ann Arbor, MI 48103
Ph: (734)761-4700
Fax: (734)997-4222
Co. E-mail: info@proquest.com
URL: http://www.csa.com
Availability: Online: ProQuest LLC - CSA; STN International. **Type:** Bibliographic.

47532 ■ *State Health Care Regulatory Developments™*
1801 S Bell St.
Arlington, VA 22202
Free: 800-372-1033
Co. E-mail: customercare@bna.com
URL: http://www.bna.com
Availability: Online: Bloomberg LP-Bloomberg BNA; Thomson Reuters - Westlaw. **Type:** Full-text.

LIBRARIES

47533 ■ Ameren Corporation Library
1901 Chouteau Ave.
Box 66149
St. Louis, MO 63166-6149
Ph: (314)554-3094
Fax: (314)554-2888
Co. E-mail: khayes2@ameren.com
URL: http://www.ameren.com
Contact: Katharine A. Hayes, Librarian, Technical Services
Scope: Business, the environment, engineering, occupational safety and health, nuclear power, public utilities, public-private power. **Founded:** 1913. **Holdings:** Figures not available. **Subscriptions:** 400 journals and other serials.

47534 ■ BNA Library
1801 S. Bell St.
Arlington, VA 22202-4501
Ph: (703)341-3303
Free: 800-372-1033
Fax: (703)341-1610
Co. E-mail: mbromley@bna.com
URL: http://www.bna.com
Contact: Laura Gordon-Murnane
Scope: Law, labor-management relations, economics, government regulation, business, the environment, industrial safety and health. **Services:** Interlibrary loan; library open by special arrangement only. **Founded:** 1974. **Holdings:** 20,000 volumes. **Subscriptions:** 650 journals and other serials; 20 newspapers. **Telecommunication Services:** library@bna.com; books@bna.com.

47535 ■ CELOTEX Technical Center Library
10301 9th St., N.
St. Petersburg, FL 33716
Ph: (813)576-4171
Fax: (813)576-0318
Contact: David Brzana, Specialist
Scope: Polymer chemistry, specialty chemicals, building materials, materials science. **Services:** Interlibrary loan; center not open to the public. **Founded:** 1966. **Holdings:** 2000 books. **Subscriptions:** 150 journals and other serials.

47536 ■ CIGNA Corporation Philadelphia Research Library
2 Liberty Pl.
1601 Chestnut St.
Philadelphia, PA 19192
Ph: (215)761-1000
Free: 800-997-1654
Fax: (215)761-5588
Co. E-mail: daniel.mullan@cigna.com
URL: http://www.cigna.com
Contact: Dan Mullan, Manager
Scope: Insurance, management, occupational and environmental safety and health. **Services:** Interlibrary loan; library not open to the public. **Founded:** 1947. **Holdings:** 2000 books. **Subscriptions:** 400 journals and other serials.

47537 ■ Cogswell College Library—Cogswell Polytechnical College.
1175 Bordeaux Dr.
Sunnyvale, CA 94089-9772
Ph: (408)541-0100, x-144
Free: 800-264-7955
Fax: (408)747-0764
Co. E-mail: library@cogswell.edu
URL: http://www.cogswell.edu/library.htm
Contact: Bruce G. Dahms, Librarian
Scope: Fire science, electrical engineering, software engineering, computer and video imaging, digital motion pictures, digital audio technology. **Services:** Interlibrary loan; copying; library open to the public for reference use only. **Founded:** 1871. **Holdings:** 13,024 books; CDs; DVDs. **Subscriptions:** 100 journals and other serials; 3 newspapers. **Telecommunication Services:** bdahms@cogswell.edu; info@cogswell.edu.

47538 ■ Consad Research Corporation Library
211 N. Whitfield St., Ste. 250
Pittsburgh, PA 15206
Ph: (412)363-5500
Fax: (412)363-5509
Co. E-mail: info@consad.com
URL: http://www.consad.com
Contact: Wilbur Steger, President
Scope: Social science methodology, statistics, urban planning, drug abuse, healthcare, economics, occupational safety and health. **Services:** Library open to the public with restrictions. **Founded:** 1963. **Holdings:** 10,000 books; 10,000 reports. **Subscriptions:** 54 journals and other serials.

47539 ■ Cornell University - School of Industrial and Labor Relations - Martin P. Catherwood Library
309 Ives Hall
Ithaca, NY 14853-3901
Ph: (607)255-5435
Fax: (607)255-9641
Co. E-mail: smb6@cornell.edu
URL: http://www.ilr.cornell.edu/library/
Contact: Gordon Law, Director
Scope: Labor-management relations, labor law and legislation, labor Organization, industrial and labor conditions, labor economics, human resources, income security, human resources management, supervision, occupational safety and health, International and comparative labor relations, organizational behavior and negotiation, and conflict resolution. **Services:** Interlibrary loan; copying; library open to the public. **Founded:** 1945. **Holdings:** 232,000 volumes; 44,368 microforms; 19,000 cubic feet of manuscripts; 647 motion pictures; 1016 filmstrips and slides; 878 videotapes; 2123 sound recordings; 373 computer files; 350,000 images. **Subscriptions:** 3998 journals and other serials; 4 newspapers.

47540 ■ Exxon Research and Engineering Company Information, Computing, and Business Systems
Rte. 22 E.
Annandale, NJ 08801
Ph: (908)730-2924
Fax: (908)730-2925
Co. E-mail: mjbarne@erenj.com
Contact: Mary Jo Barnello, Analyst
Scope: Petroleum refining processes and products, petrochemical processes and products, chemistry, physics, metallurgy, mathematics, industrial safety. **Services:** Services not open to the public. **Founded:** 1983. **Holdings:** 35,000 volumes and microforms; patent holdings. **Subscriptions:** 350 journals and other serials.

47541 ■ The Hartford Financial Services Company - Loss Control Library
690 Asylum Ave.
Hartford Plaza
COGS 2-45
Hartford, CT 06105
Ph: (860)547-5000
Fax: (860)547-6004
Co. E-mail: lynn.zweiflet@thehartford.com
URL: http://www.thehartford.com/corporate/losscontrol/aboutlc.html
Contact: Lynn A. Zweifler, Librarian
Scope: Safety engineering, toxicology, chemistry, fire protection, transportation, occupational safety and health, industrial hygiene, ergonomics, risk management. **Services:** Interlibrary loan; library open to the public by special arrangement only. **Founded:** 1940. **Holdings:** 2000 books; government documents; 15 VF drawers. **Subscriptions:** 200 journals and other serials.

47542 ■ Industrial Health Foundation, Inc. Library
34 Penn Cir., W.
Pittsburgh, PA 15206
Ph: (412)363-6600

Fax: (412)363-6605
Co. E-mail: admin@infipcorp.com
Contact: Janice O'Polka, Project Manager
Scope: Industrial hygiene, occupational safety and health, toxicology, environmental issues. **Services:** Interlibrary loan; Library not open to the public. **Founded:** 1935. **Holdings:** 3000 books; 100 bound periodical volumes; 78,000 abstracts; 50 VF drawers of pamphlets and reprints. **Subscriptions:** 60 journals and other serials.

47543 ■ Institute for Business and Home Safety Library
4775 E. Fowler Ave.
Tampa, FL 33617
Ph: (813)286-3400
Fax: (813)286-9960
Co. E-mail: info@ibhs.org
URL: http://www.disastersafety.org/
Contact: Hilary Thomson, Manager, Information Services
Scope: Insurance, natural disasters, building codes, wind and seismic engineering. **Services:** Interlibrary loan; research for member companies. **Holdings:** 3000 books, periodicals, and audio/visuals. **Subscriptions:** 159 journals and other serials; 3 newspapers.

47544 ■ International Union of Operating Engineers - Research Department Library
1125 17th St., NW
Washington, DC 20036
Ph: (202)429-9100
Fax: (202)778-2691
URL: http://www.iuoe.org
Scope: Union history, productivity of heavy equipment, industrial safety. **Services:** Library not open to the public. **Holdings:** 2000 books; industrial surveys; slides; motion pictures; microfiche.

47545 ■ J.J. Keller & Associates, Inc. - Editorial Resource Center - Research & Technical Library—Keller's Research & Technical Library.
3003 W. Breezewwod Ln.
Neenah, WI 54957-0368
Free: 877-564-2333
Fax: (800)727-7516
Co. E-mail: infopros@jjkeller.com
URL: http://www.jjkeller.com
Contact: Webb A. Shaw, Vice President
Scope: Transportation, motor carrier regulations, workplace safety regulations and practices, hazardous materials, hazardous wastes, industry regulations and compliance, food safety, human resources. **Services:** Copying; library open to the public by referral. **Founded:** 1958. **Holdings:** 8000 books, 500 periodicals; 7600 books, AV programs, and government documents (Department of Transportation, Environmental Protection Agency, and Department of Labor). **Subscriptions:** 1100 journals and other serials.

47546 ■ Lakehead University - Resource Centre for Occupational Health and Safety
University Ctr., Rm. 3
955 Oliver Rd.
Thunder Bay, ON, Canada P7B 5E1
Ph: (807)343-8334
Fax: (807)343-7701
Co. E-mail: ursula.macdonald@lakeheadu.ca
URL: http://hr.lakeheadu.ca/wp/?pg=140
Contact: Ursula MacDonald
Scope: Occupational health and safety, the environment. **Services:** Interlibrary loan; copying; library open to the public. **Founded:** 1978. **Holdings:** 10,000 books and articles. **Subscriptions:** 10 journals and other serials; 2 newspapers.

47547 ■ Manitoba Department of Labour & Immigration - Workplace Safety and Health Division - Client Resource Centre
200-401 York Ave.
Winnipeg, MB, Canada R3C 0P8
Ph: (204)945-3446

Free: 800-282-8069
URL: http://www.gov.mb.ca/labour/safety/index.html
Contact: Darlene Muise, Editor
Scope: Toxicology, occupational health and safety, industrial hygiene. **Services:** Library not open to the public. **Holdings:** Figures not available.

47548 ■ Montana Tech of the University of Montana - Montana Tech Library
1300 W. Park St.
Butte, MT 59701-8997
Ph: (406)496-4281
Fax: (406)496-4133
Co. E-mail: astclair@mtech.edu
URL: http://www.mtech.edu/library
Contact: Ann St. Clair, Director
Scope: Geology, mining, mineral processing, geochemistry, geophysics, petroleum, environmental engineering, occupational safety, mineral economics, industrial hygiene, nursing, healthcare informatics. **Services:** Interlibrary loan; scanning; color copying. **Founded:** 1900. **Holdings:** 59,039 books; 81,794 bound periodical volumes. **Subscriptions:** 394 journals and other serials. **Telecommunication Services:** mlubick@mtech.edu; librequests@mtech.edu.

47549 ■ National Safety Council Library
1121 Spring Lake Dr.
Itasca, IL 60143-3200
Ph: (630)775-2199
Free: 800-621-7615
Fax: (630)285-1315
Co. E-mail: library@nsc.org
URL: http://www.nsc.org/
Contact: Alaina Kolosh, Librarian
Scope: Accident prevention in general, occupational safety and health, industrial hygiene, traffic/transportation safety, and safety research. **Services:** Interlibrary loan; copying; library open to the public with prior contact required. **Founded:** 1915. **Holdings:** 4100 books; 500 bound periodical volumes; 95,400 other cataloged items; 40,300 research reports; 510 reels of microfilm; 4000 microfiche. **Subscriptions:** 250 journals and other serials.

47550 ■ New Mexico Department of Environment - NMED Library
1190 St. Francis Dr., Ste. N4050
Santa Fe, NM 87502
Ph: (505)827-2855
Free: 800-219-6157
Fax: (505)827-2818
Co. E-mail: ann_baumgarn@nmenv.state.nm.us
URL: http://www.nmenv.state.nm.us
Scope: Ground water protection, surface water protection, hazardous waste disposal, radiation protection, occupational health and safety, air quality protection. **Services:** Copying; Library open to the public for reference use only. **Founded:** 1980. **Holdings:** 700 books; 154 bound periodical volumes; 6500 reports and documents. **Subscriptions:** 35 journals and other serials.

47551 ■ New York Department of State - Office of Fire Prevention and Control - Academy of Fire Science - Library
600 College Ave.
Montour Falls, NY 14865-9634
Ph: (607)535-7136
Fax: (607)535-4841
Co. E-mail: ofpc.library@dhses.ny.gov
URL: http://www.dhses.ny.gov/ofpc/training/fire-academy/library.cfm
Contact: Diana Robinson, Librarian
Scope: Fire protection, prevention, and control; rescue; fire department administration and management; New York state codes, standards, and regulations; emergency medical services; hazardous materials; arson prevention; fire investigation; history of fire service in New York State. **Services:** Interlibrary loan; copying; answers to email, mail and telephone inquiries from patrons in New York state; library open to the public. **Founded:** 1971. **Holdings:** 6000 books; 250 bound periodical volumes; 16 VF drawers; 200 microfiche; 3300 videocassettes; CDs and DVDs. **Subscriptions:** 45000 journals and other serials.

47552 ■ North Carolina Department of Labor - Charles H. Livengood, Jr. Memorial Library
1101 Mail Service Ctr.
Raleigh, NC 27699-1101
Ph: (919)807-2850
Co. E-mail: dol.library@labor.nc.gov
URL: http://www.nclabor.com/lib/lib2.htm
Contact: Nick Vincelli, Librarian
Scope: Labor law and history, occupational safety, health, and training. **Services:** Interlibrary loan; copying; SDI; library open to the public by appointment. **Founded:** 1975. **Holdings:** 13,000 volumes; 533 bound periodical volumes; 1200 audiocassettes; vertical files; state government documents. **Subscriptions:** 120 journals and other serials.

47553 ■ Ohio Bureau of Workers' Compensation - BWC Library
30 W. Spring St., 3rd Fl.
Columbus, OH 43215-2256
Ph: (614)466-7388
Free: 800-644-6292
Fax: (614)365-4980
Co. E-mail: library@bwc.state.oh.us
URL: http://www.ohiobwc.com
Contact: Karen Jensen
Scope: Occupational safety, industrial hygiene, workers' compensation, occupational rehabilitation. **Services:** Interlibrary loan; copying; Center open to the public. **Founded:** 1974. **Holdings:** 6000 books; 850 standards; 650 subject headings; 900 videos. **Subscriptions:** 100 journals and other serials.

47554 ■ PACE International Union - Irene Glaus Memorial Library
3340 Perimeter Hill Dr.
Box 1475
Nashville, TN 37202
Ph: (615)834-8590
Fax: (615)831-6792
Co. E-mail: mdimoff@paceunion.org
URL: http://www.paceunion.org
Contact: Mary Alyce Dimoff, Specialist
Scope: Labor relations, law, and history; occupational safety and health. **Services:** Interlibrary loan; copying; library open to the public for reference use only. **Founded:** 1981. **Holdings:** 10,100 books; 1600 bound periodical volumes; 12,250 microfiche; 60 audiotapes; 310 videotapes; 600 government documents; UPIU archival material (39 linear feet of folders, boxes, bound periodical volumes, microfilm); AIW, IWNA and OCAW archival material. **Subscriptions:** 183 journals and other serials; 44 newspapers.

47555 ■ Triodyne Inc. - Beth Hamilton Safety Library
3054 North Lake Terrace
Glenview, IL 60026
Ph: (847)677-4730
Fax: (847)647-2047
Co. E-mail: infoserv@triodyne.com
URL: http://www.triodyne.com/Library.htm
Contact: John Kristelli, Manager, Information Services
Scope: Engineering - forensic, mechanical, automotive, civil; industrial safety; materials science. **Services:** Interlibrary loan; Center not open to the public. **Founded:** 1979. **Holdings:** 3000 monograph titles; 600 VF drawers of technical reports; 1200 VF drawers of manufacturers' literature and catalogs; 800 VF of subject files, bibliographies, and ephemera, 120 VF drawers of engineering standards and specifications. **Subscriptions:** 212 journals and other serials.

47556 ■ U.S. Army Public Health Command Library
5158 Blackhawk Rd.
Aberdeen Proving Ground, MD 21010
Ph: (410)436-4311
Free: 800-222-9698
Fax: (410)436-7301
Co. E-mail: usachppm-pao@amedd.army.mil
URL: http://phc.amedd.army.mil/Pages/default.aspx
Contact: Krishan S. Goel, Librarian
Scope: Occupational medicine, safety and health; chemistry and toxicology; audiology; medical entomology; laser, microwave, and radiological safety and health; air and water pollution; sanitary engineer-

ing. **Services:** Interlibrary loan; copying; SDI. **Founded:** 1955. **Holdings:** 9000 books; 8000 bound periodical volumes; 8400 R&D reports; 3000 microfiche. **Subscriptions:** 250 journals and other serials.

47557 ■ U.S. Bureau of Mines - Twin Cities Research Center Library
201 Federal Dr.
St. Paul, MN 55111
Ph: (612)725-4503
Fax: (612)725-4784
Contact: Marilynn R. Anderson, Librarian
Scope: Mining engineering, metallurgy, mineral industries, geology, industrial safety, environmental remediation. **Services:** Interlibrary loan; Library open to the public. **Founded:** 1962. **Holdings:** 8200 books; 2270 bound periodical volumes; 120 VF drawers of reports, documents, patents. **Subscriptions:** 190 journals and other serials.

47558 ■ U.S. Dept. of Labor - Occupational Safety and Health Administration - Region VIII Library
1999 Broadway, Ste. 1690
Denver, CO 80202-5709
Ph: (720)264-6550
Fax: (720)264-6585
URL: http://www.osha.gov
Contact: Carolyn Leslie, Librarian
Scope: Occupational safety, Occupational health, OSHA regulations, any questions about OSHA - federal or state. **Services:** Interlibrary loan; copying; library open to the public for reference use only; OSHA publications are distributed from this office (one copy per request/title). Help with using OSHA's public website (http://www.osha.gov). **Founded:** 1982. **Holdings:** 600 books; 1100 reports.

47559 ■ U.S. Dept. of Labor - OSHA Billings Area Office Library
2900 4th Ave. N., Ste. 303
Billings, MT 59101
Ph: (406)247-7494
Fax: (406)247-7499
URL: http://www.osha.gov
Contact: Bonnie Albright, Clerk
Scope: Safety and health in the workplace. **Services:** Library open to the public. **Founded:** 1974. **Holdings:** 500 books.

47560 ■ U.S. Dept. of Labor - OSHA Office of Training & Education - H. Lee Saltsgaver Library
2020 S. Arlington Heights Rd.
Arlington Heights, IL 60005
Ph: (847)759-7736
Fax: (847)297-4874
Co. E-mail: perlman.elizabeth@dol.gov
URL: http://www.osha.gov/
Contact: Elizabeth Perlman, Librarian
Scope: Industrial hygiene, occupational safety, industrial toxicology. **Services:** Library open to the public for reference use only. **Founded:** 1972. **Holdings:** 1550 government documents; 1250 standards. **Subscriptions:** 46 journals and other serials.

47561 ■ U.S. Dept. of Labor - OSHA Region III Library
Curtis Center, Ste. 740 W.
170 S. Independence Mall W.
Philadelphia, PA 19106
Ph: (215)861-4900
Fax: (215)861-4904
URL: http://www.osha.gov
Contact: Barbara Bray, Librarian
Scope: Occupational health and safety, industrial hygiene, toxic substances. **Services:** Library open to the public. **Holdings:** 2000 books. **Subscriptions:** 12 journals and other serials.

47562 ■ U.S. Dept. of Labor - OSHA Region X Library
1111 3rd Ave., Ste. 715
Seattle, WA 98101-3216
Ph: (206)553-7620

Fax: (206)553-6499
URL: http://www.osha.gov
Scope: Industrial hygiene, toxic substances, industrial safety, toxicology, safety, engineering. **Services:** Interlibrary loan; copying; library open to the public for reference use only. **Founded:** 1971. **Holdings:** 1600 titles. **Subscriptions:** 10 journals and other serials.

47563 ■ U.S. Dept. of Labor - OSHA Technical Data Center
200 Constitution Ave. NW, Rm. N-2625
Washington, DC 20210
Ph: (202)693-2350
Fax: (202)693-1648
URL: http://www.osha.gov/dts/tdc/index.html
Contact: Amanda Edens, Director
Scope: Occupational safety, industrial hygiene, toxicology, control technology, hazardous materials, fire safety, electrical safety, noise, carcinogens, material safety, farm safety, process safety, ergonomics, occupational health nursing, blood-borne pathogens, indoor air quality, Occupational Safety & Health Administration (OSHA) rulemaking docket. **Services:** Interlibrary loan; Center open to the public for reference use only. **Founded:** 1972. **Holdings:** 6000 books and bound periodical volumes; 500,000 microfiche; standards from more than 370 organizations and societies. **Subscriptions:** 200 journals and other serials.

47564 ■ U.S. National Institute for Occupational Safety and Health - Library C-21
4676 Columbia Pkwy.
Cincinnati, OH 45226
Ph: (513)533-8302
Free: 888-232-6348
Co. E-mail: cdcinfo@cdc.gov
URL: http://www.cdc.gov/niosh
Contact: Lawrence Q. Foster, Librarian
Scope: Occupational safety and health, industrial hygiene and toxicology. **Services:** Interlibrary loan; Library open to the public. **Founded:** 1970. **Holdings:** 8000 books; 10,000 bound periodical volumes. **Subscriptions:** 125 journals and other serials.

47565 ■ University of California, Berkeley - School of Public Health - Labor Occupational Health Program Library
2223 Fulton St., 4th Fl.
Berkeley, CA 94720-5120
Ph: (510)643-4335
Fax: (510)643-5698
Co. E-mail: andrews2@berkeley.edu
URL: http://www.lohp.org/library/
Contact: Karen Andrews, Librarian
Scope: Chemical and physical occupational hazards, medical and industrial hygiene, standards and regulations, workers' compensation and education. **Services:** Library open to the public for reference use only (technical assistance by phone and e-mail). **Founded:** 1974. **Holdings:** 10,000 books, pamphlets, periodicals, and videos; 180 unbound periodicals; newspaper clipping file. **Subscriptions:** 50 journals and other serials; 110 newspapers. **Telecommunication Services:** info@lohp.org.

47566 ■ WorkSafeNB - Communications Department
1 Portland St.
St. John, NB, Canada E2L 3X9
Ph: (506)632-2200
Free: 800-222-9775
Fax: (506)453-7982
Co. E-mail: communications@ws-ts.nb.ca
URL: http://www.worksafenb.ca
Contact: Jill Breen, Communications Specialist
Scope: Social affairs, education, occupational health and safety, training, mining safety. **Holdings:** Figures not available.

RESEARCH CENTERS

47567 ■ National Farm Medicine Center (NFMC)
1000 N Oak Ave.
Marshfield, WI 54449-5790

Ph: (715)389-4999
Free: 800-662-6900
Fax: (715)389-4996
Co. E-mail: lee.barbara@mcrf.mfldclin.edu
URL: http://www.marshfieldclinic.org/nfmc/
Contact: Barbara C. Lee, Director
Founded: 1981. **Publications:** *Cultivate newsletter*; *Nurture newsletter*; *Progress Report*; *Year in Review annual report*. **Telecommunication Services:** nfmcsh@mcrf.mfldclin.edu.

47568 ■ University of Michigan - Center for Ergonomics
1205 Beal Ave.
Ann Arbor, MI 48109-2117
Ph: (734)763-2243
Fax: (734)764-3451
Co. E-mail: rrabourn@umich.edu
URL: http://www.engin.umich.edu/dept/ioe/C4E
Contact: Thomas J. Armstrong, Director
Founded: 1959. **Educational Activities:** 15 one- to five-day courses for engineers, managers, and occupational health professionals (Annual). **Telecommunication Services:** centerforergonomics@umich.edu.

47569 ■ University of Montreal - Health and Prevention Social Research Group—University of Montreal - Groupe de Recherche sur les Aspects Sociaux de la Sante et de la Prevention (GRASP)
2801 Édouard-Montpetit Blvd., Ste. 168
Station Centre-ville, Box 6128
Montreal, QC, Canada H3C 3J7
Ph: (514)343-6193
Fax: (514)343-2334
Co. E-mail: andree.demers@umontreal.ca
URL: http://www.grasp.umontreal.ca
Contact: Andrée Demers, Director
Services: Policy consultation: to health and welfare organizations, advocacy groups, and government. **Founded:** 1984. **Educational Activities:** Multidisciplinary university seminars (Monthly); Health and Prevention Social Research Group Conferences (Monthly). **Telecommunication Services:** grasp@umontreal.ca.

47570 ■ University of Utah - Rocky Mountain Center for Occupational and Environmental Health (RMCOEH)—University of Utah - National Institute for Occupational Safety and Health Education and Research Center
391 Chipeta Way, Ste. C
Salt Lake City, UT 84108
Ph: (801)581-4800
Fax: (801)581-7224
Co. E-mail: kurt.hegmann@hsc.utah.edu
URL: http://medicine.utah.edu/rmcoeh
Contact: Dr. Kurt T. Hegmann, Director
Services: Consulting: for federal, state, and local governments, industry, and other organizations. **Founded:** 1977. **Educational Activities:** Continuing education programs, in industrial hygiene, occupational medicine, and occupational safety and ergonomics, with more than 2,000 attendees yearly; Graduate programs in industrial hygiene and occupational medicine; Residency program in occupational medicine.

47571 ■ West Virginia University - Institute of Occupational and Environmental Health (IOEH)
Robert C. Byrd Health Sciences Ctr.
School of Medicine
Morgantown, WV 26506-9190
Ph: (304)293-0741
Fax: (304)293-2629
Co. E-mail: raltobello@hsc.wvu.edu
URL: http://www.hsc.wvu.edu/ioeh
Contact: Robin Altobello, Program Manager
Services: Community consultations: on toxic exposure risk; Patient care: for toxic exposure. **Founded:** 1988. **Publications:** *Occupational Health*. **Educational Activities:** Residencies, in preventive occupational and environmental medicine; Master's degree, in public health; IOEH Workshops.

START-UP INFORMATION

47572 ■ *101 Businesses You Can Start with Less Than One Thousand Dollars: for Students*
Pub: Atlantic Publishing Company
Ed: Heather Lee Shepherd. **Released:** September 2007. **Price:** $21.95. **Description:** More than 100 business ideas for busy students; these ideas can be started for very little money yet provide striving students with more money than they would make working a job paying an hourly wage. Web links for additional information are provides along with detailed instruction and examples for starting a successful business.

47573 ■ *"On Their Own: Bronx High School Students Open a Bank Branch" in Black Enterprise (Vol. 38, February 2008, No. 7, pp. 42)*
Pub: Earl G. Graves Publishing Co. Inc.
Ed: Jessica Jones. **Description:** Students at Fordham Leadership Academy for Business and Technology in New York City opened a student-run bank branch at their high school. The business paid high school seniors $11 per hour to work as tellers. Students were also taught interviewing basics.

47574 ■ *Prepare to Be a Teen Millionaire*
Pub: Health Communications, Inc.
Contact: Peter Vegso, President
Ed: Robyn Collins; Kimberly Spinks Burleson. **Released:** April 1, 2008. **Price:** $16.95. **Description:** Business reference for any teenager wishing to become a successful entrepreneur; advice is given from successful teenage millionaires. Topics covered include: choosing a business name, type, and location; use of the Internet; legal issues; branding, sales, and marketing; funding and financial management; return on investment; retirement; development of a sound business plan; and certification for minority or women-owned companies.

ASSOCIATIONS AND OTHER ORGANIZATIONS

47575 ■ **Entrepreneurs' Organization (EO)**
500 Montgomery St., Ste. 500
Alexandria, VA 22314
Ph: (703)519-6700
Fax: (703)519-1864
Co. E-mail: info@eonetwork.org
URL: http://www.eonetwork.org
Contact: Samer Kurdi, Chairman
Description: Entrepreneurs under the age of 50 who have either founded, co-founded, are a controlling shareholder of, or own a firm with annual gross revenues exceeding $1,000,000 (membership is by invitation only). Engages leading entrepreneurs to learn and grow. Serves as a focal point for networking and development of members through small group learning sessions, regular local chapter social and learning events, and global conference-based education programs. **Founded:** 1987. **Publications:**

Octane (Quarterly); *Overdrive* (Monthly). **Educational Activities:** Universities and Leadership Conference (Annual); Universities and Leadership Conference (Periodic).

47576 ■ **National Foundation for Teaching Entrepreneurship (NFTE)**
120 Wall St., 18th Fl.
New York, NY 10005
URL: http://www.nfte.com
Contact: Steve Mariotti, Founder
Description: Devoted to teaching entrepreneurship education to low-income young people, ages 11 through 18. **Founded:** 1987. **Publications:** *NFTE News* (Quarterly).

47577 ■ **Young Presidents' Organization (YPO)**
600 E Las Colinas Blvd., Ste. 1000
Irving, TX 75039
Ph: (972)587-1500
Free: 800-773-7976
Fax: (972)587-1611
Co. E-mail: askypo@ypo.org
URL: http://www.ypo.org
Description: Presidents or chief executive officers of corporations with minimum of 50 employees; each member must have been elected president before his/her 40th birthday and must retire by June 30th the year after his/her 50th birthday. Assists members in becoming better presidents through education and idea exchange. Conducts courses for members and spouses, in business, arts and sciences, world affairs, and family and community life, during a given year at various locations, including graduate business schools. **Founded:** 1950.

REFERENCE WORKS

47578 ■ *"Are You a Young Canadian Entrepreneur Looking for Recognition?" in CNW Group (November 10, 2010)*
Pub: Comtex
Description: Business Development Bank of Canada is looking for young Canadian entrepreneurs ages 19 to 35 for its 2011 Young Entrepreneur Awards. The awards pay tribute to remarkable young Canadian entrepreneurs for their creativity, innovative spirit and community development, as well as business success.

47579 ■ *"Biz U: Cool for School" in Entrepreneur (Vol. 35, October 2007, No. 10, pp. 144)*
Pub: Entrepreneur Media Inc.
Ed: Nichole L. Torres. **Description:** Forming a high technology business while still in college has its advantages such as having information resources nearby and having students from various fields to ask for help and advice. School business competitions are also helpful in building networks with investors. Ways that the college environment can be useful to aspiring entrepreneurs, particularly to those who are into high technology business, are discussed.

47580 ■ *"Business Start-Up a Learning Experience for Young Bellingham Entrepreneur" in Bellingham Herald (July 18, 2010)*
Pub: Bellingham Herald
Ed: Dave Gallagher. **Description:** Profile of 21-year-old entrepreneur, Chase Larabee, who developed an online program that helps airport fixed-based operators handle refueling, hotel and transportation reservations and other requests from private airplane pilots.

47581 ■ *Capitalism for Kids: Growing Up to Be Your Own Boss*
Pub: Bluestocking Press
Ed: Karl Hess. **Released:** June 2006. **Price:** $8.95. **Description:** Capitalism, democratic socialism, socialism, communism, and totalitarianism is explained to children. The book explains to young people how to build a profitable business.

47582 ■ *Creating Success from the Inside Out: Develop the Focus and Strategy to Uncover the Life You Want*
Pub: John Wiley and Sons, Inc.
Ed: Ephren W. Taylor. **Released:** November 16, 2007. **Price:** $24.95. **Description:** Ephren Taylor founded his first business at age 12 and was a multimillionaire CEO ten years later. Taylor explains how he and other successful young entrepreneurs think about success and achievement.

47583 ■ *"Creativity: A Key Link to Entrepreneurial Behavior" in Business Horizons (September-October 2007, pp. 365)*
Pub: Elsevier Technology Publications
Ed: Stephen Ko, John E. Butler. **Description:** Importance of creativity and its link to entrepreneurial behavior is examined. In a study of various entrepreneurs, studies concluded that a solid knowledge base, a well-developed social network, and a strong focus on identifying opportunities are relevant to entrepreneurial behavior.

47584 ■ *"Elastic Path Software Joins Canada in G20 Young Entrepreneur Summit" in Internet Wire (June 14, 2010)*
Pub: Comtex
Description: The Canadian Youth Business Foundation hosted the G20 Young Entrepreneur Summit and announced that Harry Chemko of British Columbia's Elastic Path Software will be a member of the Canadian delegation at the G20 Young Entrepreneur Summit. Details are included.

47585 ■ *"G20 Young Entrepreneur Alliance Signs Charter Outlining Commitment to Entrepreneurship" in Internet Wire (November 10, 2010)*
Pub: Comtex
Description: G20 Young Entrepreneur Summit members created a charter document that outlines their support for the G20 process to include entrepreneurship on its agenda. Details of the Summit are included.

47586 ■ *Here Come the Regulars: How to Run a Record Label on a Shoestring Budget*
Pub: Faber & Faber, Inc.

Ed: Ian Anderson. **Released:** October 1, 2009. **Price:** $15.00. **Description:** Author, Ian Anderson launched his own successful record label, Afternoon Records when he was 18 years old. Anderson shares insight into starting a record label, focusing on label image, budget, blogging, potential artists, as well as legal aspects.

47587 ■ *"Identify and Conquer" in Black Enterprise (Vol. 38, December 2007, No. 5, pp. 76)*
Pub: Earl G. Graves Publishing Co. Inc.

Ed: Tennille M. Robinson. **Description:** Twenty-two-year-old entrepreneur wants to expand her wholesale body oil and skincare products business.

47588 ■ *"Kid-Friendly Business Sources" in Black Enterprise (Vol. 37, January 2007, No. 6, pp. 40)*
Pub: Earl G. Graves Publishing Co. Inc.

Ed: Carolyn M. Brown. **Description:** Financial or business camps are a great way to encourage a child who interested in starting his or her own business. A number of these camps are available each year including Kidpreneurs Conference and Bull and Bear Investment Camp. Other resources are available online. Resources included.

47589 ■ *"Labor of Love" in Green Industry Pro (Vol. 23, March 2011, No. 3, pp. 14)*
Pub: Cygnus Business Media

Ed: Gregg Wartgow. **Description:** Profile of CLS Landscape Management in Chino, California and its owner who started the company when he was 21 years old. Kevin Davis built his landscape firm into a $20 million a year business without using any dedicated salesperson.

47590 ■ *Lessons of a Lipstick Queen: Finding and Developing the Great Idea That Can Change Your Life*
Pub: Simon and Schuster Inc.
Contact: Carolyn Reidy, President
E-mail: carolyn.reidy@simonandschuster.com

Ed: Poppy King. **Released:** May 1, 2009. **Price:** $14.00. **Description:** Poppy King tells how she started her lipstick brand at age eighteen. She reveals how she managed to launch her business using a good idea and finding financing, marketing the product and how she became successful.

47591 ■ *"Meet the Dropouts: the Students Who Chose Start-Ups Over College" in Inc.*

(Vol. 33, September 2011, No. 7, pp. 32)
Pub: Inc. Magazine
Ed: Eric Markowitz. **Description:** Profiles of 24 college students who left school in order to work on their own startup companies. Each new company is receiving $100,000 from Peter Thiel, cofounder of PayPal and an angel investor.

47592 ■ *My Start-Up Life: What a (Very) Young C.E.O. Learned on His Journey Through Silicon Valley*
Pub: Jossey-Bass Publishers
Ed: Ben Casnocha. **Released:** May 25, 2007. **Price:** $24.95. **Description:** Profile of Ben Casnocha, a young entrepreneur who shares insight into starting a running a new business.

47593 ■ *"Screen Time" in Canadian Business (Vol. 81, October 13, 2008, No. 17, pp. 93)*
Pub: Rogers Media Ltd.
Ed: Calvin Leung. **Description:** Young Canadian entertainment business up-and-comers like Ari Lantos and Brian Mossof plan to produce movies that cold earn and entertain audiences rather than focusing on winning awards. English movies continue to struggle in Canada, while French-language films continue to thrive. Details on Canada's movie industry are furnished.

47594 ■ *"Tech Giving 2.0" in Boston Business Journal (Vol. 31, August 5, 2011, No. 28, pp. 1)*
Pub: Boston Business Journal
Ed: Mary Moore. **Description:** Entrepreneurs and venture capitalists in Boston have launched Technology Underwriting Greater Good, the tech industry's answer to the criticism that they are not charitable. The foundation finances nonprofits that aid young people through entrepreneurship, education and life experience. Other tech firms in Boston doing charitable works are discussed.

47595 ■ *Young Bucks: How to Raise a Future Millionaire*
Pub: Thomas Nelson Inc.
Ed: Troy Dunn. **Released:** November 2007. **Price:** $17.99. **Description:** Advice is given to parents to teach their children how to save money, invest wisely and even start their own business.

47596 ■ *"Young Entrepreneur Gets Some Recognition and Some Help for College" in Philadelphia Inquirer (August 30, 2010)*
Pub: Philadelphia Inquirer
Ed: Susan Snyder. **Description:** Profile of Zachary Gosling, age 18, who launched an online auction Website from his bedroom, using advertising and sponsorship funds rather than charging fees to users.

47597 ■ *"Young Entrepreneur's Business Plan? An Ice Cream Boat? Really Floats: Maine at Work" in Portland Press Herald (August 9, 2010)*
Pub: Portland Press Herald
Ed: Ray Routhier. **Description:** Profile of Jake Viola, founder of and ice cream boat located near Portland, Maine. Viola is a sophomore at Yale University and sells ice cream from his pontoon boat on Little Sebago lake.

47598 ■ *"Young Millionaires" in Entrepreneur (Vol. 35, October 2007, No. 10, pp. 76)*
Pub: Entrepreneur Media Inc.
Ed: Jessica Chen, Lindsay Hollway, Amanda C. Kooser, Kim Orr, James Park, Nichole L. Torres, and Sarah Wilson. **Description:** Young successful entrepreneurs of 2007 were chosen to talk about their success story and their business strategies in the past and those for the future. Among those featured are Kelly Flatley, Brendan Synnott, Herman Flores, Myles Kovacs, Haythem Haddad, Jim Wetzel, Lance Lawson, Jacob DeHart, Jake Nickell, Tim Vanderhook, Chris Vanderhook, Russell Vanderhook, Megan Duckett, Brad Sugars, John Vechey, Brian Fiete, Jason Kapalka, Nathan Jones, Devon Rifkin, Ryan Black, Ed Nichols, Jeremy Black, Amy Smilovic, Bob Shallenberger, and John Cavanagh.

TRADE PERIODICALS

47599 ■ *Futures*
Pub: Junior Achievement
Contact: Mr. Sean C. Rush, President
Released: Quarterly. **Description:** Carries feature articles on various aspects of the Junior Achievement program and the volunteers and funders who support it. Promotes the principles of the free enterprise system. Recurring features include board member and volunteer profiles, and strategic initiatives.

VIDEOCASSETTES/AUDIOCASSETTES

47600 ■ *Baby-Sitting the Responsible Way*
Cambridge Educational
c/o Films Media Group
132 West 31st Street, 17th Floor
Ste. 124
New York, NY 10001
Free: 800-257-5126
Fax: (609)671-0266
Co. E-mail: custserve@films.com
URL: http://www.cambridgeol.com
Released: 19??. **Price:** $49.00. **Description:** Covers issues in responsible babysitting, including handling emergencies, keeping children on schedule, mealtime, handling behavior problems, and accident avoidance. Outlines behaviors to avoid such as talking extensively on the phone, failing to clean-up, and doing homework. Includes manual. **Availability:** VHS.

SMALL BUSINESS DEVELOPMENT CENTERS

47601 ■ Alabama A&M University Small Business Development Center
PO Box 429
Normal, AL 35762
Ph: (256)372-8487
Fax: (256)372-5874
Co. E-mail: uchenna.elike@aamu.edu
URL: http://www.aamu.edu/academics/bpa/center-sandprograms/smallbusinessdevelopmentcenter/pages/default.aspx
Contact: Uchenna Elike, Director
Description: Represents and promotes the small business sector. Provides management assistance to current and prospective small business owners. Helps to improve management skills and expand the products and services of members.

47602 ■ Alabama Small Business Development Consortium, Lead Office (ASBDC)
University of Alabama
Box 870396
Tuscaloosa, AL 35487-0396
Ph: (205)348-1582
Free: 877-825-7232
Fax: (205)348-6974
Co. E-mail: asbdc@ua.edu
URL: http://www.asbdc.org
Contact: Mr. Brian Davis, Director
Description: Represents and promotes the small business sector. Provides management assistance to current and prospective small business owners. Helps to improve management skills and expand the products and services of members.

47603 ■ Alabama State University Small Business Development Center
c/o Lorenza Patrick, Dir.
915 S Jackson St.
Montgomery, AL 36104
Ph: (334)229-4138
Fax: (334)269-1102
Co. E-mail: lpatrick@alasu.edu
URL: http://www.asbdc.org
Contact: Lorenza Patrick, Director
Description: Represents and promotes the small business sector. Provides management assistance to current and prospective small business owners. Helps to improve management skills and expand the products and services of members.

47604 ■ Auburn University Small Business Development Center
114 Lowder Business Bldg.
Auburn, AL 36849
Ph: (334)844-4220
Co. E-mail: dipofja@auburn.edu
URL: http://business.auburn.edu/research-centers/centers/small-business-development-center
Contact: Dr. Jackie Alexander Di Pofi, Director
Description: Represents and promotes the small business sector. Provides management assistance to

current and prospective small business owners. Helps to improve management skills and expand the products and services of members.

47605 ■ Jacksonville State University Small Business Development Center
College of Commerce and Business Administration
Merrill Hall, Rm. 114
700 Pelham Rd. N
Jacksonville, AL 36265
Ph: (256)782-5271
Co. E-mail: sbdc@jsu.edu
URL: http://www.jsusbdc.com
Contact: Pat Shaddix, Director
Description: Represents and promotes the small business sector. Provides management assistance to current and prospective small business owners. Helps to improve management skills and expand the products and services of members. **Founded:** 1981.

47606 ■ Troy University Small Business Development Center
Troy Campus
100 Industrial Blvd.
Troy, AL 36081
Ph: (334)674-2425
Co. E-mail: slucas@troy.edu
URL: http://cibed.troy.edu/sbdc
Contact: Sandra Lucas, Director
Description: Represents and promotes the small business sector. Provides management assistance to current and prospective small business owners. Helps to improve management skills and expand the products and services of members.

47607 ■ University of Alabama in Huntsville Small Business Development Center
301 Sparkman Dr.
Huntsville, AL 35899
Ph: (256)824-6422
Fax: (256)824-4339
Co. E-mail: sbdc@uah.edu
URL: http://sbdc.uah.edu
Contact: Foster Perry, Director
Description: Represents and promotes the small business sector. Provides management assistance to current and prospective small business owners. Helps to improve management skills and expand the products and services of members.

47608 ■ University of Alabama Small Business Development Center
Box 870396
Tuscaloosa, AL 35487-0396
Ph: (205)348-1582
Free: 877-825-7232
Fax: (205)348-6974
Co. E-mail: asbdc@ua.edu
URL: http://www.asbdc.org
Contact: Mr. Brian Davis, Director
Description: Represents and promotes the small business sector. Provides management assistance to current and prospective small business owners. Helps to improve management skills and expand the products and services of members.

47609 ■ University of North Alabama - Small Business Development Center (UNA-SBDC)
c/o Carolyn Long, Assoc. Dir.
135 Keller Hall
1 Harrison Plz.
Florence, AL 35632
Ph: (256)765-4599
Fax: (256)765-4813
Co. E-mail: cmlong@una.edu
URL: http://business.una.edu/sbdc
Contact: Mr. David Black, Director
Description: Represents and promotes the small business sector. Provides management assistance to current and prospective small business owners. Helps to improve management skills and expand the products and services of members.

47610 ■ University of South Alabama Small Business Development Center
MCOB, Rm. 118
307 University Blvd.
Mobile, AL 36688
Ph: (251)460-6004
Fax: (251)460-6246
Co. E-mail: sbdc@usouthal.edu
URL: http://www.southalabama.edu/sbdc
Description: Represents and promotes the small business sector. Provides management assistance to current and prospective small business owners. Helps to improve management skills and expand the products and services of members.

47611 ■ University of West Alabama Small Business Development Center
c/o Mr. Donald Mills, Dir.
Guy Hunt Technical Complex, R122, Sta. 35
Livingston, AL 35470
Ph: (205)652-3665
URL: http://www.asbdc.org
Contact: Mr. Donald Mills, Director
Description: Represents and promotes the small business sector. Provides management assistance to current and prospective small business owners. Helps to improve management skills and expand the products and services of members.

SMALL BUSINESS ASSISTANCE PROGRAMS

47612 ■ Alabama Department of Economic and Community Affairs - Community and Economic Development Programs
401 Adams Ave.
Montgomery, AL 36103-5690
Ph: (334)242-5100
Fax: (334)242-5099
URL: http://www.adeca.state.al.us
Contact: Doni M. Ingram, Director
Description: Provides consultation services to small and developing businesses; provides information on federal grants and projects; and helps businesses to develop export contacts and markets.

47613 ■ University of Alabama - Alabama International Trade Center
500 Colonial Dr., 201 Bidgood Hall
Box 870396
Tuscaloosa, AL 35487-0396
Ph: (205)348-7621
Free: 800-747-2482
Fax: (205)348-6974
Co. E-mail: aitc@ua.edu
URL: http://www.aitc.ua.edu
Contact: Brian K. Davis, Director
Description: Offers consulting services and seminars to help businesses develop international activities. Compiles information on foreign business climates. Services provided free of charge to smaller businesses; others must pay a fee.

SCORE OFFICES

47614 ■ Anniston SCORE
Co. E-mail: score0638@aol.com

BETTER BUSINESS BUREAUS

47615 ■ Better Business Bureau, Birmingham
PO Box 55268
Birmingham, AL 35255-5268
Ph: (205)558-2222
Free: 800-824-5274
Fax: (205)558-2239
Co. E-mail: info@centralalabama.bbb.org
URL: http://www.birmingham-al.bbb.org
Contact: David C. Smitherman, President
Description: Seeks to promote and foster the highest ethical relationship between businesses and the public through voluntary self-regulation, consumer and business education, and service excellence. Provides information to help consumers and businesses make informed purchasing decisions and avoid costly scams and frauds; settles consumer complaints through arbitration and other means.

47616 ■ Better Business Bureau of North Alabama
PO Box 383
Huntsville, AL 35804-0383
Ph: (256)533-1640
Free: 800-239-1642
Fax: (256)533-1177
Co. E-mail: info@northalabama.bbb.org
URL: http://northalabama.bbb.org
Contact: Michele Mason, President
Description: Fosters ethical relationship between businesses and the community through voluntary self-regulation, consumer and business education and service excellence. **Founded:** 1965. **Awards:** Torch Award for Marketplace Ethics (Annual).

47617 ■ Better Business Bureau of South Alabama
3361-E Cottage Hill Rd.
Mobile, AL 36606
Ph: (251)433-5494
Free: 800-544-4714
Fax: (251)438-3191
Co. E-mail: info@bbsouthal.org
URL: http://mobile.bbb.org
Contact: Tina Waller, President
Description: Seeks to promote and foster the highest ethical relationship between businesses and the public through voluntary self-regulation, consumer and business education, and service excellence. Provides information to help consumers and businesses make informed purchasing decisions and avoid costly scams and frauds; settles consumer complaints through arbitration and other means. **Founded:** 1954.

CHAMBERS OF COMMERCE

47618 ■ Action Bulletin
PO Box 973
Scottsboro, AL 35769
Ph: (256)259-5500
Free: 800-259-5508

Fax: (256)259-4447
Co. E-mail: roden@scottsboro.org
URL: http://www.jacksoncountychamber.com
Contact: Rick Roden, President
Released: Monthly **Price:** $12, /year.

47619 ■ Alabama Gulf Coast Area Chamber of Commerce (AGCACC)
3150 Gulf Shores Pkwy.
PO Drawer 3869
Gulf Shores, AL 36547-3869
Ph: (251)968-6904
Fax: (251)968-5332
Co. E-mail: info@alagulfcoastchamber.com
URL: http://www.alagulfcoastchamber.com
Contact: Linda Whitlock, President
Description: Promotes business and community development in Gulf Shores, AL. **Publications:** *Coast Commerce* (Monthly). **Educational Activities:** Business After Hours (Monthly). **Awards:** Island Spirit Award (Monthly).

47620 ■ Alexander City Chamber of Commerce (ACCC)
120 Tallapoosa St.
Alexander City, AL 35010
Ph: (256)234-3461
Fax: (256)234-0094
Co. E-mail: susan@charter.net
URL: http://www.alexandercity.org
Contact: Marvin Wagoner, President
Description: Promotes business and community development in Alexander City, Lake Martin Area. **Founded:** 1910. **Publications:** *Chamber Currents* (Monthly). **Telecommunication Services:** mwagoner@alexandercitychamber.com.

47621 ■ Aliceville Area Chamber of Commerce (AACC)
419 Memorial Pkwy. NE
Aliceville, AL 35442
Ph: (205)373-2820
Co. E-mail: acc@nctv.com
URL: http://www.cityofaliceville.com
Contact: Gale Ammerman, Chairman
Description: Promotes business and community development in the Aliceville, AL area. **Founded:** 1928. **Publications:** *Connecting Point* (Quarterly). **Awards:** Citizen of the Year (Annual); WWII Commemorative Community Award.

47622 ■ Arab Chamber of Commerce
1157 N Main St.
Arab, AL 35016
Ph: (256)586-3138
Co. E-mail: knorton@arab-chamber.org
URL: http://www.arab-chamber.org
Contact: Katy Norton, President
Description: Seeks to promote and perpetuate business growth, economic development, civic interest, general welfare and prosperity of the Arab area. Aims to stimulate public interest to these ends. **Awards:** Business of the Month (Monthly); Circle of Excellence Business Award (Annual); Outstanding Citizen Achievement Award (Annual); Teacher of the Year (Annual).

47623 ■ Atmore Area Chamber of Commerce (AACC)
501 S Pensacola Ave.
Atmore, AL 36502
Ph: (251)368-3305
Fax: (251)368-0800
Co. E-mail: atmoreal@frontiernet.net
URL: http://www.atmorechamber.com
Description: Promotes business and community development in the Atmore, AL area.

47624 ■ Auburn Advantage
PO Box 1370
Auburn, AL 36830
Ph: (334)887-7011
Fax: (334)821-5500
Co. E-mail: lolly@auburnchamber.com
URL: http://www.auburnchamber.com
Contact: Lolly Stainer, President
Released: Quarterly **Price:** $25.

47625 ■ Auburn Chamber of Commerce (ACC)
PO Box 1370
Auburn, AL 36830
Ph: (334)887-7011
Fax: (334)821-5500
Co. E-mail: lolly@auburnchamber.com
URL: http://www.auburnchamber.com
Contact: Lolly Stainer, President
Description: Promotes business, community, and economic development in Auburn, AL. **Founded:** 1836. **Publications:** *Auburn Advantage* (Quarterly).

47626 ■ Bayou La Batre Chamber of Commerce (BLBCC)
PO Box 486
Bayou La Batre, AL 36509
Ph: (251)824-4088
Fax: (251)824-4088
Co. E-mail: info@bayoulabatrechamber.com
URL: http://www.bayoulabatrechamber.com
Description: Promotes business and community development in Bayou La Batre, AL. Conducts taste of the Bayou festival. **Founded:** 1940.

47627 ■ Bessemer Area Today
Released: Annual

47628 ■ Bessemer Area Wage/Salary Research 2000

47629 ■ Birmingham Business Alliance (BBA)
505 N 20th St., Ste. 200
Birmingham, AL 35203
Ph: (205)324-2100
Fax: (205)324-2560
Co. E-mail: bhilson@birminghambusinessalliance.com
URL: http://www.birminghambusinessalliance.com
Contact: Brian Hilson, III, President
Description: Promotes business and community development in the Birmingham, AL region. Provides liaison with local agencies. **Founded:** 1887. **Publications:** *Birmingham Magazine* (Monthly); *Birmingham Regional International Business Directory*; *Birminghamchamber.com Newsletter* (Monthly); *Major Employers Directory* (Annual); *Who's Who Directory* (Annual); *Small Business Guide/Business Start-up Checklist*.

47630 ■ Birmingham Magazine
505 N 20th St., Ste. 200
Birmingham, AL 35203
Ph: (205)324-2100
Fax: (205)324-2560
Co. E-mail: bhilson@birminghambusinessalliance.com
URL: http://www.birminghambusinessalliance.com
Contact: Brian Hilson, III, President
Released: Monthly **Price:** included in membership dues; $15, /year subscription for nonmembers; $3, single issue for nonmembers; $3.50, single issue by mail for nonmembers.

47631 ■ Birmingham Regional International Business Directory
505 N 20th St., Ste. 200
Birmingham, AL 35203
Ph: (205)324-2100
Fax: (205)324-2560
Co. E-mail: bhilson@birminghambusinessalliance.com
URL: http://www.birminghambusinessalliance.com
Contact: Brian Hilson, III, President
Price: $20.

47632 ■ Birminghamchamber.com Newsletter
505 N 20th St., Ste. 200
Birmingham, AL 35203
Ph: (205)324-2100
Fax: (205)324-2560
Co. E-mail: bhilson@birminghambusinessalliance.com
URL: http://www.birminghambusinessalliance.com
Contact: Brian Hilson, III, President
Released: Monthly **Price:** included in membership dues.

47633 ■ Blount-Oneonta Chamber of Commerce
PO Box 1487
Oneonta, AL 35121
Ph: (205)274-2153
Fax: (205)274-2099
Co. E-mail: info@blountoneontachamber.org
URL: http://www.blountoneontachamber.org
Contact: Kelley Cochran, President
Description: Individuals interested in preserving the history of Blount County, AL. **Publications:** *Chamber News* (Monthly). **Awards:** Outstanding Citizen Award; Outstanding Teachers Award.

47634 ■ Boaz Chamber of Commerce (BCC)
100 E Bartlett Ave.
Boaz, AL 35957
Ph: (256)593-8154
Fax: (256)593-1233
Co. E-mail: chamber@boazchamberofcommerce. com
URL: http://www.boazchamberofcommerce.com
Contact: Tony King, Chairman
Description: Promotes business and community development in Boaz, Alabama. **Founded:** 1947. **Publications:** *Boaz Vision* (Monthly). **Awards:** Citizen of the Year (Annual); Educator of the Year (Annual).

47635 ■ *Boaz Vision*
100 E Bartlett Ave.
Boaz, AL 35957
Ph: (256)593-8154
Fax: (256)593-1233
Co. E-mail: chamber@boazchamberofcommerce. com
URL: http://www.boazchamberofcommerce.com
Contact: Tony King, Chairman
Released: Monthly

47636 ■ *Business News*
PO Box 1117
Foley, AL 36536
Ph: (251)943-3291
Free: 877-461-3712
Fax: (251)943-6810
Co. E-mail: infodesk@southbaldwinchamber.com
URL: http://www.southbaldwinchamber.com
Contact: Glenn Manning, Chairman
Released: Monthly **Price:** free for members.

47637 ■ *Business View*
451 Government St.
Mobile, AL 36652-2187
Ph: (251)433-6951
Free: 800-422-6951
Fax: (251)432-1143
Co. E-mail: info@mobilechamber.com
URL: http://www.mobilechamber.com
Contact: Michael Pierce, Chairman
Released: Monthly

47638 ■ Central Baldwin Chamber of Commerce (CBCC)
PO Box 587
Robertsdale, AL 36567
Ph: (251)947-2626
Fax: (251)947-4809
URL: http://www.centralbaldwin.com
Contact: Steve Brooks, Chairman
Description: Promotes business and community development in the Robertsdale, AL area.

47639 ■ *Chamber Chatter*
PO Box 66
Clanton, AL 35046
Ph: (205)755-2400
Fax: (205)755-8444
Co. E-mail: info@chiltonchamberonline.com
URL: http://chiltonchamberonline.com
Contact: Mike Robertson, Executive Director
Released: Bimonthly

47640 ■ Chamber of Commerce - Bessemer Area (BACC)
321 N 18th St.
Bessemer, AL 35020
Ph: (205)425-3253
Free: 888-423-7736

Fax: (205)425-4979
Co. E-mail: mmilan1@bellsouth.net
URL: http://www.bessemerchamber.com
Contact: Ronald W. Acker, President
Description: Promotes business and community development in the Bessemer and Southwest Metro area. **Founded:** 1922. **Publications:** *Communique* (Monthly). **Telecommunication Services:** ronacker@bellsouth.net.

47641 ■ Chamber of Commerce of Huntsville/ Madison County (CCHMC)
225 Church St.
Huntsville, AL 35801
Ph: (256)535-2000
Fax: (255)535-2015
Co. E-mail: info@hsvchamber.org
URL: http://www.huntsvillealabamausa.com
Contact: Chip Cherry, President
Description: Promotes business and community development in Madison County, AL. **Publications:** *ChamberLink* (Monthly); *Initiatives Review*; *Community Organizations Directory*; *Chamber of Commerce of Huntsville/Madison County--Industrial Directory*; *Membership Directory and Business Guide for Huntsville and Madison County*.

47642 ■ Chamber of Commerce of Walker County
204 19th St. E, Ste. 101
Jasper, AL 35501
Ph: (205)384-4571
Fax: (205)384-4901
Co. E-mail: linda@walkerchamber.us
URL: http://www.walkerchamber.us
Contact: Linda Lewis, President
Description: Promotes business and community development in the Jasper, AL area. Conducts annual Heritage Day festival. **Founded:** 1938.

47643 ■ Chamber of Commerce of West Alabama (CCWA)
2200 University Blvd.
Tuscaloosa, AL 35402
Ph: (205)758-7588
Fax: (205)391-0565
Co. E-mail: chamber@dbtech.net
URL: http://www.tuscaloosachamber.com
Contact: Johnnie R. Aycock, President
Description: Promotes business and community development in western Alabama. Sponsors cable television channel. **Founded:** 1911. **Publications:** *The Commerce* (Monthly); *Perspectives*. **Awards:** Entrepreneur of the Year (Annual).

47644 ■ *Chamber Connections*
102 Jamestown Blvd.
Dothan, AL 36301
Ph: (334)792-5138
Free: 800-221-1027
Fax: (334)794-4796
Co. E-mail: lrobinson@dothan.com
URL: http://www.dothan.com
Contact: Trip Wheelless, Chairman
Released: Monthly

47645 ■ *Chamber Connections*
PO Box 310
Daphne, AL 36526
Ph: (251)621-8222
Fax: (251)621-8001
Co. E-mail: office@eschamber.com
URL: http://www.eschamber.com
Contact: Phil Cusa, Chairman
Released: Monthly

47646 ■ *Chamber Currents*
120 Tallapoosa St.
Alexander City, AL 35010
Ph: (256)234-3461
Fax: (256)234-0094
Co. E-mail: susan@charter.net
URL: http://www.alexandercity.org
Contact: Marvin Wagoner, President
Released: Monthly

47647 ■ *Chamber Focus*
210 E St. S
Talladega, AL 35160

Ph: (256)362-9075
Fax: (256)362-9093
Co. E-mail: information@talladegachamber.com
URL: http://www.talladegachamber.com
Contact: Mr. Mack Ferguson, Executive Director
Released: Monthly **Price:** free.

47648 ■ The Chamber of Gadsden/Etowah County
1 Commerce Sq.
Gadsden, AL 35901
Ph: (256)543-3472
Co. E-mail: info@gadsdenchamber.com
URL: http://www.gadsdenchamber.com
Contact: Heather New, President
Description: Promotes business and community development in Etowah County, AL.

47649 ■ *Chamber News*
801 Cedar Bluff Rd., Bldg. A
Centre, AL 35960
Ph: (256)927-8455
Fax: (256)927-2768
Co. E-mail: cccoc@tds.net
URL: http://www.cherokee-chamber.org
Contact: Johnny Roberts, Chairman
Released: Quarterly

47650 ■ *Chamber News*
PO Box 1487
Oneonta, AL 35121
Ph: (205)274-2153
Fax: (205)274-2099
Co. E-mail: info@blountoneontachamber.org
URL: http://www.blountoneontachamber.org
Contact: Kelley Cochran, President
Released: Monthly

47651 ■ *Chamber Notes*
1 Depot Sq.
Greenville, AL 36037
Ph: (334)382-3251
Free: 800-959-0717
Fax: (334)382-3181
Co. E-mail: chamber@greenville-alabama.com
URL: http://www.greenville-alabama.com
Contact: Francine Wasden, Executive Director
Released: Monthly

47652 ■ *Chamber Notes*
2109 Moncrief Rd., Ste. 115
Gardendale, AL 35071
Ph: (205)631-9195
Free: 888-631-4422
Fax: (205)631-9034
Co. E-mail: info@gardendalechamberofcommerce. com
URL: http://www.gardendalechamberofcommerce. com
Contact: Kris Marshall, Executive Director (Acting)
Released: Monthly **Price:** free for members.

47653 ■ *Chamber Outlook*
101 S Beaty St.
Athens, AL 35612
Ph: (256)232-2600
Free: 866-953-6565
Fax: (256)232-2609
Co. E-mail: info@tourathens.com
URL: http://tourathens.com
Contact: Jennifer Williamson, President
Released: Monthly **Price:** free to members.

47654 ■ *Chamber Pipeline*
Released: Periodic

47655 ■ *Chamber Update*
PO Box 2366
Opelika, AL 36803-2366
Ph: (334)745-4861
Free: 877-418-3889
Fax: (334)749-4740
Co. E-mail: coc@opelika.com
URL: http://www.opelika.com
Contact: Brian Henderson, Chairman
Released: Bimonthly

47656 ■ *Chamber Voice*
PO Box 527
Childersburg, AL 35044
Ph: (256)378-5482
Fax: (256)378-5833
Co. E-mail: pbstorey@childersburg.com
URL: http://www.childersburg.com
Contact: Marian Martin, Chairperson

47657 ■ *ChamberLink*
225 Church St.
Huntsville, AL 35801
Ph: (256)535-2000
Fax: (255)535-2015
Co. E-mail: info@hsvchamber.org
URL: http://www.huntsvillealabamausa.com
Contact: Chip Cherry, President
Released: Monthly **Price:** for members.

47658 ■ *ChamberLink*
PO Box 79
Montgomery, AL 36101
Ph: (334)834-5200
Fax: (334)265-4745
Co. E-mail: rgeorge@montgomerychamber.com
URL: http://www.montgomerychamber.com/Page.
  aspx?pid=195
Contact: Randall L. George, President
Released: Monthly

**47659 ■ Cherokee County Chamber of
Commerce (CCCoC)**
801 Cedar Bluff Rd., Bldg. A
Centre, AL 35960
Ph: (256)927-8455
Fax: (256)927-2768
Co. E-mail: cccoc@tds.net
URL: http://www.cherokee-chamber.org
Contact: Johnny Roberts, Chairman
Description: Promotes business and community
development in, and tourism the Cherokee County,
AL area. **Founded:** 1946. **Publications:** *Chamber
News* (Quarterly).

**47660 ■ Childersburg Chamber of Commerce
(CCC)**
PO Box 527
Childersburg, AL 35044
Ph: (256)378-5482
Fax: (256)378-5833
Co. E-mail: pbstorey@childersburg.com
URL: http://www.childersburg.com
Contact: Marian Martin, Chairperson
Description: Promotes business and community
development in Childersburg, AL. **Publications:**
Chamber Voice. **Educational Activities:** Chamber
Coffees (Monthly).

**47661 ■ Chilton County Chamber of
Commerce (CCCC)**
PO Box 66
Clanton, AL 35046
Ph: (205)755-2400
Fax: (205)755-8444
Co. E-mail: info@chiltonchamberonline.com
URL: http://chiltonchamberonline.com
Contact: Mike Robertson, Executive Director
Description: Promotes business and community
development in Chilton County, AL. **Publications:**
Chamber Chatter (Bimonthly). **Awards:** Youth Citizen
of the Year (Annual).

47662 ■ *Cities on the Move: Alabaster/
Pelham/Helena*
1301 County Services Dr.
Pelham, AL 35124
Ph: (205)663-4542
Fax: (205)663-4524
Co. E-mail: info@shelbychamber.org
URL: http://www.shelbychamber.org/GSCHome.as-
p?ID=2
Contact: Jennifer Whisenant, President
Released: Annual

47663 ■ *City/County Maps*
PO Box 817
Hartselle, AL 35640
Ph: (256)773-4370

Free: 800-294-0692
Fax: (256)773-4379
Co. E-mail: haleyvillechamberofcommerce@gmail.
  com
URL: http://www.hartsellechamber.com
Contact: Mark Waters, Chairman
Price: included in membership dues.

**47664 ■ Clay County Chamber of Commerce,
Alabama**
PO Box 85
Lineville, AL 36266
Ph: (256)396-2828
Fax: (256)396-5532
Co. E-mail: claychamber@centurytel.net
URL: http://claycochamber.com
Contact: Mary Patchunka-Smith, Executive Director
Description: Promotes business and community
development in Clay County, AL. **Founded:** 1990.

47665 ■ *Coast Commerce*
3150 Gulf Shores Pkwy.
PO Drawer 3869
Gulf Shores, AL 36547-3869
Ph: (251)968-6904
Fax: (251)968-5332
Co. E-mail: info@alagulfcoastchamber.com
URL: http://www.alagulfcoastchamber.com
Contact: Linda Whitlock, President
Released: Monthly

47666 ■ *The Commerce*
2200 University Blvd.
Tuscaloosa, AL 35402
Ph: (205)758-7588
Fax: (205)391-0565
Co. E-mail: chamber@dbtech.net
URL: http://www.tuscaloosachamber.com
Contact: Johnnie R. Aycock, President
Released: Monthly

47667 ■ *Communigator*
939 Hwy. 43 S
Saraland, AL 36571
Ph: (251)675-4444
Fax: (251)675-2307
Co. E-mail: cocsara@bellsouth.net
URL: http://www.saralandcoc.com
Contact: Rick Schaffer, Chairman

47668 ■ *Communique*
321 N 18th St.
Bessemer, AL 35020
Ph: (205)425-3253
Free: 888-423-7736
Fax: (205)425-4979
Co. E-mail: mmilan1@bellsouth.net
URL: http://www.bessemerchamber.com
Contact: Ronald W. Acker, President
Released: Monthly

47669 ■ *Connecting Point*
419 Memorial Pkwy. NE
Aliceville, AL 35442
Ph: (205)373-2820
Co. E-mail: acc@nctv.com
URL: http://www.cityofaliceville.com
Contact: Gale Ammerman, Chairman
Released: Quarterly **Price:** included in membership
dues.

**47670 ■ Cullman Area Chamber of
Commerce (CACC)**
PO Box 1104
Cullman, AL 35056-1104
Ph: (256)734-0454
Free: 800-313-5114
Fax: (256)737-7443
Co. E-mail: info@cullmanchamber.org
URL: http://www.cullmanchamber.org
Contact: Kirk Mancer, President
Description: Promotes business and community
development in Cullman County, AL. **Founded:** 1943.
Publications: *Dateline Cullman* (Monthly).

**47671 ■ Dadeville Area Chamber of
Commerce**
185 S Tallassee St., Ste. 103
Dadeville, AL 36853

Ph: (256)825-4019
Fax: (256)825-0547
Co. E-mail: chamber@dadeville.com
URL: http://www.dadeville.com
Contact: Larry Whitfield, President
Description: Promotes business and community
development in Tallapoosa County, AL. Sponsors an-
nual Chamber Day and annual Christmas pageant.
Founded: 1950.

47672 ■ *Dateline Cullman*
PO Box 1104
Cullman, AL 35056-1104
Ph: (256)734-0454
Free: 800-313-5114
Fax: (256)737-7443
Co. E-mail: info@cullmanchamber.org
URL: http://www.cullmanchamber.org
Contact: Kirk Mancer, President
Released: Monthly

**47673 ■ Decatur Morgan County Chamber of
Commerce (DCC)**
515 6th Ave. NE
Decatur, AL 35602-2003
Ph: (256)353-5312
Fax: (256)353-2384
Co. E-mail: john@dcc.org
URL: http://www.dcc.org
Contact: Blake McAnally, Chairman
Description: Promotes business and community
development in Decatur, AL. **Founded:** 1820.

**47674 ■ Demopolis Area Chamber of
Commerce (DACC)**
PO Box 667
Demopolis, AL 36732
Ph: (334)289-0270
Fax: (334)289-1382
Co. E-mail: dacc@westal.net
URL: http://www.demopolischamber.com
Contact: John Scales, Chairman
Description: Promotes business and community
development in the Demopolis, AL area. Encourages
integrity, good faith, and just and equitable practices
in business. Sponsors Fourth of July fireworks, Arts
in the Park, and Christmas on the River. **Founded:**
1915.

47675 ■ Dothan Area Chamber of Commerce
102 Jamestown Blvd.
Dothan, AL 36301
Ph: (334)792-5138
Free: 800-221-1027
Fax: (334)794-4796
Co. E-mail: lrobinson@dothan.com
URL: http://www.dothan.com
Contact: Trip Wheelless, Chairman
Description: Promotes business, industry, and com-
munity development in the Dothan, AL area. Spon-
sors trade shows. **Founded:** 1919. **Publications:**
Chamber Connections (Monthly).

**47676 ■ Eastern Shore Chamber of
Commerce (ESCC)**
PO Box 310
Daphne, AL 36526
Ph: (251)621-8222
Fax: (251)621-8001
Co. E-mail: office@eschamber.com
URL: http://www.eschamber.com
Contact: Phil Cusa, Chairman
Description: Promotes business and community
development in Daphne, Fairhope, Montrose, Point
Clear, and Spanish Fort, AL. Provides assistance to
new businesses and industry. Sponsors Jubilee
Festival, Arts and Crafts Festival, Mayors' Prayer
Breakfast, Polo Tournament, Christmas Open House,
Christmas Parades, Community Expo and Seminars.
Founded: 1924. **Publications:** *Chamber Connec-
tions* (Monthly). **Telecommunication Services:**
dbender@eschamber.com.

47677 ■ Enterprise Chamber of Commerce
PO Box 310577
Enterprise, AL 36331-0577
Ph: (334)347-0581
Free: 800-235-4730

Fax: (334)393-8204
Co. E-mail: chamberpresident@centurytel.net
URL: http://www.enterprisealabama.com
Contact: Phil Thomas, President
Description: Promotes business and community development in Enterprise, AL area.

47678 ■ Eufaula - Barbour County Chamber of Commerce
333 E Broad St.
Eufaula, AL 36072-0697
Ph: (334)687-6664
Free: 800-524-7529
Fax: (334)687-5240
Co. E-mail: info@eufaulachamber.com
Contact: James D. Bradley, Executive Director
Description: Seeks to promote and perpetuate business growth, economic development, civic interest, general welfare and prosperity of the Eufaula - Barbour County. Aims to stimulate public interest to these ends.

47679 ■ Eutaw Area Chamber of Commerce
111 Main St.
Eutaw, AL 35462
Ph: (205)372-9002
Fax: (205)372-1393
Co. E-mail: eutawchamber@bellsouth.net
URL: http://www.eutawchamber.com
Description: Promotes business and community development in Eutaw, AL area.

47680 ■ Evergreen/Conecuh Chamber of Commerce
100 Depot Sq.
Evergreen, AL 36401
Ph: (251)578-1707
Fax: (251)578-5660
Co. E-mail: emma0916@bellsouth.net
URL: http://www.evergreenchamberofcommerce.org
Contact: Ms. Emma Johnson, Administrator
Description: Promotes business and community development in Evergreen/Conecuh area. **Awards:** Business of the Month (Monthly).

47681 ■ Fayette Area Chamber of Commerce
102 2nd Ave.
Fayette, AL 35555
Ph: (205)932-4587
Co. E-mail: info@fayetteareachamber.org
URL: http://www.fayetteareachamber.org
Description: Provides leadership and coordination for the advancement of economic growth and quality of life in Fayette and its surrounding area. **Founded:** 1960.

47682 ■ Focus
131 N Court St.
Prattville, AL 36067
Ph: (334)365-7392
Free: 800-588-2796
Fax: (334)361-1314
Co. E-mail: jprochazka@prattvillechamber.com
URL: http://www.prattvillechamber.com
Contact: Clay McConnell, Chairman of the Board
Released: Monthly

47683 ■ Fort Payne Chamber of Commerce (FPCC)
300 Gault Ave. N
Fort Payne, AL 35967
Ph: (256)845-2741
Fax: (256)845-5849
URL: http://www.fortpaynechamber.com
Contact: Carol Beddingfield, Director
Description: Promotes business and community development in Fort Payne, AL. **Founded:** 1947.

47684 ■ Franklin County Chamber of Commerce
103 N Jackson Ave.
Russellville, AL 35653
Ph: (256)332-1760

Fax: (256)332-1740
Co. E-mail: franklincountyhelp@charterinternet.com
URL: http://www.franklincountychamber.org
Contact: Danny Brown, President
Description: Promotes business and community development in Franklin County, AL. **Founded:** 1840. **Publications:** *Franklin Findings* (Monthly). **Awards:** Small Business Award (Annual).

47685 ■ *Franklin Findings*
103 N Jackson Ave.
Russellville, AL 35653
Ph: (256)332-1760
Fax: (256)332-1740
Co. E-mail: franklincountyhelp@charterinternet.com
URL: http://www.franklincountychamber.org
Contact: Danny Brown, President
Released: Monthly

47686 ■ Gardendale Chamber of Commerce
2109 Moncrief Rd., Ste. 115
Gardendale, AL 35071
Ph: (205)631-9195
Free: 888-631-4422
Fax: (205)631-9034
Co. E-mail: info@gardendalechamberofcommerce.com
URL: http://www.gardendalechamberofcommerce.com
Contact: Kris Marshall, Executive Director (Acting)
Description: Businesses, clubs and individual members. Promotes business and community development in Gardendale, AL. **Founded:** 1987. **Publications:** *Chamber Notes* (Monthly). **Educational Activities:** Gardendale Chamber of Commerce Banquet (Annual).

47687 ■ Greater Brewton Area Chamber of Commerce (GBACC)
1010 B Douglas Ave.
Brewton, AL 36426
Ph: (251)867-3224
Fax: (251)809-1793
Co. E-mail: jcrane@brewtonchamber.com
URL: http://www.brewtonchamber.com
Contact: Andrew Clark, President
Description: Promotes business and community development in the Brewton, AL area.

47688 ■ Greater Geneva Area Chamber of Commerce
406 S Commerce St.
Geneva, AL 36340
Ph: (334)684-6582
Co. E-mail: genevacountychamber@centurylink.net
URL: http://www.genevaalabama.org
Contact: Ron Justice, President
Description: Promotes business and community development in Geneva/Geneva County, AL.

47689 ■ Greater Jackson County Chamber of Commerce (SJCCC)
PO Box 973
Scottsboro, AL 35769
Ph: (256)259-5500
Free: 800-259-5508
Fax: (256)259-4447
Co. E-mail: roden@scottsboro.org
URL: http://www.jacksoncountychamber.com
Contact: Rick Roden, President
Description: Promotes business and community development in Jackson County, AL. Conducts charitable programs; sponsors festival. **Founded:** 1956. **Publications:** *Action Bulletin* (Monthly).

47690 ■ Greater Limestone County Chamber of Commerce
101 S Beaty St.
Athens, AL 35612
Ph: (256)232-2600
Free: 866-953-6565
Fax: (256)232-2609
Co. E-mail: info@tourathens.com
URL: http://tourathens.com
Contact: Jennifer Williamson, President
Description: Works to create an environment which promotes the general welfare and prosperity of its membership, the Athens-Limestone County Area and

the municipalities and citizens within that area. Sponsors the Tennessee Valley Old Time Fiddler's Convention, Walk Through the Past, Business on Display, the Dogwood Festival and tours. **Founded:** 1938. **Publications:** *Chamber Outlook* (Monthly).

47691 ■ Greater Shelby County Chamber of Commerce
1301 County Services Dr.
Pelham, AL 35124
Ph: (205)663-4542
Fax: (205)663-4524
Co. E-mail: info@shelbychamber.org
URL: http://www.shelbychamber.org/GSCHome.asp?ID=2
Contact: Jennifer Whisenant, President
Description: Promotes business and community development in the North Shelby area. **Founded:** 1979. **Publications:** *Viewpoint* (Monthly); *Cities on the Move: Alabaster/Pelham/Helena* (Annual). **Educational Activities:** Focus Meeting (Monthly).

47692 ■ Greater Talladega Area Chamber of Commerce (GTACC)
210 E St. S
Talladega, AL 35160
Ph: (256)362-9075
Fax: (256)362-9093
Co. E-mail: information@talladegachamber.com
URL: http://www.talladegachamber.com
Contact: Mr. Mack Ferguson, Executive Director
Description: Promotes business, community, and tourism development in the Talladega, AL area. Seeks to attract new business and promote the expansion of existing industry. Sponsors local programs and events which recognize the accomplishments of chamber members. **Founded:** 1909. **Publications:** *Chamber Focus* (Monthly). **Telecommunication Services:** info@talladegachamber.com.

47693 ■ Greater Tallassee Area Chamber of Commerce (TCC)
650 Gilmer Ave.
Tallassee, AL 36078
Ph: (334)283-5151
Fax: (334)252-0774
Co. E-mail: chamber@tallasseechamber.com
URL: http://www.tallassee.al.us
Contact: Jeanna W. Kervin, Executive Director
Description: Promotes business and community development in Tallassee, AL. Sponsors festival. **Founded:** 1948.

47694 ■ Greater Valley Area Chamber of Commerce (GVACC)
PO Box 205
Lanett, AL 36863
Ph: (334)642-1411
Fax: (334)642-1410
Co. E-mail: ecrowder@greatervalleyarea.com
URL: http://www.greatervalleyarea.com
Contact: Edwin Garrison, President
Description: Promotes business and community development in Chambers County, AL and West Point, GA. **Founded:** 1963.

47695 ■ Greenville Area Chamber of Commerce (GACC)
1 Depot Sq.
Greenville, AL 36037
Ph: (334)382-3251
Free: 800-959-0717
Fax: (334)382-3181
Co. E-mail: chamber@greenville-alabama.com
URL: http://www.greenville-alabama.com
Contact: Francine Wasden, Executive Director
Description: Promotes business and community development in the Greenville, AL area. **Founded:** 1941. **Publications:** *Chamber Notes* (Monthly).

47696 ■ *Guide to the Shoals*
PO Box 1331
Florence, AL 35630
Ph: (256)764-4661
Free: 877-764-4661

Fax: (256)766-9017
Co. E-mail: shoals@shoalschamber.com
URL: http://www.shoalschamber.com
Contact: Jackie Hendrix, Chairperson
Released: Annual

47697 ■ Haleyville Area Chamber of Commerce (HCC)
PO Box 634
Haleyville, AL 35565
Ph: (205)486-4611
Fax: (205)486-5074
Co. E-mail: haleyvillechamberofcommerce@gmail.com
URL: http://www.haleyvillechamber.org
Contact: Barry Burleson, President
Description: Promotes business and community development in Haleyville, AL. **Founded:** 1988.

47698 ■ Hartselle Area Chamber of Commerce (HACC)
PO Box 817
Hartselle, AL 35640
Ph: (256)773-4370
Free: 800-294-0692
Fax: (256)773-4379
Co. E-mail: haleyvillechamberofcommerce@gmail.com
URL: http://www.hartsellechamber.com
Contact: Mark Waters, Chairman
Description: Promotes business and community development in Hartselle, AL. **Founded:** 1988. **Publications:** City/County Maps.

47699 ■ Headland Chamber of Commerce (HCC)
105 Cleveland St.
Headland, AL 36345
Ph: (334)693-3303
Co. E-mail: headlandchamber@centurytel.net
URL: http://headlandal.org/index.php?option=com_contact&Itemid=3
Contact: Stephanie Blankenship, President
Description: Promotes business and community development in Headland, AL. Sponsors various activities throughout promoting the Headland area and quality of life for its residents. **Founded:** 1980. **Publications:** Headland Observer. **Educational Activities:** Daylily (Annual).

47700 ■ Homewood Chamber of Commerce (HCC)
1721 Oxmoor Rd.
Homewood, AL 35209
Ph: (205)871-5631
Co. E-mail: johnchristopher_batts@colonialbank.com
URL: http://www.homewoodchamber.org
Contact: John Christopher Batts, Executive Vice President
Description: Promotes business and community development in the Homewood, AL area. **Founded:** 1950. **Publications:** Homewood Magazine (Annual). **Educational Activities:** Business Development Breakfast (Monthly). **Awards:** Firm of the Year (Annual); Member of the Year (Annual); Top Student in School System (Annual).

47701 ■ Homewood Magazine
1721 Oxmoor Rd.
Homewood, AL 35209
Ph: (205)871-5631
Co. E-mail: johnchristopher_batts@colonialbank.com
URL: http://www.homewoodchamber.org
Contact: John Christopher Batts, Executive Vice President
Released: Annual

47702 ■ Hoover Chamber of Commerce
c/o Bill Powell, Exec. Dir.
PO Box 36005
Hoover, AL 35236
Ph: (205)988-5672

Fax: (205)988-8383
Co. E-mail: bill@hooverchamber.org
URL: http://www.hooverchamber.org
Contact: Bill Powell, Executive Director
Description: Promotes business and community development in Hoover, AL area. **Awards:** Freedom Award (Annual).

47703 ■ Hueytown Chamber of Commerce
2058-A High School Rd.
Hueytown, AL 35023
Ph: (205)491-8039
Co. E-mail: hueyoed@bellsouth.net
URL: http://www.hueytownchamber.com
Contact: George Hudson, President
Description: Promotes business and community development in the Hueytown, AL area.

47704 ■ Industrial List
PO Box 1331
Florence, AL 35630
Ph: (256)764-4661
Free: 877-764-4661
Fax: (256)766-9017
Co. E-mail: shoals@shoalschamber.com
URL: http://www.shoalschamber.com
Contact: Jackie Hendrix, Chairperson
Released: Periodic **Price:** $15, /copy.

47705 ■ Initiatives Review
225 Church St.
Huntsville, AL 35801
Ph: (256)535-2000
Fax: (255)535-2015
Co. E-mail: info@hsvchamber.org
URL: http://www.huntsvillealabamausa.com
Contact: Chip Cherry, President
Released: 6/year. **Price:** for members.

47706 ■ Insight
939 Hwy. 43 S
Saraland, AL 36571
Ph: (251)675-4444
Fax: (251)675-2307
Co. E-mail: cocsara@bellsouth.net
URL: http://www.saralandcoc.com
Contact: Rick Schaffer, Chairman
Released: Monthly

47707 ■ Lake Guntersville Chamber of Commerce (LGCC)
PO Box 577
Guntersville, AL 35976
Ph: (256)582-3612
Free: 800-869-LAKE
Fax: (256)582-3682
Co. E-mail: gcc@lakeguntersville.org
URL: http://www.lakeguntersville.org
Contact: Morri Yancy, President
Description: Promotes business and community development in Guntersville, AL. Conducts annual fishing tournament. **Founded:** 1938. **Publications:** Lake Views (Monthly). **Telecommunication Services:** morri@lakeguntersville.org.

47708 ■ Lawrence County Chamber of Commerce, Alabama
PO Box 325
Moulton, AL 35650
Ph: (256)974-1658
Fax: (256)974-2400
Co. E-mail: lawrence@lawrencealabama.com
URL: http://www.lawrencealabama.com
Contact: Tami Reist, Chairperson
Description: Promotes business and community development in Lawrence County, AL. **Publications:** Living in Lawrence (Annual). **Awards:** ACT Scholarships (Annual).

47709 ■ Leeds Area Chamber of Commerce
PO Box 900
Leeds, AL 35094-0900
Ph: (205)699-5001

Fax: (205)699-1777
Co. E-mail: leedschamber@windstream.net
URL: http://leedsareachamber.com
Contact: Julie Ferrell, President
Description: Promotes business and community development in the Greater Leeds, AL area. **Awards:** Teacher of the Year (Annual); Business of the Year (Annual); Non-Profit Organization/Club of the Year (Annual); Citizen of the Year (Annual).

47710 ■ Living in Lawrence
PO Box 325
Moulton, AL 35650
Ph: (256)974-1658
Fax: (256)974-2400
Co. E-mail: lawrence@lawrencealabama.com
URL: http://www.lawrencealabama.com
Contact: Tami Reist, Chairperson
Released: Annual

47711 ■ Major Employers Directory
505 N 20th St., Ste. 200
Birmingham, AL 35203
Ph: (205)324-2100
Fax: (205)324-2560
Co. E-mail: bhilson@birminghambusinessalliance.com
URL: http://www.birminghambusinessalliance.com
Contact: Brian Hilson, III, President
Released: Annual **Price:** $15, for members; $25, for nonmembers.

47712 ■ Membership Directory and Newcomer's Guide
131 N Court St.
Prattville, AL 36067
Ph: (334)365-7392
Free: 800-588-2796
Fax: (334)361-1314
Co. E-mail: jprochazka@prattvillechamber.com
URL: http://www.prattvillechamber.com
Contact: Clay McConnell, Chairman of the Board
Released: Annual

47713 ■ Mobile Area Chamber of Commerce (MACC)
451 Government St.
Mobile, AL 36652-2187
Ph: (251)433-6951
Free: 800-422-6951
Fax: (251)432-1143
Co. E-mail: info@mobilechamber.com
URL: http://www.mobilechamber.com
Contact: Michael Pierce, Chairman
Description: Promotes business and community development in the Mobile, AL area. Serves as a progressive advocate for business needs to promote the Mobile Alabama area's economic well-being. **Founded:** 1836. **Publications:** Business View (Monthly); The Weekly Business View (Weekly). **Awards:** All American City 95-96 (Annual).

47714 ■ Monroeville/Monroe County Chamber of Commerce
86 N Alabama Ave.
Monroeville, AL 36460
Ph: (251)743-2879
Fax: (251)743-2189
Co. E-mail: sandy@monroecountyal.com
URL: http://www.monroecountyal.com
Contact: Al Brewton, President
Description: Promotes business and community development in Monroe County, AL. Sponsors festivals and annual Christmas Parade; conducts seminars. **Founded:** 1936.

47715 ■ Montevallo Chamber of Commerce
720 Oak St.
Montevallo, AL 35115
Ph: (205)665-1519
Fax: (205)665-0759
Co. E-mail: montevallocc@bellsouth.net
Contact: Ben McCrory, President
Description: Aims to advance the commercial, industrial, professional and civic interests of Montevallo. Provides support and assistance to existing businesses and industries. **Publications:** Chamber Chatter (Monthly).

47716 ■ Montgomery Area Chamber of Commerce (MACOC)
PO Box 79
Montgomery, AL 36101
Ph: (334)834-5200
Fax: (334)265-4745
Co. E-mail: rgeorge@montgomerychamber.com
URL: http://www.montgomerychamber.com/Page.aspx?pid=195
Contact: Randall L. George, President
Description: Promotes business and community development in the Montgomery, AL area. **Publications:** *ChamberLink* (Monthly).

47717 ■ *News and Views*
1975 Merryvale Rd.
Vestavia Hills, AL 35216
Ph: (205)823-5011
Free: 866-402-VHCC
Fax: (205)823-8974
Co. E-mail: chamber@vestaviahills.org
URL: http://www.vestaviahills.org
Contact: Karen J. Odle, Executive Director
Released: Monthly

47718 ■ *Newscope*
PO Box 185
Sylacauga, AL 35150
Ph: (256)249-0308
Fax: (256)249-0315
Co. E-mail: cbates@sylacauga.net
URL: http://www.sylacaugachamber.com
Contact: Carol Emlich-Bates, Executive Director
Released: Periodic

47719 ■ North Baldwin Chamber of Commerce (NBCC)
PO Box 310
Bay Minette, AL 36507
Ph: (251)937-5665
Fax: (251)937-5670
Co. E-mail: director@northbaldwinchamber.com
URL: http://www.northbaldwinchamber.com
Contact: Margo Allen, Executive Director
Description: Promotes and enhances economic growth and community development.

47720 ■ *North Mobile Business*
939 Hwy. 43 S
Saraland, AL 36571
Ph: (251)675-4444
Fax: (251)675-2307
Co. E-mail: cocsara@bellsouth.net
URL: http://www.saralandcoc.com
Contact: Rick Schaffer, Chairman
Released: Biennial **Price:** free.

47721 ■ Northwest Alabama Junior Chamber of Commerce
c/o Martin Dean, Pres.
2808 Jackson Hwy.
Sheffield, AL 35660
Ph: (256)740-0255
Co. E-mail: nwajcc@mail.com
URL: http://nwajcc.tripod.com
Contact: Martin Dean, President
Description: Works with businesses and local governments to provide training, events and services in the area.

47722 ■ Opelika Chamber of Commerce (OCC)
PO Box 2366
Opelika, AL 36803-2366
Ph: (334)745-4861
Free: 877-418-3889
Fax: (334)749-4740
Co. E-mail: coc@opelika.com
URL: http://www.opelika.com
Contact: Brian Henderson, Chairman
Description: Promotes business and community development in Opelika, AL. **Founded:** 1941. **Publications:** *Chamber Update* (Bimonthly); *Return on Investment*. **Awards:** Small Business Person & Ambassador (Annual).

47723 ■ Opp and Covington County Area Chamber of Commerce
PO Box 148
Opp, AL 36467
Ph: (334)493-3070
Fax: (334)493-1060
Co. E-mail: info@oppchamber.com
URL: http://www.oppchamber.com
Contact: Dr. Joshua Driver, President
Description: Promotes business and community development in Covington County, AL. Sponsors Old Home Folks Day festival; maintains Opp Hall of Fame and administers United Fund. **Founded:** 1947.

47724 ■ *Perspectives*
2200 University Blvd.
Tuscaloosa, AL 35402
Ph: (205)758-7588
Fax: (205)391-0565
Co. E-mail: chamber@dbtech.net
URL: http://www.tuscaloosachamber.com
Contact: Johnnie R. Aycock, President

47725 ■ Phenix City-Russell County Chamber of Commerce
1107 Broad St.
Phenix City, AL 36867
Ph: (334)298-3639
Free: 800-892-2248
Fax: (334)298-3846
Co. E-mail: pcrccham@ldl.net
URL: http://pc-rcchamber.com
Contact: Victor W. Cross, President
Description: Promotes business and community development in Russell County, AL. Seeks to attract commercial developments. **Founded:** 1926. **Publications:** *Quality of Life* (Periodic).

47726 ■ Prattville Area Chamber of Commerce
131 N Court St.
Prattville, AL 36067
Ph: (334)365-7392
Free: 800-588-2796
Fax: (334)361-1314
Co. E-mail: jprochazka@prattvillechamber.com
URL: http://www.prattvillechamber.com
Contact: Clay McConnell, Chairman of the Board
Description: Promotes business and community development in Autauga County, AL. **Founded:** 1973. **Publications:** *Focus* (Monthly); *Membership Directory and Newcomer's Guide* (Annual).

47727 ■ *Quality of Life*
PO Box 1331
Florence, AL 35630
Ph: (256)764-4661
Free: 877-764-4661
Fax: (256)766-9017
Co. E-mail: shoals@shoalschamber.com
URL: http://www.shoalschamber.com
Contact: Jackie Hendrix, Chairperson
Released: Annual

47728 ■ *Quality of Life*
1107 Broad St.
Phenix City, AL 36867
Ph: (334)298-3639
Free: 800-892-2248
Fax: (334)298-3846
Co. E-mail: pcrccham@ldl.net
URL: http://pc-rcchamber.com
Contact: Victor W. Cross, President
Released: Periodic

47729 ■ *Quality of Life Magazine*
225 Parkway Dr.
Trussville, AL 35173
Ph: (205)655-7535
Free: 800-949-8222
Fax: (205)655-3705
Co. E-mail: info@trussvillechamber.com
URL: http://www.trussvillechamber.com
Contact: Diane Poole, Executive Director
Released: Periodic

47730 ■ Rainsville Chamber of Commerce
PO Box 396
Rainsville, AL 35986
Ph: (256)638-7800
Co. E-mail: timeberhart@farmerstel.com
URL: http://www.rainsville.info
Contact: Bill Paymar, President
Description: Promotes business and community development in Rainsville, AL. Seeks to attract tourism business. Sponsors activities. **Founded:** 1965.

47731 ■ *Return on Investment*
PO Box 2366
Opelika, AL 36803-2366
Ph: (334)745-4861
Free: 877-418-3889
Fax: (334)749-4740
Co. E-mail: coc@opelika.com
URL: http://www.opelika.com
Contact: Brian Henderson, Chairman

47732 ■ Saraland Area Chamber of Commerce
939 Hwy. 43 S
Saraland, AL 36571
Ph: (251)675-4444
Fax: (251)675-2307
Co. E-mail: cocsara@bellsouth.net
URL: http://www.saralandcoc.com
Contact: Rick Schaffer, Chairman
Description: Promotes business and community development in Saraland, AL. **Scope:** topics about starting your own business, incorporating a business, selling techniques, tips on small business success, business law and business loan information. **Founded:** 1984. **Subscriptions:** audio recordings books video recordings. **Publications:** *Communigator; Insight* (Monthly); *North Mobile Business* (Biennial); *North Mobile Business* (Biennial). **Educational Activities:** Saraland Area Chamber of Commerce Board meeting (Monthly). **Awards:** Saraland Citizen of the Year (Annual); Public Safety Officer of the Year Awards (Annual). **Telecommunication Services:** info@saralandcoc.com.

47733 ■ Shoals Chamber of Commerce (SCC)
PO Box 1331
Florence, AL 35630
Ph: (256)764-4661
Free: 877-764-4661
Fax: (256)766-9017
Co. E-mail: shoals@shoalschamber.com
URL: http://www.shoalschamber.com
Contact: Jackie Hendrix, Chairperson
Description: Promotes business and community development in Colbert and Lauderdale counties, AL. Provides information to newcomers and tourists. Sponsors Leadership Shoals, a 9-month program for business people. Conducts small business week. **Publications:** *Guide to the Shoals* (Annual); *Industrial List* (Periodic); *Quality of Life* (Annual); *Shoals Chamber of Commerce--Membership Directory and Business Reference Guide* (Annual). **Educational Activities:** Business After Hours (Annual); Chambermart (Periodic); Shoals Chamber of Commerce Tradeshow (Semiannual). **Awards:** Shoals Small Business Awards.

47734 ■ *Small Business Guide/Business Start-up Checklist*
505 N 20th St., Ste. 200
Birmingham, AL 35203
Ph: (205)324-2100
Fax: (205)324-2560
Co. E-mail: bhilson@birminghambusinessalliance.com
URL: http://www.birminghambusinessalliance.com
Contact: Brian Hilson, III, President
Price: $10.

47735 ■ South Baldwin Chamber of Commerce (SBCC)
PO Box 1117
Foley, AL 36536
Ph: (251)943-3291
Free: 877-461-3712

Fax: (251)943-6810
Co. E-mail: infodesk@southbaldwinchamber.com
URL: http://www.southbaldwinchamber.com
Contact: Glenn Manning, Chairman
Description: Seeks to promote business and community development by providing information, services, and leadership for economic development. **Founded:** 1944. **Publications:** *Business News* (Monthly). **Awards:** Walton M. Vines Free Enterprise Person of the Year (Annual).

47736 ■ Springville Area Chamber of Commerce (SACC)
6496 U.S. Hwy. 11
Springville, AL 35146
Ph: (205)467-2339
Co. E-mail: bwisner@springvillealabama.org
URL: http://www.springvillealabama.org/sacoc/index.html
Contact: Cason Catts, President
Description: Promotes business and community development in the Springville, AL area.

47737 ■ Sylacauga Chamber of Commerce (SCC)
PO Box 185
Sylacauga, AL 35150
Ph: (256)249-0308
Fax: (256)249-0315
Co. E-mail: cbates@sylacauga.net
URL: http://www.sylacaugachamber.com
Contact: Carol Emlich-Bates, Executive Director
Description: Promotes business and community development in Talladega County, AL. **Founded:** 1939. **Publications:** *Newscope* (Periodic); *Sylacauga* (Annual). **Telecommunication Services:** chamber@sylacauga.net.

47738 ■ Trussville Area Chamber of Commerce (TACC)
225 Parkway Dr.
Trussville, AL 35173
Ph: (205)655-7535
Free: 800-949-8222
Fax: (205)655-3705
Co. E-mail: info@trussvillechamber.com
URL: http://www.trussvillechamber.com
Contact: Diane Poole, Executive Director
Description: Promotes business and community development in Trussville, AL. Sponsors activities, promotions, and special projects. **Founded:** 1946. **Publications:** *Quality of Life Magazine* (Periodic); *Trussville Community Directory* (Annual).

47739 ■ *Trussville Community Directory*
225 Parkway Dr.
Trussville, AL 35173
Ph: (205)655-7535
Free: 800-949-8222
Fax: (205)655-3705
Co. E-mail: info@trussvillechamber.com
URL: http://www.trussvillechamber.com
Contact: Diane Poole, Executive Director
Released: Annual

47740 ■ Union Springs/Bullock County Chamber of Commerce
PO Box 5006
Union Springs, AL 36089
Ph: (334)738-2424
Co. E-mail: info@usacoc.com
URL: http://www.usacoc.com
Contact: Evelyn Smart, President
Description: Promotes business and community development in Bullock County, AL. Sponsors civic activities and supports local schools. **Founded:** 1965.

47741 ■ Vestavia Hills Chamber of Commerce (VHCC)
1975 Merryvale Rd.
Vestavia Hills, AL 35216
Ph: (205)823-5011
Free: 866-402-VHCC

Fax: (205)823-8974
Co. E-mail: chamber@vestaviahills.org
URL: http://www.vestaviahills.org
Contact: Karen J. Odle, Executive Director
Description: Promotes business and community development in Vestavia Hills, AL. **Publications:** *News and Views* (Monthly). **Educational Activities:** I Love America Day (Annual). **Telecommunication Services:** kareno@vestaviahills.org.

47742 ■ *Viewpoint*
1301 County Services Dr.
Pelham, AL 35124
Ph: (205)663-4542
Fax: (205)663-4524
Co. E-mail: info@shelbychamber.org
URL: http://www.shelbychamber.org/GSCHome.asp?ID=2
Contact: Jennifer Whisenant, President
Released: Monthly

47743 ■ *The Weekly Business View*
451 Government St.
Mobile, AL 36652-2187
Ph: (251)433-6951
Free: 800-422-6951
Fax: (251)432-1143
Co. E-mail: info@mobilechamber.com
URL: http://www.mobilechamber.com
Contact: Michael Pierce, Chairman
Released: Weekly

47744 ■ *Who's Who Directory*
505 N 20th St., Ste. 200
Birmingham, AL 35203
Ph: (205)324-2100
Fax: (205)324-2560
Co. E-mail: bhilson@birminghambusinessalliance.com
URL: http://www.birminghambusinessalliance.com
Contact: Brian Hilson, III, President
Released: Annual **Price:** free for members; $25, for members (additional copy); $100, for nonmembers.

47745 ■ Winfield Chamber of Commerce (WCC)
PO Box 1557
Winfield, AL 35594
Ph: (205)487-8841
Co. E-mail: chamberofcommerce@winfieldcity.org
URL: http://www.winfieldcity.org
Contact: Mike Nolen, President
Description: Promotes business and community development in the Winfield, AL area.

MINORITY BUSINESS ASSISTANCE PROGRAMS

47746 ■ Alabama Minority Business Enterprise Center
450A Government St.
Mobile, AL 36602
Ph: (251)433-2250
Fax: (251)433-2208
Co. E-mail: pramos@mbecalabama.org
URL: http://www.mbecalabama.org
Contact: Pamela Ramos
Description: Provides business and technical support for emerging and existing minority businesses in Alabama.

47747 ■ Alabama Minority Business Opportunity Center
4715 Alton Ct.
Birmingham, AL 35210
Ph: (205)957-9779
Fax: (205)957-2114
Co. E-mail: info@mbocalabama.org
URL: http://www.mbocalabama.org
Contact: Henry A. Turner, Executive Director
Description: Assists corporations, government agencies, and universities in developing business opportunites to support minority enterprises.

47748 ■ Birmingham Business Resource Center
1500 1st Ave. N, Ste. 106, Unit 2
Birmingham, AL 35203
Ph: (205)250-6380
Fax: (205)250-6384
Co. E-mail: info@bbrc.biz
URL: http://www.mybbrc.biz/
Description: Offers small business finance and related technical assistance.

47749 ■ Women's Business Center Inc.
1301 Azalea Rd., Ste. 201A
Mobile, AL 36693
Ph: (251)660-2725
Fax: (251)660-8854
Co. E-mail: info@womenbiz.biz
URL: http://www.womenbiz.biz
Contact: Kathryn Kahalley Cariglino, Executive Director
Description: Works to assist and empower women in starting or growing small businesses.

FINANCING AND LOAN PROGRAMS

47750 ■ Bonaventure Capital
3104 Blue Lake Dr., Ste. 120
Birmingham, AL 35243
Ph: (205)588-6024
Fax: (205)870-8050
URL: http://www.bonaventurecapital.net
Contact: Steve Dauphin, Partner
E-mail: sdauphin@bonaventurecapital.net
Preferred Investment Size: $500,000 to $1,500,000. **Investment Policies:** Early stage. **Industry Preferences:** Computer software, industrial and energy, financial services, and utilities. **Geographic Preference:** Southeast.

47751 ■ FHL Capital Corp.
2 20th Street N., Ste. 860
Birmingham, AL 35203
Ph: (205)328-3098
Fax: (205)323-0001
Co. E-mail: officemgr@fhlcapital.com
URL: http://www.fhlcapital.com
Contact: Edwin W. Finch, III, Chief Executive Officer
E-mail: efinch@fhlcapital.com
Preferred Investment Size: $1,000,000 to $75,000,000. **Geographic Preference:** U.S.

47752 ■ Harbert Management Corp.
2100 3rd Ave. N, Ste. 600
Birmingham, AL 35203
Ph: (205)987-5500
Fax: (205)987-5568
Co. E-mail: slrogers@harbert.net
URL: http://www.harbert.net
Contact: John Harrison, Manager
Preferred Investment Size: $1,000,000 to $4,000,000. **Industry Preferences:** Technology, semiconductors and other electronics, medical and health, biotechnology, communications, software and services. **Geographic Preference:** Southeastern U.S.

47753 ■ Hickory Venture Capital Corp. / Hickory Venture Group
301 Washington St., Ste. 301
Huntsville, AL 35801
Ph: (256)539-1931
Fax: (256)539-5130
Co. E-mail: info@hvcc.com
URL: http://www.hvcc.com
Contact: J. Thomas Noojin, Principal
Preferred Investment Size: $1,000,000 to $7,000,000. **Industry Preferences:** Communications and media, computer software and services, computer hardware, Internet specific, consumer related, industrial and energy, semiconductors and other electronics, medical and health, other products, and biotechnology. **Geographic Preference:** Southeast, Midwest, and Texas.

47754 ■ Southeastern Technology Fund
207 East Side Sq., 1st Fl.
Huntsville, AL 35801
Ph: (256)883-8711
Fax: (256)883-8558
URL: http://www.setfund.com
Contact: Chris Horgen, Managing Partner
Preferred Investment Size: $1,000,000 to
$3,000,000. **Industry Preferences:** Communications
and media, Internet specific, computer software and
services. **Geographic Preference:** Southeast.

PROCUREMENT ASSISTANCE PROGRAMS

47755 ■ Alabama Department of Finance - Division of Purchasing
100 N Union St., Ste. 192
Montgomery, AL 36130-3620
Ph: (334)242-7250
Fax: (334)242-4419
URL: http://www.purchasing.state.al.us
Contact: Isaac Kervin, Director, Purchasing
Description: Contact for the state's list of bidders for
government purchasing contracts. A small business
representative is available.

47756 ■ Alabama Procurement Center Representatives
Bldg. 5303, Rm. 3135 US SBA
Redstone Arsenal, AL 35898-5150
Ph: (256)842-6240
Fax: (256)842-0085
Co. E-mail: gary.heard@sba.gov
URL: http://www.sba.gov
Contact: Gary Heard, Representative
E-mail: gary.heard@sba.gov
Description: Covers activities for Army Aviation &
Missile Command (Huntsville, AL).

47757 ■ Alabama Procurement Technical Assistance Center - University of Alabama
Box 870396
Tuscaloosa, AL 35487-0396
Ph: (205)348-1687
Fax: (205)348-6974
Co. E-mail: asbdc@ua.edu
URL: http://www.al-ptac.org
Contact: Pat Phillips, Director
Description: Identifies and implements innovative
procurement practices in support of the efforts of our
customers, and assists the University with its mission
of teaching, research and public service by safe-
guarding the integrity of the purchasing and payables
process.

47758 ■ Alabama Small Business Development Consortium
Box 870396
Tuscaloosa, AL 35487-0396
Ph: (205)348-1582
Free: 877-825-7232
Fax: (205)348-6974
Co. E-mail: rlgrover@ua.edu
URL: http://www.asbdc.org
Contact: William Campbell, Director
Description: Notifies businesses of bidding op-
portunities. Offers counseling in areas such as bid
package preparation, minority programs, military
packaging, pricing, bonding, and quality assurance.
Holds training seminars and procurement confer-
ences.

INCUBATORS/RESEARCH AND TECHNOLOGY PARKS

47759 ■ Baldwin County Business Incubator
PO Box 1340
Robertsdale, AL 36567
Ph: (251)947-2445
Free: 800-947-2445
Fax: (251)947-4229
Co. E-mail: info@baldwinincubator.com
URL: http://www.baldwinincubator.com/
Contact: Bob Higgins, Director
Description: A small business incubator that offers
qualifying start-up companies a structured two-to-
three-year program of advice and professional as-
sistance to help ensure success.

47760 ■ Bessemer Business Incubation System
1020 Ninth Ave. SW
Bessemer, AL 35022
Ph: (205)481-2000
Fax: (205)481-2100
Co. E-mail: Bessemerincubator@yahoo.com
URL: http://bessemerincubator.net
Description: A division of the Bessemer Development Board that provides in-house services for businesses with revenues up to $5,000,000. It serves not
only startup operations, but challenged, former home-
based, geographically-expanding and those operations still in the research/feasibility phase. Businesses
can remain in the incubator for up to 5 years.

47761 ■ Business Technology Development Center
515 Sparkman Dr.
Huntsville, AL 35816
Ph: (256)704-6000
Fax: (256)704-6002
URL: http://www.biztech.org/
Contact: Gary Tauss, Chief Executive Officer
Description: BizTech is a technology incubator
designed to help small companies develop emerging
technologies for the global marketplace, providing
mentoring, access to investors, training, a ready-
made network of contacts, and various business support services designed to improve the likelihood of
success.

47762 ■ Innovation Depot
1500 First Ave. N.
Birmingham, AL 35203
Ph: (205)250-8000
Fax: (205)250-8013
Co. E-mail: ecinfo@entrepreneurialctr.com
URL: http://www.innovationdepot.net
Contact: Kevin Herren, Director
Description: Innovation Depot is a business incuba-
tor housing 70 start-up businesses. The Depot is a
non-profit partnership formed by the combination of
the Entrepreneurial Center and the University of
Alabama at Birmingham's Office for the Advance-
ment of Developing Industries.

47763 ■ Montgomery Area Chamber of Commerce Incubation Program
600 S Court St.
Montgomery, AL 36101
Ph: (334)834-5200
Fax: (334)265-4745
Co. E-mail: lmcginty@montgomerychamber.com
URL: http://www.montgomerychamber.com
Contact: Lisa McGinty, Director
Description: A non-profit small business incubator
program for new service and light manufacturing busi-
nesses in the Montgomery area.

47764 ■ Northeast Alabama Entrepreneurial System
1400 Commerce Blvd., Ste. 1
Anniston, AL 36207
Ph: (256)831-5215
Fax: (256)831-8728
Co. E-mail: giles@neaes.org
URL: http://www.neaes.org
Contact: Giles McDaniel
Description: The Entrepreneurial Center is a busi-
ness incubator. A business incubator is a building in
which start-up companies locate during their initial
growth phase which can range from one to five years.

47765 ■ Shoals Entrepreneurial Center
3115 Northington Ct.
Florence, AL 35630
Ph: (256)760-9014
Fax: (256)740-5530
Co. E-mail: ContactUs@shoalsec.com
URL: http://www.shoalsec.com
Contact: Giles H. McDaniel, Executive Director
Description: A private, non-profit corporation whose
purpose is to assist new or fledgling businesses to
grow in a sheltered environment until they are ready
to be self-sustaining within the business community.

LEGISLATIVE ASSISTANCE

47766 ■ Alabama State House of Representatives - Bill Status Office
Alabama State House, Rm. 512
11 S. Union St. 5th Fl.
Montgomery, AL 36130
Ph: (334)242-7627
Free: 800-499-3051
Fax: (334)353-9040
Co. E-mail: alsenate@mindspring.com
URL: http://www.legislature.state.al.us
Contact: Jennifer Dabbou, Clerk

47767 ■ Alabama State House of Representatives - House Commerce Committee
Alabama State House
11 S. Union St., Rm. 522-B
Montgomery, AL 36130
Ph: (334)242-7697
Fax: (334)353-0828
Co. E-mail: house3@mindspring.com
URL: http://www.legislature.state.al.us
Contact: Frank McDaniel, Chairperson

PUBLICATIONS

47768 ■ *Atlanta Business Chronicle*
1801 Peachtree St., Ste. 150
Atlanta, GA 30309
Ph: (404)249-1000
Fax: (404)249-1048
Co. E-mail: atlanta@amcity.com
URL: http://www.amcity.com/atlanta

47769 ■ *Starting and Operating a Business in Alabama: A Step-by-Step Guide*
PSI Research
300 N. Valley Dr.
Grants Pass, OR 97526
Ph: (503)479-9464
Free: 800-228-2275
Fax: (503)476-1479
Co. E-mail: psi2@magick.net
Ed: Michael D. Jenkins. **Released:** Revised edition,
1992. **Price:** $29.95 (looseleaf binder); $24.95
(paper). **Description:** Part of the Successful Busi-
ness Library series.

SMALL BUSINESS DEVELOPMENT CENTERS

47770 ■ Alaska Small Business Development Center - Central Region
201 N Lucille St., Ste. 2A
Wasilla, AK 99654
Ph: (907)373-7232
Free: 877-373-7232
Fax: (907)373-7234
Co. E-mail: anjin@uaa.alaska.edu
URL: http://www.aksbdc.org
Contact: Julie Nolen, Director
Description: Represents and promotes the small business sector. Provides management assistance to current and prospective small business owners. Helps to improve management skills and expand the products and services of members.

47771 ■ Alaska Small Business Development Center - Great North Region
UAF Tanana Valley Campus
604 Barnette St., Ste. 220
Fairbanks, AK 99701
Ph: (907)456-7232
Free: 800-478-1701
Fax: (907)456-7233
Co. E-mail: aygreatnorth@uaa.alaska.edu
URL: http://www.tvc.uaf.edu/sbdc.html
Description: Represents and promotes the small business sector. Provides management assistance to current and prospective small business owners. Helps to improve management skills and expand the products and services of members.

47772 ■ Alaska Small Business Development Center - South Central Region
430 W 7th Ave., Ste. 110
Anchorage, AK 99501
Ph: (907)274-7232
Free: 800-478-7232
Fax: (907)274-9524
Co. E-mail: antjf@uaa.alaska.edu
URL: http://www.aksbdc.org
Contact: Tom Flanagan, Director (Acting)
Description: Represents and promotes the small business sector. Provides management assistance to current and prospective small business owners. Helps to improve management skills and expand the products and services of members.

47773 ■ Alaska Small Business Development Center - South West Region
43335 Kalifornsky Beach Rd., Ste. 12
Soldotna, AK 99669
Ph: (907)260-5629
Fax: (907)260-1695
Co. E-mail: inbz@uaa.alaska.edu
URL: http://www.aksbdc.org
Contact: Bryan Zak, Director
Description: Represents and promotes the small business sector. Provides management assistance to current and prospective small business owners. Helps to improve management skills and expand the products and services of members.

47774 ■ Alaska Small Business Development Center - Southeast Region
3100 Channel Dr., Ste. 306
Juneau, AK 99801
Ph: (907)463-3789
Fax: (907)463-3430
Co. E-mail: animg@uaa.alaska.edu
URL: http://www.aksbdc.org
Contact: Ian Grant, Director
Description: Represents and promotes the small business sector. Provides management assistance to current and prospective small business owners. Helps to improve management skills and expand the products and services of members.

SMALL BUSINESS ASSISTANCE PROGRAMS

47775 ■ Alaska Department of Commerce, Community, and Economic Development
PO Box 110800
Juneau, AK 99811-0800
Ph: (907)465-2500
Fax: (907)465-3767
Co. E-mail: questions@alaska.gov
URL: http://www.commerce.state.ak.us
Contact: Emil Notti, Commissioner
Description: Assists entrepreneurs in starting new businesses or expanding existing businesses. Helps prepare applications for economic development programs. Holds seminars and workshops on various aspects of business management.

BETTER BUSINESS BUREAUS

47776 ■ Better Business Bureau of Alaska
341 W Tudor Rd.
Anchorage, AK 99503
Ph: (907)562-0704
Fax: (907)562-4061
Co. E-mail: info@thebbb.org
URL: http://www.alaska.bbb.org
Contact: Robert W.G. Andrew, President
Description: Seeks to promote and foster the highest ethical relationship between businesses and the public through voluntary self-regulation, consumer and business education, and service excellence. Provides information to help consumers and businesses make informed purchasing decisions and avoid costly scams and frauds; settles consumer complaints through arbitration and other means.

CHAMBERS OF COMMERCE

47777 ■ Alaska State Chamber of Commerce (ASCC)
217 2nd St., Ste. 201
Juneau, AK 99801-1267
Ph: (907)586-2323
Fax: (907)463-5515
Co. E-mail: info@alaskachamber.com
URL: http://www.alaskachamber.com
Contact: Wayne A. Stevens, President
Description: Promotes business and community development in Alaska. **Founded:** 1952. **Publications:** *The Chamber* (Quarterly). **Educational Activities:** Legislative Miniconference. **Awards:** Alaskan of the Year (Annual); Local Chamber of the Year (Annual); Small Business of the Year (Annual).

47778 ■ *Anchor Point Brochure/Visitor Guide*
PO Box 610
Anchor Point, AK 99556-0610
Ph: (907)235-2600
Fax: (907)235-2600
Co. E-mail: info@anchorpointchamber.org
URL: http://www.anchorpointchamber.org
Contact: Jesse Clutts, President
Released: Periodic

47779 ■ Anchor Point Chamber of Commerce (APCOC)
PO Box 610
Anchor Point, AK 99556-0610
Ph: (907)235-2600
Fax: (907)235-2600
Co. E-mail: info@anchorpointchamber.org
URL: http://www.anchorpointchamber.org
Contact: Jesse Clutts, President
Description: Seeks to promote and perpetuate business; to promote the general welfare of the Anchor Point area; and to stimulate public interest to these ends. **Founded:** 1960. **Publications:** *Anchor Point Brochure/Visitor Guide* (Periodic); *Business Directory* (Periodic); *The Resolution* (Monthly). **Educational Activities:** Anchor Point Chamber of Commerce Meeting (Weekly).

47780 ■ Anchorage Chamber of Commerce (ACC)
1016 W 6th Ave., Ste. 303
Anchorage, AK 99501-2309
Ph: (907)272-2401
Fax: (907)272-4117
Co. E-mail: info@anchoragechamber.org
URL: http://www.anchoragechamber.org
Contact: Bruce Bustamante, Chairman
Description: Promotes business and community development in Anchorage, AK. **Founded:** 1915. **Publications:** *News and Views* (Monthly). **Awards:** Anchorage Chamber Gold Pan (Annual).

47781 ■ Big Lake Chamber of Commerce
PO Box 520067
Big Lake, AK 99652
Ph: (907)892-6109
Fax: (907)892-6120
Co. E-mail: info@biglakechamber.org
URL: http://www.biglakechamber.org
Contact: Margaret Billinger, President
Description: Promotes business and community development in Big Lake, AK area. **Publications:** *Business Connection* (Monthly).

47782 ■ Business Connection
415 E Railroad Ave.
Wasilla, AK 99654
Ph: (907)376-1299
Fax: (907)373-2560
Co. E-mail: contact@wasillachamber.org
URL: http://www.wasillachamber.org
Contact: Paula Nance, President
Released: Monthly **Price:** free.

47783 ■ Business Connection
PO Box 520067
Big Lake, AK 99652
Ph: (907)892-6109
Fax: (907)892-6120
Co. E-mail: info@biglakechamber.org
URL: http://www.biglakechamber.org
Contact: Margaret Billinger, President
Released: Monthly

47784 ■ Business Directory
PO Box 610
Anchor Point, AK 99556-0610
Ph: (907)235-2600
Fax: (907)235-2600
Co. E-mail: info@anchorpointchamber.org
URL: http://www.anchorpointchamber.org
Contact: Jesse Clutts, President
Released: Periodic

47785 ■ The Chamber
217 2nd St., Ste. 201
Juneau, AK 99801-1267
Ph: (907)586-2323
Fax: (907)463-5515
Co. E-mail: info@alaskachamber.com
URL: http://www.alaskachamber.com
Contact: Wayne A. Stevens, President
Released: Quarterly

47786 ■ Chamber Focus
PO Box 5957
Ketchikan, AK 99901
Ph: (907)225-3184
Fax: (907)225-3187
Co. E-mail: info@ketchikanchamber.com
URL: http://www.ketchikanchamber.com
Contact: Miguel Torres, President
Released: Monthly

47787 ■ Chamber News
PO Box 987
Delta Junction, AK 99737-0987
Ph: (907)895-5068
Free: 877-895-5068
Fax: (907)895-5141
Co. E-mail: deltacc@deltachamber.org
URL: http://www.deltachamber.org
Contact: Chuck Creamer, President
Released: Monthly **Price:** included in membership dues.

47788 ■ Chamber POWer
PO Box 490
Klawock, AK 99925-0490
Ph: (907)755-2626
Fax: (907)755-2627
Co. E-mail: info@princeofwalescoc.org
URL: http://www.princeofwalescoc.org
Contact: Jan Bush, President
Released: Monthly

47789 ■ Chugiak-Eagle River Business & Service Directory
11401 Old Glenn Hwy., Ste. 105
Eagle River, AK 99577-0353
Ph: (907)694-4702
Fax: (907)694-1205
Co. E-mail: info@cer.com
URL: http://www.cer.org
Contact: Susan Gorski, Executive Director

47790 ■ Chugiak-Eagle River Chamber of Commerce
11401 Old Glenn Hwy., Ste. 105
Eagle River, AK 99577-0353
Ph: (907)694-4702

Fax: (907)694-1205
Co. E-mail: info@cer.com
URL: http://www.cer.org
Contact: Susan Gorski, Executive Director
Description: Seeks to promote and perpetuate economic development, civic interest, general welfare and prosperity of the Chugiak-Eagle River area. Aims to stimulate public interest to these ends. **Publications:** *Chugiak-Eagle River Business & Service Directory.* **Educational Activities:** Chugiak-Eagle River Chamber of Commerce Board meeting (Semimonthly). **Awards:** Community Service Award (Annual); Distinguished Bear Paw Award (Annual).

47791 ■ Cordova Chamber of Commerce
c/o Martin Moe, Exec. Dir.
PO Box 99
Cordova, AK 99574
Ph: (907)424-7260
Fax: (907)424-7259
URL: http://www.cordovachamber.com
Contact: Martin Moe, Executive Director
Description: Promotes business, community development, and tourism in Cordova, Alaska.

47792 ■ Delta Chamber of Commerce (DCC)
PO Box 987
Delta Junction, AK 99737-0987
Ph: (907)895-5068
Free: 877-895-5068
Fax: (907)895-5141
Co. E-mail: deltacc@deltachamber.org
URL: http://www.deltachamber.org
Contact: Chuck Creamer, President
Description: Promotes business and community development in Delta Junction, Alaska. Conducts charitable activities; Operates and maintains Visitor Information Center and Sullivan Roadhouse Historical Museum. Sponsors annual community clean-up, Festival of Lights, Friendly Frontier Days, Old Fashioned July 4th Celebration, Halloween Bash, Holiday Decorating Contest, Annual Holiday Coloring Contest, Gingerbread House Contest. **Founded:** 1977. **Publications:** *Chamber News* (Monthly); *Delta Junction Chamber of Commerce* (Annual); *Delta Junction Visitor Guide* (Annual).

47793 ■ Delta Junction Chamber of Commerce
PO Box 987
Delta Junction, AK 99737-0987
Ph: (907)895-5068
Free: 877-895-5068
Fax: (907)895-5141
Co. E-mail: deltacc@deltachamber.org
URL: http://www.deltachamber.org
Contact: Chuck Creamer, President
Released: Annual

47794 ■ Delta Junction Visitor Guide
PO Box 987
Delta Junction, AK 99737-0987
Ph: (907)895-5068
Free: 877-895-5068
Fax: (907)895-5141
Co. E-mail: deltacc@deltachamber.org
URL: http://www.deltachamber.org
Contact: Chuck Creamer, President
Released: Annual

47795 ■ Denali Chamber of Commerce
PO Box 437
Healy, AK 99743-0437
Ph: (907)683-4636
Co. E-mail: denali.chamber@gmail.com
URL: http://www.denalichamber.com
Contact: Mrs. Connie MacMaster, Administrative Assistant
Description: Aims to promote and perpetuate the business, commercial, manufacturing and civic interest; to promote and perpetuate the general welfare and prosperity of Healy/Denali and its environs, and to stimulate public interest in these ends. **Founded:** 1991.

47796 ■ Greater Copper Valley Chamber of Commerce
PO Box 469
Glennallen, AK 99588-0469

Ph: (907)822-5555
Fax: (907)822-5558
Co. E-mail: chamber@cvinternet.net
URL: http://www.coppervalleychamber.com
Contact: Warren Ulrich, President
Description: Maintains a visitor center to promote and advertise businesses in the Copper Valley area. Seeks to promote economic growth.

47797 ■ Greater Fairbanks Chamber of Commerce
100 Cushman St., Ste. 102
Fairbanks, AK 99701
Ph: (907)452-1105
Fax: (907)456-6968
Co. E-mail: info@fairbankschamber.org
URL: http://www.fairbankschamber.org
Contact: Lisa Herbert, Executive Director
Description: Promotes business and community development in the Greater Fairbanks, AK area. **Founded:** 1952. **Publications:** *Membership.*

47798 ■ Greater Ketchikan Chamber of Commerce (GKCC)
PO Box 5957
Ketchikan, AK 99901
Ph: (907)225-3184
Fax: (907)225-3187
Co. E-mail: info@ketchikanchamber.com
URL: http://www.ketchikanchamber.com
Contact: Miguel Torres, President
Description: Seeks to encourage leadership by business and professional individuals to improve business relations, economic well-being and the quality of living in Ketchikan. Monitors legislation and local, state, and federal issues. Sponsors Fourth of July parade, sales promotions, Salmon Derby, and local trade show. **Founded:** 1967. **Publications:** *Chamber Focus* (Monthly). **Awards:** Citizen of the Year (Annual); Community Service Award (Annual); Economic Development Award (Annual); Entrepreneur of the Year (Annual); Outstanding Youth Leader (Annual); Business of the Year (Annual).

47799 ■ Greater Palmer Chamber of Commerce
550 S Alaska St., Ste. 101
Palmer, AK 99645
Ph: (907)745-2880
Fax: (907)746-4164
Co. E-mail: jthompson@mta-telco.com
URL: http://www.palmerchamber.org
Contact: Jessica Thompson, President
Description: Promotes business and community development in the Palmer, AK area. **Founded:** 1971. **Publications:** *Matanuska Tradewinds.*

47800 ■ Greater Sitka Chamber of Commerce (GSCC)
PO Box 638
Sitka, AK 99835
Ph: (907)747-8604
Fax: (907)747-7413
Co. E-mail: jen@sitkachamber.com
URL: http://www.sitkachamber.com
Contact: Jennifer Robinson, Executive Director
Description: Promotes business and community development in Sitka, AK. **Founded:** 1904.

47801 ■ Greater Soldotna Chamber of Commerce (GSCC)
44790 Sterling Hwy.
Soldotna, AK 99669
Ph: (907)262-9814
Fax: (907)262-3566
Co. E-mail: info@soldotnachamber.com
URL: http://visitsoldotna.com/chamber
Contact: Evy Gebhardt, President
Description: Promotes business and community development in the Soldotna, AK area. Sponsors Soldotna Progress Days. **Founded:** 1957. **Publications:** *Your Chamber Today; Soldotna Recreation and Visitors Guide* (Annual). **Awards:** Local H.S. Scholarship Award.

47802 ■ Greater Wasilla Chamber of Commerce
415 E Railroad Ave.
Wasilla, AK 99654

Ph: (907)376-1299
Fax: (907)373-2560
Co. E-mail: contact@wasillachamber.org
URL: http://www.wasillachamber.org
Contact: Paula Nance, President
Description: Creates a positive economic and civic climate in the greater Wasilla area, thereby making possible for members and the community to grow and prosper. Provides education and information for members and the community. Facilitates group action on the part of the business community. **Founded:** 1976. **Publications:** *Business Connection* (Monthly). **Educational Activities:** Chamber After Hours (Monthly).

47803 ■ Haines Chamber of Commerce
PO Box 1449
Haines, AK 99827-1449
Ph: (907)766-2202
Fax: (907)766-2271
Co. E-mail: chamber@haineschamber.org
URL: http://www.haineschamber.org
Contact: Karl Heinz, President
Description: Promotes business and community development. Works to advance the interests of the area under the democratic system of free enterprise. Conducts activities beneficial to the community and its citizens.

47804 ■ Homer Chamber of Commerce
201 Sterling Hwy.
Homer, AK 99603
Ph: (907)235-7740
Fax: (907)235-8766
Co. E-mail: info@homeralaska.org
URL: http://www.homeralaska.org
Contact: Monte Davis, Executive Director
Description: Promotes business and community development in Homer, AK. **Founded:** 1955.

47805 ■ Juneau Chamber of Commerce
3100 Channel Dr., Ste. 300
Juneau, AK 99801
Ph: (907)463-3488
Fax: (907)463-3489
Co. E-mail: juneauchamber@gci.net
URL: http://www.juneauchamber.com
Contact: Cathie Roemmich, Chief Executive Officer
Description: Promotes business and community development in the Juneau, AK area.

47806 ■ Kenai Chamber of Commerce
402 Overland St.
Kenai, AK 99611
Ph: (907)283-7989
Fax: (907)283-7183
Co. E-mail: info@kenaichamber.org
URL: http://www.kenaichamber.org
Contact: Johna Beech, Executive Director
Description: Promotes business and community development in the Kenai, AK area. **Awards:** Business of the Year (Annual); Community Service (Annual); President's Choice (Annual); Volunteer of the Year (Annual).

47807 ■ Kodiak Chamber of Commerce (KCC)
100 E Marine Way, Ste. 300
Kodiak, AK 99615-1485
Ph: (907)486-5557
Fax: (907)486-7605
Co. E-mail: chamber@kodiak.org
URL: http://www.kodiak.org/business/kodiak-chamber-of-commerce.html
Contact: Trevor Brown, Executive Director
Description: Promotes business and community development in the Kodiak, AK area. Co-sponsors Koniag's Kodiak Crab Festival and Comfish Alaska commercial fishing show. **Founded:** 1939. **Educational Activities:** ComFish Alaska (Annual).

47808 ■ *Matanuska Tradewinds*
550 S Alaska St., Ste. 101
Palmer, AK 99645
Ph: (907)745-2880
Fax: (907)746-4164
Co. E-mail: jthompson@mta-telco.com
URL: http://www.palmerchamber.org
Contact: Jessica Thompson, President

47809 ■ *Membership*
100 Cushman St., Ste. 102
Fairbanks, AK 99701
Ph: (907)452-1105
Fax: (907)456-6968
Co. E-mail: info@fairbankschamber.org
URL: http://www.fairbankschamber.org
Contact: Lisa Herbert, Executive Director

47810 ■ *News and Views*
1016 W 6th Ave., Ste. 303
Anchorage, AK 99501-2309
Ph: (907)272-2401
Fax: (907)272-4117
Co. E-mail: info@anchoragechamber.org
URL: http://www.anchoragechamber.org
Contact: Bruce Bustamante, Chairman
Released: Monthly

47811 ■ Nome Chamber of Commerce
PO Box 250
Nome, AK 99762
Ph: (907)443-3879
Fax: (907)443-3892
Co. E-mail: nomechamber@gci.net
URL: http://www.nomechamber.org
Contact: Mitch Erickson, Executive Director
Description: Promotes business and community development in Nome, AK. **Founded:** 1981. **Publications:** *Nome Focus.*

47812 ■ Petersburg Chamber of Commerce
PO Box 649
Petersburg, AK 99833
Ph: (907)772-3646
Fax: (907)772-2453
Co. E-mail: chamber@petersburg.org
URL: http://www.petersburg.org
Contact: Ryan McFarland, President
Description: Seeks to promote a strong and diversified economy. Serves the business community of Petersburg through leadership, service, marketing, and communications.

47813 ■ Prince of Wales Chamber of Commerce
PO Box 490
Klawock, AK 99925-0490
Ph: (907)755-2626
Fax: (907)755-2627
Co. E-mail: info@princeofwalescoc.org
URL: http://www.princeofwalescoc.org
Contact: Jan Bush, President
Description: Promotes business and community development in Prince of Wales Island, AK. **Founded:** 1989. **Publications:** *Chamber POWer* (Monthly). **Educational Activities:** Prince of Wales Chamber of Commerce Meeting (Monthly). **Awards:** Business Person of the Year (Annual); Citizen of the Year (Annual); Outstanding Business of the Year (Annual); President's Award (Annual); Volunteer of the Year (Annual); Youth Leader of the Year (Annual). **Telecommunication Services:** belle@aptalaska.net.

47814 ■ *The Resolution*
PO Box 610
Anchor Point, AK 99556-0610
Ph: (907)235-2600
Fax: (907)235-2600
Co. E-mail: info@anchorpointchamber.org
URL: http://www.anchorpointchamber.org
Contact: Jesse Clutts, President
Released: Monthly

47815 ■ Seldovia Chamber of Commerce
PO Drawer F
Seldovia, AK 99663
Ph: (907)234-7612
Co. E-mail: president@seldoviachamber.org
URL: http://www.seldoviachamber.org
Contact: Peggy Keesecker, President
Description: Promotes business and community development in Seldovia, AK. Conducts charitable activities. Sponsors festivals. Publications: none. **Awards:** Citizen of the Year Award (Annual).

47816 ■ Seward Chamber of Commerce (SCC)
PO Box 749
Seward, AK 99664-0749
Ph: (907)224-8051
Fax: (907)224-5353
Co. E-mail: director@seward.net
URL: http://www.sewardak.org
Contact: Laura Cloward, Executive Director
Description: Promotes business and community development in the Seward, AK area. Sponsors festival and competitions. **Founded:** 1910.

47817 ■ *Skagway Business Directory*
PO Box 194
Skagway, AK 99840-0194
Ph: (907)983-1898
Fax: (907)983-2031
Co. E-mail: chamber@aptalaska.net
URL: http://www.skagwaychamber.org
Contact: Emily Deach, President
E-mail: emilyadalia@yahoo.com
URL(s): www.skagwaychamber.org/skagbiz.html. **Released:** Annual **Price:** free; Free. **Covers:** Comprehensive listing of area businesses.

47818 ■ Skagway Chamber of Commerce
PO Box 194
Skagway, AK 99840-0194
Ph: (907)983-1898
Fax: (907)983-2031
Co. E-mail: chamber@aptalaska.net
URL: http://www.skagwaychamber.org
Contact: Emily Deach, President
E-mail: emilyadalia@yahoo.com
Description: Strives to provide members with information of importance to business and residents of Skagway, AK. Represents members regarding city and state issues that affect Skagway. **Founded:** 1898. **Publications:** *Skagway Business Directory* (Annual).

47819 ■ *Soldotna Recreation and Visitors Guide*
44790 Sterling Hwy.
Soldotna, AK 99669
Ph: (907)262-9814
Fax: (907)262-3566
Co. E-mail: info@soldotnachamber.com
URL: http://visitsoldotna.com/chamber
Contact: Evy Gebhardt, President
Released: Annual

47820 ■ Talkeetna Chamber of Commerce
PO Box 334
Talkeetna, AK 99676-0334
Ph: (907)733-2330
Co. E-mail: info@talkeetnachamber.org
URL: http://www.talkeetnachamber.org
Contact: Trisha Costello, President
Description: Promotes business and community development in Talkeetna, AK area. **Founded:** 1975. **Awards:** Post Secondary Education Scholarship (Annual).

47821 ■ Tok Chamber of Commerce
PO Box 389
Tok, AK 99780-0389
Ph: (907)883-5775
Co. E-mail: info@tokalaskainfo.com
URL: http://www.tokalaskainfo.com
Contact: Bonnie Jenkins, Manager
Description: Promotes business and community development in Tok, AK area.

47822 ■ Willow Chamber of Commerce
PO Box 183
Willow, AK 99688
Ph: (907)495-6800
Fax: (907)495-6800
Co. E-mail: mail@willowchamber.org
URL: http://www.willowchamber.org
Contact: Mr. Houston Stanley, Vice President
Description: Seeks to provide a forum for the business community to exchange information on matters of mutual concern; to promote the economic welfare of the Willow area in general; and to undertake

projects designed to improve the business climate in Willow in particular and the surrounding area and state in general. **Founded:** 1987.

47823 ■ Wrangell Chamber of Commerce (WCC)
PO Box 49
Wrangell, AK 99929
Ph: (907)874-3901
Free: 800-367-9745
Fax: (907)874-3905
Co. E-mail: wrangellchamber@gmail.com
URL: http://www.wrangellchamber.org
Contact: Janell Privett, President

Description: Aims to advance the business, professional, civic and cultural interests of the City of Wrangell. Encourages the growth of existing businesses. Supports activities beneficial to the community and its citizens.

47824 ■ *Your Chamber Today*
44790 Sterling Hwy.
Soldotna, AK 99669
Ph: (907)262-9814
Fax: (907)262-3566
Co. E-mail: info@soldotnachamber.com
URL: http://visitsoldotna.com/chamber
Contact: Evy Gebhardt, President

MINORITY BUSINESS ASSISTANCE PROGRAMS

47825 ■ Alaska Minority Business Development Center - Tanana Chief Conference, Inc.
122 First Ave., Ste. 600
Fairbanks, AK 99701
Ph: (907)452-8251
Fax: (907)459-3851
Co. E-mail: info@tananachiefs.org
URL: http://www.tananachiefs.org

47826 ■ YWCA Anchorage Women's Business Solutions
324 E 5th Ave.
Anchorage, AK 99501
Ph: (907)644-9611
Fax: (907)644-9650
Co. E-mail: cailleo@ywcaak.org
URL: http://www.ywcaak.org/finances.htm
Contact: Caren Ailleo, Director

Description: Provides business development services for women in Alaska who want to start or grow a business.

EDUCATIONAL PROGRAMS

47827 ■ Matanuska-Susitna College
PO Box 2889
Palmer, AK 99645

Ph: (907)745-9774
Fax: (907)745-9711
Co. E-mail: info@matsu.alaska.edu
URL: http://www.matsu.alaska.edu
Description: Two-year college offering a program in small business management.

PUBLICATIONS

47828 ■ *Alaska Business Monthly*
PO Box 241288
Anchorage, AK 99524-1288
Ph: (907)276-4373
Fax: (907)279-2900
Co. E-mail: info@akbizmag.com
URL: http://www.akbizmag.com

47829 ■ *Starting and Operating a Business in Alaska: A Step-by-Step Guide*
PSI Research
300 N. Valley Dr.
Grants Pass, OR 97526
Ph: (503)479-9464
Free: 800-228-2275
Fax: (503)476-1479
Co. E-mail: psi2@magick.net
Ed: Michael D. Jenkins. **Released:** Revised edition, 1992. **Price:** $29.95 (looseleaf binder); $24.95 (paper). **Description:** Part of the Successful Business Library series.

SMALL BUSINESS DEVELOPMENT CENTERS

47830 ■ Arizona Western College Small Business Development Center
1351 S Redondo Center Dr., Ste. 101
Yuma, AZ 85365
Ph: (928)317-6151
Co. E-mail: randy.nelson@azwestern.edu
URL: http://www.azsbdc.net
Contact: Randy Nelson, Director
Description: Represents and promotes the small business sector. Provides management assistance to current and prospective small business owners. Helps to improve management skills and expand the products and services of members.

47831 ■ Central Arizona College Small Business Development Center
540 N Camino Mercado, No. 1
Casa Grande, AZ 85222
Ph: (520)494-6610
Fax: (520)494-6612
Co. E-mail: sbdc@centralaz.edu
URL: http://www.centralaz.edu/biz
Contact: Jim Rhodes, Director
Description: Represents and promotes the small business sector. Provides management assistance to current and prospective small business owners. Helps to improve management skills and expand the products and services of members.

47832 ■ Cochise College Small Business Development Center
901 N Colombo Ave., Rm. 717
Sierra Vista, AZ 85635
Ph: (520)515-5478
Free: 800-966-7943
Co. E-mail: schmittm@cochise.edu
URL: http://www.cochise.edu
Contact: Mark Schmitt, Director
Description: Represents and promotes the small business sector. Provides management assistance to current and prospective small business owners. Helps to improve management skills and expand the products and services of members.

47833 ■ Coconino Community College Small Business Development Center
3000 N 4th St.
Flagstaff, AZ 86004
Ph: (928)526-7653
Fax: (928)526-8693
Co. E-mail: sbdc@coconino.edu
URL: http://www.coconino.edu/academics/community/sbdc/Pages/default.aspx
Contact: Kurt Haskell, Director
Description: Represents and promotes the small business sector. Provides management assistance to current and prospective small business owners. Helps to improve management skills and expand the products and services of members.

47834 ■ Eastern Arizona College Small Business Development Center (EAC SBDC)
Student Services Bldg., Rm. 113
615 N Stadium Ave.
Thatcher, AZ 85552
Ph: (928)428-8590
Free: 888-322-5780
Fax: (928)428-2578
Co. E-mail: sbdc@eac.edu
URL: http://www.eac.edu/sbdc
Contact: Kevin Peck, Director
Description: Represents and promotes the small business sector. Provides management assistance to current and prospective small business owners. Helps to improve management skills and expand the products and services of members.

47835 ■ Maricopa Community Colleges at Phoenix Small Business Development Center
2400 N Central Ave., Ste. 104
Phoenix, AZ 85004
Ph: (480)784-0590
Co. E-mail: mark.engle@domail.maricopa.edu
URL: http://www.maricopa-sbdc.com/maricopasbdc/maricopasbdc.htm
Contact: Mark Engle, Director
Description: Represents and promotes the small business sector. Provides management assistance to current and prospective small business owners. Helps to improve management skills and expand the products and services of members.

47836 ■ Mesa Minority/Micro Small Business Development Center (M3SBDC)
c/o Mesa Community College Downtown Campus
165 N Centennial Way, Rm. 209
Mesa, AZ 85201
Ph: (480)461-6125
Co. E-mail: claudia.smietana@maricopasbdc.com
URL: http://www.azsbdc.net/locations/all-locations
Contact:
Description: Represents and promotes the small business sector. Provides management assistance to current and prospective small business owners. Helps to improve management skills and expand the products and services of members.

47837 ■ Mohave Community College Small Business Development Center (MCC SBDC)
1971 E Jagerson Ave.
Kingman, AZ 86409
Ph: (928)757-0894
Fax: (928)692-3038
Co. E-mail: kmarsh@mohave.edu
URL: http://www.mohave.edu/pages/195.asp
Contact: Kelley Marsh, Director
Description: Represents and promotes the small business sector. Provides management assistance to current and prospective small business owners. Helps to improve management skills and expand the products and services of members.

47838 ■ Northland Pioneer College's Small Business Development Center
PO Box 610
Holbrook, AZ 86025

Ph: (928)532-6170
Fax: (928)532-6171
Co. E-mail: tracy.mancuso@npc.edu
URL: http://www.npcsbdc.com
Contact: Tracy Mancuso, Director
Description: Represents and promotes the small business sector. Provides management assistance to current and prospective small business owners. Helps to improve management skills and expand the products and services of members.

47839 ■ Pima College's Small Business Development Center
Microbusiness Advancement Center
330 N Commerce Park Loop, Ste. 160
Tucson, AZ 85745-2790
Ph: (520)620-1241
URL: http://mac-sa.org/programs-2/sbdc
Contact: Ellen Kirton, Director
Description: Represents and promotes the small business sector. Provides management assistance to current and prospective small business owners. Helps to improve management skills and expand the products and services of members.

SCORE OFFICES

47840 ■ Southern Arizona SCORE
Co. E-mail: score@dakotacom.net

BETTER BUSINESS BUREAUS

47841 ■ Better Business Bureau, Central/Northern Arizona
4428 N 12th St.
Phoenix, AZ 85014-4585
Ph: (602)264-1721
Free: 877-291-6222
Fax: (602)263-0997
Co. E-mail: info@arizonabbb.org
URL: http://central-northern-western-arizona.bbb.org
Contact: Matthew Fehling, President
Description: Seeks to promote and foster the highest ethical relationship between businesses and the public through voluntary self-regulation, consumer and business education, and service excellence. Provides information to help consumers and businesses make informed purchasing decisions and avoid costly scams and frauds; settles consumer complaints through arbitration and other means. **Founded:** 1938. **Awards:** Business Ethics Award (Annual).

47842 ■ Better Business Bureau of Tucson
434 S Williams Blvd., Ste. 102
Tucson, AZ 85711
Ph: (520)888-5353
Fax: (520)888-6262
Co. E-mail: info@tucson.bbb.org
URL: http://tucson.bbb.org
Contact: Kim States, President
Description: Seeks to promote and foster the highest ethical relationship between businesses and the public through voluntary self-regulation, consumer

and business education, and service excellence. Provides information to help consumers and businesses make informed purchasing decisions and avoid costly scams and frauds; settles consumer complaints through arbitration and other means. **Founded:** 1952.

CHAMBERS OF COMMERCE

47843 ■ *Accept Report*
1850 N Central Ave., Ste. 1433
Phoenix, AZ 85004
Ph: (602)248-9172
Fax: (602)265-1262
Co. E-mail: info@azchamber.com
URL: http://www.azchamber.com
Contact: Glenn Hamer, President
Released: Periodic

47844 ■ **Ahwatukee Foothills Chamber of Commerce**
4435 E Chandler Blvd., No. 140
Phoenix, AZ 85048-7650
Ph: (480)753-7676
Fax: (480)753-3898
Co. E-mail: info@ahwatukeechamber.com
URL: http://www.ahwatukeechamber.com
Contact: Anne Gill, President
Description: Promotes business and community development in Ahwatukee Foothills, AZ. **Founded:** 1994. **Publications:** *The Forum.*

47845 ■ **Ajo District Chamber of Commerce**
400 Taladro St.
Ajo, AZ 85321
Ph: (520)387-7742
Fax: (520)387-3641
Co. E-mail: ajocofc@tabletoptelephone.com
URL: http://www.ajochamber.com
Contact: Silvia Howard, Executive Director
Description: Promotes business and community development in Ajo, AZ. Sponsors St. Patrick's Day celebration, Fourth of July festivities, and Octoberfest.

47846 ■ **Alpine Chamber of Commerce**
PO Box 410
Alpine, AZ 85920
Ph: (928)339-4330
Co. E-mail: chamber@alpinearizona.com
URL: http://www.alpinearizona.com
Contact: Anne MacGregor, President
Description: Promotes business and community development in Alpine, AZ. Conducts benefit bull riding event. Sponsors Fishing Derby, Logger Jamboree, and Harvest Ball.

47847 ■ **Apache Junction Chamber of Commerce (AJCC)**
PO Box 1747
Apache Junction, AZ 85217-1747
Ph: (480)982-3141
Fax: (480)982-3234
Co. E-mail: jan@ajchamber.com
URL: http://www.apachejunctioncoc.com
Contact: Steve Lewis, Chairman
Description: Promotes business and community development in the Apache Junction, Gold Canyon and San Tan, AZ area. Sponsors Lost Dutchman Days festival. **Founded:** 1960.

47848 ■ **Arizona Chamber of Commerce and Industry**
1850 N Central Ave., Ste. 1433
Phoenix, AZ 85004
Ph: (602)248-9172
Fax: (602)265-1262
Co. E-mail: info@azchamber.com
URL: http://www.azchamber.com
Contact: Glenn Hamer, President
Description: Works to promote a business climate that enhances economic vitality and improves the quality of life for all Arizonans. **Founded:** 1974. **Publications:** *Accept Report* (Periodic); *VOX Negotium* (Periodic); *Arizona Employment Law Handbook.*

47849 ■ **Arizona City Chamber of Commerce (AZC)**
PO Box 5
Arizona City, AZ 85223-0005
Ph: (520)466-5141
Fax: (520)466-8204
Co. E-mail: azchamber@cgmailbox.com
URL: http://www.azcchamber.com
Contact: Yvonne Jenkins, President
Description: Promotes business and community development in the Arizona City, AZ area.

47850 ■ *Arizona Employment Law Handbook*
1850 N Central Ave., Ste. 1433
Phoenix, AZ 85004
Ph: (602)248-9172
Fax: (602)265-1262
Co. E-mail: info@azchamber.com
URL: http://www.azchamber.com
Contact: Glenn Hamer, President

47851 ■ **Arizona Hispanic Chamber of Commerce (AZHCC)**
255 E Osborne Rd., Ste. 201
Phoenix, AZ 85012
Ph: (602)279-1800
Fax: (602)279-8900
Co. E-mail: info@azhcc.com
URL: http://www.azhcc.com
Contact: Izzy Gonzalez, Chairman
Description: Promotes business and community development in the Hispanic community of Arizona. **Founded:** 1948. **Publications:** *Comercio.*

47852 ■ *Arizona Industrial Directory*
201 N Central Ave., 27th Fl.
Phoenix, AZ 85004
Ph: (602)495-2195
Fax: (602)495-8913
Co. E-mail: info@phoenixchamber.com
URL: http://www.phoenixchamber.com
Contact: Todd Sanders, President
Released: Annual **Price:** $87, for members; $97, for nonmembers.

47853 ■ *Arizona Informant*
201 E Washington St., Ste. 350
Phoenix, AZ 85004
Ph: (602)307-5200
Fax: (602)307-5204
Co. E-mail: info@phoenixblackchamber.com
URL: http://www.phoenixblackchamber.com
Contact: Kerwin V. Brown, Chief Executive Officer
Released: Weekly **Price:** $50.

47854 ■ **Asian Chamber of Commerce**
c/o Madeline Ong-Sakata, Sec./Exec. Dir.
7217 N 6th St.
Phoenix, AZ 85020
Ph: (602)371-8452
Co. E-mail: asiansun@aol.com
URL: http://www.asianchamber.org
Contact: Madeline Ong-Sakata, Executive Director
Description: Seeks to support, promote, and foster business, cultural, and educational relationships between chamber members and the general public. Provides consultancy and technical assistance to the members. **Publications:** *Asian SUNews* (Monthly).

47855 ■ *Asian SUNews*
c/o Madeline Ong-Sakata, Sec./Exec. Dir.
7217 N 6th St.
Phoenix, AZ 85020
Ph: (602)371-8452
Co. E-mail: asiansun@aol.com
URL: http://www.asianchamber.org
Contact: Madeline Ong-Sakata, Executive Director
Released: Monthly

47856 ■ *Back to Business Buckeye*
508 E Monroe Ave.
Buckeye, AZ 85326
Ph: (623)386-2727
Free: 877-850-2600
Fax: (623)386-7527
Co. E-mail: kala@buckeyevalleychamber.org
URL: http://www.buckeyevalleychamber.org
Contact: Kevin Johnson, Chairman
Released: Monthly

47857 ■ **Benson - San Pedro Valley Chamber of Commerce**
168 E 4th St.
Benson, AZ 85602
Ph: (520)265-8031
Co. E-mail: downbytheriverbb@hotmail.com
URL: http://www.bensonchamberaz.com
Contact: Mike Hug, President (Acting)
Description: Promotes business and community development in Benson, AZ. Conducts annual Butterfield Overland Stage Days. Sponsors local festivals. Convention/Meeting: none. **Publications:** *We Mean Business* (Monthly).

47858 ■ *Bisbee Business to Business*
1326 W Hwy. 92, Ste. 9
Bisbee, AZ 85603
Ph: (520)432-5421
Co. E-mail: chamber@bisbeearizona.com
URL: http://bisbeearizona.com/content
Contact: Cathe Wright, President
Released: Monthly

47859 ■ **Bisbee Chamber of Commerce and Visitor Center (BCCVC)**
1326 W Hwy. 92, Ste. 9
Bisbee, AZ 85603
Ph: (520)432-5421
Co. E-mail: chamber@bisbeearizona.com
URL: http://bisbeearizona.com/content
Contact: Cathe Wright, President
Description: Promotes business, tourism, and community development in Bisbee, AZ. **Scope:** business, economic development, tax laws. **Subscriptions:** 200 articles books periodicals. **Publications:** *Bisbee Business to Business* (Monthly).

47860 ■ **Bouse Chamber of Commerce**
PO Box 817
Bouse, AZ 85325-0817
Ph: (928)851-2509
Co. E-mail: bousecofc@yahoo.com
URL: http://www.bousechamberofcommerce.com
Description: Strives to promote tourism in Bouse. Encourages senior citizen to retire to the community. **Founded:** 1987. **Awards:** Bouse Community Christmas Light (Annual).

47861 ■ **Buckeye Valley Chamber of Commerce**
508 E Monroe Ave.
Buckeye, AZ 85326
Ph: (623)386-2727
Free: 877-850-2600
Fax: (623)386-7527
Co. E-mail: kala@buckeyevalleychamber.org
URL: http://www.buckeyevalleychamber.org
Contact: Kevin Johnson, Chairman
Description: Strives to enhance community development in Buckeye, AZ. **Publications:** *Back to Business Buckeye* (Monthly). **Educational Activities:** Buckeye Valley Chamber of Commerce Luncheon (Monthly). **Telecommunication Services:** kj@teamkj.com.

47862 ■ **Bullhead Area Chamber of Commerce**
1251 Hwy. 95
Bullhead City, AZ 86429
Ph: (928)754-4121
Free: 800-987-7457
Fax: (928)754-5514
Co. E-mail: info@bullheadchamber.com
URL: http://www.bullheadchamber.com
Contact: Chris Barton, Executive Director
Description: Promotes business and community development in the Bullhead, AZ area. **Publications:** *Bullhead Area Chamber of Commerce--Membership Directory*; *The Business Frontline* (Monthly); *Hot Prospects* (Annual); *Hot Prospects* (Annual); *Hot Prospects* (Annual). **Telecommunication Services:** cbarton@bullheadchamber.com.

47863 ■ *The Business Advocate*
PO Box 28500
Tempe, AZ 85285-8500
Ph: (480)967-7891

Fax: (480)966-5365
Co. E-mail: info@tempechamber.org
URL: http://www.tempechamber.org
Contact: Mary Ann Miller, President
Released: Monthly

47864 ■ *Business Bylines*
289 N Litchfield Rd.
Goodyear, AZ 85338
Ph: (623)932-2260
Fax: (623)932-9057
Co. E-mail: info@southwestvalleychamber.org
URL: http://www.southwestvalleychamber.org
Contact: Sharolyn Hohman, President
Released: Monthly **Price:** free for members.

47865 ■ *Business Connection*
14001 N 7th St., Bldg. C, Ste. 106
Phoenix, AZ 85022
Ph: (602)482-3344
Co. E-mail: edward@health-fx.com
URL: http://www.northphoenixchamber.com
Contact: Edward Gomillion, Executive Director
Released: Monthly **Price:** included in membership dues.

47866 ■ *Business Connection*
25 S Arizona Pl., Ste. 201
Chandler, AZ 85225
Ph: (480)963-4571
Free: 800-963-4571
Fax: (480)963-0188
Co. E-mail: info@chandlerchamber.com
URL: http://www.chandlerchamber.com
Contact: Terri Kimble, President
Released: Monthly

47867 ■ *Business Directory*
PO Box 274
Dolan Springs, AZ 86441
Ph: (928)767-4473
Co. E-mail: president@dolanspringschamberofcommerce.com
URL: http://www.dolanspringschamberofcommerce.com
Contact: Lee Mac William, President
Released: Semiannual

47868 ■ *Business Directory*
1500 N Circle I Rd.
Willcox, AZ 85643
Ph: (520)384-2272
Free: 800-200-2272
Fax: (520)384-0293
Co. E-mail: willcoxchamber@vtc.net
URL: http://www.willcoxchamber.com
Contact: Wayne Crane, President
Released: Periodic

47869 ■ *Business Directory*
200 W Railroad Ave.
Williams, AZ 86046
Ph: (928)635-0273
Free: 800-863-0546
Fax: (928)635-1417
Co. E-mail: info@williamschamber.com
URL: http://www.williamschamber.com
Contact: Ms. Rhonda Rosinski, President
Released: Annual

47870 ■ *The Business Frontline*
1251 Hwy. 95
Bullhead City, AZ 86429
Ph: (928)754-4121
Free: 800-987-7457
Fax: (928)754-5514
Co. E-mail: info@bullheadchamber.com
URL: http://www.bullheadchamber.com
Contact: Chris Barton, Executive Director
Released: Monthly

47871 ■ *Business Pages*
117 W Goodwin St.
Prescott, AZ 86303-3954
Ph: (928)445-2000
Free: 800-266-7534

Fax: (928)445-0068
Co. E-mail: chamber@prescott.org
URL: http://www.prescott.org
Contact: David Maurer, Chief Executive Officer
Released: Monthly **Price:** $12, /year for members.

47872 ■ *Business Perspective*
120 N Center St.
Mesa, AZ 85201
Ph: (480)969-1307
Fax: (480)827-0727
Co. E-mail: info@mesachamber.org
URL: http://www.mesachamber.org
Contact: Peter Sterling, President
Released: Monthly

47873 ■ *Business Review*
PO Box 527
Gilbert, AZ 85299-0527
Ph: (480)892-0056
Fax: (480)892-1980
Co. E-mail: info@gilbertchamber.com
URL: http://www.gilbertaz.com
Contact: Kathy Tilque, President
Released: Monthly

47874 ■ *The Business Review*
1111 Thatcher Blvd.
Safford, AZ 85546
Ph: (928)428-2511
Free: 888-837-1841
Fax: (928)428-0744
Co. E-mail: info@graham-chamber.com
URL: http://www.graham-chamber.com
Contact: Steve Junion, Chairman
Released: Monthly

47875 ■ *Business Services Guide*
201 N Central Ave., 27th Fl.
Phoenix, AZ 85004
Ph: (602)495-2195
Fax: (602)495-8913
Co. E-mail: info@phoenixchamber.com
URL: http://www.phoenixchamber.com
Contact: Todd Sanders, President
Released: Annual **Price:** $25, for members; $30, for nonmembers.

47876 ■ *Calendar of Events*
305 N Stuart Blvd.
Eloy, AZ 85131
Ph: (520)466-3411
Fax: (520)466-4698
Co. E-mail: info@eloychamber.com
URL: http://www.eloychamber.com
Contact: Toni Lorona, President

47877 ■ **Camp Verde Chamber of Commerce (CVCC)**
c/o Tracie Schimikowsky, Dir. of Operations
385 S Main St.
Camp Verde, AZ 86322
Ph: (928)567-9294
Fax: (928)567-4793
Co. E-mail: info@campverde.org
URL: http://www.visitcampverde.com
Contact: Tracie Schimikowsky, Executive Director
Description: Promotes business and community development in the Verde valley area of Arizona. **Founded:** 1980.

47878 ■ *Chamber Chatter*
100 W Main St.
Payson, AZ 85547
Ph: (928)474-4515
Free: 800-672-9766
Fax: (928)474-8812
Co. E-mail: chamber@npgcable.com
URL: http://www.rimcountrychamber.com
Contact: Robert Henley, Chairman
Released: Monthly **Price:** free for members.

47879 ■ *Chamber of Commerce Newsletter*
110 N Main St., Ste. A
Snowflake, AZ 85937
Ph: (928)536-4331

Fax: (928)536-5656
Co. E-mail: info@snowflaketaylorchamber.org
URL: http://www.snowflaketaylorchamber.org
Contact: Greg Hudson, Executive Director
Released: Monthly

47880 ■ *Chamber News*
200 W Railroad Ave.
Williams, AZ 86046
Ph: (928)635-0273
Free: 800-863-0546
Fax: (928)635-1417
Co. E-mail: info@williamschamber.com
URL: http://www.williamschamber.com
Contact: Ms. Rhonda Rosinski, President
Released: Monthly

47881 ■ *Chamber Newsletter*
3001 N Main St., Ste. 2A
Prescott Valley, AZ 86314
Ph: (928)772-8857
Fax: (928)772-4267
Co. E-mail: info@pvchamber.org
URL: http://www.pvchamber.org
Contact: Marnie Uhl, President
Released: Monthly **Price:** free to members.

47882 ■ *The Chamber Vista*
21 E Wilcox Dr.
Sierra Vista, AZ 85635
Ph: (520)458-6940
Free: 888-399-2948
Fax: (520)452-0878
Co. E-mail: info@sierravistachamber.org
URL: http://sierravistachamber.org
Contact: Susan Tegmeyer, President
Released: Monthly

47883 ■ *The Chamber Voice*
305 N Stuart Blvd.
Eloy, AZ 85131
Ph: (520)466-3411
Fax: (520)466-4698
Co. E-mail: info@eloychamber.com
URL: http://www.eloychamber.com
Contact: Toni Lorona, President
Released: Monthly

47884 ■ **Chandler Chamber of Commerce**
25 S Arizona Pl., Ste. 201
Chandler, AZ 85225
Ph: (480)963-4571
Free: 800-963-4571
Fax: (480)963-0188
Co. E-mail: info@chandlerchamber.com
URL: http://www.chandlerchamber.com
Contact: Terri Kimble, President
Description: Promotes business and community development in Chandler, AZ. **Founded:** 1912. **Publications:** *Business Connection* (Monthly).

47885 ■ **Chino Valley Area Chamber of Commerce**
PO Box 419
Chino Valley, AZ 86323
Ph: (928)636-2493
Co. E-mail: chamber@chinovalley.org
URL: http://www.chinovalley.org
Contact: Charlie Arnold, President
Description: Promotes business growth in Chino. Serves members with professional development opportunities. Acts on public policy decisions for the benefit of the Chino business community. **Publications:** *The Chino Valley Connection* (Monthly).

47886 ■ *The Chino Valley Connection*
PO Box 419
Chino Valley, AZ 86323
Ph: (928)636-2493
Co. E-mail: chamber@chinovalley.org
URL: http://www.chinovalley.org
Contact: Charlie Arnold, President
Released: Monthly

47887 ■ **Chloride Chamber of Commerce (CCC)**
PO Box 268
Chloride, AZ 86431-0268

Ph: (928)565-9419
Co. E-mail: chloride_az@yahoo.com
URL: http://www.chloridearizona.com
Contact: Donna Meyer, President
Description: Promotes business and community development in Chloride, AZ. Sponsors community social and promotional events.

47888 ■ Clarkdale Chamber of Commerce
PO Box 161
Clarkdale, AZ 86324
Ph: (928)634-9438
Fax: (928)634-9438
Co. E-mail: cccinfo@clarkdalechamber.com
URL: http://www.clarkdalechamber.com
Contact: Becky O'Banion, President
Description: Promotes business and community development in Clarkdale, AZ area.

47889 ■ Comercio
255 E Osborne Rd., Ste. 201
Phoenix, AZ 85012
Ph: (602)279-1800
Fax: (602)279-8900
Co. E-mail: info@azhcc.com
URL: http://www.azhcc.com
Contact: Izzy Gonzalez, Chairman

47890 ■ Community Book
575 N Marshall St.
Casa Grande, AZ 85222-5246
Ph: (520)836-2125
Free: 800-916-1515
Fax: (520)836-6233
Co. E-mail: info@casagrandechamber.org
URL: http://www.casagrandechamber.org
Contact: Ms. Helen Neuharth, President
Released: Annual

47891 ■ Copper Basin Chamber of Commerce (CBCC)
PO Box 206
Kearny, AZ 85237
Ph: (520)363-7607
Fax: (520)363-7551
Co. E-mail: angela@copperbasinaz.com
URL: http://www.copperbasinaz.com
Contact: Rosalind Padilla, President
Description: Promotes business and community development in Hayden, Kearny, and Winkelman, AZ. Sponsors Pioneer Days and children's programs. Convention/Meeting: none. Publications: none. **Founded:** 1968.

47892 ■ Cottonwood Chamber of Commerce
1010 S Main St.
Cottonwood, AZ 86326
Ph: (928)634-7593
Fax: (928)634-7594
Co. E-mail: info@cottonwoodchamberaz.org
Contact: Debbie Wilden, President
Description: Promotes business and community development in the Cottonwood, AZ area. **Publications:** Chamber Update (Monthly). **Educational Activities:** Cottonwood Chamber of Commerce Meeting (Monthly).

47893 ■ Destination Flagstaff
101 W Rte. 66
Flagstaff, AZ 86001
Ph: (928)774-4505
Fax: (928)779-1209
Co. E-mail: info@flagstaffchamber.com
URL: http://www.flagstaffchamber.com
Contact: Julie Pastrick, President
Released: Annual **Price:** $6.50.

47894 ■ Discover
123 W Kino Park
Nogales, AZ 85621
Ph: (520)287-3685
Fax: (520)287-3687
Co. E-mail: info@thenogaleschamber.com
URL: http://www.thenogaleschamber.com/portal
Contact: Ms. Olivia Ainza-Kramer, President
Released: Annual

47895 ■ Dolan Springs Chamber of Commerce
PO Box 274
Dolan Springs, AZ 86441
Ph: (928)767-4473
Co. E-mail: president@dolanspringschamberofcommerce.com
URL: http://www.dolanspringschamberofcommerce.com
Contact: Lee Mac William, President
Description: Promotes business and community development in Dolan Springs, AZ. Sponsors annual Dolan Springs Days during the third weekend in September. Convention/Meeting: none. **Founded:** 1958. **Publications:** Business Directory (Semiannual); Dolan Springs Information (Periodic).

47896 ■ Dolan Springs Information
PO Box 274
Dolan Springs, AZ 86441
Ph: (928)767-4473
Co. E-mail: president@dolanspringschamberofcommerce.com
URL: http://www.dolanspringschamberofcommerce.com
Contact: Lee Mac William, President
Released: Periodic

47897 ■ Eloy Chamber of Commerce (ECC)
305 N Stuart Blvd.
Eloy, AZ 85131
Ph: (520)466-3411
Fax: (520)466-4698
Co. E-mail: info@eloychamber.com
URL: http://www.eloychamber.com
Contact: Toni Lorona, President
Description: Promotes business, tourism, and community development in the Eloy, AZ area. Provides referrals to members' businesses; conducts publicity campaigns for local tourist attractions. **Founded:** 1972. **Publications:** Calendar of Events; The Chamber Voice (Monthly); Eloy Living Offers You (Periodic). **Awards:** Beautification Award (Quarterly); Good Neighbor of the Year (Annual).

47898 ■ Eloy Living Offers You
305 N Stuart Blvd.
Eloy, AZ 85131
Ph: (520)466-3411
Fax: (520)466-4698
Co. E-mail: info@eloychamber.com
URL: http://www.eloychamber.com
Contact: Toni Lorona, President
Released: Periodic **Price:** free.

47899 ■ Experience Sedona
PO Box 478
Sedona, AZ 86339
Ph: (928)282-7722
Free: 800-288-7336
Fax: (928)204-1064
Co. E-mail: info@sedonachamber.com
URL: http://www.sedonachamber.com
Contact: Jennifer Wesselhoff, President
Released: Annual

47900 ■ Flagstaff Chamber of Commerce
101 W Rte. 66
Flagstaff, AZ 86001
Ph: (928)774-4505
Fax: (928)779-1209
Co. E-mail: info@flagstaffchamber.com
URL: http://www.flagstaffchamber.com
Contact: Julie Pastrick, President
Description: Promotes business and community development in Flagstaff, AZ. **Founded:** 1892. **Publications:** Destination Flagstaff (Annual); Flagstaff Today (Bimonthly).

47901 ■ Flagstaff Today
101 W Rte. 66
Flagstaff, AZ 86001
Ph: (928)774-4505

Fax: (928)779-1209
Co. E-mail: info@flagstaffchamber.com
URL: http://www.flagstaffchamber.com
Contact: Julie Pastrick, President
Released: Bimonthly **Price:** included in membership dues.

47902 ■ The Forum
4435 E Chandler Blvd., No. 140
Phoenix, AZ 85048-7650
Ph: (480)753-7676
Fax: (480)753-3898
Co. E-mail: info@ahwatukeechamber.com
URL: http://www.ahwatukeechamber.com
Contact: Anne Gill, President

47903 ■ Fountain Hills Chamber of Commerce
PO Box 17598
Fountain Hills, AZ 85269-7598
Ph: (480)837-1654
Fax: (480)837-3077
Co. E-mail: frank@fountainhillschamber.com
URL: http://www.fountainhillschamber.com
Contact: Frank S. Ferrara, President
Description: Promotes business and community development in Fountain Hills, AZ. **Founded:** 1974. **Publications:** News and Views (Monthly). **Educational Activities:** Arts and Crafts Show (Annual). **Awards:** Business Person of the Year (Annual); Not-for-Profit of the Year (Annual).

47904 ■ Gilbert Chamber of Commerce (GCC)
PO Box 527
Gilbert, AZ 85299-0527
Ph: (480)892-0056
Fax: (480)892-1980
Co. E-mail: info@gilbertchamber.com
URL: http://www.gilbertaz.com
Contact: Kathy Tilque, President
Description: Promotes business and community development in Gilbert, AZ. **Founded:** 1978. **Publications:** Business Review (Monthly).

47905 ■ Glendale Chamber of Commerce
PO Box 249
Glendale, AZ 85311
Ph: (623)937-4754
Free: 800-437-8669
Fax: (623)937-3333
Co. E-mail: info@glendaleazchamber.org
URL: http://www.glendaleazchamber.org
Contact: Don Rinehart, President
Description: Serves as a voice of commerce within the community. Seeks to improve economic environment and the quality of life in the community through programs and services. **Publications:** Pulse (Monthly).

47906 ■ Globe-Miami Regional Chamber of Commerce and Economic Development Corporation
1360 N Broad St.
Globe, AZ 85501
Ph: (928)425-4495
Free: 800-804-5623
Fax: (928)425-3410
Co. E-mail: visitorinfo@globemiamichamber.com
URL: http://www.globemiamichamber.com
Contact: Stanley Gibson, President
Description: Promotes tourism, community and economic development in Southern Gila County. **Scope:** area and community history. **Founded:** 1992. **Subscriptions:** 40 books periodicals reports video recordings.

47907 ■ Golden Valley Chamber of Commerce
c/o Bobbi Case, Pres.
3395 Verde
Golden Valley, AZ 86413
Ph: (928)565-3311

Fax: (928)565-3133
Co. E-mail: info@goldenvalleychamber.com
URL: http://www.goldenvalleychamber.com
Contact: Bobbi Case, President
Description: Promotes business and community development in the Golden Valley area of Arizona. Makes available maps. **Scope:** county, state, business information. **Founded:** 1983. **Subscriptions:** 200.

47908 ■ Graham County Chamber of Commerce (GCCC)
1111 Thatcher Blvd.
Safford, AZ 85546
Ph: (928)428-2511
Free: 888-837-1841
Fax: (928)428-0744
Co. E-mail: info@graham-chamber.com
URL: http://www.graham-chamber.com
Contact: Steve Junion, Chairman
Description: Promotes business, industrial, agricultural, and community development in Graham County, Arizona. Seeks to increase public involvement in community improvement projects. **Founded:** 1926. **Publications:** *The Business Review* (Monthly).

47909 ■ *Grand Canyon*
PO Box 3007
Grand Canyon, AZ 86023
Free: 888-472-2696
Fax: (928)638-4095
Co. E-mail: info@grandcanyonvisitorbureau.com
URL: http://grandcanyonvisitorbureau.com

47910 ■ Grand Canyon Chamber of Commerce
PO Box 3007
Grand Canyon, AZ 86023
Free: 888-472-2696
Fax: (928)638-4095
Co. E-mail: info@grandcanyonvisitorbureau.com
URL: http://grandcanyonvisitorbureau.com
Description: Promotes business and community development in Grand Canyon, AZ. **Publications:** *Grand Canyon*.

47911 ■ Greater Casa Grande Chamber of Commerce
575 N Marshall St.
Casa Grande, AZ 85222-5246
Ph: (520)836-2125
Free: 800-916-1515
Fax: (520)836-6233
Co. E-mail: info@casagrandechamber.org
URL: http://www.casagrandechamber.org
Contact: Ms. Helen Neuharth, President
Description: Promotes business and community development in the Casa Grande, AZ area and tourism in Arizona and nationwide. **Founded:** 1925. **Publications:** *Community Book* (Annual); *The Voice of Business* (Monthly). **Telecommunication Services:** president@casagrandechamber.org.

47912 ■ Greater Phoenix Black Chamber of Commerce (GPBCC)
201 E Washington St., Ste. 350
Phoenix, AZ 85004
Ph: (602)307-5200
Fax: (602)307-5204
Co. E-mail: info@phoenixblackchamber.com
URL: http://www.phoenixblackchamber.com
Contact: Kerwin V. Brown, Chief Executive Officer
Description: Improves the economic development of business entrepreneur in Phoenix, AZ. **Founded:** 1998. **Publications:** *Arizona Informant* (Weekly). **Awards:** Business of the Year (Annual); Community Advocate of the Year (Annual); Corporate of the Year (Annual).

47913 ■ Greater Phoenix Chamber of Commerce
201 N Central Ave., 27th Fl.
Phoenix, AZ 85004
Ph: (602)495-2195

Fax: (602)495-8913
Co. E-mail: info@phoenixchamber.com
URL: http://www.phoenixchamber.com
Contact: Todd Sanders, President
Description: Supports the growth and development of business and the quality of life in the Phoenix, AZ area. Champions the voice of business in government and keeps businesses informed, connected, and prosperous. **Founded:** 1888. **Publications:** *Arizona Industrial Directory* (Annual); *Business Services Guide* (Annual); *Chamber Membership Directory/Consumer Guide*; *Greater Phoenix Chamber of Commerce Membership Directory & Business Services Guide* (Annual); *Greater Phoenix Ultimate Guide to Living Here* (Annual); *Greater Phoenix Chamber Membership List--Minority-Owned or Operated Businesses*; *Greater Phoenix Chamber Membership List--Women-Owned or Operated Businesses*; *Greater Phoenix Chamber Membership List--Home-Based Businesses*; *Greater Phoenix Chamber Membership List--International Trade Businesses*. **Educational Activities:** Arizona Sports Awards Luncheon (Annual); ATHENA Luncheon (Annual); Outlook (Annual).

47914 ■ *Greater Phoenix Ultimate Guide to Living Here*
201 N Central Ave., 27th Fl.
Phoenix, AZ 85004
Ph: (602)495-2195
Fax: (602)495-8913
Co. E-mail: info@phoenixchamber.com
URL: http://www.phoenixchamber.com
Contact: Todd Sanders, President
Released: Annual **Price:** $13, for members; $15, for nonmembers.

47915 ■ Greater Sierra Vista Area Chamber of Commerce
21 E Wilcox Dr.
Sierra Vista, AZ 85635
Ph: (520)458-6940
Free: 888-399-2948
Fax: (520)452-0878
Co. E-mail: info@sierravistachamber.org
URL: http://sierravistachamber.org
Contact: Susan Tegmeyer, President
Description: Promotes business and community development in the Sierra Vista, AZ area. **Publications:** *The Chamber Vista* (Monthly); *Sierra Vista Tourism* (Monthly). **Educational Activities:** Festival of Color (Annual); Buffalo Soldier Days (Annual).

47916 ■ *The Guide to Living in Scottsdale*
4725 N Scottsdale Rd., No. 210
Scottsdale, AZ 85251-4498
Ph: (480)355-2700
Fax: (480)355-2710
Co. E-mail: info@scottsdalechamber.com
URL: http://www.scottsdalechamber.com
Contact: Rick Kidder, President
Released: Monthly

47917 ■ *The Hassayampa Alert*
216 N Frontier St.
Wickenburg, AZ 85390
Ph: (928)684-5479
Free: 800-942-5242
Fax: (928)684-5470
Co. E-mail: info@wickenburgchamber.com
URL: http://www.wickenburgchamber.com
Contact: Tom Hunt, President
Released: Periodic

47918 ■ Heber - Overgaard Chamber of Commerce
PO Box 1926
Overgaard, AZ 85933
Ph: (928)535-5777
Fax: (928)535-3254
Co. E-mail: coc@heberovergaard.org
URL: http://www.heberovergaard.org
Description: Promotes business and community development in Heber and Overgaard, AZ. **Publications:** *Splendor on the Rim*.

47919 ■ *Hot Prospects*
1251 Hwy. 95
Bullhead City, AZ 86429
Ph: (928)754-4121

Free: 800-987-7457
Fax: (928)754-5514
Co. E-mail: info@bullheadchamber.com
URL: http://www.bullheadchamber.com
Contact: Chris Barton, Executive Director
Released: Annual

47920 ■ Jerome Chamber of Commerce
PO Box K
Jerome, AZ 86331
Ph: (928)634-2900
Co. E-mail: info@jeromechamber.com
URL: http://www.jeromechamber.com
Contact: Lisa Rappaport, President
Description: Promotes business and community development in Jerome, AZ. Assists charitable programs and annual home tour. **Founded:** 1974.

47921 ■ Kingman Area Chamber of Commerce
120 W Andy Devine Ave.
Kingman, AZ 86402-1150
Ph: (928)753-6253
Fax: (928)753-1049
Co. E-mail: beverly@kingmanchamber.org
URL: http://www.kingmanchamber.org
Contact: Pamela Wilkinson, President
Description: Promotes business and community development in the Kingman, AZ area. **Scope:** customer service, goal setting, financial statements, leadership, motivation. **Subscriptions:** audio recordings books video recordings. **Publications:** *Kingman Area Chamber Report* (Monthly).

47922 ■ *Kingman Area Chamber Report*
120 W Andy Devine Ave.
Kingman, AZ 86402-1150
Ph: (928)753-6253
Fax: (928)753-1049
Co. E-mail: beverly@kingmanchamber.org
URL: http://www.kingmanchamber.org
Contact: Pamela Wilkinson, President
Released: Monthly **Price:** free.

47923 ■ Lake Havasu Area Chamber of Commerce (LHACC)
314 London Bridge Rd.
Lake Havasu City, AZ 86403-5772
Ph: (928)855-4115
Fax: (928)680-0010
Co. E-mail: info@havasuchamber.com
URL: http://www.havasuchamber.com
Contact: Lisa Krueger, President
Description: Promotes business and community development in west-central Arizona. Sponsors London Bridge Days. **Founded:** 1971.

47924 ■ Marana Chamber of Commerce
13881 N Casa Grande Hwy.
Marana, AZ 85653-9312
Ph: (520)682-4314
Fax: (520)682-2303
Co. E-mail: info@maranachamber.com
URL: http://www.maranachamber.com
Contact: Ed Stolmaker, President
Description: Promotes the community and the businesses in the community. Encourages the retention, expansion, and relocation of business locally. Provides value-added services to members by promoting business and providing assistance aimed at helping the community prosper. **Founded:** 1987. **Publications:** *Marana Community Profile and Membership Directory* (Quarterly); *Marana Community Profile and Membership Directory* (Annual); *Marana Chamber Newsletter* (Monthly). **Educational Activities:** Marana Chamber of Commerce Luncheon (Monthly).

47925 ■ *Marana Chamber Newsletter*
13881 N Casa Grande Hwy.
Marana, AZ 85653-9312
Ph: (520)682-4314
Fax: (520)682-2303
Co. E-mail: info@maranachamber.com
URL: http://www.maranachamber.com
Contact: Ed Stolmaker, President
Released: Monthly **Price:** free.

47926 ■ *Marana Community Profile and Membership Directory*
Released: Annual **Price:** free.

47927 ■ **McMullen Valley Chamber of Commerce**
PO Box 700
Salome, AZ 85348-0700
Ph: (928)859-3846
URL: http://www.azoutback.com
Description: Promotes business and community development in Salome, Wenden, Harcuvar, Vicksburg and Brenda, AZ. **Founded:** 1989.

47928 ■ **Mesa Chamber of Commerce (MCC)**
120 N Center St.
Mesa, AZ 85201
Ph: (480)969-1307
Fax: (480)827-0727
Co. E-mail: info@mesachamber.org
URL: http://www.mesachamber.org
Contact: Peter Sterling, President
Description: Promotes business, tourism, and community development in Mesa, AZ. Encourages civic involvement in tourism, community betterment, and winter visitor marketing. Conducts annual Business Showcase. **Founded:** 1912. **Publications:** *Business Perspective* (Monthly); *Mesa Chamber Directory* (Annual).

47929 ■ *Mesa Chamber Directory*
120 N Center St.
Mesa, AZ 85201
Ph: (480)969-1307
Fax: (480)827-0727
Co. E-mail: info@mesachamber.org
URL: http://www.mesachamber.org
Contact: Peter Sterling, President
Released: Annual

47930 ■ *Messenger*
81 E Deuce of Clubs
Show Low, AZ 85901
Ph: (928)537-2326
Free: 888-SHOW-LOW
Fax: (928)532-7610
Co. E-mail: info@showlowchamberofcommerce.com
URL: http://www.showlowchamberofcommerce.com
Contact: Rob Turnwall, President
Price: $300, /year (business card ad); $1300, /year (sponsorship).

47931 ■ **Mohave Valley Chamber of Commerce**
PO Box 5439
Mohave Valley, AZ 86446
Ph: (928)768-2777
Fax: (928)768-6610
Co. E-mail: info@mohavevalleychamber.com
URL: http://www.mohavevalleychamber.com
Contact: Emma J. Watson, President
Description: Promotes business and community development in the Mohave Valley area of Arizona. **Founded:** 1991. **Publications:** *MVCC Newsletter* (Monthly).

47932 ■ *News and Views*
PO Box 17598
Fountain Hills, AZ 85269-7598
Ph: (480)837-1654
Fax: (480)837-3077
Co. E-mail: frank@fountainhillschamber.com
URL: http://www.fountainhillschamber.com
Contact: Frank S. Ferrara, President
Released: Monthly **Price:** included in membership dues.

47933 ■ **Nogales-Santa Cruz County Chamber of Commerce (NSCCC)**
123 W Kino Park
Nogales, AZ 85621
Ph: (520)287-3685
Fax: (520)287-3687
Co. E-mail: info@thenogaleschamber.com
URL: http://www.thenogaleschamber.com/portal
Contact: Ms. Olivia Ainza-Kramer, President
Description: Promotes business and community development in Santa Cruz County, AZ. Sponsors festivals and parades; conducts competitions. Assists

charitable efforts. **Scope:** arc. **Founded:** 1914. **Subscriptions:** artwork business records clippings maps photographs reports. **Publications:** *Discover* (Annual); *Santa Cruz County Visitors Guide* (Annual); *2010 Shanghai Expo Customized Commercial Delegations* (Annual). **Educational Activities:** Business Expo (Annual). **Awards:** Nogales-Santa Cruz County Scholarship (Annual).

47934 ■ **North Phoenix Chamber of Commerce**
14001 N 7th St., Bldg. C, Ste. 106
Phoenix, AZ 85022
Ph: (602)482-3344
Co. E-mail: edward@health-fx.com
URL: http://www.northphoenixchamber.com
Contact: Edward Gomillion, Executive Director
Description: Strives to unite the people of commerce, industry, education, and of the professions to work together for the development of the greater North Phoenix area. **Founded:** 1963. **Publications:** *Business Connection* (Monthly).

47935 ■ **Northwest Valley Chamber of Commerce**
12801 W Bell Rd., Ste. 14
Surprise, AZ 85374
Ph: (623)583-0692
Fax: (623)583-0694
Co. E-mail: danderson@surpriseregionalchamber.com
URL: http://www.surpriseregionalchamber.com
Contact: Jeanne Blackman, Chairperson
Description: Promotes business and community development in the Sun City, AZ area. **Scope:** business decisions. **Founded:** 1963. **Publications:** *Business Directories and Communities* (Semiannual); *Northwest Valley Business* (Monthly).

47936 ■ **Oatman-Goldroad Chamber of Commerce**
PO Box 423
Oatman, AZ 86433
Ph: (928)768-6222
Co. E-mail: oatman@oatmangoldroad.org
URL: http://www.oatmangoldroad.org
Description: Promotes business and community development in the Oatman, AZ area. Sponsors Gold Camp Days. Conducts International Burro Biscuit Throwing Contest. Offers "ghost town" atmosphere; wild burros petting areas and gunfights in the streets.

47937 ■ **Page-Lake Powell Chamber of Commerce (PLPCC)**
PO Box 727
Page, AZ 86040
Ph: (928)645-2741
Free: 888-261-PAGE
Fax: (928)645-3181
Co. E-mail: chamber@pagechamber.com
URL: http://www.pagechamber.com
Contact: Cecilia Cobb, Executive Director
Description: Promotes business and community development in the Page-Lake Powell area. Seeks to enhance the quality of life and promote relocation to the area. Sponsors area festivals. Operates a tourism information source and visitor guide. **Founded:** 1958.

47938 ■ **Parker Area Chamber of Commerce (PACC)**
1217 S California Ave.
Parker, AZ 85344
Ph: (928)669-2174
Fax: (928)669-6304
Co. E-mail: info@parkerareachamberofcommerce.com
URL: http://www.parkeraz.org
Contact: Heather Wilson, President
Description: Promotes business and community development in the Parker, AZ area. Encourages tourism; sponsors festivals. **Founded:** 1952.

47939 ■ **Pearce - Sunsites Chamber of Commerce**
PO Box 536
Pearce, AZ 85625-0536

Ph: (520)507-3520
Co. E-mail: info@pearcesunsiteschamber.org
URL: http://www.pearcesunsiteschamber.org/portal
Contact: Murray McClelland, President
Description: Promotes business and community development in Pearce, AZ.

47940 ■ **Peoria Chamber of Commerce (PCC)**
8765 W Kelton Ln., Bldg. C-1
Peoria, AZ 85382
Ph: (623)979-3601
Free: 800-580-2645
Fax: (623)486-4729
Co. E-mail: diana@peoriachamber.com
URL: http://www.peoriachamber.com
Contact: Diana Bedient, Chief Executive Officer
Description: Promotes business and community development in the Peoria, AZ area. **Founded:** 1919.

47941 ■ **Pinetop-Lakeside Chamber of Commerce**
PO Box 4220
Pinetop, AZ 85935
Ph: (928)367-4290
Free: 800-573-4031
Fax: (928)367-1247
Co. E-mail: info@pinetoplakesidechamber.com
URL: http://www.pinetoplakesidechamber.com
Contact: Bev Stepp, Executive Director
Description: Promotes business and community development in Pinetop-Lakeside, AZ. Sponsors Heritage Festival, Mountain Native American, Blue Grass, and Fall Festivals. **Founded:** 1984.

47942 ■ **Prescott Chamber of Commerce (PCC)**
117 W Goodwin St.
Prescott, AZ 86303-3954
Ph: (928)445-2000
Free: 800-266-7534
Fax: (928)445-0068
Co. E-mail: chamber@prescott.org
URL: http://www.prescott.org
Contact: David Maurer, Chief Executive Officer
Description: Promotes business and community development in the Prescott, AZ area. Sponsors Bluegrass Festival and arts and crafts show. **Founded:** 1938. **Publications:** *Business Pages* (Monthly).

47943 ■ **Prescott Valley Chamber of Commerce (PVCC)**
3001 N Main St., Ste. 2A
Prescott Valley, AZ 86314
Ph: (928)772-8857
Fax: (928)772-4267
Co. E-mail: info@pvchamber.org
URL: http://www.pvchamber.org
Contact: Marnie Uhl, President
Description: Promotes business, industrial, and community development in North Central Arizona. Conducts monthly business mixer. **Founded:** 1966. **Publications:** *Chamber Newsletter* (Monthly); *Visitors Guide*. **Awards:** Roast of Outstanding Citizen (Annual).

47944 ■ *Pulse*
PO Box 249
Glendale, AZ 85311
Ph: (623)937-4754
Free: 800-437-8669
Fax: (623)937-3333
Co. E-mail: info@glendaleazchamber.org
URL: http://www.glendaleazchamber.org
Contact: Don Rinehart, President
Released: Monthly

47945 ■ **Quartzsite Chamber of Commerce**
PO Box 2566
Quartzsite, AZ 85346-0085
Ph: (928)927-9321
Co. E-mail: info@qzchamber.com
URL: http://www.quartzsitechamber.org
Contact: Richard Oldham, President
Description: Promotes business and community development in Quartzsite, AZ. **Telecommunication Services:** admin@quartzsitearizona.us.

47946 ■ Relocation Packet
180 W 1st St., Ste. A
Yuma, AZ 85364
Ph: (928)782-2567
Free: 877-782-0438
Fax: (928)343-0038
Co. E-mail: info@yumachamber.org
URL: http://www.yumachamber.org
Contact: Ken Rosevear, Executive Director
Price: $10.

47947 ■ Rim Country Regional Chamber of Commerce
100 W Main St.
Payson, AZ 85547
Ph: (928)474-4515
Free: 800-672-9766
Fax: (928)474-8812
Co. E-mail: chamber@npgcable.com
URL: http://www.rimcountrychamber.com
Contact: Robert Henley, Chairman
Description: Promotes business and community development in the Rim Country, AZ. Sponsors rodeo and parade, and June Festival. **Founded:** 1954. **Publications:** *Chamber Chatter* (Monthly); *Spirit of Payson* (Periodic); *Rim County Lifestyle & Visitor Guide* (Annual). **Educational Activities:** Strategic Retreat - Board of Directors (Annual). **Awards:** Volunteer of the Year (Annual).

47948 ■ Rim County Lifestyle & Visitor Guide
100 W Main St.
Payson, AZ 85547
Ph: (928)474-4515
Free: 800-672-9766
Fax: (928)474-8812
Co. E-mail: chamber@npgcable.com
URL: http://www.rimcountrychamber.com
Contact: Robert Henley, Chairman
Released: Annual

47949 ■ St. Johns Regional Chamber of Commerce
PO Box 929
St. Johns, AZ 85936
Ph: (928)337-2000
Fax: (928)337-2020
Co. E-mail: info@stjohnschamber.com
URL: http://www.stjohnschamber.com
Contact: Sean Kienle, President
Description: Promotes business and community development in St. Johns, Arizona.

47950 ■ Santa Cruz County Visitors Guide
123 W Kino Park
Nogales, AZ 85621
Ph: (520)287-3685
Fax: (520)287-3687
Co. E-mail: info@thenogaleschamber.com
URL: http://www.thenogaleschamber.com/portal
Contact: Ms. Olivia Ainza-Kramer, President
Released: Annual

47951 ■ Scottsdale Area Chamber of Commerce
4725 N Scottsdale Rd., No. 210
Scottsdale, AZ 85251-4498
Ph: (480)355-2700
Fax: (480)355-2710
Co. E-mail: info@scottsdalechamber.com
URL: http://www.scottsdalechamber.com
Contact: Rick Kidder, President
Description: Seeks to build a vibrant and prosperous community through business leadership. **Publications:** *Scottsdale at Work*; *Start-Up Guide*; *The Guide to Living in Scottsdale* (Monthly).

47952 ■ Scottsdale at Work
4725 N Scottsdale Rd., No. 210
Scottsdale, AZ 85251-4498
Ph: (480)355-2700
Fax: (480)355-2710
Co. E-mail: info@scottsdalechamber.com
URL: http://www.scottsdalechamber.com
Contact: Rick Kidder, President

47953 ■ Sedona-Oak Creek Canyon Chamber of Commerce (SOCCCC)
PO Box 478
Sedona, AZ 86339
Ph: (928)282-7722
Free: 800-288-7336
Fax: (928)204-1064
Co. E-mail: info@sedonachamber.com
URL: http://www.sedonachamber.com
Contact: Jennifer Wesselhoff, President
Description: Promotes business and community development in Sedona, AZ and the Oak Creek Canyon area. **Founded:** 1949. **Publications:** *Experience Sedona* (Annual). **Educational Activities:** Members Exhibition (Annual). **Telecommunication Services:** admin@sedonachamber.com.

47954 ■ Show Low Regional Chamber of Commerce
81 E Deuce of Clubs
Show Low, AZ 85901
Ph: (928)537-2326
Free: 888-SHOW-LOW
Fax: (928)532-7610
Co. E-mail: info@showlowchamberofcommerce.com
URL: http://www.showlowchamberofcommerce.com
Contact: Rob Turnwall, President
Description: Promotes business and community development in Show Low, AZ. **Publications:** *Messenger*.

47955 ■ Sierra Vista Tourism
21 E Wilcox Dr.
Sierra Vista, AZ 85635
Ph: (520)458-6940
Free: 888-399-2948
Fax: (520)452-0878
Co. E-mail: info@sierravistachamber.org
URL: http://sierravistachamber.org
Contact: Susan Tegmeyer, President
Released: Monthly

47956 ■ Snowflake - Taylor Chamber of Commerce
110 N Main St., Ste. A
Snowflake, AZ 85937
Ph: (928)536-4331
Fax: (928)536-5656
Co. E-mail: info@snowflaketaylorchamber.org
URL: http://www.snowflaketaylorchamber.org
Contact: Greg Hudson, Executive Director
Description: Promotes business, community development, and tourism in the Snowflake and Taylor, AZ area. Works to bring new industry and residents to area. **Publications:** *Chamber of Commerce Newsletter* (Monthly).

47957 ■ Southwest Valley Chamber of Commerce
289 N Litchfield Rd.
Goodyear, AZ 85338
Ph: (623)932-2260
Fax: (623)932-9057
Co. E-mail: info@southwestvalleychamber.org
URL: http://www.southwestvalleychamber.org
Contact: Sharolyn Hohman, President
Description: Promotes business and community development in the Southwest Valley areas of Avondale, Goodyear, Litchfield Park, and Tolleson, AZ. Sponsors festival. **Founded:** 1958. **Publications:** *Business Bylines* (Monthly). **Awards:** Chamber Member of the Month (Monthly).

47958 ■ Spirit of Payson
100 W Main St.
Payson, AZ 85547
Ph: (928)474-4515
Free: 800-672-9766
Fax: (928)474-8812
Co. E-mail: chamber@npgcable.com
URL: http://www.rimcountrychamber.com
Contact: Robert Henley, Chairman
Released: Periodic

47959 ■ Splendor on the Rim
PO Box 1926
Overgaard, AZ 85933
Ph: (928)535-5777

Fax: (928)535-3254
Co. E-mail: coc@heberovergaard.org
URL: http://www.heberovergaard.org

47960 ■ Springerville-Eagar Regional Chamber of Commerce
PO Box 31
Springerville, AZ 85938-0031
Ph: (928)333-2123
Fax: (928)333-5690
Co. E-mail: info@springerville-eagarchamber.com
URL: http://www.springerville-eagarchamber.com
Contact: Jennifer Prochnow, Executive Director
Description: Promotes business, tourism, and community development in the White Mountain, AZ area. Assists and cooperates with the Springerville and Eagar, AZ economic development commissions. Sponsors rodeos, parades, arts and crafts shows, and athletic tournaments. **Founded:** 1959.

47961 ■ Start-Up Guide
4725 N Scottsdale Rd., No. 210
Scottsdale, AZ 85251-4498
Ph: (480)355-2700
Fax: (480)355-2710
Co. E-mail: info@scottsdalechamber.com
URL: http://www.scottsdalechamber.com
Contact: Rick Kidder, President

47962 ■ Superior Chamber of Commerce
PO Box 95
Superior, AZ 85173-1301
Ph: (520)689-0200
Fax: (520)689-0200
URL: http://www.superiorazchamber.net
Contact: Leslie Martin, President
Description: Promotes business and community development in Superior, AZ area.

47963 ■ Swedish-American Chamber of Commerce, Arizona
c/o The Swedish Consulate of Phoenix
4300 N Miller Rd., Ste. 125
Scottsdale, AZ 85251
Ph: (602)399-7300
Co. E-mail: contact@saccarizona.org
URL: http://www.saccarizona.org
Contact: Tobias Lofstrand, President

47964 ■ Tempe Business Review
PO Box 28500
Tempe, AZ 85285-8500
Ph: (480)967-7891
Fax: (480)966-5365
Co. E-mail: info@tempechamber.org
URL: http://www.tempechamber.org
Contact: Mary Ann Miller, President
Released: Periodic

47965 ■ Tempe Chamber of Commerce (TCC)
PO Box 28500
Tempe, AZ 85285-8500
Ph: (480)967-7891
Fax: (480)966-5365
Co. E-mail: info@tempechamber.org
URL: http://www.tempechamber.org
Contact: Mary Ann Miller, President
Description: Promotes business and community development in Tempe, AZ. **Founded:** 1931. **Publications:** *The Business Advocate* (Monthly); *Tempe Business Review* (Periodic).

47966 ■ Tombstone Chamber of Commerce
PO Box 995
Tombstone, AZ 85638-0995
Free: 888-457-3929
Co. E-mail: info@tombstone.com
URL: http://www.tombstonechamber.com
Description: Seeks to advance the general welfare and prosperity of the Tombstone area. **Founded:** 1809.

47967 ■ Tubac Chamber of Commerce
PO Box 1866
Tubac, AZ 85646

Ph: (520)398-2704
Co. E-mail: assistance@tubacaz.com
URL: http://www.tubacaz.com
Contact: Mindy Maddock, President
Description: Promotes business and community development in Tubac, AZ.

47968 ■ **Tucson Metropolitan Chamber of Commerce (TMCC)**
PO Box 991
Tucson, AZ 85701
Ph: (520)792-1212
Fax: (520)882-5704
Co. E-mail: jcamper@tucsonchamber.org
URL: http://www.tucsonchamber.org
Contact: Michael V. Varney, President
Description: Promotes business and community development in the Tucson, AZ area. **Founded:** 1902.

47969 ■ *Vantage Point*
180 W 1st St., Ste. A
Yuma, AZ 85364
Ph: (928)782-2567
Free: 877-782-0438
Fax: (928)343-0038
Co. E-mail: info@yumachamber.org
URL: http://www.yumachamber.org
Contact: Ken Rosevear, Executive Director
Released: Monthly

47970 ■ *Visitors Guide*
3001 N Main St., Ste. 2A
Prescott Valley, AZ 86314
Ph: (928)772-8857
Fax: (928)772-4267
Co. E-mail: info@pvchamber.org
URL: http://www.pvchamber.org
Contact: Marnie Uhl, President

47971 ■ *The Voice of Business*
575 N Marshall St.
Casa Grande, AZ 85222-5246
Ph: (520)836-2125
Free: 800-916-1515
Fax: (520)836-6233
Co. E-mail: info@casagrandechamber.org
URL: http://www.casagrandechamber.org
Contact: Ms. Helen Neuharth, President
Released: Monthly

47972 ■ *VOX Negotium*
1850 N Central Ave., Ste. 1433
Phoenix, AZ 85004
Ph: (602)248-9172
Fax: (602)265-1262
Co. E-mail: info@azchamber.com
URL: http://www.azchamber.com
Contact: Glenn Hamer, President
Released: Periodic

47973 ■ *We Mean Business*
168 E 4th St.
Benson, AZ 85602
Ph: (520)265-8031
Co. E-mail: downbytheriverbb@hotmail.com
URL: http://www.bensonchamberaz.com
Contact: Mike Hug, President (Acting)
Released: Monthly

47974 ■ **Wickenburg Chamber of Commerce**
216 N Frontier St.
Wickenburg, AZ 85390
Ph: (928)684-5479
Free: 800-942-5242
Fax: (928)684-5470
Co. E-mail: info@wickenburgchamber.com
URL: http://www.wickenburgchamber.com
Contact: Tom Hunt, President
Description: Promotes business and community development in Wickenburg, AZ. **Founded:** 1931. **Publications:** *The Hassayampa Alert* (Periodic). **Educational Activities:** Fiesta Septiembre (Annual).

47975 ■ **Willcox Chamber of Commerce and Agriculture (WCCA)**
1500 N Circle I Rd.
Willcox, AZ 85643
Ph: (520)384-2272

Free: 800-200-2272
Fax: (520)384-0293
Co. E-mail: willcoxchamber@vtc.net
URL: http://www.willcoxchamber.com
Contact: Wayne Crane, President
Description: Promotes business, community, and agricultural development in Willcox, AZ and surrounding trade areas. **Founded:** 1915. **Publications:** *Business Directory* (Periodic). **Educational Activities:** Cowboy Hall of Fame (Annual). **Awards:** Citizen of the Year (Annual); Cowboy Hall of Fame Induction (Annual).

47976 ■ **Williams-Grand Canyon Chamber of Commerce (WGCCC)**
200 W Railroad Ave.
Williams, AZ 86046
Ph: (928)635-0273
Free: 800-863-0546
Fax: (928)635-1417
Co. E-mail: info@williamschamber.com
URL: http://www.williamschamber.com
Contact: Ms. Rhonda Rosinski, President
Description: Promotes business and community development in Williams and northern Arizona. Sponsors Rendezvous Days. **Founded:** 1974. **Publications:** *Business Directory* (Annual); *Chamber News* (Monthly). **Educational Activities:** Board Retreat (Annual).

47977 ■ **Winslow Chamber of Commerce**
PO Box 460
Winslow, AZ 86047
Ph: (928)289-2434
Fax: (928)289-5660
Co. E-mail: info@winslowarizona.org
URL: http://www.winslowarizona.org
Contact: John Dalton, President
Description: Promotes business and community development in Winslow, AZ.

47978 ■ **Yuma County Chamber of Commerce**
180 W 1st St., Ste. A
Yuma, AZ 85364
Ph: (928)782-2567
Free: 877-782-0438
Fax: (928)343-0038
Co. E-mail: info@yumachamber.org
URL: http://www.yumachamber.org
Contact: Ken Rosevear, Executive Director
Description: Works for the preservation of the free enterprise system in the Yuma, AZ area. **Founded:** 1905. **Publications:** *Relocation Packet*; *Vantage Point* (Monthly). **Educational Activities:** Good Morning YUMA (Monthly).

MINORITY BUSINESS ASSISTANCE PROGRAMS

47979 ■ **Arizona Minority Business Enterprise Center**
255 E Osborn Rd., Ste. 202
Phoenix, AZ 85012
Ph: (602)248-0007
Fax: (602)279-8900
Co. E-mail: info@azmbec.com
URL: http://www.azmbec.com
Contact: Alika Kumar, Director

47980 ■ **Arizona Native American Business Development Center - National Center for American Indian Enterprise Development Center**
953 E Juanita Ave.
Mesa, AZ 85204
Ph: (480)545-1298
Fax: (480)545-4208
Co. E-mail: ncaiedcln@aol.com
URL: http://www.ncaied.org
Contact: Joan Notah, Director

FINANCING AND LOAN PROGRAMS

47981 ■ **Miller Capital Corp.**
4909 E. McDowell Rd.
Phoenix, AZ 85008-4293
Ph: (602)225-0505
Fax: (602)225-9024
URL: http://www.themillergroup.net
Contact: Rudy R. Miller, Chief Executive Officer
Preferred Investment Size: $1,000,000 to $5,000,000. **Industry Preferences:** Consumer related. **Geographic Preference:** U.S.

47982 ■ **Valley Ventures / Arizona Growth Partners, L.P.**
1275 W. Washington St., Ste. 101
Tempe, AZ 85281
Ph: (480)661-6600
Fax: (602)286-5284
Co. E-mail: businessplans@valleyventures.com
URL: http://www.valleyventures.com
Contact: Jock Holliman, III, Partner
Industry Preferences: Computer software, Internet specific, semiconductors and other electronics, biotechnology, and medical and health. **Geographic Preference:** Arizona, Colorado, Nevada, New Mexico, Southern California, Southwest, Texas, and Utah.

PROCUREMENT ASSISTANCE PROGRAMS

47983 ■ **Arizona Procurement Technical Assistance Center - The National Center for AIED**
National Center Headquarters
953 E Juanita Ave.
Mesa, AZ 85204
Ph: (480)545-1298
Free: 800-462-2433
Fax: (480)454-4208
Co. E-mail: ken.robbins@ncaied.org
URL: http://www.ncaied.org
Contact: Ken Robbins, Chief Executive Officer
Description: Committed to Business Development for Indian People.

47984 ■ **Maricopa County Procurement Technical Assistance Center - APTAN - Bid Source**
201 N Central Ave., 27th Fl.
Phoenix, AZ 85073
Ph: (602)495-6467
Fax: (602)495-8913
Co. E-mail: bidsource@phoenixchamber.com
URL: http://www.phoenixchamber.com
Contact: Daniel Ayala, Director
E-mail: cmccroskey@phoenixchamber.com

INCUBATORS/RESEARCH AND TECHNOLOGY PARKS

47985 ■ **Arizona Center for Innovation**
9040 S Rita Rd., Ste. 1100
Tucson, AZ 85747
Ph: (520)382-3260
Fax: (520)382-3299
Co. E-mail: info@azinnovation.com
URL: http://www.azinnovation.org/
Contact: Marie Wesselhoft, Director
Description: A high-tech incubator promoting the development of high technology companies in Southern Arizona through a disciplined program of business development.

47986 ■ **Northern Arizona Center for Entrepreneurship and Technology**
2225 N Gemini Dr.
Flagstaff, AZ 86001
Ph: (928)213-9234

Fax: (928)213-9720
Co. E-mail: info@nacet.org
URL: http://www.nacet.org/
Contact: Russ Yelton, Chief Executive Officer
Description: An incubator supporting the creation of science and technology-based businesses in Arizona.

47987 ■ Stealthmode Partners
260 S Arizona Ave.
Chandler, AZ 85225
Ph: (816)974-8836
Fax: (602)532-7087
Co. E-mail: francine@stealthmode.com
URL: http://stealthmode.com/
Description: A network of people and companies working together behind the scenes (in 'stealth-mode') to help its portfolio companies grow bigger, better, faster. Companies accepted into the Stealth-mode Partners portfolio receive coaching, consulting, and connections to the people and resources they need to reach success.

47988 ■ Thunderbird Global Entrepreneurship Incubator
Thunderbird School of Global Management
Voris Bldg.
1 Global Pl.
Glendale, AZ 85306
Ph: (602)978-7571
Fax: (602)439-1435
Co. E-mail: cge@thunderbird.edu
URL: http://www.thunderbird.edu
Description: A small business incubator offering entrepreneurs a unique environment to increase their chances for success, providing low-cast office space, professional and support services, and fostering entrepreneurial ideas from the early stages of company development until the graduation from the incubator.

EDUCATIONAL PROGRAMS

47989 ■ Eastern Arizona College
615 N Stadium Ave.
Thatcher, AZ 85552-0769

Ph: (928)428-8472
Free: 800-678-3808
Fax: (928)428-8462
URL: http://www.eac.edu
Description: Two-year college offering a small business management program.

47990 ■ Rio Salado Community College
2323 W 14th St.
Tempe, AZ 85281
Ph: (480)517-8000
Free: 800-729-1197
Fax: (480)517-8519
URL: http://www.rio.maricopa.edu
Description: Two-year college offering a program in small business management.

PUBLICATIONS

47991 ■ *Starting and Operating a Business in Arizona: A Step-by-Step Guide*
PSI Research
300 N. Valley Dr.
Grants Pass, OR 97526
Ph: (503)479-9464
Free: 800-228-2275
Fax: (503)476-1479
Co. E-mail: psi2@magick.net
Ed: Michael D. Jenkins. **Released:** Revised edition, 1992. **Price:** $29.95 (looseleaf binder); $24.95 (paper). **Description:** Part of the Successful Business Library series.

PUBLISHERS

47992 ■ Center for Competitiveness and Prosperity Research
W. P. Carey School of Business
Tempe, AZ 85287-4011
Ph: (480)965-3961

Fax: (480)965-5458
Co. E-mail: wpcarey.ccpr@asu.edu
URL: http://wpcarey.asu.edu/seid/ccpr
Contact: Tom R. Rex, Director
E-mail: tom.rex@asu.edu
Description: Description: Publishes books on economics, real estate, consumer price index and demographics. Reports and documents in microform distributed by University Microfilms, Information Access Company and the Institute for Scientific Information. Printed publications available from the Center. Does not accept unsolicited manuscripts. **Founded:** 1954.

47993 ■ Sohnen-Moe Associates Inc.—SMA Inc.
8340 N Thornydale Rd., Ste. 110-261
Tucson, AZ 85741
Ph: (520)743-3936
Free: 800-786-4774
Fax: (520)743-3656
Co. E-mail: sma.info@sohnen-moe.com
URL: http://www.sohnen-moe.com
Contact: Virginia Anthony, President
Description: Description: Publishes materials for small business owners, especially health care practitioners. **Founded:** 1984.

47994 ■ Success Showcase Publishing—Debbie Allen International
10115 E Bell Rd., Ste. 107-616
Scottsdale, AZ 85260
Ph: (480)634-7691
Free: 800-359-4544
Fax: (480)634-7692
Co. E-mail: info@debbieallen.com
URL: http://www.debbieallen.com
Contact: Debbie Allen, President
E-mail: debbie@debbieAllen.com
Description: Description: Publishes books on general business and marketing titles. Does not accept unsolicited manuscripts. Reaches market through direct mail, reviews and listings. **Founded:** 1996.

SMALL BUSINESS DEVELOPMENT CENTERS

47995 ■ Arkansas State University Small Business Development Center (ASU SBDC)
PO Box 2650
Jonesboro, AR 72402
Ph: (870)972-3517
Fax: (870)972-3678
Co. E-mail: asusbtdc@astate.edu
URL: http://www.astate.edu/a/business/sbtdc
Contact: Herb Lawrence, Director
Description: Represents and promotes the small business sector. Provides management assistance to current and prospective small business owners. Helps to improve management skills and expand the products and services of members.

47996 ■ Southern Arkansas University Small Business Development Center (SAU SBDC)
PO Box 9192
Magnolia, AR 71754-9379
Ph: (870)235-5033
Co. E-mail: fabozeman@saumag.edu
URL: http://asbdc.ualr.edu/locations
Description: Represents and promotes the small business sector. Provides management assistance to current and prospective small business owners. Helps to improve management skills and expand the products and services of members.

SCORE OFFICES

47997 ■ Garland County SCORE
Co. E-mail: score@hotspringschamber.com

47998 ■ Harrison SCORE
Co. E-mail: info@nwascore.org

47999 ■ River Valley SCORE
Co. E-mail: gcampbell@attglobal.net

48000 ■ South Central Arkansas SCORE
Co. E-mail: score@suddenlinkmail.com

BETTER BUSINESS BUREAUS

48001 ■ Better Business Bureau of Arkansas
12521 Kanis Rd.
Little Rock, AR 72211
Ph: (501)664-4888
Fax: (501)664-0024
Co. E-mail: info@bbbarkansas.org
URL: http://arkansas.bbb.org
Contact: Janet J. Robb, President
Description: Seeks to promote and foster the highest ethical relationship between businesses and the public through voluntary self-regulation, consumer and business education, and service excellence. Provides information to help consumers and businesses make informed purchasing decisions and avoid costly scams and frauds; settles consumer complaints through arbitration and other means.

CHAMBERS OF COMMERCE

48002 ■ Alma Area Chamber of Commerce
725 Fayetteville Ave.
Alma, AR 72921-3603
Ph: (479)632-4127
Fax: (479)632-4037
Co. E-mail: almachamber@centurytel.net
URL: http://www.almachamber.com
Contact: Charlotte Gibson, President
Description: Promotes business and community development in Alma, AR area. **Founded:** 1984.

48003 ■ Arkadelphia Area Chamber of Commerce
c/o Mr. Blain Smith, Exec. Dir.
PO Box 38
Arkadelphia, AR 71923-0038
Ph: (870)246-5542
Free: 800-874-4289
Fax: (870)246-5543
Co. E-mail: chamber@cityofarkadelphia.com
URL: http://www.arkadelphia.org
Contact: Mr. Blain Smith, Executive Director
Description: Promotes business and community development in Arkadelphia, AR.

48004 ■ Arkansas State Chamber of Commerce
PO Box 3645
Little Rock, AR 72203-3645
Ph: (501)372-2222
Fax: (501)372-2722
Co. E-mail: rzook@arkansasstatechamber.com
URL: http://www.arkansasstatechamber.com
Contact: Randy Zook, President
Description: Promotes business and community development in Arkansas. **Founded:** 1928.

48005 ■ Bald Knob Area Chamber of Commerce
411 S Elm St.
Bald Knob, AR 72010
Ph: (501)724-3140
Fax: (501)724-3140
Co. E-mail: baldknobchamber@centurytel.net
URL: http://www.baldknobchamber.com/baldknob
Description: Promotes business and community development in Bald Knob, AR. Sponsors annual Homefest. Publications: none.

48006 ■ Batesville
409 Vine St.
Batesville, AR 72501
Ph: (870)793-2378
Fax: (870)793-3061
Co. E-mail: info@mybatesville.org
URL: http://www.mybatesville.org
Contact: Tony Stephens, Chairman
Price: free.

48007 ■ Batesville Area Chamber of Commerce (BACC)
409 Vine St.
Batesville, AR 72501
Ph: (870)793-2378
Fax: (870)793-3061
Co. E-mail: info@mybatesville.org
URL: http://www.mybatesville.org
Contact: Tony Stephens, Chairman
Description: Promotes business and community development in Independence County, AR. **Founded:** 1919. **Publications:** *Batesville*; *City of Batesville/ Independence County Maps*. **Educational Activities:** White River Water Carnival (Annual).

48008 ■ Benton Area Chamber of Commerce
607 N Market St.
Benton, AR 72015
Ph: (501)315-8272
Fax: (501)315-8290
Co. E-mail: reception@bentonchamber.com
URL: http://www.bentonchamber.com
Contact: Gary James, Executive Director
Description: Provides business and community development in the Benton, AR area.

48009 ■ Bentonville-Bella Vista Chamber of Commerce
PO Box 330
Bentonville, AR 72712
Ph: (479)273-2841
Fax: (479)273-2180
Co. E-mail: esanders@bbvchamber.com
URL: http://www.bbvchamber.com
Contact: Ed Clifford, President
Description: Promotes business and community development in Bentonville, AR area. **Founded:** 1926. **Publications:** *Bentonville/Bella Vista Chamber of Commerce--Business Directory*.

48010 ■ Booneville Development Corporation - South Logan County Chamber of Commerce
PO Box 55
Booneville, AR 72927
Ph: (479)675-2666
Fax: (479)675-5158
Co. E-mail: information@booneville.com
URL: http://www.booneville.com
Contact: Stacey McCollough, Executive Director
Description: Promotes business and community development in Booneville, AR.

48011 ■ Bradley County Chamber of Commerce
104 N Myrtle St.
Warren, AR 71671
Ph: (870)226-5225
Fax: (870)226-6285
Co. E-mail: bcc.warren@sbcglobal.net
URL: http://www.bradleychamber.com
Description: Promotes business and community development in Bradley County, AR. **Founded:** 1924.

48012 ■ Brinkley Chamber of Commerce
217 W Cypress
Brinkley, AR 72021
Ph: (870)734-2262

Fax: (870)589-2020
Co. E-mail: brinkleyar@msn.com
URL: http://www.brinkleychamber.com
Contact: Justin McCoy, President
Description: Promotes business and community development in Brinkley, AR.

48013 ■ *Bryant Business Chronicle*
PO Box 261
Bryant, AR 72089-0261
Ph: (501)847-4702
Fax: (501)847-7576
Co. E-mail: bryantcofc@aristotle.net
URL: http://www.bryant-ar.com
Contact: Jason Brown, President
Released: Periodic

48014 ■ *Bryant Chamber of Commerce (BCC)*
PO Box 261
Bryant, AR 72089-0261
Ph: (501)847-4702
Fax: (501)847-7576
Co. E-mail: bryantcofc@aristotle.net
URL: http://www.bryant-ar.com
Contact: Jason Brown, President
Description: Promotes business and community development in Bryant, AR. **Founded:** 1974. **Publications:** *Bryant Business Chronicle* (Periodic).

48015 ■ *Bull Shoals Lake - White River Chamber of Commerce*
PO Box 354
Bull Shoals, AR 72619
Ph: (870)445-4443
Free: 800-447-1290
Co. E-mail: havefun@bullshoals.org
URL: http://www.bullshoals.org
Contact: Terry Partee, President
Description: Promotes business and community development in Bull Shoals, AR. **Publications:** *Bull Shoals Lake - White River Visitor's Guide.*

48016 ■ *Bull Shoals Lake - White River Visitor's Guide*
PO Box 354
Bull Shoals, AR 72619
Ph: (870)445-4443
Free: 800-447-1290
Co. E-mail: havefun@bullshoals.org
URL: http://www.bullshoals.org
Contact: Terry Partee, President
Price: free.

48017 ■ *Business Connection*
708 W Main St.
Russellville, AR 72801-3617
Ph: (479)968-2530
Fax: (479)968-5894
Co. E-mail: chamber@russellville.org
URL: http://www.russellvillechamber.org
Contact: Jeff Pipkin, President
Released: Monthly

48018 ■ *Business Directory and Relocation Guide*
621 E Rush
Harrison, AR 72601
Ph: (870)741-2659
Free: 800-880-6265
Co. E-mail: cocinfo@harrison-chamber.com
URL: http://www.harrison-chamber.com
Contact: Patty Methvin, President
Released: Annual

48019 ■ *Cabot Chamber of Commerce*
101 S 1st St.
Cabot, AR 72023
Ph: (501)843-2136
Fax: (501)843-1861
Co. E-mail: chamber@cabotcc.org
URL: http://www.cabotcc.org
Contact: Billye Everett, Executive Director
Description: Promotes business and community development in Cabot, AR. **Founded:** 1891.

48020 ■ *Calendar of Events*
301 W Walnut St.
Paris, AR 72855-3731
Ph: (479)963-2244

Fax: (479)963-8321
Co. E-mail: pariscoc@gmail.com
URL: http://www.parisaronline.com
Released: Monthly

48021 ■ *The Catalyst*
612 Garrison Ave.
Fort Smith, AR 72901
Ph: (479)783-6118
Fax: (479)783-6110
Co. E-mail: info@fortsmithchamber.com
URL: http://www.fortsmithchamber.org
Contact: Paul Harvel, President
Released: Monthly

48022 ■ *Cave City Area Chamber of Commerce*
PO Box 274
Cave City, AR 72521
Ph: (870)283-5959
Co. E-mail: laura@frontiercs.com
URL: http://www.cavecityarkansas.info
Contact: John Beller, President
Description: Promotes business and community development in Cave City, AR. Participates in charitable programs; sponsors beauty pageants and Yard-of-the-Month competitions; conducts Watermelon Festival. Convention/Meeting: none. **Founded:** 1973.

48023 ■ *Central Arkansas Manufacturing Directory*
One Chamber Plz.
Little Rock, AR 72201-1618
Ph: (501)374-2001
Fax: (501)374-6018
Co. E-mail: chamber@littlerockchamber.com
URL: http://www.littlerockchamber.com/cwt/external/wcpages/index.aspx
Contact: Jay Chesshir, President
Price: free for members (first copy only); $10, additional copy for members; $20, for nonmembers.

48024 ■ *The Chamber*
204 S Main St.
Hope, AR 71801-4318
Ph: (870)777-3640
Fax: (870)722-6154
Co. E-mail: hopemelonfest@yahoo.com
URL: http://www.hopechamberofcommerce.com
Contact: Mark Keith, Director
Released: Monthly

48025 ■ *Chamber Business Directory*
PO Box 652
Marion, AR 72364-0652
Ph: (870)739-6041
Fax: (870)739-5448
Co. E-mail: chamber@marionarkansas.org
URL: http://www.marionarkansas.org
Contact: Craig Brown, President
Released: Annual; every January.

48026 ■ *Chamber E-Flash*
300 W Walnut St.
Blytheville, AR 72315-2832
Ph: (870)762-2012
Fax: (870)762-0551
Co. E-mail: info@blythevillegosnell.com
URL: http://www.blythevillegosnell.com
Contact: Elizabeth Smith, Executive Director
Released: Monthly

48027 ■ *Chamber Memo*
1001 W Main St.
Heber Springs, AR 72543-2946
Ph: (501)362-2444
Co. E-mail: chamber@heber-springs.com
URL: http://www.heber-springs.com
Contact: Melisa Gardner, Executive Director
Released: Monthly

48028 ■ *The Chamber Newsletter*
111 W Main St.
El Dorado, AR 71730
Ph: (870)863-6113

Fax: (870)863-6115
Co. E-mail: chamber@boomtown.org
URL: http://www.boomtown.org
Contact: Henry Florsheim, President
Released: Monthly **Price:** $5, /year for nonmembers; included in membership dues.

48029 ■ *Chamber Outlook*
202 W Emma Ave.
Springdale, AR 72764-4307
Ph: (479)872-2222
Free: 800-972-7261
Fax: (479)751-4699
Co. E-mail: info@springdale.com
URL: http://www.springdale.com
Contact: Perry Webb, President
Released: Semimonthly

48030 ■ *Chamber Post*
335 E Gaines St.
Monticello, AR 71655
Ph: (870)367-6741
Fax: (870)367-6741
Co. E-mail: monticellochamber@sbcglobal.net
URL: http://www.montdrewchamber.com
Released: Bimonthly **Price:** included in membership dues.

48031 ■ *Chamber Talk*
507 S Main St.
Stuttgart, AR 72160
Ph: (870)673-1602
Fax: (870)673-1604
Co. E-mail: stuttgartchamber@centurytel.net
URL: http://stuttgartarkansas.org
Contact: Mr. Stephen R. Bell, Executive Vice President
Released: Monthly

48032 ■ *Chamber Today*
1709 E Nettleton Ave.
Jonesboro, AR 72401-5165
Ph: (870)932-6691
Fax: (870)933-5758
Co. E-mail: myoung@jonesborochamber.com
URL: http://www.jonesborochamber.org
Contact: Mark Young, President
Released: Bimonthly

48033 ■ *City of Batesville/Independence County Maps*
409 Vine St.
Batesville, AR 72501
Ph: (870)793-2378
Fax: (870)793-3061
Co. E-mail: info@mybatesville.org
URL: http://www.mybatesville.org
Contact: Tony Stephens, Chairman
Price: $1.

48034 ■ *Clarendon Chamber of Commerce (CCC)*
PO Box 153
Clarendon, AR 72029-0153
Ph: (870)747-5414
Co. E-mail: clarendoncityhall@centurytel.net
URL: http://www.clarendon-ar.com
Contact: Ladon Edens, Secretary Treasurer
Description: Promotes business and community development in Clarendon, AR.

48035 ■ *Clarksville-Johnson County Chamber of Commerce*
101 N Johnson St.
Clarksville, AR 72830
Ph: (479)754-2340
Fax: (479)754-4923
Co. E-mail: cjccofc@centurytel.net
URL: http://www.clarksvillearchamber.com
Contact: Karl Mace, President
Description: Promotes business and community development in Clarksville and Johnson County, AR. **Founded:** 1921. **Publications:** *Johnson County Chamber Newsletter* (Monthly). **Educational Activities:** Ambassadors Meeting (Monthly). **Awards:** Member of the Month (Monthly).

48036 ■ Clinton Chamber of Commerce
290 Main St.
Clinton, AR 72031-7060
Ph: (501)745-6500
Co. E-mail: info@clintonchamber.com
URL: http://www.clintonarchamber.com
Description: Promotes business and community development in Clinton, AR. **Founded:** 1936.

48037 ■ *Communique*
659 Ouachita Ave.
Hot Springs, AR 71901
Ph: (501)321-1700
Free: 800-467-INFO
Fax: (501)321-3551
Co. E-mail: info@hotspringschamber.com
URL: http://www.hotspringschamber.com
Contact: Dave Byerly, President
Released: Monthly

48038 ■ Conway Area Chamber of Commerce (CACC)
900 Oak St.
Conway, AR 72032-4402
Ph: (501)327-7788
Fax: (501)327-7790
Co. E-mail: getsmart@conwayarkansas.org
URL: http://www.conwayarkcc.org
Contact: Brad Lacy, President
Description: Promotes business and community development in Conway, AR. **Founded:** 1890. **Publications:** *Directory of Manufacturing* (Annual).

48039 ■ Corning Area Chamber of Commerce
1621 W Main St.
Corning, AR 72422-0093
Ph: (870)857-3874
URL: http://www.corningarchamber.org
Description: Promotes business and community development in the Corning, AR area.

48040 ■ Cotter Chamber of Commerce
PO Box 489
Cotter, AR 72626-0489
Ph: (870)321-1243
Co. E-mail: office@cotterarkansas.com
URL: http://www.cotterarkansas.com
Contact: Gary Flippin, President
Description: Works to the betterment of Cotter and its people.

48041 ■ Cross County Chamber of Commerce and Economic Development Corporation (CCCEDC)
1790 Falls Blvd. N
Wynne, AR 72396-4022
Ph: (870)238-2601
Fax: (870)238-7844
Co. E-mail: brian@crosscountychamber.com
URL: http://www.crosscountychamber.com
Contact: Dianna Sisk, President
Description: Promotes business and community development in Wynne, AR.

48042 ■ Crossett Area Chamber of Commerce (CACC)
101 W 1st Ave.
Crossett, AR 71635
Ph: (870)364-6591
Fax: (870)364-7488
Co. E-mail: emorrison@fsbcrossett.com
URL: http://www.crossettchamber.org
Contact: Edith Morrison, President
Description: Promotes business and community development in the Crossett, AR area. Sponsors annual Buddy Bass Tournament and Wiggins Cabin Festival. **Founded:** 1951.

48043 ■ De Queen/Sevier County Chamber of Commerce
315 W Stilwell Ave.
De Queen, AR 71832-2860
Ph: (870)584-3225
Fax: (870)642-7959
Co. E-mail: dqscoc@ipa.net
URL: http://www.dequeenchamberofcommerce.com
Contact: Angie Walker, President
Description: Promotes business and community development in Sevier County, AR.

48044 ■ *Demographic Journal*
100 Main St.
North Little Rock, AR 72114
Ph: (501)372-5959
Fax: (501)372-5955
Co. E-mail: nlrchamber@nlrchamber.org
URL: http://www.nlrchamber.org
Contact: Terry C. Hartwick, President
Released: Periodic

48045 ■ Dermott Area Chamber of Commerce (DACC)
PO Box 147
Dermott, AR 71638-0147
Ph: (870)538-5656
Fax: (870)538-5493
Co. E-mail: email@dermottchamber.com
URL: http://www.dermottchamber.com
Contact: Frank Henry, Jr., Executive Director
Description: Promotes business and community development in Chicot County, AR. **Founded:** 1939. **Publications:** *McGohen Dermott Times News* (Monthly). **Educational Activities:** Dermott Crawfish Festival (Annual).

48046 ■ Dierks Chamber of Commerce (DCC)
PO Box 292
Dierks, AR 71833-0292
Ph: (870)286-3163
Co. E-mail: dierkscoc@alltel.net
URL: http://www.dierkschamberofcommerce.com
Contact: Brenda Ward, President
Description: Promotes business and community development in Dierks, AR.

48047 ■ *Directory of Manufacturing*
900 Oak St.
Conway, AR 72032-4402
Ph: (501)327-7788
Fax: (501)327-7790
Co. E-mail: getsmart@conwayarkansas.org
URL: http://www.conwayarkcc.org
Contact: Brad Lacy, President
Released: Annual

48048 ■ Dumas Chamber of Commerce (DCC)
c/o Sammye Owen, Exec. Dir.
PO Box 431
Dumas, AR 71639-0431
Ph: (870)382-5447
Fax: (870)382-3031
Co. E-mail: dumaschamber@centurytel.net
URL: http://www.dumasar.net
Contact: Sammye Owen, Executive Director
Description: Promotes business industrial and community development in Southern Arkansas. Sponsors Dumas Ding Dong Days activities. **Founded:** 1955. **Awards:** Employee Appreciation Award (Annual); Outstanding Man and Woman of the Year (Annual).

48049 ■ El Dorado Chamber of Commerce (EDCC)
111 W Main St.
El Dorado, AR 71730
Ph: (870)863-6113
Fax: (870)863-6115
Co. E-mail: chamber@boomtown.org
URL: http://www.boomtown.org
Contact: Henry Florsheim, President
Description: Promotes business and community development in El Dorado, AR. **Publications:** *The Chamber Newsletter* (Monthly). **Awards:** Teachers of the Year (Annual).

48050 ■ Fayetteville Chamber of Commerce (FCC)
123 W Mountain St.
Fayetteville, AR 72701
Ph: (479)521-1710
Fax: (479)521-1791
Co. E-mail: chamber@fayettevillear.com
URL: http://www.fayettevillear.com
Contact: Steve Clark, President
Description: Promotes business and community development in Fayetteville, AR. **Founded:** 1889.

48051 ■ Flippin Chamber of Commerce (FCC)
PO Box 118
Flippin, AR 72634-0118
Ph: (870)453-8480
Co. E-mail: jcheek@fnbmh.com
URL: http://www.flippinchamber.com
Contact: Jennifer Cheek, President
Description: Promotes business, community development, and tourism in Flippin and Marion counties, AR. Sponsors Ozark Mountain Air Festival.

48052 ■ Fordyce Chamber of Commerce (FCC)
c/o Darrell Crutchfield
PO Box 930
Fordyce, AR 71742
Ph: (870)352-5137
Fax: (870)352-5159
Co. E-mail: cityoffordyce@alltel.net
URL: http://cityoffordyce.com/?page_id=214
Description: Aims to advance and promote the well-being of commerce, industry, agriculture, civic interests, and the citizenry of Fordyce and its trade territory. **Founded:** 1920.

48053 ■ Forrest City Area Chamber of Commerce (FCCC)
203 N Izard
Forrest City, AR 72335
Ph: (870)633-1651
Fax: (870)633-9500
Co. E-mail: info@forrestcitychamber.com
URL: http://www.forrestcitychamber.com
Contact: David K. Dunn, Executive Director
Description: Promotes business and community development in Forrest City, AR. Sponsors annual harvest festival, Christmas parade, and triathlon. Also conducts all industrial recruitment. **Publications:** *The Forum Express* (Monthly).

48054 ■ Fort Smith Chamber of Commerce
612 Garrison Ave.
Fort Smith, AR 72901
Ph: (479)783-6118
Fax: (479)783-6110
Co. E-mail: info@fortsmithchamber.org
URL: http://www.fortsmithchamber.org
Contact: Paul Harvel, President
Description: Promotes business and community development in Ft. Smith, AR. **Founded:** 1887. **Publications:** *Fort Smith Regional Community Guide; The Catalyst* (Monthly); *Forth Smith Regional Community Guide; Forth Smith Regional Industrial Directory.* **Educational Activities:** Business & Industrial EXPO (Annual).

48055 ■ *Forth Smith Regional Community Guide*
612 Garrison Ave.
Fort Smith, AR 72901
Ph: (479)783-6118
Fax: (479)783-6110
Co. E-mail: info@fortsmithchamber.com
URL: http://www.fortsmithchamber.org
Contact: Paul Harvel, President

48056 ■ *Forth Smith Regional Industrial Directory*
612 Garrison Ave.
Fort Smith, AR 72901
Ph: (479)783-6118
Fax: (479)783-6110
Co. E-mail: info@fortsmithchamber.com
URL: http://www.fortsmithchamber.org
Contact: Paul Harvel, President

48057 ■ *The Forum Express*
203 N Izard
Forrest City, AR 72335
Ph: (870)633-1651
Fax: (870)633-9500
Co. E-mail: info@forrestcitychamber.com
URL: http://www.forrestcitychamber.com
Contact: David K. Dunn, Executive Director
Released: Monthly

48058 ■ Grant County Chamber of Commerce
202 N Oak St.
Sheridan, AR 72150-2132
Ph: (870)942-3021
Fax: (870)942-3378
Co. E-mail: gccc@windstream.net
URL: http://www.grantcountychamber.com
Contact: Kim Hollinger, President
Description: Promotes business and community development in Grant County, AR. **Founded:** 1955.

48059 ■ Greater Blytheville Area Chamber of Commerce (BGCC)
300 W Walnut St.
Blytheville, AR 72315-2832
Ph: (870)762-2012
Fax: (870)762-0551
Co. E-mail: info@blythevillegosnell.com
URL: http://www.blythevillegosnell.com
Contact: Elizabeth Smith, Executive Director
Description: Promotes business and community development in Blytheville, AR. Sponsors spring and fall festival. **Founded:** 1917. **Publications:** *Chamber E-Flash* (Monthly).

48060 ■ Greater Eureka Springs Chamber of Commerce
PO Box 551
Eureka Springs, AR 72632-0551
Ph: (479)253-8737
Free: 800-6-EUREKA
Fax: (479)253-5037
Co. E-mail: jeff@eurekaspringschamber.com
URL: http://www.eurekaspringschamber.com
Contact: Jeffrey B. Feldman, President
Description: Fosters personal, economic, and cultural growth of Eureka Springs community.

48061 ■ Greater Hot Springs Chamber of Commerce (GHSCC)
659 Ouachita Ave.
Hot Springs, AR 71901
Ph: (501)321-1700
Free: 800-467-INFO
Fax: (501)321-3551
Co. E-mail: info@hotspringschamber.com
URL: http://www.hotspringschamber.com
Contact: Dave Byerly, President
Description: Promotes business, community development, and tourism in the Hot Springs, AR area. Sponsors Oktoberfest and Healthfest. **Founded:** 1897. **Publications:** *Communique* (Monthly).

48062 ■ *Greater Little Rock Guest Guide*
One Chamber Plz.
Little Rock, AR 72201-1618
Ph: (501)374-2001
Fax: (501)374-6018
Co. E-mail: chamber@littlerockchamber.com
URL: http://www.littlerockchamber.com/cwt/external/wcpages/index.aspx
Contact: Jay Chesshir, President
Price: $15, for members; $20, for nonmembers.

48063 ■ Greater Pine Bluff Chamber of Commerce
c/o Ann Williams, Co-Dir.
510 S Main St.
Pine Bluff, AR 71601-4328
Ph: (870)535-0110
Fax: (870)535-1643
Co. E-mail: info@pinebluffchamber.com
URL: http://www.pinebluffchamber.com
Contact: Chris Hart, Chairman
Description: Promotes business and community development in the Pine Bluff, AR area. **Founded:** 1911. **Publications:** *Investor's Report* (Monthly); *Who's Who in Pine Bluff Business* (Annual).

48064 ■ Greenwood Chamber of Commerce (GCC)
No. 16 Town Square
Greenwood, AR 72936
Ph: (479)996-6357

Fax: (479)996-1162
Co. E-mail: info@greenwoodchamber.net
URL: http://www.greenwoodarkansas.com
Contact: Doris Tate, Director
Description: Promotes business and community development in the Arkansas River Valley, AR area. Sponsors Miss Sebastian County Pageant and annual July 4th Freedomfest. **Awards:** Citizens of the Year (Annual).

48065 ■ Greers Ferry Area Chamber of Commerce
PO Box 1354
Greers Ferry, AR 72067
Ph: (501)825-7188
Free: 888-825-7199
Co. E-mail: ceswl-gf@usace.army.mil
URL: http://greersferry.com
Description: Promotes business and community development in Greers Ferry, AR. Sponsors events, including fishing tournaments, rodeos, Chamber Chili Challenge in November, Christmas Lighting Contest, and Christmas Tree Lighting. **Publications:** *The Heart of the Lake, Greers Ferry, Arkansas.*

48066 ■ Gurdon Chamber of Commerce
PO Box 187
Gurdon, AR 71743-0187
Ph: (870)353-2661
URL: http://www.gurdonchamberofcommerce.com
Description: Promotes business and community development in Gurdon, AR.

48067 ■ Hamburg Area Chamber of Commerce (HCC)
6122 S Park Ave.
Hamburg, NY 14075
Ph: (716)649-7917
Fax: (716)649-6362
Co. E-mail: hccmail@hamburg-chamber.org
URL: http://www.hamburg-chamber.org
Contact: Betty B. Newell, President
Description: Promotes business and community development in Ashley County, AR. **Founded:** 1965. **Awards:** Business of the Year (Annual); Fred La-Grone Life Achievement Award (Annual); Man of the Year (Annual); Outstanding Citizens of the Year (Annual); Teacher of the Year (Annual); Woman of the Year (Annual); Ashley County Farm Family of the Year (Annual).

48068 ■ Harrisburg Area Chamber of Commerce (HACC)
200 E Jackson St.
Harrisburg, AR 72432-1916
Ph: (870)578-5461
Fax: (870)578-9467
Co. E-mail: harrisburgchamber@pcsii.com
URL: http://www.harrisburgchamber.com
Contact: Mark Weston, President
Description: Promotes business and community development in the Harrisburg, AR area. **Founded:** 1965.

48069 ■ Harrison Chamber of Commerce (HCC)
621 E Rush
Harrison, AR 72601
Ph: (870)741-2659
Free: 800-880-6265
Co. E-mail: cocinfo@harrison-chamber.com
URL: http://www.harrison-chamber.com
Contact: Patty Methvin, President
Description: Promotes business and community development in the Harrison, AR area. **Publications:** *Business Directory and Relocation Guide* (Annual).

48070 ■ *The Heart of the Lake, Greers Ferry, Arkansas*
PO Box 1354
Greers Ferry, AR 72067
Ph: (501)825-7188
Free: 888-825-7199
Co. E-mail: ceswl-gf@usace.army.mil
URL: http://greersferry.com

48071 ■ Heber Springs Area Chamber of Commerce (HSACC)
1001 W Main St.
Heber Springs, AR 72543-2946
Ph: (501)362-2444
Co. E-mail: chamber@heber-springs.com
URL: http://www.heber-springs.com
Contact: Melisa Gardner, Executive Director
Description: Promotes business and community development in Cleburne County, AR. **Founded:** 1957. **Publications:** *Chamber Memo* (Monthly).

48072 ■ Hope-Hempstead County Chamber of Commerce (HHCCC)
204 S Main St.
Hope, AR 71801-4318
Ph: (870)777-3640
Fax: (870)722-6154
Co. E-mail: hopemelonfest@yahoo.com
URL: http://www.hopechamberofcommerce.com
Contact: Mark Keith, Director
Description: Promotes business and community development in Hempstead County, AR. Sponsors annual Hope Watermelon Festival in August. Holds seminars and periodic board meeting. **Publications:** *The Chamber* (Monthly). **Educational Activities:** Hope Watermelon Festival (Annual).

48073 ■ Horseshoe Bend Area Chamber of Commerce (HBACC)
811 2nd St., No. 18
Horseshoe Bend, AR 72512
Ph: (870)670-5433
Free: 800-239-9338
Co. E-mail: horseshoebendarcc@yahoo.com
URL: http://www.horseshoebendarcc.com
Contact: Brenda Doty, President
Description: Promotes business and community development in the Horseshoe Bend, AR area. Sponsors annual Dogwood Days festival in April. **Founded:** 1969.

48074 ■ Huntsville Chamber of Commerce
104 E Main St.
Huntsville, AR 72740-0950
Ph: (479)738-6000
Co. E-mail: service@huntsvillearchamber.com
URL: http://www.huntsvillearchamber.com
Contact: Mr. Richard Gillham, Treasurer
Description: Promotes business and community development in Huntsville, AR. **Founded:** 1839. **Awards:** Community Service Award (Annual); Employee of the Year (Annual); Hero Award (Annual); Outstanding Citizen of the Year (Annual); Presidents Award (Annual); Best New Large and/or Small Business (Annual).

48075 ■ *Investor's Report*
c/o Ann Williams, Co-Dir.
510 S Main St.
Pine Bluff, AR 71601-4328
Ph: (870)535-0110
Fax: (870)535-1643
Co. E-mail: info@pinebluffchamber.com
URL: http://www.pinebluffchamber.com
Contact: Chris Hart, Chairman
Released: Monthly

48076 ■ *Johnson County Chamber Newsletter*
101 N Johnson St.
Clarksville, AR 72830
Ph: (479)754-2340
Fax: (479)754-4923
Co. E-mail: cjccofc@centurytel.net
URL: http://www.clarksvillearchamber.com
Contact: Karl Mace, President
Released: Monthly **Price:** free.

48077 ■ Jonesboro Regional Chamber of Commerce
1709 E Nettleton Ave.
Jonesboro, AR 72401-5165
Ph: (870)932-6691

Fax: (870)933-5758
Co. E-mail: myoung@jonesborochamber.com
URL: http://www.jonesborochamber.org
Contact: Mark Young, President
Description: Promotes business and community development in the Craighead County, AR area. **Founded:** 1915. **Publications:** *Chamber Today* (Bimonthly).

48078 ■ Lake Village Chamber of Commerce (LVCC)
PO Box 752
Lake Village, AR 71653
Ph: (870)265-5997
Fax: (870)265-5254
Co. E-mail: lvccdirector@sbcglobal.net
URL: http://www.lakevillagechamber.com
Contact: Lisa V. Raby, Director
Description: Promotes business and community development in Lake Village, AR. **Publications:** *News Exchange.* **Educational Activities:** General Membership (Monthly).

48079 ■ *Leader Academy*
116 N Maple St.
Osceola, AR 72370-2538
Ph: (870)563-2281
Fax: (870)563-5385
Co. E-mail: osceolachamber@sbcglobal.net
URL: http://www.osceolachamber.net
Contact: Eric Golde, Executive Director

48080 ■ Little River Chamber of Commerce (LRCC)
180 E Whitaker St.
Ashdown, AR 71822-2724
Ph: (870)898-2758
Co. E-mail: director@littlerivercounty.org
URL: http://www.littlerivercounty.org
Description: Promotes business and community development in Little River County. **Founded:** 1867. **Awards:** Beautification Award; Citizen of the Year (Annual); Continuous Service; Educator of the Year (Annual); Public Servant of the Year (Annual).

48081 ■ Little Rock Regional Chamber of Commerce
One Chamber Plz.
Little Rock, AR 72201-1618
Ph: (501)374-2001
Fax: (501)374-6018
Co. E-mail: chamber@littlerockchamber.com
URL: http://www.littlerockchamber.com/cwt/external/
wcpages/index.aspx
Contact: Jay Chesshir, President
Description: Promotes business and community development in the Little Rock, AR area. **Founded:** 1866. **Publications:** *Central Arkansas Manufacturing Directory*; *Greater Little Rock Guest Guide*; *Taking Care of Business.* **Educational Activities:** Columbus Day Chamber Ambassadors Golf Scramble (Annual).

48082 ■ Magnolia-Columbia County Chamber of Commerce
PO Box 866
Magnolia, AR 71754-0866
Ph: (870)234-4352
Fax: (870)234-9291
Co. E-mail: ea@ccalliance.us
URL: http://www.magnoliachamber.com
Contact: Cammie Hambrice, Executive Director
Description: Promotes economic and community development in Columbia County, AR. **Founded:** 1940.

48083 ■ *Maps*
100 Main St.
North Little Rock, AR 72114
Ph: (501)372-5959
Fax: (501)372-5955
Co. E-mail: nlrchamber@nlrchamber.org
URL: http://www.nlrchamber.org
Contact: Terry C. Hartwick, President

48084 ■ Marion Chamber of Commerce
PO Box 652
Marion, AR 72364-0652
Ph: (870)739-6041

Fax: (870)739-5448
Co. E-mail: chamber@marionarkansas.org
URL: http://www.marionarkansas.org
Contact: Craig Brown, President
Description: Promotes business and community development in Marion, AR. **Publications:** *Chamber Business Directory* (Annual); *Chamber Business Directory* (Annual). **Educational Activities:** Marion Chamber of Commerce Luncheon (Monthly).

48085 ■ Maumelle Area Chamber of Commerce (MACC)
115 Audubon Dr., Ste. 14
Maumelle, AR 72113-7410
Ph: (501)851-9700
Fax: (501)851-6690
Co. E-mail: info@maumellechamber.com
URL: http://www.maumellechamber.com
Contact: Julianne Cole, Executive Director
Description: Seeks to promote high quality of business for members and community through leadership in economic and civic development.

48086 ■ McGehee Chamber of Commerce
PO Box 521
McGehee, AR 71654
Ph: (870)222-4451
Fax: (870)222-5729
Co. E-mail: admin@mcgeheechamber.com
URL: http://www.mcgeheechamber.com
Contact: Mike Smith, President
Description: Promotes business and community development in the McGehee, AR area. **Founded:** 1879.

48087 ■ *McGohen Dermott Times News*
PO Box 147
Dermott, AR 71638-0147
Ph: (870)538-5656
Fax: (870)538-5493
Co. E-mail: email@dermottchamber.com
URL: http://www.dermottchamber.com
Contact: Frank Henry, Jr., Executive Director
Released: Monthly **Price:** free.

48088 ■ Monticello Drew County Chamber of Commerce
335 E Gaines St.
Monticello, AR 71655
Ph: (870)367-6741
Fax: (870)367-6741
Co. E-mail: monticellochamber@sbcglobal.net
URL: http://www.montdrewchamber.com
Description: Promotes business and community development in Drew County, AR. **Publications:** *Chamber Post* (Bimonthly). **Awards:** Industry of the Year (Annual); Man/Woman of the Year (Annual); Retail Business of the Year (Annual).

48089 ■ Morrilton Area Chamber of Commerce (MACC)
120 N Division St.
Morrilton, AR 72110-2930
Ph: (501)354-2393
Fax: (501)354-8642
Co. E-mail: brandonbaker@morrilton.com
URL: http://www.morrilton.com
Contact: Brandon Baker, President
Description: Promotes business and community development in Morrilton, AR. Sponsors Great Arkansas Pig Out Festival. **Founded:** 1915.

48090 ■ Mount Ida Area Chamber of Commerce (MIACC)
PO Box 6
Mount Ida, AR 71957-0006
Ph: (870)867-2723
Co. E-mail: director@mtidachamber.com
URL: http://www.mtidachamber.com/chamber_page.
htm
Contact: Phillip Carr, President
Description: Promotes business and community development in Mt. Ida, AR area. Sponsors festival. **Founded:** 1960. **Publications:** *Mount Ida Area Visitor Guide* (Annual).

48091 ■ *Mount Ida Area Visitor Guide*
PO Box 6
Mount Ida, AR 71957-0006

Ph: (870)867-2723
Co. E-mail: director@mtidachamber.com
URL: http://www.mtidachamber.com/chamber_page.
htm
Contact: Phillip Carr, President
Released: Annual

48092 ■ Mountain Home Area Chamber of Commerce
PO Box 488
Mountain Home, AR 72654-0488
Ph: (870)425-5111
Free: 800-822-3536
Fax: (870)425-4446
Co. E-mail: emajeste@enjoymountainhome.com
URL: http://enjoymountainhome.com
Contact: Eddie Majeste, Executive Director
Description: Promotes business and community development in the Mountain Home area of Baxter and Marion counties, AR. **Founded:** 1888. **Publications:** *The Spirit* (Monthly); *Three Rivers, Two Lakes...One Beautiful Life.*

48093 ■ *News Exchange*
PO Box 752
Lake Village, AR 71653
Ph: (870)265-5997
Fax: (870)265-5254
Co. E-mail: lvccdirector@sbcglobal.net
URL: http://www.lakevillagechamber.com
Contact: Lisa V. Raby, Director

48094 ■ *News & Views*
108 E University St.
Siloam Springs, AR 72761-2756
Ph: (479)524-6466
Co. E-mail: info@siloamchamber.com
URL: http://www.siloamchamber.com
Contact: Wayne Mays, President
Released: Monthly

48095 ■ North Little Rock Chamber of Commerce (NLRCC)
100 Main St.
North Little Rock, AR 72114
Ph: (501)372-5959
Fax: (501)372-5955
Co. E-mail: nlrchamber@nlrchamber.org
URL: http://www.nlrchamber.org
Contact: Terry C. Hartwick, President
Description: Promotes business and community development in North Little Rock, AR. Sponsors trade show. **Founded:** 1984. **Subscriptions:** 250000. **Publications:** *Demographic Journal* (Periodic); *Maps*; *North Little Rock, Your Metropolitan Home: Industrial and Commercial Location Factors.* **Educational Activities:** Markets North Little Rock (Annual). **Awards:** Educational Scholarships (Annual).

48096 ■ *North Little Rock, Your Metropolitan Home: Industrial and Commercial Location Factors*
100 Main St.
North Little Rock, AR 72114
Ph: (501)372-5959
Fax: (501)372-5955
Co. E-mail: nlrchamber@nlrchamber.org
URL: http://www.nlrchamber.org
Contact: Terry C. Hartwick, President

48097 ■ Osceola-South Mississippi County Chamber of Commerce
116 N Maple St.
Osceola, AR 72370-2538
Ph: (870)563-2281
Fax: (870)563-5385
Co. E-mail: osceolachamber@sbcglobal.net
URL: http://www.osceolachamber.net
Contact: Eric Golde, Executive Director
Description: Promotes business and community development in southern Mississippi County, AR. **Founded:** 1947. **Publications:** *Leader Academy.* **Educational Activities:** Osceola Junior Auxiliary Golf Tournament (Annual).

48098 ■ Ozark Area Chamber of Commerce
300 W Commercial
Ozark, AR 72949
Ph: (479)667-2525

Fax: (479)667-5750
Co. E-mail: ozarkareacoc@centurytel.net
URL: http://www.ozarkareacoc.org
Contact: Susan McIlroy-Stokes, Director
Description: Promotes business and community development in the Ozark, AR area. **Founded:** 1835.

48099 ■ Paragould Regional Chamber of Commerce
300 W Court St.
Paragould, AR 72450-4318
Ph: (870)236-7684
Fax: (870)236-7142
Co. E-mail: ceo@paragould.org
URL: http://www.paragould.org
Contact: Sue McGowan, Chief Executive Officer
Description: Promotes business and community development in the Paragould, AR area. **Founded:** 1915.

48100 ■ Paris Area Chamber of Commerce
301 W Walnut St.
Paris, AR 72855-3731
Ph: (479)963-2244
Fax: (479)963-8321
Co. E-mail: pariscoc@gmail.com
URL: http://www.parisaronline.com
Description: Promotes business and community development in northern Logan County, AR. Conducts Frontier Days Festivals and the Butterfly Festival. Participates in charitable programs. **Founded:** 1945. **Publications:** *Calendar of Events* (Monthly).

48101 ■ Prairie Grove Chamber of Commerce
PO Box 23
Prairie Grove, AR 72753
Ph: (479)846-2197
Co. E-mail: info@pgchamber.com
URL: http://www.pgchamber.com
Contact: Casey Copeland, President
Description: Promotes business and community development in Prairie Grove, AR.

48102 ■ Randolph County Chamber of Commerce
107 E Everett St.
Pocahontas, AR 72455-3310
Ph: (870)892-3956
Fax: (870)892-5399
Co. E-mail: chamber010@centurytel.net
URL: http://www.randolphchamber.com
Contact: Mr. Tim Scott, Executive Director
Description: Promotes business and community development in the Pocahontas, AR area. Conducts Agriculture Appreciation Day, Industry Appreciation Day, sports show, Christmas festival, and Veterans Day parade. **Founded:** 1856. **Publications:** *Randolph County Newsletter* (Monthly).

48103 ■ *Randolph County Newsletter*
107 E Everett St.
Pocahontas, AR 72455-3310
Ph: (870)892-3956
Fax: (870)892-5399
Co. E-mail: chamber010@centurytel.net
URL: http://www.randolphchamber.com
Contact: Mr. Tim Scott, Executive Director
Released: Monthly

48104 ■ Rector Chamber of Commerce
c/o Ms. Nancy J. Kemp, Pres.
PO Box 307
Rector, AR 72461-0307
Ph: (870)595-3549
Fax: (870)595-3611
Co. E-mail: ccd@rectorarkansas.com
URL: http://asccreg.weknowarkansas.org/chamber-execs
Contact: Ms. Nancy J. Kemp, President
Description: Promotes business and community development in Rector, AR.

48105 ■ Rogers Lowell Area Chamber of Commerce (RACC)
317 W Walnut St.
Rogers, AR 72756-4566
Ph: (479)636-1240

Fax: (479)636-5485
Co. E-mail: info@rogerslowell.com
URL: http://www.rogerslowell.com
Contact: Mr. Raymond M. Burns, President
Description: Promotes business and community development in Rogers, AR. Sponsors Air Show. **Founded:** 1921.

48106 ■ Russellville Chamber of Commerce (RCC)
708 W Main St.
Russellville, AR 72801-3617
Ph: (479)968-2530
Fax: (479)968-5894
Co. E-mail: chamber@russellville.org
URL: http://www.russellvillechamber.org
Contact: Jeff Pipkin, President
Description: Promotes business and community development in Pope County, AR. Sponsors local festivals. **Founded:** 1920. **Publications:** *Business Connection* (Monthly). **Educational Activities:** First Friday Luncheon (Monthly). **Awards:** Citizen of the Year (Annual).

48107 ■ Sherwood Chamber of Commerce (SCC)
295 W Kiehl Ave.
Sherwood, AR 72120
Ph: (501)835-7600
Fax: (501)835-2326
Co. E-mail: shwdchamber@att.net
URL: http://www.sherwoodchamber.net
Contact: Steve Cobb, President
Description: Promotes business and community development in Sherwood, AR.

48108 ■ Siloam Springs Chamber of Commerce (SSCC)
108 E University St.
Siloam Springs, AR 72761-2756
Ph: (479)524-6466
Co. E-mail: info@siloamchamber.com
URL: http://www.siloamchamber.com
Contact: Wayne Mays, President
Description: Promotes business and community development in Siloam Springs, AR. **Founded:** 1930. **Publications:** *News & Views* (Monthly).

48109 ■ *The Spirit*
PO Box 488
Mountain Home, AR 72654-0488
Ph: (870)425-5111
Free: 800-822-3536
Fax: (870)425-4446
Co. E-mail: emajeste@enjoymountainhome.com
URL: http://enjoymountainhome.com
Contact: Eddie Majeste, Executive Director
Released: Monthly

48110 ■ Spring River Area Chamber of Commerce
2852D Hwy. 62/412
Highland, AR 72542
Ph: (870)856-3210
Fax: (870)856-3320
Co. E-mail: sracc@centurytel.net
URL: http://www.sracc.com
Contact: Beth McEntire-Bess, President
Description: Represents business interests of members in Northeastern Arkansas. Enhances members' success in business through programs, benefits and services, and other business related information.

48111 ■ Springdale Chamber of Commerce (SCC)
202 W Emma Ave.
Springdale, AR 72764-4307
Ph: (479)872-2222
Free: 800-972-7261
Fax: (479)751-4699
Co. E-mail: info@springdale.com
URL: http://www.springdale.com
Contact: Perry Webb, President
Description: Promotes business and community development in Springdale, AR. **Founded:** 1946. **Publications:** *Chamber Outlook* (Semimonthly). **Edu-**

cational Activities: Business After Hours (Bimonthly). **Telecommunication Services:** info@chamber.springdale.com.

48112 ■ Stuttgart Chamber of Commerce
507 S Main St.
Stuttgart, AR 72160
Ph: (870)673-1602
Fax: (870)673-1604
Co. E-mail: stuttgartchamber@centurytel.net
URL: http://stuttgartarkansas.org
Contact: Mr. Stephen R. Bell, Executive Vice President
Description: Promotes business and community development in Stuttgart, AR. **Founded:** 1940. **Publications:** *Chamber Talk* (Monthly). **Awards:** Grant for Educators and Teachers (Annual).

48113 ■ *Taking Care of Business*
One Chamber Plz.
Little Rock, AR 72201-1618
Ph: (501)374-2001
Fax: (501)374-6018
Co. E-mail: chamber@littlerockchamber.com
URL: http://www.littlerockchamber.com/cwt/external/wcpages/index.aspx
Contact: Jay Chesshir, President
Price: free for members (first copy only); $10, additional copy for members; $20, for nonmembers.

48114 ■ *Three Rivers, Two Lakes...One Beautiful Life*
PO Box 488
Mountain Home, AR 72654-0488
Ph: (870)425-5111
Free: 800-822-3536
Fax: (870)425-4446
Co. E-mail: emajeste@enjoymountainhome.com
URL: http://enjoymountainhome.com
Contact: Eddie Majeste, Executive Director

48115 ■ Van Buren Chamber of Commerce (VBCC)
510 Main St.
Van Buren, AR 72956
Ph: (479)474-2761
Fax: (479)474-6259
Co. E-mail: jackie@vanburenchamber.org
URL: http://www.vanburenchamber.org
Contact: Jackie Krutsch, Executive Director
Description: Promotes business, tourism, and community development in Van Buren, AR. Sponsors community forums and social activities. Holds periodic board meeting. **Founded:** 1845. **Publications:** *Van Buren Today* (Monthly).

48116 ■ *Van Buren Today*
510 Main St.
Van Buren, AR 72956
Ph: (479)474-2761
Fax: (479)474-6259
Co. E-mail: jackie@vanburenchamber.org
URL: http://www.vanburenchamber.org
Contact: Jackie Krutsch, Executive Director
Released: Monthly

48117 ■ Waldron Area Chamber of Commerce
PO Box 1985
Waldron, AR 72958-1985
Ph: (479)637-2775
Co. E-mail: jbrewer3860@yahoo.com
URL: http://www.waldronareachamberofcommerce.com
Contact: Jeff Brewer, President
Description: Promotes business and community development in the Waldron, AR area. Sponsors various community activities.

48118 ■ White Hall Chamber of Commerce (WHCC)
PO Box 20429
White Hall, AR 71612-0429

Ph: (870)247-5502
Co. E-mail: whitehallchamber@gmail.com
URL: http://www.whitehallarchamber.com
Contact: Tommy Castleberry, President
Description: Promotes business and community development in White Hall, AR. **Founded:** 1983. **Awards:** Community Service Award (Annual).

48119 ■ *Who's Who in Pine Bluff Business*
c/o Ann Williams, Co-Dir.
510 S Main St.
Pine Bluff, AR 71601-4328
Ph: (870)535-0110
Fax: (870)535-1643
Co. E-mail: info@pinebluffchamber.com
URL: http://www.pinebluffchamber.com
Contact: Chris Hart, Chairman
Released: Annual **Price:** free for members.

48120 ■ **Yellville Area Chamber of Commerce**
PO Box 369
Yellville, AR 72687
Ph: (870)449-4676
Co. E-mail: chamber@yellville.com
URL: http://www.yellville.com
Description: Promotes business and community development in Yellville, AR. **Founded:** 1872.

MINORITY BUSINESS ASSISTANCE PROGRAMS

48121 ■ **Arkansas Economic Development Commission - Small and Minority Business Division**
900 W Capitol
Little Rock, AR 72201
Ph: (501)682-6105
Fax: (501)682-7394
Co. E-mail: info@arkansasedc.com
URL: http://arkansasedc.com/
Contact: Maria Haley, Executive Director
Description: Provides financial assistance, training seminars, and technical and management assistance to new and expanding minority businesses. Also refers these businesses to other organizations that offer assistance.

FINANCING AND LOAN PROGRAMS

48122 ■ **Arkansas Capital Corp.**
200 River Market Ave., Ste. 400
Little Rock, AR 72201-1766
Ph: (501)374-9247
Free: 800-216-7237
Fax: (501)374-9425
Co. E-mail: sbryan@arcapital.com
URL: http://www.arcapital.com
Contact: C. Sam Walls, III, President
Founded: 1957. **Preferred Investment Size:** $50,000 to $500,000. **Industry Preferences:** Communications and media, Internet specific, computer software and services, communications and computer hardware. **Geographic Preference:** Arkansas.

PROCUREMENT ASSISTANCE PROGRAMS

48123 ■ **Arkansas Procurement Assistance Center (APAC)**
127 W 5th St.
Malvern, AR 72104
Ph: (501)337-5355
Fax: (501)337-5045
Co. E-mail: apac@uaex.edu
URL: http://www.arcommunities.org/APAC.htm
Contact: Sue Coates, Director, Programs
E-mail: aptan@primenet.com
Description: Provide training and resources that help Arkansas businesses generate revenues and thereby create or retain jobs for Arkansans through effective government contracting.

48124 ■ **Arkansas Procurement Assistance Center - Metro Satellite - University of Arkansas - Cooperative Extension Service**
2301 S University Ave., Rm. 110
Little Rock, AR 72203
Ph: (501)671-2390
Fax: (501)671-2394
Co. E-mail: apac@uaex.edu
URL: http://www.arcommunities.org/apac.htm
Contact: Delbert Taylor, Assistant
E-mail: dtaylor@uaex.edu
Description: Provide training and resources that help Arkansas businesses generate revenues and thereby create or retain jobs for Arkansans through effective government contracting.

48125 ■ **Arkansas Procurement Technical Assistance Center - Satellite Office**
2301 S University
Little Rock, AR 72203
Ph: (501)671-2390
Fax: (501)671-2394
Co. E-mail: apac@uaex.edu
URL: http://www.arcommunities.org
Contact: Delbert Taylor, Counselor
Description: Serves Arkansas businesses in all 75 counties at no charge from the main office in Malvern, supported by a fully staffed satellite office in Little Rock.

INCUBATORS/RESEARCH AND TECHNOLOGY PARKS

48126 ■ **Arkansas Biotechnology Incubator - Biomedical Biotechnology Center**
4301 W Markham St.
Little Rock, AR 72205
Ph: (501)686-6696
Fax: (501)686-8501
Co. E-mail: biotech@uams.edu
URL: http://www.uamsbiotech.com
Contact: Amanda Stephens, Specialist
Description: The BBC was established to promote Arkansas' biotechnology. The Center seeks to support technology transfer and startup company development as well as forge alliances between industry and research institutions.

48127 ■ **BioVentures**
University of Arkansas for Medical Sciences
4301 W Markham St.
Little Rock, AR 72205
Ph: (501)686-6696
Fax: (501)686-8501
Co. E-mail: biotech@uams.edu
URL: http://www.uams.edu/bioventures/
Description: A formal outgrowth of the University of Arkansas for Medical Sciences, established to maximize global and industrial interaction with the University of Arkansas faculty, as well as to facilitate technology transfer, the creation of startup companies that are based on UAMS technology, and contributions to Arkansas' economic development.

48128 ■ **Genesis Technology Incubator**
Engineering Research Center
University of Arkansas
700 Research Center Blvd.
Fayetteville, AR 72701
Ph: (479)575-7227
Fax: (479)575-7446
Co. E-mail: awrc@uark.edu
URL: http://www.genesis.uark.edu/ua/artp/facilities/genesis.html
Contact: Phillip Stafford, Director
Description: GENESIS provides office space and shared services to technology-based entrepreneurs, enhanced by the resources of the University of Arkansas.

LEGISLATIVE ASSISTANCE

48129 ■ **Arkansas House and Senate Committees on Insurance and Commerce**
State Capitol Bldg, Rm. 315
Little Rock, AR 72201
Ph: (501)682-1937
Fax: (501)682-1936
URL: http://www.arkleg.state.ar.us

PUBLICATIONS

48130 ■ *Arkansas Business*
201 E. Markham, Ste. 220
Little Rock, AR 72201-1651
Ph: (501)372-1443
Fax: (501)375-0933
Co. E-mail: abnews@abnews.com
URL: http://www.arkansasbusiness.com

48131 ■ *Starting and Operating a Business in Arkansas: A Step-by-Step Guide*
PSI Research
300 N. Valley Dr.
Grants Pass, OR 97526
Ph: (503)479-9464
Free: 800-228-2275
Fax: (503)476-1479
Co. E-mail: psi2@magick.net
Ed: Michael D. Jenkins. **Released:** Revised edition, 1992. **Price:** $29.95 (looseleaf binder); $24.95 (paper). **Description:** Part of the Successful Business Library series.

SMALL BUSINESS DEVELOPMENT CENTERS

48132 ■ Alameda County Small Business Development Center
1330 Broadway, Ste. 705
Oakland, CA 94612
Ph: (510)208-0410
Fax: (510)208-0413
URL: http://www.acsbdc.org
Contact: Rick Ohlrich, Director
Description: Represents and promotes the small business sector. Provides management assistance to current and prospective small business owners. Helps to improve management skills and expand the products and services of members.

48133 ■ Alameda Small Business Development Center
1330 Broadway, Ste. 705
Oakland, CA 94612
Ph: (510)208-0410
Fax: (510)208-0413
Co. E-mail: rick@acsbdc.org
URL: http://acsbdc.org
Contact: Rick Ohlrich, Director
Description: Represents and promotes the small business sector. Provides management assistance to current and prospective small business owners. Helps to improve management skills and expand the products and services of members.

48134 ■ Alliance Small Business Development Center
1020 10th St., Ste. 102
Modesto, CA 95354
Ph: (209)567-4910
Fax: (209)567-4955
Co. E-mail: genovaja@stanalliance.com
URL: http://www.alliancesbdc.com
Contact: Kurtis Clark, Director
Description: Represents and promotes the small business sector. Provides management assistance to current and prospective small business owners. Helps to improve management skills and expand the products and services of members.

48135 ■ Alliance Small Business Development Center - Mariposa
5078 Bullion St.
Mariposa, CA 95338
Ph: (209)386-1008
Fax: (209)381-6552
URL: http://www.alliancesbdc.com
Contact: Bill Andersen, Assistant Director
URL(s): sbdc.ucmerced.edu/contact-us/service-centers. **Description:** Represents and promotes the small business sector. Provides management assistance to current and prospective small business owners. Helps to improve management skills and expand the products and services of members.

48136 ■ Alliance Small Business Development Center - Merced
1810 K St.
Merced, CA 95340
Ph: (209)386-1008
Fax: (209)381-6552
Co. E-mail: genovaja@stanalliance.com
URL: http://www.alliancesbdc.com
Contact: William Anderson, Manager
URL(s): sbdc.ucmerced.edu/contact-us/service-centers. **Description:** Represents and promotes the small business sector. Provides management assistance to current and prospective small business owners. Helps to improve management skills and expand the products and services of members.

48137 ■ Alpine County Small Business Development Center
PO Box 265
Markleeville, CA 96120
Ph: (530)694-2475
Fax: (530)694-2478
Co. E-mail: alpcntv@powernet.net
URL: http://www.sbdc.deltacollege.edu
Description: Represents and promotes the small business sector. Provides management assistance to current and prospective small business owners. Helps to improve management skills and expand the products and services of members.

48138 ■ Amador County Small Business Development Center
PO Box 1077
Jackson, CA 95642
Ph: (530)223-0351
Fax: (530)223-2261
Co. E-mail: aedc@cdepot.net
URL: http://www.sbdc.deltacollege.edu
Description: Represents and promotes the small business sector. Provides management assistance to current and prospective small business owners. Helps to improve management skills and expand the products and services of members.

48139 ■ Butte College Small Business Development Center
19 Williamsburg Ln.
Chico, CA 95928
Ph: (530)895-9017
Fax: (530)566-9851
Co. E-mail: konuwaso@butte.edu
URL: http://www.bcsbdc.org
Contact: Sophie Konuwa, Director
Description: Represents and promotes the small business sector. Provides management assistance to current and prospective small business owners. Helps to improve management skills and expand the products and services of members.

48140 ■ Calaveras County Small Business Development Center
700 Mountain Ranch Rd., Ste. A
San Andreas, CA 95249
Ph: (209)754-9791

Fax: (209)754-9792
URL: http://www.sbdc.deltacollege.edu
Description: Represents and promotes the small business sector. Provides management assistance to current and prospective small business owners. Helps to improve management skills and expand the products and services of members.

48141 ■ Central California Small Business Development Center - Fresno
Manchester Center
3302 N Blackstone Ave., Ste. 225
Fresno, CA 93726
Ph: (559)230-4056
Co. E-mail: info@ccsbdc.org
URL: http://www.ccsbdc.org
Description: Represents and promotes the small business sector. Provides management assistance to current and prospective small business owners. Helps to improve management skills and expand the products and services of members.

48142 ■ Central California Small Business Development Center - Visalia
PO Box 787
Visalia, CA 93279
Ph: (559)625-3051
URL: http://www.ccsbdc.org
Contact: Gil Jaramillo, Manager
Description: Represents and promotes the small business sector. Provides management assistance to current and prospective small business owners. Helps to improve management skills and expand the products and services of members.

48143 ■ Central Coast Small Business Development Center
Cabrillo College
6500 Soquel Dr.
Aptos, CA 95003
Ph: (831)479-6136
Fax: (831)479-6166
Co. E-mail: sbdc@cabrillo.edu
URL: http://centralcoastsbdc.org
Description: Represents and promotes the small business sector. Provides management assistance to current and prospective small business owners. Helps to improve management skills and expand the products and services of members.

48144 ■ CHARO Small Business Development Center
4301 E Valley Blvd.
Los Angeles, CA 90032
Ph: (323)269-0751
Co. E-mail: dgmorales@charocorp.com
URL: http://www.smallbusinesscalifornia.org/sbdc.htm
Description: Represents and promotes the small business sector. Provides management assistance to current and prospective small business owners. Helps to improve management skills and expand the products and services of members.

48145 ■ Coachella Valley Small Business Development Center
500 S Palm Canyon Dr., Ste. 222
Palm Springs, CA 92264
Ph: (760)864-1311
Fax: (760)864-1319
URL: http://www.leadsbdc.org/
?cat=9&lang=en&title=Locations
Description: Represents and promotes the small business sector. Provides management assistance to current and prospective small business owners. Helps to improve management skills and expand the products and services of members.

48146 ■ College of the Canyons Small Business Development Center
26455 Rockwell Canyon Rd.
Santa Clarita, CA 91355
Ph: (661)362-5900
Fax: (661)362-5596
Co. E-mail: steven.tannehill@canyons.edu
URL: http://www.sbdc4biz.org
Contact: Steve Tannehill, Director
Description: Represents and promotes the small business sector. Provides management assistance to current and prospective small business owners. Helps to improve management skills and expand the products and services of members.

48147 ■ Contra Costa Small Business Development Center (CCSBDC)
300 Ellinwood Way, No. 300
Pleasant Hill, CA 94523
Ph: (925)602-6840
Fax: (925)602-6842
Co. E-mail: bhamile@contracostasbdc.com
URL: http://www.contracostasbdc.com
Contact: Beverly Hamile, Director
Description: Represents and promotes the small business sector. Provides management assistance to current and prospective small business owners. Helps to improve management skills and expand the products and services of members.

48148 ■ Cuesta College Small Business Development Center
3211 Broad St., Ste. 109
San Luis Obispo, CA 93401
Ph: (805)549-0401
URL: http://www.ci.san-luis-obispo.ca.us/econom-icdevelopment/businessresources.asp
Description: Represents and promotes the small business sector. Provides management assistance to current and prospective small business owners. Helps to improve management skills and expand the products and services of members.

48149 ■ El Camino College Small Business Development Center
13430 Hawthorne Blvd.
Hawthorne, CA 90250
Ph: (310)973-3177
Fax: (310)973-3132
Co. E-mail: svanburen@elcamino.edu
URL: http://www.elcamino.edu/commadv/sbdc
Contact: Star Van Buren, Director
Description: Represents and promotes the small business sector. Provides management assistance to current and prospective small business owners. Helps to improve management skills and expand the products and services of members.

48150 ■ Gavilan Small Business Development Center
8351 Church St., Bldg. E
Gilroy, CA 95020
Ph: (408)847-0373
Free: 800-847-0373
URL: http://www.gavilan.edu/catalog/2005_2007/community.html#98
Description: Represents and promotes the small business sector. Provides management assistance to current and prospective small business owners. Helps to improve management skills and expand the products and services of members.

48151 ■ Imperial Valley Small Business Development Center at Imperial Valley College
301 N Imperial Ave., Ste. B
El Centro, CA 92243
Ph: (760)312-9800
Fax: (760)312-9838
Co. E-mail: greza@swccd.edu
URL: http://www.ivsbdc.org.php5-4.dfw1-1.web-sitetestlink.com/index.php
Contact: Gustavo Reza, Director
Description: Represents and promotes the small business sector. Provides management assistance to current and prospective small business owners. Helps to improve management skills and expand the products and services of members.

48152 ■ Inland Empire North Small Business Development Center
15490 Civic Dr., Ste. 102
Victorville, CA 92392
Ph: (760)951-1592
Fax: (760)951-8929
Co. E-mail: kgerke@iesmallbusiness.com
URL: http://www.leadsbdc.org
URL(s): www.iesmallbusiness.com. **Description:** Represents and promotes the small business sector. Provides management assistance to current and prospective small business owners. Helps to improve management skills and expand the products and services of members.

48153 ■ Inland Empire Small Business Development Center (IESBDC)
603 N Euclid Ave.
Ontario, CA 91762
Ph: (909)983-5005
Fax: (909)983-5515
Co. E-mail: rusher@iesmallbusiness.com
URL: http://www.iesbdc.org
Contact: Vincent McCoy, Executive Director

48154 ■ Lake County Small Business Development Center
55 First St.
Lakeport, CA 95453
Ph: (707)263-0330
URL: http://www.yubasbdc.org/Lake-County-SBDC.asp
Description: Represents and promotes the small business sector. Provides management assistance to current and prospective small business owners. Helps to improve management skills and expand the products and services of members.

48155 ■ Long Beach City College Small Business Development Center
3447 Atlantic Ave., Ste. 205
Long Beach, CA 90807
Ph: (562)570-4574
Fax: (562)570-4575
Co. E-mail: sbdcinfo@lbcc.edu
URL: http://lbsbdc.lbcc.edu
Description: Represents and promotes the small business sector. Provides management assistance to current and prospective small business owners. Helps to improve management skills and expand the products and services of members.

48156 ■ Los Angeles Small Business Development Center Network (LA SBDC)
4040 Paramount Blvd., Ste. 107
Lakewood, CA 90712
Ph: (562)938-5020
Free: 866-270-2444
URL: http://lasbdcnet.lbcc.edu
Contact: James Alva, Manager
Description: Represents and promotes the small business sector. Provides management assistance to current and prospective small business owners. Helps to improve management skills and expand the products and services of members.

48157 ■ Loyola Marymount University Small Business Development Center
1 LMU Dr.
Los Angeles, CA 90045

Ph: (310)338-2700
URL: http://www.lmu.edu
Description: Represents and promotes the small business sector. Provides management assistance to current and prospective small business owners. Helps to improve management skills and expand the products and services of members.

48158 ■ Mendocino Small Business Development Center
760B Stewart St.
Fort Bragg, CA 95437
Ph: (707)964-7571
Free: 866-604-9378
Fax: (707)964-7576
URL: http://www.westcompany.org
Contact: Pamela Patterson, Chief Executive Officer
Description: Represents and promotes the small business sector. Provides management assistance to current and prospective small business owners. Helps to improve management skills and expand the products and services of members.

48159 ■ Moreno Valley Small Business Development Center
12625 Frederick St., Ste. V-1
Moreno Valley, CA 92553
Ph: (909)888-9011
Fax: (909)888-9074
URL: http://www.leadsbdc.org
Description: Represents and promotes the small business sector. Provides management assistance to current and prospective small business owners. Helps to improve management skills and expand the products and services of members.

48160 ■ Napa Valley College Small Business Development Center
1556 First St., Ste. 103
Napa, CA 94559
Ph: (707)253-3210
Fax: (707)253-3068
Co. E-mail: vbible@napavalley.edu
URL: http://www.napasbdc.org
Description: Represents and promotes the small business sector. Provides management assistance to current and prospective small business owners. Helps to improve management skills and expand the products and services of members.

48161 ■ North San Diego Small Business Development Center
Mira Costa College
1823 Mission Ave.
Oceanside, CA 92054
Ph: (760)795-8740
Fax: (760)795-8728
Co. E-mail: centerinfo@miracosta.edu
URL: http://www.sandiegosmallbiz.com
Description: Represents and promotes the small business sector. Provides management assistance to current and prospective small business owners. Helps to improve management skills and expand the products and services of members.

48162 ■ Northcoast Small Business Development Center - Del Norte
225 H St.
Crescent City, CA 95531
Ph: (707)464-2168
Fax: (707)464-1349
Co. E-mail: burke@northcoastsbdc.org
URL: http://www.northcoastsbdc.org
Description: Represents and promotes the small business sector. Provides management assistance to current and prospective small business owners. Helps to improve management skills and expand the products and services of members.

48163 ■ Northcoast Small Business Development Center - Humboldt
Prosperity Center
520 E St.
Eureka, CA 95501
Ph: (707)445-9720
Free: 800-697-7232

Fax: (707)445-9652
URL: http://www.northcoastsbdc.org
Description: Represents and promotes the small business sector. Provides management assistance to current and prospective small business owners. Helps to improve management skills and expand the products and services of members.

48164 ■ Northern California Small Business Development Center
Humboldt State University
1 Harpst St., House 71
Arcata, CA 95521
Ph: (707)826-3919
Fax: (707)826-3912
Co. E-mail: kristin.johnson@humboldt.edu
URL: http://www.norcalsbdc.org
Contact: Kristin Johnson, Director
Description: Represents and promotes the small business sector. Provides management assistance to current and prospective small business owners. Helps to improve management skills and expand the products and services of members.

48165 ■ Orange County Small Business Development Center
2323 N Broadway, Ste. 201
Santa Ana, CA 92706
Ph: (714)564-5200
Fax: (714)647-1168
Co. E-mail: oc_sbdc@rsccd.org
URL: http://www.ocsbdc.com
Contact: Leila Mozaffari, Director

48166 ■ Redwood Empire Small Business Development Center
Santa Rosa Junior College
1808 Albany Dr.
Santa Rosa, CA 95401
Ph: (707)524-1770
Free: 888-346-SBDC
Fax: (707)524-1772
Co. E-mail: lduvernay@santarosa.edu
URL: http://sbdcsantarosa.org
Contact: Lorraine DuVernay, Director
Description: Represents and promotes the small business sector. Provides management assistance to current and prospective small business owners. Helps to improve management skills and expand the products and services of members.

48167 ■ San Francisco Small Business Development Center
City College of San Francisco
300 Montgomery St., Ste. 789
San Francisco, CA 94104
Ph: (415)841-4050
Fax: (415)398-4589
Co. E-mail: al@sfsbdc.org
URL: http://sf.norcalsbdc.org
Contact: Al Dixon, Director
Description: Represents and promotes the small business sector. Provides management assistance to current and prospective small business owners. Helps to improve management skills and expand the products and services of members.

48168 ■ San Joaquin Delta College Small Business Development Center
56 S Lincoln St.
Stockton, CA 95203
Ph: (209)954-5089
Fax: (209)939-0385
Co. E-mail: gmurphy@deltacollege.edu
URL: http://www.sbdc.deltacollege.edu
Contact: Gillian Murphy, Director
Description: Represents and promotes the small business sector. Provides management assistance to current and prospective small business owners. Helps to improve management skills and expand the products and services of members.

48169 ■ Santa Ana Regional Lead Small Business Development Center
California State University, Fullerton
800 N State College Blvd.
Fullerton, CA 92834

Ph: (714)278-2719
URL: http://www.leadsbdc.org
Contact: Adalberto Quijada, Director
Description: Represents and promotes the small business sector. Provides management assistance to current and prospective small business owners. Helps to improve management skills and expand the products and services of members.

48170 ■ Santa Monica College Small Business Development Center
1900 Pico Blvd.
Santa Monica, CA 90405
Ph: (310)434-3566
Fax: (310)434-3891
URL: http://www.smc.edu/sbdc
Contact: Michelle King, Director
Description: Represents and promotes the small business sector. Provides management assistance to current and prospective small business owners. Helps to improve management skills and expand the products and services of members.

48171 ■ Silicon Valley Small Business Development Center at West Valley/Mission College
100 E Santa Clara St., 1st Fl.
San Jose, CA 95113-1901
Ph: (408)351-3600
URL: http://www.siliconvalley-sbdc.org
Contact: Patrick Cook, Director
Description: Represents and promotes the small business sector. Provides management assistance to current and prospective small business owners. Helps to improve management skills and expand the products and services of members.

48172 ■ Small Business Development Center - Greater Sacramento
1410 Ethan Way
Sacramento, CA 95825-2205
Ph: (916)563-3210
Fax: (916)563-3266
Co. E-mail: info@sbdc.net
URL: http://www.sbdc.net
Contact: Panda Morgan, Director
Description: Represents and promotes the small business sector. Provides management assistance to current and prospective small business owners. Helps to improve management skills and expand the products and services of members.

48173 ■ Small Business Development Center at Shasta College
2990 Innsbruck Dr.
Redding, CA 96003
Ph: (530)242-7630
Fax: (530)222-8582
Co. E-mail: kanthis@sbdcsc.org
URL: http://www.sbdcsc.org
Contact: Keli Anthis, Director
Description: Represents and promotes the small business sector. Provides management assistance to current and prospective small business owners. Helps to improve management skills and expand the products and services of members.

48174 ■ Solano College Small Business Development Center
360 Campus Ln., Ste. 102
Fairfield, CA 94534
Ph: (707)864-3382
Fax: (707)864-8025
Co. E-mail: charles.eason@solano.edu
URL: http://www.solanosbdc.org
Contact: Charles Eason, Director
Description: Represents and promotes the small business sector. Provides management assistance to current and prospective small business owners. Helps to improve management skills and expand the products and services of members.

48175 ■ TriTech Small Business Development Center
111 Academy Way, Ste. 100
Irvine, CA 92617

Ph: (949)734-5635
Co. E-mail: tritech@rcc.edu
URL: http://www.leadsbdc.org
URL(s): www.tritechsbdc.com. **Description:** Represents and promotes the small business sector. Provides management assistance to current and prospective small business owners. Helps to improve management skills and expand the products and services of members.

48176 ■ UC Merced Small Business Development Center Regional Network
550 E Shaw Ave., Ste. 100
Fresno, CA 93710
Ph: (559)241-7406
Free: 877-826-7232
Fax: (559)241-7422
Co. E-mail: casbdc@ucmerced.edu
URL: http://sbdc.ucmerced.edu
Contact: Diane R. Howerton, Director
Description: Represents and promotes the small business sector. Provides management assistance to current and prospective small business owners. Helps to improve management skills and expand the products and services of members.

48177 ■ Ventura College Small Business Development Center
71 Day Rd.
Ventura, CA 93003
Ph: (805)648-8925
Fax: (805)648-8965
Co. E-mail: bwalker@vcccd.net
URL: http://www.vcsbdc.com
Contact: Becki Walker, Director
URL(s): lasbdcnet.lbcc.edu/ventura.html. **Description:** Represents and promotes the small business sector. Provides management assistance to current and prospective small business owners. Helps to improve management skills and expand the products and services of members.

48178 ■ Weill Institute Small Business Development Center at Bakersfield College
2100 Chester Ave., 1st Fl.
Bakersfield, CA 93301
Ph: (661)395-4126
Description: Represents and promotes the small business sector. Provides management assistance to current and prospective small business owners. Helps to improve management skills and expand the products and services of members.

48179 ■ Woodland Small Business Development Center
307 First St.
Woodland, CA 95695
Ph: (530)822-0140
Fax: (530)822-0163
URL: http://www.yubasbdc.org/Woodland-SBDC.asp
Description: Represents and promotes the small business sector. Provides management assistance to current and prospective small business owners. Helps to improve management skills and expand the products and services of members.

48180 ■ Yuba Community College District Small Business Development Center
1227 Bridge St., Ste. C
Yuba City, CA 95991
Ph: (530)822-0140
Fax: (530)822-0163
URL: http://www.yubasbdc.org
Contact: Ken Freeman, Director
Description: Represents and promotes the small business sector. Provides management assistance to current and prospective small business owners. Helps to improve management skills and expand the products and services of members.

SCORE OFFICES

48181 ■ Bakersfield SCORE
Co. E-mail: scorebakersfield@yahoo.com

48182 ■ Central Coast SCORE
Co. E-mail: score491@best1.net

48183 ■ Central Valley SCORE

48184 ■ Chico SCORE
Co. E-mail: scorechico@sbcglobal.net

48185 ■ Coachella Valley SCORE
Co. E-mail: info@scorecv.org

48186 ■ Redding SCORE
Co. E-mail: reddingscore@gmail.com

48187 ■ Santa Cruz County SCORE
Co. E-mail: info@scsscore.com

BETTER BUSINESS BUREAUS

48188 ■ Better Business Bureau (BBB)
11 S San Joaquin St., Ste. 803
Stockton, CA 95202-3202
Ph: (209)948-4880
Free: 800-948-4880
Fax: (209)465-6302
Co. E-mail: info@midcalbbb.org
URL: http://midcal.bbb.org
Contact: Frank K. Whitney, President
Description: Marketplace protection agency engaged in promoting the business interest of their members, as well as helping consumers with the various problems that occur daily. **Founded:** 1928. **Subscriptions:** articles video recordings. **Publications:** *The Business Standard* (Monthly). **Awards:** International Torch Award (Annual).

48189 ■ Better Business Bureau (BBB)
1000 Broadway, Ste. 625
Oakland, CA 94607-4042
Ph: (510)844-2000
Free: 866-411-2221
Fax: (510)844-2100
Co. E-mail: info@bbbemail.org
URL: http://www.oakland.bbb.org
Contact: Gene O'Neil, President
Description: Seeks to promote and foster ethical relationship between businesses and the public through voluntary self-regulation, consumer and business education, and service excellence. Provides information to help consumers and businesses make informed purchasing decisions and avoid costly scams and frauds; settles consumer complaints through arbitration and other means. **Founded:** 1912.

48190 ■ Better Business Bureau of Central California
4201 W Shaw Ave., Ste. 107
Fresno, CA 93722
Ph: (559)222-8111
Fax: (559)228-6518
Co. E-mail: info@bbbcencal.org
URL: http://cencal.bbb.org
Contact: Doug Broten, Chief Executive Officer
Description: Seeks to promote and foster ethical relationship between businesses and the public through voluntary self-regulation, consumer and business education, and service excellence. Provides information to help consumers and businesses make informed purchasing decisions and avoid costly scams and frauds; settles consumer complaints through arbitration and other means.

48191 ■ Better Business Bureau of Northeast California
3075 Beacon Blvd.
West Sacramento, CA 95691
Ph: (916)443-6843
Fax: (916)443-0376
Co. E-mail: info@necal.bbb.org
URL: http://necal.bbb.org
Contact: Gary Almond, President
Description: Seeks to promote and foster ethical relationship between businesses and the public through voluntary self-regulation, consumer and business education, and service excellence. Provides information to help consumers and businesses make informed purchasing decisions and avoid costly scams and frauds; settles consumer complaints through arbitration and other means. **Founded:** 1937.

48192 ■ Better Business Bureau of San Diego
5050 Murphy Canyon Rd., Ste. 110
San Diego, CA 92123

Ph: (858)496-2131
Fax: (858)496-2141
Co. E-mail: info@sandiego.bbb.org
URL: http://www.sandiego.bbb.org
Contact: Sheryl Bilbrey, President
Description: Seeks to promote and foster ethical relationship between businesses and the public through voluntary self-regulation, consumer and business education, and service excellence. Provides information to help consumers and businesses make informed purchasing decisions and avoid costly scams and frauds; settles consumer complaints through arbitration and other means. **Publications:** *Consumer Guide* (Semiannual); *Consumer Guide* (Semiannual).

48193 ■ Better Business Bureau of San Mateo County
1000 Broadway, Ste. 625
Millbrae, CA 94030-1966
Ph: (510)844-2000
Free: 866-411-2221
Fax: (510)844-2100
Co. E-mail: info@bbbemail.org
URL: http://goldengate.bbb.org
Description: Seeks to promote and foster ethical relationship between businesses and the public through voluntary self-regulation, consumer and business education, and service excellence. Provides information to help consumers and businesses make informed purchasing decisions and avoid costly scams and frauds; settles consumer complaints through arbitration and other means.

48194 ■ Better Business Bureau of Silicon Valley
1112 S Bascom Ave.
San Jose, CA 95128-4705
Ph: (408)278-7400
Fax: (408)278-7444
Co. E-mail: info@bbbsilicon.org
URL: http://sanjose.bbb.org
Description: Seeks to promote and foster the highest ethical relationship between businesses and the public through voluntary self-regulation, consumer and business education, and service excellence. Provides information to help consumers and businesses make informed purchasing decisions and avoid costly scams and frauds; settles consumer complaints through arbitration and other means. **Founded:** 1912.

48195 ■ Better Business Bureau of the Southland
315 N La Cadena Dr.
Colton, CA 92324
Ph: (909)825-7280
Fax: (909)825-6246
URL: http://los-angeles.bbb.org
Contact: William G. Mitchell, President
Description: Seeks to promote and foster the ethical relationship between businesses and the public through voluntary self-regulation, consumer and business education, and service excellence. Provides information to help consumers and businesses make informed purchasing decisions and avoid costly scams and frauds; settles consumer complaints through arbitration and other means.

48196 ■ Better Business Bureau of Tri-Counties
PO Box 129
Santa Barbara, CA 93102
Ph: (805)963-8657
Fax: (805)962-8557
URL: http://www.santabarbara.bbb.org
Contact: Rick Copelan, President
Description: Seeks to promote and foster ethical relationship between businesses and the public through voluntary self-regulation, consumer and business education, and service excellence. Provides information to help consumers and businesses make informed purchasing decisions and avoid costly scams and frauds; settles consumer complaints through arbitration and other means. **Founded:** 1945.

48197 ■ *The Business Standard*
11 S San Joaquin St., Ste. 803
Stockton, CA 95202-3202

Ph: (209)948-4880
Free: 800-948-4880
Fax: (209)465-6302
Co. E-mail: info@midcalbbb.org
URL: http://midcal.bbb.org
Contact: Frank K. Whitney, President
Released: Monthly

48198 ■ *Consumer Guide*
5050 Murphy Canyon Rd., Ste. 110
San Diego, CA 92123
Ph: (858)496-2131
Fax: (858)496-2141
Co. E-mail: info@sandiego.bbb.org
URL: http://www.sandiego.bbb.org
Contact: Sheryl Bilbrey, President
Released: Semiannual

CHAMBERS OF COMMERCE

48199 ■ *The Acorn*
1100 Merrill St.
Menlo Park, CA 94025-4386
Ph: (650)325-2818
Fax: (650)325-0920
Co. E-mail: info@menloparkchamber.com
URL: http://www.menloparkchamber.com
Contact: Fran Dehn, President
Released: Monthly **Price:** $12, /year.

48200 ■ *Action*
30 Ragsdale Dr., Ste. 200
Monterey, CA 93940
Ph: (831)648-5360
Fax: (831)649-3502
Co. E-mail: info@mpcc.com
URL: http://www.mpcc.com
Contact: Jody Hansen, President
Released: Monthly

48201 ■ Acton Chamber of Commerce
32039 N Crown Valley Rd.
Acton, CA 93510
Ph: (661)269-5785
Fax: (661)269-4121
Co. E-mail: actoncoc@antelecom.net
URL: http://cityofacton.org
Contact: Jim Schutte, President
URL(s): www.actoncoc.org. **Description:** Promotes Acton and its trade areas through educational, economic, legislative, civic, social and cultural programs and affairs. **Founded:** 1954.

48202 ■ *Advocate*
700 W 1st St.
Tustin, CA 92780
Ph: (714)544-5341
Fax: (714)544-2083
Co. E-mail: info@tustinchamber.org
URL: http://tustinchamber.org
Contact: Sherri Munsey, Executive Director
Released:

48203 ■ Agoura - Oak Park - Las Virgenes Chamber of Commerce
30101 Agoura Ct., Ste. 207
Agoura Hills, CA 91301
Ph: (818)889-3150
Fax: (818)889-3366
Co. E-mail: info@agourachamber.org
URL: http://www.agourachamber.org
Contact: Louis Masry, President

Description: Business owners and individuals. Works together to advance the commercial, financial, industrial, and civic interests of the community. **Awards:** Masry Award for Integrity in Community Service.

48204 ■ Alameda Chamber of Commerce
2210-D S Shore Ctr.
Alameda, CA 94501
Ph: (510)522-0414

Fax: (510)522-7677
Co. E-mail: connect@alamedachamber.com
URL: http://www.alamedachamber.com
Contact: Dennis Eloe, President
Description: Promotes business and community development in Alameda, CA. **Founded:** 1929. **Publications:** *Business Alameda Style* (Monthly). **Telecommunication Services:** alameda@alamedachamber.com.

48205 ■ Albany Chamber of Commerce
1108 Solano Ave.
Albany, CA 94706
Ph: (510)525-1771
Fax: (510)525-6068
URL: http://www.albanychamber.org
Contact: Joey Luera, President
Description: Works to maintain a terrific business climate in Albany, to represent and assist members, and help build a better community for everyone. **Founded:** 1920.

48206 ■ *Alert*
Released: Weekly; during legislative session. **Price:** included in membership dues.

48207 ■ Alhambra Chamber of Commerce
104 S 1st St.
Alhambra, CA 91801
Ph: (626)282-8481
Fax: (626)282-5596
Co. E-mail: ihernandez@alhambrachamber.org
URL: http://www.alhambrachamber.org
Contact: Mark Paulson, President
URL(s): alhambrachamber.org. **Description:** Works to encourage a strong local economy by promoting sound government and an informed membership and community. **Founded:** 1904. **Publications:** *Alhambra Chamber of Commerce--Membership Directory* (Semiannual); *Around Alhambra* (Monthly). **Educational Activities:** Business After Hours Mixers (Monthly). **Awards:** Alahambra Beautiful Award. **Telecommunication Services:** alhambrachamber@yahoo.com; alhambrachamber@sbcglobal.net.

48208 ■ *All About Folsom Business*
200 Wool St.
Folsom, CA 95630
Ph: (916)985-2698
Fax: (916)985-4117
Co. E-mail: reception@folsomchamber.com
URL: http://www.folsomchamber.com
Contact: Joseph P. Gagliardi, President
Released: Monthly

48209 ■ Alpine County Chamber of Commerce
PO Box 265
Markleeville, CA 96120
Ph: (530)694-2475
Fax: (530)694-2478
Co. E-mail: info@alpinecounty.com
URL: http://www.alpinecounty.com
Contact: Teresa Burkhauser, Executive Director
Description: Promotes business and community development in Alpine County, CA. Sponsors charitable events. **Founded:** 1964.

48210 ■ Alpine and Mountain Empire Chamber of Commerce
2157 Alpine Blvd.
Alpine, CA 91901
Ph: (619)445-2722
Fax: (619)445-2871
Co. E-mail: alpinechamber@att.net
URL: http://www.alpinechamber.com
Description: Works to advance the commercial, industrial, civic, agricultural, and general interest and prosperity of the community of Alpine and the East County region. **Founded:** 1961.

48211 ■ Altadena Chamber of Commerce (ACC)
Altadena Community Center Bldg.
730 E Altadena Dr.
Altadena, CA 91001
Ph: (626)794-3988

Fax: (626)794-6015
Co. E-mail: office@altadenachamber.org
URL: http://www.altadenachamber.org
Contact: Inger Miller, President
Description: Promotes commercial, industrial, civic, and general interests of the community of Altadena and its trade area. **Founded:** 1924. **Publications:** *Altadena: Between Wilderness and City.* **Awards:** Citizen of the Year (Annual).

48212 ■ Alturas Chamber of Commerce
600 S Main St.
Alturas, CA 96101
Ph: (530)233-4434
Co. E-mail: contactus@alturaschamber.org
URL: http://www.alturaschamber.org
Description: Promotes business and community development in the Modoc County, CA area. **Founded:** 1992.

48213 ■ Amador County Chamber of Commerce and Visitors Bureau
PO Box 596
Jackson, CA 95642-0596
Ph: (209)223-0350
Co. E-mail: gold49@amadorcountychamber.com
URL: http://www.amadorcountychamber.com
Contact: Mark Borchin, President
Description: Promotes business and community development in Amador County, CA. **Publications:** *Chamber News* (Monthly). **Educational Activities:** Mixers (Monthly).

48214 ■ *Anaheim Business Advocate*
201 E Center St.
Anaheim, CA 92805
Ph: (714)758-0222
Fax: (714)758-0468
Co. E-mail: info@anaheimchamber.org
URL: http://www.anaheimchamber.org
Contact: Ben Seybold, Chairman
Released: Monthly

48215 ■ Anaheim Chamber of Commerce
201 E Center St.
Anaheim, CA 92805
Ph: (714)758-0222
Fax: (714)758-0468
Co. E-mail: info@anaheimchamber.org
URL: http://www.anaheimchamber.org
Contact: Ben Seybold, Chairman
Description: Works to promote and support healthy diverse and broad-based economic growth in Anaheim. **Founded:** 1895. **Publications:** *Anaheim Business Advocate* (Monthly).

48216 ■ Anderson Valley Chamber of Commerce
PO Box 275
Boonville, CA 95415
Ph: (707)895-2379
Co. E-mail: info@andersonvalleychamber.com
URL: http://www.andersonvalleychamber.com
Description: Promotes business and community development in the Anderson Valley, CA.

48217 ■ Angwin Community Council
PO Box 747
Angwin, CA 94508
Ph: (707)965-2867
Co. E-mail: jenniferk@angwincouncil.org
URL: http://www.angwincouncil.org
Contact: Jennifer Klingbeil, President
Description: Provides community service and representation to Angwin village and its citizen.

48218 ■ *Annual Business Directory*
109 N 19th St.
Montebello, CA 90640
Ph: (323)721-1153
Fax: (323)721-7946
Co. E-mail: andrea@montebellochamber.org
URL: http://www.montebellochamber.org
Contact: Andrea Wagg, President
Released: Annual

48219 ■ Antelope Highlands Chamber of Commerce
PO Box 20
North Highlands, CA 95660
Ph: (916)725-5652
Contact: Keith Weber, President
Description: Promotes business and community development in North Highlands, CA.

48220 ■ Antelope Valley Board of Trade (AVBOT)
548 W Lancaster Blvd., Ste. 103
Lancaster, CA 93534-2534
Ph: (661)942-9581
Fax: (661)723-9279
Co. E-mail: info@avbot.org
URL: http://www.avbot.org
Contact: Drew Mercy, President
Description: Strives to maintain and promote diverse business and industry, quality infrastructures, and a strong legislative voice for the benefit of the members and the Greater Antelope Valley. **Founded:** 1957. **Publications:** *Antelope Valley Business News* (Monthly).

48221 ■ *Antelope Valley Business News*
548 W Lancaster Blvd., Ste. 103
Lancaster, CA 93534-2534
Ph: (661)942-9581
Fax: (661)723-9279
Co. E-mail: info@avbot.org
URL: http://www.avbot.org
Contact: Drew Mercy, President
Released: Monthly

48222 ■ Antelope Valley Chambers of Commerce - Rosamond
2861 Diamond St.
Rosamond, CA 93560
Ph: (661)256-3248
Fax: (661)256-3249
Co. E-mail: mdavey@avfcu.org
URL: http://www.avchambers.com
Contact: Mark Davey, Chairman
Description: Promotes business and community development in Rosamond, CA. **Publications:** *Business Connection* (Monthly). **Educational Activities:** General Meeting (Monthly). **Awards:** Educational Scholarship.

48223 ■ Antioch Chamber of Commerce
101 H St., Unit 4
Antioch, CA 94509
Ph: (925)757-1800
Fax: (925)757-5286
Co. E-mail: info@antiochamber.com
URL: http://www.antiochchamber.com
Contact: Donna McGee, Chairman
Description: Promotes business and community development in Antioch, CA. **Founded:** 1938. **Publications:** *The Voice of Business* (Monthly).

48224 ■ Anza Valley Chamber of Commerce
PO Box 391460
Anza, CA 92539
Ph: (951)763-0141
Free: 888-930-0222
Co. E-mail: designer@folioflare.com
URL: http://www.anzavalleychamber.com
Contact: Sandi Hughes, President
Description: Promotes business and community development in the Anza Valley, CA area. Sponsors local festivals. Convention/Meeting: none. **Publications:** *The Scope* (Monthly).

48225 ■ Apple Valley Chamber of Commerce
16010 Apple Valley Rd.
Apple Valley, CA 92307
Ph: (760)242-2753
Fax: (760)242-0303
Co. E-mail: info@avchamber.org
URL: http://www.avchamber.org
Contact: Janice Moore, President
Description: Promotes prosperous business environment in the community. **Founded:** 1948.

48226 ■ Aptos Chamber of Commerce
7605A Old Dominion Ct.
Aptos, CA 95003

Ph: (831)688-1467
Fax: (831)688-6961
Co. E-mail: info@aptoschamber.com
URL: http://www.aptoschamber.com
Contact: Karen Hibble, Executive Director
Description: Promotes business and community development in Aptos, CA. **Publications:** *Business Bulletin.*

48227 ▪ Arcadia Chamber of Commerce (ACC)
388 W Huntington Dr.
Arcadia, CA 91007-3402
Ph: (626)447-2159
Fax: (626)445-0273
URL: http://www.arcadiacachamber.org
Contact: Pete Siberell, President
Description: Works to maintain a healthy business environment, contributes to the economic growth and to enhance the city's image. **Founded:** 1910. **Publications:** *Business Directory* (Biennial); *City Map* (Biennial); *The Power of Connection* (Monthly). **Educational Activities:** Awards Dinner (Annual); Business Expo (Annual); Golf Tournament (Annual); Networking Breakfast (Monthly); Planning Conference (Annual).

48228 ▪ Arcata Chamber of Commerce (AACC)
1635 Heindon Rd.
Arcata, CA 95521
Ph: (707)822-3619
Fax: (707)822-3515
Co. E-mail: arcata@arcatachamber.com
URL: http://www.arcatachamber.com
Contact: Gene Joyce, President
Description: Promotes business, tourism, and community development in Arcata, CA. Sponsors Fourth of July Jubilee. **Founded:** 1905.

48229 ▪ Around Alhambra
104 S 1st St.
Alhambra, CA 91801
Ph: (626)282-8481
Fax: (626)282-5596
Co. E-mail: ihernandez@alhambrachamber.org
URL: http://www.alhambrachamber.org
Contact: Mark Paulson, President
Released: Monthly

48230 ▪ Arroyo Grande Chamber of Commerce
800 W Branch St.
Arroyo Grande, CA 93420-1999
Ph: (805)489-1488
Fax: (805)489-2239
Co. E-mail: info@agchamber.com
URL: http://www.agchamber.com
Contact: Terence Concannon, Chairman
Description: Promotes positive, balanced, and vital economy, and preserve the unique qualities of Arroyo Grande.

48231 ▪ Art Guide - Cultural Arts in Los Gatos
10 Station Way
Los Gatos, CA 95030-5926
Ph: (408)354-9300
Fax: (408)399-1594
Co. E-mail: chamber@losgatosweb.com
URL: http://losgatoschamber.com
Contact: Ronee Nassi, Executive Director
Released: Periodic

48232 ▪ Arvin Chamber of Commerce
PO Box 645
Arvin, CA 93203
Ph: (661)854-2265
Fax: (661)854-2265
Co. E-mail: arvinchamberofcommerce@yahoo.com
URL: http://www.arvinchamberofcommerce.com
Contact: Robert Brennan, President
Description: Promotes business and community development in Arvin, CA.

48233 ▪ Atascadero Chamber of Commerce
6904 El Camino Real
Atascadero, CA 93422
Ph: (805)466-2044

Fax: (805)466-9218
Co. E-mail: info@atascaderochamber.org
URL: http://www.atascaderochamber.org
Contact: Linda Hendy, President
Description: Promotes business and community development in Atascadero, CA. **Founded:** 1926. **Publications:** *Business Reporter.*

48234 ▪ Attorney Guide
811 S Sunset Ave.
West Covina, CA 91790-3599
Ph: (626)338-8496
Fax: (626)960-0511
Co. E-mail: glawson@westcovinachamber.com
URL: http://www.westcovinachamber.com

48235 ▪ Atwater Chamber of Commerce
1181 Third St.
Atwater, CA 95301
Ph: (209)358-4251
Fax: (209)358-0934
Co. E-mail: chamber@atwaterchamberofcommerce.org
URL: http://www.atwaterchamberofcommerce.org
Contact: Jeff Stopper, President
Description: Promotes business and community development in Atwater, CA. Sponsors fall festival.

48236 ▪ Auburn Area Chamber of Commerce (AACC)
601 Lincoln Way
Auburn, CA 95603
Ph: (530)885-5616
Free: 800-971-1888
Fax: (530)885-5854
Co. E-mail: info@auburnchamber.net
URL: http://www.auburnchamber.net
Contact: Bruce L. Cosgrove, Chief Executive Officer
Description: Works to provide services that strengthen the members, advocate policies that improve the business climate, promote the economic development of the Auburn area, and develop coalitions with organizations to build a better community. **Founded:** 1906. **Publications:** *Auburn Journal* (Monthly).

48237 ▪ Auburn Journal
601 Lincoln Way
Auburn, CA 95603
Ph: (530)885-5616
Free: 800-971-1888
Fax: (530)885-5854
Co. E-mail: info@auburnchamber.net
URL: http://www.auburnchamber.net
Contact: Bruce L. Cosgrove, Chief Executive Officer
Released: Monthly

48238 ▪ Available Properties Listing Guide
101 W Pine St.
Exeter, CA 93221
Ph: (559)592-2919
Fax: (559)592-3720
Co. E-mail: chamber@exeterchamber.com
URL: http://Zwww.exeterchamber.com
Contact: Sandy Blankenship, Executive Director
Released: Monthly **Price:** free.

48239 ▪ Azusa Chamber of Commerce
240 W Foothill Blvd.
Azusa, CA 91702
Ph: (626)334-1507
Fax: (626)334-5217
Co. E-mail: info@azusachamber.org
URL: http://www.azusachamber.org
Contact: Steve Castro, Chief Executive Officer
Description: Works to serve as a catalyst in transformation of business and economic climate, resulting in a healthier, more prosperous Azusa. **Founded:** 1893. **Publications:** *Azusa Factbook* (Periodic); *The Azusan* (Monthly).

48240 ▪ Azusa Factbook
240 W Foothill Blvd.
Azusa, CA 91702
Ph: (626)334-1507

Fax: (626)334-5217
Co. E-mail: info@azusachamber.org
URL: http://www.azusachamber.org
Contact: Steve Castro, Chief Executive Officer
Released: Periodic

48241 ▪ The Azusan
240 W Foothill Blvd.
Azusa, CA 91702
Ph: (626)334-1507
Fax: (626)334-5217
Co. E-mail: info@azusachamber.org
URL: http://www.azusachamber.org
Contact: Steve Castro, Chief Executive Officer
Released: Monthly

48242 ▪ B2B
2410 Camino Ramon, Ste. 125
Bishop Ranch 6
San Ramon, CA 94583
Ph: (925)242-0600
Fax: (925)242-0603
Co. E-mail: info@sanramon.org
URL: http://www.sanramon.org
Contact: Stewart Bambino, President

48243 ▪ Baldwin Park Chamber of Commerce
3942 Maine Ave.
Baldwin Park, CA 91706
Ph: (626)960-4848
Fax: (626)960-2990
Co. E-mail: dluevano@bpchamber.com
URL: http://www.bpchamber.com
Contact: Jose Barrera, President
Description: Promotes business and community membership, action oriented, responsive, and demonstrate outstanding leadership. **Founded:** 1906. **Publications:** *Baldwin Park NOW* (Monthly).

48244 ▪ Baldwin Park NOW
3942 Maine Ave.
Baldwin Park, CA 91706
Ph: (626)960-4848
Fax: (626)960-2990
Co. E-mail: dluevano@bpchamber.com
URL: http://www.bpchamber.com
Contact: Jose Barrera, President
Released: Monthly **Price:** $50.

48245 ▪ Banning Chamber of Commerce
PO Box 665
Banning, CA 92220
Ph: (951)849-4695
Fax: (951)849-9395
Co. E-mail: info@banningchamber.net
URL: http://www.banningchamber.net
Contact: Joni Taylor, Executive Director
Description: Advocates the commercial, industrial, civic and general interests of the City of Banning and the San Gorgonio Pass. **Founded:** 1928. **Publications:** *Banning Mail Pouch* (Monthly).

48246 ▪ Banning Mail Pouch
PO Box 665
Banning, CA 92220
Ph: (951)849-4695
Fax: (951)849-9395
Co. E-mail: info@banningchamber.net
URL: http://www.banningchamber.net
Contact: Joni Taylor, Executive Director
Released: Monthly **Price:** free for members (for 1 year).

48247 ▪ Barstow Area Chamber of Commerce
PO Box 698
Barstow, CA 92312
Ph: (760)256-8617
Fax: (760)256-7675
Co. E-mail: chamberboard@barstowchamber.com
URL: http://www.barstowchamber.com
Contact: Dianna Ross, Executive Director
Description: Seeks to foster a better community by providing leadership which promotes economic success and enriches the quality of life. Sponsors leadership program, military mixer, community awards banquet, golf tournament, procurement seminar, and summer street festival. **Founded:** 1907. **Publications:** *Business Connection* (Monthly).

48248 ■ Bass Lake Chamber of Commerce
PO Box 126
Bass Lake, CA 93604
Ph: (559)642-3676
Co. E-mail: chamber@basslakechamber.com
URL: http://www.basslakechamber.com
Description: Promotes business and community development in Bass Lake, CA. Sponsors local festival; holds competitions. Publications: none.

48249 ■ *Beach Business*
200 N Pacific Coast Hwy.
Redondo Beach, CA 90277
Ph: (310)376-6911
Free: 800-282-0333
Fax: (310)374-7373
Co. E-mail: info@redondochamber.org
URL: http://www.redondochamber.org
Contact: Steve Goldstein, Chairman
Released: Monthly **Price:** $25, /year for individuals.

48250 ■ *Bear Valley Review*
630 Bartlett Rd.
Big Bear Lake, CA 92315-2860
Ph: (909)866-4607
Fax: (909)866-5412
Co. E-mail: info@bigbearchamber.com
URL: http://www.bigbearchamber.com
Contact: Marlene Cain, Chairperson
Released: Periodic

48251 ■ Beaumont Chamber of Commerce
726 Beaumont Ave.
Beaumont, CA 92223
Ph: (951)845-9541
Fax: (951)769-9080
Co. E-mail: assistant@beaumontcachamber.com
URL: http://www.beaumontcachamber.com
Contact: Sean Balingit, President
Description: Works to help small business grow and succeed. Creates and maintains a climate for business growth and strong quality of life, serves as business advocate in city and provides credibility for business through association. **Founded:** 1954.

48252 ■ Bell Gardens Association of Merchants and Commerce (BGAMC)
7535 Pery Rd.
Bell Gardens, CA 90201-4502
Ph: (562)806-2355
Fax: (562)806-1585
Co. E-mail: carlos@bellgardenschamber.org
URL: http://www.bellgardenschamber.org
Contact: Carlos Cruz, Executive Director
Description: Promotes business and community development in Bell Gardens, CA. **Founded:** 1997.

48253 ■ Belmont Chamber of Commerce (BCC)
1059A Alameda de las Pulgas
Belmont, CA 94002
Ph: (650)595-8696
Fax: (650)204-6232
Co. E-mail: execdirector@belmontchamber.org
URL: http://www.belmontchamber.org
Contact: George Burgess, President
Description: Promotes business and community development in Belmont, CA.

48254 ■ Benicia Chamber of Commerce and Visitors' Center
601 1st St., Ste. 100
Benicia, CA 94510-3211
Ph: (707)745-2120
Free: 800-559-7377
Fax: (707)745-2275
Co. E-mail: beniciachamber@aol.com
URL: http://www.beniciachamber.com
Contact: Stephanie Christiansen, President
Description: Promotes business and community development in Benicia, CA. **Founded:** 1847.

48255 ■ *Berkeley Business Advocate*
1834 University Ave.
Berkeley, CA 94703-1516
Ph: (510)549-7000

Fax: (510)549-1789
Co. E-mail: info@berkeleychamber.com
URL: http://www.berkeleychamber.com
Contact: Polly Armstrong, Chief Executive Officer
Released: Bimonthly

48256 ■ Berkeley Chamber of Commerce—Berkeley Richmond Jewish Community Center
1834 University Ave.
Berkeley, CA 94703-1516
Ph: (510)549-7000
Fax: (510)549-1789
Co. E-mail: info@berkeleychamber.com
URL: http://www.berkeleychamber.com
Contact: Polly Armstrong, Chief Executive Officer
Description: Works to represent Berkeley's business interests. Strives to join with the general community to promote understanding and act on issues of common concern. **Scope:** Jewish topics. **Founded:** 1900. **Subscriptions:** 5000. **Publications:** *Berkeley Business Advocate* (Bimonthly); *BRJCC Directory* (Annual).

48257 ■ Bethel Island Chamber of Commerce
PO Box 263
Bethel Island, CA 94511
Ph: (925)684-3220
Fax: (925)684-9025
Co. E-mail: bicc@bethelisland-chamber.com
URL: http://www.bethelisland-chamber.com
Contact: Doris Anderson, President (Acting)
Description: Promotes business and community development in Bethel Island, CA.

48258 ■ Beverly Hills Chamber of Commerce
239 S Beverly Dr.
Beverly Hills, CA 90212
Ph: (310)248-1000
Fax: (310)248-1020
Co. E-mail: stettinski@beverlyhillschamber.com
URL: http://www.beverlyhillschamber.com
Contact: Alexander Stettinski, Executive Director

48259 ■ Big Bear Chamber of Commerce (BBCC)
630 Bartlett Rd.
Big Bear Lake, CA 92315-2860
Ph: (909)866-4607
Fax: (909)866-5412
Co. E-mail: info@bigbearchamber.com
URL: http://www.bigbearchamber.com
Contact: Marlene Cain, Chairperson
Description: Promotes business and community development in the Big Bear Lake, CA area. **Founded:** 1947. **Publications:** *Bear Valley Review* (Periodic).

48260 ■ Bishop Area Chamber of Commerce and Visitors Bureau
690 N Main St.
Bishop, CA 93514
Ph: (760)873-8405
Free: 888-395-2395
Fax: (760)873-6999
Co. E-mail: info@bishopvisitor.com
URL: http://www.bishopvisitor.com
Contact: Tawni Thomson, Executive Director
Description: Promotes business, tourism, and community development in Bishop, CA. **Publications:** *Bishop Chamber Bulletin* (Quarterly).

48261 ■ *Bishop Chamber Bulletin*
690 N Main St.
Bishop, CA 93514
Ph: (760)873-8405
Free: 888-395-2395
Fax: (760)873-6999
Co. E-mail: info@bishopvisitor.com
URL: http://www.bishopvisitor.com
Contact: Tawni Thomson, Executive Director
Released: Quarterly

48262 ■ *Biz Buzz*
700 Seacoast Dr.
Imperial Beach, CA 91932-1871
Ph: (619)424-3151

Fax: (619)424-3008
Co. E-mail: joann_barrows@yahoo.com
URL: http://www.ib-chamber.com
Contact: Joann Barrows, President
Released: Bimonthly

48263 ■ *Bizline*
1 Capitol Mall, Ste. 300
Sacramento, CA 95814
Ph: (916)552-6800
Fax: (916)443-2672
Co. E-mail: mmahood@metrochamber.org
URL: http://www.metrochamber.org
Contact: Martha Clark Lofgren, Chief Executive Officer

48264 ■ Black Business Association of Los Angeles
PO Box 43159
Los Angeles, CA 90043
Ph: (323)857-4600
Fax: (323)857-4610
Co. E-mail: mail@bbala.org
URL: http://www.bbala.org
Contact: Earl Cooper, II, President
Description: Represents the interests of black-owned business entrepreneurs. **Founded:** 1970.

48265 ■ Bonsall Chamber of Commerce
5256 S Mission Road 311
Bonsall, CA 92003
Ph: (760)630-1933
Fax: (760)630-7658
Co. E-mail: bonsallchamber@att.net
URL: http://www.bonsallchamber.org
Contact: Ronald Coulombe, President
Description: Promotes business and community development in Bonsall, CA area. **Founded:** 1990.

48266 ■ Boron Chamber of Commerce
26922 Twenty Mule Team Rd.
Boron, CA 93516
Ph: (760)762-5810
Co. E-mail: chamber@boronchamber.com
URL: http://boronchamber.com
Contact: James Welling, President
Description: Promotes business and community development in Boron, CA.

48267 ■ Borrego Springs Chamber of Commerce (BSCC)
786 Palm Canyon Dr.
Borrego Springs, CA 92004-0420
Ph: (760)767-5555
Free: 800-559-5524
Fax: (760)767-5976
Co. E-mail: info@borregospringschamber.com
URL: http://www.borregospringschamber.com
Contact: Dan Wright, President
Description: Promotes business, tourism, and community development in Borrego Springs, CA. **Founded:** 1949. **Publications:** *Chamber Views* (Bimonthly).

48268 ■ Brawley Chamber of Commerce and Economic Development Commission (BCCEDC)
204 S Imperial Ave.
Brawley, CA 92227
Ph: (760)344-3160
Fax: (760)344-7611
Co. E-mail: info@brawleychamber.com
URL: http://www.brawleychamber.com
Contact: Ryan Johansen, President
Description: Promotes business and community development in the Brawley, CA area. Sponsors Brawley Cattle Call Festival. **Founded:** 1904. **Publications:** *Brawley Update* (Monthly).

48269 ■ *Brawley Update*
204 S Imperial Ave.
Brawley, CA 92227
Ph: (760)344-3160
Fax: (760)344-7611
Co. E-mail: info@brawleychamber.com
URL: http://www.brawleychamber.com
Contact: Ryan Johansen, President
Released: Monthly

48270 ■ Brea Chamber of Commerce (BCC)
1 Civic Center Cir.
Brea, CA 92821
Ph: (714)529-4938
Fax: (714)529-6103
Co. E-mail: answers@breachamber.com
URL: http://www.breachamber.com
Contact: Sharon Wagner, Chief Executive Officer
Description: Promotes business and community development in Brea, CA. **Founded:** 1945. **Publications:** *Business Directory and Community Guide* (Annual); *The Communique* (Monthly).

48271 ■ Brentwood Chamber of Commerce (BCC)
8440 Brentwood Blvd.
Brentwood, CA 94513
Ph: (925)634-3344
Fax: (925)634-3731
Co. E-mail: bcoc240@sbcglobal.net
URL: http://www.brentwoodchamber.com
Contact: Paul Kelly, President
Description: Promotes business and community development in eastern Contra Costa County, CA. Conducts mixers, festivals, and parades; bestows Citizen of the Year Award. **Founded:** 1952. **Publications:** *The Clarion* (Monthly). **Educational Activities:** Brentwood Cornfest (Annual). **Telecommunication Services:** paul@brentwoodpartyrentals.com.

48272 ■ Bridgeport Chamber of Commerce
PO Box 541
Bridgeport, CA 93517
Ph: (760)932-7500
Co. E-mail: bridgeportcalifornia@bridgeportcalifornia.com
URL: http://www.bridgeportcalifornia.com
Description: Promotes business and community development in Bridgeport, CA.

48273 ■ Brisbane Chamber of Commerce
50 Park Pl.
Brisbane, CA 94005
Ph: (415)467-7283
Fax: (415)467-5421
Co. E-mail: growyourbusiness@brisbanechamber.com
URL: http://www.brisbanechamber.com
Contact: Mitch Bull, President
Description: Provides support and services to enhance business and residential community in Brisbane. **Founded:** 1944. **Publications:** *The Luminary* (Monthly). **Awards:** Award Banquet (Annual); Business Person of the Year (Annual).

48274 ■ *BRJCC Directory*
1834 University Ave.
Berkeley, CA 94703-1516
Ph: (510)549-7000
Fax: (510)549-1789
Co. E-mail: info@berkeleychamber.com
URL: http://www.berkeleychamber.com
Contact: Polly Armstrong, Chief Executive Officer
Released: Annual **Price:** free.

48275 ■ Buena Park Area Chamber of Commerce
8081 Stanton Ave., Ste. 306
Buena Park, CA 90620
Ph: (714)484-1420
Fax: (714)484-1806
Co. E-mail: info@buenaparkchamber.org
URL: http://www.buenaparkchamber.org
Contact: Connie Pedenko, President
Description: Promotes business and community development in the Buena Park, CA area. Takes legislative action on behalf of business. Offers networking opportunities. Provides business related seminars. **Founded:** 1927. **Publications:** *Buena Park Business Journal* (Monthly); *Buena Park Map*. **Educational Activities:** Ambassador Meeting (Monthly); Networking Meeting (Semimonthly).

48276 ■ *Buena Park Business Journal*
8081 Stanton Ave., Ste. 306
Buena Park, CA 90620
Ph: (714)484-1420

Fax: (714)484-1806
Co. E-mail: info@buenaparkchamber.org
URL: http://www.buenaparkchamber.org
Contact: Connie Pedenko, President
Released: Monthly

48277 ■ *Buena Park Map*
8081 Stanton Ave., Ste. 306
Buena Park, CA 90620
Ph: (714)484-1420
Fax: (714)484-1806
Co. E-mail: info@buenaparkchamber.org
URL: http://www.buenaparkchamber.org
Contact: Connie Pedenko, President
Released: every 18 months.

48278 ■ *Burbank Business Journal*
200 W Magnolia Blvd.
Burbank, CA 91502-1724
Ph: (818)846-3111
Fax: (818)846-0109
Co. E-mail: info@burbankchamber.org
URL: http://www.burbankchamber.org
Contact: Gary Olson, President
Released: Monthly

48279 ■ Burbank Chamber of Commerce
200 W Magnolia Blvd.
Burbank, CA 91502-1724
Ph: (818)846-3111
Fax: (818)846-0109
Co. E-mail: info@burbankchamber.org
URL: http://www.burbankchamber.org
Contact: Gary Olson, President
Description: Promotes business and community development in Burbank, CA. **Founded:** 1922. **Publications:** *Burbank Business Journal* (Monthly); *Enterprise* (Monthly); *The Guide to Burbank* (Annual). **Educational Activities:** Business Connection (Monthly).

48280 ■ *Burlingame Business*
290 California Dr.
Burlingame, CA 94010
Ph: (650)344-1735
Fax: (650)344-1763
Co. E-mail: info@burlingamechamber.org
URL: http://burlingamechamber.org
Contact: Georgette Naylor, President
Released: Monthly

48281 ■ Burlingame Chamber of Commerce
290 California Dr.
Burlingame, CA 94010
Ph: (650)344-1735
Fax: (650)344-1763
Co. E-mail: info@burlingamechamber.org
URL: http://burlingamechamber.org
Contact: Georgette Naylor, President
Description: Promotes business and community development in Burlingame, CA. Sponsors community events. **Founded:** 1913. **Publications:** *Burlingame Business* (Monthly); *Welcome to Burlingame* (Periodic).

48282 ■ Burney Chamber of Commerce
PO Box 36
Burney, CA 96013
Ph: (530)335-2111
Fax: (530)335-2122
Co. E-mail: burneychamber@frontiernet.net
URL: http://www.burneychamber.com
Description: Promotes business and community development in the Burney Basin, CA area. **Founded:** 1943. **Subscriptions:** 160 books. **Publications:** *Intermountain Area Map*. **Educational Activities:** Burney Basin Days (Annual).

48283 ■ *Business*
2855 E Coast Hwy., Ste. 101
Corona Del Mar, CA 92625
Ph: (949)673-4050
Fax: (949)673-3940
Co. E-mail: info@cdmchamber.com
URL: http://www.cdmchamber.com
Contact: Linda Leonhard, President
Price: included in membership dues.

48284 ■ *Business*
1225 Park St.
Paso Robles, CA 93446
Ph: (805)238-0506
Free: 800-406-4040
Fax: (805)238-0527
Co. E-mail: mgibson@pasorobleschamber.com
URL: http://www.pasorobleschamber.com
Contact: Mike Gibson, President
Released: Monthly

48285 ■ *Business*
581 Dolliver St.
Pismo Beach, CA 93449
Ph: (805)773-4382
Free: 800-443-7778
Fax: (805)773-6772
Co. E-mail: pbcoc@charter.net
URL: http://www.pismochamber.com
Contact: Peter Candela, Chief Executive Officer

48286 ■ *Business*
747 Auditorium Dr.
Redding, CA 96001
Ph: (530)225-4433
Fax: (530)225-4398
Co. E-mail: info@reddingchamber.com
URL: http://www.reddingchamber.com
Contact: Frank J. Strazzarino, Jr., President
Released: Annual **Price:** free for members; $25, for nonmembers.

48287 ■ *Business Advocate*
720 N Broadway
Escondido, CA 92025-1893
Ph: (760)745-2125
Fax: (760)745-1183
Co. E-mail: info@escondidochamber.org
URL: http://www.escondidochamber.org
Contact: Harvey J. Mitchell, President
Released: Monthly

48288 ■ *The Business Advocate*
42-520 Bob Hope Dr., Ste. B
Rancho Mirage, CA 92270
Ph: (760)568-9351
Fax: (760)779-9684
Co. E-mail: info@ranchomirage.org
URL: http://www.ranchomirage.org
Contact: Stuart W. Ackley, President
Released: Monthly

48289 ■ *Business Alameda Style*
2210-D S Shore Ctr.
Alameda, CA 94501
Ph: (510)522-0414
Fax: (510)522-7677
Co. E-mail: connect@alamedachamber.com
URL: http://www.alamedachamber.com
Contact: Dennis Eloe, President
Released: Monthly

48290 ■ *Business Beacon*
390 W 7th St.
San Pedro, CA 90731
Ph: (310)832-7272
Fax: (310)832-0685
Co. E-mail: info@sanpedrochamber.com
URL: http://www.sanpedrochamber.com
Contact: Randy Bowers, President
Released: Monthly **Price:** free for members.

48291 ■ *Business Briefs*
1234 6th St., Ste. 100
Santa Monica, CA 90401
Ph: (310)393-9825
Fax: (310)394-1868
Co. E-mail: info@smchamber.com
URL: http://www.smchamber.com
Contact: Laurel Rosen, President
Released: Monthly

48292 ■ *Business Bulletin*
7605A Old Dominion Ct.
Aptos, CA 95003
Ph: (831)688-1467

Fax: (831)688-6961
Co. E-mail: info@aptoschamber.com
URL: http://www.aptoschamber.com
Contact: Karen Hibble, Executive Director

48293 ■ *Business to Business*
72559 Hwy. 111
Palm Desert, CA 92260
Ph: (760)346-6111
Fax: (760)346-3263
Co. E-mail: info@pdcc.org
URL: http://www.pdcc.org
Contact: Ms. Barbara deBoom, President
Released: Monthly

48294 ■ *Business Bylines*
128-B E California Ave., Ste. B
Ridgecrest, CA 93555
Ph: (760)375-8331
Fax: (760)375-0365
Co. E-mail: chamber@ridgecrestchamber.com
URL: http://www.ridgecrestchamber.com
Contact: Jay Chun, President
Released: Monthly **Price:** free.

48295 ■ *Business Communique*
3467 Castro Valley Blvd.
Castro Valley, CA 94546
Ph: (510)537-5300
Fax: (510)537-5335
Co. E-mail: info@castrovalleychamber.com
URL: http://www.edenareachamber.com
Contact: Brian Morrison, President
Released: Monthly

48296 ■ *Business and Community Directory*
122 Hamilton Ave.
Palo Alto, CA 94301
Ph: (650)324-3121
Fax: (650)324-1215
Co. E-mail: info@paloaltochamber.com
URL: http://www.paloaltochamber.com
Contact: Paula Sandas, President
Released: Annual

48297 ■ *Business and Community Directory*
1500 Laurel St., Ste. B
San Carlos, CA 94070-5103
Ph: (650)593-1068
Fax: (650)593-9108
Co. E-mail: staff@sancarloschamber.org
URL: http://www.sancarloschamber.org/default.aspx
Contact: David Bouchard, Chief Executive Officer
Released: Annual

48298 ■ *The Business and Community Guide*
PO Box 175
San Dimas, CA 91773-0175
Ph: (909)592-3818
Fax: (909)592-8178
Co. E-mail: info@sandimaschamber.com
URL: http://www.sandimaschamber.com
Contact: Karen Gaffney, President
Released: Biennial

48299 ■ *Business and Community Services Directory*
3131 Foothill Blvd., Ste. D
La Crescenta, CA 91214
Ph: (818)248-4957
Fax: (818)248-9625
Co. E-mail: cvcoc@aol.com
URL: http://www.lacrescenta.org
Contact: Julia Rabago, Executive Director

48300 ■ *Business Connection*
2485 McCabe Way, Ste. 150
Irvine, CA 92614
Ph: (949)660-9112
Fax: (949)660-0829
Co. E-mail: icc@irvinechamber.com
URL: http://www.irvinechamber.com
Contact: Massis Chahbazian, President
Released: Monthly

48301 ■ *Business Connection*
3516 N Verdugo Rd.
Glendale, CA 91208
Ph: (818)249-7171

Fax: (818)249-8919
Co. E-mail: mvcc@montrosechamber.org
URL: http://www.montrosechamber.org
Contact: Melina Clarke, Executive Director
Released: Quarterly

48302 ■ *Business Connection*
2861 Diamond St.
Rosamond, CA 93560
Ph: (661)256-3248
Fax: (661)256-3249
Co. E-mail: mdavey@avfcu.org
URL: http://www.avchambers.com
Contact: Mark Davey, Chairman
Released: Monthly **Price:** included in membership dues.

48303 ■ *Business Connection*
PO Box 698
Barstow, CA 92312
Ph: (760)256-8617
Fax: (760)256-7675
Co. E-mail: chamberboard@barstowchamber.com
URL: http://www.barstowchamber.com
Contact: Dianna Ross, Executive Director
Released: Monthly

48304 ■ *Business Connection*
9047 Arrow Rte., Ste. 180
Rancho Cucamonga, CA 91730
Ph: (909)987-1012
Fax: (909)987-5917
Co. E-mail: info@ranchochamber.org
URL: http://www.ranchochamber.org
Contact: Michelle Alonzo, President
Released: Monthly

48305 ■ *Business Directory*
321 E La Habra Blvd.
La Habra, CA 90631
Ph: (562)697-1704
Fax: (562)697-8359
Co. E-mail: info@lahabrachamber.com
URL: http://www.lahabrachamber.com
Contact: Mark Sturdevant, President
Price: included in membership dues.

48306 ■ *Business Directory*
388 W Huntington Dr.
Arcadia, CA 91007-3402
Ph: (626)447-2159
Fax: (626)445-0273
URL: http://www.arcadiacachamber.org
Contact: Pete Siberell, President
Released: Biennial

48307 ■ *Business Directory*
c/o Catherine Gaughen, Exec. Dir.
13259 E South St.
Cerritos, CA 90703
Ph: (562)467-0800
Fax: (562)467-0840
Co. E-mail: catherine@cerritos.org
URL: http://www.cerritos.org
Contact: Ann Smith, President
Released: Annual

48308 ■ *Business Directory*
904 E 6th St.
Corona, CA 92879
Ph: (951)737-3350
Fax: (951)737-3531
Co. E-mail: info@coronachamber.org
URL: http://www.mychamber.org
Contact: Bobby Spiegel, President
Released: Annual

48309 ■ *Business Directory*
200 Wool St.
Folsom, CA 95630
Ph: (916)985-2698
Fax: (916)985-4117
Co. E-mail: reception@folsomchamber.com
URL: http://www.folsomchamber.com
Contact: Joseph P. Gagliardi, President
Released: Annual **Price:** included in membership dues.

48310 ■ *Business Directory*
375 5th St.
Gustine, CA 95322
Ph: (209)854-6975
Fax: (209)854-3511
Co. E-mail: gustinechamber@inreach.com
URL: http://www.gustinechamberofcommerce.com
Contact: Glen Beard, President
Released: Periodic

48311 ■ *Business Directory*
82-921 Indio Blvd.
Indio, CA 92201
Ph: (760)347-0676
Free: 800-755-8440
Fax: (760)347-6069
Co. E-mail: info@indiochamber.org
URL: http://www.indiochamber.org
Contact: Patrick Swarthout, Chairman
Released: Annual

48312 ■ *Business Directory*
330 E Queen St.
Inglewood, CA 90301-1817
Ph: (310)677-1121
Fax: (310)677-1001
Co. E-mail: inglewoodchamber@sbcglobal.net
URL: http://www.inglewoodchamber.com
Contact: Shannon R. Howe, Executive Vice President
Released: Annual

48313 ■ *Business Directory*
2078 Bonita Ave.
La Verne, CA 91750
Ph: (909)593-5265
Fax: (909)596-0579
Co. E-mail: info@lavernechamber.org
URL: http://www.lavernechamber.org
Contact: Brian McNerney, President
Released: every 18 months.

48314 ■ *Business Directory*
c/o Peggy Lemons, Exec. Dir.
15357 Paramount Blvd.
Paramount, CA 90723-4338
Ph: (562)634-3980
Fax: (562)634-0891
Co. E-mail: plemons@paramountchamber.com
URL: http://www.paramountchamber.com
Contact: Peggy Lemons, Executive Director

48315 ■ *Business Directory*
844 E Green St., Ste. 208
Pasadena, CA 91101
Ph: (626)795-3355
Fax: (626)795-5603
Co. E-mail: info@pasadena-chamber.org
URL: http://www.pasadena-chamber.org
Contact: Paul Little, President
Released: Periodic

48316 ■ *Business Directory*
581 Dolliver St.
Pismo Beach, CA 93449
Ph: (805)773-4382
Free: 800-443-7778
Fax: (805)773-6772
Co. E-mail: pbcoc@charter.net
URL: http://www.pismochamber.com
Contact: Peter Candela, Chief Executive Officer

48317 ■ *Business Directory*
542 Main St.
Placerville, CA 95667-5610
Ph: (530)621-5885
Free: 800-457-6279
Fax: (530)642-1624
Co. E-mail: admin@eldoradocounty.org
URL: http://www.eldoradocounty.org
Contact: Kirk Bone, President
Released: Annual

48318 ■ *Business Directory*
390 W 7th St.
San Pedro, CA 90731
Ph: (310)832-7272

Fax: (310)832-0685
Co. E-mail: info@sanpedrochamber.com
URL: http://www.sanpedrochamber.com
Contact: Randy Bowers, President
Released: Annual

48319 ■ *Business Directory*
817 Mission Ave.
San Rafael, CA 94901
Ph: (415)454-4163
Fax: (415)454-7039
Co. E-mail: frontdesk@srchamber.com
URL: http://www.sanrafaelchamber.com
Contact: Rick Wells, President
Released: Annual

48320 ■ *Business Directory*
PO Box 341
Shingle Springs, CA 95682
Ph: (530)677-8000
Fax: (530)676-8313
Co. E-mail: info@sscpchamber.org
URL: http://www.sscpchamber.org
Contact: Peter Fordham, President
E-mail: pfordham@comcast.net
Released: Biennial **Price:** free.

48321 ■ *Business Directory*
8158 Painter Ave.
Whittier, CA 90602
Ph: (562)698-9554
Fax: (562)693-2700
Co. E-mail: info@whittierchamber.com
URL: http://www.whittierchamber.com
Contact: Dean Harako, President
Released: Annual

48322 ■ *Business Directory*
118 W Sycamore
Willows, CA 95988
Ph: (530)934-8150
Free: 888-EZW-AY4U
Fax: (530)934-2681
Co. E-mail: info@willowschamber.com
URL: http://www.willowschamber.com
Contact: Jamie Millen, President
Released: Annual **Price:** included in membership dues.

48323 ■ *Business Directory*
50 Victoria Ave., Ste. 103
Millbrae, CA 94030-2622
Ph: (650)697-7324
Fax: (650)259-7918
Co. E-mail: chamber@millbrae.com
URL: http://www.millbrae.com
Contact: John Ford, President
Released: Annual

48324 ■ *Business Directory and Community Guide*
1 Civic Center Cir.
Brea, CA 92821
Ph: (714)529-4938
Fax: (714)529-6103
Co. E-mail: answers@breachamber.com
URL: http://www.breachamber.com
Contact: Sharon Wagner, Chief Executive Officer
Released: Annual

48325 ■ *Business Directory and Community Guide*
11900 La Mirada Blvd., Ste. 9
La Mirada, CA 90638
Ph: (562)902-1970
Fax: (562)902-1218
Co. E-mail: info@lmchamber.org
URL: http://lmchamber.org
Contact: Demian Ross, Director
Released: Annual

48326 ■ *Business Directory and Community Guide*
215 N 2nd Ave., Ste. D
Upland, CA 91786
Ph: (909)204-4465

Fax: (909)204-4464
Co. E-mail: realpeople@uplandchamber.org
URL: http://www.uplandchamber.org
Contact: Sonnie S. Faires, President
Price: included in membership dues.

48327 ■ *Business Directory and Community Guide*
600 Hampshire Rd., Ste. 200
Westlake Village, CA 91361-2571
Ph: (805)370-0035
Fax: (805)370-1083
Co. E-mail: jlederer@conejochamber.org
URL: http://www.conejochamber.org
Contact: Jill Lederer, President
Released: Annual

48328 ■ *Business Directory & Destination Planning Guide*
PO Box 786
Morgan Hill, CA 95038-0786
Ph: (408)779-9444
Fax: (408)779-5405
Co. E-mail: info@morganhill.org
URL: http://www.morganhill.org
Contact: Christine Giusiana, President
Released: Annual

48329 ■ *Business Focus*
27451 Tourney Rd., Ste. 160
Santa Clarita, CA 91355
Ph: (661)702-6977
Fax: (661)702-6980
Co. E-mail: info@scvchamber.com
URL: http://www.scvchamber.com
Contact: Terri K. Crain, President
Released: Monthly

48330 ■ *Business Focus*
8158 Painter Ave.
Whittier, CA 90602
Ph: (562)698-9554
Fax: (562)693-2700
Co. E-mail: info@whittierchamber.com
URL: http://www.whittierchamber.com
Contact: Dean Harako, President
Released: Monthly

48331 ■ *Business Link*
931 High St.
Delano, CA 93215
Ph: (661)725-2518
Co. E-mail: info@chamberofdelano.com
URL: http://www.chamberofdelano.com

48332 ■ *Business Link*
2331 Fresno St.
Fresno, CA 93721
Ph: (559)495-4817
Fax: (559)495-4811
Co. E-mail: info@cchcc.net
URL: http://www.cchcc.net
Contact: John Hernandez, Executive Director
Released: Monthly

48333 ■ *Business Matters*
190 W Amado Rd.
Palm Springs, CA 92262
Ph: (760)325-1577
Fax: (760)325-8549
Co. E-mail: janetcook@pschamber.org
URL: http://www.pschamber.org
Contact: Nona Watson, Chief Executive Officer
Released: Monthly **Price:** $200, delivery for chamber partner members.

48334 ■ *Business News*
PO Box 4444
Carmel, CA 93921
Ph: (831)624-2522
Free: 800-550-4333
Fax: (831)624-1329
Co. E-mail: info@carmelchamber.org
URL: http://www.carmelcalifornia.org
Contact: Monta Potter, Chief Executive Officer
Released: Monthly

48335 ■ *Business News*
c/o Catherine Gaughen, Exec. Dir.
13259 E South St.
Cerritos, CA 90703
Ph: (562)467-0800
Fax: (562)467-0840
Co. E-mail: catherine@cerritos.org
URL: http://www.cerritos.org
Contact: Ann Smith, President
Released: Monthly

48336 ■ *Business News*
1204 6th St.
Norco, CA 92860
Ph: (951)737-2531
Fax: (951)737-2574
Co. E-mail: staff@norcochamber.com
URL: http://www.norcochamber.com
Released: Monthly

48337 ■ *The Business News*
1225 Park St.
Paso Robles, CA 93446
Ph: (805)238-0506
Free: 800-406-4040
Fax: (805)238-0527
Co. E-mail: mgibson@pasorobleschamber.com
URL: http://www.pasorobleschamber.com
Contact: Mike Gibson, President
Released: Monthly

48338 ■ *Business News*
5016 Passons Blvd.
Pico Rivera, CA 90660
Ph: (562)949-2473
Fax: (562)949-8320
Co. E-mail: elena@picoriverachamber.org
URL: http://www.picoriverachamber.org
Contact: Mary Ann Bakotich, Executive Director
Released: Monthly

48339 ■ *Business News*
93 N Main St., Ste. A
Porterville, CA 93257
Ph: (559)784-7502
Fax: (559)784-0770
Co. E-mail: chamber@porterville.com
URL: http://www.chamber.porterville.com
Contact: Donnette Silva Carter, President
Released: Monthly

48340 ■ *Business News*
91 Gregory Ln., Ste. 11
Pleasant Hill, CA 94523-4914
Ph: (925)687-0700
Fax: (925)676-7422
Co. E-mail: info@pleasanthillchamber.com
URL: http://www.pleasanthillchamber.com
Contact: Charley Daly, Chief Executive Officer
Released: Monthly

48341 ■ *Business News*
8381 Katella Ave., Ste. H
Stanton, CA 90680
Ph: (714)995-1485
Fax: (714)995-1184
Co. E-mail: service@stantonchamber.org
URL: http://www.stantonchamber.org
Contact: Don Martinez, President
Released: Quarterly **Price:** included in membership dues.

48342 ■ *Business News*
580 Castro St.
Mountain View, CA 94041
Ph: (650)968-8378
Fax: (650)968-5668
Co. E-mail: info@chambermv.org
URL: http://www.mountainviewchamber.org
Contact: Oscar Garcia, President
Released: Bimonthly **Price:** included in membership dues.

48343 ■ *Business News Network*
122 Hamilton Ave.
Palo Alto, CA 94301
Ph: (650)324-3121

Fax: (650)324-1215
Co. E-mail: info@paloaltochamber.com
URL: http://www.paloaltochamber.com
Contact: Paula Sandas, President
Released: Bimonthly **Price:** free for members.

48344 ■ *Business Outlook*
1700 Adams Ave., Ste. 101
Costa Mesa, CA 92626
Ph: (714)885-9090
Fax: (714)885-9094
Co. E-mail: info@costamesachamber.com
URL: http://www.costamesachamber.com
Contact: Ed Fawcett, President
Released: Periodic

48345 ■ *Business Outlook*
811 S Sunset Ave.
West Covina, CA 91790-3599
Ph: (626)338-8496
Fax: (626)960-0511
Co. E-mail: glawson@westcovinachamber.com
URL: http://www.westcovinachamber.com
Released: 10/year

48346 ■ *Business Progress*
260 S Sunnyvale Ave., Ste. 4
Sunnyvale, CA 94086-6193
Ph: (408)736-4971
Fax: (408)736-1919
Co. E-mail: info@svcoc.org
URL: http://www.svcoc.org
Contact: Don Eagleston, President
Released: Monthly

48347 ■ *Business Referral*
190 W Amado Rd.
Palm Springs, CA 92262
Ph: (760)325-1577
Fax: (760)325-8549
Co. E-mail: janetcook@pschamber.org
URL: http://www.pschamber.org
Contact: Nona Watson, Chief Executive Officer
Released: Annual

48348 ■ *Business Referral Directory*
c/o Stuart McElhinney, Pres.
Morro Bay, CA 93442
Ph: (805)772-4467
Free: 800-231-0592
Co. E-mail: brownpelican@morrobay.org
URL: http://www.morrobay.org
Contact: Craig Schmidt, Chief Executive Officer
Released: Annual

48349 ■ *Business Referral Directory*
402 W Broadway, Ste. 1000
San Diego, CA 92101-3585
Ph: (619)544-1300
Co. E-mail: webinfo@sdchamber.org
URL: http://www.sdchamber.org
Contact: Ruben Barrales, President
E-mail: rbarrales@sdchamber.org
Released: Annual **Price:** $39, plus $6 postage.

48350 ■ *Business Report*
2341 El Toro Rd, Ste. 300
Laguna Hills, CA 92653
Ph: (949)600-5470
Fax: (949)635-1635
Co. E-mail: info@socchambers.com
URL: http://socchamber.com
Contact: James M. Leach, Chief Executive Officer
Released: Quarterly **Price:** free for members.

48351 ■ *Business Reporter*
6904 El Camino Real
Atascadero, CA 93422
Ph: (805)466-2044
Fax: (805)466-9218
Co. E-mail: info@atascaderochamber.org
URL: http://www.atascaderochamber.org
Contact: Linda Hendy, President

48352 ■ *Business Resource Directory*
720 N Broadway
Escondido, CA 92025-1893
Ph: (760)745-2125

Fax: (760)745-1183
Co. E-mail: info@escondidochamber.org
URL: http://www.escondidochamber.org
Contact: Harvey J. Mitchell, President
Released: Annual

48353 ■ *Business Resource Directory*
30 Ragsdale Dr., Ste. 200
Monterey, CA 93940
Ph: (831)648-5360
Fax: (831)649-3502
Co. E-mail: info@mpcc.com
URL: http://www.mpcc.com
Contact: Jody Hansen, President
Released: Annual

48354 ■ *Business Resource Directory*
1241 S Main St.
Angels Camp, CA 95222
Ph: (209)736-2580
Fax: (209)736-2576
Co. E-mail: chamber@calaveras.org
URL: http://www.calaveras.org
Contact: Diane Gray, Executive Director
Released: Annual

48355 ■ *Business Resource Directory*
101 Golf Course Dr. C-7
Rohnert Park, CA 94928
Ph: (707)584-1415
Fax: (707)584-2945
Co. E-mail: info@rohnertparkchamber.org
URL: http://www.rohnertparkchamber.org
Contact: Roy Gugliotta, President
Released: Annual **Price:** free.

48356 ■ *Business Review*
132 W Graham Ave.
Lake Elsinore, CA 92530
Ph: (951)245-8848
Fax: (951)245-9127
Co. E-mail: info@lakeelsinorechamber.com
URL: http://www.lakeelsinorechamber.com
Contact: Kim Joseph Cousins, President
Released: Monthly

48357 ■ *Business Review*
PO Box 786
Morgan Hill, CA 95038-0786
Ph: (408)779-9444
Fax: (408)779-5405
Co. E-mail: info@morganhill.org
URL: http://www.morganhill.org
Contact: Christine Giusiana, President
Released: Monthly

48358 ■ *Business Roundup*
1204 6th St.
Norco, CA 92860
Ph: (951)737-2531
Fax: (951)737-2574
Co. E-mail: staff@norcochamber.com
URL: http://www.norcochamber.com
Price: included in membership dues.

48359 ■ *Business Santa Cruz*
611 Ocean St., Ste. 1
Santa Cruz, CA 95060
Ph: (831)457-3713
Fax: (831)423-1847
Co. E-mail: info@santacruzchamber.org
URL: http://www.santacruzchamber.org
Contact: William R. Tysseling, Chief Executive Officer
Released: Monthly

48360 ■ *Business Today*
PO Box 1429
Marysville, CA 95901
Ph: (530)743-6501
Fax: (530)741-8645
Co. E-mail: chamber@yubasutterchamber.com
URL: http://www.yubasutterchamber.com
Contact: Kristy Santucci, Chief Executive Officer
Released: Weekly

48361 ■ *Business Today*
985 Railroad Ave.
Pittsburg, CA 94565

Ph: (925)432-7301
Fax: (925)427-5555
Co. E-mail: mconig@pittsburg.org
URL: http://www.pittsburg.org
Contact: Meredith B. Ladich, Chief Executive Officer
Released: Monthly

48362 ■ *Business Update*
105 N Cloverdale Blvd.
Cloverdale, CA 95425-0356
Ph: (707)894-4470
Fax: (707)894-9568
Co. E-mail: chamberinfo@cloverdale.com
URL: http://www.cloverdale.net
Contact: Mike Nixon, Chairman
Released: Monthly **Price:** free for members.

48363 ■ *Business View*
131 E Foothill Blvd.
Glendora, CA 91741-3336
Ph: (626)963-4128
Fax: (626)914-4822
Co. E-mail: info@glendora-chamber.org
URL: http://www.glendora-chamber.org
Contact: Linda Hermann, President
Released: Monthly **Price:** included in membership dues.

48364 ■ *Business Voice*
400 E Esplanade Dr., Ste. 302
Oxnard, CA 93036
Ph: (805)983-6118
Fax: (805)604-7331
Co. E-mail: info@oxnardchamber.org
URL: http://www.oxnardchamber.org
Contact: Nancy Lindholm, President
Released: Monthly

48365 ■ *Business Voice*
3801 Santa Fe Ave.
Vernon, CA 90058
Ph: (323)583-3313
Co. E-mail: molguin@vernonchamber.org
URL: http://vernonchamber.org
Contact: Marisa Olguin, Executive Director

48366 ■ Buttonwillow Chamber of Commerce (BCC)
PO Box 251
Buttonwillow, CA 93206
Ph: (661)764-5406
Fax: (661)764-5406
URL: http://www.buttonwillowchamber.com
Contact: Gloria Selvidge, Office Manager Secretary
Description: Promotes business and community development in Buttonwillow, CA. Sponsors Cotton Harvest Festival, Country Christmas celebration, and Mayor's Race. **Founded:** 1943.

48367 ■ *Buyer's Guide and Chamber Directory*
11131 Brookshire Ave.
Downey, CA 90241-3860
Ph: (562)923-2191
Fax: (562)869-0461
Co. E-mail: info@downeychamber.com
URL: http://www.downeychamber.com
Contact: Susan Nordin, Executive Director
Released: Semiannual

48368 ■ *Byline*
PO Box 538
El Cerrito, CA 94530
Ph: (510)705-1202
Co. E-mail: info@elcerritochamber.org
URL: http://www.elcerritochamber.org
Contact: Judy Pope, President
Released: Monthly

48369 ■ Calabasas Chamber of Commerce
23564 Calabasas Rd., Ste. 101
Calabasas, CA 91302
Ph: (818)222-5680

Fax: (818)222-5690
Co. E-mail: info@calabasaschamber.com
URL: http://www.calabasaschamber.com
Contact: Bridget Karl, President
Description: Promotes business and community development in Calabasas, CA. **Founded:** 1955. **Publications:** *Calabasas Post.* **Telecommunication Services:** bkarl@calabasaschamber.com.

48370 ■ *Calabasas Post*
23564 Calabasas Rd., Ste. 101
Calabasas, CA 91302
Ph: (818)222-5680
Fax: (818)222-5690
Co. E-mail: info@calabasaschamber.com
URL: http://www.calabasaschamber.com
Contact: Bridget Karl, President

48371 ■ Calaveras County Chamber of Commerce
1241 S Main St.
Angels Camp, CA 95222
Ph: (209)736-2580
Fax: (209)736-2576
Co. E-mail: chamber@calaveras.org
URL: http://www.calaveras.org
Contact: Diane Gray, Executive Director
Description: Promotes business and community development in the Calaveras County, CA area. Sponsors community events and social activities. Maintains business resource center. **Founded:** 1948. **Publications:** *Business Resource Directory* (Annual); *Chamber Newsletter* (Monthly). **Educational Activities:** Mixer (Monthly).

48372 ■ *Calendar of Community Events*
30 Ragsdale Dr., Ste. 200
Monterey, CA 93940
Ph: (831)648-5360
Fax: (831)649-3502
Co. E-mail: info@mpcc.com
URL: http://www.mpcc.com
Contact: Jody Hansen, President
Released: Annual

48373 ■ *CALEXICO California, City Directory and Tourist Guide*
PO Box 948
Calexico, CA 92232
Ph: (760)357-1166
Fax: (760)357-9043
Co. E-mail: hildy@calexicochamber.net
URL: http://www.calexicochamber.net
Contact: Robert Rubio, President
Released: Annual

48374 ■ Calexico Chamber of Commerce (CCC)
PO Box 948
Calexico, CA 92232
Ph: (760)357-1166
Fax: (760)357-9043
Co. E-mail: hildy@calexicochamber.net
URL: http://www.calexicochamber.net
Contact: Robert Rubio, President
Description: Promotes business and community development in Calexico, CA. Sponsors festival. Convention/Meeting : none. **Founded:** 1949. **Publications:** *CALEXICO California, City Directory and Tourist Guide* (Annual).

48375 ■ *California Chamber Advocate*
PO Box 538
El Cerrito, CA 94530
Ph: (510)705-1202
Co. E-mail: info@elcerritochamber.org
URL: http://www.elcerritochamber.org
Contact: Judy Pope, President
Released: Periodic

48376 ■ California Chamber of Commerce (CCC)
PO Box 1736
Sacramento, CA 95812-1736
Ph: (916)444-6670
Free: 800-331-8877

Fax: (916)325-1272
Co. E-mail: techsupport@calchamber.com
URL: http://www.calchamber.com
Contact: Allan Zaremberg, President
E-mail: debi.hobson@calchamber.com
Description: Works to act as legislative advocate for all California business interests. Offers educational seminars. Issues publications. **Founded:** 1890.

48377 ■ California Chamber of Commerce, Southern California Office
PO Box 8230
La Verne, CA 91750-8230
Ph: (909)593-0449
Fax: (909)593-0449
Co. E-mail: marlene.carney@calchamber.com
URL: http://www.scacce.org
Contact: Sonnie S. Faires, President

48378 ■ California Israel Chamber of Commerce (CICC)
440 N Wolfe Rd.
Sunnyvale, CA 94085
Ph: (408)343-0917
Fax: (408)343-1197
Co. E-mail: info@ca-israelchamber.org
URL: http://www.ca-israelchamber.org
Contact: Shuly Galili, Executive Director
Description: Aims to strengthen business and trade relations between California and Israel. Serves as facilitator and active supporter for joint venture programs between the two communities. Conducts networking events, mentorship programs, investment forums, and educational seminars. **Telecommunication Services:** shuly@ca-israelchamber.org.

48379 ■ *California.Calm, A Guide to San Benito County*
650 San Benito St., Ste. 130
Hollister, CA 95023-3988
Ph: (831)637-5315
Fax: (831)637-1008
Co. E-mail: info1@sanbenitocountychamber.com
URL: http://www.sanbenitocountychamber.com
Contact: Jessica French, President
Price: included in membership dues.

48380 ■ Calistoga Chamber of Commerce (CCC)
1133 Washington St.
Calistoga, CA 94515
Ph: (707)942-6333
Free: 866-306-5588
Fax: (707)942-9287
Co. E-mail: ralbright@calistogachamber.net
URL: http://www.calistogachamber.com
Contact: Chris Canning, Executive Director
URL(s): www.calistogavisitors.com. **Description:** Seeks to promote business, tourism and community development in Calistoga, CA. Sponsors several entertainment shows and festivals. **Founded:** 1944. **Publications:** *Calistoga Visitors Guide*; *Guide to Calistoga* (Annual). **Awards:** Scholarship (Annual).

48381 ■ Camarillo Chamber of Commerce
2400 E Ventura Blvd.
Camarillo, CA 93010
Ph: (805)484-4383
Fax: (805)484-1395
Co. E-mail: info@camarillochamber.org
URL: http://www.camarillochamber.org
Contact: Jennifer Wells, President
Description: Seeks to further commercial, professional, economic, and educational well being of Camarillo community. **Founded:** 1940. **Publications:** *Communicator* (Monthly). **Awards:** Business of the Year (Annual); Educator of the Year (Annual); Entrepreneur of the Year (Annual); Man/Woman of the Year (Annual); Public Servant of the Year (Annual); Service Organization of the Year (Annual); Volunteer of the Year (Annual); Youth/Senior of the Year (Annual).

48382 ■ Cambria Chamber of Commerce
767 Main St.
Cambria, CA 93428
Ph: (805)927-3624

Fax: (805)927-9426
Co. E-mail: info@cambriachamber.org
URL: http://cambriachamber.org
Contact: Mel McColloch, President
Description: Promotes business and community development in Cambria, CA.

48383 ■ Campbell Chamber of Commerce (CCC)
1628 W Campbell Ave.
Campbell, CA 95008
Ph: (408)378-6252
Fax: (408)378-0192
Co. E-mail: ccoc@pacbell.net
URL: http://www.campbellchamber.com
Contact: Neil Collins, Executive Director
Description: Promotes business and community development in Campbell, CA. Conducts business/education partnership programs. Sponsors festival. Informs Campbell business as to pending local, state, and federal legislation that will affect their business. **Founded:** 1958. **Publications:** *Campbell Connection* (Monthly). **Telecommunication Services:** info@campbellchamber.net.

48384 ■ *Campbell Connection*
1628 W Campbell Ave.
Campbell, CA 95008
Ph: (408)378-6252
Fax: (408)378-0192
Co. E-mail: ccoc@pacbell.net
URL: http://www.campbellchamber.com
Contact: Neil Collins, Executive Director
Released: Monthly **Price:** free for members.

48385 ■ *Capital Gains*
5770 Freeport Blvd., Ste. 44
Sacramento, CA 95822
Ph: (916)231-0416
Fax: (916)706-0477
URL: http://www.sacblackchamber.org
Contact: Azizza Davis Goines, President
Released: Quarterly

48386 ■ *Capitola*
716-G Capitola Ave.
Capitola, CA 95010
Ph: (831)475-6522
Fax: (831)475-6530
Co. E-mail: lfalcon@comericabank.com
URL: http://www.capitolachamber.com
Contact: Lynn Falcon, Chairperson
Released: Monthly

48387 ■ Capitola-Soquel Chamber of Commerce
716-G Capitola Ave.
Capitola, CA 95010
Ph: (831)475-6522
Fax: (831)475-6530
Co. E-mail: lfalcon@comericabank.com
URL: http://www.capitolachamber.com
Contact: Lynn Falcon, Chairperson
Description: Promotes Capitola business community. **Publications:** *Capitola* (Monthly). **Educational Activities:** Capitola-Soquel Chamber of Commerce Festival (Annual). **Telecommunication Services:** capcham@capitolachamber.com.

48388 ■ Cardiff-by-the-Sea Chamber of Commerce
PO Box 552
Cardiff-by-the-Sea, CA 92007
Ph: (760)436-0431
Fax: (760)753-0144
Co. E-mail: cardiff101chamber@gmail.com
URL: http://www.cardiffbythesea.org
Contact: Brenda Dizon, President
Description: Promotes business and community development within the city of Encinitas.

48389 ■ *Carlsbad Business Journal*
5934 Priestly Dr.
Carlsbad, CA 92008
Ph: (760)931-8400

Fax: (760)931-9153
Co. E-mail: carlsbadchamber@carlsbad.org
URL: http://www.carlsbad.org
Contact: Gina McBride, Chairperson
Released: Monthly

48390 ■ Carlsbad Chamber of Commerce (CCC)
5934 Priestly Dr.
Carlsbad, CA 92008
Ph: (760)931-8400
Fax: (760)931-9153
Co. E-mail: carlsbadchamber@carlsbad.org
URL: http://www.carlsbad.org
Contact: Gina McBride, Chairperson
Description: Promotes business and community development in the Carlsbad, CA area. Sponsors Carlsbad Village Fair. **Founded:** 1962. **Publications:** *Carlsbad Chamber Members* (Annual); *Carlsbad Business Journal* (Monthly). **Awards:** Outstanding Educational Program Award (Annual).

48391 ■ Carmel Chamber of Commerce
PO Box 4444
Carmel, CA 93921
Ph: (831)624-2522
Free: 800-550-4333
Fax: (831)624-1329
Co. E-mail: info@carmelchamber.org
URL: http://www.carmelcalifornia.org
Contact: Monta Potter, Chief Executive Officer
Description: Promotes business, marketing, and networking opportunities to benefit the members professionally and economically. **Founded:** 1932. **Publications:** *Business News* (Monthly); *Guide to Camel* (Annual).

48392 ■ Carmel Valley Chamber of Commerce
PO Box 288
Carmel Valley, CA 93924
Ph: (831)659-4000
Fax: (831)644-9476
Co. E-mail: info@carmelvalleychamber.com
URL: http://www.carmelvalleychamber.com
Contact: Sonia Werk, President
Description: Promotes business and community development in the Carmel Valley, CA area. **Founded:** 1953. **Publications:** *The Chamber Chronicle* (Quarterly).

48393 ■ Carmichael Chamber of Commerce (CCC)
6825 Fair Oaks Blvd., Ste. 100
Carmichael, CA 95608
Ph: (916)481-1002
Fax: (916)481-1003
Co. E-mail: admin@carmichaelchamber.com
URL: http://www.carmichaelchamber.com
Contact: Trish Harrington, President
Description: Promotes business and community development in Carmichael, CA. Represents members' interests before state, local, and federal government agencies. Conducts public education campaigns. **Founded:** 1948. **Publications:** *Commentator* (Monthly).

48394 ■ *Carpinteria Valley Business*
1056-B Eugenia Pl.
Carpinteria, CA 93013-2050
Ph: (805)684-5479
Fax: (805)684-3477
Co. E-mail: info@carpinteriachamber.org
URL: http://www.carpchamber.org
Contact: Ms. Lynda Lang, President
Released: Monthly

48395 ■ Carpinteria Valley Chamber of Commerce
1056-B Eugenia Pl.
Carpinteria, CA 93013-2050
Ph: (805)684-5479

Fax: (805)684-3477
Co. E-mail: info@carpinteriachamber.org
URL: http://www.carpchamber.org
Contact: Ms. Lynda Lang, President
Description: Promotes business and community development in the Carpinteria, CA area. **Founded:** 1912. **Publications:** *Carpinteria Valley Business* (Monthly); *Carpinteria Valley, Member Directory and Visitors Guide* (Annual).

48396 ■ *Carpinteria Valley, Member Directory and Visitors Guide*
1056-B Eugenia Pl.
Carpinteria, CA 93013-2050
Ph: (805)684-5479
Fax: (805)684-3477
Co. E-mail: info@carpinteriachamber.org
URL: http://www.carpchamber.org
Contact: Ms. Lynda Lang, President
Released: Annual

48397 ■ Carson Chamber of Commerce (CCC)
530 E Del Amo Blvd.
Carson, CA 90746
Ph: (310)217-4590
Fax: (310)217-4591
Co. E-mail: carsonchamber@carsonchamber.com
URL: http://www.carsonchamber.com
Contact: Walter Neil, Chairman
Description: Promotes business and community development in Carson, CA.

48398 ■ Castro Valley Chamber of Commerce (CVCC)
3467 Castro Valley Blvd.
Castro Valley, CA 94546
Ph: (510)537-5300
Fax: (510)537-5335
Co. E-mail: info@castrovalleychamber.com
URL: http://www.edenareachamber.com
Contact: Brian Morrison, President
Description: Promotes business and community development in the eastern San Francisco Bay area of California. Conducts annual community festival and business exchange night. **Founded:** 1937. **Publications:** *Business Communique* (Monthly); *Community Guide* (Biennial). **Educational Activities:** Business After Hours Mixer (Monthly). **Awards:** Business and Education Achievement Awards.

48399 ■ Castroville Chamber of Commerce
PO Box 744
Castroville, CA 95012
Ph: (831)633-2465
Fax: (831)633-0485
Co. E-mail: artifest@att.net
URL: http://www.northmontereycountychamber.org
Contact: Gary DeAmaral, President
Description: Promotes business and community development in Castroville, CA.

48400 ■ Catalina Island Chamber of Commerce and Visitors' Bureau
PO Box 217
Avalon, CA 90704-0217
Ph: (310)510-1520
Fax: (310)510-7607
Co. E-mail: info@catalinachamber.com
URL: http://www.catalinachamber.com
Contact: Wayne G. Griffin, President
Description: Promotes business, community development, and tourism on Santa Catalina Island, CA. **Founded:** 1944. **Publications:** *Visitor's Guide* (Annual).

48401 ■ Cayucos Chamber of Commerce
PO Box 346
Cayucos, CA 93430
Ph: (805)995-1200
Co. E-mail: cayucoschamber@charter.net
URL: http://www.cayucoschamber.com
Contact: Myles Crebs, President
Description: Promotes business and community development in Cayucos, CA. Sponsors semiannual antique sale, periodic flea market, and seafood festival.

48402 ■ Central California Hispanic Chamber of Commerce (CCHCC)
2331 Fresno St.
Fresno, CA 93721
Ph: (559)495-4817
Fax: (559)495-4811
Co. E-mail: info@cchcc.net
URL: http://www.cchcc.net
Contact: John Hernandez, Executive Director
Description: Seeks to promote, stimulate, and support Hispanic-owned businesses in the central California area by creating, maintaining, and improving a favorable business environment. **Founded:** 1984. **Publications:** *Business Link* (Monthly).

48403 ■ Century City Chamber of Commerce
2029 Century Park E, Concourse Level
Los Angeles, CA 90067
Ph: (310)553-2222
Fax: (310)553-4623
Co. E-mail: contact@centurycitycc.com
URL: http://www.centurycitycc.com
Contact: Susan Bursk, President
Description: Promotes business and community development in Los Angeles, CA. **Founded:** 1965. **Telecommunication Services:** susan@centurycitycc.com.

48404 ■ Ceres Chamber of Commerce (CCC)
2491 Lawrence St.
Ceres, CA 95307
Ph: (209)537-2601
Fax: (209)537-2699
Co. E-mail: chamber@cereschamber.org
URL: http://www.cereschamber.org
Contact: Cary Pope, Chairman
Description: Encourages a strong local economy by maintaining and advancing business. Leadership provides an informed membership through the Chamber newsletter, the business directory, and business surveys. Serves as an active watchdog to review current legislation at the local, state and federal levels that impact the local business community. Promotes an advancement of business through information and recognition programs. **Founded:** 1967. **Publications:** *Ceres Directory and Fact Book* (Periodic); *Chamber Report* (Periodic).

48405 ■ *Ceres Directory and Fact Book*
2491 Lawrence St.
Ceres, CA 95307
Ph: (209)537-2601
Fax: (209)537-2699
Co. E-mail: chamber@cereschamber.org
URL: http://www.cereschamber.org
Contact: Cary Pope, Chairman
Released: Periodic

48406 ■ Cerritos Chamber of Commerce (CCOC)
c/o Catherine Gaughen, Exec. Dir.
13259 E South St.
Cerritos, CA 90703
Ph: (562)467-0800
Fax: (562)467-0840
Co. E-mail: catherine@cerritos.org
URL: http://www.cerritos.org
Contact: Ann Smith, President
Description: Promotes business and community development in the Cerritos, CA area. Sponsors business expo. **Founded:** 1963. **Publications:** *Business Directory* (Annual); *Business News* (Monthly). **Educational Activities:** Cerritos Chamber of Commerce Luncheon (Monthly).

48407 ■ *The Chamber*
111 S 1 St.
Lompoc, CA 93436
Ph: (805)736-4567
Free: 800-240-0999
Co. E-mail: chamber@lompoc.com
URL: http://www.lompoc.com
Contact: Chris Ames, Chairman
Released: Monthly **Price:** $15, /year.

48408 ■ *Chamber Action*
PO Box 178
Sebastopol, CA 95473-0178
Ph: (707)823-3032

Free: 877-828-4748
Fax: (707)823-8439
Co. E-mail: info@sebastopol.org
URL: http://www.sebastopol.org
Contact: Teresa Ramondo, Chief Executive Officer
Released: Monthly **Price:** free.

48409 ■ *Chamber Action*
17670 Yorba Linda Blvd.
Yorba Linda, CA 92886
Ph: (714)993-9537
Co. E-mail: phyllisylcc@sbcglobal.net
URL: http://www.yorbalindachamber.org
Contact: Phyllis A. Coleman, Executive Director
Released: Monthly

48410 ■ *The Chamber Advantage*
321 University Ave.
Los Altos, CA 94022
Ph: (650)948-1455
Fax: (650)948-6238
Co. E-mail: info@losaltoschamber.org
URL: http://www.losaltoschamber.org
Contact: Julie Rose, President
Released: Bimonthly

48411 ■ *Chamber Advocate*
101 W Santa Clara St.
San Jose, CA 95113
Ph: (408)291-5250
Fax: (408)286-5019
Co. E-mail: info@sjchamber.com
URL: http://www.sjchamber.com
Contact: Pat Dando, President
Released: Monthly

48412 ■ *Chamber Annual Business and Community Directory*
580 Castro St.
Mountain View, CA 94041
Ph: (650)968-8378
Fax: (650)968-5668
Co. E-mail: info@chambermv.org
URL: http://www.mountainviewchamber.org
Contact: Oscar Garcia, President
Released: Annual

48413 ■ *Chamber Business*
2134 St., Ste. 100
Huntington Beach, CA 92648
Ph: (714)536-8888
Fax: (714)960-7654
Co. E-mail: hbchamber@hbcoc.com
URL: http://www.hbchamber.org
Contact: Jerry L. Wheeler, Sr., President
Released: Monthly

48414 ■ *Chamber Business Journal*
2157 1st St.
Livermore, CA 94550
Ph: (925)447-1606
Fax: (925)447-1641
Co. E-mail: ttikalsky@rina.com
URL: http://www.livermorechamber.org
Contact: Dale Kaye, President
Released: Monthly

48415 ■ *Chamber Challenge*
614 S Broadway
Santa Maria, CA 93454-5111
Ph: (805)925-2403
Free: 800-331-3779
Fax: (805)928-7559
Co. E-mail: info@santamaria.com
URL: http://www.santamaria.com/cm/Home.html
Contact: Robert P. Hatch, President
Released: Monthly

48416 ■ *Chamber Chat*
PO Box 338
Susanville, CA 96130-0338
Ph: (530)257-4323
Fax: (530)251-2561
Co. E-mail: director@lassencountychamber.org
URL: http://www.lassencountychamber.org
Contact: Patricia Hagata, Executive Director
Released: Monthly

48417 ■ *Chamber Chatter*
PO Box 6204
San Pablo, CA 94806
Ph: (510)234-2067
URL: http://www.ci.san-pablo.ca.us/index.aspx-
?nid=955
Contact: Jerry Sattler, President
Released: Monthly

48418 ■ *Chamber Chatter*
PO Box 998
Larkspur, CA 94977
Ph: (415)838-0038
Co. E-mail: info@larkspurchamber.org
URL: http://www.larkspurchamber.org
Contact: Donna Craft, Executive Secretary
Released: Monthly

48419 ■ *The Chamber Chronicle*
PO Box 288
Carmel Valley, CA 93924
Ph: (831)659-4000
Fax: (831)644-9476
Co. E-mail: info@carmelvalleychamber.com
URL: http://www.carmelvalleychamber.com
Contact: Sonia Werk, President
Released: Quarterly

48420 ■ **Chamber of Commerce of Dana Point**
24681 La Plaza, Ste. 115
Dana Point, CA 92629-0012
Ph: (949)496-1555
Fax: (949)496-5321
Co. E-mail: chamber@danapointchamber.com
URL: http://www.danapointchamber.com
Contact: Heather Johnston, Executive Director
Description: Promotes business and community development in the Dana Point, CA area.

48421 ■ *Chamber of Commerce Membership Directory*
1114 J St.
Modesto, CA 95354-0806
Ph: (209)577-5757
Fax: (209)577-2623
Co. E-mail: info@modchamber.org
URL: http://www.modchamber.org
Contact: Joy Madison, President
E-mail: jmadison@modchamber.org
Released: Annual **Price:** $10.

48422 ■ *Chamber of Commerce Membership Directory*
924 Anacapa St., Ste. 1
Santa Barbara, CA 93101
Ph: (805)965-3023
Fax: (805)966-5954
Co. E-mail: info@sbchamber.org
URL: http://www.sbchamber.org
Contact: Zoe Taylor, President
Price: $300, for nonmembers; $20, for members.

48423 ■ **Chamber of Commerce Mountain View**
580 Castro St.
Mountain View, CA 94041
Ph: (650)968-8378
Fax: (650)968-5668
Co. E-mail: info@chambermv.org
URL: http://www.mountainviewchamber.org
Contact: Oscar Garcia, President
Description: Promotes business and community development in Mountain View, CA. **Founded:** 1922.
Publications: *Business News* (Bimonthly); *Chamber Annual Business and Community Directory* (Annual).

48424 ■ *Chamber Communications*
PO Box 1211
Spring Valley, CA 91979-1211
Ph: (619)670-9902
Fax: (619)670-9924
URL: http://www.springvalleychamber.org
Contact: Tina Carlson, Executive Director
Released: Monthly

48425 ■ *The Chamber Communicator*
c/o Connie Librenjak, Exec. Dir.
Riverside, CA 92501

Ph: (951)683-7100
Fax: (951)683-2670
Co. E-mail: croth@riverside-chamber.com
URL: http://www.riverside-chamber.com
Contact: Cindy Roth, President

48426 ■ *Chamber Connection*
19401 S Vermont Ave., Ste. G104
Torrance, CA 90502
Ph: (310)516-7933
Fax: (310)516-7734
Co. E-mail: hchgchamber@sbcglobal.net
URL: http://www.hchgchamber.com
Contact: Lou Baglietto, President
Released: Monthly

48427 ■ *Chamber Connection*
c/o Vince Reinig, Pres.
300 Pine St.
Mount Shasta, CA 96067
Ph: (530)926-4865
Free: 800-926-4865
Fax: (530)926-0976
Co. E-mail: info@mtshastachamber.com
URL: http://mtshastachamber.com/index.php
Contact: Jim Mullins, President
Released: Monthly

48428 ■ *Chamber Connection*
118 W Sycamore
Willows, CA 95988
Ph: (530)934-8150
Free: 888-EZW-AY4U
Fax: (530)934-2681
Co. E-mail: info@willowschamber.com
URL: http://www.willowschamber.com
Contact: Jamie Millen, President
Released: Monthly

48429 ■ *Chamber Directory*
26790 Ynez Ct.
Temecula, CA 92591
Ph: (951)676-5090
Free: 866-676-5090
Fax: (951)676-5090
Co. E-mail: info@temecula.org
URL: http://www.temecula.org
Contact: Alice Sullivan, President
Released: Periodic

48430 ■ *Chamber E-News*
40637 Hwy. 41
Oakhurst, CA 93644
Ph: (559)683-7766
Fax: (559)683-0784
Co. E-mail: chamber@oakhurstchamber.com
URL: http://www.oakhurstchamber.com
Contact: Janet Stanovich, President
Released: Semimonthly

48431 ■ *Chamber Member Business and Resource Directory*
9047 Arrow Rte., Ste. 180
Rancho Cucamonga, CA 91730
Ph: (909)987-1012
Fax: (909)987-5917
Co. E-mail: info@ranchochamber.org
URL: http://www.ranchochamber.org
Contact: Michelle Alonzo, President

48432 ■ *Chamber Membership Directory*
1 E Redlands Blvd.
Redlands, CA 92373
Ph: (909)793-2546
Fax: (909)335-6388
Co. E-mail: info@redlandschamber.org
URL: http://www.redlandschamber.org
Contact: Paul Barich, Director
Released: Annual

48433 ■ *Chamber Membership Directory and Business Resource Guide*
350 S Bixel St.
Los Angeles, CA 90017
Ph: (213)580-7500

Fax: (213)580-7511
Co. E-mail: info@lachamber.org
URL: http://www.lachamber.com
Contact: Gary Toebben, President
Released: Annual

48434 ■ Chamber News
904 E 6th St.
Corona, CA 92879
Ph: (951)737-3350
Fax: (951)737-3531
Co. E-mail: info@coronachamber.org
URL: http://www.mychamber.org
Contact: Bobby Spiegel, President
Released: Monthly

48435 ■ Chamber News
19401 S Vermont Ave., Ste. G104
Torrance, CA 90502
Ph: (310)516-7933
Fax: (310)516-7734
Co. E-mail: hchgchamber@sbcglobal.net
URL: http://www.hchgchamber.com
Contact: Lou Baglietto, President
Released: Monthly

48436 ■ Chamber News
650 San Benito St., Ste. 130
Hollister, CA 95023-3988
Ph: (831)637-5315
Fax: (831)637-1008
Co. E-mail: info1@sanbenitocountychamber.com
URL: http://www.sanbenitocountychamber.com
Contact: Jessica French, President
Released: Monthly

48437 ■ Chamber News
901 National City Blvd.
National City, CA 91950-3203
Ph: (619)477-9339
Fax: (619)477-5018
Co. E-mail: reynoso@nationalcitychamber.org
URL: http://www.nationalcitychamber.org
Contact: Jacqueline L. Reynoso, President
Released: Bimonthly

48438 ■ Chamber News
222 S Shepherd St.
Sonora, CA 95370
Ph: (209)532-4212
Free: 877-532-4212
Fax: (209)532-8068
Co. E-mail: info@tcchamber.com
URL: http://www.tcchamber.com
Contact: George Segarini, Executive Director
Released: Monthly

48439 ■ Chamber News
PO Box 596
Jackson, CA 95642-0596
Ph: (209)223-0350
Co. E-mail: gold49@amadorcountychamber.com
URL: http://www.amadorcountychamber.com
Contact: Mark Borchin, President
Released: Monthly

48440 ■ Chamber Newsletter
1241 S Main St.
Angels Camp, CA 95222
Ph: (209)736-2580
Fax: (209)736-1571
Co. E-mail: chamber@calaveras.org
URL: http://www.calaveras.org
Contact: Diane Gray, Executive Director
Released: Monthly

48441 ■ Chamber Notes
PO Box 1429
Marysville, CA 95901
Ph: (530)743-6501
Fax: (530)741-8645
Co. E-mail: chamber@yubasutterchamber.com
URL: http://www.yubasutterchamber.com
Contact: Kristy Santucci, Chief Executive Officer
Released: Weekly

48442 ■ Chamber Progress
c/o Melony Newman, Pres./CEO
117-E Town and Country Dr.
Danville, CA 94526
Ph: (925)837-4400
Fax: (925)837-5709
URL: http://www.danvilleareachamber.com
Contact: Melony Newman, President

48443 ■ Chamber Report
2491 Lawrence St.
Ceres, CA 95307
Ph: (209)537-2601
Fax: (209)537-2699
Co. E-mail: chamber@cereschamber.org
URL: http://www.cereschamber.org
Contact: Cary Pope, Chairman
Released: Periodic

48444 ■ Chamber Report
101 W Pine St.
Exeter, CA 93221
Ph: (559)592-2919
Fax: (559)592-3720
Co. E-mail: chamber@exeterchamber.com
URL: http://Zwww.exeterchamber.com
Contact: Sandy Blankenship, Executive Director
Released: Monthly

48445 ■ Chamber Report
2729 Prospect Park Dr., Ste. 117
Rancho Cordova, CA 95670
Ph: (916)273-5688
Fax: (916)273-5727
Co. E-mail: jlunn@ranchocordova.org
URL: http://www.ranchocordova.org
Contact: Jane Daly, Chief Executive Officer

48446 ■ Chamber Report
100 Main St.
Red Bluff, CA 96080
Ph: (530)527-6220
Free: 800-655-6225
Fax: (530)527-2908
Co. E-mail: rbchamber@att.net
URL: http://www.redbluffchamberofcommerce.com
Contact: Dave Gowan, President
Released: Monthly

48447 ■ Chamber Reporter
1110 Solano St.
Corning, CA 96021
Ph: (530)824-5550
Co. E-mail: corningchamber@sbcglobal.net
URL: http://corningchamber.org
Contact: Barbara Landavazo, President
Released: Monthly **Price:** free for members.

48448 ■ Chamber Spotlight
200 Broadway St., Ste. 40
King City, CA 93930
Ph: (831)385-3814
Fax: (831)386-9462
Co. E-mail: kingcitychamber@sbcglobal.net
URL: http://www.kingcitychamber.com
Contact: Sarah Cummings, President
Released: Monthly

48449 ■ The Chamber Times
PO Box 45
Yucaipa, CA 92399-0045
Ph: (909)790-1841
Fax: (909)363-7373
Co. E-mail: info@yucaipachamber.org
URL: http://www.yucaipachamber.org
Contact: Pamela Emenger, President
Released: Monthly

48450 ■ Chamber Today
7120 Hayvenhurst Ave., Ste. 114
Van Nuys, CA 91406-3813
Ph: (818)989-0300
URL: http://www.midvalleychamber.com
Contact: Nancy Hoffman Vanyek, Chief Executive
  Officer
Released: Monthly **Price:** $25, /year for individuals.

48451 ■ Chamber Update
99 S Railroad Ave.
Colfax, CA 95713
Ph: (530)346-8888
URL: http://www.colfaxarea.com
Contact: Frank Klein, President

48452 ■ Chamber Views
786 Palm Canyon Dr.
Borrego Springs, CA 92004-0420
Ph: (760)767-5555
Free: 800-559-5524
Fax: (760)767-5976
Co. E-mail: info@borregospringschamber.com
URL: http://www.borregospringschamber.com
Contact: Dan Wright, President
Released: Bimonthly **Price:** included in membership
dues.

48453 ■ Chamber Waves
10 Liberty Ship Way, Bay 2, Ste. 250
Sausalito, CA 94965
Ph: (415)331-7262
Fax: (415)332-0323
Co. E-mail: chamber@sausalito.org
URL: http://www.sausalito.org
Contact: Oonagh Kavanagh, Chief Executive Officer
Released: Monthly

48454 ■ ChamberLine 2.0
2020 N Broadway, 2nd Fl.
Santa Ana, CA 92702
Ph: (714)541-5353
Fax: (714)541-2238
Co. E-mail: info@santaanachamber.com
URL: http://www.santaanachamber.com
Contact: David Elliott, President
Released: Biweekly

**48455 ■ Chatsworth - Porter Ranch Chamber
of Commerce**
10038 Old Depot Plaza Rd.
Chatsworth, CA 91311
Ph: (818)341-2428
Fax: (818)341-4930
Co. E-mail: info@chatsworthchamber.com
URL: http://www.chatsworthchamber.com
Contact: Kevin Huling, President
Description: Promotes business and community
development in Chatsworth, CA. **Founded:** 1914.

**48456 ■ Chester/Lake Almanor Chamber of
Commerce**
PO Box 1198
Chester, CA 96020
Ph: (530)258-2426
Free: 800-350-4838
Co. E-mail: info@lakealmanorarea.com
URL: http://chester-lakealmanor.com
URL(s): www.lakealmanorarea.com. **Description:**
Promotes business and community development in
the Chester and Lake Almanor, CA areas. **Awards:**
Person of the Year (Annual).

48457 ■ Chico Business
300 Salem St.
Chico, CA 95928
Ph: (530)891-5556
Free: 800-852-8570
Co. E-mail: info@chicochamber.com
URL: http://www.chicochamber.com
Contact: Katie Simmons, President
Released: Monthly

48458 ■ Chico Chamber of Commerce
300 Salem St.
Chico, CA 95928
Ph: (530)891-5556
Free: 800-852-8570
Co. E-mail: info@chicochamber.com
URL: http://www.chicochamber.com
Contact: Katie Simmons, President
Description: Promotes business and community
development in the Chico, CA area. Sponsors annual
business-to-business and consumer trade shows,
industrial barbecue, and promotes local economy
and tourism. **Founded:** 1938. **Publications:** *Chico*

Business (Monthly); *Information and Business Directory* (Annual); *Chico Chamber of Commerce--Membership Directory.*

48459 ■ Chino Valley Chamber of Commerce
13150 7th St.
Chino, CA 91710
Ph: (909)627-6177
Fax: (909)627-4180
Co. E-mail: dbas@verizon.net
URL: http://www.chinovalleychamber.com
Contact: Vicki Finklestein, Executive Director
Description: Promotes business and community development in the Chino Valley, CA area. **Founded:** 1913.

48460 ■ Chronicle
615 N San Jacinto St.
Hemet, CA 92543
Ph: (951)658-3211
Free: 800-334-9344
Fax: (951)766-5013
Co. E-mail: info@hemetsanjacintochamber.com
URL: http://hemetsanjacintochamber.com
Contact: Patti Drusky, President
Released: Monthly

48461 ■ Chula Vista Chamber of Commerce
233 4th Ave.
Chula Vista, CA 91910
Ph: (619)420-6603
Fax: (619)420-1269
Co. E-mail: info@chulavistachamber.org
URL: http://www.chulavistachamber.org
Contact: Lisa Johnson, President
Description: Seeks to enhance the partnership between business and professional people promoting free enterprise system. **Founded:** 1927. **Publications:** *News and Views* (Quarterly).

48462 ■ Citrus Heights Chamber of Commerce
PO Box 191
Citrus Heights, CA 95611
Ph: (916)722-4545
Fax: (916)722-4543
Co. E-mail: chamber@chchamber.com
URL: http://www.chchamber.com
Contact: Bettie Cosby, Chief Executive Officer
Description: Promotes business and community development in Citrus Heights, CA. **Founded:** 1958. **Publications:** *Horizons* (Monthly). **Educational Activities:** Membership Luncheon (Monthly). **Awards:** Student of the Month (Monthly); Kids Choice Teacher of the Year Award (Annual).

48463 ■ City of Industry News
15651 Stafford St.
City of Industry, CA 91744
Ph: (626)968-3737
Fax: (626)330-5060
Co. E-mail: chamber@cityofindustry.org
URL: http://www.cityofindustry.org/news.php
Contact: Donald Sachs, Executive Director
Released: Monthly

48464 ■ City Map
388 W Huntington Dr.
Arcadia, CA 91007-3402
Ph: (626)447-2159
Fax: (626)445-0273
URL: http://www.arcadiacachamber.org
Contact: Pete Siberell, President
Released: Biennial **Price:** $1.

48465 ■ City Map
c/o Peggy Lemons, Exec. Dir.
15357 Paramount Blvd.
Paramount, CA 90723-4338
Ph: (562)634-3980
Fax: (562)634-0891
Co. E-mail: plemons@paramountchamber.com
URL: http://www.paramountchamber.com
Contact: Peggy Lemons, Executive Director

48466 ■ City Map
14460 Big Basin Way
Saratoga, CA 95070
Ph: (408)867-0753

Fax: (408)867-5213
Co. E-mail: info@saratogachamber.org
URL: http://www.saratogachamber.org
Contact: Vicki Seelig, Treasurer
Released: Biennial **Price:** $1.

48467 ■ City Map/Business and Tourist Directory
PO Box 202
Venice, CA 90294
Ph: (310)822-5425
Co. E-mail: info@venicechamber.net
URL: http://www.venicechamber.net
Contact: Donna Lasman, Executive Director
Released: Annual

48468 ■ CityLine
2020 N Broadway, 2nd Fl.
Santa Ana, CA 92702
Ph: (714)541-5353
Fax: (714)541-2238
Co. E-mail: info@santaanachamber.com
URL: http://www.santaanachamber.com
Contact: David Elliott, President
Released: Bimonthly

48469 ■ The Clarion
8440 Brentwood Blvd.
Brentwood, CA 94513
Ph: (925)634-3344
Fax: (925)634-3731
Co. E-mail: bcoc240@sbcglobal.net
URL: http://www.brentwoodchamber.com
Contact: Paul Kelly, President
Released: Monthly

48470 ■ Clear Lake Chamber of Commerce
3245 Bowers Ave.
Clearlake, CA 95422
Ph: (707)994-3600
Fax: (707)994-3603
Co. E-mail: office@clearlakechamber.com
URL: http://www.clearlakechamber.com
Contact: Joey Luiz, President
Description: Promotes business and community development in Clearlake, CA. **Founded:** 1943. **Publications:** *Clear Lake Chamber Newsletter* (Monthly); *Map Directory* (Annual); *Map Directory* (Annual); *Clear Lake Chamber of Commerce--Map Directory* (Annual). **Telecommunication Services:** clearlakechamber@yahoo.com.

48471 ■ Clear Lake Chamber Newsletter
3245 Bowers Ave.
Clearlake, CA 95422
Ph: (707)994-3600
Fax: (707)994-3603
Co. E-mail: office@clearlakechamber.com
URL: http://www.clearlakechamber.com
Contact: Joey Luiz, President
Released: Monthly

48472 ■ Clements Lockeford Chamber of Commerce (CLCC)
PO Box 971
Lockeford, CA 95237-0971
Ph: (209)727-3142
Fax: (209)727-3365
Co. E-mail: clchamber@sbcglobal.net
URL: http://www.clementslockefordchamber.org
Contact: Cynthia L. Haynes, President
Description: Promotes business and community development in the Clements-Lockeford, CA area. Sponsors semiannual Lockeford Street Faire and Community Support Day.

48473 ■ Cloverdale Chamber of Commerce
105 N Cloverdale Blvd.
Cloverdale, CA 95425-0356
Ph: (707)894-4470
Fax: (707)894-9568
Co. E-mail: chamberinfo@cloverdale.com
URL: http://www.cloverdale.net
Contact: Mike Nixon, Chairman
Description: Promotes business and community development in Cloverdale, CA. **Founded:** 1926. **Publications:** *Business Update* (Monthly).

48474 ■ Clovis Directory and Visitor Guide
325 Pollasky Ave.
Clovis, CA 93612-1139
Ph: (559)299-7363
Fax: (559)299-2969
Co. E-mail: info@clovischamber.com
URL: http://www.clovischamber.com
Contact: Jim Ware, President
Released: Annual

48475 ■ Clovis District Chamber of Commerce
325 Pollasky Ave.
Clovis, CA 93612-1139
Ph: (559)299-7363
Fax: (559)299-2969
Co. E-mail: info@clovischamber.com
URL: http://www.clovischamber.com
Contact: Jim Ware, President
Description: Strengthens the connections of homes, business, and community within Clovis area. **Publications:** *Clovis Directory and Visitor Guide* (Annual); *The Voice of Business* (Monthly).

48476 ■ Clubs and Organizations Directory
8158 Painter Ave.
Whittier, CA 90602
Ph: (562)698-9554
Fax: (562)693-2700
Co. E-mail: info@whittierchamber.com
URL: http://www.whittierchamber.com
Contact: Dean Harako, President
Released: Annual **Price:** $10.

48477 ■ Colfax Area Chamber of Commerce
99 S Railroad Ave.
Colfax, CA 95713
Ph: (530)346-8888
URL: http://www.colfaxarea.com
Contact: Frank Klein, President
Description: Promotes business and community development in Colfax, CA area. **Publications:** *Chamber Update.*

48478 ■ Colton Chamber of Commerce
655 N La Cadena Dr.
Colton, CA 92324
Ph: (909)825-2222
Fax: (909)824-1650
Co. E-mail: info@lomalindachamber.com
URL: http://coltonchamber.org
Contact: Tony Myrell, President
Description: Promotes business and community development in Colton, CA. **Founded:** 1906.

48479 ■ Commentator
6825 Fair Oaks Blvd., Ste. 100
Carmichael, CA 95608
Ph: (916)481-1002
Fax: (916)481-1003
Co. E-mail: admin@carmichaelchamber.com
URL: http://www.carmichaelchamber.com
Contact: Trish Harrington, President
Released: Monthly

48480 ■ Comments
300 Main St., Ste. A
Vacaville, CA 95688
Ph: (707)448-6424
Fax: (707)448-0424
Co. E-mail: jennifer@vacavillechamber.com
URL: http://www.vacavillechamber.com
Contact: Mark Creffield, President
Released: Monthly **Price:** included in membership dues.

48481 ■ Commerce
1556 1st St.
Napa, CA 94559
Ph: (707)226-7455
Fax: (707)226-1171
Co. E-mail: chris@napachamber.com
URL: http://www.napachamber.com
Contact: Chris Messina, President
Released: Monthly

48482 ■ Commerce Industrial Council Chamber of Commerce
6055 E Washington Blvd., No. 120
Commerce, CA 90040
Ph: (323)728-7222
Fax: (323)728-7565
URL: http://www.industrialcouncil.org
Contact: Helene Simmons, President
Description: Promotes commercial, industrial, education, and legislative actions that will benefit its members and all those concerned for the welfare of the community. **Founded:** 1959.

48483 ■ *Commerce Magazine Real Estate Guide*
924 Anacapa St., Ste. 1
Santa Barbara, CA 93101
Ph: (805)965-3023
Fax: (805)966-5954
Co. E-mail: info@sbchamber.org
URL: http://www.sbchamber.org
Contact: Zoe Taylor, President
Released: Monthly **Price:** $2.

48484 ■ *Communicator*
2400 E Ventura Blvd.
Camarillo, CA 93010
Ph: (805)484-4383
Fax: (805)484-1395
Co. E-mail: info@camarillochamber.org
URL: http://www.camarillochamber.org
Contact: Jennifer Wells, President
Released: Monthly **Price:** included in membership dues.

48485 ■ *The Communicator*
929 W Main St.
Ripon, CA 95366
Ph: (209)599-7519
Fax: (209)599-2286
Co. E-mail: execdirector@riponchamber.org
URL: http://www.riponchamber.org
Contact: Dorothy Booth, Executive Director

48486 ■ *The Communique*
1 Civic Center Cir.
Brea, CA 92821
Ph: (714)529-4938
Fax: (714)529-6103
Co. E-mail: answers@breachamber.com
URL: http://www.breachamber.com
Contact: Sharon Wagner, Chief Executive Officer
Released: Monthly

48487 ■ *Communique*
PO Box 868
Poway, CA 92074-0868
Ph: (858)748-0016
Fax: (858)748-1710
Co. E-mail: chamber@poway.com
URL: http://www.poway.com
Contact: Luanne Hulsizer, President
Released: Monthly

48488 ■ *Community Directory*
1100 Merrill St.
Menlo Park, CA 94025-4386
Ph: (650)325-2818
Fax: (650)325-0920
Co. E-mail: info@menloparkchamber.com
URL: http://www.menloparkchamber.com
Contact: Fran Dehn, President
Released: Annual

48489 ■ *Community Economic Profile*
1556 1st St.
Napa, CA 94559
Ph: (707)226-7455
Fax: (707)226-1171
Co. E-mail: chris@napachamber.com
URL: http://www.napachamber.com
Contact: Chris Messina, President
Released: Annual

48490 ■ *Community Guide*
3467 Castro Valley Blvd.
Castro Valley, CA 94546
Ph: (510)537-5300

Fax: (510)537-5335
Co. E-mail: info@castrovalleychamber.com
URL: http://www.edenareachamber.com
Contact: Brian Morrison, President
Released: Biennial

48491 ■ *Community Guide*
844 E Green St., Ste. 208
Pasadena, CA 91101
Ph: (626)795-3355
Fax: (626)795-5603
Co. E-mail: info@pasadena-chamber.org
URL: http://www.pasadena-chamber.org
Contact: Paul Little, President
Released: Periodic

48492 ■ *Community Guide*
PO Box 936
San Mateo, CA 94403
Ph: (650)401-2440
Fax: (650)401-2446
Co. E-mail: info@sanmateochamber.org
URL: http://www.sanmateoca.org
Contact: Linda Asbury, President
Released: Annual

48493 ■ *Community Guide*
73484 29th Palms Hwy.
Twentynine Palms, CA 92277
Ph: (760)367-3445
Fax: (760)367-3366
Co. E-mail: 29chamber@29chamber.org
URL: http://www.29chamber.org
Contact: Jodi Callahan, Executive Director
Released: Annual

48494 ■ *Community Guide and Membership Directory*
c/o Debi Bray, Pres./CEO
120 NE St.
Madera, CA 93638
Ph: (559)673-3563
Fax: (559)673-5009
Co. E-mail: dbray@maderachamber.com
URL: http://www.maderachamber.com
Contact: Debi Bray, President
Released: Annual

48495 ■ *Community Information and Business Guide*
811 S Sunset Ave.
West Covina, CA 91790-3599
Ph: (626)338-8496
Fax: (626)960-0511
Co. E-mail: glawson@westcovinachamber.com
URL: http://www.westcovinachamber.com
Released: Semiannual **Price:** free for members.

48496 ■ Compton Chamber of Commerce
c/o Ms. Lestean M. Johnson, Pres.
700 N Bullins Rd., Ste. 6-A
Compton, CA 90221
Ph: (310)631-8611
Co. E-mail: cptchamber@aol.com
URL: http://www.comptonchamberofcommerce.com
Contact: Ms. Lestean M. Johnson, President
Description: Promotes business and community development in Compton, CA. Sponsors festival. Publications: none. **Founded:** 1928.

48497 ■ *Conejo Business Times*
600 Hampshire Rd., Ste. 200
Westlake Village, CA 91361-2571
Ph: (805)370-0035
Fax: (805)370-1083
Co. E-mail: jlederer@conejochamber.org
URL: http://www.conejochamber.org
Contact: Jill Lederer, President
Released: Monthly

48498 ■ *The Connection*
781 Los Osos Valley Rd.
Los Osos, CA 93402
Ph: (805)528-4884

Fax: (805)528-8401
Co. E-mail: info@lobpchamber.org
URL: http://www.lobpchamber.org
Contact: Jim Stanfill, President
Released: Monthly **Price:** free for members; $15, /year for nonmembers.

48499 ■ Corning District Chamber of Commerce (CCC)
1110 Solano St.
Corning, CA 96021
Ph: (530)824-5550
Co. E-mail: corningchamber@sbcglobal.net
URL: http://corningchamber.org
Contact: Barbara Landavazo, President
Description: Promotes business and community development in Corning, CA. **Founded:** 1921. **Publications:** *Chamber Reporter* (Monthly).

48500 ■ Corona Chamber of Commerce
904 E 6th St.
Corona, CA 92879
Ph: (951)737-3350
Fax: (951)737-3531
Co. E-mail: info@coronachamber.org
URL: http://www.mychamber.org
Contact: Bobby Spiegel, President
Description: Promotes business and community development in Corona, CA. Sponsors Street Faire. **Founded:** 1914. **Publications:** *Business Directory* (Annual); *Chamber News* (Monthly). **Educational Activities:** Good Morning Corona (Monthly); New Member Orientation (Bimonthly).

48501 ■ Corona Del Mar Chamber of Commerce (CDMCC)
2855 E Coast Hwy., Ste. 101
Corona Del Mar, CA 92625
Ph: (949)673-4050
Fax: (949)673-3940
Co. E-mail: info@cdmchamber.com
URL: http://www.cdmchamber.com
Contact: Linda Leonhard, President
Description: Promotes business and community development in Corona Del Mar, CA. **Founded:** 1957. **Publications:** *Business*; *Village Voice* (Monthly).

48502 ■ Coronado Chamber of Commerce (CCC)
1125 10th St.
Coronado, CA 92118
Ph: (619)435-9260
Fax: (619)522-6577
Co. E-mail: info@coronadochamber.com
URL: http://www.coronadochamber.com
Contact: Karen Finch, Chief Executive Officer
Description: Promotes business and community development in Coronado, CA. Offers marketing consulting and relocation services. Conducts networking activities. Sponsors Christmas Open House. **Founded:** 1937. **Publications:** *Village Voice* (Monthly). **Telecommunication Services:** karen@coronadochamber.com.

48503 ■ Corte Madera Chamber of Commerce
129 Town Ctr.
Corte Madera, CA 94925
Ph: (415)924-0441
Fax: (415)924-1839
Co. E-mail: chamber@cortemadera.org
URL: http://www.cortemadera.org
Contact: Julie Kritzberger, Executive Director
Description: Promotes business and community development in Corte Madera, CA area.

48504 ■ Costa Mesa Chamber of Commerce
1700 Adams Ave., Ste. 101
Costa Mesa, CA 92626
Ph: (714)885-9090
Fax: (714)885-9094
Co. E-mail: info@costamesachamber.com
URL: http://www.costamesachamber.com
Contact: Ed Fawcett, President
Description: Promotes business and community development in Costa Mesa, CA. **Publications:** *Business Outlook* (Periodic); *Daily Pilot*.

48505 ■ Cotati Chamber of Commerce (CCC)
PO Box 592
Cotati, CA 94931
Ph: (707)795-5508
Fax: (707)795-5868
Co. E-mail: chamber@cotati.org
URL: http://www.cotati.org
Contact: Suzanne Whipple, Executive Director
Description: Promotes business and community development in Cotati, CA. **Founded:** 1940.

48506 ■ Cottonwood Chamber of Commerce
PO Box 584
Cottonwood, CA 96022-0584
Ph: (530)347-6800
Fax: (530)347-6800
Co. E-mail: cskudlarek@novb.com
URL: http://www.cottonwoodcofc.org
Description: Promotes business and community development in Cottonwood, CA area.

48507 ■ Covina Business
c/o Dawn Nelson, Pres./CEO
935 W Badillo St., Ste. 100
Covina, CA 91722
Ph: (626)967-4191
Fax: (626)966-9660
Co. E-mail: chamber@covina.org
URL: http://www.covina.org
Contact: Dawn Nelson, President
Released: 10/year **Price:** included in membership dues.

48508 ■ Covina Chamber of Commerce
c/o Dawn Nelson, Pres./CEO
935 W Badillo St., Ste. 100
Covina, CA 91722
Ph: (626)967-4191
Fax: (626)966-9660
Co. E-mail: chamber@covina.org
URL: http://www.covina.org
Contact: Dawn Nelson, President
Description: Promotes business and community development in Covina, CA. **Founded:** 1900. **Publications:** *Covina Business* (10/year). **Educational Activities:** Covina Open Golf Tournament (Annual). **Awards:** Citizen of the Year (Annual).

48509 ■ Crescent City-Del Norte County Chamber of Commerce
1001 Front St.
Crescent City, CA 95531
Ph: (707)464-3174
Free: 800-343-8300
Fax: (707)465-3891
URL: http://exploredelnorte.com
Contact: Lisa McKeown, President
URL(s): www.delnorte.org. **Description:** Promotes business and community development in the Del Norte County, CA area. Sponsors festivals, Crab races, Fourth of July, Sea Cruise Car Show. **Founded:** 1929.

48510 ■ Crescenta Valley Chamber of Commerce (CVCC)
3131 Foothill Blvd., Ste. D
La Crescenta, CA 91214
Ph: (818)248-4957
Fax: (818)248-9625
Co. E-mail: cvcoc@aol.com
URL: http://www.lacrescenta.org
Contact: Julia Rabago, Executive Director
URL(s): www.crescentavalleychamber.org. **Description:** Promotes business and community development in La Canada, La Crescenta, Montrose, and Sunland-Tujunga, CA. Sponsors Fourth of July Festival, Mayor's Prayer Breakfast, Tri-City Golf Tournament, 4 Cities Casino Night, annual Tea, Mary Pinola Smart-a-thon, and annual Family Festival of Fun. **Founded:** 1925. **Publications:** *Crescenta Valley Chamber of Commerce Business Directory*; *Foothill Business* (Monthly); *Crescenta Valley Chamber of Commerce Business Directory* (Annual); *Business and Community Services Directory*. **Educational Activities:** Crescenta Valley Chamber of Commerce Banquet (Annual). **Awards:** Business of the Year (Annual); Man and Woman of the Year (Annual); Volunteer of the Year (Annual).

48511 ■ Crestline Chamber of Commerce
PO Box 926
Crestline, CA 92325
Ph: (909)338-2706
Fax: (909)338-6588
Co. E-mail: info@crestlinechamber.net
URL: http://crestlinechamber.co
Contact: Jody Glaviano, President
Description: Promotes business and community development in Crestline, CA area.

48512 ■ Crockett Chamber of Commerce
PO Box 191
Crockett, CA 94525
Ph: (510)787-1155
Co. E-mail: crockettchamber@aol.com
URL: http://www.crockettca-chamber.org
Contact: Norma Black, President
Description: Promotes business and community development in Crockett, CA.

48513 ■ Culver City Business
6000 Sepulveda Blvd., Ste. 1260
Culver City, CA 90230
Ph: (310)287-3850
Fax: (310)390-0935
Co. E-mail: barbara@culvercitychamber.com
URL: http://www.culvercitychamber.com
Contact: Steven J. Rose, President
Released: Monthly

48514 ■ Culver City Chamber of Commerce
6000 Sepulveda Blvd., Ste. 1260
Culver City, CA 90230
Ph: (310)287-3850
Fax: (310)390-0935
Co. E-mail: barbara@culvercitychamber.com
URL: http://www.culvercitychamber.com
Contact: Steven J. Rose, President
Description: Promotes business and community development in Culver City, CA. **Founded:** 1923. **Publications:** *Culver City Business* (Monthly).

48515 ■ Cupertino Business
20455 Silverado Ave.
Cupertino, CA 95014
Ph: (408)252-7054
Fax: (408)252-0638
Co. E-mail: info@cupertino-chamber.org
URL: http://www.cupertino-chamber.org
Contact: John Zirelli, President
Released: Monthly **Price:** $1.25, /issue.

48516 ■ Cupertino Chamber of Commerce
20455 Silverado Ave.
Cupertino, CA 95014
Ph: (408)252-7054
Fax: (408)252-0638
Co. E-mail: info@cupertino-chamber.org
URL: http://www.cupertino-chamber.org
Contact: John Zirelli, President
Description: Promotes business and community development in Cupertino, CA. Collaborates with government, education, and private industry to assist and strengthen local businesses, to be an advocate for business, and affect the high quality of life for which Cupertino is known. Provides leadership and direction for community action. **Founded:** 1954. **Publications:** *Cupertino Business* (Monthly). **Educational Activities:** Finance Meeting (Monthly). **Awards:** Business of the Year (Annual); Citizen of the Year (Annual).

48517 ■ The Current
PO Box 1141
Fort Bragg, CA 95437
Ph: (707)961-6300
Fax: (707)964-2056
Co. E-mail: chamber@mcn.org
URL: http://www.mendocinocoast.com
Contact: Debra DeGraw, Executive Director
Released: Monthly

48518 ■ Currents
16209 1st St.
Guerneville, CA 95446
Ph: (707)869-9000
Free: 877-644-9001
Fax: (707)869-9009
Co. E-mail: news@russianriver.com
URL: http://www.russianriver.com
Contact: Margaret Kennett, President
Released: Monthly **Price:** included in membership dues.

48519 ■ Cypress Chamber of Commerce
5550 Cerritos Ave., Ste. D
Cypress, CA 90630
Ph: (714)827-2430
Fax: (714)827-1229
Co. E-mail: info@cypresschamber.org
URL: http://www.cypresschamber.org
Contact: Ed Munson, President
Description: Promotes business and community development in Cypress, CA area.

48520 ■ Daily Pilot
1700 Adams Ave., Ste. 101
Costa Mesa, CA 92626
Ph: (714)885-9090
Fax: (714)885-9094
Co. E-mail: info@costamesachamber.com
URL: http://www.costamesachamber.com
Contact: Ed Fawcett, President

48521 ■ Daly City - Colma Chamber of Commerce
355 Gellert Blvd., No. 138
Daly City, CA 94015-2665
Ph: (650)755-3900
Fax: (650)755-5160
Co. E-mail: gsarles@dalycity-colmachamber.org
URL: http://www.dalycity-colmachamber.org
Contact: Georgette Sales, President
Description: Promotes business and community development in the Daly City/Colma, CA area. Sponsors annual festival and annual scholarship competition. **Founded:** 1953.

48522 ■ Danville Area Chamber of Commerce (DACC)
c/o Melony Newman, Pres./CEO
117-E Town and Country Dr.
Danville, CA 94526
Ph: (925)837-4400
Fax: (925)837-5709
URL: http://www.danvilleareachamber.com
Contact: Melony Newman, President
Description: Promotes business and community development in the Danville, CA area. **Founded:** 1948. **Publications:** *Chamber Progress*.

48523 ■ Davis Chamber of Commerce
604 Third St.
Davis, CA 95616
Ph: (530)756-5160
Fax: (530)756-5190
Co. E-mail: director@davischamber.com
URL: http://www.davischamber.com
Contact: Kemble K Pope, Executive Director
Description: Promotes business and community development in the Davis, CA area. Sponsors competitions and festivals. **Founded:** 1905. **Publications:** *Davis Chamber Viewpoint* (Monthly). **Educational Activities:** Tour Day (Biennial). **Telecommunication Services:** ceo@davischamber.com.

48524 ■ Davis Chamber Viewpoint
604 Third St.
Davis, CA 95616
Ph: (530)756-5160
Fax: (530)756-5190
Co. E-mail: director@davischamber.com
URL: http://www.davischamber.com
Contact: Kemble K Pope, Executive Director
Released: Monthly

48525 ■ Death Valley Chamber of Commerce
PO Box 157
Shoshone, CA 92384

Ph: (760)852-4524
Co. E-mail: deathvalleychamber@gmail.com
URL: http://www.deathvalleychamber.org
Contact: Amy L. Noel, President
Description: Seeks to advance the general welfare and prosperity of Death Valley. Promotes business community and upholds the economic, civil, commercial, industrial, and educational interests of the community. **Founded:** 1988.

48526 ■ Delano Chamber of Commerce
931 High St.
Delano, CA 93215
Ph: (661)725-2518
Co. E-mail: info@chamberofdelano.com
URL: http://www.chamberofdelano.com
Description: Promotes business and community development in Delano, CA. **Founded:** 1924. **Publications:** *Business Link.*

48527 ■ Desert Hot Springs Chamber of Commerce
11-999 Palm Dr.
Desert Hot Springs, CA 92240
Ph: (760)329-6403
Free: 800-346-3347
Fax: (760)329-2833
Co. E-mail: info2@deserthotsprings.com
URL: http://www.deserthotsprings.com
Contact: Gary Piotrowski, President
URL(s): www.dhschamber.org. **Description:** Promotes business and community development in Desert Hot Springs, CA. Operates visit information center. Sponsors monthly mixer. **Founded:** 1965.

48528 ■ Diamond Bar Chamber of Commerce
21845 E Copley Dr., Ste. 1170
Diamond Bar, CA 91765-6401
Ph: (909)860-1904
Co. E-mail: info@diamondbarchamber.com
URL: http://www.ci.diamond-bar.ca.us/Index.aspx?page=219
Contact: Steve Smith, Chief Executive Officer
Description: Aims to advance the interests of the business community in the City of Diamond Bar and the surrounding region. **Founded:** 1983. **Publications:** *Diamond Bar Business View* (Monthly). **Educational Activities:** Diamond Bar Chamber of Commerce Board meeting (Monthly).

48529 ■ Dinuba Chamber of Commerce
210 N L St.
Dinuba, CA 93618
Ph: (559)591-2707
Fax: (559)591-2712
Co. E-mail: info@dinubacommerce.org
URL: http://www.dinubachamber.com
Contact: Tony Carillo, President
Description: Promotes business and community development in Dinuba, CA. Conducts Raisin Day festival. **Founded:** 1912.

48530 ■ DIRECTIONS
14491 Beach Blvd., Ste. B
Westminster, CA 92683
Ph: (714)898-9648
Fax: (714)373-1499
Co. E-mail: biz@westminsterchamber.org
URL: http://westminsterchamber.org
Contact: Crystal R. Wadsworth, Executive Director
Released: Quarterly

48531 ■ Directory of Businesses
11650 Iberia Pl., Ste. 220
San Diego, CA 92128
Ph: (858)487-1767
Fax: (858)487-8051
URL: http://www.sdncc.com
Contact: Debra Rosen, President
Released: Periodic

48532 ■ Discover Gilroy
7471 Monterey St.
Gilroy, CA 95020
Ph: (408)842-6437

Fax: (408)842-6010
Co. E-mail: chamber@gilroy.org
URL: http://www.gilroy.org
Contact: Susan Valenta, President
Released: Annual

48533 ■ Dixon District Chamber of Commerce
PO Box 159
Dixon, CA 95620
Ph: (707)678-2650
Fax: (707)678-3654
Co. E-mail: info@dixonchamber.org
URL: http://dixonchamber.org
Contact: Tiffany Wing, Executive Director
Description: Promotes business and community development in the Dixon, CA area. **Founded:** 1909. **Awards:** Citizen of the Year (Annual).

48534 ■ Downey Business
11131 Brookshire Ave.
Downey, CA 90241-3860
Ph: (562)923-2191
Fax: (562)869-0461
Co. E-mail: info@downeychamber.com
URL: http://www.downeychamber.com
Contact: Susan Nordin, Executive Director

48535 ■ Downey Chamber of Commerce (DCC)
11131 Brookshire Ave.
Downey, CA 90241-3860
Ph: (562)923-2191
Fax: (562)869-0461
Co. E-mail: info@downeychamber.com
URL: http://www.downeychamber.com
Contact: Susan Nordin, Executive Director
Description: Promotes business and community development in Downey, CA. Seeks to advocate and support a healthy and profitable business environment which improves the quality of life in Downey. **Founded:** 1903. **Publications:** *Buyer's Guide and Chamber Directory* (Semiannual); *Downey Business.*

48536 ■ Duarte Business
PO Box 1438
Duarte, CA 91009-4438
Ph: (626)357-3333
Fax: (626)357-3645
Co. E-mail: diana@duartechamber.com
URL: http://www.duartechamber.com
Contact: Jim Kirchner, President
Released: Biennial

48537 ■ Duarte Chamber of Commerce (DCC)
PO Box 1438
Duarte, CA 91009-4438
Ph: (626)357-3333
Fax: (626)357-3645
Co. E-mail: diana@duartechamber.com
URL: http://www.duartechamber.com
Contact: Jim Kirchner, President
Description: Promotes business and community development in Duarte, CA. **Founded:** 1921. **Publications:** *Duarte View* (Bimonthly); *Duarte Business* (Biennial); *Duarte Overview* (Annual); *Duarte View* (Bimonthly). **Telecommunication Services:** jim@duartechamber.com.

48538 ■ Duarte Overview
PO Box 1438
Duarte, CA 91009-4438
Ph: (626)357-3333
Fax: (626)357-3645
Co. E-mail: diana@duartechamber.com
URL: http://www.duartechamber.com
Contact: Jim Kirchner, President
Released: Annual **Price:** free.

48539 ■ Duarte View
PO Box 1438
Duarte, CA 91009-4438
Ph: (626)357-3333
Fax: (626)357-3645
Co. E-mail: diana@duartechamber.com
URL: http://www.duartechamber.com
Contact: Jim Kirchner, President
Released: Bimonthly

48540 ■ Dublin Chamber of Commerce
7080 Donlon Way, Ste. 110
Dublin, CA 94568
Ph: (925)828-6200
Fax: (925)828-4247
Co. E-mail: info2@dublinchamberofcommerce.org
URL: http://www.dublinchamberofcommerce.org
Contact: Chuck Tyler, Chairman
Description: Promotes business and community development in Dublin, CA. **Founded:** 1968.

48541 ■ Dunsmuir Chamber of Commerce
5915 Dunsmuir Ave., Ste. No. 100
Dunsmuir, CA 96025
Ph: (530)235-2177
Free: 800-386-7684
Fax: (530)235-0911
URL: http://dunsmuir.com/index.php
Contact: Barbara Cross, President
Description: Promotes business and community development in Dunsmuir, CA.

48542 ■ E-Commerce Newsletter
26790 Ynez Ct.
Temecula, CA 92591
Ph: (951)676-5090
Free: 866-676-5090
Fax: (951)676-5090
Co. E-mail: info@temecula.org
URL: http://www.temecula.org
Contact: Alice Sullivan, President
Released: Monthly

48543 ■ Eagle Rock Chamber of Commerce
PO Box 41354
Eagle Rock, CA 90041
Ph: (323)257-2197
Fax: (323)257-4245
Co. E-mail: erccwebguy@aol.com
URL: http://www.eaglerockchamberofcommerce.com
Contact: Michael Tolj, President
Description: Promotes business and community development in Eagle Rock, CA area.

48544 ■ East County Business News
c/o Scott Alevy, Pres./CEO
201 S Magnolia Ave.
El Cajon, CA 92020-4525
Ph: (619)440-6161
Fax: (619)440-6164
Co. E-mail: ceo@eastcountychamber.org
URL: http://www.eastcountychamber.org
Contact: Scott Alevy, President
Released: Monthly **Price:** $10, /year.

48545 ■ East Los Angeles Chamber of Commerce (ELACOC)
PO Box 63220
Los Angeles, CA 90063-0220
Ph: (323)722-2005
Fax: (323)722-2405
Co. E-mail: elacoc@pacbell.net
URL: http://www.elacoc.com
Contact: Joe Sandoval, President
Description: Promotes business and community development in East Los Angeles, CA. **Founded:** 1988.

48546 ■ East Valley Business
82-921 Indio Blvd.
Indio, CA 92201
Ph: (760)347-0676
Free: 800-755-8440
Fax: (760)347-6069
Co. E-mail: info@indiochamber.org
URL: http://www.indiochamber.org
Contact: Patrick Swarthout, Chairman
Released: Monthly

48547 ■ Eastern Plumas Chamber of Commerce
PO Box 1043
Blairsden, CA 96103
Ph: (530)836-6811
Free: 800-995-6057

Fax: (530)836-6809
Co. E-mail: epluchmb@psln.com
URL: http://www.easternplumaschamber.com
Contact: Linda Johnson, Assistant
Description: Promotes business and community development in Eastern Plumas, CA. Sponsors local festivals; conducts competitions.

48548 ■ *Echo*
10315 Mission Gorge Rd.
Santee, CA 92071
Ph: (619)449-6572
Fax: (619)562-7906
Co. E-mail: info@santee-chamber.org
URL: http://www.santee-chamber.org
Contact: Warren H. Savage, Jr., Executive Director
Released: Monthly

48549 ■ *Economic Bulletin*
402 W Broadway, Ste. 1000
San Diego, CA 92101-3585
Ph: (619)544-1300
Co. E-mail: webinfo@sdchamber.org
URL: http://www.sdchamber.org
Contact: Ruben Barrales, President
E-mail: rbarrales@sdchamber.org
Released: Monthly

48550 ■ El Centro Chamber of Commerce and Visitors Bureau
1095 S 4th St.
El Centro, CA 92243
Ph: (760)352-3681
Fax: (760)352-3246
Co. E-mail: info@elcentrochamber.com
URL: http://www.elcentrochamber.org
Contact: Darletta D. Willis, Chief Executive Officer
Description: Promotes business and community development in El Centro, CA. **Founded:** 1933. **Awards:** Star Award (Monthly).

48551 ■ El Cerrito Chamber of Commerce (ECCC)
PO Box 538
El Cerrito, CA 94530
Ph: (510)705-1202
Co. E-mail: info@elcerritochamber.org
URL: http://www.elcerritochamber.org
Contact: Judy Pope, President
Description: Promotes business and community development in El Cerrito, CA. **Founded:** 1936. **Publications:** *Byline* (Monthly); *California Chamber Advocate* (Periodic); *Membership and Business Directory* (Periodic).

48552 ■ El Dorado County Chamber of Commerce
542 Main St.
Placerville, CA 95667-5610
Ph: (530)621-5885
Free: 800-457-6279
Fax: (530)642-1624
Co. E-mail: admin@eldoradocounty.org
URL: http://www.eldoradocounty.org
Contact: Kirk Bone, President
Description: Promotes business and community development in El Dorado County, CA. **Founded:** 1915. **Publications:** *Business Directory* (Annual); *El Dorado Magazine*; *Ranch Marketing Guide*. **Awards:** College and Adult Education Scholarship (Annual).

48553 ■ El Dorado Hills Chamber of Commerce
2085 Vine St., Ste. 105
El Dorado Hills, CA 95762
Ph: (916)933-1335
Fax: (916)933-5908
Co. E-mail: chamber@eldoradohillschamber.com
URL: http://www.eldoradohillschamber.com
Contact: Debbie Manning, President
Description: Aims to advance the interests of the business community in the City of El Dorado Hills, CA.

48554 ■ *El Dorado Magazine*
542 Main St.
Placerville, CA 95667-5610
Ph: (530)621-5885
Free: 800-457-6279

Fax: (530)642-1624
Co. E-mail: admin@eldoradocounty.org
URL: http://www.eldoradocounty.org
Contact: Kirk Bone, President

48555 ■ El Segundo Chamber of Commerce
427 Main St.
El Segundo, CA 90245
Ph: (310)322-1220
Fax: (310)322-6880
Co. E-mail: director@elsegundochamber.org
URL: http://www.elsegundochamber.org
Contact: Marsha Hansen, Executive Director
Description: Promotes business and community development in El Segundo, CA. Sponsors Main St. Run, Richmond St. Fair, and Christmas Parade. Conducts Business Outlook, business expo, seminars, and networking breakfasts. **Founded:** 1948. **Awards:** Ambassador of the Year (Annual); Business of the Year (Annual); Business Person of the Year (Annual); Chamber Salute to El Segundo; Salute to Businesses Supporting Education.

48556 ■ El Sobrante Chamber of Commerce
3769 San Pablo Dam Rd.
El Sobrante, CA 94803
Ph: (510)223-0757
URL: http://elsobrantechamber.com
Contact: Jennifer Arrouzet, President
Description: Promotes business and community development in the El Sobrante, CA area.

48557 ■ Elk Grove Chamber of Commerce
9370 Studio Ct., Ste. 110
Elk Grove, CA 95758
Ph: (916)691-3760
Fax: (916)691-3810
Co. E-mail: chamber@elkgroveca.com
URL: http://www.elkgroveca.com
Contact: Angela Perry, Executive Director
Description: Promotes business and community development in Elk Grove, CA. **Founded:** 1953. **Publications:** *Focus on Business*. **Educational Activities:** Business Expo (Annual).

48558 ■ Emeryville Chamber of Commerce
3980 Harlan St.
Emeryville, CA 94608-3771
Ph: (510)652-5223
Fax: (510)652-4223
Co. E-mail: info@emeryvillechamber.com
URL: http://www.emeryvillechamber.com
Contact: Bob Canter, President
Description: Promotes business and community development in Emeryville, CA. **Publications:** *San Francisco Business Times* (Weekly). **Educational Activities:** Golf Tournament (Annual).

48559 ■ Encinitas Chamber and Visitors Center
No. 112, 1106 2nd St.
Encinitas, CA 92024
Ph: (760)753-6041
Fax: (760)753-6270
Co. E-mail: asst@encinitaschamber.com
URL: http://www.encinitaschamber.com
Contact: Bob Gattinella, President
Description: Promotes business and community development in Encinitas, CA. **Founded:** 1966. **Publications:** *What to Know* (Monthly). **Telecommunication Services:** info@encinitaschamber.com.

48560 ■ Encino Chamber of Commerce
4933 Balboa Blvd.
Encino, CA 91316-3497
Ph: (818)789-4711
Fax: (818)789-2485
Co. E-mail: info@encinochamber.org
URL: http://www.encinochamber.org
Contact: Ms. Diana Donovan, Chief Executive Officer
Description: Promotes business and community development in Encino, CA. **Founded:** 1936. **Publications:** *Encino Chamber of Commerce Envoy* (Monthly).

48561 ■ *Encino Chamber of Commerce Envoy*
4933 Balboa Blvd.
Encino, CA 91316-3497
Ph: (818)789-4711
Fax: (818)789-2485
Co. E-mail: info@encinochamber.org
URL: http://www.encinochamber.org
Contact: Ms. Diana Donovan, Chief Executive Officer
Released: Monthly **Price:** free for members.

48562 ■ *Enterprise*
10224 Fair Oaks Blvd.
Fair Oaks, CA 95628
Ph: (916)967-2903
Fax: (916)967-8536
Co. E-mail: info@fairoakschamber.com
URL: http://www.fairoakschamber.com
Contact: Jan Bass Otto, Executive Director
Released: Monthly

48563 ■ *Enterprise*
200 W Magnolia Blvd.
Burbank, CA 91502-1724
Ph: (818)846-3111
Fax: (818)846-0109
Co. E-mail: info@burbankchamber.org
URL: http://www.burbankchamber.org
Contact: Gary Olson, President
Released: Monthly

48564 ■ Escalon Chamber of Commerce
PO Box 222
Escalon, CA 95320
Ph: (209)838-2793
Co. E-mail: escaloncofc@gmail.com
URL: http://www.escalonchamberofcommerce.org
Contact: Pat Brown, President
Description: Promotes business and community development in the Escalon, CA area. Conducts charitable activities; sponsors competitions and festivals. **Founded:** 1950.

48565 ■ Escondido Chamber of Commerce
720 N Broadway
Escondido, CA 92025-1893
Ph: (760)745-2125
Fax: (760)745-1183
Co. E-mail: info@escondidochamber.org
URL: http://www.escondidochamber.org
Contact: Harvey J. Mitchell, President
Description: Promotes business and community development in Escondido, CA. **Founded:** 1910. **Publications:** *Business Advocate* (Monthly); *Business Resource Directory* (Annual). **Educational Activities:** Business Expo (Annual); Escondido Street Faires (Semiannual). **Awards:** Business Leader of the Year (Annual); Business of the Year (Annual).

48566 ■ Esparto District Chamber of Commerce
PO Box 194
Esparto, CA 95627
Ph: (530)787-3242
Fax: (530)787-3373
Co. E-mail: espartonews@ymail.com
URL: http://www.espartochamber.com
URL(s): www.espartoregionalchamber.com. **Description:** Promotes business and community development in Esparto District, CA. Sponsors Capay Valley Almond Festival.

48567 ■ *The Eureka Chamber Review*
2112 Broadway
Eureka, CA 95501
Ph: (707)442-3738
Free: 800-356-6381
Fax: (707)442-0079
URL: http://www.eurekachamber.com
Contact: J. Warren Hockaday, President
Released: Monthly

48568 ■ *The Exchange*
2078 Bonita Ave.
La Verne, CA 91750
Ph: (909)593-5265

Fax: (909)596-0579
Co. E-mail: info@lavernechamber.org
URL: http://www.lavernechamber.org
Contact: Brian McNerney, President
Released: Bimonthly

48569 ■ Exeter Chamber of Commerce
101 W Pine St.
Exeter, CA 93221
Ph: (559)592-2919
Fax: (559)592-3720
Co. E-mail: chamber@exeterchamber.com
URL: http://Zwww.exeterchamber.com
Contact: Sandy Blankenship, Executive Director
Description: Promotes and supports business and community development in Exeter, CA. **Founded:** 1921. **Publications:** *Available Properties Listing Guide* (Monthly); *Chamber Report* (Monthly). **Educational Activities:** Exeter Chamber of Commerce Festival (Annual).

48570 ■ *Explore 99 Things*
PO Box 1429
Marysville, CA 95901
Ph: (530)743-6501
Fax: (530)741-8645
Co. E-mail: chamber@yubasutterchamber.com
URL: http://www.yubasutterchamber.com
Contact: Kristy Santucci, Chief Executive Officer
Released: Annual

48571 ■ *Fair Oaks Business Directory*
10224 Fair Oaks Blvd.
Fair Oaks, CA 95628
Ph: (916)967-2903
Fax: (916)967-8536
Co. E-mail: info@fairoakschamber.com
URL: http://www.fairoakschamber.com
Contact: Jan Bass Otto, Executive Director
Released: Annual

48572 ■ Fair Oaks Chamber of Commerce
10224 Fair Oaks Blvd.
Fair Oaks, CA 95628
Ph: (916)967-2903
Fax: (916)967-8536
Co. E-mail: info@fairoakschamber.com
URL: http://www.fairoakschamber.com
Contact: Jan Bass Otto, Executive Director
Description: Promotes business and community development in Fair Oaks, CA. Sponsors Fiesta, Business/Networking Fair, Octoberfest, Safe Halloween, Business/Education Internships, Christmas in Village, and Summer Concerts In The Park. **Founded:** 1954. **Publications:** *Enterprise* (Monthly); *Fair Oaks Business Directory* (Annual). **Educational Activities:** Mixer (Monthly); Fair Oaks Chamber of Commerce Party (Monthly).

48573 ■ Fallbrook Chamber of Commerce
111 South Main Ave.
Fallbrook, CA 92028-2848
Ph: (760)728-5845
Co. E-mail: richard.kennedy@fallbrookchamber-ofcommerce.com
URL: http://www.fallbrookchamberofcommerce.org
Contact: Richard Kennedy, Chief Executive Officer
Description: Promotes business and community development in Fallbrook, CA. Sponsors Avocado Harvest Festival and Avocado Open Golf Tournament. **Founded:** 1943. **Publications:** *Village Voice* (Monthly). **Educational Activities:** Sundowners (Monthly).

48574 ■ Fillmore Chamber of Commerce
PO Box 815
Fillmore, CA 93016-0815
Ph: (805)524-0351
Fax: (805)524-2551
Co. E-mail: info@fillmorechamber.com
URL: http://www.fillmorechamber.com
Description: Promotes business and community development in Fillmore, CA. **Founded:** 1948.

48575 ■ *Focus on Business*
9370 Studio Ct., Ste. 110
Elk Grove, CA 95758
Ph: (916)691-3760

Fax: (916)691-3810
Co. E-mail: chamber@elkgroveca.com
URL: http://www.elkgroveca.com
Contact: Angela Perry, Executive Director

48576 ■ *Focus on Business*
475 14th St.
Oakland, CA 94612-1903
Ph: (510)874-4800
Fax: (510)839-8817
Co. E-mail: lana@oaklandchamber.com
URL: http://www.oaklandchamber.com
Contact: Joseph Haraburda, President
Released: Monthly **Price:** free.

48577 ■ Folsom Chamber of Commerce
200 Wool St.
Folsom, CA 95630
Ph: (916)985-2698
Fax: (916)985-4117
Co. E-mail: reception@folsomchamber.com
URL: http://www.folsomchamber.com
Contact: Joseph P. Gagliardi, President
Description: Promotes business and community development in Folsom, CA. **Publications:** *Folsom Magazine* (Annual); *All About Folsom Business* (Monthly); *Business Directory* (Annual); *Folsom Magazine* (Annual). **Educational Activities:** Folsom Chamber of Commerce Luncheon (Monthly).

48578 ■ *Folsom Magazine*
200 Wool St.
Folsom, CA 95630
Ph: (916)985-2698
Fax: (916)985-4117
Co. E-mail: reception@folsomchamber.com
URL: http://www.folsomchamber.com
Contact: Joseph P. Gagliardi, President
Released: Annual **Price:** included in membership dues.

48579 ■ Fontana Chamber of Commerce (FCC)
8491 Sierra Ave.
Fontana, CA 92335-3860
Ph: (909)822-4433
Fax: (909)822-6238
Co. E-mail: info@fontanachamber.com
URL: http://www.fontanachamber.com
Contact: Jan Hudson, President
Description: Promotes business and community development in the Fontana, CA area. **Founded:** 1941.

48580 ■ *Foothill Business*
3131 Foothill Blvd., Ste. D
La Crescenta, CA 91214
Ph: (818)248-4957
Fax: (818)248-9625
Co. E-mail: cvcoc@aol.com
URL: http://www.lacrescenta.org
Contact: Julia Rabago, Executive Director
Released: Monthly **Price:** included in membership dues.

48581 ■ Foresthill Divide Chamber of Commerce
PO Box 346
Foresthill, CA 95631
Ph: (530)367-2474
Fax: (530)367-2474
Co. E-mail: foresthillchamber@ftcnet.net
URL: http://www.foresthillchamber.org
Contact: Rick Velgos, President
Description: Promotes business and community development in Foresthill, CA.

48582 ■ Fort Bragg - Mendocino Coast Chamber of Commerce
PO Box 1141
Fort Bragg, CA 95437
Ph: (707)961-6300
Fax: (707)964-2056
Co. E-mail: chamber@mcn.org
URL: http://www.mendocinocoast.com
Contact: Debra DeGraw, Executive Director
Description: Promotes business and community development in the Mendocino Coast area. Sponsors whale festivals every March. **Founded:** 1951. **Publi-**

cations: *The Current* (Monthly); *Medocino Coast Business Directory*; *Mendocino Map and Visitor Information Guide* (Annual).

48583 ■ Fortuna Chamber of Commerce
735 14th St.
Fortuna, CA 95540
Ph: (707)725-3959
Free: 800-426-8166
Fax: (707)725-4766
Co. E-mail: chamber@sunnyfortuna.com
URL: http://www.chamber.sunnyfortuna.com
Description: Promotes business and community development in Fortuna, CA. Sponsors festival.

48584 ■ Foster City Chamber of Commerce
1031 E Hillside Blvd., Ste. F
Foster City, CA 94404
Ph: (650)573-7600
Fax: (650)573-5201
Co. E-mail: chamber@fostercitychamber.com
URL: http://www.fostercitychamber.com
Contact: Mae Heagerty-Matos, Chief Executive Officer
Description: Promotes business and community development in Foster City, CA. Sponsors annual Art and Wine Festival. **Founded:** 1972.

48585 ■ Fountain Valley Chamber of Commerce
8840 Warner Ave., Ste. 207
Fountain Valley, CA 92708
Ph: (714)841-3822
Fax: (714)841-3877
Co. E-mail: bwhite@fvchamber.com
URL: http://www.fvchamber.com
Contact: Leslie VanDeusen, President
Description: Promotes business and community development in Fountain Valley, CA. **Awards:** Ambassador of the Year (Annual); Business of the Year (Annual); Corporate Sponsor Awards (Annual); Ethics in America Award (Annual); Firefighter of the Year (Annual); Police Officer of the Year (Annual).

48586 ■ *Fremont Business Review*
39488 Stevenson Pl., Ste. 100
Fremont, CA 94539
Ph: (510)795-2244
Fax: (510)795-2240
Co. E-mail: fmtcc@fremontbusiness.com
URL: http://www.fremontbusiness.com
Contact: Cindy Bonior, President
Released: Monthly

48587 ■ Fremont Chamber of Commerce (FCC)
39488 Stevenson Pl., Ste. 100
Fremont, CA 94539
Ph: (510)795-2244
Fax: (510)795-2240
Co. E-mail: fmtcc@fremontbusiness.com
URL: http://www.fremontbusiness.com
Contact: Cindy Bonior, President
Description: Promotes business and community development in Fremont, CA. Sponsors Festival of the Arts. Conducts business education and assistance programs. **Founded:** 1956. **Publications:** *Fremont Business Review* (Monthly); *Fremont Chamber of Commerce Membership Directory and Community Guide* (Annual). **Educational Activities:** Festival of the Arts (Annual). **Telecommunication Services:** cbonior@fremontbusiness.com.

48588 ■ *Fremont Chamber of Commerce Membership Directory and Community Guide*
39488 Stevenson Pl., Ste. 100
Fremont, CA 94539
Ph: (510)795-2244
Fax: (510)795-2240
Co. E-mail: fmtcc@fremontbusiness.com
URL: http://www.fremontbusiness.com
Contact: Cindy Bonior, President
Released: Annual **Price:** $10, /year for nonmembers; $5, /year for members.

48589 ■ *Fresno Business Newsletter*
2331 Fresno St.
Fresno, CA 93721
Ph: (559)495-4800

Fax: (559)495-4811
Co. E-mail: info@fresnochamber.com
URL: http://www.fresnochamber.com
Contact: Al Smith, President
Released: Monthly

48590 ■ Fullerton Business Review
444 N Harbor Blvd., No. 200
Fullerton, CA 92832
Ph: (714)871-3100
Fax: (714)871-2871
Co. E-mail: tharvey@fullertonchamber.com
URL: http://www.fullertonchamber.com
Contact: Theresa Harvey, Executive Director
Released: Biweekly

48591 ■ Fullerton Chamber of Commerce
444 N Harbor Blvd., No. 200
Fullerton, CA 92832
Ph: (714)871-3100
Fax: (714)871-2871
Co. E-mail: tharvey@fullertonchamber.com
URL: http://www.fullertonchamber.com
Contact: Theresa Harvey, Executive Director
Description: Promotes business and community development in Fullerton, CA. **Founded:** 1895. **Publications:** Fullerton Business Review (Biweekly). **Educational Activities:** Government Affairs (Monthly).

48592 ■ Galt District Chamber of Commerce (GCC)
PO Box 1446
Galt, CA 95632
Ph: (209)745-2529
Co. E-mail: info@galtchamber.com
URL: http://www.galtchamber.com
Contact: David Herburger, Secretary
Description: Promotes business and community development in Galt, CA. Sponsors the Merchant's Fair and Galt Strawberry Festival. **Founded:** 1940. **Publications:** Galt Today (Bimonthly). **Awards:** Annual President of Chamber Award (Annual); Business of the Year (Annual).

48593 ■ Galt Today
PO Box 1446
Galt, CA 95632
Ph: (209)745-2529
Co. E-mail: info@galtchamber.com
URL: http://www.galtchamber.com
Contact: David Herburger, Secretary
Released: Bimonthly **Price:** free.

48594 ■ Garberville-Redway Area Chamber of Commerce (GRCC)
782 Redwood Dr.
Garberville, CA 95542
Ph: (707)923-2613
Fax: (707)923-4789
Co. E-mail: chamber@garberville.org
URL: http://www.garberville.org
Contact: Dee Way, Executive Director
Description: Promotes business, tourism, and community development in Southern Humboldt County, CA. Sponsors Shakespeare at Benbow Lake, Culpepper, and Merriweather circus. Operates visitor and business information center. **Founded:** 1941.

48595 ■ Garden Grove Chamber of Commerce
12866 Main St., Ste. 102
Garden Grove, CA 92840-5298
Ph: (714)638-7950
Free: 800-959-5560
Fax: (714)636-6672
Co. E-mail: elizabeth@gardengrovechamber.com
URL: http://gardengrovechamber.org
Contact: Jeremy Harris, President
Description: Aims to serve the needs of the Garden Grove business community. Represents professionals from a wide variety of companies who are committed to promoting business in the community. **Founded:** 1907.

48596 ■ Gardena Chamber News
1204 W Gardena Blvd., Ste. E
Gardena, CA 90247
Ph: (310)532-9905

Free: 888-399-2948
Fax: (310)329-7307
Co. E-mail: info@gardenachamber.org
URL: http://www.gardenachamber.com
Contact: Henry Hoskins, President
Released: Monthly

48597 ■ Gardena Valley Chamber of Commerce (GVCC)
1204 W Gardena Blvd., Ste. E
Gardena, CA 90247
Ph: (310)532-9905
Free: 888-399-2948
Fax: (310)329-7307
Co. E-mail: info@gardenachamber.org
URL: http://www.gardenachamber.com
Contact: Henry Hoskins, President
Description: Promotes business and community development in Gardena, CA. Conducts Business Expo and golf tournament. Sponsors fundraising activities. **Founded:** 1912. **Publications:** Gardena Valley Business Directory; Gardena Chamber News (Monthly); Gardena Valley Chamber of Commerce Business Directory (Annual); Gardena Valley Business Directory (Annual).

48598 ■ Gardena Valley Chamber of Commerce Business Directory
1204 W Gardena Blvd., Ste. E
Gardena, CA 90247
Ph: (310)532-9905
Free: 888-399-2948
Fax: (310)329-7307
Co. E-mail: info@gardenachamber.org
URL: http://www.gardenachamber.com
Contact: Henry Hoskins, President
Released: Annual

48599 ■ The Gem
78-275 Calle Tampico
La Quinta, CA 92253
Ph: (760)564-3199
Fax: (760)564-3111
Co. E-mail: david@lqchamber.com
URL: http://www.lqchamber.com
Contact: David Archer, President
Released: Monthly

48600 ■ Geyserville Chamber of Commerce
PO Box 276
Geyserville, CA 95441
Ph: (707)857-3745
Co. E-mail: moreinfo@geyservillecc.com
URL: http://www.geyservillecc.com
Contact: Vickie Norris, Secretary, Administration
Description: Promotes business and community development in Geyserville, CA. **Founded:** 1976. **Awards:** Geyserville Citizens of the Year (Annual).

48601 ■ Gilroy Business Focus
7471 Monterey St.
Gilroy, CA 95020
Ph: (408)842-6437
Fax: (408)842-6010
Co. E-mail: chamber@gilroy.org
URL: http://www.gilroy.org
Contact: Susan Valenta, President
Released: Monthly

48602 ■ Gilroy Chamber of Commerce (GCC)
7471 Monterey St.
Gilroy, CA 95020
Ph: (408)842-6437
Fax: (408)842-6010
Co. E-mail: chamber@gilroy.org
URL: http://www.gilroy.org
Contact: Susan Valenta, President
Description: Seeks to promote economic vitality in the Gilroy community. Provides marketing opportunities for businesses for an increased network. Has partnerships with City of Gilroy, Gilroy Economic Development Corp., Gilroy Visitors Bureau, Leadership Gilroy, Gilroy Downtown Development Corp. and school district. **Founded:** 1952. **Publications:** Discover Gilroy (Annual); Gilroy Business Focus (Monthly).

48603 ■ Glendale Business
200 S Louise St.
Glendale, CA 91205
Ph: (818)240-7870
Fax: (818)240-2872
Co. E-mail: info@glendalechamber.com
URL: http://www.glendalechamber.com
Contact: Sharon Beauchamp, Executive Vice President
Released: Monthly

48604 ■ Glendale Chamber of Commerce (GCC)
200 S Louise St.
Glendale, CA 91205
Ph: (818)240-7870
Fax: (818)240-2872
Co. E-mail: info@glendalechamber.com
URL: http://www.glendalechamber.com
Contact: Sharon Beauchamp, Executive Vice President
Description: Promotes business and community development in Glendale, CA. **Founded:** 1910. **Publications:** Glendale Business (Monthly).

48605 ■ Glendora Chamber of Commerce
131 E Foothill Blvd.
Glendora, CA 91741-3336
Ph: (626)963-4128
Fax: (626)914-4822
Co. E-mail: info@glendora-chamber.org
URL: http://www.glendora-chamber.org
Contact: Linda Hermann, President
Description: Promotes business and community development in Glendora, CA. **Founded:** 1916. **Publications:** Business View (Monthly). **Educational Activities:** Expo (Annual).

48606 ■ Golden Triangle Chamber of Commerce
1011 Camino Del Mar, No. 256
Del Mar, CA 92014
Ph: (858)350-1253
Co. E-mail: financialbodyguard@yahoo.com
URL: http://goldentrianglechamber.com
Contact: George Schmall, President
Description: Strengthens business and the community through leadership, prosperity, information, communication, and community involvement. **Founded:** 1985.

48607 ■ Goleta Business Update
PO Box 781
Goleta, CA 93117
Ph: (805)967-2500
Free: 800-646-5382
Co. E-mail: info@goletavalley.com
URL: http://goletavalley.com
Contact: Kristen Miller Amyx, President
Released: Monthly

48608 ■ Goleta Magazine
PO Box 781
Goleta, CA 93117
Ph: (805)967-2500
Free: 800-646-5382
Co. E-mail: info@goletavalley.com
URL: http://goletavalley.com
Contact: Kristen Miller Amyx, President
Released: Annual

48609 ■ Goleta Valley Chamber of Commerce (GVCOC)
PO Box 781
Goleta, CA 93117
Ph: (805)967-2500
Free: 800-646-5382
Co. E-mail: info@goletavalley.com
URL: http://goletavalley.com
Contact: Kristen Miller Amyx, President
Description: Promotes business and community development in the Goleta Valley, CA area. Provides guest speakers. Sponsors Goleta Valley Days Lemon Festival. **Founded:** 1947. **Publications:** Goleta Business Update (Monthly); Goleta Magazine (Annual); Discovery Dining Coupon (Semiannual).

48610 ■ Gonzales Chamber of Commerce
PO Box 216
Gonzales, CA 93926
Ph: (831)675-9019
Co. E-mail: email@gonzaleschamber.org
URL: http://www.gonzaleschamber.org
Contact: David Celedon, Secretary Treasurer
Description: Promotes business development in Gonzales, CA.

48611 ■ Granada Hills Chamber of Commerce
17723 Chatsworth St.
Granada Hills, CA 91344
Ph: (818)368-3235
Fax: (818)366-7425
Co. E-mail: email@granadachamber.com
URL: http://www.granadachamber.com
Contact: Steve Baker, Treasurer
Description: Promotes business and community development in Granada Hills, CA. **Founded:** 1927.

48612 ■ Grand Terrace Area Chamber of Commerce
22365 Barton Rd., Ste. 101
Grand Terrace, CA 92313
Ph: (909)783-3581
Fax: (909)370-2906
Co. E-mail: office@gtchamber.com
URL: http://www.gtchamber.com
Contact: Sally McGuire, President
Description: Promotes business and community development in Grand Terrace, CA. Sponsors monthly luncheon, quarterly business mixers. **Founded:** 1962.

48613 ■ Greater Bakersfield Chamber of Commerce
PO Box 1947
Bakersfield, CA 93301
Ph: (661)327-4421
Fax: (661)327-8751
Co. E-mail: info@bakersfieldchamber.org
URL: http://www.bakersfieldchamber.org
Contact: Debra L. Moreno, President
Description: Bankers and beauticians, communications consultants and caterers. Provides leadership to promote a healthy environment for business through networking, advocacy, learning and community service.

48614 ■ Greater Concord Chamber of Commerce
2280 Diamond Blvd., Ste. 200
Concord, CA 94520
Ph: (925)685-1181
Fax: (925)685-5623
Co. E-mail: mfowler@concordchamber.com
URL: http://www.concordchamber.com
Contact: Kim Trupiano, Chairman of the Board
Description: Promotes business and community development in Concord, CA. **Founded:** 1937.

48615 ■ Greater Cornejo Valley Chamber of Commerce
600 Hampshire Rd., Ste. 200
Westlake Village, CA 91361-2571
Ph: (805)370-0035
Fax: (805)370-1083
Co. E-mail: jlederer@conejochamber.org
URL: http://www.conejochamber.org
Contact: Jill Lederer, President
Description: Promotes business and community development in Thousand Oaks and Westlake Village, CA. Holds fundraisers and seminars. Offers networking opportunities. **Founded:** 1939. **Publications:** *Conejo Business Times* (Monthly); *Business Directory and Community Guide* (Annual). **Educational Activities:** Chamber After Five Mixer (Monthly); Networking Breakfast of Champions (Monthly).

48616 ■ Greater Eureka Chamber of Commerce
2112 Broadway
Eureka, CA 95501
Ph: (707)442-3738
Free: 800-356-6381

Fax: (707)442-0079
URL: http://www.eurekachamber.com
Contact: J. Warren Hockaday, President
Description: Promotes business and community development in Eureka, CA. **Founded:** 1891. **Publications:** *The Eureka Chamber Review* (Monthly).

48617 ■ Greater Fresno Area Chamber of Commerce
2331 Fresno St.
Fresno, CA 93721
Ph: (559)495-4800
Fax: (559)495-4811
Co. E-mail: info@fresnochamber.com
URL: http://www.fresnochamber.com
Contact: Al Smith, President
Description: Promotes business and community development in the Fresno County, CA area. Serves as a voice of business on local and state level. **Founded:** 1895. **Publications:** *Fresno Business Newsletter* (Monthly); *Resource Guide*.

48618 ■ Greater Huntington Park Area Chamber of Commerce
6330 Pacific Blvd., Ste. 208
Huntington Park, CA 90255
Ph: (323)585-1155
Fax: (323)585-2176
Co. E-mail: info@hpchamber1.com
URL: http://www.hpchamber1.com
Contact: Don Brabant, President
Description: Promotes business and community development in Huntington Park, CA. **Founded:** 1906.

48619 ■ Greater Merced Chamber of Commerce
360 E Yosemite Ave., Ste. No. 100
Merced, CA 95340
Ph: (209)384-7092
Fax: (209)384-8472
Co. E-mail: info@merced-chamber.com
URL: http://www.merced-chamber.com
Contact: Scott Crawford, Chairman
Description: Promotes business and community development in Greater Merced, CA area. **Publications:** *Merced Today*; *Merced Today*.

48620 ■ Greater Redding Chamber of Commerce
747 Auditorium Dr.
Redding, CA 96001
Ph: (530)225-4433
Fax: (530)225-4398
Co. E-mail: info@reddingchamber.com
URL: http://www.reddingchamber.com
Contact: Frank J. Strazzarino, Jr., President
Description: Promotes business and community development in the Greater Redding, CA area. **Founded:** 1921. **Publications:** *Business Directory* (Annual); *Redding Directions* (Monthly); *Business* (Annual); *Redding Directions* (Monthly).

48621 ■ Greater Riverside Chamber of Commerce (GRCC)
c/o Connie Librenjak, Exec. Dir.
Riverside, CA 92501
Ph: (951)683-7100
Fax: (951)683-2670
Co. E-mail: croth@riverside-chamber.com
URL: http://www.riverside-chamber.com
Contact: Cindy Roth, President
Description: Promotes business and community development in the Riverside, CA area. **Publications:** *The Chamber Communicator*. **Awards:** Raincross Trophy Dinner (Annual).

48622 ■ Greater Santa Ana Business Alliance
2020 N Broadway, 2nd Fl.
Santa Ana, CA 92702
Ph: (714)541-5353

Fax: (714)541-2238
Co. E-mail: info@santaanachamber.com
URL: http://www.santaanachamber.com
Contact: David Elliott, President
Description: Promotes business and community development in the Santa Ana, CA area. **Founded:** 1889. **Publications:** *ChamberLine 2.0* (Biweekly); *CityLine* (Bimonthly); *Santa Ana Community Guide and Business Directory* (Annual).

48623 ■ Greater Sherman Oaks Chamber of Commerce
14827 Ventura Blvd., Ste. 207
Sherman Oaks, CA 91403-5224
Ph: (818)906-1951
Fax: (818)783-3100
Co. E-mail: ourchamber@aol.com
URL: http://www.shermanoakschamber.org
Contact: Lisa Clayden, Executive Director
Description: Promotes business and community development in Sherman Oaks, CA. **Founded:** 1947. **Publications:** *Sherman Oaks Chamber NEWS* (Monthly). **Telecommunication Services:** chamber@shermanoakschamber.org.

48624 ■ Greater Stockton Chamber of Commerce (GSCC)
445 W Weber Ave., Ste. 220
Stockton, CA 95203
Ph: (209)547-2770
Fax: (209)466-5271
Co. E-mail: schamber@stocktonchamber.org
URL: http://www.stocktonchamber.org
Contact: Douglass W. Wilhoit, Jr., Chief Executive Officer
Description: Promotes business and community development in the Stockton, CA area. **Founded:** 1901. **Publications:** *Port O Call* (Monthly). **Awards:** Agricultural Hall of Fame (Annual). **Telecommunication Services:** doug@stocktonchamber.org.

48625 ■ Greater Tehachapi Chamber of Commerce
209 E Tehachapi Blvd.
Tehachapi, CA 93581
Ph: (661)822-4180
Fax: (661)822-9036
Co. E-mail: chamber@tehachapi.com
URL: http://www.tehachapi.com/chamber
Contact: Ida Perkins, President
Description: Promotes business and community development in the greater Tehachapi, CA area. Sponsors rodeo and Mountain Festival. **Founded:** 1962. **Awards:** Business of the Year (Annual); Citizen of the Year (Annual).

48626 ■ Greater Trinidad Chamber of Commerce
PO Box 356
Trinidad, CA 95570
Ph: (707)677-1610
Co. E-mail: info@discovertrinidadca.com
URL: http://www.discovertrinidadca.com
Description: Promotes business and community development in the greater Trinidad, CA area. **Founded:** 1950.

48627 ■ Greater Ukiah Chamber of Commerce (GUCC)
309 E. Perkins St.
Ukiah, CA 95482
Ph: (707)462-4705
Fax: (707)462-5059
URL: http://www.ukiahchamber.com
Contact: Bret Cooperrider, Chairman
Description: Promotes business and community development in the greater Ukiah, CA area. Conducts business networking and community promotional events.

48628 ■ *The Green Sheet*
1800 Huntington Dr.
San Marino, CA 91108
Ph: (626)286-1022
Fax: (626)286-7765
Co. E-mail: sanmarinochamber@att.net
URL: http://www.sanmarinochamber.org
Contact: Sandra Troup, President
Released: Monthly

48629 ■ Greenfield Chamber of Commerce
One Courthouse Pl.
Greenfield, IN 46140
Ph: (317)477-4188
Fax: (317)477-4189
Co. E-mail: info2@greenfieldcc.org
URL: http://www.greenfieldcc.org
Contact: Retta Livengood, President
Description: Promotes business and community development in Greenfield, CA.

48630 ■ Gridley Area Chamber of Commerce
613 Kentucky St.
Gridley, CA 95948
Ph: (530)846-3142
Fax: (530)846-7165
Co. E-mail: gridleychamber@hotmail.com
URL: http://gridleyareachamber.com
Contact: Christine Cunningham, Secretary
Description: Promotes business and community development in Gridley, CA. Sponsors Red Suspenders Day in May, the Pioneer Christmas Parade in December. **Founded:** 1946. **Publications:** *The Gridley Herald* (Semiweekly); *Guide to Gridley* (Annual); *Map of Gridley*. **Educational Activities:** Gridley Area Chamber of Commerce Meeting (Bimonthly). **Awards:** Community Recognition Awards (Annual).

48631 ■ *The Gridley Herald*
613 Kentucky St.
Gridley, CA 95948
Ph: (530)846-3142
Fax: (530)846-7165
Co. E-mail: gridleychamber@hotmail.com
URL: http://gridleyareachamber.com
Contact: Christine Cunningham, Secretary
Released: Semiweekly

48632 ■ Guadalupe Chamber of Commerce and Visitor Center
873 Guadalupe St.
Guadalupe, CA 93434
Ph: (805)343-2236
Fax: (805)343-2236
Co. E-mail: info@guadalupechamber.org
URL: http://www.guadalupechamber.org
Contact: Rhonda Walker, President
Description: Promotes business and community development in Guadalupe, CA.

48633 ■ *Guide to the Area's Fifteen Shopping and Professional Centers*
11650 Iberia Pl., Ste. 220
San Diego, CA 92128
Ph: (858)487-1767
Fax: (858)487-8051
URL: http://www.sdncc.com
Contact: Debra Rosen, President
Released: Periodic

48634 ■ *The Guide to Burbank*
200 W Magnolia Blvd.
Burbank, CA 91502-1724
Ph: (818)846-3111
Fax: (818)846-0109
Co. E-mail: info@burbankchamber.org
URL: http://www.burbankchamber.org
Contact: Gary Olson, President
Released: Annual **Price:** free for members.

48635 ■ *Guide to Calistoga*
1133 Washington St.
Calistoga, CA 94515
Ph: (707)942-6333
Free: 866-306-5588
Fax: (707)942-9287
Co. E-mail: ralbright@calistogachamber.net
URL: http://www.calistogachamber.com
Contact: Chris Canning, Executive Director
Released: Annual

48636 ■ *Guide to Camel*
PO Box 4444
Carmel, CA 93921
Ph: (831)624-2522
Free: 800-550-4333

Fax: (831)624-1329
Co. E-mail: info@carmelchamber.org
URL: http://www.carmelcalifornia.org
Contact: Monta Potter, Chief Executive Officer
Released: Annual **Price:** included in membership dues.

48637 ■ *Guide to Gridley*
613 Kentucky St.
Gridley, CA 95948
Ph: (530)846-3142
Fax: (530)846-7165
Co. E-mail: gridleychamber@hotmail.com
URL: http://gridleyareachamber.com
Contact: Christine Cunningham, Secretary
Released: Annual; not available until June. **Price:** $2.

48638 ■ Gustine Chamber of Commerce
375 5th St.
Gustine, CA 95322
Ph: (209)854-6975
Fax: (209)854-3511
Co. E-mail: gustinechamber@inreach.com
URL: http://www.gustinechamberofcommerce.com
Contact: Glen Beard, President
Description: Promotes business and community development in Gustine, CA. Sponsors Farmer's Market. **Publications:** *Business Directory* (Periodic).

48639 ■ Half Moon Bay - Coastside Chamber of Commerce and Visitors' Bureau (HMBCCCVB)
235 Main St.
Half Moon Bay, CA 94019
Ph: (650)726-8380
Fax: (650)726-8389
Co. E-mail: info@hmbchamber.com
URL: http://www.halfmoonbaychamber.org
Contact: Charise Hale McHugh, President
Description: Promotes business and community development in Half Moon Bay, CA. Sponsors community events. **Founded:** 1963.

48640 ■ Hanford Chamber of Commerce
200 Santa Fe, Ste. D
Hanford, CA 93230
Ph: (559)582-0483
Fax: (559)582-0960
Co. E-mail: hope@hanfordchamber.com
Contact: Hope Williams-Morikawa, Chief Executive Officer
Description: Promotes business and community development in Hanford, CA. Provides program of action that meets the evolving needs and challenges of the community. **Publications:** *Strictly Business* (Monthly); *TIPS* (Monthly). **Awards:** Business of the Year (Annual); Distinguished Man and Woman of the Year (Annual).

48641 ■ Harbor City - Harbor Gateway Chamber of Commerce (HCHGCC)
19401 S Vermont Ave., Ste. G104
Torrance, CA 90502
Ph: (310)516-7933
Fax: (310)516-7734
Co. E-mail: hchgchamber@sbcglobal.net
URL: http://www.hchgchamber.com
Contact: Lou Baglietto, President
Description: Promotes business and community development in Harbor City, CA. **Founded:** 1948. **Publications:** *Chamber Connection* (Monthly); *Chamber News* (Monthly).

48642 ■ Hawthorne Chamber of Commerce (HCC)
4444 El Segundo Blvd.
Hawthorne, CA 90250
Ph: (310)676-1163
Fax: (310)676-7661
Co. E-mail: info@hawthorne-chamber.com
URL: http://www.hawthorne-chamber.com
Contact: Patricia Feldman-Donaldson, President
Description: Promotes business and community development in Hawthorne, CA. Sponsors Video Public Information Program. **Founded:** 1919. **Publications:** *The Hawthorne Hotline* (Monthly).

48643 ■ *The Hawthorne Hotline*
4444 El Segundo Blvd.
Hawthorne, CA 90250
Ph: (310)676-1163
Fax: (310)676-7661
Co. E-mail: info@hawthorne-chamber.com
URL: http://www.hawthorne-chamber.com
Contact: Patricia Feldman-Donaldson, President
Released: Monthly

48644 ■ *Healdsburg Area Business*
217 Healdsburg Ave.
Healdsburg, CA 95448-4103
Ph: (707)433-6935
Free: 800-648-9922
Fax: (707)433-7562
Co. E-mail: info@healdsburg.com
URL: http://www.healdsburg.org
Contact: Craig Schmidt, President
Released: Monthly **Price:** included in membership dues.

48645 ■ Healdsburg Chamber of Commerce and Visitors Bureau
217 Healdsburg Ave.
Healdsburg, CA 95448-4103
Ph: (707)433-6935
Free: 800-648-9922
Fax: (707)433-7562
Co. E-mail: info@healdsburg.com
URL: http://www.healdsburg.org
Contact: Craig Schmidt, President
Description: Promotes business and community development in Healdsburg, CA. **Publications:** *Healdsburg Area Business* (Monthly).

48646 ■ *Health Providers Guide*
811 S Sunset Ave.
West Covina, CA 91790-3599
Ph: (626)338-8496
Fax: (626)960-0511
Co. E-mail: glawson@westcovinachamber.com
URL: http://www.westcovinachamber.com

48647 ■ Hemet San Jacinto Valley Chamber of Commerce
615 N San Jacinto St.
Hemet, CA 92543
Ph: (951)658-3211
Free: 800-334-9344
Fax: (951)766-5013
Co. E-mail: info@hemetsanjacintochamber.com
URL: http://hemetsanjacintochamber.com
Contact: Patti Drusky, President
Description: Promotes business and community development in Hemet, CA. **Publications:** *Chronicle* (Monthly).

48648 ■ Hercules Chamber of Commerce
PO Box 5283
Hercules, CA 94547
Ph: (510)741-7945
Fax: (510)741-8965
Co. E-mail: sylvia@herculeschamber.com
URL: http://www.herculeschamber.com
Contact: Sylvia Villa-Serrano, Executive Director
Description: Promotes business and community development in Hercules, CA area.

48649 ■ Hermosa Beach Chamber of Commerce and Visitors Bureau
1007 Hermosa Ave.
Hermosa Beach, CA 90254
Ph: (310)376-0951
Fax: (310)798-2594
Co. E-mail: info@hbchamber.net
URL: http://www.hbchamber.net
Contact: Carla Merriman, Executive Director
Description: Promotes business and community development in Hermosa Beach, CA. Sponsors arts and crafts show. **Founded:** 1912. **Telecommunication Services:** carla@hbchamber.net.

48650 ■ High Desert Hispanic Chamber of Commerce (HDHCC)
14286 California Ave., Ste. 104
Victorville, CA 92392
Ph: (760)241-6661

Free: 866-791-2133
URL: http://www.hdhcc.org
Contact: Vickie Cabriales, President
Description: Promotes the economic development of a culturally diverse business community through education, networking, and business community partnerships.

48651 ■ Highland Area Chamber of Commerce
2755 Messina St.
Highland, CA 92346
Ph: (909)864-4073
Fax: (909)864-4583
Co. E-mail: members@highlandchamber.org
URL: http://www.highlandchamber.org
Contact: Nanette Peykani, Executive Director
Description: Promotes business and community development in the Highland, CA area. Encourage residence through its maintenance, rehabilitation, development and occupation. **Founded:** 1906.

48652 ■ *Hill Street News*
2201 E Willow St., Ste. D
Signal Hill, CA 90755
Ph: (562)424-6489
Co. E-mail: president@signalhillchamber.com
URL: http://www.signalhillchamber.com
Contact: Shari Blackwell, President
Released: Quarterly **Price:** free.

48653 ■ Hispanic Chamber of Commerce of Sonoma County (HCCSC)
PO Box 11392
Santa Rosa, CA 95406
Ph: (707)575-3648
Fax: (707)575-3693
Co. E-mail: hccadmin@hcc-sc.org
URL: http://www.hcc-sc.org
Contact: Marcos J. Suarez, President
Founded: 1988.

48654 ■ Historic Sonora Chamber of Commerce (HSCC)
PO Box 884
Sonora, CA 95370-0251
Ph: (209)588-9625
Co. E-mail: hscc@um.att.com
URL: http://www.sonorachamber.com
Description: Strives to develop an economically prosperous business district while maintaining the character and integrity of Historic Sonora, making it the "heartbeat" of the community. Promotes commerce, culture, trade, good fellowship, and cooperative relationships among individuals and businesses. **Founded:** 2000.

48655 ■ *Historic Walking Tour*
584 Central Ave.
Pacific Grove, CA 93950
Ph: (831)373-3304
Free: 800-656-6650
Fax: (831)373-3317
Co. E-mail: chamber@pacificgrove.org
URL: http://www.pacificgrove.org
Contact: Moe Ammar, President

48656 ■ *Hollywood Business*
7018 Hollywood Blvd.
Hollywood, CA 90028
Ph: (323)469-8311
Fax: (323)469-2805
Co. E-mail: info@hollywoodchamber.net
URL: http://hollywoodchamber.net
Contact: Sam Smith, Chairman
Released: Monthly **Price:** included in membership dues.

48657 ■ *Hollywood Business Resource Book*
7018 Hollywood Blvd.
Hollywood, CA 90028
Ph: (323)469-8311
Fax: (323)469-2805
Co. E-mail: info@hollywoodchamber.net
URL: http://hollywoodchamber.net
Contact: Sam Smith, Chairman
Released: Annual **Price:** $25.

48658 ■ *Hollywood Business Weekly*
7018 Hollywood Blvd.
Hollywood, CA 90028
Ph: (323)469-8311
Fax: (323)469-2805
Co. E-mail: info@hollywoodchamber.net
URL: http://hollywoodchamber.net
Contact: Sam Smith, Chairman
Released: Weekly **Price:** included in membership dues.

48659 ■ Hollywood Chamber of Commerce
7018 Hollywood Blvd.
Hollywood, CA 90028
Ph: (323)469-8311
Fax: (323)469-2805
Co. E-mail: info@hollywoodchamber.net
URL: http://hollywoodchamber.net
Contact: Sam Smith, Chairman
Description: Promotes business and community development in Hollywood, CA. **Founded:** 1921.
Publications: *Hollywood Business* (Monthly); *Hollywood Business Resource Book* (Annual); *Hollywood Business Weekly* (Weekly); *Hollywood Business* (Monthly).

48660 ■ Holtville Chamber of Commerce
101 W 5th St.
Holtville, CA 92250
Ph: (760)356-2923
Fax: (760)356-2925
Co. E-mail: holtvillechamber@yahoo.com
URL: http://www.holtvillechamber.org
Contact: Matt Hester, President
Description: Promotes business and community development in Holtville, CA.

48661 ■ *Horizons*
PO Box 191
Citrus Heights, CA 95611
Ph: (916)722-4545
Fax: (916)722-4543
Co. E-mail: chamber@chchamber.com
URL: http://www.chchamber.com
Contact: Bettie Cosby, Chief Executive Officer
Released: Monthly

48662 ■ Huntington Beach Chamber of Commerce
2134 St., Ste. 100
Huntington Beach, CA 92648
Ph: (714)536-8888
Fax: (714)960-7654
Co. E-mail: hbchamber@hbcoc.com
URL: http://www.hbchamber.org
Contact: Jerry L. Wheeler, Sr., President
Description: Promotes business and supports the growth and development of the community in the Huntington Beach, CA area. **Founded:** 1904. **Publications:** *Chamber Business* (Monthly). **Educational Activities:** Economic Outlook Conference (Annual). **Awards:** Ambassador of the Year (Annual); Member of the Year (Annual).

48663 ■ Idyllwild Chamber of Commerce
PO Box 304
Idyllwild, CA 92549
Ph: (951)659-3259
Co. E-mail: info@idyllwildchamber.com
URL: http://www.idyllwildchamber.com
Contact: Richmond Blake, President
Description: Supports businesses by promoting Idyllwild and its surrounding areas as a visitor destination. Develops and participate in activities that benefit the community as a whole. Act as a communication network for businesses and citizens and to provide leadership in enhancing Idyllwild's quality of life. **Founded:** 1946.

48664 ■ Imperial Beach Chamber of Commerce and Visitor's Bureau (IBCC)
700 Seacoast Dr.
Imperial Beach, CA 91932-1871
Ph: (619)424-3151

Fax: (619)424-3008
Co. E-mail: joann_barrows@yahoo.com
URL: http://www.ib-chamber.com
Contact: Joann Barrows, President
Description: Promotes business and community development in Imperial Beach, CA. **Founded:** 1951. **Publications:** *Biz Buzz* (Bimonthly).

48665 ■ Imperial Chamber of Commerce (ICC)
400 S Imperial Ave., No. 2
Imperial, CA 92251-1637
Ph: (760)355-1609
Fax: (760)355-3920
URL: http://www.imperialchamber.org
Description: Promotes business and community development in Imperial, CA. **Founded:** 1904.

48666 ■ Indian Valley Chamber of Commerce
PO Box 516
Greenville, CA 95947
Ph: (530)284-6633
Fax: (530)284-6907
Co. E-mail: indianvalleychamber@frontiernet.net
URL: http://indianvalleychamber.snappages.com
Description: Promotes business and community development in the Indian Valley, CA area. Conducts charitable programs; sponsors concerts and other social events; holds competitions.

48667 ■ *The Indicator*
2 Park Plz., Ste. 100
Irvine, CA 92614-5904
Ph: (949)476-2242
Fax: (949)476-0443
Co. E-mail: ldunn@ocbc.org
URL: http://www.ocbc.org
Contact: Lucy Dunn, President
Released: Quarterly

48668 ■ *Indio*
82-921 Indio Blvd.
Indio, CA 92201
Ph: (760)347-0676
Free: 800-755-8440
Fax: (760)347-6069
Co. E-mail: info@indiochamber.org
URL: http://www.indiochamber.org
Contact: Patrick Swarthout, Chairman
Released: Annual

48669 ■ Indio Chamber of Commerce
82-921 Indio Blvd.
Indio, CA 92201
Ph: (760)347-0676
Free: 800-755-8440
Fax: (760)347-6069
Co. E-mail: info@indiochamber.org
URL: http://www.indiochamber.org
Contact: Patrick Swarthout, Chairman
Description: Promotes business and community development in Indio, CA. Sponsors Southwest Arts Festival and International Tamale Festival. **Founded:** 1946. **Publications:** *Business Directory* (Annual); *East Valley Business* (Monthly); *Indio* (Annual). **Awards:** Business Person of the Year (Annual); Indio Image Award (Monthly).

48670 ■ *Individual Map*
PO Box 404
West Sacramento, CA 95691-3209
Ph: (916)371-7042
Fax: (916)371-7007
Co. E-mail: wsinfo@westsacramentochamber.com
URL: http://www.westsacramentochamber.com
Contact: Denice A. Seals, Chief Executive Officer
Released: Biennial **Price:** $1.50.

48671 ■ Industry Manufacturers Council (IMC)
15651 Stafford St.
City of Industry, CA 91744
Ph: (626)968-3737

Fax: (626)330-5060
Co. E-mail: chamber@cityofindustry.org
URL: http://www.cityofindustry.org/news.php
Contact: Donald Sachs, Executive Director
Description: Works to serve the needs of its members and also provide services as a public relations agency for the City of Industry. **Founded:** 1962. **Publications:** *City of Industry News* (Monthly).

48672 ■ *Information and Business Directory*
300 Salem St.
Chico, CA 95928
Ph: (530)891-5556
Free: 800-852-8570
Co. E-mail: info@chicochamber.com
URL: http://www.chicochamber.com
Contact: Katie Simmons, President
Released: Annual

48673 ■ *Informe*
3443 Camino Del Rio S, Ste. 101
San Diego, CA 92108
Ph: (619)702-0790
Fax: (619)521-6722
Co. E-mail: marcocortes@sdchcc.com
URL: http://www.sdchcc.com
Contact: Minnie Rzeslawski, President
Released: Bimonthly

48674 ■ Inglewood/Airport Area Chamber of Commerce (IAACC)
330 E Queen St.
Inglewood, CA 90301-1817
Ph: (310)677-1121
Fax: (310)677-1001
Co. E-mail: inglewoodchamber@sbcglobal.net
URL: http://www.inglewoodchamber.com
Contact: Shannon R. Howe, Executive Vice President
Description: Promotes business and community development in Inglewood, CA. **Founded:** 1922. **Publications:** *Business Directory* (Annual); *Let's Talk Business* (Monthly).

48675 ■ *The Insider*
PO Box 404
West Sacramento, CA 95691-3209
Ph: (916)371-7042
Fax: (916)371-7007
Co. E-mail: wsinfo@westsacramentochamber.com
URL: http://www.westsacramentochamber.com
Contact: Denice A. Seals, Chief Executive Officer

48676 ■ *Insight*
14174 Green Tree Blvd.
Victorville, CA 92395
Ph: (760)245-6506
Fax: (760)245-6505
Co. E-mail: vvchamber@vvchamber.com
URL: http://vvchamber.com
Contact: Michele Spears, President
Released: Monthly

48677 ■ *Insights*
16102 Arrow Hwy.
Irwindale, CA 91706
Ph: (626)960-6606
Fax: (626)960-3868
Co. E-mail: info@irwindalechamber.org
URL: http://www.irwindalechamber.org
Contact: Lisa Bailey, President
Released: Monthly

48678 ■ *Intermountain Area Map*
PO Box 36
Burney, CA 96013
Ph: (530)335-2111
Fax: (530)335-2122
Co. E-mail: burneychamber@frontiernet.net
URL: http://www.burneychamber.com

48679 ■ Irvine Chamber of Commerce (ICC)
2485 McCabe Way, Ste. 150
Irvine, CA 92614
Ph: (949)660-9112

Fax: (949)660-0829
Co. E-mail: icc@irvinechamber.com
URL: http://www.irvinechamber.com
Contact: Massis Chahbazian, President
Description: Promotes business and community development in Irvine, CA. **Founded:** 1979. **Publications:** *Business Connection* (Monthly).

48680 ■ Irwindale Chamber of Commerce
16102 Arrow Hwy.
Irwindale, CA 91706
Ph: (626)960-6606
Fax: (626)960-3868
Co. E-mail: info@irwindalechamber.org
URL: http://www.irwindalechamber.org
Contact: Lisa Bailey, President
Description: Promotes business and community development in Irwindale, CA. **Founded:** 1980. **Publications:** *Insights* (Monthly). **Awards:** Business of the Year (Annual); Citizen of the Year (Annual).

48681 ■ Isleton Chamber of Commerce (ICC)
PO Box 758
Isleton, CA 95641
Ph: (916)777-5880
Fax: (916)777-4330
URL: http://www.isletoncoc.org
Description: Promotes business and community development in Isleton, CA. **Founded:** 1970.

48682 ■ *It's Our Business*
10 Station Way
Los Gatos, CA 95030-5926
Ph: (408)354-9300
Fax: (408)399-1594
Co. E-mail: chamber@losgatosweb.com
URL: http://losgatoschamber.com
Contact: Ronee Nassi, Executive Director
Released: Bimonthly

48683 ■ Japanese Chamber of Commerce of Southern California (JCCSC)
244 San Pedro St., No. 504
Los Angeles, CA 90012
Ph: (213)626-3067
Fax: (213)626-3070
Co. E-mail: office@jccsc.com
URL: http://www.jccsc.com
Contact: Toshio Handa, President
Description: Supports the business activities of Japanese and Japanese Americans in Southern California. Promotes mutual understanding and friendship between Japanese and Americans. Seeks to propagate the culture of Japan. **Founded:** 1947.

48684 ■ Joshua Tree Chamber of Commerce
6448 Hallee Rd., Ste. 9
Joshua Tree, CA 92252
Ph: (760)366-3723
Fax: (760)366-2573
Co. E-mail: info@joshuatreechamber.org
URL: http://joshuatreechamber.org
Contact: Eva Soltes, President
Description: Promotes business and community development in Joshua Tree, CA.

48685 ■ Julian Chamber of Commerce
PO Box 1866
Julian, CA 92036
Ph: (760)765-1857
Fax: (760)765-2544
Co. E-mail: chamber@julianca.com
URL: http://www.julianca.com
Description: Local businesses and individuals. Promotes tourism while maintaining the historic flavor of small town. **Founded:** 1930. **Subscriptions:** books periodicals. **Publications:** *Julian Guide*; *What to See and Do in Julian* (Daily).

48686 ■ *Julian Guide*
PO Box 1866
Julian, CA 92036
Ph: (760)765-1857
Fax: (760)765-2544
Co. E-mail: chamber@julianca.com
URL: http://www.julianca.com

48687 ■ June Lake Chamber of Commerce
PO Box 2
June Lake, CA 93529
URL: http://junelakeloop.org
Description: Promotes business and community development in June Lake, California.

48688 ■ Kerman District Chamber of Commerce
783 S Madera Ave.
Kerman, CA 93630-1796
Ph: (559)846-6343
Fax: (559)846-6344
Co. E-mail: info@kermanchamber.org
URL: http://www.kermanchamber.org
Description: Promotes business and community development in Kerman, CA. **Founded:** 1946. **Awards:** College Scholarships (Annual).

48689 ■ Kern River Valley Chamber of Commerce
PO Box 567
Lake Isabella, CA 93240
Ph: (760)379-5236
Free: 866-578-4386
Fax: (760)379-5457
Co. E-mail: office@kernrivervalley.com
URL: http://www.kernrivervalley.com
Contact: Rex Emerson, President
Description: Promotes business and community development and tourism in Lake Isabella and surrounding communities. **Founded:** 1958. **Publications:** *Lake Lines* (Monthly). **Awards:** Man & Woman of the Year (Annual).

48690 ■ Kernville Chamber of Commerce (KCC)
11447 Kernville Rd.
Kernville, CA 93238-0397
Ph: (760)376-2629
Free: 866--
Fax: (760)376-4371
Co. E-mail: office@kernvillechamber.org
URL: http://www.kernvillechamber.org
Contact: Jill Sloan-Thurman, President
Description: Promotes business, community development, and tourism in Kernville, CA. Works to attract visitors, new residents and jobs creating businesses in the area. Provides service and support to its members. **Founded:** 1957. **Publications:** *Kernville Express* (3/year).

48691 ■ *Kernville Express*
11447 Kernville Rd.
Kernville, CA 93238-0397
Ph: (760)376-2629
Free: 866--
Fax: (760)376-4371
Co. E-mail: office@kernvillechamber.org
URL: http://www.kernvillechamber.org
Contact: Jill Sloan-Thurman, President
Released: 3/year **Price:** free.

48692 ■ King City and Southern Monterey Chamber of Commerce and Agriculture
200 Broadway St., Ste. 40
King City, CA 93930
Ph: (831)385-3814
Fax: (831)386-9462
Co. E-mail: kingcitychamber@sbcglobal.net
URL: http://www.kingcitychamber.com
Contact: Sarah Cummings, President
Description: Promotes business and community development in King City, CA. **Founded:** 1911. **Publications:** *Chamber Spotlight* (Monthly). **Awards:** Citizen of the Year Award (Annual).

48693 ■ Kingsburg District Chamber of Commerce
1475 Draper St.
Kingsburg, CA 93631
Ph: (559)897-1111

Fax: (559)897-4621
Co. E-mail: jessatkingsburg@aol.com
URL: http://www.kingsburgchamberofcommerce.com
Contact: Jess Chambers, Executive Director
Description: Promotes business and community development in Kingsburg, CA. Sponsors festival. Operates California Welcome Center.

48694 ■ *LA Area Chamber Voice*
350 S Bixel St.
Los Angeles, CA 90017
Ph: (213)580-7500
Fax: (213)580-7511
Co. E-mail: info@lachamber.org
URL: http://www.lachamber.org
Contact: Gary Toebben, President
Released: Monthly

48695 ■ La Canada - Flintridge Chamber of Commerce
4529 Angeles Crest Hwy., Ste. 102
La Canada, CA 91011
Ph: (818)790-4289
Fax: (818)790-8930
Co. E-mail: exec@lacanadaflintridge.com
URL: http://www.lacanadaflintridge.com
Contact: Pat Anderson, President
Description: Promotes business and community development in La Canada Flintridge, CA. **Founded:** 1912. **Awards:** Miss La Canada Flintridge (Annual).

48696 ■ La Habra Area Chamber of Commerce
321 E La Habra Blvd.
La Habra, CA 90631
Ph: (562)697-1704
Fax: (562)697-8359
Co. E-mail: info@lahabrachamber.com
URL: http://www.lahabrachamber.com
Contact: Mark Sturdevant, President
Description: Works with businesses, retailers, and residents dedicated to commerce in its growing community. Serves as an advocate for its business membership as well as an essential link between business, government, and the community. **Founded:** 1914. **Publications:** *Business Directory.*

48697 ■ La Mirada Chamber of Commerce
11900 La Mirada Blvd., Ste. 9
La Mirada, CA 90638
Ph: (562)902-1970
Fax: (562)902-1218
Co. E-mail: info@lmchamber.org
URL: http://lmchamber.org
Contact: Demian Ross, Director
Description: Promotes business and community development in La Mirada, CA. **Publications:** *Your City Insider* (Monthly); *Business Directory and Community Guide* (Annual). **Educational Activities:** La Mirada Morning View (Monthly). **Telecommunication Services:** stacey@lmchamber.org.

48698 ■ La Quinta Chamber of Commerce (LQCC)
78-275 Calle Tampico
La Quinta, CA 92253
Ph: (760)564-3199
Fax: (760)564-3111
Co. E-mail: david@lqchamber.com
URL: http://www.lqchamber.com
Contact: David Archer, President
Description: Promotes business and community development in La Quinta, CA. **Founded:** 1950. **Publications:** *The Gem* (Monthly). **Educational Activities:** Mayor's Luncheons (Monthly).

48699 ■ La Verne Chamber of Commerce (LVCC)
2078 Bonita Ave.
La Verne, CA 91750
Ph: (909)593-5265
Fax: (909)596-0579
Co. E-mail: info@lavernechamber.org
URL: http://www.lavernechamber.org
Contact: Brian McNerney, President
Description: Promotes business and community development in La Verne, CA. Sponsors community marketplace and business showcase. **Founded:** 1941. **Publications:** *Business Directory; The Ex-*

change (Bimonthly). **Awards:** Business of the Year (Annual); Member of the Year (Annual); New Business of the Year (Annual).

48700 ■ Lafayette Chamber of Commerce
100 Lafayette Cir., Ste. 103
Lafayette, CA 94549
Ph: (925)284-7404
Fax: (925)284-3109
Co. E-mail: info@lafayettechamber.org
URL: http://lafayettechamber.org
Contact: Jay Lifson, Executive Director
Description: Promotes business and community development in Lafayette, CA. **Founded:** 1947. **Awards:** Business Person of the Year (Annual).

48701 ■ *Laguna Beach Business Directory & Relocation Guide*
357 Glenneyre Ave.
Laguna Beach, CA 92651
Ph: (949)494-1018
Fax: (949)376-8916
Co. E-mail: info@lagunabeachchamber.org
URL: http://www.lagunabeachchamber.org
Contact: Rose Hancock, Executive Director
Released: Annual

48702 ■ *Laguna Beach Business News*
357 Glenneyre Ave.
Laguna Beach, CA 92651
Ph: (949)494-1018
Fax: (949)376-8916
Co. E-mail: info@lagunabeachchamber.org
URL: http://www.lagunabeachchamber.org
Contact: Rose Hancock, Executive Director
Released: Monthly

48703 ■ Laguna Beach Chamber of Commerce (LBCC)
357 Glenneyre Ave.
Laguna Beach, CA 92651
Ph: (949)494-1018
Fax: (949)376-8916
Co. E-mail: info@lagunabeachchamber.org
URL: http://www.lagunabeachchamber.org
Contact: Rose Hancock, Executive Director
Description: Promotes business and community development in Laguna Beach, CA. **Founded:** 1917. **Publications:** *Laguna Beach Business News* (Monthly); *Laguna Beach Community Directory* (Annual); *Laguna Beach Business Directory & Relocation Guide* (Annual). **Educational Activities:** Mixers (Monthly).

48704 ■ *Laguna Beach Community Directory*
357 Glenneyre Ave.
Laguna Beach, CA 92651
Ph: (949)494-1018
Fax: (949)376-8916
Co. E-mail: info@lagunabeachchamber.org
URL: http://www.lagunabeachchamber.org
Contact: Rose Hancock, Executive Director
Released: Annual **Price:** $1.

48705 ■ Laguna Niguel Chamber of Commerce
30111 Crown Valley Pkwy.
Laguna Niguel, CA 92677
Ph: (949)363-0136
Fax: (949)363-9026
Co. E-mail: lncc@lnchamber.com
URL: http://lagunaniguelchamber.net
Contact: Debbie Newman, President
Description: Promotes business and community development in Laguna Niguel, CA. **Founded:** 1982. **Publications:** *Sea Country News* (Monthly).

48706 ■ Lake Arrowhead Communities Chamber of Commerce
PO Box 219
Lake Arrowhead, CA 92352
Ph: (909)337-3715

Fax: (909)336-1548
Co. E-mail: info@lakearrowhead.net
URL: http://www.lakearrowhead.net
Contact: Lewis Murray, President
Description: Promotes business and community development in Lake Arrowhead, CA. Sponsors summer music festivals; supports charitable programs. **Founded:** 1950. **Telecommunication Services:** lewis@lakearrowhead.net.

48707 ■ Lake County Chamber of Commerce
PO Box 295
Lakeport, CA 95453
Ph: (707)263-5092
Free: 866-525-3767
Fax: (707)263-5104
Co. E-mail: info@lakecochamber.com
URL: http://www.lakeportchamber.com
Contact: Melissa Fulton, Chief Executive Officer
Description: Works to support and promote business and economic growth and encourage the improvement of tourism activities in Lakeport area, CA.

48708 ■ Lake Elsinore Valley Chamber of Commerce
132 W Graham Ave.
Lake Elsinore, CA 92530
Ph: (951)245-8848
Fax: (951)245-9127
Co. E-mail: info@lakeelsinorechamber.com
URL: http://www.lakeelsinorechamber.com
Contact: Kim Joseph Cousins, President
Description: Promotes business and community development in the Lake Elsinore, CA area. Sponsors Frontier Days Rodeo, Play Days, and horse shows. **Founded:** 1949. **Publications:** *Business Review* (Monthly). **Awards:** Business of the Month (Monthly); Student of the Month (Monthly). **Telecommunication Services:** kim@lakeelsinorechamber.com.

48709 ■ *Lake Lines*
PO Box 567
Lake Isabella, CA 93240
Ph: (760)379-5236
Free: 866-578-4386
Fax: (760)379-5457
Co. E-mail: office@kernrivervalley.com
URL: http://www.kernrivervalley.com
Contact: Rex Emerson, President
Released: Monthly **Price:** free.

48710 ■ Lake Los Angeles Chamber of Commerce
PO Box 500071
Lake Los Angeles, CA 93550-0071
Ph: (661)264-2786
Co. E-mail: info@lakelachamber.com
URL: http://www.lakelachamber.com
Contact: Manuel Magana, President
Description: Promotes business and community development in the Lake Los Angeles, CA area.

48711 ■ Lakeside Chamber of Commerce (LCC)
9924 Vine St.
Lakeside, CA 92040
Ph: (619)561-1031
Fax: (619)561-7951
Co. E-mail: info@lakesideca.com
URL: http://www.lakesideca.com
Contact: Steve Menefee, President
URL(s): www.lakesideca.com/chamber/newsletter/2010-02.pdf. **Description:** Promotes business and community development in Lakeside, CA. **Founded:** 1932. **Publications:** *Lakeside Community and Business Directory; The Link* (Monthly). **Educational Activities:** Lakeside Chamber of Commerce Board meeting (Monthly); Chamber Networking Luncheon (Monthly). **Awards:** Lakeside Citizen of the Year (Annual). **Telecommunication Services:** chamber@lakesideca.com.

48712 ■ *Lakeside Community and Business Directory*
9924 Vine St.
Lakeside, CA 92040
Ph: (619)561-1031

Fax: (619)561-7951
Co. E-mail: info@lakesideca.com
URL: http://www.lakesideca.com
Contact: Steve Menefee, President

48713 ■ Larkspur Chamber of Commerce (LCC)
PO Box 998
Larkspur, CA 94977
Ph: (415)838-0038
Co. E-mail: info@larkspurchamber.org
URL: http://www.larkspurchamber.org
Contact: Donna Craft, Executive Secretary
Description: Promotes business and community development in Greenbrae, Kentfield, Larkspur, and Ross, CA. Sponsors local festivals. **Founded:** 1958. **Publications:** Chamber Chatter (Monthly). **Awards:** Business Citizen of the Year (Annual). **Telecommunication Services:** lcc07@comcast.net.

48714 ■ Lassen County Chamber of Commerce (LCCC)
PO Box 338
Susanville, CA 96130-0338
Ph: (530)257-4323
Fax: (530)251-2561
Co. E-mail: director@lassencountychamber.org
URL: http://www.lassencountychamber.org
Contact: Patricia Hagata, Executive Director
Description: Promotes business and community development in Susanville and Lassen County, CA. **Founded:** 1888. **Publications:** Chamber Chat (Monthly).

48715 ■ Lathrop Chamber of Commerce
PO Box 313
Lathrop, CA 95330
Ph: (209)740-6503
Co. E-mail: typp12@sbcglobal.net
URL: http://www.lathropchamber.org
Contact: Mary Kennedy Bracken, President
Description: Promotes business and community development in the Lathrop, CA area.

48716 ■ Lee Vining Chamber of Commerce
PO Box 130
Lee Vining, CA 93541
Ph: (760)647-6629
Fax: (760)647-6377
Co. E-mail: info@leevining.com
URL: http://www.leevining.com
Contact: Nancy Boman, Coordinator
Description: Promotes business and community development in Lee Vining, CA.

48717 ■ Let's Talk Business
330 E Queen St.
Inglewood, CA 90301-1817
Ph: (310)677-1121
Fax: (310)677-1001
Co. E-mail: inglewoodchamber@sbcglobal.net
URL: http://www.inglewoodchamber.com
Contact: Shannon R. Howe, Executive Vice President
Released: Monthly

48718 ■ Lincoln Area Chamber of Commerce
540 F St.
Lincoln, CA 95648
Ph: (916)645-2035
Fax: (916)645-9455
Co. E-mail: info@lincolnchamber.com
URL: http://www.lincolnchamber.com
Contact: Bob Ramness, Chief Executive Officer
Description: Promotes business and community development in Lincoln, CA. **Founded:** 1905.

48719 ■ Linden-Peters Chamber of Commerce
PO Box 557
Linden, CA 95236
Ph: (209)547-3046
URL: http://www.lindenchamber.net
Description: Promotes business and community development in the Linden-Peters, CA area.

48720 ■ Lindsay Chamber of Commerce
PO Box 989
Lindsay, CA 93247-0989

Ph: (559)562-4929
Fax: (559)562-5219
URL: http://thelindsaychamber.com
Contact: Virginia Loya, Executive Director
Description: Promotes business and community development in Lindsay, CA.

48721 ■ The Link
9924 Vine St.
Lakeside, CA 92040
Ph: (619)561-1031
Fax: (619)561-7951
Co. E-mail: info@lakesideca.com
URL: http://www.lakesideca.com
Contact: Steve Menefee, President
Released: Monthly

48722 ■ The Link
PO Box 425
Mariposa, CA 95338
Ph: (209)966-2456
Fax: (209)966-4193
Co. E-mail: mariposachamber@sti.net
URL: http://www.mariposachamber.org
Contact: Peter Schimmelfennig, Executive Director
Released: Monthly **Price:** included in membership dues.

48723 ■ Littlerock Chamber of Commerce
PO Box 326
Littlerock, CA 93543
Ph: (661)944-6990
Co. E-mail: jackt@qnet.com
URL: http://www.littlerock-ca.us
Contact: Ronni Di Giovanni, President
Description: Promotes business and community development in Littlerock, CA. Holds annual Community Queen Pageant. Sponsors annual Harvest Festival and Parade. **Founded:** 1949.

48724 ■ Live Oak District Chamber of Commerce
PO Box 391
Live Oak, CA 95953
Ph: (530)695-1519
Co. E-mail: liveoakchamber@syix.com
URL: http://www.liveoakchamber.org
Contact: Annette Bertolini, President
Description: Works to represent local business owners, organizations, churches, and individuals of Live Oak, California. **Founded:** 1946.

48725 ■ Livermore Business Journal
2157 1st St.
Livermore, CA 94550
Ph: (925)447-1606
Fax: (925)447-1641
Co. E-mail: ttikalsky@rina.com
URL: http://www.livermorechamber.org
Contact: Dale Kaye, President
Released: Monthly **Price:** $35, /year.

48726 ■ Livermore Chamber of Commerce
2157 1st St.
Livermore, CA 94550
Ph: (925)447-1606
Fax: (925)447-1641
Co. E-mail: ttikalsky@rina.com
URL: http://www.livermorechamber.org
Contact: Dale Kaye, President
Description: Promotes business and community development in Livermore, CA. **Founded:** 1926. **Publications:** Chamber Business Journal (Monthly); Livermore Business Journal (Monthly); Livermore Chamber of Commerce Business Directory (Annual). **Telecommunication Services:** lccinfo@livermore-chamber.org.

48727 ■ Livermore Chamber of Commerce Business Directory
2157 1st St.
Livermore, CA 94550
Ph: (925)447-1606
Fax: (925)447-1641
Co. E-mail: ttikalsky@rina.com
URL: http://www.livermorechamber.org
Contact: Dale Kaye, President
Released: Annual

48728 ■ Local Business Directory
PO Box 404
West Sacramento, CA 95691-3209
Ph: (916)371-7042
Fax: (916)371-7007
Co. E-mail: wsinfo@westsacramentochamber.com
URL: http://www.westsacramentochamber.com
Contact: Denice A. Seals, Chief Executive Officer
Released: Triennial

48729 ■ Lodi Business
35 S School St.
Lodi, CA 95240
Ph: (209)367-7840
Co. E-mail: info@lodichamber.com
URL: http://www.lodichamber.com
Contact: Pat Patrick, President
Released: Monthly

48730 ■ Lodi Chamber of Commerce
35 S School St.
Lodi, CA 95240
Ph: (209)367-7840
Co. E-mail: info@lodichamber.com
URL: http://www.lodichamber.com
Contact: Pat Patrick, President
Description: Promotes business and community development in the Lodi District, CA. Conducts semiannual Lodi Street Fair. **Founded:** 1923. **Publications:** Lodi Business (Monthly).

48731 ■ Loma Linda Chamber of Commerce
25541 Barton Rd., Ste. 4
Loma Linda, CA 92354
Ph: (909)799-2828
Fax: (909)799-2825
Co. E-mail: info@lomalindachamber.org
URL: http://www.lomalindachamber.org
Contact: Phil Carlisle, Chief Executive Officer
Description: Promotes business and community development in Loma Linda, CA. **Founded:** 1956. **Publications:** Loma Linda Report (Bimonthly). **Awards:** Chamber Ambassador of the Year (Annual); Chamber Business of the Year (Annual); Chamber Member of the Year (Annual); Chamber of Commerce Citizen of the Year (Annual); City Employee of the Year (Annual); Firefighter of the Year (Annual); Outstanding Member of the Year (Annual); Police Officer of the Year (Annual).

48732 ■ Loma Linda Report
25541 Barton Rd., Ste. 4
Loma Linda, CA 92354
Ph: (909)799-2828
Fax: (909)799-2825
Co. E-mail: info@lomalindachamber.org
URL: http://www.lomalindachamber.org
Contact: Phil Carlisle, Chief Executive Officer
Released: Bimonthly

48733 ■ Lomita Chamber of Commerce
25332 Narbonne Ave., Ste. 250
Lomita, CA 90717
Ph: (310)326-6378
Fax: (310)326-2904
Co. E-mail: info@lomitacoc.com
URL: http://lomitacoc.com
Contact: George Kivett, Executive Director
Description: Promotes business and community development in Lomita, CA. Conducts charitable activities. Sponsors festival. **Founded:** 1949.

48734 ■ Lompoc Valley Chamber of Commerce and Visitors' Bureau (LVCCVB)
111 S 1 St.
Lompoc, CA 93436
Ph: (805)736-4567
Free: 800-240-0999
Co. E-mail: chamber@lompoc.com
URL: http://www.lompoc.com
Contact: Chris Ames, Chairman
Description: Promotes business, community development, and tourism in the Lompoc, CA area. Operates committees responsible for business, tourism, governmental affairs, military aerospace affairs, and economic development. Maintains community resource center and tourist information center. Conducts downtown fair. **Founded:** 1903. **Publications:** The Chamber (Monthly).

48735 ■ Lone Pine Chamber of Commerce (LPCC)
PO Box 749
Lone Pine, CA 93545
Ph: (760)876-4444
Fax: (760)876-9205
Co. E-mail: info@lonepinechamber.org
URL: http://www.lonepinechamber.org
Description: Promotes business, tourism, and economic development in southern Inyo County, CA. Sponsors bicycle road race. **Founded:** 1944.

48736 ■ Long Beach Area Chamber of Commerce (LBACC)
1 World Trade Ctr., Ste. 206
Long Beach, CA 90831-0206
Ph: (562)436-1251
Fax: (562)436-7099
Co. E-mail: info@lbchamber.com
URL: http://www.lbchamber.com
Contact: Randy Gordon, President
Description: Promotes business and community development in the Long Beach, CA area. **Founded:** 1891. **Publications:** *Long Beach Business* (Monthly); *Member Referral Guide*. **Educational Activities:** Long Beach Area Chamber of Commerce Breakfast (Weekly).

48737 ■ *Long Beach Business*
1 World Trade Ctr., Ste. 206
Long Beach, CA 90831-0206
Ph: (562)436-1251
Fax: (562)436-7099
Co. E-mail: info@lbchamber.com
URL: http://www.lbchamber.com
Contact: Randy Gordon, President
Released: Monthly **Price:** free for members.

48738 ■ *Lookout*
1470 Jamboree Rd.
Newport Beach, CA 92660
Ph: (929)729-4400
Fax: (929)729-4417
Co. E-mail: rluehrs@newportbeach.com
URL: http://www.newportbeach.com
Contact: Richard R. Luehrs, President
Released: Monthly

48739 ■ Loomis Basin Chamber of Commerce
6090 Horseshoe Bar Rd.
Loomis, CA 95650
Ph: (916)652-7252
Fax: (916)652-7211
Co. E-mail: manager@loomischamber.com
URL: http://www.loomischamber.com
Contact: Michelle Jahnsen, Manager
Description: Promotes business and community development in Loomis, CA. **Founded:** 1984.

48740 ■ Los Alamitos Area Chamber of Commerce
3231 Katella Ave.
Los Alamitos, CA 90720
Ph: (562)598-6659
Fax: (562)598-7035
Co. E-mail: info@losalchamber.org
URL: http://www.losalchamber.org
Contact: Johnie Strohmyer, Chief Executive Officer
Description: Promotes business and community development in Los Alamitos, CA. **Founded:** 1907. **Publications:** *Los Alamitos Business* (Monthly). **Awards:** Ambassador of the Year (Annual); Business of the Year (Annual); Employee of the Year (Annual); Teacher of the Year (Annual).

48741 ■ *Los Alamitos Business*
3231 Katella Ave.
Los Alamitos, CA 90720
Ph: (562)598-6659
Fax: (562)598-7035
Co. E-mail: info@losalchamber.org
URL: http://www.losalchamber.org
Contact: Johnie Strohmyer, Chief Executive Officer
Released: Monthly **Price:** free.

48742 ■ Los Altos Chamber of Commerce
321 University Ave.
Los Altos, CA 94022
Ph: (650)948-1455
Fax: (650)948-6238
Co. E-mail: info@losaltoschamber.org
URL: http://www.losaltoschamber.org
Contact: Julie Rose, President
Description: Promotes business and community development in Los Altos, CA. Sponsors Los Altos Fall Festival. **Founded:** 1951. **Publications:** *The Chamber Advantage* (Bimonthly); *Los Altos Chamber of Commerce Directory* (Annual). **Educational Activities:** Los Altos Chamber of Commerce Festival (Annual). **Awards:** Ambassador of the Year (Annual); Community Legacy Award; Community Partnership Award; Member of the Year (Annual); New Business of the Year (Annual); Outstanding Service to the Chamber.

48743 ■ *Los Altos Chamber of Commerce Directory*
321 University Ave.
Los Altos, CA 94022
Ph: (650)948-1455
Fax: (650)948-6238
Co. E-mail: info@losaltoschamber.org
URL: http://www.losaltoschamber.org
Contact: Julie Rose, President
Released: Annual

48744 ■ Los Angeles Area Chamber of Commerce
350 S Bixel St.
Los Angeles, CA 90017
Ph: (213)580-7500
Fax: (213)580-7511
Co. E-mail: info@lachamber.org
URL: http://www.lachamber.com
Contact: Gary Toebben, President
Description: Promotes business and community development in the Los Angeles, CA area. **Founded:** 1888. **Publications:** *LA Area Chamber Voice* (Monthly); *Los Angeles Business Journal*; *Southern California Business* (Monthly); *Chamber Membership Directory and Business Resource Guide* (Annual); *Chamber Membership Directory and Business Resource Guide* (Annual); *Southern California Business Trends* (Quarterly). **Educational Activities:** Referral Network (Weekly). **Telecommunication Services:** info@lachamber.com.

48745 ■ *Los Angeles Business Journal*
350 S Bixel St.
Los Angeles, CA 90017
Ph: (213)580-7500
Fax: (213)580-7511
Co. E-mail: info@lachamber.org
URL: http://www.lachamber.com
Contact: Gary Toebben, President

48746 ■ *Los Banos Business Journal*
503 J St.
Los Banos, CA 93635
Ph: (209)826-2495
Fax: (209)826-9689
Co. E-mail: lbchamber@pacbell.net
URL: http://www.losbanos.com
Contact: Geneva Brett, President
Released: Monthly

48747 ■ Los Banos Chamber of Commerce (LBCC)
503 J St.
Los Banos, CA 93635
Ph: (209)826-2495
Fax: (209)826-9689
Co. E-mail: lbchamber@pacbell.net
URL: http://www.losbanos.com
Contact: Geneva Brett, President
Description: Promotes business and community development in Los Banos, CA. **Founded:** 1929. **Publications:** *Los Banos Business Journal* (Monthly); *Los Banos Chamber Directory* (Periodic).

48748 ■ *Los Banos Chamber Directory*
503 J St.
Los Banos, CA 93635
Ph: (209)826-2495
Fax: (209)826-9689
Co. E-mail: lbchamber@pacbell.net
URL: http://www.losbanos.com
Contact: Geneva Brett, President
Released: Periodic **Price:** $2.

48749 ■ Los Osos/Baywood Park Chamber of Commerce
781 Los Osos Valley Rd.
Los Osos, CA 93402
Ph: (805)528-4884
Fax: (805)528-8401
Co. E-mail: info@lobpchamber.org
URL: http://www.lobpchamber.org
Contact: Jim Stanfill, President
Description: Promotes business and community development in the Los Osos-Baywood Park, CA area. **Founded:** 1955. **Publications:** *The Connection* (Monthly). **Educational Activities:** Chamber Board of Directors Meeting (Monthly). **Awards:** Business of the Year (Annual); Citizen of the Year (Annual); Volunteer of the Year (Annual); Business Person of the Year (Annual).

48750 ■ Lucerne Valley Chamber of Commerce
PO Box 491
Lucerne Valley, CA 92356-0491
Ph: (760)248-7215
Fax: (760)248-2024
Co. E-mail: chamber@lucernevalley.net
URL: http://www.lvcal.org/chamber
Description: Promotes business and community development in Lucerne Valley, CA. **Founded:** 1957.

48751 ■ *The Luminary*
50 Park Pl.
Brisbane, CA 94005
Ph: (415)467-7283
Fax: (415)467-5421
Co. E-mail: growyourbusiness@brisbanechamber.com
URL: http://www.brisbanechamber.com
Contact: Mitch Bull, President
Released: Monthly

48752 ■ Lynwood Chamber of Commerce (LCC)
3651 E Imperial Hwy.
Lynwood, CA 90262
Ph: (310)527-1431
Co. E-mail: lynwoodchamber@gmail.com
URL: http://www.lynwoodchamber.org
Contact: Maria Garcia, President
Description: Promotes business and community development in Lynwood, CA. Conducts Career Day, Job Fair and scholarship competition. **Founded:** 1946.

48753 ■ *Madera Business Beat*
c/o Debi Bray, Pres./CEO
120 NE St.
Madera, CA 93638
Ph: (559)673-3563
Fax: (559)673-5009
Co. E-mail: dbray@maderachamber.com
URL: http://www.maderachamber.com
Contact: Debi Bray, President
Released: Monthly

48754 ■ Madera Chamber of Commerce
c/o Debi Bray, Pres./CEO
120 NE St.
Madera, CA 93638
Ph: (559)673-3563
Fax: (559)673-5009
Co. E-mail: dbray@maderachamber.com
URL: http://www.maderachamber.com
Contact: Debi Bray, President
Description: Promotes business and community development in Madera District, CA. **Publications:** *Community Guide and Membership Directory* (Annual); *Madera Business Beat* (Monthly). **Educational Activities:** Business Extravaganza (Annual); Governmental Affairs Breakfast Meeting (Monthly).

48755 ■ Malibu Chamber of Commerce
23805 Stuart Ranch Rd., Ste. 100
Malibu, CA 90265

Ph: (310)458-9025
Fax: (310)456-0195
Co. E-mail: info@malibu.org
URL: http://www.malibu.org
Contact: Ed Gillespie, President
Description: Promotes business and community development in Malibu, CA. **Publications:** *Malibu Business and Community Directory.*

48756 ■ Manhattan Beach Chamber of Commerce (MBCC)
425 15th St.
Manhattan Beach, CA 90266
Ph: (310)545-5313
Fax: (310)545-7203
Co. E-mail: james@manhattanbeachchamber.net
URL: http://www.manhattanbeachchamber.net
Contact: James O'callaghan, President
Description: Promotes business and community development in Manhattan Beach, CA. Sponsors special events. **Founded:** 1941. **Publications:** *Sandollar* (Monthly).

48757 ■ Manteca Chamber of Commerce
183 W N St., Ste. 6
Manteca, CA 95337
Ph: (209)823-6121
Fax: (209)239-6131
Co. E-mail: directordebby@manteca.org
URL: http://www.manteca.org
Contact: Debby Moorhead, Chief Executive Officer
Description: Promotes business and community development in Manteca District, CA. **Founded:** 1929. **Publications:** *Manteca First* (Bimonthly). **Educational Activities:** Executive Board Meeting (Monthly).

48758 ■ Manteca First
183 W N St., Ste. 6
Manteca, CA 95337
Ph: (209)823-6121
Fax: (209)239-6131
Co. E-mail: directordebby@manteca.org
URL: http://www.manteca.org
Contact: Debby Moorhead, Chief Executive Officer
Released: Bimonthly

48759 ■ Map
14174 Green Tree Blvd.
Victorville, CA 92395
Ph: (760)245-6506
Fax: (760)245-6505
Co. E-mail: vvchamber@vvchamber.com
URL: http://vvchamber.com
Contact: Michele Spears, President
Released: Annual **Price:** $0.75.

48760 ■ Map
811 S Sunset Ave.
West Covina, CA 91790-3599
Ph: (626)338-8496
Fax: (626)960-0511
Co. E-mail: glawson@westcovinachamber.com
URL: http://www.westcovinachamber.com

48761 ■ Map/Directory
336 Pacific Ave.
Shafter, CA 93263
Ph: (661)746-2600
Fax: (661)746-0607
URL: http://www.shafter.com
Contact: Karen Wilkins, Director
Released: Periodic

48762 ■ Map Directory
3245 Bowers Ave.
Clearlake, CA 95422
Ph: (707)994-3600
Fax: (707)994-3603
Co. E-mail: office@clearlakechamber.com
URL: http://www.clearlakechamber.com
Contact: Joey Luiz, President
Released: Annual **Price:** included in membership dues; $1.07, for nonmembers.

48763 ■ Map of Gridley
613 Kentucky St.
Gridley, CA 95948
Ph: (530)846-3142

Fax: (530)846-7165
Co. E-mail: gridleychamber@hotmail.com
URL: http://gridleyareachamber.com
Contact: Christine Cunningham, Secretary

48764 ■ Marina Chamber of Commerce
PO Box 425
Marina, CA 93933
Ph: (831)384-9155
Co. E-mail: info@marinachamber.com
URL: http://www.marinachamber.com
Contact: Mike Mast, President
Description: Promotes business and community development in Marina, CA.

48765 ■ Mariposa County Chamber of Commerce
PO Box 425
Mariposa, CA 95338
Ph: (209)966-2456
Fax: (209)966-4193
Co. E-mail: mariposachamber@sti.net
URL: http://www.mariposachamber.org
Contact: Peter Schimmelfennig, Executive Director
Description: Promotes business and community development in Mariposa County, CA. Encourages travel and tourism. Sponsors monthly storytelling festival. **Publications:** *The Link* (Monthly).

48766 ■ Mark West Area Chamber of Commerce
4787 Old Redwood Hwy., Ste. 101
Santa Rosa, CA 95403
Ph: (707)578-7975
Fax: (707)578-0397
Co. E-mail: office@markwest.org
URL: http://www.markwest.org
Contact: Will Brodt, President
Description: Promotes business and community development in Mark West, CA area. **Founded:** 1980.

48767 ■ Martinez Area Chamber of Commerce and Visitors and Information Center
603 Marina Vista
Martinez, CA 94553
Ph: (925)228-2345
Fax: (925)228-2356
Co. E-mail: info@martinezchamber.com
URL: http://www.martinezchamber.com
Contact: Marie Knutson, Chairperson
Description: Promotes business and community development in Martinez, CA. Conducts local 4th of July and Columbus Day festivities. **Founded:** 1913. **Publications:** *Networker* (Monthly).

48768 ■ Maywood Chamber of Commerce (MCC)
5720 Heliothrope Ave.
Maywood, CA 90270
Ph: (323)562-3373
Fax: (323)562-2905
Co. E-mail: sjimenez@cityofmaywood.com
URL: http://www.cityofmaywood.com
Contact: Susan Jimenez, General Manager
Description: Promotes business and community development in Maywood, CA. **Founded:** 1926.

48769 ■ McCloud Chamber of Commerce
PO Box 372
McCloud, CA 96057
Ph: (530)964-3113
Co. E-mail: askus@mccloudchamber.com
URL: http://www.mccloudchamber.com
Description: Strives to enhance and protect the natural and historic resources of McCloud to the benefit, enjoyment and pride of both local citizens and the tourists. Enhances existing businesses, encourages new opportunities and promotes tourism.

48770 ■ McKinleyville Chamber of Commerce
1640 Central Ave.
McKinleyville, CA 95519
Ph: (707)839-2449

Fax: (707)839-1205
Co. E-mail: executivedirector@mckinleyvillechamber.com
URL: http://www.mckinleyvillechamber.com
Contact: Cindy Harrington, Executive Director
Description: Promotes business and community development in McKinleyville, CA. **Founded:** 1967.

48771 ■ Medocino Coast Business Directory
PO Box 1141
Fort Bragg, CA 95437
Ph: (707)961-6300
Fax: (707)964-2056
Co. E-mail: chamber@mcn.org
URL: http://www.mendocinocoast.com
Contact: Debra DeGraw, Executive Director

48772 ■ Member Referral Guide
1 World Trade Ctr., Ste. 206
Long Beach, CA 90831-0206
Ph: (562)436-1251
Fax: (562)436-7099
Co. E-mail: info@lbchamber.com
URL: http://www.lbchamber.com
Contact: Randy Gordon, President

48773 ■ Membership and Business Directory
PO Box 538
El Cerrito, CA 94530
Ph: (510)705-1202
Co. E-mail: info@elcerritochamber.org
URL: http://www.elcerritochamber.org
Contact: Judy Pope, President
Released: Periodic

48774 ■ Membership Directory and Business Referral Guide
901 National City Blvd.
National City, CA 91950-3203
Ph: (619)477-9339
Fax: (619)477-5018
Co. E-mail: reynoso@nationalcitychamber.org
URL: http://www.nationalcitychamber.org
Contact: Jacqueline L. Reynoso, President
Price: included in membership dues.

48775 ■ Membership Directory and Buyers Guide
1556 1st St.
Napa, CA 94559
Ph: (707)226-7455
Fax: (707)226-1171
Co. E-mail: chris@napachamber.com
URL: http://www.napachamber.com
Contact: Chris Messina, President
Released: Annual

48776 ■ Membership Directory and Buyers Guide
1234 6th St., Ste. 100
Santa Monica, CA 90401
Ph: (310)393-9825
Fax: (310)394-1868
Co. E-mail: info@smchamber.com
URL: http://www.smchamber.com
Contact: Laurel Rosen, President
Released: Annual

48777 ■ Membership Directory and Buyer's Guide
700 W 1st St.
Tustin, CA 92780
Ph: (714)544-5341
Fax: (714)544-2083
Co. E-mail: info@tustinchamber.org
URL: http://tustinchamber.org
Contact: Sherri Munsey, Executive Director
Released: Annual

48778 ■ Membership Directory and Community Guide to Visalia
220 N Santa Fe Ave.
Visalia, CA 93292
Ph: (559)734-5876
Free: 877-VIS-ALIA

Fax: (559)734-7479
Co. E-mail: info@visaliachamber.org
URL: http://www.visaliachamber.org
Contact: Glenn Morris, President
Released: Annual **Price:** included in membership dues.

48779 ■ *Mendocino Map and Visitor Information Guide*
PO Box 1141
Fort Bragg, CA 95437
Ph: (707)961-6300
Fax: (707)964-2056
Co. E-mail: chamber@mcn.org
URL: http://www.mendocinocoast.com
Contact: Debra DeGraw, Executive Director
Released: Annual

48780 ■ Menifee Valley Chamber of Commerce
29683 New Hub Dr., Ste. C
Menifee, CA 92586
Ph: (951)672-1991
Fax: (951)672-4022
URL: http://www.menifeevalleychamber.com
Contact: Dorothy Wolons, Chief Executive Officer
Description: Seeks to enhance the quality of individual living in Menifee Valley by promoting local business enterprise, strengthening the relationship of residents and businesses and establishing programs for development and economic growth.

48781 ■ Menlo Park Chamber of Commerce (MPCC)
1100 Merrill St.
Menlo Park, CA 94025-4386
Ph: (650)325-2818
Fax: (650)325-0920
Co. E-mail: info@menloparkchamber.com
URL: http://www.menloparkchamber.com
Contact: Fran Dehn, President
Description: Promotes business and community development in Menlo Park, Portola Valley, and Atherton, CA. **Founded:** 1926. **Publications:** *The Acorn* (Monthly); *Community Directory* (Annual). **Educational Activities:** Women in Business Breakfast (Monthly). **Awards:** Golden Acorn Award (Annual); Jerry Jacob Scholarship (Annual).

48782 ■ Merced County Chamber of Commerce
PO Box 1112
Merced, CA 95341-1112
Ph: (209)722-3864
Fax: (209)722-2406
Co. E-mail: info@mercedcountychamber.com
URL: http://www.mercedcountychamber.com
Contact: Nelson Crabb, President
Description: Promotes business and community development in Merced County, CA. **Founded:** 1925. **Publications:** *Chamber Business Gazette* (Monthly).

48783 ■ *Merced Today*
360 E Yosemite Ave., Ste. No. 100
Merced, CA 95340
Ph: (209)384-7092
Fax: (209)384-8472
Co. E-mail: info@merced-chamber.com
URL: http://www.merced-chamber.com
Contact: Scott Crawford, Chairman
Released: every 18 months.

48784 ■ *Metro Business*
1 Capitol Mall, Ste. 300
Sacramento, CA 95814
Ph: (916)552-6800
Fax: (916)443-2672
Co. E-mail: mmahood@metrochamber.org
URL: http://www.metrochamber.org
Contact: Martha Clark Lofgren, Chief Executive Officer
Released: Weekly

48785 ■ *Mid-month Update*
1234 6th St., Ste. 100
Santa Monica, CA 90401
Ph: (310)393-9825

Fax: (310)394-1868
Co. E-mail: info@smchamber.com
URL: http://www.smchamber.com
Contact: Laurel Rosen, President
Released: Monthly

48786 ■ Mid Valley Chamber of Commerce
7120 Hayvenhurst Ave., Ste. 114
Van Nuys, CA 91406-3813
Ph: (818)989-0300
URL: http://www.midvalleychamber.com
Contact: Nancy Hoffman Vanyek, Chief Executive Officer
Description: Promotes business and community development in the Van Nuys, CA area. **Founded:** 1989. **Publications:** *Chamber Today* (Monthly); *Speakers' Bureau Listing.* **Educational Activities:** Inaugural Ball (Annual); Latino Consumer Expo (Annual).

48787 ■ *Mill Valley Business*
85 Throckmorton Ave.
Mill Valley, CA 94941
Ph: (415)388-9700
Fax: (415)388-9770
Co. E-mail: info@millvalley.org
URL: http://www.millvalley.org
Contact: Daniel Escalzo, Executive Director
Released: Monthly

48788 ■ *Mill Valley Business Directory*
85 Throckmorton Ave.
Mill Valley, CA 94941
Ph: (415)388-9700
Fax: (415)388-9770
Co. E-mail: info@millvalley.org
URL: http://www.millvalley.org
Contact: Daniel Escalzo, Executive Director

48789 ■ Mill Valley Chamber of Commerce
85 Throckmorton Ave.
Mill Valley, CA 94941
Ph: (415)388-9700
Fax: (415)388-9770
Co. E-mail: info@millvalley.org
URL: http://www.millvalley.org
Contact: Daniel Escalzo, Executive Director
Description: Promotes business and community development in Mill Valley, CA. **Publications:** *Mill Valley Business* (Monthly); *Mill Valley Business Directory*; *Mill Valley Business Directory*; *Mill Valley Business* (Monthly). **Educational Activities:** Government Affairs (Monthly); Wine and Gourmet Food Tasting (Annual).

48790 ■ Millbrae Chamber of Commerce (MCC)
50 Victoria Ave., Ste. 103
Millbrae, CA 94030-2622
Ph: (650)697-7324
Fax: (650)259-7918
Co. E-mail: chamber@millbrae.com
URL: http://www.millbrae.com
Contact: John Ford, President
Description: Promotes business and community development in Millbrae, CA. Conducts forums and luncheons. Sponsors Art and Wine Festival, held on Labor Day weekend. **Scope:** significant events throughout Millbrae's history, Millbrae's local issues, accomplishments and concerns. **Founded:** 1949. **Subscriptions:** archival material articles clippings photographs. **Publications:** *Business Directory* (Annual). **Awards:** Business of the Year (Annual); Chamber Excellence Award (Annual); Youth Ambassador Scholarship Program (Annual).

48791 ■ Milpitas Chamber of Commerce
828 N Hillview Dr.
Milpitas, CA 95035-4544
Ph: (408)262-2613
Fax: (408)262-2823
Co. E-mail: info@milpitaschamber.com
URL: http://www.milpitaschamber.com
Contact: Robert Paedon, Vice President
Description: Works to ensure a healthy economic environment for Milpitas area, CA. **Founded:** 1957.

48792 ■ Modesto Chamber of Commerce
1114 J St.
Modesto, CA 95354-0806
Ph: (209)577-5757
Fax: (209)577-2623
Co. E-mail: info@modchamber.org
URL: http://www.modchamber.org
Contact: Joy Madison, President
E-mail: jmadison@modchamber.org
Description: Promotes business and community development in Modesto, CA. **Publications:** *Chamber of Commerce Membership Directory* (Annual); *Modesto Progress* (Annual); *Stanislaus County Industrial Directory*; *Chamber of Commerce Membership Directory* (Annual); *Modesto Chamber of Commerce Membership Directory* (Annual); *United Way of Etowah County--Directory of Community Service Resources* (Biennial). **Educational Activities:** Oktoberfest (Annual). **Awards:** Ambassador of the Year (Annual); Business Hall of Fame (Annual); Distinguished Service Award (Annual); Member of the Year (Annual); Non-Profit Organization of the Year (Annual); Robert J. Cardoza Award (Annual); Small Business of the Year (Annual); Welcome Team Member of the Year (Annual).

48793 ■ Modesto Junior Chamber of Commerce
PO Box 76
Modesto, CA 95354
Ph: (209)450-3810
Co. E-mail: mickiemodestojc@yahoo.com
URL: http://www.jayceesmodesto.org
Contact: Vincent Sandoval, III, President
Description: Leadership and community service training organization. **Publications:** *Modesto Memo* (Quarterly).

48794 ■ *Modesto Memo*
PO Box 76
Modesto, CA 95354
Ph: (209)450-3810
Co. E-mail: mickiemodestojc@yahoo.com
URL: http://www.jayceesmodesto.org
Contact: Vincent Sandoval, III, President
Released: Quarterly

48795 ■ *Modesto Progress*
1114 J St.
Modesto, CA 95354-0806
Ph: (209)577-5757
Fax: (209)577-2623
Co. E-mail: info@modchamber.org
URL: http://www.modchamber.org
Contact: Joy Madison, President
E-mail: jmadison@modchamber.org
Released: Annual **Price:** free for members.

48796 ■ Monrovia Chamber of Commerce (MCC)
620 S Myrtle Ave.
Monrovia, CA 91016-2805
Ph: (626)358-1159
Fax: (626)357-6036
Co. E-mail: chamber@monroviacc.com
URL: http://www.monroviacc.com
Contact: Marilyn Johnson, President
Description: Promotes business and community development in the San Gabriel Valley, CA. Conducts workshops and expos. Holds community forum. **Founded:** 1897. **Publications:** *Monrovia Insider* (Monthly); *Monrovia Chamber of Commerce--Membership Directory and Community Guide.* **Educational Activities:** Monrovia Chamber of Commerce Breakfast (Bimonthly). **Awards:** Dick Lord Award (Annual); Iris Award (Annual); Monroe Award (Annual).

48797 ■ *Monrovia Insider*
620 S Myrtle Ave.
Monrovia, CA 91016-2805
Ph: (626)358-1159
Fax: (626)357-6036
Co. E-mail: chamber@monroviacc.com
URL: http://www.monroviacc.com
Contact: Marilyn Johnson, President
Released: Monthly **Price:** $36, /year.

48798 ■ Montclair Chamber of Commerce
5222 Benito St.
Montclair, CA 91763
Ph: (909)624-4569
Fax: (909)625-2009
Co. E-mail: info@montclairchamber.com
URL: http://www.montclairchamber.com
Contact: Darleen Curley, President
Description: Promotes business and community development in Montclair, CA area. Supports local charities; conducts political and business networking forums. **Founded:** 1958.

48799 ■ Monte Rio Chamber of Commerce (MRCC)
PO Box 220
Monte Rio, CA 95462-0220
Ph: (707)865-2304
Co. E-mail: mrcc@sonic.net
URL: http://monterio.org
Description: Promotes business and community development in the Monte Rio and Russian River area of western Sonoma County, CA. **Founded:** 1921.

48800 ■ Montebello Chamber of Commerce
109 N 19th St.
Montebello, CA 90640
Ph: (323)721-1153
Fax: (323)721-7946
Co. E-mail: andrea@montebellochamber.org
URL: http://www.montebellochamber.org
Contact: Andrea Wagg, President
Description: Promotes business and community development in Montebello, CA. **Founded:** 1912. **Publications:** *Annual Business Directory* (Annual); *Spotlight* (Bimonthly).

48801 ■ Monterey Peninsula Chamber of Commerce (MPCC)
30 Ragsdale Dr., Ste. 200
Monterey, CA 93940
Ph: (831)648-5360
Fax: (831)649-3502
Co. E-mail: info@mpcc.com
URL: http://www.mpcc.com
Contact: Jody Hansen, President
Description: Promotes business and community development in the Monterey Peninsula area of California. **Founded:** 1908. **Publications:** *Action* (Monthly); *Business Resource Directory* (Annual); *Calendar of Community Events* (Annual); *Monterey Peninsula Chamber of Commerce--Membership Directory & Business Referral Guide* (Annual). **Awards:** Business Excellence Awards (Annual); Business of the Year (Annual); Citizen of the Year (Annual); Public Official of the Year (Annual); Robert C. Littlefield Award (Annual); Volunteer of the Month (Monthly).

48802 ■ Montrose-Verdugo City Chamber of Commerce (MVCCC)
3516 N Verdugo Rd.
Glendale, CA 91208
Ph: (818)249-7171
Fax: (818)249-8919
Co. E-mail: mvcc@montrosechamber.org
URL: http://www.montrosechamber.org
Contact: Melina Clarke, Executive Director
Description: Promotes business and community development in Montrose, Verdugo City, Glendale, and La Crescenta, CA. Sponsors charitable and service activities. Sponsors arts and crafts fairs, Memorial Day services, Oktoberfest, and Christmas Parade. **Founded:** 1923. **Publications:** *Business Connection* (Quarterly). **Educational Activities:** Mixers (Monthly). **Awards:** Organization of the Year (Annual); Volunteers of the Year (Annual); Business Person of the Year (Annual).

48803 ■ Morgan Hill Chamber of Commerce (MHCC)
PO Box 786
Morgan Hill, CA 95038-0786
Ph: (408)779-9444

Fax: (408)779-5405
Co. E-mail: info@morganhill.org
URL: http://www.morganhill.org
Contact: Christine Giusiana, President
Description: Promotes business and community development in Morgan Hill, CA. Sponsors business seminars. **Founded:** 1964. **Publications:** *Business Review* (Monthly); *Business Directory & Destination Planning Guide* (Annual). **Educational Activities:** Monthly Networking Mixers (Monthly); Wake Up Morgan Hill Networking Breakfast (Monthly). **Awards:** Big Business of the Year (Annual); Chamber Volunteer of the Year (Annual); Educator of the Year (Annual); Man of the Year (Annual); Past Citizen of the Year (Annual); Small Business of the Year (Annual); Student of the Year (Annual); Woman of the Year (Annual).

48804 ■ Morro Bay Chamber of Commerce (MBCC)
c/o Stuart McElhinney, Pres.
Morro Bay, CA 93442
Ph: (805)772-4467
Free: 800-231-0592
Co. E-mail: brownpelican@morrobay.org
URL: http://www.morrobay.org
Contact: Craig Schmidt, Chief Executive Officer
Description: Promotes business and community development in Morro Bay, CA. **Publications:** *Business Referral Directory* (Annual); *Soundings* (Monthly); *Business Referral Directory* (Annual).

48805 ■ Moss Landing Chamber of Commerce
PO Box 41
Moss Landing, CA 95039
Ph: (831)633-4501
URL: http://www.mosslandingchamber.com
Description: Promotes business and community development in Moss Landing, CA.

48806 ■ Mount Shasta Chamber of Commerce
c/o Vince Reinig, Pres.
300 Pine St.
Mount Shasta, CA 96067
Ph: (530)926-4865
Free: 800-926-4865
Fax: (530)926-0976
Co. E-mail: info@mtshastachamber.com
URL: http://mtshastachamber.com/index.php
Contact: Jim Mullins, President
Description: Promotes business and community development in Mt. Shasta, CA. **Founded:** 1939. **Publications:** *Chamber Connection* (Monthly). **Awards:** Business of the Year (Annual); Citizen of the Year (Annual); Meritorious Service Award (Annual).

48807 ■ Napa Chamber of Commerce (NCC)
1556 1st St.
Napa, CA 94559
Ph: (707)226-7455
Fax: (707)226-1171
Co. E-mail: chris@napachamber.com
URL: http://www.napachamber.com
Contact: Chris Messina, President
Description: Promotes the Napa County, CA area's economic vitality and quality of life through leadership development, advocacy, facilitation, and education. **Founded:** 1889. **Publications:** *Commerce* (Monthly); *Community Economic Profile* (Annual); *Membership Directory and Buyers Guide* (Annual); *Visitor Booklet*. **Educational Activities:** Committee Meeting (Monthly). **Awards:** Business of the Year (Annual); Citizen of the Year (Annual); Healthcare Professional of the Year (Annual); Public Safety Employee (Annual); Teacher of the Year (Annual). **Telecommunication Services:** info@napachamber.com.

48808 ■ National City Chamber of Commerce (NCCC)
901 National City Blvd.
National City, CA 91950-3203
Ph: (619)477-9339

Fax: (619)477-5018
Co. E-mail: reynoso@nationalcitychamber.org
URL: http://www.nationalcitychamber.org
Contact: Jacqueline L. Reynoso, President
Description: Promotes business and community development in National City, CA. **Founded:** 1911. **Publications:** *Chamber News* (Bimonthly); *Membership Directory and Business Referral Guide*. **Telecommunication Services:** thechamber@nationalcitychamber.org.

48809 ■ Needles Area Chamber of Commerce
PO Box 705
Needles, CA 92363-0705
Ph: (760)326-2050
Fax: (760)326-2194
Co. E-mail: needleschamber@frontier.com
URL: http://www.needleschamber.com
Contact: Sue Godnick, Executive Director
Description: Promotes an active, healthy business environment throughout Needles so that its citizens and all of its business community shall prosper.

48810 ■ Networker
603 Marina Vista
Martinez, CA 94553
Ph: (925)228-2345
Fax: (925)228-2356
Co. E-mail: info@martinezchamber.com
URL: http://www.martinezchamber.com
Contact: Marie Knutson, Chairperson
Released: Monthly

48811 ■ Networkers of the Costa Mesa Chamber of Commerce
1700 Adams Ave., Ste. 101
Costa Mesa, CA 92626-4865
Ph: (714)885-9090
Fax: (714)885-9094
URL: http://www.costamesachamber.com
Contact: Larry Weichman, Chairman
Description: Promotes business and community development in Costa Mesa, CA.

48812 ■ Nevada City Chamber of Commerce (NCCC)
132 Main St.
Nevada City, CA 95959-2520
Ph: (530)265-2692
Free: 800-655-NJOY
Fax: (530)265-3892
URL: http://www.nevadacitychamber.com
Description: Promotes business and community development in Nevada City, CA. **Founded:** 1931.

48813 ■ Newark Chamber of Commerce—North Silicon Valley Chamber of Commerce
37101 Newark Blvd.
Newark, CA 94560
Ph: (510)744-1000
Fax: (510)744-1003
Co. E-mail: info@newark-chamber.com
URL: http://www.newark-chamber.com
Contact: Linda Ashley, President
Description: Promotes business and community development in Newark, CA. Sponsors Winter Art and Wine Festival and Monarch Festival. **Founded:** 1906. **Publications:** *The Voice of Business* (Monthly). **Educational Activities:** Mixers (Monthly).

48814 ■ Newport Beach Chamber of Commerce
1470 Jamboree Rd.
Newport Beach, CA 92660
Ph: (929)729-4400
Fax: (929)729-4417
Co. E-mail: rluehrs@newportbeach.com
URL: http://www.newportbeach.com
Contact: Richard R. Luehrs, President
Description: Promotes business and community development in the Newport Beach, CA area. **Founded:** 1906. **Publications:** *Lookout* (Monthly). **Educational Activities:** Fire and Lifeguard Appreciation (Annual).

48815 ■ News and Views
9050 Las Tunas Dr.
Temple City, CA 91780

Ph: (626)286-3101
Fax: (626)286-2590
Co. E-mail: info@templecitychamber.org
URL: http://www.templecitychamber.org
Contact: Linda Payne, President
Released: Monthly

48816 ■ *News and Views*
233 4th Ave.
Chula Vista, CA 91910
Ph: (619)420-6603
Fax: (619)420-1269
Co. E-mail: info@chulavistachamber.org
URL: http://www.chulavistachamber.org
Contact: Lisa Johnson, President
Released: Quarterly

48817 ■ Nipomo Chamber of Commerce
671 W Tefft St., Ste. 13
Nipomo, CA 93444
Ph: (805)929-1583
Fax: (805)929-5835
Co. E-mail: nipomochamber@yahoo.com
URL: http://www.nipomochamber.org
Contact: Cees Dobbe, President
Description: Promotes business and community development in Nipomo, CA.

48818 ■ Norco Chamber of Commerce (NCC)
1204 6th St.
Norco, CA 92860
Ph: (951)737-2531
Fax: (951)737-2574
Co. E-mail: staff@norcochamber.com
URL: http://www.norcochamber.com
Description: Promotes business and community development in Norco, CA. **Publications:** *Business News* (Monthly); *Business Roundup.* **Educational Activities:** Beth Stone Holiday Decorating Contest (Annual); Business and Community Expo (Annual).

48819 ■ North Fork Chamber of Commerce
PO Box 426
North Fork, CA 93643
Ph: (559)877-2410
Fax: (559)877-2332
Co. E-mail: info@north-fork-chamber.com
URL: http://www.north-fork-chamber.com
Contact: Jack McGowan, President
Description: Promotes business and community development in North Fork, CA.

48820 ■ North Monterey County Chamber of Commerce
PO Box 744
Castroville, CA 95012
Ph: (831)633-2465
Fax: (831)633-0485
Co. E-mail: artifest@att.net
URL: http://www.northmontereycountychamber.org
Contact: Gary DeAmaral, President
Description: Promotes business and community development in North Monterey County, CA. **Publications:** *North Monterey County Chamber Times* (Bimonthly).

48821 ■ *North Monterey County Chamber Times*
PO Box 744
Castroville, CA 95012
Ph: (831)633-2465
Fax: (831)633-0485
Co. E-mail: artifest@att.net
URL: http://www.northmontereycountychamber.org
Contact: Gary DeAmaral, President
Released: Bimonthly

48822 ■ North Sacramento Chamber of Commerce
PO Box 15468
Sacramento, CA 95851
Ph: (916)925-6773
Co. E-mail: leadership@northsacramentochamber.org
URL: http://northsacramentochamber.org
Contact: Rob Kerth, President
Description: Promotes business and community development in Sacramento, CA area. **Founded:** 1940.

48823 ■ North Valley Regional Chamber of Commerce (NVRCC)
9401 Reseda Blvd., Ste. 100
Northridge, CA 91324
Ph: (818)349-5676
Fax: (818)349-4343
Co. E-mail: info@nvrcc.com
URL: http://www.nvrcc.com
Contact: Wayne Adelstein, President
Description: Promotes business and community development in North Valley area, CA. **Publications:** *Northridge and Chatsworth Business and Community News* (Monthly).

48824 ■ *Northridge and Chatsworth Business and Community News*
9401 Reseda Blvd., Ste. 100
Northridge, CA 91324
Ph: (818)349-5676
Fax: (818)349-4343
Co. E-mail: info@nvrcc.com
URL: http://www.nvrcc.com
Contact: Wayne Adelstein, President
Released: Monthly

48825 ■ Norwalk Chamber of Commerce
12040 Foster Rd.
Norwalk, CA 90650
Ph: (562)864-7785
Fax: (562)864-8539
URL: http://www.norwalkchamber.com
Contact: Lynda Fisher, President
Description: Promotes business and community development in Norwalk, CA. **Publications:** *Norwalk Chamber News* (Monthly).

48826 ■ *Norwalk Chamber News*
12040 Foster Rd.
Norwalk, CA 90650
Ph: (562)864-7785
Fax: (562)864-8539
URL: http://www.norwalkchamber.com
Contact: Lynda Fisher, President
Released: Monthly **Price:** included in membership dues.

48827 ■ Novato Chamber of Commerce
807 DeLong Ave.
Novato, CA 94945
Ph: (415)897-1164
Fax: (415)898-9097
Co. E-mail: info@novatochamber.com
URL: http://www.novatochamber.com
Contact: Coy Smith, Chief Executive Officer
Description: Promotes business and community development in Novato, CA. **Founded:** 1915. **Publications:** *Novato Business News* (Monthly). **Educational Activities:** B2B Economic Breakfast (Bimonthly).

48828 ■ *Oakdale Business News*
590 N Yosemite Ave.
Oakdale, CA 95361-2732
Ph: (209)847-2244
Fax: (209)847-0826
Co. E-mail: info@oakdalechamber.com
URL: http://www.oakdalechamber.com
Contact: Mary Guardiola, Chief Executive Officer
Released: Monthly

48829 ■ Oakdale District Chamber of Commerce
590 N Yosemite Ave.
Oakdale, CA 95361-2732
Ph: (209)847-2244
Fax: (209)847-0826
Co. E-mail: info@oakdalechamber.com
URL: http://www.oakdalechamber.com
Contact: Mary Guardiola, Chief Executive Officer
Description: Promotes business and community development in Oakdale, CA. Sponsors annual Antique and Craft Show and Chocolate Festival. **Founded:** 1917. **Publications:** *Oakdale Business News* (Monthly). **Educational Activities:** Oakdale Chocolate Ball Chocolate Bliss (Annual).

48830 ■ Oakhurst Area Chamber of Commerce (OACC)
40637 Hwy. 41
Oakhurst, CA 93644
Ph: (559)683-7766
Fax: (559)683-0784
Co. E-mail: chamber@oakhurstchamber.com
URL: http://www.oakhurstchamber.com
Contact: Janet Stanovich, President
Description: Works to advance the commercial, financial, industrial and civic interests of Oakhurst Area. **Founded:** 1959. **Publications:** *Chamber E-News* (Semimonthly).

48831 ■ Oakland African-American Chamber of Commerce (OAACC)
449 15th St., Ste. 410
Oakland, CA 94612
Ph: (510)268-1600
Fax: (510)268-1602
Co. E-mail: info@oaacc.org
URL: http://www.oaacc.org
Contact: Mr. Wil Hardee, Jr., President
Description: Promotes business and development for the African-American community in Oakland.

48832 ■ *Oakland Business Review*
475 14th St.
Oakland, CA 94612-1903
Ph: (510)874-4800
Fax: (510)839-8817
Co. E-mail: lana@oaklandchamber.com
URL: http://www.oaklandchamber.com
Contact: Joseph Haraburda, President
Released: Monthly **Price:** included in membership dues; $195, /year for nonmembers.

48833 ■ Oakland Chinatown Chamber of Commerce
Pacific Renaissance Plz.
388 9th St., Ste. 258
Oakland, CA 94607
Ph: (510)893-8979
Fax: (510)893-8988
Co. E-mail: oaklandctchamber@aol.com
URL: http://www.oaklandchinatownchamber.org
Contact: Jennie Ong, Executive Director
Description: Promotes business and community development in Oakland, Chinatown area.

48834 ■ Oakland Metropolitan Chamber of Commerce
475 14th St.
Oakland, CA 94612-1903
Ph: (510)874-4800
Fax: (510)839-8817
Co. E-mail: lana@oaklandchamber.com
URL: http://www.oaklandchamber.com
Contact: Joseph Haraburda, President
Description: Promotes business and community development in Oakland, CA. **Founded:** 1905. **Publications:** *Focus on Business* (Monthly); *Oakland Business Review* (Monthly). **Educational Activities:** Oakland Metropolitan Chamber of Commerce Breakfast (Monthly). **Awards:** Arts Organization Award (Annual); Community Service/Education Award (Annual); Entrepreneur of the Year (Annual); Individual Artist (Annual); Oakland on the Map Award (Annual); Special Recognition (Annual); Volunteer of the Year (Annual); Woman-Owned Business of the Year (Annual).

48835 ■ Oakley Chamber of Commerce
PO Box 1340
Oakley, CA 94561
Ph: (925)625-1035
Fax: (925)625-4051
Co. E-mail: oakleychamber@sbcglobal.net
URL: http://www.oakleychamber.com
Contact: Steve Nosanchuck, President
Description: Promotes business and community development in Oakley, CA area.

48836 ■ Oceanside Chamber of Commerce (OCC)
928 N Coast Hwy.
Oceanside, CA 92054
Ph: (760)722-1534

Fax: (760)722-8336
Co. E-mail: info@oceansidechamber.com
URL: http://www.oceansidechamber.com
Contact: David L. Nydegger, Chief Executive Officer
Description: Promotes business and community development in Oceanside, CA. **Founded:** 1895.
Publications: Oceanside Chronicle (Monthly).

48837 ■ *Oceanside Chronicle*
928 N Coast Hwy.
Oceanside, CA 92054
Ph: (760)722-1534
Fax: (760)722-8336
Co. E-mail: info@oceansidechamber.com
URL: http://www.oceansidechamber.com
Contact: David L. Nydegger, Chief Executive Officer
Released: Monthly **Price:** free.

48838 ■ *Ojai Valley Chamber Business Journal*
PO Box 1134
Ojai, CA 93024
Ph: (805)646-8126
Fax: (805)646-9762
Co. E-mail: info@ojaichamber.com
URL: http://www.ojaichamber.org
Contact: Bob Kemper, President
Released: Monthly **Price:** free.

48839 ■ *Ojai Valley Chamber of Commerce*
PO Box 1134
Ojai, CA 93024
Ph: (805)646-8126
Fax: (805)646-9762
Co. E-mail: info@ojaichamber.com
URL: http://www.ojaichamber.org
Contact: Bob Kemper, President
Description: Promotes business and community development in the Ojai, CA area. **Founded:** 1956.
Publications: Ojai Valley Chamber Business Journal (Monthly). **Awards:** Citizen of the Year (Annual); Educator of the Year (Annual); Youth of the Year (Annual).

48840 ■ *On Point*
1260 N Dutton Ave., Ste. 272
Santa Rosa, CA 95401
Ph: (707)545-1414
Co. E-mail: info@santarosachamber.com
URL: http://www.santarosachamber.com
Contact: Jonathan Coe, President
Released: Monthly

48841 ■ *On Point On Line*
1260 N Dutton Ave., Ste. 272
Santa Rosa, CA 95401
Ph: (707)545-1414
Co. E-mail: info@santarosachamber.com
URL: http://www.santarosachamber.com
Contact: Jonathan Coe, President
Released: Weekly

48842 ■ *The Ontario Business Journal*
520 N Euclid Ave.
Ontario, CA 91762
Ph: (909)984-2458
Fax: (909)984-6439
Co. E-mail: info@ontario.org
URL: http://www.ontario.org
Contact: Bob Brown, Chairman
Released: Monthly

48843 ■ *Ontario Chamber of Commerce*
520 N Euclid Ave.
Ontario, CA 91762
Ph: (909)984-2458
Fax: (909)984-6439
Co. E-mail: info@ontario.org
URL: http://www.ontario.org
Contact: Bob Brown, Chairman
Description: Strives to help develop, enhance, and promote commerce in the city of Ontario and its trade area. Sponsors business golf tournament in April, police officers' recognition luncheon in May, Christmas on Euclid craft show, Police and Fire Safety Fair, health fair, chili cook, Christmas tree decorating contest for local schools and Nativity scene.
Founded: 1909. **Publications:** The Ontario Business Journal (Monthly); Who's Who in Chamber

Membership (Annual). **Educational Activities:** Ontario Chamber of Commerce Luncheon (Monthly); Ontario Chamber of Commerce Meeting (Weekly).

48844 ■ *Orange Business News*
307 E Chapman Ave.
Orange, CA 92866
Ph: (714)538-3581
Fax: (714)532-1675
Co. E-mail: hlarkin-reed@orangechamber.com
URL: http://www.orangechamber.com
Contact: Heidi Larkin-Reed, President
Released: Monthly

48845 ■ *Orange Bytes*
307 E Chapman Ave.
Orange, CA 92866
Ph: (714)538-3581
Fax: (714)532-1675
Co. E-mail: hlarkin-reed@orangechamber.com
URL: http://www.orangechamber.com
Contact: Heidi Larkin-Reed, President
Released: Weekly

48846 ■ *Orange Chamber of Commerce and Visitor Bureau (OCCVB)*
307 E Chapman Ave.
Orange, CA 92866
Ph: (714)538-3581
Fax: (714)532-1675
Co. E-mail: hlarkin-reed@orangechamber.com
URL: http://www.orangechamber.com
Contact: Heidi Larkin-Reed, President
Description: Promotes business and community development in Orange, CA. **Founded:** 1946. **Publications:** Orange Business News (Monthly); Orange Bytes (Weekly). **Educational Activities:** Golf Tournament (Annual).

48847 ■ *Orange County Business Council (OCBC)*
2 Park Plz., Ste. 100
Irvine, CA 92614-5904
Ph: (949)476-2242
Fax: (949)476-0443
Co. E-mail: ldunn@ocbc.org
URL: http://www.ocbc.org
Contact: Lucy Dunn, President
Description: Promotes business and community development in Orange County, CA. **Founded:** 1888.
Publications: The Indicator (Quarterly). **Educational Activities:** Economic Forecast (Annual). **Awards:** The Advocacy Award (Annual); The Chairman Award (Annual); The Economic Development Award (Annual); The Segerstrom Lifetime Achievement Award (Annual); The Workforce Development Award (Annual).

48848 ■ *Orange County Chamber of Commerce Profit Connection*
307 E Chapman Ave.
Orange, CA 92866-1509
Ph: (714)538-3581
Fax: (714)532-1675
Co. E-mail: info@orangechamber.com
URL: http://www.orangechamber.com
Contact: Heide Larkin-Reed, President
Description: Promotes business and community development in Orange County, CA area. **Founded:** 1946.

48849 ■ *Orange County Hispanic Chamber of Commerce (OCHCC)*
2130 E 4th St., Ste. 160
Santa Ana, CA 92705
Ph: (714)953-4289
Fax: (714)953-0273
Co. E-mail: eddie.marquez@sce.com
URL: http://www.ochcc.com
Contact: Eddie Marquez, Chairman
Description: Promotes business and community development in Orange County, CA area. **Founded:** 1986.

48850 ■ *Orangevale Chamber of Commerce (OCC)*
9267 Greenback Ln., Ste. B97
Orangevale, CA 95662-4865
Ph: (916)988-0175

Fax: (916)988-1049
Co. E-mail: info@orangevalechamber.com
URL: http://www.orangevalechamber.com
Contact: Darlene Lyons, President
Description: Promotes business and community development in Sacramento County, CA. **Founded:** 1955. **Publications:** Orangevale Chamber of Commerce Business Directory (Annual); Orangevale Juice (Periodic); Orangevale History. **Educational Activities:** Chamber Ambassador Meeting (Monthly); Pow Wow Days (Annual).

48851 ■ *Orangevale Chamber of Commerce Business Directory*
9267 Greenback Ln., Ste. B97
Orangevale, CA 95662-4865
Ph: (916)988-0175
Fax: (916)988-1049
Co. E-mail: info@orangevalechamber.com
URL: http://www.orangevalechamber.com
Contact: Darlene Lyons, President
Released: Annual

48852 ■ *Orangevale Juice*
9267 Greenback Ln., Ste. B97
Orangevale, CA 95662-4865
Ph: (916)988-0175
Fax: (916)988-1049
Co. E-mail: info@orangevalechamber.com
URL: http://www.orangevalechamber.com
Contact: Darlene Lyons, President
Released: Periodic

48853 ■ *Orinda Chamber of Commerce (OCC)*
PO Box 2271
Orinda, CA 94563
Ph: (925)254-3909
Fax: (925)254-8312
Co. E-mail: info@orindachamber.org
URL: http://www.orindachamber.org
Contact: Candy Kattenburg, Executive Director
Description: Promotes business and community development in Contra Costa County, CA. **Founded:** 1952.

48854 ■ *Oroville Area Chamber of Commerce (OACC)*
1789 Montgomery St.
Oroville, CA 95965
Ph: (530)538-2542
Free: 800-655-GOLD
Fax: (530)538-2546
Co. E-mail: info@orovillechamber.net
URL: http://www.orovillechamber.net
Contact: Linda Dahlmeier, President
Description: Promotes business and community development in the Oroville, CA area.

48855 ■ *Otay Action*
9163 Siempre Viva Rd., Ste. I-2
San Diego, CA 92154-7608
Ph: (619)661-6111
Fax: (619)661-6178
Co. E-mail: lenriquez@otaymesa.org
URL: http://www.otaymesa.org
Contact: Lnda Greenberg, President
Released: Bimonthly **Price:** included in membership dues.

48856 ■ *Otay Mesa Chamber of Commerce*
9163 Siempre Viva Rd., Ste. I-2
San Diego, CA 92154-7608
Ph: (619)661-6111
Fax: (619)661-6178
Co. E-mail: lenriquez@otaymesa.org
URL: http://www.otaymesa.org
Contact: Lnda Greenberg, President
Description: Promotes business and community development in Otay Mesa, CA. Sponsors Trade Show. **Founded:** 1987. **Publications:** Otay Action (Bimonthly).

48857 ■ *Oxnard Chamber of Commerce (OCC)*
400 E Esplanade Dr., Ste. 302
Oxnard, CA 93036
Ph: (805)983-6118

Fax: (805)604-7331
Co. E-mail: info@oxnardchamber.org
URL: http://www.oxnardchamber.org
Contact: Nancy Lindholm, President
Description: Promotes business and community development in Oxnard, CA area. **Founded:** 1923. **Publications:** *Business Voice* (Monthly). **Educational Activities:** Good Morning Oxnard Breakfasts (Monthly).

48858 ■ Pacific Grove Chamber of Commerce (PGCC)
584 Central Ave.
Pacific Grove, CA 93950
Ph: (831)373-3304
Free: 800-656-6650
Fax: (831)373-3317
Co. E-mail: chamber@pacificgrove.org
URL: http://www.pacificgrove.org
Contact: Moe Ammar, President
Description: Promotes business and community development and operates visitor information center in Pacific Grove, CA. **Publications:** *Historic Walking Tour; Rap Up* (Bimonthly). **Educational Activities:** Mixer (Monthly). **Awards:** City Employee of the Year Award (Annual); James Hughes Community Service Award (Annual).

48859 ■ Pacific Palisades Chamber of Commerce
15330 Antioch St.
Pacific Palisades, CA 90272
Ph: (310)459-7963
Fax: (310)459-9534
Co. E-mail: info@palisadeschamber.com
URL: http://www.palisadeschamber.com
Contact: John Petrick, President
Description: Promotes business and community development in Pacific Palisades, CA. **Founded:** 1949.

48860 ■ Pacifica Chamber of Commerce and Visitor Center (PCC)
225 Rockaway Beach Ave., Ste. 1
Pacifica, CA 94044
Ph: (650)355-4122
Fax: (650)355-6949
Co. E-mail: debbie@pacificachamber.com
URL: http://www.pacificachamber.com
Description: Promotes business and community development in Pacifica, CA. **Founded:** 1957.

48861 ■ Pajaro Valley Chamber of Commerce
444 Main St.
Watsonville, CA 95077-1748
Ph: (831)724-3900
Fax: (831)728-5300
Co. E-mail: info@pajarovalleychamber.com
URL: http://www.pajarovalleychamber.com
Contact: Theo Wierdsma, Chairman
Description: Promotes business and community development in the Watsonville and Pajaro Valley, CA area. **Publications:** *The Progress* (Monthly). **Awards:** Business of the Year (Annual); Man and Woman of the Year (Annual); Organization of the Year (Annual).

48862 ■ Palm Desert Chamber of Commerce
72559 Hwy. 111
Palm Desert, CA 92260
Ph: (760)346-6111
Fax: (760)346-3263
Co. E-mail: info@pdcc.org
URL: http://www.pdcc.org
Contact: Ms. Barbara deBoom, President
Description: Promotes business and community development in Palm Desert, CA. **Founded:** 1954. **Publications:** *Business to Business* (Monthly). **Awards:** Art and Business Award (Annual); Award of Excellence (Annual); Business Person of the Year (Annual); Community Service Award (Annual); George V. Berkey Award (Annual).

48863 ■ Palm Springs Chamber of Commerce (PSCC)
190 W Amado Rd.
Palm Springs, CA 92262
Ph: (760)325-1577

Fax: (760)325-8549
Co. E-mail: janetcook@pschamber.org
URL: http://www.pschamber.org
Contact: Nona Watson, Chief Executive Officer
Description: Promotes business and community development in the Palm Springs, CA area. **Founded:** 1940. **Publications:** *Business Matters* (Monthly); *Business Referral* (Annual); *Business Referral* (Annual). **Educational Activities:** Board Retreat (Annual); Leadership Conference/Retreat (Monthly). **Telecommunication Services:** info@pschamber.org

48864 ■ Palmdale Chamber of Commerce
817 East Ave., Q-9
Palmdale, CA 93550
Ph: (661)273-3232
Fax: (661)273-8508
Co. E-mail: chamberstaff@palmdalechamber.org
URL: http://www.palmdalechamber.org
Contact: Chris Buchanan, Chairperson
Description: Promotes business and community development in Palmdale, CA. Sponsors Miss Palmdale Pageant. **Founded:** 1941. **Publications:** *Vantage* (Monthly). **Educational Activities:** Mixers (Monthly).

48865 ■ Palo Alto Chamber of Commerce (PACC)
122 Hamilton Ave.
Palo Alto, CA 94301
Ph: (650)324-3121
Fax: (650)324-1215
Co. E-mail: info@paloaltochamber.com
URL: http://www.paloaltochamber.com
Contact: Paula Sandas, President
Description: Promotes business and community development in Palo Alto, CA. **Founded:** 1910. **Publications:** *Business and Community Directory* (Annual); *Business News Network* (Bimonthly). **Educational Activities:** Golf Tournament (Annual). **Awards:** Tall Tree Award (Annual).

48866 ■ Palos Verdes Peninsula Chamber of Commerce
707 Silver Spur Rd., Ste. 100
Rolling Hills Estates, CA 90274
Ph: (310)377-8111
Fax: (310)377-0614
Co. E-mail: office@palosverdeschamber.com
URL: http://palosverdeschamber.com
Contact: Kay Finer, President
Description: Promotes business and community development in Palos Verdes Peninsula, California area. **Founded:** 1956. **Publications:** *Peninsula Business Journal* (Monthly).

48867 ■ Paradise Ridge Chamber of Commerce
5550 Skyway, No. 1
Paradise, CA 95969
Ph: (530)877-9356
Free: 888-845-2769
Fax: (530)877-1865
Co. E-mail: info@paradisechamber.com
URL: http://www.paradisechamber.com
Contact: Monica Nolan, Officer, Membership
Description: Promotes business and community development on the Paradise Ridge in Northern California.

48868 ■ Paramount Chamber of Commerce (PCC)
c/o Peggy Lemons, Exec. Dir.
15357 Paramount Blvd.
Paramount, CA 90723-4338
Ph: (562)634-3980
Fax: (562)634-0891
Co. E-mail: plemons@paramountchamber.com
URL: http://www.paramountchamber.com
Contact: Peggy Lemons, Executive Director
Description: Promotes business and community development in Paramount, CA. Maintains business resource center. **Scope:** business. **Founded:** 1924. **Subscriptions:** books. **Publications:** *Business Directory; City Map; PulseBeat* (Monthly). **Educational Activities:** Paramount Fiesta (Annual).

48869 ■ Pasadena Chamber of Commerce and Civic Association
844 E Green St., Ste. 208
Pasadena, CA 91101
Ph: (626)795-3355
Fax: (626)795-5603
Co. E-mail: info@pasadena-chamber.org
URL: http://www.pasadena-chamber.org
Contact: Paul Little, President
Description: Promotes business and community development in Pasadena, CA. **Founded:** 1888. **Publications:** *Business Directory* (Periodic); *Community Guide* (Periodic); *Pasadena Commerce* (Monthly). **Educational Activities:** Connection (Monthly); Luncheon Alliance (Monthly).

48870 ■ *Pasadena Commerce*
844 E Green St., Ste. 208
Pasadena, CA 91101
Ph: (626)795-3355
Fax: (626)795-5603
Co. E-mail: info@pasadena-chamber.org
URL: http://www.pasadena-chamber.org
Contact: Paul Little, President
Released: Monthly

48871 ■ Paso Robles Chamber of Commerce (PRCC)
1225 Park St.
Paso Robles, CA 93446
Ph: (805)238-0506
Free: 800-406-4040
Fax: (805)238-0527
Co. E-mail: mgibson@pasorobleschamber.com
URL: http://www.pasorobleschamber.com
Contact: Mike Gibson, President
Description: Promotes business and community development in northern San Luis Obispo County, CA. **Founded:** 1921. **Publications:** *Business* (Monthly); *The Business News* (Monthly). **Educational Activities:** Agri-Business (Annual); Business Expo (Annual). **Awards:** Roblan of the Year (Annual).

48872 ■ Patterson-Westley Chamber of Commerce (PWCC)
PO Box 365
Patterson, CA 95363
Ph: (209)895-8094
Co. E-mail: chamberofcommerce@gvni.com
URL: http://www.patterson-westleychamber.com
Contact: Carolyn Harr, President
Description: Promotes business and community development in the Patterson and Westley, CA area. **Founded:** 1912. **Publications:** *The Sentinel* (Quarterly).

48873 ■ Pearblossom Chamber of Commerce
PO Box 591
Pearblossom, CA 93553
Ph: (661)944-2564
URL: http://pearblossomchamber.com
Contact: Duane Carles, President
Description: Promotes business and community development in the Pearblossom, CA area.

48874 ■ *Pelican Post*
PO Box 5185
Salton City, CA 92275-5185
Ph: (760)394-4112
Fax: (760)394-4112
Co. E-mail: wscc.secretary@gmail.com
URL: http://www.westshoreschamber.org
Contact: Lavon Jaksch, President
Released: Monthly; except July and August. **Price:** free.

48875 ■ *Peninsula Business Journal*
707 Silver Spur Rd., Ste. 100
Rolling Hills Estates, CA 90274
Ph: (310)377-8111
Fax: (310)377-0614
Co. E-mail: office@palosverdeschamber.com
URL: http://palosverdeschamber.com
Contact: Kay Finer, President
Released: Monthly

48876 ■ Perris Valley Chamber of Commerce
11 S D St.
Perris, CA 92571

Ph: (951)657-3555
Fax: (951)657-3085
Co. E-mail: perrischamberofcommerce@yahoo.com
URL: http://www.perrischamber.org
Contact: Robert Turner, President
Description: Promotes business and community development in the Parris Valley, CA area. **Founded:** 1911.

48877 ■ Petaluma Area Chamber of Commerce
6 Petaluma Blvd. N, Ste. A2
Petaluma, CA 94952
Ph: (707)762-2785
Fax: (707)762-4721
Co. E-mail: pacc@petalumachamber.com
URL: http://www.petalumachamber.com
Contact: Ms. Onita Pellegrini, Chief Executive Officer
Description: Promotes business and community development in the Petaluma Area, CA area. **Founded:** 1906. **Subscriptions:** archival material clippings papers periodicals video recordings. **Publications:** *Petaluma Business* (Monthly); *Petaluma Street Map* (Annual); *Petaluma Business* (Monthly); *Petaluma Chamber Directory and Relocation Guide* (Annual). **Awards:** Citizen of the Year (Annual).

48878 ■ *Petaluma Business*
6 Petaluma Blvd. N, Ste. A2
Petaluma, CA 94952
Ph: (707)762-2785
Fax: (707)762-4721
Co. E-mail: pacc@petalumachamber.com
URL: http://www.petalumachamber.com
Contact: Ms. Onita Pellegrini, Chief Executive Officer
Released: Monthly

48879 ■ *Petaluma Chamber Directory and Relocation Guide*
6 Petaluma Blvd. N, Ste. A2
Petaluma, CA 94952
Ph: (707)762-2785
Fax: (707)762-4721
Co. E-mail: pacc@petalumachamber.com
URL: http://www.petalumachamber.com
Contact: Ms. Onita Pellegrini, Chief Executive Officer
Released: Annual

48880 ■ *Petaluma Street Map*
6 Petaluma Blvd. N, Ste. A2
Petaluma, CA 94952
Ph: (707)762-2785
Fax: (707)762-4721
Co. E-mail: pacc@petalumachamber.com
URL: http://www.petalumachamber.com
Contact: Ms. Onita Pellegrini, Chief Executive Officer
Released: Annual

48881 ■ Phelan Chamber of Commerce
PO Box 290010
Phelan, CA 92329-0010
Ph: (760)868-3291
Fax: (760)868-3291
Co. E-mail: phelanchamber@verizon.net
URL: http://www.phelanchamber.org
Contact: Rosella Bernal, President
Description: Works to advance the general welfare and prosperity of the Phelan area.

48882 ■ Pico Rivera Chamber of Commerce
5016 Passons Blvd.
Pico Rivera, CA 90660
Ph: (562)949-2473
Fax: (562)949-8320
Co. E-mail: elena@picoriverachamber.org
URL: http://www.picoriverachamber.org
Contact: Mary Ann Bakotich, Executive Director
Description: Promotes business and community development in Pico Rivera, CA. Conducts beautification and business of the year competitions. Sponsors business expo, golf tournaments, mixers, and other special events. **Founded:** 1958. **Publications:** *Business News* (Monthly).

48883 ■ Pinole Chamber of Commerce (PCC)
PO Box 1
Pinole, CA 94564
Ph: (510)724-4484

Fax: (510)724-4408
Co. E-mail: pinolechamber@yahoo.com
URL: http://www.pinolechamber.org
Contact: Ivette Ricco, President
Description: Promotes business and community development in Pinole, CA.

48884 ■ Pinon Hills Chamber of Commerce
PO Box 720095
Pinon Hills, CA 92372
Ph: (760)868-5801
Co. E-mail: pinonhillschamber@verizon.net
URL: http://www.pinonhillschamber.com
Contact: Jane Rowan, President
Description: Promotes business and community development in Pinon Hills, CA area.

48885 ■ *Pioneer*
PO Box 175
San Dimas, CA 91773-0175
Ph: (909)592-3818
Fax: (909)592-8178
Co. E-mail: info@sandimaschamber.com
URL: http://www.sandimaschamber.com
Contact: Karen Gaffney, President
Released: Monthly; except February and September.

48886 ■ Pismo Beach Chamber of Commerce and Visitors' Information Center
581 Dolliver St.
Pismo Beach, CA 93449
Ph: (805)773-4382
Free: 800-443-7778
Fax: (805)773-6772
Co. E-mail: pbcoc@charter.net
URL: http://www.pismochamber.com
Contact: Peter Candela, Chief Executive Officer
Description: Promotes business and community development in Pismo Beach, CA. **Publications:** *Business*; *Business Directory*. **Telecommunication Services:** info@pismochamber.com

48887 ■ Pittsburg Chamber of Commerce
985 Railroad Ave.
Pittsburg, CA 94565
Ph: (925)432-7301
Fax: (925)427-5555
Co. E-mail: mconig@pittsburg.org
URL: http://www.pittsburg.org
Contact: Meredith B. Ladich, Chief Executive Officer
Description: Promotes business and community development in Pittsburg, CA. **Scope:** business. **Publications:** *Business Today* (Monthly). **Telecommunication Services:** chamber@pittsburgchamber. org.

48888 ■ *Placentia Business Link*
201 E Yorba Linda Blvd., Ste. C
Placentia, CA 92870-3418
Ph: (714)528-1873
Fax: (714)528-1879
Co. E-mail: info@placentiachamber.com
URL: http://www.placentiachamber.com
Contact: Ms. Erin Coggins, President
Released: Monthly

48889 ■ Placentia Chamber of Commerce
201 E Yorba Linda Blvd., Ste. C
Placentia, CA 92870-3418
Ph: (714)528-1873
Fax: (714)528-1879
Co. E-mail: info@placentiachamber.com
URL: http://www.placentiachamber.com
Contact: Ms. Erin Coggins, President
Description: Promotes business and community development in northern Orange County, CA. **Founded:** 1924. **Publications:** *Placentia Business Link* (Monthly).

48890 ■ *Pleasant Hill Chamber*
91 Gregory Ln., Ste. 11
Pleasant Hill, CA 94523-4914
Ph: (925)687-0700
Fax: (925)676-7422
Co. E-mail: info@pleasanthillchamber.com
URL: http://www.pleasanthillchamber.com
Contact: Charley Daly, Chief Executive Officer

48891 ■ Pleasant Hill Chamber of Commerce (PHCC)
91 Gregory Ln., Ste. 11
Pleasant Hill, CA 94523-4914
Ph: (925)687-0700
Fax: (925)676-7422
Co. E-mail: info@pleasanthillchamber.com
URL: http://www.pleasanthillchamber.com
Contact: Charley Daly, Chief Executive Officer
Description: Promotes business and community development in the central Contra Costa County, CA. Sponsors local festivals and charitable events. Conducts competitions. **Founded:** 1954. **Publications:** *Business News* (Monthly); *Pleasant Hill Chamber*. **Educational Activities:** Art, Jazz & Wine (Annual); Summer Bash (Annual). **Awards:** Business Person of the Year (Annual); Chamber Board (Annual); Citizen of the Year (Annual); Community Plus Award (Annual); Educator of the Year (Annual); Teen of the Year (Annual).

48892 ■ Pleasanton Chamber of Commerce
777 Peters Ave.
Pleasanton, CA 94566-6500
Ph: (925)846-5858
Fax: (925)846-9697
Co. E-mail: info@pleasanton.org
URL: http://www.pleasanton.org
Contact: Scott Raty, President
Description: Promotes business and community development in Pleasanton, CA. **Founded:** 1949. **Publications:** *Business Connection* (Monthly). **Educational Activities:** Community Service Awards Luncheon (Annual). **Awards:** Community Service Award (Annual).

48893 ■ *Pomona Chamber Business Monthly*
PO Box 1457
Pomona, CA 91769-1457
Ph: (909)622-8484
Fax: (909)620-5986
Co. E-mail: info@pomonachamber.org
URL: http://www.pomonachamber.org
Contact: Simon Concepcion, President
Released: Monthly

48894 ■ Pomona Chamber of Commerce
PO Box 1457
Pomona, CA 91769-1457
Ph: (909)622-8484
Fax: (909)620-5986
Co. E-mail: info@pomonachamber.org
URL: http://www.pomonachamber.org
Contact: Simon Concepcion, President
Description: Promotes business and community development in Pomona, CA. **Scope:** community directory, community map. **Founded:** 1888. **Subscriptions:** 3 articles maps. **Publications:** *Pomona Chamber Business Monthly* (Monthly); *Pomona Chamber of Commerce Membership Directory/Community Guide* (Annual); *Pomona Chamber of Commerce Membership Directory/Community Guide* (Annual). **Awards:** Community Service Award (Annual).

48895 ■ *Pomona Chamber of Commerce Membership Directory/Community Guide*
PO Box 1457
Pomona, CA 91769-1457
Ph: (909)622-8484
Fax: (909)620-5986
Co. E-mail: info@pomonachamber.org
URL: http://www.pomonachamber.org
Contact: Simon Concepcion, President
Released: Annual **Price:** free.

48896 ■ Port Hueneme Chamber of Commerce (PHCC)
220 N Market St.
Port Hueneme, CA 93041-3204
Ph: (805)488-2023
Fax: (805)488-6993
URL: http://www.huenemechamber.com
Contact: Kathleen Misewitch, President
Description: Promotes business and community development in Port Hueneme, Oxnard Harbor District, and surrounding areas. **Founded:** 1940.

48897 ■ *Port O Call*
445 W Weber Ave., Ste. 220
Stockton, CA 95203
Ph: (209)547-2770
Fax: (209)466-5271
Co. E-mail: schamber@stocktonchamber.org
URL: http://www.stocktonchamber.org
Contact: Douglass W. Wilhoit, Jr., Chief Executive
Officer
Released: Monthly

48898 ■ Porterville Chamber of Commerce
93 N Main St., Ste. A
Porterville, CA 93257
Ph: (559)784-7502
Fax: (559)784-0770
Co. E-mail: chamber@porterville.com
URL: http://www.chamber.porterville.com
Contact: Donnette Silva Carter, President
URL(s): irisfestival.porterville.com, www.porterville.
com/business, www.chamber.porterville.com/attrac-
tions. **Description:** Promotes business and com-
munity development in southeastern Tulare County,
CA. Sponsors local festivals. **Founded:** 1907. **Publi-
cations:** *Business News* (Monthly); *Porterville Fact
Book* (Periodic). **Educational Activities:** Iris (An-
nual). **Awards:** Community Service Project of the
Year (Annual); Female Youth of the Year (Annual);
Large Business of the Year (Annual); Male Youth of
the Year (Annual); Man of the Year (Annual); Small
Business of the Year (Annual); Volunteer of the Year
(Annual); Woman of the Year (Annual).

48899 ■ *Porterville Fact Book*
93 N Main St., Ste. A
Porterville, CA 93257
Ph: (559)784-7502
Fax: (559)784-0770
Co. E-mail: chamber@porterville.com
URL: http://www.chamber.porterville.com
Contact: Donnette Silva Carter, President
Released: Periodic

48900 ■ Poway Chamber of Commerce
PO Box 868
Poway, CA 92074-0868
Ph: (858)748-0016
Fax: (858)748-1710
Co. E-mail: chamber@poway.com
URL: http://www.poway.com
Contact: Luanne Hulsizer, President
Description: Promotes business and community
development in Poway, CA. **Founded:** 1951. **Publi-
cations:** *Communique* (Monthly); *Poway Telephone
Directory* (Annual).

48901 ■ *Poway Telephone Directory*
PO Box 868
Poway, CA 92074-0868
Ph: (858)748-0016
Fax: (858)748-1710
Co. E-mail: chamber@poway.com
URL: http://www.poway.com
Contact: Luanne Hulsizer, President
Released: Annual **Price:** free.

48902 ■ *The Power of Connection*
388 W Huntington Dr.
Arcadia, CA 91007-3402
Ph: (626)447-2159
Fax: (626)445-0273
URL: http://www.arcadiacachamber.org
Contact: Pete Siberell, President
Released: Monthly

48903 ■ *The Progress*
444 Main St.
Watsonville, CA 95077-1748
Ph: (831)724-3900
Fax: (831)728-5300
Co. E-mail: info@pajarovalleychamber.com
URL: http://www.pajarovalleychamber.com
Contact: Theo Wierdsma, Chairman
Released: Monthly

48904 ■ *The Progress*
307 1st St.
Woodland, CA 95695-3412
Ph: (530)662-7327

Free: 888-843-2636
Fax: (530)662-4086
Co. E-mail: staff@woodlandchamber.org
URL: http://www.woodlandchamber.org
Contact: Kristy Wright, Chief Executive Officer
E-mail: kristyw@woodlandchamber.com
Released: Monthly **Price:** included in membership
dues.

48905 ■ *PulseBeat*
c/o Peggy Lemons, Exec. Dir.
15357 Paramount Blvd.
Paramount, CA 90723-4338
Ph: (562)634-3980
Fax: (562)634-0891
Co. E-mail: plemons@paramountchamber.com
URL: http://www.paramountchamber.com
Contact: Peggy Lemons, Executive Director
Released: Monthly **Price:** free.

48906 ■ *Quartz Hill Breeze*
42043 50th St. W
Quartz Hill, CA 93536
Ph: (661)722-4811
Fax: (661)722-3235
Co. E-mail: info@quartzhillchamber.org
URL: http://www.qhchamber.com
Contact: Mr. Lee Barron, President
Price: free for members.

48907 ■ Quartz Hill Chamber of Commerce
42043 50th St. W
Quartz Hill, CA 93536
Ph: (661)722-4811
Fax: (661)722-3235
Co. E-mail: info@quartzhillchamber.org
URL: http://www.qhchamber.com
Contact: Mr. Lee Barron, President
Description: Promotes business and community
development in Quartz Hill, CA. **Founded:** 1948.
Publications: *Quartz Hill Breeze.* **Educational Ac-
tivities:** Quartz Hill Chamber of Commerce Workshop
(Monthly). **Awards:** Quartz Hill Queen (Annual).

**48908 ■ Quincy Chamber of Commerce
(QCC)**
464 W Main St.
Quincy, CA 95971
Ph: (530)283-0188
Free: 888-EZW-AY4U
Fax: (530)283-5864
Co. E-mail: office@quincychamber.com
URL: http://www.quincychamber.com
Contact: Kent Barrett, President
Description: Promotes business and community
development in Quincy, CA. Sponsors community
events.

**48909 ■ *Ramona Business and Community
News***
960 Main St.
Ramona, CA 92065
Ph: (760)789-1311
Fax: (760)789-1317
Co. E-mail: info@ramonachamber.com
URL: http://www.ramonachamber.com
Contact: Thad Clendenen, President
Released: Monthly

**48910 ■ Ramona Chamber of Commerce
(RCC)**
960 Main St.
Ramona, CA 92065
Ph: (760)789-1311
Fax: (760)789-1317
Co. E-mail: info@ramonachamber.com
URL: http://www.ramonachamber.com
Contact: Thad Clendenen, President
Description: Promotes business and community
development in Ramona, CA. Holds annual country
fair, golf tournament, and rodeo. **Founded:** 1902.
Publications: *Ramona Business and Community
News* (Monthly).

48911 ■ *Ranch Marketing Guide*
542 Main St.
Placerville, CA 95667-5610
Ph: (530)621-5885
Free: 800-457-6279

Fax: (530)642-1624
Co. E-mail: admin@eldoradocounty.org
URL: http://www.eldoradocounty.org
Contact: Kirk Bone, President

**48912 ■ Rancho Cordova Chamber of
Commerce**
2729 Prospect Park Dr., Ste. 117
Rancho Cordova, CA 95670
Ph: (916)273-5688
Fax: (916)273-5727
Co. E-mail: jlunn@ranchocordova.org
URL: http://www.ranchocordova.org
Contact: Jane Daly, Chief Executive Officer
Description: Promotes business and community
development in the southeastern Sacramento, CA
area. Conducts small business seminars and work-
shops; sponsors Talk to Expert series. Issues annual
and monthly publications. **Founded:** 1963. **Publica-
tions:** *Chamber Report.*

**48913 ■ Rancho Cucamonga Chamber of
Commerce**
9047 Arrow Rte., Ste. 180
Rancho Cucamonga, CA 91730
Ph: (909)987-1012
Fax: (909)987-5917
Co. E-mail: info@ranchochamber.org
URL: http://www.ranchochamber.org
Contact: Michelle Alonzo, President
Description: Promotes business and community
development in Rancho Cucamonga, CA area.
Founded: 1951. **Publications:** *Business Connection*
(Monthly); *Chamber Member Business and Resource
Directory; The Shop Rancho Retail Guide and
Service Directory* (Annual). **Educational Activities:**
Business Connection Network (Weekly); The Grape
Harvest Festival (Annual).

**48914 ■ Rancho Mirage Chamber of
Commerce (RMCC)**
42-520 Bob Hope Dr., Ste. B
Rancho Mirage, CA 92270
Ph: (760)568-9351
Fax: (760)779-9684
Co. E-mail: info@ranchomirage.org
URL: http://www.ranchomirage.org
Contact: Stuart W. Ackley, President
Description: Promotes business and community
development in the Coachella Valley area of Califor-
nia. Sponsors Mayor's Breakfast. **Founded:** 1955.
Subscriptions: 18000. **Publications:** *The Business
Advocate* (Monthly); *Rancho Mirage City Guide* (An-
nual); *Rancho Mirage Chamber of Commerce--
Membership Directory & Buyers Guide* (Annual).
Awards: Business Award (Annual).

48915 ■ *Rancho Mirage City Guide*
42-520 Bob Hope Dr., Ste. B
Rancho Mirage, CA 92270
Ph: (760)568-9351
Fax: (760)779-9684
Co. E-mail: info@ranchomirage.org
URL: http://www.ranchomirage.org
Contact: Stuart W. Ackley, President
Released: Annual

48916 ■ *Rap Up*
584 Central Ave.
Pacific Grove, CA 93950
Ph: (831)373-3304
Free: 800-656-6650
Fax: (831)373-3317
Co. E-mail: chamber@pacificgrove.org
URL: http://www.pacificgrove.org
Contact: Moe Ammar, President
Released: Bimonthly

**48917 ■ Red Bluff-Tehama County Chamber
of Commerce**
100 Main St.
Red Bluff, CA 96080
Ph: (530)527-6220
Free: 800-655-6225

Fax: (530)527-2908
Co. E-mail: rbchamber@att.net
URL: http://www.redbluffchamberofcommerce.com
Contact: Dave Gowan, President
Description: Promotes business and community development in Red Bluff-Tehama County, CA. Sponsors Memorial Day Championship Drag Boat Races and art and crafts fair. **Publications:** *Chamber Report* (Monthly).

48918 ■ *Redding Directions*
747 Auditorium Dr.
Redding, CA 96001
Ph: (530)225-4433
Fax: (530)225-4398
Co. E-mail: info@reddingchamber.com
URL: http://www.reddingchamber.com
Contact: Frank J. Strazzarino, Jr., President
Released: Monthly

48919 ■ **Redlands Chamber of Commerce**
1 E Redlands Blvd.
Redlands, CA 92373
Ph: (909)793-2546
Fax: (909)335-6388
Co. E-mail: info@redlandschamber.org
URL: http://www.redlandschamber.org
Contact: Paul Barich, Director
Description: Promotes business and community development in Redlands, CA. Issues publications. **Founded:** 1893. **Publications:** *Chamber Membership Directory* (Annual); *Redlands Chamber Today* (Monthly). **Educational Activities:** Rise 'n Shine Redlands (Monthly).

48920 ■ *Redlands Chamber Today*
1 E Redlands Blvd.
Redlands, CA 92373
Ph: (909)793-2546
Fax: (909)335-6388
Co. E-mail: info@redlandschamber.org
URL: http://www.redlandschamber.org
Contact: Paul Barich, Director
Released: Monthly **Price:** included in membership dues.

48921 ■ **Redondo Beach Chamber of Commerce and Visitors Bureau**
200 N Pacific Coast Hwy.
Redondo Beach, CA 90277
Ph: (310)376-6911
Free: 800-282-0333
Fax: (310)374-7373
Co. E-mail: info@redondochamber.org
URL: http://www.redondochamber.org
Contact: Steve Goldstein, Chairman
URL(s): www.redondoadvocacy.biz. **Description:** Promotes business and community development in Redondo Beach, CA. Sponsors festivals, competitions, and charitable events. **Founded:** 1907. **Publications:** *Beach Business* (Monthly); *Update* (Monthly).

48922 ■ *Report to the Community*
400 Kern St.
Taft, CA 93268
Ph: (661)765-2165
Fax: (661)765-6639
Co. E-mail: taftchamber@bak.rr.com
URL: http://www.taftchamber.com
Contact: Fred Schell, Executive Director
Released: Monthly **Price:** free.

48923 ■ *Resource Guide*
2331 Fresno St.
Fresno, CA 93721
Ph: (559)495-4800
Fax: (559)495-4811
Co. E-mail: info@fresnochamber.com
URL: http://www.fresnochamber.com
Contact: Al Smith, President
Price: $40, for nonmembers; $35, for members.

48924 ■ **Rialto Chamber of Commerce**
120 N Riverside Ave.
Rialto, CA 92376
Ph: (909)875-5364

Fax: (909)875-6790
Co. E-mail: lisa@rialtochamber.com
URL: http://www.rialtochamber.org
Description: Promotes business and community development in Rialto, CA. Issues publications. **Founded:** 1907.

48925 ■ **Richmond Chamber of Commerce**
3925 Macdonald Ave.
Richmond, CA 94805
Ph: (510)234-3512
Fax: (510)234-3540
Co. E-mail: judy@rcoc.com
URL: http://www.rcoc.com
Contact: Ms. Judith Morgan, President
Description: Membership is made up of a dynamic range of businesses from sole-proprietors to major corporations. Provides a voice for each and encourages participation by all. Strives to provides services, resources, and advocacy to foster growth in the business community and benefit West Contra Costa County. Offers information about the city and its business opportunities, policies, and trends. **Founded:** 1924. **Publications:** *Richmond Magazine* (Biennial); *Richmond Chamber News* (Monthly); *Richmond Magazine* (Biennial). **Educational Activities:** Chamber Breakfast for Business (Monthly).

48926 ■ *Richmond Chamber News*
3925 Macdonald Ave.
Richmond, CA 94805
Ph: (510)234-3512
Fax: (510)234-3540
Co. E-mail: judy@rcoc.com
URL: http://www.rcoc.com
Contact: Ms. Judith Morgan, President
Released: Monthly **Price:** included in membership dues.

48927 ■ *Richmond Magazine*
3925 Macdonald Ave.
Richmond, CA 94805
Ph: (510)234-3512
Fax: (510)234-3540
Co. E-mail: judy@rcoc.com
URL: http://www.rcoc.com
Contact: Ms. Judith Morgan, President
Released: Biennial **Price:** $20, for nonmembers; included in membership dues.

48928 ■ **Ridgecrest Chamber of Commerce**
128-B E California Ave., Ste. B
Ridgecrest, CA 93555
Ph: (760)375-8331
Fax: (760)375-0365
Co. E-mail: chamber@ridgecrestchamber.com
URL: http://www.ridgecrestchamber.com
Contact: Jay Chun, President
Description: Promotes business and community development in eastern Kern County, CA. Sponsors Adopt-A-School program. Conducts Ridgecrest Follies, IWV Outlook Conference, Business Expo, Retail Promotion Seminars, and Military Shopping Tour. **Founded:** 1946. **Publications:** *Business Bylines* (Monthly). **Educational Activities:** Business After Hours (Monthly).

48929 ■ **Rio Linda-Elverta Chamber of Commerce**
PO Box 75
Rio Linda, CA 95673
Ph: (916)991-9344
Fax: (916)922-9074
Co. E-mail: jculley@rlechamber.com
URL: http://www.rlechamber.com/
Contact: Hal Morris, President
Description: Promotes business and community development in Rio Linda-Elverta, CA. **Publications:** *Welcome to Rio Linda-Elverta* (Monthly). **Telecommunication Services:** info@rlechamber.com.

48930 ■ **Rio Vista Chamber of Commerce**
6 N Front St.
Rio Vista, CA 94571
Ph: (707)374-2700

Fax: (707)374-2424
Co. E-mail: volunteer@riovista.org
URL: http://www.riovista.org
Contact: Mary Peinado, Executive Director
Description: Promotes business and community development in Rio Vista, CA. **Founded:** 1929.

48931 ■ **Ripon Chamber of Commerce**
929 W Main St.
Ripon, CA 95366
Ph: (209)599-7519
Fax: (209)599-2286
Co. E-mail: execdirector@riponchamber.org
URL: http://www.riponchamber.org
Contact: Dorothy Booth, Executive Director
Description: Promotes business and community development in Ripon, CA area. **Publications:** *The Communicator*. **Educational Activities:** Fashion Show (Annual).

48932 ■ **Rocklin Area Chamber of Commerce**
3700 Rocklin Rd.
Rocklin, CA 95677
Ph: (916)624-2548
Fax: (916)624-5743
Co. E-mail: info@rocklinchamber.com
URL: http://www.rocklinchamber.com
Contact: Robin Trimble, Chief Executive Officer
Description: Promotes business and community development in Rocklin, CA area. **Publications:** *Rocklin Chamber of Commerce City Guide and Membership Directory* (Annual); *Rocklin Chamber Membership Directory and Community Guide.*

48933 ■ *Rocklin Chamber of Commerce City Guide and Membership Directory*
3700 Rocklin Rd.
Rocklin, CA 95677
Ph: (916)624-2548
Fax: (916)624-5743
Co. E-mail: info@rocklinchamber.com
URL: http://www.rocklinchamber.com
Contact: Robin Trimble, Chief Executive Officer
Released: Annual

48934 ■ **Rohnert Park Chamber of Commerce**
101 Golf Course Dr. C-7
Rohnert Park, CA 94928
Ph: (707)584-1415
Fax: (707)584-2945
Co. E-mail: info@rohnertparkchamber.org
URL: http://www.rohnertparkchamber.org
Contact: Roy Gugliotta, President
Description: Business people in the Rohnert Park, CA area committed to creating and maintaining an environment in which businesses can grow and prosper economically, socially, and culturally. Emphasis is placed on leadership, advocacy, building community, and partnerships. **Founded:** 1963. **Publications:** *Business Resource Directory* (Annual); *Rohnert Park Chamber of Commerce Business News* (Monthly). **Educational Activities:** A.M. Rohnert Park (Monthly).

48935 ■ *Rohnert Park Chamber of Commerce Business News*
101 Golf Course Dr. C-7
Rohnert Park, CA 94928
Ph: (707)584-1415
Fax: (707)584-2945
Co. E-mail: info@rohnertparkchamber.org
URL: http://www.rohnertparkchamber.org
Contact: Roy Gugliotta, President
Released: Monthly

48936 ■ **Rosemead Chamber of Commerce**
3953 Muscatel Ave.
Rosemead, CA 91770
Ph: (626)288-0811
Fax: (626)288-2514
Co. E-mail: office@rosemeadchamber.org
URL: http://www.rosemeadchamber.org
Contact: Amy Wu, President
Description: Promotes business and community development in Rosemead, CA. Sponsors golf tournament and principal for a day program. **Founded:** 1927. **Publications:** *Rosemead Report* (Monthly).

48937 ■ *Rosemead Report*
3953 Muscatel Ave.
Rosemead, CA 91770
Ph: (626)288-0811
Fax: (626)288-2514
Co. E-mail: office@rosemeadchamber.org
URL: http://www.rosemeadchamber.org
Contact: Amy Wu, President
Released: Monthly

48938 ■ Roseville Chamber of Commerce
650 Douglas Blvd.
Roseville, CA 95678
Ph: (916)783-8136
Fax: (916)783-5261
Co. E-mail: admin@rosevillechamber.com
URL: http://www.rosevillechamber.com
Contact: Wendy A. Gerig, Chief Executive Officer
Description: Promotes business and community development in Placer County, CA. **Founded:** 1906. **Publications:** *Roseville Insight* (Monthly).

48939 ■ *Roseville Insight*
650 Douglas Blvd.
Roseville, CA 95678
Ph: (916)783-8136
Fax: (916)783-5261
Co. E-mail: admin@rosevillechamber.com
URL: http://www.rosevillechamber.com
Contact: Wendy A. Gerig, Chief Executive Officer
Released: Monthly

48940 ■ Rough and Ready Chamber of Commerce
PO Box 801
Rough and Ready, CA 95975
Ph: (530)272-4320
Co. E-mail: evburka@cwnet.com
URL: http://www.roughandreadychamber.com
Contact: Charles Crecilius, President
Description: Promotes business and community development in Rough and Ready, CA. **Founded:** 1958. **Awards:** Chili Cook-Off (Annual).

48941 ■ Running Springs Area Chamber of Commerce
PO Box 96
Running Springs, CA 92382-0096
Ph: (909)867-2411
Co. E-mail: info@runningspringschamber.com
URL: http://www.runningspringschamber.com
Contact: Linda Peabody, Administrative Assistant
Description: Promotes business and community development in Running Springs, CA.

48942 ■ Russian River Chamber of Commerce and Visitor Center
16209 1st St.
Guerneville, CA 95446
Ph: (707)869-9000
Free: 877-644-9001
Fax: (707)869-9009
Co. E-mail: news@russianriver.com
URL: http://www.russianriver.com
Contact: Margaret Kennett, President
Description: Promotes business and community development in Guerneville, CA. **Publications:** *Currents* (Monthly).

48943 ■ Sacramento Black Chamber of Commerce (SBCC)
5770 Freeport Blvd., Ste. 44
Sacramento, CA 95822
Ph: (916)231-0416
Fax: (916)706-0477
URL: http://www.sacblackchamber.org
Contact: Azizza Davis Goines, President
Description: Local businesses within Greater Sacramento, CA region providing the latest information on local and national issues that may impact the community; brings local business owners together to create a solid economic structure within the Sacramento business community. **Founded:** 1985. **Publications:** *Capital Gains* (Quarterly).

48944 ■ *Sacramento Hispanic*
1491 River Park Dr., Ste. No. 101
Sacramento, CA 95825
Ph: (916)486-7700

Fax: (916)486-7728
Co. E-mail: info@sachcc.org
URL: http://www.sachcc.org
Contact: Celia Cortez, Executive Director
Released: Monthly **Price:** $25, /year.

48945 ■ Sacramento Hispanic Chamber of Commerce (SHCC)
1491 River Park Dr., Ste. No. 101
Sacramento, CA 95825
Ph: (916)486-7700
Fax: (916)486-7728
Co. E-mail: info@sachcc.org
URL: http://www.sachcc.org
Contact: Celia Cortez, Executive Director
Description: Business owners, corporations, and individuals in Sacramento, CA. Creates and promotes a positive environment for Hispanic business. Coordinates efforts aimed at furthering economic and business development. Sponsors annual fundraisers and various festivals. **Founded:** 1972. **Publications:** *Sacramento Hispanic* (Monthly); *Sacramento Hispanic* (Monthly). **Awards:** SHCC Scholarships (Annual).

48946 ■ Sacramento Metro Chamber of Commerce
1 Capitol Mall, Ste. 300
Sacramento, CA 95814
Ph: (916)552-6800
Fax: (916)443-2672
Co. E-mail: mmahood@metrochamber.org
URL: http://www.metrochamber.org
Contact: Martha Clark Lofgren, Chief Executive Officer
Description: Promotes business and community development in the Sacramento, CA area. **Founded:** 1895. **Publications:** *Bizline*; *Metro Business* (Weekly). **Awards:** Business Hall of Fame (Annual); Businessman and Businesswoman of the Year Awards (Annual). **Telecommunication Services:** chamber@metrochamber.org.

48947 ■ St. Helena Chamber of Commerce (SHCC)
1010 Main St., Ste. A
St. Helena, CA 94574
Ph: (707)963-4456
Free: 800-799-6456
Fax: (707)963-5396
Co. E-mail: info@sthelena.com
URL: http://www.sthelena.com
Contact: Nancy Levenberg, President
Description: Promotes business and community development in St. Helena, CA. **Founded:** 1940.

48948 ■ *Salinas Valley Business Journal*
119 E Alisal St.
Salinas, CA 93901
Ph: (831)751-7725
Fax: (831)424-8639
Co. E-mail: info@salinaschamber.com
URL: http://www.salinaschamber.com
Contact: Tom Carvey, President
Released: Bimonthly

48949 ■ Salinas Valley Chamber of Commerce
119 E Alisal St.
Salinas, CA 93901
Ph: (831)751-7725
Fax: (831)424-8639
Co. E-mail: info@salinaschamber.com
URL: http://www.salinaschamber.com
Contact: Tom Carvey, President
Description: Promotes business and community development in the Salinas, CA area. **Publications:** *Salinas Valley Business Journal* (Bimonthly). **Awards:** Business Woman of the Year (Annual); Citizen of the Year (Annual); Member of the Year (Annual).

48950 ■ San Anselmo Chamber of Commerce
PO Box 2844
San Anselmo, CA 94979-2844
Ph: (415)454-2510

Fax: (415)258-9458
Co. E-mail: info@sananselmochamber.org
URL: http://www.sananselmochamber.org
Contact: Connie S. Rodgers, President
Description: Promotes business and community development in San Anselmo, CA area.

48951 ■ San Benito County Chamber of Commerce
650 San Benito St., Ste. 130
Hollister, CA 95023-3988
Ph: (831)637-5315
Fax: (831)637-1008
Co. E-mail: info1@sanbenitocountychamber.com
URL: http://www.sanbenitocountychamber.com
Contact: Jessica French, President
Description: Promotes business and community development in San Benito, CA. **Founded:** 1921. **Publications:** *Chamber News* (Monthly); *California. Calm, A Guide to San Benito County*; *California.Calm, A Guide to San Benito County*. **Educational Activities:** Chamber Mixers (Monthly).

48952 ■ San Bernardino Area Chamber of Commerce (SBACC)
PO Box 658
San Bernardino, CA 92402
Ph: (909)885-7515
Fax: (909)384-9979
Co. E-mail: sba.chamber@verizon.net
URL: http://www.sbachamber.org
Contact: Judi Penman, President
Description: Promotes business and community development in the San Bernardino, CA area. **Founded:** 1925. **Publications:** *San Bernardino Business* (Monthly).

48953 ■ *San Bernardino Business*
PO Box 658
San Bernardino, CA 92402
Ph: (909)885-7515
Fax: (909)384-9979
Co. E-mail: sba.chamber@verizon.net
URL: http://www.sbachamber.org
Contact: Judi Penman, President
Released: Monthly

48954 ■ *San Carlos Business*
1500 Laurel St., Ste. B
San Carlos, CA 94070-5103
Ph: (650)593-1068
Fax: (650)593-9108
Co. E-mail: staff@sancarloschamber.org
URL: http://www.sancarloschamber.org/default.aspx
Contact: David Bouchard, Chief Executive Officer
Released: Monthly

48955 ■ San Carlos Chamber of Commerce
1500 Laurel St., Ste. B
San Carlos, CA 94070-5103
Ph: (650)593-1068
Fax: (650)593-9108
Co. E-mail: staff@sancarloschamber.org
URL: http://www.sancarloschamber.org/default.aspx
Contact: David Bouchard, Chief Executive Officer
Description: Works to insure a vital local economy and to enhance the quality of life in San Carlos, California through business promotion, economic development and advocacy on business issues. **Founded:** 1926. **Publications:** *Business and Community Directory* (Annual); *San Carlos Business* (Monthly). **Telecommunication Services:** dbouchard@sancarloschamber.org.

48956 ■ San Clemente Chamber of Commerce
1100 N El Camino Real
San Clemente, CA 92672-4653
Ph: (949)492-1131
Fax: (949)492-3764
Co. E-mail: info@scchamber.com
URL: http://www.scchamber.com
Contact: Lynn Wood, President
Description: Promotes business and community development in San Clemente, CA. **Publications:** *The San Clemente Current* (Monthly); *South Coast Area Directory* (Annual). **Educational Activities:** San Clemente Seafest (Annual).

48957 ■ *The San Clemente Current*
1100 N El Camino Real
San Clemente, CA 92672-4653
Ph: (949)492-1131
Fax: (949)492-3764
Co. E-mail: info@scchamber.com
URL: http://www.scchamber.com
Contact: Lynn Wood, President
Released: Monthly

48958 ■ San Diego Coastal Chamber of Commerce (SDCC)
1104 Camino Del Mar, Ste. 1
Del Mar, CA 92014
Ph: (858)755-4844
Fax: (858)793-5293
Co. E-mail: info@sandiegocoastalchamber.com
URL: http://www.delmarchamber.org
Contact: Nancy Wasko, President
URL(s): www.sandiegocoastalchamber.com. **Description:** Promotes business and community development in the Del Mar, CA area. Conducts charitable activities. **Founded:** 1946. **Awards:** Member of the Month (Monthly).

48959 ■ San Diego County Hispanic Chamber of Commerce (SDCHCC)
3443 Camino Del Rio S, Ste. 101
San Diego, CA 92108
Ph: (619)702-0790
Fax: (619)521-6722
Co. E-mail: marcocortes@sdchcc.com
URL: http://www.sdchcc.com
Contact: Minnie Rzeslawski, President
Description: Promotes business and community development in the Hispanic community of San Diego, CA. **Founded:** 1989. **Publications:** *Informe* (Bimonthly). **Awards:** Scholarship Program (Annual).

48960 ■ San Diego East County Chamber of Commerce
c/o Scott Alevy, Pres./CEO
201 S Magnolia Ave.
El Cajon, CA 92020-4525
Ph: (619)440-6161
Fax: (619)440-6164
Co. E-mail: ceo@eastcountychamber.org
URL: http://www.eastcountychamber.org
Contact: Scott Alevy, President
Description: Promotes business and community development in San Diego East County which includes El Cajon and La Mesa, CA. **Founded:** 1912. **Publications:** *East County Business News* (Monthly). **Educational Activities:** Networking (Monthly). **Awards:** Business of the Year (Annual).

48961 ■ San Diego North Chamber of Commerce (SDNCC)
11650 Iberia Pl., Ste. 220
San Diego, CA 92128
Ph: (858)487-1767
Fax: (858)487-8051
URL: http://www.sdncc.com
Contact: Debra Rosen, President
Description: Promotes business and community development in Rancho Penasquitos, Carmel Mountain Ranch, Sabre Springs, Mira Mesa/Miramar and Scripps Ranch, CA. Sponsors Miss Penasquitos Pageant, Carmel Mountain Ranch Fall Festival, Fiesta de Los Penasquitos Street Fair, education scholarships, and golf tournament. **Founded:** 1980. **Publications:** *Directory of Businesses* (Periodic); *Guide to the Area's Fifteen Shopping and Professional Centers* (Periodic); *Street and Area Map.*

48962 ■ San Diego Regional Chamber of Commerce
402 W Broadway, Ste. 1000
San Diego, CA 92101-3585
Ph: (619)544-1300
Co. E-mail: webinfo@sdchamber.org
URL: http://www.sdchamber.org
Contact: Ruben Barrales, President
E-mail: rbarrales@sdchamber.org
Description: Promotes business and community development in the Greater San Diego, CA area. **Founded:** 1870. **Publications:** *Business Referral Directory* (Annual); *Economic Bulletin* (Monthly); *Wel-*

come (Periodic); *Chambers of Commerce* (Annual); *Small Business Assistance Directory; Greater San Diego Chamber of Commerce Business Referral Directory; Executives Listing* (Annual); *Greater San Diego Chamber of Commerce Business Referral Directory* (Annual); *San Diego Metro Guide; Headquarters, San Diego County; Major Retail Centers, San Diego County; Real Estate Services, San Diego County* (Annual); *San Diego World Trade Directory; California Bioscience Directory.* **Educational Activities:** INSIGHTS (Annual).

48963 ■ San Dimas Chamber of Commerce
PO Box 175
San Dimas, CA 91773-0175
Ph: (909)592-3818
Fax: (909)592-8178
Co. E-mail: info@sandimaschamber.com
URL: http://www.sandimaschamber.com
Contact: Karen Gaffney, President
Description: Strives to foster and promote growth of business and professional community while enhancing the quality of life in San Dimas. **Founded:** 1914. **Publications:** *Pioneer* (Monthly); *The Business and Community Guide* (Biennial); *The Business and Community Guide* (Biennial).

48964 ■ *San Francisco Business Times*
3980 Harlan St.
Emeryville, CA 94608-3771
Ph: (510)652-5223
Fax: (510)652-4223
Co. E-mail: info@emeryvillechamber.com
URL: http://www.emeryvillechamber.com
Contact: Bob Canter, President
Released: Weekly **Price:** free, for members only.

48965 ■ San Francisco Chamber of Commerce
235 Montgomery St., 12th Fl.
San Francisco, CA 94104
Ph: (415)392-4520
Fax: (415)392-0485
Co. E-mail: sfalk@sfchamber.com
URL: http://www.sfchamber.com
Contact: Rhea Serpan, President
Description: Promotes business and community development in San Francisco, CA. Convention/Meeting: none. **Founded:** 1911. **Publications:** *San Francisco Chamber of Commerce Membership Directory; Business Meeting & More; San Francisco Industry and Commerce Directory* (Annual); *San Francisco Business Resource Guide and International Business Directory* (Annual); *Northern California Business Directory; California Manufacturers Register: 2008 Edition* (Annual); *Directory of California Technology Companies; San Francisco Bay Area Silicon Valley International Business Directory; Trade Association Directory--San Francisco Chamber of Commerce* (Annual); *World Trade Association International Business Directory* (Annual); *San Francisco Business--Top 51 Public Companies Issue* (Annual).

48966 ■ San Gabriel Chamber of Commerce (SGCC)
620 W Santa Anita St.
San Gabriel, CA 91776
Ph: (626)576-2525
Fax: (626)289-2901
Co. E-mail: rosco_sandy@yahoo.com
URL: http://www.sangabrielchamber.com/default.
  php?page=main
Contact: Lou Costanzo, President
Description: Promotes the interests of local businesses as well as its products and services.

48967 ■ San Jose - Silicon Valley Chamber of Commerce
101 W Santa Clara St.
San Jose, CA 95113
Ph: (408)291-5250
Fax: (408)286-5019
Co. E-mail: info@sjchamber.com
URL: http://www.sjchamber.com
Contact: Pat Dando, President
Description: Promotes economic development and the improvement of quality of life in the Silicon Valley area of CA by being the leading voice for business through delivering innovative products and services,

engaging in aggressive government advocacy, and producing premier networking opportunities. **Founded:** 1886. **Publications:** *Chamber Advocate* (Monthly). **Telecommunication Services:** patd@sjchamber.com.

48968 ■ San Juan Bautista Chamber of Commerce (SJBCC)
209 3rd St.
San Juan Bautista, CA 95045
Ph: (831)623-2454
Fax: (831)623-0674
Co. E-mail: sjbcc@sbcglobal.net
URL: http://www.sjbchamber.com
Contact: Carolyn Roe-Gargiulo, President
Description: Strives to promote business and tourism in San Juan Bautista, CA as well as to support the local merchant base. Holds annual street shows, including two-day peddler's fair, original outdoor antiques flea market, and art and wine festival. **Scope:** history of San Juan Bautista. **Founded:** 1935. **Subscriptions:** books. **Publications:** *Business Directory* (Periodic). **Awards:** Outstanding Sponsor of the Year (Annual); Volunteer Recognition Certificates (Annual); Philanthropic Volunteer of the Year (Annual).

48969 ■ San Juan Capistrano Chamber of Commerce (SJC)
PO Box 1878
San Juan Capistrano, CA 92693
Ph: (949)493-4700
Fax: (949)489-2695
Co. E-mail: info@sanjuanchamber.com
URL: http://www.sanjuanchamber.com
Contact: Mark Bodenhamer, Executive Director
Description: Promotes business and community development in San Juan Capistrano, CA. **Founded:** 1984.

48970 ■ San Leandro Chamber of Commerce (SLCC)
15555 E 14th St., Ste. 100
San Leandro, CA 94578
Ph: (510)317-1400
Fax: (510)317-1404
Co. E-mail: info@sanleandrochamber.com
URL: http://www.sanleandrochamber.com
Contact: David P. Johnson, Chief Executive Officer
Description: Promotes business and community development in San Leandro, CA. **Founded:** 1939.

48971 ■ San Luis Obispo Chamber of Commerce
1041 Chorro St.
San Luis Obispo, CA 93401
Ph: (805)781-2670
Fax: (805)543-1255
Co. E-mail: ermina@slochamber.org
URL: http://www.slochamber.org/cm/Home.html
Contact: Ermina Karim, President
URL(s): www.visitslo.com. **Description:** Promotes business and community development in San Luis Obispo, CA. Conducts lobbying activities. **Founded:** 1905. **Publications:** *San Luis Obispo Chamber of Commerce Visitors Guide.* **Educational Activities:** Electronic Village Conference (Biennial). **Awards:** San Luis Obispo Citizen of the Year (Annual).

48972 ■ *San Luis Obispo Chamber of Commerce Visitors Guide*
1041 Chorro St.
San Luis Obispo, CA 93401
Ph: (805)781-2670
Fax: (805)543-1255
Co. E-mail: ermina@slochamber.org
URL: http://www.slochamber.org/cm/Home.html
Contact: Ermina Karim, President

48973 ■ *San Marcos Business Update*
939 Grand Ave.
San Marcos, CA 92078
Ph: (760)744-1270
Fax: (760)744-5230
Co. E-mail: andy@sanmarcoschamber.com
URL: http://www.sanmarcoschamber.com
Contact: Jeff Ritchie, Chairman
Released: Monthly

48974 ■ San Marcos Chamber of Commerce
939 Grand Ave.
San Marcos, CA 92078
Ph: (760)744-1270
Fax: (760)744-5230
Co. E-mail: andy@sanmarcoschamber.com
URL: http://www.sanmarcoschamber.com
Contact: Jeff Ritchie, Chairman
Description: Promotes business and community development in San Marcos, CA. Offers networking service. Sponsors annual sanctioned Chili Cook-off. **Founded:** 1967. **Publications:** *San Marcos Business Update* (Monthly); *San Marcos Chamber of Commerce Business & Relocation Directory* (Annual).

48975 ■ *San Marcos Chamber of Commerce Business & Relocation Directory*
939 Grand Ave.
San Marcos, CA 92078
Ph: (760)744-1270
Fax: (760)744-5230
Co. E-mail: andy@sanmarcoschamber.com
URL: http://www.sanmarcoschamber.com
Contact: Jeff Ritchie, Chairman
Released: Annual **Price:** $5.

48976 ■ San Marino Chamber of Commerce (SMCC)
1800 Huntington Dr.
San Marino, CA 91108
Ph: (626)286-1022
Fax: (626)286-7765
Co. E-mail: sanmarinochamber@att.net
URL: http://www.sanmarinochamber.org
Contact: Sandra Troup, President
Description: Promotes business and community development in San Marino, CA. **Founded:** 1959. **Publications:** *The Green Sheet* (Monthly).

48977 ■ San Mateo Chamber of Commerce (SMCC)
PO Box 936
San Mateo, CA 94403
Ph: (650)401-2440
Fax: (650)401-2446
Co. E-mail: info@sanmateochamber.org
URL: http://www.sanmateoca.org
Contact: Linda Asbury, President
Description: Promotes business and the public interest through representation, advocacy and sponsorship. Organizes and funds programs that support the economic, civic, cultural, and educational excellence of the San Mateo area. **Founded:** 1939. **Publications:** *Community Guide* (Annual).

48978 ■ San Pablo Chamber of Commerce (SPCC)
PO Box 6204
San Pablo, CA 94806
Ph: (510)234-2067
URL: http://www.ci.san-pablo.ca.us/index.aspx-?nid=955
Contact: Jerry Sattler, President
Description: Promotes business and community development in San Pablo, CA. **Founded:** 1902. **Publications:** *Chamber Chatter* (Monthly).

48979 ■ San Pedro Peninsula Chamber of Commerce (SPPCC)
390 W 7th St.
San Pedro, CA 90731
Ph: (310)832-7272
Fax: (310)832-0685
Co. E-mail: info@sanpedrochamber.com
URL: http://www.sanpedrochamber.com
Contact: Randy Bowers, President
Description: Promotes, supports and advocates the interests of the business community. **Founded:** 1906. **Publications:** *Business Beacon* (Monthly); *Business Directory* (Annual); *Visitors Guide* (Biennial). **Educational Activities:** Taste in San Pedro (Annual); Harbor Area Business Outlook Conference (Annual).

48980 ■ *San Rafael Business*
817 Mission Ave.
San Rafael, CA 94901
Ph: (415)454-4163

Fax: (415)454-7039
Co. E-mail: frontdesk@srchamber.com
URL: http://www.sanrafaelchamber.com
Contact: Rick Wells, President
Released: Monthly

48981 ■ San Rafael Chamber of Commerce (SRCC)
817 Mission Ave.
San Rafael, CA 94901
Ph: (415)454-4163
Fax: (415)454-7039
Co. E-mail: frontdesk@srchamber.com
URL: http://www.sanrafaelchamber.com
Contact: Rick Wells, President
Description: Works to provide a strong voice in support of the economic vitality of the community. **Founded:** 1920. **Publications:** *Business Directory* (Annual); *San Rafael Business* (Monthly). **Educational Activities:** Leadership Institute (Annual).

48982 ■ San Ramon Chamber of Commerce (SRCC)
2410 Camino Ramon, Ste. 125
Bishop Ranch 6
San Ramon, CA 94583
Ph: (925)242-0600
Fax: (925)242-0603
Co. E-mail: info@sanramon.org
URL: http://www.sanramon.org
Contact: Stewart Bambino, President
Description: Works to enhance the quality of life and economic vitality of the San Ramon Valley by representing business and community interests. **Publications:** *B2B*. **Educational Activities:** East Bay Business Symposium (Annual). **Awards:** Community Service Awards (Annual).

48983 ■ San Simeon Chamber of Commerce
250 San Simeon, Ste. 3A
San Simeon, CA 93452
Ph: (805)927-3500
Co. E-mail: sansimeonchamber@yahoo.com
URL: http://www.sansimeonchamber.org
Description: Promotes business and community development in San Simeon, CA. **Founded:** 1961.

48984 ■ San Ysidro Chamber of Commerce and Visitor Information Center
663 E San Ysidro Blvd.
San Ysidro, CA 92173
Ph: (619)428-1281
Fax: (619)428-1294
Co. E-mail: info@sanysidrochamber.org
URL: http://www.sanysidrochamber.org
Contact: Israel Adato, President
Description: Promotes business and commerce of the distinct community of San Ysidro through networking, communication of pertinent information, and sponsoring of community enhancing events, benefiting from its unique location along the international border. **Founded:** 1923. **Publications:** *San Ysidro in Motion* (Quarterly). **Educational Activities:** San Ysidro Chamber of Commerce and Visitor Information Center Board meeting (Monthly).

48985 ■ *San Ysidro in Motion*
663 E San Ysidro Blvd.
San Ysidro, CA 92173
Ph: (619)428-1281
Fax: (619)428-1294
Co. E-mail: info@sanysidrochamber.org
URL: http://www.sanysidrochamber.org
Contact: Israel Adato, President
Released: Quarterly

48986 ■ *Sandollar*
425 15th St.
Manhattan Beach, CA 90266
Ph: (310)545-5313
Fax: (310)545-7203
Co. E-mail: james@manhattanbeachchamber.net
URL: http://www.manhattanbeachchamber.net
Contact: James O'callaghan, President
Released: Monthly

48987 ■ Sanger District Chamber of Commerce
1789 Jensen Ave., Ste. B
Sanger, CA 93657
Ph: (559)875-4575
Fax: (559)875-0745
Co. E-mail: sanger@psnw.com
URL: http://www.sanger.org
Contact: Nettie Inouye, President
Description: Promotes business and community development in Sanger, CA. **Founded:** 1927. **Publications:** *Sanger District Chamber of Commerce--Business Directory* (Biennial).

48988 ■ *Santa Ana Community Guide and Business Directory*
2020 N Broadway, 2nd Fl.
Santa Ana, CA 92702
Ph: (714)541-5353
Fax: (714)541-2238
Co. E-mail: info@santaanachamber.com
URL: http://www.santaanachamber.com
Contact: David Elliott, President
Released: Annual

48989 ■ Santa Barbara Hispanic Chamber of Commerce (SBHCC)
PO Box 6592
Santa Barbara, CA 93160
Ph: (805)637-3680
Fax: (805)681-1260
Co. E-mail: info@sbhispanicchamber.org
URL: http://www.sbhispanicchamber.org
Contact: Sergio Villa, Chairman
Description: Promotes the Hispanic business and community development in Santa Barbara, CA area.

48990 ■ Santa Barbara Region Chamber of Commerce (SBCC)
924 Anacapa St., Ste. 1
Santa Barbara, CA 93101
Ph: (805)965-3023
Fax: (805)966-5954
Co. E-mail: info@sbchamber.org
URL: http://www.sbchamber.org
Contact: Zoe Taylor, President
Description: Promotes business and community development in Santa Barbara, CA. Conducts seminars. **Founded:** 1871. **Publications:** *Chamber of Commerce Membership Directory*; *Commerce Magazine Real Estate Guide* (Monthly).

48991 ■ Santa Clara Chamber of Commerce and Convention and Visitors Bureau
1850 Warburton Ave.
Santa Clara, CA 95050
Ph: (408)244-9660
Free: 800-272-6822
Fax: (408)244-9202
Co. E-mail: steve.vandorn@santaclara.org
URL: http://www.santaclara.org
Contact: Steve VanDorn, President
Description: Promotes business, community development, tourism and the convention trade in Santa Clara, CA. **Founded:** 1947.

48992 ■ Santa Clarita Valley Chamber of Commerce (SCVCC)
27451 Tourney Rd., Ste. 160
Santa Clarita, CA 91355
Ph: (661)702-6977
Fax: (661)702-6980
Co. E-mail: info@scvchamber.com
URL: http://www.scvchamber.com
Contact: Terri K. Crain, President
Description: Promotes business and community development in the Santa Clarita Valley, CA area. Sponsors business expo. **Publications:** *Business Focus* (Monthly); *Santa Clarita Valley Chamber of Commerce Business Directory* (Annual); *SCVCC E-News* (Monthly). **Educational Activities:** Business After Hours (Monthly); Business Expo (Annual).

48993 ■ *Santa Clarita Valley Chamber of Commerce Business Directory*
27451 Tourney Rd., Ste. 160
Santa Clarita, CA 91355
Ph: (661)702-6977

Fax: (661)702-6980
Co. E-mail: info@scvchamber.com
URL: http://www.scvchamber.com
Contact: Terri K. Crain, President
Released: Annual

48994 ■ Santa Cruz Chamber of Commerce
611 Ocean St., Ste. 1
Santa Cruz, CA 95060
Ph: (831)457-3713
Fax: (831)423-1847
Co. E-mail: info@santacruzchamber.org
URL: http://www.santacruzchamber.org
Contact: William R. Tysseling, Chief Executive Officer

Description: Promotes business and community development in the Santa Cruz, CA area. **Publications:** *Santa Cruz Chamber of Commerce-- Membership Directory*; *Business Santa Cruz* (Monthly). **Educational Activities:** Women in Business EXTRAVAGANZA (Annual). **Awards:** Community Recognition Awards (Annual).

48995 ■ Santa Fe Springs Chamber of Commerce and Industrial League
12016 E Telegraph Rd., Ste. 100
Santa Fe Springs, CA 90670
Ph: (562)944-1616
Fax: (562)946-3976
Co. E-mail: mail@sfschamber.com
URL: http://www.sfschamber.com
Contact: Michael J. Foley, President

Description: Promotes business and community development in Santa Fe Springs, CA. **Founded:** 1974. **Awards:** Destiny Fund Scholarship (Annual); The Don and Jackie Powell Grant (Annual).

48996 ■ Santa Maria Valley Chamber of Commerce (SMVCC)
614 S Broadway
Santa Maria, CA 93454-5111
Ph: (805)925-2403
Free: 800-331-3779
Fax: (805)928-7559
Co. E-mail: info@santamaria.com
URL: http://www.santamaria.com/cm/Home.html
Contact: Robert P. Hatch, President

Description: Works to improve the economy and increase its tax base by attracting visitors to the Santa Maria Valley. **Founded:** 1902. **Publications:** *Chamber Challenge* (Monthly). **Educational Activities:** Santa Maria Valley Chamber of Commerce Luncheon (Annual).

48997 ■ Santa Monica Chamber of Commerce (SMCC)
1234 6th St., Ste. 100
Santa Monica, CA 90401
Ph: (310)393-9825
Fax: (310)394-1868
Co. E-mail: info@smchamber.com
URL: http://www.smchamber.com
Contact: Laurel Rosen, President

Description: Promotes business and community development in the Santa Monica, CA area. Provides information, research assistance, and business counseling. Offers business referrals and Certificates of Origin for members exporting goods overseas. Sponsors semiannual art festival. Holds annual community health fair. Offers business seminars. **Founded:** 1925. **Publications:** *Santa Monica Chamber of Commerce Business Profile and Membership Directory*; *Business Briefs* (Monthly); *Mid-month Update* (Monthly); *Membership Directory and Buyers Guide* (Annual); *Santa Monica Chamber of Commerce Business Profile and Membership Directory* (Annual). **Educational Activities:** Mini-Expo (Periodic).

48998 ■ Santa Paula Chamber of Commerce (SPCC)
PO Box 1
Santa Paula, CA 93060
Ph: (805)525-5561

Fax: (805)525-8950
Co. E-mail: info@santapaulachamber.com
URL: http://www.santapaulachamber.com
Contact: Chris Sayer, Chairman
Description: Promotes business and community development in the Santa Paula, CA area. **Founded:** 1940.

48999 ■ Santa Rosa Chamber of Commerce
1260 N Dutton Ave., Ste. 272
Santa Rosa, CA 95401
Ph: (707)545-1414
Co. E-mail: info@santarosachamber.com
URL: http://www.santarosachamber.com
Contact: Jonathan Coe, President
URL(s): www.visitsantarosa.com. **Description:** Promotes business and community development in Santa Rosa, CA. **Publications:** *On Point* (Monthly); *On Point On Line* (Weekly).

49000 ■ Santee Chamber of Commerce (SCC)
10315 Mission Gorge Rd.
Santee, CA 92071
Ph: (619)449-6572
Fax: (619)562-7906
Co. E-mail: info@santee-chamber.org
URL: http://www.santee-chamber.org
Contact: Warren H. Savage, Jr., Executive Director
Description: Seeks to encourage economic growth in a free enterprise environment and enhance the community's image through collaboration with various civic and governmental entities. **Founded:** 1955. **Publications:** *Echo* (Monthly). **Educational Activities:** Business After Five Mixers (Monthly).

49001 ■ *Saratoga Business Focus*
14460 Big Basin Way
Saratoga, CA 95070
Ph: (408)867-0753
Fax: (408)867-5213
Co. E-mail: info@saratogachamber.org
URL: http://www.saratogachamber.org
Contact: Vicki Seelig, Treasurer
Released: Bimonthly

49002 ■ Saratoga Chamber of Commerce
14460 Big Basin Way
Saratoga, CA 95070
Ph: (408)867-0753
Fax: (408)867-5213
Co. E-mail: info@saratogachamber.org
URL: http://www.saratogachamber.org
Contact: Vicki Seelig, Treasurer
Description: Works to invigorate the business environment and enhance the quality of life in the community. **Founded:** 1956. **Publications:** *City Map* (Biennial); *Saratoga Business Focus* (Bimonthly); *Special Events Resource*.

49003 ■ Sausalito Chamber of Commerce
10 Liberty Ship Way, Bay 2, Ste. 250
Sausalito, CA 94965
Ph: (415)331-7262
Fax: (415)332-0323
Co. E-mail: chamber@sausalito.org
URL: http://www.sausalito.org
Contact: Oonagh Kavanagh, Chief Executive Officer
Description: Strives to promote the economic health and well-being of Sausalito, CA by providing leadership and representation for issues affecting the business community, the citizens and visitors. Seeks to promote business and community development in Sausalito. **Founded:** 1945. **Publications:** *Chamber Waves* (Monthly); *Sausalito Chamber of Commerce-- Membership Directory*.

49004 ■ *The Scope*
PO Box 391460
Anza, CA 92539
Ph: (951)763-0141
Free: 888-930-0222
Co. E-mail: designer@folioflare.com
URL: http://www.anzavalleychamber.com
Contact: Sandi Hughes, President
Released: Monthly

49005 ■ *Scotts Valley Business Today*
360 Kings Village Rd.
Scotts Valley, CA 95066
Ph: (831)438-1010
Fax: (831)438-6544
Co. E-mail: info@scottsvalleychamber.com
URL: http://www.scottsvalleychamber.com
Contact: Sharolynn Ullestad, Executive Director
Released: Monthly

49006 ■ Scotts Valley Chamber of Commerce
360 Kings Village Rd.
Scotts Valley, CA 95066
Ph: (831)438-1010
Fax: (831)438-6544
Co. E-mail: info@scottsvalleychamber.com
URL: http://www.scottsvalleychamber.com
Contact: Sharolynn Ullestad, Executive Director
Description: Promotes business and community development in Scotts Valley, CA. **Founded:** 1966. **Publications:** *Scotts Valley Business Today* (Monthly); *Scotts Valley Directory and Annual Review* (Annual). **Awards:** Beautification Project of the Year (Annual); Business of the Year (Annual); Man of the Year (Annual); Organization of the Year (Annual); Woman of the Year (Annual); Youth of the Year (Annual).

49007 ■ *Scotts Valley Directory and Annual Review*
360 Kings Village Rd.
Scotts Valley, CA 95066
Ph: (831)438-1010
Fax: (831)438-6544
Co. E-mail: info@scottsvalleychamber.com
URL: http://www.scottsvalleychamber.com
Contact: Sharolynn Ullestad, Executive Director
Released: Annual

49008 ■ *SCVCC E-News*
27451 Tourney Rd., Ste. 160
Santa Clarita, CA 91355
Ph: (661)702-6977
Fax: (661)702-6980
Co. E-mail: info@scvchamber.com
URL: http://www.scvchamber.com
Contact: Terri K. Crain, President
Released: Monthly

49009 ■ *Sea Country News*
30111 Crown Valley Pkwy.
Laguna Niguel, CA 92677
Ph: (949)363-0136
Fax: (949)363-9026
Co. E-mail: lncc@lnchamber.com
URL: http://lagunaniguelchamber.net
Contact: Debbie Newman, President
Released: Monthly

49010 ■ Seal Beach Chamber of Commerce - California
201 8th St., Ste. 120
Seal Beach, CA 90740
Ph: (562)799-0179
Fax: (562)795-5637
Co. E-mail: info@sealbeachchamber.org
URL: http://www.sealbeachchamber.org
Contact: Erik Dreyer-Goldman, President
Description: Promotes business and community development in Seal Beach, CA.

49011 ■ Sebastopol Area Chamber of Commerce and Visitors Center
PO Box 178
Sebastopol, CA 95473-0178
Ph: (707)823-3032
Free: 877-828-4748
Fax: (707)823-8439
Co. E-mail: info@sebastopol.org
URL: http://www.sebastopol.org
Contact: Teresa Ramondo, Chief Executive Officer
Description: Promotes civic and commercial progress in the Sebastopol, CA area. **Founded:** 1921. **Publications:** *Chamber Action* (Monthly). **Educational Activities:** Business and Community Showcase (Annual).

49012 ■ *Selma Business*
1821 Tucker St.
Selma, CA 93662
Ph: (559)891-2235
Fax: (559)896-7075
Co. E-mail: cindyh@cityofselma.com
URL: http://www.cityofselma.com/chamber/index.htm
Contact: Cindy L. Howell, Executive Director
Released: Monthly **Price:** free.

49013 ■ Selma District Chamber of Commerce (SDCC)
1821 Tucker St.
Selma, CA 93662
Ph: (559)891-2235
Fax: (559)896-7075
Co. E-mail: cindyh@cityofselma.com
URL: http://www.cityofselma.com/chamber/index.htm
Contact: Cindy L. Howell, Executive Director
Description: Large business/industry, small business, medical, professional, individual and retirees. Promotes business and community development in the Selma, CA area. Sponsors Annual Crab Feed & Auction, Raisin Festival, July 3rd Community Celebration, August Summer Concerts in the Park, Car Show Marching Band Festival & Field Competition and a Holiday Street Faire and Santa Arrival. Hosts fund raising event. **Founded:** 1890. **Publications:** *Selma Business* (Monthly). **Awards:** Citizen of the Year (Annual).

49014 ■ *The Sentinel*
PO Box 365
Patterson, CA 95363
Ph: (209)895-8094
Co. E-mail: chamberofcommerce@gvni.com
URL: http://www.patterson-westleychamber.com
Contact: Carolyn Harr, President
Released: Quarterly

49015 ■ Shafter Chamber of Commerce (SCC)
336 Pacific Ave.
Shafter, CA 93263
Ph: (661)746-2600
Fax: (661)746-0607
URL: http://www.shafter.com
Contact: Karen Wilkins, Director
Description: Promotes business and community development in Shafter, CA. Sponsors Street Faires, May Festival, Cinco de Mayo, and Business/Student Exchange Day. **Founded:** 1947. **Publications:** *Map/Directory* (Periodic). **Awards:** Agricultural Award (Annual); Business of the Year (Annual); Citizen of the Year (Annual); Community Service Award (Annual); Crystal Award (Annual); Humanitarian (Annual).

49016 ■ *Sherman Oaks Chamber NEWS*
14827 Ventura Blvd., Ste. 207
Sherman Oaks, CA 91403-5224
Ph: (818)906-1951
Fax: (818)783-3100
Co. E-mail: ourchamber@aol.com
URL: http://www.shermanoakschamber.org
Contact: Lisa Clayden, Executive Director
Released: Monthly

49017 ■ Shingle Springs/Cameron Park Chamber of Commerce
PO Box 341
Shingle Springs, CA 95682
Ph: (530)677-8000
Fax: (530)676-8313
Co. E-mail: info@sscpchamber.org
URL: http://www.sscpchamber.org
Contact: Peter Fordham, President
E-mail: pfordham@comcast.net
Description: "Connecting With the Community". Works to advocate, promote, and preserve the quality of life in the area by means of a strong, healthy, and diverse business community. **Founded:** 1967. **Publications:** *Business Directory* (Biennial); *Shingle Springs/Cameron Park Chamber of Commerce Business Directory*; *Shingle Springs/Cameron Park Chamber of Commerce--Business Directory* (Biennial); *Business Directory* (Biennial); *Shingle Springs/*

Cameron Park Chamber of Commerce Chamber News (Monthly). **Awards:** Myrtle Baker Community Service Award (Annual).

49018 ■ *Shingle Springs/Cameron Park Chamber of Commerce Chamber News*
PO Box 341
Shingle Springs, CA 95682
Ph: (530)677-8000
Fax: (530)676-8313
Co. E-mail: info@sscpchamber.org
URL: http://www.sscpchamber.org
Contact: Peter Fordham, President
E-mail: pfordham@comcast.net
Released: Monthly

49019 ■ *The Shop Rancho Retail Guide and Service Directory*
9047 Arrow Rte., Ste. 180
Rancho Cucamonga, CA 91730
Ph: (909)987-1012
Fax: (909)987-5917
Co. E-mail: info@ranchochamber.org
URL: http://www.ranchochamber.org
Contact: Michelle Alonzo, President
Released: Annual

49020 ■ Sierra Madre Chamber of Commerce
20 W Montecito Ave., Ste. C
Sierra Madre, CA 91024
Ph: (626)355-5111
Fax: (626)306-1150
Co. E-mail: info@sierramadrechamber.com
URL: http://www.sierramadrechamber.com
Contact: Ed Chen, President
Description: Promotes business and community development in Sierra Madre, CA. **Awards:** Citizen of the Year (Annual).

49021 ■ Signal Hill Chamber of Commerce
2201 E Willow St., Ste. D
Signal Hill, CA 90755
Ph: (562)424-6489
Co. E-mail: president@signalhillchamber.com
URL: http://www.signalhillchamber.com
Contact: Shari Blackwell, President
Description: Promotes business and community development in Signal Hill, CA. **Founded:** 1941. **Publications:** *Hill Street News* (Quarterly).

49022 ■ Simi Valley Chamber of Commerce
40 W Cochran St., Ste. 100
Simi Valley, CA 93065
Ph: (805)526-3900
Fax: (805)526-6234
Co. E-mail: info@simichamber.org
URL: http://simivalleychamber.org
Contact: Leigh Nixon, President
Description: Promotes business and community development in Simi Valley, CA.

49023 ■ Solana Beach Chamber of Commerce
210 W Plaza St.
Solana Beach, CA 92075-0623
Ph: (858)755-4775
Fax: (858)755-4889
Co. E-mail: info@solanabeachchamber.com
URL: http://www.solanabeachchamber.com
Contact: Carolyn Cohen, President
Description: Works to promote and support local business by encouraging and facilitating tourism, business to business relationships, community involvement and communications with local county and regional governments. **Publications:** *Solana Business Sounds*.

49024 ■ *Solana Business Sounds*
210 W Plaza St.
Solana Beach, CA 92075-0623
Ph: (858)755-4775
Fax: (858)755-4889
Co. E-mail: info@solanabeachchamber.com
URL: http://www.solanabeachchamber.com
Contact: Carolyn Cohen, President

49025 ■ Solvang Chamber of Commerce (SCC)
PO Box 465
Solvang, CA 93464
Ph: (805)688-0701
Co. E-mail: linda@solvangcc.org
URL: http://www.solvangcc.com
Contact: Linda Jackson, Executive Director
Description: Promotes business and community development in Solvang, CA. **Founded:** 1911.

49026 ■ Sonoma Valley Chamber of Commerce
651A Broadway
Sonoma, CA 95476
Ph: (707)996-1033
Fax: (707)996-9402
Co. E-mail: info@sonomachamber.com
URL: http://www.sonomachamber.com
Contact: Jennifer Yankovich, Chief Executive Officer
Description: Promotes business and community development in the Sonoma Valley area of California. **Founded:** 1914.

49027 ■ *Soundings*
c/o Stuart McElhinney, Pres.
Morro Bay, CA 93442
Ph: (805)772-4467
Free: 800-231-0592
Co. E-mail: brownpelican@morrobay.org
URL: http://www.morrobay.org
Contact: Craig Schmidt, Chief Executive Officer
Released: Monthly

49028 ■ *South Coast Area Directory*
1100 N El Camino Real
San Clemente, CA 92672-4653
Ph: (949)492-1131
Fax: (949)492-3764
Co. E-mail: info@scchamber.com
URL: http://www.scchamber.com
Contact: Lynn Wood, President
Released: Annual

49029 ■ South Lake Tahoe Chamber of Commerce
2572 Lake Tahoe Blvd., Ste. 3
South Lake Tahoe, CA 96150
Ph: (530)542-5060
Co. E-mail: southtahoechamberofcommerce@gmail.com
URL: http://www.tahoeinfo.com
Contact: David Kelly, Executive Director
URL(s): www.southlaketahoechamber.com. **Description:** Promotes business and community development in South Lake Tahoe, CA. **Publications:** *Business Matters* (Monthly).

49030 ■ South Orange County Regional Chambers of Commerce
2341 El Toro Rd, Ste. 300
Laguna Hills, CA 92653
Ph: (949)600-5470
Fax: (949)635-1635
Co. E-mail: info@socchambers.com
URL: http://socchamber.com
Contact: James M. Leach, Chief Executive Officer
Description: Promotes the social and economic development in South Orange County. **Founded:** 1967. **Publications:** *Business Report* (Quarterly). **Educational Activities:** Legislative Action Committee (Monthly).

49031 ■ South San Francisco Chamber of Commerce
213 Linden Ave.
South San Francisco, CA 94080
Ph: (650)588-1911
Fax: (650)588-2534
Co. E-mail: info@ssfchamber.com
URL: http://www.ssfchamber.com
Contact: Maria Martinucci, Chief Executive Officer
Description: Promotes business and community development in South San Francisco, CA. **Founded:** 1913.

49032 ■ *Southern California Business*
350 S Bixel St.
Los Angeles, CA 90017

Ph: (213)580-7500
Fax: (213)580-7511
Co. E-mail: info@lachamber.org
URL: http://www.lachamber.com
Contact: Gary Toebben, President
Released: Monthly **Price:** $17.34, for nonmembers.

49033 ■ *Speakers' Bureau Listing*
7120 Hayvenhurst Ave., Ste. 114
Van Nuys, CA 91406-3813
Ph: (818)989-0300
URL: http://www.midvalleychamber.com
Contact: Nancy Hoffman Vanyek, Chief Executive
Officer
Price: $10, for members.

49034 ■ *Special Events Guide*
811 S Sunset Ave.
West Covina, CA 91790-3599
Ph: (626)338-8496
Fax: (626)960-0511
Co. E-mail: glawson@westcovinachamber.com
URL: http://www.westcovinachamber.com

49035 ■ *Special Events Resource*
14460 Big Basin Way
Saratoga, CA 95070
Ph: (408)867-0753
Fax: (408)867-5213
Co. E-mail: info@saratogachamber.org
URL: http://www.saratogachamber.org
Contact: Vicki Seelig, Treasurer
Price: $3.

49036 ■ *Spotlight*
109 N 19th St.
Montebello, CA 90640
Ph: (323)721-1153
Fax: (323)721-7946
Co. E-mail: andrea@montebellochamber.org
URL: http://www.montebellochamber.org
Contact: Andrea Wagg, President
Released: Bimonthly

**49037 ■ Spring Valley Chamber of Commerce
(SVCC)**
PO Box 1211
Spring Valley, CA 91979-1211
Ph: (619)670-9902
Fax: (619)670-9924
URL: http://www.springvalleychamber.org
Contact: Tina Carlson, Executive Director
Description: Promotes business and community
development in Spring Valley, CA. Sponsors parade
and business fair. **Founded:** 1935. **Publications:**
Chamber Communications (Monthly). **Awards:** Busi-
ness of the Year (Annual); Individual of the Year (An-
nual); President's Award for Volunteerism (Annual).

49038 ■ Springville Chamber of Commerce
PO Box 104
Springville, CA 93265
Ph: (559)539-0100
Co. E-mail: chamber@springville.ca.us
URL: http://springville.ca.us
Contact: Mr. Rick Mitchell, President
Description: Promotes business and communica-
tions among Springville citizens and its surroundings.
Founded: 1948. **Awards:** Business of the Year (An-
nual); Organization of the Year (Annual); Person of
the Year (Annual); Youth of the Year (Annual).

**49039 ■ *Stanislaus County Industrial
Directory***
1114 J St.
Modesto, CA 95354-0806
Ph: (209)577-5757
Fax: (209)577-2623
Co. E-mail: info@modchamber.org
URL: http://www.modchamber.org
Contact: Joy Madison, President
E-mail: jmadison@modchamber.org
Price: $16.

49040 ■ Stanton Chamber of Commerce
8381 Katella Ave., Ste. H
Stanton, CA 90680
Ph: (714)995-1485

Fax: (714)995-1184
Co. E-mail: service@stantonchamber.org
URL: http://www.stantonchamber.org
Contact: Don Martinez, President
Description: Promotes business and community
development in Stanton, CA. Sponsors annual Miss
Stanton Scholarship Pageant. **Founded:** 1952. **Pub-
lications:** *Business News* (Quarterly); *Stanton
Chamber Directory* (Annual). **Educational Activities:**
Stanton Chamber of Commerce Luncheon (Monthly).

49041 ■ *Stanton Chamber Directory*
8381 Katella Ave., Ste. H
Stanton, CA 90680
Ph: (714)995-1485
Fax: (714)995-1184
Co. E-mail: service@stantonchamber.org
URL: http://www.stantonchamber.org
Contact: Don Martinez, President
Released: Annual

49042 ■ *Street and Area Map*
11650 Iberia Pl., Ste. 220
San Diego, CA 92128
Ph: (858)487-1767
Fax: (858)487-8051
URL: http://www.sdncc.com
Contact: Debra Rosen, President

49043 ■ *Studio City Business*
4024 Radford Ave., Ed. 2, Ste. F
Studio City, CA 91604
Ph: (818)655-5916
Fax: (818)655-8392
Co. E-mail: sccc@mptp.com
URL: http://www.studiocitychamber.com
Contact: Esther Walker, Executive Director
Released: Monthly

**49044 ■ Studio City Chamber of Commerce
(SCCC)**
4024 Radford Ave., Ed. 2, Ste. F
Studio City, CA 91604
Ph: (818)655-5916
Fax: (818)655-8392
Co. E-mail: sccc@mptp.com
URL: http://www.studiocitychamber.com
Contact: Esther Walker, Executive Director
Description: Promotes business and community
development in Studio City, CA. Sponsors running
and race walking competitions. **Founded:** 1934. **Pub-
lications:** *Studio City Business* (Monthly). **Telecom-
munication Services:** admin@studiocitychamber.
com.

**49045 ■ Sun Valley Area Chamber of
Commerce**
PO Box 308
Sun Valley, CA 91353
Ph: (818)768-2014
Fax: (818)767-1947
Co. E-mail: info@svacc.com
Contact: Jessa Dizon, Executive Director
Description: Seeks to advance commercial, indus-
trial, and public interests of Sun Valley trade and com-
merce. **Founded:** 1925. **Publications:** *Sun Times*
(Bimonthly). **Educational Activities:** Sun Valley Area
Chamber of Commerce Board meeting (Monthly).

**49046 ■ Sunland-Tujunga Chamber of
Commerce**
8250 Foothill Blvd., No. A
Sunland, CA 91040
Ph: (818)352-4433
Fax: (818)353-7551
Co. E-mail: stchamber91040@gmail.com
URL: http://www.stchamber.com
Contact: Sonia Tatulian, President
Description: Promotes business and community
development in the Sunland-Tujunga, CA area.

49047 ■ Sunnyvale Chamber of Commerce
260 S Sunnyvale Ave., Ste. 4
Sunnyvale, CA 94086-6193
Ph: (408)736-4971

Fax: (408)736-1919
Co. E-mail: info@svcoc.org
URL: http://www.svcoc.org
Contact: Don Eagleston, President
Description: Promotes policies designed to connect,
educate, and energize the business community to
achieve economic vitality. **Publications:** *Business
Progress* (Monthly). **Awards:** Murphy Awards (An-
nual).

**49048 ■ Swedish American Chamber of
Commerce of Greater Los Angeles
(SACC-GLA)**
1956 Cotner Ave.
Los Angeles, CA 90025
Ph: (310)393-9893
Co. E-mail: info@sacc-gla.org
URL: http://www.sacc-gla.org
Contact: Lotta Alsen, President

**49049 ■ Swedish-American Chamber of
Commerce, San Diego/Tijuana**
4350 Executive Dr., Ste. 304
San Diego, CA 92121
Ph: (858)598-4809
Co. E-mail: info@san-diego.org
URL: http://www.sacc-sandiego.org
Contact: Andreas Fried, President
Description: Promotes, develops and increases the
Swedish-American contacts and interactions in the
San Diego area. Facilitates mutually beneficial
relationships between Swedish and American compa-
nies. **Founded:** 1989.

**49050 ■ Taft District Chamber of
Commerce—Taft Chamber of Commerce**
400 Kern St.
Taft, CA 93268
Ph: (661)765-2165
Fax: (661)765-6639
Co. E-mail: taftchamber@bak.rr.com
URL: http://www.taftchamber.com
Contact: Fred Schell, Executive Director
Description: Promotes business and community
development in Taft, CA. Conducts annual fundrais-
ers, Taft District Chamber of Commerce Gala and an-
nual Taft District Chamber of Commerce Trout Derby.
Founded: 1910. **Publications:** *Report to the Com-
munity* (Monthly).

**49051 ■ Tarzana Chamber of Commerce
(TOCC)**
PO Box 570414
Tarzana, CA 91356
Ph: (818)343-3687
Fax: (818)705-0127
Co. E-mail: info.chamber@sbcglobal.net
URL: http://www.tarzanachamber.com
Contact: Steve Hornstein, President
Description: Promotes business and community
development in Tarzana, CA. Conducts charitable
events. **Founded:** 1935. **Publications:** *Topics*
(Monthly). **Educational Activities:** Tarzana Chamber
of Commerce Meeting (Monthly).

49052 ■ *TCC Business News*
c/o Sharon Silva, Pres./CEO
115 S Golden State Blvd.
Turlock, CA 95380
Ph: (209)632-2221
Fax: (209)632-5289
Co. E-mail: info@turlockchamber.com
URL: http://www.turlockchamber.com
Contact: Sharon Silva, President
Released: Bimonthly

49053 ■ *Temecula Today*
26790 Ynez Ct.
Temecula, CA 92591
Ph: (951)676-5090
Free: 866-676-5090
Fax: (951)676-5090
Co. E-mail: info@temecula.org
URL: http://www.temecula.org
Contact: Alice Sullivan, President
Released: Monthly

49054 ■ Temecula Valley Chamber of Commerce (TVCC)
26790 Ynez Ct.
Temecula, CA 92591
Ph: (951)676-5090
Free: 866-676-5090
Fax: (951)676-5090
Co. E-mail: info@temecula.org
URL: http://www.temecula.org
Contact: Alice Sullivan, President
Description: Promotes business and community development in the Temecula Valley, CA area. **Founded:** 1966. **Publications:** *Chamber Directory* (Periodic); *E-Commerce Newsletter* (Monthly); *Temecula Today* (Monthly).

49055 ■ Temple City Chamber of Commerce
9050 Las Tunas Dr.
Temple City, CA 91780
Ph: (626)286-3101
Fax: (626)286-2590
Co. E-mail: info@templecitychamber.org
URL: http://www.templecitychamber.org
Contact: Linda Payne, President
Description: Promotes business and community development in Temple City, CA. **Founded:** 1924. **Publications:** *News and Views* (Monthly).

49056 ■ Templeton Chamber of Commerce
c/o Robert Rosales, Pres.
PO Box 701
Templeton, CA 93465
Ph: (805)434-2099
Co. E-mail: info@templetonchamber.com
URL: http://www.templetonchamber.com
Contact: Robert Rosales, President
Description: Promotes business and community development in Templeton, CA. Sponsors local charities and festivals. **Founded:** 1913. **Telecommunication Services:** robert@templetonchamber.com.

49057 ■ Thousand Palms Chamber of Commerce
c/o Rosemarie Tessier, Exec. Admin.
PO Box 365
Thousand Palms, CA 92276
Ph: (760)343-1988
Fax: (760)343-1988
Co. E-mail: info@thousandpalmschamber.com
URL: http://www.thousandpalmscc.com
Contact: Patricia Saleh, Secretary
Description: Promotes business and community development in Thousand Palms, CA.

49058 ■ Tiburon Peninsula Chamber of Commerce (TPCC)
PO Box 563
Tiburon, CA 94920
Ph: (415)435-5633
Fax: (415)435-1132
Co. E-mail: tibcc@sbcglobal.net
URL: http://www.tiburonchamber.org
Contact: Christine Koehler, Executive Director
Description: Promotes business and community development in the Tiburon, CA area. Sponsors Chili Cook-off and Wine Festival. Conducts Fourth of July activities, picnic, and charitable activities. **Founded:** 1960.

49059 ■ Torrance Area Chamber of Commerce (TACC)
3400 Torrance Blvd., Ste. 100
Torrance, CA 90503
Ph: (310)540-5858
Fax: (310)540-7662
Co. E-mail: info@torrancechamber.com
URL: http://www.torrancechamber.com
Contact: Donna Duperron, President
Description: Promotes business and community development in Torrance, CA area.

49060 ■ Town of Los Gatos Chamber of Commerce (TLGCC)
10 Station Way
Los Gatos, CA 95030-5926
Ph: (408)354-9300

Fax: (408)399-1594
Co. E-mail: chamber@losgatosweb.com
URL: http://losgatoschamber.com
Contact: Ronee Nassi, Executive Director
Description: Promotes business and community development in Los Gatos, CA. Offers programs, services and resources for business and community vitality. Operates the official Town of Los Gatos Information Office. **Founded:** 1997. **Publications:** *Art Guide - Cultural Arts in Los Gatos* (Periodic); *It's Our Business* (Bimonthly).

49061 ■ Tracy Chamber of Commerce
c/o Dan Maloney, Exec. Dir.
223 E 10th St.
Tracy, CA 95376
Ph: (209)835-2131
Fax: (209)833-9526
Co. E-mail: info@tracychamber.org
URL: http://www.tracychamber.org
Contact: Art Vallejo, Chairman
Description: Works to strengthen the business community and take a leadership role in promoting economic vitality, influencing public policy and promoting the welfare of members. **Founded:** 1909. **Publications:** *Inside Advantage* (Monthly). **Educational Activities:** Winter Gala (Annual). **Awards:** Agri-business Person of the Year (Annual); Male and Female Citizen of the Year (Annual).

49062 ■ Trinity County Chamber of Commerce (TCCC)
509 Main St., State Hwy. 299
Weaverville, CA 96093
Ph: (530)623-6101
Free: 800-4-TRINITY
Fax: (530)623-3753
Co. E-mail: chamber@trinitycounty.com
URL: http://www.trinitycounty.com
Contact: Carol Eli, Executive Director
Description: Promotes business and community development in Trinity County, CA. **Founded:** 1966.

49063 ■ Truckee-Donner Chamber of Commerce
10065 Donner Pass Rd.
Truckee, CA 96161
Ph: (530)587-8808
Fax: (530)587-2439
Co. E-mail: info@truckee.com
URL: http://truckeechamber.com
Contact: Lynn Saunders, President
Description: Promotes and develops local business and tourism, while improving the community's quality of life. **Publications:** *Truckee Tracks* (Monthly); *Truckee-Donner Chamber of Commerce--Business Directory*.

49064 ■ *Truckee Tracks*
10065 Donner Pass Rd.
Truckee, CA 96161
Ph: (530)587-8808
Fax: (530)587-2439
Co. E-mail: info@truckee.com
URL: http://truckeechamber.com
Contact: Lynn Saunders, President
Released: Monthly

49065 ■ Tuolumne County Chamber of Commerce
222 S Shepherd St.
Sonora, CA 95370
Ph: (209)532-4212
Free: 877-532-4212
Fax: (209)532-8068
Co. E-mail: info@tcchamber.com
URL: http://www.tcchamber.com
Contact: George Segarini, Executive Director
Description: Works to provide leadership for a better business environment. Promotes the economic well-being of Tuolumne County, CA. **Founded:** 1921. **Publications:** *Chamber News* (Monthly).

49066 ■ Turlock Chamber of Commerce
c/o Sharon Silva, Pres./CEO
115 S Golden State Blvd.
Turlock, CA 95380
Ph: (209)632-2221

Fax: (209)632-5289
Co. E-mail: info@turlockchamber.com
URL: http://www.turlockchamber.com
Contact: Sharon Silva, President
Description: Promotes business and community development in Turlock, CA. Conducts charitable activities. Sponsors Turlock Poultry and Dairy Festival. **Publications:** *TCC Business News* (Bimonthly). **Telecommunication Services:** ssilva@turlockchamber.com.

49067 ■ Tustin Chamber of Commerce (TCC)
700 W 1st St.
Tustin, CA 92780
Ph: (714)544-5341
Fax: (714)544-2083
Co. E-mail: info@tustinchamber.org
URL: http://tustinchamber.org
Contact: Sherri Munsey, Executive Director
Description: Promotes business and community development in Tustin, CA. **Founded:** 1957. **Publications:** *Advocate* (Monthly); *Membership Directory and Buyer's Guide* (Annual).

49068 ■ Twain Harte Area Chamber of Commerce (THCC)
PO Box 404
Twain Harte, CA 95383
Ph: (209)586-4482
Fax: (209)586-0360
Co. E-mail: info@twainhartecc.com
URL: http://www.twainhartecc.com
Contact: Rebecca Halvorsen, President
Description: Promotes business and community development in Twain Harte, CA area. **Founded:** 1955.

49069 ■ Twentynine Palms Chamber of Commerce (TPCC)
73484 29th Palms Hwy.
Twentynine Palms, CA 92277
Ph: (760)367-3445
Fax: (760)367-3366
Co. E-mail: 29chamber@29chamber.org
URL: http://www.29chamber.org
Contact: Jodi Callahan, Executive Director
Description: Promotes business and community development in Twentynine Palms, CA. Sponsors Pioneer Days, Rodeo in October, and Bluegrass Festival in April. **Founded:** 1936. **Publications:** *Community Guide* (Annual); *Twentynine Palms Chamber of Commerce--Membership Directory*.

49070 ■ Union City Chamber of Commerce
3939 Smith St.
Union City, CA 94587
Ph: (510)952-9637
Fax: (510)952-9647
Co. E-mail: info@unioncitychamber.com
URL: http://www.unioncitychamber.com
Contact: Heidi Finberg, Chairman
Description: Promotes business and community development in Union City, CA. **Founded:** 1912.

49071 ■ Universal City-North Hollywood Chamber of Commerce
6369 Bellingham Ave.
North Hollywood, CA 91606-3202
Ph: (818)508-5155
Fax: (818)508-5156
Co. E-mail: info@noho.org
URL: http://www.noho.org
Contact: Kirk Jaffe, President
Description: Promotes business and community development in the Universal City-North Hollywood, CA area. Conducts charitable activities. Sponsors festival. **Founded:** 1914.

49072 ■ *Update*
200 N Pacific Coast Hwy.
Redondo Beach, CA 90277
Ph: (310)376-6911
Free: 800-282-0333
Fax: (310)374-7373
Co. E-mail: info@redondochamber.org
URL: http://www.redondochamber.org
Contact: Steve Goldstein, Chairman
Released: Monthly

49073 ■ Upland Chamber of Commerce
215 N 2nd Ave., Ste. D
Upland, CA 91786
Ph: (909)204-4465
Fax: (909)204-4464
Co. E-mail: realpeople@uplandchamber.org
URL: http://www.uplandchamber.org
Contact: Sonnie S. Faires, President
Description: Promotes business and community development in Upland, CA. **Founded:** 1963. **Publications:** *Business Directory and Community Guide.* **Educational Activities:** Ambassador Team (Monthly).

49074 ■ Vacaville Chamber of Commerce (VCC)
300 Main St., Ste. A
Vacaville, CA 95688
Ph: (707)448-6424
Fax: (707)448-0424
Co. E-mail: jennifer@vacavillechamber.com
URL: http://www.vacavillechamber.com
Contact: Mark Creffield, President
Description: Promotes business and community development in Vacaville, CA. Sponsors local charities and festivals. **Founded:** 1913. **Publications:** *Comments* (Monthly). **Awards:** Ambassador of the Year (Annual); ATHENA Award (Annual); Business of the Year (Annual).

49075 ■ Vallejo Chamber of Commerce
427 York St.
Vallejo, CA 94590
Ph: (707)644-5551
Fax: (707)644-5590
Co. E-mail: info@vallejochamber.com
URL: http://www.vallejochamber.com
Contact: Anita Hawkes, President
Description: Promotes business and community development in Vallejo, CA. **Founded:** 1874.

49076 ■ Valley Center Chamber of Commerce (VCCC)
27301 Valley Center Rd.
Valley Center, CA 92082
Ph: (760)751-1666
Fax: (760)749-8483
Co. E-mail: info@vcchamber.com
URL: http://www.vcchamber.com
Contact: Claudia Johnson, President
Description: Promotes business and community development in Valley Center, CA.

49077 ■ *Vantage*
817 East Ave., Q-9
Palmdale, CA 93550
Ph: (661)273-3232
Fax: (661)273-8508
Co. E-mail: chamberstaff@palmdalechamber.org
URL: http://www.palmdalechamber.org
Contact: Chris Buchanan, Chairperson
Released: Monthly

49078 ■ Venice Area Chamber of Commerce
PO Box 202
Venice, CA 90294
Ph: (310)822-5425
Co. E-mail: info@venicechamber.net
URL: http://www.venicechamber.net
Contact: Donna Lasman, Executive Director
Description: Promotes business and community development in the Venice, CA area. **Founded:** 1922. **Publications:** *Venice Area Chamber of Commerce Newsletter* (Bimonthly); *City Map/Business and Tourist Directory* (Annual). **Educational Activities:** Venice Area Chamber of Commerce Dinner (Annual); Mixer (Quarterly). **Awards:** Humanitarian of the Year (Annual).

49079 ■ *Venice Area Chamber of Commerce Newsletter*
PO Box 202
Venice, CA 90294
Ph: (310)822-5425
Co. E-mail: info@venicechamber.net
URL: http://www.venicechamber.net
Contact: Donna Lasman, Executive Director
Released: Bimonthly

49080 ■ *Ventura Business*
505 Poli St., 2nd Fl.
Ventura, CA 93003
Ph: (805)643-7222
Fax: (805)650-1414
Co. E-mail: info@ventura-chamber.org
URL: http://www.venturachamber.com
Contact: Ed Summers, President
Released: Monthly

49081 ■ *Ventura Chamber Business Directory*
505 Poli St., 2nd Fl.
Ventura, CA 93003
Ph: (805)643-7222
Fax: (805)650-1414
Co. E-mail: info@ventura-chamber.org
URL: http://www.venturachamber.com
Contact: Ed Summers, President

49082 ■ Ventura Chamber of Commerce
505 Poli St., 2nd Fl.
Ventura, CA 93003
Ph: (805)643-7222
Fax: (805)650-1414
Co. E-mail: info@ventura-chamber.org
URL: http://www.venturachamber.com
Contact: Ed Summers, President
Description: Promotes business and community development in the Ventura, CA area. **Founded:** 1899. **Publications:** *Ventura Business* (Monthly); *Ventura Chamber Business Directory*; *Ventura County Industry Guide.*

49083 ■ *Ventura County Industry Guide*
505 Poli St., 2nd Fl.
Ventura, CA 93003
Ph: (805)643-7222
Fax: (805)650-1414
Co. E-mail: info@ventura-chamber.org
URL: http://www.venturachamber.com
Contact: Ed Summers, President
Price: $53.63, plus $4 for postage and handling.

49084 ■ Vernon Chamber of Commerce
3801 Santa Fe Ave.
Vernon, CA 90058
Ph: (323)583-3313
Co. E-mail: molguin@vernonchamber.org
URL: http://vernonchamber.org
Contact: Marisa Olguin, Executive Director
Description: Seeks to enhance the economic and socio-economic health of Vernon community. **Founded:** 1950. **Publications:** *Business Voice.*

49085 ■ Victorville Chamber of Commerce (VCC)
14174 Green Tree Blvd.
Victorville, CA 92395
Ph: (760)245-6506
Fax: (760)245-6505
Co. E-mail: vvchamber@vvchamber.com
URL: http://vvchamber.com
Contact: Michele Spears, President
Description: Promotes business and community development in Victorville, CA. **Founded:** 1913. **Publications:** *Insight* (Monthly); *Map* (Annual); *Victorville Chamber of Commerce Business Directory* (Semiannual). **Educational Activities:** High Desert Opportunity Business Conference (Annual); Mixers (Quarterly).

49086 ■ *Victorville Chamber of Commerce Business Directory*
14174 Green Tree Blvd.
Victorville, CA 92395
Ph: (760)245-6506
Fax: (760)245-6505
Co. E-mail: vvchamber@vvchamber.com
URL: http://vvchamber.com
Contact: Michele Spears, President
Released: Semiannual

49087 ■ Vietnamese Chamber of Commerce
9121 Bolsa Ave., Ste. 203
Westminster, CA 92683
Ph: (714)892-6928
Fax: (714)892-6938
Co. E-mail: info@vacoc.com
URL: http://vacoc.com/index_en.php
Contact: Tam Nguyen, Chairman
Description: Provides leadership for the community, promotes local resources, enhances local programs, and coordinates development efforts.

49088 ■ *Village Voice*
2855 E Coast Hwy., Ste. 101
Corona Del Mar, CA 92625
Ph: (949)673-4050
Fax: (949)673-3940
Co. E-mail: info@cdmchamber.com
URL: http://www.cdmchamber.com
Contact: Linda Leonhard, President
Released: Monthly **Price:** included in membership dues.

49089 ■ *Village Voice*
111 South Main Ave.
Fallbrook, CA 92028-2848
Ph: (760)728-5845
Co. E-mail: richard.kennedy@fallbrookchamber-ofcommerce.com
URL: http://www.fallbrookchamberofcommerce.org
Contact: Richard Kennedy, Chief Executive Officer
Released: Monthly

49090 ■ *Visalia Business*
220 N Santa Fe Ave.
Visalia, CA 93292
Ph: (559)734-5876
Free: 877-VIS-ALIA
Fax: (559)734-7479
Co. E-mail: info@visaliachamber.org
URL: http://www.visaliachamber.org
Contact: Glenn Morris, President
Released: Monthly

49091 ■ Visalia Chamber of Commerce (VCC)
220 N Santa Fe Ave.
Visalia, CA 93292
Ph: (559)734-5876
Free: 877-VIS-ALIA
Fax: (559)734-7479
Co. E-mail: info@visaliachamber.org
URL: http://www.visaliachamber.org
Contact: Glenn Morris, President
Description: Promotes business and community development in Visalia, CA. Holds seminars. **Founded:** 1899. **Publications:** *Visalia Business* (Monthly); *Membership Directory and Community Guide to Visalia* (Annual). **Educational Activities:** Business Networking Breakfast (Periodic); Christmas Tree Auction and Holiday (Annual). **Awards:** College of the Sequoias Scholarship (Annual); Large Business of the Year (Annual); Man of the Year (Annual); Small Business of the Year (Annual); Woman of the Year (Annual). **Telecommunication Services:** glenn@visaliachamber.com.

49092 ■ *Visitor Booklet*
1556 1st St.
Napa, CA 94559
Ph: (707)226-7455
Fax: (707)226-1171
Co. E-mail: chris@napachamber.com
URL: http://www.napachamber.com
Contact: Chris Messina, President

49093 ■ *Visitor's Guide*
PO Box 217
Avalon, CA 90704-0217
Ph: (310)510-1520
Fax: (310)510-7607
Co. E-mail: info@catalinachamber.com
URL: http://www.catalinachamber.com
Contact: Wayne G. Griffin, President
Released: Annual

49094 ■ *Visitors Guide*
390 W 7th St.
San Pedro, CA 90731
Ph: (310)832-7272

Fax: (310)832-0685
Co. E-mail: info@sanpedrochamber.com
URL: http://www.sanpedrochamber.com
Contact: Randy Bowers, President
Released: Biennial

49095 ■ Vista Chamber of Commerce
201 Washington St.
Vista, CA 92084
Ph: (760)726-1122
Fax: (760)726-8654
Co. E-mail: info@vistachamber.com
URL: http://www.vistachamber.com
Contact: Bret Schanzenbach, President
Description: Promotes business and community development in Vista, CA.

49096 ■ *The Voice of Business*
101 H St., Unit 4
Antioch, CA 94509
Ph: (925)757-1800
Fax: (925)757-5286
Co. E-mail: info@antiochchamber.com
URL: http://www.antiochchamber.com
Contact: Donna McGee, Chairman
Released: Monthly

49097 ■ *The Voice of Business*
37101 Newark Blvd.
Newark, CA 94560
Ph: (510)744-1000
Fax: (510)744-1003
Co. E-mail: info@newark-chamber.com
URL: http://www.newark-chamber.com
Contact: Linda Ashley, President
Released: Monthly

49098 ■ *The Voice of Business*
325 Pollasky Ave.
Clovis, CA 93612-1139
Ph: (559)299-7363
Fax: (559)299-2969
Co. E-mail: info@clovischamber.com
URL: http://www.clovischamber.com
Contact: Jim Ware, President
Released: Monthly

49099 ■ *WACC Perspective*
118 W Sycamore
Willows, CA 95988
Ph: (530)934-8150
Free: 888-EZW-AY4U
Fax: (530)934-2681
Co. E-mail: info@willowschamber.com
URL: http://www.willowschamber.com
Contact: Jamie Millen, President
Released: Bimonthly

49100 ■ *Walnut Creek Business Focus*
1777 Botelho Dr., Ste. 103
Walnut Creek, CA 94596-4233
Ph: (925)934-2007
Fax: (925)934-2404
Co. E-mail: chamber@walnut-creek.com
URL: http://www.walnut-creek.com
Contact: Jay Hoyer, President

49101 ■ Walnut Creek Chamber of Commerce
1777 Botelho Dr., Ste. 103
Walnut Creek, CA 94596-4233
Ph: (925)934-2007
Fax: (925)934-2404
Co. E-mail: chamber@walnut-creek.com
URL: http://www.walnut-creek.com
Contact: Jay Hoyer, President
Description: Promotes business and community development in Walnut Creek, CA. **Founded:** 1926. **Publications:** *Walnut Creek Business Focus*; *Walnut Creek Chamber Membership Directory* (Annual). **Educational Activities:** Art and Wine (Annual); Ask the Experts (Weekly).

49102 ■ *Walnut Creek Chamber Membership Directory*
1777 Botelho Dr., Ste. 103
Walnut Creek, CA 94596-4233
Ph: (925)934-2007

Fax: (925)934-2404
Co. E-mail: chamber@walnut-creek.com
URL: http://www.walnut-creek.com
Contact: Jay Hoyer, President
Released: Annual

49103 ■ Wasco Chamber of Commerce and Agriculture
c/o Vickie Hight, Office Mgr.
700 G St.
Wasco, CA 93280
Ph: (661)758-2746
Co. E-mail: vhight@ci.wasco.ca.us
URL: http://www.ci.wasco.ca.us
Contact: Vickie Hight, Office Manager
Description: Promotes business and community development in Wasco, CA. Conducts charitable activities. Sponsors Wasco Farm Festival. **Founded:** 1946.

49104 ■ *Weed Chamber Chatter*
34 Main St.
Weed, CA 96094-2522
Ph: (530)938-4624
Free: 877-938-4624
Fax: (530)938-1658
Co. E-mail: weedchamber@ncen.org
URL: http://www.weedchamber.com
Contact: Brenda Woods, President
Released: Periodic

49105 ■ Weed Chamber of Commerce (WCC)
34 Main St.
Weed, CA 96094-2522
Ph: (530)938-4624
Free: 877-938-4624
Fax: (530)938-1658
Co. E-mail: weedchamber@ncen.org
URL: http://www.weedchamber.com
Contact: Brenda Woods, President
Description: Promotes business and community development in Weed, CA. **Founded:** 1953. **Publications:** *Weed Chamber Chatter* (Periodic).

49106 ■ *Welcome*
402 W Broadway, Ste. 1000
San Diego, CA 92101-3585
Ph: (619)544-1300
Co. E-mail: webinfo@sdchamber.org
URL: http://www.sdchamber.org
Contact: Ruben Barrales, President
E-mail: rbarrales@sdchamber.org
Released: Periodic **Price:** $16.

49107 ■ *Welcome to Burlingame*
290 California Dr.
Burlingame, CA 94010
Ph: (650)344-1735
Fax: (650)344-1763
Co. E-mail: info@burlingamechamber.org
URL: http://burlingamechamber.org
Contact: Georgette Naylor, President
Released: Periodic

49108 ■ *Welcome to Rio Linda-Elverta*
PO Box 75
Rio Linda, CA 95673
Ph: (916)991-9344
Fax: (916)922-9074
Co. E-mail: jculley@rlechamber.com
URL: http://www.rlechamber.com/
Contact: Hal Morris, President
Released: Monthly **Price:** free.

49109 ■ *Wellspring*
PO Box 416
Wrightwood, CA 92397
Ph: (760)249-4320
Fax: (760)249-6822
Co. E-mail: info@wrightwoodchamber.org
URL: http://www.wrightwoodchamber.org
Contact: Clark Fleeup, President

49110 ■ West Covina Chamber of Commerce
811 S Sunset Ave.
West Covina, CA 91790-3599
Ph: (626)338-8496

Fax: (626)960-0511
Co. E-mail: glawson@westcovinachamber.com
URL: http://www.westcovinachamber.com
Description: Promotes business and community development in West Covina, CA. Sponsors summer concert series and public safety luncheon; bestows Citizen of the Year award. **Founded:** 1953. **Publications:** *Business Outlook* (10/year); *Health Providers Guide*; *Map*; *Special Events Guide*; *Attorney Guide*; *Community Information and Business Guide* (Semiannual). **Educational Activities:** West Covina Chamber of Commerce Breakfast (Monthly).

49111 ■ *West Los Angeles Business Monthly*
2370 Westwood Blvd., Ste. J
Los Angeles, CA 90064
Ph: (310)441-2900
Fax: (310)441-2904
Co. E-mail: info@westlachamber.org
URL: http://www.westlachamber.org
Contact: Ronald Adams, President
Released: Monthly

49112 ■ West Los Angeles Chamber of Commerce
2370 Westwood Blvd., Ste. J
Los Angeles, CA 90064
Ph: (310)441-2900
Fax: (310)441-2904
Co. E-mail: info@westlachamber.org
URL: http://www.westlachamber.org
Contact: Ronald Adams, President
Description: Promotes business and community development in West Los Angeles, CA. **Founded:** 1945. **Publications:** *West Los Angeles Business Monthly* (Monthly).

49113 ■ West Marin Chamber of Commerce
PO Box 1045
Point Reyes Station, CA 94956
Ph: (415)663-9232
Co. E-mail: info@pointreyes.org
URL: http://www.pointreyes.org
Description: Promotes business and community development in Point Reyes Station, CA.

49114 ■ West Sacramento Chamber and Visitors Bureau
PO Box 404
West Sacramento, CA 95691-3209
Ph: (916)371-7042
Fax: (916)371-7007
Co. E-mail: wsinfo@westsacramentochamber.com
URL: http://www.westsacramentochamber.com
Contact: Denice A. Seals, Chief Executive Officer
Description: Promotes business and community development in the West Sacramento, CA area. Conducts toy drive and food drive. Sponsors golf tournament, port fest, annual barbecue, river front celebration, July 3 fireworks and community day parade. **Scope:** business survival. **Founded:** 1947. **Subscriptions:** books periodicals. **Publications:** *Individual Map* (Biennial); *The Insider*; *Local Business Directory* (Triennial). **Educational Activities:** West Sacramento Business and Trade Fair (Annual).

49115 ■ West Shores Chamber of Commerce of the Salton Sea
PO Box 5185
Salton City, CA 92275-5185
Ph: (760)394-4112
Fax: (760)394-4112
Co. E-mail: wscc.secretary@gmail.com
URL: http://www.westshoreschamber.org
Contact: Lavon Jaksch, President
Description: Promotes business and community development at the west shores of the Salton Sea. **Founded:** 1959. **Publications:** *Pelican Post* (Monthly).

49116 ■ Western Association of Chamber Executives (WACE)
PO Box 1736
Sacramento, CA 95812-1736
Ph: (916)442-2223

Fax: (916)444-6685
Co. E-mail: info@waceonline.com
URL: http://www.waceonline.com
Contact: Ken Moore, Chairman of the Board
Description: Seeks to enhance and promote the professional growth and competence of Chamber of Commerce Executives. **Founded:** 1995.

49117 ■ Westminster Chamber of Commerce
14491 Beach Blvd., Ste. B
Westminster, CA 92683
Ph: (714)898-9648
Fax: (714)373-1499
Co. E-mail: biz@westminsterchamber.org
URL: http://westminsterchamber.org
Contact: Crystal R. Wadsworth, Executive Director
Description: Promotes business and community development in Westminster, CA. Sponsors Quarterly Breakfasts, Networking Luncheons & Mixers, Legislative Meetings & Mixer, Taste and Tour of Little Saigon, Business Expo, Bowling Tournament, Annual Business Awards Dinner and Business Forums. Conducts community activities including Salute to Seniors Luncheon and Public Service Awards luncheon. **Founded:** 1907. **Publications:** *DIRECTIONS* (Quarterly). **Awards:** Chamber Member of the Year (Annual); Citizen of the Year (Annual); Employee of the Year (Annual); Major Business of the Year (Annual); Organization of the Year (Annual); Public Service Awards (Annual); Small Business of the Year (Annual).

49118 ■ *What to Know*
No. 112, 1106 2nd St.
Encinitas, CA 92024
Ph: (760)753-6041
Fax: (760)753-6270
Co. E-mail: asst@encinitaschamber.com
URL: http://www.encinitaschamber.com
Contact: Bob Gattinella, President
Released: Monthly

49119 ■ *What to See and Do in Julian*
PO Box 1866
Julian, CA 92036
Ph: (760)765-1857
Fax: (760)765-2544
Co. E-mail: chamber@julianca.com
URL: http://www.julianca.com
Released: Daily **Price:** free.

49120 ■ Whittier Area Chamber of Commerce (WACC)
8158 Painter Ave.
Whittier, CA 90602
Ph: (562)698-9554
Fax: (562)693-2700
Co. E-mail: info@whittierchamber.com
URL: http://www.whittierchamber.com
Contact: Dean Harako, President
Description: Promotes business and community development in the Whittier, CA area. **Founded:** 1914. **Publications:** *Clubs and Organizations Directory* (Annual); *Business Directory* (Annual); *Business Focus* (Monthly); *Clubs and Organizations Directory* (Annual); *Whittier Area Chamber of Commerce--Membership Directory* (Annual); *Whittier Area Chamber of Commerce--Clubs and Organizations Directory* (Annual). **Educational Activities:** Hathaway Golf Classic (Annual); Wake Up Whittier (Monthly). **Awards:** Silver Shield Awards (Annual).

49121 ■ *Who's Who in Chamber Membership*
520 N Euclid Ave.
Ontario, CA 91762
Ph: (909)984-2458
Fax: (909)984-6439
Co. E-mail: info@ontario.org
URL: http://www.ontario.org
Contact: Bob Brown, Chairman
Released: Annual

49122 ■ Wildomar Chamber of Commerce
PO Box 885
Wildomar, CA 92595

Ph: (909)245-0437
Co. E-mail: info@wildomarchamber.org
URL: http://www.wildomarchamber.org
Contact: Craig McKenzie, Chairman
Description: Promotes business and community development in Wildomar, CA area.

49123 ■ Willits Chamber of Commerce (WCC)
239 S Main St.
Willits, CA 95490
Ph: (707)459-7910
Fax: (707)459-7914
Co. E-mail: info@willits.org
URL: http://www.willits.org
Contact: Lynn R. Kennelly, Executive Director
Description: Promotes business and community development in Willits, CA. Sponsors annual community festival. **Founded:** 1926. **Publications:** *Chamber ... Updates* (Quarterly). **Educational Activities:** Willits Chamber of Commerce Meeting (Annual).

49124 ■ Willow Creek Chamber of Commerce
PO Box 704
Willow Creek, CA 95573
Ph: (530)629-2693
Free: 800-628-5156
Co. E-mail: info@willowcreekchamber.com
URL: http://www.willowcreekchamber.com
Contact: Tangie Markle, President
Description: Promotes business and community development in Willow Creek, CA.

49125 ■ Willows Area Chamber of Commerce
118 W Sycamore
Willows, CA 95988
Ph: (530)934-8150
Free: 888-EZW-AY4U
Fax: (530)934-2681
Co. E-mail: info@willowschamber.com
URL: http://www.willowschamber.com
Contact: Jamie Millen, President
Description: Promotes business and community development in the Willows, CA area. **Publications:** *Business Directory* (Annual); *Chamber Connection* (Monthly); *WACC Perspective* (Bimonthly).

49126 ■ Wilmington Chamber of Commerce
PO Box 90
Wilmington, CA 90748
Ph: (310)834-8586
Fax: (310)834-8887
Co. E-mail: info@wilmington-chamber.com
URL: http://www.wilmington-chamber.com
Contact: Dan Hoffman, Executive Director
Description: Promotes business and community development in Wilmington, CA. **Founded:** 1904. **Awards:** Board Members of the Year (Annual); Company of the Year (Annual); Organization of the Year (Annual); Volunteer Citizen of the Year (Annual).

49127 ■ Windsor Chamber of Commerce and Visitors Center (WCC)—Windsor Chamber of Commerce
PO Box 367
Windsor, CA 95492
Ph: (707)838-7285
Co. E-mail: info@windsorchamber.com
URL: http://www.windsorchamber.com
Contact: Gary Quackenbush, President
Description: Promotes business and community development in Windsor, CA. Sponsors Windsor Day Festival and Windsor Business Expo. **Founded:** 1965.

49128 ■ Winters District Chamber of Commerce
11 Main St.
Winters, CA 95694
Ph: (530)795-2329
Fax: (530)795-3202
Co. E-mail: chamberwinters@yahoo.com
URL: http://www.winterschamber.com
Description: Works to strengthen businesses and serve the community through involvement and volunteers.

49129 ■ Women in Business Roundtable (WIBR)
c/o San Francisco Chamber of Commerce
235 Montgomery St., 12th Fl.
San Francisco, CA 94104
Ph: (415)392-4520
Fax: (415)392-0485
Co. E-mail: nchan@sfchamber.com
URL: http://www.sfchamber.com/eventsprogs/bizdev/
  programs_wibr.php
Description: Aims to attract, develop and retain business in San Francisco. Provides information, education and networking opportunities for women and minorities. **Founded:** 1993.

49130 ■ Woodland Area Chamber of Commerce
307 1st St.
Woodland, CA 95695-3412
Ph: (530)662-7327
Free: 888-843-2636
Fax: (530)662-4086
Co. E-mail: staff@woodlandchamber.org
URL: http://www.woodlandchamber.org
Contact: Kristy Wright, Chief Executive Officer
E-mail: kristyw@woodlandchamber.com
Description: Promotes business and community development in Woodland, CA. Sponsors festival. **Founded:** 1931. **Publications:** *The Progress* (Monthly); *Membership Directory/Buyers Guide* (Periodic); *Woodland Area Chamber of Commerce--Membership Directory/Buyers Guide* (Periodic).

49131 ■ Wrightwood Chamber of Commerce
PO Box 416
Wrightwood, CA 92397
Ph: (760)249-4320
Fax: (760)249-6822
Co. E-mail: info@wrightwoodchamber.org
URL: http://www.wrightwoodchamber.org
Contact: Clark Fleeup, President
Description: Promotes business and community development in Wrightwood, CA. **Publications:** *Wellspring.* **Educational Activities:** Wrightwood Chamber of Commerce Board meeting (Monthly).

49132 ■ Yorba Linda Chamber of Commerce (YLCC)
17670 Yorba Linda Blvd.
Yorba Linda, CA 92886
Ph: (714)993-9537
Co. E-mail: phyllisylcc@sbcglobal.net
URL: http://www.yorbalindachamber.org
Contact: Phyllis A. Coleman, Executive Director
Description: Promotes business and community development in Yorba Linda, CA. **Founded:** 1913. **Publications:** *Chamber Action* (Monthly). **Awards:** Outstanding Student Awards (Annual); Senior High School Scholarships (Annual).

49133 ■ Yountville Chamber of Commerce
6484 Washington St., Ste. F
Yountville, CA 94599
Ph: (707)944-0904
Fax: (707)944-4465
Co. E-mail: info@yountville.com
URL: http://www.yountville.com
Contact: Katja Loeffelholz, President
Description: Promotes business and community development in the Yountville, CA area.

49134 ■ *Your City Insider*
11900 La Mirada Blvd., Ste. 9
La Mirada, CA 90638
Ph: (562)902-1970
Fax: (562)902-1218
Co. E-mail: info@lmchamber.org
URL: http://lmchamber.org
Contact: Demian Ross, Director
Released: Monthly **Price:** included in membership dues.

49135 ■ Yreka Chamber of Commerce (YCC)
117 W Miner St.
Yreka, CA 96097

Ph: (530)842-1649
Co. E-mail: info@yrekachamber.com
URL: http://www.yrekachamber.com
Contact: Jill Harris, Executive Director
Description: Promotes business, tourism, and community development in Siskiyou County, CA. **Founded:** 1923.

49136 ■ Yuba-Sutter Chamber of Commerce (YSCOC)
PO Box 1429
Marysville, CA 95901
Ph: (530)743-6501
Fax: (530)741-8645
Co. E-mail: chamber@yubasutterchamber.com
URL: http://www.yubasutterchamber.com
Contact: Kristy Santucci, Chief Executive Officer
Description: Promotes business and community development in Sutter and Yuba counties, CA. **Founded:** 1970. **Publications:** *Business Today* (Weekly); *Chamber Notes* (Weekly); *Explore 99 Things* (Annual); *Innerview* (Monthly); *Explore Yuba-Sutter* (Annual). **Educational Activities:** Business Connection Breakfasts (Monthly). **Awards:** Ambassador of the Year (Annual); Athena Award (Annual); Business of the Year (Annual); Civic Entrepreneur of the Year (Annual); Civic Organization of the Year (Annual); Non-Profit Business of the Year (Annual); Small Business of the Year (Annual); Volunteer of the Year (Annual).

49137 ■ Yucaipa Valley Chamber of Commerce (YVCC)
PO Box 45
Yucaipa, CA 92399-0045
Ph: (909)790-1841
Fax: (909)363-7373
Co. E-mail: info@yucaipachamber.org
URL: http://www.yucaipachamber.org
Contact: Pamela Emenger, President
Description: Promotes a vibrant business environment by cooperative interaction between business, government and community. **Founded:** 1915. **Publications:** *The Chamber Times* (Monthly); *Yucaipa Valley Chamber of Commerce Business Directory* (Biennial). **Educational Activities:** Installation of Officers & Community Awards Banquet (Annual). **Awards:** Chamber Member of the Year (Annual); Citizen of the Year (Annual); Firefighter of the Year (Annual); Peace Officer of the Year (Annual).

49138 ■ *Yucaipa Valley Chamber of Commerce Business Directory*
PO Box 45
Yucaipa, CA 92399-0045
Ph: (909)790-1841
Fax: (909)363-7373
Co. E-mail: info@yucaipachamber.org
URL: http://www.yucaipachamber.org
Contact: Pamela Emenger, President
Released: Biennial

MINORITY BUSINESS ASSISTANCE PROGRAMS

49139 ■ ASIAN
1167 Mission St., 4th Fl.
San Francisco, CA 94103
Ph: (415)928-5910
Fax: (415)921-0182
Co. E-mail: info@asianinc.org
URL: http://www.asianinc.org
Contact: Michael A. Chan, President
Description: Assisting in the business development and growth of African Americans and other minorities in Northern California. **Founded:** 1971. **Telecommunication Services:** supplier@asianinc.org.

49140 ■ California Native American Business Center - National Center for American Indian Enterprise
11138 Valley Mall, Ste. 200
El Monte, CA 91731
Ph: (626)442-3701

Fax: (626)442-7115
Co. E-mail: schambers@ncaied.org
URL: http://www.canabec.org
Contact: Sharon Chambers, Director

49141 ■ East Los Angeles Minority Business Development Center
5271 E Beverly Blvd.
Los Angeles, CA 90022
Ph: (323)726-7734
Fax: (323)721-9794
Co. E-mail: eastlambdc@ibm.net

49142 ■ Inland Empire Minority Business Enterprise Center - CHARO Community Development Corp.
1485 Spruce St., Ste. C-100
Riverside, CA 92507
Ph: (951)320-7020
Fax: (951)320-7023
Co. E-mail: kgutierrez@charo.corp.com
URL: http://www.charocorp.com
Contact: Karla V. Gonzalez-Gutierrez
Description: Provides certification, technical assistance, and training services to minority businesses in the Inland Empire, Orange County, and San Diego areas.

49143 ■ Los Angeles Minority Business Enterprise Center
2801 S Hoover St.
Los Angeles, CA 90089
Ph: (213)743-1966
Fax: (213)743-4511
Co. E-mail: info@losangelesmbec.org
URL: http://www.losangelesmbec.org/
Contact: Sergio Gascon, Director
Description: Provides access to educational and technical resources that foster business expansion and job creation throughout Los Angeles County.

49144 ■ Los Angeles Minority Business Opportunity Center - City of Los Angeles
City Hall
200 N Spring St., 13th Fl.
Los Angeles, CA 90012
Ph: (213)978-0671
Fax: (213)978-0690
Co. E-mail: lambdc@lacity.org
URL: http://www.lamboc.org/
Contact: Linda Smith, Executive Director
Description: LA MBOC's vision is to achieve entrepreneurial parity for local Minority Business Enterprises by actively promoting their ability to grow and compete in the global economy.

49145 ■ Los Angeles Urban League Entrepreneur Center
3450 Mount Vernon Dr.
Los Angeles, CA 90008
Ph: (323)299-9660
Fax: (323)299-0618
Co. E-mail: info@laul.org
URL: http://www.laul.org
Contact: Blair Taylor, Director
Description: Provides business development and support to African Americans and other minorities in Los Angeles.

49146 ■ Northern California Minority Business Enterprise Center
111 N Market St., Ste. 920
San Jose, CA 95113
Ph: (408)998-8058
Fax: (408)998-8872
Co. E-mail: aserrudo@norcalmbec.com
URL: http://www.norcalmbec.com
Description: Works to promote the growth and competitiveness of minority businsses in Northern California. Offers access to capital, contracting, and technical assistance.

49147 ■ Small & Minority Business - OSMB - Department of General Services - Office of Small Business and DVBE Services
707 3rd St., 1st Fl., Rm. 400
West Sacramento, CA 95605-2811
Ph: (916)375-4940

Fax: (916)375-4950
Co. E-mail: osdchelp@dgs.ca.gov
URL: http://www.pd.dgs.ca.gov/pd/Programs.aspx
Description: Offers technical assistance to small and minority business and promotes their procurement of government contracts for purchases, construction, and services.

49148 ■ Women's Initiative for Self-Employment
1398 Valencia St.
San Francisco, CA 94110
Ph: (415)641-3460
Fax: (415)826-1885
Co. E-mail: jabrams@womensinitiative.org
URL: http://www.womensinitiative.org
Contact: Julie Castro Abrams, Chief Executive Officer
Description: Provides business development services to women-owned businesses in the San Francisco area, with a focus on traditionally underserved groups including low-income and minority women. Maintains seven training sites.

FINANCING AND LOAN PROGRAMS

49149 ■ 5AM Ventures / 5AM Partners
2200 Sand Hill Rd., Ste. 110
Menlo Park, CA 94025
Ph: (650)233-8600
Fax: (650)233-8923
URL: http://www.5amventures.com
Contact: Mark S. Colella, Principal
Investment Policies: Seed and early stage. **Industry Preferences:** Biotechnology. **Geographic Preference:** East and West Coast.

49150 ■ 21st Century Internet Venture Partners
2 South Park, 2nd Fl.
San Francisco, CA 94107
Ph: (415)512-1221
Fax: (415)512-2650
URL: http://www.21vc.com
Contact: Peter Ziebelman, Partner
Preferred Investment Size: $3,000,000 minimum. **Industry Preferences:** Internet specific, Computer software and services, communications and media, and consumer related. **Geographic Preference:** U.S. and Canada.

49151 ■ Aberdare Ventures
1 Embarcadero Ctr., Ste. 4000
San Francisco, CA 94111
Ph: (415)392-7442
Fax: (415)392-4264
URL: http://www.aberdare.com
Contact: Paul Klingenstein, Managing Partner
Preferred Investment Size: $1,000,000 to $7,000,000. **Industry Preferences:** Healthcare technology, including biopharmaceutical products, medical devices, and related therapeutic technologies. **Geographic Preference:** U.S.

49152 ■ Acacia Venture Partners
7912 Radnor Rd., Ste. 700
Bethesda, MD 20817
Ph: (301)263-1071
Fax: (301)560-6540
Co. E-mail: jlaubach@acaciavp.com
URL: http://www.acaciavp.com
Contact: David Heer, Managing Director
Preferred Investment Size: $5,000,000 minimum. **Investment Policies:** Seed, start-up, first and second stage, leveraged buyout, and mezzanine. **Industry Preferences:** Internet specific, medical and health, computer software and services, industrial and energy, and communications and media. **Geographic Preference:** U.S.

49153 ■ Accel-KKR, LLC
2500 Sand Hill Rd., Ste. 300
Menlo Park, CA 94025
Ph: (650)289-2460

Fax: (650)289-2461
Co. E-mail: inquires@accel-kkr.com
URL: http://www.accel-kkr.com
Contact: Tom Barnds, Managing Director
Preferred Investment Size: $10,000,000 to
$50,000,000. **Industry Preferences:** Communications and media, Internet specific, computer related, and semiconductors and other electronics. **Geographic Preference:** Canada.

49154 ■ Accel Partners
428 University Ave.
Palo Alto, CA 94301
Ph: (650)614-4800
Fax: (650)614-4880
Co. E-mail: siliconvalley@accel.com
URL: http://www.accel.com
Contact: Jim Breyer, Managing Partner
Preferred Investment Size: $1,000,000 minimum.
Investment Policies: Seed, start-up, and early stage. **Industry Preferences:** Internet specific, computer software and services, communications and media, semiconductors and other electronics, other products, medical and health, computer hardware, biotechnology, industrial and energy, and consumer related. **Geographic Preference:** U.S.

49155 ■ Acorn Campus
3 Results Way
Cupertino, CA 95014-5924
Ph: (408)777-8090
Fax: (408)777-8091
Co. E-mail: info@acorncampus.com
URL: http://www.acorncampus.com
Contact: Wu-fu Chen, Founder
Preferred Investment Size: $250,000 to $5,000,000.
Investment Policies: Seed, start-up, and early stage. **Industry Preferences:** Communications, computer software, semiconductors and other electronics. **Geographic Preference:** Northern California.

49156 ■ Acorn Ventures, Inc.
2635 North First St., Ste. 148
San Jose, CA 95131
Ph: (510)459-6500
Fax: (925)249-1748
Co. E-mail: Partner@Acorn-Ventures.com
URL: http://www.acorn-ventures.com
Contact: Cliff Girard, Chief Executive Officer
Preferred Investment Size: $1,000,000 to $5,000,000. **Industry Preferences:** Communications and media, Internet specific, computer software and services, semiconductors and other electronics, other products, and computer hardware. **Geographic Preference:** West Coast.

49157 ■ Acuity Ventures LLC
1960 The Alameda, Ste. 200
San Jose, CA 95126-1441
Ph: (408)261-4286
Fax: (408)557-6555
URL: http://www.acuityventures.com
Contact: Eric Hardgrave, Managing Partner
E-mail: eric@acuityventures.com
Investment Policies: Early stage. **Industry Preferences:** Software.

49158 ■ Advanced Technology Ventures (Palo Alto)
485 Ramona St.
Palo Alto, CA 94301
Ph: (650)321-8601
Fax: (650)321-0934
Co. E-mail: info@atvcapital.com
URL: http://www.atvcapital.com
Contact: Steve Baloff, Partner
Preferred Investment Size: $15,000,000 to $35,000,000. **Industry Preferences:** Internet specific, computer software and services, computer hardware, semiconductors and other electronics, communications and media, medical and health, biotechnology, industrial and energy, consumer related, and other products. **Geographic Preference:** U.S. and Canada.

49159 ■ Advent International Corp. (New York)
375 Park Ave.
New York, NY 10152

Ph: (212)813-8300
Fax: (212)451-6503
Co. E-mail: news@adventinternational.com
URL: http://www.adventinternational.com
Contact: Chris Pike, Managing Director
Preferred Investment Size: $1,000,000 minimum.
Industry Preferences: Communications and media, consumer related, Internet specific, industrial and energy, medical and health, computer software and services, computer hardware, semiconductors and other electronics, and biotechnology, and other products. **Geographic Preference:** U.S and Canada.

49160 ■ Agilent Ventures
395 Page Mill Rd.
Palo Alto, CA 94303-0870
Ph: (650)752-5000
Fax: (650)752-5772
Co. E-mail: agilent_ventures@agilent.com
URL: http://www.agilentventures.com
Contact: Maximilian Schroeck, Managing Director
Preferred Investment Size: $500,000 to $10,000,000. **Industry Preferences:** Communications and media, semiconductors and other electronics, biotechnology, medical and health, and industrial and energy. **Geographic Preference:** U.S and Canada.

49161 ■ Allegis Capital LLC / Media Technology Ventures
525 University Ave., Ste. 220
Palo Alto, CA 94301
Ph: (650)687-0500
Fax: (650)687-0234
Co. E-mail: vc@allegiscapital.com
URL: http://www.allegiscapital.com
Contact: Barry M. Weinman, Managing Director
Preferred Investment Size: $3,000,000 to $5,000,000. **Investment Policies:** Seed, start-up, early stage, and research and development. **Industry Preferences:** Internet specific, computer software and services, communications and media, semiconductors and other electronics, computer hardware, and other products. **Geographic Preference:** West Coast.

49162 ■ Alloy Ventures, L.P.
400 Hamilton Ave., 4th Fl.
Palo Alto, CA 94301
Ph: (650)687-5000
Fax: (650)687-5010
Co. E-mail: info@alloyventures.com
URL: http://www.alloyventures.com
Contact: David Pidwell, Partner
E-mail: pidwell@alloyventures.com
Industry Preferences: Internet specific, computer software and services, medical and health, biotechnology, communications and media, semiconductors and other electronics, computer hardware, and industrial and energy. **Geographic Preference:** U.S.

49163 ■ Alpine Technology Ventures
20300 Stevens Creek Blvd., Ste. 495
Cupertino, CA 95014
Ph: (408)725-1810
Fax: (408)725-1207
URL: http://www.alpineventures.com
Contact: Chuck Chan, Partner
Preferred Investment Size: $2,000,000 to $4,000,000. **Industry Preferences:** Internet specific, computer software and services, computer hardware, communications and media, semiconductors and other electronics, other products, industrial and energy. **Geographic Preference:** California.

49164 ■ Alta Partners
1 Embarcadero Ctr., 37th Fl.
San Francisco, CA 94111
Ph: (415)362-4022
Fax: (415)362-6178
Co. E-mail: alta@altapartners.com
URL: http://www.altapartners.com
Contact: Alison Kiley, Director
Preferred Investment Size: $2,000,000 to $15,000,000. **Industry Preferences:** Internet specific, computer software and services, industrial and energy, consumer related, communications and

media, medical and health, computer hardware, biotechnology, semiconductors and other electronics, and other products. **Geographic Preference:** West Coast.

49165 ■ Alto Tech Ventures LLC
1010 El Camino Real, Ste. 340
Menlo Park, CA 94025
Ph: (650)330-0881
Fax: (650)330-0881
Co. E-mail: info@altotechventures.com
URL: http://www.altotechventures.com
Contact: Gloria Wahl, Partner
Investment Policies: Early stage. **Industry Preferences:** Communications, computer software, Internet specific, semiconductors and other electronics, and biotechnology. **Geographic Preference:** U.S.

49166 ■ Altos Ventures
2882 Sand Hill Rd., Ste. 100
Menlo Park, CA 94025
Ph: (650)234-9771
Fax: (650)233-9821
Co. E-mail: info@altosventures.com
URL: http://www.altosvc.com
Contact: Anthony Lee, Principal
Preferred Investment Size: $1,000,000 to $3,000,000. **Industry Preferences:** Internet specific, computer software and services, other products, consumer related, communications and media. **Geographic Preference:** Northern California and West Coast.

49167 ■ American River Ventures
2270 Douglas Blvd., Ste. 212
Roseville, CA 95661
Ph: (916)780-2828
Fax: (916)780-5443
Co. E-mail: info@arventures.com
URL: http://www.arventures.com
Contact: Dr. Barbara Grant, Managing Director
Preferred Investment Size: $500,000 to $2,000,000.
Investment Policies: Start-up, seed, early, first and second stage. **Industry Preferences:** Communications, computer software and hardware, Internet specific, semiconductors and other electronics, and business service. **Geographic Preference:** Arizona, California, Colorado, Idaho, Nevada, New Mexico, Oregon, Utah, Washington, and West Coast.

49168 ■ Amgen Inc.
1 Amgen Center Dr.
Thousand Oaks, CA 91320-1799
Ph: (805)447-1000
Free: 888-762-6436
Fax: (805)447-1010
Co. E-mail: info@amgen.com
URL: http://www.amgen.com
Contact: Robert Bradway, President
Founded: 1980. **Preferred Investment Size:** $1,000,000 to $3,000,000. **Investment Policies:** Early stage. **Industry Preferences:** Biotechnology. **Geographic Preference:** U.S. **Telecommunication Services:** investor.relations@amgen.com.

49169 ■ Amidzad, LLC
370 Convention Way, 3rd Fl.
Redwood City, CA 94063
Ph: (650)678-0123
Fax: (650)323-4044
URL: http://www.amidzad.com
Contact: Pejman Nozad, Partner
E-mail: pejman@amidzad.com
Investment Policies: Seed and early stage. **Industry Preferences:** Technology and life sciences. **Geographic Preference:** West Coast.

49170 ■ Anthem Venture Partners
225 Arizona Ave., Ste. 200
Santa Monica, CA 90401
Ph: (310)899-6225
Fax: (310)899-6234
Co. E-mail: info@anthemvp.com
URL: http://www.anthemvp.com
Contact: William Woodward, Managing Director
Preferred Investment Size: $500,000 to $400,000,000. **Investment Policies:** Early and later stage. **Industry Preferences:** Communications and media, Internet specific, computer hardware, con-

sumer related, business services, computer software and services, semiconductors and other electronics, other products. **Geographic Preference:** California.

49171 ■ Applied Materials Ventures
1142 Crane St., Ste. 4
Menlo Park, CA 94025
Ph: (650)833-0400
Co. E-mail: info@appliedvc.com
Contact: Julien Nguyen, Managing Partner
Investment Policies: Seed and early stage. **Industry Preferences:** Communications.

49172 ■ Asset Management Company Venture Capital
2100 Geng Rd., Ste. 200
Palo Alto, CA 94303
Ph: (650)494-7400
Fax: (650)856-1826
URL: http://www.assetman.com
Contact: Bennett S. Dubin, Managing Partner
Preferred Investment Size: $500,000 to $2,000,000. **Industry Preferences:** Computer software and services, medical and health, biotechnology, computer hardware, semiconductors and other electronics, Internet specific, communications and media, consumer related, industrial and energy, and other products. **Geographic Preference:** West Coast.

49173 ■ Athena Technology Ventures
100 Hamilton Ave., Ste. 225
Palo Alto, CA 94301
Ph: (650)470-0370
Fax: (650)470-0378
Co. E-mail: info@athenatv.com
URL: http://www.athenatv.com
Contact: Perry Ha, Managing Director
Industry Preferences: Internet specific, communications and media, computer software and services, computer hardware, semiconductors and other electronics, and consumer related. **Geographic Preference:** West Coast.

49174 ■ August Capital
2480 Sand Hill Rd., Ste. 101
Menlo Park, CA 94025
Ph: (650)234-9900
Fax: (650)234-9910
URL: http://www.augustcap.com
Contact: Andrew Rappaport, Partner
Industry Preferences: Internet specific, computer software, and services, communications and media, computer hardware, semiconductors and other electronics. **Geographic Preference:** Northwest, Southwest, Rocky mountains, and West Coast.

49175 ■ AVI Capital LP
100 Hamilton Ave., Ste. 250
Palo Alto, CA 94301
Ph: (650)687-0235
Fax: (650)687-0234
URL: http://www.avicapital.com
Contact: Brian J. Grossi, Partner
E-mail: grossi@avicapital.com
Preferred Investment Size: $1,000,000 to $2,000,000. **Industry Preferences:** Computer software, hardware, and services Internet specific, communications and media, semiconductors and other electronics, industrial and energy, and medical and health. **Geographic Preference:** West Coast.

49176 ■ Band of Angels
535 Middlefield Rd., Ste. 190
Menlo Park, CA 94025
Ph: (650)321-0854
Fax: (650)321-1968
Co. E-mail: contact@bandangels.com
URL: http://www.bandangels.com
Contact: Ian Patrick Sobieski, Managing Director
Preferred Investment Size: $300,000 to $860,000. **Investment Policies:** Seed, early stage, and balanced. **Industry Preferences:** Communications, computer software, semiconductors and other electronics, biotechnology, industrial and energy. **Geographic Preference:** California.

49177 ■ Barrington Partners
77 Franklin St., Ste. 802
Boston, MA 02110

Ph: (617)482-3300
Fax: (617)482-3325
URL: http://www.barringtonpartners.com
Contact: James Baker, Partner
Investment Policies: Seed and early stage. **Industry Preferences:** Internet specific, other products, communications and media.

49178 ■ Bay Partners
490 S. California Ave., Ste. 200
Palo Alto, CA 94306
Ph: (650)854-1500
Fax: (650)854-1515
Co. E-mail: partners@baypartners.com
URL: http://www.baypartners.com
Contact: Neal Dempsey, Partner
E-mail: neal@baypartners.com
Preferred Investment Size: $250,000. **Industry Preferences:** Communications and media, Internet specific, computer software and services, computer hardware, semiconductors and other electronics, consumer related, medical and health, and biotechnology. **Geographic Preference:** West Coast and Canada.

49179 ■ Benchmark Capital
2480 Sand Hill Rd., Ste.200
Menlo Park, CA 94025-6925
Ph: (650)854-8180
Fax: (650)854-8183
Co. E-mail: informationUS@benchmark.com
URL: http://www.benchmark.com
Contact: Alex Balkanski, Partner
E-mail: abalkanski@benchmark.com
Founded: 1995. **Preferred Investment Size:** $100,000 to $15,000,000. **Industry Preferences:** Internet specific, communications and media, computer software and services, computer hardware, industrial and energy, semiconductors and other electronics, and consumer related. **Geographic Preference:** Southwest and West Coast.

49180 ■ Berkeley International Capital Corp.
650 California St., 26th Fl.
San Francisco, CA 94108-2607
Ph: (415)249-0450
Co. E-mail: info@berkeleyvc.com
URL: http://www.berkeleyvc.com
Contact: Halsted W. Wheeler, Principal
Preferred Investment Size: $1,000,000 to $50,000,000. **Industry Preferences:** Semiconductors and other electronics, communications and media, computer software and services, computer hardware, biotechnology, medical and health, other products, Internet specific, industrial and energy. **Geographic Preference:** U.S.

49181 ■ Bessemer Venture Partners (Menlo Park)
535 Middlefield Rd., Ste. 245
Menlo Park, CA 94025
Ph: (650)853-7000
Fax: (650)853-7001
URL: http://www.bessemervp.com
Contact: David Cowan, Partner
Preferred Investment Size: $1,000,000 to $10,000,000. **Industry Preferences:** Communications and media, Internet specific, computer software and services, semiconductors and other electronics, consumer related, medical and health, industrial and energy, and biotechnology, computer hardware, and other products. **Geographic Preference:** U.S.

49182 ■ Blueprint Ventures
The Embaracadero
Pier 33 South, Ste. 201
San Francisco, CA 94111
Ph: (415)901-4000
Fax: (415)901-4035
URL: http://www.blueprintventures.com
Contact: Bart Schachter, Managing Director
E-mail: bart@blueprintventures.com
Preferred Investment Size: $500,000 to $3,000,000. **Industry Preferences:** Communications and media, computer related, and semiconductors and other electronics. **Geographic Preference:** West Coast.

49183 ■ Blumberg Capital Ventures
580 Howard St., Ste. 101
San Francisco, CA 94105
Ph: (415)905-5000
Fax: (415)357-5027
Co. E-mail: info@blumbergcapital.com
URL: http://www.blumbergcapital.com
Contact: David J. Blumberg, Managing Partner
Preferred Investment Size: $500,000 to $3,000,000. **Investment Policies:** Seed, early and first stage. **Industry Preferences:** Communications, computer software, and Internet specific. **Geographic Preference:** U.S.

49184 ■ Brentwood Venture Capital
11150 Santa Monica Blvd., Ste. 1200
Los Angeles, CA 90025
Ph: (310)477-7678
Fax: (310)312-1868
URL: http://www.brentwoodvc.com
Contact: Brian Atwood, Partner
Investment Policies: Seed, start-up, and second stage. **Industry Preferences:** Communications and media, computer software, Internet specific, biotechnology, and medical and health. **Geographic Preference:** West Coast.

49185 ■ Burrill & Company
1 Embarcadero Ctr., Ste. 2700
San Francisco, CA 94111-3776
Ph: (415)591-5400
Fax: (415)591-5401
Co. E-mail: burrill@b-c.com
URL: http://www.burrillandco.com
Contact: Ann F. Hanham, Managing Director
Preferred Investment Size: $5,000,000 to $15,000,000. **Industry Preferences:** Biotechnology, medical and health, Internet specific, computer software and services, and consumer related. **Geographic Preference:** U.S. and Canada.

49186 ■ BV Capital / Bertelsmann Ventures, LP (San Francisco)
600 Montgomery St., 43rd Fl.
San Francisco, CA 94111
Ph: (415)869-5200
Fax: (415)869-5200
Co. E-mail: info@bvcapital.biz
URL: http://www.bvcapital.com
Contact: Jan Henric Buettner, Partner
E-mail: jan@bvcapital.com
Preferred Investment Size: $1,000,000 to $5,000,000. **Industry Preferences:** Communications and media, computer software and services, and Internet specific. **Geographic Preference:** West Coast.

49187 ■ California Technology Ventures, LLC
670 N. Rosemead Blvd., Ste. 201
Pasadena, CA 91107
Ph: (626)351-3700
Fax: (626)351-3702
Co. E-mail: info@ctventures.com
URL: http://www.ctventures.com
Contact: Alexander B. Suh, Managing Director
E-mail: asuh@CTVentures.com
Preferred Investment Size: $250,000 to $2,000,000. **Investment Policies:** Early, first, second and later stage. **Industry Preferences:** Communications, computer software and hardware, Internet specific, semiconductors and other electronics, biotechnology, medical and health, and industrial and energy. **Geographic Preference:** California, Northern California, and Southern California.

49188 ■ The Cambria Group
2055 Woodside Rd., Ste. 195
Redwood City, CA 94061
Ph: (650)241-6400
Fax: (650)241-6401
URL: http://www.cambriagroup.com
Contact: Christopher Sekula, Principal
Preferred Investment Size: $5,000,000 to $25,000,000. **Industry Preferences:** Communications and media, semiconductors and other electronics, medical and health, consumer related, industrial and energy, transportation, business service, manufacturing, agriculture, forestry and fishing. **Geographic Preference:** U.S.

49189 ■ Cambrian Ventures, Inc.
444 Castro St., Ste. 109
Mountain View, CA 94041
Ph: (650)938-5900
Fax: (650)938-5959
Co. E-mail: info@cambrianventures.com
URL: http://www.cambrianventures.com
Contact: Anand Rajaraman, Founder
Industry Preferences: Internet specific. **Geographic Preference:** U.S.

49190 ■ CampVentures
280 2nd St., Ste. 280
Los Altos, CA 94022
Ph: (650)949-0804
Fax: (650)618-1719
URL: http://www.campventures.com
Contact: Jerome Camp, Partner
E-mail: jerry@campventures.com
Preferred Investment Size: $500,000 to $1,500,000. **Investment Policies:** Seed and early stage. **Industry Preferences:** Communications and media, computer software, and semiconductors and other electronics. **Geographic Preference:** California.

49191 ■ Canaan Partners (Menlo Park)
2765 Sand Hill Rd., Ste. 115
Menlo Park, CA 94025-7019
Ph: (650)854-8092
Fax: (650)854-8127
URL: http://www.canaan.com
Contact: Mark Biestman, Chief Executive Officer
Founded: 1987. **Preferred Investment Size:** $3,000,000 to $25,000,000. **Industry Preferences:** Internet specific, computer software and services, computer hardware, medical and health, communications and media, biotechnology, semiconductors and other electronics, consumer related, and industrial and energy. **Geographic Preference:** Northeast, West Coast, and U.S.

49192 ■ Charter Life Sciences
2031 Mission College Blvd., Ste. 210
Santa Clara, CA 94054
Ph: (408)758-4700
Fax: (408)758-4848
URL: http://www.charterls.com
Contact: Andrew K. Klatt, Chief Financial Officer
Preferred Investment Size: $1,000,000 to $5,000,000. **Investment Policies:** Early stage. **Industry Preferences:** Biotechnology, and medical and health. **Geographic Preference:** Midwest and West Coast.

49193 ■ Charter Venture Capital / Charter Ventures
525 University Ave., Ste. 1400
Palo Alto, CA 94301
Ph: (650)325-6953
Fax: (650)325-4762
URL: http://www.charterventures.com
Contact: Bob Kondamoori, Partner
Preferred Investment Size: $500,000 to $10,000,000. **Investment Policies:** Early stage. **Industry Preferences:** Internet specific, biotechnology, medical and health, computer software and services, communications and media, computer hardware, semiconductors and other electronics, other products, and other products. **Geographic Preference:** U.S.

49194 ■ Clearstone Venture Partners / Idealab! Capital Partners
1351 4th St., 4th Fl.
Santa Monica, CA 90401
Ph: (310)460-7900
Fax: (310)460-7901
Co. E-mail: info@clearstone.com
URL: http://www.clearstone.com
Contact: Erik Lassila, Managing Director
Preferred Investment Size: $2,000,000 to $10,000,000. **Industry Preferences:** Internet specific, computer software and services, computer hardware, communications and media, industrial and energy, semiconductors and other electronics, and other products. **Geographic Preference:** Northern and Southern California, California, and West Coast.

49195 ■ CMEA Capital / Chemicals & Materials Enterprise Association
1750 Montgomery St.
San Francisco, CA 94111
Ph: (415)352-1520
Fax: (415)352-1524
URL: http://www.cmeaventures.com
Contact: Thomas R. Baruch, Founder
E-mail: tom@cmeaventures.com
Preferred Investment Size: $250,000 to $10,000,000. **Industry Preferences:** Medical and health, biotechnology, communications and media, computer software and services, semiconductors and other electronics, Internet specific, industrial and energy, computer hardware, other products. **Geographic Preference:** Northwest and West Coast.

49196 ■ Compass Technology Partners, L.P.
261 Hamilton Ave., Ste. 200
Palo Alto, CA 94301
Ph: (650)322-7595
Fax: (650)322-0588
URL: http://www.compasstechpartners.com
Contact: David G. Arscott, Partner
Preferred Investment Size: $250,000 to $1,250,000. **Industry Preferences:** Internet specific, medical and health, communications and media, semiconductors and other electronics, computer software and services. **Geographic Preference:** California and U.S.

49197 ■ Convergence Partners
800 W. El Camino Real, Ste. 180
Mountain View, CA 94040
Ph: (650)854-3010
Fax: (650)462-8415
Co. E-mail: info@convergencepartners.com
URL: http://www.convergencepartners.com
Contact: Eric DiBenedetto, Founder
Preferred Investment Size: $2,000,000 to $10,000,000. **Industry Preferences:** Internet specific, computer software and services, semiconductors and other electronics, computer hardware, other products, industrial and energy, communications and media. **Geographic Preference:** U.S.

49198 ■ Crocker Capital
1 Post St., Ste. 2515
San Francisco, CA 94104
Ph: (415)956-5250
Fax: (415)956-5710
Co. E-mail: info@crocker-capital.com
URL: http://www.crocker-capital.com
Contact: Charles Crocker, Chairman
Industry Preferences: Communications and media, semiconductors and other electronics, medical and health, consumer related, industrial and energy, manufacturing, and environment. **Geographic Preference:** West Coast.

49199 ■ Crosslink Capital
Two Embarcadero Ctr., Ste. 2200
San Francisco, CA 94111
Ph: (415)617-1800
Fax: (415)617-1801
Co. E-mail: ewinterhalter@crosslinkcapital.com
URL: http://www.crosslinkcapital.com
Contact: Peter Van Camp, Chief Executive Officer
Scope: An independent venture capital and investment firm. Firm focuses on strategic business and technology questions as well as to discuss tactical approaches to addressing these challenges. **Founded:** 1989. **Preferred Investment Size:** $8,000,000 to $20,000,000. **Industry Preferences:** Internet specific, computer software and services, semiconductors and other electronics, communications and media, biotechnology, computer hardware, other products, consumer related, medical and health, industrial and energy. **Geographic Preference:** California and U.S. **Telecommunication Services:** info@crosslinkcapital.com.

49200 ■ De Novo Ventures
2180 Sand Hill Rd.
Menlo Park, CA 94025-6929
Ph: (650)329-1999

Fax: (650)329-1315
Co. E-mail: andrea@denovovc.com
URL: http://www.denovovc.com
Contact: Frederick J. Dotzler, President
Founded: 2000. **Preferred Investment Size:** $1,000,000 to $3,000,000. **Investment Policies:** Start-up, seed, first and early stage, and expansion. **Industry Preferences:** Internet specific, biotechnology, and medical and health. **Geographic Preference:** Northwest, Rocky Mountains, Southwest, and West Coast.

49201 ■ Defta Partners
111 Pine St., Ste. 1410
San Francisco, CA 94111-5619
Ph: (415)433-2262
Fax: (415)433-2264
URL: http://www.deftapartners.com
Contact: George Hara, Chief Executive Officer
URL(s): www.defta-partners.com. **Preferred Investment Size:** $500,000 to $3,000,000. **Investment Policies:** Start-up, seed, and early stage. **Industry Preferences:** computer software and services, semiconductors and other electronics, Internet specific, communications and media, medical and health, and computer hardware. **Geographic Preference:** National.

49202 ■ Delphi Ventures
3000 Sand Hill Rd.
Bldg. 1, Ste. 135
Menlo Park, CA 94025
Ph: (650)854-9650
Fax: (650)854-2961
URL: http://www.delphiventures.com
Contact: David L. Douglass, Partner
Preferred Investment Size: $500,000 to $12,000,000. **Industry Preferences:** Medical and health, and biotechnology. **Geographic Preference:** U.S.

49203 ■ DFJ Frontier
800 Anacapa St., Ste. A
Santa Barbara, CA 93101
Ph: (805)963-2277
Co. E-mail: businessplan@dfjfrontier.com
URL: http://www.dfjfrontier.com
Contact: David Cremin, Managing Director
E-mail: david@dfjfrontier.com
Preferred Investment Size: $100,000 to $1,000,000. **Investment Policies:** Seed and early stage. **Industry Preferences:** Communications and media, computer software, Internet specific, semiconductors and other electronics, biotechnology, consumer related, industrial and energy, financial services, agriculture, forestry and fishing. **Geographic Preference:** California.

49204 ■ Diamondhead Ventures, L.P.
c/o Onset Ventures
2400 Sand Hill Rd.
Menlo Park, CA 94025
Ph: (650)529-0700
Fax: (650)529-0777
URL: http://www.dhven.com
Contact: Raman Khanna, Founder
Preferred Investment Size: $500,000 to $5,000,000. **Industry Preferences:** Communications and media, computer software, Internet specific, semiconductors and other electronics. **Geographic Preference:** Northern California and West Coast.

49205 ■ Doll Capital Management
2420 Sand Hill Rd., Ste. 200
Menlo Park, CA 94025
Ph: (650)233-1400
Fax: (650)854-9159
URL: http://www.dcmvc.com
Contact: Ruby Lu, Principal
E-mail: rlu@dcm.com
Preferred Investment Size: $3,000,000 to $15,000,000. **Industry Preferences:** Internet specific, computer software and services, communications and media, semiconductors and other electronics, computer hardware, other products, and consumer related. **Geographic Preference:** Midwestern states of Minnesota, Ohio, Iowa, Wisconsin, Michigan, Indiana, Illinois, and Missouri.

49206 ■ Dominion Ventures, Inc.
1646 N. California Blvd., Ste. 230
Walnut Creek, CA 94596
Ph: (925)280-6300
Fax: (925)280-6338
Co. E-mail: info@dominion.com
URL: http://www.dominion.com
Contact: Brian Smith, Partner
E-mail: bsmith@dominion.com
Preferred Investment Size: $2,000,000 to $4,000,000. **Industry Preferences:** Internet specific, computer software and services, computer hardware, other products, medical and health, semiconductors and other electronics, communications and media, consumer related, biotechnology, industrial and energy. **Geographic Preference:** U.S.

49207 ■ Dorset Capital
343 Sansome St., Ste. 1210
San Francisco, CA 94104
Ph: (415)398-7101
Fax: (415)398-7141
URL: http://www.dorsetcapital.com
Contact: John Berg, Managing Partner
Preferred Investment Size: $5,000,000 to $30,000,000. **Industry Preferences:** Consumer related, financial services, business service, and manufacturing. **Geographic Preference:** U.S.

49208 ■ Dot Edu Ventures
514 Bryant St., Ste. 101
Palo Alto, CA 94301
Ph: (650)321-3804
Fax: (650)321-3808
Co. E-mail: priya@doteduventures.com
URL: http://www.doteduventures.com
Contact: Asha Jadeja, Founder
Industry Preferences: Internet specific. **Geographic Preference:** U.S.

49209 ■ Draper, Fisher, Jurvetson / Draper Associates
2882 Sand Hill Rd., Ste. 150
Menlo Park, CA 94025
Ph: (650)233-9000
Fax: (650)233-9233
Co. E-mail: mail@dfj.com
URL: http://www.dfj.com
Contact: Jennifer Fonstad, Managing Director
Preferred Investment Size: $500,000 to $20,000,000. **Industry Preferences:** Computer software and services, communications and media, semiconductors and other electronics, industrial and energy, consumer related, medical and health, Internet specific, computer hardware, other products, and biotechnology. **Geographic Preference:** Northeast U.S. and Canada.

49210 ■ Draper International
50 California St., Ste. 2925
San Francisco, CA 94111-4779
Ph: (415)616-4050
Fax: (415)616-4060
URL: http://www.draperintl.com
Contact: William Draper, Managing Director
Preferred Investment Size: $250,000 to $1,000,000. **Industry Preferences:** Internet specific, computer hardware, computer software and services, consumer related, communications and media. **Geographic Preference:** Mid Atlantic, Northeast, Northwest, Southeast and West Coast.

49211 ■ Draper Richards L.P.
50 California St., Ste. 2925
San Francisco, CA 94111
Ph: (415)616-4050
Fax: (415)616-4060
URL: http://www.draperrichards.com
Contact: William H. Draper, III, Partner
E-mail: bill@draperrichards.com
Industry Preferences: Internet specific, computer software and services, communications and media, consumer related, semiconductors and other electronics, biotechnology, and other products. **Geographic Preference:** Mid Atlantic, Northeast, Northern California, and West Coast.

49212 ■ DynaFund Ventures
21515 Hawthorne Blvd., Ste. 700
Torrance, CA 90503
Ph: (310)543-5477
Fax: (310)543-8733
Co. E-mail: cgray@dynafundventures.com
URL: http://www.dynafundventures.com
Contact: Tony Hung, Partner
Preferred Investment Size: $1,000,000 to $5,000,000. **Industry Preferences:** Semiconductors and other electronics, communications and media, Internet specific, computer software and services, computer hardware, and biotechnology. **Geographic Preference:** U.S.

49213 ■ E
1000 Wilshire Blvd., Ste. 830
Los Angeles, CA 90017
Ph: (213)688-8080
Fax: (213)688-8095
URL: http://www.e-cap.com
Contact: Eric Wedbush, Managing Director
Preferred Investment Size: $2,000,000 to $10,000,000. **Industry Preferences:** Business and financial services, consumer products and services, and niche manufacturing. **Geographic Preference:** Western U.S.

49214 ■ Ecompanies
2120 Colorado Ave., 3rd Fl.
Santa Monica, CA 90404
Ph: (310)586-4000
Fax: (310)586-4425
URL: http://www.ecompanies.com
Contact: Steve Ledger, Partner
Industry Preferences: Internet specific, computer software and services, industrial and energy, and other products.

49215 ■ El Dorado Ventures
2440 Sand Hill Rd., Ste. 200
Menlo Park, CA 94025
Ph: (650)854-1200
Fax: (650)854-1202
Co. E-mail: bizplans@eldorado.com
URL: http://www.eldoradoventures.com
Contact: Ray Schuder, Principal
Preferred Investment Size: $250,000 to $1,000,000. **Industry Preferences:** Internet specific, computer software and services, computer hardware, communications and media, semiconductors and other electronics, medical and health, other products, consumer related, and biotechnology. **Geographic Preference:** West Coast.

49216 ■ Electronics for Imaging / EFI
303 Velocity Way
Foster City, CA 94404
Ph: (650)357-3500
Fax: (650)357-3907
URL: http://www.efi.com
Contact: Guy Gecht, Chief Executive Officer

49217 ■ Emergence Capital Partners, L.L.C.
160 Bovet Rd., Ste. 300
San Mateo, CA 94402
Ph: (650)573-3100
Fax: (650)573-3119
Co. E-mail: info@emcap.com
URL: http://www.emergencecap.com
Contact: Kevin Spain, Principal
Preferred Investment Size: $1,000,000 to $10,000,000. **Investment Policies:** Start-up, seed, early stage, and expansion. **Industry Preferences:** Computer software, Internet specific, consumer related, financial services, and business service. **Geographic Preference:** U.S.

49218 ■ Enterprise Partners Venture Capital / EPVC
2223 Avenida de la Playa, Ste. 300
La Jolla, CA 92037-3218
Ph: (858)731-0300
Fax: (858)731-0235
URL: http://www.epvc.com
Contact: Bob Conn, Managing Director
Preferred Investment Size: $3,000,000 to $10,000,000. **Industry Preferences:** Communications and media, computer software and services, In-

ternet specific, computer hardware, other products, medical and health, biotechnology, semiconductors and other electronics, consumer related, industrial and energy. **Geographic Preference:** Southern California and Southwest.

49219 ■ Falcon Fund
100 N. Barranca St., Ste., 920
West Covina, CA 91791
Ph: (626)966-6235
Fax: (626)966-0193
URL: http://www.falconfund.com
Contact: Edward Tuck, Principal
Investment Policies: Seed and early stage. **Industry Preferences:** Communications, computer software, and transportation.

49220 ■ Far East Capital Corp.
2 California Plz.
350 S. Grand Ave., Lobby Level
Los Angeles, CA 90071
Ph: (213)687-1260
Fax: (213)626-3884
Co. E-mail: free@fareastnationalbank.com
URL: http://www.fareastnationalbank.com
Contact: Fredrick C. Copeland, Chairman
Preferred Investment Size: $100,000 to $300,000. **Industry Preferences:** Communications and media, computer software and hardware, Internet specific, semiconductors and other electronics, medical and health. **Geographic Preference:** West coast.

49221 ■ Finaventures
3340 Ocean Park Blvd., Ste. 1050
Santa Monica, CA 90405
Ph: (310)399-5011
Fax: (310)452-5492
Co. E-mail: contact@finaventures.com
URL: http://www.finaventures.com
Contact: Rachid Sefrioui, Managing Director
Preferred Investment Size: $500,000 to $3,000,000. **Investment Policies:** Early, first, and second stage, balanced, and expansion. **Industry Preferences:** Communications, computer software, and semiconductors and other electronics. **Geographic Preference:** Northern and Southern California.

49222 ■ Flywheel Ventures
341 E. Alameda St.
Santa Fe, NM 87501-2229
Ph: (800)750-7870
Fax: (800)750-7870
URL: http://www.flywheelventures.com
Contact: Trevor R. Loy, Partner
E-mail: trevor@flywheelventures.com
Preferred Investment Size: $100,000 to $1,000,000. **Investment Policies:** Seed and early stage. **Industry Preferences:** Communications, computer software, and semiconductors and other electronics. **Geographic Preference:** New Mexico, Rocky Mountains, and West Coast.

49223 ■ Forrest Binkley and Brown
19800 MacArthur Blvd. Ste. 690
Irvine, CA 92612-2491
Ph: (949)222-1987
Fax: (949)222-1988
Co. E-mail: fbb@fbbvc.com
URL: http://www.fbbvc.com
Contact: Ashish Kaul, Principal
Founded: 1993. **Investment Policies:** $2,000,000 to $4,000,000. **Industry Preferences:** Computer software and services, Internet specific, semiconductors and other electronics, biotechnology, communications and media, other products, computer hardware, medical and health, and consumer related. **Geographic Preference:** California.

49224 ■ Forward Ventures
9393 Towne Centre Dr., Ste. 200
San Diego, CA 92121
Ph: (858)677-6077

Fax: (858)452-8799
Co. E-mail: info@forwardventures.com
URL: http://www.forwardventure.com
Contact: Ivor Royston, Founder
Preferred Investment Size: $1,000,000 to $6,000,000. **Industry Preferences:** Biotechnology, medical and health, and Internet specific. **Geographic Preference:** U.S. and Canada.

49225 ■ Foundation Capital
250 Middlefield Rd.
Menlo Park, CA 94025
Ph: (650)614-0500
Fax: (650)614-0505
Co. E-mail: info@foundationcapital.com
URL: http://www.foundationcapital.com
Contact: Adam Grosser, Partner
E-mail: agrosser@foundationcapital.com
Preferred Investment Size: $1,000,000 to $10,000,000. **Industry Preferences:** Internet specific, communications and media, computer software and services, computer hardware, semiconductors and other electronics, industrial and energy, other products, industrial and energy, medical and health, and consumer related. **Geographic Preference:** West Coast.

49226 ■ Gabriel Venture Partners
350 Marine Pky., Ste. 200
Redwood Shores, CA 94065
Ph: (650)551-5000
Fax: (650)551-5001
Co. E-mail: info@GabrielVP.com
URL: http://www.gabrielvp.com
Contact: Rick Bolander, Managing Director
Preferred Investment Size: $500,000 to $10,000,000. **Industry Preferences:** Internet specific, computer software and services, communications and media, computer hardware, semiconductors and other electronics, medical and health. **Geographic Preference:** California, Mid Atlantic, Northeast, Northern California, and West Coast.

49227 ■ Garage Technology Ventures / Garage.com
502 Waverly St., Ste. 300
Palo Alto, CA 94301
Ph: (650)838-0811
Fax: (650)838-0813
URL: http://www.garage.com
Contact: Bill Reichert, Managing Director
E-mail: reichert@garage.com
Preferred Investment Size: $500,000 to $3,000,000. **Investment Policies:** Seed, early, first and second stage. **Industry Preferences:** Communications, computer software, Internet specific, and semiconductors and other electronics. **Geographic Preference:** California and West Coast.

49228 ■ Glynn Capital Management
3000 Sand Hill Rd.
Bldg. 4, Ste. 230
Menlo Park, CA 94025
Ph: (650)854-2215
Fax: (650)854-8083
URL: http://www.glynncapital.com
Contact: Steven J. Rosston, Managing Director
Preferred Investment Size: $300,000 to 500,000. **Industry Preferences:** Internet specific, communications and media, medical and health, computer software and services. **Geographic Preference:** Northeast, Northwest, Southeast and West Coast.

49229 ■ Greylock Partners (San Mateo)
2550 Sand Hill Rd., Ste. 200
San Mateo, CA 94025
Ph: (650)493-5525
Fax: (650)493-5575
URL: http://www.greylock.com
Contact: Isaac Fehrenbach, Principal
E-mail: isaac@greylock.com
Preferred Investment Size: $250,000 minimum. **Industry Preferences:** Internet specific, computer hardware, computer software and services, communications and media, semiconductors and other electronics, consumer related, and other products. **Geographic Preference:** U.S.

49230 ■ GRP Partners / Global Retail Partners
2121 Avenue of the Stars, Ste. 1630
Los Angeles, CA 90067
Ph: (310)785-5100
Fax: (310)785-5111
Co. E-mail: la@grpvc.com
URL: http://www.grpvc.com
Contact: Steven Dietz, Managing Partner
Preferred Investment Size: $3,000,000 to $25,000,000. **Industry Preferences:** Internet specific, consumer related, business and financial services, computer hardware, computer software and services, communications and media, and other products. **Geographic Preference:** U.S.

49231 ■ Hallador Venture Partners
PO Box 15299
Sacramento, CA 95851
Ph: (916)920-5187
Fax: (916)920-5188
URL: http://www.hallador.com
Contact: Chris L. Branscum, Managing Director
E-mail: chris@shallador.com
Preferred Investment Size: $500,000 to $1,000,000. **Industry Preferences:** Communications and media, computer software, Internet specific, semiconductors and other electronics. **Geographic Preference:** West Coast.

49232 ■ Hamilton Bioventures / Hamilton Apex Technology Ventures
990 Highland Dr., Ste. 314
Solana Beach, CA 92075
Ph: (858)314-2350
Fax: (858)314-2355
Co. E-mail: info@HamiltonBioVenturers.com
URL: http://www.hamiltonbioventures.com
Contact: Richard J. Crosby, Managing Director
E-mail: Richard@hamiltonbioventures.com
Preferred Investment Size: $1,000,000 to $5,000,000. **Investment Policies:** Early, first, second and later stage. **Industry Preferences:** Biotechnology, and medical and health. **Geographic Preference:** Southern California.

49233 ■ Headland Ventures, LP / Sterling Payot Capital
65 Cloudview Rd.
Sausalito, CA 94965
Ph: (415)289-2590
Fax: (415)289-2591
URL: http://www.headlandventures.com
Contact: Larry Stites, Chief Financial Officer
Investment Policies: Early stage. **Industry Preferences:** Computer software, Internet specific, and consumer related. **Geographic Preference:** U.S.

49234 ■ Hewlett Packard / Compaq Computer Corporation
3000 Hanover St.
Palo Alto, CA 94304-1185
Ph: (650)857-1501
Fax: (650)857-5518
URL: http://www.hp.com
Contact: Michael Duggan, Managing Director
Investment Policies: Early stage. **Industry Preferences:** Biotechnology. **Geographic Preference:** National.

49235 ■ HighBAR Ventures
3150 Porter Dr.
Palo Alto, CA 94304
Co. E-mail: info@highbarventures.com
URL: http://www.highbarventures.com
Contact: Roy Thiele-Sardina, Managing Partner
Investment Policies: Seed and early stage. **Industry Preferences:** Technology.

49236 ■ Horizon Ventures
4 Main St., Ste. 50
Los Altos, CA 94022
Ph: (650)917-4100

Fax: (650)917-4109
URL: http://www.horizonvc.com
Contact: Doug Tsui, Managing Director
E-mail: doug@horizonvc.com
Preferred Investment Size: $500,000 to $3,500,000. **Industry Preferences:** Internet specific, computer hardware, computer software and services, semiconductors and other electronics, medical and health, communications and media, and other products. **Geographic Preference:** West Coast.

49237 ■ iD Ventures America, LLC
5201 Great America Pky., Ste. 270
Santa Clara, CA 95054
Ph: (408)894-7900
Fax: (408)894-7939
Co. E-mail: info@idsoftcapital.com
URL: http://www.acervc.com
Contact: James C. Lu, Managing Director
Preferred Investment Size: $500,000 to $3,000,000. **Investment Policies:** Start-up, seed, first and second stage. **Industry Preferences:** Communications and media, computer software and hardware, Internet specific, semiconductors and other electronics, consumer related, and financial services. **Geographic Preference:** U.S. and Canada.

49238 ■ Idanta Partners, Ltd. (San Diego)
9255 Towne Centre Dr., Ste. 925
San Diego, CA 92121
Ph: (858)452-9690
Fax: (858)452-2013
URL: http://www.idanta.com
Contact: David Dunn, Managing Partner
Preferred Investment Size: $1,000,000 to $10,000,000. **Industry Preferences:** Semiconductors and other electronics, communications and media, computer software and services, Internet specific, computer hardware, consumer related, medical and health, and other products. **Geographic Preference:** U.S.

49239 ■ Idealab!
130 W. Union St.
Pasadena, CA 91103
Ph: (626)585-6900
Fax: (626)535-2701
Co. E-mail: info@idealab.com
URL: http://www.idealab.com
Contact: Douglas McPherson, Managing Director
Investment Policies: Start-up and early stage. **Industry Preferences:** Internet specific.

49240 ■ IDG Ventures (San Francisco)
1 Letterman Dr.
Bldg. D, Ste. 100
San Francisco, CA 94129
Ph: (415)439-4420
Fax: (415)439-4428
Co. E-mail: Plans_sf@idgventures.com
URL: http://www.idgventures.com
Contact: Pat Kenealy, Managing Director
Preferred Investment Size: 1,000,000 to $5,000,000. **Industry Preferences:** Internet specific, computer software and services, computer hardware, communications and media, medical and health, semiconductors and other electronics, biotechnology, consumer related, and other products. **Geographic Preference:** U.S.

49241 ■ The Ignite Group / Ignite Associates, LLC
255 Shoreline Dr., Ste. 510
Redwood City, CA 94065
Ph: (650)622-2000
Fax: (650)622-2015
Co. E-mail: info@ignitegroup.com
URL: http://www.ignitegroup.com
Contact: Nobuo Mii, Managing Partner
E-mail: nmii@ignitegroup.com
Preferred Investment Size: $2,000,000 to $10,000,000. **Industry Preferences:** Internet specific, communications and media, computer software and services, computer hardware, semiconductors and other electronics, medical and health. **Geographic Preference:** Northern and Southern California.

STATE LISTINGS

49242 ■ Infinity Capital, L.L.C.
480 Cowper St., Ste. 200
Palo Alto, CA 94301
Ph: (650)462-8400
Fax: (650)462-8415
URL: http://www.infinityllc.com
Contact: Bruce Graham, Managing Director
E-mail: bruce@infinityllc.com
Preferred Investment Size: $275,000 to $10,000,000. **Industry Preferences:** Internet specific, communications and media, computer hardware, medical and health, other products, computer software and services, semiconductors and other electronics. **Geographic Preference:** U.S.

49243 ■ Information Technology Ventures
100 Hamilton Ave., Ste. 400
Palo Alto, CA 94301
Ph: (650)462-8400
Fax: (650)462-8415
URL: http://www.itventures.com
Contact: George Kitagawa, Chief Financial Officer
Industry Preferences: Internet specific, computer software and services, communications and media, semiconductors and other electronics, computer hardware, industrial and energy, and other products. **Geographic Preference:** Northeast, Northwest, and West Coast.

49244 ■ Inglewood Ventures
12526 High Bluff Dr., Ste. 300
San Diego, CA 92130
Ph: (858)792-3579
Fax: (858)792-3417
Co. E-mail: info@inglewoodventures.com
URL: http://www.inglewoodventures.com
Contact: M. Blake Ingle, Principal
E-mail: blake@inglewoodventures.com
Preferred Investment Size: $500,000 to $1,500,000. **Industry Preferences:** Biotechnology, medical and health. **Geographic Preference:** Northern and Southern California, and West Coast.

49245 ■ Innocal Venture Capital
Center Tower, Ste. 770
650 Town Center Dr.
Costa Mesa, CA 92626
Ph: (714)850-6784
Fax: (714)850-6798
URL: http://www.innocal.com
Contact: Harry Lambert, Managing Director
E-mail: hlambert@innocal.com
Preferred Investment Size: $1,000,000 to $5,000,000. **Industry Preferences:** Computer software and services, Internet specific, medical and health, communications and media, industrial and energy, semiconductors and other electronics, and biotechnology. **Geographic Preference:** Northern and Southern California, and the West Coast.

49246 ■ Institutional Venture Partners
3000 Sand Hill Rd.
Bldg. 2, Ste. 250
Menlo Park, CA 94025
Ph: (650)854-0132
Fax: (650)854-2009
URL: http://www.ivp.com
Contact: Dennis Phelps, Partner
Preferred Investment Size: $10,000,000 to $100,000,000. **Industry Preferences:** Internet specific, communications and media, computer hardware, computer software and services, semiconductors and other electronics, consumer related, and other products. **Geographic Preference:** U.S.

49247 ■ Interwest Partners (Menlo Park)
2710 Sand Hill Rd., 2nd Fl.
Menlo Park, CA 94025
Ph: (650)854-8585
Fax: (650)854-4706
Co. E-mail: info@interwest.com
URL: http://www.interwest.com
Contact: Doug Pepper, Principal
Preferred Investment Size: $10,000,000 to $15,000,000. **Industry Preferences:** Medical and health, Internet specific, consumer related, biotechnology, communications and media, computer hard-

ware, computer software and services, semiconductors and other electronics, industrial and energy, and other products. **Geographic Preference:** U.S.

49248 ■ Invencor, Inc.
PO Box 7355
Menlo Park, CA 94026
Ph: (650)330-1210
Fax: (650)330-1222
Co. E-mail: plans@invencor.com
URL: http://www.invencor.com
Contact: Debra R. Guerin, Principal
E-mail: debra@invencor.com
Preferred Investment Size: $300,000 to $2,000,000. **Geographic Preference:** Primarily in Arizona, California, Hawaii, New Mexico, and Utah.

49249 ■ Jafco Ventures
505 Hamilton Ave., Ste. 310
Palto Alto, CA 94301
Ph: (650)463-8800
Fax: (650)463-8801
Co. E-mail: info@jafco.com
URL: http://www.jafco.com
Contact: Joseph Horowitz, Partner
E-mail: joe@jafco.com
Preferred Investment Size: $4,000,000 to $8,000,000. **Industry Preferences:** Communications and media, computer software and services, and semiconductors and other electronics. **Geographic Preference:** U.S.

49250 ■ Kaiser Permanente Ventures
1 Kaiser Plz., 22nd Fl.
Oakland, CA 94612
Ph: (510)267-7300
Fax: (510)891-7943
URL: http://www.kpventures.com
Contact: Chris Grant, Managing Director
E-mail: chris.m.grant@kp.org
Preferred Investment Size: $500,000 to $2,000,000. **Industry Preferences:** Biotechnology, and medical and health. **Geographic Preference:** Canada.

49251 ■ Kleiner Perkins Caufield & Byers (Menlo Park)
2750 Sand Hill Rd.
Menlo Park, CA 94025
Ph: (650)233-2750
Fax: (650)233-0300
Co. E-mail: plans@kpcb.com
URL: http://www.kpcb.com
Contact: John Denniston, Partner
E-mail: johnde@kpcb.com
Preferred Investment Size: $500,000 minimum. **Industry Preferences:** Internet specific, computer software and services, computer hardware, communications and media, semiconductors and other electronics, medical and health, biotechnology, industrial and energy, consumer related, and other products. **Geographic Preference:** West Coast.

49252 ■ Kline Hawkes & Co.
11726 San Vicente Blvd., Ste. 300
Los Angeles, CA 90049
Ph: (310)442-4700
Fax: (310)442-4707
Co. E-mail: cwood@klinehawkes.com
URL: http://www.klinehawkes.com
Contact: Jay Ferguson, Principal
E-mail: jferg@klinehawkes.com
Preferred Investment Size: $5,000,000 to $10,000,000. **Industry Preferences:** Communications and media, Internet specific, semiconductors and other electronics, Business services, computer software, and services, computer hardware, industrial and energy, and other products. **Geographic Preference:** Northwest, Southwest, and West Coast.

49253 ■ KLM Capital Group
19925 Stevens Creek Blvd., Ste. 100
Cupertino, CA 95014
Ph: (408)970-8888

Fax: (408)970-8885
Co. E-mail: info@klmcapital.com
URL: http://www.klmtech.com
Contact: Peter Mok, Partner
E-mail: petermok@klmcapital.com
Preferred Investment Size: $500,000 to $5,000,000. **Industry Preferences:** Semiconductors and other electronics, Internet specific, computer software and services, communications and media, and consumer related. **Geographic Preference:** U.S.

49254 ■ KTB Ventures / KTB Venture Capital
203 Redwood Shores Pky., Ste. 610
Redwood City, CA 94065
Ph: (650)324-4681
Fax: (650)324-4682
Co. E-mail: info@ktbvc.com
URL: http://www.ktbvc.com
Contact: Sung Y. Yoon, Managing Partner
Preferred Investment Size: $500,000 to $5,000,000. **Industry Preferences:** Internet specific, semiconductors and other electronics, communications and media, computer software and services, computer hardware, and consumer and business service. **Geographic Preference:** U.S.

49255 ■ Kyocera International, Inc.
Corporate Development
8611 Balboa Ave.
San Diego, CA 92123
Ph: (858)576-2600
Fax: (858)492-1456
URL: http://global.kyocera.com
Contact: Makoto Kawamura, President
Preferred Investment Size: $300,000 to $500,000. **Industry Preferences:** Communications and media, computer related, semiconductors and other electronics, biotechnology, medical and health, consumer related, industrial and energy, business service, agriculture, forestry and fishing. **Geographic Preference:** West Coast.

49256 ■ Labrador Ventures
101 University Ave., 4th Fl.
Palo Alto, CA 94301
Ph: (650)366-6000
Fax: (650)366-6430
Co. E-mail: businessplans@labrador.com
URL: http://www.labrador.com
Contact: Larry Kubal, Partner
Preferred Investment Size: $1,000,000 to $6,000,000. **Investment Policies:** Start-up, seed, early and first stage. **Industry Preferences:** Communications, computer software, and semiconductors and other electronics. **Geographic Preference:** Northern California and West Coast.

49257 ■ Latterell Venture Partners
1 Embarcadero Centre, Ste. 4050
San Francisco, CA 94111-4106
Ph: (415)399-9880
Fax: (415)399-9879
Co. E-mail: support@LVPcapital.com
URL: http://www.lvpcapital.com
Contact: Patrick Latterell, Managing Director
E-mail: pat@lvpcapital.com
Preferred Investment Size: $50,000 to $10,000,000. **Investment Policies:** Early stage and balanced. **Industry Preferences:** Biotechnology, and medical and health. **Geographic Preference:** U.S.

49258 ■ Lawrence Financial Group
13320 Westcove Dr.
Box 491773
Los Angeles, CA 90049-2520
Ph: (310)230-1188
Fax: (310)943-2232
Co. E-mail: info@lawrencefinancial.com
URL: http://www.lawrencefinancial.com
Contact: Lawrence Hurwitz, President
E-mail: LNHurwitz@LawrenceFinancial.com
Preferred Investment Size: $500,000 to $1,000,000. **Industry Preferences:** Communications and media, computer related, semiconductors and other electronics, biotechnology, medical and health, consumer related, industrial and energy, financial services, business service, agriculture, forestry and fishing. **Geographic Preference:** West Coast.

49259 ■ Leapfrog Ventures
Ph: (650)926-9900
Fax: (650)233-1301
Co. E-mail: plans@leapfrogventures.com
URL: http://www.leapfrogventures.com
Contact: Pete Sinclair, Managing Director
E-mail: pete@leapfrogventures.com
Preferred Investment Size: $1,000,000 to $3,000,000. **Investment Policies:** Start-up, seed, early and first stage. **Industry Preferences:** Communications and media, computer software, and Internet specific. **Geographic Preference:** Northern California and West Coast.

49260 ■ Legacy Venture
180 Lytton Ave.
Palo Alto, CA 94301
Ph: (650)324-5980
Fax: (650)324-5982
Co. E-mail: info@legacyventure.com
URL: http://www.legacyventure.com
Contact: Chris A. Eyre, Managing Partner
Preferred Investment Size: $3,000,000 to $10,000,000. **Investment Policies:** Early stage, and fund of funds. **Industry Preferences:** Communications and media. **Geographic Preference:** U.S.

49261 ■ LF USA Investment, Inc.
4 Embarcadero Ctr., Ste. 3400
San Francisco, CA 94111
Ph: (415)315-7440
Co. E-mail: contact.usa@lfvc.com
URL: http://www.lfvc.com
Contact: Michael Hsieh, President
Preferred Investment Size: $1,000,000 to $10,000,000. **Industry Preferences:** Consumer related, technology, software and services. **Geographic Preference:** U.S.

49262 ■ Lighthouse Capital Partners, Inc.
500 Drake's Landing Rd., Ste. 210
Greenbrae, CA 94904-3011
Ph: (415)464-5900
Fax: (415)925-3387
Co. E-mail: info@lcpartners.com
URL: http://www.lcpartners.com
Contact: Rick Stubblefield, Founder
Preferred Investment Size: $1,000,000 to $10,000,000. **Industry Preferences:** Internet specific, computer software and services, other products, semiconductors and other electronics, communications and media. **Geographic Preference:** California and Massachusetts.

49263 ■ Lightspeed Venture Partners / Weiss, Peck and Greer
2200 Sand Hill Rd.
Menlo Park, CA 94025
Ph: (650)234-8300
Fax: (650)234-8333
Co. E-mail: info@lightspeedvp.com
URL: http://www.lightspeedvp.com
Contact: Eric O'Brien, Managing Director
E-mail: eric@lightspeedvp.com
Preferred Investment Size: $500,000 to $20,000,000. **Industry Preferences:** Communications and media, Internet specific, computer software and services, computer hardware, semiconductors and other electronics, medical and health, industrial and energy, biotechnology, consumer related, and other products. **Geographic Preference:** U.S.

49264 ■ Magic Venture Capital, LLC
335 Lowell Ave.
Palo Alto, CA 94301
Ph: (650)327-7719
URL: http://www.magicvc.com
Contact: Erin McGurk, Managing Director
Preferred Investment Size: $300,000 to $1,000,000. **Investment Policies:** Start-up, seed, and first stage. **Industry Preferences:** Medical and health. **Geographic Preference:** West Coast.

49265 ■ Manitou Ventures, LLC
460 Bush St., 2nd Fl.
San Francisco, CA 94108
Ph: (415)288-0727

Fax: (415)627-9079
Co. E-mail: info@maniven.com
URL: http://www.manitouventures.com
Contact: Chris Wadsworth, Partner
Preferred Investment Size: $500,000 to $1,500,000. **Investment Policies:** Early stage. **Industry Preferences:** Communications and media, computer hardware, semiconductors and other electronics. **Geographic Preference:** National.

49266 ■ Marwit Capital, LLC
100 Bayview Cir., Ste. 550
Newport Beach, CA 92660
Ph: (949)861-3636
Fax: (949)861-3637
Co. E-mail: info@marwit.com
URL: http://www.marwit.com
Contact: Chris Britt, President
Preferred Investment Size: $3,000,000 to $15,000,000. **Industry Preferences:** Medical and health, transportation, industrial and energy, business service, and manufacturing. **Geographic Preference:** Western U.S.

49267 ■ Maton Venture
1601 S. De Anza Blvd., Ste. 115
Cupertino, CA 95014
Ph: (408)786-5168
Fax: (408)996-0728
Co. E-mail: info@maton.com
URL: http://www.maton.com
Contact: James Chen, Managing Partner
Preferred Investment Size: $200,000 to $2,000,000. **Industry Preferences:** Communications and media, computer software and hardware, Internet specific, semiconductors and other electronics. **Geographic Preference:** Northern California.

49268 ■ Matrix Partners (Palo Alto)
260 Homer Ave., Ste. 201
Palo Alto, CA 94025
Ph: (650)798-1600
Fax: (650)798-1601
Co. E-mail: info@matrixpartners.com
URL: http://www.matrixpartners.com
Contact: Bob Lisbonne, Partner
E-mail: blisbonne@matrixpartners.com
Preferred Investment Size: $2,000,000 to $10,000,000. **Industry Preferences:** Communications and media, Internet specific, computer software and services, computer hardware, semiconductors and other electronics. **Geographic Preference:** California and Massachusetts.

49269 ■ Mayfield Fund
2800 Sand Hill Rd., Ste. 250
Menlo Park, CA 94025
Ph: (650)854-5560
Fax: (650)854-5712
Co. E-mail: info@mayfield.com
URL: http://www.mayfield.com
Contact: Rajeev Batra, Principal
E-mail: rbatra@mayfield.com
Preferred Investment Size: $1,000,000 to $3,000,000. **Industry Preferences:** Computer software and services, computer hardware, Internet specific, communications and media, semiconductors and other electronics, consumer related, industrial and energy, and other products. **Geographic Preference:** U.S.

49270 ■ McCown De Leeuw and Co.
950 Tower Ln., Ste. 800
Foster City, CA 94025-7111
Ph: (650)854-6000
Fax: (650)854-0853
URL: http://www.mdcpartners.com
Contact: George McCown, Managing Director
Preferred Investment Size: $20,000,000 to $50,000,000. **Industry Preferences:** Consumer related, computer software and services, medical and health, Internet specific, communications and media, computer hardware, semiconductors and other electronics, industrial and energy, and other products. **Geographic Preference:** U.S.

49271 ■ Media Technology Ventures
525 University Ave., Ste. 220
Palo Alto, CA 94301

Ph: (650)687-0500
Fax: (650)687-0234
Co. E-mail: vc@allegiscapital.com
URL: http://www.allegiscapital.com
Contact: Robert R. Ackerman, Founder
Preferred Investment Size: $3,000,000 to $5,000,000. **Industry Preferences:** Communications and media, Internet specific, and computer software and services, other products, computer hardware, semiconductors and other electronics. **Geographic Preference:** U.S.

49272 ■ Media Venture Partners
244 Jackson St., 4th Fl.
San Francisco, CA 94111
Ph: (415)391-4877
Fax: (415)391-4912
URL: http://www.mediaventurepartners.com
Contact: Elliot Evers, Managing Director
E-mail: eevers@mediaventurepartners.com
Preferred Investment Size: $500,000 to $1,000,000. **Industry Preferences:** Communications and media, computer software and hardware, consumer related, and manufacturing. **Geographic Preference:** U.S. and Canada.

49273 ■ Medventure Associates
5980 Horton St., Ste. 390
Emeryville, CA 94608
Ph: (510)597-7979
Fax: (510)597-9920
Co. E-mail: medven@medven.com
URL: http://www.medven.com
Contact: Annette Campbell-White, Managing Partner
E-mail: annette.cw@medven.com
Preferred Investment Size: $200,000 to $500,000. **Industry Preferences:** Medical and health, Internet specific, biotechnology, communications and media, computer software and services. **Geographic Preference:** West Coast.

49274 ■ Menlo Ventures
3000 Sand Hill Rd.
Bldg. 4, Ste. 100
Menlo Park, CA 94025
Ph: (650)854-8540
Fax: (650)854-7059
Co. E-mail: info@menloventures.com
URL: http://www.menloventures.com
Contact: H. DuBose Montgomery, Managing Director
E-mail: dubose@menloventures.com
Preferred Investment Size: $5,000,000 to $20,000,000. **Industry Preferences:** Internet specific, communications and media, computer software and services, computer hardware, medical and health, semiconductors and other electronics, biotechnology, consumer related, industrial and energy, and other products. **Geographic Preference:** U.S.

49275 ■ Millennium Hanson
4519 Admiralty Way, Ste. A
Marina del Rey, CA 90292
Ph: (310)550-1995
Fax: (310)482-6944
Co. E-mail: associates@millhanson.com
URL: http://www.millhanson.com
Contact: Jonathan Mork, Officer
Preferred Investment Size: $1,000,000. **Investment Policies:** Early stage, expansion and acquisition. **Industry Preferences:** Internet specific. **Geographic Preference:** National.

49276 ■ Mission Ventures
11455 El Camino Real, Ste. 450
San Diego, CA 92130
Ph: (858)350-2100
Fax: (858)350-2101
URL: http://www.missionventures.com
Contact: David Ryan, Managing Partner
Preferred Investment Size: $2,000,000 to $10,000,000. **Industry Preferences:** Internet specific, communications and media, computer software and services, consumer related, semiconductors and other electronics, and other products. **Geographic Preference:** Southern California.

49277 ■ Mobius Venture Capital / Softbank Venture Capital
1050 Walnut St., Ste. 210
Boulder, CO 80302
Ph: (303)642-4000
URL: http://www.mobiusvc.com
Contact: Brad Feld, Principal
Preferred Investment Size: $2,000,000 to $100,000,000. **Industry Preferences:** Internet specific, computer software and services, computer hardware, communications and media, consumer related, semiconductors and other electronics, biotechnology, industrial and energy, and other products. **Geographic Preference:** California, East and West Coast.

49278 ■ Mohr Davidow Ventures (Menlo Park)
3000 Sand Hill Rd.
Bldg. 3, Ste. 290
Menlo Park, CA 94025
Ph: (650)854-7236
Fax: (650)854-7365
Co. E-mail: info@mdv.com
URL: http://www.mdv.com
Contact: Jim Smith, Partner
E-mail: jsmith@mdv.com
Preferred Investment Size: $500,000 to $10,000,000. **Industry Preferences:** Internet specific, computer software and services, computer hardware, semiconductors and other electronics, communications and media, medical and health, consumer related, biotechnology, industrial and energy, and other products. **Geographic Preference:** Northwest, Mid Atlantic, and West Coast.

49279 ■ National Investment Management, Inc.
2601 Airport Dr., Ste. 210
Torrance, CA 90505
Ph: (310)784-7600
Co. E-mail: robins621@aol.com
URL: http://www.wallstreetdex.com
Contact: Richard Robins, President
Preferred Investment Size: $1,000,000 minimum. **Industry Preferences:** Internet specific, computer software and services, consumer related, industrial and energy, communications and media, semiconductors and other electronics, computer hardware, and other products. **Geographic Preference:** U.S.

49280 ■ NetFuel Inc.
3 1/2 N. Santa Cruz Ave., Ste. D
Los Gatos, CA 95030
Ph: (408)384-9938
Fax: (408)384-5203
URL: http://www.netfuel.com
Contact: Jim Harlow, Principal
E-mail: jim@netfuel.com
Investment Policies: Seed and start-up. **Industry Preferences:** Internet specific. **Geographic Preference:** Midwest.

49281 ■ New Enterprise Associates (Menlo Park)
2855 Sand Hill Rd.
Menlo Park, CA 94025
Ph: (650)854-9499
Fax: (650)854-9397
URL: http://www.nea.com
Contact: Mohamad Makhzoumi, Principal
E-mail: mmakhzoumi@nea.com
Preferred Investment Size: $200,000 to $20,000,000. **Industry Preferences:** Communications and media, Internet specific, medical and health, computer software and services, computer hardware, semiconductors and other electronics, biotechnology, consumer related, industrial and energy, and other products. **Geographic Preference:** U.S.

49282 ■ New Vista Capital, LLC
161 E. Evelyn Ave.
Mountain View, CA 94041
Ph: (650)864-2553

Fax: (650)864-2599
URL: http://www.nvcap.com
Contact: Frank S. Greene, Managing Partner
E-mail: fgreene@nvcap.com
Industry Preferences: Internet specific, computer software and services, computer hardware, semiconductors and other electronics, communications and media, consumer related, and other products. **Geographic Preference:** Northwest, Rocky Mountains, Southwest, and West Coast.

49283 ■ Newbury Ventures
255 Shoreline Dr., Ste. 520
Redwood Shores, CA 94065
Ph: (650)486-2444
Fax: (650)595-2442
Co. E-mail: chehrzad@newburyven.com
URL: http://www.newburyven.com
Contact: Bruce Bauer, Managing Director
E-mail: bruce@newburyven.com
Preferred Investment Size: $5,000,000 to $10,000,000. **Industry Preferences:** Internet specific, semiconductors and other electronics, communications and media, computer software and services, computer hardware, medical and health. **Geographic Preference:** Northwest U.S. and Eastern Canada.

49284 ■ Norwest Venture Partners
525 University Ave., Ste. 800
Palo Alto, CA 94301-1922
Ph: (650)321-8000
Fax: (650)321-8010
Co. E-mail: bizplans@nvp.com
URL: http://www.nvp.com
Contact: Promod Haque, Partner
Preferred Investment Size: $1,000,000 to $30,000,000. **Industry Preferences:** Internet specific, computer software and services, communications and media, semiconductors and other electronics, consumer related, industrial and energy, medical and health, computer hardware, other products, and biotechnology. **Geographic Preference:** U.S.

49285 ■ Novus Ventures
20111 Stevens Creek Blvd., Ste. 130
Cupertino, CA 95014
Ph: (408)252-3900
Fax: (408)252-1713
Co. E-mail: info@novusventures.com
URL: http://www.novusventures.com
Contact: Daniel Tompkins, Partner
Preferred Investment Size: $25,000 to $10,000,000. **Industry Preferences:** Communications and media, computer software and services, Internet specific, semiconductors and other electronics, medical and health. **Geographic Preference:** California and West Coast.

49286 ■ Oak Investment Partners (Palo Alto)
525 University Ave., Ste. 1300
Palo Alto, CA 94301
Ph: (650)614-3700
Fax: (650)328-6345
URL: http://www.oakvc.com
Contact: Bandel Carano, Managing Partner
E-mail: bandel@oakvc.com
Preferred Investment Size: $25,000,000 to $150,000,000. **Industry Preferences:** Communications and media, Internet specific, computer software and services, semiconductors and other electronics, computer hardware, consumer related, medical and health, biotechnology, industrial and energy, and other products. **Geographic Preference:** U.S.

49287 ■ Omninet Capital, LLC
9420 Wilshire Blvd., 4th Fl.
Beverly Hills, CA 90212
Ph: (310)300-4100
Fax: (310)300-4101
Co. E-mail: info@omninet.com
URL: http://www.omninet.com
Contact: Benjamin Nazarian, Managing Partner
Investment Policies: Start-up and early stage. **Industry Preferences:** Communications, and Internet specific. **Geographic Preference:** U.S.

49288 ■ Onset Ventures
2400 Sand Hill Rd.
Menlo Park, CA 94025
Ph: (650)529-0700
Fax: (650)529-0777
Co. E-mail: mp@onset.com
URL: http://www.onset.com
Contact: Stephen Bernardez, Principal
Preferred Investment Size: $8,000,000 to $12,000,000. **Industry Preferences:** Computer software and services, computer hardware, Internet specific, communications and media, semiconductors and other electronics, medical and health, other products, and biotechnology. **Geographic Preference:** West Coast and U.S.

49289 ■ Opportunity Capital Partners
2201 Walnut Ave., Ste. 210
Fremont, CA 94538
Ph: (510)795-7000
Fax: (510)494-5439
URL: http://www.ocpcapital.com
Contact: J. Peter Thompson, Managing Partner
Preferred Investment Size: $2,000,000 to $10,000,000. **Industry Preferences:** Communications and media, computer software and services, computer hardware, consumer related, Internet specific, medical and health, industrial and energy, other products, and semiconductors and other electronics. **Geographic Preference:** California and West Coast.

49290 ■ Oracle Venture Fund
500 Oracle Pky.
Redwood Shores, CA 94065
Ph: (650)506-7000
Fax: (650)633-0272
URL: http://www.oracle.com
Contact: Laurent Sandrolini, Managing Director
Preferred Investment Size: $2,000,000 to $5,000,000. **Industry Preferences:** Internet specific, computer software and services, medical and health, biotechnology, communications and media, computer hardware, and other products. **Geographic Preference:** U.S.

49291 ■ Osprey Ventures, L.P.
502 Waverley St.
Palo Alto, CA 94065
Ph: (650)620-9450
Fax: (650)620-9458
Co. E-mail: admin@ospreyventures.com
URL: http://www.ospreyventures.com
Contact: David Stastny, Managing Director
Industry Preferences: Internet specific, semiconductors and other electronics, communications and media, computer software and services, computer hardware, medical and health. **Geographic Preference:** West Coast.

49292 ■ Outlook Ventures / Iminds, Interactive Minds
3000F Danville, Blvd., Ste. 110
Alamo, CA 94105
Ph: (415)547-0000
Fax: (415)547-0010
Co. E-mail: info@outlookventures.com
URL: http://www.outlookventures.com
Contact: Carl Nichols, Managing Director
Preferred Investment Size: $500,000 to $5,000,000. **Investment Policies:** Start-up, seed, early and first stage. **Industry Preferences:** Internet specific, computer software and services, computer hardware, and other products. **Geographic Preference:** Northern California and West Coast.

49293 ■ Pacifica Fund
5150 El Camino Real, Ste. A-32
Los Altos, CA 94022
Ph: (650)318-0063
Fax: (650)318-0290
URL: http://www.pacificafund.com
Contact: Tim Oren, Managing Director
Preferred Investment Size: $1,000,000 to $5,000,000. **Industry Preferences:** Communications and media, computer hardware and software, Internet specific, semiconductors and other electronics, and industrial and energy. **Geographic Preference:** Northern California and West Coast.

49294 ■ PacRim Venture Partners
535 Middlefield Rd., Ste. 280
Menlo Park, CA 94025
Ph: (650)330-0880
Fax: (650)330-0785
Co. E-mail: info@pacrimpartners.com
URL: http://www.pacrimpartners.com
Contact: Thomas J. Toy, Managing Director
E-mail: ttoy@pacrimpartners.com
Preferred Investment Size: $100,000 to $2,000,000.
Industry Preferences: Communications and media, computer hardware and software, Internet specific, semiconductors and other electronics. **Geographic Preference:** West Coast.

49295 ■ Palo Alto Venture Partners / 21VC Oartners
300 Hamilton Ave., 4th Fl.
Palo Alto, CA 94301
Ph: (650)462-1221
Fax: (650)462-1227
URL: http://www.pavp.com
Contact: Neil Weintraut, Partner
E-mail: nweintraut@pavp.com
Preferred Investment Size: $1,000,000 to $10,000,000. **Investment Policies:** Start-up, seed, early and first stage. **Industry Preferences:** Internet specific, computer software and services, communications and media, other products, and consumer related. **Geographic Preference:** U.S.

49296 ■ Palomar Ventures
100 Wilshire Blvd., Ste. 1700
Santa Monica, CA 90401
Ph: (310)260-6050
Fax: (310)656-4150
URL: http://www.palomarventures.com
Contact: Jim Gauer, Managing Director
E-mail: jgauer@palomarventures.com
Preferred Investment Size: $2,000,000 to $5,000,000. **Industry Preferences:** Communications and media, Internet specific, computer software and services, computer hardware, consumer releated, and other products. **Geographic Preference:** Northern California, Southwest, West Coast, and U.S.

49297 ■ Partech International
50 California St., Ste. 3200
San Francisco, CA 94111
Ph: (415)788-2929
Fax: (415)788-6763
URL: http://www.partechvc.com
Contact: Vincent Worms, Managing Partner
Preferred Investment Size: $1,000,000 to $10,000,000. **Industry Preferences:** Internet specific, computer software, hardware and services, communications and media, semiconductors and other electronics, medical and health, consumer related, biotechnology, industrial and energy. **Geographic Preference:** U.S.

49298 ■ Peninsula Equity Partners
3000 Sand Hill Rd.
Bldg. 2, Ste. 100
Menlo Park, CA 94025
Ph: (650)854-0314
Fax: (650)854-0670
Co. E-mail: info@peninsulaequity.com
URL: http://www.peninsulaequity.com
Contact: Gregory Robinson, Principal
Investment Policies: Early, first and second stage.
Industry Preferences: Information technology, computer software, hardware and services, semiconductors and other electronics. **Geographic Preference:** U.S.

49299 ■ Phoenix Growth Capital Corp.
2401 Kerner Blvd.
San Rafael, CA 94901
Ph: (415)485-4519
Free: 866-895-5050
Fax: (415)485-4663
Co. E-mail: info@phxa.com
URL: http://www.phxa.com
Contact: Gus Constantin, Chief Executive Officer
Preferred Investment Size: $250,000 to $1,000,000.
Industry Preferences: Communications, computer related, consumer retailing, distribution, electronics, genetic engineering, medical and health related, education, publishing, and transportation. **Geographic Preference:** U.S.

49300 ■ Prescient Capital LLC
2 Harrison St., Ste. 600
San Francisco, CA 94133
Ph: (415)675-6750
Fax: (415)675-6755
URL: http://www.prcap.com
Contact: Eric Mathewson, Managing Director
Industry Preferences: Communications and media, computer hardware and software, Internet specific, and consumer related. **Geographic Preference:** Colorado and Northern California.

49301 ■ Prospect Venture Partners / Prospect Management LLC
435 Tasso St., Ste. 200
Palo Alto, CA 94301
Ph: (650)327-8800
Fax: (650)324-8838
URL: http://www.prospectventures.com
Contact: Alex Barkas, Managing Director
Preferred Investment Size: $500,000 to $10,000,000. **Industry Preferences:** Biotechnology, medical and health, computer software and services, semiconductors and other electronics. **Geographic Preference:** U.S.

49302 ■ Putnam Lovell NBF Capital Partners, L.P.
The Plz. at Continental Park
2141 Rosecrans Ave., Ste. 5150
El Segundo, CA 90245
Ph: (310)414-6160
Fax: (310)607-9942
Co. E-mail: Capital@PutnamLovellNBF.com
URL: http://www.putnamlovellcapital.com
Contact: Robert M. Belke, Principal
Preferred Investment Size: $20,000,000 to $100,000,000. **Industry Preferences:** Financial services. **Geographic Preference:** U.S. and Canada.

49303 ■ Red Rock Ventures
530 Lytton Ave., 2nd Fl.
Palo Alto, CA 94301
Ph: (650)325-3111
Fax: (650)853-7044
URL: http://www.redrockventures.com
Contact: Laura Gwosden, Chief Financial Officer
Preferred Investment Size: $500,000 to $5,000,000.
Investment Policies: Seed, early and first stage.
Industry Preferences: Computer software and services, Internet specific, communications and media, computer hardware, and industrial and energy. **Geographic Preference:** West Coast.

49304 ■ Redleaf Venture Management
14395 Saratoga Ave., Ste. 130
Saratoga, CA 95070
Ph: (408)868-0800
Fax: (408)868-0810
URL: http://www.redleaf.com
Contact: Michael B. Nelson, Managing Director
Preferred Investment Size: $1,000,000 to $20,000,000. **Industry Preferences:** Computer software and services, Internet specific, medical and health, communications and media, consumer related, and other products. **Geographic Preference:** California.

49305 ■ Rembrandt Venture Partners
2440 Sand Hill Rd., Ste. 100
Menlo Park, CA 94025
Ph: (650)326-7070
Fax: (650)326-3780
Co. E-mail: inquiries@rembrandtvc.com
URL: http://www.rembrandtvc.com
Contact: In Sik Rhee, Partner
Founded: 2004. **Investment Policies:** Early stage.
Industry Preferences: Communications, and Internet specific. **Geographic Preference:** U.S.

49306 ■ Riordan Lewis & Haden
10900 Wilshire Blvd., Ste. 850
Los Angeles, CA 90024
Ph: (310)405-7200
Fax: (310)405-7222
URL: http://www.rlhinvestors.com
Contact: J. Christopher Lewis, Managing Director
E-mail: clewis@rlhequity.com
Preferred Investment Size: $10,000,000 to $50,000,000. **Industry Preferences:** Computer software, medical and health, consumer related, industrial and energy, transportation, business service, and manufacturing. **Geographic Preference:** West Coast.

49307 ■ Rocket Ventures
2200 Sand Hill Rd., Ste. 240
Menlo Park, CA 94025
Ph: (650)561-9100
URL: http://www.rocketventures.com
Contact: David Adams, Managing Director
Preferred Investment Size: $1,000,000 to $8,000,000. **Industry Preferences:** Communications and media, computer software, and Internet specific. **Geographic Preference:** California and West Coast.

49308 ■ Rosewood Capital, L.P.
1 Maritime Plz., Ste. 1575
San Francisco, CA 94111
Ph: (415)362-5526
Fax: (415)362-1192
URL: http://www.rosewoodvc.com
Contact: Kevin Reilly, Managing Director
E-mail: kevin@rosewoodvc.com
Preferred Investment Size: $10,000,000 to $40,000,000. **Industry Preferences:** Consumer related, Internet specific, Computer software and services, communications and Media, business and financial services, and other products. **Geographic Preference:** U.S.

49309 ■ RWI Ventures
545 Middlefiels Rd., Ste. 220
Menlo Park, CA 94025
Ph: (650)543-3300
Fax: (650)543-3339
URL: http://www.rwigroup.com
Contact: Donald A. Lucas, Managing Director
Preferred Investment Size: $500,000 to $8,000,000.
Industry Preferences: Internet specific, computer software and services, computer hardware, communications and media, semiconductors and other electronics, medical and health, other products, industrial and energy. **Geographic Preference:** U.S.

49310 ■ Saderling Ventures
400 S. El Camino Real, Ste. 1200
Menlo Park, CA 94402
Ph: (650)401-2000
Fax: (650)375-7077
Co. E-mail: info@sanderling.com
URL: http://www.saderling.com
Contact: Timothy Wollaeger, Managing Director
Preferred Investment Size: $500,000 to $5,000,000.
Industry Preferences: Biotechnology, medical and health, Internet specific, computer software and services, computer hardware, semiconductors and other electronics, industrial and energy, communications and media, and consumer related. **Geographic Preference:** U.S. and Canada.

49311 ■ Saints Ventures
475 Sansome St., Ste. 1850
San Francisco, CA 94111
Ph: (415)773-2080
Fax: (415)835-5970
Co. E-mail: info@saintsvc.com
URL: http://www.saintsvc.com
Contact: Kenneth B. Sawyer, Managing Director
Preferred Investment Size: $5,000,000 to $100,000,000. **Investment Policies:** Special situation and acquisition. **Industry Preferences:** Consumer related, industrial, computer software, and Internet specific. **Geographic Preference:** U.S.

49312 ■ SBV Venture Partners / Sigefi, Burnette & Vallee
454 Ruthven Ave.
Palo Alto, CA 94301
Ph: (650)522-0085

Fax: (650)522-0087
Co. E-mail: info@sbvpartners.com
URL: http://www.sbvpartners.com
Contact: Jacques F. Vallee, Partner
Preferred Investment Size: $500,000 to $2,500,000. **Investment Policies:** Seed, start-up, research and development, early and first stage. **Industry Preferences:** Communications, computer hardware and software, Internet specific, semiconductors and other electronics, biotechnology, and medical and health. **Geographic Preference:** U.S. and Canada.

49313 ■ Selby Venture Partners
3500 Alameda de las Pulgas, Ste. 200
Menlo Park, CA 94025
Ph: (650)854-7399
Fax: (650)854-7039
URL: http://www.selbyventures.com
Contact: Robert Marshall, Managing Director
Preferred Investment Size: $500,000 to $7,000,000. **Industry Preferences:** Internet specific, communications and media, consumer related, computer software, and services, computer hardware, semiconductors and other electronics. **Geographic Preference:** Northern California, Southern California, and West Coast.

49314 ■ Semper Ventures
325M Sharon Park Dr., Ste. 460
Menlo Park, CA 94025
Ph: (847)589-4197
URL: http://www.semperventures.com
Contact: Victor J. Lee, Chief Executive Officer
Preferred Investment Size: $500,000 to $2,000,000. **Investment Policies:** Early and later stage. **Industry Preferences:** Computer software. **Geographic Preference:** National.

49315 ■ Sequoia Capital
3000 Sand Hill Rd.
Bldg. 4, Ste. 250
Menlo Park, CA 94025
Ph: (650)854-3927
Fax: (650)854-2977
URL: http://www.sequoiacap.com
Contact: Greg McAdoo, Partner
E-mail: mcadoo@sequoiacap.com
Preferred Investment Size: $100,000 to $100,000,000. **Industry Preferences:** Internet specific, communications and media, computer software and services, computer hardware, other products, semiconductors and other electronics, medical and health, consumer related, biotechnology, industrial and energy. **Geographic Preference:** West Coast.

49316 ■ Shoreline Venture Management, LLC
Mariners Plz.
675 Mariners Island Blvd., Ste. 109
San Mateo, CA 94404
Ph: (650)854-6685
Co. E-mail: info@shorelineventures.com
URL: http://www.shorelineventures.com
Contact: Peter Craddock, Managing Director
Investment Policies: Seed and early stage. **Industry Preferences:** Consumer related, computer software and services, information technology, and medical and health. **Geographic Preference:** National.

49317 ■ Sienna Ventures / Sienna Holdings Inc.
100 Drakes Landing Rd., Ste. 115
Greenbrae, CA 94965
Ph: (415)464-2040
Fax: (415)464-2043
URL: http://www.siennaventures.com
Contact: Daniel L. Skaff, Managing Partner
Preferred Investment Size: $35,000,000 minimum. **Industry Preferences:** Internet specific, computer software and services, consumer related, computer hardware, communications and media, other products, and semiconductors and other electronics. **Geographic Preference:** U.S. and Canada.

49318 ■ Sierra Ventures
2884 Sand Hill Rd., Ste. 100
Menlo Park, CA 94025
Ph: (650)854-1000

Fax: (650)854-5593
Co. E-mail: info@sierraventures.com
URL: http://www.sierraventures.com
Contact: Mark Fernandes, Managing Director
E-mail: mfernandes@sierraventures.com
Preferred Investment Size: $2,000,000 to $25,000,000. **Industry Preferences:** Internet specific, computer software and services, computer hardware, communications and media, semiconductors and other electronics, industrial and energy, biotechnology, and consumer related. **Geographic Preference:** U.S. and Canada.

49319 ■ Sigma Partners (Menlo Park)
1600 El Camino Real, Ste. 280
Menlo Park, CA 94025
Ph: (650)853-1700
Fax: (650)853-1717
URL: http://www.sigmapartners.com
Contact: Lawrence G. Finch, Managing Director
E-mail: lgf@sigmapartners.com
Preferred Investment Size: $2,000,000 to $8,000,000. **Industry Preferences:** Internet specific, computer hardware, computer software and services, communications and media, semiconductors and other electronics, consumer related, and other products. **Geographic Preference:** U.S.

49320 ■ Silicon Valley Bancventures / Silicon Valley Bank (Menlo Park)
3000 Sand Hill Rd.
Bldg. 3, Ste. 150
Menlo Park, CA 94025
Ph: (650)233-7420
Fax: (650)233-6611
URL: http://www.svb.com
Contact: Kenneth P. Wilcox, Chief Executive Officer
Preferred Investment Size: $500,000 to $1,000,000. **Industry Preferences:** Internet specific, communications and media, semiconductors and other electronics, computer software and services, medical and health, consumer related, computer hardware, other products, biotechnology, and industrial and energy. **Geographic Preference:** U.S.

49321 ■ Skyline Ventures
525 University Ave., Ste. 520
Palo Alto, CA 94301
Ph: (650)462-5800
Fax: (650)329-1090
URL: http://www.skylineventures.com
Contact: John G. Freund, Managing Director
Preferred Investment Size: $15,000,000 to $25,000,000. **Industry Preferences:** Medical and health, biotechnology, computer software and services, Internet specific, semiconductors and other electronics. **Geographic Preference:** U.S.

49322 ■ Sofinnova Ventures
2800 Sand Hill Rd., Ste. 150
Menlo Park, CA 94025
Ph: (650)681-8420
Fax: (650)322-2037
Co. E-mail: info@sofinnova.com
URL: http://www.sofinnova.com
Contact: Eric Buatois, Partner
E-mail: eric@sofinnova.com
Preferred Investment Size: $100,000 to $30,000,000. **Industry Preferences:** Internet specific, computer software and services, computer hardware, communications and media, semiconductors and other electronics, and other products. **Geographic Preference:** Northeast and West Coast.

49323 ■ Sorrento Ventures
12250 El Camino Real, Ste. 100
San Diego, CA 92130
Ph: (858)792-2700
Fax: (858)792-5070
Co. E-mail: investment@sorrentoventures.com
URL: http://www.sorrentoventures.com
Contact: Robert M. Jaffe, President
Preferred Investment Size: $1,000,000 to $10,000,000. **Industry Preferences:** Medical and health, computer software and services, Internet specific, biotechnology, communications and media, consumer related, computer hardware, industrial and energy. **Geographic Preference:** Southern California.

49324 ■ Summit Partners (Palo Alto)
499 Hamilton Ave.
Palo Alto, CA 94301
Ph: (650)321-1166
Fax: (650)321-1188
URL: http://www.summitpartners.com
Contact: C.J. Fitzgerald, Managing Director
E-mail: cfitzgerald@summitpartners.com
Preferred Investment Size: $5,000,000 to $500,000,000. **Industry Preferences:** Computer software and services, computer hardware, communications and media, Internet specific, semiconductors and other electronics, medical and health, business services, consumer related, biotechnology, industrial and energy, and other products. **Geographic Preference:** U.S. and Canada.

49325 ■ Sutter Hill Ventures
755 Page Mill Rd., Ste. A-200
Palo Alto, CA 94304-1005
Ph: (650)493-5600
Fax: (650)858-1854
Co. E-mail: shv@shv.com
URL: http://www.shv.com
Contact: David L. Anderson, Managing Director
Preferred Investment Size: $100,000 to $10,000,000. **Industry Preferences:** Computer software and services, Internet specific, computer hardware, communications and media, semiconductors and other electronics, consumer related, industrial and energy, and other products. **Geographic Preference:** U.S.

49326 ■ Sybase Inc.—Sybase
1 Sybase Dr.
Dublin, CA 94568-7976
Ph: (925)236-5000
Free: 800-792-2735
URL: http://www.sybase.com
Contact: John S. Chen, President
Founded: 1984. **Publications:** *SQL Anywhere Studio; PowerDesigner Viewer; Sybase EnterpriseConnect; Sybase Financial Server; InfoHub; jConnect; PowerDimensions; Sybase Character Sets; Watcom-FORTRAN 77; Gain Momentum; SA Companion; Sybase APT Workbench; Sybase Ada Workbench; PC-NET Library; QuickStart DataMart; Sybase Audit Server; Sybase Data Workbench; Sybase IQ; Build Momentum; Replication Server; WATCOM C/C++; Sybase Distribution Director; OmniConnect; Open ClientConnect; Open ServerConnect; dbComplete; Power Designer; ClearConnect; Sybase Replication Server; Sybase Open Server; Sybase XA-Library; InfoMaker; Sybase Warehouse WORKS; Warehouse Now; DirectConnect; PowerJ; Gain Interplay; Powersoft Portfolio; PowerSite Enterprise; QuickStart ReportMart; PowerBuilder Desktop; PowerBuilder; PowerBuilder Professional; PowerDesigner AppModeler; PowerDesigner DataArchitect; PowerDesigner MetaWorks; PowerDesigner ProcessAnalyst; PowerDesigner WarehouseArchitect; PowerStudio Enterprise; ImpactNow; Sybase web.sql; dbQueue; Sybase MPP; Sybase Ebteroruse Data Studio; Sybase Enterprise Event Broker; Adaptive Server IQ 12; Adaptive Server IQ 12 - Multiplex; Adaptive Server Enterprise Replication; Enterprise Data Studio; UDK: Developer's Kit for Unicode; URK: Runtime Kit for Unicode; Industry Warehouse Studio; Sybase Enterprise Portal (EP); EMS (Enterprise Messaging Service); Embedded SQL (11.1); Expressway Design Support Query Accelerator; Database Gateway for AS/400; Database Gateway for SQL/DS with DRDA; Database Gateway for VSE; Replication Agent for DB2 (11.2); Replication Agent for Lotus Notes; Replication Agent for Oracle; Omni SQL Access Module; Enterprise Application Server (EAServer); Telecommunications e-Business Support Systems Portal Plus Intelligence (Telecom B2B+I); jConnect for JDBC; Replication Toolkit for MVS; Sybase Distribution Agent for MVS; DirectConnect for AS/400; DirectConnect for MVS; DirectConnect for Oracle; Distribution Agent for MVS; MainframeConnect for DB2; Sybase Replication Agent for IMS & VSAM; Intellidex Warehouse Control Center; Advanced Developer Toolkit for PowerBuilder; Internet Developer Toolkit for PowerBuilder; ObjectCONNECT for C++; ObjectCONNECT for OLE; Sybase New Media Studio; PowerBuilder Library for Lotus Notes; Enterprise Application Server; Enterprise Application Studio.* **Preferred Investment Size:**

$500,000 to $5,000,000. **Industry Preferences:** Computer software, and Internet specific. **Geographic Preference:** U.S.

49327 ■ Synopsys Inc.—Synopsys
700 E Middlefield Rd.
Mountain View, CA 94043-4024
Ph: (650)584-5000
Free: 800-541-7737
Fax: (650)584-4249
Co. E-mail: webmaster@synopsys.com
URL: http://www.synopsys.com
Contact: Alain Labat, President
URL(s): www.viragelogic.com, www.coware.com, www.vastsystems.com. **Scope:** Firm develops semiconductor design software and electronic design automation (EDA) software, as well as design consulting and support services for the ASIC design process. **Founded:** 1986. **Publications:** "Synopsys Insight "; "Design Ware Technical Bulletin"; "Verification Avenue Technical Bulletin"; "Synopsys Journal"; "Flexible Analysis is Key to Power Integrity," Oct, 2008; "Accelerate Rolls Power Plan," Oct, 2008; "Synopsys bets on mixed-signal implementation market," Sep, 2008; "Full frontal attack," Sep, 2008; "Synopsys revamps IC Complier with multi-threaded routing technology," May, 2008. **Preferred Investment Size:** $500,000 to $5,000,000. **Industry Preferences:** Semiconductors and other electronics, computer software and services, manufacturing, and computer hardware. **Seminars:** Verification Acceleration with CHIP it Automated Rapid Prototyping Series; Custom Design Solution Series; FPGA Implementation Series; Galaxy 2009Series; Introduction to 3GPP LTE Series; Manufacturing Asia Pacific Seminar Series; Reducing Costs and Improving Competitiveness for all your ASIC Projects; Reduce Semiconductor Technology Development Time and Cost; Hands-on Training for Synopsys Tools and Methodologies. **Special Services:** Galaxy?; Discovery?; DesignWare? IP.

49328 ■ TA Associates, Inc. (Menlo Park)
64 Willow Pl., Ste. 100
Menlo Park, CA 94025
Ph: (650)473-2200
Fax: (650)473-2235
URL: http://www.ta.com
Contact: Michael C. Child, Managing Director
E-mail: mchild@ta.com
Preferred Investment Size: $60,000,000 to $500,000,000. **Industry Preferences:** Computer software and services, other products, communications and media, Internet specific, medical and health, semiconductors and other electronics, consumer related, computer hardware, financial and business services, medical and health. **Geographic Preference:** U.S. and Canada.

49329 ■ Tallwood Venture Capital
3000 Sand Hill Rd., Bldg. 3, Ste. 240
Menlo Park, CA 94025-7113
Ph: (650)473-6750
Free: 877-380-6490
Fax: (650)473-6755
Co. E-mail: information@tallwoodvc.com
URL: http://www.tallwoodvc.com
Contact: Jane Cai, Manager
Investment Policies: start-up, early stage, and balanced. **Industry Preferences:** Communications, and semiconductors and other electronics. **Geographic Preference:** U.S.

49330 ■ Techfarm Ventures / Techfund Capital
1800 Embarcadero Rd.
Palo Alto, CA 94303
Ph: (650)856-8500
Fax: (650)856-8510
URL: http://www.techfarm.com
Contact: Gordon Campbell, Managing Director
E-mail: gordon@techfarm.com
Preferred Investment Size: $1,500,000 to $8,000,000. **Industry Preferences:** Semiconductors and other electronics, computer software and services, Internet specific, communications and media. **Geographic Preference:** U.S.

49331 ■ Technology Crossover Ventures
528 Ramona St.
Palo Alto, CA 94301-1709
Ph: (650)614-8200
Fax: (650)614-8222
Co. E-mail: IR@tcv.com
URL: http://www.tcv.com
Contact: John Rosenberg, Principal
Founded: 1995. **Preferred Investment Size:** $20,000 to $200,000,000. **Industry Preferences:** Internet specific, computer software, hardware and services, financial services, communications and media, consumer related, semiconductors and other electronics, and biotechnology. **Geographic Preference:** U.S and Canada.

49332 ■ Technology Funding
1107 Investment Blvd., Ste. 180
El Dorado Hills, CA 95762
Ph: (916)941-1400
Fax: (916)941-7551
Co. E-mail: businessplans@technologyfunding.com
URL: http://technologyfunding.com
Contact: Charles R. Kokesh, Partner
Preferred Investment Size: $500,000 to $2,000,000. **Industry Preferences:** Industrial and energy, biotechnology, medical and health, computer software and services, computer hardware, other products, Internet specific, semiconductors and other electronics, communications and media. **Geographic Preference:** Northern California.

49333 ■ Technology Partners
550 University Ave.
Palo Alto, CA 94301
Ph: (650)289-9000
Fax: (650)289-9001
Co. E-mail: admin@technologypartners.com
URL: http://www.technologypartners.com
Contact: Ira Ehrenpreis, Partner
E-mail: ira@technologypartners.com
Preferred Investment Size: $1,000,000 to $15,000,000. **Industry Preferences:** Internet specific, medical and health, communications and media, computer software and services, consumer related, biotechnology, semiconductors and other electronics, computer hardware, industrial and energy, and other products. **Geographic Preference:** West Coast.

49334 ■ Telos Venture Partners
835 Page Mill Rd.
Palo Alto, CA 94304
Ph: (650)949-1343
URL: http://www.telosvp.com
Contact: Bruce R. Bourbon, Partner
E-mail: bourbob@telosvp.com
Preferred Investment Size: $1,000,000 to $3,000,000. **Industry Preferences:** Internet specific, computer software and services, computer hardware, semiconductors and other electronics, communications and media, and other products. **Geographic Preference:** Northern California, Northwest, and West Coast.

49335 ■ Ticonderoga Capital Inc.
25 Braintree Hill Park, Ste. 200
Braintree, MA 02184
Ph: (781)416-3409
Fax: (781)416-9868
URL: http://www.ticcap.com
Contact: Craig Jones, Managing Partner
E-mail: craig@ticcap.com
Preferred Investment Size: $2,000,000 to $5,000,000. **Industry Preferences:** Computer software, and services, Business services, biotechnology, computer hardware, consumer related, semiconductors and other electronics, medical and health, communications and media, Internet specific, and other products. **Geographic Preference:** U.S. and Canada.

49336 ■ Trinity Ventures
3000 Sand Hill Rd., Bldg. 4
Menlo Park, CA 94025-7113
Ph: (650)854-9500
Fax: (650)854-9501
Co. E-mail: info@trinityventures.com
URL: http://www.trinityventures.com
Contact: Jim Tybur, Principal
E-mail: jim@trinityventures.com
Founded: 1986. **Preferred Investment Size:** $5,000,000 to $20,000,000. **Industry Preferences:** Internet specific, computer software and services, computer hardware, communications and media, consumer related, semiconductors and other electronics, medical and health, industrial and energy, and other products. **Geographic Preference:** U.S.

49337 ■ U.S. Venture Partners
2735 Sand Hill Rd.
Menlo Park, CA 94025
Ph: (650)854-9080
Fax: (650)854-3018
URL: http://www.usvp.com
Contact: William K. Bowes, Jr., Founder
E-mail: bbowes@usvp.com
Preferred Investment Size: $250,000 to $25,000,000. **Industry Preferences:** Internet specific, computer software and services, computer hardware, communications and media, semiconductors and other electronics, consumer related, medical and health, biotechnology, industrial and energy, and other products. **Geographic Preference:** U.S.

49338 ■ Vanguard Ventures
PO Box 20068
San Jose, CA 95160
Ph: (650)321-2900
Fax: (650)321-2902
URL: http://www.vanguardventures.com
Contact: Donald Wood, Managing Director
Preferred Investment Size: $500,000 to $10,000,000. **Industry Preferences:** Communications and media, Internet specific, medical and health, semiconductors and other electronics, computer software and services, biotechnology, computer hardware, semiconductors and other electronics, industrial and energy, and other products. **Geographic Preference:** U.S.

49339 ■ Venrock Associates (Palo Alto)
3340 Hillview Ave.
Palo Alto, CA 94304
Ph: (650)561-9580
Fax: (650)561-9180
URL: http://www.venrock.com
Contact: Brian Ascher, Partner
Preferred Investment Size: $5,000,000 to $15,000,000. **Industry Preferences:** Biotechnology, Internet specific, computer software and services, computer hardware, communications and media, medical and health, semiconductors and other electronics, industrial and energy, consumer related, and other products. **Geographic Preference:** U.S.

49340 ■ Ventana Capital Management, Inc.
22431 Antonio Pkwy., Ste. B160-1002
Rancho Santa Margarita, CA 92688
Ph: (949)481-4200
Fax: (949)766-4487
URL: http://www.ventanaglobal.com
Contact: Thomas O. Gephart, Managing Partner
Preferred Investment Size: $1,000,000 minimum. **Industry Preferences:** Communications and media, semiconductors and other electronics, biotechnology, medical and health, and industrial and energy. **Geographic Preference:** Southern California.

49341 ■ Walden International
1 California St.
San Francisco, CA 94111-5429
Ph: (415)765-7100
Fax: (415)765-7200
Co. E-mail: usa@waldenintl.com
URL: http://www.waldenintl.com
Contact: Mary Coleman, Managing Director
E-mail: mcoleman@waldenintl.com
Founded: 1987. **Preferred Investment Size:** $10,000,000 to $25,000,000. **Industry Preferences:** Communications and media, computer hardware, other products, Internet specific, semiconductors and other electronics, computer Software and services, medical and health, biotechnology, consumer related, industrial and energy. **Geographic Preference:** U.S.

49342 ■ Wedbush Capital Partners
1000 Wilshire Blvd.
Los Angeles, CA 90017
Ph: (213)688-8000
Fax: (213)688-8095
URL: http://www.wedbush.com
Contact: Geoff Bland, Managing Director
Preferred Investment Size: $500,000 minimum. **Industry Preferences:** Computer software and hardware, Internet specific, medical and health, consumer related, and business service. **Geographic Preference:** West Coast.

49343 ■ Westar Capital (Costa Mesa)
949 South Coast Dr., Ste. 170
Costa Mesa, CA 92626
Ph: (714)481-5160
Fax: (714)481-5166
Co. E-mail: contact@westarcapital.com
URL: http://www.westarcapital.com
Contact: Sharon Bujacich, Partner
E-mail: sbujacich@westarcapital.com
Preferred Investment Size: $5,000,000 to $25,000,000. **Industry Preferences:** Communications and media, computer related, semiconductors and other electronics, medical and health, consumer related, industrial and energy, transportation, financial services, and manufacturing. **Geographic Preference:** Northwest, Southwest, Rocky Mountains, and West Coast.

49344 ■ Western States Investment Group
6335 Ferris Sq., Ste. A
San Diego, CA 92121
Ph: (858)678-0800
Fax: (858)678-0900
Co. E-mail: info@wsig.com
URL: http://www.wsig.com
Contact: Scott R. Pancoast, Executive Vice President
Preferred Investment Size: $1,000,000 minimum. **Industry Preferences:** Industrial and energy, medical and health, communications and media, semiconductors and other electronics, computer software and services, and biotechnology. **Geographic Preference:** Southwest and West Coast.

49345 ■ Western Technology Investment
104 La mesa Dr., Ste. 102
Portola Valley, CA 94028
Ph: (650)234-4300
Fax: (650)234-4343
Co. E-mail: info@westerntech.com
URL: http://www.westerntech.com
Contact: Ron Swenson, Founder
E-mail: rons@westerntech.com
Preferred Investment Size: $250,000 to $30,000,000. **Industry Preferences:** Communications and media, semiconductors and other electronics, biotechnology, medical and health. **Geographic Preference:** U.S.

49346 ■ Windward Ventures (Thousand Oaks)
PO Box 7688
Thousand Oaks, CA 91359
Ph: (805)499-7338
Co. E-mail: mailbox@windwardventures.com
URL: http://www.windwardventures.com
Contact: James A. Cole, Managing Partner
E-mail: cole@windwardventures.com
Preferred Investment Size: $1,000,000 to $5,000,000. **Industry Preferences:** Medical and health, Internet specific, computer software and services, communications and media, semiconductors and other electronics, and other products. **Geographic Preference:** Southern California.

49347 ■ Woodside Fund
350 Marine Pky., Ste. 300
Redwood City, CA 94065
Ph: (650)610-8050
Fax: (650)610-8051
Co. E-mail: info@woodsidefund.com
URL: http://www.woodsidefund.com
Contact: Thomas A. Shields, Partner
Preferred Investment Size: $5,000,000 to $10,000,000. **Industry Preferences:** Computer software and services, communications and media, Internet specific, consumer related, computer hardware, other products, semiconductors and other electronics. **Geographic Preference:** Northern California and West Coast.

49348 ■ Worldview Technology Partners
2207 Bridgepointe Pkwy., Ste. 100
San Mateo, CA 94404
Ph: (650)322-3800
Fax: (650)322-3880
URL: http://www.worldview.com
Contact: Terence Tan, Managing Director
Founded: 1996. **Industry Preferences:** Communications and media, Internet specific, semiconductors and other electronics, computer software, and services, computer hardware, and other products. **Geographic Preference:** U.S.

PROCUREMENT ASSISTANCE PROGRAMS

49349 ■ California Procurement Technical Assistance Center - The Federal Technology Center (The FTC)
4600 Roseville Rd., Ste. 100
North Highlands, CA 95660
Ph: (916)334-9388
Fax: (916)334-9078
Co. E-mail: jack@theftc.org
URL: http://www.theftc.org
Contact: Jack Toney, Director
E-mail: Jaxk@TheFTC.org
Description: Promotes economic development by facilitating technology transfer between government and the private sector, and by helping small businesses successfully compete for government contracts.

49350 ■ California Procurement Technical Assistance Center - Federal Technology Center Procurement Technical Assistance Center
4600 Roseville Rd., Ste. 100
North Highlands, CA 95660
Ph: (916)334-9388
Fax: (916)334-9078
Co. E-mail: jack@theftc.org
URL: http://www.theftc.org/PTAC
Contact: Jack Toney, Director
Description: Promotes economic development by facilitating technology transfer between government and the private sector, and by helping small businesses successfully compete for government contracts.

49351 ■ California Procurement Technical Assistance Center - Los Angeles County Office of Small Business
1100 N Eastern Ave., No. G115
Los Angeles, CA 90063
Ph: (323)881-3964
Fax: (323)881-1871
Co. E-mail: dcabreira@isd.lacounty.gov
URL: http://www.laosb.org
Contact: Debbie Cabreira Johnson, Program Director
E-mail: dcabreira@isd.lacounty.gov
Description: Los Angeles County Office of Small Business (OSB) is a source of information on procurement opportunities, certification, financing, and technical assistance. OSB also serves as the County Procurement Technical Assistance Center (PTAC), funded by the U.S. Department of Defense (DoD) to help small businesses get contracts with prime defense contractors.

49352 ■ California Procurement Technical Assistance Center - Pacific American Indian Development (PAID) - Procurement Technical Assistance Center
Bldg. R1
2000 East El Segundo Blvd.
El Segundo, CA 90245
Ph: (480)545-1298
URL: http://www.ncaied.org/american-indian-procurement-assistance.php
Contact: Oscar Padilla, Director
E-mail: oscar.padilla@p-aid.org
Description: Assists Indian owned and tribally owned businesses succeed in government contracting.

49353 ■ California Procurement Technical Assistance Center - Riverside Community College District
14745 Riverside Dr.
Riverside, CA 92518
Ph: (951)571-6475
Free: 866-267-7986
Fax: (951)653-1051
Co. E-mail: susanne.adams@rcc.edu
URL: http://www.rcchelpsbusiness.com
Contact: Julie Ann Padilla, Director
Description: Helps business firms market their goods and services to federal, state and local government agencies.

49354 ■ California Procurement Technical Assistance Center - San Diego Contracting Opportunities Center
4007 Camino Del Rio S., Ste. 210
San Diego, CA 92108-4189
Ph: (619)285-7020
Fax: (619)285-7030
Co. E-mail: sbdcoc@ptac-sandiego.org
URL: http://www.ptac-sandiego.org

INCUBATORS/RESEARCH AND TECHNOLOGY PARKS

49355 ■ Business Technology Center of Los Angeles County
2400 N Lincoln Ave.
Altadena, CA 91001
Ph: (626)296-6300
Fax: (626)296-6301
Co. E-mail: info@labtc.org
URL: http://www.labtc.org
Contact: Mark Loeberman, Manager
Description: The BTC committed to developing high technology firms by providing financial, technical, and business management assistance.

49356 ■ Central Valley Business Incubator
1630 E. Shaw, Ste. 163
Fresno, CA 93710
Ph: (559)292-9033
Fax: (559)294-6537
URL: http://www.cvbi.org/
Contact: Travis Sheridan, Director
Description: A public/private partnership, fueled with community resources and helping start-up companies launch successfully by creating an entrepreneurial community where people learn how to balance their passion and ideas with the structure of running a successful business.

49357 ■ Communications Technology Cluster (CTC)
300 Frank H. Ogawa Plaza, Ste. 210
Oakland, CA 94612-1932
Ph: (510)903-1902
Fax: (510)903-1952
Co. E-mail: info@ctcluster.com
URL: http://www.ctcluster.com/main/index.htm
Contact: Joe Gross, Chief Executive Officer
Description: CTC is a business incubator supporting entrepreneurs and growth-oriented small to mid-sized companies in the fields of business services, consumer products, financial services, healthcare, and technology.

49358 ■ Daly City Business Center
355 Gellert Blvd., Ste. 230
Daly City, CA 94015
Ph: (650)757-2060

Fax: (650)757-2075
Co. E-mail: info@DalyCityBusinessCenter.com
URL: http://www.dalycity.org/services_for_business/
Economic_Development/dcbzctr.htm
Description: A small business incubator providing a proven growth environment for small businesses and entrepreneurs.

49359 ■ El Pajaro Community Development Corporation
23 E Beach St., Ste. 209
Watsonville, CA 95076
Ph: (831)722-1224
Fax: (831)722-3128
Co. E-mail: info@elpajarocdc.org/
URL: http://www.elpajarocdc.org/
Contact: Carmen Herrera-Mansir, Executive Director
Description: A small business incubator with more than twenty years of experience in the provision of bilingual/bicultural small business assistance and job creation for primarily minority and low-income entrepreneurs.

49360 ■ The Greater Antelope Valley Economic Alliance
1028 West Ave., L-12, No. 101
Lancaster, CA 93534
Ph: (661)945-2741
Free: 800-888-7483
Fax: (661)945-7711
Co. E-mail: info@aveconomy.org
URL: http://www.aveconomy.org
Contact: Mel Layne, President
Description: Provides a thriving environment for economic growth and offers a wide range of benefits to businesses seeking to relocate or expand into our area.

49361 ■ Los Angeles Business Owner Outreach Support and Training (LABOOST)
2 Coral Circle
Monterey Park, CA 91755
Ph: (323)890-7110
Free: 866-632-6678
Fax: (323)890-8575
Co. E-mail: Mark.Lieberman@lacdc.org
URL: http://www.lacdc.org/CDCWebsite/la-boost/
home.aspx
Contact: Mark Lieberman, Director
Description: Provides emerging small businesses with professional training, outreach, counseling, and advisory services. Formerly Athens Westmont Business Center.

49362 ■ San Jose Software Business Cluster
2 N First St., Fourth Fl.
San Jose, CA 95113
Ph: (408)535-2701
Fax: (408)535-2711
Co. E-mail: info@sjsbc.org
URL: http://www.sjsbc.org
Contact: Chuck Erickson, Director
Description: Small business incubator with capacity for 20 to 30 emerging software firms.

49363 ■ SARTA CleanStart
3801 Power Inn Rd.
Sacramento, CA 95826
Ph: (916)231-0770
Co. E-mail: gary@cleanstart.org
URL: http://www.sarta.org/go/cs/
Description: An initiative of McClellan Technology Incubator (MTI) and Sacramento Area Regional Technology Alliance (SARTA) designed to accelerate the development of clean energy technology ventures within the Greater Sacramento Region.

49364 ■ US Market Access Center
10 S 3rd St., 3rd Fl.
San Jose, CA 95113-1101
Ph: (408)351-3300
Fax: (408)351-3330
Co. E-mail: info@usmarketaccess.com
URL: http://www.usmarketaccess.com
Contact: Omar Mencin, President
Description: US Market Access Center is a non-profit business incubator sponsored by a collaboration of business, government, and academic organi-

zations. The Center is a leading business gateway into the United States. Formerly International Business Incubator (IBI).

EDUCATIONAL PROGRAMS

49365 ■ American River College
4700 College Oak Dr.
Sacramento, CA 95841-4286
Ph: (916)484-8011
Fax: (916)484-8037
Co. E-mail: info@arc.losrios.edu
URL: http://www.arc.losrios.edu
Contact: Dr. David Viar, President
Description: Two-year college offering small business management classes. **Founded:** 1955. **Publications:** *The Current* (Weekly (Wed.)). **Telecommunication Services:** viard@arc.losrios.edu.

49366 ■ Chabot College
25555 Hesperian Blvd.
Hayward, CA 94545
Ph: (510)723-6700
Fax: (510)723-7510
URL: http://www.chabotcollege.edu
Description: Two-year college offering a program in entrepreneurship.

49367 ■ Cypress College
Business Office
9200 Valley View St.
Cypress, CA 90630
Ph: (714)484-7000
Fax: (714)527-4733
Co. E-mail: info@cypresscollege.edu
URL: http://www.cypress.cc.ca.us
Description: Regular business program includes courses on small business management, human relations, and related topics.

49368 ■ De Anza College
21250 Stevens Creek Blvd.
Cupertino, CA 95014
Ph: (408)864-5678
Fax: (408)864-5433
URL: http://www.deanza.fhda.edu
Description: Two-year college offering a small business management program. Certificate program includes marketing, finance, and management.

49369 ■ Empire College - School of Business
3035 Cleveland Ave.
Santa Rosa, CA 95403
Ph: (707)546-4000
Free: 800-705-0567
Fax: (707)546-4058
Co. E-mail: rhurd@empcol.com
URL: http://www.empcol.com
Description: College offering a small business management program.

49370 ■ Lake Tahoe Community College
1 College Dr.
South Lake Tahoe, CA 96150-4524
Ph: (530)541-4660
Fax: (530)541-7852
URL: http://www.ltcc.cc.ca.us
Description: Two-year college offering a small business management program.

49371 ■ Ohlone College
43600 Mission Blvd.
Fremont, CA 94539
Ph: (510)659-6000
Fax: (510)659-7321
URL: http://www.ohlone.cc.ca.us
Description: Two-year college offering a small business management program.

49372 ■ Saddleback College
28000 Marguerite Pky.
Mission Viejo, CA 92692
Ph: (949)582-4500
Fax: (949)347-0438
URL: http://www.saddleback.cc.ca.us
Description: Two-year college offering a small business management program.

49373 ■ Santa Ana College
1530 W 17th St.
Santa Ana, CA 92706
Ph: (714)564-6000
Fax: (714)564-6455
URL: http://www.sac.edu
Description: Two-year college offering a small business management program.

49374 ■ Southwestern College
900 Otay Lakes Rd.
Chula Vista, CA 91910
Ph: (619)421-6700
Fax: (619)482-6402
URL: http://www.swc.cc.ca.us
Description: Two-year college offering a program in small business management.

TRADE PERIODICALS

49375 ■ *California Employer Advisor*
Pub: Employer Resource Institute Inc.
Ed: Larry J. Shapiro, Esq., Editor, lshapiro@arthcink. net. **Released:** Monthly. **Price:** $177, individuals. **Description:** The award-winning guide to California employment law and employee relations.

49376 ■ *California Labor and Employment ALERT Newsletter*
Pub: Castle Publications Ltd.
Contact: Richard Simmons, President
Released: Bimonthly. **Price:** $90; $105 includes 3-ring binder. **Description:** Reports on current developments in California and federal laws concerning personnel and employment issues. Recurring features include notices of publications available.

49377 ■ *California Labor and Employment Law Quarterly*
Pub: State Bar of California
Contact: Marty Fassler, Managing Editor
Released: Quarterly. **Description:** Contains information and news on California's labor and employment laws and regulations.

PUBLICATIONS

49378 ■ *The Business Journal Serving San Jose and Silicon Valley*
96 N. 3rd St., Ste. 100
San Jose, CA 95112-5560
Ph: (408)295-3800
Fax: (408)295-5028
Co. E-mail: sanjose@amcity.com
URL: http://www.amcity.com

49379 ■ *California Corporation Formation Package and Minute Book*
Oasis Press
300 N. Valley Dr.
Grants Pass, OR 97526
Ph: (541)479-9464
Free: 800-228-2275
Fax: (541)476-1479
Co. E-mail: psi2@magick.net
Ed: Kevin W. Finck. **Released:** Seventh edition, 1992. **Price:** $29.95 (paper); $39.95 (ringbound).

49380 ■ *How to Form Your Own California Corporation*
950 Parker St.
Berkeley, CA 94710
Ph: (510)549-1976
Free: 800-992-6656
Fax: (800)645-0895
URL: http://www.nolo.com
Ed: Anthony Mancuso. **Released:** Seventh edition, 1988. **Price:** $29.95 (paper).

49381 ■ *Orange County Business Journal*
4590 McArthur, Ste. 100
Newport Beach, CA 92660
Ph: (714)833-8373
Fax: (714)833-8751
Co. E-mail: cox@ocbj.com
URL: http://www.ocbj.com

49382 ■ Sacramento Business Journal
1401 21st St., Ste. 200
Sacramento, CA 95814-3120
Ph: (916)447-7661
Fax: (916)444-7779
Co. E-mail: tbj@ns.net
URL: http://www.amcity.com/sacramento

49383 ■ San Diego Business Journal
4909 Murphy Canyon Rd., Ste. 200
San Diego, CA 92123-4300
Ph: (619)277-6359
Fax: (619)571-3628
Co. E-mail: sdbj@sdbj.com
URL: http://www.sdbj.com

49384 ■ Small Business Success
101 Spear St., Rm. 429
San Francisco, CA 94105
Ph: (415)995-3899
Ed: Andrea Hine, editor. **Price:** Free. **Description:** Contains articles on small business development in California. Includes a resource directory.

49385 ■ Starting and Operating a Business in California: A Step-by-Step Guide
PSI Research
300 N. Valley Dr.
Grants Pass, OR 97526
Ph: (503)479-9464
Free: 800-228-2275
Fax: (503)476-1479
Co. E-mail: psi2@magick.net
Ed: Michael D. Jenkins. **Released:** Revised edition, 1992. **Price:** $29.95 (looseleaf binder); $24.95 (paper). **Description:** Part of the Successful Business Library series.

PUBLISHERS

49386 ■ Adams-Blake Company Inc.—Adams-Blake Publishing
8041 Sierra St., Ste. 102
Fair Oaks, CA 95628-7530
Ph: (916)962-9296
Free: 800-368-2326
Fax: (916)962-9296
Co. E-mail: info@adams-blake.com
URL: http://www.adams-blake.com
Contact: Alan N. Canton, President
Description: Description: Publishes business, career and technology books. Accepts unsolicited manuscripts. Reaches market through direct mail and wholesalers and distributors. **Founded:** 1990.

49387 ■ Advisor Media Inc.
12463 Rancho Bernardo Rd., Ste. 509
San Diego, CA 92128-3350
Ph: (858)278-5600
Fax: (858)947-3993
URL: http://advisormedia.com/adv/AdvisorLegal
Contact: John L. Hawkins, Chief Executive Officer
Description: Description: Publishes business related materials. **Founded:** 1983. **Publications:** FoxPro Advisor (Monthly); SharePoint Advisor (Monthly); Mobile Business Advisor (Bimonthly); Lotus Advisor Magazine (Monthly); Security Advisor (Monthly); Access VB- SQL Advisor (Monthly); Compliance Solutions Advisor: The Advisor Guide to Corporate Compliance Strategies & Solutions (Bimonthly); E-Discovery Advisor: The Advisor Guide to Law Electronic Discovery Strategies & Solutions (Monthly); Databased Web Advisor (Monthly); Internet Java & ActiveX Advisor (Monthly).

49388 ■ Alliance of Area Business Publications (AABP)
1970 E Grand Ave., Ste. 330
El Segundo, CA 90245
Ph: (310)364-0193
Fax: (310)364-0196
Co. E-mail: info@bizpubs.org
URL: http://www.bizpubs.org
Contact: Mark Singletary, President
E-mail: mark.singletary@nopg.com
Description: Local area business publications. Encourages high journalistic standards among area business publications. Acts as a forum for the

exchange of ideas and information, especially on common issues such as editorial excellence, postal regulations, government regulations, and advertising. Compiles statistics of business patterns in markets of members and engages in cooperative member market research. **Founded:** 1979. **Publications:** Alliance of Area Business Publications--Membership Directory (Annual); Association of Area Business Publications--Directory (Annual). **Educational Activities:** Editorial and Design Awards Banquet (Annual); Editorial and Design Awards Banquet (Annual). **Awards:** Editorial and Design Award (Annual).

49389 ■ Ashar Press
1002 Elk Hills Dr.
Galt, CA 95632
Ph: (209)745-2756
Free: 877-266-5117
Fax: (209)745-7538
Co. E-mail: beverly@asharpress.com
URL: http://www.asharpress.com
Contact: Tammy J. Deruyter, Editor
Description: Description: Publishes books on religion. **Founded:** 1999.

49390 ■ Bay Tree Publishing
1400 Pinnacle Ct., Ste. 406
Point Richmond, CA 94801-4178
Ph: (510)236-1475
Fax: (866)552-7329
Co. E-mail: dcole@baytreepublish.com
URL: http://www.baytreepublish.com
Contact: Mary Lee Cole, Publisher
Description: Description: Publishes nonfiction in the areas of current affairs, business and psychology. **Founded:** 2002.

49391 ■ Bell Springs Publishing
106 State St.
Willits, CA 95490-3118
Ph: (707)459-6372
Free: 800-515-8050
Fax: (707)459-8614
Co. E-mail: publisher@bellsprings.com
URL: http://www.bellsprings.com
Contact: Sam Leandro, Publisher
Description: Description: Publishes small business guidebooks and pinball machine repair manuals. Reaches market through trade sales and wholesalers. Does not accept unsolicited manuscripts. **Founded:** 1976.

49392 ■ BizBest Media Corp.
881 Alma Real Dr., Ste. 220
Pacific Palisades, CA 90272
Ph: (310)230-6868
Free: 800-873-5205
Fax: (310)454-6130
Co. E-mail: info@bizbest.com
URL: http://www.bizbest.com
Contact: Shara Karasic, Manager
E-mail: skarasic@work.com
Description: Description: Publishes a small business resources directory. **Founded:** 1999.

49393 ■ Blueprint Books
7734 Creekside Dr.
Pleasanton, CA 94588-3686
Ph: (925)425-9513
Free: 800-605-2913
Fax: (800)605-2914
Contact: Bette Daoust, Manager
Description: Description: Publishes business books.

49394 ■ Business Coach Press
48 Matthews Pl.
Alamo, CA 94507-2600
Free: 866-500-1183
Co. E-mail: info@businesscoachpress.biz
URL: http://www.businesscoachpress.biz
Contact: Steven Hilferty, Manager
Description: Description: Publishes books that assist small business owners.

49395 ■ California State University Press
2380 E Keats MS/MB99
Fresno, CA 93740-8024
Ph: (559)278-3056

Fax: (559)278-6758
Co. E-mail: press@csufresno.edu
URL: http://www.csufresno.edu/artshum/press/index.shtml
Contact: Lee Ann Jansen, Director
E-mail: ljansen@csufresno.edu
Description: Description: Publishes books on art, drama, music, film, media, architecture, politics, business and auto-biography. Reaches market through southern Illinois University Press. Does not accept unsolicited manuscripts. **Founded:** 1982.

49396 ■ CMP Books
6600 Silacci Way
Gilroy, CA 95020-7005
Ph: (408)848-3854
Free: 800-500-6875
Fax: (408)848-5784
Co. E-mail: cmp@rushorder.com
Contact: Junia Ziblay, Manager
E-mail: jziblay@cmp.com
Description: Description: Publishes information on computing, design and communications solutions.

49397 ■ Collins Publications
3233 Grand Ave., Ste. N-294C
Chino Hills, CA 91709-1489
Ph: (909)590-2471
Free: 800-795-8999
Fax: (909)628-9330
Co. E-mail: collins@collinspub.com
URL: http://www.collinspub.com
Contact: Rachel Anderson, Director
Description: Description: Publishes how-to, business, and self-help products. Offers an array of software training materials, such as videos, books and CD-ROMs. Also offers self publishing services. Reaches market through commission representatives, direct mail, trade sales and wholesalers and distributors, including Baker and Taylor and Brodart. Does not accept unsolicited manuscripts. **Founded:** 1991.

49398 ■ D.M.R. Consulting Group—Fujitsu Consulting
225 S Lake Ave., Ste. 300
Pasadena, CA 91101-3005
Ph: (626)440-8365
Contact: Mark Dunnet, President
Description: Description: Publishes home-based business success manuals and other specialized information on various subjects. Distributes for premier Publishers. Reaches market through commission representatives, direct mail, and telephone and trade sales. **Founded:** 1980.

49399 ■ Vince Emery Productions
781 Prague St.
San Francisco, CA 94112
Ph: (415)337-6000
Free: 800-888-4741
Fax: (650)697-6048
Co. E-mail: vince@emery.com
URL: http://www.emerybooks.com
Contact: Vince Emery, Manager
E-mail: vince@emery.com
Description: Description: Publishes books on Internet businesses.

49400 ■ Frontal Lobe
836 Starlite Ln.
Los Altos, CA 94024
Ph: (650)941-8561
Co. E-mail: masonc2@earthlink.net
Contact: Mason A. Clark, Editor
Description: Description: Publishes small business management, entrepreneurship, religion and how-to books. **Founded:** 1978.

49401 ■ Hunter Arts Publishing
PO Box 66578E
Los Angeles, CA 90066
Ph: (310)842-8864

Fax: (310)842-8868
Co. E-mail: publisher@hunterarts.com
URL: http://www.headhuntersrevealed.com/reviews.
html
Contact: Darrell W. Gurney, Manager
Description: Description: Publishes Headhunters
Revealed! Career Secrets for Choosing and Using
Professional Recruiters -an executive recruiter that
exposes the mind and mechanics of the search
industry to job-seeking professionals. Does not ac-
cept unsolicited manuscripts. **Founded:** 1999. **Publi-**
cations: *Headhunters Revealed: Career Secrets for*
Choosing and Using Professional Recruiters (Quarterly).

49402 ■ IBIS/Business Information Services
International—International Business &
Management InstituteInternational Business
Information Services;
PO Box 3271
Tustin, CA 92781-3271
Ph: (949)552-8494
Fax: (501)432-5112
Contact: Ray B. Debby, Manager
Description: Description: Publishes book, audio-tape
and video sets on various business topics for entre-
preneurs and enterprising managers, business
students, and business groups. Also publishes busi-
ness manuals on a variety of topics. Reaches market
through direct mail, trade sales, and through the
distributor. Does not accept unsolicited manuscripts.
Founded: 1980.

49403 ■ International Business &
Management Institute (IBMI Business Books)
IBMI Ctr.
Tustin, CA 92781-3271
Ph: (949)552-8494
Fax: (501)432-5112
Co. E-mail: ibmi-books@juno.com
Contact: T. R. Balla, Director
Description: Description: Publishes on diverse busi-
ness and management topics focusing on interna-
tional trade and finance for entrepreneurs and
managers. Also publishes booklets. Offers consulting
and in-house educational programs. Distributes IBIS
Business Reports. Reaches market through direct
mail, internet and trade promotions. Does not accept
unsolicited manuscripts. **Founded:** 1970.

49404 ■ Jardin Publishing
2325 Fatjo Pl., Ste. 105
Santa Clara, CA 95050
Ph: (408)454-6650
Free: 866-896-8946
Contact: David T. Riveness, Manager
Description: Description: Publishes books on busi-
ness and leadership.

49405 ■ Juice Gallery Multimedia
2042 Big Oak Ave.
Chino Hills, CA 91709-4710
Ph: (909)597-0791
Free: 800-710-8163
Fax: (909)597-0791
Co. E-mail: info@juicegallery.com
URL: http://www.juicegallery.com
Contact: Dan Titus, President
Description: Description: Publishes materials related
to staring a restaurant business. Accepts unsolicited
manuscripts. Reaches market through direct mail,
reviews, listings, telephone sales and wholesalers
and Baker & Taylor. **Founded:** 1992.

49406 ■ Monterey Home Video
566 St. Charles Dr.
Thousand Oaks, CA 91360-3953
Ph: (805)494-7199
Free: 800-424-2593
Fax: (805)496-6061
Co. E-mail: customerservice@montereymedia.com
URL: http://www.montereymedia.com
Contact: Scott Mansfield, President
Description: Description: Publishes educational
audio and video cassettes. Does not accept unsolic-
ited manuscripts. Reaches market through wholesal-
ers, distributors and direct to store sales. **Founded:**
1979.

49407 ■ Out of Your Mind and into the
Marketplace—OM...IM
13381 White Sand Dr.
Tustin, CA 92780-4565
Ph: (714)544-0248
Free: 800-419-1513
Fax: (714)730-1414
Co. E-mail: lpinson@business-plan.com
URL: http://www.business-plan.com
Contact: Ndaba Mdhlongwa, Director, Marketing
E-mail: ndaba@business-plan.com
Description: Description: Publishes on small and
home-based business concerns, stressing step-by-
step, hands-on approach to business start-up, record
keeping, marketing and business plan preparation.
Offers a business plan software program for windows.
Reaches market through commission representa-
tives, direct mail, trade sales and wholesalers. Does
not accept unsolicited manuscripts. **Founded:** 1987.

49408 ■ Pleasanton Publishing
55 New Montgomery St.
San Francisco, CA 94105-3412
Ph: (925)249-9112
Fax: (925)249-1807
Description: Description: Publishes literary works for
holistic and natural healing using a teddy bear
metaphor to connect reader. Does not accept unsolicited manuscripts. Reaches market through distributors. **Founded:** 2000.

49409 ■ Power2BE Media
2975 Seahorse Ave.
Ventura, CA 93001
Ph: (805)650-1248
Fax: (805)650-1249
Co. E-mail: info@powerselling.com
URL: http://www.powerselling.com
Contact: Steven Power, President
E-mail: spower@powerselling.com
Description: Description: Publishes business books
about power selling. Does not accept unsolicited
manuscripts. Reaches market through commission
representatives, direct mail and via e-mail. **Founded:**
2002.

49410 ■ Rampant Lion Publishers Inc.
c/o L. H. Joseph Jr., 8344 Melrose Ave., Ste. 23
Los Angeles, CA 90069
Fax: (323)651-0624
Contact: Lawrence H. Joseph, Jr., President
Description: Description: Publishes management
and how-to books for business people. Reaches
market through business organizations. **Founded:**
1980.

49411 ■ Rhino's Press
PO Box 3520
Laguna Hills, CA 92654
Free: 800-872-3274
Fax: (714)244-3256
Contact: Scott Alexander, Owner
Description: Description: Publishes motivation, small
business books. **Founded:** 1980.

49412 ■ Sun Publications
300 Carlsbad Village Dr., Ste. 108A-78
Carlsbad, CA 92008
Ph: (760)476-0777
Free: 888-786-3777
Fax: (760)462-4752
Co. E-mail: debra@debrapestrak.com
URL: http://www.debrapestrak.com
Contact: Steve Pestrak, President
Description: Description: Publishes business leader-
ship and women's issues books and tapes. They are
concerned with helping business people succeed and
reach their goals. Does not accept unsolicited
manuscripts. Reaches market through direct mail,
wholesalers and distributors, seminars and speaking
engagements. **Founded:** 2000.

49413 ■ WBusiness Books
9682 Telstar Ave., Ste. 110
El Monte, CA 91731-3009
Ph: (626)448-3448
Fax: (626)602-3817
Co. E-mail: info@academiclearningcompany.com
URL: http://www.wbusinessbooks.com
Contact: Troy Hazard, Manager
Description: Description: Publishes business books.
Accepts unsolicited manuscripts. Reaches market
through commission representatives. **Founded:**
2005.

SMALL BUSINESS DEVELOPMENT CENTERS

49414 ■ Boulder Small Business Development Center
2440 Pearl St.
Boulder, CO 80302
Ph: (303)442-1475
URL: http://www.bouldersbdc.com
Description: Represents and promotes the small business sector. Provides management assistance to current and prospective small business owners. Helps to improve management skills and expand the products and services of members.

49415 ■ Boulder Small Business Development Center (Longmont, Colorado)
528 Main St.
Longmont, CO 80501
Ph: (303)442-1475
Co. E-mail: sharon.king@boulderchamber.com
URL: http://www.bouldersbdc.com
Description: Represents and promotes the small business sector. Provides management assistance to current and prospective small business owners. Helps to improve management skills and expand the products and services of members.

49416 ■ Colorado Springs Small Business Development Center
Citti Bldg.
1420 Austin Bluffs Pkwy.
Colorado Springs, CO 80933
Ph: (719)262-3844
URL: http://cssbdc.org
Contact: Janna Hoiberg, Counselor
Description: Represents and promotes the small business sector. Provides management assistance to current and prospective small business owners. Helps to improve management skills and expand the products and services of members.

49417 ■ Denver Metro Small Business Development Center
1445 Market St.
Denver, CO 80202
Ph: (303)620-8076
Fax: (303)534-2145
Co. E-mail: denver.sbdc@den-chamber.org
URL: http://www.denversbdc.org
Contact: Tameka Montgomery, Executive Director
Description: Represents and promotes the small business sector. Provides management assistance to current and prospective small business owners. Helps to improve management skills and expand the products and services of members.

49418 ■ Fort Morgan Small Business Development Center
300 Main St.
Fort Morgan, CO 80701

Ph: (970)542-3263
Co. E-mail: kristi.rorabaugh@morgancc.edu
URL: http://www.coloradosbdc.org
Contact: Kristi Rorabaugh, Coordinator
Description: Represents and promotes the small business sector. Provides management assistance to current and prospective small business owners. Helps to improve management skills and expand the products and services of members.

49419 ■ Grand Junction Small Business Development Center
2591 B 3/4 Rd.
Grand Junction, CO 81503
Ph: (970)243-5242
Co. E-mail: jmorey@gjincubator.org
URL: http://www.coloradosbdc.org
Contact: Julie Morey, Director
Description: Represents and promotes the small business sector. Provides management assistance to current and prospective small business owners. Helps to improve management skills and expand the products and services of members.

49420 ■ Greeley/Weld Small Business Development Center
902 7th Ave.
Greeley, CO 80631
Ph: (970)352-3661
Fax: (970)352-3572
Co. E-mail: richard@pickett.unco.edu
URL: http://www.neeccosbdc.org
Contact: Richard Pickett, Director
Description: Represents and promotes the small business sector. Provides management assistance to current and prospective small business owners. Helps to improve management skills and expand the products and services of members.

49421 ■ La Junta Small Business Development Center
Otero Junior College
1802 Colorado Ave.
La Junta, CO 81050
Ph: (719)384-6959
Co. E-mail: bill.dutro@ojc.edu
URL: http://www.coloradosbdc.org
Contact: Bill Dutro, Director
Description: Represents and promotes the small business sector. Provides management assistance to current and prospective small business owners. Helps to improve management skills and expand the products and services of members.

49422 ■ Larimer County Small Business Development Center
125 S Howes St., Ste. 150
Fort Collins, CO 80521
Ph: (970)498-9295
Fax: (970)498-8924
Co. E-mail: admin@larimersbdc.org
URL: http://www.larimersbdc.org
Description: Represents and promotes the small business sector. Provides management assistance to current and prospective small business owners. Helps to improve management skills and expand the products and services of members.

49423 ■ Loveland Small Business Development Center
441 E 4th St., Ste. 101A
Loveland, CO 80537
Ph: (970)667-4106
Co. E-mail: info@lovelandsbdc.org
URL: http://www.coloradosbdc.org
Contact: Robin Shuckle-Shea, Director
URL(s): www.lovelandsbdc.org. **Description:** Represents and promotes the small business sector. Provides management assistance to current and prospective small business owners. Helps to improve management skills and expand the products and services of members.

49424 ■ North Metro Small Business Development Center
Front Range Community College
3645 W 112th Ave., Rm. C2006
Westminster, CO 80031
Ph: (303)460-1032
Fax: (303)469-7143
Co. E-mail: wcicpd@frontrange.edu
URL: http://www.frontrange.edu/FRCCTemplates/ FRCC7.aspx?id=132
Contact: Chris Luchs, Director
Description: Represents and promotes the small business sector. Provides management assistance to current and prospective small business owners. Helps to improve management skills and expand the products and services of members.

49425 ■ Pueblo Small Business Development Center
Business & Technology Center
301 N Main St., Ste. 205
Pueblo, CO 81003
Ph: (719)549-3224
Co. E-mail: caroline.parra@pueblocc.edu
URL: http://www.coloradosbdc.org
Contact: Caroline Parra, Director
Description: Represents and promotes the small business sector. Provides management assistance to current and prospective small business owners. Helps to improve management skills and expand the products and services of members.

49426 ■ San Luis Valley Small Business Development Center
610 State Ave., Ste. 120
Alamosa, CO 81102
Ph: (719)589-3682
Co. E-mail: donna@slv-sbdc.com
URL: http://www.coloradosbdc.org
Contact: Donna Wehe, Director
Description: Represents and promotes the small business sector. Provides management assistance to current and prospective small business owners. Helps to improve management skills and expand the products and services of members.

49427 ■ South Metro Denver Small Business Development Center - Aurora
6840 S University Blvd.
Centennial, CO 80122

Ph: (303)795-0142
Co. E-mail: info@smallbusinessdenver.com
URL: http://www.coloradosbdc.org
Contact: Marcia McGilley, Director
URL(s): www.smallbusinessdenver.com. **Description:** Represents and promotes the small business sector. Provides management assistance to current and prospective small business owners. Helps to improve management skills and expand the products and services of members.

49428 ■ South Metro Denver Small Business Development Center - Centennial
6840 S University Blvd.
Centennial, CO 80122
Ph: (303)795-0142
Fax: (303)795-7520
Co. E-mail: info@smallbusinessdenver.com
URL: http://www.smallbusinessdenver.com
Description: Provides assistance to individuals who are interested in starting a new business. Provides free or low-cost training through workshops and programs as well as one-on-one consulting with experienced entrepreneurs. Helps small business owners develop a one-page strategic plan for their businesses using the Rockefeller Habits methodology and a combination of application, assessment, coaching and weekly action steps.

49429 ■ Southwest Colorado Small Business Development Center - Durango
2700 Main Ave.
Durango, CO 81301
Ph: (970)247-7009
Co. E-mail: asano_l@fortlewis.edu
URL: http://www.coloradosbdc.org/center.
  aspx?center=2170&subloc=4
Contact: Joe Keck, Director
Description: Represents and promotes the small business sector. Provides management assistance to current and prospective small business owners. Helps to improve management skills and expand the products and services of members.

49430 ■ Southwest Colorado Small Business Development Center - Pagosa
402 San Juan Dr.
Pagosa Springs, CO 81147
Ph: (970)247-7009
Co. E-mail: asano_l@fortlewis.edu
URL: http://www.coloradosbdc.org/center.
  aspx?center=2170&subloc=2
Contact: Joe Keck, Director
Description: Represents and promotes the small business sector. Provides management assistance to current and prospective small business owners. Helps to improve management skills and expand the products and services of members.

49431 ■ Southwestern Colorado Small Business Development Center
1000 Rim Dr., EBH 140
Durango, CO 81301
Ph: (970)247-7009
Co. E-mail: sbdc@fortlewis.edu
URL: http://www.coloradosbdc.org
Contact: Joe Keck, Director
URL(s): soba.fortlewis.edu/sbdc. **Description:** Represents and promotes the small business sector. Provides management assistance to current and prospective small business owners. Helps to improve management skills and expand the products and services of members.

49432 ■ West Central Small Business Development Center
211 Savage Library
Western State College of Colorado
600 N Adams St.
Gunnison, CO 81231
Ph: (970)943-3157
Co. E-mail: sbdc@western.edu
URL: http://www.coloradosbdc.org/center.
  aspx?center=2160&subloc=0
Contact: Marilyn Laverty, Director
URL(s): www.western.edu/academics/sbdc. **Description:** Represents and promotes the small business sector. Provides management assistance to current

and prospective small business owners. Helps to improve management skills and expand the products and services of members.

49433 ■ West Central Small Business Development Center - Chaffee and Lake County
448 E 1st St., Ste. 209
Salida, CO 81201
Ph: (719)395-4099
Co. E-mail: mlaverty@western.edu
URL: http://www.coloradosbdc.org/center.
  aspx?center=2160&subloc=1
Contact: Marilyn Laverty, Director
Description: Represents and promotes the small business sector. Provides management assistance to current and prospective small business owners. Helps to improve management skills and expand the products and services of members.

49434 ■ West Metro Small Business Development Center
1667 Cole Blvd.
Bldg. 19, Ste. 400
Lakewood, CO 80401
Ph: (303)620-8076
Co. E-mail: sara.reimnitz@denversbdc.org
URL: http://www.coloradosbdc.org
Description: Represents and promotes the small business sector. Provides management assistance to current and prospective small business owners. Helps to improve management skills and expand the products and services of members.

SMALL BUSINESS ASSISTANCE PROGRAMS

49435 ■ Colorado Office of Economic Development and International Trade - Colorado International Trade Office
1625 Broadway, Ste. 2700
Denver, CO 80202
Ph: (303)892-3840
Fax: (303)892-3848
Co. E-mail: ito@state.co.us
URL: http://www.state.co.us/oed
Contact: Pam Reichert, Director
Description: Promotes the export of Colorado's products and assists businesses in many aspects of exporting.

49436 ■ Colorado Office of Economic Development and International Trade - Small Business Development Center
1625 Broadway, Ste. 2700
Denver, CO 80202
Ph: (303)892-3840
Free: 800-333-7798
Fax: (303)892-3848
Co. E-mail: kelly.manning@state.co.us
URL: http://www.coloradosbdc.org
Contact: Kelly Manning, Director
Description: Answers small business inquiries or refers them to an appropriate resource. Provides information on starting a business, marketing, financing, and other aspects of running a business.

49437 ■ Denver Metro Chamber of Commerce - Small Business Development Center
1445 Market St.
Denver, CO 80202
Ph: (303)620-8076
Fax: (303)534-2145
Co. E-mail: denver.sbdc@den-chamber.org
URL: http://www.denversbdc.org
Contact: Tameka Montgomery, Executive Director
Description: Assists companies with 100 or fewer employees. The Management Education Division provides management education and training; the Information/Networking Division sponsors meetings for small business chief executive officers for the exchange of information; and the Special Services Division is involved in such activities as legislative lobbying and sponsoring group health insurance programs for small businesses.

SCORE OFFICES

49438 ■ Grand Junction SCORE
Co. E-mail: bob@ahinet.com

BETTER BUSINESS BUREAUS

49439 ■ Better Business Bureau of Denver
1020 Cherokee St.
Denver, CO 80204-4039
Ph: (303)758-2100
Fax: (303)577-8101
Co. E-mail: info@denver.bbb.org
URL: http://denver.bbb.org
Contact: Dale Mingilton, President
Description: Seeks to build and ensure a fair, honest, safe, marketplace in the Denver, CO area community by fostering ethical, fair, and honest relations between buyers and sellers. Promotes business self resolution in the traditional and electronic marketplace, while providing credibility and exceptional value for members. **Founded:** 1951. **Publications:** Torch Report (Bimonthly). **Awards:** Consumer Choice Award (Annual).

49440 ■ Better Business Bureau of the Mountain States
8020 S County Rd. 5, Ste. 100
Fort Collins, CO 80528-8994
Ph: (970)484-1348
Free: 800-564-0371
Fax: (970)221-1239
Co. E-mail: info@wynco.bbb.org
URL: http://wynco.bbb.org
Contact: Pamela King, President
Description: Seeks to promote and foster ethical relationship between businesses and the public through voluntary self-regulation, consumer and business education, and service excellence. Provides information to help consumers and businesses make informed purchasing decisions and avoid costly scams and frauds; settles consumer complaints through arbitration and other means.

49441 ■ Better Business Bureau of Southern Colorado
25 N Wahsatch Ave.
Colorado Springs, CO 80903
Ph: (719)636-1155
Free: 866-206-1800
Fax: (719)636-5078
Co. E-mail: info@bbbsc.org
URL: http://www.southerncolorado.bbb.org
Contact: Carol Odell, Chief Executive Officer
Description: Seeks to promote and foster the highest ethical relationship between businesses and the public through voluntary self-regulation, consumer and business education, and service excellence. Provides information to help consumers and businesses make informed purchasing decisions and avoid costly scams and frauds; settles consumer complaints through arbitration and other means. **Telecommunication Services:** janeb@bbbsc.org.

49442 ■ Torch Report
1020 Cherokee St.
Denver, CO 80204-4039
Ph: (303)758-2100
Fax: (303)577-8101
Co. E-mail: info@denver.bbb.org
URL: http://denver.bbb.org
Contact: Dale Mingilton, President
Released: Bimonthly

CHAMBERS OF COMMERCE

49443 ■ Activity Guidelines
PO Box 774408
Steamboat Springs, CO 80477-4408
Ph: (970)879-0880
Free: 877-754-2269
Fax: (970)285-3550
Co. E-mail: info@steamboatchamber.com
URL: http://www.steamboat-chamber.com
Contact: Tom Kern, Chief Executive Officer
Price: included in membership dues.

49444 ■ *Advocate*
300 Main St.
Fort Morgan, CO 80701
Ph: (970)867-6702
Free: 800-354-8660
Fax: (970)867-6121
Co. E-mail: fortmorganchamber@flci.net
URL: http://www.fortmorganchamber.org
Contact: Kelley Kreegar-Baugh, Executive Director

49445 ■ Alamosa County Chamber of Commerce (ACCC)
610 State St.
Alamosa, CO 81101
Ph: (719)589-3681
Fax: (719)589-1773
Co. E-mail: office@alamosachamber.com
URL: http://alamosa.com
Contact: Ms. Barbara McGinnis, Office Manager
Description: Promotes business and community development in Alamosa County, CO. **Founded:** 1923. **Publications:** *Chamber Chatter* (Monthly).

49446 ■ Arvada Chamber of Commerce
7305 Grandview Ave.
Arvada, CO 80002-9960
Ph: (303)424-0313
Fax: (303)424-5370
Co. E-mail: dot@arvadachamber.org
URL: http://www.arvadachamber.org
Contact: Dot Wright, President
Description: Promotes business and community development in the Arvada/Westminster area. Facilitates communication and cooperation among area businesspeople. **Founded:** 1925. **Publications:** *Insider* (Weekly); *Membership Directory/Community Resource Guide* (Annual); *Northwest Metro Business Network Book* (Annual). **Educational Activities:** Arvada Chamber of Commerce Breakfast (Semiweekly); Arvada Chamber of Commerce Luncheon (Semiweekly).

49447 ■ Aspen Chamber Resort Association (ACRA)
425 Rio Grande Pl.
Aspen, CO 81611
Ph: (970)925-1940
Free: 800-670-0792
Fax: (970)920-1173
Co. E-mail: info@aspenchamber.org
URL: http://www.aspenchamber.org
Contact: Debbie Contini Braun, President
Description: Serves the Aspen business and residential community by: attracting visitors to the resort, providing valuable services to member businesses, and facilitating community synergy among government and local civic organizations.

49448 ■ Aurora Chamber of Commerce
562 Sable Blvd., Ste. 200
Aurora, CO 80011-0809
Ph: (303)344-1500
Fax: (303)344-1564
Co. E-mail: info@aurorachamber.org
URL: http://www.aurorachamber.org
Contact: Kevin Hougen, President
Description: Strives to maintain a strong business climate and a thriving community. Provide business networking and services in Aurora, CO area. **Founded:** 1901. **Publications:** *Impact* (Monthly). **Educational Activities:** Business for the Arts Committee (Monthly). **Awards:** Business for the Arts Award (Annual); Business Person of the Year (Annual); Community Leadership Award (Annual); Humanitarian of the Year (Annual); Man of the Year (Annual); Small Business Person of the Year (Annual); Woman of the Year (Annual).

49449 ■ *Aware*
5400 Stone Creek Cir.
Loveland, CO 80538-8838
Ph: (970)667-6311
Fax: (970)667-5211
Co. E-mail: info@loveland.org
URL: http://www.loveland.org
Contact: Brian Willms, President
Released: Monthly

49450 ■ Basalt Chamber of Commerce
PO Box 514
Basalt, CO 81621-0514
Ph: (970)927-4031
Fax: (970)927-2833
Co. E-mail: info@basaltchamber.com
URL: http://www.basaltchamber.org
Contact: Heather Smith, Executive Director
Description: Promotes business and community development in Basalt, Eljebel and old Snowmass, CO.

49451 ■ Berthoud Area Chamber of Commerce
345 Mountain Ave.
Berthoud, CO 80513
Ph: (970)532-4200
Fax: (970)532-7690
Co. E-mail: bcc@berthoudcolorado.com
URL: http://www.berthoudcolorado.com
Contact: Don Dana, Executive Director
Description: Promotes business and community development in Berthoud, CO. **Publications:** *The Garden Spot of Colorado* (Monthly); *Berthoud Area Chamber of Commerce--Member Directory and Visitor Guide*.

49452 ■ Boulder Chamber of Commerce
PO Box 73
Boulder, CO 80302
Ph: (303)442-1044
Fax: (303)938-8837
Co. E-mail: susan.graf@boulderchamber.com
URL: http://www.boulderchamber.com
Contact: Susan Graf, President
Description: Promotes business and community development in Boulder, CO. **Founded:** 1905. **Publications:** *Chamber Today.*

49453 ■ Breckenridge Resort Chamber of Commerce (BRC)
PO Box 1909
Breckenridge, CO 80424-1909
Ph: (970)453-2918
Free: 888-251-2417
Fax: (970)453-7238
Co. E-mail: gobreck@gobreck.com
URL: http://www.gobreck.com
Contact: John McMahon, President
Description: Promotes business, community development, and tourism in Breckenridge, CO. **Founded:** 1971. **Publications:** *Great Times.* **Educational Activities:** Breckenridge Resort Chamber of Commerce Tradeshow (Annual).

49454 ■ Broomfield Chamber of Commerce—Chamber Serving the Broomfield Area
2095 W 6th Ave., Ste. 109
Broomfield, CO 80020
Ph: (303)466-1775
Fax: (303)466-4481
Co. E-mail: info@broomfieldchamber.com
URL: http://www.broomfieldchamber.com
Contact: Jennifer Kerr, President
Description: Promotes business and community development in the Broomfield, CO area. **Founded:** 1975. **Publications:** *The Broomfielder* (Monthly); *Update* (Periodic); *The Broomfielder* (Monthly). **Educational Activities:** Business After Hours (Monthly).

49455 ■ *The Broomfielder*
2095 W 6th Ave., Ste. 109
Broomfield, CO 80020
Ph: (303)466-1775
Fax: (303)466-4481
Co. E-mail: info@broomfieldchamber.com
URL: http://www.broomfieldchamber.com
Contact: Jennifer Kerr, President
Released: Monthly

49456 ■ Brush Chamber of Commerce—Brush Area Chamber of Commerce
1215 Edison St.
Brush, CO 80723
Ph: (970)842-2666
Free: 800-354-8659

Fax: (970)842-3828
Co. E-mail: brush@brushchamber.org
URL: http://www.brushchamber.org
Contact: Dr. Ronald Prascher, Executive Director
Description: Promotes business and community development in the Brush, CO area. **Founded:** 1902.

49457 ■ Buena Vista Area Chamber of Commerce
343 Hwy. 24 S
Buena Vista, CO 81211
Ph: (719)395-6612
Co. E-mail: buenavista@vtinet.com
URL: http://www.buenavistacolorado.org
Contact: Judy Hassell, Executive Director
Description: Promotes business, community development, and tourism in Buena Vista, CO. Maintains visitor's bureau. Sponsors Fourth of July Celebration, Gold Rush Days, Christmas Opening, and trade show. **Founded:** 1929. **Publications:** *Buena Vista Chamber of Commerce Newsletter* (Monthly); *Business and Information Directory* (Annual). **Educational Activities:** Buena Vista Area Chamber of Commerce Board meeting (Weekly); Business After Hours (Monthly). **Awards:** Attaboys (Annual); Citizen of the Year (Annual); Honorary Members (Annual).

49458 ■ *Business Connection*
PO Box 1018
Lafayette, CO 80026
Ph: (303)666-9555
Fax: (303)666-4392
Co. E-mail: info@lafayettecolorado.com
URL: http://www.lafayettecolorado.com
Contact: Vicki Trumbo, Executive Director
Released: Monthly

49459 ■ *Business Directory and Community Guide*
PO Box 1018
Lafayette, CO 80026
Ph: (303)666-9555
Fax: (303)666-4392
Co. E-mail: info@lafayettecolorado.com
URL: http://www.lafayettecolorado.com
Contact: Vicki Trumbo, Executive Director
Released: Annual

49460 ■ *Calendar of Events*
PO Box 81
Westcliffe, CO 81252-0081
Ph: (719)783-9163
Free: 877-793-3170
Fax: (719)783-2724
Co. E-mail: info@custercountyco.com
URL: http://www.custercountyco.com
Contact: Donna Hood, President

49461 ■ Canon City Chamber of Commerce
403 Royal Gorge Blvd.
Canon City, CO 81212
Ph: (719)275-2331
Free: 800-876-7922
Fax: (719)275-2332
Co. E-mail: chamber@canoncity.com
URL: http://www.canoncity.com/index.php
Contact: Larry Oddo, President
Description: Promotes business and community development in Canon City, CO. **Founded:** 1892. **Publications:** *Chamber Update* (Monthly). **Awards:** Designate Canon City Distinguished Citizen (Annual).

49462 ■ Carbondale Community Chamber of Commerce (CCCC)
PO Box 1645
Carbondale, CO 81623
Ph: (970)963-1890
Fax: (970)963-4719
Co. E-mail: chamber@carbondale.com
URL: http://www.carbondale.com
Contact: Ms. Sherri Harrison, Executive Director
Description: Promotes business and community development in Carbondale, CO. **Founded:** 1947. **Publications:** *Membership Directory and Area Guide* (Annual).

49463 ▪ Castle Rock Chamber of Commerce (CRCC)
420 Jerry St.
Castle Rock, CO 80104
Ph: (303)688-4597
Free: 866-441-8508
Fax: (303)688-2688
Co. E-mail: info@castlerock.org
URL: http://www.castlerock.org
Contact: Pam Ridler, President
Description: Promotes the economic well-being of Castle Rock, CO; provides a forum for members to promote their businesses; and serves as the voice of the Castle Rock business community. Sponsors art festival. **Founded:** 1954.

49464 ▪ Cedaredge Area Chamber of Commerce (CCC)
245 W Main St.
Cedaredge, CO 81413
Ph: (970)856-6961
Fax: (970)856-7292
Co. E-mail: cedaredgech@tds.net
URL: http://www.cedaredgechamber.com
Contact: Eileen Liles, President
Description: Promotes business, community development, and tourism in Cedaredge, CO. Hosts Little Britches Rodeo; sponsors Apple Days Festival and other activities. **Founded:** 1976.

49465 ▪ Chamber Chat
PO Box 147
Monument, CO 80132
Ph: (719)481-3282
Fax: (719)481-1638
Co. E-mail: kstensland@trilakeschamber.com
URL: http://www.trilakeschamber.com
Contact: Mr. David T. Van Ness, Executive Director
Released: Weekly

49466 ▪ Chamber Chatter
610 State St.
Alamosa, CO 81101
Ph: (719)589-3681
Fax: (719)589-1773
Co. E-mail: office@alamosachamber.com
URL: http://alamosa.com
Contact: Ms. Barbara McGinnis, Office Manager
Released: Monthly **Price:** included in membership dues.

49467 ▪ Chamber Commentaries
PO Box 968
Cortez, CO 81321
Ph: (970)565-3414
Fax: (970)565-8373
Co. E-mail: cortezchamber@cityofcortez.com
URL: http://www.cortezchamber.com
Contact: Dena Guttridge, Executive Director
Released: Monthly **Price:** free for members.

49468 ▪ Chamber Communique
PO Box 201
Fountain, CO 80817-0201
Ph: (719)382-3190
Fax: (719)322-9395
Co. E-mail: fvcc@qwest.net
URL: http://www.fountaincolorado.org/department/
index.asp?fDD=25-0
Contact: Scott Turner, President
Released: Quarterly

49469 ▪ The Chamber Compass
225 S Meldrum St.
PO Drawer D
Fort Collins, CO 80521
Ph: (970)482-3746
Fax: (970)482-3774
Co. E-mail: general@fcchamber.org
URL: http://www.fortcollinschamber.com
Contact: David L. May, President
Released: Monthly

49470 ▪ The Chamber Connection
111 S Camino Del Rio
Durango, CO 81302
Ph: (970)247-0312
Free: 888-414-0835

Fax: (970)385-7884
Co. E-mail: chamber@durangobusiness.org
URL: http://www.durangobusiness.org
Contact: Jack Llewellyn, Executive Director
Released: Monthly

49471 ▪ Chamber Connection
PO Box 501
Johnstown, CO 80534-0501
Ph: (970)587-7042
Co. E-mail: info@johnstownmillikenchamber.com
URL: http://jmchamber.com
Contact: Tanis Roeder, President
Released: Bimonthly

49472 ▪ Chamber Currents
1519 E Main St.
Montrose, CO 81401-3807
Ph: (970)249-5000
Free: 800-923-5515
Fax: (970)249-2907
Co. E-mail: info@montrosechamber.com
URL: http://www.montrosechamber.com
Contact: Ken Brengle, President
Released: Monthly

49473 ▪ Chamber E-News
PO Box 861
Leadville, CO 80461-0861
Ph: (719)486-3900
Free: 888-532-3845
Fax: (719)486-8478
Co. E-mail: leadville@leadvilleusa.com
URL: http://www.leadvilleusa.com
Contact: Heather Scanlon, Executive Director
Released: Monthly **Price:** free for members.

49474 ▪ Chamber Highlights
PO Box 1683
Sterling, CO 80751
Ph: (970)522-5070
Free: 866-522-5070
Fax: (970)522-4082
Co. E-mail: loganccc@logancountychamber.com
URL: http://www.logancountychamber.com
Contact: Rocky Joy, President
Released: Periodic

49475 ▪ Chamber Report
902 7th Ave.
Greeley, CO 80631-4603
Ph: (970)352-3566
Free: 800-449-3866
Fax: (970)352-3572
Co. E-mail: info@greeleychamber.com
URL: http://www.greeleychamber.com
Contact: Sarah MacQuiddy, President
Released: Monthly

49476 ▪ Chamber Today
PO Box 73
Boulder, CO 80302
Ph: (303)442-1044
Fax: (303)938-8837
Co. E-mail: susan.graf@boulderchamber.com
URL: http://www.boulderchamber.com
Contact: Susan Graf, President

49477 ▪ Chamber Update
403 Royal Gorge Blvd.
Canon City, CO 81212
Ph: (719)275-2331
Free: 800-876-7922
Fax: (719)275-2332
Co. E-mail: chamber@canoncity.com
URL: http://www.canoncity.com/index.php
Contact: Larry Oddo, President
Released: Monthly **Price:** $0.35.

49478 ▪ Chamber View
6 S Tejon St., Ste. 700
Colorado Springs, CO 80903
Ph: (719)635-1551
Fax: (719)635-1571
Co. E-mail: info@cscc.org
URL: http://www.coloradospringschamber.org
Contact: Dave Csintyan, President
Released: Monthly

49479 ▪ The Chamber Weekly
225 S Meldrum St.
PO Drawer D
Fort Collins, CO 80521
Ph: (970)482-3746
Fax: (970)482-3774
Co. E-mail: general@fcchamber.org
URL: http://www.fortcollinschamber.com
Contact: David L. May, President
Released: Weekly

49480 ▪ Comercio
924 W Colfax Ave., Ste. No. 201
Denver, CO 80204
Ph: (303)534-7783
Fax: (303)595-8977
Co. E-mail: info@hispanicchamberdenver.org
URL: http://www.dhcc.com
Contact: Jeffrey Campos, President
Released: Monthly **Price:** free.

49481 ▪ Conifer Chamber of Commerce
PO Box 127
Conifer, CO 80433
Ph: (303)838-5711
Fax: (303)838-5712
Co. E-mail: director@goconifer.com
URL: http://www.goconifer.com
Contact: Dawn Smith, Executive Director
Description: Provides leadership for the community, promotes local resources, enhances local programs, and coordinates development efforts.

49482 ▪ Cortez Area Chamber of Commerce (CACC)
PO Box 968
Cortez, CO 81321
Ph: (970)565-3414
Fax: (970)565-8373
Co. E-mail: cortezchamber@cityofcortez.com
URL: http://www.cortezchamber.com
Contact: Dena Guttridge, Executive Director
Description: Promotes business and community development in the Cortez, CO area. Sponsors area festivals and charitable events. Conducts competitions. Convention/Meeting: none. **Founded:** 1926.
Publications: *Chamber Commentaries* (Monthly).

49483 ▪ Costilla County Chamber of Commerce
PO Box 428
Fort Garland, CO 81133
Ph: (719)379-3512
Co. E-mail: sanluis2@fone.net
URL: http://slvguide.com/COSTILLA/CONTACTUS.
HTML
Description: Promotes business, community development, and tourism in Costilla County, Colorado.

49484 ▪ Craig Chamber of Commerce
360 E Victory Way
Craig, CO 81625
Ph: (970)824-5689
Free: 800-864-4405
Fax: (970)824-0231
Co. E-mail: info@craig-chamber.com
URL: http://www.craig-chamber.com
Contact: Christina Curie, Executive Director
Description: Promotes business, community development, and tourism in Moffat County, CO. **Founded:** 1947.

49485 ▪ Crawford Area Chamber of Commerce (CACC)
PO Box 22
Crawford, CO 81415
Ph: (970)921-4000
Co. E-mail: info@crawfordcountry.org
URL: http://www.crawfordcountry.org
Description: Promotes cooperation among businesses, professionals and community citizens to improve the business environment of the Crawford area.

49486 ▪ Creede - Mineral County Chamber of Commerce
PO Box 580
Creede, CO 81130-0580
Ph: (719)658-2374

Free: 800-327-2102
Fax: (719)658-2717
Co. E-mail: chamber@creede.com
URL: http://www.creede.com/chamber.htm
Description: Seeks to encourage, foster, and protect the growth and integrity of the Mineral County, CO area through careful economic and community planning and promotion.

49487 ■ Crested Butte/Mount Crested Butte Chamber of Commerce (CBCC)
601 Elk Ave.
Crested Butte, CO 81224
Ph: (970)349-6438
Free: 800-545-4505
Fax: (970)349-1023
Co. E-mail: cbinfo@cbchamber.com
URL: http://www.cbchamber.com/index.html
Contact: Richard Bond, Executive Director
Description: Promotes business and community development in Crested Butte, and Mt. Crested Butte, CO. **Founded:** 1972.

49488 ■ Cripple Creek Chamber of Commerce (CCCC)
PO Box 430
Cripple Creek, CO 80813
Ph: (719)689-3461
Free: 877-858-4653
Fax: (719)689-2774
Co. E-mail: info@cripple-creek.co.us
URL: http://www.cripple-creek.co.us
Description: Promotes business and community development in Cripple Creek, CO. **Founded:** 1984.

49489 ■ Custer County Merchants and Chamber of Commerce
PO Box 81
Westcliffe, CO 81252-0081
Ph: (719)783-9163
Free: 877-793-3170
Fax: (719)783-2724
Co. E-mail: info@custercountyco.com
URL: http://www.custercountyco.com
Contact: Donna Hood, President
Description: Promotes business and community development in Custer County, CO. Sponsors bike race and Fourth of July celebration. **Founded:** 1938. **Publications:** Calendar of Events.

49490 ■ Del Norte Chamber of Commerce (DNCC)
505 Grande Ave.
Del Norte, CO 81132
Ph: (719)657-2845
Free: 888-616-4638
Co. E-mail: mail@delnortechamber.org
URL: http://www.delnortechamber.org
Description: Promotes business, community development, and tourism in Del Norte, CO. Sponsors Covered Wagon Days, Christmas Merchants' open house and logging events. **Founded:** 1972.

49491 ■ Delta Area Chamber of Commerce
301 Main St.
Delta, CO 81416-1881
Ph: (970)874-8616
Fax: (970)874-8618
Co. E-mail: chamber@deltacolorado.org
URL: http://www.deltacolorado.org
Description: Promotes business and community development in the Delta, CO area.

49492 ■ Denver Hispanic Chamber of Commerce
924 W Colfax Ave., Ste. No. 201
Denver, CO 80204
Ph: (303)534-7783
Fax: (303)595-8977
Co. E-mail: info@hispanicchamberdenver.org
URL: http://www.dhcc.com
Contact: Jeffrey Campos, President
Description: Promotes business and community development in the Hispanic community Denver, CO. **Publications:** Comercio (Monthly). **Educational Activities:** Business After Hours (Monthly).

49493 ■ Denver Metro Chamber of Commerce
1445 Market St.
Denver, CO 80202
Ph: (303)534-8500
Fax: (303)534-3200
Co. E-mail: info@denverchamber.org
URL: http://www.denverchamber.org
Contact: Kelly J. Brough, President
Description: Works to promote the development of civic leadership in the business community and fosters opportunities for increased cooperation among the private, public, and nonprofit sectors in Denver, CO area. **Founded:** 1876. **Publications:** Denver Metro Chamber of Commerce--Membership Directory and Buyer's Guide.

49494 ■ Dining Guide
PO Box 774408
Steamboat Springs, CO 80477-4408
Ph: (970)879-0880
Free: 877-754-2269
Fax: (970)285-3550
Co. E-mail: info@steamboatchamber.com
URL: http://www.steamboat-chamber.com
Contact: Tom Kern, Chief Executive Officer
Price: included in membership dues.

49495 ■ Dolores Chamber of Commerce
201 Railroad Ave.
Dolores, CO 81323
Ph: (970)882-4018
Co. E-mail: doloreschamber@centurytel.net
URL: http://www.doloreschamber.com
Contact: Larry Engel, Treasurer
Description: Promotes business and community development in Dolores, CO.

49496 ■ Durango Chamber of Commerce
111 S Camino Del Rio
Durango, CO 81302
Ph: (970)247-0312
Free: 888-414-0835
Fax: (970)385-7884
Co. E-mail: chamber@durangobusiness.org
URL: http://www.durangobusiness.org
Contact: Jack Llewellyn, Executive Director
Description: Works to promote and support the local business community. Acts as a resource of information for its members, the community, and relocation inquirers. **Founded:** 1931. **Publications:** The Chamber Connection (Monthly).

49497 ■ EACOC Connection
166 Main St., Ste. E
Elizabeth, CO 80107
Ph: (303)646-4287
Fax: (303)646-2509
Co. E-mail: director@elizabethchamber.org
URL: http://www.elizabethchamber.org
Contact: Beverly Durant, Director

49498 ■ Eads Chamber of Commerce (ECC)
PO Box 163
Eads, CO 81036-0163
Ph: (719)438-5590
Co. E-mail: dennis.pearson@state.co.us
URL: http://www.kiowacountycolo.com/chamber-ofcommerce.htm
Contact: Dennis Pearson, President
Description: Promotes business and community development in Eads, CO. Sponsors Eads Appreciation Day and Mixed Bag Hunt.

49499 ■ Eagle Valley Chamber of Commerce (EVCC)
PO Box 964
Eagle, CO 81631
Ph: (970)328-5220
Fax: (970)328-1120
Co. E-mail: evcc@centurytel.net
URL: http://www.eaglevalley.org
Description: Promotes business and community development in Eagle, CO. **Founded:** 1948. **Awards:** Citizen of the Year Extravaganza (Annual); Community Involvement Scholarship (Annual).

49500 ■ Economic Profile
210 E Midland Ave.
Woodland Park, CO 80866-9022
Ph: (719)687-9885
Free: 800-551-7886
Fax: (719)687-8216
Co. E-mail: info@gwpcc.biz
URL: http://www.woodlandparkchamber.com
Contact: Ms. Debbie Miller, President
Released: Annual

49501 ■ Elizabeth Area Chamber of Commerce (EACOC)
166 Main St., Ste. E
Elizabeth, CO 80107
Ph: (303)646-4287
Fax: (303)646-2509
Co. E-mail: director@elizabethchamber.org
URL: http://www.elizabethchamber.org
Contact: Beverly Durant, Director
Description: Promotes business and community development in Elizabeth, CO and the surrounding area in Elbert County. Sponsors ElizaBash, Harvest Festival, Olde Country Christmas and Art in the Pines. **Founded:** 1948. **Publications:** EACOC Connection.

49502 ■ Erie Chamber of Commerce
235 Wells St.
Erie, CO 80516
Ph: (303)828-3440
Fax: (303)828-3330
Co. E-mail: erie@eriechamber.org
URL: http://www.eriechamber.org
Contact: Elle Cabbage, Executive Director
Description: Works to advance the commercial, financial, industrial and civic interests of Erie, CO.

49503 ■ Estes Park Chamber of Commerce (EPCC)
500 Big Thompson Ave.
Estes Park, CO 80517
Ph: (970)577-9900
Free: 800-378-3708
URL: http://www.estesparkresort.com
Description: Promotes business and community development in the Estes Park, CO area. **Founded:** 1997.

49504 ■ Evergreen
30480 Stagecoach Blvd., Ste. C
Evergreen, CO 80439
Ph: (303)674-3412
Fax: (303)674-8463
Co. E-mail: info@evergreenchamber.org
URL: http://www.evergreenchamber.org
Contact: Lin Browning, President

49505 ■ Evergreen Area Chamber of Commerce
30480 Stagecoach Blvd., Ste. C
Evergreen, CO 80439
Ph: (303)674-3412
Fax: (303)674-8463
Co. E-mail: info@evergreenchamber.org
URL: http://www.evergreenchamber.org
Contact: Lin Browning, President
Description: Promotes business and community development in Evergreen, CO. **Scope:** business. **Founded:** 1970. **Subscriptions:** 150. **Publications:** Evergreen; The Voice (Monthly). **Awards:** Business of the Year (Annual). **Telecommunication Services:** admin@evergreenchamber.org; president@evergreenchamber.org.

49506 ■ Florence Chamber of Commerce
117 S Pikes Peak
Florence, CO 81226
Ph: (719)784-3544
Fax: (719)784-9324
URL: http://www.florencecolorado.net
Description: Promotes business and community development in eastern Fremont county, Florence, CO. Conducts Snowball Softball competition, annual Pioneer Day festival, and Hardscrabble 100 Mile Bicycle Race. Sponsors charitable Christmas activities.

49507 ■ Fort Collins Area Chamber of Commerce
225 S Meldrum St.
PO Drawer D
Fort Collins, CO 80521
Ph: (970)482-3746
Fax: (970)482-3774
Co. E-mail: general@fcchamber.org
URL: http://www.fortcollinschamber.com
Contact: David L. May, President
Description: Promotes business and community development in the Ft. Collins, CO area. **Founded:** 1904. **Publications:** *The Chamber Compass* (Monthly); *The Chamber Weekly* (Weekly). **Educational Activities:** Business Before Hours (Monthly).

49508 ■ Fort Morgan Area Chamber of Commerce
300 Main St.
Fort Morgan, CO 80701
Ph: (970)867-6702
Free: 800-354-8660
Fax: (970)867-6121
Co. E-mail: fortmorganchamber@flci.net
URL: http://www.fortmorganchamber.org
Contact: Kelley Kreegar-Baugh, Executive Director
Description: Promotes business and community development in the Ft. Morgan, CO area. **Founded:** 1919. **Publications:** *Advocate.*

49509 ■ Fountain Valley Chamber of Commerce
PO Box 201
Fountain, CO 80817-0201
Ph: (719)382-3190
Fax: (719)322-9395
Co. E-mail: fvcc@qwest.net
URL: http://www.fountaincolorado.org/department/index.asp?fDD=25-0
Contact: Scott Turner, President
Description: Promotes business and community development in Fountain, CO. **Publications:** *Chamber Communique* (Quarterly).

49510 ■ *Fruit & Wine Directory*
319 S Main St.
Palisade, CO 81526
Ph: (970)464-7458
Fax: (970)464-4757
Co. E-mail: info@palisadecoc.com
URL: http://www.palisadecoc.com
Contact: Ms. Margie Latta, Chairperson
Released: Annual

49511 ■ Fruita Chamber of Commerce
432 E Aspen Ave.
Fruita, CO 81521
Ph: (970)858-3894
Fax: (970)858-3121
Co. E-mail: info@fruitachamber.org
URL: http://www.fruitachamber.org
Contact: Mary Lou Wilson, Director
Description: Promotes business and community development in Fruita, CO.

49512 ■ *The Garden Spot of Colorado*
345 Mountain Ave.
Berthoud, CO 80513
Ph: (970)532-4200
Fax: (970)532-7690
Co. E-mail: bcc@berthoudcolorado.com
URL: http://www.berthoudcolorado.com
Contact: Don Dana, Executive Director
Released: Monthly

49513 ■ Granby Chamber of Commerce (GCC)
PO Box 35
Granby, CO 80446
Ph: (970)887-2311
Free: 800-325-1661
Fax: (970)887-3895
Co. E-mail: grcoc@rkymtnhi.com
URL: http://granbychamber.com
Contact: Kim Burner, Chairperson
Description: Works to advance economic welfare and civic pride in the greater Granby area while preserving its unique cultural heritage and sense of

community. **Founded:** 1947. **Subscriptions:** clippings. **Publications:** *The Heart Beat* (Monthly). **Awards:** Business Person of the Year (Annual).

49514 ■ Grand Junction Area Chamber of Commerce
360 Grand Ave.
Grand Junction, CO 81501
Ph: (970)242-3214
Free: 800-352-5286
Fax: (970)242-3694
Co. E-mail: diane@gjchamber.org
URL: http://www.gjchamber.org
Contact: Diane Schwenke, President
Description: Promotes business and community development in the Grand Junction, CO area. **Publications:** *Grand Junction Area Chamber of Commerce--Business Directory.*

49515 ■ Grand Lake Area Chamber of Commerce
PO Box 429
Grand Lake, CO 80447
Ph: (970)627-3402
Free: 800-531-1019
Fax: (970)627-8007
Co. E-mail: glinfo@grandlakechamber.com
URL: http://www.grandlakechamber.com
Contact: Sara Sable, Executive Director
Description: Promotes business and community development in the Grand Lake, CO area. **Founded:** 1946. **Publications:** *Investment Report* (Monthly).

49516 ■ *Great Times*
PO Box 1909
Breckenridge, CO 80424-1909
Ph: (970)453-2918
Free: 888-251-2417
Fax: (970)453-7238
Co. E-mail: gobreck@gobreck.com
URL: http://www.gobreck.com
Contact: John McMahon, President

49517 ■ Greater Brighton Area Chamber of Commerce
36 S Main St.
Brighton, CO 80601
Ph: (303)655-2169
Fax: (303)655-2153
Co. E-mail: kwelch@brightonedc.org
URL: http://www.brightonchamber.com
Contact: Brian Lewis, Chairman
Description: Promotes business and community development in the Brighton, CO area.

49518 ■ Greater Colorado Springs Chamber of Commerce (GCSCC)
6 S Tejon St., Ste. 700
Colorado Springs, CO 80903
Ph: (719)635-1551
Fax: (719)635-1571
Co. E-mail: info@cscc.org
URL: http://www.coloradospringschamber.org
Contact: Dave Csintyan, President
Description: Promotes business and community development in Colorado Springs, CO. **Founded:** 1892. **Publications:** *Chamber View* (Monthly); *Magazine* (Monthly).

49519 ■ Greater Englewood Chamber of Commerce (ECC)
3501 S Broadway, 2nd Fl.
Englewood, CO 80110-3629
Ph: (303)789-4473
Fax: (303)789-0098
URL: http://www.myenglewoodchamber.com
Contact: Colleen Mello, Director
E-mail: colleen@myenglewoodchamber.com
Description: Promotes business and community development in the Englewood, CO area. **Founded:** 1983. **Publications:** *Greater Englewood Chamber of Commerce Membership Directory and Buyers Guide* (Biennial).

49520 ■ Greater Golden Chamber of Commerce (GGCC)
1010 Washington Ave.
Golden, CO 80401
Ph: (303)279-3113

Free: 800-590-3113
Fax: (303)279-0332
Co. E-mail: info@goldencochamber.org
URL: http://www.goldencochamber.org
Contact: Gary L. Wink, President
Description: Promotes business and community development in Golden, CO. **Founded:** 1920. **Publications:** *Greater Golden Chamber of Commerce Network* (Monthly).

49521 ■ *Greater Golden Chamber of Commerce Network*
1010 Washington Ave.
Golden, CO 80401
Ph: (303)279-3113
Free: 800-590-3113
Fax: (303)279-0332
Co. E-mail: info@goldencochamber.org
URL: http://www.goldencochamber.org
Contact: Gary L. Wink, President
Released: Monthly **Price:** free.

49522 ■ Greater Pueblo Chamber of Commerce
302 N Santa Fe Ave.
Pueblo, CO 81003-4102
Ph: (719)542-1704
Free: 800-233-3446
Co. E-mail: rod.slyhoff@usa.net
URL: http://www.pueblochamber.org
Contact: Rod Slyhoff, President
Description: Promotes business and community development in Pueblo County, CO. Acts as "the collective voice of 1,150 businesses and professionals working to improve and promote an atmosphere that not only enables the community to grow and prosper but be an outstanding place to visit, live and conduct business". **Founded:** 1910. **Publications:** *The Horizon* (Monthly); *Passport to Pueblo.*

49523 ■ Greater Woodland Park Chamber of Commerce (GWPCC)
210 E Midland Ave.
Woodland Park, CO 80866-9022
Ph: (719)687-9885
Free: 800-551-7886
Fax: (719)687-8216
Co. E-mail: info@gwpcc.biz
URL: http://www.woodlandparkchamber.com
Contact: Ms. Debbie Miller, President
Description: As the primary regional business advocate, the Greater Woodland Park Chamber of Commerce provides valuable member services, pro active leadership, economic opportunity and preservation of the free enterprise system. **Founded:** 1964. **Publications:** *Economic Profile* (Annual).

49524 ■ Greeley/Weld Chamber of Commerce
902 7th Ave.
Greeley, CO 80631-4603
Ph: (970)352-3566
Free: 800-449-3866
Fax: (970)352-3572
Co. E-mail: info@greeleychamber.com
URL: http://www.greeleychamber.com
Contact: Sarah MacQuiddy, President
Description: Promotes business and community development in the Greeley and Weld County, CO area. Provides a small business development center. **Founded:** 1920. **Publications:** *Chamber Report* (Monthly); *Greeleychamber.com* (Monthly). **Educational Activities:** Business After Hours (Monthly); Business Before Hours (Monthly). **Telecommunication Services:** sarah@greeleychamber.com.

49525 ■ *Greeleychamber.com*
902 7th Ave.
Greeley, CO 80631-4603
Ph: (970)352-3566
Free: 800-449-3866
Fax: (970)352-3572
Co. E-mail: info@greeleychamber.com
URL: http://www.greeleychamber.com
Contact: Sarah MacQuiddy, President
Released: Monthly

49526 ■ Gunnison County Chamber of Commerce (GCCC)
500 E Tomichi Ave.
Gunnison, CO 81230-0036
Ph: (970)641-1501
Fax: (970)641-3467
Co. E-mail: info@gunnisonchamber.com
URL: http://www.gunnison-co.com
Contact: Tammy Scott, Executive Director
Description: Promotes business and community development in Gunnison County, CO. Sponsors local festivals.

49527 ■ Haxtun Chamber of Commerce
145 S Colorado Ave.
Haxtun, CO 80731
Ph: (970)774-6104
Fax: (970)774-5875
Co. E-mail: webmaster@haxtunchamber.org
URL: http://www.haxtunchamber.org
Description: Promotes business and community development in the Haxtun, CO area.

49528 ■ *The Heart Beat*
PO Box 35
Granby, CO 80446
Ph: (970)887-2311
Free: 800-325-1661
Fax: (970)887-3895
Co. E-mail: grcoc@rkymtnhi.com
URL: http://granbychamber.com
Contact: Kim Burner, Chairperson
Released: Monthly

49529 ■ Heart of the Rockies Chamber of Commerce (HRCC)
406 W Hwy. 50
Salida, CO 81201
Ph: (719)539-2068
Free: 877-772-5432
Fax: (719)539-7844
Co. E-mail: info@salidachamber.org
URL: http://salidachamber.org
Contact: John Engelbrecht, Executive Director
Description: Promotes business and community development in Salida, CO.

49530 ■ Holyoke Chamber of Commerce
212 S Interocean
Holyoke, CO 80734-0134
Ph: (970)854-3517
Fax: (970)854-3514
Co. E-mail: holyokec@pctelcom.coop
URL: http://www.holyokechamber.org
Contact: Mary Tomky, Director
Description: Promotes business and community development in Holyoke, CO.

49531 ■ *The Horizon*
302 N Santa Fe Ave.
Pueblo, CO 81003-4102
Ph: (719)542-1704
Free: 800-233-3446
Co. E-mail: rod.slyhoff@usa.net
URL: http://www.pueblochamber.org
Contact: Rod Slyhoff, President
Released: Monthly

49532 ■ Hotchkiss Chamber of Commerce (HCC)
PO Box 158
Hotchkiss, CO 81419-0158
Ph: (970)872-3226
Co. E-mail: hotchkiss@hotchkisschamber.com
URL: http://www.hotchkisschamber.com
Contact: Nathan Sponseller, President
Description: Promotes business and community development in Hotchkiss area. Co-sponsors Hotchkiss Sheepcamp Stockdog trials and North Fork Valley Bluegrass Festival. **Founded:** 1950.

49533 ■ *Insider*
7305 Grandview Ave.
Arvada, CO 80002-9960
Ph: (303)424-0313

Fax: (303)424-5370
Co. E-mail: dot@arvadachamber.org
URL: http://www.arvadachamber.org
Contact: Dot Wright, President
Released: Weekly

49534 ■ *Investment Report*
PO Box 429
Grand Lake, CO 80447
Ph: (970)627-3402
Free: 800-531-1019
Fax: (970)627-8007
Co. E-mail: glinfo@grandlakechamber.com
URL: http://www.grandlakechamber.com
Contact: Sara Sable, Executive Director
Released: Monthly **Price:** $10, /year.

49535 ■ Johnstown-Milliken Chamber of Commerce
PO Box 501
Johnstown, CO 80534-0501
Ph: (970)587-7042
Co. E-mail: info@johnstownmillikenchamber.com
URL: http://jmchamber.com
Contact: Tanis Roeder, President
Description: Promotes business and community development in Johnstown, CO. Sponsors charitable events, competitions, and summer festival. **Publications:** *Chamber Connection* (Bimonthly). **Educational Activities:** Business After Hours (Monthly).

49536 ■ Kersey Area Chamber of Commerce
PO Box 397
Kersey, CO 80644-0397
Ph: (970)304-6171
Co. E-mail: sandie@unitedway-weld.org
URL: http://www.kerseycolorado.com/tp40/Default.
    asp?ID=86026
Contact: Sandie Cantrell, President
Description: Promotes business and community development in the Kersey, CO area.

49537 ■ Kremmling Area Chamber of Commerce and Visitor Center
PO Box 471
Kremmling, CO 80459
Ph: (970)724-3472
Free: 877-573-6654
Fax: (970)724-0397
Co. E-mail: info@kremmlingchamber.com
URL: http://www.kremmlingchamber.com
Description: Provides leadership for the community, promotes local resources, enhances local programs, offers good places for relocation and coordinates development efforts. **Founded:** 1984.

49538 ■ La Junta Chamber of Commerce (LJCC)
110 Santa Fe Ave.
La Junta, CO 81050
Ph: (719)384-7411
Fax: (719)384-2217
Co. E-mail: info@lajuntachamber.com
URL: http://www.lajuntachamber.com
Contact: Chandra Ochoa, President
Description: Promotes business and community development in La Junta, CO. Sponsors Early Settlers Day, community "Wake Up" breakfasts and other social and promotional events. **Founded:** 1930. **Awards:** Agriculture Award (Periodic); Community Service Award (Periodic).

49539 ■ La Veta/Cuchara Chamber of Commerce
PO Box 32
La Veta, CO 81055
Ph: (719)742-3676
Free: 866-615-3676
Co. E-mail: email@lavetacucharachamber.com
URL: http://www.lavetacucharachamber.com
Contact: Bob Baker, President
Description: Promotes business and community development in La Veta, CO.

49540 ■ Lafayette Chamber of Commerce (LCC)
PO Box 1018
Lafayette, CO 80026
Ph: (303)666-9555

Fax: (303)666-4392
Co. E-mail: info@lafayettecolorado.com
URL: http://www.lafayettecolorado.com
Contact: Vicki Trumbo, Executive Director
Description: Promotes business and community development in Lafayette, CO. **Founded:** 1954. **Publications:** *Business Connection* (Monthly); *Business Directory and Community Guide* (Annual); *Lafayette Chamber Directory* (Annual). **Educational Activities:** Celebrate Lafayette (Annual).

49541 ■ *Lafayette Chamber Directory*
PO Box 1018
Lafayette, CO 80026
Ph: (303)666-9555
Fax: (303)666-4392
Co. E-mail: info@lafayettecolorado.com
URL: http://www.lafayettecolorado.com
Contact: Vicki Trumbo, Executive Director
Released: Annual

49542 ■ Lake City - Hinsdale County Chamber of Commerce (LCCCC)
800 N Gunnison Ave.
Lake City, CO 81235
Ph: (970)944-2527
Free: 800-569-1874
Co. E-mail: info@lakecity.com
URL: http://www.lakecity.com
Description: Promotes business, community development, and tourism in Hinsdale County, CO. **Founded:** 1953.

49543 ■ Lamar Chamber of Commerce (LCC)
109A E Beech St.
Lamar, CO 81052
Ph: (719)336-4379
Fax: (719)336-4370
Co. E-mail: lamarchamber@bresnan.net
URL: http://www.lamarchamber.com
Contact: Chana Reed, Office Manager
Description: Promotes business and community development in Lamar, CO. **Founded:** 1897.

49544 ■ Las Animas - Bent County Chamber of Commerce
332 Ambassador Thompson Blvd.
Las Animas, CO 81054
Ph: (719)456-0453
Fax: (719)456-0455
Co. E-mail: russellatchamber@yahoo.com
URL: http://bentcounty.org
Contact: Russell Smith, Executive Director
Description: Aims to promote trade, commerce, general prosperity, education, social and cultural interests, commercial uniformity, integrity and interdependence among businessmen; and to disseminate information relating to the commercial, financial, industrial and cultural interest of Las Animas and Bent County.

49545 ■ Leadville/Lake County Chamber of Commerce
PO Box 861
Leadville, CO 80461-0861
Ph: (719)486-3900
Free: 888-532-3845
Fax: (719)486-8478
Co. E-mail: leadville@leadvilleusa.com
URL: http://www.leadvilleusa.com
Contact: Heather Scanlon, Executive Director
Description: Promotes business and community development in Lake County, CO. **Founded:** 1913. **Publications:** *Chamber E-News* (Monthly); *The Chamber Corner* (Weekly). **Awards:** Business of the Year (Annual); Citizen of the Year (Annual).

49546 ■ Limon Chamber of Commerce
PO Box 101
Limon, CO 80828
Ph: (719)775-9418
Co. E-mail: limonchamber@yahoo.com
URL: http://www.limonchamber.com
Contact: Donna Metcalf, President
Description: Works to advance the commercial, financial, industrial and civic interests of Limon, CO.

49547 ■ *Listing Business Directory*
PO Box 774408
Steamboat Springs, CO 80477-4408
Ph: (970)879-0880
Free: 877-754-2269
Fax: (970)285-3550
Co. E-mail: info@steamboatchamber.com
URL: http://www.steamboat-chamber.com
Contact: Tom Kern, Chief Executive Officer
Price: included in membership dues.

49548 ■ Logan County Chamber of Commerce
PO Box 1683
Sterling, CO 80751
Ph: (970)522-5070
Free: 866-522-5070
Fax: (970)522-4082
Co. E-mail: loganccc@logancountychamber.com
URL: http://www.logancountychamber.com
Contact: Rocky Joy, President
Description: Promotes business and community development in Logan County, CO. **Scope:** tax structure for start-up, board governance, business start-up info. **Founded:** 1937. **Subscriptions:** 1. **Publications:** *Chamber Highlights* (Periodic). **Awards:** Ambassador of the Year (Annual); Best Supporting Business (Annual); Business Person of the Year (Annual); Citizen of the Year (Annual); Customer Service All-Star (Annual).

49549 ■ *Longmont Area Best of Business Directory and Community Guide*
528 Main St.
Longmont, CO 80501-5537
Ph: (303)776-5295
Fax: (303)776-5657
Co. E-mail: kharding@longmontchamber.org
URL: http://www.longmontchamber.org
Contact: Kathy Weber-Harding, President
Released: Annual **Price:** free for members.

49550 ■ Longmont Area Chamber of Commerce
528 Main St.
Longmont, CO 80501-5537
Ph: (303)776-5295
Fax: (303)776-5657
Co. E-mail: kharding@longmontchamber.org
URL: http://www.longmontchamber.org
Contact: Kathy Weber-Harding, President
Description: Promotes business and community development in the Longmont, CO area. **Publications:** *Longmont Area Best of Business Directory and Community Guide* (Annual).

49551 ■ Louisville Chamber of Commerce
901 Main St.
Louisville, CO 80027
Ph: (303)666-5747
Fax: (303)666-4285
Co. E-mail: info@louisvillechamber.com
URL: http://www.louisvillechamber.com
Contact: Shelley Angell, Executive Director
Description: Works to advance the commercial, financial, industrial and civic interests of Louisville, CO.

49552 ■ Loveland Chamber of Commerce and Visitors Center
5400 Stone Creek Cir.
Loveland, CO 80538-8838
Ph: (970)667-6311
Fax: (970)667-5211
Co. E-mail: info@loveland.org
URL: http://www.loveland.org
Contact: Brian Willms, President
Description: Promotes business and community development in the Loveland, CO area. Conducts Corn Roast Festival. **Founded:** 1902. **Publications:** *Aware* (Monthly); *Membership Directory/Relocation Guide* (Annual).

49553 ■ Loveland Info Chamber of Commerce
5400 Stone Creek Cir.
Loveland, CO 80538
Ph: (970)667-6311

Fax: (970)667-5211
Co. E-mail: info@loveland.org
URL: http://www.loveland.org
Contact: Mindy McCloughan, President
Description: Promotes business and community development in the Loveland, CO area.

49554 ■ Lyons Chamber of Commerce (LCC)
PO Box 426
Lyons, CO 80540
Ph: (303)823-5215
Free: 877-LYO-NSCO
Co. E-mail: admin@lyons-colorado.com
URL: http://www.lyons-colorado.com
Contact: Jayne Rhode, President
Description: Promotes business and community development in Lyons, CO. Sponsors Lyons Good Ole Days (end of June), Colorado Fly-Casting Open Championship (late July), Safety programs, May Day (cake walk, ice cream, and wind may pole), Lyons Arborfest (late April), Sandstone Institute and special events at Christmas, Halloween, and Valentine's Day. **Founded:** 1970. **Publications:** *Lyons Directory* (Periodic). **Educational Activities:** Informational Safety Meeting (Monthly).

49555 ■ *Lyons Directory*
PO Box 426
Lyons, CO 80540
Ph: (303)823-5215
Free: 877-LYO-NSCO
Co. E-mail: admin@lyons-colorado.com
URL: http://www.lyons-colorado.com
Contact: Jayne Rhode, President
Released: Periodic **Price:** free.

49556 ■ Manitou Springs Chamber of Commerce (MSCC)—Manitou Springs Chamber of Commerce and Visitors Bureau
354 Manitou Ave.
Manitou Springs, CO 80829
Ph: (719)685-5089
Free: 800-642-2567
Fax: (719)685-0355
URL: http://www.manitousprings.org
Contact: Leslie Lewis, Executive Director
Description: Promotes business, community development and tourism in Manitou Springs, CO. **Founded:** 1961. **Publications:** *News and Views* (Monthly).

49557 ■ Meeker Chamber of Commerce
PO Box 869
Meeker, CO 81641-0869
Ph: (970)878-5510
Fax: (970)878-0271
Co. E-mail: info@meekerchamber.com
URL: http://www.meekerchamber.net
Contact: Margie Joy, President
Description: Promotes business and community development in Meeker, CO. Sponsors yearly festival.

49558 ■ *Membership Directory and Area Guide*
PO Box 1645
Carbondale, CO 81623
Ph: (970)963-1890
Fax: (970)963-4719
Co. E-mail: chamber@carbondale.com
URL: http://www.carbondale.com
Contact: Ms. Sherri Harrison, Executive Director
Released: Annual

49559 ■ *Membership Directory and Buyers' Guide*
2921 W 120th Ave., Ste. 210
Westminster, CO 80234
Ph: (303)288-1000
Fax: (303)227-1050
Co. E-mail: info@metronorthchamber.com
URL: http://www.metronorthchamber.com
Contact: Deborah Obermeyer, President

49560 ■ *Membership Directory and Buyers' Guide*
PO Box 5450
Frisco, CO 80443
Ph: (970)668-2051
Free: 800-530-3099

Fax: (970)668-1515
Co. E-mail: info@summitchamber.org
URL: http://www.summitchamber.org
Released: Annual

49561 ■ *Membership Directory/Community Resource Guide*
7305 Grandview Ave.
Arvada, CO 80002-9960
Ph: (303)424-0313
Fax: (303)424-5370
Co. E-mail: dot@arvadachamber.org
URL: http://www.arvadachamber.org
Contact: Dot Wright, President
Released: Annual

49562 ■ *Membership Directory/Relocation Guide*
5400 Stone Creek Cir.
Loveland, CO 80538-8838
Ph: (970)667-6311
Fax: (970)667-5211
Co. E-mail: info@loveland.org
URL: http://www.loveland.org
Contact: Brian Willms, President
Released: Annual

49563 ■ *Messenger*
2921 W 120th Ave., Ste. 210
Westminster, CO 80234
Ph: (303)288-1000
Fax: (303)227-1050
Co. E-mail: info@metronorthchamber.com
URL: http://www.metronorthchamber.com
Contact: Deborah Obermeyer, President
Released: Monthly

49564 ■ Metro North Chamber of Commerce (MNCC)
2921 W 120th Ave., Ste. 210
Westminster, CO 80234
Ph: (303)288-1000
Fax: (303)227-1050
Co. E-mail: info@metronorthchamber.com
URL: http://www.metronorthchamber.com
Contact: Deborah Obermeyer, President
Description: Promotes the economic vitality of the Metro North region. **Founded:** 1957. **Publications:** *Messenger* (Monthly); *Membership Directory and Buyers' Guide*. **Educational Activities:** Taste of the Chamber (Annual). **Awards:** Business Person of the Year (Annual); Leadership Person of the Year (Annual); Outstanding Chamber Partner of the Year (Annual); Small Business Person of the Year (Annual).

49565 ■ Monte Vista Chamber of Commerce (MVCC)
947 1st Ave.
Monte Vista, CO 81144
Ph: (719)852-2731
Free: 800-562-7085
Fax: (719)852-9382
Co. E-mail: chamber@monte-vista.org
URL: http://www.monte-vista.org
Contact: Peggy Jo Pepper, President
Description: Promotes business and community development in Monte Vista, CO. Gathers and disseminates business, industrial and general relocation information. Conducts business education programs. **Founded:** 1922. **Publications:** *Monte Vista F.Y.I.* (Monthly); *Mountain of Facts* (Annual). **Educational Activities:** Forage/Livestock Conference and Agricultural Exhibition (Annual); Potato-Grain Conference & Agricultural Exhibition (Annual).

49566 ■ *Monte Vista F.Y.I.*
947 1st Ave.
Monte Vista, CO 81144
Ph: (719)852-2731
Free: 800-562-7085
Fax: (719)852-9382
Co. E-mail: chamber@monte-vista.org
URL: http://www.monte-vista.org
Contact: Peggy Jo Pepper, President
Released: Monthly

49567 ■ Montrose Chamber of Commerce
1519 E Main St.
Montrose, CO 81401-3807

Ph: (970)249-5000
Free: 800-923-5515
Fax: (970)249-2907
Co. E-mail: info@montrosechamber.com
URL: http://www.montrosechamber.com
Contact: Ken Brengle, President
Description: Promotes business and community development in Montrose County, CO. **Publications:** *Chamber Currents* (Monthly). **Telecommunication Services:** information@montrosechamber.com.

49568 ■ *Mountain Bike Trail Map*
PO Box 3236
Winter Park, CO 80482-3236
Ph: (970)726-4118
Free: 800-903-7275
Fax: (970)726-9449
Co. E-mail: visitorcenter@playwinterpark.com
URL: http://www.playwinterpark.com
Contact: Catherine Ross, Executive Director
Released: Annual

49569 ■ *Mountain of Facts*
947 1st Ave.
Monte Vista, CO 81144
Ph: (719)852-2731
Free: 800-562-7085
Fax: (719)852-9382
Co. E-mail: chamber@monte-vista.org
URL: http://www.monte-vista.org
Contact: Peggy Jo Pepper, President
Released: Annual

49570 ■ Nederland Area Chamber of Commerce (NACC)
PO Box 85
Nederland, CO 80466
Ph: (303)258-3936
Co. E-mail: info@nederlandchamber.org
URL: http://www.nederlandchamber.org
Contact: Matt Bennett, Treasurer
Description: Works to advance the commercial, financial, industrial and civic interests of Nederland, CO.

49571 ■ *Network*
19751 E Main St., R12
Parker, CO 80138
Ph: (303)841-4268
Fax: (303)841-8061
URL: http://www.parkerchamber.com
Contact: Joe Sandoval, Chairman
Released: Monthly

49572 ■ New Castle Area Chamber of Commerce
PO Box 983
New Castle, CO 81647
Ph: (970)984-2897
Co. E-mail: info@newcastlechamber.org
URL: http://www.newcastlechamber.org
Description: Promotes new and existing businesses in the New Castle Area. Provides relocation and new resident packets to organizations and individuals.

49573 ■ *News and Views*
354 Manitou Ave.
Manitou Springs, CO 80829
Ph: (719)685-5089
Free: 800-642-2567
Fax: (719)685-0355
URL: http://www.manitousprings.org
Contact: Leslie Lewis, Executive Director
Released: Monthly

49574 ■ *Northwest Metro Business Network Book*
7305 Grandview Ave.
Arvada, CO 80002-9960
Ph: (303)424-0313
Fax: (303)424-5370
Co. E-mail: dot@arvadachamber.org
URL: http://www.arvadachamber.org
Contact: Dot Wright, President
Released: Annual **Price:** $5, /year for nonmembers; free for members.

49575 ■ Ouray Chamber Resort Association (OCRA)
PO Box 145
Ouray, CO 81427-0145
Ph: (970)325-4746
Free: 800-228-1876
Fax: (970)325-4868
Co. E-mail: ouray@ouraycolorado.com
URL: http://www.ouraycolorado.com
Contact: Ms. Jennifer Loshaw, Executive Director
Description: Promotes business and community development in Ouray County, CO. Sponsors Octoberfest and New Year's Eve fireworks display. **Founded:** 1993.

49576 ■ Pagosa Springs Area Chamber of Commerce (PSACC)
PO Box 787
Pagosa Springs, CO 81147
Ph: (970)264-2360
Free: 800-252-2204
Co. E-mail: info@pagosachamber.com
URL: http://pagosachamber.com
Contact: Mary Jo Coulehan, Executive Director
Description: Promotes business and community development in the Pagosa Springs, CO area. Sponsors Colorfest and Arts and Crafts Festival. Publications: none. **Founded:** 1976.

49577 ■ Palisade Chamber of Commerce (PCC)
319 S Main St.
Palisade, CO 81526
Ph: (970)464-7458
Fax: (970)464-4757
Co. E-mail: info@palisadecoc.com
URL: http://www.palisadecoc.com
Contact: Ms. Margie Latta, Chairperson
Description: Promotes agriculture, business and community development in the Palisade, CO area. Sponsors annual Palisade Peach Festival. **Founded:** 1982. **Publications:** *Fruit & Wine Directory* (Annual). **Educational Activities:** Awards Banquet (Annual).

49578 ■ Paonia Chamber of Commerce (PCC)
PO Box 366
Paonia, CO 81428-0366
Ph: (970)527-3886
Co. E-mail: regnajones@yahoo.com
URL: http://www.paoniachamber.com
Contact: Regna Jones, President
Description: Promotes business and community development in Paonia, CO. Sponsors October Chili Cookoff, 4th of July Cherry Day celebration, Easter egg hunt, guilt show, and Christmas festival. Publications: none. **Founded:** 1960.

49579 ■ Parker Chamber of Commerce (PCC)
19751 E Main St., R12
Parker, CO 80138
Ph: (303)841-4268
Fax: (303)841-8061
URL: http://www.parkerchamber.com
Contact: Joe Sandoval, Chairman
Description: Supports and promotes the success of the members through working, professional development, advocacy, leadership and community development. **Founded:** 1965. **Publications:** *Parker Country Magazine* (Annual); *Network* (Monthly); *Parker Country Magazine* (Annual); *Parker Country Map* (Annual); *Parker Country Map* (Annual). **Educational Activities:** Parker Country Festival (Annual). **Awards:** Dransfeldt Organization of the Year (Annual); Jim Adkins Community Service Award (Annual); O'Brien Chamber Citizen of the Year (Annual).

49580 ■ *Parker Country Magazine*
19751 E Main St., R12
Parker, CO 80138
Ph: (303)841-4268
Fax: (303)841-8061
URL: http://www.parkerchamber.com
Contact: Joe Sandoval, Chairman
Released: Annual; May.

49581 ■ *Parker Country Map*
19751 E Main St., R12
Parker, CO 80138

Ph: (303)841-4268
Fax: (303)841-8061
URL: http://www.parkerchamber.com
Contact: Joe Sandoval, Chairman
Released: Annual; April.

49582 ■ *Passport to Pueblo*
302 N Santa Fe Ave.
Pueblo, CO 81003-4102
Ph: (719)542-1704
Free: 800-233-3446
Co. E-mail: rod.slyhoff@usa.net
URL: http://www.pueblochamber.org
Contact: Rod Slyhoff, President

49583 ■ Rangely Area Chamber of Commerce (RACC)
209 E Main St.
Rangely, CO 81648
Ph: (970)675-5290
Co. E-mail: brooke@rangelychamber.com
URL: http://www.rangelychamber.com
Contact: Henry Hames, President
Description: Seeks to enhance the economic health and business climate of Rangely community.

49584 ■ Rifle Area Chamber of Commerce (RACC)
200 Lions Park Cir.
Rifle, CO 81650-0809
Ph: (970)625-2085
Free: 800-842-2085
Fax: (970)625-4757
Co. E-mail: mail@riflechamber.com
URL: http://www.riflechamber.com
Contact: Annick Pruett, President
Description: Promotes business and community development in the Rifle, CO area. Sponsors County Fair Parade and other community events. **Publications:** *Rifle Chamber Scope* (Monthly).

49585 ■ *Rifle Chamber Scope*
200 Lions Park Cir.
Rifle, CO 81650-0809
Ph: (970)625-2085
Free: 800-842-2085
Fax: (970)625-4757
Co. E-mail: mail@riflechamber.com
URL: http://www.riflechamber.com
Contact: Annick Pruett, President
Released: Monthly

49586 ■ *SCWCC Enews*
PO Box 49218
Colorado Springs, CO 80949
Ph: (719)442-2007
Co. E-mail: info@scwcc.com
URL: http://www.scwcc.com/CMS
Contact: Linda Mojer, Executive Director
Released: Monthly

49587 ■ Silverton Chamber of Commerce (SCC)
PO Box 565
Silverton, CO 81433-0565
Ph: (970)387-5654
Free: 800-752-4494
Fax: (970)387-0282
Co. E-mail: mail@silvertoncolorado.com
URL: http://www.silvertoncolorado.com
Description: Promotes business, community development, and tourism in Silverton, CO. Sponsors Brass Band Festival, Iron Horse Bicycle Classic, Handgliding Festival, and Hardrockers Holidays Mining Celebration. **Founded:** 1956.

49588 ■ Snowmass Village Resort Association
PO Box 5010
Snowmass Village, CO 81615-5010
Ph: (970)922-2297
Free: 866-352-1763
Fax: (970)922-1139
URL: http://www.snowmassvillage.com
Description: Promotes the social and economic development in Snowmass Village, CO.

49589 ■ South Fork Chamber of Commerce and Visitors Center
c/o South Fork Visitor Center
PO Box 1030
South Fork, CO 81154
Ph: (719)873-5512
Free: 800-571-0881
Fax: (719)873-5693
Co. E-mail: southfrk@amigo.net
URL: http://www.southfork.org
Description: Promotes business, tourism, and community development in South Fork, CO.

49590 ■ South Metro Denver Chamber of Commerce
6840 S University Blvd.
Centennial, CO 80122
Ph: (303)795-0142
Fax: (303)795-7520
Co. E-mail: jbrackney@bestchamber.com
URL: http://www.bestchamber.com
Contact: John Brackney, President
Description: Promotes business and community development in the southern metropolitan Denver, CO area. Conducts seminars. **Scope:** business, careers. **Founded:** 1929. **Subscriptions:** 500 audio recordings books. **Awards:** Small Business of the Year (Annual).

49591 ■ Southern Colorado Women's Chamber of Commerce (SCWCC)
PO Box 49218
Colorado Springs, CO 80949
Ph: (719)442-2007
Co. E-mail: info@scwcc.com
URL: http://www.scwcc.com/CMS
Contact: Linda Mojer, Executive Director
Description: Promotes economic development among women-owned or operated businesses in Southern Colorado. **Founded:** 1993. **Publications:** SCWCC Enews (Monthly). **Awards:** Business Leader of the Year (Annual).

49592 ■ Springfield Chamber of Commerce
948 Main St.
Springfield, CO 81073
Ph: (719)523-4061
Co. E-mail: springfieldcochamber@springfieldco.info
URL: http://www.springfieldcochamber.com
Description: Promotes business and community development in the Springfield, CO area.

49593 ■ Steamboat Springs Chamber Resort Association (SSCRA)
PO Box 774408
Steamboat Springs, CO 80477-4408
Ph: (970)879-0880
Free: 877-754-2269
Fax: (970)285-3550
Co. E-mail: info@steamboatchamber.com
URL: http://www.steamboat-chamber.com
Contact: Tom Kern, Chief Executive Officer
Description: Seeks to support, encourage and sustain a vibrant, healthy economy in Steamboat Springs, CO and the surrounding communities. **Publications:** Activity Guidelines; Dining Guide; Listing Business Directory; Visitors Guide.

49594 ■ The Summit
PO Box 5450
Frisco, CO 80443
Ph: (970)668-2051
Free: 800-530-3099
Fax: (970)668-1515
Co. E-mail: info@summitchamber.org
URL: http://www.summitchamber.org
Released: Bimonthly

49595 ■ Summit County Chamber of Commerce (SCCC)
PO Box 5450
Frisco, CO 80443
Ph: (970)668-2051
Free: 800-530-3099

Fax: (970)668-1515
Co. E-mail: info@summitchamber.org
URL: http://www.summitchamber.org
URL(s): www.experiencethesummit.com. **Description:** Promotes business and community development in Summit County, CO. **Founded:** 1976. **Publications:** The Summit (Bimonthly); Membership Directory and Buyers' Guide (Annual).

49596 ■ Swedish-American Chamber of Commerce, Colorado
1720 S Bellaire St., Ste. 310
Denver, CO 80222-4316
Ph: (720)515-9421
Co. E-mail: info@saccco.org
URL: http://sacc-usa.org/regional-chambers-3/sacc-colorado
Contact: Rikard Lundberg, Director
URL(s): www.sacc-co.org.

49597 ■ Tri-Lakes Chamber of Commerce (TLCC)
PO Box 147
Monument, CO 80132
Ph: (719)481-3282
Fax: (719)481-1638
Co. E-mail: kstensland@trilakeschamber.com
URL: http://www.trilakeschamber.com
Contact: Mr. David T. Van Ness, Executive Director
Description: Promotes business and community development in Tri-Lakes, CO area. Conducts charitable activities. Sponsors area festivals. **Founded:** 1976. **Publications:** Chamber Chat (Weekly).

49598 ■ Update
2095 W 6th Ave., Ste. 109
Broomfield, CO 80020
Ph: (303)466-1775
Fax: (303)466-4481
Co. E-mail: info@broomfieldchamber.com
URL: http://www.broomfieldchamber.com
Contact: Jennifer Kerr, President
Released: Periodic

49599 ■ Vallecito Lake Chamber of Commerce
17252 County Rd. 501
Bayfield, CO 81122
Ph: (970)247-1573
Co. E-mail: info@vallecitolakechamber.com
URL: http://www.vallecitolakechamber.com
Description: Works to advance the commercial, financial, industrial and civic interests of the area.

49600 ■ Valley View
PO Box 3236
Winter Park, CO 80482-3236
Ph: (970)726-4118
Free: 800-903-7275
Fax: (970)726-9449
Co. E-mail: visitorcenter@playwinterpark.com
URL: http://www.playwinterpark.com
Contact: Catherine Ross, Executive Director
Released: Monthly **Price:** included in membership dues.

49601 ■ Visitors Guide
PO Box 774408
Steamboat Springs, CO 80477-4408
Ph: (970)879-0880
Free: 877-754-2269
Fax: (970)285-3550
Co. E-mail: info@steamboatchamber.com
URL: http://www.steamboat-chamber.com
Contact: Tom Kern, Chief Executive Officer
Price: included in membership dues.

49602 ■ Visitors Guide
PO Box 3236
Winter Park, CO 80482-3236
Ph: (970)726-4118
Free: 800-903-7275
Fax: (970)726-9449
Co. E-mail: visitorcenter@playwinterpark.com
URL: http://www.playwinterpark.com
Contact: Catherine Ross, Executive Director

49603 ■ The Voice
30480 Stagecoach Blvd., Ste. C
Evergreen, CO 80439
Ph: (303)674-3412
Fax: (303)674-8463
Co. E-mail: info@evergreenchamber.org
URL: http://www.evergreenchamber.org
Contact: Lin Browning, President
Released: Monthly

49604 ■ West Chamber of Commerce Serving Jefferson County
1667 Cole Blvd., Bldg. 19, Ste. 400
Lakewood, CO 80401
Ph: (303)233-5555
Co. E-mail: bwillms@westchamber.org
URL: http://www.westchamber.org
Contact: Brian Willms, President
Description: Seeks to support member businesses through business growth opportunities. **Founded:** 1947.

49605 ■ West Yuma County Chamber of Commerce
14 W 2nd Ave.
Yuma, CO 80759
Ph: (970)848-2704
Fax: (970)848-5700
Co. E-mail: director@westyumachamber.com
URL: http://westyumachamber.com
Description: Promotes business and community development in western Yuma County, CO. Holds Community Chest Drive and St. Patrick's Benefit Auction for local charity. Sponsors Yuma Fest, Old Threshers Day, and Business Expo. Conducts seminars and workshops. **Founded:** 1926.

49606 ■ Windsor Chamber of Commerce (WCC)
421 Main St.
Windsor, CO 80550
Ph: (970)686-7189
Fax: (970)686-0352
Co. E-mail: michal@windsorchamber.net
URL: http://www.windsorchamber.net
Contact: Erich E. Ehrlich, President
Description: Promotes business and community development in Windsor, CO. Sponsors harvest and summer festival and pool day. Holds Business After Hours mixers. Conducts promotional campaigns. Presents Student of the Year award to high school students. Holds monthly board meeting. **Founded:** 1951. **Publications:** Windsor Chamber of Commerce Newsletter (Monthly). **Educational Activities:** Windsor Chamber of Commerce Dinner (Bimonthly). **Awards:** Windsor Chamber/Harvest Festival Scholarship Award.

49607 ■ Windsor Chamber of Commerce Newsletter
421 Main St.
Windsor, CO 80550
Ph: (970)686-7189
Fax: (970)686-0352
Co. E-mail: michal@windsorchamber.net
URL: http://www.windsorchamber.net
Contact: Erich E. Ehrlich, President
Released: Monthly

49608 ■ Winter Park-Fraser Valley Chamber of Commerce (WPFVCC)
PO Box 3236
Winter Park, CO 80482-3236
Ph: (970)726-4118
Free: 800-903-7275
Fax: (970)726-9449
Co. E-mail: visitorcenter@playwinterpark.com
URL: http://www.playwinterpark.com
Contact: Catherine Ross, Executive Director
Description: Promotes business, community development, and tourism in Winter Park and the Fraser River valley, CO. **Founded:** 1975. **Publications:** Valley View (Monthly); Visitors Guide; Mountain Bike Trail Map (Annual).

49609 ■ Wray Chamber of Commerce
110 E 3rd St.
Wray, CO 80758
Ph: (970)332-3484

Fax: (970)332-3486
Co. E-mail: director@wraychamber.net
URL: http://www.wraychamber.net
Contact: Kyle Hansen, Executive Director
Description: Promotes business and community development in Wray, CO. **Publications:** *Wray Chamber of Commerce News* (Monthly).

49610 ■ *Wray Chamber of Commerce News*
110 E 3rd St.
Wray, CO 80758
Ph: (970)332-3484
Fax: (970)332-3486
Co. E-mail: director@wraychamber.net
URL: http://www.wraychamber.net
Contact: Kyle Hansen, Executive Director
Released: Monthly

MINORITY BUSINESS ASSISTANCE PROGRAMS

49611 ■ Colorado Office of Economic Development and International Trade - Minority Business Office
1625 Broadway, Ste. 2700
Denver, CO 80202
Ph: (303)892-3840
Fax: (303)892-3848
Co. E-mail: lromero@state.co.us
URL: http://www.state.co.us
Contact: LeRoy Romero, Director
Description: Provides information and assistance to minority- and women-owned businesses in Colorado.

FINANCING AND LOAN PROGRAMS

49612 ■ 5280 Partners
360 S. Monroe St., Ste. 600
Denver, CO 80209
Ph: (303)333-1215
Fax: (303)322-3553
URL: http://www.5280partners.com
Contact: Jeffrey D. Bennis, Principal
Preferred Investment Size: $500,000 to $2,500,000. **Investment Policies:** Early, first and second stage. **Industry Preferences:** Communications, computer software, and Internet specific. **Geographic Preference:** Western United States, primarily in the Rocky Mountain region.

49613 ■ Access Venture Partners
8787 Turnpike Dr., Ste. 260
Westminster, CO 80031
Ph: (303)426-8899
Fax: (303)426-8828
Co. E-mail: mail@accessvp.com
URL: http://www.accessventurepartners.com
Contact: Jay Campion, Managing Director
Preferred Investment Size: $250,000 to $2,000,000. **Industry Preferences:** Internet specific, communications and media, biotechnology, computer software and services, semiconductors and other electronics, and industrial and energy. **Geographic Preference:** U.S.

49614 ■ Altira Group LLC
1675 Broadway, Ste. 2400
Denver, CO 80202
Ph: (303)592-5500
Fax: (303)592-5519
Co. E-mail: info@altiragroup.com
URL: http://www.altiragroup.com
Contact: Dick McDermott, Managing Partner
Preferred Investment Size: $5,000,000 to $10,000,000. **Industry Preferences:** Industrial and energy, and environment. **Geographic Preference:** U.S. and Canada.

49615 ■ Appian Ventures
1512 Larimer St., Ste. 200
Denver, CO 80202
Ph: (303)830-2450

Fax: (303)830-2449
Co. E-mail: admin@appianvc.com
URL: http://www.appianvc.com
Contact: Chris Onan, Managing Director
Preferred Investment Size: $1,000,000 to $2,000,000. **Investment Policies:** Seed, early and later stage. **Industry Preferences:** Communications, and computer software. **Geographic Preference:** Colorado, Rocky Mountains, and West Coast.

49616 ■ Aweida Venture Partners
500 Discovery Pky., Ste. 300
Superior, CO 80027
Ph: (303)664-9520
Fax: (303)664-9530
Co. E-mail: info@aweida.com
URL: http://www.aweida.com
Contact: Daniel Aweida, Managing Partner
Preferred Investment Size: $500,000 to $1,000,000. **Industry Preferences:** Computer software and hardware, Internet specific, biotechnology, and medical and health. **Geographic Preference:** Rocky Mountains.

49617 ■ Centennial Ventures
1125 17th St., Ste. 740
Denver, CO 80202
Ph: (303)405-7500
Fax: (303)405-7575
URL: http://www.centennial.com
Contact: Duncan Butler, Managing Director
Preferred Investment Size: $100,000 minimum. **Industry Preferences:** Communications and media, Internet specific, computer hardware, computer software and services, semiconductors and other electronics, medical and health, biotechnology, consumer related, other products, and industrial and energy. **Geographic Preference:** U.S.

49618 ■ Meritage Private Equity Funds
1600 Wynkoop, Ste. 300
Denver, CO 80202-1157
Ph: (303)352-2040
Fax: (303)352-2050
URL: http://www.meritagefunds.com
Contact: Laura Beller, Managing Director
Founded: 1998. **Preferred Investment Size:** $5,000,000 to $15,000,000. **Industry Preferences:** Internet specific, communications and media, computer hardware, and computer software and services. **Geographic Preference:** U.S.

49619 ■ Roser Ventures LLC
1105 Spruce St.
Boulder, CO 80302
Ph: (303)443-7924
Fax: (303)443-1885
URL: http://www.roserventures.com
Contact: Christopher W. Roser, Partner
E-mail: croser@roseventures.com
Preferred Investment Size: $100,000 to $3,000,000. **Industry Preferences:** Internet specific, communications and media, industrial and energy, semiconductors and other electronics, computer software and services, medical and health, computer hardware, other products, biotechnology, and consumer related. **Geographic Preference:** Colorado and the Rocky Mountains.

49620 ■ Sequel Venture Partners
4430 Arapahoe Ave., Ste. 220
Boulder, CO 80303
Ph: (303)546-0400
Fax: (303)546-9728
Co. E-mail: info@sequelvc.com
URL: http://www.sequelvc.com
Contact: Ron Bernal, Partner
Preferred Investment Size: $2,000,000 to $12,000,000. **Industry Preferences:** Internet specific, computer software and services, medical and health, semiconductors and other electronics, biotechnology, communications and media, computer hardware, and other products. **Geographic Preference:** Colorado and Rocky Mountains.

PROCUREMENT ASSISTANCE PROGRAMS

49621 ■ Colorado Procurement Technical Assistance Center - Denver Small Business Development Procurement Center
1445 Market St.
Denver, CO 80202
Ph: (303)620-8076
Fax: (303)534-2145
URL: http://www.denversbdc.org/
Contact: Tameka Montgomery, Director

INCUBATORS/RESEARCH AND TECHNOLOGY PARKS

49622 ■ Colorado Springs Technology Incubator
3595 E Fountain Blvd., Ste. B2
Colorado Springs, CO 80910
Ph: (719)685-7877
Fax: (719)685-7878
Co. E-mail: info@cstionline.org
URL: http://www.cstionline.org/
Description: A small incubator assisting in the launch of high-technology companies in the greater Colorado Springs area, through business advice, office facilities and access to educational resources.

49623 ■ The Denver Enterprise Center
3003 Arapahoe St.
Denver, CO 80205
Ph: (303)296-9400
Fax: (303)296-5542
Co. E-mail: decinfo@thedec.org
URL: http://www.thedec.org/
Contact: Pat Durand, Executive Director
Description: A small business incubator that assists entrepreneurs in the business start-up process and gives aid to new businesses to help ensure their survival.

49624 ■ Fitzsimons BioBusiness Partners
12635 E Montview Blvd.
Aurora, CO 80045
Ph: (720)859-4107
Fax: (720)859-4110
Co. E-mail: ddrake@colobio.com
URL: http://www.fbbp.org
Description: An incubator dedicated to promoting the growth and success of bioscience businesses in Colorado, with a special emphasis on forming a bioscience cluster at Fitzsimons. Connects ideas, technology and people to deliver targeted assistance to start-up companies and entrepreneurs; unites industry experts, venture capitalists, private investors, and the researchers the move discoveries from the lab to the commercial marketplace.

49625 ■ Fitzsimons Life Science District
12635 E. Montview Blvd.
Aurora, CO 80045-7336
Ph: (720)859-4107
Fax: (720)859-4110
URL: http://www.fitzscience.com
Description: A development facility stimulating economic growth by creating a word-class scientific community at Fitzsimons which includes, but is not limited to, entrepreneurial life science organizations, related support services and high-quality amenities.

49626 ■ Fremont County Business Development Corporation
402 Valley Rd.
Canon City, CO 81212
Ph: (719)275-8601
Free: 800-426-4794
Fax: (719)275-4400
Co. E-mail: Edie@qwestoffice.net
URL: http://www.fremontedc.org
Description: A small business incubator that assists entrepreneurs in the business start-up process and gives aid to new businesses to help ensure their survival.

49627 ■ Longmont Entrepreneurial Network
2400 Trade Center Ave.
Longmont, CO 80305
Ph: (303)678-8000
Fax: (303)678-8505
Co. E-mail: alex.sammoury@ctek.biz
URL: http://www.ctek.biz
Contact: Alex Sammoury, Executive Director
Description: Provides housing and laboratory space for young technology companies. A CTek venture center.

49628 ■ Pueblo Business and Technology Center
301 N Main St.
Pueblo, CO 81003
Ph: (719)546-1133
Free: 800-522-1120
Fax: (719)546-1942
Co. E-mail: btc@pedco.org
URL: http://www.btc-pueblo.com
Description: A small business incubator that assists entrepreneurs in the business start-up process and gives aid to new businesses to help ensure their survival.

49629 ■ Rocky Mountain Innosphere
320 E Vine Dr., Ste. 101
Fort Collins, CO 80524
Ph: (970)221-1301
Fax: (970)221-9423
URL: http://www.rmi2.org/
Description: A business incubator assisting startup companies and rapidly growing young firms. Formerly the Fort Collins Technology Incubator.

49630 ■ Western Colorado Business Development Corp. - Business Incubator Center
2591B 3/4 Rd.
Grand Junction, CO 81503
Ph: (970)243-5242
Fax: (970)241-0771
Co. E-mail: administrative@gjincubator.org
URL: http://www.gjincubator.org
Contact: Chris Reddin, Executive Director
Description: Assists entrepreneurs in the business start-up process and in managing new businesses.

EDUCATIONAL PROGRAMS

49631 ■ Aims Community College
PO Box 69
Greeley, CO 80632
Ph: (970)330-8008
Free: 800-301-5388
Co. E-mail: info@aims.edu
URL: http://www.aims.edu
Description: Two-year college offering a small business management program.

49632 ■ Colorado Northwestern Community College (Craig)
2801 W 9th St.
Craig, CO 81625
Ph: (970)824-1101
Free: 800-562-1105
Fax: (970)824-1134
URL: http://www.cncc.edu
Description: Two-year college offering a small business management program.

49633 ■ Emily Griffith Opportunity School
1250 Welton St.
Denver, CO 80204

Ph: (720)423-4700
Fax: (720)575-4840
URL: http://www.egos-school.com
Description: Trade and technical school offering classes in entrepreneurship.

49634 ■ Lamar Community College
2401 S Main St.
Lamar, CO 81052
Ph: (719)336-2248
Free: 800-968-6920
Fax: (719)336-2448
Co. E-mail: admissions@lamarcc.edu
URL: http://www.lamarcc.edu
Description: Two-year college offering a small business management program.

TRADE PERIODICALS

49635 ■ *Colorado Job Finder*
Pub: Colorado Municipal League
Released: Semimonthly, 1st and 3rd Wednesday of each month. **Price:** individuals; $30 for 6 months.
Description: Consists of local government employment opportunities in Colorado and surrounding area.

PUBLICATIONS

49636 ■ *The Denver Business Journal*
1700 Broadway, Ste. 515
Denver, CO 80290
Ph: (303)837-3500
Fax: (303)837-3535
URL: http://www.amcity.com/denver

49637 ■ *Smart Start your Colorado Business*
PSI Research
300 N. Valley Dr.
Grants Pass, OR 97526
Ph: (503)479-9464
Free: 800-228-2275
Fax: (503)476-1479
Co. E-mail: info@psi-research.com
URL: http://www.psi-research.com
Ed: Michael D. Jenkins. **Released:** Revised edition, 1992. **Price:** $29.95 (looseleaf binder); $24.95 (paper). **Description:** Part of the Successful Business Library series.

49638 ■ *Starting and Operating a Business in Colorado: A Step-by-Step Guide*
PSI Research
300 N. Valley Dr.
Grants Pass, OR 97526
Ph: (503)479-9464
Free: 800-228-2275
Fax: (503)476-1479
Co. E-mail: psi2@magick.net
Ed: Michael D. Jenkins. **Released:** Revised edition, 1992. **Price:** $29.95 (looseleaf binder); $24.95 (paper). **Description:** Part of the Successful Business Library series.

PUBLISHERS

49639 ■ Center for Self-Sufficiency - Publishing Div.
1001 Logan St., Apt. 108
Denver, CO 80203-3081
Ph: (303)575-5676

Fax: (303)575-1187
Contact: A. C. Doyle, Owner
Description: Description: Publishes how-to, consumer, recycling, and small business titles. Does not accept unsolicited manuscripts. Reaches market through direct mail. **Founded:** 1982. **Publications:** *Herb, Health, Vitamin & Natural Food Catalogs: An International Directory* (Irregular).

49640 ■ Restaurant Publishing
c/o Prosperity & Profit Unlimited, Distribution Services
Denver, CO 80201-0416
Ph: (303)575-5676
Fax: (303)575-1187
Co. E-mail: street@gmail.com
Contact: A. Doyle, President
Description: Description: Publishes and distributes cook books, food how-to book and newsletters for restaurants, cafes and catering services. Distributes-Recipe Greetings, Recipe Multiplication Forms, and Herbal Verbal cassettes. Reaches market through direct mail, trade sales and Prosperity and Profits Unlimited. Does not accept unsolicited manuscripts. **Founded:** 1989.

49641 ■ Rollaway Bay Publications Inc.
6334 S Racine Cir., Ste. 100
Centennial, CO 80111-6405
Ph: (303)799-8320
Fax: (303)799-4220
Contact: Marsha Haigh Arend, Manager
Description: Description: Publishes business titles. **Founded:** 2003.

49642 ■ Update Publicare Co.
c/o Prosperity & Profits Unlimited
Denver, CO 80201-0416
Ph: (303)575-5676
Fax: (303)575-1187
Co. E-mail: mail@breadpudding.net
Contact: A. C. Doyle
Description: Description: Publishes for consumers and businesses. Offers newsletters on recycling, self employment, publishing, and small business. Does not accept unsolicited manuscripts. **Founded:** 1989.

49643 ■ World Economic Processing Zones Association (WEPZA)
3 Bullet Hill Rd.
Danbury, CT 06811-2906
Ph: (203)798-9394
Fax: (203)798-9394
Co. E-mail: director@wepza.org
URL: http://www.wepza.org
Description: Attracts enterprise investment to all countries. Comprise many types of free zones, special economic zones, export processing zones, foreign trade zones, free ports, and logistics zones. Provides sites and infrastructure which attract firms assembling and manufacturing products, warehousing, financing, and servicing clients to add speed and efficiency to global marketing. **Founded:** 1978. **Publications:** *Journal of the Flagstaff Institute* (Semiannual); *The Dynamic Transformation of Economic Zones*; *Export Processing Zones Move to High Technology*; *Free Zones and Export Processing Zones in Central*; *The Global Network of Free Zones in the 21st Century*; *The Impact of 57 New EPZs in Mercosur*; *Mainline Free Zones: Mediterranean, Gulf*; *The World Impact of NAFTA*.

SMALL BUSINESS DEVELOPMENT CENTERS

49644 ■ Connecticut Small Business Development Center - Eastern Connecticut State University
Beckert Hall
83 Windham St.
Willimantic, CT 06226
Ph: (860)832-0650
Fax: (860)832-0656
Co. E-mail: reedhel@ccsu.edu
URL: http://www.ctsbdc.org
Contact: Henry Reed, Manager, Business Development
Description: Represents and promotes the small business sector. Provides management assistance to current and prospective small business owners. Helps to improve management skills and expand the products and services of members.

49645 ■ Connecticut Small Business Development Center - Southern Connecticut State University
Temporary Bldg.
501 Crescent St.
New Haven, CT 06515
Ph: (860)832-0650
Fax: (860)832-0656
Co. E-mail: kollmeyerkes@ccsu.edu
URL: http://www.ctsbdc.org
Contact: Owen Cheevers, Manager, Business Development
Description: Represents and promotes the small business sector. Provides management assistance to current and prospective small business owners. Helps to improve management skills and expand the products and services of members.

49646 ■ Connecticut Small Business Development Center - Western Connecticut State University
Westside Campus - Classroom Bldg.
43 Lake Ave. Ext.
Danbury, CT 06810
Ph: (860)832-0650
Fax: (860)832-0656
Co. E-mail: cilleychj@ccsu.edu
URL: http://www.ctsbdc.org
Contact: Charlotte Cilley, Manager, Business Development
Description: Represents and promotes the small business sector. Provides management assistance to current and prospective small business owners. Helps to improve management skills and expand the products and services of members.

SMALL BUSINESS ASSISTANCE PROGRAMS

49647 ■ Connecticut Economic Resource Center
805 Brook St., Bldg. 4
Rocky Hill, CT 06067-3405
Ph: (860)571-7136
Free: 800-392-2122
Fax: (860)571-7150
Co. E-mail: solutions@cerc.com
URL: http://www.cerc.com
Contact: Connie Maffeo, Director
Description: Provides managerial assistance and assists in preparing applications for financing.

49648 ■ Department of Economic & Community Development - Office of Business and Industry Development
505 Hudson St.
Hartford, CT 06106-7106
Ph: (860)270-8000
Free: 800-392-2122
Fax: (860)270-8070
Co. E-mail: DECD@po.state.ct.us
URL: http://www.ct.gov/ecd
Description: Promotes trade; publishes a brochure on licensing and joint ventures; and administers the Exporters Revolving Loan Fund for small and medium-sized businesses.

SCORE OFFICES

49649 ■ Northwest Connecticut SCORE
Co. E-mail: score@nwctchamberofcommerce.org

49650 ■ Southeastern Connecticut SCORE
Co. E-mail: score579@hotmail.com

BETTER BUSINESS BUREAUS

49651 ■ BBB Consumer Guide
94 S Turnpike Rd.
Wallingford, CT 06492
Ph: (203)269-2700
Fax: (203)269-3124
URL: http://www.connecticut.bbb.org
Contact: Paulette N. Hotton, President
Released: Annual **Price:** free.

49652 ■ Better Business Bureau, Connecticut
94 S Turnpike Rd.
Wallingford, CT 06492
Ph: (203)269-2700
Fax: (203)269-3124
URL: http://www.connecticut.bbb.org
Contact: Paulette N. Hotton, President
Description: Promotes and fosters the highest ethical relationship between businesses and the public. Provides arbitration, mediation, conciliation services, and educational marketplace information. **Scope:** consumer education. **Founded:** 1952. **Subscriptions:** periodicals. **Publications:** BBB Consumer Guide (Annual); Marketplace Report (Periodic); What Is a Better Business Bureau. **Awards:** BBB Torch Award for Marketplace Ethics (Annual).

49653 ■ Marketplace Report
94 S Turnpike Rd.
Wallingford, CT 06492
Ph: (203)269-2700
Fax: (203)269-3124
URL: http://www.connecticut.bbb.org
Contact: Paulette N. Hotton, President
Released: Periodic

49654 ■ What Is a Better Business Bureau
94 S Turnpike Rd.
Wallingford, CT 06492
Ph: (203)269-2700
Fax: (203)269-3124
URL: http://www.connecticut.bbb.org
Contact: Paulette N. Hotton, President

CHAMBERS OF COMMERCE

49655 ■ Avon Chamber of Commerce (ACOC)
412 W Avon Rd.
Avon, CT 06001
Ph: (860)675-4832
Fax: (860)675-0469
Co. E-mail: avonchamber@sbcglobal.net
URL: http://www.avonchamber.com
Contact: Lisa Bohman, Executive Director
Description: Works to advance the economic and civic development of the community.

49656 ■ Bare Bones
30 Lafayette Sq.
Vernon, CT 06066-4527
Ph: (860)872-0587
Fax: (860)872-0588
Co. E-mail: tccc@tollandcountychamber.org
URL: http://www.tollandcountychamber.org
Contact: Candice Corcione, Executive Director
Released: Quarterly

49657 ■ Berlin Chamber of Commerce (BCC)
40 Chamberlain Hwy., Ferndale Ctr.
Kensington, CT 06037
Ph: (860)829-1033
Fax: (860)829-1243
Co. E-mail: director@berlinctchamber.org
URL: http://www.berlinctchamber.org
Contact: Katherine A. Fuechsel, Executive Director
Description: Promotes business development in Berlin, Kensington and East Berlin. Conducts various programs to assist small business to compete successfully. **Publications:** Chamber Channel.

49658 ■ Bethel Chamber of Commerce
184 Greenwood Ave.
Bethel, CT 06801
Ph: (203)743-6500
Fax: (203)743-6500
Co. E-mail: contactus@bethelchamber.com
URL: http://www.bethelchamber.com
Contact: Bobbi Jo Beers, Executive Director
Description: Promotes business and community development in Bethel, CT area. **Subscriptions:** maps.

49659 ■ BizLink
900 Bridgeport Ave., 2nd Fl.
Shelton, CT 06484

Ph: (203)925-4981
Fax: (203)925-4984
Co. E-mail: info@greatervalleychamber.com
URL: http://greatervalleychamber.com
Contact: William E. Purcell, President
Released: Weekly

49660 ■ Bloomfield Chamber of Commerce (BCC)
PO Box 938
Bloomfield, CT 06002
Ph: (860)242-3710
Fax: (860)242-6129
Co. E-mail: webmail@bloomfieldchamber.org
URL: http://www.bloomfieldchamber.org
Contact: Vera Smith-Winfree, Executive Director
Description: Strives to be the principal advocate, networking organization, and service and resource provider for local businesses. Supports business and community efforts so that Bloomfield continues to be an economically attractive place to live and do business. **Founded:** 1965. **Publications:** The Forum (Bimonthly). **Awards:** BCC Scholarship Competition (Annual); Business Leadership Circle Award (Annual).

49661 ■ Branford Chamber of Commerce
239 N Main St.
Branford, CT 06405-3020
Ph: (203)488-5500
Fax: (203)488-5046
Co. E-mail: ed@branfordct.com
URL: http://www.branfordct.com
Contact: Edward Lazarus, President
Description: Works to enhance business opportunity for the economic success of Branford, CT. **Publications:** Moving Forward (Quarterly).

49662 ■ Bridgeport Regional Business Council (BRBC)
10 Middle St., 14th Fl.
Bridgeport, CT 06604
Ph: (203)335-3800
Fax: (203)366-0105
Co. E-mail: info@brbc.org
URL: http://www.brbc.org
Contact: Paul S. Timpanelli, President
Description: Promotes business and community development in Bridgeport region. **Founded:** 1986. **Publications:** enews (Monthly); IMPACT (Quarterly). **Telecommunication Services:** timpanelli@brbc.org.

49663 ■ Business
641 Main St.
Monroe, CT 06468
Ph: (203)268-6518
Fax: (203)268-3337
Co. E-mail: info@monroe-chamber.com
URL: http://www.monroe-chamber.com
Contact: Jo-Ellen Stipak, Executive Director
Released: Periodic

49664 ■ Business Directory and Relocation Guide
14 Holmes St.
Mystic, CT 06355
Ph: (860)572-9578
Free: 866-572-9578
Fax: (860)572-9273
Co. E-mail: tricia@mysticchamber.org
URL: http://www.mysticchamber.org
Contact: Tricia Cunningham, President
Released: Annual

49665 ■ Business Matters
900 Bridgeport Ave., 2nd Fl.
Shelton, CT 06484
Ph: (203)925-4981
Fax: (203)925-4984
Co. E-mail: info@greatervalleychamber.com
URL: http://greatervalleychamber.com
Contact: William E. Purcell, President
Released: Bimonthly

49666 ■ Business Review
195 S Main St.
Cheshire, CT 06410
Ph: (203)272-2345

Fax: (203)271-3044
Co. E-mail: info@cheshirechamber.com
URL: http://www.cheshirechamber.com
Contact: Sheldon Dill, President
Released: Quarterly

49667 ■ Business United
261 Broad St.
Windsor, CT 06095
Ph: (860)688-5165
Fax: (860)688-0809
Co. E-mail: info@windsorcc.org
URL: http://www.windsorcc.org
Contact: Martin McMahon, President
Released: Bimonthly

49668 ■ Canton Chamber of Commerce
PO Box 704
Canton, CT 06019
Ph: (860)693-0405
Fax: (860)693-9105
Co. E-mail: info@cantonchamberofcommerce.com
URL: http://www.cantonchamberofcommerce.com
Contact: Phil Worley, Executive Director
Description: Works to advance the economic and civic development of the Canton Community.

49669 ■ Chamber Channel
40 Chamberlain Hwy., Ferndale Ctr.
Kensington, CT 06037
Ph: (860)829-1033
Fax: (860)829-1243
Co. E-mail: director@berlinctchamber.org
URL: http://www.berlinctchamber.org
Contact: Katherine A. Fuechsel, Executive Director

49670 ■ Chamber of Commerce of Eastern Connecticut
914 Hartford Tpke.
Waterford, CT 06385
Ph: (860)701-9113
Free: 866-274-5587
Fax: (860)701-9902
Co. E-mail: info@chamberect.com
URL: http://www.chamberect.com
Contact: Thomas A. Sheridan, President
Description: Promotes business and community development in New London County, CT. **Founded:** 1915. **Publications:** Chamber Update (Monthly). **Awards:** Citizen of the Year Award (Annual); William Crawford Distinguished Service Award (Annual).

49671 ■ Chamber of Commerce Newsletter
215 Main St.
Westport, CT 06880
Ph: (203)227-9234
Fax: (203)454-4019
Co. E-mail: info@westportchamber.com
URL: http://westportchamber.com
Contact: Paul Gehr, Chairman
Released: Monthly **Price:** free for members.

49672 ■ Chamber of Commerce of Newtown
PO Box 314
Newtown, CT 06470
Ph: (203)426-2695
Fax: (203)426-2695
Co. E-mail: chamber@newtown-ct.com
URL: http://www.newtown-ct.com
Contact: Pat Linnell, President
Description: Promotes business and community development in Newtown, CT. Sponsors Christmas Tree Poster contest, Christmas Tree Lighting, and Pizza and Politics Forum for local candidates. **Founded:** 1996.

49673 ■ Chamber of Commerce of Northwest Connecticut
PO Box 59
Torrington, CT 06790
Ph: (860)482-6586
Fax: (860)489-8851
Co. E-mail: info@nwctchamberofcommerce.org
URL: http://www.nwctchamberofcommerce.org
Contact: JoAnn Ryan, President
Description: Promotes business and community development in Northwestern Connecticut. **Founded:** 1901. **Publications:** Personal Services Booklet.

49674 ■ Chamber of Commerce, Windham Region
PO Box 43
Willimantic, CT 06226-0043
Ph: (860)423-6389
Fax: (860)423-8235
Co. E-mail: info@windhamchamber.com
URL: http://www.windhamchamber.com
Contact: Roger Adams, Executive Director
Description: Works in building a vibrant, growing regional community that supports a 21st century lifestyle.

49675 ■ Chamber Connections
100 S Turnpike Rd.
Wallingford, CT 06492
Ph: (203)269-9891
Fax: (203)269-1358
Co. E-mail: robin@quinncham.com
URL: http://www.quinncham.com
Contact: Robin Wilson, President
Released: Monthly

49676 ■ Chamber Directory
2400 Main St.
Glastonbury, CT 06033
Ph: (860)659-3587
Fax: (860)659-0102
Co. E-mail: info@glastonburychamber.com
URL: http://www.glastonburychamber.net
Contact: Mary Ellen Dombrowski, President
Released: Annual **Price:** included in membership dues.

49677 ■ Chamber News
PO Box 334
Clinton, CT 06413
Ph: (860)669-3889
Fax: (860)669-3889
Co. E-mail: chamber@clintonct.com
URL: http://clintonct.com
Contact: Bruce Langevin, Chairman
Released: Monthly **Price:** free for members.

49678 ■ Chamber News
3 Colony St., Ste. 301
Meriden, CT 06450
Ph: (203)235-7901
Fax: (203)686-0172
Co. E-mail: info@meridenchamber.com
URL: http://www.meridenchamber.com
Contact: Sean W. Moore, President
Released: Monthly

49679 ■ Chamber News
PO Box 7094
Wilton, CT 06897-7094
Ph: (203)762-0567
Fax: (203)762-9096
Co. E-mail: wiltoncoc@snet.net
URL: http://www.wiltonchamber.com
Contact: Ms. Stephanie R. Barksdale, Executive Director
Released: Quarterly

49680 ■ Chamber Pulse
2400 Main St.
Glastonbury, CT 06033
Ph: (860)659-3587
Fax: (860)659-0102
Co. E-mail: info@glastonburychamber.com
URL: http://www.glastonburychamber.net
Contact: Mary Ellen Dombrowski, President
Released: Monthly **Price:** included in membership dues.

49681 ■ Chamber Update
914 Hartford Tpke.
Waterford, CT 06385
Ph: (860)701-9113
Free: 866-274-5587
Fax: (860)701-9902
Co. E-mail: info@chamberect.com
URL: http://www.chamberect.com
Contact: Thomas A. Sheridan, President
Released: Monthly **Price:** free for members.

49682 ■ *Chamber Waves*
PO Box 706
Madison, CT 06443
Ph: (203)245-7394
Fax: (203)245-4279
Co. E-mail: chamber@madisonct.com
URL: http://www.madisonct.com
Contact: Eileen Banisch, Executive Director
Released: Semimonthly

49683 ■ *Chamberlights*
PO Box 625
Old Saybrook, CT 06475-0625
Ph: (860)388-3266
Fax: (860)388-9433
Co. E-mail: info@oldsaybrookchamber.com
URL: http://www.oldsaybrookchamber.com
Contact: Judy Sullivan, Executive Director
Released: Monthly

49684 ■ Cheshire Chamber of Commerce (CCC)
195 S Main St.
Cheshire, CT 06410
Ph: (203)272-2345
Fax: (203)271-3044
Co. E-mail: info@cheshirechamber.com
URL: http://www.cheshirechamber.com
Contact: Sheldon Dill, President
Description: Promotes business and community development in Cheshire, CT. **Publications:** *Business Review* (Quarterly).

49685 ■ Clinton Chamber of Commerce
PO Box 334
Clinton, CT 06413
Ph: (860)669-3889
Fax: (860)669-3889
Co. E-mail: chamber@clintonct.com
URL: http://clintonct.com
Contact: Bruce Langevin, Chairman
Description: Promotes business and community development in Clinton, CT. Sponsors business expo, summer concert series. **Founded:** 1983. **Publications:** *Chamber News* (Monthly); *Community Guide* (Annual).

49686 ■ *Community Profile and Membership Directory*
3 Colony St., Ste. 301
Meriden, CT 06450
Ph: (203)235-7901
Fax: (203)686-0172
Co. E-mail: info@meridenchamber.com
URL: http://www.meridenchamber.com
Contact: Sean W. Moore, President
Released: Annual

49687 ■ *Company List*
45 E Putnam Ave., Ste. 121
Greenwich, CT 06830
Ph: (203)869-3500
Fax: (203)869-3502
Co. E-mail: info@greenwichchamber.com
URL: http://www.greenwichchamber.com
Contact: Mary Ann Morrison, President
Released: Periodic

49688 ■ Connecticut Business and Industry Association (CBIA)
350 Church St.
Hartford, CT 06103-1126
Ph: (860)244-1900
Fax: (860)278-8562
Co. E-mail: joe.dias@cbia.com
URL: http://www.cbia.com/home.php
Contact: Joe Dias, Director, Member Services
Description: Promotes a regulatory system that responds to businesses' needs.

49689 ■ *Cutting Edge*
PO Box 668
Norwalk, CT 06852-0668
Ph: (203)866-2521

Fax: (203)852-0583
Co. E-mail: info@norwalkchamberofcommerce.com
URL: http://www.norwalkchamberofcommerce.com
Contact: Edward J. Musante, Jr., President
Released: Bimonthly

49690 ■ *Danbury Difference*
39 West St.
Danbury, CT 06810
Ph: (203)743-5565
Fax: (203)794-1439
Co. E-mail: info@danburychamber.com
URL: http://www.danburychamber.com
Contact: Stephen A. Bull, President
Released: Bimonthly

49691 ■ Darien Chamber of Commerce (DCC)
10 Corbin Dr.
Darien, CT 06820
Ph: (203)655-3600
Fax: (203)655-2074
Co. E-mail: ctdarienchamber@optonline.net
URL: http://www.darienchamberonline.com
Contact: Carol Wilder-Tamme, President
Description: Promotes business and community development in Darien, CT. Sponsors the Darien Citizens Awards Program, Sidewalk Sales Days and annual Christmas Lighting program. **Founded:** 1957. **Publications:** *The Guide* (Annual). **Awards:** Citizen of the Year.

49692 ■ East Granby Chamber of Commerce
PO Box 1335
East Granby, CT 06026
Ph: (860)653-3833
Fax: (860)653-3855
Co. E-mail: admin@eastgranbycoc.org
URL: http://www.eastgranbycoc.org
Contact: Mark J. Hann, President
Description: Promotes business and community development in East Grandy, CT area. **Telecommunication Services:** president@eastgranbycoc.org.

49693 ■ East Hartford Chamber of Commerce
1137 Main St.
East Hartford, CT 06108
Ph: (860)289-0239
URL: http://www.ehcoc.biz
Contact: Ron J. Pugliese, President
Description: Represents and promotes business and professional firms in East Hartford, CT. **Founded:** 1915.

49694 ■ East Haven Chamber of Commerce (EHCC)
PO Box 120055
East Haven, CT 06512
Ph: (203)467-4305
Co. E-mail: east.haven@sbcglobal.net
URL: http://easthavenchamber.com
Contact: Mary W. Cacace, President
Description: Promotes business and community development in East Haven, CT area.

49695 ■ *enews*
10 Middle St., 14th Fl.
Bridgeport, CT 06604
Ph: (203)335-3800
Fax: (203)366-0105
Co. E-mail: info@brbc.org
URL: http://www.brbc.org
Contact: Paul S. Timpanelli, President
Released: Monthly

49696 ■ Fairfield Chamber of Commerce
1597 Post Rd.
Fairfield, CT 06824
Ph: (203)255-1011

Fax: (203)256-9990
Co. E-mail: info@fairfieldctchamber.com
URL: http://www.fairfieldctchamber.com/online/home/index.asp
Contact: Patricia L. Ritchie, President
Description: Promotes business and community development in Fairfield, CT. Sponsors holiday events and revitalization efforts. Encourages cultural involvement. **Founded:** 1946. **Publications:** *Fairfield Town Map* (Annual); *Resource Guide* (Annual).

49697 ■ *Fairfield Town Map*
1597 Post Rd.
Fairfield, CT 06824
Ph: (203)255-1011
Fax: (203)256-9990
Co. E-mail: info@fairfieldctchamber.com
URL: http://www.fairfieldctchamber.com/online/home/index.asp
Contact: Patricia L. Ritchie, President
Released: Annual

49698 ■ Farmington Chamber of Commerce (FCC)
827 Farmington Ave.
Farmington, CT 06032
Ph: (860)676-8490
Fax: (860)677-8332
Co. E-mail: raygagnon@farmingtonchamber.com
URL: http://www.farmingtonchamber.com
Contact: Lisa Whitney, President
Description: Works together to advance the economic and civic development in Farmington, CT.

49699 ■ *The Forum*
PO Box 938
Bloomfield, CT 06002
Ph: (860)242-3710
Fax: (860)242-6129
Co. E-mail: webmail@bloomfieldchamber.org
URL: http://www.bloomfieldchamber.org
Contact: Vera Smith-Winfree, Executive Director
Released: Bimonthly

49700 ■ *Getting To Know Ridgefield*
9 Bailey Ave.
Ridgefield, CT 06877
Ph: (203)438-5992
Fax: (203)438-9175
Co. E-mail: jkouroupas@ridgefieldchamber.org
URL: http://www.ridgefieldchamber.org
Contact: Marion Roth, Executive Director
Released: Annual

49701 ■ Glastonbury Chamber of Commerce (GCC)
2400 Main St.
Glastonbury, CT 06033
Ph: (860)659-3587
Fax: (860)659-0102
Co. E-mail: info@glastonburychamber.com
URL: http://www.glastonburychamber.net
Contact: Mary Ellen Dombrowski, President
Description: Promotes business and community development in Glastonbury, CT. Sponsors Apple Harvest Festival and the summer music series. **Founded:** 1902. **Publications:** *Chamber Directory* (Annual); *Chamber Pulse* (Monthly).

49702 ■ Granby Chamber of Commerce (GCC)
PO Box 211
Granby, CT 06035
Ph: (860)653-5085
Fax: (860)844-8692
Co. E-mail: gcoc@granbycoc.org
URL: http://www.granbycoc.org
Contact: Rebecca Taylor, Administrator
Description: Promotes business and community development in Granby, CT area. **Founded:** 1965. **Awards:** Business Person of the Year (Annual); Humanitarian of the Year (Annual).

49703 ■ *Greater Danbury Business Directory and Buyers Guide*
39 West St.
Danbury, CT 06810
Ph: (203)743-5565

Fax: (203)794-1439
Co. E-mail: info@danburychamber.com
URL: http://www.danburychamber.com
Contact: Stephen A. Bull, President

49704 ■ Greater Danbury Chamber of Commerce (GDCC)
39 West St.
Danbury, CT 06810
Ph: (203)743-5565
Fax: (203)794-1439
Co. E-mail: info@danburychamber.com
URL: http://www.danburychamber.com
Contact: Stephen A. Bull, President
Description: Represents the ten town Connecticut business community of Bethel, Bridgewater, Brookfield, Danbury, New Fairfield, New Milford, Newtown, Redding, Ridgefield, Sherman and the surrounding area. Promotes business and community development. **Founded:** 1936. **Publications:** *Danbury Difference* (Bimonthly); *Inside Business* (Quarterly); *Greater Danbury Business Directory and Buyers Guide.*

49705 ■ Greater Manchester Chamber of Commerce (GMCC)
20 Hartford Rd.
Manchester, CT 06040
Ph: (860)646-2223
Fax: (860)646-5871
Co. E-mail: staffgmcc@manchesterchamber.com
URL: http://www.manchesterchamber.com
Contact: Sue O'Connor, President
Description: Promotes business and community development in the Manchester, CT area. **Founded:** 1901. **Publications:** *News and Views* (Bimonthly).

49706 ■ Greater Meriden Chamber of Commerce (GMCC)
3 Colony St., Ste. 301
Meriden, CT 06450
Ph: (203)235-7901
Fax: (203)686-0172
Co. E-mail: info@meridenchamber.com
URL: http://www.meridenchamber.com
Contact: Sean W. Moore, President
Description: Encourages and promotes commerce, industry, and community. **Founded:** 1915. **Publications:** *Chamber News* (Monthly); *Community Profile and Membership Directory* (Annual); *Community Profile and Membership Directory* (Annual). **Educational Activities:** Business After Hours (Monthly); Business Expo (Annual).

49707 ■ Greater New Haven Chamber of Commerce (GNHCC)
900 Chapel St., 10th Fl.
New Haven, CT 06510
Ph: (203)787-6735
Fax: (203)782-4329
Co. E-mail: info@gnhcc.com
URL: http://www.gnhcc.com
Contact: Anthony P. Rescigno, President
Description: Provides leadership in marshalling the physical, economic, and human resources of the South Central Connecticut region. **Publications:** *The Source--Greater New Haven Market Directory* (Annual).

49708 ■ Greater New Milford Chamber of Commerce (GNMCC)
11 Railroad St.
New Milford, CT 06776-2717
Ph: (860)354-6080
Fax: (860)354-8526
Co. E-mail: nmcc@newmilford-chamber.com
URL: http://www.newmilford-chamber.com
Contact: Denise Del Mastro, Executive Director
Description: Promotes business and community development in New Milford, CT. Sponsors Village Fair and Business Expo. **Founded:** 1931. **Publications:** *New Milford Magazine* (Periodic); *New Milford Visitor's Guide* (Periodic). **Awards:** Lamp of Learning.

49709 ■ Greater Norwalk Chamber of Commerce
PO Box 668
Norwalk, CT 06852-0668

Ph: (203)866-2521
Fax: (203)852-0583
Co. E-mail: info@norwalkchamberofcommerce.com
URL: http://www.norwalkchamberofcommerce.com
Contact: Edward J. Musante, Jr., President
Description: Promotes business and community development in the Norwalk, CT area. **Founded:** 1889. **Publications:** *Cutting Edge* (Bimonthly); *Who's Who Greater Norwalk Business Directory* (Annual). **Educational Activities:** Business Exchange (Monthly); Small Business Awards (Annual).

49710 ■ Greater Southington Chamber of Commerce
1 Factory Sq.
Southington, CT 06489
Ph: (860)628-8036
Fax: (860)276-9696
Co. E-mail: info@southingtoncoc.com
URL: http://www.southingtoncoc.com
Contact: Art Secondo, President
Description: Promotes business and community development in the Southington, CT area. **Founded:** 1938. **Publications:** *Southington at a Glance* (Annual); *Southington CC Express* (Weekly). **Awards:** Beautification Award (Annual); Community Spirit Award (Annual); Business Person of the Year, Riccio Brothers Award (Annual); Employee of the Year, Ann Hauver Award (Annual).

49711 ■ *Greater Valley Business and Resource Guide*
900 Bridgeport Ave., 2nd Fl.
Shelton, CT 06484
Ph: (203)925-4981
Fax: (203)925-4984
Co. E-mail: info@greatervalleychamber.com
URL: http://greatervalleychamber.com
Contact: William E. Purcell, President
Released: Annual

49712 ■ Greater Valley Chamber of Commerce
900 Bridgeport Ave., 2nd Fl.
Shelton, CT 06484
Ph: (203)925-4981
Fax: (203)925-4984
Co. E-mail: info@greatervalleychamber.com
URL: http://greatervalleychamber.com
Contact: William E. Purcell, President
Description: Represents the business community of Ansonia, Beacon Falls, Derby, Oxford, Seymour, Shelton and the surrounding area. **Founded:** 1964. **Subscriptions:** 100 books reports video recordings. **Publications:** *BizLink* (Weekly); *Business Matters* (Bimonthly); *Greater Valley Business and Resource Guide* (Annual). **Educational Activities:** Business Showcase (Annual); Valley Business Expo featuring a Taste of the Valley (Annual). **Awards:** Silver Medal Gold Seal Platinum Award (Annual).

49713 ■ Greenwich Chamber of Commerce (GCC)
45 E Putnam Ave., Ste. 121
Greenwich, CT 06830
Ph: (203)869-3500
Fax: (203)869-3502
Co. E-mail: info@greenwichchamber.com
URL: http://www.greenwichchamber.com
Contact: Mary Ann Morrison, President
Description: Promotes business and community development in Greenwich, CT. **Founded:** 1917. **Publications:** *Company List* (Periodic).

49714 ■ *The Guide*
10 Corbin Dr.
Darien, CT 06820
Ph: (203)655-3600
Fax: (203)655-2074
Co. E-mail: ctdarienchamber@optonline.net
URL: http://www.darienchamberonline.com
Contact: Carol Wilder-Tamme, President
Released: Annual **Price:** $25, for nonmembers.

49715 ■ Guilford Chamber of Commerce
1300 Boston Post Rd.
Guilford, CT 06437
Ph: (203)453-9677

Fax: (203)453-6022
Co. E-mail: chamber@guilfordct.com
URL: http://www.guilfordct.com
Contact: Terry McGuire, Executive Director
Description: Promotes business and community development in Guilford, CT area.

49716 ■ Hamden Chamber of Commerce
2969 Whitney Ave.
Hamden, CT 06518
Ph: (203)288-6431
Fax: (203)288-4499
Co. E-mail: hcc@hamdenchamber.com
URL: http://www.hamdenchamber.com/chamber.html
Contact: Meegia Wojcik, Administrative Assistant
Description: Promotes business and community development in Hamden, CT. **Publications:** *In Hamden* (Monthly); *In Hamden* (Monthly).

49717 ■ *IMPACT*
10 Middle St., 14th Fl.
Bridgeport, CT 06604
Ph: (203)335-3800
Fax: (203)366-0105
Co. E-mail: info@brbc.org
URL: http://www.brbc.org
Contact: Paul S. Timpanelli, President
Released: Quarterly

49718 ■ *In Hamden*
2969 Whitney Ave.
Hamden, CT 06518
Ph: (203)288-6431
Fax: (203)288-4499
Co. E-mail: hcc@hamdenchamber.com
URL: http://www.hamdenchamber.com/chamber.html
Contact: Meegia Wojcik, Administrative Assistant
Released: Monthly **Price:** free.

49719 ■ *Inside Business*
39 West St.
Danbury, CT 06810
Ph: (203)743-5565
Fax: (203)794-1439
Co. E-mail: info@danburychamber.com
URL: http://www.danburychamber.com
Contact: Stephen A. Bull, President
Released: Quarterly

49720 ■ Kent Chamber of Commerce
PO Box 124
Kent, CT 06757-0124
Ph: (860)927-1463
Co. E-mail: president@kentct.com
URL: http://www.kentct.com
Contact: Elissa Potts, President
Description: Promotes business and community development in Kent, CT area.

49721 ■ Madison Chamber of Commerce (MCC)
PO Box 706
Madison, CT 06443
Ph: (203)245-7394
Fax: (203)245-4279
Co. E-mail: chamber@madisonct.com
URL: http://www.madisonct.com
Contact: Eileen Banisch, Executive Director
Description: Promotes business and community development in Madison, CT. **Founded:** 1948. **Publications:** *Chamber Waves* (Semimonthly). **Educational Activities:** Madison Expo (Annual).

49722 ■ *Member and Business Directory*
215 Main St.
Westport, CT 06880
Ph: (203)227-9234
Fax: (203)454-4019
Co. E-mail: info@westportchamber.com
URL: http://westportchamber.com
Contact: Paul Gehr, Chairman
Released: Annual

49723 ■ *Member Business Directory*
PO Box 386
Lakeville, CT 06039

Ph: (860)435-0740
Co. E-mail: info@tristatechamber.com
URL: http://www.tristatechamber.com
Contact: Susan Dickinson, President

49724 ■ MetroHartford Chamber of Commerce
31 Pratt St., 5th Fl.
Hartford, CT 06103
Ph: (860)525-4451
Fax: (860)293-2592
Co. E-mail: oz@metrohartford.com
URL: http://www.metrohartford.com
Contact: Oz Griebel, President
Description: Promotes business and community development in the Metro Hartford area. **Publications:** *The Regional Review* (Bimonthly).

49725 ■ Middlesex County Chamber of Commerce (MCCC)
393 Main St.
Middletown, CT 06457
Ph: (860)347-6924
Fax: (860)346-1043
Co. E-mail: info@middlesexchamber.com
URL: http://www.middlesexchamber.com
Contact: Larry McHugh, President
Description: Promotes business and community development in Middlesex County, CT. Sponsors Business After Hours program. **Founded:** 1895. **Publications:** *Middlesex Magazine and Business Review* (Monthly); *We're on the Move*; *Middlesex Magazine and Business Review* (Monthly). **Educational Activities:** Central Business Bureau Meeting (Monthly). **Awards:** Chief Michael L. Green Award (Annual); Distinguished Citizen Award (Annual); Robert Briggs Good Guy Award (Annual); Judge Raymond E. Baldwin Scholarship (Annual).

49726 ■ *Middlesex Magazine and Business Review*
393 Main St.
Middletown, CT 06457
Ph: (860)347-6924
Fax: (860)346-1043
Co. E-mail: info@middlesexchamber.com
URL: http://www.middlesexchamber.com
Contact: Larry McHugh, President
Released: Monthly

49727 ■ Milford Chamber of Commerce
5 Broad St.
Milford, CT 06460
Ph: (203)878-0681
Fax: (203)876-8517
Co. E-mail: chamber@milfordct.com
URL: http://www.milfordct.com
Contact: Kathleen Alagno, President
Description: Promotes business and community development in Milford, CT. **Founded:** 1954. **Awards:** Ambassador of the Year (Annual); Service to the Chamber (Annual).

49728 ■ *Monroe Business Bulletin*
641 Main St.
Monroe, CT 06468
Ph: (203)268-6518
Fax: (203)268-3337
Co. E-mail: info@monroe-chamber.com
URL: http://www.monroe-chamber.com
Contact: Jo-Ellen Stipak, Executive Director
Released: Monthly

49729 ■ Monroe Chamber of Commerce (MCC)
641 Main St.
Monroe, CT 06468
Ph: (203)268-6518
Fax: (203)268-3337
Co. E-mail: info@monroe-chamber.com
URL: http://www.monroe-chamber.com
Contact: Jo-Ellen Stipak, Executive Director
Description: Promotes business and community development in the Monroe, CT area. Sponsors Monroe Spirit Week festival. **Founded:** 1966. **Publications:** *Business* (Periodic); *Monroe Business Bulletin* (Monthly). **Awards:** Business Award; Community Service Award; Public Service Award; Student Award.

49730 ■ *Moving Forward*
239 N Main St.
Branford, CT 06405-3020
Ph: (203)488-5500
Fax: (203)488-5046
Co. E-mail: ed@branfordct.com
URL: http://www.branfordct.com
Contact: Edward Lazarus, President
Released: Quarterly

49731 ■ Mystic Chamber of Commerce
14 Holmes St.
Mystic, CT 06355
Ph: (860)572-9578
Free: 866-572-9578
Fax: (860)572-9273
Co. E-mail: tricia@mysticchamber.org
URL: http://www.mysticchamber.org
Contact: Tricia Cunningham, President
Description: Promotes business and community development in Mystic, CT area. **Publications:** *Business Directory and Relocation Guide* (Annual); *The Mystic Four Seasons Discovery Guide* (Annual).

49732 ■ *The Mystic Four Seasons Discovery Guide*
14 Holmes St.
Mystic, CT 06355
Ph: (860)572-9578
Free: 866-572-9578
Fax: (860)572-9273
Co. E-mail: tricia@mysticchamber.org
URL: http://www.mysticchamber.org
Contact: Tricia Cunningham, President
Released: Annual

49733 ■ New Britain Chamber of Commerce
1 Court St.
New Britain, CT 06051
Ph: (860)229-1665
Fax: (860)223-8341
Co. E-mail: bill@newbritainchamber.com
URL: http://www.newbritainchamber.com
Contact: William F. Millerick, President
Description: Promotes business and community development in New Britain, CT area. **Publications:** *Positively New Britain* (Monthly).

49734 ■ New Canaan Chamber of Commerce
91 Elm St.
New Canaan, CT 06840
Ph: (203)966-2004
URL: http://www.newcanaanchamber.com
Contact: Tucker Murphy, Executive Director
Description: Promotes business and community development in New Canaan, CT. Bestows Citizen's Award. Sponsors village fair. **Founded:** 1956.

49735 ■ *New Milford Magazine*
11 Railroad St.
New Milford, CT 06776-2717
Ph: (860)354-6080
Fax: (860)354-8526
Co. E-mail: nmcc@newmilford-chamber.com
URL: http://www.newmilford-chamber.com
Contact: Denise Del Mastro, Executive Director
Released: Periodic

49736 ■ *New Milford Visitor's Guide*
11 Railroad St.
New Milford, CT 06776-2717
Ph: (860)354-6080
Fax: (860)354-8526
Co. E-mail: nmcc@newmilford-chamber.com
URL: http://www.newmilford-chamber.com
Contact: Denise Del Mastro, Executive Director
Released: Periodic

49737 ■ Newington Chamber of Commerce
1046 Main St.
Newington, CT 06111
Ph: (860)666-2089
Fax: (860)665-7551
Co. E-mail: office@newingtonchamber.com
URL: http://www.newingtonchamber.com
Contact: Joan-Alice Taylor, President
Description: Promotes business and community development in Newington, CT. **Founded:** 1945.

49738 ■ *News and Views*
20 Hartford Rd.
Manchester, CT 06040
Ph: (860)646-2223
Fax: (860)646-5871
Co. E-mail: staffgmcc@manchesterchamber.com
URL: http://www.manchesterchamber.com
Contact: Sue O'Connor, President
Released: Bimonthly **Price:** included in membership dues.

49739 ■ *News and Views*
PO Box 257
Windsor Locks, CT 06096
Ph: (860)623-9319
Fax: (860)831-1036
Co. E-mail: info@windsorlockschamber.com
URL: http://www.windsorlockschamber.org
Contact: Jared Carillo, President
Released: Quarterly

49740 ■ North Central Connecticut Chamber of Commerce (NCCCC)
PO Box 294
Enfield, CT 06083
Ph: (860)741-3838
Fax: (860)741-3512
Co. E-mail: chamber@ncccc.org
URL: http://www.ncccc.org
Contact: Sandy Zukowski, President
Description: Promotes business and community development in North Central, CT area. **Telecommunication Services:** edward_palomba@banksi.com.

49741 ■ Northeastern Connecticut Chamber of Commerce (NCCC)
3 Central St.
Danielson, CT 06239
Ph: (860)774-8001
Fax: (860)774-4299
Co. E-mail: info@nectchamber.com
URL: http://nectchamber.com
Contact: Elizabeth Kuszaj, Executive Director
Description: Promotes business and community development in Danielson, CT area.

49742 ■ Old Saybrook Chamber of Commerce
PO Box 625
Old Saybrook, CT 06475-0625
Ph: (860)388-3266
Fax: (860)388-9433
Co. E-mail: info@oldsaybrookchamber.com
URL: http://www.oldsaybrookchamber.com
Contact: Judy Sullivan, Executive Director
Description: Provides leadership, support, and networking within the business community of Old Saybrook. **Founded:** 1939. **Publications:** *Chamberlights* (Monthly). **Telecommunication Services:** executivedirector@oldsaybrookchamber.com.

49743 ■ Orange Chamber of Commerce
605A Orange Center Rd.
Orange, CT 06477
Ph: (203)795-3328
Fax: (203)795-5926
Co. E-mail: info@orangectchamber.com
URL: http://www.orangectchamber.com
Contact: Ms. Janice Lettick, Executive Director
Description: Promotes business and community development in Orange, CT. **Founded:** 1962.

49744 ■ *Personal Services Booklet*
PO Box 59
Torrington, CT 06790
Ph: (860)482-6586
Fax: (860)489-8851
Co. E-mail: info@nwctchamberofcommerce.org
URL: http://www.nwctchamberofcommerce.org
Contact: JoAnn Ryan, President

49745 ■ *Positively New Britain*
1 Court St.
New Britain, CT 06051
Ph: (860)229-1665

Fax: (860)223-8341
Co. E-mail: bill@newbritainchamber.com
URL: http://www.newbritainchamber.com
Contact: William F. Millerick, President
Released: Monthly

**49746 ■ Quinnipiac Chamber of Commerce
(QCC)**
100 S Turnpike Rd.
Wallingford, CT 06492
Ph: (203)269-9891
Fax: (203)269-1358
Co. E-mail: robin@quinncham.com
URL: http://www.quinncham.com
Contact: Robin Wilson, President
Description: Promotes business and community
development in Wallingford and North Haven, CT.
Active lobbying and activities in educational arena.
Sponsors seminars; conducts Business After Hours
mixers. Maintains Women's Council, Industrial
Council, Mayor's Advisory Council, and Legislative
Committee, Real Estate Advisory Committee, and
Small Business Council. **Founded:** 1915. **Publications:** *Chamber Connections* (Monthly). **Educational
Activities:** Business After Hours.

49747 ■ *Resource Guide*
1597 Post Rd.
Fairfield, CT 06824
Ph: (203)255-1011
Fax: (203)256-9990
Co. E-mail: info@fairfieldctchamber.com
URL: http://www.fairfieldctchamber.com/online/home/
index.asp
Contact: Patricia L. Ritchie, President
Released: Annual

49748 ■ Ridgefield Chamber of Commerce
9 Bailey Ave.
Ridgefield, CT 06877
Ph: (203)438-5992
Fax: (203)438-9175
Co. E-mail: jkouroupas@ridgefieldchamber.org
URL: http://www.ridgefieldchamber.org
Contact: Marion Roth, Executive Director
Description: Promotes business and community
development in Ridgefield, CT. Sponsors Halloween
Walk, Holiday Tree Lighting, Gift certificate program,
Sale-a-brations, and home based entrepreneur
workshop. **Founded:** 1966. **Publications:** *Getting To
Know Ridgefield* (Annual). **Awards:** President's Eagle
Award (Annual).

49749 ■ Rocky Hill Chamber of Commerce
2264 Silas Deane Hwy.
Rocky Hill, CT 06067
Ph: (860)258-7633
Fax: (860)258-7637
Co. E-mail: cbaio@baiolaw.com
URL: http://www.rhchamber.org
Contact: Claudia Baio, President
Description: Promotes business and community
development in Rocky Hill, CT. Maintains governmental affairs, economic development, civic affairs,
education, public relations, membership, retention,
meetings, and budget committees. **Founded:** 1989.

**49750 ■ Simsbury Chamber of Commerce
(SCOC)**
PO Box 224
Simsbury, CT 06070
Ph: (860)651-7307
Fax: (860)651-1933
Co. E-mail: info@simsburycoc.org
URL: http://www.simsburycoc.org
Contact: Dennis E. Jacobs, President
Description: Promotes business and community
development in Simsbury, CT. **Founded:** 1959. **Publications:** *Update* (Bimonthly).

49751 ■ *Southington CC Express*
1 Factory Sq.
Southington, CT 06489
Ph: (860)628-8036

Fax: (860)276-9696
Co. E-mail: info@southingtoncoc.com
URL: http://www.southingtoncoc.com
Contact: Art Secondo, President
Released: Weekly **Price:** free for members; $15,
/year for nonmembers.

49752 ■ *Southington at a Glance*
1 Factory Sq.
Southington, CT 06489
Ph: (860)628-8036
Fax: (860)276-9696
Co. E-mail: info@southingtoncoc.com
URL: http://www.southingtoncoc.com
Contact: Art Secondo, President
Released: Annual **Price:** free for members; $15, for
nonmembers.

49753 ■ Stamford Chamber of Commerce
733 Summer St.
Stamford, CT 06901-1019
Ph: (203)359-4761
Fax: (203)363-5069
Co. E-mail: jcondlin@stamfordchamber.com
URL: http://www.stamfordchamber.com
Contact: Jack Condlin, President
Description: Aims to advance the civic and economic
vitality of Stamford, Connecticut.

**49754 ■ Suffield Chamber of Commerce
(SCC)**
PO Box 741
Suffield, CT 06078
Ph: (860)668-4848
Co. E-mail: info@suffieldchamber.com
URL: http://www.suffieldchamber.com
Contact: John Smith, President
Description: Works to promote economic and community development within the region by offering
networking opportunities, educational seminars and
special programs to its members. **Founded:** 1994.

**49755 ■ Tolland County Chamber of
Commerce**
30 Lafayette Sq.
Vernon, CT 06066-4527
Ph: (860)872-0587
Fax: (860)872-0588
Co. E-mail: tccc@tollandcountychamber.org
URL: http://www.tollandcountychamber.org
Contact: Candice Corcione, Executive Director
Description: Promotes business and community
development in Tolland County. **Founded:** 1957.
Publications: *Bare Bones* (Quarterly). **Educational
Activities:** Consumer Showcase (Annual).

**49756 ■ Tri-State Chamber of
Commerce—Salisbury Chamber of
Commerce**
PO Box 386
Lakeville, CT 06039
Ph: (860)435-0740
Co. E-mail: info@tristatechamber.com
URL: http://www.tristatechamber.com
Contact: Susan Dickinson, President
Description: Promotes business and community
development in Lakeville, CT. **Publications:** *Member
Business Directory.*

49757 ■ *Update*
PO Box 224
Simsbury, CT 06070
Ph: (860)651-7307
Fax: (860)651-1933
Co. E-mail: info@simsburycoc.org
URL: http://www.simsburycoc.org
Contact: Dennis E. Jacobs, President
Released: Bimonthly

49758 ■ *We're on the Move*
393 Main St.
Middletown, CT 06457
Ph: (860)347-6924
Fax: (860)346-1043
Co. E-mail: info@middlesexchamber.com
URL: http://www.middlesexchamber.com
Contact: Larry McHugh, President

**49759 ■ West Hartford Chamber of
Commerce**
948 Farmington Ave.
West Hartford, CT 06107
Ph: (860)521-2300
Fax: (860)521-1996
Co. E-mail: info@whchamber.com
URL: http://www.whchamber.com
Contact: Marjorie Luke, President
Description: Promotes business and community
development in West Hartford, CT. **Founded:** 1908.
Publications: *Membership Directory/Community
Guide* (Annual). **Educational Activities:** Evening
Networking Function (Monthly). **Awards:** Noah Webster Awards (Annual).

**49760 ■ West Haven Chamber of Commerce
(WHCC)**
140 Captain Thomas Blvd.
West Haven, CT 06516
Ph: (203)933-1500
Fax: (203)931-1940
Co. E-mail: info@westhavenchamber.com
URL: http://www.westhavenchamber.com
Contact: Nicholas DeMatties, Executive Director
Description: Promotes business and community
development in West Haven, CT. **Awards:** Scholarship Award (Annual).

**49761 ■ Westport/Weston Chamber of
Commerce**
215 Main St.
Westport, CT 06880
Ph: (203)227-9234
Fax: (203)454-4019
Co. E-mail: info@westportchamber.com
URL: http://westportchamber.com
Contact: Paul Gehr, Chairman
Description: Promotes business and community
development in Westport and Weston, CT. Sponsors
Golf and Tennis Classic, Business Expo, and Business After Hours Lead-Generators. **Founded:** 1931.
Publications: *Chamber of Commerce Newsletter*
(Monthly); *Member and Business Directory* (Annual).
Educational Activities: Business After Hours
(Monthly); Westport/Weston Chamber of Commerce
Workshop (Periodic).

49762 ■ Wethersfield Chamber of Commerce
200 Main St.
Wethersfield, CT 06109
Ph: (860)721-6200
Fax: (860)721-8703
Co. E-mail: wethersfield@sbcglobal.net
URL: http://www.wethersfieldchamber.com
Contact: John O. Brien, President
Description: Promotes business and community
development in Wethersfield, CT. Convention/Meeting: none. **Founded:** 1965.

**49763 ■ *Who's Who Greater Norwalk
Business Directory***
PO Box 668
Norwalk, CT 06852-0668
Ph: (203)866-2521
Fax: (203)852-0583
Co. E-mail: info@norwalkchamberofcommerce.com
URL: http://www.norwalkchamberofcommerce.com
Contact: Edward J. Musante, Jr., President
Released: Annual

49764 ■ Wilton Chamber of Commerce
PO Box 7094
Wilton, CT 06897-7094
Ph: (203)762-0567
Fax: (203)762-9096
Co. E-mail: wiltoncoc@snet.net
URL: http://www.wiltonchamber.com
Contact: Ms. Stephanie R. Barksdale, Executive
Director
Description: Aims to advance the commercial and
civic interests of the town of Wilton. **Founded:** 1989.
Publications: *Chamber News* (Quarterly).

**49765 ■ Windsor Chamber of Commerce
(WCC)**
261 Broad St.
Windsor, CT 06095

Ph: (860)688-5165
Fax: (860)688-0809
Co. E-mail: info@windsorcc.org
URL: http://www.windsorcc.org
Contact: Martin McMahon, President
Description: Seeks to provide a voice for the business community on issues of public policy. Strives to help businesses work together for their mutual benefit. Advocates initiatives that enhance the region's economic vitality and quality of life. Sponsors annual auction, Nightmare on Broad Street at Halloween, golf tournament, school-to-career, Winter Magic, Businesses Fueling Minds and new teacher reception. **Founded:** 1949. **Publications:** *Business United* (Bimonthly). **Awards:** Citizen of the Year (Annual); Frank D. Parker Memorial Beautification Award (Annual); The Jerry Hallas Memorial Award (Annual).

49766 ■ Windsor Locks Chamber of Commerce (WLCC)
PO Box 257
Windsor Locks, CT 06096
Ph: (860)623-9319
Fax: (860)831-1036
Co. E-mail: info@windsorlockschamber.com
URL: http://www.windsorlockschamber.org
Contact: Jared Carillo, President
Description: Promotes business and community development in Windsor Locks, CT. **Founded:** 1954. **Publications:** *News and Views* (Quarterly).

MINORITY BUSINESS ASSISTANCE PROGRAMS

49767 ■ University of Hartford Entrepreneurial Center - Women's Business Center
50 Elizabeth St.
Hartford, CT 06105-2280
Ph: (860)768-5681
Co. E-mail: entrectr@hartford.edu
Contact: Sandra Cahill
Description: Provides business counseling, business workshops and resources, and referrals to SBA programs for start-up and established businesses. Serves both men and women, but emphasis is on women-owned enterprises.

FINANCING AND LOAN PROGRAMS

49768 ■ Advanced Materials Partners, Inc.
45 Pine St.
New Canaan, CT 06840
Ph: (203)966-6415
Fax: (203)966-8448
Co. E-mail: wkb@amplink.com
URL: http://amplink.com
Contact: Warner K. Babcock, Chairman
E-mail: wkb@amplink
Industry Preferences: Semiconductors and other electronics, biotechnology, medical and health, consumer related, industrial and energy, transportation, business service, manufacturing, utilities, and other products. **Geographic Preference:** U.S. and Canada.

49769 ■ Axiom Venture Partners, L.P.
CityPlace II, 17th Fl.
185 Asylum St.
Hartford, CT 06103
Ph: (860)548-7799
Fax: (860)548-7797
URL: http://www.axiomventures.com
Contact: Alan Mendelson, Partner
Preferred Investment Size: $1,000,000 to $5,000,000. **Industry Preferences:** Communications and media, biotechnology, computer software and services, medical and health, Internet specific, consumer related, semiconductors and other electronics, computer hardware, other products, industrial and energy. **Geographic Preference:** U.S. and Canada.

49770 ■ Beacon Partners Inc.
97 Libbey Pky., Ste. 310
Weymouth, MA 02189
Ph: (781)982-8400
Fax: (781)337-8469
URL: http://www.beaconpartners.com
Contact: Ralph P. Fargnoli, Jr., Chief Executive Officer
Preferred Investment Size: $300,000 to $1,000,000.
Industry Preferences: Consumer related, industrial and energy, Internet specific, other products, medical and health, semiconductors and other electronics, communications and media, computer software and services. **Geographic Preference:** Northeast.

49771 ■ BEV Capital / Brand Equity Ventures
8 Maher Ave.
Greenwich, CT 06830
Ph: (203)724-1101
Fax: (203)724-1155
URL: http://www.bevcapital.com
Contact: Christopher P. Kirchen, Partner
Preferred Investment Size: $1,000,000 to $5,000,000. **Industry Preferences:** Internet specific, consumer related, semiconductors and other electronics, computer software and services, and other products. **Geographic Preference:** Mid Atlantic and Northeast.

49772 ■ Canaan Partners (Westport)
285 Riverside Ave., Ste. 250
Westport, CT 06880
Ph: (203)855-0400
Fax: (203)854-9117
URL: http://www.canaan.com
Contact: Mickey Kim, Principal
Preferred Investment Size: $3,000,000 to $25,000,000. **Industry Preferences:** Internet specific, computer software and services, medical and health, communications and media, biotechnology, other products, computer hardware, semiconductors and other electronics, consumer related, industrial and energy. **Geographic Preference:** Northeast, West Coast, and U.S.

49773 ■ Catterton Partners
599 W. Putnam Ave.
Greenwich, CT 06830
Ph: (203)629-4901
Fax: (203)629-4903
Co. E-mail: info@cpequity.com
URL: http://www.cpequity.com
Contact: Neda Daneshzadeh, Principal
Preferred Investment Size: $5,000,000 minimum.
Industry Preferences: Consumer related, communications and media, other products. **Geographic Preference:** U.S. and Canada.

49774 ■ CHL Medical Partners / Collinson, Howe, and Lennox
1055 Washington Blvd., 6th Fl.
Stamford, CT 06901
Ph: (203)324-7700
Fax: (203)324-3636
Co. E-mail: info@chlmedical.com
URL: http://www.chlmedical.com
Contact: Jeffrey J. Collinson, Principal
E-mail: jcollinson@chlmedical.com
Preferred Investment Size: $250,000 to $6,000,000.
Industry Preferences: Medical and health, biotechnology, and Internet specific. **Geographic Preference:** U.S.

49775 ■ Connecticut Innovations, Inc.
865 Brook St.
Rocky Hill, CT 06067
Ph: (860)563-5851
Fax: (860)563-4877
URL: http://www.ctinnovations.com
Contact: Pauline M. Murphy, Managing Director
E-mail: pauline.murphy@ctinnovations.com
Preferred Investment Size: $100,000 to $2,000,000.
Industry Preferences: Internet specific, computer software and services, semiconductors and other electronics, biotechnology, medical and health, industrial and energy, communications and media, other products, computer hardware, and consumer related. **Geographic Preference:** Connecticut.

49776 ■ Endeavor Capital Management
49 Richmondville Ave., Ste. 215
Westport, CT 06880
Ph: (203)341-7788
Fax: (203)341-7799
Co. E-mail: contactus@endeavorcap.com
URL: http://www.endeavor.com
Contact: Anthony Buffa, Partner
Preferred Investment Size: $50,000 to $5,000,000.
Industry Preferences: Other products, communications and media, Internet specific, consumer related, medical and health, computer hardware, computer software and services, and industrial and energy. **Geographic Preference:** U.S. and Canada.

49777 ■ First New England Capital, L.P.
100 Pearl St.
Hartford, CT 06103
Ph: (860)293-3333
Fax: (860)293-3338
Co. E-mail: info@fnec.com
URL: http://www.firstnewenglandcapital.com
Contact: Richard C. Klaffky, Principal
E-mail: rklaffky@fnec.com
Preferred Investment Size: $2,000,000 to $7,000,000. **Industry Preferences:** Consumer related, industrial and energy, transportation, business service, manufacturing, and other products. **Geographic Preference:** U.S.

49778 ■ Generation Partners
1 Greenwich Office Park
Greenwich, CT 06831-5150
Ph: (203)422-8200
Fax: (203)422-8250
Co. E-mail: info@generation.com
URL: http://www.generation.com
Contact: Mark Jennings, Managing Partner
Founded: 1996. **Preferred Investment Size:** $10,000,000 to $40,000,000. **Industry Preferences:** Computer software and services, Internet specific, business services, communications and media, consumer related, healthcare services and technology. **Geographic Preference:** U.S. and Canada.

49779 ■ Landmark Partners, Inc.
10 Mill Pond Ln.
Simsbury, CT 06070
Ph: (860)651-9760
Fax: (860)651-8890
Co. E-mail: info@landmarkpartners.com
URL: http://www.landmarkpartners.com
Contact: Paul G. Giovacchini, Principal
E-mail: Paul.Giovacchini@landmarkpartners.com
Preferred Investment Size: $500,000 minimum. **Industry Preferences:** Other products, computer software and services, computer hardware, semiconductors and other electronics, Internet specific, biotechnology, medical and health, consumer related, industrial and energy. **Geographic Preference:** U.S. and Canada.

49780 ■ LTI Ventures Leasing Corp. / Leasing Technologies International, Inc.
221 Danbury Rd.
Wilton, CT 06897
Ph: (203)563-1100
Fax: (203)563-1112
URL: http://www.ltileasing.com
Contact: Jerry Sprole, Chief Executive Officer
E-mail: jsprole@ltileasing.com
Preferred Investment Size: $500,000 to $2,000,000.
Industry Preferences: Communications and media, computer hardware and software, Internet specific, semiconductors and other electronics, biotechnology, medical and health, consumer related, industrial and energy. **Geographic Preference:** U.S.

49781 ■ The NTC Group
3 Pickwick Plz., Ste. 200
Greenwich, CT 06830
Ph: (203)862-2850
Fax: (203)622-6538
URL: http://www.ntcgroupinc.com
Contact: Thomas C. Foley
Preferred Investment Size: $1,000,000 minimum.
Industry Preferences: Semiconductors and other electronics, and industrial and energy. **Geographic Preference:** U.S.

49782 ■ Oak Investment Partners
901 Main Ave., Ste. 600
Norwalk, CT 06851
Ph: (203)226-8346
Fax: (203)846-0282
URL: http://www.oakvc.com
Contact: Bandel Carano, Managing Partner
E-mail: bandel@oakvc.com
Preferred Investment Size: $25,000,000 to $150,000,000. **Industry Preferences:** Communications and media, Internet specific, computer software and services, semiconductors and other electronics, consumer related, medical and health, computer hardware, other products, biotechnology, industrial and energy. **Geographic Preference:** U.S.

49783 ■ Oxford Bioscience Partners (Monroe)
PO Box 573
Monroe, CT 06880
Ph: (203)261-3182
Co. E-mail: bizplan@oxbio.com
URL: http://www.oxbio.com
Contact: Alan G. Walton, Senior Partner
Preferred Investment Size: $1,000,000 to $10,000,000. **Industry Preferences:** Biotechnology, medical and health, Internet specific, computer software and services, consumer related, and semiconductors and other electronics. **Geographic Preference:** U.S. and Canada.

49784 ■ RFE Investment Partners
195 Oenoke Ridge
New Canaan, CT 06840
Ph: (203)966-2800
Fax: (203)966-3109
Co. E-mail: info@rfeip.com
URL: http://www.rfeip.com
Contact: James A. Parsons, Partner
E-mail: jparsons@rfeip.com
Preferred Investment Size: $10,000,000 to $25,000,000. **Industry Preferences:** Other products, business services, medical and health, industrial and energy, consumer related, computer software and services, computer hardware, semiconductors and other electronics, and biotechnology. **Geographic Preference:** U.S. and Canada.

49785 ■ Saugatuck Capital Company
187 Danbury Rd.
Wilton, CT 06897
Ph: (203)348-6669
Fax: (203)324-6995
Co. E-mail: saugatuck@saugatuckcapital.com
URL: http://www.saugatuckcapital.com
Contact: Frank J. Hawley, Jr., Managing Director
E-mail: fhawley@saugatuckcapital.com
Preferred Investment Size: $4,000,000 to $7,000,000. **Industry Preferences:** Other products, medical and health, consumer related, communications and media, industrial and energy, computer hardware, semiconductors and other electronics, computer software and services, and Internet specific. **Geographic Preference:** U.S.

49786 ■ Signal Lake Management LLC
606 Post Rd. E., Ste. 667
Westport, CT 06880-4549
Ph: (203)454-1133
Fax: (203)454-7142
Co. E-mail: info@signallake.com
URL: http://www.signallake.com
Contact: Bart Stuck, Managing Director
E-mail: BartStuck@signallake.com
Preferred Investment Size: $100,000 to $100,000,000. **Industry Preferences:** Internet specific, semiconductors and other electronics, communications and media, computer hardware, computer software and services. **Geographic Preference:** Northeast and U.S.

PROCUREMENT ASSISTANCE PROGRAMS

49787 ■ Connecticut Procurement Technical Assistance Center - Outreach Office
10 Middle St., 6th Fl.
Bridgeport, CT 06604-4223

Ph: (203)333-3338
Fax: (860)437-4662
Co. E-mail: ptap@ctptap.org
URL: http://www.ctptap.org
Contact: Bernie Todisco, Specialist
E-mail: skoos@sector.org
Description: Provides marketing and procurement assistance to Connecticut businesses interested in selling their goods or services to federal, state, or local governments.

49788 ■ Connecticut Procurement Technical Assistance Center - Small Business Development Procurement Center
190 Governor Winthrop Blvd., 4th Fl.
New London, CT 06320-6633
Ph: (860)437-4659
Fax: (860)437-4662
Co. E-mail: brobertson@secter.org
URL: http://www.ctptap.org
Contact: Brien Robertson, Director
Description: Covers activities for the VA Medical Center (West Haven, CT), Naval Submarine base (Groton, CT), and the U.S. Coast Guard Academy (New London, CT).

49789 ■ SouthEastern Connecticut Enterprise Region (seCTer) - Connecticut Procurement Center
190 Governor Winthrop Blvd.
New London, CT 06320
Ph: (860)437-4659
Fax: (860)437-4662
Co. E-mail: secter@secter.org
URL: http://www.secter.org
Contact: Brien Robertson, Director
E-mail: lawrence.steele@sba.gov
Description: Covers activities for the VA Medical Center (West Haven, CT), Naval Submarine base (Groton, CT), and the U.S. Coast Guard Academy (New London, CT).

49790 ■ State of Connecticut Procurement Services - Purchasing Services Division
165 Capitol Ave.
Hartford, CT 06106
Ph: (860)713-5093
Fax: (860)622-2904
Co. E-mail: carol.wilson@po.state.ct.us
URL: http://www.das.state.ct.us/Purchase/New_PurchHome/Busopp.asp
Contact: Carol Wilson, Director

INCUBATORS/RESEARCH AND TECHNOLOGY PARKS

49791 ■ Bridgeport Innovation Center
955 Connecticut Ave., Ste 5103
Bridgeport, CT 06607
Ph: (203)333-9000
Fax: (203)333-9008
Co. E-mail: reneesand@hotmail.com
URL: http://www.bridgeportinnovationcenter.com
Contact: Carleton Pierpont, General Manager
Description: Bridgeport Innovation Center provides an entrepreneurial environment for small to mid-sized growth businesses. As a Bridgeport business your company may qualify for the city's liberal tax incentives and/or for Connecticut State tax abatements, personnel job training, and/or financial assistance programs.

49792 ■ Ceebraid Signal Corp.
112 Hoyt St.
Stamford, CT 06905
Ph: (203)406-1300
Fax: (203)406-1305
URL: http://www.ceebraidsignal.com

49793 ■ Connecticut Center for Advanced Technology
222 Pitkin St., Ste. 101
East Hartford, CT 06108
Ph: (860)291-8832

Fax: (860)291-8874
Co. E-mail: info@ccat.us
URL: http://www.ccat.us/incubator/index.php
Contact: Elliot Ginsberg, Chief Executive Officer
Description: A non-profit corporation funded under federal and state sponsored grants to develop a national center that addresses military and civilian industrial manufacturing needs; promotes energy planning and policy initiatives; stimulates innovation; and enhances workforce development issues concerning technology competitiveness.

49794 ■ Connecticut Enterprise Center
200 Myrtle St.
New Britain, CT 06053
Ph: (860)229-7700
Fax: (860)229-6847
URL: http://www.cwresources.org/cec.htm
Description: A facility in which a variety of new and growing businesses operate; sharing services, equipment and experiences with other startup entrepreneurs. CEC has admission criteria, support services and encourages graduation from incubator.

49795 ■ Institute of Technology and Business Development
Central Connecticut State University
185 Main St.
New Britain, CT 06051
Ph: (860)832-0700
Fax: (860)832-0701
Co. E-mail: mullinsr@ccsu.edu
URL: http://www.ccsu.edu/itbd/
Contact: Richard Mullins, Executive Assistant
Description: A small business incubator that assists entrepreneurs in the business start-up process and gives aid to new businesses to help ensure their survival.

49796 ■ University of Connecticut Technology Incubation Program
1392 Storrs Rd., U4213
Storrs, CT 06269-4213
Ph: (860)486-3010
Fax: (860)486-3536
Co. E-mail: rita.zangari@uconn.edu
URL: http://www.tip.uconn.edu/
Description: A program that aims to accelerate the successful establishment and development of entrepreneurial companies by providing laboratory/office space and an array of support resources and services which are available through the various departments and functions at the University.

EDUCATIONAL PROGRAMS

49797 ■ Housatonic Community College
900 Lafayette Blvd.
Bridgeport, CT 06604
Ph: (203)332-5000
Fax: (203)332-5123
URL: http://www.hcc.commnet.edu
Description: Two-year college offering a small business management program.

PUBLICATIONS

49798 ■ Starting and Operating a Business in Connecticut: A Step-by-Step Guide
PSI Research
300 N. Valley Dr.
Grants Pass, OR 97526
Ph: (503)479-9464
Free: 800-228-2275
Fax: (503)476-1479
Co. E-mail: psi2@magick.net
Ed: Michael D. Jenkins. **Released:** Revised edition, 1992. **Price:** $29.95 (looseleaf binder); $24.95 (paper). **Description:** Part of the Successful Business Library series.

PUBLISHERS

49799 ■ Business Books International—De Villiers Inc.
194 Putnam Rd.
New Canaan, CT 06840

Ph: (203)966-9645
Fax: (203)966-6018
Co. E-mail: editor@businessbooksusa.com
URL: http://www.businessbooksusa.com
Contact: Les de Villiers, President
Description: Description: Publishes reference books for business and library use on regions of the world. Reaches market through advertising, direct mail, trade sales and wholesalers. Does not accept unsolicited manuscripts. **Founded:** 1982.

49800 ■ Hannacroix Creek Books Inc.
1127 High Ridge Rd., Ste. 110B
Stamford, CT 06905-1203
Ph: (203)968-8098
Fax: (203)968-0193
Co. E-mail: hannacroix@aol.com
URL: http://www.hannacroixcreekbooks.com
Contact: Peggy Stautberg, Manager
Description: Description: Publishes books and audio cassettes in the areas of deafness, friendship, business, time management and relationships. **Founded:** 1996.

49801 ■ Hunt-Scanlon Publishing
1037 E Putnam Ave.
Riverside, CT 06878
Ph: (203)344-9281
Free: 800-477-1199
Fax: (203)344-9282
Contact: Christopher W. Hunt, President
E-mail: chris@hunt-scanlon.com
Description: Description: Publishes business directories for business-to-business applications. Also publishes CD-ROMs and software, as well as a newsletter. Reaches market through direct mail. **Founded:** 1989. **Publications:** *Diversity in Corporate America* (Biennial); *RecruiterLink* (Annual); *ExecutiveSelect - Finance Executives Edition* (Annual); *ExecutiveSelect - Sales & Marketing Executives Edition*; *ExecutiveSelect - Information Technology Executives Edition* (Annual); *The Job Seekers Guide to Executive Recruiters*; *Job Seekers Guide to Personnel Managers*; *Personnel Locator*; *Hunt-Scanlon's Select Guide to Human Resource Executives* (Annual); *Hunt-Scanlon's Select Guide to Finance Executives* (Annual); *Hunt-Scanlon's Select Guide to Sales & Marketing Executives* (Annual); *Hunt-Scanlon's Select Guide to Information Technology Executives*; *Hunt-Scanlon's Executive Recruiters of North America* (Annual); *Hunt-Scanlon's Executive Recruiters of North America - Contingency Firms* (Annual); *4 Data Base* (Annual); *ExecutiveSelect - Human Resource Executives Edition* (Annual).

49802 ■ RDS Associates Inc.
41 Brainerd Rd.
Niantic, CT 06357-1722
Ph: (860)691-0081
Free: 800-363-8867
Fax: (860)691-1145
Co. E-mail: rds@businessbookpress.com
URL: http://www.businessbookpress.com
Contact: Sam Cantor, President
Description: Description: Publishes reference and business books relating to buying, selling, valuing, starting or improving a business. Accepts unsolicited manuscripts. Direct mail and Book World Services. **Founded:** 1996.

SMALL BUSINESS DEVELOPMENT CENTERS

49803 ■ Delaware Small Business Development Center - Lead Office (DSBDC)
Delaware Technology Park
One Innovation Way, Ste. 301
Newark, DE 19711
Ph: (302)831-1555
Fax: (302)831-1423
Co. E-mail: mdd@udel.edu
URL: http://www.dsbtdc.org
Contact: Clinton Tymes, Director
Awards: Small Business Administration (Annual).

49804 ■ Dover Small Business Development Center
1200 N DuPont Hwy., Ste. 108
Dover, DE 19901
Ph: (302)678-1555
Fax: (302)857-6950
Co. E-mail: apaoli@udel.edu
URL: http://www.delawaresbdc.org
Description: Represents and promotes the small business sector. Provides management assistance to current and prospective small business owners. Helps to improve management skills and expand the products and services of members.

49805 ■ Georgetown Small Business Development Center
103 W Pine St.
Georgetown, DE 19947
Ph: (302)856-1555
Co. E-mail: wpfaff@udel.edu
URL: http://www.delawaresbdc.org
Description: Represents and promotes the small business sector. Provides management assistance to current and prospective small business owners. Helps to improve management skills and expand the products and services of members.

49806 ■ Newark Small Business Development Center
1 Innovation Way, Ste. 301
Newark, DE 19711
Ph: (302)831-0770
Co. E-mail: mdd@udel.edu
URL: http://www.delawaresbdc.org
Description: Represents and promotes the small business sector. Provides management assistance to current and prospective small business owners. Helps to improve management skills and expand the products and services of members.

49807 ■ Wilmington Small Business Development Center
100 W 10th St., Ste. 812
Wilmington, DE 19801
Ph: (302)831-1555
Co. E-mail: mdd@udel.edu
URL: http://www.delawaresbdc.org
Description: Represents and promotes the small business sector. Provides management assistance to current and prospective small business owners.

Helps to improve management skills and expand the products and services of members.

SMALL BUSINESS ASSISTANCE PROGRAMS

49808 ■ Delaware Economic Development Office - Business Finance Section
99 Kings Hwy.
Dover, DE 19901
Ph: (302)739-4271
Fax: (302)739-5749
URL: http://dedo.delaware.gov
Contact: Gary Smith, Director, Finance
Description: Promotes the development and growth of new and existing businesses; trains workers, assists employers with recruiting, and develops training programs; conducts research on the state's business and economic climate; and provides publications entitled Small Business Start-Up Guide, Selling to the State, Solutions for Delaware Small Business, and The Workforce Resource. The Small Business Advocate acts as a liaison between small businesses and local, state, and federal agencies; helps businesses get into state programs; and provides information on permits, regulations, financing, and procurement programs.

BETTER BUSINESS BUREAUS

49809 ■ *BBB Consumer Resource Guide and Membership Directory*
60 Reads Way
New Castle, DE 19720
Ph: (302)221-5255
Fax: (302)221-5265
Co. E-mail: info@delaware.bbb.org
URL: http://delaware.bbb.org
Contact: Christine Sauers, President

49810 ■ Better Business Bureau of Delaware
60 Reads Way
New Castle, DE 19720
Ph: (302)221-5255
Fax: (302)221-5265
Co. E-mail: info@delaware.bbb.org
URL: http://delaware.bbb.org
Contact: Christine Sauers, President
Description: Seeks to promote and foster ethical relationship between businesses and the public through voluntary self-regulation, consumer and business education, and service excellence. Provides information to help consumers and businesses make informed purchasing decisions and avoid costly scams and frauds; settles consumer complaints through arbitration and other means. **Founded:** 1965. **Publications:** *BBB Consumer Resource Guide and Membership Directory.* **Awards:** Torch Awards for Marketplace Ethics (Annual); Edward M. Rush, Sr. Memorial Award (Annual).

CHAMBERS OF COMMERCE

49811 ■ Bethany-Fenwick Area Chamber of Commerce
36913 Coastal Hwy.
Fenwick Island, DE 19944

Ph: (302)539-2100
Free: 800-962-7873
Fax: (302)539-9434
Co. E-mail: info@bethany-fenwick.org
URL: http://www.bethany-fenwick.org
Contact: Andrew Cripps, Executive Director
Description: Promotes business and community development in Bethany Beach, Fenwick Island and surrounding areas in Delaware. Holds semiannual surf fishing tournament, annual golf tournament and ocean-to-bay bike tour. **Founded:** 1976. **Publications:** *Map and Business Guide; Map and Visitors Guide* (Annual); *The Quiet Resorts Visitors Guide.*

49812 ■ *Business Bridge*
12 Penns Way
New Castle, DE 19720
Ph: (302)737-4343
Fax: (302)322-3593
Co. E-mail: info@ncccc.com
URL: http://www.ncccc.com/cwt/external/wcpages/index.aspx
Contact: Mark Kleinschmidt, President
Released: Monthly

49813 ■ Central Delaware Chamber of Commerce (CDCC)
435 N DuPont Hwy.
Dover, DE 19901
Ph: (302)734-7513
Fax: (302)678-0189
Co. E-mail: info@cdcc.net
URL: http://www.cdcc.net
Contact: Judy Diogo, President
Description: Promotes business and community development in central Delaware. Sponsors trade shows. **Founded:** 1919. **Publications:** *Central Delaware Info Book* (Annual); *Chamber News* (Monthly). **Telecommunication Services:** jdiogo@cdcc.net.

49814 ■ *Central Delaware Info Book*
435 N DuPont Hwy.
Dover, DE 19901
Ph: (302)734-7513
Fax: (302)678-0189
Co. E-mail: info@cdcc.net
URL: http://www.cdcc.net
Contact: Judy Diogo, President
Released: Annual **Price:** free.

49815 ■ Chamber of Commerce for Greater Milford (CCGM)
411 N Rehoboth Blvd.
Milford, DE 19963
Ph: (302)422-3344
Fax: (302)422-7503
Co. E-mail: milford@milfordchamber.com
URL: http://www.milfordchamber.com
Contact: Fred Rohm, President
Description: Seeks to advance Greater Milford economy through promotion of civic, industrial, commercial, educational, agricultural, and social interests of communities within the area. **Founded:** 1989.

49816 ■ Chamber News
435 N DuPont Hwy.
Dover, DE 19901
Ph: (302)734-7513
Fax: (302)678-0189
Co. E-mail: info@cdcc.net
URL: http://www.cdcc.net
Contact: Judy Diogo, President
Released: Monthly

49817 ■ Delaware Coast Vacationland
501 Rehoboth Ave.
Rehoboth Beach, DE 19971-0216
Ph: (302)227-2233
Free: 800-441-1329
Fax: (302)227-8351
Co. E-mail: rehoboth@beach-fun.com
URL: http://www.beach-fun.com
Contact: Matt Turlinski, Chairman
Released: Annual

49818 ■ Delaware Directory of Commerce and Industry
1201 N Orange St., Ste. 200
Wilmington, DE 19899-0671
Ph: (302)655-7221
Free: 800-292-9507
Fax: (302)654-0691
Co. E-mail: info@dscc.com
URL: http://www.dscc.com
Contact: James A. Wolfe, President
URL(s): www.dscc.com/state_chamber/publications.htm. **Released:** Periodic; Annual; late in year. **Price:** $50, Members per additional copy for members; $100, Nonmembers. **Covers:** About 5,000 manufacturers, retailers, wholesalers, and service establishments. **Entries include:** Name, address, phone, name, address, phone, name and title of contact, list of products or services. **Arrangement:** Alphabetical. **Indexes:** By category.

49819 ■ Delaware State Chamber Business Journal
1201 N Orange St., Ste. 200
Wilmington, DE 19899-0671
Ph: (302)655-7221
Free: 800-292-9507
Fax: (302)654-0691
Co. E-mail: info@dscc.com
URL: http://www.dscc.com
Contact: James A. Wolfe, President
Released: Biweekly

49820 ■ Delaware State Chamber of Commerce Inc. (DSCC)
1201 N Orange St., Ste. 200
Wilmington, DE 19899-0671
Ph: (302)655-7221
Free: 800-292-9507
Fax: (302)654-0691
Co. E-mail: info@dscc.com
URL: http://www.dscc.com
Contact: James A. Wolfe, President
Description: Promotes business and community development in Delaware. **Founded:** 1837. **Publications:** Delaware State Chamber Business Journal (Biweekly); Legislative Roster (Periodic); Delaware Legislative Roster (Annual); Delaware Directory of Commerce and Industry (Periodic; Annual). **Awards:** Josiah Marvel Cup Award (Annual); Superstars in Education (Annual); Gilman Award for Superstars in Business (Annual). **Telecommunication Services:** jtaylor@dscc.com; publications@dscc.com; jwolfe@dscc.com.

49821 ■ FocusOn
501 Rehoboth Ave.
Rehoboth Beach, DE 19971-0216
Ph: (302)227-2233
Free: 800-441-1329
Fax: (302)227-8351
Co. E-mail: rehoboth@beach-fun.com
URL: http://www.beach-fun.com
Contact: Matt Turlinski, Chairman
Released: Monthly

49822 ■ Greater Seaford Chamber of Commerce (GSCC)
PO Box 26
Seaford, DE 19973
Ph: (302)629-9690
Free: 800-416-GSCC
Fax: (302)629-0281
Co. E-mail: admin@seafordchamber.com
URL: http://www.seafordchamber.com
Contact: Paula K. Gunson, Executive Director
Description: Promotes the economic health of the Seaford, DE area and contributes to the civic, economic, and social welfare of the people in the surrounding communities. **Founded:** 1936. **Publications:** Take Five (Bimonthly). **Awards:** Business Person of the Year (Annual); Volunteer of the Year (Annual); John A. Moore, Jr. Community Service Award (Annual).

49823 ■ Legislative Roster
1201 N Orange St., Ste. 200
Wilmington, DE 19899-0671
Ph: (302)655-7221
Free: 800-292-9507
Fax: (302)654-0691
Co. E-mail: info@dscc.com
URL: http://www.dscc.com
Contact: James A. Wolfe, President
Released: Periodic

49824 ■ Lewes Chamber of Commerce (LCC)
120 Kings Hwy.
Lewes, DE 19958
Ph: (302)645-8073
Free: 877-465-3937
Fax: (302)645-8412
Co. E-mail: inquiry@leweschamber.com
URL: http://www.leweschamber.com
Contact: Betsy Reamer, Executive Director
Description: Promotes business and community development in Lewes, DE. Sponsors kite festival, garden tour, and Christmas parade. **Founded:** 1935. **Publications:** Visitors Guide (Annual).

49825 ■ Map and Business Guide
36913 Coastal Hwy.
Fenwick Island, DE 19944
Ph: (302)539-2100
Free: 800-962-7873
Fax: (302)539-9434
Co. E-mail: info@bethany-fenwick.org
URL: http://www.bethany-fenwick.org
Contact: Andrew Cripps, Executive Director

49826 ■ Map and Visitors Guide
36913 Coastal Hwy.
Fenwick Island, DE 19944
Ph: (302)539-2100
Free: 800-962-7873
Fax: (302)539-9434
Co. E-mail: info@bethany-fenwick.org
URL: http://www.bethany-fenwick.org
Contact: Andrew Cripps, Executive Director
Released: Annual **Price:** free.

49827 ■ Map and Visitors Guide
501 Rehoboth Ave.
Rehoboth Beach, DE 19971-0216
Ph: (302)227-2233
Free: 800-441-1329
Fax: (302)227-8351
Co. E-mail: rehoboth@beach-fun.com
URL: http://www.beach-fun.com
Contact: Matt Turlinski, Chairman
Released: Annual

49828 ■ New Castle County Chamber of Commerce (NCCCC)
12 Penns Way
New Castle, DE 19720
Ph: (302)737-4343

Fax: (302)322-3593
Co. E-mail: info@ncccc.com
URL: http://www.ncccc.com/cwt/external/wcpages/index.aspx
Contact: Mark Kleinschmidt, President
Description: Creates a prosperous economic environment in New Castle County, DE. Strives to be the premier resource for business growth by providing programs and services that contribute to the success of the community. Offers value-added benefits, connection to business opportunities, local representation on major issues of public policy, and timely communication so that members can be proactive in growing their businesses. **Founded:** 1922. **Publications:** Business Bridge (Monthly). **Awards:** Entrepreneur of the Year (Annual).

49829 ■ Rehoboth Beach-Dewey Beach Chamber of Commerce (RBDBCC)
501 Rehoboth Ave.
Rehoboth Beach, DE 19971-0216
Ph: (302)227-2233
Free: 800-441-1329
Fax: (302)227-8351
Co. E-mail: rehoboth@beach-fun.com
URL: http://www.beach-fun.com
Contact: Matt Turlinski, Chairman
Description: Promotes business and community development in the Rehoboth Beach-Dewey Beach area. Sponsors Sea Witch Weekend Festival. **Founded:** 1940. **Publications:** FocusOn (Monthly); Delaware Coast Vacationland (Annual); Map and Visitors Guide (Annual). **Educational Activities:** Sand Castle Contest (Annual).

49830 ■ Take Five
PO Box 26
Seaford, DE 19973
Ph: (302)629-9690
Free: 800-416-GSCC
Fax: (302)629-0281
Co. E-mail: admin@seafordchamber.com
URL: http://www.seafordchamber.com
Contact: Paula K. Gunson, Executive Director
Released: Bimonthly

49831 ■ Visitors Guide
120 Kings Hwy.
Lewes, DE 19958
Ph: (302)645-8073
Free: 877-465-3937
Fax: (302)645-8412
Co. E-mail: inquiry@leweschamber.com
URL: http://www.leweschamber.com
Contact: Betsy Reamer, Executive Director
Released: Annual

MINORITY BUSINESS ASSISTANCE PROGRAMS

49832 ■ Wilmington Minority Business Enterprise Office
Louis L. Redding City/County Bldg.
800 N. French St.
Wilmington, DE 19801
Ph: (302)576-2121
Fax: (302)573-5557
URL: http://www.ci.wilmington.de.us/dbe.htm
Contact: Larraine P. Watson, Director
Description: Allows the solicitation and assistance to disadvantage businesses to participate in the procurement process and performance of City contracts.

FINANCING AND LOAN PROGRAMS

49833 ■ Blue Rock Capital
PO Box 4513
Wilmington, DE 19807-1312
Ph: (302)426-0981

Fax: (302)426-0982
URL: http://www.bluerockcapital.com
Contact: Virginia Breen, Partner
E-mail: virginia@bluerockcapital.com
Preferred Investment Size: $250,000 to $2,000,000.
Industry Preferences: Internet specific, semiconductors and other electronics, communications and media, consumer related, computer software and services, and computer hardware. **Geographic Preference:** Mid Atlantic.

PROCUREMENT ASSISTANCE PROGRAMS

49834 ■ Delaware Procurement Technical Assistance Center - Delaware Small Business Development Center Network
1 Innovation Way, Ste. 301
Newark, DE 19711
Ph: (302)831-0783
Fax: (302)831-0771
Co. E-mail: info@delawarecontracts.com
URL: http://www.delawarecontracts.com
Contact: Diane Seymour, Specialist
E-mail: jbeau@udel.edu
Description: Offers free resources to small Delaware businesses wanting to grow their sales in the public sector with federal, state and local government entities.

INCUBATORS/RESEARCH AND TECHNOLOGY PARKS

49835 ■ DE Micro Enterprise Program - Retail Incubator Program
Louis L. Redding City/County Bldg
800 French St.
Wilmington, DE 19801-3537
Ph: (302)576-2120
URL: http://www.wilmingtonde.gov/microloan_incubator.htm
Description: A facility that has been re-established to assist early-stage development businesses. Its mission is to provide emerging and new businesses opportunities to start-up operations in a shared service environment that will enable them to receive technical assistance, business and financial management, and retail salesmanship training to help sustain their respective operations.

49836 ■ Delaware Technology Park
15 Innovation Way, Ste. 300
Newark, DE 19711
Ph: (302)452-1100
Fax: (302)452-1101
Co. E-mail: info@deltechpark.org
URL: http://www.deltechpark.org/
Contact: Jane Crouch, Administrator
Description: A business research park devoted to attracting established industries and providing an incubation and acceleration for start-ups in high-technology fields, specifically those in biotechnology, information technology and advanced materials.

LEGISLATIVE ASSISTANCE

49837 ■ Delaware Senate Committee on Small Business
Legislative Hall
Dover, DE 19901
Ph: (302)744-4298
Free: 800-282-8545
Fax: (302)739-6890
Co. E-mail: LIS.Webmaster@state.de.us
URL: http://www.delaware.gov/
Contact: Robert Venables, Chairperson

PUBLICATIONS

49838 ■ *Starting and Operating a Business in Delaware: A Step-by-Step Guide*
PSI Research
300 N. Valley Dr.
Grants Pass, OR 97526
Ph: (503)479-9464
Free: 800-228-2275
Fax: (503)476-1479
Co. E-mail: psi2@magick.net
Ed: Michael D. Jenkins. **Released:** Revised edition, 1992. **Price:** $29.95 (looseleaf binder); $24.95 (paper). **Description:** Part of the Successful Business Library series.

District of Columbia

SMALL BUSINESS DEVELOPMENT CENTERS

49839 ■ District of Columbia Small Business Development Center at University of District of Columbia (DC SBDC)
4340 Connecticut Ave. NW
Washington, DC 20008
Ph: (202)274-7030
Co. E-mail: sbdcinfo@udc.edu
URL: http://www.dcsbdc.org
Description: Represents and promotes the small business sector. Provides management assistance to current and prospective small business owners. Helps to improve management skills and expand the products and services of members.

49840 ■ Washington, D.C. Small Business Development Center at Howard University
2600 6th St. NW
Washington, DC 20059
Ph: (202)806-1550
Fax: (202)806-1777
URL: http://www.dcsbdc.org
Contact: Darrell Brown, Executive Director
Description: Represents and promotes the small business sector. Provides management assistance to current and prospective small business owners. Helps to improve management skills and expand the products and services of members.

SMALL BUSINESS ASSISTANCE PROGRAMS

49841 ■ District of Columbia Office of the Deputy Mayor - Planning and Economic Development
John A. Wilson Bldg.
1350 Pennsylvania Ave., NW, Ste. 317
Washington, DC 20004
Ph: (202)727-6365
Fax: (202)727-6703
Co. E-mail: dmped.eom@dc.gov
URL: http://www.dcbiz.dc.gov
Contact: Mary Margaret Plumridge, Director
Description: Works to attract new businesses and retain existing ones. The Financial Services Division offers SBA 503/504 loans and other loan programs. The Small Business Incubator Facility Program provides affordable facilities and management assistance to new and small businesses. The Neighborhood Commercial Services Division provides loans and technical assistance to encourage the revitalization of neighborhood commercial districts.

BETTER BUSINESS BUREAUS

49842 ■ *BBB Rules of Arbitration*
1411 K St. NW, Ste. 1000
Washington, DC 20005
Ph: (202)393-8000

Fax: (202)393-1198
Co. E-mail: info@mybbb.org
URL: http://dc-easternpa.bbb.org
Contact: Edward J. Johnson, III, President

49843 ■ *BBB Rules of Mediation*
1411 K St. NW, Ste. 1000
Washington, DC 20005
Ph: (202)393-8000
Fax: (202)393-1198
Co. E-mail: info@mybbb.org
URL: http://dc-easternpa.bbb.org
Contact: Edward J. Johnson, III, President

49844 ■ Better Business Bureau Serving Metropolitan Washington, DC and Eastern Pennsylvania
1411 K St. NW, Ste. 1000
Washington, DC 20005
Ph: (202)393-8000
Fax: (202)393-1198
Co. E-mail: info@mybbb.org
URL: http://dc-easternpa.bbb.org
Contact: Edward J. Johnson, III, President
Description: Business and professional. Helps the local community to make a better place to live. Promotes integrity and business ethics through self-regulation in the marketplace. **Founded:** 1920. **Publications:** *BBB Rules of Arbitration*; *BBB Rules of Mediation*; *Memberline* (Periodic).

49845 ■ *Memberline*
1411 K St. NW, Ste. 1000
Washington, DC 20005
Ph: (202)393-8000
Fax: (202)393-1198
Co. E-mail: info@mybbb.org
URL: http://dc-easternpa.bbb.org
Contact: Edward J. Johnson, III, President
Released: Periodic **Price:** free for members.

CHAMBERS OF COMMERCE

49846 ■ District of Columbia Chamber of Commerce (DCCC)
506 9th St. NW
Washington, DC 20004
Ph: (202)347-7201
Fax: (202)638-6762
Co. E-mail: info@dcchamber.org
URL: http://www.dcchamber.org
Contact: Barbara Lang, President
Description: Promotes business and community development in Washington, DC. **Founded:** 1938.

MINORITY BUSINESS ASSISTANCE PROGRAMS

49847 ■ Government of the District of Columbia - Department of Small and Local Business Development
441 4th St. NW, Ste. 970N
Washington, DC 20001
Ph: (202)727-3900

Fax: (202)724-3786
Co. E-mail: dslbd@dc.gov
URL: http://dslbd.dc.gov/DC/DSLBD/
Contact: Lee Smith, Director (Acting)
Description: The mission of the Department of Small and Local Business Development is to foster economic growth and the development of local, small, and disadvantaged business enterprises through supportive legislation, business development programs, and agency and public/private contract compliance.

49848 ■ Washington DC Women's Business Center
727 15th St. NW, 10th Fl.
Washington, DC 20005
Ph: (202)393-8307
Co. E-mail: info@dcwbc.org
URL: http://www.dcwbc.org
Contact: Samira B. Cook, Director
Description: Provides business development and support for women-owned businesses in the field of federal procurements.

49849 ■ Washngton DC Minority Business Enterprise Center
64 New York Ave., NE, Ste. 3152
Washington, DC 20002
Ph: (202)671-1552
Fax: (202)671-3073
Co. E-mail: info@dcmbec.org
URL: http://www.dcmbec.org/home.html
Contact: Eric Rice, Director
Description: Offers business consulting and development services.

FINANCING AND LOAN PROGRAMS

49850 ■ Core Capital Partners
1401 I St., NW, Ste. 1000
Washington, DC 20005
Ph: (202)589-0090
Fax: (202)589-0091
Co. E-mail: info@core-capital.com
URL: http://www.core-capital.com
Contact: Pascal Luck, Managing Director
E-mail: pluck@core-capital.com
Preferred Investment Size: $2,000,000 to $5,000,000. **Industry Preferences:** Communications and media, computer software and computer related. **Geographic Preference:** East Coast and Washington, D.C. metropolitan area.

49851 ■ The Grosvenor Funds
1776 Eye St. NW, Ste. 890
Washington, DC 20006
Ph: (202)861-5650
Fax: (202)861-5653
Co. E-mail: anna@grosvenorfund.com
URL: http://www.grosvenorfund.com
Contact: Bruce B. Dunnan, Managing Partner
Preferred Investment Size: $1,000,000 to $3,000,000. **Industry Preferences:** Communications, Internet specific, semiconductors and other electronics, and biotechnology.

49852 ■ Next Point Partners, L.P.
701 Pennsylvania Ave. NW, Ste. 900
Washington, DC 20004
Ph: (202)434-7319
Fax: (202)434-7400
Co. E-mail: mf@nextpoingvc.com
URL: http://www.nextpointvc.com
Contact: Michael Faber, Partner
Preferred Investment Size: $250,000 to $4,000,000.
Industry Preferences: Communications and media,
computer software, computer related, Internet spe-
cific, semiconductors and other electronics, industrial
and energy, and other. **Geographic Preference:** Mid
Atlantic, Midwest, Northeast, and Southeast.

**49853 ■ Telecommunications Development
Fund (TDF)**
2 Wisconsin Cir., Ste. 920
Chevy Chase, MD 20815
Ph: (240)483-4286
Fax: (301)907-8850
URL: http://www.tdfund.com
Contact: James Pastoriza, Managing Partner
Preferred Investment Size: $500,000 to $5,000,000.
Industry Preferences: Computer software and
services, Internet specific, computer hardware, com-
munications and media, semiconductors and other
electronics. **Geographic Preference:** U.S.

49854 ■ Women's Growth Capital Fund
Canal Sq., Ste. 110
1054 31st St., NW
Washington, DC 20007
Ph: (202)342-1431
Fax: (202)342-1203
Co. E-mail: info@wgcf.com
URL: http://www.wgcf.com
Contact: Patty Abramson, Managing Director
Preferred Investment Size: $100,000 to $1,800,000.
Industry Preferences: Internet specific, computer
software and services, communications and media,
consumer related, biotechnology, medical and health.
Geographic Preference: Mid Atlantic, Northeast,
and Southeast.

PROCUREMENT ASSISTANCE PROGRAMS

49855 ■ Procurement Center Representative
Department of Health & Human Services
200 Independence Ave. SW, Rm. 517D
Washington, DC 20201
Ph: (202)690-8330
Fax: (202)827-7228
Co. E-mail: malda.brown@hhs.gov
URL: http://www.sba.gov
Contact: Malda Brown, Representative
E-mail: rlewis@os.dhhs.gov
Description: Covers activities for Department of
Health and Human Services (Washington, DC), Army
Corps of Engineers (Baltimore, MD), Social Security
Administration (Baltimore, MD).

**49856 ■ Washington, DC, Metropolitan Area
Procurement Center - Department of
Transportation**
1200 New Jersey Ave, SW
Washington, DC 20590
Ph: (202)366-9142
Fax: (202)366-7228
Co. E-mail: annette.merrion@dot.gov
URL: http://www.sba.gov
Contact: Annette Johnson-Merrion, Representative
Description: Covers activities for Department of
Transportation (Washington, DC), Department of
Commerce (Washington, DC), Department of Veter-
ans Affairs (Washington, DC), Small Business Admin-
istration (Washington, DC), GSA/Regional Office
(Washington, DC), Department of Housing and Urban
Development (Washington, DC).

LEGISLATIVE ASSISTANCE

49857 ■ Council of the District of Columbia
John A. Wilson Bldg., Ste. 5
1350 Pennsylvania Ave., NW
Washington, DC 20004

Ph: (202)724-8000
Fax: (202)347-3070
Co. E-mail: dccouncil@dccouncil.us
URL: http://www.dccouncil.us
Contact: Vincent C. Gray, Chairman

TRADE PERIODICALS

49858 ■ *DMAW Marketing Advents*
Pub: Direct Marketing Association of Washington,
DC
Ed: Nancy Scott, Editor. **Released:** Monthly. **Price:**
$165, Included in membership. **Description:** Spot-
lights direct marketing topics for members in the
Washington, DC area. Recurring features include
interviews, a calendar of events, news of educational
opportunities, and job listings.

PUBLICATIONS

**49859 ■ *Starting and Operating a Business
in District of Columbia: A Step-by-Step Guide***
PSI Research
300 N. Valley Dr.
Grants Pass, OR 97526
Ph: (503)479-9464
Free: 800-228-2275
Fax: (503)476-1479
Co. E-mail: psi2@magick.net
Ed: Michael D. Jenkins. **Released:** Revised edition,
1992. **Price:** $29.95 (looseleaf binder); $24.95
(paper). **Description:** Part of the Successful Busi-
ness Library series.

PUBLISHERS

49860 ■ Friends of the Earth (FOE)
1100 15th St. NW, 11th Fl.
Washington, DC 20005
Ph: (202)783-7400
Free: 877-843-8687
Fax: (202)783-0444
Co. E-mail: foe@foe.org
URL: http://www.foe.org
Contact: Erich Pica, President
E-mail: epica@foe.org
Description: Dedicated to protecting the planet from
environmental disaster; preserving biological and
ethnic diversity; empowers citizens to have an effective voice in environmental decision; promotes use of
tax dollars to protect the environment; other interests
include groundwater and ozone protection, toxic
waste cleanup, and reforming the World Bank and
sustainable development which addressed the need
to reduce over-consumption in the U.S. **Founded:**
1969. **Publications:** *Friends of the Earth Newsmaga-*
zine (Quarterly); *Friends of the Earth Newsmagazine*
(Quarterly). **Awards:** FOE Fellowship Program,
6-Month; Unpaid internships.

49861 ■ Gallaudet University Press
800 Florida Ave. NE
Washington, DC 20002-3695
Ph: (202)651-5488
Fax: (202)651-5489
Co. E-mail: gupress@gallaudet.edu
URL: http://gupress.gallaudet.edu
Contact: Dr. John van cleve, Director
E-mail: john.vancleve@gallaudet.edu
Description: Description: Publishes reference books,
biographies for and about deaf and hard of hearing
people, deaf culture and deaf studies. Accepts
unsolicited manuscripts. Reaches market through
direct mail, reviews, listings, wholesalers and distribu-
tors. **Founded:** 1980.

**49862 ■ International Council for Small
Business (ICSB)**
GWU School of Business
Washington, DC 20052
Ph: (202)994-0704

Fax: (202)994-4930
Co. E-mail: icsb@gwu.edu
URL: http://www.icsb.org
Contact: Sylvio Rosa, Jr., President
E-mail: srosa@parqtec.com.br
Description: Management educators, researchers,
government officials and professionals in 80 countries. Fosters discussion of topics pertaining to the
development and improvement of small business
management. **Founded:** 1955. **Publications:** *Journal*
of Small Business Management (Quarterly). **Tele-**
communication Services: aymanelt@icsb.org.

**49863 ■ International Franchise Association
(IFA)**
1501 K St. NW, Ste. 350
Washington, DC 20005-1412
Ph: (202)628-8000
Free: 800-543-1038
Fax: (202)628-0812
Co. E-mail: ifa@franchise.org
URL: http://www.franchise.org
Contact: Anne Poodiack, Director
E-mail: apoodiack@franchise.org
Description: Description: Publishes educational tools
for members, public, press and governments to
describe the workings and advantages of franchising
as a method of doing business. Offers audio cas-
settes, video tapes, computer diskettes. Distributes
for Commerce Clearing House. **Founded:** 1960. **Pub-**
lications: *Franchising World* (Monthly); *International*
Franchise Association--Franchise Opportunities
Guide (Semiannual).

49864 ■ Kiplinger Washington Editors Inc.
1729 H St. NW
Washington, DC 20006
Ph: (202)887-6400
Free: 800-544-0155
Fax: (202)223-8990
Co. E-mail: sub.services@kiplinger.com
URL: http://www.kiplinger.com
Contact: Knight A. Kiplinger, President
Description: Description: Publishes personal finance
and business forecasting books for both profession-
als and the public. Reaches market through distribu-
tors. Does not accept unsolicited manuscripts.
Founded: 1920. **Publications:** *The Kiplinger Agricul-*
ture Letter; *The Kiplinger Tax Letter*; *The Kiplinger*
Letter; *Kiplinger's Retirement Report*; *Kiplinger's*
Personal Finance (Monthly); *Kiplinger Finance &*
Forecasts (KFF); *Changing Times Financial Services*
Directory.

**49865 ■ National Association for Business
Economics (NABE)**
1233 20th St. NW, Ste. 505
Washington, DC 20036
Ph: (202)463-6223
Fax: (202)463-6239
Co. E-mail: nabe@nabe.com
URL: http://www.nabe.com
Contact: Gene Huang, President
Description: Professional society of institutions, busi-
nesses, and students with an active interest in busi-
ness economics and individuals who are employed
by academic, private, or governmental concerns in
the area of business-related economic issues.
Maintains placement service for members; conducts
several seminars per year. Maintains speakers'
bureau. **Founded:** 1959. **Publications:** *NABE News*
(Bimonthly); *NABE Policy Survey* (Semiannual); *Busi-*
ness Economics (Quarterly); *National Association for*
Business Economics Membership Directory; *Nabe*
News (Quarterly); *Nabe Quarterly Surveys* (Quarterly); *Employment Opportunities* (Quarterly); *Careers*
in Business Economics; *Salary Survey* (Biennial);
National Association for Business Economics--
Membership Directory (Annual); *NABE News*; *Busi-*
ness Economics: Designed to Serve the Needs of
People Who Use Economics in Their Work. **Awards:**
Abramson Award (Annual).

**49866 ■ National Small Business Association
(NSBA)**
1156 15th St. NW, Ste. 1100
Washington, DC 20005
Ph: (202)293-8830
Free: 800-345-6728

Fax: (202)872-8543
URL: http://www.nsba.biz
Contact: Todd O. McCracken, President
Description: Description: Publishes information pertinent to small business. Also operates an Export Opportunity Hot line providing trade information to small firms. Reaches market through direct mail. **Founded:** 1937.

49867 ■ U.S. Small Business Administration (SBA)

409 3rd St. SW
Washington, DC 20416
Ph: (202)606-4000
Free: 800-U-ASK-SBA
Fax: (202)205-6901
Co. E-mail: answerdesk@sba.gov
URL: http://www.sba.gov
Contact: Dr. Winslow Sargeant, Manager
Description: Description: Publishes books and videotapes on starting and financing your own business and on international trade. **Founded:** 1953.

Publications: *SBA OnLine*; *U.S. Business Advisor*; *www.+BusinessLaw.gov*; *SBA Online*. **Awards:** Entrepreneurial Success Award; Small Business Advocates of the Year; Small Business Exporter of the Year; National Small Business Person of the Year; Phoenix Award for Small Business Disaster Recovery; Phoenix Award for Outstanding Contributions to Disaster Recovery.

SMALL BUSINESS DEVELOPMENT CENTERS

49868 ■ **Florida Small Business Development Center at Daytona State College**
Daytona State College
Bldg. 110, Rm. 222
1200 W International Speedway Blvd.
Daytona Beach, FL 32114
Ph: (386)506-4723
Fax: (386)506-4602
Co. E-mail: sbdc@daytonastate.edu
URL: http://www.sbdcdaytona.com
Contact: Ned Harper, Director
Description: Represents and promotes the small business sector. Provides management assistance to current and prospective small business owners. Helps to improve management skills and expand the products and services of members.

49869 ■ **Florida Small Business Development Center Network (FSBDCN)**
c/o Jerry Cartwright, Dir.
11000 University Pkwy., Bldg. 38
Pensacola, FL 32514-5750
Ph: (850)473-7800
Free: 866-737-7232
Fax: (850)473-7813
Co. E-mail: info@floridasbdc.org
URL: http://www.floridasbdc.com
Contact: Jerry Cartwright, Director
Description: Provides emerging and established business owners with assistance enabling overall growth and increased profitability that contributes to the economic prosperity of the state.

49870 ■ **Florida Small Business Development Center at Seminole Community College**
1445 Dolgner Pl.
Sanford, FL 32771
Ph: (407)321-3495
Fax: (407)321-4184
Co. E-mail: goetzr@seminolestate.edu
URL: http://sbdc.seminolestate.edu
Description: Represents and promotes the small business sector. Provides management assistance to current and prospective small business owners. Helps to improve management skills and expand the products and services of members.

49871 ■ **Small Business Development Center Broward County**
Reubin O. D'Askew Tower, Rm. 525
111 Las Olas Blvd.
Fort Lauderdale, FL 33301
Ph: (954)762-5201
Co. E-mail: sbdc-broward@floridasbdc.org
URL: http://www.floridasbdc.org/broward
Contact: Rafael Cruz, Director
Description: Represents and promotes the small business sector. Provides management assistance to current and prospective small business owners. Helps to improve management skills and expand the products and services of members.

49872 ■ **Small Business Development Center at Central Florida Development Council of Polk County**
Neil Combee Administration Bldg.
330 W Church St.
Bartow, FL 33830
Ph: (863)534-5915
Fax: (863)534-5932
Co. E-mail: info@polksbdc.org
URL: http://www.polksbdc.org
Contact: Rodney Carson, Director
Description: Represents and promotes the small business sector. Provides management assistance to current and prospective small business owners. Helps to improve management skills and expand the products and services of members.

49873 ■ **Small Business Development Center at Florida A&M University - Perry**
Taylor County Chamber of Commerce
428 N Jefferson St.
Perry, FL 32347-2510
Ph: (850)584-5366
URL: http://floridasbdc.org/locations.php
Contact: Jerry Cartright, Director
URL(s): www.taylorcountychamber.com. **Description:** Represents and promotes the small business sector. Provides management assistance to current and prospective small business owners. Helps to improve management skills and expand the products and services of members.

49874 ■ **Small Business Development Center at Florida A&M University - Tallahassee**
Innovation Park
The Morgan Bldg., Ste. 130
2035 E Paul Dirac Dr.
Tallahassee, FL 32310-3700
Ph: (850)599-3407
Fax: (850)561-2049
Co. E-mail: barbara.boles@famu.edu
URL: http://www.sbdcfamu.org/new/sbdc
Contact: Mr. Keith Bowers, Executive Director
URL(s): floridasbdc.org/locations.php. **Description:** Represents and promotes the small business sector. Provides management assistance to current and prospective small business owners. Helps to improve management skills and expand the products and services of members.

49875 ■ **Small Business Development Center at Florida Atlantic University - Boca Raton**
777 Glades Rd., Bldg. T-11
Boca Raton, FL 33431-0991
Ph: (561)297-3000
Co. E-mail: kbarr@fau.edu
URL: http://www.fau.edu
Contact: Nancy Young, Director
Description: Represents and promotes the small business sector. Provides management assistance to current and prospective small business owners. Helps to improve management skills and expand the products and services of members.

49876 ■ **Small Business Development Center at Florida Atlantic University - Downtown Campus**
Reubin O'D Askew Tower, Rm. 525
111 Las Olas Blvd.
Fort Lauderdale, FL 33301
Ph: (954)762-5235
Co. E-mail: rafael.cruz@floridasbdc.org
URL: http://sbdcbroward.org
Contact: Rafael Cruz, Regional Director
Description: Represents and promotes the small business sector. Provides management assistance to current and prospective small business owners. Helps to improve management skills and expand the products and services of members.

49877 ■ **Small Business Development Center at Florida Atlantic University - Florida Keys Community College**
5901 College Rd., Rm. C-218
Key West, FL 33040
Ph: (305)809-3156
Co. E-mail: greg.baumann@floridasbdc.org
URL: http://www.floridasbdc.org/key-west
Description: Represents and promotes the small business sector. Provides management assistance to current and prospective small business owners. Helps to improve management skills and expand the products and services of members.

49878 ■ **Small Business Development Center at Florida Atlantic University - Miami-Dade County**
8500 SW 8th St., Ste. 224
Miami, FL 33144-4002
Ph: (305)261-1638
Co. E-mail: sbdc-miami@floridasbdc.org
URL: http://143.88.93.11/miami-dade
Contact: Carlos Cardenas, Regional Director
Description: Represents and promotes the small business sector. Provides management assistance to current and prospective small business owners. Helps to improve management skills and expand the products and services of members.

49879 ■ **Small Business Development Center at Florida Atlantic University - Port St. Lucie**
c/o Ken R. Stephanz
Bldg. SL, Rm. 125A
500 NW California Blvd.
Port St. Lucie, FL 34986-2601
Ph: (772)873-3428
Co. E-mail: kstepha2@fau.edu
URL: http://www.fau.edu/psl/campus-resources/SBDC.php
Description: Represents and promotes the small business sector. Provides management assistance to current and prospective small business owners. Helps to improve management skills and expand the products and services of members.

49880 ■ **Small Business Development Center at Florida Atlantic University - Treasure Coast**
500 NW California Blvd.
Port St. Lucie, FL 34986

Ph: (772)873-3300
Co. E-mail: ccarlton@fau.edu
URL: http://www.fau.edu/psl
Description: Represents and promotes the small business sector. Provides management assistance to current and prospective small business owners. Helps to improve management skills and expand the products and services of members.

49881 ■ Small Business Development Center at Florida Gulf Coast University - Cape Coral
1020 Cultural Park Blvd. S, No. 3
Cape Coral, FL 33990-1229
Ph: (239)573-2737
Fax: (239)573-2797
Co. E-mail: bsmoot@fgcu.edu
URL: http://sbdc.fgcu.edu
Description: Represents and promotes the small business sector. Provides management assistance to current and prospective small business owners. Helps to improve management skills and expand the products and services of members.

49882 ■ Small Business Development Center at Florida Gulf Coast University - Clewiston
c/o Janice Groves
One Stop Career and Service Center
215 S Franscisco St.
Clewiston, FL 33440-4002
Ph: (863)983-6138
Co. E-mail: jgroves@fgcu.edu
URL: http://sbdc.fgcu.edu
Description: Represents and promotes the small business sector. Provides management assistance to current and prospective small business owners. Helps to improve management skills and expand the products and services of members.

49883 ■ Small Business Development Center at Florida Gulf Coast University - Fort Myers
Florida Gulf Coast University
College of Business Lutgert Hall, 2nd Fl.
10501 FGCU Blvd. S
Fort Myers, FL 33965-6565
Ph: (239)745-3700
Fax: (239)745-3710
Co. E-mail: dnikolov@fgcu.edu
URL: http://sbdc.fgcu.edu
Contact: Dan Regelski, Director
Description: Represents and promotes the small business sector. Provides management assistance to current and prospective small business owners. Helps to improve management skills and expand the products and services of members.

49884 ■ Small Business Development Center at Florida Gulf Coast University - Immokalee
750 S 5th St., Ste. 710
Immokalee, FL 34142
Ph: (239)658-3327
Fax: (239)658-3355
Co. E-mail: jestreme@fgcu.edu
URL: http://sbdc.fgcu.edu/counseling
Description: Represents and promotes the small business sector. Provides management assistance to current and prospective small business owners. Helps to improve management skills and expand the products and services of members.

49885 ■ Small Business Development Center at Florida Gulf Coast University - Port Charlotte
c/o Peter Keating
2702 Tamiami Trail
Port Charlotte, FL 33952-5129
Ph: (941)627-2222
Co. E-mail: captain27pete@hotmail.com
URL: http://floridasbdc.org
URL(s): sbdc.fgcu.edu/counseling. **Description:** Represents and promotes the small business sector. Provides management assistance to current and prospective small business owners. Helps to improve management skills and expand the products and services of members.

49886 ■ Small Business Development Center at Gulf Coast Community College
2500 Minnesota Ave.
Lynn Haven, FL 32444-4815

Ph: (850)271-1108
Free: 800-542-7232
Fax: (850)271-1109
Co. E-mail: info@northfloridabiz.com
URL: http://www.northfloridabiz.com
Contact: Joe Chavarria, Director
Description: Represents and promotes the small business sector. Provides management assistance to current and prospective small business owners. Helps to improve management skills and expand the products and services of members.

49887 ■ Small Business Development Center of the Heartland at South Florida Community College
600 W College Dr.
Avon Park, FL 33825
Ph: (863)784-7379
Fax: (863)784-7355
Co. E-mail: bmckown@coba.usf.edu
URL: http://www.southflorida.edu/sbdc
Description: Represents and promotes the small business sector. Provides management assistance to current and prospective small business owners. Helps to improve management skills and expand the products and services of members.

49888 ■ Small Business Development Center at Indian River State College - Fort Pierce
3209 Virginia Ave.
Fort Pierce, FL 34981
Ph: (772)462-7296
Free: 888-283-1177
Co. E-mail: jpagano@irsc.edu
URL: http://www.cctiirsc.com/index.
cfm?fuseaction=channel.home&chanid=SBDC
Description: Represents and promotes the small business sector. Provides management assistance to current and prospective small business owners. Helps to improve management skills and expand the products and services of members.

49889 ■ Small Business Development Center at Indian River State College - Stuart
924 SE Central Pkwy.
Stuart, FL 34994
Ph: (772)419-5694
Fax: (772)283-1981
Co. E-mail: sbdc-irsc@floridasbdc.org
Description: Represents and promotes the small business sector. Provides management assistance to current and prospective small business owners. Helps to improve management skills and expand the products and services of members.

49890 ■ Small Business Development Center Miami-Dade - Hialeah Gardens
The Church in the Gardens
13090 NW 107th Ave.
Hialeah Gardens, FL 33018
Ph: (305)515-8609
URL: http://clients.floridasbdc.org/DocumentMaster.
aspx?doc=2691
Description: Represents and promotes the small business sector. Provides management assistance to current and prospective small business owners. Helps to improve management skills and expand the products and services of members.

49891 ■ Small Business Development Center at North Florida Community College
Business Education Bldg. No.7, Rm. 107
325 NW Turner Davis Dr.
Madison, FL 32340-1602
Ph: (850)973-9409
Free: 866-937-6322
Co. E-mail: sboc@nfcc.edu
Description: Represents and promotes the small business sector. Provides management assistance to current and prospective small business owners. Helps to improve management skills and expand the products and services of members.

49892 ■ Small Business Development Center at Palm Beach Community College - Boca Raton
3000 St. Lucie Ave., Ste. AD408
Boca Raton, FL 33431
Ph: (561)862-4726

Fax: (561)862-4727
Co. E-mail: sbdc@palmbeachstate.edu
URL: http://www.palmbeachstate.edu/sbdc.xml
Contact: Ted Kramer, Director
Description: Represents and promotes the small business sector. Provides management assistance to current and prospective small business owners. Helps to improve management skills and expand the products and services of members.

49893 ■ Small Business Development Center at State College of Florida Manatee-Sarasota
8000 Tamiami Trail S
Venice, FL 34293
Ph: (941)408-1412
Fax: (941)497-6433
Co. E-mail: griffic2@scf.edu
URL: http://www.scf.edu/CorporateCommunityDevelopment/SmallBusinessDevelopmentCenter
Contact: Carolyn Griffin, Assistant Director
Description: Represents and promotes the small business sector. Provides management assistance to current and prospective small business owners. Helps to improve management skills and expand the products and services of members.

49894 ■ Small Business Development Center at State College of Florida Manatee - Sarasota
Lakewood Ranch
7131 Professional Pkwy. E
Sarasota, FL 34240
Ph: (941)363-7219
URL: http://floridasbdc.org
URL(s): www.scf.edu/sbdc. **Description:** Represents and promotes the small business sector. Provides management assistance to current and prospective small business owners. Helps to improve management skills and expand the products and services of members.

49895 ■ Small Business Development Center at University of Central Florida - Clermont
Lake-Sumter Community College
Bldg. 2, Rm. 164
1250 N Hancock Rd.
Clermont, FL 34711
Ph: (352)536-2224
Co. E-mail: gromagna@bus.ucf.edu
URL: http://www.bus.ucf.edu/sbdc
Contact: Gene Romagna, Manager
Description: Represents and promotes the small business sector. Provides management assistance to current and prospective small business owners. Helps to improve management skills and expand the products and services of members.

49896 ■ Small Business Development Center at University of Central Florida - Kissimmee
1425 E Vine St.
Kissimmee, FL 34744
Ph: (407)847-2452
Co. E-mail: nperez@bus.ucf.edu
URL: http://www.bus.ucf.edu/sbdc
Contact: Janice Lopez, Manager
URL(s): www.kissimmeechamber.com/sbdc. **Description:** Represents and promotes the small business sector. Provides management assistance to current and prospective small business owners. Helps to improve management skills and expand the products and services of members.

49897 ■ Small Business Development Center at University of Central Florida - Melbourne
Brevard Community College
Bldg. 10, Rm. 117
3865 N Wickam Rd.
Melbourne, FL 32935
Ph: (321)433-5573
Co. E-mail: pfrimmers@brevardcc.edu
URL: http://www.bus.ucf.edu/sbdc
Contact: Vicky Peake, Director
Description: Represents and promotes the small business sector. Provides management assistance to current and prospective small business owners. Helps to improve management skills and expand the products and services of members.

49898 ■ Small Business Development Center at University of Central Florida - Orlando
National Entrepreneur Center
Orlando Fashion Square Mall
3201 E Colonial Dr., Ste. A-20
Orlando, FL 32803
Ph: (407)420-4850
Fax: (407)420-4862
Co. E-mail: sbdc@bus.ucf.edu
URL: http://www.bus.ucf.edu/sbdc
Contact: Eunice Choi, Regional Director
Description: Represents and promotes the small business sector. Provides management assistance to current and prospective small business owners. Helps to improve management skills and expand the products and services of members.

49899 ■ Small Business Development Center at University of North Florida - Gainesville
Gainesville Technology Enterprise Center
2153 SE Hawthorne Rd., Ste. 126
Gainesville, FL 32641
Ph: (352)334-7230
Free: 866-998-8332
URL: http://www.sbdc.unf.edu
Description: Represents and promotes the small business sector. Provides management assistance to current and prospective small business owners. Helps to improve management skills and expand the products and services of members.

49900 ■ Small Business Development Center at University of North Florida - Jacksonville
UNF University Center
12000 Alumni Dr.
Jacksonville, FL 32224
Ph: (904)620-2476
Free: 800-450-4624
Co. E-mail: smallbiz@unf.edu
URL: http://www.sbdc.unf.edu
Contact: Janice William Donaldson, Director
Description: Represents and promotes the small business sector. Provides management assistance to current and prospective small business owners. Helps to improve management skills and expand the products and services of members.

49901 ■ Small Business Development Center at University of North Florida - Ocala/Marion County
3405 SW College Rd., Ste. 201
Ocala, FL 34474
Free: 866-998-8332
Co. E-mail: sbdcoca@atlantic.net
URL: http://www.sbdc.unf.edu
Contact: Dr. Philip Geist, Director
Description: Represents and promotes the small business sector. Provides management assistance to current and prospective small business owners. Helps to improve management skills and expand the products and services of members.

49902 ■ Small Business Development Center at University of South Florida - Hillsborough County
1101 Channelside Dr., Ste. 210
Tampa, FL 33602
Ph: (813)905-5800
URL: http://www.sbdctampabay.com/category/
locations/hillsborough-county
Description: Represents and promotes the small business sector. Provides management assistance to current and prospective small business owners. Helps to improve management skills and expand the products and services of members.

49903 ■ Small Business Development Center at University of South Florida - St. Petersburg
140 7th Ave. S, Davis 108
St. Petersburg, FL 33701
Ph: (813)905-5800
URL: http://www.sbdctampabay.com
Contact: Wayne Brass, Manager
Description: Represents and promotes the small business sector. Provides management assistance to current and prospective small business owners. Helps to improve management skills and expand the products and services of members.

49904 ■ Small Business Development Center at University of South Florida - Tampa
1101 Channelside Dr., Ste. 210
Tampa, FL 33602
Ph: (813)905-5800
Fax: (813)905-5801
Co. E-mail: sbdc@coba.usf.edu
URL: http://www.sbdctampabay.com
Contact: Eileen Rodriguez, Regional Director
Description: Represents and promotes the small business sector. Provides management assistance to current and prospective small business owners. Helps to improve management skills and expand the products and services of members.

49905 ■ Small Business Development Center at University of West Florida - Fort Walton Beach
922 Mar Walt Dr., Ste. 203
Fort Walton Beach, FL 32547-6703
Ph: (850)833-9400
Co. E-mail: fwbsbdc@uwf.edu
URL: http://www.sbdc.uwf.edu
Contact: Tom Hermanson, Associate Director
Description: Represents and promotes the small business sector. Provides management assistance to current and prospective small business owners. Helps to improve management skills and expand the products and services of members.

49906 ■ Small Business Development Center at University of West Florida - Pensacola
401 E Chase St., Ste. 100
Pensacola, FL 32502-6160
Ph: (850)595-0063
Co. E-mail: dcavanaugh@uwf.edu
URL: http://www.sbdc.uwf.edu
Contact: Larry Strain, Executive Director
Description: Represents and promotes the small business sector. Provides management assistance to current and prospective small business owners. Helps to improve management skills and expand the products and services of members.

SMALL BUSINESS ASSISTANCE PROGRAMS

49907 ■ Enterprise Florida, Inc. - Marketing And Development Division
800 N. Magnolia Ave., Ste. 1100
Orlando, FL 32803
Ph: (407)956-5600
Fax: (407)956-5599
URL: http://www.eflorida.com/
Description: Administers the Business Supplier Program, which helps businesses locate suppliers of goods and services in Florida.

49908 ■ NASA/Southern Technology Applications Center
75 5th St. NW, Ste. 100
Atlanta, GA 30308-0390
Ph: (800)472-6785
Fax: (404)894-4545
Co. E-mail: nasa@edi.gatech.edu
URL: http://www.edi.gatech.edu/nasa
Description: Provides information on technology, science, industry, management, marketing, economics, and business.

SCORE OFFICES

49909 ■ Bay County SCORE
Co. E-mail: bayscore@knology.net

49910 ■ Charlotte-Desoto County SCORE
Co. E-mail: score0318@aol.com

49911 ■ Hollywood SCORE
Co. E-mail: info@scorehollywoodfl.org

49912 ■ Ocala/The Villages SCORE
Co. E-mail: seveer2cnr@aol.com

49913 ■ Pasco-Hernando County SCORE - Chapter 439
6014 US Hwy. 19, Ste. 302
New Port Richey, FL 34652
Ph: (727)842-4638
Co. E-mail: score439@verizon.net
URL: http://pascohernando.score.org
Description: Represents businessmen and women, small business owners, senior corporate executives and experienced professionals. Provides professional guidance and information to maximize the success of existing and emerging small businesses.

49914 ■ SCORE Citrus County
Bldg. L1-110
3810 S Lecanto Hwy.
Lecanto, FL 34461
Ph: (352)249-1236
Co. E-mail: citruschapter@live.com
URL: http://citrusscore.easycgi.com/ccs
URL(s): citruscounty.score.org. **Description:** Provides professional guidance and information to maximize the success of existing and emerging small businesses. Promotes entrepreneur education in Citrus County area, FL.

49915 ■ SCORE Dade
111 NW 1st St., No. 1941
Miami, FL 33128
Ph: (786)425-9119
Co. E-mail: admin@scoremiami.org
URL: http://miamidade.score.org/chapters/score-miami-dade
Description: Provides professional guidance and information to maximize the success of existing and emerging small businesses. Offers business counseling and workshops.

49916 ■ SCORE Hillsborough
Bldg. 400, Ste. 425
7402 N 56th St.
Tampa, FL 33617
Ph: (813)988-1435
URL: http://www.tampascore.org
Description: Provides resources and expertise to maximize the success of existing and emerging small businesses. Offers business counseling and workshops. **Founded:** 1964.

49917 ■ SCORE Manasota
2801 Fruitville Rd., Ste. 280
Sarasota, FL 34237
Ph: (941)955-1029
Co. E-mail: scorech116@verizon.net
URL: http://manasota.score.org
Contact: Mr. Greg Hoffman, Chairman
Description: Works for the formation, growth, and success of small businesses. Provides on-line business counseling and business improvement activities. **Scope:** small business start up and improvement. **Founded:** 1965. **Subscriptions:** 30 articles books. **Awards:** Small Business of the Year (Annual).

49918 ■ SCORE Naples
900 Goodlette Rd. N
Naples, FL 34102
Ph: (239)430-0081
URL: http://naples.score.org
Description: Creates opportunities for small business owners and potential small business owners to achieve success. Provides entrepreneur education in Naples area, in Florida. Offers individual counseling, workshops, seminars and literature. **Founded:** 1988.

49919 ■ SCORE Orlando
Orlando Fashion Sq. Mall
3201 E Colonial Dr., Unit A20
Orlando, FL 32803
Ph: (407)420-4844
Co. E-mail: score@nationalec.org
URL: http://www.scoreorlando.org
Description: All-volunteer resource partner of the Small Business Administration. Provides business management counselors for present and future small business owners in need of expert advice. Offers free and confidential one-on-one and email counseling, in addition to numerous educational seminars appropriate for entrepreneurs. **Founded:** 1966.

49920 ■ SCORE Palm Beach
500 Australian Ave. S, Ste. 115
West Palm Beach, FL 33401
Ph: (561)833-1672
Fax: (561)833-1470
Co. E-mail: z4seven@bellsouth.net
URL: http://palmbeach.score.org
Description: Represents retired entrepreneurs and corporate executives. Provides free business counseling to start-ups and small businesses. Includes primary counseling areas such as; business planning, business structure, marketing, distribution, home businesses, accounting, budgeting, personnel, operation issues, etc. **Scope:** business. **Subscriptions:** 350 periodicals.

49921 ■ SCORE Space Coast
1600 Sarno Rd., Ste. 205
Melbourne, FL 32935
Ph: (321)254-2288
Fax: (321)254-2288
Co. E-mail: scorechapter400@bellsouth.net
URL: http://www.spacecoastscore.org
Contact: Carol Wheatley, Chairperson
URL(s): spacecoast.score.org. **Description:** Strives for the formation, growth, and success of small businesses. Offers educational seminars and business counseling.

49922 ■ SCORE of Suwannee Valley
Co. E-mail: info@scoreofsuwanneevalley.org

BETTER BUSINESS BUREAUS

49923 ■ *BBB Central Florida Times*
1600 S Grant St.
Longwood, FL 32750
Ph: (407)621-3300
Fax: (407)786-2625
Co. E-mail: info@centralflorida.bbb.org
URL: http://www.orlando.bbb.org
Released: Quarterly

49924 ■ Better Business Bureau of Central Florida
1600 S Grant St.
Longwood, FL 32750
Ph: (407)621-3300
Fax: (407)786-2625
Co. E-mail: info@centralflorida.bbb.org
URL: http://www.orlando.bbb.org
Description: Seeks to promote and foster ethical relationship between businesses and the public through voluntary self-regulation, consumer and business education, and service excellence. Provides information to help consumers and businesses make informed purchasing decisions and avoid costly scams and frauds; settles consumer complaints through arbitration and other means. **Founded:** 1983. **Publications:** *BBB Central Florida Times* (Quarterly). **Educational Activities:** Golf Outing (Annual).

49925 ■ Better Business Bureau of Northeast Florida
4417 Beach Blvd., Ste. 202
Jacksonville, FL 32207
Ph: (904)721-2288
Free: 800-940-1315
Fax: (904)721-7373
Co. E-mail: info@bbbnefla.org
URL: http://northeastflorida.bbb.org
Contact: Tom Stephens, President
Description: Seeks to promote and foster ethical relationship between businesses and the public through voluntary self-regulation, consumer and business education, and service excellence. Provides information to help consumers and businesses make informed purchasing decisions and avoid costly scams and frauds; settles consumer complaints through arbitration and other means.

49926 ■ Better Business Bureau of Northwest Florida
912 E Gadsden St.
Pensacola, FL 32501
Ph: (850)429-0002
Free: 800-729-9226

Fax: (850)429-0006
Co. E-mail: info@nwfl.bbb.org
URL: http://nwfl.bbb.org
Contact: Norman Wright, President
Description: Seeks to promote and foster ethical relationship between businesses and the public through voluntary self-regulation, consumer and business education, and service excellence. Provides information to help consumers and businesses make informed purchasing decisions and avoid costly scams and frauds; settles consumer complaints through arbitration and other means. **Founded:** 1985. **Awards:** Customer Service Excellence Award (Annual); Student Ethics Scholarship (Annual); Torch Award for Marketplace Ethics (Annual).

49927 ■ Better Business Bureau of West Florida
PO Box 7950
Clearwater, FL 33758-7950
Ph: (727)535-5522
Free: 800-525-1447
Fax: (727)539-6301
Co. E-mail: info@bbbwestflorida.org
URL: http://westflorida.bbb.org
Contact: Karen Nalven, President
Description: Seeks to promote and foster ethical relationship between businesses and the public through voluntary self-regulation, consumer and business education, and service excellence. Provides information to help consumers and businesses make informed purchasing decisions and avoid costly scams and frauds; settles consumer complaints through arbitration and other means. **Publications:** *Year in Review.*

49928 ■ *Year in Review*
PO Box 7950
Clearwater, FL 33758-7950
Ph: (727)535-5522
Free: 800-525-1447
Fax: (727)539-6301
Co. E-mail: info@bbbwestflorida.org
URL: http://westflorida.bbb.org
Contact: Karen Nalven, President

CHAMBERS OF COMMERCE

49929 ■ *Accommodations Guide to Siesta Key*
5118 Ocean Blvd.
Siesta Key, FL 34242
Ph: (941)349-3800
Free: 866-831-7778
Co. E-mail: info@siestakeychamber.com
URL: http://www.siestakeychamber.com
Contact: Mark Smith, Chairman
Released: Annual

49930 ■ *Action*
16 S Volusia Ave.
Arcadia, FL 34266
Ph: (863)494-4033
Fax: (863)494-3312
Co. E-mail: desotochamber@earthlink.net
URL: http://www.desotochamberfl.com
Contact: Mary Kay Burns, President
Released: Bimonthly

49931 ■ Alachua Chamber of Commerce
PO Box 387
Alachua, FL 32616-0387
Ph: (386)462-3333
Fax: (386)462-0400
Co. E-mail: dpope@windstream.com
URL: http://www.alachua.com
Contact: David Pope, President
Description: Promotes business growth and community development in Alachua, FL.

49932 ■ Anna Maria Island Chamber of Commerce
5313 Gulf Dr. N
Holmes Beach, FL 34217
Ph: (941)778-1541

Fax: (941)778-9679
Co. E-mail: info@annamariaislandchamber.org
URL: http://www.annamariaislandchamber.org
Contact: Mary Ann Brockman, President
Description: Promotes business and community development in Anna Maria Island area of FL. Promotes tourism. Conducts workshops, seminars, trade shows, and festivals. **Publications:** *Anna Maria Island Vacation Guide* (Annual).

49933 ■ *Anna Maria Island Vacation Guide*
5313 Gulf Dr. N
Holmes Beach, FL 34217
Ph: (941)778-1541
Fax: (941)778-9679
Co. E-mail: info@annamariaislandchamber.org
URL: http://www.annamariaislandchamber.org
Contact: Mary Ann Brockman, President
Released: Annual **Price:** free.

49934 ■ *Annual Directory*
227 U.S. Hwy. N
Sebring, FL 33870
Ph: (863)385-8448
Fax: (863)385-8810
Co. E-mail: information@sebring.org
URL: http://www.greatersebringchamberofcommerce.
org
Contact: Greg Harris, President
Released: Annual

49935 ■ *Apalachicola Bay Area of Franklin County*
122 Commerce St.
Apalachicola, FL 32320
Ph: (850)653-9419
Fax: (850)653-8219
Co. E-mail: info@apalachicolabay.org
URL: http://www.apalachicolabay.org
Contact: Anita Grove, Executive Director

49936 ■ Apalachicola Bay Chamber of Commerce (ABCC)
122 Commerce St.
Apalachicola, FL 32320
Ph: (850)653-9419
Fax: (850)653-8219
Co. E-mail: info@apalachicolabay.org
URL: http://www.apalachicolabay.org
Contact: Anita Grove, Executive Director
Description: Promotes business, tourism, and community development in Franklin County, FL. **Publications:** *Apalachicola Bay Area of Franklin County; Apalachicola Times; Chuck Spicer's Coastline.*

49937 ■ *Apalachicola Times*
122 Commerce St.
Apalachicola, FL 32320
Ph: (850)653-9419
Fax: (850)653-8219
Co. E-mail: info@apalachicolabay.org
URL: http://www.apalachicolabay.org
Contact: Anita Grove, Executive Director
Price: $0.35, /week.

49938 ■ Apollo Beach Chamber of Commerce
PO Box 3686
Apollo Beach, FL 33572
Ph: (813)645-1366
Fax: (813)641-2612
Co. E-mail: abeachchamber@tampabay.rr.com
URL: http://www.apollobeachchamber.com
Contact: Joanne C. Gadek, Executive Director
Description: Seeks to promote high quality of business within the area by providing business leadership that recognize the social, political, and cultural needs of the community.

49939 ■ Apopka Area Chamber of Commerce
180 E Main St.
Apopka, FL 32703
Ph: (407)886-1441

Fax: (407)886-1131
Co. E-mail: pauls@apopkachamber.org
URL: http://www.apopkachamber.org
Contact: Wayne H. Levesque, Chairman
Description: Promotes business and community development in the Apopka, FL area. Monitors issues concerning business community. Sponsors student government day. **Founded:** 1913. **Publications:** *Foliage Locator; Membership Books* (Annual). **Educational Activities:** Apopka Business Connection/Taste of the Town Trade Show (Annual).

49940 ■ *Area Map*
1005 E Strawbridge Ave.
Melbourne, FL 32901-4782
Ph: (321)724-5400
Fax: (321)725-2093
Co. E-mail: christine@melbourneregionalchamber.com
URL: http://www.melpb-chamber.org
Contact: Christine Michaels, President
Released: Annual

49941 ■ *Area Map*
31020 Overseas Hwy.
Big Pine Key, FL 33043-0511
Ph: (305)872-2411
Free: 800-872-3722
Fax: (305)872-0752
Co. E-mail: info@lowerkeyschamber.com
URL: http://www.lowerkeyschamber.com
Contact: Carole Stevens, Secretary
Released: Annual

49942 ■ Auburndale-Mainstreet Chamber of Commerce
245 E Lake Ave.
Auburndale, FL 33823
Ph: (863)967-3400
Fax: (863)967-0880
Co. E-mail: jpruitt@auburndalechamber.com
URL: http://www.auburndalefl.com
Contact: Joy Pruitt, Executive Director
Description: Promotes business and community development in the Auburndale, FL area. Holds monthly board meeting, luncheons, seminars, socials, and town meetings. **Founded:** 1997.

49943 ■ Avon Park Chamber of Commerce (APCC)
28 E Main St.
Avon Park, FL 33825
Ph: (863)453-3350
Fax: (863)453-0973
Co. E-mail: apcc@apfla.com
URL: http://www.apfla.com
Contact: David Greenslade, Executive Director
Description: Promotes business and community development in Avon Park, FL. Sponsors annual Arts and Crafts Show and Jararanda Festival for fine arts. **Founded:** 1904. **Publications:** *Chamber Chatter* (Monthly); *Downtown Merchant Directory.* **Educational Activities:** Business/Trade Show Expo (Annual). **Awards:** Student of the Month (Monthly).

49944 ■ *Baker Bulletin*
20 E Macclenny Ave.
Macclenny, FL 32063
Ph: (904)259-6433
Co. E-mail: dregister@bakerchamberfl.com
URL: http://www.bakerchamberfl.com
Contact: Darryl Register, Executive Director
Released: Bimonthly

49945 ■ Baker County Chamber of Commerce (BCCC)
20 E Macclenny Ave.
Macclenny, FL 32063
Ph: (904)259-6433
Co. E-mail: dregister@bakerchamberfl.com
URL: http://www.bakerchamberfl.com
Contact: Darryl Register, Executive Director
Description: Promotes business and community development in Baker County, FL. **Founded:** 1980. **Publications:** *Baker Bulletin* (Bimonthly). **Awards:** Business Appreciation Awards (Annual).

49946 ■ *Bartow Chamber News*
510 N Broadway Ave.
Bartow, FL 33830-3918
Ph: (863)533-7125
Fax: (863)533-3793
Co. E-mail: discoverbartow@bartowchamber.com
URL: http://www.bartowchamber.com
Contact: Jeff Clark, Executive Director
Released: Monthly

49947 ■ *Bay Biz*
PO Box 1850
Panama City, FL 32402-1850
Ph: (850)785-5206
Fax: (850)763-6229
Co. E-mail: reception2@baychamberfl.com
URL: http://www.panamacity.org
Contact: Ms. Carol Roberts, President
Released: Monthly

49948 ■ *Bay Biz Magazine*
PO Box 1850
Panama City, FL 32402-1850
Ph: (850)785-5206
Fax: (850)763-6229
Co. E-mail: reception2@baychamberfl.com
URL: http://www.panamacity.org
Contact: Ms. Carol Roberts, President
Released: Quarterly **Price:** free.

49949 ■ Bay County Chamber of Commerce (BCCC)
PO Box 1850
Panama City, FL 32402-1850
Ph: (850)785-5206
Fax: (850)763-6229
Co. E-mail: reception2@baychamberfl.com
URL: http://www.panamacity.org
Contact: Ms. Carol Roberts, President
Description: Strives to develop, enhance, and maintain a viable business climate and to provide leadership in the development of economic growth and quality of life. **Founded:** 1913. **Publications:** *Bay Biz* (Monthly); *Bay Biz Magazine* (Quarterly).

49950 ■ *The Baysider*
315 S Tamiami Trail
Ruskin, FL 33570-4660
Ph: (813)645-3808
Fax: (813)645-2099
Co. E-mail: info@ruskinchamber.org
URL: http://www.ruskinchamber.org
Contact: Pat Warbritton, President
E-mail: pat.warbritton@verizon.net
Released: Monthly **Price:** included in membership dues.

49951 ■ *The Beach Biz*
PO Box 1536
Jensen Beach, FL 34958
Ph: (772)334-3444
Co. E-mail: info@jensenbeachchamber.biz
URL: http://www.jensenbeachchamber.biz
Contact: Sue Zachman, President
Released: Monthly

49952 ■ *Beach Business*
5118 Ocean Blvd.
Siesta Key, FL 34242
Ph: (941)349-3800
Free: 866-831-7778
Co. E-mail: info@siestakeychamber.com
URL: http://www.siestakeychamber.com
Contact: Mark Smith, Chairman
Released: Monthly

49953 ■ *Beach Waves*
6990 Gulf Blvd.
St. Pete Beach, FL 33706
Ph: (727)360-6957
Co. E-mail: info@tampabaybeaches.com
URL: http://www.tampabaybeaches.com/cwt/external/wcpages/index.aspx
Contact: Robin Sollie, President
Released: Monthly

49954 ■ *The Believer*
PO Box 457
Chipley, FL 32428

Ph: (850)638-4157
Fax: (850)638-8770
Co. E-mail: wcchamber@wfeca.net
URL: http://www.washcomall.com
Contact: Philip Pippin, President
Released: Monthly

49955 ■ Belle Glade Chamber of Commerce
540 S Main St.
Belle Glade, FL 33430
Ph: (561)996-2745
Fax: (561)996-2252
Co. E-mail: bgchamber@aol.com
URL: http://www.bellegladechamber.com
Contact: Brenda Bunting, Executive Director
Description: Promotes business and community development in Belle Glade, FL. **Publications:** *Chamber Chatter* (Monthly).

49956 ■ Belleview-South Marion Chamber of Commerce
5301 SE Abshier Blvd.
Belleview, FL 34420
Ph: (352)245-2178
Fax: (352)245-7673
Co. E-mail: info@bsmcc.org
URL: http://bsmcc.org
Contact: Sheila Lister, Executive Director
Description: Promotes business and community development in Belleview and South Marion County, FL. Sponsors Founders' Day festival, first Saturday in May, and Christmas parade. **Founded:** 1956. **Publications:** *The Gavel* (Bimonthly).

49957 ■ *Biennial Guide*
PO Box 757
Lehigh Acres, FL 33970-0757
Ph: (239)369-3322
Fax: (239)368-0500
Co. E-mail: info@lehighacreschamber.org
URL: http://www.lehighacreschamber.org
Contact: Oliver B. Conover, Executive Director
Released: Biennial **Price:** free locally; $1, by mail.

49958 ■ Boca Grande Area Chamber of Commerce
PO Box 704
Boca Grande, FL 33921
Ph: (941)964-0568
Fax: (941)964-0620
Co. E-mail: info@bocagrandechamber.com
URL: http://www.bocagrandechamber.com
Contact: Richard Edwards, President
URL(s): bocagrandechamber.net. **Description:** Seeks to enhance members' business and economic growth of Boca Grande area.

49959 ■ *Boca Raton Annual*
1800 N Dixie Hwy.
Boca Raton, FL 33432
Ph: (561)395-4433
Fax: (561)392-3780
Co. E-mail: info@bocaratonchamber.com
URL: http://www.bocaratonchamber.com
Contact: Troy M. Mclellan, President
Released: Annual **Price:** $5, /copy.

49960 ■ Bonita Springs Area Chamber of Commerce (BSACC)
25071 Chamber of Commerce Dr.
Bonita Springs, FL 34135
Ph: (239)992-2943
Free: 800-226-2943
Fax: (239)992-5011
Co. E-mail: info@bonitaspringschamber.com
URL: http://www.bonitaspringschamber.com
Contact: Christine A. Ross, President
Description: Business and community leaders promoting business and community development in Bonita Springs, FL. **Founded:** 1954. **Publications:** *Chamber Focus* (Monthly).

49961 ■ *Boomtown Gazette*
20500 E Pennsylvania Ave.
Dunnellon, FL 34432
Ph: (352)489-2320
Free: 800-830-2087

Fax: (352)489-6846
Co. E-mail: dunnellonchamber@bellsouth.net
URL: http://www.dunnellonchamber.org
Contact: Lisa Sheffield, President
Released: Annual

49962 ■ Boynton Beach Business Monthly
1880 N Congress Ave., Ste. 106
Boynton Beach, FL 33425
Ph: (561)732-9501
Fax: (561)734-4304
Co. E-mail: chamber@boyntonbeach.org
URL: http://www.boyntonbeach.org/index.
 php?sid=349cc8ac080f2b4081fffe8198df83b9
Contact: Glenn Jergensen, President
Released: Monthly

49963 ■ Brandon Area Directory
330 Pauls Dr., Ste. 100
Brandon, FL 33511
Ph: (813)689-1221
Fax: (813)689-9440
Co. E-mail: info@brandonchamber.com
URL: http://www.brandonchamber.com
Contact: Tammy C. Bracewell, President
Released: Annual **Price:** free.

49964 ■ Brandon Business
330 Pauls Dr., Ste. 100
Brandon, FL 33511
Ph: (813)689-1221
Fax: (813)689-9440
Co. E-mail: info@brandonchamber.com
URL: http://www.brandonchamber.com
Contact: Tammy C. Bracewell, President
Released: Monthly

49965 ■ The Bridge
1945 Fruitville Rd.
Sarasota, FL 34236
Ph: (941)955-8187
Fax: (941)366-5621
Co. E-mail: squeior@sarasotachamber.com
URL: http://www.sarasotachamber.com
Contact: Steve Queior, President
Released: Monthly

49966 ■ The Bridge
880 SW Martin Downs Blvd.
Palm City, FL 34990
Ph: (772)286-8121
Fax: (772)286-3331
Co. E-mail: info@palmcitychamber.com
URL: http://www.palmcitychamber.com
Contact: Carolyn Davi, Executive Director
Released: Monthly

**49967 ■ British American Chamber of
Commerce of Central Florida**
Orlando Fashion Square Mall
3201 E Colonial Dr., Unit A20
Orlando, FL 32803
Ph: (407)226-7251
Fax: (407)420-4849
Co. E-mail: admin@britishamericanchamberorlando.
 com
URL: http://www.britishamericanchamberorlando.com
Contact: David Lenox, President
Description: Promotes trade and investment. Facili-
tates social and commercial interaction among
members. Provides a forum in which members can
exchange information and ideas.

49968 ■ Bulletin
2787 N Tamiami Trail
North Fort Myers, FL 33903-2213
Ph: (239)997-9111
Co. E-mail: exec@nfmchamber.org
URL: http://nfmchamber.org
Contact: Phil Goss, President
Released: Periodic

49969 ■ Business
38550 5th Ave.
Zephyrhills, FL 33542
Ph: (813)782-1913

Fax: (813)783-6060
Co. E-mail: info@zephyrhillschamber.org
URL: http://zephyrhillschamber.org
Contact: Carolyn Hodges, President

49970 ■ Business
880 SW Martin Downs Blvd.
Palm City, FL 34990
Ph: (772)286-8121
Fax: (772)286-3331
Co. E-mail: info@palmcitychamber.com
URL: http://www.palmcitychamber.com
Contact: Carolyn Davi, Executive Director
Released: Monthly

49971 ■ Business Beat
691 W Montrose St.
Clermont, FL 34711
Ph: (352)394-4191
Fax: (352)394-5799
Co. E-mail: rays@southlakechamber-fl.com
URL: http://www.southlakechamber-fl.com
Contact: Ray San Fratello, President
Released: Monthly

49972 ■ Business Beat
PO Box 757
Lehigh Acres, FL 33970-0757
Ph: (239)369-3322
Fax: (239)368-0500
Co. E-mail: info@lehighacreschamber.org
URL: http://www.lehighacreschamber.org
Contact: Oliver B. Conover, Executive Director
Released: Monthly

49973 ■ Business Directory
PO Box 610
Cedar Key, FL 32625
Ph: (352)543-5600
Fax: (352)543-5600
Co. E-mail: info@cedarkey.org
URL: http://www.cedarkey.org
Contact: Eric Jungklaus, President
Released: Annual

49974 ■ Business Directory
c/o Dana Jones, Pres.
1100 Reid St.
Palatka, FL 32178-0550
Ph: (386)328-1503
Fax: (386)328-7076
Co. E-mail: dana@pcccfl.org
URL: http://www.putnamcountychamber.org
Contact: Dana Jones, President
Released: Annual

49975 ■ The Business Edge
15588 Aviation Loop Dr.
Brooksville, FL 34604
Ph: (352)796-0697
Fax: (352)796-3704
Co. E-mail: info@hernandochamber.com
URL: http://hernandochamber.com
Contact: John Mitten, Chairman of the Board
Released: Monthly

49976 ■ The Business Exchange
336 N Woodland Blvd.
DeLand, FL 32720
Ph: (386)734-4331
Fax: (386)734-4333
Co. E-mail: welcome@delandchamber.org
URL: http://www.delandchamber.org
Contact: Nick Conte, Executive Director
Released: Monthly

**49977 ■ Business/Investors Directory and
Visitor's Guide**
310 Julia St.
New Smyrna Beach, FL 32168-7024
Ph: (386)428-2449
Fax: (386)423-3512
Co. E-mail: sevinfo@sevchamber.com
URL: http://www.sevchamber.com
Contact: Kenneth Bohannon, President
Released: Annual

49978 ■ Business Journal Newsletter
300 E University Ave., Ste. 100
Gainesville, FL 32601
Ph: (352)334-7100
Fax: (352)334-7141
URL: http://www.gainesvillechamber.com
Contact: Brent Christensen, President
Released: Monthly

49979 ■ Business On-Line
2702 Tamiami Trail
Port Charlotte, FL 33952
Ph: (941)627-2222
Fax: (941)627-9730
Co. E-mail: askus@charlottecountychamber.org
URL: http://www.charlottecountychamber.org
Contact: Ms. Julie Mathis, Executive Director
Released: Biweekly

49980 ■ Business Views
PO Box 1639
Tallahassee, FL 32302
Ph: (850)224-8116
Fax: (850)561-3860
Co. E-mail: info@talchamber.com
URL: http://talchamber.com
Contact: Sue Dick, President

49981 ■ Business Watch
401 N Flagler Dr.
West Palm Beach, FL 33401
Ph: (561)833-3711
Fax: (561)833-5582
Co. E-mail: chamber@palmbeaches.org
URL: http://www.palmbeaches.org
Contact: Dennis Grady, President
Released: Monthly

49982 ■ Buyer's Guide
336 N Woodland Blvd.
DeLand, FL 32720
Ph: (386)734-4331
Fax: (386)734-4333
Co. E-mail: welcome@delandchamber.org
URL: http://www.delandchamber.org
Contact: Nick Conte, Executive Director
Released: Annual **Price:** $2, for mailing cost only.

49983 ■ C/N Chamber News
248 SW Range Ave.
Madison, FL 32340
Ph: (850)973-2788
Free: 877-272-3642
Fax: (850)973-8864
Co. E-mail: chamber@madisonfl.org
URL: http://www.madisonfl.org
Contact: Terri Schefbuch, Office Manager
Released: Monthly

**49984 ■ Calhoun County Chamber of
Commerce (CCCOC)**
PO Box 1087
Anniston, AL 36202
Ph: (256)237-3536
Free: 800-237-3536
Co. E-mail: info@calhounchamber.com
URL: http://calhounchamber.com
Contact: Kristy Terry, Executive Director
Description: Promotes business growth and devel-
opment in the area. **Awards:** Above and Beyond
Award (Annual); Calhoun County's Citizen of the Year
(Annual); Outstanding Chamber Member of the Year
(Annual).

49985 ■ Catalyst
1945 Fruitville Rd.
Sarasota, FL 34236
Ph: (941)955-8187
Fax: (941)366-5621
Co. E-mail: squeior@sarasotachamber.com
URL: http://www.sarasotachamber.com
Contact: Steve Queior, President
Released: Monthly **Price:** free for members only.

49986 ■ Cedar Key Chamber of Commerce
PO Box 610
Cedar Key, FL 32625
Ph: (352)543-5600

Fax: (352)543-5600
Co. E-mail: info@cedarkey.org
URL: http://www.cedarkey.org
Contact: Eric Jungklaus, President
Description: Promotes business and community development in the Cedar Key, FL area. Promotes commercial aquaculture, fishing, and tourism. Conducts annual fine arts fair and annual seafood festival. **Founded:** 1983. **Publications:** *Business Directory* (Annual).

49987 ■ Central Pasco Chamber of Commerce
2810 Land O' Lakes Blvd.
Land O' Lakes, FL 34639-0098
Ph: (813)909-2722
Fax: (813)909-0827
Co. E-mail: office@centralpascochamber.com
URL: http://centralpascochamber.com
Contact: Kathy Dunkley, Executive Director
Description: Promotes business and community development in central Pasco and northern Hillsborough counties, FL. Conducts Winter Festival. **Founded:** 1975. **Publications:** *Chamber Biz* (Monthly); *Chamber Review* (Monthly). **Educational Activities:** Business Expo (Annual).

49988 ■ CEO Report
1601 Biscayne Blvd.
Ballroom Level
Miami, FL 33132-1260
Ph: (305)350-7700
Free: 888-660-5955
Fax: (305)374-6902
Co. E-mail: reception@miamichamber.com
URL: http://www.greatermiami.com
Contact: Barry E. Johnson, President
Released: Quarterly

49989 ■ CEO Report Update
1601 Biscayne Blvd.
Ballroom Level
Miami, FL 33132-1260
Ph: (305)350-7700
Free: 888-660-5955
Fax: (305)374-6902
Co. E-mail: reception@miamichamber.com
URL: http://www.greatermiami.com
Contact: Barry E. Johnson, President
Released: Monthly

49990 ■ Chamber Biz
2810 Land O' Lakes Blvd.
Land O' Lakes, FL 34639-0098
Ph: (813)909-2722
Fax: (813)909-0827
Co. E-mail: office@centralpascochamber.com
URL: http://centralpascochamber.com
Contact: Kathy Dunkley, Executive Director
Released: Monthly

49991 ■ Chamber Bulletin
PO Box 683
Wauchula, FL 33873
Ph: (863)773-6967
Fax: (863)773-4915
Co. E-mail: casey@hardeecc.com
URL: http://www.hardeecc.com/recreation.htm
Contact: Derren Bryan, President
Released: Monthly

49992 ■ Chamber Channel
31020 Overseas Hwy.
Big Pine Key, FL 33043-0511
Ph: (305)872-2411
Free: 800-872-3722
Fax: (305)872-0752
Co. E-mail: info@lowerkeyschamber.com
URL: http://www.lowerkeyschamber.com
Contact: Carole Stevens, Secretary
Released: Monthly

49993 ■ Chamber Chatter
28 E Main St.
Avon Park, FL 33825
Ph: (863)453-3350

Fax: (863)453-0973
Co. E-mail: apcc@apfla.com
URL: http://www.apfla.com
Contact: David Greenslade, Executive Director
Released: Monthly

49994 ■ Chamber Chatter
1447 Commerce Dr.
Crestview, FL 32539
Ph: (850)682-3212
Fax: (850)682-7413
Co. E-mail: info@crestviewchamber.com
URL: http://www.crestviewchamber.com/crestview-chamber.htm
Contact: Wayne Harris, Executive Director
Released: Monthly **Price:** included in membership dues; $12, /year for nonmembers.

49995 ■ The Chamber Chatter
102 W Dania Beach Blvd.
Dania Beach, FL 33004
Ph: (954)926-2323
Fax: (954)926-2384
Co. E-mail: info@greaterdania.org
URL: http://www.greaterdania.org
Contact: Victoria Payne, Executive Director
Released: Monthly

49996 ■ Chamber Chatter
540 S Main St.
Belle Glade, FL 33430
Ph: (561)996-2745
Fax: (561)996-2252
Co. E-mail: bgchamber@aol.com
URL: http://www.belleglades chamber.com
Contact: Brenda Bunting, Executive Director
Released: Monthly

49997 ■ Chamber Chatter
23 High Dr.
Crawfordville, FL 32327-2032
Ph: (850)926-1848
Fax: (850)926-2050
Co. E-mail: info@wakullacountychamber.com
URL: http://www.wakullacountychamber.com
Contact: Amy Geiger, President
Released: Monthly

49998 ■ Chamber Chowder
510 Greene St., 1st Fl.
Key West, FL 33040
Ph: (305)294-2587
Fax: (305)294-2898
Co. E-mail: info@keywestchamber.org
URL: http://www.keywestchamber.org
Contact: Diane Gibson, President
Released: Monthly **Price:** free.

49999 ■ Chamber Chronicle
4185 Davie Rd.
Davie, FL 33314
Ph: (954)581-0790
Fax: (954)581-9684
Co. E-mail: dcch@davie-coopercity.org
URL: http://www.davie-coopercity.org
Contact: Alice Harrington, President
Released: Monthly

50000 ■ Chamber of Commerce of Cape Coral
2051 Cape Coral Pkwy. E
Cape Coral, FL 33904
Ph: (239)549-6900
Free: 800-226-9609
Fax: (239)549-9609
Co. E-mail: info@capecoralchamber.com
URL: http://www.capecoralchamber.com
Contact: Michael Quaintance, President
Description: Advocates business interest, tourism, and community development in Cape Coral, FL. **Publications:** *Chamber Trends* (Monthly). **Awards:** Big Business of the Year (Annual); Employee of the Year (Annual); Small Business of the Year (Annual).

50001 ■ Chamber of Commerce of the Palm Beaches
401 N Flagler Dr.
West Palm Beach, FL 33401
Ph: (561)833-3711

Fax: (561)833-5582
Co. E-mail: chamber@palmbeaches.org
URL: http://www.palmbeaches.org
Contact: Dennis Grady, President
Description: Advances the economic, industrial and civic interests of the Palm Beaches. Strives to support projects that lead to a stronger economy and an improved quality of life. **Founded:** 1913. **Publications:** *Business Watch* (Monthly); *Guide to Palm Beaches*; *Guide to Palm Beaches*. **Educational Activities:** Marathon of the Palm Beaches (Annual); New Member Reception (Monthly). **Awards:** Athena Award (Annual); Small Business Person of the Year (Annual). **Telecommunication Services:** dgrady@palmbeaches.org.

50002 ■ Chamber of Commerce of West Volusia
1656 S Volusia Ave.
Orange City, FL 32763-4802
Ph: (386)775-2793
Fax: (386)775-4575
Co. E-mail: contact@delandchamber.org
URL: http://www.delandchamber.org
Contact: Mark Zimmerman, President
Description: Promotes business and community development in the Orange City, FL area. Encourages public service. Sponsors community social and promotional activities. Maintains tourism center. **Founded:** 1922. **Publications:** *City Directory* (Biennial); *Dateline* (Monthly). **Educational Activities:** After Hours Connection (Monthly); Breakfast Connection (Monthly).

50003 ■ Chamber Connection
63 S Centre Trail
Santa Rosa Beach, FL 32459
Ph: (850)267-0683
Fax: (850)267-0603
Co. E-mail: wendy@waltonareachamber.com
URL: http://www.waltonareachamber.com
Contact: Cory Fosdyek, Chairperson
Released: Monthly **Price:** included in membership dues.

50004 ■ Chamber Connection
63 S Centre Trl.
Santa Rosa Beach, FL 32459
Ph: (850)892-3191
Fax: (850)267-0603
Co. E-mail: wendy@waltonareachamber.com
URL: http://www.waltonareachamber.com
Contact: Kitty Whitney, President
Released: Monthly

50005 ■ Chamber Connection
1601 E Hillsboro Blvd.
Deerfield Beach, FL 33441-4389
Ph: (954)427-1050
Fax: (954)427-1056
Co. E-mail: info@deerfieldchamber.com
URL: http://www.deerfieldchamber.com
Contact: Bud Clark, Chairman
Released: Monthly

50006 ■ The Chamber Connection
1 W Orange Ave.
Eustis, FL 32727-1210
Ph: (352)357-3434
Fax: (352)357-1392
URL: http://www.eustischamber.org
Contact: Scott Sullivan, President
Released: Monthly

50007 ■ Chamber Connection
12222 Overseas Hwy.
Marathon, FL 33050
Ph: (305)743-5417
Free: 800-262-7284
Fax: (305)289-0183
Co. E-mail: visitus@floridakeysmarathon.com
URL: http://www.floridakeysmarathon.com
Contact: Daniel Samess, Chief Executive Officer
Released: Monthly

50008 ■ Chamber Connection
PO Box 525
Matlacha, FL 33993
Ph: (239)283-0888

Fax: (239)283-0336
Co. E-mail: info@pineislandchamber.org
URL: http://www.pineislandchamber.org
Contact: Jay Johnson, President
Released: Monthly

50009 ■ *Chamber Currents*
1850 SW Fountainview Blvd., Ste. 201
Port St. Lucie, FL 34986
Ph: (772)340-1333
Fax: (772)785-7021
Co. E-mail: info@stluciechamber.org
URL: http://www.stluciechamber.org
Contact: Linda W. Cox, Executive Director
Released: Monthly

50010 ■ *Chamber Directory*
100 E Call St.
Starke, FL 32091
Ph: (904)964-5278
Fax: (904)964-2863
URL: http://www.northfloridachamber.com
Contact: Jimmie Scott, Chairman
Released: Annual **Price:** $10.

50011 ■ *Chamber Focus*
25071 Chamber of Commerce Dr.
Bonita Springs, FL 34135
Ph: (239)992-2943
Free: 800-226-2943
Fax: (239)992-5011
Co. E-mail: info@bonitaspringschamber.com
URL: http://www.bonitaspringschamber.com
Contact: Christine A. Ross, President
Released: Monthly

50012 ■ *The Chamber Focus*
11805 Heron Bay Blvd.
Coral Springs, FL 33076
Ph: (954)752-4242
Fax: (954)827-0543
Co. E-mail: mona@cschamber.com
URL: http://www.cschamber.com
Contact: Cindy Brief, President
Released: Monthly

50013 ■ *Chamber Headlines*
330 N Federal Hwy.
Hollywood, FL 33020
Ph: (954)923-4000
Free: 800-231-5562
Fax: (954)923-8737
Co. E-mail: information@hollywoodchamber.org
URL: http://www.hollywoodchamber.org
Contact: Anne Hotte, Executive Director
Released: Monthly

50014 ■ *Chamber Insider*
136 S Bronough St.
Tallahassee, FL 32302-3309
Ph: (850)521-1200
Fax: (850)521-1219
Co. E-mail: info@flchamber.com
URL: http://flchamber.com
Contact: Mark Wilson, President
Released: Weekly

50015 ■ *Chamber Line*
23 High Dr.
Crawfordville, FL 32327-2032
Ph: (850)926-1848
Fax: (850)926-2050
Co. E-mail: info@wakullacountychamber.com
URL: http://www.wakullacountychamber.com
Contact: Amy Geiger, President
Released: Monthly **Price:** free.

50016 ■ *Chamber Link*
512 NE 3rd Ave.
Fort Lauderdale, FL 33301-3236
Ph: (954)462-6000
Fax: (954)527-8766
Co. E-mail: carolyn@ftlchamber.com
URL: http://www.ftlchamber.com
Contact: Carolyn Michaels, Executive Vice President
Released: Quarterly

50017 ■ *Chamber Link Newsletter*
1216 21st St.
Vero Beach, FL 32960
Ph: (772)567-3491
Fax: (772)778-3181
Co. E-mail: info@indianriverchamber.com
URL: http://www.indianriverchamber.com
Contact: Bill Penney, Chairman of the Board
Released: Monthly

50018 ■ *Chamber Matters*
12184 W Colonial Dr.
Winter Garden, FL 34787
Ph: (407)656-1304
Fax: (407)656-0221
Co. E-mail: info@wochamber.com
URL: http://www.wochamber.com
Contact: Stina D'Uva, President

50019 ■ *The Chamber Monthly Review*
220 S Main St.
Trenton, FL 32693
Ph: (352)463-3467
Fax: (352)463-3469
Co. E-mail: chamber@gilchristcounty.com
URL: http://www.gilchristcounty.com
Contact: Tammy Beauchamp, President
Released: Monthly

50020 ■ *Chamber Music*
PO Box 369
Williston, FL 32696
Ph: (352)528-5552
Fax: (352)528-4342
Co. E-mail: wcoc@willistonfl.com
URL: http://www.willistonfl.org
Contact: Maggie Crane, President
Released: Monthly **Price:** free for members.

50021 ■ *Chamber Net*
301 Main St.
Dunedin, FL 34698
Ph: (727)733-3197
Fax: (727)734-8942
Co. E-mail: chamber@dunedin-fl.com
URL: http://www.dunedin-fl.com
Contact: Lynn Wargo, President
Released: Monthly **Price:** included in membership dues.

50022 ■ *Chamber News*
16 S Volusia Ave.
Arcadia, FL 34266
Ph: (863)494-4033
Fax: (863)494-3312
Co. E-mail: desotochamber@earthlink.net
URL: http://www.desotochamberfl.com
Contact: Mary Kay Burns, President
Released: Monthly

50023 ■ *Chamber News*
18 N Oak St.
Lake Placid, FL 33852
Ph: (863)465-4331
Fax: (863)465-2588
Co. E-mail: chamber@lpfla.com
URL: http://www.lpfla.com
Contact: Eileen M. May, Executive Director
Released: Monthly

50024 ■ *Chamber News*
5443 Main St.
New Port Richey, FL 34652
Ph: (727)842-7651
Fax: (727)848-0202
Co. E-mail: info@westpasco.com
URL: http://www.westpasco.com
Contact: Joe Alpine, President
Released: Monthly

50025 ■ *Chamber Review*
2810 Land O' Lakes Blvd.
Land O' Lakes, FL 34639-0098
Ph: (813)909-2722
Fax: (813)909-0827
Co. E-mail: office@centralpascochamber.com
URL: http://centralpascochamber.com
Contact: Kathy Dunkley, Executive Director
Released: Monthly **Price:** $75, per month.

50026 ■ *The Chamber Roadmap*
c/o Mike Horner, Pres.
Kissimmee, FL 34744
Ph: (407)847-3174
Fax: (407)870-8607
Co. E-mail: info@kissimmeechamber.com
URL: http://kissimmeechamber.com
Contact: Mike Horner, President
Released: Monthly

50027 ■ Chamber South
6410 SW 80th St.
South Miami, FL 33143
Ph: (305)661-1621
Fax: (305)666-0508
Co. E-mail: info@chambersouth.com
URL: http://www.chambersouth.com
Contact: Mary Scott Russell, President
Description: Promotes business and community development in South Dade/Kendall and Miami, FL. Sponsors South Miami Art Festival and other special events. Conducts local festivals. **Founded:** 1931. **Publications:** *Compass Points; Southword* (Monthly). **Telecommunication Services:** msrussell@chambersouth.com.

50028 ■ *Chamber Times*
1056 Ridgewood Ave.
Holly Hill, FL 32117
Ph: (386)255-7311
Fax: (386)267-0485
Co. E-mail: office@hollyhillchamber.com
URL: http://www.hollyhillchamber.com
Contact: Rose Schuhmacher, Executive Director
Released: Periodic

50029 ■ *Chamber Times*
PO Box 901544
Homestead, FL 33090
Ph: (305)247-2332
Free: 888-352-4891
Co. E-mail: info@chamberinaction.com
URL: http://www.chamberinaction.com
Contact: Ms. Mary Finlan, Executive Director
Released: Monthly

50030 ■ *Chamber Trends*
2051 Cape Coral Pkwy. E
Cape Coral, FL 33904
Ph: (239)549-6900
Free: 800-226-9609
Fax: (239)549-9609
Co. E-mail: info@capecoralchamber.com
URL: http://www.capecoralchamber.com
Contact: Michael Quaintance, President
Released: Monthly

50031 ■ *The Chamber Weekly Connection!*
1005 E Strawbridge Ave.
Melbourne, FL 32901-4782
Ph: (321)724-5400
Fax: (321)725-2093
Co. E-mail: christine@melbourneregionalchamber. com
URL: http://www.melpb-chamber.org
Contact: Christine Michaels, President
Released: Weekly

50032 ■ *The Channel*
400 E First St.
Sanford, FL 32771-1408
Ph: (407)322-2212
Fax: (407)322-8160
Co. E-mail: info@sanfordchamber.com
URL: http://www.sanfordchamber.com
Contact: Barbara Coenson, Chairperson
Released: Bimonthly **Price:** free for members; $10, /year for nonmembers.

50033 ■ Charlotte County Chamber of Commerce
2702 Tamiami Trail
Port Charlotte, FL 33952
Ph: (941)627-2222

Fax: (941)627-9730
Co. E-mail: askus@charlottecountychamber.org
URL: http://www.charlottecountychamber.org
Contact: Ms. Julie Mathis, Executive Director
Description: Promotes business and community development in Charlotte County, FL. **Founded:** 1952. **Publications:** *Business On-Line* (Biweekly); *Perspective* (Monthly).

50034 ■ *Chuck Spicer's Coastline*
122 Commerce St.
Apalachicola, FL 32320
Ph: (850)653-9419
Fax: (850)653-8219
Co. E-mail: info@apalachicolabay.org
URL: http://www.apalachicolabay.org
Contact: Anita Grove, Executive Director

50035 ■ **Citrus County Chamber of Commerce**
28 NW, US 19
Crystal River, FL 34428
Ph: (352)795-3149
Fax: (352)795-1921
Co. E-mail: meredith@citruscountychamber.com
URL: http://www.citruscountychamber.com
Contact: Rob Wardlow, Chairman
Description: Promotes business and community development in the Homosassa Springs, FL area. **Founded:** 1974. **Publications:** *The Wisecracker* (Monthly).

50036 ■ **Citrus County Chamber of Commerce, Crystal River**
28 NW Hwy. 19
Crystal River, FL 34428
Ph: (352)795-3149
Fax: (352)795-1921
Co. E-mail: josh@citruscountychamber.com
URL: http://www.citruscountychamber.com
Contact: Josh Wooten, President
Description: Promotes business and community development in Crystal River, FL area.

50037 ■ *City Directory*
1656 S Volusia Ave.
Orange City, FL 32763-4802
Ph: (386)775-2793
Fax: (386)775-4575
Co. E-mail: contact@delandchamber.org
URL: http://www.delandchamber.org
Contact: Mark Zimmerman, President
Released: Biennial

50038 ■ **Clay County Chamber of Commerce (CCCC)**
1734 Kingsley Ave.
Orange Park, FL 32073
Ph: (904)264-2651
Fax: (904)264-0070
Co. E-mail: jtabor@claychamber.com
URL: http://www.claychamber.org
Contact: John Tabor, Chief Executive Officer
Description: Promotes business and community development in Clay County, FL. Sponsors annual Health Screening, Business and Health Expo, Military Appreciation, Industry Appreciation, Golf Tournament. In addition, promote economic, tourism and film development for the county. **Founded:** 1962. **Publications:** *Links* (Monthly); *Membership and Marketplace Guide* (Semiannual).

50039 ■ **Clearwater Regional Chamber of Commerce**
401 Cleveland St.
Clearwater, FL 33755
Ph: (727)461-0011
Fax: (727)449-2889
Co. E-mail: bclifford@clearwaterflorida.org
URL: http://www.clearwaterflorida.org
Contact: Bob Clifford, President
Description: Promotes business and community development in the Clearwater, FL area. Promotes tourism. Provides governmental affairs services, networking opportunities, and small business assistance. **Founded:** 1922. **Publications:** *Relocation Guide* (Annual); *Visitors Guide* (Annual); *Voice of*

Business (Monthly). **Awards:** Business of the Year (Annual). **Telecommunication Services:** bcoleman@clearwaterflorida.org.

50040 ■ **Clewiston Chamber of Commerce**
109 Central Ave.
Clewiston, FL 33440
Ph: (863)983-7979
Fax: (863)983-7108
Co. E-mail: clewistonchamber@embarqmail.com
URL: http://www.clewiston.org
Contact: Jillian P. Sparks, Executive Director
Description: Promotes business and community development in Clewiston, FL. **Publications:** *Clewiston Chamber of Commerce Newsletter* (Monthly). **Educational Activities:** Sugar Festival (Annual).

50041 ■ *Clewiston Chamber of Commerce Newsletter*
109 Central Ave.
Clewiston, FL 33440
Ph: (863)983-7979
Fax: (863)983-7108
Co. E-mail: clewistonchamber@embarqmail.com
URL: http://www.clewiston.org
Contact: Jillian P. Sparks, Executive Director
Released: Monthly

50042 ■ *Coastlines*
PO Box 640
Fort Walton Beach, FL 32549
Ph: (850)244-8191
Fax: (850)244-1935
Co. E-mail: info@fwbchamber.org
URL: http://www.fwbchamber.org
Contact: Ted Corcoran, President
Released: Monthly

50043 ■ **Cocoa Beach Area Chamber of Commerce (CBACC)**
400 Fortenberry Rd.
Merritt Island, FL 32952
Ph: (321)459-2200
Fax: (321)459-2232
Co. E-mail: mstains@cocoabeachchamber.com
URL: http://www.cocoabeachchamber.com
Contact: Melissa Stains, President
Description: Promotes business and community development in central Brevard County, FL. **Founded:** 1925. **Publications:** *Discover Our Spirit* (Monthly); *Economic Development Council Newsletter* (Monthly); *Tourism and Convention Council Newsletter* (Periodic). **Awards:** Business of the Year (Annual).

50044 ■ **Coconut Grove Chamber of Commerce**
2820 McFarlane Rd.
Coconut Grove, FL 33133
Ph: (305)444-7270
Fax: (305)444-2498
Co. E-mail: info@coconutgrove.org
URL: http://coconutgrovechamber.com
Contact: Anthony Noboa, President
Description: Works to advance the commercial, financial, industrial and civic interests of Coconut Grove, FL. **Founded:** 1946. **Awards:** Golden Coconut Award (Annual).

50045 ■ *Communicator*
1151 Nebraska Ave.
Palm Harbor, FL 34683-4032
Ph: (727)784-4287
Co. E-mail: phcc@palmharborcc.org
URL: http://www.palmharborcc.org
Contact: Connie Davis, President
Released: Monthly

50046 ■ *Communicator*
227 U.S. Hwy. N
Sebring, FL 33870
Ph: (863)385-8448
Fax: (863)385-8810
Co. E-mail: information@sebring.org
URL: http://www.greatersebringchamberofcommerce.org
Contact: Greg Harris, President
Released: Monthly

50047 ■ *The Communicator*
PO Box 774
Sorrento, FL 32776-0774
Ph: (352)383-8801
Fax: (352)383-9343
Co. E-mail: chamber@elcchamber.com
URL: http://www.elcchamber.com
Contact: William Smalley, President
Released: Monthly

50048 ■ *Community and Buyer's Guide*
300 E University Ave., Ste. 100
Gainesville, FL 32601
Ph: (352)334-7100
Fax: (352)334-7141
URL: http://www.gainesvillechamber.com
Contact: Brent Christensen, President
Released: Annual **Price:** included in membership dues.

50049 ■ *Community and Commerce*
103 S 6th St.
Leesburg, FL 34748
Ph: (352)787-2131
Fax: (352)787-3985
Co. E-mail: info@leesburgchamber.com
URL: http://www.leesburgchamber.com
Contact: Jan Zacharchuk, Executive Director
Released: Monthly

50050 ■ *Community Directory and Buyers' Guide*
3431 Ridgewood Ave.
Port Orange, FL 32129
Ph: (386)761-1601
Fax: (386)788-9165
Co. E-mail: info@pschamber.com
URL: http://www.pschamber.com
Contact: Debbie Connors, Executive Director
Released: Annual

50051 ■ *Community Guide and Directory*
PO Box 196
Mount Dora, FL 32756-0196
Ph: (352)383-2165
Fax: (352)383-1668
Co. E-mail: chamber@mountdora.com
URL: http://www.mountdora.com
Contact: Judi Phillips Jones, Director
Released: Monthly **Price:** free.

50052 ■ *Compass Points*
6410 SW 80th St.
South Miami, FL 33143
Ph: (305)661-1621
Fax: (305)666-0508
Co. E-mail: info@chambersouth.com
URL: http://www.chambersouth.com
Contact: Mary Scott Russell, President

50053 ■ *ConTACt*
2000 S Washington Ave.
Titusville, FL 32780-4747
Ph: (321)267-3036
Fax: (321)264-0127
Co. E-mail: gaedcke@titusville.org
URL: http://www.titusville.org
Contact: Marcia Gaedcke, President
Released: Monthly

50054 ■ **Coral Gables Chamber of Commerce**
224 Catalonia Ave.
Coral Gables, FL 33134
Ph: (305)446-1657
Fax: (305)446-9900
Co. E-mail: info@coralgableschamber.org
URL: http://www.coralgableschamber.org
Contact: Mark A. Trowbridge, President
Description: Strives to foster and enhance the economic interests and quality of life in the Coral Gables community. **Telecommunication Services:** mtrowbridge@coralgableschamber.org.

50055 ■ **Coral Springs Chamber of Commerce**
11805 Heron Bay Blvd.
Coral Springs, FL 33076
Ph: (954)752-4242

Fax: (954)827-0543
Co. E-mail: mona@cschamber.com
URL: http://www.cschamber.com
Contact: Cindy Brief, President
Description: Promotes business and community development in Coral Gables, FL. Sponsors the town festival. **Founded:** 1967. **Publications:** *The Chamber Focus* (Monthly). **Awards:** Rookie Business Leader of the Year (Annual); Small Business Leader of the Year (Annual); Veteran Small Business Leader of the Year (Annual). **Telecommunication Services:** cindy@cschamber.com.

50056 ■ Crestview Area Chamber of Commerce (CACC)
1447 Commerce Dr.
Crestview, FL 32539
Ph: (850)682-3212
Fax: (850)682-7413
Co. E-mail: info@crestviewchamber.com
URL: http://www.crestviewchamber.com/crestview-chamber.htm
Contact: Wayne Harris, Executive Director
Description: Promotes business and community development in the Crestview, FL area. **Founded:** 1956. **Publications:** *Chamber Chatter* (Monthly). **Educational Activities:** Crestview Area Chamber of Commerce Meeting (Monthly). **Telecommunication Services:** execdir@crestviewchamber.com.

50057 ■ *Crossroads*
162 S Marion Ave.
Lake City, FL 32025-4354
Ph: (386)752-3690
Fax: (386)755-7744
Co. E-mail: dennille@lakecitychamber.com
URL: http://www.lakecitychamber.com
Contact: Denille Decker, Executive Director
Released: Monthly **Price:** free for members.

50058 ■ *Currents*
2390 Tamiami Trail N, Ste. 210
Naples, FL 34103
Ph: (239)262-6376
Fax: (239)262-8374
Co. E-mail: info@napleschamber.org
URL: http://www.napleschamber.org
Contact: Mike Reagen, President
Released: Monthly **Price:** included in membership dues.

50059 ■ *Dateline*
1656 S Volusia Ave.
Orange City, FL 32763-4802
Ph: (386)775-2793
Fax: (386)775-4575
Co. E-mail: contact@delandchamber.org
URL: http://www.delandchamber.org
Contact: Mark Zimmerman, President
Released: Monthly

50060 ■ Davie-Cooper City Chamber of Commerce
4185 Davie Rd.
Davie, FL 33314
Ph: (954)581-0790
Fax: (954)581-9684
Co. E-mail: dcch@davie-coopercity.org
URL: http://www.davie-coopercity.org
Contact: Alice Harrington, President
Description: Promotes business and community development in the Davie/Cooper City, FL area. Seeks to protect the public against fraud and unethical practices; earn and maintain the public's confidence in the free enterprise system; and promote tourism. Sponsors Orange Blossom festival, and the Pro-Rodeo in November. **Founded:** 1937. **Publications:** *Chamber Chronicle* (Monthly); *Membership Directory and Buyer's Guide* (Annual). **Educational Activities:** Business After Hours/Business Mixers (Monthly). **Telecommunication Services:** aharrington@davie-coopercity.org.

50061 ■ Daytona Beach - Halifax Area Chamber of Commerce (DBHACC)—Chamber, Daytona Beach and Halifax Area
126 E Orange Ave.
Daytona Beach, FL 32115
Ph: (386)255-0981

Fax: (386)258-5104
Co. E-mail: info@daytonachamber.com
URL: http://www.daytonachamber.com
Contact: Larry McKinney, President
Description: Promotes business and community development in the Daytona Beach, FL area. **Publications:** *Official Guide* (Annual). **Telecommunication Services:** ceo@daytonachamber.com.

50062 ■ DeLand Area Chamber of Commerce (DACC)
336 N Woodland Blvd.
DeLand, FL 32720
Ph: (386)734-4331
Fax: (386)734-4333
Co. E-mail: welcome@delandchamber.org
URL: http://www.delandchamber.org
Contact: Nick Conte, Executive Director
Description: Promotes business and community development in western Volusia County, FL. Seeks improved public education and transportation. Sponsors Restaurant Show and Home Show. Sponsors Leadership De Land. Administers Industrial and Tourism Development programs. **Founded:** 1890. **Publications:** *The Business Exchange* (Monthly); *Buyer's Guide* (Annual); *DeLand Data* (Bimonthly). **Awards:** President's Award (Annual). **Telecommunication Services:** contact@delandchamber.org.

50063 ■ *DeLand Data*
336 N Woodland Blvd.
DeLand, FL 32720
Ph: (386)734-4331
Fax: (386)734-4333
Co. E-mail: welcome@delandchamber.org
URL: http://www.delandchamber.org
Contact: Nick Conte, Executive Director
Released: Bimonthly

50064 ■ DeSoto County Chamber of Commerce
16 S Volusia Ave.
Arcadia, FL 34266
Ph: (863)494-4033
Fax: (863)494-3312
Co. E-mail: desotochamber@earthlink.net
URL: http://www.desotochamberfl.com
Contact: Mary Kay Burns, President
Description: Promotes business and community development in DeSoto County, FL. Provides staffed Welcome Center for local information. Sponsors All-Florida Championship Rodeo, Christmas card lane and Harvest Festival. **Founded:** 1926. **Publications:** *Action* (Bimonthly); *Chamber News* (Monthly). **Educational Activities:** Harvest Festival (Annual).

50065 ■ Destin Area Chamber of Commerce
4484 Legendary Dr., Ste. A
Destin, FL 32541
Ph: (850)837-6241
Fax: (850)654-5612
Co. E-mail: mail@destinchamber.com
URL: http://www.destinchamber.com
Contact: Shane Moody, President
Description: Promotes business and community development in the Destin, FL area. **Founded:** 1966. **Publications:** *Mini-Guide Brochure*; *Progress* (Monthly); *Guide to the Emerald Coast*. **Educational Activities:** Destin Area Chamber of Commerce Breakfast (Monthly). **Telecommunication Services:** ceo@destinchamber.com.

50066 ■ *Destination Winter Haven*
PO Box 1420
Winter Haven, FL 33882
Ph: (863)293-2138
Fax: (863)297-5818
Co. E-mail: chamber1@winterhavenfl.com
URL: http://winterhavenchamber.com
Contact: Nelson Kirkland, President
Price: free.

50067 ■ *Directory of Florida Industries*
136 S Bronough St.
Tallahassee, FL 32302-3309
Ph: (850)521-1200

Fax: (850)521-1219
Co. E-mail: info@flchamber.com
URL: http://flchamber.com
Contact: Mark Wilson, President
Released: Annual

50068 ■ *Discover Our Spirit*
400 Fortenberry Rd.
Merritt Island, FL 32952
Ph: (321)459-2200
Fax: (321)459-2232
Co. E-mail: mstains@cocoabeachchamber.com
URL: http://www.cocoabeachchamber.com
Contact: Melissa Stains, President
Released: Monthly

50069 ■ Dixie County Chamber of Commerce
PO Box 547
Cross City, FL 32628
Ph: (352)498-5454
Fax: (352)498-7549
Co. E-mail: dixiechamber@usa.net
URL: http://www.dixiechamber.org
Contact: Arthur Bellot, Vice President
Description: Promotes business and community development in Dixie County, FL.

50070 ■ *Downtown Merchant Directory*
28 E Main St.
Avon Park, FL 33825
Ph: (863)453-3350
Fax: (863)453-0973
Co. E-mail: apcc@apfla.com
URL: http://www.apfla.com
Contact: David Greenslade, Executive Director

50071 ■ *Drug Resource Guide*
1005 E Strawbridge Ave.
Melbourne, FL 32901-4782
Ph: (321)724-5400
Fax: (321)725-2093
Co. E-mail: christine@melbourneregionalchamber.com
URL: http://www.melpb-chamber.org
Contact: Christine Michaels, President
Released: Annual

50072 ■ Dunedin Chamber of Commerce
301 Main St.
Dunedin, FL 34698
Ph: (727)733-3197
Fax: (727)734-8942
Co. E-mail: chamber@dunedin-fl.com
URL: http://www.dunedin-fl.com
Contact: Lynn Wargo, President
Description: Promotes business and community development in the Dunedin, FL area. **Founded:** 1926. **Publications:** *Chamber Net* (Monthly). **Telecommunication Services:** lwargo@dunedin-fl.com.

50073 ■ Dunnellon Area Chamber of Commerce
20500 E Pennsylvania Ave.
Dunnellon, FL 34432
Ph: (352)489-2320
Free: 800-830-2087
Fax: (352)489-6846
Co. E-mail: dunnellonchamber@bellsouth.net
URL: http://www.dunnellonchamber.org
Contact: Lisa Sheffield, President
Description: Promotes business and community development in the Dunnellon, FL area. Sponsors Boomtown Days festival, 4th of July Festival. **Founded:** 1935. **Publications:** *Boomtown Gazette* (Annual).

50074 ■ *E-Communicator*
800 N U.S. Hwy. 1
Jupiter, FL 33477
Ph: (561)746-7111
Fax: (561)745-7519
Co. E-mail: info@npbchamber.com
URL: http://www.npbchamber.com/splash.php
Contact: Beth Kigel, President
Released: Monthly **Price:** included in membership dues.

50075 ■ E-Currents
1920 Meridian Ave.
Miami Beach, FL 33139-1818
Ph: (305)674-1300
Fax: (305)538-4336
Co. E-mail: bruce@miamibeachchamber.com
URL: http://www.miamibeachchamber.com
Contact: Jerry Libbin, President
Released: Weekly

50076 ■ East Lake County Chamber of Commerce
PO Box 774
Sorrento, FL 32776-0774
Ph: (352)383-8801
Fax: (352)383-9343
Co. E-mail: chamber@elcchamber.com
URL: http://www.elcchamber.com
Contact: William Smalley, President
Description: Promotes business and community development in East Lake County. **Founded:** 1986. **Publications:** *The Communicator* (Monthly).

50077 ■ East Oranger
2860 S Alafaya Trail, Ste. 130
Orlando, FL 32828
Ph: (407)277-5951
Fax: (407)381-1720
Co. E-mail: info@eocc.org
URL: http://www.eocc.org
Contact: Annie Winterbottom, President
Released: Monthly **Price:** $4, /year.

50078 ■ East Orlando Chamber of Commerce (EOCC)
2860 S Alafaya Trail, Ste. 130
Orlando, FL 32828
Ph: (407)277-5951
Fax: (407)381-1720
Co. E-mail: info@eocc.org
URL: http://www.eocc.org
Contact: Annie Winterbottom, President
Description: Promotes business and community development in East Orange County, FL. Maintains visitor's center; provides business and personal relocation assistance. **Founded:** 1954. **Publications:** *East Oranger* (Monthly); *Relo Directory* (Annual). **Awards:** Business of the Month (Monthly).

50079 ■ Economic Development Council Newsletter
400 Fortenberry Rd.
Merritt Island, FL 32952
Ph: (321)459-2200
Fax: (321)459-2232
Co. E-mail: mstains@cocoabeachchamber.com
URL: http://www.cocoabeachchamber.com
Contact: Melissa Stains, President
Released: Monthly

50080 ■ Englewood-Cape Haze Area Chamber of Commerce
601 S Indiana Ave.
Englewood, FL 34223-3788
Ph: (941)474-5511
Free: 800-603-7198
Fax: (941)475-9257
Co. E-mail: info@englewoodchamber.com
URL: http://www.englewoodchamber.com
Contact: Mary Smith, Executive Director
Description: Advocates responsible business and economic growth in Englewood community. **Publications:** *The Pulse* (Monthly). **Educational Activities:** Network at Noon (Monthly). **Awards:** Beautification Award (Annual); Member of the Year (Annual); Business/Education Partner of the Year (Annual); Hall of Fame Award (Annual).

50081 ■ ePoint!
1945 Fruitville Rd.
Sarasota, FL 34236
Ph: (941)955-8187
Fax: (941)366-5621
Co. E-mail: squeior@sarasotachamber.com
URL: http://www.sarasotachamber.com
Contact: Steve Queior, President
Released: Biweekly

50082 ■ Estero
PO Box 588
Estero, FL 33929
Ph: (239)948-7990
Fax: (239)948-5072
Co. E-mail: info@esterochamber.com
URL: http://www.esterochamber.org
Contact: Grace Fortuna, Executive Director
Released: Annual **Price:** included in membership dues.

50083 ■ Estero Chamber of Commerce
PO Box 588
Estero, FL 33929
Ph: (239)948-7990
Fax: (239)948-5072
Co. E-mail: info@esterochamber.com
URL: http://www.esterochamber.org
Contact: Grace Fortuna, Executive Director
Description: Seeks to foster and achieve a business and economic climate for all the citizens of the Estero area. **Publications:** *Estero* (Annual).

50084 ■ Eustis Area Chamber of Commerce (ECC)—Lake Eustis Area Chamber of Commerce
1 W Orange Ave.
Eustis, FL 32727-1210
Ph: (352)357-3434
Fax: (352)357-1392
URL: http://www.eustischamber.org
Contact: Scott Sullivan, President
Description: Promotes business and community development in the Eustis, FL area. Sponsors Washington Birthday Festival. **Founded:** 1902. **Publications:** *The Chamber Connection* (Monthly); *Eustis Book* (Annual); *Eustis Brochure and Membership Directory*. **Educational Activities:** Eustis Area Chamber of Commerce Breakfast (Monthly).

50085 ■ Eustis Book
1 W Orange Ave.
Eustis, FL 32727-1210
Ph: (352)357-3434
Fax: (352)357-1392
URL: http://www.eustischamber.org
Contact: Scott Sullivan, President
Released: Annual

50086 ■ Eustis Brochure and Membership Directory
1 W Orange Ave.
Eustis, FL 32727-1210
Ph: (352)357-3434
Fax: (352)357-1392
URL: http://www.eustischamber.org
Contact: Scott Sullivan, President

50087 ■ Everglades Area Chamber of Commerce
PO Box 130
Everglades City, FL 34139-0130
Ph: (239)695-3941
Co. E-mail: evergladeschamber@gmail.com
URL: http://www.florida-everglades.com
URL(s): www.evergladeschamber.net. **Description:** Promotes business and community development in Everglades, FL area.

50088 ■ Every Monday
PO Box 1234
Orlando, FL 32802-1234
Ph: (407)425-1234
Fax: (407)835-2500
Co. E-mail: info@orlando.org
URL: http://www.orlando.org
Contact: Jacob V. Stuart, President
Released: Weekly

50089 ■ Fantastic Flagler
20 Airport Rd.
Palm Coast, FL 32164
Ph: (386)437-0106
Free: 800-881-1022
Fax: (386)437-5700
Co. E-mail: info@flaglerchamber.org
URL: http://www.flaglerchamber.org
Contact: Rebecca DeLorenzo, President
Released: Annual

50090 ■ Festival and Events Guide
PO Box 901544
Homestead, FL 33090
Ph: (305)247-2332
Free: 888-352-4891
Co. E-mail: info@chamberinaction.com
URL: http://www.chamberinaction.com
Contact: Ms. Mary Finlan, Executive Director

50091 ■ First Monday
PO Box 1234
Orlando, FL 32802-1234
Ph: (407)425-1234
Fax: (407)835-2500
Co. E-mail: info@orlando.org
URL: http://www.orlando.org
Contact: Jacob V. Stuart, President
Released: Monthly

50092 ■ Flagler Beach Chamber of Commerce
PO Box 5
Flagler Beach, FL 32136-0005
Ph: (386)439-0995
Free: 800-298-0995
Co. E-mail: info@flaglerbeachchamber.com
URL: http://www.flaglerbeachchamber.com
Contact: Mary Stetler, President
Description: Promotes business and community development in Flagler Beach, FL.

50093 ■ Flagler County Directory and Shopping Guide
20 Airport Rd.
Palm Coast, FL 32164
Ph: (386)437-0106
Free: 800-881-1022
Fax: (386)437-5700
Co. E-mail: info@flaglerchamber.org
URL: http://www.flaglerchamber.org
Contact: Rebecca DeLorenzo, President
Released: Annual

50094 ■ Flagler County Palm Coast Chamber of Commerce
20 Airport Rd.
Palm Coast, FL 32164
Ph: (386)437-0106
Free: 800-881-1022
Fax: (386)437-5700
Co. E-mail: info@flaglerchamber.org
URL: http://www.flaglerchamber.org
Contact: Rebecca DeLorenzo, President
Description: Provides networking opportunities to the business community. Helps to strengthen the Economy of Flagler County. **Scope:** business. **Founded:** 1962. **Subscriptions:** 200 books. **Publications:** *Fantastic Flagler* (Annual); *The Network* (Monthly); *Relax*; *Flagler County Directory and Shopping Guide* (Annual). **Educational Activities:** Business After Hours (Monthly); Eggs and Issues (Monthly). **Awards:** Flagler County Chamber of Commerce Scholarship (Annual).

50095 ■ Florida Chamber of Commerce (FCC)
136 S Bronough St.
Tallahassee, FL 32302-3309
Ph: (850)521-1200
Fax: (850)521-1219
Co. E-mail: info@flchamber.com
URL: http://flchamber.com
Contact: Mark Wilson, President
Description: Promotes business and community development in the state of Florida. **Founded:** 1916. **Publications:** *Chamber Insider* (Weekly); *Directory of Florida Industries* (Annual); *Voice of Reason* (Monthly).

50096 ■ Focus
2787 N Tamiami Trail
North Fort Myers, FL 33903-2213
Ph: (239)997-9111
Co. E-mail: exec@nfmchamber.org
URL: http://nfmchamber.org
Contact: Phil Goss, President
Released: Monthly

50097 ■ *Foliage Locator*
180 E Main St.
Apopka, FL 32703
Ph: (407)886-1441
Fax: (407)886-1131
Co. E-mail: pauls@apopkachamber.org
URL: http://www.apopkachamber.org
Contact: Wayne H. Levesque, Chairman

50098 ■ *Forum for Business*
PO Box 3607
Lakeland, FL 33802-3607
Ph: (863)688-8551
Fax: (863)683-7454
Co. E-mail: info@lakelandchamber.com
URL: http://lakelandchamber.com
Contact: Kathleen L. Munson, President
Released: Monthly **Price:** included in membership
dues.

50099 ■ Frostproof Chamber of Commerce
15 E Wall St.
Frostproof, FL 33843
Ph: (863)635-9112
Fax: (863)635-7222
Co. E-mail: info@frostproofchamber.com
URL: http://frostproofchamber.com
Description: Promotes business and community
development in Frostproof, FL.

**50100 ■ Gadsden County Chamber of
Commerce**
PO Box 389
Quincy, FL 32353-0389
Ph: (850)627-9231
Fax: (850)875-3299
Co. E-mail: gadsdencc@tds.net
URL: http://www.gadsdencc.com
Contact: David A. Gardner, Executive Director
Description: Promotes business and economic
development in Gadsden County, Fl. **Founded:** 1946.
Telecommunication Services: davidgardner@tds.
net.

**50101 ■ Gainesville Area Chamber of
Commerce**
300 E University Ave., Ste. 100
Gainesville, FL 32601
Ph: (352)334-7100
Fax: (352)334-7141
URL: http://www.gainesvillechamber.com
Contact: Brent Christensen, President
Description: Promotes business and community
development in the Gainesville, FL area. **Founded:**
1924. **Publications:** *Business Journal Newsletter*
(Monthly); *Community and Buyer's Guide* (Annual).
Educational Activities: Business Showcase (Semi-
annual); Chamber After Hours (Monthly).

50102 ■ *The Gavel*
5301 SE Abshier Blvd.
Belleview, FL 34420
Ph: (352)245-2178
Fax: (352)245-7673
Co. E-mail: info@bsmcc.org
URL: http://bsmcc.org
Contact: Sheila Lister, Executive Director
Released: Bimonthly

**50103 ■ Gilchrist County Chamber of
Commerce**
220 S Main St.
Trenton, FL 32693
Ph: (352)463-3467
Fax: (352)463-3469
Co. E-mail: chamber@gilchristcounty.com
URL: http://www.gilchristcounty.com
Contact: Tammy Beauchamp, President
Description: Promotes business and community
development in Gilchrist County, FL. **Publications:**
The Chamber Monthly Review (Monthly); *Gilchrist
Guide*. **Educational Activities:** Annual Down Home
Days (Annual).

**50104 ■ Goldenrod Area Chamber of
Commerce**
4755 Palmetto Ave.
Goldenrod, FL 32733
Ph: (407)667-5980

Fax: (407)667-4928
Co. E-mail: director@goldenrodchamber.com
URL: http://www.goldenrodchamber.com
Contact: Darlene Dangel, Executive Director
Description: Promotes business and community
development in the Goldenrod, FL area.

**50105 ■ Greater Bartow Chamber of
Commerce (GBCC)**
510 N Broadway Ave.
Bartow, FL 33830-3918
Ph: (863)533-7125
Fax: (863)533-3793
Co. E-mail: discoverbartow@bartowchamber.com
URL: http://www.bartowchamber.com
Contact: Jeff Clark, Executive Director
Description: Works to recruit new businesses and
industries to Bartow, FL and promotes cultural life.
Founded: 1887. **Publications:** *Bartow Chamber
News* (Monthly).

**50106 ■ Greater Boca Raton Chamber of
Commerce (GBRCC)**
1800 N Dixie Hwy.
Boca Raton, FL 33432
Ph: (561)395-4433
Fax: (561)392-3780
Co. E-mail: info@bocaratonchamber.com
URL: http://www.bocaratonchamber.com
Contact: Troy M. Mclellan, President
Description: Promotes business and community
development in the Boca Raton, FL area. Provides
member services such as discount health insurance,
networking, business development workshops, etc.
Publications: *Boca Raton Annual* (Annual); *The Re-
porter* (Monthly). **Awards:** Business Person of the
Year (Annual); Small Business Leader of the Year
(Annual).

**50107 ■ Greater Boynton Beach Chamber of
Commerce (GBBCC)**
1880 N Congress Ave., Ste. 106
Boynton Beach, FL 33425
Ph: (561)732-9501
Fax: (561)734-4304
Co. E-mail: chamber@boyntonbeach.org
URL: http://www.boyntonbeach.org/index.
    php?sid=349cc8ac080f2b4081fffe8198df83b9
Contact: Glenn Jergensen, President
Description: Promotes business and community
development in the Boynton Beach, FL area. Spon-
sors business card exchanges and breakfasts and
luncheons. Conducts golf and tennis tournament,
business expo, and annual auction. **Founded:** 1924.
Publications: *Boynton Beach Business Monthly*
(Monthly); *Horizons* (Monthly).

**50108 ■ Greater Brandon Chamber of
Commerce (GBCC)**
330 Pauls Dr., Ste. 100
Brandon, FL 33511
Ph: (813)689-1221
Fax: (813)689-9440
Co. E-mail: info@brandonchamber.com
URL: http://www.brandonchamber.com
Contact: Tammy C. Bracewell, President
Description: Promotes business and community
development in the Brandon, FL area. Operates visi-
tors' bureau. Holds seminars and networking op-
portunities. **Founded:** 1959. **Publications:** *Brandon
Area Directory* (Annual); *Brandon Area Directory* (An-
nual); *Brandon Business* (Monthly). **Educational Ac-
tivities:** Business After Hours (Monthly); Coffee Club
(Monthly). **Awards:** Greater Brandon Community
Leadership Award (Annual).

**50109 ■ Greater Chiefland Area Chamber of
Commerce**
PO Box 1397
Chiefland, FL 32644
Ph: (352)493-1849
Fax: (352)493-0282
Co. E-mail: chieflandchamber@bellsouth.net
URL: http://www.chieflandchamber.com
Contact: Bennitt Patterson, President
Description: Fosters population, commerce and
finance advancement, civic and social improvement,
and other sphere of interests within greater Chiefland
area. **Awards:** Citizen of the Year (Annual).

**50110 ■ Greater Dade City Chamber of
Commerce**
14112 8th St.
Dade City, FL 33525
Ph: (352)567-3769
Fax: (352)567-3770
Co. E-mail: info@dadecitychamber.org
URL: http://www.dadecitychamber.org
Contact: Joey Wubbena, President
Description: Promotes business and community
development in the Dade City, FL area. **Founded:**
1889. **Publications:** *Annual Membership Directory*
(Annual); *Greater Dade City Chamber of Commerce--
Annual Membership Directory* (Annual).

**50111 ■ Greater Dania Beach Chamber of
Commerce**
102 W Dania Beach Blvd.
Dania Beach, FL 33004
Ph: (954)926-2323
Fax: (954)926-2384
Co. E-mail: info@greaterdania.org
URL: http://www.greaterdania.org
Contact: Victoria Payne, Executive Director
Description: Promotes business and community
development in Dania, FL. **Publications:** *The Cham-
ber Chatter* (Monthly). **Awards:** Small Business
Person of the Year (Annual).

**50112 ■ Greater Deerfield Beach Chamber of
Commerce (GDBCC)**
1601 E Hillsboro Blvd.
Deerfield Beach, FL 33441-4389
Ph: (954)427-1050
Fax: (954)427-1056
Co. E-mail: info@deerfieldchamber.com
URL: http://www.deerfieldchamber.com
Contact: Bud Clark, Chairman
Description: Promotes tourism, business and com-
munity development in Deerfield Beach, FL.
Founded: 1952. **Publications:** *Chamber Connection*
(Monthly); *Member Report* (Monthly); *Guide Book/
Buyers Guide* (Annual). **Educational Activities:** Bus-
Link Expo (Annual); Golf Outing (Annual); St. Patrick's
Pot 'O Gold Auction (Annual).

**50113 ■ Greater Delray Beach Chamber of
Commerce**
64-A SE 5th Ave.
Delray Beach, FL 33483
Ph: (561)278-0424
Fax: (561)278-0555
Co. E-mail: chamber@delraybeach.com
URL: http://www.delraybeach.com
Contact: Michael Malone, President
Description: Seeks to promote and perpetuate busi-
ness growth, economic development, civic interest,
general welfare and prosperity of the Greater Delray
Beach area. Aims to stimulate public interest to these
ends. **Publications:** *TradeWinds* (Bimonthly). **Educa-
tional Activities:** Membership Business Breakfast
(Monthly). **Awards:** Business of the Year (Annual);
Business Recognition Awards (Annual); Ken Elling-
sworth Community Service Awards (Annual); Small
Business Person of the Year (Annual). **Telecommunication Services:** mike@delraybeach.com.

**50114 ■ Greater Fort Lauderdale Chamber of
Commerce (GFLCC)**
512 NE 3rd Ave.
Fort Lauderdale, FL 33301-3236
Ph: (954)462-6000
Fax: (954)527-8766
Co. E-mail: carolyn@ftlchamber.com
URL: http://www.ftlchamber.com
Contact: Carolyn Michaels, Executive Vice President
Description: Promotes business, tourism, and com-
munity development in the Greater Ft. Lauderdale,
FL area. **Founded:** 1910. **Publications:** *Chamber
Link* (Quarterly); *The Guide*; *Guide to Greater Fort
Lauderdale* (Annual).

**50115 ■ Greater Fort Myers Chamber of
Commerce**
2310 Edwards Dr.
Fort Myers, FL 33901
Ph: (239)332-3624
Free: 800-366-3622

Fax: (239)332-7276
Co. E-mail: info@fortmyers.org
URL: http://www.fortmyers.org
Contact: Heather Christie, President
Description: Promotes civic and commercial progress of Greater Fort Myers' community. **Publications:** *Greater Network E-News.*

50116 ■ Greater Fort Walton Beach Chamber of Commerce
PO Box 640
Fort Walton Beach, FL 32549
Ph: (850)244-8191
Fax: (850)244-1935
Co. E-mail: info@fwbchamber.org
URL: http://www.fwbchamber.org
Contact: Ted Corcoran, President
Description: Promotes business and community development in the Ft. Walton Beach, FL area. **Founded:** 1946. **Publications:** *Lifestyles* (Annual); *Coastlines* (Monthly); *Lifestyles.* **Educational Activities:** First Friday Coffees (Monthly); Billy Bowlegs Pirate Festival (Annual). **Awards:** H.C. White Scholarships (Annual). **Telecommunication Services:** tedcorcoran@fwbchamber.org.

50117 ■ Greater Hernando County Chamber of Commerce
15588 Aviation Loop Dr.
Brooksville, FL 34604
Ph: (352)796-0697
Fax: (352)796-3704
Co. E-mail: info@hernandochamber.com
URL: http://hernandochamber.com
Contact: John Mitten, Chairman of the Board
Description: Business and professional men and women who promote civic, commercial, and industrial progress. **Publications:** *The Business Edge* (Monthly). **Educational Activities:** Leadership Hernando. **Telecommunication Services:** pat@hernandochamber.com.

50118 ■ Greater Hollywood Chamber of Commerce
330 N Federal Hwy.
Hollywood, FL 33020
Ph: (954)923-4000
Free: 800-231-5562
Fax: (954)923-8737
Co. E-mail: information@hollywoodchamber.org
URL: http://www.hollywoodchamber.org
Contact: Anne Hotte, Executive Director
Description: Promotes business and community development in the Hollywood, FL area. **Publications:** *Chamber Headlines* (Monthly); *Visitor Guide* (Annual).

50119 ■ Greater Homestead/Florida City Chamber of Commerce (GHFCCC)
PO Box 901544
Homestead, FL 33090
Ph: (305)247-2332
Free: 888-352-4891
Co. E-mail: info@chamberinaction.com
URL: http://www.chamberinaction.com
Contact: Ms. Mary Finlan, Executive Director
Description: Promotes business and economic development in South Miami-Dade County Florida. **Founded:** 1915. **Subscriptions:** 150 archival material articles business records maps photographs reports. **Publications:** *Chamber Times* (Monthly); *Festival and Events Guide; Membership Guide and Directory* (Annual). **Awards:** Citizen of the Year (Annual); Volunteer of the Year (Annual).

50120 ■ Greater Lake Worth Chamber of Commerce
501 Lake Ave.
Lake Worth, FL 33460
Ph: (561)582-4401
Fax: (561)547-8300
Co. E-mail: lwchamber@lwchamber.com
URL: http://www.lwchamber.com
Description: Promotes business and community development in the Lake Worth, FL area. **Founded:** 1912.

50121 ■ Greater Marathon Chamber of Commerce
12222 Overseas Hwy.
Marathon, FL 33050
Ph: (305)743-5417
Free: 800-262-7284
Fax: (305)289-0183
Co. E-mail: visitus@floridakeysmarathon.com
URL: http://www.floridakeysmarathon.com
Contact: Daniel Samess, Chief Executive Officer
Description: Promotes business and community development in the Marathon, FL area. **Founded:** 1939. **Publications:** *Chamber Connection* (Monthly).

50122 ■ Greater Miami Chamber of Commerce (GMCC)
1601 Biscayne Blvd.
Ballroom Level
Miami, FL 33132-1260
Ph: (305)350-7700
Free: 888-660-5955
Fax: (305)374-6902
Co. E-mail: reception@miamichamber.com
URL: http://www.greatermiami.com
Contact: Barry E. Johnson, President
Description: Promotes business and community development in the Miami, FL area. **Founded:** 1907. **Publications:** *CEO Report* (Quarterly); *CEO Report Update* (Monthly); *Greater Miami Chamber Membership Directory* (Annual); *New Member Profile* (Semiannual); *NewsBREAK* (Weekly). **Awards:** Health Care Heroes (Annual).

50123 ■ Greater Miami Chamber of Commerce, Women in Business Group
Omni International Complex
1601 Biscayne Blvd.
Miami, FL 33132-1260
Ph: (305)350-7700
Free: 888-660-5955
Fax: (305)374-6902
Co. E-mail: reception@miamichamber.com
URL: http://www.greatermiami.com
Contact: Lisa Showers, Executive Assistant
Description: Aims to create economic progress in Miami-Dade County. Aims to make South Florida the most business-friendly region in the Americas and to promote members' competitiveness through state of the art benefits and services, support for sustainable economic development, and advocacy to enhance the business environment. Serves as the voice of business enterprise and involves the private sector in community leadership.

50124 ■ *Greater Miami Chamber Membership Directory*
1601 Biscayne Blvd.
Ballroom Level
Miami, FL 33132-1260
Ph: (305)350-7700
Free: 888-660-5955
Fax: (305)374-6902
Co. E-mail: reception@miamichamber.com
URL: http://www.greatermiami.com
Contact: Barry E. Johnson, President
Released: Annual **Price:** $45.60, plus shipping and handling.

50125 ■ Greater Miami Shores Chamber of Commerce
9701 NE 2nd Ave.
Miami Shores, FL 33138-2310
Ph: (305)754-5466
Fax: (305)759-8872
Co. E-mail: shoreschamber@bellsouth.net
URL: http://www.miamishores.com
Contact: Lew Soli, Executive Director
Description: Strives to provide leadership for the advancement of the economic vitality, civic affairs and quality of life of the total community in Miami shores, FL. **Awards:** Outstanding Students Awards (Annual); Police Officer of the Quarter (Quarterly); Police Officer of the Year (Annual); Teacher Enhancement Awards Program (Semiannual).

50126 ■ Greater Mulberry Chamber of Commerce (GMCC)
PO Box 254
Mulberry, FL 33860-0254
Ph: (863)425-4414
Fax: (863)425-3837
URL: http://www.mulberrychamber.org
Contact: Sharron Jones, Executive Director
Description: Promotes business and community development in Mulberry, FL. Helps to bring educational information to the local businesses and helps to promote the sports and tourism in the Central Florida Area. **Publications:** *Mulberry Magic* (Monthly).

50127 ■ Greater Naples Chamber of Commerce (GNCC)
2390 Tamiami Trail N, Ste. 210
Naples, FL 34103
Ph: (239)262-6376
Fax: (239)262-8374
Co. E-mail: info@napleschamber.org
URL: http://www.napleschamber.org
Contact: Mike Reagen, President
Description: Promotes business and community development in the Naples, FL area. **Publications:** *Currents* (Monthly); *Naples on the Gulf* (Annual).

50128 ■ *Greater Nassau Chamber News*
PO Box 98
Callahan, FL 32011
Ph: (904)879-1441
Fax: (904)879-4033
Co. E-mail: gncc@juno.com
URL: http://www.greaternassaucounty.com/gn/frontpage
Contact: Louise Banks, Executive Director
Released: Monthly **Price:** free to members.

50129 ■ Greater Nassau County Chamber of Commerce
PO Box 98
Callahan, FL 32011
Ph: (904)879-1441
Fax: (904)879-4033
Co. E-mail: gncc@juno.com
URL: http://www.greaternassaucounty.com/gn/frontpage
Contact: Louise Banks, Executive Director
Description: Promotes business and community development in Nassau County, FL. **Founded:** 1974. **Publications:** *Greater Nassau Chamber News* (Monthly). **Educational Activities:** Membership Meeting (Monthly).

50130 ■ Greater North Miami Beach Chamber of Commerce
1870 NE 171st St.
North Miami Beach, FL 33162
Ph: (305)944-8500
Fax: (305)944-8191
Co. E-mail: chamber@nmbchamber.com
URL: http://www.nmbchamber.com
Contact: Yona S. Lunger, President
Description: Promotes business and community development in North Miami, FL. Sponsors annual Career Shadowing Day. **Founded:** 1947. **Publications:** *The Pink Sheet* (Monthly). **Educational Activities:** Business After Hours Expo (Monthly).

50131 ■ Greater Palm Harbor Area Chamber of Commerce (GPHACC)
1151 Nebraska Ave.
Palm Harbor, FL 34683-4032
Ph: (727)784-4287
Co. E-mail: phcc@palmharborcc.org
URL: http://www.palmharborcc.org
Contact: Connie Davis, President
Description: Promotes business and community development in the Palm Harbor, FL area. **Founded:** 1978. **Publications:** *Communicator* (Monthly).

50132 ■ Greater Panama City Beaches Chamber of Commerce
309 Beckrich Rd.
Panama City Beach, FL 32407
Ph: (850)235-1159

Fax: (850)235-2301
Co. E-mail: chamber@pcbeach.org
URL: http://www.pcbeach.org
Contact: Beth Oltman, President
Description: Promotes business and community development in Panama City Beach, FL.

50133 ■ Greater Pine Island Chamber of Commerce
PO Box 525
Matlacha, FL 33993
Ph: (239)283-0888
Fax: (239)283-0336
Co. E-mail: info@pineislandchamber.org
URL: http://www.pineislandchamber.org
Contact: Jay Johnson, President
Description: Promotes business, community development, and tourism in Pine Island, FL. Sponsors fundraising activities. **Founded:** 1961. **Publications:** *Chamber Connection* (Monthly). **Educational Activities:** Business Card Exchange (Monthly).

50134 ■ Greater Plant City Chamber of Commerce
106 N Evers St.
Plant City, FL 33563-3330
Ph: (813)754-3707
Free: 800-760-2315
Fax: (813)752-8793
Co. E-mail: info@plantcity.org
URL: http://www.plantcity.org
Contact: Marion M. Smith, President
Description: Promotes business and community development in the Plant City, FL area. **Publications:** *Greater Plant City Chamber of Commerce--Membership Directory.*

50135 ■ Greater Plantation Chamber of Commerce
7401 NW 4th St.
Plantation, FL 33317
Ph: (954)587-1410
Fax: (954)587-1886
Co. E-mail: info@plantationchamber.org
URL: http://www.plantationchamber.org
Contact: Siobhan Edwards, President
Description: Promotes business and community development in the Plantation, FL area. Encourages orderly development and growth. **Publications:** *Plantation Annual* (Annual).

50136 ■ Greater Pompano Beach Chamber of Commerce
2200 E Atlantic Blvd.
Pompano Beach, FL 33062
Ph: (954)941-2940
Fax: (954)785-8358
URL: http://www.pompanobeachchamber.com
Contact: Ric green, President
Description: Promotes business and community development in Pompano Beach, FL. **Awards:** Small Business Person of the Year (Annual).

50137 ■ Greater Riverview Chamber of Commerce (GRCC)
10011 Water Works Ln.
Riverview, FL 33578
Ph: (813)234-5944
Fax: (813)234-5945
Co. E-mail: info@riverviewchamber.com
URL: http://www.riverviewchamber.com
Contact: Tanya Doran, Executive Director
Description: Promotes business and community development in Riverview, FL. Sponsors run. **Founded:** 1966.

50138 ■ Greater Sanford - Seminole County Chamber of Commerce
400 E First St.
Sanford, FL 32771-1408
Ph: (407)322-2212

Fax: (407)322-8160
Co. E-mail: info@sanfordchamber.com
URL: http://www.sanfordchamber.com
Contact: Barbara Coenson, Chairperson
Description: Promotes business and community development in Sanford and Seminole County. **Founded:** 1920. **Publications:** *The Channel* (Bimonthly). **Educational Activities:** Bikefest.

50139 ■ Greater Sarasota Chamber of Commerce
1945 Fruitville Rd.
Sarasota, FL 34236
Ph: (941)955-8187
Fax: (941)366-5621
Co. E-mail: squeior@sarasotachamber.com
URL: http://www.sarasotachamber.com
Contact: Steve Queior, President
Description: Promotes business and community development in Sarasota County, FL. **Founded:** 1921. **Publications:** *The Bridge* (Monthly); *Catalyst* (Monthly); *ePoint!* (Biweekly); *Guide to Greater Sarasota*; *The Point* (Quarterly). **Educational Activities:** Business Connections (Monthly); Economic Development Breakfast (Monthly). **Awards:** Small Business of the Year (Annual); Young Business of the Year (Annual).

50140 ■ Greater Sebring Chamber of Commerce
227 U.S. Hwy. N
Sebring, FL 33870
Ph: (863)385-8448
Fax: (863)385-8810
Co. E-mail: information@sebring.org
URL: http://www.greatersebringchamberofcommerce.org
Contact: Greg Harris, President
Description: Promotes business and community development in the Sebring, FL area. **Founded:** 1914. **Publications:** *Annual Directory* (Annual); *Communicator* (Monthly); *Lifestyle Sebring* (Annual).

50141 ■ Greater Seffner Area Chamber of Commerce
11816 US Hwy. 92 E
Seffner, FL 33583-1920
Ph: (813)627-8686
Co. E-mail: info@seffnerchamber.com
URL: http://www.seffnerchamber.com
Contact: Rory Weiner, President
Description: Promotes business and community development in the Seffner, Mango, Dover, and Valrico FL area. **Founded:** 1986.

50142 ■ Greater Seminole Area Chamber of Commerce
7985 113th St. N, Ste. 208
Seminole, FL 33772
Ph: (727)392-3245
Fax: (727)397-7753
Co. E-mail: rogere@myseminolechamber.com
URL: http://seminolechamber.net
Contact: Roger Edelman, President
Description: Seeks to advance Seminole's economy and quality of life. **Founded:** 1963.

50143 ■ Greater Sunrise Chamber of Commerce
12801 W Sunrise Blvd.
Sunrise, FL 33323-4020
Ph: (954)835-2428
Co. E-mail: mjacobs@sunrisechamber.org
URL: http://www.sunrisechamber.org
Contact: Mike Jacobs, Executive Director
Description: Promotes business and community development in Sunrise, FL. **Publications:** *Sunlines* (Monthly). **Awards:** Small Business Person of the Year (Annual).

50144 ■ Greater Tallahassee Chamber of Commerce
PO Box 1639
Tallahassee, FL 32302
Ph: (850)224-8116

Fax: (850)561-3860
Co. E-mail: info@talchamber.com
URL: http://talchamber.com
Contact: Sue Dick, President
Description: Promotes business and community development in Tallahassee, FL. **Founded:** 1923. **Publications:** *Business Views*; *Market Directory* (Annual). **Awards:** Small Business Excellence Awards. **Telecommunication Services:** sdick@talchamber.com.

50145 ■ Greater Tampa Chamber of Commerce (GTCC)
PO Box 420
Tampa, FL 33601
Ph: (813)228-7777
Free: 800-298-2672
Fax: (813)223-7899
Co. E-mail: info@tampachamber.com
Contact: Robert J. Rohrlack, Jr., President
Description: Promotes business growth and community development in Greater Tampa area. **Publications:** *Inside View* (Quarterly); *Directory of Industries--Tampa and Greater Tampa Metropolitan Area*; *Relocation Guide and Membership Directory.* **Awards:** Small Business of the Year (Annual).

50146 ■ Greater Temple Terrace Chamber of Commerce (TTCC)
9385 N 56th St.
Temple Terrace, FL 33617
Ph: (813)989-7004
Fax: (813)989-7005
Co. E-mail: hharper@templeterracechamber.com
URL: http://www.templeterracechamber.com
Contact: Barbara Sparks-McGlinchy, Executive Director
Description: Promotes business and community development in Temple Terrace, FL. Holds art festival, Fourth of July parade and celebration, and business expo. **Founded:** 1963. **Publications:** *News and Views* (Monthly). **Awards:** Small Business of Year (Annual); Student Award (Annual); Citizen of Year (Annual); Ed Hanna Business of the Year (Annual). **Telecommunication Services:** ltice@templeterracechamber.com; bsparks@templeterracechamber.com.

50147 ■ Greater Winter Haven Chamber of Commerce
PO Box 1420
Winter Haven, FL 33882
Ph: (863)293-2138
Fax: (863)297-5818
Co. E-mail: chamber1@winterhavenfl.com
URL: http://winterhavenchamber.com
Contact: Nelson Kirkland, President
Description: Promotes business and community development in Winter Haven, FL. **Founded:** 1926. **Publications:** *Destination Winter Haven.*

50148 ■ *The Guide*
512 NE 3rd Ave.
Fort Lauderdale, FL 33301-3236
Ph: (954)462-6000
Fax: (954)527-8766
Co. E-mail: carolyn@ftlchamber.com
URL: http://www.ftlchamber.com
Contact: Carolyn Michaels, Executive Vice President
Price: $6, each.

50149 ■ *Guide Book*
11 E Orange St.
Tarpon Springs, FL 34689-3439
Ph: (727)937-6100
Fax: (727)937-2879
Co. E-mail: chamber@tarponsprings.com
URL: http://tarponspringschamber.com
Contact: Sue Thomas, President
Released: Annual **Price:** free.

50150 ■ *Guide Book/Buyers Guide*
1601 E Hillsboro Blvd.
Deerfield Beach, FL 33441-4389
Ph: (954)427-1050
Fax: (954)427-1056
Co. E-mail: info@deerfieldchamber.com
URL: http://www.deerfieldchamber.com
Contact: Bud Clark, Chairman
Released: Annual

50151 ■ *Guide to Greater Fort Lauderdale*
512 NE 3rd Ave.
Fort Lauderdale, FL 33301-3236
Ph: (954)462-6000
Fax: (954)527-8766
Co. E-mail: carolyn@ftlchamber.com
URL: http://www.ftlchamber.com
Contact: Carolyn Michaels, Executive Vice President
Released: Annual

50152 ■ *Guide to Greater Sarasota*
1945 Fruitville Rd.
Sarasota, FL 34236
Ph: (941)955-8187
Fax: (941)366-5621
Co. E-mail: squeior@sarasotachamber.com
URL: http://www.sarasotachamber.com
Contact: Steve Queior, President
Price: $4.95.

50153 ■ *Guide to Palm Beaches*
401 N Flagler Dr.
West Palm Beach, FL 33401
Ph: (561)833-3711
Fax: (561)833-5582
Co. E-mail: chamber@palmbeaches.org
URL: http://www.palmbeaches.org
Contact: Dennis Grady, President

50154 ■ *Guidebook*
6990 Gulf Blvd.
St. Pete Beach, FL 33706
Ph: (727)360-6957
Co. E-mail: info@tampabaybeaches.com
URL: http://www.tampabaybeaches.com/cwt/external/
 wcpages/index.aspx
Contact: Robin Sollie, President
Released: Annual

50155 ■ Gulf Breeze Area Chamber of Commerce
409 Gulf Breeze Pkwy.
Gulf Breeze, FL 32561
Ph: (850)932-7888
Fax: (850)934-4601
Co. E-mail: reception@gulfbreezechamber.com
URL: http://www.gulfbreezechamber.com
Contact: Ms. Meg Peltier, President
Description: Develops an attractive business environment that provides opportunity for economic growth while improving the quality of life and enhancing the standard of living for the entire Gulf Breeze area. **Founded:** 1988. **Publications:** *Gulf Breeze Magazine* (Quarterly); *Gulf Breeze Area Chamber of Commerce--Membership Directory and Relocation Guide* (Annual).

50156 ■ *Gulf Breeze Magazine*
409 Gulf Breeze Pkwy.
Gulf Breeze, FL 32561
Ph: (850)932-7888
Fax: (850)934-4601
Co. E-mail: reception@gulfbreezechamber.com
URL: http://www.gulfbreezechamber.com
Contact: Ms. Meg Peltier, President
Released: Quarterly **Price:** $10, for nonmembers; free for members.

50157 ■ Gulf County Chamber of Commerce
406 Marina Dr.
Port St. Joe, FL 32456
Ph: (850)227-1223
Fax: (850)227-9684
Co. E-mail: info@gulfchamber.org
URL: http://www.gulfchamber.org
Contact: Bobby Pickels, President
Description: Promotes the growth of local businesses by keeping members informed of news that may affect their businesses; by discovering and communicating members' interests on questions affecting the welfare of cities, county, state and the country at large; by linking the people of the entire communities together in a common enterprise; and by making possible great public and business-forward movements. **Founded:** 1938.

50158 ■ Haines City Chamber of Commerce
35610 U.S. Hwy. 27
Haines City, FL 33844

Ph: (863)422-3751
Free: 855-233-6362
Fax: (863)422-4704
Co. E-mail: info@hainescity.com
URL: http://www.hainescity.com
Contact: Steve Shealey, Chairperson
Description: Promotes business and community development in Haines City, FL. **Founded:** 1960.
Publications: *Heart-Beat* (Monthly).

50159 ■ Hamilton County Chamber of Commerce (HCCC)
PO Box 366
Jasper, FL 32052
Ph: (386)792-1300
Fax: (386)792-1300
Co. E-mail: hamcoc@windstream.net
URL: http://www.hamiltoncountycoc.com
Contact: Samantha Prueter, President
Description: Promotes business and community development in Hamilton County, FL. **Founded:** 1958.

50160 ■ *Harbor News*
200 Main St.
Safety Harbor, FL 34695
Ph: (727)726-2890
Fax: (727)726-2733
Co. E-mail: info@safetyharborchamber.com
URL: http://www.safetyharborchamber.com
Contact: Marie Padavich, Chairperson
Released: Monthly

50161 ■ Hardee County Chamber of Commerce (HCCC)
PO Box 683
Wauchula, FL 33873
Ph: (863)773-6967
Fax: (863)773-4915
Co. E-mail: casey@hardeecc.com
URL: http://www.hardeecc.com/recreation.htm
Contact: Derren Bryan, President
Description: Promotes business and community development in Hardee County, FL. **Publications:** *Chamber Bulletin* (Monthly); *The Voice of Business* (Monthly).

50162 ■ Hawthorne Area Chamber of Commerce
PO Box 125
Hawthorne, FL 32640-0125
Ph: (352)481-2432
Co. E-mail: hawthornechamber@hotmail.com
URL: http://www.hawthorneflorida.org
Contact: Chris Carson, President
Description: Promotes business and community development in Hawthorne, FL area.

50163 ■ *Heart-Beat*
35610 U.S. Hwy. 27
Haines City, FL 33844
Ph: (863)422-3751
Free: 855-233-6362
Fax: (863)422-4704
Co. E-mail: info@hainescity.com
URL: http://www.hainescity.com
Contact: Steve Shealey, Chairperson
Released: Monthly

50164 ■ Hialeah Chamber of Commerce and Industry (HCC)
240 E 1st Ave., Ste. 217
Hialeah, FL 33010
Ph: (305)888-7780
Fax: (305)888-7804
Co. E-mail: info@hialeahchamber.org
URL: http://www.hialeahchamber.org
Contact: Daniel Hernandez, President
Description: Provides information to small, medium, and large sized businesses in the community. Develops business opportunities throughout the community through the use of trade missions to Latin America, the Caribbean, and Europe.

50165 ■ High Springs Chamber of Commerce
PO Box 863
High Springs, FL 32655-0863
Ph: (386)454-3120

Fax: (386)454-5848
Co. E-mail: chamber@highsprings.com
URL: http://www.highsprings.com/home/index.php
Contact: Donna Mogler, President
Description: Promotes business and community development in High Springs, FL. Sponsors annual Pioneer Days festival. **Telecommunication Services:** thomaswellerattorneyatlaw@alltel.net.

50166 ■ Hobe Sound Chamber of Commerce
11954 SE Bridge Rd.
Hobe Sound, FL 33475
Ph: (772)546-4724
Fax: (772)546-9969
Co. E-mail: info@hobesound.org
URL: http://hobesound.org
Contact: Angela Hoffman
Description: Promotes business and community development in Hobe Sound, FL. **Telecommunication Services:** ahoffman@hobesound.org.

50167 ■ Holly Hill Chamber of Commerce
1056 Ridgewood Ave.
Holly Hill, FL 32117
Ph: (386)255-7311
Fax: (386)267-0485
Co. E-mail: office@hollyhillchamber.com
URL: http://www.hollyhillchamber.com
Contact: Rose Schuhmacher, Executive Director
Description: Promotes business and community development in Holly Hill, FL. **Founded:** 1960. **Publications:** *Chamber Times* (Periodic).

50168 ■ *Horizon Lines*
101 State St. W
Oldsmar, FL 34677
Ph: (813)855-4233
Fax: (813)854-1237
Co. E-mail: jcustin@utbchamber.com
URL: http://www.oldsmarchamber.com
Contact: Jerry Custin, President
Released: Monthly **Price:** free.

50169 ■ *Horizons*
1880 N Congress Ave., Ste. 106
Boynton Beach, FL 33425
Ph: (561)732-9501
Fax: (561)734-4304
Co. E-mail: chamber@boyntonbeach.org
URL: http://www.boyntonbeach.org/index.
 php?sid=349cc8ac080f2b4081fffe8198df83b9
Contact: Glenn Jergensen, President
Released: Monthly

50170 ■ Immokalee Chamber of Commerce
1300 N 15th St., Ste. 2
Immokalee, FL 34142
Ph: (239)657-3237
Fax: (239)657-5450
Co. E-mail: ecoc@comcast.net
URL: http://www.immokaleechamber.com
Contact: Bernardo Barnhart, President
Description: Promotes business and community development in Immokalee, FL.

50171 ■ Indian River County Chamber of Commerce
1216 21st St.
Vero Beach, FL 32960
Ph: (772)567-3491
Fax: (772)778-3181
Co. E-mail: info@indianriverchamber.com
URL: http://www.indianriverchamber.com
Contact: Bill Penney, Chairman of the Board
Description: Business and professional membership. Promotion, expansion and retention of business. Provides leadership for growth and change. Promotes tourism. **Founded:** 1923. **Publications:** *Chamber Link Newsletter* (Monthly). **Telecommunication Services:** director@indianriverchamber.com.

50172 ■ Indiantown Western Martin County Chamber of Commerce
15935 SW Warfield Blvd.
Indiantown, FL 34956-0602

Ph: (772)597-2184
Co. E-mail: info@indiantownchamber.com
URL: http://indiantownfl.org
Contact: Hilary McKeich, Executive Director
Description: Promotes business growth and community development in Indiantown, FL.

50173 ■ *Inside View*
PO Box 420
Tampa, FL 33601
Ph: (813)228-7777
Free: 800-298-2672
Fax: (813)223-7899
Co. E-mail: info@tampachamber.com
Contact: Robert J. Rohrlack, Jr., President
Released: Quarterly

50174 ■ Islamorada Chamber of Commerce
PO Box 915
Islamorada, FL 33036-0915
Ph: (305)664-4503
Free: 800-322-5397
Fax: (305)664-4289
Co. E-mail: info@islamoradachamber.com
URL: http://www.islamoradachamber.com
Contact: Judy Hull, Executive Director
Description: Promotes business and community development in Islamorada, FL.

50175 ■ *Island Guide*
1159 Causeway Rd.
Sanibel, FL 33957
Ph: (239)472-1080
Fax: (239)472-1070
Co. E-mail: island@sanibel-captiva.org
URL: http://www.sanibel-captiva.org
Contact: Mr. Ric Base, President

50176 ■ Jackson County Chamber of Commerce
PO Box 130
Marianna, FL 32447
Ph: (850)482-8060
Fax: (850)482-8002
Co. E-mail: info@jacksoncounty.com
URL: http://www.jacksoncounty.com
Contact: Art Kimbrough, President
Description: Promotes economic and community development in Jackson County, FL. Provides public relations services. **Founded:** 1928.

50177 ■ Jacksonville Regional Chamber of Commerce
3 Independent Dr.
Jacksonville, FL 32202
Ph: (904)366-6600
Fax: (904)632-0617
Co. E-mail: info@jacksonvillechamber.org
URL: http://www.myjaxchamber.com/general.asp?id=2
Contact: Walter M. Lee, III, President
Description: Promotes business and community development in Jacksonville, FL. Conducts seminars and other programs. **Founded:** 1884.

50178 ■ Jensen Beach Chamber of Commerce
PO Box 1536
Jensen Beach, FL 34958
Ph: (772)334-3444
Co. E-mail: info@jensenbeachchamber.biz
URL: http://www.jensenbeachchamber.biz
Contact: Sue Zachman, President
Description: Seeks to promote business and community development in Jensen Beach, FL. **Publications:** *The Beach Biz* (Monthly).

50179 ■ *The Journal of Osceola County Business*
c/o Mike Horner, Pres.
Kissimmee, FL 34744
Ph: (407)847-3174
Fax: (407)870-8607
Co. E-mail: info@kissimmeechamber.com
URL: http://kissimmeechamber.com
Contact: Mike Horner, President
Released: Bimonthly

50180 ■ Key Largo Chamber of Commerce—Key Largo Chamber of Commerce and Florida Keys Visitor Center
106000 Overseas Hwy.
Key Largo, FL 33037
Ph: (305)451-4747
Free: 800-822-1088
Fax: (305)451-4726
Co. E-mail: info@keylargochamber.org
URL: http://www.keylargochamber.org
Contact: Jackie Harder, President
Description: Promotes business and community development in Key Largo, Plantation Key, and the Everglades area of Florida. Operates welcome center. Provides information to visitors and businesses and individuals considering moving to the area. **Founded:** 1956. **Publications:** *The Legend* (Monthly); *Legendary Key Largo: A Guide to Island Living.*

50181 ■ *Key Newsletter*
5118 Ocean Blvd.
Siesta Key, FL 34242
Ph: (941)349-3800
Free: 866-831-7778
Co. E-mail: info@siestakeychamber.com
URL: http://www.siestakeychamber.com
Contact: Mark Smith, Chairman
Released: Monthly

50182 ■ Key West Chamber of Commerce (KWCC)
510 Greene St., 1st Fl.
Key West, FL 33040
Ph: (305)294-2587
Fax: (305)294-2898
Co. E-mail: info@keywestchamber.org
URL: http://www.keywestchamber.org
Contact: Diane Gibson, President
Description: Promotes business and community development in the Key West, FL area. Issues tourist information. **Founded:** 1822. **Publications:** *Chamber Chowder* (Monthly). **Educational Activities:** Fantasy (Annual).

50183 ■ Kissimmee - Osceola County Chamber of Commerce
c/o Mike Horner, Pres.
Kissimmee, FL 34744
Ph: (407)847-3174
Fax: (407)870-8607
Co. E-mail: info@kissimmeechamber.com
URL: http://kissimmeechamber.com
Contact: Mike Horner, President
Description: Provides valuable member benefits, expands economic base, supports quality education, promotes tourism, and encourages good government. **Publications:** *The Chamber Roadmap* (Monthly); *The Journal of Osceola County Business* (Bimonthly); *The Journal of Osceola County Business* (Bimonthly). **Educational Activities:** Business After Hours (Monthly); Back to School, Back to Business Expo (Annual). **Awards:** Ambassador of the Month (Monthly); Ambassador of the Year (Annual); Business of the Year (Annual); Downtown Beautification Award (Monthly); Hall of Fame (Annual); Residential Beautification Award (Monthly); Small Business of the Year (Annual). **Telecommunication Services:** mhorner@kissimmeechamber.com.

50184 ■ *La Setima*
1800 E 9th Ave.
Tampa, FL 33605-9998
Ph: (813)248-3712
Fax: (813)242-0398
Co. E-mail: info@ybor.org
URL: http://www.ybor.org
Contact: Andrea Gonzmart, Chairperson
Released: Monthly

50185 ■ Lady Lake Area Chamber of Commerce
PO Box 1430
Lady Lake, FL 32158-1430
Ph: (352)753-6029

Fax: (352)753-8029
URL: http://www.ladylakechamber.com
Contact: Peggy Hayes, Executive Director
Description: Promotes business and community development in Lady Lake, FL. **Publications:** *The Heritage Express.*

50186 ■ Lafayette County Chamber of Commerce
PO Box 364
Mayo, FL 32066
Ph: (386)294-2705
Co. E-mail: lafayettecnty@aol.com
URL: http://www.lafayettecountychamber.com
Contact: Jim Hollis, President
Description: Promotes business and community development in the Mayo, FL area. **Founded:** 1980.

50187 ■ Lake Alfred Chamber of Commerce (LACC)
115 E Pomelo St.
Lake Alfred, FL 33850
Ph: (863)875-7800
Co. E-mail: lachamber@lake-alfred.com
URL: http://www.lake-alfred.com
Contact: Judy Gay, President
Description: Promotes business and community development in Lake Alfred, FL.

50188 ■ Lake City - Columbia County Chamber of Commerce
162 S Marion Ave.
Lake City, FL 32025-4354
Ph: (386)752-3690
Fax: (386)755-7744
Co. E-mail: dennille@lakecitychamber.com
URL: http://www.lakecitychamber.com
Contact: Denille Decker, Executive Director
Description: Promotes business and community development in the Lake City/Columbia County area. **Founded:** 1921. **Publications:** *Crossroads* (Monthly).

50189 ■ Lake Placid Chamber of Commerce (LPCC)
18 N Oak St.
Lake Placid, FL 33852
Ph: (863)465-4331
Fax: (863)465-2588
Co. E-mail: chamber@lpfla.com
URL: http://www.lpfla.com
Contact: Eileen M. May, Executive Director
Description: Promotes business and community development in the Lake Placid, FL area. **Scope:** literacy and genealogy collection. **Founded:** 1958. **Subscriptions:** 35000 articles books clippings papers video recordings. **Publications:** *Chamber News* (Monthly); *Lake Placid Map.* **Educational Activities:** Lake Placid Chamber of Commerce Luncheon (Monthly).

50190 ■ *Lake Placid Map*
18 N Oak St.
Lake Placid, FL 33852
Ph: (863)465-4331
Fax: (863)465-2588
Co. E-mail: chamber@lpfla.com
URL: http://www.lpfla.com
Contact: Eileen M. May, Executive Director

50191 ■ Lake Wales Area Chamber of Commerce (LWACC)
340 W Central Ave.
Lake Wales, FL 33859-0191
Ph: (863)676-3445
Fax: (863)676-3446
Co. E-mail: info@lakewaleschamber.com
URL: http://www.lakewaleschamber.com
Contact: Mike Morrow, President
Description: Promotes business and community development in Lake Wales, FL. **Founded:** 1911. **Publications:** *Progressions* (Monthly); *Membership Directory/Buyers Guide* (Annual); *Lake Wales Area Chamber of Commerce--Membership Directory/Buyers Guide* (Annual); *Membership Directory/Buyers Guide* (Annual); *Membership Directory/Buyers Guide* (Annual).

50192 ■ Lakeland Area Chamber of Commerce
PO Box 3607
Lakeland, FL 33802-3607
Ph: (863)688-8551
Fax: (863)683-7454
Co. E-mail: info@lakelandchamber.com
URL: http://lakelandchamber.com
Contact: Kathleen L. Munson, President
Description: Promotes business and community development in the Lakeland, FL area. **Founded:** 1921. **Publications:** *Forum for Business* (Monthly). **Awards:** Scott Linder Small Business of the Year Award (Annual).

50193 ■ Lauderdale By The Sea Chamber of Commerce (LSCC)
4201 Ocean Dr.
Lauderdale by the Sea, FL 33308
Ph: (954)776-1000
Fax: (954)769-1560
Co. E-mail: info@lbts.com
URL: http://www.lbts.com
Contact: Paul Novak, Treasurer
Description: Promotes business and community development in Lauderdale-by-the-Sea, FL. **Founded:** 1955. **Publications:** *Visitors Guide* (Annual).

50194 ■ Leesburg Area Chamber of Commerce (LACC)
103 S 6th St.
Leesburg, FL 34748
Ph: (352)787-2131
Fax: (352)787-3985
Co. E-mail: info@leesburgchamber.com
URL: http://www.leesburgchamber.com
Contact: Jan Zacharchuk, Executive Director
Description: Promotes business and community development in the Leesburg, FL area. Maintains committees; sponsors parades; conducts fishing tournaments. **Founded:** 1937. **Publications:** *Community and Commerce* (Monthly).

50195 ■ *The Legend*
106000 Overseas Hwy.
Key Largo, FL 33037
Ph: (305)451-4747
Free: 800-822-1088
Fax: (305)451-4726
Co. E-mail: info@keylargochamber.org
URL: http://www.keylargochamber.org
Contact: Jackie Harder, President
Released: Monthly

50196 ■ *Legendary Key Largo: A Guide to Island Living*
106000 Overseas Hwy.
Key Largo, FL 33037
Ph: (305)451-4747
Free: 800-822-1088
Fax: (305)451-4726
Co. E-mail: info@keylargochamber.org
URL: http://www.keylargochamber.org
Contact: Jackie Harder, President

50197 ■ Lehigh Acres Chamber of Commerce (LACC)
PO Box 757
Lehigh Acres, FL 33970-0757
Ph: (239)369-3322
Fax: (239)368-0500
Co. E-mail: info@lehighacreschamber.org
URL: http://www.lehighacreschamber.org
Contact: Oliver B. Conover, Executive Director
Description: Promotes business and community development in Lehigh Acres, FL. **Founded:** 1970. **Publications:** *Biennial Guide* (Biennial); *Business Beat* (Monthly). **Educational Activities:** Membership Meeting (Monthly). **Awards:** High Senior Scholarships (Annual).

50198 ■ *Lifestyle Sebring*
227 U.S. Hwy. N
Sebring, FL 33870
Ph: (863)385-8448

Fax: (863)385-8810
Co. E-mail: information@sebring.org
URL: http://www.greatersebringchamberofcommerce.org
Contact: Greg Harris, President
Released: Annual

50199 ■ *Lifestyles*
PO Box 640
Fort Walton Beach, FL 32549
Ph: (850)244-8191
Fax: (850)244-1935
Co. E-mail: info@fwbchamber.org
URL: http://www.fwbchamber.org
Contact: Ted Corcoran, President

50200 ■ *Links*
1734 Kingsley Ave.
Orange Park, FL 32073
Ph: (904)264-2651
Fax: (904)264-0070
Co. E-mail: jtabor@claychamber.com
URL: http://www.claychamber.org
Contact: John Tabor, Chief Executive Officer
Released: Monthly **Price:** free.

50201 ■ *Lodging, Dining and Things To Do*
700 Main St.
Sebastian, FL 32958
Ph: (772)589-5969
Free: 888-881-7568
Fax: (772)589-5993
Co. E-mail: info@sebastianchamber.com
URL: http://www.sebastianchamber.com
Contact: Beth L. Mitchell, Executive Director
Released: Annual

50202 ■ Longboat Key Chamber of Commerce (LKCC)
5570 Gulf of Mexico Dr.
Longboat Key, FL 34228
Ph: (941)383-2466
Fax: (941)383-8217
Co. E-mail: taposporos@longboatkeychamber.com
URL: http://longboatkeychamber.com
Contact: David Miller, Chairperson
Description: Promotes business and community development in Longboat Key, FL. Provides business resource information and convention/meeting planning, relocation, and tourist assistance. Holds seminars. Sponsors fishing and golfing tournaments and annual one-day Islandfest and Business Expo. **Founded:** 1961. **Publications:** *Map of Longboat Key, Florida; Restaurant and Accommodations Directory* (Periodic); *Vacation Guide* (Periodic).

50203 ■ Lower Keys Chamber of Commerce (LKCC)
31020 Overseas Hwy.
Big Pine Key, FL 33043-0511
Ph: (305)872-2411
Free: 800-872-3722
Fax: (305)872-0752
Co. E-mail: info@lowerkeyschamber.com
URL: http://www.lowerkeyschamber.com
Contact: Carole Stevens, Secretary
Description: Promotes business and community development in the lower Florida keys. Holds monthly business social and three fundraising events per year. Conducts annual Jazz Festival, Dolphin Fishing Tournament and Underwater Music Festival. **Founded:** 1963. **Publications:** *Area Map* (Annual); *Chamber Channel* (Monthly); *Visitors Guide.*

50204 ■ Madison County Chamber of Commerce (MCCC)
248 SW Range Ave.
Madison, FL 32340
Ph: (850)973-2788
Free: 877-272-3642
Fax: (850)973-8864
Co. E-mail: chamber@madisonfl.org
URL: http://www.madisonfl.org
Contact: Terri Schefbuch, Office Manager
Description: Promotes business and community development in Madison County, FL. Conducts local charitable projects; sponsors annual Down Home Days festival. **Founded:** 1962. **Publications:** *Madi-*

son Magazine (Periodic); *C/N Chamber News* (Monthly); *Madison Magazine* (Periodic); *Reflections of Madison County* (Annual); *Reflections of Madison County* (Annual).

50205 ■ *Madison Magazine*
248 SW Range Ave.
Madison, FL 32340
Ph: (850)973-2788
Free: 877-272-3642
Fax: (850)973-8864
Co. E-mail: chamber@madisonfl.org
URL: http://www.madisonfl.org
Contact: Terri Schefbuch, Office Manager
Released: Periodic

50206 ■ Maitland Area Chamber of Commerce
110 N Maitland Ave.
Maitland, FL 32751
Ph: (407)644-0741
Fax: (407)539-2529
Co. E-mail: msimmons@maitlandchamber.com
URL: http://www.maitlandchamber.com
Contact: Maria Alvarez-Simmons, Executive Director
Description: Promotes business and community development in southern Seminole County, FL. Sponsors Annual Spring Festival during the third weekend in April, the Live and Silent Auction the third Friday in August, and Business Expo and non-profit showcase in October. **Founded:** 1958.

50207 ■ Manatee Chamber of Commerce
PO Box 321
Bradenton, FL 34206-0321
Ph: (941)748-3411
Fax: (941)745-1877
Co. E-mail: info@manateechamber.com
URL: http://www.manateechamber.com
Contact: Bob Bartz, President
Description: Promotes business and community development in the Manatee County, FL area. **Founded:** 1962.

50208 ■ *Manufacturers Guide*
PO Box 1234
Orlando, FL 32802-1234
Ph: (407)425-1234
Fax: (407)835-2500
Co. E-mail: info@orlando.org
URL: http://www.orlando.org
Contact: Jacob V. Stuart, President

50209 ■ *Map of Longboat Key, Florida*
5570 Gulf of Mexico Dr.
Longboat Key, FL 34228
Ph: (941)383-2466
Fax: (941)383-8217
Co. E-mail: taposporos@longboatkeychamber.com
URL: http://longboatkeychamber.com
Contact: David Miller, Chairperson

50210 ■ *Marco Island*
1102 N Collier Blvd.
Marco Island, FL 34145
Ph: (239)394-7549
Free: 800-788-6272
Fax: (239)394-3061
Co. E-mail: info@marcoislandchamber.org
URL: http://www.marcoislandchamber.org
Released: Annual

50211 ■ Marco Island Area Chamber of Commerce
1102 N Collier Blvd.
Marco Island, FL 34145
Ph: (239)394-7549
Free: 800-788-6272
Fax: (239)394-3061
Co. E-mail: info@marcoislandchamber.org
URL: http://www.marcoislandchamber.org
Description: Promotes business and community development in the Marco, FL area. **Founded:** 1977. **Publications:** *Marco Island* (Annual); *Marco Island Chamber of Commerce Newsletter* (Monthly); *Marco Island* (Annual).

50212 ■ *Marco Island Chamber of Commerce Newsletter*
1102 N Collier Blvd.
Marco Island, FL 34145
Ph: (239)394-7549
Free: 800-788-6272
Fax: (239)394-3061
Co. E-mail: info@marcoislandchamber.org
URL: http://www.marcoislandchamber.org
Released: Monthly

50213 ■ *Market Directory*
PO Box 1639
Tallahassee, FL 32302
Ph: (850)224-8116
Fax: (850)561-3860
Co. E-mail: info@talchamber.com
URL: http://talchamber.com
Contact: Sue Dick, President
Released: Annual

50214 ■ Melbourne-Palm Bay Area Chamber of Commerce (M-PBACC)
1005 E Strawbridge Ave.
Melbourne, FL 32901-4782
Ph: (321)724-5400
Fax: (321)725-2093
Co. E-mail: christine@melbourneregionalchamber.
   com
URL: http://www.melpb-chamber.org
Contact: Christine Michaels, President
Description: Promotes business and economic development in South Brevard County, FL. **Founded:** 1960. **Publications:** *Area Map* (Annual); *Relocation Guide*; *Visitor Guide* (Annual); *The Chamber Weekly Connection!* (Weekly); *Drug Resource Guide* (Annual). **Educational Activities:** Corporate Health Challenge (Annual).

50215 ■ *Member Connection*
10100 Pines Blvd., 4th Fl.
Pembroke Pines, FL 33026-3900
Ph: (954)432-9808
Fax: (954)432-9193
Co. E-mail: info@miramarpembrokepines.org
URL: http://www.miramarpembrokepines.org
Contact: Mr. Robert Goltz, President
Released: Bimonthly

50216 ■ *Member Report*
1601 E Hillsboro Blvd.
Deerfield Beach, FL 33441-4389
Ph: (954)427-1050
Fax: (954)427-1056
Co. E-mail: info@deerfieldchamber.com
URL: http://www.deerfieldchamber.com
Contact: Bud Clark, Chairman
Released: Monthly

50217 ■ *Members in Action*
597 Tamiami Trail S
Venice, FL 34285
Ph: (941)488-2236
Co. E-mail: vchamber@venicechamber.com
URL: http://www.venicechamber.com
Contact: John G. Ryan, President

50218 ■ *Membership Books*
180 E Main St.
Apopka, FL 32703
Ph: (407)886-1441
Fax: (407)886-1131
Co. E-mail: pauls@apopkachamber.org
URL: http://www.apopkachamber.org
Contact: Wayne H. Levesque, Chairman
Released: Annual

50219 ■ *Membership Directory and Buyer's Guide*
4185 Davie Rd.
Davie, FL 33314
Ph: (954)581-0790
Fax: (954)581-9684
Co. E-mail: dcch@davie-coopercity.org
URL: http://www.davie-coopercity.org
Contact: Alice Harrington, President
Released: Annual

50220 ■ *Membership Directory/Buyers Guide*
340 W Central Ave.
Lake Wales, FL 33859-0191
Ph: (863)676-3445
Fax: (863)676-3446
Co. E-mail: info@lakewaleschamber.com
URL: http://www.lakewaleschamber.com
Contact: Mike Morrow, President
Released: Annual

50221 ■ *Membership Directory and Buyers Guide*
212 N Ohio Ave.
Live Oak, FL 32064
Ph: (386)362-3071
Fax: (386)362-4758
URL: http://www.suwanneechamber.com
Contact: Dennis Cason, President
Released: Periodic

50222 ■ *Membership Guide and Directory*
PO Box 901544
Homestead, FL 33090
Ph: (305)247-2332
Free: 888-352-4891
Co. E-mail: info@chamberinaction.com
URL: http://www.chamberinaction.com
Contact: Ms. Mary Finlan, Executive Director
Released: Annual

50223 ■ *Membership and Marketplace Guide*
1734 Kingsley Ave.
Orange Park, FL 32073
Ph: (904)264-2651
Fax: (904)264-0070
Co. E-mail: jtabor@claychamber.com
URL: http://www.claychamber.org
Contact: John Tabor, Chief Executive Officer
Released: Semiannual

50224 ■ Miami Beach Chamber of Commerce
1920 Meridian Ave.
Miami Beach, FL 33139-1818
Ph: (305)674-1300
Fax: (305)538-4336
Co. E-mail: bruce@miamibeachchamber.com
URL: http://www.miamibeachchamber.com
Contact: Jerry Libbin, President
Description: Promotes business and community development in Miami Beach, FL. **Founded:** 1921. **Publications:** *E-Currents* (Weekly); *Miami Beach Visitors Guide* (Annual). **Educational Activities:** Chamber Networkers (Semimonthly); Miami Beach Chamber of Commerce Luncheon. **Awards:** Citizen of the Year (Annual); Jan Pfeiffer Distinguished Service Award (Annual); Leonard A. 'Doc' Baker Lifetime Achievement Award (Annual). **Telecommunication Services:** info@miamibeachchamber.com.

50225 ■ *Miami Beach Visitors Guide*
1920 Meridian Ave.
Miami Beach, FL 33139-1818
Ph: (305)674-1300
Fax: (305)538-4336
Co. E-mail: bruce@miamibeachchamber.com
URL: http://www.miamibeachchamber.com
Contact: Jerry Libbin, President
Released: Annual

50226 ■ Miami-Dade County Chamber of Commerce
1951 NW 7th Ave., Ste. 13-139
Miami, FL 33136
Ph: (305)751-8648
Fax: (305)758-3839
Co. E-mail: bdiggs@m-dcc.org
URL: http://www.m-dcc.org
Contact: Bill Diggs, President
Description: Promotes business and economic interest of the black community throughout Dade County. **Founded:** 1974. **Awards:** Board Member of the Year (Annual); Corporate Business of the Year (Annual); Small Business of the Year (Annual); Top 5 Small Business (Annual). **Telecommunication Services:** bjames@m-dcc.org; mcrance@m-dcc.org; jgeter@m-dcc.org.

50227 ■ *Mini-Guide Brochure*
4484 Legendary Dr., Ste. A
Destin, FL 32541
Ph: (850)837-6241
Fax: (850)654-5612
Co. E-mail: mail@destinchamber.com
URL: http://www.destinchamber.com
Contact: Shane Moody, President

50228 ■ Miramar-Pembroke Pines Regional Chamber of Commerce
10100 Pines Blvd., 4th Fl.
Pembroke Pines, FL 33026-3900
Ph: (954)432-9808
Fax: (954)432-9193
Co. E-mail: info@miramarpembrokepines.org
URL: http://www.miramarpembrokepines.org
Contact: Mr. Robert Goltz, President
Description: Works to provide a variety of venues to assist the business owners of the region to become better businesses by becoming better business leaders. **Founded:** 1969. **Publications:** *Member Connection* (Bimonthly).

50229 ■ Monticello-Jefferson County Chamber of Commerce
420 W Washington St.
Monticello, FL 32344
Ph: (850)997-5552
Fax: (850)997-1020
Co. E-mail: info@monticellojeffersonfl.com
URL: http://www.monticellojeffersonfl.com/home.cfm
Contact: Mary Frances Drawdy, Director
Description: Promotes business and community development in Jefferson County, FL.

50230 ■ Mount Dora Area Chamber of Commerce
PO Box 196
Mount Dora, FL 32756-0196
Ph: (352)383-2165
Fax: (352)383-1668
Co. E-mail: chamber@mountdora.com
URL: http://www.mountdora.com
Contact: Judi Phillips Jones, Director
Description: Promotes business and community development in the Mount Dora, FL area. Sponsors community activities. **Founded:** 1923. **Publications:** *Community Guide and Directory* (Monthly).

50231 ■ *Mulberry Magic*
PO Box 254
Mulberry, FL 33860-0254
Ph: (863)425-4414
Fax: (863)425-3837
URL: http://www.mulberrychamber.org
Contact: Sharron Jones, Executive Director
Released: Monthly

50232 ■ *Naples on the Gulf*
2390 Tamiami Trail N, Ste. 210
Naples, FL 34103
Ph: (239)262-6376
Fax: (239)262-8374
Co. E-mail: info@napleschamber.org
URL: http://www.napleschamber.org
Contact: Mike Reagen, President
Released: Annual

50233 ■ Navarre Beach Area Chamber of Commerce
8543 Navarre Pkwy.
Navarre, FL 32566
Ph: (850)939-3267
Free: 800-480-7263
Fax: (850)939-0085
Co. E-mail: info@navarrechamber.com
URL: http://www.navarrechamber.com
Contact: Kelley Fuller, President
Description: Promotes business and community development in the Navarre, FL area. Encourages industrial development and tourism. Sponsors local festival. **Founded:** 1975. **Publications:** *Guide Book* (Annual).

50234 ■ *The Network*
20 Airport Rd.
Palm Coast, FL 32164
Ph: (386)437-0106

Free: 800-881-1022
Fax: (386)437-5700
Co. E-mail: info@flaglerchamber.org
URL: http://www.flaglerchamber.org
Contact: Rebecca DeLorenzo, President
Released: Monthly

50235 ■ New Member Profile
1601 Biscayne Blvd.
Ballroom Level
Miami, FL 33132-1260
Ph: (305)350-7700
Free: 888-660-5955
Fax: (305)374-6902
Co. E-mail: reception@miamichamber.com
URL: http://www.greatermiami.com
Contact: Barry E. Johnson, President
Released: Semiannual **Price:** free for members; $25,
for nonmembers.

**50236 ■ Newberry Area Chamber of
Commerce**
PO Box 495
Newberry, FL 32669
Ph: (352)472-6611
Co. E-mail: joyglanzer@cox.net
URL: http://www.newberrychamber.com
Contact: Joy Glanzer, President
Description: Promotes business and community
development in the Newberry, FL area.

50237 ■ News and Views
Park Sta.
5851 Park Blvd.
Pinellas Park, FL 33781
Ph: (727)544-4777
Fax: (727)209-0837
Co. E-mail: info@pinellasparkchamber.com
URL: http://www.pinellasparkchamber.com
Contact: Paul P. Ziegler, President
Released: Monthly **Price:** free for members; $25,
/year for nonmembers.

50238 ■ News and Views
9385 N 56th St.
Temple Terrace, FL 33617
Ph: (813)989-7004
Fax: (813)989-7005
Co. E-mail: hharper@templeterracechamber.com
URL: http://www.templeterracechamber.com
Contact: Barbara Sparks-McGlinchy, Executive
 Director
Released: Monthly

50239 ■ NewsBREAK
1601 Biscayne Blvd.
Ballroom Level
Miami, FL 33132-1260
Ph: (305)350-7700
Free: 888-660-5955
Fax: (305)374-6902
Co. E-mail: reception@miamichamber.com
URL: http://www.greatermiami.com
Contact: Barry E. Johnson, President
Released: Weekly

50240 ■ Newsline
12184 W Colonial Dr.
Winter Garden, FL 34787
Ph: (407)656-1304
Fax: (407)656-0221
Co. E-mail: info@wochamber.com
URL: http://www.wochamber.com
Contact: Stina D'Uva, President
Released: Monthly

**50241 ■ Niceville-Valparaiso Bay Area
Chamber of Commerce**
1055 E John Sims Pkwy.
Niceville, FL 32578
Ph: (850)678-2323

Fax: (850)678-2602
Co. E-mail: info@nicevillechamber.com
URL: http://www.nicevillechamber.com
Contact: Tricia Brunson, President
Description: Promotes business and community
development in Niceville and Valparaiso, FL area.
Sponsors business seminars and leadership school.
Founded: 1956. **Telecommunication Services:** tri-
ciabrunson@nicevillechamber.com.

**50242 ■ North Dade Regional Chamber of
Commerce**
1300 NW 167th St., Ste. 1
Miami, FL 33169
Ph: (305)690-9123
Fax: (305)690-9124
Co. E-mail: thechamber@thechamber.cc
URL: http://www.thechamber.cc
Description: Promotes business and community
development in North Dade area.

**50243 ■ North Florida Regional Chamber of
Commerce**
100 E Call St.
Starke, FL 32091
Ph: (904)964-5278
Fax: (904)964-2863
URL: http://www.northfloridachamber.com
Contact: Jimmie Scott, Chairman
Description: Promotes business and community
development in Bradford County, FL. Sponsors Arts
Festival, Christmas Parade, and a Fourth of July
celebration. Operates small business resource library.
Scope: business and industry. **Founded:** 1945. **Sub-
scriptions:** 50 books periodicals. **Publications:**
Chamber Directory (Annual); Tri County Connection
(Quarterly); Taking Care of Business (Weekly).

**50244 ■ North Fort Myers Chamber of
Commerce (NFMCC)**
2787 N Tamiami Trail
North Fort Myers, FL 33903-2213
Ph: (239)997-9111
Co. E-mail: exec@nfmchamber.org
URL: http://nfmchamber.org
Contact: Phil Goss, President
Description: Promotes business and community
development in North Ft. Myers, FL. Sponsors
Cracker Festival. **Founded:** 1958. **Publications:** Bul-
letin (Periodic); Focus (Monthly).

**50245 ■ North Miami Beach Chamber of
Commerce**
1870 NE 171 St.
North Miami Beach, FL 33162
Ph: (305)944-8500
Fax: (305)944-8191
Co. E-mail: chamber@nmbchamber.com
URL: http://www.nmbchamber.com
Description: Promotes business and community
development in North Miami Beach, FL. **Founded:**
1949.

**50246 ■ North Palm Beach County Chamber
of Commerce**
800 N U.S. Hwy. 1
Jupiter, FL 33477
Ph: (561)746-7111
Fax: (561)745-7519
Co. E-mail: info@npbchamber.com
URL: http://www.npbchamber.com/splash.php
Contact: Beth Kigel, President
Description: Promotes business and community
development in northern Palm Beach County. **Publi-
cations:** E-Communicator (Monthly).

**50247 ■ North Port Area Chamber of
Commerce**
15141 Tamiami Trail
North Port, FL 34287-2711
Ph: (941)564-3040
Fax: (941)423-5042
Co. E-mail: info@northportareachamber.com
URL: http://www.northportareachamber.com
Contact: Kim Quigley, President
Description: Promotes business and community
development in North Port, FL.

50248 ■ North Tampa Chamber of Commerce
PO Box 82043
Tampa, FL 33682
Ph: (813)961-2420
Fax: (813)961-2903
Co. E-mail: info@northtampachamber.com
URL: http://www.northtampachamber.com
Contact: Ginger Rockey-Johnson, President
Description: Promotes business interests in North
Tampa, FL. **Founded:** 1947. **Awards:** The Outstand-
ing Chamber Member of the Year Award (Annual);
The Phyllis Ellis Memorial Giver Award (Annual).

**50249 ■ Ocala-Marion County Chamber of
Commerce**
310 SE 3rd St.
Ocala, FL 34471
Ph: (352)629-8051
Fax: (352)629-7651
Co. E-mail: ourguest@ocalacc.com
URL: http://www.ocalacc.com
Contact: Jaye Baillie, President
Description: Promotes business and community
development in Marion County, FL. Sponsors Christ-
mas parade and Horse and Agriculture Festival.
Founded: 1887. **Publications:** Sunlines (Monthly);
Who's Who in Business (Annual); Who's Who in Busi-
ness (Annual). **Telecommunication Services:**
jaye@ocalacc.com.

50250 ■ Official Buyer's Guide
63 S Centre Trl.
Santa Rosa Beach, FL 32459
Ph: (850)892-3191
Fax: (850)267-0603
Co. E-mail: wendy@waltonareachamber.com
URL: http://www.waltonareachamber.com
Contact: Kitty Whitney, President
Released: Annual

50251 ■ Official Guide
126 E Orange Ave.
Daytona Beach, FL 32115
Ph: (386)255-0981
Fax: (386)258-5104
Co. E-mail: info@daytonachamber.com
URL: http://www.daytonachamber.com
Contact: Larry McKinney, President
Released: Annual

50252 ■ Official Guide to Palm Beach
400 Royal Palm Way, Ste. 106
Palm Beach, FL 33480
Ph: (561)655-3282
Co. E-mail: info@palmbeachchamber.com
URL: http://www.palmbeachchamber.com
Contact: Laurel Baker, Executive Director
Price: $10.

50253 ■ Official Guide to Wellington
12230 Forest Hill Blvd., Ste. 183
Wellington, FL 33414
Ph: (561)792-6525
Fax: (561)792-6200
Co. E-mail: info@wellingtonchamber.com
URL: http://wellingtonchamber.com
Contact: Alexander L. Domb, President

50254 ■ Official SE Volusia County Map
310 Julia St.
New Smyrna Beach, FL 32168-7024
Ph: (386)428-2449
Fax: (386)423-3512
Co. E-mail: sevinfo@sevchamber.com
URL: http://www.sevchamber.com
Contact: Kenneth Bohannon, President
Released: Annual

50255 ■ Okeechobee Chamber of Commerce
55 S Parrott Ave.
Okeechobee, FL 34972
Ph: (863)763-6464
Fax: (863)763-3467
Co. E-mail: commerce@okeechobeechamberofcom-
 merce.com
URL: http://okeechobeechamberofcommerce.com
Contact: Matthew Buxton, President
Description: Promotes business and community
development in Okeechobee County, FL.

50256 ■ Oldsmar/Upper Tampa Bay Regional Chamber of Commerce
101 State St. W
Oldsmar, FL 34677
Ph: (813)855-4233
Fax: (813)854-1237
Co. E-mail: jcustin@utbchamber.com
URL: http://www.oldsmarchamber.com
Contact: Jerry Custin, President
Description: Promotes business and community development in the Oldsmar, FL area. Holds business after hours gatherings and coffee socials, intergovernmental relations and city public relations. **Founded:** 1960. **Publications:** *Horizon Lines* (Monthly); *Visitors Guide* (Annual). **Educational Activities:** Oldsmar Days (Annual).

50257 ■ Orlando Regional Chamber of Commerce
PO Box 1234
Orlando, FL 32802-1234
Ph: (407)425-1234
Fax: (407)835-2500
Co. E-mail: info@orlando.org
URL: http://www.orlando.org
Contact: Jacob V. Stuart, President
Description: Promotes business and community development in Orange, Osceola, and Seminole, FL. Provides governmental activities, small business and international trade programs, and Goals 2000. **Founded:** 1913. **Publications:** *Every Monday* (Weekly); *First Monday* (Monthly); *Manufacturers Guide*.

50258 ■ Ormond Beach Chamber of Commerce
165 W Granada Blvd.
Ormond Beach, FL 32174
Ph: (386)677-3454
Fax: (386)677-4363
Co. E-mail: tony@ormondchamber.com
Contact: Tony Capozzi, Executive Director
Description: Promotes business and community development in Ormond Beach, FL. Sponsors art show and jazz festival. **Awards:** Beautification Awards (Quarterly).

50259 ■ *Osceola Business Journal*
1200 New York Ave.
St. Cloud, FL 34769-3742
Ph: (407)892-3671
Fax: (407)892-5289
Co. E-mail: info@stcloudflchamber.com
URL: http://stcloudflchamber.com/Content/index.aspx
Contact: David C. Lane, President
Released: Monthly

50260 ■ Oviedo-Winter Springs Regional Chamber of Commerce
PO Box 621236
Oviedo, FL 32762
Ph: (407)365-6500
Fax: (407)650-2712
Co. E-mail: cory@oviedowintersprings.org
URL: http://www.oviedowintersprings.org
Contact: Corydon G. Skeates, President
Description: Promotes business and community development in the Oviedo, FL area. **Scope:** business. **Founded:** 1982. **Subscriptions:** 25 periodicals. **Awards:** Business of the Year (Annual).

50261 ■ Pahokee Chamber of Commerce
115 E Main St.
Pahokee, FL 33476
Ph: (561)924-5579
Fax: (561)924-8116
Co. E-mail: pahokeechamber@att.net
URL: http://www.pahokee.com
Contact: Hal Stankard, President
Description: Promotes business and community development in Pahokee, FL. **Founded:** 1950.

50262 ■ Palm Beach Chamber of Commerce
400 Royal Palm Way, Ste. 106
Palm Beach, FL 33480
Ph: (561)655-3282
Co. E-mail: info@palmbeachchamber.com
URL: http://www.palmbeachchamber.com
Contact: Laurel Baker, Executive Director
Description: Provides leadership, education, and advocacy for the Town of Palm Beach to continue to thrive. **Founded:** 1929. **Publications:** *Official Guide to Palm Beach*. **Educational Activities:** Palm Beach Chamber of Commerce Breakfast (Monthly).

50263 ■ Palm City Chamber of Commerce
880 SW Martin Downs Blvd.
Palm City, FL 34990
Ph: (772)286-8121
Fax: (772)286-3331
Co. E-mail: info@palmcitychamber.com
URL: http://www.palmcitychamber.com
Contact: Carolyn Davi, Executive Director
Description: Promotes business and community development in Palm City, FL. Participates in community and environmental projects. Holds monthly social networking meeting. **Founded:** 1927. **Publications:** *The Bridge* (Monthly); *Business* (Monthly). **Educational Activities:** Palm City Chamber of Commerce Breakfast (Monthly).

50264 ■ Palms West Chamber of Commerce (PWCC)
13901 Southern Blvd.
Loxahatchee, FL 33470-1062
Ph: (561)790-6200
Free: 800-790-2364
Co. E-mail: jaene@cpbchamber.com
URL: http://www.palmswest.com
Contact: Jaene Miranda, Chief Executive Officer
Description: Promotes business and community development in the Acreage, Loxahatchee, Royal Palm Beach, Greenacres and Wellington areas. **Founded:** 1983. **Awards:** Member of the Year (Annual); Small Business of the Year (Annual).

50265 ■ Pensacola Area Chamber of Commerce
117 W Garden St.
Pensacola, FL 32502
Ph: (850)438-4081
Fax: (850)438-6369
Co. E-mail: jhizer@pensacolachamber.com
URL: http://www.pensacolachamber.com
Contact: James Hizer, President
Description: Promotes business and community development in the Pensacola, FL area. **Founded:** 1889.

50266 ■ *Perspective*
2702 Tamiami Trail
Port Charlotte, FL 33952
Ph: (941)627-2222
Fax: (941)627-9730
Co. E-mail: askus@charlottecountychamber.org
URL: http://www.charlottecountychamber.org
Contact: Ms. Julie Mathis, Executive Director
Released: Monthly

50267 ■ Pinellas Park/Mid-County Chamber of Commerce
Park Sta.
5851 Park Blvd.
Pinellas Park, FL 33781
Ph: (727)544-4777
Fax: (727)209-0837
Co. E-mail: info@pinellasparkchamber.com
URL: http://www.pinellasparkchamber.com
Contact: Paul P. Ziegler, President
Description: Promotes business and economic development in the Pinellas Park, FL area. Conducts annual Legislative Day and Country in the Park. Maintains high-tech work center. **Founded:** 1915. **Publications:** *News and Views* (Monthly). **Educational Activities:** Corporate Golf Tournament (Annual).

50268 ■ *The Pink Sheet*
1870 NE 171st St.
North Miami Beach, FL 33162
Ph: (305)944-8500
Fax: (305)944-8191
Co. E-mail: chamber@nmbchamber.com
URL: http://www.nmbchamber.com
Contact: Yona S. Lunger, President
Released: Monthly

50269 ■ *Plantation Annual*
7401 NW 4th St.
Plantation, FL 33317
Ph: (954)587-1410
Fax: (954)587-1886
Co. E-mail: info@plantationchamber.org
URL: http://www.plantationchamber.org
Contact: Siobhan Edwards, President
Released: Annual **Price:** free.

50270 ■ *The Point*
1945 Fruitville Rd.
Sarasota, FL 34236
Ph: (941)955-8187
Fax: (941)366-5621
Co. E-mail: squeior@sarasotachamber.com
URL: http://www.sarasotachamber.com
Contact: Steve Queior, President
Released: Quarterly

50271 ■ Port Orange/South Daytona Chamber of Commerce
3431 Ridgewood Ave.
Port Orange, FL 32129
Ph: (386)761-1601
Fax: (386)788-9165
Co. E-mail: info@pschamber.com
URL: http://www.pschamber.com
Contact: Debbie Connors, Executive Director
Description: Promotes business and community development in the Port Orange, FL area. **Founded:** 1975. **Publications:** *Community Directory and Buyers' Guide* (Annual); *The Trade Winds* (Monthly).

50272 ■ *Progress*
4484 Legendary Dr., Ste. A
Destin, FL 32541
Ph: (850)837-6241
Fax: (850)654-5612
Co. E-mail: mail@destinchamber.com
URL: http://www.destinchamber.com
Contact: Shane Moody, President
Released: Monthly

50273 ■ *Progressions*
340 W Central Ave.
Lake Wales, FL 33859-0191
Ph: (863)676-3445
Fax: (863)676-3446
Co. E-mail: info@lakewaleschamber.com
URL: http://www.lakewaleschamber.com
Contact: Mike Morrow, President
Released: Monthly

50274 ■ *The Pulse*
601 S Indiana Ave.
Englewood, FL 34223-3788
Ph: (941)474-5511
Free: 800-603-7198
Fax: (941)475-9257
Co. E-mail: info@englewoodchamber.com
URL: http://www.englewoodchamber.com
Contact: Mary Smith, Executive Director
Released: Monthly

50275 ■ Putnam County Chamber of Commerce
c/o Dana Jones, Pres.
1100 Reid St.
Palatka, FL 32178-0550
Ph: (386)328-1503
Fax: (386)328-7076
Co. E-mail: dana@pcccfl.org
URL: http://www.putnamcountychamber.org
Contact: Dana Jones, President
Description: Promotes business and community development in Putnam County, FL. **Scope:** economic development, demographics. **Founded:** 1926. **Subscriptions:** 100 books periodicals. **Publications:** *Business Directory* (Annual); *Return on Investment* (Monthly). **Awards:** Bob Hudson Small Business Person of the Year (Annual).

50276 ■ *Reflections of Madison County*
248 SW Range Ave.
Madison, FL 32340
Ph: (850)973-2788
Free: 877-272-3642
Fax: (850)973-8864
Co. E-mail: chamber@madisonfl.org
URL: http://www.madisonfl.org
Contact: Terri Schefbuch, Office Manager
Released: Annual

50277 ■ *Relax*
20 Airport Rd.
Palm Coast, FL 32164
Ph: (386)437-0106
Free: 800-881-1022
Fax: (386)437-5700
Co. E-mail: info@flaglerchamber.org
URL: http://www.flaglerchamber.org
Contact: Rebecca DeLorenzo, President

50278 ■ *Relo Directory*
2860 S Alafaya Trail, Ste. 130
Orlando, FL 32828
Ph: (407)277-5951
Fax: (407)381-1720
Co. E-mail: info@eocc.org
URL: http://www.eocc.org
Contact: Annie Winterbottom, President
Released: Annual **Price:** free.

50279 ■ *Relocation Guide*
401 Cleveland St.
Clearwater, FL 33755
Ph: (727)461-0011
Fax: (727)449-2889
Co. E-mail: bclifford@clearwaterflorida.org
URL: http://www.clearwaterflorida.org
Contact: Bob Clifford, President
Released: Annual

50280 ■ *Relocation Guide*
1005 E Strawbridge Ave.
Melbourne, FL 32901-4782
Ph: (321)724-5400
Fax: (321)725-2093
Co. E-mail: christine@melbourneregionalchamber.
com
URL: http://www.melpb-chamber.org
Contact: Christine Michaels, President

50281 ■ *Relocation Guide and Membership Directory*
PO Box 420
Tampa, FL 33601
Ph: (813)228-7777
Free: 800-298-2672
Fax: (813)223-7899
Co. E-mail: info@tampachamber.com
Contact: Robert J. Rohrlack, Jr., President

50282 ■ *The Reporter*
1800 N Dixie Hwy.
Boca Raton, FL 33432
Ph: (561)395-4433
Fax: (561)392-3780
Co. E-mail: info@bocaratonchamber.com
URL: http://www.bocaratonchamber.com
Contact: Troy M. Mclellan, President
Released: Monthly

50283 ■ *Restaurant and Accommodations Directory*
5570 Gulf of Mexico Dr.
Longboat Key, FL 34228
Ph: (941)383-2466
Fax: (941)383-8217
Co. E-mail: taposporos@longboatkeychamber.com
URL: http://longboatkeychamber.com
Contact: David Miller, Chairperson
Released: Periodic

50284 ■ *Return on Investment*
c/o Dana Jones, Pres.
1100 Reid St.
Palatka, FL 32178-0550
Ph: (386)328-1503

Fax: (386)328-7076
Co. E-mail: dana@pcccfl.org
URL: http://www.putnamcountychamber.org
Contact: Dana Jones, President
Released: Monthly **Price:** free for members.

50285 ■ Ruskin Chamber of Commerce
315 S Tamiami Trail
Ruskin, FL 33570-4660
Ph: (813)645-3808
Fax: (813)645-2099
Co. E-mail: info@ruskinchamber.org
URL: http://www.ruskinchamber.org
Contact: Pat Warbritton, President
E-mail: pat.warbritton@verizon.net
Description: Promotes business and community development in southern Hillsborough County, FL. Sponsors annual Seafood Fest and Ruskin Tomato Festival. Maintains Economic-Industrial Committee. Holds monthly coffee socials, quarterly after-hours mixers, and holiday socials such as Valentine's Day, St. Patrick's Day and Christmas. **Founded:** 1928. **Publications:** *The Baysider* (Monthly); *Ruskin Chamber of Commerce--Area Guide: Ruskin By the Bay Membership Directory* (Annual). **Awards:** Juried Arts and Crafts (Annual).

50286 ■ Safety Harbor Chamber of Commerce
200 Main St.
Safety Harbor, FL 34695
Ph: (727)726-2890
Fax: (727)726-2733
Co. E-mail: info@safetyharborchamber.com
URL: http://www.safetyharborchamber.com
Contact: Marie Padavich, Chairperson
Description: Promotes business and community development in Safety Harbor, FL. Sponsors Safety Harbor Sprints, Arbor Day Volleyball Tournament, and Safety Harbor Fall Street Festival. Donates to local and national charities. **Founded:** 1930. **Publications:** *Harbor News* (Monthly). **Awards:** Business of the Year (Annual).

50287 ■ St. Cloud Greater Osceola County Chamber of Commerce
1200 New York Ave.
St. Cloud, FL 34769-3742
Ph: (407)892-3671
Fax: (407)892-5289
Co. E-mail: info@stcloudflchamber.com
URL: http://stcloudflchamber.com/Content/index.aspx
Contact: David C. Lane, President
Description: Promotes business and community development in St. Cloud, FL. Economic development, tourism, governmental affairs and education in Osceola County. **Publications:** *Osceola Business Journal* (Monthly); *St. Cloud Visitors Guide and Area Map.*

50288 ■ *St. Cloud Visitors Guide and Area Map*
1200 New York Ave.
St. Cloud, FL 34769-3742
Ph: (407)892-3671
Fax: (407)892-5289
Co. E-mail: info@stcloudflchamber.com
URL: http://stcloudflchamber.com/Content/index.aspx
Contact: David C. Lane, President

50289 ■ St. Lucie County Chamber of Commerce
1850 SW Fountainview Blvd., Ste. 201
Port St. Lucie, FL 34986
Ph: (772)340-1333
Fax: (772)785-7021
Co. E-mail: info@stluciechamber.org
URL: http://www.stluciechamber.org
Contact: Linda W. Cox, Executive Director
Description: Promotes business and community development in Ft. Pierce and St. Lucie County, FL. **Founded:** 1906. **Publications:** *Chamber Currents* (Monthly).

50290 ■ St. Petersburg Area Chamber of Commerce
The Chamber Bldg.
100 Second Ave. N, Ste. 150
St. Petersburg, FL 33701-3351

Ph: (727)821-4069
Fax: (727)895-6326
Co. E-mail: csteinocher@stpete.com
URL: http://www.stpete.com
Contact: Chris Steinocher, President
Description: Promotes business and community development in the St. Petersburg, FL area.

50291 ■ Sanibel-Captiva Islands Chamber of Commerce
1159 Causeway Rd.
Sanibel, FL 33957
Ph: (239)472-1080
Fax: (239)472-1070
Co. E-mail: island@sanibel-captiva.org
URL: http://www.sanibel-captiva.org
Contact: Mr. Ric Base, President
Description: Promotes business and community development in Sanibel, FL and the Captiva Islands. **Founded:** 1954. **Publications:** *Island Guide.* **Awards:** Ken Meeker Annual Travel Media Awards (Annual).

50292 ■ Santa Rosa County Chamber of Commerce
5247 Stewart St.
Milton, FL 32570-4737
Ph: (850)623-2339
Fax: (850)623-4413
Co. E-mail: director@srcchamber.com
URL: http://www.srcchamber.com
Contact: Ron Fields, President
Description: Promotes business and community development in Santa Rosa County, FL. Provides advice to prospective business owners. **Publications:** *Santa Rosan* (Monthly). **Awards:** Business of the Year (Annual); Community Achievement Award (Annual); Community Leader of the Year (Annual); Emerging Leader of the Year (Annual); Hall of Fame Award (Annual); Industry of the Year (Annual); Man of the Year (Annual); President's Award (Annual); Volunteer of the Year (Annual); Woman of the Year (Annual).

50293 ■ *Santa Rosan*
5247 Stewart St.
Milton, FL 32570-4737
Ph: (850)623-2339
Fax: (850)623-4413
Co. E-mail: director@srcchamber.com
URL: http://www.srcchamber.com
Contact: Ron Fields, President
Released: Monthly

50294 ■ Sebastian River Area Chamber of Commerce
700 Main St.
Sebastian, FL 32958
Ph: (772)589-5969
Free: 888-881-7568
Fax: (772)589-5993
Co. E-mail: info@sebastianchamber.com
URL: http://www.sebastianchamber.com
Contact: Beth L. Mitchell, Executive Director
Description: Promotes business and community development in the Sebastian, FL area. **Founded:** 1958. **Publications:** *Lodging, Dining and Things To Do* (Annual). **Educational Activities:** Tourism Committee Meeting (Monthly). **Awards:** Ambassador of the Year (Annual); Chamber Member of the Year (Annual); Director of the Year (Annual); Volunteer of the Year (Annual).

50295 ■ Seminole County Regional Chamber of Commerce
1055 AAA Dr., Ste. 153
Heathrow, FL 32746
Ph: (407)333-4748
Fax: (407)708-4615
Co. E-mail: info@seminolebusiness.org
URL: http://www.seminolebusiness.org
Contact: Frank S. Hale, President
Description: Promotes business and economic growth in the Seminole County, FL area. **Founded:** 1974.

50296 ■ Siesta Key Chamber of Commerce (SKCC)
5118 Ocean Blvd.
Siesta Key, FL 34242
Ph: (941)349-3800
Free: 866-831-7778
Co. E-mail: info@siestakeychamber.com
URL: http://www.siestakeychamber.com
Contact: Mark Smith, Chairman
Description: Promotes business and community development in, and provides visitor information in Siesta Key, FL. Conducts Christmas parade, Sand Fest, July 4th Fireworks. **Founded:** 1958. **Publications:** *Accommodations Guide to Siesta Key* (Annual); *Beach Business* (Monthly); *Key Newsletter* (Monthly); *Visitor's Guide.* **Educational Activities:** Siesta Key Chamber 4th of July Fireworks (Annual).

50297 ■ South Lake Chamber of Commerce (SLCC)
691 W Montrose St.
Clermont, FL 34711
Ph: (352)394-4191
Fax: (352)394-5799
Co. E-mail: rays@southlakechamber-fl.com
URL: http://www.southlakechamber-fl.com
Contact: Ray San Fratello, President
Description: Promotes business and community development in Clermont, FL. Sponsors Labor Day Festival, Light Up Clermont Christmas Festival, and Business Expo. **Founded:** 1947. **Publications:** *Business Beat* (Monthly); *Clermont Guide Book* (Annual). **Awards:** Citizen of the Year (Annual).

50298 ■ South Tampa Chamber of Commerce (STCOC)
2113 S Dale Mabry Hwy.
Tampa, FL 33629
Ph: (813)637-0156
Fax: (813)514-1885
Co. E-mail: executivedirector@southtampachamber. org
URL: http://www.southtampachamber.org
Contact: Ms. Judy Y. Gay, Executive Director
Description: Promotes business and community development in the southern section of Tampa, FL. Supports local charities; conducts political and business networking forums. **Founded:** 1926. **Awards:** Business of the Year (Annual); Citizen of the Year (Annual).

50299 ■ Southeast Volusia Chamber of Commerce
310 Julia St.
New Smyrna Beach, FL 32168-7024
Ph: (386)428-2449
Fax: (386)423-3512
Co. E-mail: sevinfo@sevchamber.com
URL: http://www.sevchamber.com
Contact: Kenneth Bohannon, President
Description: Promotes business and community development in southeastern Volusia County, FL. **Founded:** 1932. **Publications:** *Volusia News* (Monthly); *Business/Investors Directory and Visitor's Guide* (Annual); *Official SE Volusia County Map* (Annual). **Educational Activities:** East Coast Cruiser Night (Monthly); Membership Meeting (Monthly). **Telecommunication Services:** suewilliams2@cfl.rr. com.

50300 ■ Southword
6410 SW 80th St.
South Miami, FL 33143
Ph: (305)661-1621
Fax: (305)666-0508
Co. E-mail: info@chambersouth.com
URL: http://www.chambersouth.com
Contact: Mary Scott Russell, President
Released: Monthly

50301 ■ Sun City Center Area Chamber of Commerce
1651 Sun City Center Plz.
Sun City Center, FL 33573
Ph: (813)634-5111

Fax: (813)634-8438
Co. E-mail: info@scccchamber.com
URL: http://www.suncitycenterchamber.org
Contact: Dana Dittmar, Executive Director
Description: Aims to promote commercial, professional, financial and general business interests in the Greater Sun City Center Area and to promote the general interests and welfare of the community.

50302 ■ Sunlines
310 SE 3rd St.
Ocala, FL 34471
Ph: (352)629-8051
Fax: (352)629-7651
Co. E-mail: ourguest@ocalacc.com
URL: http://www.ocalacc.com
Contact: Jaye Baillie, President
Released: Monthly **Price:** included in membership dues.

50303 ■ Sunlines
12801 W Sunrise Blvd.
Sunrise, FL 33323-4020
Ph: (954)835-2428
Co. E-mail: mjacobs@sunrisechamber.org
URL: http://www.sunrisechamber.org
Contact: Mike Jacobs, Executive Director
Released: Monthly

50304 ■ Suwanee Notes
212 N Ohio Ave.
Live Oak, FL 32064
Ph: (386)362-3071
Fax: (386)362-4758
URL: http://www.suwanneechamber.com
Contact: Dennis Cason, President
Released: Periodic

50305 ■ Suwannee County Chamber of Commerce (SCCC)
212 N Ohio Ave.
Live Oak, FL 32064
Ph: (386)362-3071
Fax: (386)362-4758
URL: http://www.suwanneechamber.com
Contact: Dennis Cason, President
Description: Promotes business and community development in Suwannee County, FL. Sponsors Christmas on the Square Festival and Suwanee Bicycle Festival. **Founded:** 1946. **Publications:** *Suwanee Notes* (Periodic); *Membership Directory and Buyers Guide* (Periodic).

50306 ■ Tampa Bay Beaches Chamber of Commerce
6990 Gulf Blvd.
St. Pete Beach, FL 33706
Ph: (727)360-6957
Co. E-mail: info@tampabaybeaches.com
URL: http://www.tampabaybeaches.com/cwt/external/ wcpages/index.aspx
Contact: Robin Sollie, President
Description: Promotes business and community development in the Pinellas County beaches area of Florida. Sponsors a triathlon, and the Taste of the Beaches festival. **Founded:** 1997. **Publications:** *Beach Waves* (Monthly); *Guidebook* (Annual).

50307 ■ Tarpon Springs Chamber of Commerce (TSCC)
11 E Orange St.
Tarpon Springs, FL 34689-3439
Ph: (727)937-6100
Fax: (727)937-2879
Co. E-mail: chamber@tarponsprings.com
URL: http://tarponspringschamber.com
Contact: Sue Thomas, President
Description: Promotes business and community development in the Tarpon Springs, FL area. **Founded:** 1921. **Publications:** *Guide Book* (Annual).

50308 ■ Titusville Area Chamber of Commerce
2000 S Washington Ave.
Titusville, FL 32780-4747
Ph: (321)267-3036

Fax: (321)264-0127
Co. E-mail: gaedcke@titusville.org
URL: http://www.titusville.org
Contact: Marcia Gaedcke, President
Description: Promotes business and community development in the Titusville, FL area. **Founded:** 1928. **Publications:** *ConTACt* (Monthly). **Awards:** Business with a Heart Scholarship (Annual).

50309 ■ Tourism and Convention Council Newsletter
400 Fortenberry Rd.
Merritt Island, FL 32952
Ph: (321)459-2200
Fax: (321)459-2232
Co. E-mail: mstains@cocoabeachchamber.com
URL: http://www.cocoabeachchamber.com
Contact: Melissa Stains, President
Released: Periodic

50310 ■ The Trade Winds
3431 Ridgewood Ave.
Port Orange, FL 32129
Ph: (386)761-1601
Fax: (386)788-9165
Co. E-mail: info@pschamber.com
URL: http://www.pschamber.com
Contact: Debbie Connors, Executive Director
Released: Monthly

50311 ■ TradeWinds
64-A SE 5th Ave.
Delray Beach, FL 33483
Ph: (561)278-0424
Fax: (561)278-0555
Co. E-mail: chamber@delraybeach.com
URL: http://www.delraybeach.com
Contact: Michael Malone, President
Released: Bimonthly

50312 ■ Tri County Connection
100 E Call St.
Starke, FL 32091
Ph: (904)964-5278
Fax: (904)964-2863
URL: http://www.northfloridachamber.com
Contact: Jimmie Scott, Chairman
Released: Quarterly

50313 ■ Umatilla Chamber of Commerce
PO Box 300
Umatilla, FL 32784
Ph: (352)669-3511
Fax: (352)669-8900
Co. E-mail: umatilla@umatillachamber.org
URL: http://www.umatillachamber.org
Contact: Shananne Cain, President
Description: Promotes business and community development in Umatilla, FL. Sponsors festival. **Founded:** 1904.

50314 ■ Upper Tampa Bay Regional Chamber of Commerce
163 State Rd., 580 W
Oldsmar, FL 34677
Ph: (813)855-4233
Fax: (813)854-1237
Co. E-mail: jcustin@utbchamber.com
URL: http://www.oldsmarchamber.org
Contact: Jerry Custin, President
Description: Promotes business and community development in Upper Tampa Bay Region.

50315 ■ Vacation Guide
5570 Gulf of Mexico Dr.
Longboat Key, FL 34228
Ph: (941)383-2466
Fax: (941)383-8217
Co. E-mail: taposporos@longboatkeychamber.com
URL: http://longboatkeychamber.com
Contact: David Miller, Chairperson
Released: Periodic

50316 ■ Venice Area Chamber of Commerce (VACC)
597 Tamiami Trail S
Venice, FL 34285

Ph: (941)488-2236
Co. E-mail: vchamber@venicechamber.com
URL: http://www.venicechamber.com
Contact: John G. Ryan, President
Description: Promotes business and community development in the Venice, FL area. **Publications:** *Members in Action.*

50317 ■ Villages Chamber of Commerce
1000 Lake Sumter Landing
The Villages, FL 32162
Ph: (352)753-2270
Free: 800-245-1081
Co. E-mail: info@thevillages.com
URL: http://www.thevillages.com
Description: Promotes business and community development in The Villages, FL. **Founded:** 2000. **Publications:** *The Villages Chamber Connection* (Quarterly).

50318 ■ *The Villages Chamber Connection*
1000 Lake Sumter Landing
The Villages, FL 32162
Ph: (352)753-2270
Free: 800-245-1081
Co. E-mail: info@thevillages.com
URL: http://www.thevillages.com
Released: Quarterly

50319 ■ *Visitor Guide*
330 N Federal Hwy.
Hollywood, FL 33020
Ph: (954)923-4000
Free: 800-231-5562
Fax: (954)923-8737
Co. E-mail: information@hollywoodchamber.org
URL: http://www.hollywoodchamber.org
Contact: Anne Hotte, Executive Director
Released: Annual **Price:** free.

50320 ■ *Visitor Guide*
1005 E Strawbridge Ave.
Melbourne, FL 32901-4782
Ph: (321)724-5400
Fax: (321)725-2093
Co. E-mail: christine@melbourneregionalchamber.
  com
URL: http://www.melpb-chamber.org
Contact: Christine Michaels, President
Released: Annual

50321 ■ *Visitors Guide*
401 Cleveland St.
Clearwater, FL 33755
Ph: (727)461-0011
Fax: (727)449-2889
Co. E-mail: bclifford@clearwaterflorida.org
URL: http://www.clearwaterflorida.org
Contact: Bob Clifford, President
Released: Annual

50322 ■ *Visitors Guide*
4201 Ocean Dr.
Lauderdale by the Sea, FL 33308
Ph: (954)776-1000
Fax: (954)769-1560
Co. E-mail: info@lbts.com
URL: http://www.lbts.com
Contact: Paul Novak, Treasurer
Released: Annual

50323 ■ *Visitors Guide*
101 State St. W
Oldsmar, FL 34677
Ph: (813)855-4233
Fax: (813)854-1237
Co. E-mail: jcustin@utbchamber.com
URL: http://www.oldsmarchamber.com
Contact: Jerry Custin, President
Released: Annual

50324 ■ *Visitor's Guide*
5118 Ocean Blvd.
Siesta Key, FL 34242
Ph: (941)349-3800
Free: 866-831-7778
Co. E-mail: info@siestakeychamber.com
URL: http://www.siestakeychamber.com
Contact: Mark Smith, Chairman

50325 ■ *Visitors Guide*
31020 Overseas Hwy.
Big Pine Key, FL 33043-0511
Ph: (305)872-2411
Free: 800-872-3722
Fax: (305)872-0752
Co. E-mail: info@lowerkeyschamber.com
URL: http://www.lowerkeyschamber.com
Contact: Carole Stevens, Secretary

50326 ■ *Voice of Business*
401 Cleveland St.
Clearwater, FL 33755
Ph: (727)461-0011
Fax: (727)449-2889
Co. E-mail: bclifford@clearwaterflorida.org
URL: http://www.clearwaterflorida.org
Contact: Bob Clifford, President
Released: Monthly

50327 ■ *The Voice of Business*
PO Box 683
Wauchula, FL 33873
Ph: (863)773-6967
Fax: (863)773-4915
Co. E-mail: casey@hardeecc.com
URL: http://www.hardeecc.com/recreation.htm
Contact: Derren Bryan, President
Released: Monthly

50328 ■ *Volusia News*
310 Julia St.
New Smyrna Beach, FL 32168-7024
Ph: (386)428-2449
Fax: (386)423-3512
Co. E-mail: sevinfo@sevchamber.com
URL: http://www.sevchamber.com
Contact: Kenneth Bohannon, President
Released: Monthly

50329 ■ Wakulla County Chamber of Commerce
23 High Dr.
Crawfordville, FL 32327-2032
Ph: (850)926-1848
Fax: (850)926-2050
Co. E-mail: info@wakullacountychamber.com
URL: http://www.wakullacountychamber.com
Contact: Amy Geiger, President
Description: Promotes business and community development in Wakulla County, FL. **Publications:** *Chamber Chatter* (Monthly); *Chamber Line* (Monthly).

50330 ■ Walton Area Chamber of Commerce
63 S Centre Trail
Santa Rosa Beach, FL 32459
Ph: (850)267-0683
Fax: (850)267-0603
Co. E-mail: wendy@waltonareachamber.com
URL: http://www.waltonareachamber.com
Contact: Cory Fosdyek, Chairperson
Description: Works to help members improve and enhance their business. Provides vision leadership within Walton County. **Publications:** *Chamber Connection* (Monthly).

50331 ■ Walton County Chamber of Commerce (WCCC)
63 S Centre Trl.
Santa Rosa Beach, FL 32459
Ph: (850)892-3191
Fax: (850)267-0603
Co. E-mail: wendy@waltonareachamber.com
URL: http://www.waltonareachamber.com
Contact: Kitty Whitney, President
Description: Promotes business and community development in the Walton County, FL area. Promotes tourism. **Founded:** 1925. **Publications:** *Chamber Connection* (Monthly); *Official Buyer's Guide* (Annual). **Educational Activities:** Walton County Chamber of Commerce Breakfast (Monthly).

50332 ■ Washington County Chamber of Commerce (WCCC)
PO Box 457
Chipley, FL 32428
Ph: (850)638-4157

Fax: (850)638-8770
Co. E-mail: wcchamber@wfeca.net
URL: http://www.washcomall.com
Contact: Philip Pippin, President
Description: Promotes business and community development in Washington County, FL. **Founded:** 1954. **Publications:** *The Believer* (Monthly).

50333 ■ Wellington Chamber of Commerce
12230 Forest Hill Blvd., Ste. 183
Wellington, FL 33414
Ph: (561)792-6525
Fax: (561)792-6200
Co. E-mail: info@wellingtonchamber.com
URL: http://wellingtonchamber.com
Contact: Alexander L. Domb, President
Description: Promotes the general welfare and prosperity of the village of Wellington as well as its economic, civic, cultural, industrial, security and educational interests. **Founded:** 1996. **Publications:** *Official Guide to Wellington.* **Telecommunication Services:** michela@wellingtonchamber.com.

50334 ■ West Orange Chamber of Commerce
12184 W Colonial Dr.
Winter Garden, FL 34787
Ph: (407)656-1304
Fax: (407)656-0221
Co. E-mail: info@wochamber.com
URL: http://www.wochamber.com
Contact: Stina D'Uva, President
Description: Promotes business and community development in western Orange County, FL. Conducts charitable activities. Sponsors educational programs. **Founded:** 1972. **Publications:** *Chamber Matters*; *Newsline* (Monthly). **Telecommunication Services:** sduva@wochamber.com.

50335 ■ West Pasco Chamber of Commerce
5443 Main St.
New Port Richey, FL 34652
Ph: (727)842-7651
Fax: (727)848-0202
Co. E-mail: info@westpasco.com
URL: http://www.westpasco.com
Contact: Joe Alpine, President
Description: Promotes business and community development in New Port Richey, FL. **Publications:** *Chamber News* (Monthly); *West Pasco Chamber of Commerce--Member Directory.*

50336 ■ Weston Area Chamber of Commerce (WACC)
1290 Weston Rd., Ste. 200
Weston, FL 33326-1909
Ph: (954)389-0600
Fax: (954)384-6133
Co. E-mail: jack@westonchamber.com
URL: http://www.westonchamber.com
Contact: Jack Miller, President
Description: Promotes economic development, entrepreneur system, governmental affairs, education, networking, business to business networking, branding, business assistance, and new job creation. **Founded:** 1989.

50337 ■ *Who's Who in Business*
310 SE 3rd St.
Ocala, FL 34471
Ph: (352)629-8051
Fax: (352)629-7651
Co. E-mail: ourguest@ocalacc.com
URL: http://www.ocalacc.com
Contact: Jaye Baillie, President
Released: Annual **Price:** included in membership dues; $20, for nonmembers.

50338 ■ Williston Area Chamber of Commerce
PO Box 369
Williston, FL 32696
Ph: (352)528-5552
Fax: (352)528-4342
Co. E-mail: wcoc@willistonfl.com
URL: http://www.willistonfl.org
Contact: Maggie Crane, President
Description: Promotes business and community development in the Williston, FL area. **Founded:** 1985. **Publications:** *Chamber Music* (Monthly). **Edu-**

cational Activities: Membership Conference (Annual). Awards: Appearance Improvement Award (Quarterly); Member of the Month (Monthly); Member of the Year (Annual).

50339 ■ Winter Park Chamber of Commerce
151 W Lyman Ave.
Winter Park, FL 32789
Ph: (407)644-8281
Fax: (407)644-7826
Co. E-mail: wpcc@winterpark.org
URL: http://www.winterpark.org
Contact: Maritza Martinez, Chairman
Description: Strives to develop, promote, and sustain a vital, thriving business climate throughout the community. Seeks to support and enhance the civic, educational, economical well-being of the Winter Park, FL area.

50340 ■ *The Wisecracker*
28 NW, US 19
Crystal River, FL 34428
Ph: (352)795-3149
Fax: (352)795-1921
Co. E-mail: meredith@citruscountychamber.com
URL: http://www.citruscountychamber.com
Contact: Rob Wardlow, Chairman
Released: Monthly **Price:** free to members.

50341 ■ Ybor City Chamber of Commerce
1800 E 9th Ave.
Tampa, FL 33605-9998
Ph: (813)248-3712
Fax: (813)242-0398
Co. E-mail: info@ybor.org
URL: http://www.ybor.org
Contact: Andrea Gonzmart, Chairperson
Description: Represents and assists local businesses. **Founded:** 1930. **Publications:** *La Setima* (Monthly).

50342 ■ Zephyrhills Chamber of Commerce
38550 5th Ave.
Zephyrhills, FL 33542
Ph: (813)782-1913
Fax: (813)783-6060
Co. E-mail: info@zephyrhillschamber.org
URL: http://zephyrhillschamber.org
Contact: Carolyn Hodges, President
Description: Promotes business and community development in Zephyrhills, FL. **Publications:** *Business.*

MINORITY BUSINESS ASSISTANCE PROGRAMS

50343 ■ Florida Black Business Investment Board
1030-9 E Lafayette St.
Tallahassee, FL 32302
Ph: (850)878-0826
Fax: (850)878-4578
Co. E-mail: info@fbbib.com
URL: http://www.fbbib.com
Contact: Paula Duncan, President (Acting)
Description: Obtains and provides loans for Black-owned and -operated businesses.

50344 ■ Florida Minority Supplier Development Council (FMSDC)
7453 Brokerage Dr.
Orlando, FL 32809
Ph: (407)404-6700
Fax: (407)857-8647
Co. E-mail: malik@fmsdc.org
URL: http://fmsdc.org
Contact: Malik Ali, President
URL(s): www.cnfmsdc.com. **Description:** The purpose of the FMSDC is to provide major corporations and government agencies with easy access to minority owned and operated businesses.

50345 ■ Minority Business Enterprise Center
970 SW 1st St., Ste. 405 and 406
Miami, FL 33130
Ph: (786)316-0888

Fax: (786)316-0090
Co. E-mail: info@mbdcsouthflorida.org
URL: http://www.mbecflorida.org
Contact: Marie Gill, Director
Description: Providing general and specific business assistance, counseling and training to help establish, maintain and grow eligible minority business enterprises.

50346 ■ Palm Beach County Resource Center, Inc.
2001 Broadway, Ste. 250
Riviera Beach, FL 33404
Ph: (561)863-0895
Fax: (561)863-0897
Co. E-mail: p_skyers@pbcrc.org
URL: http://www.pbcrc.org
Contact: Paul Skyers, Director

50347 ■ Southern Florida Minority Supplier Development Counsel
9499 NE 2nd Ave., Ste. 201
Miami, FL 33138
Ph: (305)762-6151
Free: 800-79FRMPC
Fax: (305)762-6158
Co. E-mail: info@frmbc.org
URL: http://www.frmbc.org
Contact: Beatrice Louissaint, Chief Executive Officer
Description: Private-sector corporation that promotes the procurement of goods and services from minority businesses. Provides technical assistance and referral services to minority businesses.

FINANCING AND LOAN PROGRAMS

50348 ■ CEO Advisors
848 Brickel Ave., Ste. 603
Miami, FL 33131
Ph: (305)371-8560
Fax: (305)371-8563
URL: http://www.ceoadvisors.com
Contact: Robert J. Arguello, President
E-mail: rjarguello@ceoadvisors.com
Preferred Investment Size: $300,000 to $500,000. **Industry Preferences:** Communications and media, computer hardware and software, semiconductors and other electronics, biotechnology, medical and health, consumer related. **Geographic Preference:** Southeast.

50349 ■ Florida Capital Partners
500 N. Westshore Blvd., Ste. 605
Tampa, FL 33609
Ph: (813)222-8000
Fax: (813)222-8001
Co. E-mail: bhc@fcinvestors.com
URL: http://www.fcpinvestors.com
Contact: Peter B. Franz, Managing Director
E-mail: Franz@fcpinvestors.com
Preferred Investment Size: $500,000 minimum. **Industry Preferences:** Communications and media, semiconductors and other electronics, medical and health, consumer related, industrial and energy, transportation, business service, manufacturing, agriculture, forestry and fishing. **Geographic Preference:** U.S.

50350 ■ Grace Venture Partners
SunTrust Ctr., Ste. 1850
200 S. Orange Ave.
Orlando, FL 32801
Ph: (407)835-7900
Fax: (407)835-7901
URL: http://www.graceventure.com
Contact: Edward P. Grace, III, Managing Director
E-mail: ngrace@graceventure.com
Preferred Investment Size: $2,000,000 to $10,000,000. **Investment Policies:** Early and later stage, and mezzanine rounds. **Industry Preferences:** Communications, computer software, semiconductors and other electronics, and consumer related. **Geographic Preference:** East Coast, Northeast, and Southeast.

50351 ■ LM Capital Securities, Inc.
619 Datura St.
West Palm Beach, FL 33401-5309
Ph: (561)623-1700
Co. E-mail: info@LMCapitalSecurities.com
URL: http://www.lmcapitalsecurities.com
Contact: Leslie Corley, President
E-mail: LeslieCorley@LMCapitalSecurities.com
Preferred Investment Size: $5,000,000 minimum. **Industry Preferences:** Computer hardware, semiconductors and other electronics, medical and health, consumer related, industrial and energy, and financial services.

50352 ■ Lovett Miller & Co. Incorporated
1 Independent Sq., Ste. 1600
Jacksonville, FL 32202
Ph: (813)222-1477
Fax: (813)222-1478
Co. E-mail: info@lovettmiller.com
URL: http://www.lovettmiller.com
Contact: W. Radford Lovett, II
E-mail: rad@lovettmiller.com
Preferred Investment Size: $3,000,000 to $10,000,000. **Industry Preferences:** Computer software and services, Internet specific, communications and media, consumer related, business services, financial services, medical and health, and other products. **Geographic Preference:** Southeastern U.S. and Texas.

50353 ■ North American Business Development Co., L.L.C.
135 S. LaSalle St., Ste. 3225
Chicago, IL 60603
Ph: (312)332-4950
Fax: (312)332-1540
Co. E-mail: information@northamericanfund.com
URL: http://www.northamericanfund.com
Contact: Robert L. Underwood, Managing Partner
Preferred Investment Size: $500,000 minimum. **Industry Preferences:** Manufacturing and service.

50354 ■ SI Ventures
12600 Gateway Blvd.
Ft. Myers, FL 33913
Ph: (239)561-4760
Fax: (239)561-4916
Co. E-mail: info@siventures.com
URL: http://www.siventures.com
Contact: Brian C. Beach, Managing Director
Preferred Investment Size: $2,000,000 to $5,000,000. **Industry Preferences:** Internet specific, computer software, hardware and services, communications and media, medical and health, semiconductors and other electronics. **Geographic Preference:** Southeastern U.S.

50355 ■ South Atlantic Venture Funds, L.P.
614 W. Bay St.
Tampa, FL 33606-2704
Ph: (813)253-2500
Fax: (813)253-2360
URL: http://www.southatlantic.com
Contact: Sandra P. Barber, Managing Director
E-mail: spbarber@southatlantic.com
Preferred Investment Size: $1,500,000 to $7,500,000. **Industry Preferences:** Communications and media, medical and health, Other products, Internet specific, consumer related, semiconductors and other electronics, computer software and services, computer hardware, industrial and energy. **Geographic Preference:** Southeast, as far as Baltimore, MD and Washington, DC and Texas.

PROCUREMENT ASSISTANCE PROGRAMS

50356 ■ Florida Department of Management Services - Division of Purchasing
4050 Esplanade Way
Tallahassee, FL 32399-0950
Ph: (850)488-2786

Fax: (850)922-6149
URL: http://dms.myflorida.com/support/contact_dms
Contact: Russ Rothman, Director
Description: Publishes Doing Business with the State of Florida. Potential vendors should contact each state agency's purchasing office, since the Department of General Services does not make purchases for all agencies.

50357 ■ Florida Procurement Center Representatives
Naval Air Warfare Center
Training Systems Division
12350 Research Blvd.
Orlando, FL 32826-3224
Ph: (407)380-8252
Fax: (407)380-8232
Co. E-mail: walter.wallace@sba.gov
URL: http://www.sba.gov
Contact: Walter Wallace, Representative
E-mail: walter.wallace@sba.gov
Description: Covers activities for Naval Training Systems Center (Orlando, FL). McDill Air Force Base (Tampa, FL), Patrick Air Force Base (Cocoa Beach, FL), and NASA, Kennedy Space Flight Center (Cape Canaveral, FL).

50358 ■ Florida Procurement Technical Assistance Center - Florida Gulf Coast University
Lutgert College of Business, Unit 2313
10501 FGCU Blvd. S.
Ft. Myers, FL 33965-6565
Ph: (239)745-3708
Co. E-mail: dtelep@fgcu.edu
URL: http://www.fptac.org
Contact: Dan Telep, Specialist
E-mail: dtelep@fgcu.edu
Description: Helps Florida businesses interested in obtaining contracts with the Department of Defense, other federal agencies, and state/local government agencies and participating prime contractors covering Lee, Collier, Charlotte, Glades, and Hendry counties.

50359 ■ Florida Procurement Technical Assistance Center - Jacksonville Chamber of Commerce - Small Business Center (SBC)
3 Independent Dr.
Jacksonville, FL 32202-5004
Ph: (904)366-6650
Fax: (904)632-0617
Co. E-mail: info@jacksonvillechamber.org
URL: http://www.myjaxchamber.com
Contact: Barbara English, Director
E-mail: paul.arrington@myjaxchamber.com
Description: Assists the growth and development of Jacksonville's small businesses community by constantly assessing their needs, collaborating with service providers and offering technical assistance, mentoring and access to capital.

50360 ■ Florida Procurement Technical Assistance Center - Palm Beach Community PTAC
3000 St. Lucie Ave., Rm. CB 221
Boca Raton, FL 33431-6490
Ph: (561)862-4782
Co. E-mail: carole.hart@floridaptac.org
URL: http://www.fptac.org
Contact: Carole Hart, Specialist
E-mail: chart@fau.edu
Description: Helps Florida businesses interested in obtaining contracts with the Department of Defense, other federal agencies, and state/local government agencies and participating prime contractors covering Boca Raton area, Palm Beach, and Martin County.

50361 ■ Florida Procurement Technical Assistance Center - Pinellas Park Office - University of South Florida
Technical Services Bldg.
6051 78th Ave.
Pinellas Park, FL 33780

Ph: (727)541-0805
URL: http://www.fptac.org
Description: Helps Florida businesses interested in obtaining contracts with the Department of Defense, other federal agencies, and state/local government agencies and participating prime contractors covering St. Petersburg, Sarasota, and Pasco Counties.

50362 ■ Florida Procurement Technical Assistance Center - Tampa Office - University of South Florida
1101 Channelside Dr., Ste. 210
Tampa, FL 33602-3613
Ph: (813)905-5800
Co. E-mail: cbostic@coba.usf.edu
URL: http://www.fptac.org
Contact: Charlene Bostic, Specialist
E-mail: cbostic@coba.usf.edu
Description: Helps Florida businesses interested in obtaining contracts with the Department of Defense, other federal agencies, and state/local government agencies and participating prime contractors covering Tampa, Bartow, Ocala, and Melbourne areas.

50363 ■ Florida Procurement Technical Assistance Center - University of Central Florida
315 E Robinson St., Ste. 100
Orlando, FL 32805
Ph: (407)420-4850
Co. E-mail: tespinosa@bus.ucf.edu
URL: http://www.fptac.org
Contact: Tony Espinosa, Specialist
E-mail: tespinosa@bus.ucf.edu
Description: Helps Florida businesses interested in obtaining contracts with the Department of Defense, other federal agencies, and state/local government agencies and participating prime contractors covering the Orlando area.

50364 ■ Florida Procurement Technical Assistance Center - University of West Florida
401 E Chase St., Ste 100
Pensacola, FL 32502-6160
Ph: (850)473-7806
Fax: (850)473-7813
Co. E-mail: lsubel@uwf.edu
URL: http://www.fptac.org
Contact: Laura Subel, Program Manager
E-mail: lsubel@uwf.edu
Description: Helps Florida businesses interested in obtaining contracts with the Department of Defense, other federal agencies, and state/local government agencies and participating prime contractors covering the Pensacola area.

50365 ■ Florida Procurement Technical Assistance Center - University of West Florida - FWB Branch Office
409 Racetrack Rd.
Ft. Walton Beach, FL 32547
Ph: (850)301-3514
Co. E-mail: pbriere@uwf.edu
URL: http://www.fptac.org
Contact: Paul Briere, Specialist
E-mail: pbriere@uwf.edu
Description: Helps Florida businesses interested in obtaining contracts with the Department of Defense, other federal agencies, and state/local government agencies and participating prime contractors covering Ft. Walton Beach and Crestview areas.

INCUBATORS/RESEARCH AND TECHNOLOGY PARKS

50366 ■ Bay County Small Business Incubator
2500 Minnesota Ave.
Lynn Haven, FL 32444
Ph: (850)271-1107
Co. E-mail: info@nfci.org
URL: http://www.nfci.org/
Contact: Joe Chavarria, Director
Description: A non-profit small business incubator program established with a mission to give new and existing service and light manufacturing businesses the training and tools to become successful.

50367 ■ Beaver Street Enterprise Center
1225 W. Beaver St.
Jacksonville, FL 32204
Ph: (904)265-4700
Fax: (904)265-4740
Co. E-mail: info@bsecenter.net
URL: http://www.bsecenter.net/
Description: A small business incubator established to launch new businesses, to assist existing business through growing pains, to create jobs, and enhance economic development in Jacksonville.

50368 ■ Center for Technology, Enterprise & Development Business Incubator
401 W Atlantic Ave., Ste. 09
Delray Beach, FL 33444
Ph: (561)265-3790
Free: 866-353-3790
Fax: (561)265-0806
Co. E-mail: tedcenter@tedcenter.org
URL: http://www.tedcenter.org/BusinessIncubator.html
Contact: Seaborn A. Smith, Executive Director
Description: A business incubator helping businesses grow in order to employ more people from the community in the services industry (janitorial, lawn service, etc.), professional services (accountants, consultants, legal, etc.), food preparation, and the construction industry.

50369 ■ Enterprise Development Corporation of South Florida
3701 FAU Blvd., Ste. 210
Boca Raton, FL 33431
Ph: (561)620-8494
Fax: (561)620-8493
Co. E-mail: edcinfo@edc-tech.org
URL: http://www.edc-tech.org/
Description: A non profit organization that assists emerging science and technology companies.

50370 ■ Enterprise North Florida Corporation, Inc. (ENFC)
4905 Belfort Rd. Ste.110
Jacksonville, FL 32256
Ph: (904)730-4700
Fax: (904)730-4711
Co. E-mail: admin@enfc.org
URL: http://www.enfc.org
Contact: Alan Rossiter, Chief Executive Officer
Description: ENFC is a non-profit corporation that assists emerging high technology firms in northern Florida.

50371 ■ Florida Atlantic Research and Development Authority
3701 FAU Blvd., Ste. 210
Boca Raton, FL 33431
Ph: (561)416-6092
Fax: (561)620-8493
Co. E-mail: aduffell@research-park.org
URL: http://www.research-park.org/
Description: Research and development facility offering applied research directed at the industry partners' specific needs.

50372 ■ Florida/NASA Business Incubation Center - Technology Research and Development Authority
TRDA
1050 W NASA Blvd., Ste. 125
Melbourne, FL 32901
Ph: (321)872-1050
Fax: (321)872-1051
Co. E-mail: admin@trda.org
URL: http://www.trda.org/incubation-programs/
Description: The goal of this incubator is to increase the number of successful technology-based small companies in Brevard County, Florida. Tenants must be producing a technology-intensive product or be commercializing a NASA technology.

50373 ■ Gainesville Technology Enterprise Center
2153 SE Hawthorne Rd., Ste. 101
Gainesville, FL 32641-7553
Ph: (352)393-6000

Fax: (352)393-6015
Co. E-mail: contact@gtecflorida.com
URL: http://www.gtecflorida.com/
Description: A community organization providing early stage technology startup companies with the tools, training, and infrastructure to become self-sufficient, financially-viable technology enterprises.

50374 ■ Seminole Technology Business Incubation Center
1445 Dolgner Pl.
Sanford, FL 32771
Ph: (407)321-3495
Fax: (407)321-4184
Co. E-mail: hardyw@scc-fl.edu
URL: http://www.seminoleinc.com/
Description: A joint venture of Seminole County, Seminole County Port Authority, and Seminole Community College providing a nurturing environment for technology-based companies in the early stages of development.

EDUCATIONAL PROGRAMS

50375 ■ Florida Keys Community College
5901 College Rd.
Key West, FL 33040
Ph: (305)296-9081
Fax: (305)292-5155
URL: http://www.fkcc.edu
Description: Two-year college offering degree and certificate programs in small business management program.

50376 ■ St. Johns River Community College
5001 St. Johns Ave.
Palatka, FL 32177
Ph: (386)312-4200
Fax: (386)312-4292
URL: http://www.sjrcc.cc.fl.us
Description: Two-year college offering a small business management program.

50377 ■ Santa Fe Community College
3000 NW 83rd St., Rm. 112
Gainesville, FL 32606
Ph: (352)395-5443
Fax: (352)395-5286
Co. E-mail: info@sfcc.edu
URL: http://www.santafe.edu
URL(s): www.sfcollege.edu, www.sfcc.edu. **Description:** Two-year college offering a program in small business management. **Telecommunication Services:** information@sfcc.edu.

50378 ■ Seminole Community College
100 Weldon Blvd.
Sanford, FL 32773-6199
Ph: (407)708-4722

Fax: (407)708-2029
Co. E-mail: admissions@scc-fl.edu
URL: http://www.scc-fl.com
Description: Two-year college offering a small business administration program.

PUBLICATIONS

50379 ■ *Business in Broward*
PO Box 460669
Ft. Lauderdale, FL 33346-0669
Ph: (954)763-3338
Co. E-mail: sfbiz@mindspring.com

50380 ■ *Daily Business Review*
1 SE 3rd Ave., Ste. 900
Miami, FL 33131-1820
Ph: (305)377-3721
Fax: (305)347-6678

50381 ■ *How to Form Your Own Florida Corporation*
950 Parker St.
Berkeley, CA 94710
Ph: (510)549-1976
Free: 800-992-6656
Fax: (510)548-5902
URL: http://www.nolo.com
Ed: Anthony Mancuso. **Released:** Third edition, 1990. **Price:** $24.95.

50382 ■ *Incorporation and Business Guide for Florida*
Self-Counsel Press, Inc.
1704 N. State St.
Bellingham, WA 98225
Ph: (360)676-4530
Free: 800-663-3007
Fax: (360)676-4549
Ed: Robert C. Waters. **Released:** 1992. **Price:** $21.95. **Description:** Includes forms to help entrepreneurs incorporate in Florida.

50383 ■ *Silver River Marine Institute*

50384 ■ *Starting and Operating a Business in Florida: A Step-by-Step Guide*
PSI Research
300 N. Valley Dr.
Grants Pass, OR 97526
Ph: (503)479-9464
Free: 800-228-2275
Fax: (503)476-1479
Co. E-mail: psi2@magick.net
Ed: Michael D. Jenkins. **Released:** Revised edition, 1992. **Price:** $29.95 (looseleaf binder); $24.95 (paper). **Description:** Part of the Successful Business Library series.

PUBLISHERS

50385 ■ DC Press—Diogenes Consortium
2445 River Tree Cir.
Sanford, FL 32771-8334
Ph: (407)688-1156
Free: 866-602-1476
Fax: (877)203-1805
Co. E-mail: info@focusonethics.com
URL: http://www.focusonethics.com
Contact: Dennis McClellan, President
E-mail: dennis@focusonethics.com
Description: Description: Publishes ethical books in a variety of areas. **Founded:** 2001.

50386 ■ Famaco Publishers L.L.C.
6001-21 Argyle Forest Blvd., Ste. 323
Jacksonville, FL 32244-0665
Ph: (904)434-5901
Fax: (904)777-5901
Co. E-mail: famapub@aol.com
Contact: Darlene Miller Muhammad, President
Description: Description: Publishes scholarly non-fiction works on religion, politics and social commentary. Does not accept unsolicited manuscripts. Reaches market through commission representatives, direct mail, telephone sales, wholesalers and distributors and broadcast Internet. **Founded:** 1996.

50387 ■ Financial Research Association Inc. (FRA)
203 A Ave, NW., Ste. 202
Winter Haven, FL 33881
Ph: (863)299-3969
Fax: (863)299-2131
Co. E-mail: sales@frafssb.com
Contact: Karen E. Klein, Manager
Description: Description: Publishes financial ratio analysis for small business, which is useful for bank loan officers, CPA's, business consultants, leasing companies, and individual business owners. Reaches market through direct mail and wholesalers. **Founded:** 1976. **Publications:** *Financial Studies of the Small Business* (Annual).

50388 ■ Donald Wade Johnson
7911 Old Kings Rd. S
Jacksonville, FL 32217-4107
Ph: (904)737-4901
Fax: (904)737-4901
Co. E-mail: dowajo41@cs.com
Contact: Donald Wade Johnson, Publisher
Description: Description: Publishes a manual on piano care. **Founded:** 1999.

SMALL BUSINESS DEVELOPMENT CENTERS

50389 ■ Clayton State University Small Business Development Center
Center for Continuing Education
2000 Clayton State Blvd.
Morrow, GA 30260
Ph: (678)466-5100
Fax: (678)466-5109
Co. E-mail: heatherchaney@clayton.edu
URL: http://business.clayton.edu/SBDC
Contact: Heather Chaney, Program Manager
Description: Represents and promotes the small business sector. Provides management assistance to current and prospective small business owners. Helps to improve management skills and expand the products and services of members.

50390 ■ Georgia Small Business Development Center - Lead Office
University of Georgia
Chicopee Complex
1180 E Broad St.
Athens, GA 30602-5412
Ph: (706)542-2762
Fax: (706)542-7935
URL: http://www.georgiasbdc.org
Contact: Allan Adams, Director

50391 ■ Georgia Southern University Small Business Development Center
1100 Brampton Ave., Ste. C
Statesboro, GA 30458
Ph: (912)478-7232
Fax: (912)478-0648
URL: http://www.georgiasbdc.org/index.aspx?page_name=Statesboro_people
Description: Represents and promotes the small business sector. Provides management assistance to current and prospective small business owners. Helps to improve management skills and expand the products and services of members.

50392 ■ Georgia State University Small Business Development Center
10 Park Pl. S, Ste. 450
Atlanta, GA 30303
Ph: (404)413-7830
Fax: (404)413-7832
Co. E-mail: sbdmbp@langate.gsu.edu
URL: http://www2.gsu.edu/~wwwsbp
Contact: Bernard J. Meineke, Director
Description: Represents and promotes the small business sector. Provides management assistance to current and prospective small business owners. Helps to improve management skills and expand the products and services of members.

50393 ■ Kennesaw State University Small Business Development Center (KSU SBDC)
KSU Center, Ste. 500
1000 Chastain Rd., No. 3303
Kennesaw, GA 30144
Ph: (770)423-6450
Fax: (770)423-6564
URL: http://sbdc.kennesaw.edu
Contact: Drew Tonsmeire, Director
Description: Represents and promotes the small business sector. Provides management assistance to current and prospective small business owners. Helps to improve management skills and expand the products and services of members.

50394 ■ University of Georgia Small Business Development Center - Albany
125 Pine Ave., Ste. 142
Albany, GA 31701
Ph: (229)420-1144
Fax: (229)430-3933
Co. E-mail: dfinney@georgiasbdc.org
URL: http://www.georgiasbdc.org
Contact: Debbie Finney, Director
Description: Represents and promotes the small business sector. Provides management assistance to current and prospective small business owners. Helps to improve management skills and expand the products and services of members.

50395 ■ University of Georgia Small Business Development Center - Athens
Chicopee Complex
1180 E Broad St.
Athens, GA 30602
Ph: (706)542-7436
Fax: (706)542-6803
Co. E-mail: cmcdonell@georgiasbdc.org
URL: http://www.georgiasbdc.org
Contact: Carol McDonell, Director
Description: Represents and promotes the small business sector. Provides management assistance to current and prospective small business owners. Helps to improve management skills and expand the products and services of members.

50396 ■ University of Georgia Small Business Development Center - Augusta
1450 Greene St., Ste. 3500
Augusta, GA 30901
Ph: (706)721-4545
Fax: (706)721-4554
Co. E-mail: scaldwell@georgiasbdc.org
URL: http://www.georgiasbdc.org
Contact: Susan Caldwell, Director
Description: Represents and promotes the small business sector. Provides management assistance to current and prospective small business owners. Helps to improve management skills and expand the products and services of members.

50397 ■ University of Georgia Small Business Development Center - Brunswick
501 Gloucester St., Ste. 200
Brunswick, GA 31520
Ph: (912)264-7343
Fax: (912)262-3095
Co. E-mail: dlewis@georgiasbdc.org
URL: http://www.georgiasbdc.org
Contact: David Lewis, Director
Description: Represents and promotes the small business sector. Provides management assistance to

current and prospective small business owners. Helps to improve management skills and expand the products and services of members.

50398 ■ University of Georgia Small Business Development Center - Columbus
Columbus State University
Cunningham Conference Ctr., Ste. 119
3100 Gentian Blvd.
Columbus, GA 31907
Ph: (706)569-2651
Fax: (706)569-2657
Co. E-mail: lauten@georgiasbdc.org
URL: http://www.georgiasbdc.org
Contact: Lori Auten, Director
Description: Represents and promotes the small business sector. Provides management assistance to current and prospective small business owners. Helps to improve management skills and expand the products and services of members.

50399 ■ University of Georgia Small Business Development Center - Dalton
Continuing Education Bldg., Rm. 309
550 N College Dr.
Dalton, GA 30720
Ph: (706)272-2700
Fax: (706)272-2701
Co. E-mail: rriedrich@georgiasbdc.org
URL: http://www.georgiasbdc.org
Contact: Rand Riedrich, Director
Description: Represents and promotes the small business sector. Provides management assistance to current and prospective small business owners. Helps to improve management skills and expand the products and services of members.

50400 ■ University of Georgia Small Business Development Center - DeKalb
2296 Henderson Mill Rd., Ste. 404B
Atlanta, GA 30345
Ph: (770)414-3110
Fax: (770)414-3109
Co. E-mail: smacaluso@georgiasbdc.org
URL: http://www.georgiasbdc.org
Contact: Sharon Macaluso, Director
Description: Represents and promotes the small business sector. Provides management assistance to current and prospective small business owners. Helps to improve management skills and expand the products and services of members.

50401 ■ University of Georgia Small Business Development Center - Gainesville
The Featherbone Center
999 Chestnut St.
Gainesville, GA 30501
Ph: (770)531-5681
Fax: (770)531-5684
Co. E-mail: rsimmons@georgiasbdc.org
URL: http://www.georgiasbdc.org
Contact: Ron E. Simmons, Director
Description: Represents and promotes the small business sector. Provides management assistance to current and prospective small business owners. Helps to improve management skills and expand the products and services of members.

50402 ■ University of Georgia Small Business Development Center - Gwinnett
2530 Sever Rd., Ste. 202
Lawrenceville, GA 30043
Ph: (678)985-6820
Fax: (678)985-6819
Co. E-mail: randoh@georgiasbdc.org
URL: http://www.georgiasbdc.org
Contact: Robert Andoh, Director
Description: Represents and promotes the small business sector. Provides management assistance to current and prospective small business owners. Helps to improve management skills and expand the products and services of members.

50403 ■ University of Georgia Small Business Development Center - Macon
4875 Riverside Dr., Ste. 202
Macon, GA 31210
Ph: (478)757-3609
Fax: (478)471-0637
Co. E-mail: smalloy@georgiasbdc.org
URL: http://www.georgiasbdc.org
Contact: Donald Rhodes, Director
Description: Represents and promotes the small business sector. Provides management assistance to current and prospective small business owners. Helps to improve management skills and expand the products and services of members.

50404 ■ University of Georgia Small Business Development Center - Savannah
111 E Liberty St., Ste. 200
Savannah, GA 31401
Ph: (912)651-3200
Fax: (912)651-3209
Co. E-mail: lvos@georgiasbdc.org
URL: http://www.georgiasbdc.org
Contact: Lynn Vos, Director
Description: Represents and promotes the small business sector. Provides management assistance to current and prospective small business owners. Helps to improve management skills and expand the products and services of members.

50405 ■ University of West Georgia Small Business Development Center
105 Adamson Hall
Carrollton, GA 30118
Ph: (678)839-5082
Fax: (678)839-5083
Co. E-mail: donnar@westga.edu
URL: http://www.westga.edu/~sbdc
Contact: Donna L. Robinson, Director
Description: Represents and promotes the small business sector. Provides management assistance to current and prospective small business owners. Helps to improve management skills and expand the products and services of members.

50406 ■ Valdosta State University Small Business Development Center
1500 N Patterson St.
Valdosta, GA 31698-0077
Ph: (229)245-3738
Fax: (229)245-3741
URL: http://valdostastate.info/sbdc
Contact: Ruby Riesinger, Director
Description: Represents and promotes the small business sector. Provides management assistance to current and prospective small business owners. Helps to improve management skills and expand the products and services of members.

SMALL BUSINESS ASSISTANCE PROGRAMS

50407 ■ Georgia Department of Community Affairs, Business and Financial Assistance Division
60 Executive Park South, NE
Atlanta, GA 30329
Ph: (404)679-4940
Free: 800-359-4663

Fax: (404)679-0572
Co. E-mail: jthompso@dca.state.ga.us
URL: http://www.dca.state.ga.us
Contact: James L. Thompson, Manager
Description: Coordinates technical and financial assistance programs for rural development.

50408 ■ Georgia Department of Economic Development - Entrepreneur and Small Business Office
75 5th St. NW, Ste. 1200
Atlanta, GA 30308
Ph: (404)962-4000
Fax: (404)962-4829
Co. E-mail: smallbusiness@georgia.org
URL: http://www.georgia.org
Contact: Mary Ellen McClanahan, Director
Description: Promotes the interests of small businesses at trade fairs and through a network of resources.

SCORE OFFICES

50409 ■ Dalton-Whitfield SCORE
Co. E-mail: score554@hotmail.com

50410 ■ SCORE Alpharetta

50411 ■ SCORE Atlanta
233 Peachtree St. NE, Ste. 1900
Atlanta, GA 30303
Ph: (404)331-0121
Co. E-mail: scoreatlanta@joimail.com
URL: http://atlanta.score.org
Description: Works to provide free counseling to small business community. **Scope:** various types of business, financing, marketing, staffing. **Founded:** 1969. **Subscriptions:** 200 audio recordings books periodicals video recordings. **Awards:** Eddie and Pearl Award (Annual); Gold Award (Annual); Platinum Award (Annual); Years of Service Awards (Annual).

50412 ■ SCORE Augusta
Co. E-mail: score48@hotmail.com

50413 ■ SCORE Blue Ridge
Co. E-mail: fanninchamber@tds.net

50414 ■ SCORE Buford

50415 ■ SCORE Columbus
Co. E-mail: score671@bellsouth.net

50416 ■ SCORE Conyers

50417 ■ SCORE Cumming
Co. E-mail: cfccoc@cummingforsythchamber.org

50418 ■ SCORE Fayetteville
Co. E-mail: info@fayettechamber.og

50419 ■ SCORE Griffin

50420 ■ SCORE Macon
Co. E-mail: info@maconchamber.com

50421 ■ SCORE Marietta
Co. E-mail: info@cobbchamber.org

50422 ■ SCORE McDonough

50423 ■ SCORE Newnan
Co. E-mail: info@newnancowetachamber.org

50424 ■ SCORE Savannah
111 E Liberty St., Ste. 103
Savannah, GA 31401
Ph: (912)652-4335
Fax: (912)652-4184
Co. E-mail: info@scoresav.org
URL: http://savannah.score.org
Contact: Majorie Young, President
Description: Provides professional guidance and information to maximize the success of existing and emerging small businesses. Develops business plans and evaluates financial projections. Identifies problems and potential solutions.

BETTER BUSINESS BUREAUS

50425 ■ Better Business Bureau of Central Georgia
277 Martin Luther King Jr. Blvd., Ste. 102
Macon, GA 31201
Ph: (478)742-7999
Free: 800-763-4222
Fax: (478)742-8191
Co. E-mail: info@centralgeorgia.bbb.org
URL: http://centralgeorgia.bbb.org
Contact: Kelvin Collins, Chief Executive Officer
Description: Seeks to promote and foster ethical relationship between businesses and the public through voluntary self-regulation, consumer and business education, and service excellence. Provides information to help consumers and businesses make informed purchasing decisions and avoid costly scams and frauds; settles consumer complaints through arbitration and other means.

50426 ■ Better Business Bureau of Metro Atlanta, Athens and Northeast Georgia
503 Oak Pl., Ste. 590
Atlanta, GA 30349
Ph: (404)766-0875
Fax: (404)768-1085
Co. E-mail: info@atlanta.bbb.org
URL: http://atlanta.bbb.org
Description: Seeks to promote and foster the highest ethical relationship between businesses and the public through voluntary self-regulation, consumer and business education, and service excellence. Provides information to help consumers and businesses make informed purchasing decisions and avoid costly scams and frauds; settles consumer complaints through arbitration and other means.

50427 ■ Better Business Bureau Southeast Atlantic
6555 Abercorn St., Ste. 120
Savannah, GA 31405
Ph: (912)354-7521
Fax: (912)354-5068
Co. E-mail: bbbsea@bellsouth.net
URL: http://savannah.bbb.org
Description: Seeks to promote and foster ethical relationship between businesses and the public through voluntary self-regulation, consumer and business education, and service excellence. Provides information to help consumers and businesses make informed purchasing decisions and avoid costly scams and frauds; settles consumer complaints through arbitration and other means.

50428 ■ Better Business Bureau of West Georgia - East Alabama
PO Box 2587
Columbus, GA 31902
Ph: (706)324-0712
Fax: (706)324-2181
Co. E-mail: info@columbus-ga.bbb.org
URL: http://columbus-ga.bbb.org
Description: Seeks to promote and foster the highest ethical relationship between businesses and the public through voluntary self-regulation, consumer and business education, and service excellence. Provides information to help consumers and businesses make informed purchasing decisions and avoid costly scams and frauds; settles consumer complaints through arbitration and other means. **Awards:** Local Torch Awards (Annual); Students of Integrity Scholarship Award (Annual).

CHAMBERS OF COMMERCE

50429 ■ *Action*
c/o Griffin Regional Welcome Center
143 N Hill St.
Griffin, GA 30223
Ph: (770)228-8200
Fax: (770)228-8031
Co. E-mail: griffinchamber@cityofgriffin.com
URL: http://www.griffinchamber.com
Contact: John Tidwell, Chairman
Released: Monthly

50430 ■ Adel-Cook County Chamber of Commerce
100 S Hutchinson Ave.
Adel, GA 31620
Ph: (229)896-2281
Fax: (229)869-8201
Co. E-mail: cookcochamber@windstream.net
URL: http://adelcookchamber.org
Description: Promotes business and community development in Cook County, GA. Sponsors local festival. **Scope:** statistics. **Founded:** 1958. **Subscriptions:** books. **Publications:** *The Informer* (Monthly).

50431 ■ Airport Area Chamber of Commerce
600 S Central Ave., Ste. 100
Hapeville, GA 30354
Ph: (404)209-0910
Fax: (404)389-0271
Co. E-mail: info@airportchamber.com
URL: http://www.airportchamber.com
Contact: Ann Ray, President
Description: Promotes business and community development in Airport area, GA. **Founded:** 1945.

50432 ■ Albany Area Chamber of Commerce, Georgia
225 W Broad Ave.
Albany, GA 31701
Ph: (229)434-8700
Free: 800-475-8700
Fax: (229)434-8716
Co. E-mail: info@albanyga.com
URL: http://www.albanyga.com
Contact: Chris Hardy, President
Description: Promotes business and community development in the Albany-Daugherty County, GA area. **Founded:** 1911. **Publications:** *Business* (Bimonthly); *Business in Brief* (Bimonthly); *Manufacturing Directory*.

50433 ■ Alma/Bacon County Chamber of Commerce
1120 W 12th St.
Alma, GA 31510
Ph: (912)632-5859
Fax: (912)632-7710
Co. E-mail: abcchamber@accessatc.net
URL: http://almaone.com
Contact: Cherry Rewis, Executive Assistant
Description: Promotes business and community development in Bacon County, GA. **Founded:** 1965.

50434 ■ Americus-Sumter County Chamber of Commerce
409 Elm Ave. Ste. A
Americus, GA 31709
Ph: (229)924-2646
Fax: (229)924-8784
Co. E-mail: rachael@americus.net
URL: http://www.americus-sumterchamber.com
Contact: Angela Westra, President
Description: Promotes business and community development in Sumter County, GA. **Founded:** 1920. **Publications:** *What's News* (Quarterly); *Speakers Bureau.* **Educational Activities:** Americus-Sumter County Chamber of Commerce Banquet (Annual). **Telecommunication Services:** info@americus-sumterchamber.com; rachael@americus-sumterchamber.com.

50435 ■ *Apple Blossom*
668 441 Business Hwy.
Cornelia, GA 30531
Ph: (706)778-4654
Free: 800-835-2559
Fax: (706)776-1416
Co. E-mail: taylorjudy@windstream.net
URL: http://www.habershamchamber.com
Contact: Judy Taylor, President
Released: Monthly

50436 ■ Ashburn - Turner County Chamber of Commerce
238 E College Ave.
Ashburn, GA 31714
Ph: (229)567-9696
Free: 800-471-9696

Fax: (229)567-2541
Co. E-mail: szorn@windstream.net
URL: http://www.turnerchamber.com
Contact: Shelly Zorn, President
Description: Promotes business and community development in Turner County, GA.

50437 ■ Athens Area Chamber of Commerce (AACC)
246 W Hancock Ave.
Athens, GA 30601
Ph: (706)549-6800
Fax: (706)549-5636
Co. E-mail: info@athensga.com
URL: http://www.athenschamber.net
Contact: Doc Eldridge, President
E-mail: doc@athensga.com
Description: Promotes business and community development in the Athens, GA area. **Founded:** 1903. **Publications:** *It's Your Business* (Semimonthly); *Athens Area Chamber of Commerce Basic Package*; *Athens Area Chamber of Commerce Deluxe Package*; *Athens Area Chamber of Commerce Business Package*; *Athens Area Chamber of Commerce Community Overview*; *Athens Area Chamber of Commerce Largest Employers*; *Athens Area Chamber Membership Directory*; *Athens Area Chamber of Commerce Manufacturer's Guide*; *Athens Area Chamber of Commerce Membership Directory*. **Awards:** AACC Industry of the Year Award (Annual); Spirit of Athens Award (Annual); Small Business Person of the Year Award (Annual). **Telecommunication Services:** doc@athensga.com; info@athens-chamber.net.

50438 ■ *The Augusta Chronicle*
701 Greene St.
Augusta, GA 30901
Ph: (706)821-1300
Free: 888-639-8188
Fax: (706)821-1330
Co. E-mail: info@augustagausa.com
URL: http://augustachamber.net
Contact: Mrs. Susan E. Parr, President
Released: Monthly

50439 ■ Augusta Metro Chamber of Commerce
701 Greene St.
Augusta, GA 30901
Ph: (706)821-1300
Free: 888-639-8188
Fax: (706)821-1330
Co. E-mail: info@augustagausa.com
URL: http://augustachamber.net
Contact: Mrs. Susan E. Parr, President
Description: Promotes business and community development in the Augusta, GA area. **Founded:** 1905. **Publications:** *The Augusta Chronicle* (Monthly); *Capitol Updates* (Semimonthly). **Telecommunication Services:** sparr@augustagausa.com.

50440 ■ *The Bagpiper*
1111 Magnolia Bluff Way SW Ste. 255
Darien, GA 31305
Ph: (912)437-6684
Fax: (912)437-5251
Co. E-mail: info@mcintoshchamber.com
URL: http://www.mcintoshcounty.com
Contact: Chris Harper, Chairman

50441 ■ Bainbridge-Decatur County Chamber of Commerce
PO Box 755
Bainbridge, GA 39818
Ph: (229)246-4774
Free: 800-243-4774
Fax: (229)243-7633
Co. E-mail: info@bainbridgechamber.org
URL: http://www.bainbridgegachamber.com
Contact: Rick McCaskill, President
Description: Promotes business and community development in Decatur County, GA. **Scope:** education, growth. **Founded:** 1924. **Subscriptions:** 100000. **Awards:** STAR Program, Mentor & Mentee (Annual).

50442 ■ Banks County Chamber of Commerce (BCCC)
105 US Hwy. N
Homer, GA 30547-0057
Ph: (706)677-2108
Free: 800-638-5004
Fax: (706)677-2109
Co. E-mail: bankscountychamber@windstream.net
URL: http://bankscountychamber.com
Contact: Danny Lewis, Executive Director
Description: Promotes business and community development in Banks County, GA. Banks County Holiday Festival for arts and crafts. **Founded:** 1972. **Publications:** *The Chamber Connection* (Monthly).

50443 ■ Barnesville-Lamar County Chamber of Commerce
100 Commerce Pl.
Barnesville, GA 30204
Ph: (770)358-5884
Fax: (770)358-5886
Co. E-mail: amandarose@barnesville.org
URL: http://www.barnesville.org
Contact: Amanda Rose, President
Description: Promotes business and community development in Lamar County, GA. Sponsors Health Fair and Buggy Days festival. **Founded:** 1959. **Publications:** *Business Builder* (Monthly).

50444 ■ Barrow County Chamber of Commerce (BCCC)
6 Porter St.
Winder, GA 30680-1731
Ph: (770)867-9444
Fax: (770)867-6366
Co. E-mail: mmilner@barrowchamber.com
URL: http://www.barrowchamber.com
Contact: Thomas R. Jennings, President
Description: Promotes business and community development in Barrow County, GA. Sponsors annual Summer's End Festival. **Founded:** 1948. **Publications:** *Barrowvision Newsletter* (Monthly); *Chamber Chat* (Bimonthly). **Educational Activities:** Barrow County Chamber of Commerce Meeting (Monthly). **Awards:** Citizen of the Year (Annual); Star Student of the Year (Annual).

50445 ■ *Barrowvision Newsletter*
6 Porter St.
Winder, GA 30680-1731
Ph: (770)867-9444
Fax: (770)867-6366
Co. E-mail: mmilner@barrowchamber.com
URL: http://www.barrowchamber.com
Contact: Thomas R. Jennings, President
Released: Monthly

50446 ■ Baxley-Appling County Chamber of Commerce
305 W Parker St.
Baxley, GA 31515
Ph: (912)367-7731
Fax: (912)367-2073
Co. E-mail: glennkk@bellsouth.net
URL: http://www.baxley.org
Contact: Karen Glenn, Executive Director
Description: Promotes business and community development in Appling County, GA. **Scope:** business operation. **Founded:** 1948. **Publications:** *Partners in Progress* (Monthly); *South Georgia Business* (Monthly). **Telecommunication Services:** baxleychamber@bellsouth.net.

50447 ■ Blairsville - Union County Chamber of Commerce (BUCCC)
PO Box 789
Blairsville, GA 30514
Ph: (706)745-5789
Free: 877-745-5789
Co. E-mail: admin@blairsvillechamber.com
URL: http://www.blairsvillechamber.com
Contact: Joseph Garner, Chairman
URL(s): www.visitblairsvillega.com. **Description:** Seeks to develop leadership qualities in individuals that have the potential to affect great, positive change in Union County through their particular economic,

civic, and social responsibilities and interactions with current and future contributing members of the community. **Publications:** *BUCCC Monthly News* (Monthly).

50448 ■ Blakely-Early County Chamber of Commerce
214 Court Sq.
Blakely, GA 39823
Ph: (229)723-3741
Fax: (229)723-6876
Co. E-mail: info@blakelyearlycountychamber.com
URL: http://www.blakelyearlycountychamber.com
Contact: Hilary Halford, President
Description: Promotes business and community development in Early County, GA.

50449 ■ Brunswick-Golden Isles Chamber of Commerce (BGICC)
4 Glynn Ave.
Brunswick, GA 31520
Ph: (912)265-0620
Fax: (912)265-0629
Co. E-mail: info@brunswickgoldenisleschamber.com
URL: http://www.brunswickgoldenisleschamber.com
Contact: Mike Maloy, Chairman
Description: Promotes business and community development in Glynn County, GA. **Founded:** 1952. **Publications:** *Brunswick-Golden Isles Today* (Annual); *Chamber Clipper*.

50450 ■ Brunswick-Golden Isles Today
4 Glynn Ave.
Brunswick, GA 31520
Ph: (912)265-0620
Fax: (912)265-0629
Co. E-mail: info@brunswickgoldenisleschamber.com
URL: http://www.brunswickgoldenisleschamber.com
Contact: Mike Maloy, Chairman
Released: Annual

50451 ■ BUCCC Monthly News
PO Box 789
Blairsville, GA 30514
Ph: (706)745-5789
Free: 877-745-5789
Co. E-mail: admin@blairsvillechamber.com
URL: http://www.blairsvillechamber.com
Contact: Joseph Garner, Chairman
Released: Monthly

50452 ■ Business
200 Northside Dr.
Carrollton, GA 30117
Ph: (770)832-2446
Fax: (770)832-1300
Co. E-mail: carrollchamber@carroll-ga.org
URL: http://www.carroll-ga.org
Contact: Mr. Daniel Jackson, President

50453 ■ Business
225 W Broad Ave.
Albany, GA 31701
Ph: (229)434-8700
Free: 800-475-8700
Fax: (229)434-8716
Co. E-mail: info@albanyga.com
URL: http://www.albanyga.com
Contact: Chris Hardy, President
Released: Bimonthly **Price:** free for members; $50, /year for nonmembers.

50454 ■ Business in Brief
225 W Broad Ave.
Albany, GA 31701
Ph: (229)434-8700
Free: 800-475-8700
Fax: (229)434-8716
Co. E-mail: info@albanyga.com
URL: http://www.albanyga.com
Contact: Chris Hardy, President
Released: Bimonthly

50455 ■ Business Builder
100 Commerce Pl.
Barnesville, GA 30204
Ph: (770)358-5884

Fax: (770)358-5886
Co. E-mail: amandarose@barnesville.org
URL: http://www.barnesville.org
Contact: Amanda Rose, President
Released: Monthly **Price:** free to members.

50456 ■ Business Bulletin
1228 Watson Blvd.
Warner Robins, GA 31093
Ph: (478)922-8585
Fax: (478)328-7745
Co. E-mail: info@warner-robins.com
URL: http://www.warner-robins.com
Contact: Edward M. Rodriguez, President
Released: Quarterly

50457 ■ Business Directory
300 S Wall St.
Calhoun, GA 30701
Ph: (706)625-3200
Fax: (706)625-5062
Co. E-mail: contact@gordonchamber.org
URL: http://gordonchamber.org
Contact: Jimmy Phillips, President
Released: Annual

50458 ■ Business Macon
PO Box 169
Macon, GA 31202-0169
Ph: (478)621-2000
Fax: (478)621-2021
Co. E-mail: info@maconchamber.com
URL: http://www.maconchamber.com
Contact: Chip Cherry, President
Released: Monthly

50459 ■ Business Month
200 Northside Dr.
Carrollton, GA 30117
Ph: (770)832-2446
Fax: (770)832-1300
Co. E-mail: carrollchàmber@carroll-ga.org
URL: http://www.carroll-ga.org
Contact: Mr. Daniel Jackson, President
Released: Monthly

50460 ■ Business Progress
1200 6th Ave.
Columbus, GA 31902-1200
Ph: (706)327-1566
Free: 800-360-8552
Fax: (706)327-7512
Co. E-mail: mgaymon@columbusgachamber.com
URL: http://www.columbusgachamber.com
Contact: Mike Gaymon, President
Released: Monthly

50461 ■ BusinessLink
PO Box 374
Gainesville, GA 30503
Ph: (770)532-6206
Fax: (770)535-8419
Co. E-mail: info@ghcc.com
URL: http://www.ghcc.com
Contact: Kit Dunlap, President
Released: Monthly

50462 ■ Camden County Chamber of Commerce
2603 Osborne Rd., Ste. R
St. Marys, GA 31558
Ph: (912)729-5840
Fax: (912)576-7924
Co. E-mail: information@camdenchamber.com
URL: http://www.camdenchamber.com
Contact: Bert Guy, Chairman
Description: Promotes business and community development in Camden-Kings Bay area of Georgia. **Publications:** *Teamwork, Leadership, Commitment.*

50463 ■ Camilla Chamber of Commerce
212 E Broad St.
Camilla, GA 31730

Ph: (229)336-5255
Co. E-mail: eric@camillageorgia.com
URL: http://www.camillageorgia.com
Contact: Jennifer Burnum, Executive Director
Description: Promotes business and community development in Camilla, GA. Sponsors Gnat Days Summer Celebration.

50464 ■ Capitol Updates
701 Greene St.
Augusta, GA 30901
Ph: (706)821-1300
Free: 888-639-8188
Fax: (706)821-1330
Co. E-mail: info@augustagausa.com
URL: http://augustachamber.net
Contact: Mrs. Susan E. Parr, President
Released: Semimonthly

50465 ■ Carroll County Chamber of Commerce
200 Northside Dr.
Carrollton, GA 30117
Ph: (770)832-2446
Fax: (770)832-1300
Co. E-mail: carrollchamber@carroll-ga.org
URL: http://www.carroll-ga.org
Contact: Mr. Daniel Jackson, President
Description: Promotes business and community development in Carroll County, GA. **Scope:** small business. **Subscriptions:** books video recordings. **Publications:** *Business*; *Business Month* (Monthly); *Existing Industry Resource.*

50466 ■ Cartersville-Bartow County Chamber of Commerce
122 W Main St.
Cartersville, GA 30120
Ph: (770)382-1466
Fax: (770)382-2704
Co. E-mail: reception@cartersvillechamber.com
URL: http://www.cartersvillechamber.com
Contact: Joe Frank Harris, Jr., President
Description: Promotes business and community development in Bartow County, GA. **Founded:** 1949.

50467 ■ Catoosa County Chamber of Commerce
264 Catoosa Cir.
Ringgold, GA 30736
Ph: (706)965-5201
Free: 877-965-5201
Fax: (706)965-8224
Co. E-mail: meaker@catoosachamberofcommerce.com
URL: http://www.catoosachamberofcommerce.com
Contact: Martha Eaker, President
Description: Promotes business and community development in the Catoosa County, GA area. **Founded:** 1929. **Publications:** *Chamber Network* (Bimonthly); *Common Cents* (Biweekly).

50468 ■ The Chamber
PO Box 818
Dublin, GA 31040-0818
Ph: (478)272-5546
Fax: (478)275-0811
Co. E-mail: chamber@dublin-georgia.com
URL: http://www.dublin-georgia.com
Contact: Willie Paulk, President

50469 ■ The Chamber Advocate
122 N Main St.
Cleveland, GA 30528
Ph: (706)865-5356
Free: 800-392-8279
Fax: (706)865-0758
Co. E-mail: melissa@whitecountychamber.org
URL: http://www.whitecountychamber.org
Contact: Melissa Leitzsey, President
Released: Monthly

50470 ■ The Chamber Chat
425 W Oglethorpe Hwy.
Hinesville, GA 31313
Ph: (912)368-4445

Fax: (912)368-4677
Co. E-mail: info@libertycounty.org
URL: http://www.libertycounty.org
Contact: Leah Poole, Executive Director
Released: Monthly

50471 ■ *Chamber Chat*
6 Porter St.
Winder, GA 30680-1731
Ph: (770)867-9444
Fax: (770)867-6366
Co. E-mail: mmilner@barrowchamber.com
URL: http://www.barrowchamber.com
Contact: Thomas R. Jennings, President
Released: Bimonthly

50472 ■ *Chamber Chatter*
502 S 2nd St.
Cordele, GA 31015
Ph: (229)273-1668
Fax: (229)273-5132
Co. E-mail: msimmons@cordele-crisp-chamber.com
URL: http://www.cordelecrispga.com
Contact: Monica G. Simmons, President
Released: Periodic

50473 ■ *Chamber Chatter*
PO Box 27
Warrenton, GA 30828
Ph: (706)465-9604
Fax: (706)465-1789
Co. E-mail: chamber@warrencountyga.com
URL: http://www.warrencountyga.com/docs/chamber/
    chamber_home.htm
Contact: O.B. McCorkle, Secretary
Released: Monthly

50474 ■ *Chamber Clipper*
4 Glynn Ave.
Brunswick, GA 31520
Ph: (912)265-0620
Fax: (912)265-0629
Co. E-mail: info@brunswickgoldenisleschamber.com
URL: http://www.brunswickgoldenisleschamber.com
Contact: Mike Maloy, Chairman

50475 ■ *Chamber Comment*
213 E Gordon St.
Thomaston, GA 30286
Ph: (706)647-9686
Fax: (706)647-1703
Co. E-mail: lorishowalter@windstream.net
URL: http://www.thomastonchamber.com
Released: Monthly **Price:** included in membership
dues.

**50476 ■ Chamber of Commerce for the City
of Loganville**
PO Box 2390
Loganville, GA 30052
Ph: (770)466-1601
Fax: (770)466-1668
Co. E-mail: info@loganvillechamber.com
URL: http://loganvillechamber.com
Contact: Betty McCullers, President

50477 ■ *The Chamber Connection*
PO Box 629
Jefferson, GA 30549
Ph: (706)387-0300
Fax: (706)387-0304
Co. E-mail: info@jacksoncountyga.com
URL: http://www.jacksoncountyga.com
Contact: Keith Johnson, Chairman
Released: Quarterly

50478 ■ *The Chamber Connection*
105 US Hwy. N
Homer, GA 30547-0057
Ph: (706)677-2108
Free: 800-638-5004
Fax: (706)677-2109
Co. E-mail: bankscountychamber@windstream.net
URL: http://bankscountychamber.com
Contact: Danny Lewis, Executive Director
Released: Monthly

50479 ■ *Chamber Connection*
PO Box 303
Statesboro, GA 30459
Ph: (912)764-6111
Fax: (912)489-3108
Co. E-mail: peggychapman@statesboro-chamber.org
URL: http://www.statesboro-chamber.org
Contact: Peggy Chapman, President
Released: Monthly

50480 ■ *Chamber Corner*
PO Box 4088
Eatonton, GA 31024
Ph: (706)485-7701
Fax: (706)485-3277
Co. E-mail: info@eatonton.com
URL: http://www.eatonton.com
Contact: Roddie Anne Blackwell, President
Released: Monthly

50481 ■ *The Chamber Express*
1200 6th Ave.
Columbus, GA 31902-1200
Ph: (706)327-1566
Free: 800-360-8552
Fax: (706)327-7512
Co. E-mail: mgaymon@columbusgachamber.com
URL: http://www.columbusgachamber.com
Contact: Mike Gaymon, President
Released: Semimonthly

50482 ■ *Chamber Focus*
111 N Main St.
Greensboro, GA 30642
Ph: (706)453-7592
Free: 800-886-5253
Fax: (706)453-1430
Co. E-mail: chamber@greeneccoc.org
URL: http://www.greeneccoc.org
Contact: Becky Cronic, President
Released: Monthly

50483 ■ *Chamber Focus*
PO Box 790
Valdosta, GA 31603
Ph: (229)247-8100
Fax: (229)245-0071
Co. E-mail: chamberinfo@valdostachamber.com
URL: http://www.valdostachamber.com
Contact: Myrna Ballard, President
Released: Weekly

50484 ■ *Chamber/Gram*
302 E Broad St.
Louisville, GA 30434
Ph: (478)625-8134
Free: 866-527-2642
Fax: (478)625-9060
Co. E-mail: info@jeffersoncounty.org
URL: http://www.jeffersoncounty.org
Contact: Lil Easterlin, Executive Director
Released: Quarterly

50485 ■ *Chamber Highlights*
102 S Main St.
Swainsboro, GA 30401
Ph: (478)237-6426
Fax: (478)237-7460
Co. E-mail: swainsborochambr@bellsouth.net
URL: http://www.emanuelchamber.org
Contact: Bill Rogers, Jr., Executive Director

50486 ■ *Chamber In Motion*
PO Box 790
Valdosta, GA 31603
Ph: (229)247-8100
Fax: (229)245-0071
Co. E-mail: chamberinfo@valdostachamber.com
URL: http://www.valdostachamber.com
Contact: Myrna Ballard, President
Released: Biweekly

50487 ■ *The Chamber Link*
100 S Hamilton St.
Dalton, GA 30720
Ph: (706)278-7373

Fax: (706)226-8739
Co. E-mail: info@daltonchamber.org
URL: http://www.daltonchamber.org
Contact: Brian Anderson, President
Released: Monthly

50488 ■ *Chamber Network*
264 Catoosa Cir.
Ringgold, GA 30736
Ph: (706)965-5201
Free: 877-965-5201
Fax: (706)965-8224
Co. E-mail: meaker@catoosachamberofcommerce.
    com
URL: http://www.catoosachamberofcommerce.com
Contact: Martha Eaker, President
Released: Bimonthly

50489 ■ *Chamber News*
10052 Hwy. 27 N
Rock Spring, GA 30739
Ph: (706)375-7702
Fax: (706)375-7797
Co. E-mail: info@walkercochamber.com
URL: http://www.walkercochamber.com
Contact: Vickie Hodge, Chairperson
Released: Bimonthly

50490 ■ *Chamber News*
2805 E 1st St.
Vidalia, GA 30474
Ph: (912)537-4466
Fax: (912)537-1805
Co. E-mail: information@toombschamber.com
URL: http://www.toombsmontgomerychamber.com/
    cwt/external/wcpages/index.aspx
Contact: Bill Mitchell, President
Released: Monthly

50491 ■ *Chamber News*
c/o Jennie English, Pres.
70 Murphy Campus Blvd.
Waco, GA 30182
Ph: (770)537-5594
Fax: (770)537-5873
Co. E-mail: hccoc@haralson.org
URL: http://www.haralson.org
Contact: Jennie English, President

50492 ■ *Chamber Report*
126 N 3rd Ave.
Chatsworth, GA 30705
Ph: (706)695-6060
Free: 800-969-9490
Fax: (706)517-0198
Co. E-mail: murraychamber@windstream.net
URL: http://www.murraycountychamber.org
Contact: Dinah Rowe, President
Released: Monthly **Price:** free to members.

50493 ■ *The Chambergram*
111 Railway Ln.
Trenton, GA 30752
Ph: (706)657-4488
Co. E-mail: information@dadecogachamber.com
URL: http://www.dadecogachamber.com
Contact: Debbie Tinker, Executive Director
Released: Monthly **Price:** free.

50494 ■ *ChamberLink*
11605 Haynes Bridge Rd., Ste. 100
Alpharetta, GA 30009
Ph: (770)993-8806
Free: 866-840-5770
Fax: (770)594-1059
Co. E-mail: info@gnfcc.com
URL: http://www.gnfcc.com
Contact: Lou Douglass, Chairman
Released: Weekly

**50495 ■ Chatsworth-Murray County Chamber
of Commerce**
126 N 3rd Ave.
Chatsworth, GA 30705
Ph: (706)695-6060
Free: 800-969-9490

Fax: (706)517-0198
Co. E-mail: murraychamber@windstream.net
URL: http://www.murraycountychamber.org
Contact: Dinah Rowe, President
Description: Promotes business and community development in Murray County, GA. Sponsors North Georgia Mountain Christmas Parade. **Founded:** 1975. **Publications:** *Chamber Report* (Monthly); *Quality of Life.* **Awards:** Business of the Year (Annual); Man of the Year (Annual); Woman of the Year (Annual).

50496 ■ Chattooga County Chamber of Commerce
PO Box 217
Summerville, GA 30747
Ph: (706)857-4033
Fax: (706)857-6963
Co. E-mail: chattooga_chamber@windstream.net
URL: http://www.chattooga-chamber.org
Contact: Mr. David Tidmore, President
Description: Promotes tourism, business and community development in Chattooga County, GA. Conducts educational and leadership development programs. **Founded:** 1977. **Subscriptions:** archival material articles clippings maps photographs. **Publications:** *Essentials* (Monthly); *The Source* (Periodic).

50497 ■ Cherokee County Chamber of Commerce
3605 Marietta Hwy.
Canton, GA 30114
Ph: (770)345-0400
Fax: (770)345-0030
Co. E-mail: pam@cherokeechamber.com
URL: http://www.cherokeechamber.com
Contact: Thomas Heard, Chairman
Description: Promotes business and community development in Cherokee County, GA. **Founded:** 1970. **Publications:** *Visions* (Bimonthly).

50498 ■ Claxton-Evans County Chamber of Commerce
4 N Duval St.
Claxton, GA 30417
Ph: (912)739-1391
Fax: (912)739-3827
Co. E-mail: info@claxtonevanschamber.com
URL: http://www.claxtonevanschamber.com
Contact: Tammi Rogers Hall, Executive Director
Description: Promotes business and community development in Evans County, GA. **Founded:** 1912. **Publications:** *Membership Notes* (Monthly); *It's Good for Business*; *The Only Thing Missing.*

50499 ■ Clayton County Chamber of Commerce
2270 Mt. Zion Rd.
Jonesboro, GA 30236
Ph: (678)610-4021
Fax: (678)610-4025
Co. E-mail: info@claytonchamber.org
URL: http://www.claytonchamber.org
Contact: Yulonda Darden Beauford, President
Description: Promotes business growth and enhances the overall business climate for a prosperous Clayton County. **Founded:** 1953. **Publications:** *Economic Focus* (Quarterly); *FOCUS* (Monthly).

50500 ■ Cobb Chamber of Commerce
PO Box 671868
Marietta, GA 30006
Ph: (770)980-2000
Fax: (770)980-9510
Co. E-mail: info@cobbchamber.org
URL: http://www.cobbchamber.org
Contact: David Connell, President
Description: Promotes business and community development in the Marietta, GA area. **Founded:** 1942. **Publications:** *Direct* (Monthly).

50501 ■ Colquitt - Miller County Chamber of Commerce
302 E College St.
Colquitt, GA 39837
Ph: (229)758-2400

Fax: (229)758-8140
Co. E-mail: cmccoc@bellsouth.net
URL: http://www.colquitt-georgia.com
Description: Works to improve the economic and cultural vitality of the community.

50502 ■ *Comercio*
2801 Buford Hwy., Ste. 500
Atlanta, GA 30329
Ph: (404)929-9998
Fax: (404)929-9908
Co. E-mail: ttallman@ghcc.org
URL: http://www.ghcc.org
Contact: Tisha Tallman, President
Released: Quarterly

50503 ■ *Common Cents*
264 Catoosa Cir.
Ringgold, GA 30736
Ph: (706)965-5201
Free: 877-965-5201
Fax: (706)965-8224
Co. E-mail: meaker@catoosachamberofcommerce.com
URL: http://www.catoosachamberofcommerce.com
Contact: Martha Eaker, President
Released: Biweekly

50504 ■ *Community Connection*
101 S Main St.
Sylvania, GA 30467
Ph: (912)564-7878
Fax: (912)564-7245
Co. E-mail: hjeffers@planters.net
URL: http://www.screvencounty.com
Contact: Heidi Jeffers, Director
Released: Quarterly

50505 ■ *Community Image*
115 E Jefferson St.
Madison, GA 30650-0826
Ph: (706)342-4454
Free: 800-709-7406
Fax: (706)342-4455
Co. E-mail: marguerite@madisonga.org
URL: http://www.madisonga.org
Contact: Marguerite Copelan, President
Released: Biennial

50506 ■ *Community Magazine*
PO Box 4088
Eatonton, GA 31024
Ph: (706)485-7701
Fax: (706)485-3277
Co. E-mail: info@eatonton.com
URL: http://www.eatonton.com
Contact: Roddie Anne Blackwell, President
Released: Biennial

50507 ■ Conyers-Rockdale Chamber of Commerce
1186 Scott St.
Conyers, GA 30012
Ph: (770)483-7049
Fax: (770)922-8415
Co. E-mail: info@conyers-rockdale.com
URL: http://www.conyers-rockdale.com
Contact: Fred Boscarino, President
Description: Promotes business and community development in the Conyers/Rockdale area. **Founded:** 1954.

50508 ■ Cordele-Crisp Chamber of Commerce
502 S 2nd St.
Cordele, GA 31015
Ph: (229)273-1668
Fax: (229)273-5132
Co. E-mail: msimmons@cordele-crisp-chamber.com
URL: http://www.cordelecrispga.com
Contact: Monica G. Simmons, President
Description: Works to advance the economic, industrial, professional, cultural, and civic welfare of Crisp County, GA. Sponsors annual Watermelon Festival. **Founded:** 1888. **Publications:** *Cordele-Crisp Chamber of Commerce--Business Directory* (Annual); *Chamber Chatter* (Periodic).

50509 ■ Cumming-Forsyth County Chamber of Commerce
212 Kelly Mill Rd.
Cumming, GA 30040
Ph: (770)887-6461
Fax: (770)781-8800
Co. E-mail: cfccoc@cummingforsythchamber.org
URL: http://www.cummingforsythchamber.org
Contact: James McCoy, President
Description: Promotes business and community development in Forsyth County, GA. **Publications:** *Minds for Business* (Monthly).

50510 ■ Dade County Chamber of Commerce
111 Railway Ln.
Trenton, GA 30752
Ph: (706)657-4488
Co. E-mail: information@dadecogachamber.com
URL: http://www.dadecogachamber.com
Contact: Debbie Tinker, Executive Director
Description: Promotes business and community development in Dade County, GA. **Publications:** *The Chambergram* (Monthly). **Educational Activities:** Dade County Chamber of Commerce Meeting (Monthly). **Telecommunication Services:** dcoc@tvn.net.

50511 ■ Dahlonega Lumpkin County Chamber of Commerce
13 S Park St.
Dahlonega, GA 30533-2082
Ph: (706)864-3711
Fax: (706)864-0139
Co. E-mail: amy@dahlonega.org
URL: http://thechamber.dahlonega.org
Contact: Amy Booker, President
Description: Promotes business and community development in Lumpkin County, GA.

50512 ■ Dalton-Whitfield Chamber of Commerce
100 S Hamilton St.
Dalton, GA 30720
Ph: (706)278-7373
Fax: (706)226-8739
Co. E-mail: info@daltonchamber.org
URL: http://www.daltonchamber.org
Contact: Brian Anderson, President
Description: Promotes business and community development in Dalton and Whitfield County, GA. **Founded:** 1940. **Publications:** *The Chamber Link* (Monthly); *Manufacturer's Directory* (Biennial). **Telecommunication Services:** anderson@daltonchamber.org.

50513 ■ Darien-McIntosh Chamber of Commerce
1111 Magnolia Bluff Way SW Ste. 255
Darien, GA 31305
Ph: (912)437-6684
Fax: (912)437-5251
Co. E-mail: info@mcintoshchamber.com
URL: http://www.mcintoshcounty.com
Contact: Chris Harper, Chairman
Description: Promotes economic growth, represents the business community and enhances the quality of life while protecting cultural and natural resources. **Publications:** *The Bagpiper.*

50514 ■ Dawson County Chamber of Commerce
PO Box 299
Dawsonville, GA 30534
Ph: (706)265-6278
Free: 877-302-9271
Fax: (706)265-6279
Co. E-mail: info@dawson.org
URL: http://www.dawson.org
Contact: Christie Haynes, President
Description: Businesses, professionals, retirees and concerned individuals representing the best interest of Dawson County. Promotes, assists, and encourages the development of Dawson County's economic, educational, social, and natural resources in a manner consistent with preserving the county's uniquely desirable quality of life.

50515 ■ *Direct*
PO Box 671868
Marietta, GA 30006
Ph: (770)980-2000
Fax: (770)980-9510
Co. E-mail: info@cobbchamber.org
URL: http://www.cobbchamber.org
Contact: David Connell, President
Released: Monthly

50516 ■ *Dividends*
101 Gen. Courtney Hodges Blvd.
Perry, GA 31069
Ph: (478)987-1234
Fax: (478)988-1234
Co. E-mail: mail@perrygachamber.com
URL: http://www.perrygachamber.com
Contact: Megan Smith, President
Released: Quarterly

50517 ■ Donalsonville-Seminole County Chamber of Commerce
PO Box 713
Donalsonville, GA 39845
Ph: (229)524-2588
Fax: (229)524-8406
Co. E-mail: staff@donalsonvillega.com
URL: http://www.donalsonvillega.com
Contact: Monroe Bonner, Chairman
Description: Promotes business and community development in Seminole County, GA. Contributes weekly newspaper column and radio report. Sponsors Harvest Festival. **Founded:** 1920.

50518 ■ Dooly County Chamber of Commerce
117 E Union St.
Vienna, GA 31092
Ph: (229)268-8275
Fax: (229)268-8200
Co. E-mail: dccofc@sowega.net
URL: http://www.doolychamber.com
Description: Promotes business and community development in Dooly County, GA. **Founded:** 1977.

50519 ■ Douglas - Coffee County Chamber of Commerce
211 Gaskin Ave. S
Douglas, GA 31533
Ph: (912)384-1873
Fax: (912)383-6304
Co. E-mail: chamber@douglasga.org
URL: http://www.douglasga.org
Contact: JoAnne Lewis, President
Description: Entrepreneurs, small business partners, and industries. Enhances the quality of life in Douglas-Coffee County, Georgia. **Awards:** Business Development Award (Annual); Entrepreneurship Award (Annual); Industry Partner Award (Annual).

50520 ■ Douglas County Chamber of Commerce
6658 Church St.
Douglasville, GA 30134
Ph: (770)942-5022
Fax: (770)942-5876
Co. E-mail: info@douglascountygeorgia.com
URL: http://www.douglascountygeorgia.com
Contact: Kali Boatright, President
Description: Promotes business and community development in Douglas County, GA. Sponsors local festivals; conducts promotional activities. **Scope:** business operation and promotion. **Founded:** 1945. **Subscriptions:** 300 articles books. **Publications:** *New Horizons* (Monthly). **Educational Activities:** Business to Business Expo (Annual). **Awards:** Douglas County Citizen of the Year (Annual); Industry of the Year (Annual); Small Business of the Year (Annual).

50521 ■ Dublin - Laurens County Chamber of Commerce
PO Box 818
Dublin, GA 31040-0818
Ph: (478)272-5546
Fax: (478)275-0811
Co. E-mail: chamber@dublin-georgia.com
URL: http://www.dublin-georgia.com
Contact: Willie Paulk, President
Description: Promotes business and community development in Dublin, Georgia. **Publications:** *The Chamber.*

50522 ■ Eastman - Dodge County Chamber of Commerce
PO Box 550
Eastman, GA 31023
Ph: (478)374-4723
Fax: (478)374-4626
URL: http://www.eastman-georgia.com
Description: Works for the advancement of the economic, commercial, industrial, professional, educational, cultural and civic welfare of the Dodge County area. Encourages the growth of existing industries and businesses while giving all proper assistance to any new firms or individuals seeking to locate to the area.

50523 ■ Eatonton-Putnam County Chamber of Commerce
PO Box 4088
Eatonton, GA 31024
Ph: (706)485-7701
Fax: (706)485-3277
Co. E-mail: info@eatonton.com
URL: http://www.eatonton.com
Contact: Roddie Anne Blackwell, President
Description: Promotes business and community development in Putnam County, GA. **Founded:** 1979. **Publications:** *Chamber Corner* (Monthly); *Community Magazine* (Biennial); *The Putnam Pages* (Annual).

50524 ■ *Economic Focus*
2270 Mt. Zion Rd.
Jonesboro, GA 30236
Ph: (678)610-4021
Fax: (678)610-4025
Co. E-mail: info@claytonchamber.org
URL: http://www.claytonchamber.org
Contact: Yulonda Darden Beauford, President
Released: Quarterly

50525 ■ Effingham County Chamber of Commerce
520 W 3rd St.
Springfield, GA 31329
Ph: (912)754-3301
Fax: (912)754-1236
Co. E-mail: effingham@windstream.net
URL: http://www.effinghamcounty.com
Contact: Rick Lott, Executive Director
Description: Promotes economic development in Effingham County. Helps existing businesses become more competitive. Encourages new businesses to locate in the county. Facilitates cooperation among governmental leaders in addressing growth management issues.

50526 ■ *Enterprise*
PO Box 636
LaGrange, GA 30241
Ph: (706)884-8671
Fax: (706)882-8012
Co. E-mail: pestes@lagrangechamber.com
URL: http://www.lagrangechamber.com
Contact: Page Estes, President
Released: Monthly

50527 ■ *Essentials*
PO Box 217
Summerville, GA 30747
Ph: (706)857-4033
Fax: (706)857-6963
Co. E-mail: chattooga_chamber@windstream.net
URL: http://www.chattooga-chamber.org
Contact: Mr. David Tidmore, President
Released: Monthly

50528 ■ *Existing Industry Resource*
200 Northside Dr.
Carrollton, GA 30117
Ph: (770)832-2446
Fax: (770)832-1300
Co. E-mail: carrollchamber@carroll-ga.org
URL: http://www.carroll-ga.org
Contact: Mr. Daniel Jackson, President

50529 ■ Fannin County Chamber of Commerce
152 Orvin Lance Dr.
Blue Ridge, GA 30513
Ph: (706)632-5680
Free: 800-899-6867
Fax: (706)632-2241
Co. E-mail: fanninchamber@tds.net
URL: http://blueridgemountains.com/chamber_info.html
Contact: Jan Hackett, President
Description: Promotes business and community development in northwestern Georgia and Polk County, TN. Encourages tourism in the area. Convention/Meeting: none. **Founded:** 1983. **Publications:** *Mountain Update* (Quarterly). **Telecommunication Services:** jahackett@tds.net.

50530 ■ Fayette County Chamber of Commerce
200 Courthouse Sq.
Fayetteville, GA 30214
Ph: (770)461-9983
Fax: (770)461-9622
Co. E-mail: info@fayettechamber.org
URL: http://www.fayettechamber.org
Contact: Virginia Gibbs, President
Description: Promotes business and community development in Fayette County, GA. **Founded:** 1965. **Publications:** *Images Directory* (Annual); *The Voice of Business* (Monthly). **Educational Activities:** Business After Hours (Monthly); Business Person of the Year Award Presentation (Annual). **Awards:** Business Partner of the Year (Annual); Spirit of the Industry Awards (Quarterly).

50531 ■ *FOCUS*
2270 Mt. Zion Rd.
Jonesboro, GA 30236
Ph: (678)610-4021
Fax: (678)610-4025
Co. E-mail: info@claytonchamber.org
URL: http://www.claytonchamber.org
Contact: Yulonda Darden Beauford, President
Released: Monthly

50532 ■ *Foresight*
300 S Wall St.
Calhoun, GA 30701
Ph: (706)625-3200
Fax: (706)625-5062
Co. E-mail: contact@gordonchamber.org
URL: http://gordonchamber.org
Contact: Jimmy Phillips, President
Released: Monthly

50533 ■ Forsyth-Monroe County Chamber of Commerce
68 N Lee St.
Forsyth, GA 31029
Ph: (478)994-9239
Free: 888-642-4628
Fax: (478)994-9240
Co. E-mail: jennifer@forsyth-monroechamber.com
URL: http://www.forsyth-monroechamber.com
Contact: Tiffany G. Andrews, Chief Executive Officer
Description: Promotes business and community development in Monroe County, GA. Provides funding for the Monroe County Historical Society. **Publications:** *Keynotes* (Monthly). **Educational Activities:** Georgia State Wild Game Cook-Off.

50534 ■ *Future Focus*
10052 Hwy. 27 N
Rock Spring, GA 30739
Ph: (706)375-7702
Fax: (706)375-7797
Co. E-mail: info@walkercochamber.com
URL: http://www.walkercochamber.com
Contact: Vickie Hodge, Chairperson
Released: Monthly

50535 ■ Georgia Association of Chamber of Commerce Executives (GACCE)
c/o Tiffany Fulmer, Exec. Dir.
1622 Tarklin Valley Rd.
Knoxville, TN 37920
Ph: (404)312-0524
Fax: (865)573-4994
Co. E-mail: tfulmer@gacce.org
URL: http://www.gacce.org
Contact: Kali Boatright, Chairperson
Description: Provides exceptional services to members in the areas of professional development, information and networking opportunities. Advocates the local Chamber's role in economic and community development. **Awards:** GACCE Executive of the Year Honoring Kent Lawrence (Annual).

50536 ■ Georgia Chamber of Commerce
233 Peachtree St. NE, Ste. 2000
Atlanta, GA 30303-1564
Ph: (404)233-2264
Free: 800-241-2286
Fax: (404)233-2290
Co. E-mail: lga@gachamber.com
URL: http://www.gachamber.com
Contact: Doug Carter, President
Description: Serves as the voice of business community. Advocates the business viewpoint in the shaping of public policy, encouraging ethical business practices and ensuring the state's future as economically prosperous, educationally competitive, and environmentally responsible. **Founded:** 1915. **Publications:** *Profile* (Monthly).

50537 ■ Georgia Hispanic Chamber of Commerce (GHCC)
2801 Buford Hwy., Ste. 500
Atlanta, GA 30329
Ph: (404)929-9998
Fax: (404)929-9908
Co. E-mail: ttallman@ghcc.org
URL: http://www.ghcc.org
Contact: Tisha Tallman, President
Description: Promotes business and community development in the Hispanic community of the State of Georgia. **Founded:** 1984. **Publications:** *Comercio* (Quarterly). **Awards:** Business of the Year (Annual); Businessman of the Year (Annual); Businesswoman of the Year (Annual); Corporation of the Year (Annual); Entrepreneur of the Year (Annual); Legislative Award (Annual); Member of the Year (Annual); Special Recognition Award (Annual).

50538 ■ Gilmer County Chamber of Commerce
PO Box 505
East Ellijay, GA 30540
Ph: (706)635-7400
Fax: (706)635-7410
Co. E-mail: info@gilmerchamber.com
URL: http://www.gilmerchamber.com
Contact: Paige Green, President
Description: Promotes business and community development in Ellijay and East Ellijay, GA. Sponsors Georgia Apple Festival. Convention/Meeting: none. Publications: none. **Founded:** 1979.

50539 ■ Gordon County Chamber of Commerce (GCCC)
300 S Wall St.
Calhoun, GA 30701
Ph: (706)625-3200
Fax: (706)625-5062
Co. E-mail: contact@gordonchamber.org
URL: http://gordonchamber.org
Contact: Jimmy Phillips, President
Description: Promotes business and community development in Gordon County, GA. Convention/Meeting: none. **Founded:** 1953. **Publications:** *Business Directory* (Annual); *Foresight* (Monthly).

50540 ■ Greater Columbus Chamber of Commerce (GCCC)
1200 6th Ave.
Columbus, GA 31902-1200
Ph: (706)327-1566
Free: 800-360-8552

Fax: (706)327-7512
Co. E-mail: mgaymon@columbusgachamber.com
URL: http://www.columbusgachamber.com
Contact: Mike Gaymon, President
Description: Promotes business and community development in Columbus, GA. Sponsors Columbus Day celebration. Conducts 10K Run and Criterium. **Founded:** 1845. **Publications:** *Business Progress* (Monthly); *The Chamber Express* (Semimonthly).

50541 ■ Greater Hall Chamber of Commerce (GHCC)
PO Box 374
Gainesville, GA 30503
Ph: (770)532-6206
Fax: (770)535-8419
Co. E-mail: info@ghcc.com
URL: http://www.ghcc.com
Contact: Kit Dunlap, President
Description: Promotes business and community development in Hall County, GA. **Founded:** 1907. **Publications:** *BusinessLink* (Monthly). **Educational Activities:** Business Expo, Career and Job Fair (Annual).

50542 ■ Greater Helen Area Chamber of Commerce
PO Box 192
Helen, GA 30545
Ph: (706)878-1908
Co. E-mail: office@helenchamber.com
URL: http://www.helenchamber.com/Helen/Helen_Chamber.html
Description: Local merchants. Sponsors 7 major events during the year to bring tourists to the area.

50543 ■ Greater Macon Chamber of Commerce (GMCC)
PO Box 169
Macon, GA 31202-0169
Ph: (478)621-2000
Fax: (478)621-2021
Co. E-mail: info@maconchamber.com
URL: http://www.maconchamber.com
Contact: Chip Cherry, President
Description: Promotes business and community development in Macon, GA. **Founded:** 1861. **Publications:** *Business Macon* (Monthly).

50544 ■ Greater North Fulton Chamber of Commerce (GNFCC)
11605 Haynes Bridge Rd., Ste. 100
Alpharetta, GA 30009
Ph: (770)993-8806
Free: 866-840-5770
Fax: (770)594-1059
Co. E-mail: info@gnfcc.com
URL: http://www.gnfcc.com
Contact: Lou Douglass, Chairman
Description: Promotes business and community development in northern Fulton County, GA. **Founded:** 1972. **Publications:** *ChamberLink* (Weekly); *Your Business Connection* (Monthly). **Educational Activities:** Business After Hours (Monthly).

50545 ■ Greater Tattnall Chamber of Commerce
PO Box 759
Reidsville, GA 30453
Ph: (912)557-6323
Fax: (912)557-3046
Co. E-mail: davidavery61@yahoo.com
URL: http://www.tattnall.com
Contact: David Avery, Executive Director
Description: Promotes business and community development in Tattnall County, GA. **Founded:** 1991.

50546 ■ Greene County Chamber of Commerce
111 N Main St.
Greensboro, GA 30642
Ph: (706)453-7592
Free: 800-886-5253

Fax: (706)453-1430
Co. E-mail: chamber@greeneccoc.org
URL: http://www.greeneccoc.org
Contact: Becky Cronic, President
Description: Promotes business and community development in Greene County, GA. Sponsors Lake Ocunee/Downtown Festival. **Publications:** *Chamber Focus* (Monthly); *The Greene Pages* (Annual).

50547 ■ *The Greene Pages*
111 N Main St.
Greensboro, GA 30642
Ph: (706)453-7592
Free: 800-886-5253
Fax: (706)453-1430
Co. E-mail: chamber@greeneccoc.org
URL: http://www.greeneccoc.org
Contact: Becky Cronic, President
Released: Annual

50548 ■ Griffin-Spalding Chamber of Commerce (GSCC)
c/o Griffin Regional Welcome Center
143 N Hill St.
Griffin, GA 30223
Ph: (770)228-8200
Fax: (770)228-8031
Co. E-mail: griffinchamber@cityofgriffin.com
URL: http://www.griffinchamber.com
Contact: John Tidwell, Chairman
Description: Promotes business and community development in Spalding County, GA. Sponsors Mayfling festival and Business After Hours. Holds annual retreat and board meeting. **Founded:** 1913. **Publications:** *Action* (Monthly). **Educational Activities:** Business After Hours (Monthly). **Awards:** General Griffin Nomination (Annual); Outstanding Citizen Award (Annual); Outstanding Organization Award (Annual); Lon Touchstone Small Business of the Year Award (Annual). **Telecommunication Services:** swindham@beckowen.com.

50549 ■ Gwinnett Chamber of Commerce
6500 Sugarloaf Pkwy.
Duluth, GA 30097
Ph: (770)232-3000
Fax: (770)232-8807
Co. E-mail: info@gwinnettchamber.org
URL: http://www.gwinnettchamber.org
Contact: James J. Maran, President
Description: Works to promote and sustain a responsible pro-business environment in Gwinnett County. **Founded:** 1947. **Publications:** *Inside Gwinnett* (Quarterly); *Inside Gwinnett* (Quarterly).

50550 ■ Habersham County Chamber of Commerce
668 441 Business Hwy.
Cornelia, GA 30531
Ph: (706)778-4654
Free: 800-835-2559
Fax: (706)776-1416
Co. E-mail: taylorjudy@windstream.net
URL: http://www.habershamchamber.com
Contact: Judy Taylor, President
Description: Promotes business and community development in Habersham, Hall, Rabun, Stephens, and White counties, GA. **Publications:** *Apple Blossom* (Monthly).

50551 ■ Haralson County Chamber of Commerce
c/o Jennie English, Pres.
70 Murphy Campus Blvd.
Waco, GA 30182
Ph: (770)537-5594
Fax: (770)537-5873
Co. E-mail: hccoc@haralson.org
URL: http://www.haralson.org
Contact: Jennie English, President
Description: Promotes the civic, educational civic and industrial progress of the community. **Publications:** *Chamber News*.

50552 ■ Harris County Chamber of Commerce
PO Box 426
Hamilton, GA 31811
Ph: (706)628-0010

Free: 888-478-0010
Fax: (706)628-4429
Co. E-mail: info@harriscountychamber.org
URL: http://www.harriscountychamber.org
Contact: Tammy Segura, Chairperson
Description: Provides leadership aimed at promoting controlled growth, economic development and, in general, to enhance and preserve the quality of life experienced by all citizens of Harris County, Georgia. **Scope:** brochures on tourism, economic development and small business development in Harris County. **Founded:** 1991. **Subscriptions:** 100.

50553 ■ Hart County Chamber of Commerce
31 E Howell St.
Hartwell, GA 30643
Ph: (706)376-8590
Fax: (706)376-5177
Co. E-mail: hartchamber@hartcom.net
URL: http://www.hart-chamber.org
Contact: Kiera Partlow, President (Acting)
Description: Promotes business and community development in Hart County, GA. Sponsors Antique Boat Festival and Lake Hartwell Dam Run. **Founded:** 1949. **Awards:** Star Student/Teacher (Annual).

50554 ■ Hawkinsville-Pulaski County Chamber of Commerce (HPCCC)
46 Lumpkin St.
Hawkinsville, GA 31036
Ph: (478)783-1717
Fax: (478)783-1700
Co. E-mail: kimberly@hawkinsvillechamber.org
URL: http://www.hawkinsvillechamber.org
Contact: Kimberly Brown, Executive Director
Description: Promotes business and community development in Pulaski County, GA. **Founded:** 1975.

50555 ■ Henry County Chamber of Commerce
1709 Hwy. 20 W
McDonough, GA 30253
Ph: (770)957-5786
Fax: (770)957-8030
Co. E-mail: memberservices@henrycounty.com
URL: http://www.henrycounty.com
Contact: Kay Pippin, Executive Director
Description: Promotes business and community development in Henry County, GA.

50556 ■ Homerville - Clinch County Chamber of Commerce
23 W Plant Ave.
Homerville, GA 31634
Ph: (912)487-2360
Fax: (912)487-2384
Co. E-mail: clinchcountychamberofcommerce@windstream.net
URL: http://www.clinchcountychamber.org
Contact: Jeff Brown, President
Description: Promotes business and community development in Clinch County, GA area.

50557 ■ *Images Directory*
200 Courthouse Sq.
Fayetteville, GA 30214
Ph: (770)461-9983
Fax: (770)461-9622
Co. E-mail: info@fayettechamber.org
URL: http://www.fayettechamber.org
Contact: Virginia Gibbs, President
Released: Annual

50558 ■ *Industrial Development Brochure*
122 N Main St.
Cleveland, GA 30528
Ph: (706)865-5356
Free: 800-392-8279
Fax: (706)865-0758
Co. E-mail: melissa@whitecountychamber.org
URL: http://www.whitecountychamber.org
Contact: Melissa Leitzsey, President
Released: Semiannual

50559 ■ *The Informer*
100 S Hutchinson Ave.
Adel, GA 31620
Ph: (229)896-2281

Fax: (229)869-8201
Co. E-mail: cookcochamber@windstream.net
URL: http://adelcookchamber.org
Released: Monthly

50560 ■ *Inside Gwinnett*
6500 Sugarloaf Pkwy.
Duluth, GA 30097
Ph: (770)232-3000
Fax: (770)232-8807
Co. E-mail: info@gwinnettchamber.org
URL: http://www.gwinnettchamber.org
Contact: James J. Maran, President
Released: Quarterly **Price:** free.

50561 ■ *It's Good for Business*
4 N Duval St.
Claxton, GA 30417
Ph: (912)739-1391
Fax: (912)739-3827
Co. E-mail: info@claxtonevanschamber.com
URL: http://www.claxtonevanschamber.com
Contact: Tammi Rogers Hall, Executive Director
Price: $0.50, /copy.

50562 ■ *It's Your Business*
246 W Hancock Ave.
Athens, GA 30601
Ph: (706)549-6800
Fax: (706)549-5636
Co. E-mail: info@athensga.com
URL: http://www.athenschamber.net
Contact: Doc Eldridge, President
E-mail: doc@athensga.com
Released: Semimonthly

50563 ■ Jackson County Area Chamber of Commerce
PO Box 629
Jefferson, GA 30549
Ph: (706)387-0300
Fax: (706)387-0304
Co. E-mail: info@jacksoncountyga.com
URL: http://www.jacksoncountyga.com
Contact: Keith Johnson, Chairman
Description: Works to encourage the growth of existing industries and businesses while giving all proper assistance to any new firms or individuals seeking to locate in the Jackson County area. **Publications:** *The Chamber Connection* (Quarterly).

50564 ■ Jefferson County Chamber of Commerce
302 E Broad St.
Louisville, GA 30434
Ph: (478)625-8134
Free: 866-527-2642
Fax: (478)625-9060
Co. E-mail: info@jeffersoncounty.org
URL: http://www.jeffersoncounty.org
Contact: Lil Easterlin, Executive Director
Description: Promotes business and community development in Jefferson County, GA. **Founded:** 1981. **Publications:** *Chamber/Gram* (Quarterly). **Telecommunication Services:** asterlin@jefferson-county.org.

50565 ■ *Keynotes*
68 N Lee St.
Forsyth, GA 31029
Ph: (478)994-9239
Free: 888-642-4628
Fax: (478)994-9240
Co. E-mail: jennifer@forsyth-monroechamber.com
URL: http://www.forsyth-monroechamber.com
Contact: Tiffany G. Andrews, Chief Executive Officer
Released: Monthly

50566 ■ LaGrange - Troup County Chamber of Commerce
PO Box 636
LaGrange, GA 30241
Ph: (706)884-8671

Fax: (706)882-8012
Co. E-mail: pestes@lagrangechamber.com
URL: http://www.lagrangechamber.com
Contact: Page Estes, President
Description: Promotes international understanding through cultural exchange. **Founded:** 1935. **Publications:** *Enterprise* (Monthly).

50567 ■ Lake Park Area Chamber of Commerce and Visitors Center
PO Box 278
Lake Park, GA 31636
Ph: (229)559-5302
Fax: (229)559-0828
Co. E-mail: lpacocv@bellsouth.net
URL: http://www.lakeparkga.com
Contact: Michelle Mullins, Executive Director

50568 ■ Lavonia Chamber of Commerce
PO Box 564
Lavonia, GA 30553
Ph: (706)356-8202
Fax: (706)356-4694
Co. E-mail: lavoniacofc@alltel.net
URL: http://www.lavonia-ga.com
Contact: Vivian Young, Executive Secretary
Description: Promotes business and community development in Lavonia, GA.

50569 ■ Liberty County Chamber of Commerce
425 W Oglethorpe Hwy.
Hinesville, GA 31313
Ph: (912)368-4445
Fax: (912)368-4677
Co. E-mail: info@libertycounty.org
URL: http://www.libertycounty.org
Contact: Leah Poole, Executive Director
Description: Businesses, professionals, and individuals interested in promoting a healthy business climate and supporting economic development and improved quality of life in Liberty County, GA. Sponsors festival. **Publications:** *The Chamber Chat* (Monthly).

50570 ■ Lincolnton - Lincoln County Chamber of Commerce and Development Authority
112 N Washington St.
Lincolnton, GA 30817
Ph: (706)359-7970
Fax: (706)359-5477
Co. E-mail: sbanks@lincolncountyga.com
URL: http://www.lincolncountyga.org
Contact: Debbie Justice, Executive Director
Description: Promotes business and community development in Lincolnton, GA area.

50571 ■ Madison County Chamber of Commerce and Industrial Authority
PO Box 381
Danielsville, GA 30633-5961
Ph: (706)795-3473
Fax: (706)795-3262
Co. E-mail: mccc@madisoncountyga.org
URL: http://www.madisoncountyga.org
Contact: Jean Mullis, Chairperson
Description: Promotes business and community development in Madison County, Georgia. **Founded:** 1811.

50572 ■ Madison-Morgan County Chamber of Commerce
115 E Jefferson St.
Madison, GA 30650-0826
Ph: (706)342-4454
Free: 800-709-7406
Fax: (706)342-4455
Co. E-mail: marguerite@madisonga.org
URL: http://www.madisonga.org
Contact: Marguerite Copelan, President
Description: Promotes business and community development in Madison, GA. **Founded:** 1984. **Publications:** *Community Image* (Biennial).

50573 ■ *Manufacturer's Directory*
100 S Hamilton St.
Dalton, GA 30720
Ph: (706)278-7373

Fax: (706)226-8739
Co. E-mail: info@daltonchamber.org
URL: http://www.daltonchamber.org
Contact: Brian Anderson, President
Released: Biennial **Price:** $12, walk in; $15, mailed.

50574 ■ *Manufacturing Directory*
225 W Broad Ave.
Albany, GA 31701
Ph: (229)434-8700
Free: 800-475-8700
Fax: (229)434-8716
Co. E-mail: info@albanyga.com
URL: http://www.albanyga.com
Contact: Chris Hardy, President
Price: $15, /copy.

50575 ■ *MCCC Newsletter*
PO Box 9
Warm Springs, GA 31830
Ph: (706)655-2558
Fax: (706)655-2812
Co. E-mail: meriwetherchamber@windstream.net
URL: http://www.meriwethercountychamberofcom-
   merce.com
Contact: Carolyn McKinley, Executive Director
Released: Monthly **Price:** free.

50576 ■ *Membership Notes*
4 N Duval St.
Claxton, GA 30417
Ph: (912)739-1391
Fax: (912)739-3827
Co. E-mail: info@claxtonevanschamber.com
URL: http://www.claxtonevanschamber.com
Contact: Tammi Rogers Hall, Executive Director
Released: Monthly **Price:** $0.32, /copy.

50577 ■ Meriwether County Chamber of Commerce (MCCC)
PO Box 9
Warm Springs, GA 31830
Ph: (706)655-2558
Fax: (706)655-2812
Co. E-mail: meriwetherchamber@windstream.net
URL: http://www.meriwethercountychamberofcom-
   merce.com
Contact: Carolyn McKinley, Executive Director
Description: Promotes business and community
development in Meriwether County, GA. **Publica-
tions:** *MCCC Newsletter* (Monthly).

50578 ■ Metro Atlanta Chamber of Commerce (MACOC)
235 Andrew Young International Blvd. NW
Atlanta, GA 30303-2718
Ph: (404)880-9000
Co. E-mail: president@macoc.com
URL: http://www.metroatlantachamber.com
Contact: Sam A. Williams, President
E-mail: swilliams@macoc.com
Description: Aims to improve the quality of life and
promote economic growth in Atlanta. **Founded:** 1988.
Publications: *Metropolitan Atlanta Manufacturing
Directory* (Biennial); *Bioscience Directory; Fortune
1000 Companies in Metro Atlanta; Media Guide for
Metro Atlanta; Executive Recruiting Agencies; Major
Atlanta Headquartered Firms* (Biennial); *Larger Em-
ployers; Education; New Business Quarterly* (Quar-
terly); *Atlanta Chamber of Commerce--Education Di-
rectory* (Biennial); *Metro Atlanta Chamber of
Commerce--Who's Who in Metro Atlanta Business;
Atlanta Larger Employers* (Biennial); *Who's Who in
Metro Atlanta Business: Membership Directory &
Buyers Guide* (Annual); *Metro Atlanta Area Health
Care Facilities Directory* (Biennial); *Atlanta Chamber
of Commerce--Transportation* (Biennial); *Arts and
Business Council; Atlanta Area Hospitals; Sports and
Recreation; Atlanta Consular Corps; Management
Services and Technical Assistance: Small Business
Resource; Small Business Sources of Capital Hand-
book; Atlanta Consulates, Trade and Tourism Offices
and Foreign-American Chambers of Commerce* (An-
nual); *International Atlanta* (Annual); *Atlanta Business Chronicle's Book of Lists; Metro Atlanta Chamber of Commerce--Who's Who in Metro Atlanta Business: Membership Directory* (Annual); *Atlanta
Employment Services* (Annual). **Telecommunication
Services:** rblumenthal@macoc.com.

50579 ■ Metter-Candler Chamber of Commerce
c/o Mrs. Sue S. Holland, Coor.
Metter I-16 Welcome Ctr.
Metter, GA 30439-0497
Ph: (912)685-2159
Fax: (912)685-2108
Co. E-mail: ebim@pineland.net
URL: http://www.metter-candlercounty.com
Contact: Mrs. Lynda Williamson, Chairperson
Description: Promotes business and community
development in Metter and Candler County, GA.
Founded: 1956.

50580 ■ Milledgeville-Baldwin County Chamber of Commerce
130 S Jefferson St.
Milledgeville, GA 31061
Ph: (478)453-9311
Fax: (478)453-0051
Co. E-mail: mbcchamber@windstream.net
URL: http://www.milledgevillega.com
Contact: Tara Peters, President
Description: Promotes business and community
development in Baldwin County. **Founded:** 1947.

50581 ■ *Minds for Business*
212 Kelly Mill Rd.
Cumming, GA 30040
Ph: (770)887-6461
Fax: (770)781-8800
Co. E-mail: cfccoc@cummingforsythchamber.org
URL: http://www.cummingforsythchamber.org
Contact: James McCoy, President
Released: Monthly

50582 ■ Monticello-Jasper County Chamber of Commerce
119 W Washington St.
Monticello, GA 31064
Ph: (706)468-8994
URL: http://www.historicmonticello.com/Chamber-
   OfCommerce.html
Description: Promotes business and community
development in Monticello, GA. Sponsors Jasper
Jubilee festival and Fourth of July celebration.
Founded: 1954.

50583 ■ Moultrie-Colquitt County Chamber of Commerce
116 1st Ave. SE
Moultrie, GA 31776-0487
Ph: (229)985-2131
Free: 888-408-4748
Fax: (229)890-2638
Co. E-mail: contact@moultriechamber.com
URL: http://www.moultriechamber.com
Contact: Darrell Moore, President
Description: Promotes business and community
development in Moultrie, GA.

50584 ■ *Mountain Update*
152 Orvin Lance Dr.
Blue Ridge, GA 30513
Ph: (706)632-5680
Free: 800-899-6867
Fax: (706)632-2241
Co. E-mail: fanninchamber@tds.net
URL: http://blueridgemountains.com/chamber_info.
   html
Contact: Jan Hackett, President
Released: Quarterly **Price:** free.

50585 ■ Nashville-Berrien Chamber of Commerce
201 N Jefferson St.
Nashville, GA 31639
Ph: (229)686-5123
Fax: (229)686-1905
URL: http://www.berrienchamber.com
Contact: Crissy Staley, Executive Director
Description: Promotes business and community
development in Berrien County, GA.

50586 ■ *New Horizons*
6658 Church St.
Douglasville, GA 30134
Ph: (770)942-5022

Fax: (770)942-5876
Co. E-mail: info@douglascountygeorgia.com
URL: http://www.douglascountygeorgia.com
Contact: Kali Boatright, President
Released: Monthly **Price:** free.

50587 ■ *News Blast*
10052 Hwy. 27 N
Rock Spring, GA 30739
Ph: (706)375-7702
Fax: (706)375-7797
Co. E-mail: info@walkercochamber.com
URL: http://www.walkercochamber.com
Contact: Vickie Hodge, Chairperson
Released: Weekly

50588 ■ Ocilla - Irwin Chamber of Commerce
PO Box 104
Ocilla, GA 31774
Ph: (229)468-9114
Fax: (229)468-4452
URL: http://www.ocillachamber.net
Contact: Allan Smith, Chairman
Description: Promotes business and community
development in Ocilla - Irwin, GA area.

50589 ■ Oconee County Chamber of Commerce
PO Box 348
Watkinsville, GA 30677
Ph: (706)769-7947
Fax: (706)769-7948
Co. E-mail: zgattie@occoc.org
URL: http://www.occoc.org
Contact: JR Whitfield, President
Description: Promotes business and community
development in Oconee County, GA. Sponsors Fall
Craft Festival. **Founded:** 1975. **Awards:** Agribusi-
ness of the Year (Annual); Sharon Johnson Volunteer
of the Year (Annual); STAR (Annual); Teacher of the
Year (Annual).

50590 ■ Okefenokee Chamber of Commerce and Folkston and Charlton County Development Authority
3795 Main St.
Folkston, GA 31537
Ph: (912)496-2536
Fax: (912)496-4601
Co. E-mail: generalinfo@folkston.com
URL: http://www.folkston.com
Contact: Dawn Malin, Executive Director
Description: Promotes business and community
development in Charlton County, GA. Encourages
tourism. Sponsors annual Okefenokee Festival.
Founded: 1965.

50591 ■ *The Only Thing Missing*
4 N Duval St.
Claxton, GA 30417
Ph: (912)739-1391
Fax: (912)739-3827
Co. E-mail: info@claxtonevanschamber.com
URL: http://www.claxtonevanschamber.com
Contact: Tammi Rogers Hall, Executive Director
Price: $0.50, /copy.

50592 ■ *The Outlook*
455 Jimmy Campbell Pkwy.
Dallas, GA 30132
Ph: (770)445-6016
Fax: (770)445-3050
Co. E-mail: cwright@pauldingchamber.org
URL: http://www.pauldingcountychamber.org
Contact: Carolyn S. Wright, President
Released: Monthly

50593 ■ *Outlook*
101 E Bay St.
Savannah, GA 31401
Ph: (912)644-6400
Fax: (912)644-6499
Co. E-mail: bhubbard@savannahchamber.com
URL: http://www.savannahchamber.com
Contact: Bert Tenenbaum, President
Released: Monthly

50594 ■ _Partners in Progress_
305 W Parker St.
Baxley, GA 31515
Ph: (912)367-7731
Fax: (912)367-2073
Co. E-mail: glennkk@bellsouth.net
URL: http://www.baxley.org
Contact: Karen Glenn, Executive Director
Released: Monthly

50595 ■ _Paulding Chamber Business Directory_
455 Jimmy Campbell Pkwy.
Dallas, GA 30132
Ph: (770)445-6016
Fax: (770)445-3050
Co. E-mail: cwright@pauldingchamber.org
URL: http://www.pauldingcountychamber.org
Contact: Carolyn S. Wright, President
Released: Annual

50596 ■ Paulding Chamber of Commerce
455 Jimmy Campbell Pkwy.
Dallas, GA 30132
Ph: (770)445-6016
Fax: (770)445-3050
Co. E-mail: cwright@pauldingchamber.org
URL: http://www.pauldingcountychamber.org
Contact: Carolyn S. Wright, President
Description: Promotes community and economic development in Paulding County, GA. Assists existing business and industry with planned expansions and/or local relocations. Sponsors fundraisers and events for investors. **Founded:** 1962. **Publications:** _The Outlook_ (Monthly); _Paulding Chamber Business Directory_ (Annual); _Paulding Chamber Quality of Life_ (Biennial). **Educational Activities:** Paulding Chamber of Commerce Banquet (Annual); First Thursday Forum (Monthly).

50597 ■ _Paulding Chamber Quality of Life_
455 Jimmy Campbell Pkwy.
Dallas, GA 30132
Ph: (770)445-6016
Fax: (770)445-3050
Co. E-mail: cwright@pauldingchamber.org
URL: http://www.pauldingcountychamber.org
Contact: Carolyn S. Wright, President
Released: Biennial

50598 ■ Peach County Chamber of Commerce
201 Oakland Heights Pkwy.
Fort Valley, GA 31030
Ph: (478)825-3733
Fax: (478)825-2501
Co. E-mail: pswanson@peachchamber.com
URL: http://www.peachchamber.com
Contact: Perry Swanson, President
Description: Promotes business and community development in Peach County, GA. **Publications:** _Chamber Connections_ (Monthly).

50599 ■ Perry Area Chamber of Commerce (PACC)
101 Gen. Courtney Hodges Blvd.
Perry, GA 31069
Ph: (478)987-1234
Fax: (478)988-1234
Co. E-mail: mail@perrygachamber.com
URL: http://www.perrygachamber.com
Contact: Megan Smith, President
Description: Promotes business and enhance the quality of life for the greater Perry area. **Founded:** 1955. **Publications:** _Dividends_ (Quarterly). **Educational Activities:** Perry Area Chamber of Commerce Meeting (Annual). **Awards:** C.B. Hickson Award (Annual); Volunteer Award (Annual).

50600 ■ Pine Mountain Chamber of Commerce
PO Box 483
Pine Mountain, GA 31822

Ph: (706)663-8850
Co. E-mail: support@pinemountainchamber.com
URL: http://www.pinemountainchamber.com
Contact: Judy Adams, President
Description: Works to enhance, preserve and protect the quality of life experienced by all the citizens of Pine Mountain, Georgia.

50601 ■ _Profile_
233 Peachtree St. NE, Ste. 2000
Atlanta, GA 30303-1564
Ph: (404)233-2264
Free: 800-241-2286
Fax: (404)233-2290
Co. E-mail: lga@gachamber.com
URL: http://www.gachamber.com
Contact: Doug Carter, President
Released: Monthly

50602 ■ _Progress_
PO Box 790
Valdosta, GA 31603
Ph: (229)247-8100
Fax: (229)245-0071
Co. E-mail: chamberinfo@valdostachamber.com
URL: http://www.valdostachamber.com
Contact: Myrna Ballard, President
Released: Monthly

50603 ■ _The Putnam Pages_
PO Box 4088
Eatonton, GA 31024
Ph: (706)485-7701
Fax: (706)485-3277
Co. E-mail: info@eatonton.com
URL: http://www.eatonton.com
Contact: Roddie Anne Blackwell, President
Released: Annual

50604 ■ _Quality of Life_
126 N 3rd Ave.
Chatsworth, GA 30705
Ph: (706)695-6060
Free: 800-969-9490
Fax: (706)517-0198
Co. E-mail: murraychamber@windstream.net
URL: http://www.murraycountychamber.org
Contact: Dinah Rowe, President

50605 ■ Quitman-Brooks County Chamber of Commerce
900 E Screven St.
Quitman, GA 31643
Ph: (229)263-4841
Fax: (229)263-4822
Co. E-mail: bcchamber@quitmangeorgia.org
URL: http://quitmangeorgia.org/2005/index.php
Contact: John Cox, President
Description: Promotes economic development in Quitman, GA and Brooks County. **Publications:** _Quitman-Brooks County Chamber of Commerce Newsletter_.

50606 ■ _Quitman-Brooks County Chamber of Commerce Newsletter_
900 E Screven St.
Quitman, GA 31643
Ph: (229)263-4841
Fax: (229)263-4822
Co. E-mail: bcchamber@quitmangeorgia.org
URL: http://quitmangeorgia.org/2005/index.php
Contact: John Cox, President

50607 ■ Rabun County Chamber of Commerce
PO Box 750
Clayton, GA 30525-0019
Ph: (706)782-4812
Fax: (706)782-4810
Co. E-mail: rabunchamber@gamountains.com
URL: http://www.gamountains.com/index.php
Contact: Sean Brady, President
Description: Promotes business and community development in Rabun County, GA. **Publications:** _Special Events_ (Periodic).

50608 ■ Roberta - Crawford County Chamber of Commerce
PO Box 417
Roberta, GA 31078
Ph: (478)836-3825
Fax: (478)836-4509
Co. E-mail: rcccoc@pstel.net
URL: http://www.robertacrawfordchamber.org
Contact: Charles Cook, President
Founded: 1986.

50609 ■ Savannah Area Chamber of Commerce, Georgia (SACC)
101 E Bay St.
Savannah, GA 31401
Ph: (912)644-6400
Fax: (912)644-6499
Co. E-mail: bhubbard@savannahchamber.com
URL: http://www.savannahchamber.com
Contact: Bert Tenenbaum, President
Description: Promotes business and community development in the Savannah, GA area. **Founded:** 1806. **Publications:** _Outlook_ (Monthly); _Sharing Savannah_ (Weekly); _Small Street_ (Quarterly).

50610 ■ Screven County Chamber of Commerce
101 S Main St.
Sylvania, GA 30467
Ph: (912)564-7878
Fax: (912)564-7245
Co. E-mail: hjeffers@planters.net
URL: http://www.screvencounty.com
Contact: Heidi Jeffers, Director
Description: Works to build a shared vision for the future, promote lifelong learning, provide community leadership, achieve economic growth, and improve the quality of life and represent the interests of members. **Publications:** _Community Connection_ (Quarterly).

50611 ■ _Sharing Savannah_
101 E Bay St.
Savannah, GA 31401
Ph: (912)644-6400
Fax: (912)644-6499
Co. E-mail: bhubbard@savannahchamber.com
URL: http://www.savannahchamber.com
Contact: Bert Tenenbaum, President
Released: Weekly

50612 ■ _Small Street_
101 E Bay St.
Savannah, GA 31401
Ph: (912)644-6400
Fax: (912)644-6499
Co. E-mail: bhubbard@savannahchamber.com
URL: http://www.savannahchamber.com
Contact: Bert Tenenbaum, President
Released: Quarterly

50613 ■ Soperton - Treutlen Chamber of Commerce
402 2nd St.
Soperton, GA 30457
Ph: (912)529-4496
Co. E-mail: johnlee@millionpines.com
URL: http://www.soperton.org
Contact: John Lee, Executive Director
Description: Promotes business and community development in Treutlen County, GA.

50614 ■ _The Source_
PO Box 217
Summerville, GA 30747
Ph: (706)857-4033
Fax: (706)857-6963
Co. E-mail: chattooga_chamber@windstream.net
URL: http://www.chattooga-chamber.org
Contact: Mr. David Tidmore, President
Released: Periodic

50615 ■ South Fulton Chamber of Commerce (SFCC)
5155 Westpark Dr. SW
Atlanta, GA 30336
Ph: (770)964-1984

Fax: (770)969-1969
Co. E-mail: office@southfultonchamber.org
URL: http://www.sfcoc.org
Contact: Y. Dyan Matthews, Chairperson
Description: Promotes business and community development in southern Fulton County, GA. Supports local vocational center. Sponsors golf tournament. **Founded:** 1962.

50616 ■ *South Georgia Business*
305 W Parker St.
Baxley, GA 31515
Ph: (912)367-7731
Fax: (912)367-2073
Co. E-mail: glennkk@bellsouth.net
URL: http://www.baxley.org
Contact: Karen Glenn, Executive Director
Released: Monthly

50617 ■ *Special Events*
PO Box 750
Clayton, GA 30525-0019
Ph: (706)782-4812
Fax: (706)782-4810
Co. E-mail: rabunchamber@gamountains.com
URL: http://www.gamountains.com/index.php
Contact: Sean Brady, President
Released: Periodic

50618 ■ Statesboro-Bulloch Chamber of Commerce
PO Box 303
Statesboro, GA 30459
Ph: (912)764-6111
Fax: (912)489-3108
Co. E-mail: peggychapman@statesboro-chamber.org
URL: http://www.statesboro-chamber.org
Contact: Peggy Chapman, President
Description: Promotes business and economic development in Bulloch County, GA. **Founded:** 1921. **Publications:** *Chamber Connection* (Monthly).

50619 ■ Swainsboro-Emanuel County Chamber of Commerce
102 S Main St.
Swainsboro, GA 30401
Ph: (478)237-6426
Fax: (478)237-7460
Co. E-mail: swainsborochambr@bellsouth.net
URL: http://www.emanuelchamber.org
Contact: Bill Rogers, Jr., Executive Director
Description: Promotes business and community development in Emanuel County, GA. **Founded:** 1954. **Publications:** *Chamber Highlights.* **Educational Activities:** Washpot Cookoff (Annual).

50620 ■ *Teamwork, Leadership, Commitment*
2603 Osborne Rd., Ste. R
St. Marys, GA 31558
Ph: (912)729-5840
Fax: (912)576-7924
Co. E-mail: information@camdenchamber.com
URL: http://www.camdenchamber.com
Contact: Bert Guy, Chairman

50621 ■ Telfair County Chamber of Commerce (TCCC)
9 E Oak St.
McRae, GA 31055
Ph: (229)868-6365
Fax: (229)868-7970
Co. E-mail: telfaircounty@yahoo.com
URL: http://www.telfairco.org
Contact: Kory Tokar, Chairman
Description: Promotes commercial and industrial development, as well as community development throughout Telfair County, GA. **Founded:** 1940.

50622 ■ Terrell County Chamber of Commerce (TCCC)
PO Box 405
Dawson, GA 39842-0405
Ph: (229)995-2011

Fax: (229)995-3971
Co. E-mail: tccc@windstream.net
URL: http://www.terrellcountygeorgia.org
Contact: Ms. Gina H. Webb, Executive Director
Description: Promotes business and community development in Terrell County, GA. **Founded:** 1946. **Awards:** Citizen of the Year (Annual).

50623 ■ Thomaston - Upson Chamber of Commerce
213 E Gordon St.
Thomaston, GA 30286
Ph: (706)647-9686
Fax: (706)647-1703
Co. E-mail: lorishowalter@windstream.net
URL: http://www.thomastonchamber.com
Description: Promotes business and community development in Upson County, GA. **Founded:** 1947. **Publications:** *Chamber Comment* (Monthly).

50624 ■ Thomasville-Thomas County Chamber of Commerce
PO Box 560
Thomasville, GA 31799
Ph: (229)226-9600
Fax: (229)226-9603
Co. E-mail: chamber@rose.net
URL: http://www.thomasvillechamber.com
Contact: Donald P. Sims, President
Description: Promotes business and community development in Thomas County, GA. Sponsors festival and competitions; conducts charitable activities. **Founded:** 1921. **Awards:** Community Service Award (Annual); Distinguished Service Award (Annual); Humanitarian Award (Annual); Lifetime Achievement Award (Annual); Man of the Year (Annual); Woman of the Year (Annual).

50625 ■ Toombs-Montgomery Chamber of Commerce
2805 E 1st St.
Vidalia, GA 30474
Ph: (912)537-4466
Fax: (912)537-1805
Co. E-mail: information@toombschamber.com
URL: http://www.toombsmontgomerychamber.com/cwt/external/wcpages/index.aspx
Contact: Bill Mitchell, President
Description: Promotes business and community development in Toombs County, GA. **Founded:** 1947. **Publications:** *Chamber News* (Monthly). **Telecommunication Services:** bmitchell@toombschamber.com.

50626 ■ *Tourism Brochure*
122 N Main St.
Cleveland, GA 30528
Ph: (706)865-5356
Free: 800-392-8279
Fax: (706)865-0758
Co. E-mail: melissa@whitecountychamber.org
URL: http://www.whitecountychamber.org
Contact: Melissa Leitzsey, President
Released: Annual

50627 ■ Towns County Chamber of Commerce
1411 Jack Dayton Cir.
Young Harris, GA 30582
Ph: (706)896-4966
Free: 800-984-1543
Fax: (706)896-5441
Co. E-mail: info@mountaintopga.com
URL: http://www.mountaintopga.com
Contact: Brett Beazley, Chairperson
Description: Provides support, leadership, and education through planned development, marketing, and communications to enhance the quality of life while maintaining the heritage of Towns County.

50628 ■ Valdosta-Lowndes County Chamber of Commerce (VLCCC)
PO Box 790
Valdosta, GA 31603
Ph: (229)247-8100

Fax: (229)245-0071
Co. E-mail: chamberinfo@valdostachamber.com
URL: http://www.valdostachamber.com
Contact: Myrna Ballard, President
Description: Promotes business and community development in Lowndes County, GA. **Founded:** 1912. **Publications:** *Chamber Focus* (Weekly); *Chamber In Motion* (Biweekly); *Progress* (Monthly).

50629 ■ *Visions*
3605 Marietta Hwy.
Canton, GA 30114
Ph: (770)345-0400
Fax: (770)345-0030
Co. E-mail: pam@cherokeechamber.com
URL: http://www.cherokeechamber.com
Contact: Thomas Heard, Chairman
Released: Bimonthly

50630 ■ *The Voice of Business*
200 Courthouse Sq.
Fayetteville, GA 30214
Ph: (770)461-9983
Fax: (770)461-9622
Co. E-mail: info@fayettechamber.org
URL: http://www.fayettechamber.org
Contact: Virginia Gibbs, President
Released: Monthly

50631 ■ Walker County Chamber of Commerce
10052 Hwy. 27 N
Rock Spring, GA 30739
Ph: (706)375-7702
Fax: (706)375-7797
Co. E-mail: info@walkercochamber.com
URL: http://www.walkercochamber.com
Contact: Vickie Hodge, Chairperson
Description: Promotes business and community development in the Walker County, GA area. **Publications:** *Quality of Life*; *Chamber News* (Bimonthly); *Future Focus* (Monthly); *News Blast* (Weekly).

50632 ■ Walton County Chamber of Commerce
PO Box 89
Monroe, GA 30655
Ph: (770)267-6594
Fax: (770)267-0961
Co. E-mail: teri@waltonchamber.org
URL: http://www.waltonchamber.org
Contact: Teri H. Wommack, President
Description: Promotes business and community development in Walton County, GA. **Founded:** 1819.

50633 ■ Warner Robins Area Chamber of Commerce
1228 Watson Blvd.
Warner Robins, GA 31093
Ph: (478)922-8585
Fax: (478)328-7745
Co. E-mail: info@warner-robins.com
URL: http://www.warner-robins.com
Contact: Edward M. Rodriguez, President
Description: Promotes business and community development in the Warner Robins, GA area. **Founded:** 1948. **Publications:** *Business Bulletin* (Quarterly). **Awards:** Employee of the Month (Monthly); Small Business of the Month (Monthly); L.V. Osigian Teacher of the Year (Annual). **Telecommunication Services:** erodriguez@warner-robins.com.

50634 ■ Warren County Chamber of Commerce
PO Box 27
Warrenton, GA 30828
Ph: (706)465-9604
Fax: (706)465-1789
Co. E-mail: chamber@warrencountyga.com
URL: http://www.warrencountyga.com/docs/chamber/chamber_home.htm
Contact: O.B. McCorkle, Secretary
Description: Promotes business and community development in Warren County, GA. **Founded:** 1990. **Publications:** *Chamber Chatter* (Monthly).

50635 ■ Washington County Chamber of Commerce
131 W Haynes St., Ste. B
Sandersville, GA 31082-0582
Ph: (478)552-3288
Fax: (478)552-1449
Co. E-mail: wacocofc@bellsouth.net
URL: http://www.washingtoncounty-ga.com
Contact: Ree Garrett, President
Description: Promotes business and community development in Washington County, GA. **Founded:** 1956.

50636 ■ Washington-Wilkes Chamber of Commerce
PO Box 661
Washington, GA 30673
Ph: (706)678-2013
Fax: (706)678-3033
Co. E-mail: chamber@washingtonwilkes.org
URL: http://www.washingtonwilkes.org
Contact: Allan Soto, President
Description: Businesses, organizations, and individuals concerned with the socioeconomic climate of Washington-Wilkes. Promotes business and community development in the Washington, GA area.

50637 ■ Wayne County Chamber of Commerce
124 NW Broad St.
Jesup, GA 31545-2708
Ph: (912)427-2028
Free: 888-224-5983
Fax: (912)427-2778
Co. E-mail: jriddle@waynechamber.com
URL: http://www.waynechamber.com
Contact: John Riddle, President
Description: Promotes business and community development in Wayne County, GA. **Founded:** 1948.

50638 ■ *What's News*
409 Elm Ave. Ste. A
Americus, GA 31709
Ph: (229)924-2646
Fax: (229)924-8784
Co. E-mail: rachael@americus.net
URL: http://www.americus-sumterchamber.com
Contact: Angela Westra, President
Released: Quarterly

50639 ■ Wheeler County Chamber of Commerce
PO Box 654
Alamo, GA 30411
Ph: (912)568-7808
Fax: (912)568-7808
Co. E-mail: wchamber1@windstream.net
URL: http://www.wheelercounty.org
Description: Promotes business and community development in Wheeler County, Georgia.

50640 ■ White County Chamber of Commerce and Development Authority (WCCCDA)
122 N Main St.
Cleveland, GA 30528
Ph: (706)865-5356
Free: 800-392-8279
Fax: (706)865-0758
Co. E-mail: melissa@whitecountychamber.org
URL: http://www.whitecountychamber.org
Contact: Melissa Leitzsey, President
Description: Promotes business and community development in White County, GA. Sponsors Easter Eggstravaganza Festival. **Scope:** small business. **Founded:** 1983. **Subscriptions:** books video recordings. **Publications:** *Tourism Brochure* (Annual); *The Chamber Advocate* (Monthly); *Industrial Development Brochure* (Semiannual); *Tourism Brochure* (Annual). **Educational Activities:** Business After Hours (Monthly). **Telecommunication Services:** whitecountychamber@whitecountychamber.org.

50641 ■ Wrightsville - Johnson County Chamber of Commerce
PO Box 94
Wrightsville, GA 31096
Ph: (478)864-7200

Fax: (478)864-7200
Co. E-mail: commerce@wrightsville-johnsoncounty.com
URL: http://www.wrightsville-johnsoncounty.com
Contact: Teresa Lamb, President
Description: Works to advance the commercial, agricultural, industrial, civic, and general interests of the City of Wrightsville, Johnson County, Georgia and its trade area.

50642 ■ *Your Business Connection*
11605 Haynes Bridge Rd., Ste. 100
Alpharetta, GA 30009
Ph: (770)993-8806
Free: 866-840-5770
Fax: (770)594-1059
Co. E-mail: info@gnfcc.com
URL: http://www.gnfcc.com
Contact: Lou Douglass, Chairman
Released: Monthly

MINORITY BUSINESS ASSISTANCE PROGRAMS

50643 ■ Atlanta Urban League - Entrepreneurship Center
100 Edgewood Ave. NE, No. 600
Atlanta, GA 30303-3070
Ph: (404)523-0131
Contact: Nancy Flake-Johnson, Chief Executive Officer
Description: Provides business mentoring and networking services to minority business owners in Atlanta.

50644 ■ Georgia Minority Business Enterprise Center - Georgia Tech Enterprise Innovation Institute
75 5th St., Ste. 700
Atlanta, GA 30308-0640
Ph: (404)894-2096
Fax: (404)894-8194
Co. E-mail: donna.ennis@innovate.gatech.edu
URL: http://www.georgiambec.org
Description: Provides emerging and existing minority businesses with business development and technical assistance.

50645 ■ Governor's Small Business Center
State Bldg.
1102 West Tower
200 Piedmont Ave.
1306 West Tower
Atlanta, GA 30334
Ph: (404)656-6315
Free: 800-495-0053
Fax: (404)657-4681
Co. E-mail: gsbc@doas.ga.gov
URL: http://www.doas.ga.gov
Description: Assists the development of small and minority-owned businesses.

FINANCING AND LOAN PROGRAMS

50646 ■ Accuitive Medical Ventures LLC / AMV Partners
2905 Premiere Pky., Ste. 150
Duluth, GA 30097
Ph: (678)812-1101
Fax: (678)417-7325
Co. E-mail: albert@amvpartners.com
URL: http://www.amvpartners.com
Contact: Charles E. Larsen, Managing Director
Investment Policies: Early stage and expansion. **Industry Preferences:** Medical and health. **Geographic Preference:** Southeast.

50647 ■ Alliance Technology Ventures
1990 Main St., Ste. 750
Sarasota, FL 34236
Ph: (678)336-2000

Fax: (678)336-2001
URL: http://www.alliancetechventures.com
Contact: Michael A. Henos, Partner
Preferred Investment Size: $500,000 to $5,000,000. **Industry Preferences:** Internet specific, semiconductors and other electronics, biotechnology, communications and media, computer software and services, computer hardware, medical and health. **Geographic Preference:** U.S.

50648 ■ C & B Capital LP
4200 Northside Pky., NW, Bldg. 1, Ste., 100
Atlanta, GA 30327
Ph: (404)841-3131
Fax: (404)841-3135
Co. E-mail: info@croft-bender.com
URL: http://www.croft-bender.com
Contact: Edward S. Croft, III, Managing Director
Industry Preferences: Internet specific, computer software and services, medical and health, industrial, communications and media. **Geographic Preference:** Southeast.

50649 ■ CGW Southeast Partners / Cravey, Green & Wahlen Inc.
1 Buckhead Plz.
3060 Peachtree Rd., Ste. 895
Atlanta, GA 30305
Ph: (404)841-3255
Fax: (678)705-9940
URL: http://www.cgwlp.com
Contact: Edwin Wahlen, Jr., Managing Partner
Preferred Investment Size: $25,000,000 to $200,000,000. **Industry Preferences:** Other products, industrial and energy, consumer related, medical and health, and communications and media. **Geographic Preference:** U.S.

50650 ■ Cordova Ventures
4080 McGinnis Ferry Rd., Ste. 1201
Alpharetta, GA 30005
Ph: (678)942-0300
Fax: (678)942-0301
URL: http://www.cordovaventures.com
Contact: Gerald F. Schmidt, Founder
E-mail: js@cordovaventures.com
Preferred Investment Size: $1,000,000 to $5,000,000. **Industry Preferences:** Computer software and services, medical and health, Internet specific, communications and media, other products, industrial and health, biotechnology, consumer related, semiconductors and other electronics. **Geographic Preference:** Southeast.

50651 ■ EGL Ventures
11 Piedmont Ctr., Ste. 412
3495 Piedmont Rd.
Atlanta, GA 30305
Ph: (404)949-8300
Fax: (404)949-8311
Co. E-mail: info@eglventures.com
URL: http://www.eglventures.com
Contact: Salvatore Massaro, Managing Partner
E-mail: samassaro@eglholdings.com
Preferred Investment Size: $500,000 to $6,000,000. **Industry Preferences:** Communications, computer hardware and software, Internet specific, semiconductors and other electronics, medical and health, industrial and energy, and manufacturing. **Geographic Preference:** Mid Atlantic, Midwest, Northeast, Midwest, and Southeast.

50652 ■ Equity-South Advisors, LLC / Grubb & Williams Ltd.
6 Piedmont Ctr., Ste. 130
Atlanta, GA 31119-1606
Ph: (404)237-6222
Fax: (404)261-1578
URL: http://www.equity-south.com
Contact: Douglas L. Diamond, Managing Director
Preferred Investment Size: $1,000,000 to $6,000,000. **Industry Preferences:** Communications, computer software, semiconductors and other electronics, medical and health, consumer related, industrial and energy, business service, and manufacturing. **Geographic Preference:** Mid Atlantic, Midwest, and Southeast.

50653 ■ First Growth Capital, Inc.
Best Western Plaza, Ste. 105
Forsyth, GA 31029
Ph: (478)994-9260
Fax: (478)994-1280
Contact: Vijay K. Patel, President
Preferred Investment Size: $100,000 to $300,000.

50654 ■ Healthcare Capital Partners
6065 Roswell Rd., Ste. 800
Atlanta, GA 30328
Ph: (678)244-5874
Fax: (404)250-9431
Co. E-mail: bplans@healthcarecp.com
URL: http://www.healthcarecp.com
Contact: Thomas Brooks, Founder
Preferred Investment Size: $100,000 to $1,500,000.
Investment Policies: Seed and early stage. **Industry Preferences:** Medical and health. **Geographic Preference:** Southeast.

50655 ■ Liveoak Equity Partners
1266 Park Vista Dr.
Atlanta, GA 30319
Ph: (404)790-2666
Fax: (404)842-1502
URL: http://www.liveoakequity.com
Contact: James Gilbert, Managing Partner
Preferred Investment Size: $500,000 to $6,000,000.
Industry Preferences: Computer software and services, Internet specific, communications and media, medical and health, biotechnology, semiconductors and other electronics. **Geographic Preference:** Southeast.

50656 ■ Noro-Moseley Partners
9 N. Pky. Sq.
4200 Northside Pky., NW
Atlanta, GA 30327-3054
Ph: (404)233-1966
Fax: (404)239-9280
Co. E-mail: info@noro-moseley.com
URL: http://www.noro-moseley.com
Contact: George Mackie, Partner
Preferred Investment Size: $3,000,000 to $10,000,000. **Industry Preferences:** Internet specific, computer software and services, medical and health, consumer related, other products, communications and media, computer hardware, semiconductors and other electronics, industrial and energy, and biotechnology. **Geographic Preference:** Southeast.

50657 ■ River Capital
2 Midtown Plz.
4200 Northside Pky., Bldg. 14, Ste. 250
Atlanta, GA 30327
Ph: (404)873-2166
Fax: (404)873-2158
Co. E-mail: info@river-capital.com
URL: http://www.river-capital.com
Contact: Jerry D. Wethington, Principal
E-mail: jwethington@river-capital.com
Preferred Investment Size: $3,000,000 to $50,000,000. **Industry Preferences:** Semiconductors and other electronics, medical and health, consumer related, industrial and energy, transportation, and manufacturing. **Geographic Preference:** U.S.

50658 ■ UPS Strategic Enterprise Fund
55 Glenlake Pky., NE
Bldg. 1, 4th Fl.
Atlanta, GA 30328
Ph: (404)828-8814
Fax: (404)828-8088
Co. E-mail: sef@ups.com
URL: http://www.ups.com/sef/sef_home.html
Preferred Investment Size: $250,000 to $1,500,000.
Industry Preferences: Internet specific, computer software and services, other products, computer hardware, communications and media, semiconductors and other electronics. **Geographic Preference:** U.S. and Canada.

50659 ■ Wachovia Capital Associates, Inc. (WCA)
191 Peachtree St., NE, 26th Fl.
Atlanta, GA 30303

Ph: (404)332-5000
Fax: (404)332-1392
URL: http://www.wachovia.com/wca
Contact: Andy Rose, Vice President
Preferred Investment Size: $5,000,000 to $15,000,000. **Industry Preferences:** Communications and media, industrial and energy, consumer related, other products, medical and health, Internet specific, computer software and services, semiconductors and other electronics, and computer hardware. **Geographic Preference:** Southeast.

PROCUREMENT ASSISTANCE PROGRAMS

50660 ■ Department of Administrative Services - Office of Small and Minority Business Division
200 Piedmont Ave. SE, Ste. 1804, W Tower
Atlanta, GA 30334-9010
Ph: (404)656-5514
Free: 800-495-0053
Fax: (404)651-9595
Co. E-mail: customerservice@doas.ga.gov
URL: http://doas.georgia.gov
Contact: Brad Douglas, Commissioner
Description: Helps small and minority businesses secure government procurement contracts.

50661 ■ Georgia Procurement Technical Assistance Center - Georgia Institute of Technology - Enterprise Innovation Institute
151 Osigian Blvd., Ste. 157
Warner Robins, GA 31088-7810
Ph: (478)953-1460
Fax: (478)953-3169
Co. E-mail: larry.selman@innovate.gatech.edu
URL: http://www.gtpac.org
Contact: Larry O. Selman, Counselor
E-mail: zack.osborne@edi.gatech.edu
Description: Provides marketing and procurement technical assistance to Georgia businesses, large and small, operating in the government procurement markets at the federal, state, and local levels as a prime contractor or subcontractor.

50662 ■ Georgia Procurement Technical Assistance Center - Outreach Center
125 Pine Ave., Ste. 220
Albany, GA 31702
Ph: (229)430-4189
Fax: (229)430-4200
Co. E-mail: clovia.hamilton@innovate.gatech.edu
URL: http://www.gtpac.org
Contact: Clovia Hamilton, Counselor
E-mail: helen.daughtry@innovate.gatech.edu
Description: Provides marketing and procurement technical assistance to Georgia businesses, large and small, operating in the government procurement markets at the federal, state, and local levels as a prime contractor or subcontractor.

50663 ■ Georgia Procurement Technical Assistance Center - Outreach Center
1054 Claussen Rd., Ste. 301
Augusta, GA 30907
Ph: (706)729-2076
Fax: (706)737-1420
Co. E-mail: todd.hurd@innovate.gatech.edu
URL: http://www.gtpac.org
Contact: Todd Heard, Counselor
E-mail: lloyd.watts@innovate.gatech.edu
Description: Provides marketing and procurement technical assistance to Georgia businesses, large and small, operating in the government procurement markets at the federal, state, and local levels as a prime contractor or subcontractor.

50664 ■ Georgia Procurement Technical Assistance Center - Outreach Center
The Burson Ctr.
500 Old Bremen Rd.
Carrollton, GA 30117
Ph: (678)890-2342

Fax: (770)834-2232
Co. E-mail: jerry.shadinger@innovate.gatech.edu
URL: http://www.gtpac.org
Contact: Jerry Shadinger, Counselor
E-mail: jerry.shadinger@innovate.gatech.edu
Description: Provides marketing and procurement technical assistance to Georgia businesses, large and small, operating in the government procurement markets at the federal, state, and local levels as a prime contractor or subcontractor.

50665 ■ Georgia Procurement Technical Assistance Center - Outreach Center
190 Technology Cir., Rm. 145
Savannah, GA 31407-3039
Ph: (912)963-2524
Fax: (912)963-2522
Co. E-mail: larry.blige@innovate.gatech.edu
URL: http://www.gtpac.org
Contact: Larry Blige, Counselor
E-mail: larry.blige@innovate.gatech.edu
Description: Provides marketing and procurement technical assistance to Georgia businesses, large and small, operating in the government procurement markets at the federal, state, and local levels as a prime contractor or subcontractor.

50666 ■ Georgia Procurement Technical Assistance Center - Outreach Center
3100 Gentian Blvd., Ste. 115
Columbus, GA 31907
Ph: (706)569-2688
Fax: (706)562-8447
Co. E-mail: roy.leggett@innovate.gatech.edu
URL: http://www.gtpac.org
Contact: Roy Leggett, Counselor
E-mail: roy.leggett@innovate.gatech.edu
Description: Provides marketing and procurement technical assistance to Georgia businesses, large and small, operating in the government procurement markets at the federal, state, and local levels as a prime contractor or subcontractor.

50667 ■ Georgia Procurement Technical Assistance Center - Outreach Center
Featherstone Center
999 Chestnut St. SE, Ste. 7
Gainesville, GA 30501
Ph: (770)535-5844
Fax: (770)535-5847
Co. E-mail: joe.beaulieu@innovate.gatech.edu
URL: http://www.gtpac.org
Contact: Joe Beaulieu, Counselor
E-mail: joe.beaulieu@innovate.gatech.edu
Description: Provides marketing and procurement technical assistance to Georgia businesses, large and small, operating in the government procurement markets at the federal, state, and local levels as a prime contractor or subcontractor.

50668 ■ Georgia Procurement Technical Assistance Center - UIDA Business Services
86 S. Cobb Dr.
MZ0510
Marietta, GA 30063
Ph: (770)494-0431
Fax: (770)494-1236
Co. E-mail: georgew@uida.org
URL: http://www.uida.org
Contact: George Williams, Program Manager
E-mail: georgew@uida.org
Description: Helps establish business relationships between Indian enterprises and private industry.

50669 ■ US Small Business Administration
PO Box 611
Warner Robins, GA 31099-0611
Ph: (478)926-7446
Fax: (478)926-3832
Co. E-mail: thomas.hollingsworth@robins.af.mil
URL: http://www.sba.gov/
Contact: T.C. Hollingsworth
E-mail: tholling@wrdisol.robins.af.mil
Description: Covers activities for Warner Robins ALC (Warner Robins, GA) and the Marine Corps Logistics Command (Albany, GA).

INCUBATORS/RESEARCH AND TECHNOLOGY PARKS

50670 ■ Advanced Technology Development Center
Georgia Institute of Technology
Enterprise Innovation Institute
75 5th St. NW, Ste. 202
Atlanta, GA 30308
Ph: (404)894-3575
Fax: (404)894-4545
URL: http://www.atdc.org
Contact: Barbara Miller, Coordinator, Administration
Description: A start-up accelerator helping technology entrepreneurs in Georgia.

50671 ■ Columbus State University Regional Technology Incubator
Cunningham Center for Leadership Development
3100 Gentian Blvd.
Columbus, GA 31907
Ph: (706)568-8339
Fax: (706)562-8447
Co. E-mail: Miller_Susan@colstate.edu
URL: http://www.columbusincubator.org/
Description: A non-profit organization dedicated to housing and nurturing new companies by providing the space and the support needed to grow technology-related jobs in the Chattahoochee Valley area.

50672 ■ Computer Link Professional Services and Software Training Center
3140 Augusta Tech Dr.
Augusta, GA 30906
Ph: (706)792-0900
Fax: (706)792-9905
Co. E-mail: info@ComputerLinkAugusta.com
URL: http://www.computerlinkaugusta.com

50673 ■ Georgia BioBusiness Center
University of Georgia
220 Riverbend Rd.
Athens, GA 30602-7411
Ph: (706)583-8209
Fax: (706)542-3804
Co. E-mail: gbbc@uga.edu
URL: http://www.ovpr.uga.edu/gbbc/
Contact: Margaret Wagner Dahl, Director
Description: A small business incubator affiliated with several established and startup bioscience companies with research and technology ties to UGA. The program enables bioscience startup companies to accelerate their early growth through access to management expertise and state-of-the-art instrumentation.

50674 ■ Gwinnett Innovation Park
4355 Shackleford Rd.
Norcross, GA 30093
Ph: (770)564-5666
Co. E-mail: info@gwinnettinnovationpark.com
URL: http://gwinnettinnovationpark.com/
Contact: Bonnie Herron, Director
Description: A small business incubator that supports entrepreneurs and their companies though its Launch Pad for small and fast-growing businesses.

50675 ■ Hispanic American Center for Economic Development
Georgia Hispanic Chamber of Commerce
99 W Paces Ferry, Ste. 200
Atlanta, GA 30305
Ph: (770)457-6770

Fax: (770)457-6944
Co. E-mail: info@haced.org
URL: http://www.ghcc.org/haced.asp
Description: A small business incubator founded in 2001 by the Georgia Hispanic Chamber of Commerce in order to advance the formation and growth of Hispanic Businesses in the state of Georgia.

50676 ■ MicroBusiness Enterprise Center
230 S. Jackson St., Ste. 315
Albany, GA 31701
Ph: (229)483-7650
Fax: (229)430-3989
Co. E-mail: jcraft@albany.ga.us
URL: http://www.albany.ga.us/ced/ced_enterprise_ctr.htm
Description: A community resource providing assistance and facilities to create an environment that will stimulate small business formation, growth and survival.

50677 ■ South DeKalb Business Incubator
1599-A Memorial Dr., SE
Atlanta, GA 30317
Ph: (404)329-4508
Fax: (404)378-0768
URL: http://www.sdbusinc.net
Contact: Tonya Weaver, Office Manager

50678 ■ Southwest Georgia Business Development Center
1150 Industrial Dr.
Vienna, GA 31092
Ph: (229)268-8944
Co. E-mail: foster2@sowega.net
URL: http://www.crispdooly.org/
Description: A small business incubator established to create an environment for the development, growth, and success of emerging service and light manufacturing businesses in the southwest region of Georgia.

EDUCATIONAL PROGRAMS

50679 ■ East Georgia College
131 College Cir.
Swainsboro, GA 30401
Ph: (478)289-2017
Fax: (478)289-2140
URL: http://www.ega.edu
Description: Two-year college offering a program in small business management.

50680 ■ Emory University - Center for Lifelong Learning
Center For Longlife Learning Mailstop 1256/001/1AD
Atlanta, GA 30322-1790
Ph: (404)727-6000
Fax: (404)727-6001
Co. E-mail: evening@emory.edu
URL: http://www.cll.emory.edu
Description: Offers courses for owners--or potential owners--of small business enterprises. Also offers courses through the School of Business Administration.

50681 ■ Georgia Highlands College - Floyd Campus
3175 Cedartown Hwy.
Rome, GA 30162-1864
Ph: (706)802-5000
Free: 800-332-2406
Fax: (706)295-6341
URL: http://www.highlands.edu
Description: Two-year college offering a small business management program.

50682 ■ University of West Georgia - Richards College of Business
1601 Maple St.
Carrollton, GA 30118
Ph: (678)839-6467
Fax: (678)839-5040
Co. E-mail: khannah@westga.edu
URL: http://www.westga.edu
Description: Presents business-related courses, seminars, and workshops to persons interested in professional and staff development. Also provides counseling, databases, and case studies to those interested in starting or building a small business.

LEGISLATIVE ASSISTANCE

50683 ■ Georgia House of Representatives
State Capitol
Atlanta, GA 30334
Ph: (404)656-0305
Fax: (404)656-6897
Co. E-mail: riley.lowry@house.ga.us
URL: http://www.legis.state.ga.us
Contact: Riley Lowry, Director

PUBLICATIONS

50684 ■ *Atlanta Magazine*
1330 West Peachtree St., Ste. 450
Atlanta, GA 30309-3214
Ph: (404)872-3100
Fax: (404)870-6230
Co. E-mail: atlmag@atlanta.com
URL: http://atlantamag.atlanta.com

50685 ■ *The Atlanta Small Business Monthly*
6129 Oakbrook Pkwy.
Norcross, GA 30093
Ph: (770)446-5434
Fax: (770)446-3970
Co. E-mail: asbm@bellsouth.net

50686 ■ *Starting and Operating a Business in Georgia: A Step-by-Step Guide*
PSI Research
300 N. Valley Dr.
Grants Pass, OR 97526
Ph: (503)479-9464
Free: 800-228-2275
Fax: (503)476-1479
Co. E-mail: psi2@magick.net
Ed: Michael D. Jenkins. **Released:** Revised edition, 1992. **Price:** $29.95 (looseleaf binder); $24.95 (paper). **Description:** Part of the Successful Business Library series.

PUBLISHERS

50687 ■ Franklin-Sarrett Publishers L.L.C. (FSP)
3761 Vineyard Trace NE
Marietta, GA 30062-5227
Ph: (770)578-9410
Free: 800-346-0656
Fax: (770)573-2222
Co. E-mail: info@franklin-sarrett.com
URL: http://www.franklin-sarrett.com
Contact: Ed Katz, President
Description: Description: Publishes material for small business. Accepts unsolicited manuscripts. Reaches market through reviews and listings and wholesalers. **Founded:** 1992.

50688 ■ Toca Family Publishing
245 N Highland Ave., Ste. 230-230
Atlanta, GA 30307-1919
Ph: (404)348-4065
Fax: (404)348-4469
Contact: Tiffany Wright, Manager
Description: Description: Publishes books on small business financing.

SMALL BUSINESS DEVELOPMENT CENTERS

50689 ■ Hawaii Small Business Development Center - Lead Office
308 Kamehameha Ave., Ste. 201
Hilo, HI 96720
Ph: (808)974-7515
Fax: (808)974-7683
URL: http://www.hawaii-sbdc.org
Contact: John Furstenwerth, Director (Acting)
Description: Represents and promotes the small business sector. Provides management assistance to current and prospective small business owners. Helps to improve management skills and expand the products and services of members.

50690 ■ Honolulu Small Business Development Center
1833 Kalakaua Ave., Ste. 400
Honolulu, HI 96815
Ph: (808)945-1430
Fax: (808)945-1432
URL: http://www.hawaii-sbdc.org/honolulucenter.htm
Contact: Joseph Burns, Director
Description: Represents and promotes the small business sector. Provides management assistance to current and prospective small business owners. Helps to improve management skills and expand the products and services of members.

50691 ■ Kaua'i Small Business Development Center
Kaua'i Community College
3-1901 Kaumuali'i Hwy.
Lihue, HI 96766
Ph: (808)241-3148
Fax: (808)241-3229
URL: http://www.hawaii-sbdc.org/kauaicenter.htm
Contact: John Latkiewicz, Director
Description: Represents and promotes the small business sector. Provides management assistance to current and prospective small business owners. Helps to improve management skills and expand the products and services of members.

50692 ■ Maui Small Business Development Center
1300 N Holopono St., Ste. 213
Kihei, HI 96753
Ph: (808)875-5990
Fax: (808)875-5989
URL: http://www.hawaii-sbdc.org/mauicenter.htm
Description: Represents and promotes the small business sector. Provides management assistance to current and prospective small business owners. Helps to improve management skills and expand the products and services of members.

SMALL BUSINESS ASSISTANCE PROGRAMS

50693 ■ Chamber of Commerce of Hawaii - Small Business Council
1132 Bishop St., Ste. 402
Honolulu, HI 96813
Ph: (808)545-4300
Fax: (808)545-4369
Co. E-mail: info@cochawaii.org
URL: http://www.cochawaii.org
Contact: Jim Tollefson, Chief Executive Officer
Description: Offers business referrals, financial planning, loan packaging, and business, marketing, and entrepreneurship counseling. **Publications:** *Chamber of Commerce of Hawaii--Business Networking Directory.* **Telecommunication Services:** customerservice@harrisinfo.com.

50694 ■ Hawaii Department of Business, Economic Development, and Tourism - Strategic Marketing & Support
PO Box 2359
Honolulu, HI 96804
Ph: (808)586-2423
Fax: (808)587-2790
Co. E-mail: library@dbedt.hawaii.gov
URL: http://www.hawaii.gov/dbedt
Contact: Theodore E. Liu, Director
Description: Promotes new enterprise development in Hawaii from the U.S. mainland and international business centers.

50695 ■ University of Hawaii - Pacific Business Center Program
College of Business Administration
2404 Maile Way, A413
Honolulu, HI 96822
Ph: (808)956-6286
Fax: (808)956-6278
Co. E-mail: pbcp@hawaii.edu
URL: http://pbchawaii.com/Default.asp
Description: Provides counseling and referral services to businesses. Conduct some research for program clients.

SCORE OFFICES

50696 ■ SCORE of Hawaii
500 Ala Moana Blvd., Rm. 1-306A
Honolulu, HI 96813
Ph: (808)547-2700
Fax: (808)541-2950
Co. E-mail: hawaiiscore@hawaiiscore.org
URL: http://www.hawaiiscore.org
Contact: Cliff Silverstein, Chairman
Description: Creates opportunities for small business owners and potential business owners to achieve success. Provides business assistance to develop business plans, stimulate business growth and identify problems and potential solutions. Promotes entrepreneur education in Hawaii.

BETTER BUSINESS BUREAUS

50697 ■ Better Business Bureau of Hawaii
1132 Bishop St., Ste. 615
Honolulu, HI 96813-2813
Ph: (808)536-6956
Free: 877-222-6551
Fax: (808)628-3970
URL: http://hawaii.bbb.org
Contact: Bonnie Horibata, Vice President
Description: Seeks to promote and foster ethical relationship between businesses and the public through voluntary self-regulation, consumer and business education, and service excellence. Provides information to help consumers and businesses make informed purchasing decisions and avoid costly scams and frauds; settles consumer complaints through arbitration and other means.

CHAMBERS OF COMMERCE

50698 ■ Australian/American Chamber of Commerce - Hawaii
1000 Bishop St., Penthouse
Honolulu, HI 96813
Ph: (808)526-2242
Fax: (808)534-0475
Co. E-mail: info@aacchawaii.org
URL: http://www.aacchawaii.org
Contact: John Fyfe, President
Description: Provides forum for the discussion of vital issues and for the dissemination of useful information on Australian/American trade and economic relations. **Founded:** 1985.

50699 ■ Chamber of Commerce of Hawaii
1132 Bishop St., Ste. 402
Honolulu, HI 96813
Ph: (808)545-4300
Fax: (808)545-4369
URL: http://www.cochawaii.com
Contact: Jim Tollefson, President
E-mail: jtollefson@cochawaii.org
Description: Promotes business and economic growth throughout the state. **Founded:** 1850. **Publications:** *Chamber of Commerce of Hawaii--Business Networking Directory* (Annual); *Who's Who in Government in Hawaii* (Biennial).

50700 ■ *The Chamber Connection*
106 Kamehameha Ave.
Hilo, HI 96720
Ph: (808)935-7178
Fax: (808)961-4435
Co. E-mail: admin@hicc.biz
URL: http://www.hicc.biz
Contact: Mike Gleason, President
Released: Monthly

50701 ■ *Connections*
270 Ho'okahi St., Ste. 212
Wailuku, HI 96793
Ph: (808)224-0081
Fax: (808)244-0083
Co. E-mail: info@mauichamber.com
URL: http://www.mauichamber.com
Contact: Pamela Tumpap, President
Released: Quarterly

50702 ■ *Connections*
75-5737 Kaukini Hwy., Ste. 208
Kailua Kona, HI 96740-1725

Ph: (808)329-1758
Fax: (808)329-8564
Co. E-mail: info@kona-kohala.com
URL: http://www.kona-kohala.com
Contact: Vivian Landrum, President
Released: Monthly

**50703 ■ Hawaii Island Chamber of
Commerce (HICC)**
106 Kamehameha Ave.
Hilo, HI 96720
Ph: (808)935-7178
Fax: (808)961-4435
Co. E-mail: admin@hicc.biz
URL: http://www.hicc.biz
Contact: Mike Gleason, President
Description: Business and professional people in
the community who work together to make Hawaii
Island a better place to live and do business. Provides
leadership via services and advocacy for the busi-
ness community and to promote the economic well-
being of the community as a whole. **Founded:** 1898.
Publications: The Chamber Connection (Monthly);
The Hawaii Island Chamber of Commerce Directory
& Guide (Annual). **Awards:** ATHENA Award (Annual).

**50704 ■ The Hawaii Island Chamber of
Commerce Directory & Guide**
106 Kamehameha Ave.
Hilo, HI 96720
Ph: (808)935-7178
Fax: (808)961-4435
Co. E-mail: admin@hicc.biz
URL: http://www.hicc.biz
Contact: Mike Gleason, President
Released: Annual

**50705 ■ Hawaii Island Portuguese Chamber
of Commerce**
PO Box 1839
Hilo, HI 96721
Ph: (808)974-6262
Co. E-mail: mmiranda50@hotmail.com
URL: http://www.hipcc.org
Contact: Marc W. Miranda, President
Description: Promotes commerce, industry, and
agriculture throughout the County and State of
Hawaii. **Founded:** 1982. **Awards:** Hawaii Island
Portuguese Chamber of Commerce Scholarship Fund
(Biennial).

**50706 ■ Hawaii Korean Chamber of
Commerce (HKCC)**
PO Box 2296
Honolulu, HI 96804
Ph: (808)544-3581
Co. E-mail: gina.nakamura@centralpacificbank.com
URL: http://www.hkccweb.org/en
Contact: Gina Nakamura, President
Description: Strives to fulfill the goals and purposes
of supporting the Korean people and its business
community. **Founded:** 1940. **Awards:** Hawaii Korean
Chamber of Commerce Annual Scholarship Award
(Annual).

**50707 ■ Honolulu Japanese Chamber of
Commerce (HJCC)**
2454 S Beretania St., Ste. 201
Honolulu, HI 96826
Ph: (808)949-5531
Fax: (808)949-3020
Co. E-mail: info@honolulujapanesechamber.org
URL: http://www.honolulujapanesechamber.org
Contact: Wayne Ishihara, President
Description: Provides the organizational means for
support of functions of groups within the Hawaiian
community or Japan-related groups in pursuit of
cultural, economic, governmental, and social develop-
ment. **Founded:** 1900. **Publications:** Shoko News-
letter (Monthly); Honolulu Japanese Chamber of
Commerce--Membership Directory (Annual).

**50708 ■ Honolulu Japanese Junior Chamber
of Commerce (HJCC)**
2454 S Beretania St., Ste. 201
Honolulu, HI 96826
Ph: (808)949-5531

Fax: (808)949-3020
Co. E-mail: info@honolulujapanesechamber.org
URL: http://www.honolulujapanesechamber.org
Contact: Wayne Ishihara, President
Description: Aims to provide young people of
Honolulu a medium for leadership training and civic
improvement. **Founded:** 1900. **Publications:**
SHOKO.

**50709 ■ Kailua Chamber of Commerce
(KCOC)**
PO Box 1496
Kailua, HI 96734
Ph: (808)261-2727
Free: 888-261-7997
Co. E-mail: kcoc@kailuachamber.com
URL: http://www.kailuachamber.com
Contact: Puna Nam, President
Description: Promotes Kailua as a community, and
supports members and businesses individually and
collectively. **Founded:** 1957. **Awards:** Volunteer of
the Year Award (Annual).

50710 ■ Kauai Chamber of Commerce
PO Box 1969
Lihue, HI 96766
Ph: (808)245-7363
Fax: (808)245-8815
Co. E-mail: info@kauaichamber.org
URL: http://www.kauaichamber.org
Contact: Randall Francisco, President
Description: Businesses and professional men and
women. Represents all elements of Kauai's business
and industry. Works to advance the commercial,
financial, industrial, civic and social well-being of the
county of Kaua'i and the state of Hawaii. **Founded:**
1913. **Publications:** Update (Monthly); Kauai Cham-
ber of Commerce--Community Guide & Business Directory; Kaua'i The Garden Island.

**50711 ■ Kona Kohala Chamber of Commerce
(KKCC)**
75-5737 Kaukini Hwy., Ste. 208
Kailua Kona, HI 96740-1725
Ph: (808)329-1758
Fax: (808)329-8564
Co. E-mail: info@kona-kohala.com
URL: http://www.kona-kohala.com
Contact: Vivian Landrum, President
Description: Promotes business and community
development in West Hawaii. **Publications:** Connec-
tions (Monthly). **Educational Activities:** Membership
Meeting (Periodic).

50712 ■ Maui Chamber of Commerce
270 Ho'okahi St., Ste. 212
Wailuku, HI 96793
Ph: (808)224-0081
Fax: (808)244-0083
Co. E-mail: info@mauichamber.com
URL: http://www.mauichamber.com
Contact: Pamela Tumpap, President
Description: Promotes a healthy economic environment for business. Advocates responsive government and quality education, while preserving the
unique community characteristics of Maui. Supports
civic, social, and cultural programs designed to
increase the functional and aesthetic values of the
community. **Publications:** Connections (Quarterly).

50713 ■ Moloka'i Chamber of Commerce
PO Box 515
Kaunakakai, HI 96748-0515
Ph: (808)553-4482
Fax: (808)553-4482
Co. E-mail: molokaichamber@hawaiiantel.biz
URL: http://www.molokaichamber.org
Contact: Robert Stephenson, President
Description: Promotes business and community
development in the Moloka'i area.

**50714 ■ Native Hawaiian Chamber of
Commerce (NHCC)**
PO Box 597
Honolulu, HI 96809
Ph: (808)531-3744

Fax: (808)732-7059
Co. E-mail: robson@hawaii.rr.com
URL: http://www.nativehawaiian.cc
Description: Participates in economic, social, and
public affairs in Hawaiian community. **Founded:**
1974. **Publications:** The Voice of Hawaiian Business
(Monthly).

50715 ■ Update
PO Box 1969
Lihue, HI 96766
Ph: (808)245-7363
Fax: (808)245-8815
Co. E-mail: info@kauaichamber.org
URL: http://www.kauaichamber.org
Contact: Randall Francisco, President
Released: Monthly

50716 ■ The Voice of Hawaiian Business
PO Box 597
Honolulu, HI 96809
Ph: (808)531-3744
Fax: (808)732-7059
Co. E-mail: robson@hawaii.rr.com
URL: http://www.nativehawaiian.cc
Released: Monthly

MINORITY BUSINESS
ASSISTANCE PROGRAMS

**50717 ■ Honolulu Minority Business
Enterprise Center**
University of Hawaii at Manoa
Shidler College of Business
2404 Maile Way, D-307
Honolulu, HI 96822
Ph: (808)956-0850
Fax: (808)956-0851
Co. E-mail: info@honolulu-mbdc.org
URL: http://www.honolulu-mbdc.org
Contact: Dana Hauanio, Director
Description: Established to increase the number of
minority-owned businesses and strengthen existing
ones.

FINANCING AND LOAN
PROGRAMS

50718 ■ HMS Hawaii Management Partners
Davies Pacific Ctr.
841 Bishop St., Ste. 860
Honolulu, HI 96813
Ph: (808)545-3755
Fax: (808)531-2611
Co. E-mail: info@hmshawaii.com
URL: http://www.hmshawaii.com
Contact: Richard G. Grey, Partner
Preferred Investment Size: $500,000 to $1,500,000.
Industry Preferences: Communications and media,
Internet specific, medical and health, other products,
and industrial and energy. **Geographic Preference:**
Hawaii and West Coast.

INCUBATORS/RESEARCH AND
TECHNOLOGY PARKS

50719 ■ Agribusiness Incubator Program
University of Hawaii
3050 Maile Way, Gilmore 115
Honolulu, HI 96822
Ph: (808)956-3530
Fax: (808)956-3547
Co. E-mail: agincubator@ctahr.hawaii.edu
URL: http://aip.hawaii.edu/default.aspx
Contact: Steven Chiang, Director
Description: A small business incubator providing
business consulting services to agriculture-related
businesses throughout the State of Hawaii, maximiz-
ing their chance of business viability and success, in
order to grow the State's diversified agriculture
industry.

50720 ■ Manoa Innovation Center (MIC)
2800 Woodlawn Dr.
Honolulu, HI 96822

Ph: (808)539-3806
Fax: (808)539-3795
Co. E-mail: htdc@htdc.org
URL: http://www.htdc.org
Contact: Philip Bossert, Executive Director
Description: The MIC is a high technology small business incubator that forges ties between entrepreneurs and university-oriented research and development.

LEGISLATIVE ASSISTANCE

50721 ■ Hawaii House Labor and Public Employment Committee
Hawaii State Capital, Rm 326
415 S. Beretania St.
Honolulu, HI 96813
Ph: (808)586-6180
Fax: (808)586-6189
Co. E-mail: reprhoads@capitol.hawaii.gov
URL: http://www.capitol.hawaii.gov
Contact: Karl Rhoads, Chairperson

50722 ■ Hawaii Senate Consumer Protection Committee
Hawaii State Capitol, Rm. 320
415 S Beretania St.
Honolulu, HI 96813
Ph: (808)586-8400
Fax: (808)586-8404
Co. E-mail: repherkes@capitol.hawaii.gov
URL: http://www.capitol.hawaii.gov
Contact: Robert N. Herkes, Chairperson

50723 ■ Hawaii Senate Water and Land Use Planning Committee
State Capitol Bldg., Rm. 201
415 S. Beretania St.
Honolulu, HI 96813
Ph: (808)586-7335
Fax: (808)586-7339
Co. E-mail: seninouye@capital.hawaii.gov
URL: http://www.capitol.hawaii.gov

PUBLICATIONS

50724 ■ *Business Basics in Hawaii: Secrets of Starting Your Own Business in Our State*
2840 Kolowalu St.
Honolulu, HI 96822
Ph: (808)956-8694
Fax: (808)988-6052
Co. E-mail: uhpbook@hawaii.edu
Ed: Dennis K. Kondo. **Released:** 1988. **Price:** $14.95.

50725 ■ *Hawaii Business*
825 Keeaumoku
Honolulu, HI 96808
Ph: (808)537-9500
Fax: (808)537-6455
Co. E-mail: hawbus@pixi.com
URL: http://www.hawaiibusinessmagizine.com

50726 ■ *Pacific Business News*
PO Box 833
Honolulu, HI 96808-0833

Ph: (808)596-2021
Fax: (808)591-2321
URL: http://www.amcity.com

50727 ■ *Smart Start your Hawaii Business*
PSI Research
300 N. Valley Dr.
Grants Pass, OR 97526
Ph: (503)479-9464
Free: 800-228-2275
Fax: (503)476-1479
Co. E-mail: info@psi-research.com
URL: http://www.psi-research.com
Ed: Michael D. Jenkins and Franklin Forbes. **Released:** Revised edition, 1992. **Price:** $29.95 (looseleaf binder); $24.95 (paper). **Description:** Part of the Successful Business Library series.

50728 ■ *Starting and Operating a Business in Hawaii: A Step-by-Step Guide*
PSI Research
300 N. Valley Dr.
Grants Pass, OR 97526
Ph: (503)479-9464
Free: 800-228-2275
Fax: (503)476-1479
Co. E-mail: psi2@magick.net
Ed: Michael D. Jenkins. **Released:** Revised edition, 1992. **Price:** $29.95 (looseleaf binder); $24.95 (paper). **Description:** Part of the Successful Business Library series.

SMALL BUSINESS DEVELOPMENT CENTERS

50729 ■ College of Southern Idaho Small Business Development Center
PO Box 1238
Twin Falls, ID 83303-1238
Ph: (208)732-6221
Free: 800-680-0274
Fax: (208)736-4705
Co. E-mail: info@csi.edu
URL: http://www.csi.edu/support/isbdc/SBDC.html
Contact: Bryan J. Matsuoka, Director
Description: Represents and promotes the small business sector. Provides management assistance to current and prospective small business owners. Helps to improve management skills and expand the products and services of members.

50730 ■ Idaho Small Business Development Center - Lead Office
Boise State University
1910 University Dr.
Boise, ID 83725-1655
Ph: (208)426-1640
Free: 800-225-3815
Fax: (208)426-3877
Co. E-mail: info@idahosbdc.org
URL: http://www.idahosbdc.org
Contact: James E. Hogge, Director
Founded: 1986. **Publications:** *Your Idaho Business Plan.* **Educational Activities:** Small Business Information Fair (Quarterly).

50731 ■ *Your Idaho Business Plan*
Boise State University
1910 University Dr.
Boise, ID 83725-1655
Ph: (208)426-1640
Free: 800-225-3815
Fax: (208)426-3877
Co. E-mail: info@idahosbdc.org
URL: http://www.idahosbdc.org
Contact: James E. Hogge, Director
Price: $15.75, plus 5 percent Idaho Sales tax.

SMALL BUSINESS ASSISTANCE PROGRAMS

50732 ■ Idaho Department of Commerce - Department of Economic Development
700 W State St.
Boise, ID 83720
Ph: (208)334-2470
Free: 800-842-5858
Fax: (208)334-2631
URL: http://commerce.idaho.gov/business
Contact: Lane Packwood, Administrator
Description: Provides information on regulations, permits, and licenses. Sponsors the Idaho Business Network. Offers international trade assistance, and travel and tourism promotion.

SCORE OFFICES

50733 ■ SCORE Eastern Idaho
2300 N Yellowstone Hwy., Ste. 100B
Idaho Falls, ID 83401
Ph: (208)523-1022
Fax: (208)528-7127
Co. E-mail: score295@iictr.com
URL: http://www.scoreideast.org
Founded: 1985.

50734 ■ SCORE Treasure Valley
380 E Parkcenter Blvd., Ste. 330
Boise, ID 83706
Ph: (208)334-1696
Fax: (208)334-9353
Co. E-mail: tvscore240@yahoo.com
URL: http://www.idahotvscore.org
Contact: Jeff Weeks, Chairman
Description: Provides professional guidance and information to maximize the success of existing and merging small businesses. Promotes entrepreneur education in Treasure Valley area, Idaho. **Founded:** 1964.

BETTER BUSINESS BUREAUS

50735 ■ Better Business Bureau of Eastern Idaho and Western Wyoming
453 River Pkwy.
Idaho Falls, ID 83402-3615
Ph: (208)523-9754
Fax: (208)227-1603
Co. E-mail: info@idahofalls.bbb.org
URL: http://idahofalls.bbb.org
Contact: Donna Oe, President
Description: Seeks to promote and foster the highest ethical relationship between businesses and the public through voluntary self-regulation, consumer and business education, and service excellence. Provides information to help consumers and businesses make informed purchasing decisions and avoid costly scams and frauds; settles consumer complaints through arbitration and other means. **Founded:** 1987.

50736 ■ Better Business Bureau of Southwest Idaho and Eastern Oregon
4355 Emerald St., Ste. 290
Boise, ID 83706
Ph: (208)342-4649
Fax: (208)342-5116
Co. E-mail: info@boise.bbb.org
URL: http://boise.bbb.org
Contact: Nora Carpenter, Executive Director
Description: Seeks to promote and foster ethical relationship between businesses and the public through voluntary self-regulation, consumer and business education, and service excellence. Provides information to help consumers and businesses make informed purchasing decisions and avoid costly scams and frauds; settles consumer complaints through arbitration and other means.

CHAMBERS OF COMMERCE

50737 ■ Bayview Chamber of Commerce
PO Box 121
Bayview, ID 83803-0121
Ph: (208)683-3293
Co. E-mail: manska2@aol.com
URL: http://www.bayviewidaho.org
Contact: Bob Prince, President
Description: Promotes business, community development, and tourism in Bayview, ID. Sponsors Bayview Days and July 4th Festival. **Founded:** 1958.

50738 ■ *Boise Metro Business Today*
PO Box 2368
Boise, ID 83701
Ph: (208)472-5200
Fax: (208)472-5201
Co. E-mail: info@boisechamber.org
URL: http://www.boisechamber.org
Contact: Bill Connors, President
Released: Monthly **Price:** $24, /year for nonmembers.

50739 ■ Boise Metro Chamber of Commerce
PO Box 2368
Boise, ID 83701
Ph: (208)472-5200
Fax: (208)472-5201
Co. E-mail: info@boisechamber.org
URL: http://www.boisechamber.org
Contact: Bill Connors, President
Description: Promotes business and community development in the Boise, ID area. **Founded:** 1885. **Publications:** *Boise Metro Business Today* (Monthly).

50740 ■ Buhl Chamber of Commerce
716 U.S. Hwy. 30 E
Buhl, ID 83316
Ph: (208)543-6682
Fax: (208)543-2185
Co. E-mail: michelle@buhlchamber.org
URL: http://www.buhlchamber.org
Contact: Rick Stoltenburg, President
Description: Promotes business and community development in Buhl, ID. **Founded:** 1920. **Awards:** Extra Mile Award (Monthly).

50741 ■ *Business Connection*
PO Box 123
Kuna, ID 83634
Ph: (208)922-9254
Co. E-mail: information@kunachamber.com
URL: http://www.kunachamber.com
Contact: Sherry Maestas, President
Released: Quarterly **Price:** $10, /year.

50742 ■ *Business Directory*
PO Box 571
Cascade, ID 83611
Ph: (208)382-3833
Fax: (208)382-3833
Co. E-mail: info@cascadechamber.com
URL: http://www.cascadechamber.com
Released: Periodic

50743 ■ Business Journal
PO Box 8936
Moscow, ID 83843-0180
Ph: (208)882-1800
Free: 800-380-1801
Fax: (208)882-6186
Co. E-mail: info@moscowchamber.com
URL: http://www.moscowchamber.com
Contact: Steven Hacker, Executive Director
Released: Quarterly **Price:** free for members.

50744 ■ Business Lines
231 N 3rd Ave.
Sandpoint, ID 83864
Ph: (208)263-2161
Free: 800-800-2106
Fax: (208)265-5289
Co. E-mail: info@sandpointchamber.com
URL: http://sandpointchamber.org
Contact: Kate McAlister, President
Released: Monthly

50745 ■ Business News
PO Box 819
Caldwell, ID 83606
Ph: (208)459-7493
Free: 866-206-6944
Fax: (208)454-1284
Co. E-mail: chamber@ci.caldwell.id.us
URL: http://chamber.cityofcaldwell.com
Contact: Theresa Hardin, Executive Director
Released: Monthly

50746 ■ Business and Relocation Guide
PO Box 2420
Sun Valley, ID 83353
Ph: (208)726-3423
Free: 866-305-0408
Fax: (208)726-4533
Co. E-mail: chamberinfo@visitsunvalley.com
URL: http://www.visitsunvalley.com
Contact: Carol Waller, Executive Director
Released: Annual **Price:** $15, /year.

50747 ■ Caldwell Chamber of Commerce (CCC)
PO Box 819
Caldwell, ID 83606
Ph: (208)459-7493
Free: 866-206-6944
Fax: (208)454-1284
Co. E-mail: chamber@ci.caldwell.id.us
URL: http://chamber.cityofcaldwell.com
Contact: Theresa Hardin, Executive Director
Description: Promotes business and community development in Caldwell, ID. **Founded:** 1897. **Publications:** Business News (Monthly).

50748 ■ Cascade Chamber of Commerce (CCC)
PO Box 571
Cascade, ID 83611
Ph: (208)382-3833
Fax: (208)382-3833
Co. E-mail: info@cascadechamber.com
URL: http://www.cascadechamber.com
Description: Promotes business and community development in Cascade, ID. Sponsors Thunder Mountain Days, Winter Jamboree, and Annual Christmas Lighting Contest. **Publications:** Business Directory (Periodic).

50749 ■ Chamber Chatter
10 River St.
Wallace, ID 83873
Ph: (208)753-7151
Fax: (208)753-7151
Co. E-mail: director@wallaceidahochamber.com
URL: http://www.wallaceidahochamber.com
Contact: Diane Reifer, Coordinator
Released: Quarterly

50750 ■ Chamber of Commerce Newsletter
PO Box 162
St. Maries, ID 83861
Ph: (208)245-3563

Fax: (208)245-3477
Co. E-mail: manager@stmarieschamber.org
URL: http://www.stmarieschamber.org
Contact: Shirley Ackerman, President
Released: Monthly **Price:** free.

50751 ■ Chamber News
309 State St.
Weiser, ID 83672
Ph: (208)414-0452
Fax: (208)414-0451
Co. E-mail: info@weiserchamber.com
URL: http://www.weiserchamber.com
Contact: Glory Gray, President
Released: Monthly

50752 ■ Chamber Notes
PO Box 626
Pocatello, ID 83204
Ph: (208)233-1525
Fax: (208)233-1527
Co. E-mail: dbeckett@pocatelloidaho.com
URL: http://www.pocatelloidaho.com
Contact: Mathew Hunter, President
Released: Monthly

50753 ■ Chamber Reminder
PO Box 592
Emmett, ID 83617
Ph: (208)365-3485
Fax: (208)365-3220
Co. E-mail: chamber@emmettidaho.com
URL: http://www.emmettidaho.com
Contact: Chuck Rolland, President
Released: Weekly

50754 ■ Chamber Today
PO Box 626
Pocatello, ID 83204
Ph: (208)233-1525
Fax: (208)233-1527
Co. E-mail: dbeckett@pocatelloidaho.com
URL: http://www.pocatelloidaho.com
Contact: Mathew Hunter, President
Released: Monthly

50755 ■ Coeur d'Alene Area Chamber of Commerce (CDACC)
105 N 1st St.
Coeur d'Alene, ID 83814
Ph: (208)664-3194
Free: 877-782-9232
Fax: (208)667-9338
Co. E-mail: info@cdachamber.com
URL: http://www.cdachamber.com/default.aspx
Contact: Todd Christensen, President
Description: Promotes business and community development in Kootenai County, ID. **Publications:** Visitor Guide; A Report to Membership (Monthly). **Educational Activities:** Upbeat Breakfast (Monthly).

50756 ■ Come Out and Play
PO Box 250
Driggs, ID 83422
Ph: (208)354-2500
Fax: (208)354-2517
Co. E-mail: tvcc@tetonvalleychamber.com
URL: http://www.tetonvalleychamber.com
Contact: Kevin Owyang, President

50757 ■ Council Chamber of Commerce
PO Box 527
Council, ID 83612
Ph: (208)253-6830
Co. E-mail: councilchamber@ctcweb.net
URL: http://www.councilchamberofcommerce.com
Contact: Ken Bell, President
Description: Strives to promote and perpetuate the business, commercial, manufacturing, agriculture, and civic interests of the City of Council and its nearby territory.

50758 ■ Donnelly Area Chamber of Commerce
PO Box 83
Donnelly, ID 83615-0083

Ph: (208)325-3978
Co. E-mail: donnellychamber@frontiernet.net
URL: http://www.donnellychamber.org
Contact: Cheryl Teed, President
Description: Promotes business and community development in the Donnelly, ID area. Sponsors festivals and hall of fame; presents business and service awards. Operates county welcome center and tourism development.

50759 ■ Fruitland Chamber of Commerce (FCC)
PO Box 408
Fruitland, ID 83619
Ph: (208)452-4350
Fax: (208)452-5028
Co. E-mail: chamber@fmtc.com
URL: http://www.fruitlandidaho.org
Contact: Judy Cordezia, Board Member
Description: Promotes business and community development in Fruitland, ID. Conducts annual Spring Festival and Auction.

50760 ■ Gem County Chamber of Commerce (GCCC)
PO Box 592
Emmett, ID 83617
Ph: (208)365-3485
Fax: (208)365-3220
Co. E-mail: chamber@emmettidaho.com
URL: http://www.emmettidaho.com
Contact: Chuck Rolland, President
Description: Promotes business and community development in Gem County, ID. **Publications:** Chamber Reminder (Weekly).

50761 ■ Glenns Ferry Chamber of Commerce (GFCC)
7 E 1st Ave.
Glenns Ferry, ID 83623
URL: http://www.glennsferryidaho.org
Contact: Susan Case, President
Description: Promotes business and community development in Glenns Ferry, ID. Sponsors annual Oregon Trail historical re-enactment. Conducts charitable activities. **Publications:** Glenns Ferry Directory.

50762 ■ Glenns Ferry Directory
7 E 1st Ave.
Glenns Ferry, ID 83623
URL: http://www.glennsferryidaho.org
Contact: Susan Case, President

50763 ■ Grangeville Chamber of Commerce (GCC)
PO Box 212
Grangeville, ID 83530
Ph: (208)983-0460
Fax: (208)983-1429
Co. E-mail: gvillecc@camasnet.com
URL: http://www.grangevilleidaho.com
Contact: Melinda Hall, President
Description: Promotes business and community development in Grangeville, ID. **Founded:** 1906. **Telecommunication Services:** chamber@grangevilleidaho.com.

50764 ■ Greater Bear Lake Valley Chamber of Commerce
915 Washington St.
Montpelier, ID 83254
Ph: (208)847-0067
Co. E-mail: info@bearlakechamber.org
URL: http://bearlakechamber.org
Contact: Lance Fitzsimmons, Chairman
Description: Promotes business and tourism for the economic growth of Montpelier, ID.

50765 ■ Greater Blackfoot Area Chamber of Commerce (GBACC)
PO Box 801
Blackfoot, ID 83221-0801
Ph: (208)785-0510

Fax: (208)785-7974
Co. E-mail: chamber@blackfootchamber.org
URL: http://www.blackfootchamber.org
Contact: Stephanie Govatos, Executive Director
Description: Promotes business and community development in the Blackfoot, ID area. **Founded:** 1939. **Awards:** Top Senior Student Awards (Annual).

50766 ■ Greater Bonners Ferry Chamber of Commerce (GBFCC)
PO Box X
Bonners Ferry, ID 83805
Ph: (208)267-5277
Fax: (208)267-5922
Co. E-mail: info@bonnersferrychamber.com
URL: http://www.bonnersferrychamber.com
Contact: Mike Sloan, President
Description: Promotes business, community development, and tourism in Boundary County, ID. **Founded:** 1908.

50767 ■ Greater Pocatello Chamber of Commerce (GPCC)
PO Box 626
Pocatello, ID 83204
Ph: (208)233-1525
Fax: (208)233-1527
Co. E-mail: dbeckett@pocatelloidaho.com
URL: http://www.pocatelloidaho.com
Contact: Mathew Hunter, President
Description: Promotes business and community development in the Pocatello, ID area. Sponsors leadership program. **Founded:** 1901. **Publications:** *Chamber Notes* (Monthly); *Chamber Today* (Monthly); *Welcome to Pocatello* (Semiannual).

50768 ■ Greater Sandpoint Chamber of Commerce (GSCC)
231 N 3rd Ave.
Sandpoint, ID 83864
Ph: (208)263-2161
Free: 800-800-2106
Fax: (208)265-5289
Co. E-mail: info@sandpointchamber.com
URL: http://sandpointchamber.org
Contact: Kate McAlister, President
Description: Promotes business and community development in the Sandpoint, ID area. **Founded:** 1978. **Publications:** *Business Lines* (Monthly). **Awards:** Business of the Month (Monthly); Tourism Member of the Year (Annual). **Telecommunication Services:** judy@sandpointchamber.com.

50769 ■ Greater Weiser Area Chamber of Commerce (GWACC)
309 State St.
Weiser, ID 83672
Ph: (208)414-0452
Fax: (208)414-0451
Co. E-mail: info@weiserchamber.com
URL: http://www.weiserchamber.com
Contact: Glory Gray, President
Description: Promotes business and community development in Weiser, ID. Sponsors National Old-time Fiddlers' Contest, Christmas Parade, Spring Crab Feed and Auction, and Fall Chili Cook-Off and Mud Bog. Operates Vendome Event Center. **Founded:** 1948. **Publications:** *Chamber News* (Monthly). **Awards:** Community Award (Annual); Nick Speropolus Sportsmanship Award (Annual).

50770 ■ Hagerman Valley Chamber of Commerce (HVCC)
PO Box 599
Hagerman, ID 83332-0599
Ph: (208)837-9131
Co. E-mail: info@hagermanchamber.com
URL: http://www.hagermanchamber.com
Contact: Mark Bulduc, President
Description: Promotes business and community development in the Hagerman, ID area.

50771 ■ Hailey Chamber of Commerce
PO Box 100
Hailey, ID 83333
Ph: (208)788-3484

Fax: (208)578-1595
Co. E-mail: info@haileyidaho.com
URL: http://www.haileyidaho.com
Contact: Heather La Monica Deckard, Executive Director
Description: Promotes business and community development in Hailey, ID. **Publications:** *Hailey Chamber News* (Monthly).

50772 ■ *Hailey Chamber News*
PO Box 100
Hailey, ID 83333
Ph: (208)788-3484
Fax: (208)578-1595
Co. E-mail: info@haileyidaho.com
URL: http://www.haileyidaho.com
Contact: Heather La Monica Deckard, Executive Director
Released: Monthly

50773 ■ Historic Silver Valley Chamber of Commerce
10 Station Ave.
Kellogg, ID 83837
Ph: (208)784-0821
Fax: (208)783-4343
Co. E-mail: rachelhopper@minershatrealty.com
URL: http://www.silvervalleychamber.com
Contact: Debbie Angle, President
Description: Promotes business and community development in Kellogg and the Silver Valley, ID area.

50774 ■ Jerome Chamber of Commerce
104 W Main St., Ste. 101
Jerome, ID 83338
Ph: (208)324-2711
Fax: (208)324-6881
Co. E-mail: jeromechamber@visitjeromeidaho.com
URL: http://visitjeromeidaho.com
Contact: Jon Melone, Executive Director
Description: Promotes business and community development in Jerome, ID. **Founded:** 1920. **Publications:** *News and Views* (Quarterly). **Educational Activities:** General Membership (Monthly).

50775 ■ Kamiah Chamber of Commerce
PO Box 1124
Kamiah, ID 83536-1124
Ph: (208)935-2290
Fax: (208)935-2290
Co. E-mail: info@kamiahchamber.com
URL: http://www.kamiahchamber.com
Contact: Robert Simmons, President
Description: Promotes business and community development in Kamiah, ID.

50776 ■ Kuna Chamber of Commerce
PO Box 123
Kuna, ID 83634
Ph: (208)922-9254
Co. E-mail: information@kunachamber.com
URL: http://www.kunachamber.com
Contact: Sherry Maestas, President
Description: Promotes business and community development in Kuna, ID. **Publications:** *Business Connection* (Quarterly); *Kuna Directory* (Periodic).

50777 ■ Lava Hot Springs Chamber of Commerce (LHSCC)
PO Box 238
Lava Hot Springs, ID 83246
Ph: (208)776-5500
Co. E-mail: findout@lavahotsprings.org
URL: http://www.lavahotsprings.org
Contact: Vicky Lyon, President
Description: Promotes business and community development in the Lava Hot Springs, ID area.

50778 ■ Lewiston Chamber of Commerce (LCC)
111 Main St., Ste. 120
Lewiston, ID 83501
Ph: (208)743-3531
Free: 800-473-3543

Fax: (208)743-2176
Co. E-mail: info@lewistonchamber.org
URL: http://www.lewistonchamber.org
Contact: Keith Havens, President
Description: Promotes business and community development in Lewiston, ID. Sponsors the Great Snake Lake Steelhead Derby. **Founded:** 1908. **Publications:** *Local Organizations List* (Annual); *Membership and Buyer's Guide*; *Valley Currents* (Monthly).

50779 ■ *Local Organizations List*
111 Main St., Ste. 120
Lewiston, ID 83501
Ph: (208)743-3531
Free: 800-473-3543
Fax: (208)743-2176
Co. E-mail: info@lewistonchamber.org
URL: http://www.lewistonchamber.org
Contact: Keith Havens, President
Released: Annual

50780 ■ *Member in the Spotlight*
PO Box 7
Meridian, ID 83680-0007
Ph: (208)888-2817
Fax: (208)888-2682
Co. E-mail: info@meridianchamber.org
URL: http://www.meridianchamber.org
Contact: Teri Sackman, President
Released: Monthly

50781 ■ *Membership and Buyer's Guide*
111 Main St., Ste. 120
Lewiston, ID 83501
Ph: (208)743-3531
Free: 800-473-3543
Fax: (208)743-2176
Co. E-mail: info@lewistonchamber.org
URL: http://www.lewistonchamber.org
Contact: Keith Havens, President

50782 ■ *Membership Directory and Buyers' Guide*
127 E Main St.
Rexburg, ID 83440
Ph: (208)356-5700
Free: 888-463-6880
Fax: (208)356-5799
Co. E-mail: info@rexburgchamber.com
URL: http://www.rexcc.com
Contact: Donna Benfield, Executive Director
Released: Annual

50783 ■ *Meridian Buyer's Guide*
PO Box 7
Meridian, ID 83680-0007
Ph: (208)888-2817
Fax: (208)888-2682
Co. E-mail: info@meridianchamber.org
URL: http://www.meridianchamber.org
Contact: Teri Sackman, President
Released: Annual

50784 ■ Meridian Chamber of Commerce
PO Box 7
Meridian, ID 83680-0007
Ph: (208)888-2817
Fax: (208)888-2682
Co. E-mail: info@meridianchamber.org
URL: http://www.meridianchamber.org
Contact: Teri Sackman, President
Description: Provides ways to become involved in the community through leadership opportunities, business advocacy, networking, and promotion of individual businesses in Meridian, ID. **Publications:** *Member in the Spotlight* (Monthly); *Meridian Buyer's Guide* (Annual). **Educational Activities:** Business After Hours (Monthly). **Awards:** Meridian Small Business Person of the Year (Annual); Small Business of the Year (Annual).

50785 ■ Mini-Cassia Chamber of Commerce
1177 7th St.
Heyburn, ID 83336
Ph: (208)679-4793

Fax: (208)679-4794
Co. E-mail: director@pmt.org
URL: http://www.minicassiachamber.com
Contact: Kae Cameron, Executive Director
Description: Promotes business and community development and tourism in the Minidoka/Cassia County, IL area. Sponsors festivals. **Founded:** 1993.

50786 ■ Moscow Chamber of Commerce
PO Box 8936
Moscow, ID 83843-0180
Ph: (208)882-1800
Free: 800-380-1801
Fax: (208)882-6186
Co. E-mail: info@moscowchamber.com
URL: http://www.moscowchamber.com
Contact: Steven Hacker, Executive Director
Description: Promotes business, community development, and tourism in the Moscow, Idaho area. **Founded:** 1949. **Publications:** *Business Journal* (Quarterly). **Educational Activities:** The Business Forum. **Awards:** Agricultural Scholarship (Annual). **Telecommunication Services:** staff@moscowchamber.com.

50787 ■ Mountain Home Chamber of Commerce
205 N 3rd St. E
Mountain Home, ID 83647
Ph: (208)587-4334
Fax: (208)587-0042
Co. E-mail: chamber@mountainhomechamber.com
URL: http://www.mountainhomechamber.com
Contact: Mindy Cuevas, Executive Director
Description: Provides a format in which members can share and grow in ideas, leadership, community commitment and economic vitality. Promotes business and community development. Sponsors Air Force Appreciation Day. **Founded:** 1948.

50788 ■ *Nampa Chamber*
315 11th Ave. S
Nampa, ID 83651
Ph: (208)466-4641
Free: 877-20-NAMPA
Fax: (208)466-4677
Co. E-mail: info@nampa.com
URL: http://www.nampa.com
Contact: Debbie Kling, President
Released: Monthly

50789 ■ Nampa Chamber of Commerce
315 11th Ave. S
Nampa, ID 83651
Ph: (208)466-4641
Free: 877-20-NAMPA
Fax: (208)466-4677
Co. E-mail: info@nampa.com
URL: http://www.nampa.com
Contact: Debbie Kling, President
Description: Promotes business and community development in Nampa, ID. **Founded:** 1892. **Publications:** *Nampa Chamber* (Monthly).

50790 ■ *News and Views*
104 W Main St., Ste. 101
Jerome, ID 83338
Ph: (208)324-2711
Fax: (208)324-6881
Co. E-mail: jeromechamber@visitjeromeidaho.com
URL: http://visitjeromeidaho.com
Contact: Jon Melone, Executive Director
Released: Quarterly

50791 ■ Post Falls Chamber of Commerce (PFCC)
201 E 4th Ave.
Post Falls, ID 83854
Ph: (208)773-5016
Free: 800-292-2553
Fax: (208)773-3843
Co. E-mail: info@postfallschamber.com
URL: http://www.postfallschamber.com
Contact: Ms. Pam Houser, President
Description: Promotes business and community development in Post Falls, ID. Sponsors Old-Time Fiddler's Contest, Post Falls Pioneer Festival, Christmas tree lighting ceremony, and Summer Community Picnic. **Founded:** 1964.

50792 ■ Preston Chamber of Commerce
49 N State, Ste. A
Preston, ID 83263
Ph: (208)852-2703
Co. E-mail: pacc@ida.net
URL: http://www.prestonidaho.org
Contact: Pennie Christensen, Executive Director
Description: Promotes business and community development in the Preston, ID area.

50793 ■ Priest Lake Chamber of Commerce
PO Box 174
Coolin, ID 83821
Ph: (208)443-3191
Free: 888-774-3785
Fax: (208)443-4061
Co. E-mail: info@priestlake.org
URL: http://www.priestlake.org
Contact: Kathleen Martin, President
Description: Promotes business and community development in the Coolin, ID area.

50794 ■ Priest River Chamber of Commerce
PO Box 929
Priest River, ID 83856
Ph: (208)448-2721
Co. E-mail: prchamber@conceptcable.com
URL: http://www.priestriverchamber.com
Contact: Kerri Martin, President
Description: Unites local businesses and citizens towards the common goal of prosperity for the community.

50795 ■ *A Report to Membership*
105 N 1st St.
Coeur d'Alene, ID 83814
Ph: (208)664-3194
Free: 877-782-9232
Fax: (208)667-9338
Co. E-mail: info@cdachamber.com
URL: http://www.cdachamber.com/default.aspx
Contact: Todd Christensen, President
Released: Monthly

50796 ■ Rexburg Chamber of Commerce
127 E Main St.
Rexburg, ID 83440
Ph: (208)356-5700
Free: 888-463-6880
Fax: (208)356-5799
Co. E-mail: info@rexburgchamber.com
URL: http://www.rexcc.com
Contact: Donna Benfield, Executive Director
Description: Enhances the vitality and economic health of Rexburg and Madison County. Sponsors many activities throughout the year to bring thousands of people to Rexburg like Sunbird Program, Idaho International Dance and Music Festival, and July 4th Whoopee Days Celebrations. **Publications:** *Membership Directory and Buyers' Guide* (Annual); *Rexburg Chamber of Commerce--Membership Directory and Buyers Guide* (Annual). **Educational Activities:** Folk Dance (Annual). **Telecommunication Services:** info@rexcc.com.

50797 ■ St. Maries Chamber of Commerce
PO Box 162
St. Maries, ID 83861
Ph: (208)245-3563
Fax: (208)245-3477
Co. E-mail: manager@stmarieschamber.org
URL: http://www.stmarieschamber.org
Contact: Shirley Ackerman, President
Description: Promotes business and community development in St. Maries, ID and the surrounding area. **Publications:** *Chamber of Commerce Newsletter* (Monthly).

50798 ■ Salmon River Chamber of Commerce
PO Box 289
Riggins, ID 83549
Ph: (208)628-3778
Free: 866-221-3901
Co. E-mail: cfriend@frontiernet.net
URL: http://www.rigginsidaho.com
Description: Promotes business and community development in Salmon River, ID area.

50799 ■ Salmon Valley Chamber of Commerce
200 Main St., Ste. 1
Salmon, ID 83467
Ph: (208)756-2100
Free: 800-727-2540
Co. E-mail: info@salmonchamber.com
URL: http://www.salmonchamber.com
Contact: Cori Allen, President
Description: Works to generate support for and promote the well-being of the businesses in the greater Salmon Valley.

50800 ■ Soda Springs Chamber of Commerce
PO Box 697
Soda Springs, ID 83276
Ph: (208)547-2600
Fax: (208)547-2601
Co. E-mail: sodacoc@sodachamber.com
URL: http://www.sodachamber.com
Description: Promotes business and community development in Soda Springs, ID.

50801 ■ Stanley - Sawtooth Chamber of Commerce
PO Box 8
Stanley, ID 83278-0008
Ph: (208)774-3411
Free: 800-878-7950
Co. E-mail: info@stanleycc.org
URL: http://www.stanleycc.org
Description: Helps to promote the Stanley area.

50802 ■ Sun Valley-Ketchum Chamber and Visitors Bureau
PO Box 2420
Sun Valley, ID 83353
Ph: (208)726-3423
Free: 866-305-0408
Fax: (208)726-4533
Co. E-mail: chamberinfo@visitsunvalley.com
URL: http://www.visitsunvalley.com
Contact: Carol Waller, Executive Director
Description: Promotes business development and tourism in the Sun Valley-Ketchum, ID area. **Publications:** *Vacation Planner* (Annual); *Business and Relocation Guide* (Annual). **Telecommunication Services:** cwaller@visitsunvalley.com.

50803 ■ Teton Valley Chamber of Commerce (TVCC)
PO Box 250
Driggs, ID 83422
Ph: (208)354-2500
Fax: (208)354-2517
Co. E-mail: tvcc@tetonvalleychamber.com
URL: http://www.tetonvalleychamber.com
Contact: Kevin Owyang, President
Description: Promotes business and community development in Driggs, ID. **Subscriptions:** maps. **Publications:** *Come Out and Play.*

50804 ■ Twin Falls Area Chamber of Commerce
858 Blue Lakes Blvd. N
Twin Falls, ID 83301
Ph: (208)733-3974
Free: 866-TWIN-FALLS
Fax: (208)733-9216
Co. E-mail: info@twinfallschamber.com
URL: http://www.twinfallschamber.com
Contact: Shawn Barigar, President
Description: Promotes business and community development in the Twin Falls, ID area. **Founded:** 1920. **Telecommunication Services:** shawn@twinfallschamber.com; bobbi@twinfallschamber.com.

50805 ■ *Vacation Planner*
PO Box 2420
Sun Valley, ID 83353
Ph: (208)726-3423
Free: 866-305-0408
Fax: (208)726-4533
Co. E-mail: chamberinfo@visitsunvalley.com
URL: http://www.visitsunvalley.com
Contact: Carol Waller, Executive Director
Released: Annual **Price:** free.

50806 ■ *Valley Currents*
111 Main St., Ste. 120
Lewiston, ID 83501
Ph: (208)743-3531
Free: 800-473-3543
Fax: (208)743-2176
Co. E-mail: info@lewistonchamber.org
URL: http://www.lewistonchamber.org
Contact: Keith Havens, President
Released: Monthly

50807 ■ *Visitor Guide*
105 N 1st St.
Coeur d'Alene, ID 83814
Ph: (208)664-3194
Free: 877-782-9232
Fax: (208)667-9338
Co. E-mail: info@cdachamber.com
URL: http://www.cdachamber.com/default.aspx
Contact: Todd Christensen, President

50808 ■ Wallace Chamber of Commerce
10 River St.
Wallace, ID 83873
Ph: (208)753-7151
Fax: (208)753-7151
Co. E-mail: director@wallaceidahochamber.com
URL: http://www.wallaceidahochamber.com
Contact: Diane Reifer, Coordinator
Description: Promotes business and community development in Wallace, ID and surrounding Silver Valley area. Sponsors Huckleberry/Heritage Festival, 5K Fun Run, Yuletide Lighting Celebration, and Joint Chamber Auction. **Founded:** 1964. **Publications:** *Chamber Chatter* (Quarterly). **Educational Activities:** Wallace Chamber of Commerce Luncheon (Semimonthly). **Awards:** Chamber Member of the Year (Annual); Citizen of the Year (Annual); Volunteer of the Year (Annual).

50809 ■ *Welcome to Pocatello*
PO Box 626
Pocatello, ID 83204
Ph: (208)233-1525
Fax: (208)233-1527
Co. E-mail: dbeckett@pocatelloidaho.com
URL: http://www.pocatelloidaho.com
Contact: Mathew Hunter, President
Released: Semiannual

FINANCING AND LOAN PROGRAMS

50810 ■ Akers Capital, LLC
5207 Sunrise Blvd., Ste. 220
Fair Oaks, CA 95628
Ph: (916)966-2236
Fax: (916)966-2239
URL: http://www.akerscapital.com
Contact: Roger Akers, Managing Partner
Preferred Investment Size: $500,000 to $3,000,000. **Investment Policies:** Early, first, and second stage. **Industry Preferences:** Communications, software, and Internet specific. **Geographic Preference:** Northern California and Northwest.

PROCUREMENT ASSISTANCE PROGRAMS

50811 ■ Idaho Procurement Technical Assistance Center - Idaho Department of Commerce
700 W State St.
Boise, ID 83720-0093
Ph: (208)334-2650
Fax: (208)334-2631
Co. E-mail: sundi.smith@commerce.idaho.gov
URL: http://idahoworks.com
Contact: Sundi Smith, Program Manager

INCUBATORS/RESEARCH AND TECHNOLOGY PARKS

50812 ■ Bonner Business Center (BBC)
804 Airport Way
Sandpoint, ID 83864
Ph: (208)263-4073
Fax: (208)263-4609
Co. E-mail: info@bonnerbusinesscenter.com
URL: http://www.bonnerbusinesscenter.com/
Contact: Wally Schmidt, Manager
Description: A small business incubator assisting the development of new firms in northern Idaho. The BBC is also equipped with a fully licensed shared-use food production facility.

50813 ■ College of Southern Idaho - Small Business Incubator
Evergreen Bldg. C77
315 Falls Ave.
Twin Falls, ID 83303-1238
Ph: (208)732-6451
Fax: (208)455-1492
Co. E-mail: bmatsuoka@csi.edu
URL: http://www.csi.edu/support/isbdc/incubator/bus-inc.htm
Contact: Brian J. Matsuoka, Manager
Description: Using the resources of the College of Southern Idaho, this small business incubator offers emerging firms affordable office space, business consulting, and a variety of other services.

50814 ■ CSI Business Incubator
College of Southern Idaho
315 Falls Ave., Evergreen Bldg. C77
Twin Falls, ID 83303-1238
Ph: (208)732-6450
Fax: (208)733-9316
Co. E-mail: bMatsuoka@csi.edu
URL: http://www.csi.edu/support/isbdc/incubator/bus-inc.htm
Description: A small business incubator providing entrepreneurs with adequate facilities and resources needed to develop new businesses; expanding the economic base of South-Central Idaho by assisting value-added, non-competing new businesses; creating jobs in the Magic Valley area; and improving new businesses' chances for success.

50815 ■ East Central Idaho Planning Development Association - Upper Snake River Valley Incubator
310 N 2nd E
Rexburg, ID 83440
Ph: (208)356-4524
Fax: (208)356-4544
URL: http://www.ecipda.org
Contact: Ted Hendricks, Manager

50816 ■ Idaho Innovation Center, Inc.
2300 N Yellowstone Hwy.
Idaho Falls, ID 83401
Ph: (208)523-1026
Fax: (208)528-7127
URL: http://www.iictr.com
Contact: Jeff Krantz, Executive Director
Description: A small business incubator.

50817 ■ North Central Idaho Business Technology Incubator
121 W Sweet Ave.
Moscow, ID 83843
Ph: (208)885-3800
Fax: (208)885-3803
Co. E-mail: edc@moscow.com
URL: http://www.bti.uro.uidaho.edu
Contact: Barbara Crouch, Director
Description: A small business incubator offering affordable space for emerging technology-based firms. Space can be configured to suit the needs of tenants.

50818 ■ Panhandle Area Council - Business Center for Innovation and Development
11100 N Airport Dr.
Hayden, ID 83835-9798
Ph: (208)772-0584

Fax: (208)772-6196
URL: http://www.pacni.org/incubator.html
Contact: Jeff Deffenbaugh, Executive Director
Description: A small business incubator that assists entrepreneurs in the business start-up process and gives aid to new businesses to help ensure their survival.

50819 ■ Salmon Valley Business Innovation Center
803 Monroe St.
Salmon, ID 83467
Ph: (208)756-1505
Fax: (208)756-1506
Co. E-mail: wayne@centurytel.net
URL: http://www.svbic.com/
Contact: Rene Toman, Executive Director
Description: A project developed to encourage new business growth in the community while creating greater employment opportunities for residents of the Salmon Valley. Its objective is to help new and relocating businesses become successful by providing capital cost reductions during their start up phase, in the form of lease rate discounts, shared office equipment and resources, and business development assistance.

EDUCATIONAL PROGRAMS

50820 ■ BYU Idaho
525 S Center St.
Rexburg, ID 83460-0800
Ph: (208)496-2411
Fax: (208)496-9803
Co. E-mail: infodesk@byui.edu
URL: http://www.byui.edu
Description: General studies associates degrees.

50821 ■ College of Southern Idaho - School of Vo-Tech Education
PO Box 1238
Twin Falls, ID 83303-1238
Ph: (208)733-9554
Free: 800-680-0274
Fax: (208)736-4705
Co. E-mail: info@csi.edu
URL: http://www.csi.edu
Description: Vocation-technical school offering customized training; industry-specific upgrade training; independent business and agribusiness management training; entry/re-entry training; and retraining for displaced workers.

50822 ■ Eastern Idaho Technical College
1600 S 25th East
Idaho Falls, ID 83404
Ph: (208)524-3000
Free: 800-662-0261
Fax: (208)524-3007
Co. E-mail: pamela.levan@my.eitc.edu
URL: http://www.eitc.edu
Description: Vocation-technical school offering customized training; industry-specific upgrade training; independent business and agribusiness management training; entry/re-entry training; and retraining for displaced workers.

50823 ■ Idaho State University - College of Technology
921 S 8th Ave., Stop 8380
Pocatello, ID 83209-8380
Ph: (208)282-2622
Fax: (208)282-5195
Co. E-mail: ctech@isu.edu
URL: http://www.isu.edu/ctech
Description: Vocation-technical school offering customized training; industry-specific upgrade training; independent business and agribusiness management training; entry/re-entry training; and retraining for displaced workers.

50824 ■ Lewis-Clark State College - School of Technology
500 8th Ave.
Lewiston, ID 83501
Ph: (208)792-5272
Free: 800-933-5272

Fax: (208)792-2816
Co. E-mail: admissions@lcsc.edu
URL: http://www.lcsc.edu
URL(s): www.lcsc.edu/ti. **Description:** Vocation-technical school offering customized training; industry-specific upgrade training; independent business and agribusiness management training; entry/re-entry training; and retraining for displaced workers.

50825 ■ North Idaho College - Professional - Technical Education
1000 W Garden Ave.
Coeur D'Alene, ID 83814
Ph: (208)769-3300
Free: 877-404-4536
Fax: (208)769-3459
URL: http://www.nic.edu
Description: Vocation-technical school offering customized training; industry-specific upgrade training; independent business and agribusiness manage-

ment training; entry/re-entry training; and retraining for displaced workers.

LEGISLATIVE ASSISTANCE

50826 ■ Idaho Department of Commerce
700 W State St.
Boise, ID 83720-0093
Ph: (208)334-2470
Free: 800-842-5858
Fax: (208)334-2631
URL: http://commerce.idaho.gov/

PUBLICATIONS

50827 ■ *The Idaho Business Review*
PO Box 8866
Boise, ID 83707
Ph: (208)336-3768
Fax: (208)336-5534

50828 ■ *North Idaho Business Journal*
201 N., Second St.
Coeur D'Alene, ID 83814
Ph: (208)664-8176
Fax: (208)664-0212
Co. E-mail: editor@cbapress.com

50829 ■ *Starting and Operating a Business in Idaho: A Step-by-Step Guide*
PSI Research
300 N. Valley Dr.
Grants Pass, OR 97526
Ph: (503)479-9464
Free: 800-228-2275
Fax: (503)476-1479
Co. E-mail: psi2@magick.net
Ed: Michael D. Jenkins. **Released:** Revised edition, 1992. **Price:** $29.95 (looseleaf binder); $24.95 (paper). **Description:** Part of the Successful Business Library series.

SMALL BUSINESS DEVELOPMENT CENTERS

50830 ■ Illinois Small Business Development Center at Black Hawk College
4703 16th St., Ste. G
Moline, IL 61265-7066
Ph: (309)796-5714
Co. E-mail: johnsonma@bhc.edu
URL: http://www.bhc.edu/business-training/businesses
Description: Represents and promotes the small business sector. Provides management assistance to current and prospective small business owners. Helps to improve management skills and expand the products and services of members.

50831 ■ Illinois Small Business Development Center at Bradley University
141 Jobst Hall
1501 W Bradley Ave.
Peoria, IL 61606-1048
Ph: (309)677-4321
Fax: (309)677-3386
Co. E-mail: illinoissbdc@bradley.edu
URL: http://www.bradley.edu/turnercenter/centers/sbdc.html
Contact: Ken Klotz, Director
Description: Represents and promotes the small business sector. Provides management assistance to current and prospective small business owners. Helps to improve management skills and expand the products and services of members.

50832 ■ Illinois Small Business Development Center at Chicago Community Ventures
20 S Clark St., Ste. 2650
Chicago, IL 60603
Ph: (312)960-0322
Fax: (312)960-0310
Co. E-mail: tcassell@chiventures.org
URL: http://www.chiventures.org
Contact: Tom Cassell, Director
Description: Represents and promotes the small business sector. Provides management assistance to current and prospective small business owners. Helps to improve management skills and expand the products and services of members.

50833 ■ Illinois Small Business Development Center at Chicago State University/Greater Southside
9501 S King Dr.
BHS 601
Chicago, IL 60628-1598
Ph: (773)995-3938
Fax: (773)821-2841
Co. E-mail: i-conda@csu.edu
URL: http://www.csu.edu/sbdc/contact.htm
Contact: Isabelle Conda, Director
Description: Represents and promotes the small business sector. Provides management assistance to current and prospective small business owners. Helps to improve management skills and expand the products and services of members.

50834 ■ Illinois Small Business Development Center at College of DuPage
2525 Cabot Dr.
Lisle, IL 60532
Ph: (630)942-2771
Fax: (630)505-4931
Co. E-mail: gaydav@cod.edu
URL: http://www.cod.edu/Academic/Bus_Tech/center_entrepreneur/sm_business.htm
Description: Represents and promotes the small business sector. Provides management assistance to current and prospective small business owners. Helps to improve management skills and expand the products and services of members.

50835 ■ Illinois Small Business Development Center at College of Lake County
19351 W Washington St., Rm. T-302
Grayslake, IL 60030-1198
Ph: (847)543-2033
Fax: (847)223-9371
Co. E-mail: illinoissbdc@clcillinois.edu
URL: http://www.clcillinois.edu/depts/sbd.asp
Contact: Jan Bauer, Director
URL(s): wpdi.clcillinois.edu/sbdc. **Description:** Represents and promotes the small business sector. Provides management assistance to current and prospective small business owners. Helps to improve management skills and expand the products and services of members.

50836 ■ Illinois Small Business Development Center at Danville Area Community College
2917 N Vermillion St.
Danville, IL 61832
Ph: (217)442-7232
Fax: (217)442-1897
Co. E-mail: sbdc@dacc.edu
URL: http://www.ildceo.net/dceo/Bureaus/Entrepreneurship+and+Small+Business/sbdc.htm
Contact: Michael O'Brian, Director
URL(s): www.dacc.edu/sbdc. **Description:** Represents and promotes the small business sector. Provides management assistance to current and prospective small business owners. Helps to improve management skills and expand the products and services of members.

50837 ■ Illinois Small Business Development Center at Duman Microenterprise Center
216 W Jackson Blvd., Ste. 700
Chicago, IL 60606
Ph: (312)673-3429
Co. E-mail: sbdcdumancenter@jvschicago.org
URL: http://www.jvschicago.org/duman
Description: Represents and promotes the small business sector. Provides management assistance to current and prospective small business owners. Helps to improve management skills and expand the products and services of members.

50838 ■ Illinois Small Business Development Center at Elgin Community College
1700 Spartan Dr.
Elgin, IL 60123-7193
Ph: (847)214-7488

Fax: (847)931-3911
Co. E-mail: sbdc@elgin.edu
URL: http://www.ildceo.net/dceo/Bureaus/Entrepreneurship+and+Small+Business/sbdc.htm
Description: Represents and promotes the small business sector. Provides management assistance to current and prospective small business owners. Helps to improve management skills and expand the products and services of members.

50839 ■ Illinois Small Business Development Center at Evanston Technology Innovation Center
820 Davis St., Ste. 137
Evanston, IL 60201
Ph: (847)866-1817
Fax: (847)866-1808
Co. E-mail: info@sbdc-evanston.org
URL: http://www.glrppr.org/contacts/org_view.cfm?orgid=1012
Description: Represents and promotes the small business sector. Provides management assistance to current and prospective small business owners. Helps to improve management skills and expand the products and services of members.

50840 ■ Illinois Small Business Development Center at Greater Northwest Chicago Development Corporation
6600 W Armitage Ave.
Chicago, IL 60707-3908
Ph: (773)637-2416
Fax: (773)637-2698
Co. E-mail: info@gncdc.org
URL: http://www.gncdc.org
Contact: James Lemonides, Chief Executive Officer
Description: Represents and promotes the small business sector. Provides management assistance to current and prospective small business owners. Helps to improve management skills and expand the products and services of members.

50841 ■ Illinois Small Business Development Center at Harper College
Harper Professional Bldg., Ste. 106
650 E Higgins Rd.
Schaumburg, IL 60173
Ph: (847)925-6520
Fax: (847)925-6109
Co. E-mail: brichter@harper.edu
URL: http://www.ildceo.net/dceo/Bureaus/Entrepreneurship+and+Small+Business/sbdc.htm
Description: Represents and promotes the small business sector. Provides management assistance to current and prospective small business owners. Helps to improve management skills and expand the products and services of members.

50842 ■ Illinois Small Business Development Center at Highland Community College
Bldg. H, Rm. 205
2998 W Pearl City Rd.
Freeport, IL 61032

Ph: (815)599-3654
URL: http://www.highland.edu/BusinessInstitute/sbdc.
asp
Description: Represents and promotes the small business sector. Provides management assistance to current and prospective small business owners. Helps to improve management skills and expand the products and services of members.

50843 ■ Illinois Small Business Development Center at Hull House

Jane Addams Hull House - Parkway Community House
500 E 67th St.
Chicago, IL 60637-4097
Ph: (773)955-8027
Fax: (773)955-8028
Co. E-mail: krobbins@hullhouse.org
URL: http://www.hullhouse.org/programsandcenters/
program/smallbusinessdevelopment.html
Contact: Kathleen Robbins, Director
URL(s): www.ildceo.net/dceo/Bureaus/
Entrepreneurship+and+Small+Business/sbdc.htm.
Description: Represents and promotes the small business sector. Provides management assistance to current and prospective small business owners. Helps to improve management skills and expand the products and services of members.

50844 ■ Illinois Small Business Development Center at Illinois Eastern Community College

218 E Main St.
Olney, IL 62450
Ph: (618)395-3011
Fax: (618)395-1922
Co. E-mail: sbdc@iecc.edu
URL: http://www.iecc.edu/sbdc2
Contact: Barney Brumfiel, Program Director
Description: Represents and promotes the small business sector. Provides management assistance to current and prospective small business owners. Helps to improve management skills and expand the products and services of members.

50845 ■ Illinois Small Business Development Center at Illinois State University

College of Business
Campus Box 5580
Normal, IL 61790-5580
Ph: (309)438-3610
Fax: (309)438-2114
Co. E-mail: sbdc@illinoisstate.edu
URL: http://www.sbdc.ilstu.edu
Description: Represents and promotes the small business sector. Provides management assistance to current and prospective small business owners. Helps to improve management skills and expand the products and services of members. **Founded:** 2005.

50846 ■ Illinois Small Business Development Center at Illinois State University

College of Business, Campus Box 5500
Normal, IL 61761-5500
Ph: (309)438-3610
Fax: (309)438-2114
Co. E-mail: sbdc@illinoisstate.edu
URL: http://www.sbdc.ilstu.edu
Contact: Elizabeth Binning, Director
Description: Represents and promotes the small business sector. Provides management assistance to current and prospective small business owners. Helps to improve management skills and expand the products and services of members.

50847 ■ Illinois Small Business Development Center at Illinois Valley Community College

815 N Orlando Smith Ave., Bldg. 11
Oglesby, IL 61348
Ph: (815)224-0212
Fax: (815)224-3033
Co. E-mail: bev_malooley@ivcc.edu
URL: http://www.ivcc.edu/sbdc.aspx?id=3152
Contact: Bev Malooley, Director
URL(s): www.ildceo.net/dceo/Bureaus/
Entrepreneurship+and+Small+Business/sbdc.htm.
Description: Represents and promotes the small business sector. Provides management assistance to

current and prospective small business owners. Helps to improve management skills and expand the products and services of members.

50848 ■ Illinois Small Business Development Center at Industrial Council of Nearwest Chicago

320 N Damen Ave., Ste. 100
Chicago, IL 60612
Ph: (312)433-2373
Fax: (312)421-1871
Co. E-mail: sbdc@industrialcouncil.com
URL: http://www.ildceo.net/dceo/Bureaus/
Entrepreneurship+and+Small+Business/sbdc.htm
Description: Represents and promotes the small business sector. Provides management assistance to current and prospective small business owners. Helps to improve management skills and expand the products and services of members.

50849 ■ Illinois Small Business Development Center at Joliet Jr. College

1215 Houbolt Rd.
Joliet, IL 60431
Ph: (815)280-1400
Fax: (815)280-1294
Co. E-mail: sbdc@jjc.edu
URL: http://www.jjc.edu
URL(s): www.ildceo.net/dceo/Bureaus/
Entrepreneurship+and+Small+Business/sbdc.htm.
Description: Represents and promotes the small business sector. Provides management assistance to current and prospective small business owners. Helps to improve management skills and expand the products and services of members.

50850 ■ Illinois Small Business Development Center at Joseph Center

7600 W Roosevelt Rd.
Forest Park, IL 60130
Ph: (708)697-6200
Fax: (708)488-2290
Co. E-mail: lwhite1@livingwd.org
URL: http://www.ildceo.net/dceo/Bureaus/
Entrepreneurship+and+Small+Business/sbdc.htm
Description: Represents and promotes the small business sector. Provides management assistance to current and prospective small business owners. Helps to improve management skills and expand the products and services of members.

50851 ■ Illinois Small Business Development Center at Kankakee Community College

100 College Dr.
Kankakee, IL 60901
Ph: (815)802-8222
Fax: (815)802-8101
Co. E-mail: kcrite@kcc.edu
URL: http://www.ildceo.net/dceo/Bureaus/
Entrepreneurship+and+Small+Business/sbdc.htm
Description: Represents and promotes the small business sector. Provides management assistance to current and prospective small business owners. Helps to improve management skills and expand the products and services of members.

50852 ■ Illinois Small Business Development Center at Kaskaskia College

Institute for Entrepreneurial Success
325 S Poplar St.
Centralia, IL 62801
Ph: (618)545-3260
Fax: (618)545-3258
Co. E-mail: sgroner@kaskaskia.edu
URL: http://www.kaskaskia.edu/ISBDC
Contact: Steven Groner, Director
URL(s): www.ildceo.net/dceo/Bureaus/
Entrepreneurship+and+Small+Business/sbdc.htm.
Description: Represents and promotes the small business sector. Provides management assistance to current and prospective small business owners. Helps to improve management skills and expand the products and services of members.

50853 ■ Illinois Small Business Development Center at Lincoln Land Community College

8 S Old State Capitol Plz.
Springfield, IL 62701
Ph: (217)544-7232

Fax: (217)522-3512
Co. E-mail: sbdc@llcc.edu
URL: http://www.llcc.edu/Default.aspx?alias=www.
llcc.edu/sbdc
Contact: Kevin Lust, Director
Description: Represents and promotes the small business sector. Provides management assistance to current and prospective small business owners. Helps to improve management skills and expand the products and services of members.

50854 ■ Illinois Small Business Development Center at McHenry County College

4100 W Shamrock Ln.
McHenry, IL 60050
Ph: (815)455-6098
Co. E-mail: shahcenter@mchenry.edu
URL: http://www.shahcenter.mchenry.edu
Contact: Mary Margaret Maule, Coordinator
Description: Represents and promotes the small business sector. Provides management assistance to current and prospective small business owners. Helps to improve management skills and expand the products and services of members.

50855 ■ Illinois Small Business Development Center at North Business and Industrial Council

8430 W Bryn Mawr Ave., Ste. 1000
Chicago, IL 60631
Ph: (773)594-9292
Fax: (773)594-9416
Co. E-mail: info@norbic.org
URL: http://www.norbic.org/services/busDev/main.
html
Contact: Jack McInerney, Director
Description: Represents and promotes the small business sector. Provides management assistance to current and prospective small business owners. Helps to improve management skills and expand the products and services of members.

50856 ■ Illinois Small Business Development Center at Rend Lake College

327 Potomac Blvd., Ste. A
Mount Vernon, IL 62864
Ph: (618)242-5813
Fax: (618)242-8220
Co. E-mail: mowrer@rlc.edu
URL: http://www.ildceo.net/dceo/Bureaus/
Entrepreneurship+and+Small+Business/sbdc.htm
Description: Represents and promotes the small business sector. Provides management assistance to current and prospective small business owners. Helps to improve management skills and expand the products and services of members.

50857 ■ Illinois Small Business Development Center at Rock Valley College

EIGER Lab
605 Fulton Ave., Rm. E109
Rockford, IL 61103
Ph: (815)921-2081
Fax: (815)921-2089
Co. E-mail: c.fuller@rockvalleycollege.edu
URL: http://www.rockvalleycollege.edu/Business/
sbdc.cfm
Description: Represents and promotes the small business sector. Provides management assistance to current and prospective small business owners. Helps to improve management skills and expand the products and services of members.

50858 ■ Illinois Small Business Development Center at Sauk Valley Community College

173 Illinois Rte. No. 2
Dixon, IL 61021-9188
Ph: (815)288-5511
Fax: (815)288-1880
Co. E-mail: nelsonj@svcc.edu
URL: http://www.svcc.edu/UserMenu/ppd/index.html
Description: Represents and promotes the small business sector. Provides management assistance to current and prospective small business owners. Helps to improve management skills and expand the products and services of members.

50859 ■ Illinois Small Business Development Center at Shawnee Community College
8364 Shawnee College Rd.
Ullin, IL 62992-2206
Ph: (618)634-3200
Free: 800-481-2242
Fax: (618)634-3300
Co. E-mail: candye@shawneecc.edu
URL: http://www.shawneecc.edu/community_
  services/business.asp
Contact: Candy Eastwood, Coordinator
Description: Represents and promotes the small business sector. Provides management assistance to current and prospective small business owners. Helps to improve management skills and expand the products and services of members.

50860 ■ Illinois Small Business Development Center at SIU-E/East St. Louis
601 James R. Thompson Blvd., Bldg. D, Rm. 2009
East St. Louis, IL 62201-1200
Ph: (618)482-8330
Fax: (618)482-8341
Co. E-mail: eslsiuesbdc@yahoo.com
URL: http://www.siue.edu/business/sbdc
Contact: Kwa Mister, Director
URL(s): www.ildceo.net/dceo/Bureaus/
Entrepreneurship+and+Small+Business/sbdc.htm.
Description: Represents and promotes the small business sector. Provides management assistance to current and prospective small business owners. Helps to improve management skills and expand the products and services of members.

50861 ■ Illinois Small Business Development Center at Southeastern Illinois College
2 E Locust St., Ste. 200
Harrisburg, IL 62946
Ph: (618)252-5001
Fax: (618)252-0210
Co. E-mail: lori.cox@sic.edu
URL: http://www.sic.edu/business.
  php?Page=business&Sub1=sbdc
Contact: Lori Cox, Director
URL(s): www.ildceo.net/dceo/Bureaus/
Entrepreneurship+and+Small+Business/sbdc.htm.
Description: Represents and promotes the small business sector. Provides management assistance to current and prospective small business owners. Helps to improve management skills and expand the products and services of members.

50862 ■ Illinois Small Business Development Center at Southern Illinois University (Edwardsville, Illinois)
Campus Box 1107
Alumni Hall 2126
Edwardsville, IL 62026
Ph: (618)650-2929
Fax: (618)650-2647
Co. E-mail: siuesbdc@hotmail.com
URL: http://www.siue.edu/business/sbdc
Contact: Kwa Mister, Director
URL(s): www.ildceo.net/dceo/Bureaus/
Entrepreneurship+and+Small+Business/sbdc.htm.
Description: Represents and promotes the small business sector. Provides management assistance to current and prospective small business owners. Helps to improve management skills and expand the products and services of members.

50863 ■ Illinois Small Business Development Center at Waubonsee Community College
18 S River St., Rm. 268
Aurora, IL 60506-4178
Ph: (630)906-4143
Fax: (630)892-4668
Co. E-mail: hparker@waubonsee.edu
URL: http://www.ildceo.net/dceo/Bureaus/
  Entrepreneurship+and+Small+Business/sbdc.htm
Description: Represents and promotes the small business sector. Provides management assistance to current and prospective small business owners. Helps to improve management skills and expand the products and services of members.

50864 ■ Illinois Small Business Development Center at Western Illinois University
510 N Pearl St., Ste. 1400
Macomb, IL 61455
Ph: (309)836-2640
Free: 800-526-0844
Fax: (309)837-4688
Co. E-mail: sb-center@wiu.edu
URL: http://www.ildceo.net/dceo/Bureaus/
  Entrepreneurship+and+Small+Business/sbdc.htm
URL(s): www.wiusbdc.org/services. **Description:** Represents and promotes the small business sector. Provides management assistance to current and prospective small business owners. Helps to improve management skills and expand the products and services of members.

SMALL BUSINESS ASSISTANCE PROGRAMS

50865 ■ Illinois Department of Commerce and Community Affairs - Entrepreneurship and Small Business Office
620 E Adams St.
Springfield, IL 62701
Ph: (800)252-2923
Free: 800-252-3998
URL: http://www.commerce.state.il.us/dceo
Description: Provides management, technical, and financial assistance through its Advocacy, Program Evaluation, Business Development, and Business Finance and Energy Assistance Division.

50866 ■ Illinois Department of Commerce and Economic Opportunity - Energy and Recycling
620 E Adams St.
Chicago, IL 62701
Ph: (217)785-3416
Co. E-mail: illinois.energy@illinois.gov
URL: http://www.commerce.state.il.us/dceo
Contact: Jack Lavin, Director
Description: Intervenes in the utility rate-setting process and in disputes between small businesses and utility companies. Assists in financing energy conservation measures.

SCORE OFFICES

50867 ■ Chicago SCORES
c/o Citibank Center
500 W Madison St., Ste. 1150
Chicago, IL 60661
Ph: (312)353-7724
Free: 877-727-2673
Fax: (312)886-4879
Co. E-mail: avondrastark@americascores.org
URL: http://www.scorechicago.org
Contact: Larry Lakin, Chairman
Description: Aims to empower students in urban communities using soccer, writing and creative expression, and service-learning.

50868 ■ E. Central Illinois (ECI) SCORE
Co. E-mail: score@champaigncounty.org

50869 ■ Peoria SCORE
Co. E-mail: scorepeoria@sscore.h-p.org

50870 ■ Quad Cities SCORE Newsletter
622 19th St.
Moline, IL 61265
Ph: (309)797-0082
Fax: (309)757-5435
Co. E-mail: info@quadcitiesscore.org
URL: http://www.quadcitiesscore.org
Contact: Mr. Robert Radkiewicz, Chairman
Released: Bimonthly

50871 ■ SCORE Central Illinois
121 N Main St.
Bloomington, IL 61701
Ph: (309)664-0549

Fax: (309)663-8270
Co. E-mail: webmaster@central-illinois-score.org
URL: http://www.central-illinois-score.org
Contact: Doug Miklich, Chairman
Description: Provides free consulting services to both start-up and existing small businesses in Central Illinois service area.

50872 ■ SCORE Chicago
Citibank Center, Ste. 1150
500 W Madison St.
Chicago, IL 60661-2511
Ph: (312)353-7724
Free: 877-727-2673
Fax: (312)886-4879
Co. E-mail: info@scorechicago.org
URL: http://www.scorechicago.org
Description: Works to strengthen the formation, growth and success of small businesses nationwide.
Founded: 1964.

50873 ■ SCORE Decatur
Millikin University
1184 W Main St.
Decatur, IL 62522
Ph: (217)424-6297
Co. E-mail: score@millikin.edu
URL: http://www.decatur.scorechapter.org
URL(s): www.score.org/chapter-list. **Description:** Works to strengthen the formation, growth and success of small businesses nationwide. **Founded:** 1977.

50874 ■ SCORE Fox Valley
1444 N Farnsworth Ave., Rm. 504
Aurora, IL 60505
Ph: (630)375-6026
Fax: (630)585-1903
Co. E-mail: benton2218@comcast.net
URL: http://www.scorefoxvalley.org
Contact: John Benton, Chairman
Description: Strives for the formation, growth and success of small businesses. Provides professional guidance and information to maximize the success of existing and emerging small businesses. Promotes entrepreneur education in Fox Valley area, Illinois.

50875 ■ SCORE Kankakee
Co. E-mail: score-kakakee@sbcglobal.net

50876 ■ SCORE Northern Illinois
605 Fulton Ave.
Rockford, IL 61103
Ph: (815)962-0122
Fax: (815)962-0806
Co. E-mail: info@northernillinoisscore.org
URL: http://northernillinoisscore.org
Contact: Vern Wanner, Chairman
Description: Counsels small businesses on start-up, writing a business plan, addressing problems with cash flow, inventory control, and other business-related issues. **Publications:** Scoreboard (Monthly). **Educational Activities:** Starting a Small Business/ Writing a Business Plan (Monthly).

50877 ■ SCORE Quad Cities
622 19th St.
Moline, IL 61265
Ph: (309)797-0082
Fax: (309)757-5435
Co. E-mail: info@quadcitiesscore.org
URL: http://www.quadcitiesscore.org
Contact: Mr. Robert Radkiewicz, Chairman
Description: Provides professional guidance and information to maximize the success of existing and emerging small businesses. Develops business plans and evaluate financial projections. Promotes entrepreneur education in the western Illinois/eastern Iowa Quad Cities area including Moline and Rock Island IL and Davenport and Bettendorf, IA. **Founded:** 1978. **Publications:** Quad Cities SCORE Newsletter (Bimonthly). **Awards:** SCORE Business of the Year (Annual).

50878 ■ SCORE Quincy Tri-State
c/o Quincy Area Chamber of Commerce
300 Civic Center Plz., Ste. 245
Quincy, IL 62301
Ph: (217)222-8093

Fax: (217)222-3033
Co. E-mail: info@score-tristate.org
URL: http://www.score-tristate.org
Contact: Dr. Cynthia Haliemun, Vice Chairperson
Description: Provides counseling to persons wanting to go into business as well as those already in the business. Sponsors seminars and workshops. **Founded:** 1980.

50879 ■ SCORE Springfield
3330 Ginger Creek Dr., Ste. B, S
Springfield, IL 62711
Ph: (217)793-5020
Fax: (217)793-5027
Co. E-mail: score571@aol.com
URL: http://www.scorespi.org
URL(s): springfieldil.score.org.

50880 ■ Scoreboard
605 Fulton Ave.
Rockford, IL 61103
Ph: (815)962-0122
Fax: (815)962-0806
Co. E-mail: info@northernillinoisscore.org
URL: http://northernillinoisscore.org
Contact: Vern Wanner, Chairman
Released: Monthly

50881 ■ Southeastern Illinois SCORE
Co. E-mail: score4u@eiu.ed

50882 ■ Southern Illinois SCORE
Co. E-mail: score@clearwave.com

50883 ■ Southwestern Illinois SCORE
Co. E-mail: score@ic.edu

BETTER BUSINESS BUREAUS

50884 ■ BBB Alert
330 N Wabash Ave., Ste. 3120
Chicago, IL 60611
Ph: (312)832-0500
Fax: (312)832-9985
Co. E-mail: info@chicago.bbb.org
URL: http://chicago.bbb.org
Contact: Steve J. Bernas, President
Released: Bimonthly

50885 ■ Better Business Bureau of Central Illinois
112 Harrison
Peoria, IL 61602
Ph: (309)688-3741
Co. E-mail: bbb@heart.net
URL: http://www.peoria.bbb.org
Contact: Bonnie Bakin, President
Description: Seeks to promote and foster the highest ethical relationship between businesses and the public through voluntary self-regulation, consumer and business education, and service excellence. Provides information to help consumers and businesses make informed purchasing decisions and avoid costly scams and frauds; settles consumer complaints through arbitration and other means.

50886 ■ Better Business Bureau of Chicago and Northern Illinois
330 N Wabash Ave., Ste. 3120
Chicago, IL 60611
Ph: (312)832-0500
Fax: (312)832-9985
Co. E-mail: info@chicago.bbb.org
URL: http://chicago.bbb.org
Contact: Steve J. Bernas, President
Description: Seeks to promote and foster the highest ethical relationship between businesses and the public through voluntary self-regulation, consumer and business education, and service excellence. Provides information to help consumers and businesses make informed purchasing decisions and avoid costly scams and frauds; settles consumer complaints through arbitration and other means. **Founded:** 1926. **Publications:** BBB Alert (Bimonthly); The Consumer Resource Guide (Semiannual).

50887 ■ The Consumer Resource Guide
330 N Wabash Ave., Ste. 3120
Chicago, IL 60611
Ph: (312)832-0500
Fax: (312)832-9985
Co. E-mail: info@chicago.bbb.org
URL: http://chicago.bbb.org
Contact: Steve J. Bernas, President
Released: Semiannual

CHAMBERS OF COMMERCE

50888 ■ Access DeKalb
164 E Lincoln Hwy.
DeKalb, IL 60115
Ph: (815)756-6306
Fax: (815)756-5164
Co. E-mail: chamber@dekalb.org
URL: http://www.dekalb.org
Contact: Mr. Jim Allen, Executive Director
Released: Bimonthly

50889 ■ Action News
1123 S Milwaukee Ave.
Libertyville, IL 60048
Ph: (847)680-0750
Fax: (847)680-0760
Co. E-mail: info@glmvchamber.org
URL: http://www.glmvchamber.org
Contact: Alese Campbell, Executive Director
Released: Monthly

50890 ■ Action Report
211 Locust St.
Sterling, IL 61081-3536
Ph: (815)625-2400
Fax: (815)625-9361
Co. E-mail: kewoldsen@saukvalleyareachamber.com
URL: http://www.saukvalleyareachamber.com
Contact: Kimberly Ewoldsen, Executive Director
Released: Periodic

50891 ■ Addison Chamber of Commerce and Industry (ACCI)
777 Army Trail Rd., Ste. D
Addison, IL 60101
Ph: (630)543-4300
Fax: (630)543-4355
Co. E-mail: addisonchamber@sbcglobal.net
URL: http://www.addisonaic.org
Contact: Bernadette Hanrahan, Executive Director
Description: Promotes the retention and further development of business in Addison, IL, and the representation of businesses to local and national county, state, and national governmental agencies. **Founded:** 1991. **Subscriptions:** audio recordings books video recordings. **Publications:** Accent on Members (Biennial); Addison Community Directory (Biennial); Shoptalk (Bimonthly). **Educational Activities:** Five Star Business EXPO (Annual).

50892 ■ Addison Community Directory
777 Army Trail Rd., Ste. D
Addison, IL 60101
Ph: (630)543-4300
Fax: (630)543-4355
Co. E-mail: addisonchamber@sbcglobal.net
URL: http://www.addisonaic.org
Contact: Bernadette Hanrahan, Executive Director
Released: Biennial **Price:** free.

50893 ■ Advantage
108 E Wesley St.
Wheaton, IL 60187
Ph: (630)668-6464
Fax: (630)668-2744
Co. E-mail: info@wheatonchamber.com
URL: http://wheatonchamber.com
Contact: Jill Seijo, President
Released: Monthly

50894 ■ Agri-Business Brochure
300 Bucklin
La Salle, IL 61301-0446
Ph: (815)223-0227

Fax: (815)223-4827
Co. E-mail: ivaced@ivaced.org
URL: http://www.ivaced.org
Contact: Marci Duro, Chief Executive Officer

50895 ■ Airport Brochure
300 Bucklin
La Salle, IL 61301-0446
Ph: (815)223-0227
Fax: (815)223-4827
Co. E-mail: ivaced@ivaced.org
URL: http://www.ivaced.org
Contact: Marci Duro, Chief Executive Officer

50896 ■ Albany Park Chamber of Commerce
3403 W Lawrence Ave., Ste. 201
Chicago, IL 60625
Ph: (773)478-0202
Fax: (773)478-0282
Co. E-mail: lgriffiths@northrivercommission.org
URL: http://www.albanyparkchamber.org
Contact: Andrew Levin, President
Description: Promotes business and community development in the Albany Park area of Chicago, IL. Sponsors promotions. Convention/Meeting: none. **Founded:** 1976.

50897 ■ Aledo Area Chamber of Commerce
PO Box 261
Aledo, IL 61231
Ph: (309)582-5373
Co. E-mail: aledochamber@frontiernet.net
URL: http://www.aledochamber.org
Contact: Tony Hotschlag, President
Description: Promotes business and community development in Aledo area. **Telecommunication Services:** dsharp@aledochamber.org.

50898 ■ Algonquin - Lake in the Hills Chamber of Commerce
2114 W Algonquin Rd.
Lake in the Hills, IL 60156
Ph: (847)658-5300
Co. E-mail: info@algonquin-lith-chamber.com
URL: http://www.algonquin-lith-chamber.com
Contact: Jackie Gappa, President
Description: Aims to bring area businesses and individuals together to improve the business climate and quality of life for all citizens. **Publications:** Chamber Connections (Monthly).

50899 ■ Alsip Chamber of Commerce
12159 S Pulaski Rd.
Alsip, IL 60803
Ph: (708)597-2668
Fax: (708)597-5962
Co. E-mail: info@alsipchamber.org
URL: http://www.alsipchamber.org
Contact: Mary Schmidt, Executive Director
Founded: 1961.

50900 ■ Altamont Chamber of Commerce
PO Box 141
Altamont, IL 62411
Ph: (618)483-6119
Free: 866-483-6119
Co. E-mail: info@altamontchamber.com
URL: http://www.altamontil.net
Contact: Butch Roedl, President
URL(s): www.altamontchamber.com/public. **Description:** Promotes business and community development in Altamont, IL area.

50901 ■ Antioch Chamber of Commerce and Industry (ACCI)
882 Main St.
Antioch, IL 60002
Ph: (847)395-2233
Fax: (847)395-8954
Co. E-mail: info@antiochchamber.org
URL: http://www.antiochchamber.org
Contact: Barbara Porch, Executive Director
Description: Promotes business and community development in Antioch, IL. Sponsors art and craft fair, Christmas program, Easter Program, and Taste of Antioch.

50902 ■ Arcola Chamber of Commerce
PO Box 274
Arcola, IL 61910
Ph: (217)268-4530
Fax: (217)268-3690
Co. E-mail: rcrane@arcolachamber.com
URL: http://www.arcolachamber.com
Contact: Rachael Crane, Executive Director
Description: Promotes business and community development in Arcola, IL area.

50903 ■ Arlington Heights Chamber of Commerce (AHCC)
311 S Arlington Heights Rd., Ste. 20
Arlington Heights, IL 60005
Ph: (847)253-1703
Fax: (847)253-9133
Co. E-mail: info@arlingtonhtschamber.com
URL: http://www.arlingtonhtschamber.com/web06.nsf
Contact: Jon S. Ridler, Executive Director
Description: Promotes business and community development in Arlington Heights, IL. **Founded:** 1946. **Telecommunication Services:** jridler@arlingtonhtschamber.com.

50904 ■ Around Town
50 1/2 Raupp Blvd.
Buffalo Grove, IL 60089
Ph: (847)541-7799
Fax: (847)541-7819
Co. E-mail: info@bgacc.org
URL: http://www.bgacc.org/Welcome.asp
Contact: Lynne Schneider, Executive Director
Released: Monthly **Price:** included in membership dues.

50905 ■ ATHENA International
PO Box 811188
Chicago, IL 60681
Ph: (312)580-0111
Fax: (312)580-0110
Co. E-mail: athena@athenainternational.org
URL: http://www.athenainternational.org
Contact: Dianne Dinkel, President
Description: Supports, develops and honors women leaders. Inspires women to achieve their full potential. Creates balance in leadership worldwide. **Founded:** 1982. **Publications:** *The ATHENAIAN* (3/year). **Awards:** ATHENA Award (Annual).

50906 ■ The ATHENAIAN
PO Box 811188
Chicago, IL 60681
Ph: (312)580-0111
Fax: (312)580-0110
Co. E-mail: athena@athenainternational.org
URL: http://www.athenainternational.org
Contact: Dianne Dinkel, President
Released: 3/year

50907 ■ Available Site Location Guide
907 Main St.
Highland, IL 62249
Ph: (618)654-3721
Fax: (618)654-8966
Co. E-mail: jami@highlandillinois.com
URL: http://www.highlandillinois.com
Contact: Jami Jansen, Executive Director
Released: Annual

50908 ■ Barrington Area Chamber of Commerce (BACC)
325 N Hough St.
Barrington, IL 60010
Ph: (847)381-2525
Fax: (847)381-2540
Co. E-mail: janet@barringtonchamber.com
URL: http://www.barringtonchamber.com
Contact: Janet Meyer, President
Description: Aims to promote a dynamic business environment for the community.

50909 ■ Bartlett Chamber of Commerce
138 S Oak Ave.
Bartlett, IL 60103
Ph: (630)830-0324

Fax: (630)830-9724
Co. E-mail: info@bartlettchamber.com
URL: http://www.bartlettchamber.com
Contact: Diane Hubberts, President
Description: Promotes business and community development in Bartlett, IL. **Founded:** 1977. **Publications:** *Bartletter Business and Chamber of Commerce Directory* (Annual); *Business Beat* (Monthly).

50910 ■ Bartletter Business and Chamber of Commerce Directory
138 S Oak Ave.
Bartlett, IL 60103
Ph: (630)830-0324
Fax: (630)830-9724
Co. E-mail: info@bartlettchamber.com
URL: http://www.bartlettchamber.com
Contact: Diane Hubberts, President
Released: Annual

50911 ■ Batavia Business
106 W Wilson St.
Batavia, IL 60510
Ph: (630)879-7134
Fax: (630)879-7215
Co. E-mail: info@bataviachamber.org
URL: http://www.bataviachamber.org
Contact: Mr. Roger Breisch, Executive Director
Released: Monthly

50912 ■ Batavia Chamber of Commerce (BCC)
106 W Wilson St.
Batavia, IL 60510
Ph: (630)879-7134
Fax: (630)879-7215
Co. E-mail: info@bataviachamber.org
URL: http://www.bataviachamber.org
Contact: Mr. Roger Breisch, Executive Director
Description: Businesses, organizations, and individuals interested in business and community development in Batavia, IL. Supports community improvement projects. **Founded:** 1953. **Publications:** *Batavia Business* (Monthly).

50913 ■ Beardstown Chamber of Commerce (BCC)
101 W 3rd St.
Beardstown, IL 62618
Ph: (217)323-3271
Fax: (217)323-3271
Co. E-mail: info@beardstownil.org
URL: http://www.beardstownil.org
Description: Promotes business and community development in Beardstown, IL.

50914 ■ Beecher Chamber of Commerce
PO Box 292
Beecher, IL 60401
Ph: (708)946-6803
Co. E-mail: info@beecherchamber.com
URL: http://www.beecherchamber.com
Contact: Chuck Hoehn, President
Description: Promotes business and community development in the Beecher, IL area. **Founded:** 1970.

50915 ■ Belmont-Central Chamber of Commerce
5534 W Belmont Ave.
Chicago, IL 60641
Ph: (773)647-1644
Co. E-mail: info@belmontcentral.org
URL: http://www.belmontcentral.org
Description: Maintains a strong and viable commercial district at Belmont-Central.

50916 ■ Belvidere Area Chamber of Commerce (BACC)
130 S State St., Ste. 300
Belvidere, IL 61008-3695
Ph: (815)544-4357
Fax: (815)547-7654
Co. E-mail: tlassandro@belviderechamber.com
URL: http://www.belviderechamber.com
Contact: Thomas Lassandro, Executive Director
Description: Promotes business and community development in the Boone County, IL area. Convention/Meeting: none. **Founded:** 1915. **Publications:**

Chamber HELP (Annual); *Chamber News* (Monthly). **Telecommunication Services:** officemanager@belviderechamber.com.

50917 ■ Benton-West City Area Chamber of Commerce (BACC)
211 N Main St.
Benton, IL 62812
Ph: (618)438-2121
Free: 866-536-8423
Fax: (618)438-8011
Co. E-mail: chamber@bentonwestcity.com
URL: http://www.bentonwestcity.com
Contact: Gloria Atchison, Executive Secretary
Description: Promotes business and community development in the Benton, IL area. Holds area festival. **Founded:** 1941.

50918 ■ Bloomingdale Chamber of Commerce
108 W Lake St.
Bloomingdale, IL 60108
Ph: (630)980-9082
Fax: (630)980-9092
Co. E-mail: jane@bloomingdalechamber.com
URL: http://www.bloomingdalechamber.com
Contact: Ms. Jane Hove, President
Description: Strives to promote the growth of local business for the benefit of Bloomingdale Chamber of Commerce and the community. **Founded:** 1982. **Publications:** *Chamber Outlook* (Monthly). **Awards:** Business of the Year (Annual); Business Person of the Year (Annual); Chamber Ambassador (Annual).

50919 ■ Blue Island Area Chamber of Commerce and Industry
2434 Vermont St.
Blue Island, IL 60406
Ph: (708)388-1000
Fax: (708)388-1062
Co. E-mail: blueislandchamber@sbcglobal.net
URL: http://www.blueislandchamber.org
Contact: Karen Warrick, Chairperson
Description: Coordinates marketing and networking efforts, as well as acting as a liaison with various municipal bodies. **Publications:** *Chamber Chatter* (Quarterly). **Educational Activities:** Blue Island Chamber of Commerce Community Expo (Annual).

50920 ■ Bolingbrook Area Chamber of Commerce
201-B Canterbury Ln.
Bolingbrook, IL 60440
Ph: (630)226-8420
Fax: (630)759-9937
Co. E-mail: info@bolingbrookchamber.org
URL: http://www.bolingbrookchamber.org
Contact: Mike Evans, Executive Director
Description: Fosters a competitive enterprise system of business and promotes the growth and development of businesses in the community. **Founded:** 1978. **Publications:** *The Reporter* (Monthly). **Educational Activities:** Business to Business Showcase (Annual).

50921 ■ Bradley-Bourbonnais Chamber of Commerce (BBCC)
1690 Newtowne Dr.
Bourbonnais, IL 60914
Ph: (815)932-2222
Fax: (815)932-3294
Co. E-mail: bbcc@bbchamber.com
URL: http://bbchamber.com
Contact: Jaclyn Dugan-Roof, President
Description: Promotes business and community development in Bradley and Bourbonnais, IL. Conducts charitable programs; sponsors Bradley Village Christmas Parade. **Founded:** 1989. **Publications:** *Leverage* (Monthly).

50922 ■ Breese Chamber of Commerce
PO Box 132
Breese, IL 62230
Co. E-mail: bjwade@wadesbiz.com
URL: http://www.breesechamber.org
Contact: Brandon Wade, President
Description: Works hand-in-hand with the city of Breese to promote business and residential growth and encourage tourism and shopping. Aims to improve the existing facilities and the historical aspects of the city.

50923 ■ Bridgeview Chamber of Commerce
7300 W 87th St.
Bridgeview, IL 60455
Ph: (708)598-1700
Fax: (708)598-1709
Co. E-mail: info@bridgeviewchamber.com
URL: http://www.bridgeviewchamber.com
Contact: Jerry Gresik, President
Description: Provides information from local, state and federal sources on a variety of issues that may affect the business community. Sponsors community programs such as the Toys for Needy Children Drive at Christmas, scholarships to deserving students, Fire Prevention Poster Contest, and Christmas Tree Lighting Ceremony.

50924 ■ *Briefings*
500 Broadway Ave.
Mattoon, IL 61938
Ph: (217)235-5661
Fax: (217)234-6544
Co. E-mail: matchamber@consolidated.net
URL: http://www.mattoonchamber.com
Contact: Brian Titus, President
Released: Monthly

50925 ■ Brookfield Chamber of Commerce
PO Box 38
Brookfield, IL 60513
Ph: (708)268-8080
Co. E-mail: info@brookfieldchamber.net
URL: http://www.brookfieldchamber.net
Contact: Betty LeClere, President
Description: Promotes business and community development in Brookfield, IL area. **Founded:** 1953.

50926 ■ Buffalo Grove Area Chamber of Commerce
50 1/2 Raupp Blvd.
Buffalo Grove, IL 60089
Ph: (847)541-7799
Fax: (847)541-7819
Co. E-mail: info@bgacc.org
URL: http://www.bgacc.org/Welcome.asp
Contact: Lynne Schneider, Executive Director
Description: Promotes business and community development in Buffalo Grove, IL and surrounding communities. **Founded:** 1972. **Publications:** *Around Town* (Monthly). **Educational Activities:** Buffalo Grove Area Chamber of Commerce Meeting (Monthly).

50927 ■ Bushnell Chamber of Commerce
PO Box 111
Bushnell, IL 61422
Ph: (309)772-2171
Fax: (309)772-3616
Co. E-mail: chamber@bushnellchamber.com
URL: http://www.bushnellchamber.com
Contact: Don Swartzbaugh, President
Description: Works to build a strong economic base through the promotion of local businesses and activities.

50928 ■ *Business*
PO Box 313
Monticello, IL 61856-0313
Ph: (217)762-7921
Free: 800-952-3396
Fax: (217)762-2711
Co. E-mail: info@monticellochamber.org
URL: http://www.monticellochamber.org
Contact: Sue Gortner, Executive Director
Released: Annual

50929 ■ *The Business Advocate*
1401 E Oakton St.
Des Plaines, IL 60018
Ph: (847)824-4200
Fax: (847)824-7932
Co. E-mail: info@dpchamber.com
URL: http://www.desplaineschamber.com
Contact: Jeffrey Rozovics, President
Released: Monthly **Price:** free for members; $10, /year for nonmembers.

50930 ■ *Business Beat*
138 S Oak Ave.
Bartlett, IL 60103
Ph: (630)830-0324
Fax: (630)830-9724
Co. E-mail: info@bartlettchamber.com
URL: http://www.bartlettchamber.com
Contact: Diane Hubberts, President
Released: Monthly

50931 ■ *Business Bulletin*
PO Box 42
New Lenox, IL 60451-0042
Ph: (815)485-4241
Fax: (815)485-5001
Co. E-mail: info@newlenoxchamber.com
URL: http://www.newlenoxchamber.com
Contact: Mark Stevens, President

50932 ■ *Business and Community Directory*
108 E Wesley St.
Wheaton, IL 60187
Ph: (630)668-6464
Fax: (630)668-2744
Co. E-mail: info@wheatonchamber.com
URL: http://wheatonchamber.com
Contact: Jill Seijo, President
Released: Annual

50933 ■ *Business Connection*
128 E Railroad St.
Sandwich, IL 60548
Ph: (815)312-4963
Fax: (815)786-2505
Co. E-mail: info@sandwich-il.org
URL: http://www.sandwich-il.org
Contact: John R. Lux, President
Released: Monthly

50934 ■ *Business Connection*
7727 Lake St.
River Forest, IL 60305
Ph: (708)771-5760
Co. E-mail: info@oprfchamber.org
URL: http://www.oprfchamber.org
Contact: John Lawrence, President
Released: Bimonthly

50935 ■ *Business Directory*
c/o Carol Foreman, Exec. Dir.
Edwardsville, IL 62025
Ph: (618)656-7600
Fax: (618)656-7611
Co. E-mail: cforeman@edglenchamber.com
URL: http://www.edglenchamber.com
Contact: Carol Foreman, Executive Director

50936 ■ *Business Directory and Buyer's Guide*
500 Broadway Ave.
Mattoon, IL 61938
Ph: (217)235-5661
Fax: (217)234-6544
Co. E-mail: matchamber@consolidated.net
URL: http://www.mattoonchamber.com
Contact: Brian Titus, President
Released: Annual

50937 ■ *Business Guide*
PO Box 172
Maywood, IL 60153
Ph: (708)345-7077
Fax: (708)345-9455
Co. E-mail: info@maywoodchamber.org
URL: http://maywoodchamber.com
Contact: Edwin H. Walker, IV, President

50938 ■ *Business Monthly*
43 W Galena Blvd.
Aurora, IL 60506
Ph: (630)256-3180
Fax: (630)256-3189
Co. E-mail: jhenning@aurorachamber.com
URL: http://www.aurorachamber.com
Contact: Joseph Henning, President
Released: Monthly

50939 ■ *Business News*
200 Potomac Blvd.
Mount Vernon, IL 62864
Ph: (618)242-5725
Fax: (618)242-5130
Co. E-mail: chambermarketing@mvn.net
URL: http://www.southernillinois.com
Contact: Brandon Bullard, Executive Director
Released: Monthly

50940 ■ *The Business News*
209 N State St.
Jerseyville, IL 62052-1755
Ph: (618)639-5222
Co. E-mail: agilmore@jcba-il.us
URL: http://www.jcba.us
Contact: Alan Gilmore, Chief Executive Officer
Released: Monthly

50941 ■ *Business News In Depth*
622 19th St.
Moline, IL 61265-2142
Ph: (309)757-5416
Fax: (309)757-5435
Co. E-mail: rbaker@quadcitychamber.com
URL: http://www.quadcitychamber.com
Contact: Rick L. Baker, President
Released: Bimonthly

50942 ■ *Business and Professional Directory*
5002 Oakton St.
Skokie, IL 60077
Ph: (847)673-0240
Fax: (847)673-0249
Co. E-mail: info@skokiechamber.org
URL: http://www.skokiechamber.org
Contact: Howard Meyer, Executive Director
Released: Annual

50943 ■ *Business and Professional Memo*
City Hall
120 E 3rd St.
Pana, IL 62557
Ph: (217)562-4240
Fax: (217)562-3823
Co. E-mail: panachamber@consolidated.net
URL: http://www.panachamber.com
Contact: John Allen, Director
Released: Quarterly **Price:** included in membership dues.

50944 ■ *Business Resource Guide and Membership Directory*
Aon Center
200 E Randolph St., Ste. 2200
Chicago, IL 60601-6436
Ph: (312)494-6700
Fax: (312)861-0660
Co. E-mail: info@chicagolandchamber.org
URL: http://chicagolandchamber.org/wdk_cc
Contact: Jerry Roper, President
Price: $50, for members; $150, for nonmembers.

50945 ■ *Buying Guide*
2 Community Blvd., Ste. 203
Wheeling, IL 60090-2726
Ph: (847)541-0170
Fax: (847)541-0296
Co. E-mail: info@wphchamber.com
URL: http://www.wphchamber.com
Contact: Catherine Powers, Executive Director
Released: Annual

50946 ■ Byron Area Chamber of Commerce
PO Box 405
Byron, IL 61010
Ph: (815)234-5500
Fax: (815)234-7114
Co. E-mail: byronchamber@byronil.net
URL: http://www.byronchamber.org
Contact: Blake Horras, Executive Director
Description: Promotes business and community development in Byron, IL. **Founded:** 1958. **Publications:** *Byron Chamber News* (Monthly). **Awards:** Business of the Year (Annual); Citizen of the Year (Annual); Green Business of the Year (Annual).

50947 ■ *Byron Chamber News*
PO Box 405
Byron, IL 61010
Ph: (815)234-5500

Fax: (815)234-7114
Co. E-mail: byronchamber@byronil.net
URL: http://www.byronchamber.org
Contact: Blake Horras, Executive Director
Released: Monthly

50948 ■ Cahokia Area Chamber of Commerce
103 Main St.
Cahokia, IL 62206
Ph: (618)332-4258
Co. E-mail: cahokiachamber@gmail.com
URL: http://www.cahokiachamber.com
Contact: Richard D. Laux, President
Description: Promotes business in the Cahokia, IL area.

50949 ■ Canton Area Chamber of Commerce (CACC)
45 E Side Sq., Ste. 303
Canton, IL 61520
Ph: (309)647-2677
Fax: (309)647-2712
Co. E-mail: chamber@cantonillinois.org
URL: http://www.cantonillinois.org
Contact: Missy Towery, Executive Director
Description: Businesses, organizations, and individuals promoting economic and community development in the Canton, IL area. **Founded:** 1925. **Publications:** *Chamber Courier* (Monthly). **Awards:** Business Person of the Year (Annual); Citizen of the Year (Annual); Educator of the Year (Annual). **Telecommunication Services:** mtowery@cantonillinois.org.

50950 ■ Carbondale Chamber of Commerce (CCC)
PO Box 877
Carbondale, IL 62903
Ph: (618)549-2146
Fax: (618)529-5063
Co. E-mail: carbondalechamberofcommerce@gmail.com
URL: http://www.carbondalechamber.com
Contact: Woody Thorne, President
Description: Promotes business and community development in the Carbondale, IL area. **Founded:** 1916. **Publications:** *The Communicator* (Bimonthly); *Membership Directory and Buyer's Guide* (Annual). **Awards:** Athena (Annual); Business Leader of the Year (Annual); Business of the Year (Annual); Citizen of the Year (Annual).

50951 ■ Carlinville Community Chamber of Commerce (CCCC)
112 N Side Sq.
Carlinville, IL 62626
Ph: (217)854-2141
Fax: (217)854-8548
Co. E-mail: info@carlinvillechamber.com
URL: http://www.carlinvillechamber.com
Description: Promotes business and community development in Carlinville, IL. **Founded:** 1953. **Publications:** *Chamber Insider* (Monthly). **Educational Activities:** Christmas Market (Annual).

50952 ■ Carmi Chamber of Commerce (CCC)
225 E Main St.
Carmi, IL 62821
Ph: (618)382-7606
URL: http://www.cityofcarmi.com
Contact: Sandra Irvine, Director
Description: Aims to sustain and further develop a thriving economy in the area and enhance the community's quality of life. Sponsors several activities including community food basket drives at Thanksgiving. **Founded:** 1944.

50953 ■ Carol Stream Chamber of Commerce
150 S Gary Ave.
Carol Stream, IL 60188
Ph: (630)665-3325
Fax: (630)665-6965
Co. E-mail: info@carolstreamchamber.com
URL: http://www.carolstreamchamber.com
Contact: Ms. Luanne Triolo, Executive Director
Description: Represents businesses and professional people. Works to advance the economic well-being of the greater Carol Stream area and its nearby vicinity. Offers a variety of programs to keep the

members at their competitive best. **Founded:** 1992. **Publications:** *Chamber Connection* (Quarterly). **Educational Activities:** Business After Hours (Monthly).

50954 ■ Carterville Chamber of Commerce
120 N Greenbriar
Carterville, IL 62918
Ph: (618)985-6942
Fax: (618)985-6942
Co. E-mail: chamber@cartervillechamber.com
URL: http://www.cartervillechamber.com
Contact: Ms. Andrea Frailey, Executive Director
Description: Enhances the business and social climate of the Carterville area which helps individual businesses prosper.

50955 ■ Carthage Area Chamber of Commerce (CACC)
8 S Madison
Carthage, IL 62321
Ph: (217)357-3024
Fax: (217)357-3024
Co. E-mail: chamber@carthage-il.com
URL: http://www.carthage-il.com/carthage.php?id=1
Contact: Nina Boyer, President
Description: Promotes business and community development in Hancock County, IL. Convention/Meeting: none.

50956 ■ Cary/Grove Area Chamber of Commerce (CCC)
27 E Main St.
Cary, IL 60013
Ph: (847)639-2800
Fax: (847)639-2168
Co. E-mail: info@carygrovechamber.com
URL: http://www.carygrovechamber.com
Contact: Suzanne Corr, Executive Director
Description: Promotes business and community development in the Cary, IL area. Holds bimonthly board meeting. Sponsors Home and Business Expo. **Founded:** 1964. **Publications:** *Insights* (Monthly); *Minutes of Board Meeting.*

50957 ■ *Chamber Business and Community Guide*
900 N 25th Ave.
Melrose Park, IL 60160
Ph: (708)338-1007
Fax: (708)338-9924
Co. E-mail: melroseparkchamber@sbcglobal.net
URL: http://www.melroseparkchamber.org
Contact: Mrs. Cathy K. Stenberg, Executive Director
Released: Annual

50958 ■ *Chamber Chat*
3 S Park Ave.
Herrin, IL 62948
Ph: (618)942-5163
Co. E-mail: herrincc@herrinillinois.com
URL: http://www.herrinillinois.com
Contact: Kevin Frost, President
Released: Monthly

50959 ■ *Chamber Chatter*
708 Archer Ave.
Marshall, IL 62441
Ph: (217)826-2034
Fax: (217)826-2034
Co. E-mail: marshall.chamber@frontier.com
URL: http://www.marshall-il.com
Contact: George Dallmier, President
Released: Monthly

50960 ■ *Chamber Chatter*
90 Public Sq.
Monmouth, IL 61462-0857
Ph: (309)734-3181
Co. E-mail: macc@maplecity.com
URL: http://www.monmouthilchamber.com
Contact: Angela McElwee, Executive Director
Released: Monthly

50961 ■ *Chamber Chatter*
124 N Morgan St.
Shelbyville, IL 62565
Ph: (217)774-2221

Fax: (217)774-2221
Co. E-mail: chamber01@consolidated.net
URL: http://www.shelbyvillechamberofcommerce.com
Contact: Tad Mayhall, President
Released: Bimonthly **Price:** free.

50962 ■ *Chamber Chatter*
2434 Vermont St.
Blue Island, IL 60406
Ph: (708)388-1000
Fax: (708)388-1062
Co. E-mail: blueislandchamber@sbcglobal.net
URL: http://www.blueislandchamber.org
Contact: Karen Warrick, Chairperson
Released: Quarterly

50963 ■ *The Chamber Chatter*
c/o Ms. Barbara Melnyk, Exec. Dir.
Elmwood Park, IL 60707
Ph: (708)456-8000
Fax: (708)456-8680
Co. E-mail: mcepcoc@aol.com
URL: http://www.mcepchamber.org
Contact: Mr. Jonathan Zivojnovic, President
Released: Bimonthly

50964 ■ *Chamber Chatter*
c/o Diana Johnson, Exec. Dir.
100 Heart Blvd.
Loves Park, IL 61111
Ph: (815)633-3999
Fax: (815)633-4057
Co. E-mail: diana@parkschamber.com
URL: http://www.parkschamber.com
Contact: Diana Johnson, Executive Director
Released: Monthly

50965 ■ *Chamber Chit-Chat*
900 N 25th Ave.
Melrose Park, IL 60160
Ph: (708)338-1007
Fax: (708)338-9924
Co. E-mail: melroseparkchamber@sbcglobal.net
URL: http://www.melroseparkchamber.org
Contact: Mrs. Cathy K. Stenberg, Executive Director
Released: Quarterly

50966 ■ *Chamber Chords*
101 Main St.
Lemont, IL 60439-3675
Ph: (630)257-5997
Fax: (630)257-3238
Co. E-mail: info@lemontchamber.com
URL: http://www.lemontchamber.com
Contact: Marlene Miciunas, President
Released: Monthly **Price:** free for members.

50967 ■ *Chamber of Commerce*
124 N Morgan St.
Shelbyville, IL 62565
Ph: (217)774-2221
Fax: (217)774-2221
Co. E-mail: chamber01@consolidated.net
URL: http://www.shelbyvillechamberofcommerce.com
Contact: Tad Mayhall, President

50968 ■ Chamber of Commerce of Southwestern Madison County
PO Box 370
Granite City, IL 62040-0370
Ph: (618)876-6400
Fax: (618)876-6448
Co. E-mail: chamber@chamberswmadisoncounty.com
URL: http://www.chamberswmadisoncounty.com
Contact: Chris Barnes, President
Description: Promotes business in Southwestern Madison County.

50969 ■ *Chamber Communicator*
90 Public Sq.
Monmouth, IL 61462-0857
Ph: (309)734-3181
Co. E-mail: macc@maplecity.com
URL: http://www.monmouthilchamber.com
Contact: Angela McElwee, Executive Director
Released: Monthly

50970 ■ Chamber Communicator
100 SW Water St.
Peoria, IL 61602
Ph: (309)676-0755
Fax: (309)676-7534
Co. E-mail: chamber@mail.h-p.org
URL: http://www.peoriachamber.org
Contact: Roberta M. Parks, President
Released: Weekly

50971 ■ Chamber Communicator
10003 Bunkum Rd.
Fairview Heights, IL 62208
Ph: (618)397-3127
Fax: (618)397-5563
Co. E-mail: office@fairviewheightschamber.org
URL: http://www.fairviewheightschamber.org
Contact: Scott Leas, Executive Director
Released: Monthly

50972 ■ Chamber Communique
3755 E Main St., Ste. 140
St. Charles, IL 60174
Ph: (630)584-8384
Fax: (630)584-6065
Co. E-mail: info@stcharleschamber.com
URL: http://www.stcharleschamber.com
Contact: Lori G. Hewitt, President
Released: Monthly

50973 ■ Chamber Connection
5002 Oakton St.
Skokie, IL 60077
Ph: (847)673-0240
Fax: (847)673-0249
Co. E-mail: info@skokiechamber.org
URL: http://www.skokiechamber.org
Contact: Howard Meyer, Executive Director
Released: Monthly

50974 ■ Chamber Connection
150 S Gary Ave.
Carol Stream, IL 60188
Ph: (630)665-3325
Fax: (630)665-6965
Co. E-mail: info@carolstreamchamber.com
URL: http://www.carolstreamchamber.com
Contact: Ms. Luanne Triolo, Executive Director
Released: Quarterly **Price:** free.

50975 ■ Chamber Connection
1817 S Neil St., Ste. 201
Champaign, IL 61820-7269
Ph: (217)359-1791
Fax: (217)359-1809
Co. E-mail: info@champaigncounty.org
URL: http://www.champaigncounty.org
Contact: Laura E. Weis, President
Released: Monthly

50976 ■ Chamber Connections
6440 Main St., Ste 330
Woodridge, IL 60517-1290
Ph: (630)960-7080
Fax: (630)852-2316
Co. E-mail: chamber@woodridgechamber.org
URL: http://www.woodridgechamber.org
Contact: Amy Melinder, President
Released: Monthly

50977 ■ Chamber Connections
2 Community Blvd., Ste. 203
Wheeling, IL 60090-2726
Ph: (847)541-0170
Fax: (847)541-0296
Co. E-mail: info@wphchamber.com
URL: http://www.wphchamber.com
Contact: Catherine Powers, Executive Director
Released: Bimonthly

50978 ■ Chamber Connections
2114 W Algonquin Rd.
Lake in the Hills, IL 60156
Ph: (847)658-5300
Co. E-mail: info@algonquin-lith-chamber.com
URL: http://www.algonquin-lith-chamber.com
Contact: Jackie Gappa, President
Released: Monthly

50979 ■ Chamber Connections
10 W Park Blvd.
Villa Park, IL 60181
Ph: (630)941-9133
Fax: (630)941-9134
Co. E-mail: vphamber@sbcglobal.net
URL: http://www.villaparkchamber.org
Contact: Alesia Bailey, Executive Director
Released: Monthly

50980 ■ Chamber Courier
45 E Side Sq., Ste. 303
Canton, IL 61520
Ph: (309)647-2677
Fax: (309)647-2712
Co. E-mail: chamber@cantonillinois.org
URL: http://www.cantonillinois.org
Contact: Missy Towery, Executive Director
Released: Monthly

50981 ■ Chamber Directory
6440 Main St., Ste 330
Woodridge, IL 60517-1290
Ph: (630)960-7080
Fax: (630)852-2316
Co. E-mail: chamber@woodridgechamber.org
URL: http://www.woodridgechamber.org
Contact: Amy Melinder, President
Released: Annual

50982 ■ Chamber Directory
1702 Plainfield Rd.
Darien, IL 60561-5080
Ph: (630)968-0004
Fax: (630)968-2474
Co. E-mail: info@darienchamber.com
URL: http://www.darienchamber.com
Contact: Angelo Imbrogno, President

50983 ■ Chamber Directory
203 S 13th Street
Murphysboro, IL 62966
Ph: (618)684-6421
Free: 800-406-8774
Fax: (618)684-2010
Co. E-mail: director@murphysborochamber.com
URL: http://www.murphysboro.com
Contact: Dan Bost, President
Released: Periodic

50984 ■ Chamber Focus
501 Jackson Ave.
Charleston, IL 61920
Ph: (217)345-7041
Fax: (217)345-7042
Co. E-mail: cacc@advant.com
URL: http://www.charlestonchamber.com
Contact: Cindy White, Executive Director
Released: Monthly

50985 ■ Chamber Focus
407 W State St., Ste. 10
Sycamore, IL 60178
Ph: (815)895-3456
Fax: (815)895-0125
Co. E-mail: info@sycamorechamber.com
URL: http://www.sycamorechamber.com
Contact: Rose Treml, Executive Director

50986 ■ Chamber Goods and Services Guide
800 Roosevelt Rd., Bldg. D, Ste. 108
Glen Ellyn, IL 60137
Ph: (630)469-0907
Fax: (630)469-0426
Co. E-mail: director@glenellynchamber.com
URL: http://www.glenellynchamber.com
Contact: Georgia Koch, Executive Director
Released: Annual

50987 ■ The Chamber Guide
579 First Bank Dr., Ste. 205
Palatine, IL 60067
Ph: (847)359-7200
Fax: (847)359-7246
Co. E-mail: info@palatinechamber.com
URL: http://www.palatinechamber.com
Contact: Mindy Phillips, Director
Released: Annual

50988 ■ Chamber HELP
130 S State St., Ste. 300
Belvidere, IL 61008-3695
Ph: (815)544-4357
Fax: (815)547-7654
Co. E-mail: tlassandro@belviderechamber.com
URL: http://www.belviderechamber.com
Contact: Thomas Lassandro, Executive Director
Released: Annual

50989 ■ Chamber Insider
112 N Side Sq.
Carlinville, IL 62626
Ph: (217)854-2141
Fax: (217)854-8548
Co. E-mail: info@carlinvillechamber.com
URL: http://www.carlinvillechamber.com
Released: Monthly **Price:** free.

50990 ■ Chamber Matters
107 S Main St.
Mount Prospect, IL 60056
Ph: (847)398-6616
Fax: (847)398-6780
Co. E-mail: info@mountprospectchamber.org
URL: http://www.mountprospectchamber.org
Contact: Dawn Fletcher Collins, Executive Director
Released: Bimonthly

50991 ■ The Chamber News
2169B S China Pl.
Chicago, IL 60616
Ph: (312)326-5320
Fax: (312)326-5668
Co. E-mail: info@chicagochinatown.org
URL: http://www.chicagochinatown.org/cccorg/home.
  jsp
Contact: Man-Men Lee, Executive Director
Released: Quarterly **Price:** included in membership
dues.

50992 ■ Chamber News
130 S State St., Ste. 300
Belvidere, IL 61008-3695
Ph: (815)544-4357
Fax: (815)547-7654
Co. E-mail: tlassandro@belviderechamber.com
URL: http://www.belviderechamber.com
Contact: Thomas Lassandro, Executive Director
Released: Monthly

50993 ■ Chamber News
62 N Ayer St., Ste. B
Harvard, IL 60033
Ph: (815)943-4404
Fax: (815)943-4410
Co. E-mail: info@harvcc.net
URL: http://www.harvcc.net
Contact: Crystal Musgrove, Executive Director
Released: Bimonthly

50994 ■ Chamber News
907 Main St.
Highland, IL 62249
Ph: (618)654-3721
Fax: (618)654-8966
Co. E-mail: jami@highlandillinois.com
URL: http://www.highlandillinois.com
Contact: Jami Jansen, Executive Director
Released: Monthly **Price:** free for members.

50995 ■ Chamber News
2007 Civic Center Way
Round Lake Beach, IL 60073
Ph: (847)546-2002
Fax: (847)546-2254
Co. E-mail: info@rlchamber.org
URL: http://www.rlchamber.org
Contact: Shanna Coakley, Executive Director
Released: Monthly

50996 ■ Chamber News
22 W Streamwood Blvd.
Streamwood, IL 60107
Ph: (630)837-5200

Fax: (630)837-5251
Co. E-mail: staff@streamwoodchamber.com
URL: http://www.streamwoodchamber.com
Contact: Patrick McKernan, President
Released: Bimonthly

50997 ■ *Chamber News*
63 W Washington St.
Oswego, IL 60543-0863
Ph: (630)554-3505
Fax: (630)554-0050
Co. E-mail: info@oswegochamber.org
URL: http://www.oswegochamber.org
Contact: Steve Hatcher, President
Released: Monthly

50998 ■ *Chamber News Highlights*
601 W 10th St.
Rock Falls, IL 61071-1576
Ph: (815)625-4500
Fax: (815)625-4558
Co. E-mail: doug@rockfallschamber.com
URL: http://www.rockfallschamber.com/index.html
Contact: Doug Wiersema, President
Released: Monthly

50999 ■ *Chamber News and Views*
17316 S Oak Park Ave.
Tinley Park, IL 60477
Ph: (708)532-5700
Fax: (708)532-1475
Co. E-mail: info@tinleychamber.org
URL: http://www.tinleychamber.org
Contact: Ms. Kim Scalise, President
Released: Monthly

51000 ■ *Chamber Notes*
330 S Main St.
Anna, IL 62906
Ph: (618)833-6311
Fax: (618)833-1903
Co. E-mail: uccc@ajinternet.net
URL: http://www.shawneeheartland.com
Contact: Jeannie Landis, Executive Director
Released: Quarterly

51001 ■ *Chamber Outlook*
108 W Lake St.
Bloomingdale, IL 60108
Ph: (630)980-9082
Fax: (630)980-9092
Co. E-mail: jane@bloomingdalechamber.com
URL: http://www.bloomingdalechamber.com
Contact: Ms. Jane Hove, Executive Director
Released: Monthly **Price:** free for members.

51002 ■ *Chamber Plus*
PO Box 534
Pontiac, IL 61764
Ph: (815)844-5131
Fax: (815)844-2600
Co. E-mail: clambert@pontiacchamber.org
URL: http://www.pontiacchamber.org
Contact: Cheri Lambert, President
Released: Quarterly

51003 ■ *Chamber Report*
3138 N Broadway
Chicago, IL 60657
Ph: (773)348-8608
Fax: (773)348-7409
Co. E-mail: info@lakevieweast.com
URL: http://www.lakevieweast.com
Contact: Maureen Martino, Executive Director
Released: Monthly

51004 ■ *Chamber Review*
c/o Ginny Fanning, Pres.
Jacksonville, IL 62650
Ph: (217)245-2174
Fax: (217)245-0661
Co. E-mail: chamber@jacksonvilleareachamber.org
URL: http://www.jacksonvilleareachamber.org
Contact: Ginny Fanning, President
Released: Monthly **Price:** included in membership dues.

51005 ■ *The Chamber Review*
11419 State Rte. 47
Huntley, IL 60142
Ph: (847)669-0166
Fax: (847)669-0170
Co. E-mail: info@huntleychamber.org
URL: http://www.huntleychamber.org
Contact: Rita Slawek, President
Released: Monthly **Price:** included in membership dues.

51006 ■ *Chamber Scene*
8060 W Oakton St.
Niles, IL 60714
Ph: (847)268-8180
Fax: (847)268-8186
Co. E-mail: contactus@nileschamber.com
URL: http://nileschamber.com
Contact: Katie Schneider, Executive Director
Released: Quarterly

51007 ■ *Chamber Scoop*
100 S Center St., Ste. 101
Clinton, IL 61727-1945
Ph: (217)935-3364
Free: 866-4DE-WITT
Fax: (217)935-0064
Co. E-mail: chamber@clintonilchamber.com
URL: http://www.clintonilchamber.com
Contact: Marian Brisard, Office Manager

51008 ■ *Chamber Talk*
116 S State St.
Marengo, IL 60152
Ph: (815)568-6680
Fax: (815)568-6879
Co. E-mail: chamber@marengo-union.com
URL: http://www.marengo-union.com
Contact: Christine Wienke, Managing Director
Released: Monthly

51009 ■ *The Chamber Update*
121 N 4th St.
Oregon, IL 61061
Ph: (815)732-2100
Co. E-mail: ococ@oglecom.com
URL: http://www.oregonil.com
Released: Monthly

51010 ■ *Chamber Update*
PO Box 353
Wood Dale, IL 60191-0353
Ph: (630)595-0505
Fax: (630)595-0677
Co. E-mail: info@wooddalechamber.com
URL: http://www.wooddalechamber.com
Contact: George Ellefsen, President

51011 ■ *Chamber World*
311 N Madison
Litchfield, IL 62056
Ph: (217)324-2533
Fax: (217)324-3559
Co. E-mail: info@litchfieldchamber.com
URL: http://www.litchfieldchamber.com
Contact: Adrian Baker, President
Released: Monthly

51012 ■ *Chambergram*
19820 Wolf Rd.
Mokena, IL 60448-1545
Ph: (708)479-2468
Co. E-mail: mokena@mokena.com
URL: http://www.mokena.com
Contact: Mary Maertin, President
Released: Quarterly

51013 ■ *Chambergram*
4753 N Broadway St., Ste. 822
Chicago, IL 60640-4992
Ph: (773)878-1184
Fax: (773)878-3678
Co. E-mail: info@uptownbusinesspartners.com
URL: http://www.uptownbusinesspartners.com
Contact: Christie Hahn, Executive Director
Released: Monthly **Price:** free.

51014 ■ *Chambergram*
8799 W 151st St.
Orland Park, IL 60462
Ph: (708)349-2972
Fax: (708)349-7454
Co. E-mail: info@orlandparkchamber.org
URL: http://www.orlandparkchamber.org
Contact: Keloryn Putnam, Executive Director
Released: Monthly

51015 ■ *ChamberLine*
The Esplanade at Locust Point
Downers Grove, IL 60515
Ph: (630)968-4050
Fax: (630)968-8368
Co. E-mail: chamber@downersgrove.org
URL: http://www.downersgrove.org
Contact: Laura Crawford, President
Released: Monthly

51016 ■ *Chamberlink*
607 Market St.
Metropolis, IL 62960
Ph: (618)524-2714
Free: 800-949-5740
Fax: (618)524-4780
URL: http://www.metropolischamber.com
Released: Monthly **Price:** free for members.

51017 ■ Champaign County Chamber of Commerce
1817 S Neil St., Ste. 201
Champaign, IL 61820-7269
Ph: (217)359-1791
Fax: (217)359-1809
Co. E-mail: info@champaigncounty.org
URL: http://www.champaigncounty.org
Contact: Laura E. Weis, President
Description: Works to ensure a healthy economic and socio-economic base to benefit the community. **Publications:** *Champaign County Chamber of Commerce--Membership Directory* (Annual); *Chamber Connection* (Monthly); *Images of Champaign County* (Annual). **Educational Activities:** Brown Bag (Monthly); Business After Hours (Monthly). **Awards:** Athena Award (Annual); Champaign County Most Valuable Citizen (Annual); Small Business of the Year (Annual); Top Chamber Investors (Annual). **Telecommunication Services:** lauraw@champaigncounty.org.

51018 ■ Charleston Area Chamber of Commerce (CACC)
501 Jackson Ave.
Charleston, IL 61920
Ph: (217)345-7041
Fax: (217)345-7042
Co. E-mail: cacc@advant.com
URL: http://www.charlestonchamber.com
Contact: Cindy White, Executive Director
Description: Promotes the economic climate in the greater Charleston, Illinois area. Acts as the marketing/promoting agent for the Charleston area in collaboration with other community organizations. **Founded:** 1919. **Publications:** *Chamber Focus* (Monthly); *Membership Directory & Buyers' Guide* (Annual); *Charleston Area Chamber of Commerce-- Membership Directory & Buyer's Guide* (Annual). **Telecommunication Services:** cacc@charlestonchamber.com.

51019 ■ *Chatter*
1st Bank Plz., Ste. 308
Lake Zurich, IL 60047
Ph: (847)438-5572
Fax: (847)438-5574
Co. E-mail: info@lzacc.com
URL: http://www.lzacc.com
Contact: Dale Perrin, Executive Director
Released: Monthly

51020 ■ Chester Chamber of Commerce
c/o Mike Ritter, Treas.
10 Chester By-Pass Rd.
Chester, IL 62233

Ph: (618)826-2721
Co. E-mail: chesterc@frontier.com
URL: http://www.chesterill.com/chamber
Contact: Linda Sympson, Executive Director
Description: Promotes business and community development in Chester, IL. **Founded:** 1934.

51021 ■ Chicago Area Gay and Lesbian Chamber of Commerce
3656 N Halsted St.
Chicago, IL 60613
Ph: (773)303-0167
Fax: (773)303-0168
Co. E-mail: info@glchamber.org
URL: http://www.glchamber.org
Contact: Christina Pinson, Executive Director
Description: Seeks to help gay, lesbian, bisexual and transgender business community through networking, promotions, marketing and attracting tourism. **Founded:** 1996.

51022 ■ Chicago Chinatown Chamber of Commerce
2169B S China Pl.
Chicago, IL 60616
Ph: (312)326-5320
Fax: (312)326-5668
Co. E-mail: info@chicagochinatown.org
URL: http://www.chicagochinatown.org/cccorg/home.jsp
Contact: Man-Men Lee, Executive Director
Description: Strives to improve and expand business opportunities and to educate others on the history, culture, and customs of the Chinese American community. **Founded:** 1983. **Publications:** *The Chamber News* (Quarterly).

51023 ■ Chicagoland Chamber of Commerce (CCoC)
Aon Center
200 E Randolph St., Ste. 2200
Chicago, IL 60601-6436
Ph: (312)494-6700
Fax: (312)861-0660
Co. E-mail: info@chicagolandchamber.org
URL: http://chicagolandchamber.org/wdk_cc
Contact: Jerry Roper, President
Description: Promotes business and community development in Chicago, IL. Conducts drug-free workplace program. **Publications:** *Business Resource Guide and Membership Directory; Relocation Guide for the Chicagoland Area.* **Telecommunication Services:** jroper@chicagolandchamber.org.

51024 ■ Chillicothe Chamber of Commerce (CCOC)
1028 N 2nd St.
Chillicothe, IL 61523
Ph: (309)274-4556
Co. E-mail: info@chillicothechamber.com
URL: http://www.chillicothechamber.com
Contact: Ben Alvarez, President
Description: Promotes business and community development in Chillicothe, IL. **Founded:** 1946. **Awards:** Chamber Member of the Year (Annual); Civic Award of the Year (Annual).

51025 ■ Cicero Chamber of Commerce and Industry
5801 W Cermak Rd., 2nd Fl.
Cicero, IL 60804
Ph: (708)863-6000
Fax: (708)863-8981
Co. E-mail: cicerocc@cicerochamber.org
URL: http://www.cicerochamber.org
Contact: Mary Esther Hernandez, Executive Director
Description: Promotes business and community development in Cicero, IL area.

51026 ■ *City Directory*
203 S 13th Street
Murphysboro, IL 62966
Ph: (618)684-6421
Free: 800-406-8774

Fax: (618)684-2010
Co. E-mail: director@murphysborochamber.com
URL: http://www.murphysboro.com
Contact: Dan Bost, President
Released: Periodic

51027 ■ Clinton Area Chamber of Commerce (CACC)
100 S Center St., Ste. 101
Clinton, IL 61727-1945
Ph: (217)935-3364
Free: 866-4DE-WITT
Fax: (217)935-0064
Co. E-mail: chamber@clintonilchamber.com
URL: http://www.clintonilchamber.com
Contact: Marian Brisard, Office Manager
Description: Promotes business and community development in Clinton, IL. Sponsors Clinton May Days Festival and Community Expo. **Founded:** 1953. **Publications:** *Chamber Scoop.* **Educational Activities:** Christmas Candlelight (Annual).

51028 ■ Collinsville Chamber of Commerce
221 W Main St.
Collinsville, IL 62234
Ph: (618)344-2884
Fax: (618)344-7499
Co. E-mail: info@discovercollinsville.com
URL: http://www.discovercollinsville.com
Contact: Wendi Valenti, Executive Director
Description: Promotes business and community development in Collinsville, IL. **Founded:** 1928.

51029 ■ *Commerce*
55 S Main St., Ste. 351
Naperville, IL 60540
Ph: (630)355-4141
Fax: (630)355-8335
Co. E-mail: chamber@naperville.net
URL: http://www.naperville.net
Contact: Tami Andrew, Chief Executive Officer
Released: Monthly

51030 ■ *Commerce Communicator*
28 W North St.
Danville, IL 61832-5729
Ph: (217)442-6201
Fax: (217)442-6228
Co. E-mail: vhaugen@vermilionadvantage.com
URL: http://www.vermilionadvantage.com
Contact: Vicki Haugen, President
Released: Bimonthly

51031 ■ *The Communicator*
PO Box 877
Carbondale, IL 62903
Ph: (618)549-2146
Fax: (618)529-5063
Co. E-mail: carbondalechamberofcommerce@gmail.com
URL: http://www.carbondalechamber.com
Contact: Woody Thorne, President
Released: Bimonthly **Price:** $3, /year.

51032 ■ *Communicator*
27 W Stephenson St.
Freeport, IL 61032
Ph: (815)233-1350
Fax: (815)235-4035
URL: http://www.freeportilchamber.com
Contact: Mr. Kim Grimes, President
Released: Monthly

51033 ■ *Community Development Guide and Membership Directory*
101 Bouthillier St.
Galena, IL 61036
Ph: (815)777-9050
Fax: (815)777-8465
Co. E-mail: office@galenachamber.com
URL: http://www.galenachamber.com
Contact: Ed Schmit, Executive Director
Released: Annual

51034 ■ *Community Guide*
1257 N Green St.
McHenry, IL 60050
Ph: (815)385-4300

Fax: (815)385-9142
Co. E-mail: info@mchenrychamber.com
URL: http://www.mchenrychamber.com
Contact: Kay Rial Bates, President

51035 ■ *Community Guide*
579 First Bank Dr., Ste. 205
Palatine, IL 60067
Ph: (847)359-7200
Fax: (847)359-7246
Co. E-mail: info@palatinechamber.com
URL: http://www.palatinechamber.com
Contact: Mindy Phillips, Director
Released: Monthly **Price:** $3.

51036 ■ *Community Guide*
PO Box 172
Maywood, IL 60153
Ph: (708)345-7077
Fax: (708)345-9455
Co. E-mail: info@maywoodchamber.org
URL: http://maywoodchamber.com
Contact: Edwin H. Walker, IV, President
Released: Annual

51037 ■ *Community Guide*
7727 Lake St.
River Forest, IL 60305
Ph: (708)771-5760
Co. E-mail: info@oprfchamber.org
URL: http://www.oprfchamber.org
Contact: John Lawrence, President
Released: Annual

51038 ■ *Community Guide*
22 W Streamwood Blvd.
Streamwood, IL 60107
Ph: (630)837-5200
Fax: (630)837-5251
Co. E-mail: staff@streamwoodchamber.com
URL: http://www.streamwoodchamber.com
Contact: Patrick McKernan, President
Released: Annual

51039 ■ *Community Guide*
427 W Virginia St.
Crystal Lake, IL 60014
Ph: (815)459-1300
Fax: (815)459-0243
Co. E-mail: info@clchamber.com
URL: http://www.clchamber.com
Contact: Gary Reece, President
Released: Annual; in July.

51040 ■ *Community Guide*
c/o Cheri Sisson, Exec. Dir.
2200 W Higgins Rd., Ste. 201
Hoffman Estates, IL 60169
Ph: (847)781-9100
Fax: (847)781-9172
Co. E-mail: info@hechamber.com
URL: http://www.hechamber.com
Contact: Cheri Sisson, Executive Director
Released: Annual

51041 ■ *Community Guide*
11419 State Rte. 47
Huntley, IL 60142
Ph: (847)669-0166
Fax: (847)669-0170
Co. E-mail: info@huntleychamber.org
URL: http://www.huntleychamber.org
Contact: Rita Slawek, President
Released: Annual

51042 ■ *Community Guide*
272 E Deerpath, Ste. 106
Lake Forest, IL 60045
Ph: (847)234-4282
Co. E-mail: info@lflbchamber.com
URL: http://www.lflbchamber.com/build1/index.cfm
Contact: Joanna Rolek, Executive Director
Released: Annual

51043 ■ *Community Guide*
350 May Mart Dr.
Rochelle, IL 61068-0220
Ph: (815)562-4189

Fax: (815)562-4180
Co. E-mail: chamber@rochelle.net
URL: http://www.rochellechamber.org
Contact: Peggy Friday, Chief Executive Officer
Released: Annual

51044 ■ *Community Guide and Business Listing*
107 S Main St.
Mount Prospect, IL 60056
Ph: (847)398-6616
Fax: (847)398-6780
Co. E-mail: info@mountprospectchamber.org
URL: http://www.mountprospectchamber.org
Contact: Dawn Fletcher Collins, Executive Director
Released: Annual

51045 ■ *Community Guide and Shopping, Dining, Lodging Guide, and a Street Map*
601 Deerfield Rd., Ste. 200
Deerfield, IL 60015
Ph: (847)945-4660
Fax: (847)940-0381
Co. E-mail: info@dbrchamber.com
URL: http://www.dbrchamber.com
Contact: Victoria Case, Executive Director
Released: Annual **Price:** $5, /copy.

51046 ■ *Community Map*
c/o Carol Foreman, Exec. Dir.
Edwardsville, IL 62025
Ph: (618)656-7600
Fax: (618)656-7611
Co. E-mail: cforeman@edglenchamber.com
URL: http://www.edglenchamber.com
Contact: Carol Foreman, Executive Director
Released: Monthly

51047 ■ *Community Profile on Village of Lisle*
1111 Burlington Ave., Ste. 102
Lisle, IL 60532
Ph: (630)964-0052
Fax: (630)964-2726
Co. E-mail: info@lislechamber.com
URL: http://www.lislechamber.com
Contact: Tom Althoff, President
Released: Biennial

51048 ■ *Community Resource Directory*
2320 Glenview Rd.
Glenview, IL 60025-2711
Ph: (847)724-0900
Fax: (847)724-0202
Co. E-mail: gcstaff@glenviewchamber.com
URL: http://glenviewchamber.com
Contact: Gregg Goslin, President
Released: Biennial **Price:** $10, each.

51049 ■ *Community Resource Guide*
10 S Seymour Ave.
Grayslake, IL 60030
Ph: (847)223-6888
Fax: (847)223-6895
Co. E-mail: business@grayslakechamber.com
URL: http://www.grayslakechamber.com
Contact: Karen Christian-Smith, Executive Director

51050 ■ *Community Resource Guide and Relocation Handbook*
55 S Main St., Ste. 351
Naperville, IL 60540
Ph: (630)355-4141
Fax: (630)355-8335
Co. E-mail: chamber@naperville.net
URL: http://www.naperville.net
Contact: Tami Andrew, Chief Executive Officer

51051 ■ *Connection*
136 Cass St.
Woodstock, IL 60098
Ph: (815)338-2436
Fax: (815)338-2927
Co. E-mail: info@woodstockilchamber.com
URL: http://www.woodstockilchamber.com
Contact: Todd Kinker, President (Acting)
Released: Monthly

51052 ■ *The Connector*
2775 Algonquin Rd., Ste. 310
Rolling Meadows, IL 60008
Ph: (847)398-3730
Fax: (847)398-3745
Co. E-mail: office@rmchamber.org
URL: http://www.rmchamber.org
Contact: Linda Liles Ballantine, Executive Director
Released: Bimonthly

51053 ■ *CosmoConnection*
203 N Wabash Ave., Ste. 518
Chicago, IL 60601
Ph: (312)499-0611
Fax: (312)701-0095
Co. E-mail: info@cosmococ.org
URL: http://www.cosmococ.org
Contact: Consuelo Pope, President
Released: Monthly

51054 ■ Cosmopolitan Chamber of Commerce (CCC)
203 N Wabash Ave., Ste. 518
Chicago, IL 60601
Ph: (312)499-0611
Fax: (312)701-0095
Co. E-mail: info@cosmococ.org
URL: http://www.cosmococ.org
Contact: Consuelo Pope, President
URL(s): cosmococ.org. **Description:** Individuals and businesses promoting the growth and development of minority-owned businesses in Chicago, IL. Convention/Meeting: none. **Scope:** Organized to promote the development of a broader economic base through the creation and strengthening of new businesses and the expansion of under-utilized business enterprises. **Founded:** 1933. **Publications:** *CosmoConnection* (Monthly). **Seminars:** System Formation Seminar; Estimating, Bonding and Financing; How to Start a Construction Company; Managing Construction Costs. Electronic Commerce (EDI, etc.); Basic Business Management; Marketing and Bookkeeping; Business Formation Seminar; Quarterly Networking.

51055 ■ Crete Area Chamber of Commerce
PO Box 263
Crete, IL 60417-0263
Ph: (708)672-9216
Fax: (708)672-7640
Co. E-mail: cretechamber@sbcglobal.net
URL: http://www.cretechamber.com
Contact: Pat Herbert, Executive Director
Description: Promotes business and community development in Crete, IL area. Sponsors 2-antique show, Wine Tasting, ribbon cutting, and grants scholarship. **Founded:** 1984. **Publications:** *Crete Record* (Weekly).

51056 ■ *Crete Record*
PO Box 263
Crete, IL 60417-0263
Ph: (708)672-9216
Fax: (708)672-7640
Co. E-mail: cretechamber@sbcglobal.net
URL: http://www.cretechamber.com
Contact: Pat Herbert, Executive Director
Released: Weekly

51057 ■ Crystal Lake Chamber of Commerce
427 W Virginia St.
Crystal Lake, IL 60014
Ph: (815)459-1300
Fax: (815)459-0540
Co. E-mail: info@clchamber.com
URL: http://www.clchamber.com
Contact: Gary Reece, President
Description: Provides businesses, professionals, and community organizations in the area with opportunities to meet, share interests, and develop business relationships. **Founded:** 1940. **Subscriptions:** audio recordings books video recordings. **Publications:** *Community Guide* (Annual); *News & Views* (Monthly); *Community Guide* (Annual); *Shopping and Dining Guide*. **Educational Activities:** Annual Dinner and Awards Banquet (Annual); Annual Golf Classic (Annual). **Awards:** Athena Award (Annual); Carl E. Wehde Memorial Award (Annual); Eagle Awards (Annual); Pride in Crystal Lake Award (Bimonthly); Robert Covey Award (Annual).

51058 ■ Darien Chamber of Commerce (DCC)
1702 Plainfield Rd.
Darien, IL 60561-5080
Ph: (630)968-0004
Fax: (630)968-2474
Co. E-mail: info@darienchamber.com
URL: http://www.darienchamber.com
Contact: Angelo Imbrogno, President
Description: Promotes business and community development in Darien, IL. Sponsors Easter Gala, tree lighting ceremony, and annual festival. **Founded:** 1984. **Publications:** *Chamber Directory*.

51059 ■ *Dateline*
130 S Locust St.
Centralia, IL 62801
Ph: (618)532-6789
Free: 888-533-2600
Fax: (618)533-7305
Co. E-mail: gccoc@centralil.com
URL: http://www.centraliail.com
Contact: Bob Kelsheimer, Executive Director

51060 ■ Deerfield, Bannockburn, Riverwoods Chamber of Commerce (DBRCC)
601 Deerfield Rd., Ste. 200
Deerfield, IL 60015
Ph: (847)945-4660
Fax: (847)940-0381
Co. E-mail: info@dbrchamber.com
URL: http://www.dbrchamber.com
Contact: Victoria Case, Executive Director
Description: Strives to enhance the local business climate and to promote business and community development in the Deerfield, Bannockburn, and Riverwoods, IL areas. **Founded:** 1925. **Publications:** *Community Guide and Shopping, Dining, Lodging Guide, and a Street Map* (Annual). **Awards:** College Scholarship (Annual).

51061 ■ DeKalb Chamber of Commerce (DCOC)
164 E Lincoln Hwy.
DeKalb, IL 60115
Ph: (815)756-6306
Fax: (815)756-5164
Co. E-mail: chamber@dekalb.org
URL: http://www.dekalb.org
Contact: Mr. Jim Allen, Executive Director
Description: Promotes business and community development in DeKalb County, GA. **Founded:** 1938. **Publications:** *Access DeKalb* (Bimonthly); *DeKalb Chamber Membership Guide* (Annual); *DeKalb County Map* (Semiannual). **Educational Activities:** DeKalb Chamber of Commerce Meeting (Annual). **Awards:** Mini Grants for Teachers (Annual).

51062 ■ *DeKalb Chamber Membership Guide*
164 E Lincoln Hwy.
DeKalb, IL 60115
Ph: (815)756-6306
Fax: (815)756-5164
Co. E-mail: chamber@dekalb.org
URL: http://www.dekalb.org
Contact: Mr. Jim Allen, Executive Director
Released: Annual

51063 ■ *DeKalb County Map*
164 E Lincoln Hwy.
DeKalb, IL 60115
Ph: (815)756-6306
Fax: (815)756-5164
Co. E-mail: chamber@dekalb.org
URL: http://www.dekalb.org
Contact: Mr. Jim Allen, Executive Director
Released: Semiannual

51064 ■ Des Plaines Chamber of Commerce and Industry
1401 E Oakton St.
Des Plaines, IL 60018
Ph: (847)824-4200

Fax: (847)824-7932
Co. E-mail: info@dpchamber.com
URL: http://www.desplaineschamber.com
Contact: Jeffrey Rozovics, President
Description: Promotes, supports, and assists the Des Plaines business community through effective communication and quality service. Improves the quality of life for all citizens of the area. **Publications:** *The Business Advocate* (Monthly); *Directory and Community Guide* (Annual).

51065 ■ *Destination Evanston*
1 Rotary Ctr.
1560 Sherman Ave., Ste. 860
Evanston, IL 60201
Ph: (847)328-1500
Fax: (847)328-1510
Co. E-mail: info@evchamber.com
URL: http://www.evchamber.com
Contact: Jonathan D. Perman, Executive Director
Released: Annual

51066 ■ *Dining Guide*
2775 Algonquin Rd., Ste. 310
Rolling Meadows, IL 60008
Ph: (847)398-3730
Fax: (847)398-3745
Co. E-mail: office@rmchamber.org
URL: http://www.rmchamber.org
Contact: Linda Liles Ballantine, Executive Director
Released: Semiannual

51067 ■ *Directory and Community Guide*
1401 E Oakton St.
Des Plaines, IL 60018
Ph: (847)824-4200
Fax: (847)824-7932
Co. E-mail: info@dpchamber.com
URL: http://www.desplaineschamber.com
Contact: Jeffrey Rozovics, President
Released: Annual

51068 ■ *Directory of Members*
PO Box 84
Mount Zion, IL 62549
Ph: (217)864-2526
Fax: (217)864-6115
Co. E-mail: askjudy4@aol.com
URL: http://www.mtzionchamber.org
Contact: Judy Kaiser, Administrator
Released: Annual

51069 ■ *Dixon Area Business News*
101 W 2nd St., Ste. 301
Dixon, IL 61021
Ph: (815)284-3361
Fax: (815)284-3675
Co. E-mail: dchamber@essex1.com
URL: http://www.dixonillinoischamber.com
Contact: John R. Thompson, President
Released: Monthly

51070 ■ Dixon Area Chamber of Commerce and Industry (DACCI)—Dixon Chamber of Commerce
101 W 2nd St., Ste. 301
Dixon, IL 61021
Ph: (815)284-3361
Fax: (815)284-3675
Co. E-mail: dchamber@essex1.com
URL: http://www.dixonillinoischamber.com
Contact: John R. Thompson, President
Description: Businesspersons, manufacturers, professionals, and non-profit organizations interested in promoting business and community development in the Dixon, IL area. **Founded:** 1887. **Publications:** *Dixon Area Business News* (Monthly); *Membership and Business Services Directory* (Annual).

51071 ■ Downers Grove Area Chamber of Commerce and Industry
The Esplanade at Locust Point
Downers Grove, IL 60515
Ph: (630)968-4050

Fax: (630)968-8368
Co. E-mail: chamber@downersgrove.org
URL: http://www.downersgrove.org
Contact: Laura Crawford, President
Description: Supports the business community while partnering with the residential, educational and service organizations. Helps to shape the business climate in the Downers Grove area. **Publications:** *ChamberLine* (Monthly); *Village and Business* (Annual).

51072 ■ Du Quoin Chamber of Commerce
PO Box 57
Du Quoin, IL 62832
Ph: (618)542-9570
Co. E-mail: dqchamber@comcast.net
URL: http://www.duquoin.org
Contact: Fred Huff, President
Description: Promotes the common interests and community welfare of the residents in Du Quoin, IL. Seeks to enhance the city's image and develop and encourage the various commercial, industrial, professional, financial, and civic interests of the city.

51073 ■ *E-Chamber Update*
1400 N Illinois St.
Swansea, IL 62226
Ph: (618)233-3938
Fax: (618)234-0222
Co. E-mail: swansea@swanseachamber.org
URL: http://www.swanseachamber.org
Contact: Tom Tyler, Executive Director
Released: Weekly **Price:** e-mail update for members only.

51074 ■ *E-Newsletter*
5221 W Grand Ave.
Gurnee, IL 60031
Ph: (847)249-3800
Fax: (847)249-3892
Co. E-mail: info@lakecountychamber.com
URL: http://www.lakecountychamber.com
Contact: Horacio Lopez, Chairman
Released: Weekly

51075 ■ *East Peoria Business Directory*
111 W Washington St., Ste. 290
East Peoria, IL 61611-2532
Ph: (309)699-6212
Fax: (309)699-6220
Co. E-mail: epcc@epcc.org
URL: http://www.epcc.org
Contact: Rick Swan, Executive Director
Released: Periodic

51076 ■ East Peoria Chamber of Commerce and Tourism (EPCCT)
111 W Washington St., Ste. 290
East Peoria, IL 61611-2532
Ph: (309)699-6212
Fax: (309)699-6220
Co. E-mail: epcc@epcc.org
URL: http://www.epcc.org
Contact: Rick Swan, Executive Director
Description: Represents businesses interested in promoting East Peoria, IL. **Publications:** *EP Update* (Monthly); *East Peoria Business Directory* (Periodic); *The FOLEPI Guide* (Annual). **Educational Activities:** Business After Hours (Monthly); Mayor's Prayer (Annual); Mittens for Muffins (Annual). **Awards:** Terry Brewer Memorial Scholarship (Annual).

51077 ■ *ED Update*
633 La Salle St., Ste. 401
Ottawa, IL 61350
Ph: (815)433-0084
Fax: (815)433-2405
Co. E-mail: info@ottawachamberillinois.com
URL: http://www.ottawachamberillinois.com
Contact: Boyd Palmer, Executive Director
Released: Bimonthly

51078 ■ Edgebrook Chamber of Commerce
6440 N Central Ave.
Chicago, IL 60646
Ph: (773)775-0378

Fax: (773)775-0371
URL: http://www.edgebrookchamber.com
Contact: Julie Schultz, President
Description: Promotes business and community development in the Edgebrook-Sauganash area of Chicago, IL.

51079 ■ Edwardsville - Glen Carbon Chamber of Commerce (EGCCC)
c/o Carol Foreman, Exec. Dir.
Edwardsville, IL 62025
Ph: (618)656-7600
Fax: (618)656-7611
Co. E-mail: cforeman@edglenchamber.com
URL: http://www.edglenchamber.com
Contact: Carol Foreman, Executive Director
Description: Promotes business and community development in Madison County, IL. Holds monthly Business After Hours party; sponsors annual Halloween Parade, Harvest Hometest and Annual Golf Scramble. Organizes ribbon cutting events for new local businesses. **Founded:** 1924. **Publications:** *Business Directory*; *Community Map* (Monthly). **Educational Activities:** Edwardsville - Glen Carbon Chamber of Commerce Meeting (Annual); Edwardsville - Glen Carbon Chamber of Commerce Meeting (Annual). **Awards:** Athena Award (Annual); Albert Cassens Community Service Award.

51080 ■ *Effingham Business*
PO Box 643
Effingham, IL 62401
Ph: (217)342-4147
Fax: (217)342-4228
Co. E-mail: chamber@effinghamchamber.org
URL: http://www.effinghamchamber.org
Contact: Norma Lansing, President
Released: Quarterly **Price:** free.

51081 ■ El Paso Chamber of Commerce
475 W Front St.
El Paso, IL 61738
Ph: (309)527-4005
Fax: (309)527-4717
Co. E-mail: jenmelkearney@yahoo.com
URL: http://www.elpasoil.org/chamber
Description: Promotes business and community development in El Paso, IL.

51082 ■ *Elgin Area Chamber Business Review*
31 S Grove Ave.
Elgin, IL 60120
Ph: (847)741-5660
Fax: (847)741-5677
Co. E-mail: info@elginchamber.com
URL: http://www.elginchamber.com
Contact: Leo Nelson, President
Released: Monthly

51083 ■ Elgin Area Chamber of Commerce (EACC)
31 S Grove Ave.
Elgin, IL 60120
Ph: (847)741-5660
Fax: (847)741-5677
Co. E-mail: info@elginchamber.com
URL: http://www.elginchamber.com
Contact: Leo Nelson, President
Description: Promotes economic and community development in northern Kane County, IL. **Founded:** 1908. **Publications:** *Elgin Area Chamber Business Review* (Monthly).

51084 ■ Elizabeth Chamber of Commerce
PO Box 371
Elizabeth, IL 61028
Co. E-mail: info@elizabeth-il.com
URL: http://www.elizabeth-il.com
Contact: Diane Siperia, President
Description: Promotes business and community development in Elizabeth, IL area. **Founded:** 1986.

51085 ■ Elmhurst Chamber of Commerce and Industry
242 N York St., Ste. 102
Elmhurst, IL 60126-3301
Ph: (630)834-6060

Fax: (630)834-6002
Co. E-mail: info@elmhurstchamber.org
URL: http://www.elmhurstchamber.org
Contact: John R. Quigley, President
Description: Business and professional men and
women. Sponsors annual Elmfest. Offers services,
programs and events that provide opportunities for
networking and referral, business education, development and promotion, governmental representation
and community involvement. **Founded:** 1918. **Publications:** *Elmhurst Community* (Annual); *Focus*
(Monthly).

51086 ■ Elmhurst Community
242 N York St., Ste. 102
Elmhurst, IL 60126-3301
Ph: (630)834-6060
Fax: (630)834-6002
Co. E-mail: info@elmhurstchamber.org
URL: http://www.elmhurstchamber.org
Contact: John R. Quigley, President
Released: Annual

51087 ■ EP Update
111 W Washington St., Ste. 290
East Peoria, IL 61611-2532
Ph: (309)699-6212
Fax: (309)699-6220
Co. E-mail: epcc@epcc.org
URL: http://www.epcc.org
Contact: Rick Swan, Executive Director
Released: Monthly **Price:** free for members.

**51088 ■ Evanston Chamber of Commerce
(ECC)**
1 Rotary Ctr.
1560 Sherman Ave., Ste. 860
Evanston, IL 60201
Ph: (847)328-1500
Fax: (847)328-1510
Co. E-mail: info@evchamber.com
URL: http://www.evchamber.com
Contact: Jonathan D. Perman, Executive Director
Description: Promotes business and community
development in Evanston, IL. Sponsors Fountain
Square Arts Festival and The World's Largest Garage
Sale. **Founded:** 1921. **Publications:** *Destination
Evanston* (Annual); *Evanston Community Guide* (An-
nual); *Evanston Marketplace* (Bimonthly). **Awards:**
Business Person of the Year (Annual); Community
Leadership Award (Annual).

51089 ■ Evanston Community Guide
1 Rotary Ctr.
1560 Sherman Ave., Ste. 860
Evanston, IL 60201
Ph: (847)328-1500
Fax: (847)328-1510
Co. E-mail: info@evchamber.com
URL: http://www.evchamber.com
Contact: Jonathan D. Perman, Executive Director
Released: Annual

51090 ■ Evanston Marketplace
1 Rotary Ctr.
1560 Sherman Ave., Ste. 860
Evanston, IL 60201
Ph: (847)328-1500
Fax: (847)328-1510
Co. E-mail: info@evchamber.com
URL: http://www.evchamber.com
Contact: Jonathan D. Perman, Executive Director
Released: Bimonthly

**51091 ■ Evergreen Park Chamber of
Commerce (EPCC)**
3960 W 95th St., 3rd Fl.
Evergreen Park, IL 60805
Ph: (708)423-1118
Fax: (708)423-1859
Co. E-mail: epchamber@sbcglobal.net
URL: http://www.evergreenparkchamber.org
Contact: Helen Cuprisin, President
Description: Serves the business community by
creating a positive business environment. Promotes
commerce by developing and providing information
and advocacy in a responsive and ethical manner.

51092 ■ Fairbury Chamber of Commerce
101 E Locust St.
Fairbury, IL 61739
Ph: (815)692-3899
Co. E-mail: fcc@fairburyil.org
URL: http://www.fairburyil.org
Description: Advances the commercial, industrial,
civic and professional interest of the City of Fairbury
by supporting the growth of existing industries and
assisting those firms or individuals seeking to locate
in the area. **Founded:** 1951. **Publications:** *Member
Directory & Community Guide.*

**51093 ■ Fairview Heights Chamber of
Commerce (FHCOC)**
10003 Bunkum Rd.
Fairview Heights, IL 62208
Ph: (618)397-3127
Fax: (618)397-5563
Co. E-mail: office@fairviewheightschamber.org
URL: http://www.fairviewheightschamber.org
Contact: Scott Leas, Executive Director
Description: Brings together the private sector, non-
profit entities, educational institutions and govern-
ment in Fairview Heights. Integrates the agendas of
many organizations working toward similar economic,
educational, and quality of life goals. **Founded:** 1969.
Publications: *Chamber Communicator* (Monthly).
Awards: Citizen of the Year (Annual). **Telecommunication Services:** director@fairviewheights-
chamber.org.

51094 ■ Focus
242 N York St., Ste. 102
Elmhurst, IL 60126-3301
Ph: (630)834-6060
Fax: (630)834-6002
Co. E-mail: info@elmhurstchamber.org
URL: http://www.elmhurstchamber.org
Contact: John R. Quigley, President
Released: Monthly

51095 ■ Focus
402 Court St.
Pekin, IL 61555-0636
Ph: (309)346-2106
Fax: (309)346-2104
Co. E-mail: chamber@pekin.net
URL: http://www.pekin.net
Contact: Bill Fleming, Executive Director
Released: Annual

51096 ■ The FOLEPI Guide
111 W Washington St., Ste. 290
East Peoria, IL 61611-2532
Ph: (309)699-6212
Fax: (309)699-6220
Co. E-mail: epcc@epcc.org
URL: http://www.epcc.org
Contact: Rick Swan, Executive Director
Released: Annual

51097 ■ Forest Park Chamber of Commerce
7331 W Roosevelt Rd.
Forest Park, IL 60130
Ph: (708)366-2543
Fax: (708)366-3373
Co. E-mail: info@exploreforestpark.com
URL: http://www.exploreforestpark.com
Contact: Laurie Kokenes, Executive Director
Description: Local businesses, organizations and
community-minded individuals working together to
promote business and a sense of community. Provides a climate where business can grow by strengthening, supporting, and promoting the economic viability, social needs and community cohesion of the
Village of Forest Park. **Founded:** 1912. **Publications:** *Forest Park Community Guide* (Annual). **Educational Activities:** Networking (Monthly).

51098 ■ Forest Park Community Guide
7331 W Roosevelt Rd.
Forest Park, IL 60130
Ph: (708)366-2543
Fax: (708)366-3373
Co. E-mail: info@exploreforestpark.com
URL: http://www.exploreforestpark.com
Contact: Laurie Kokenes, Executive Director
Released: Annual

**51099 ■ Fox Lake Area Chamber of
Commerce and Industry (FLACCI)**
PO Box 203
Fox Lake, IL 60020
Ph: (847)587-7474
Fax: (847)587-1725
Co. E-mail: info@discoverfoxlake.com
URL: http://www.discoverfoxlake.com
Contact: Linnea Pioro, Executive Director
Description: Promotes business and community
development in the Fox Lake, IL area. Sponsors area
festival, Miss Fox Lake competition, and trade fair;
conducts fundraising activities.

51100 ■ Frankfort Business
123 Kansas St.
Frankfort, IL 60423
Ph: (815)469-3356
Free: 877-469-3356
Fax: (815)469-4352
Co. E-mail: info@frankfortchamber.com
URL: http://www.frankfortchamber.com
Contact: Keith Ogle, President
Released: Monthly **Price:** free for members; $15, for
nonmembers.

51101 ■ Frankfort Chamber of Commerce
123 Kansas St.
Frankfort, IL 60423
Ph: (815)469-3356
Free: 877-469-3356
Fax: (815)469-4352
Co. E-mail: info@frankfortchamber.com
URL: http://www.frankfortchamber.com
Contact: Keith Ogle, President
Description: Promotes the commercial, industrial,
and civic welfare of the Frankfort area. Provides
many civic and business development programs.
Sponsors fund-raising events like Labor Day Week-
end Festival and Frankfort Fall Festival. **Founded:**
1967. **Publications:** *Frankfort Business* (Monthly).
Educational Activities: Business Expo (Annual).

**51102 ■ Franklin Park/Schiller Park Chamber
of Commerce**
PO Box 186
Franklin Park, IL 60131
Ph: (708)865-9510
Fax: (847)865-9520
Co. E-mail: info@chamberbyohare.org
URL: http://www.chamberbyohare.org
Contact: Kenneth Kollar, President
Description: Creates a strong association between
two villages that have a similar industrial and residen-
tial community base. Works toward the integration of
resources and a strong presence through community
event participation, consistent programs for business
leaders, educational opportunities and networking for
continued business interaction.

**51103 ■ Freeport Area Chamber of
Commerce (FACC)**
27 W Stephenson St.
Freeport, IL 61032
Ph: (815)233-1350
Fax: (815)235-4035
URL: http://www.freeportilchamber.com
Contact: Mr. Kim Grimes, President
Description: Promotes business and community
development in the Freeport, IL area. Conducts an-
nual Tutty Baker Days festival. **Founded:** 1947. **Pub-
lications:** *Communicator* (Monthly).

**51104 ■ French - American Chamber of
Commerce (Chicago, Illinois)**
35 E Wacker Dr., Ste. 670
Chicago, IL 60601
Ph: (312)578-0444
Fax: (312)578-0445
Co. E-mail: information@facc-chicago.com
URL: http://www.facc-chicago.com/presentation-of-
the-chamber
Contact: Emmanuele van Houdenhoven, Executive
Director
Description: Promotes and develops commercial
and financial relations between France and the
United States in Chicago land. Offers commercial
services and organizes professional events to bring

members together in the spirit of establishing contacts and expanding the economic relationship between both countries.

51105 ■ Friday Facts
100 S Water St., Ste. 103
Decatur, IL 62523-1048
Ph: (217)422-2200
Fax: (217)422-4576
Co. E-mail: mirinda.rothrock@decaturchamber.com
URL: http://www.decaturchamber.com
Contact: Mirinda Rothrock, President
E-mail: mirinda.rothrock@decaturchamber.com
Released: Weekly

51106 ■ Fulton Chamber of Commerce
415 11th Ave.
Fulton, IL 61252
Ph: (815)589-4545
Co. E-mail: chamber@cityoffulton.us
URL: http://www.cityoffulton.us
Contact: Heather Bennett, Executive Director
Description: Represents small business owners, individuals, and large corporations. Enhances the economic climate and promotes the business community for the benefit of the greater Fulton area.

51107 ■ FYI
15440 S Central Ave.
Oak Forest, IL 60452
Ph: (708)687-4600
Fax: (708)687-7878
Co. E-mail: info@oc-chamber.org
URL: http://oc-chamber.org
Contact: Kim Malecky-Iles, Executive Director

51108 ■ Galena Area Chamber of Commerce
101 Bouthillier St.
Galena, IL 61036
Ph: (815)777-9050
Fax: (815)777-8465
Co. E-mail: office@galenachamber.com
URL: http://www.galenachamber.com
Contact: Ed Schmit, Executive Director
Description: Organized on behalf of its members to promote the economic welfare of the business community and contribute to the quality of life in the Galena area. Events sponsored include a business and trade showcase, 2 golf outings, Festival of Quilts, Ladies Getaway, Business After Hours, Business A.M., Halloween Parade, Night of the Luminaria, and various community education meetings. **Founded:** 1838. **Publications:** Galenian (Semiannual); Nexus (Monthly); Community Development Guide and Membership Directory (Annual).

51109 ■ Galenian
101 Bouthillier St.
Galena, IL 61036
Ph: (815)777-9050
Fax: (815)777-8465
Co. E-mail: office@galenachamber.com
URL: http://www.galenachamber.com
Contact: Ed Schmit, Executive Director
Released: Semiannual

51110 ■ Galesburg Area Chamber of Commerce
PO Box 749
Galesburg, IL 61401
Ph: (309)343-1194
Fax: (309)343-1195
Co. E-mail: chamber@galesburg.org
URL: http://www.galesburg.org
Contact: Robert C. Maus, President
Description: Promotes business and community development in Galesburg, IL area.

51111 ■ Geneva Chamber of Commerce (GCC)
8 S 3rd St.
Geneva, IL 60134-0481
Ph: (630)232-6060
Free: 866-4-GENEVA

Fax: (630)232-6083
Co. E-mail: chamberinfo@genevachamber.com
URL: http://www.genevachamber.com
Contact: Jean Gaines, President
Description: Promotes business and community development in Geneva, IL. Sponsors local festivals. **Founded:** 1950. **Publications:** Soundings (Monthly).

51112 ■ Gibson Area Chamber of Commerce (GACC)
126 N Sangamon Ave.
Gibson City, IL 60936
Ph: (217)784-5217
URL: http://www.gibsoncityillinois.com/Business/chamber-of-commerce
Contact: Pam Bradbury, Secretary
Description: Promotes business and community development in the Gibson, IL area.

51113 ■ Glen Ellyn Chamber of Commerce (GECOC)
800 Roosevelt Rd., Bldg. D, Ste. 108
Glen Ellyn, IL 60137
Ph: (630)469-0907
Fax: (630)469-0426
Co. E-mail: director@glenellynchamber.com
URL: http://www.glenellynchamber.com
Contact: Georgia Koch, Executive Director
Description: Promotes business and community development in the Glen Ellyn, IL area. **Founded:** 1949. **Publications:** Chamber Goods and Services Guide (Annual); Navigator (Monthly).

51114 ■ Glencoe Chamber of Commerce
PO Box 575
Glencoe, IL 60022
Ph: (847)835-3333
Fax: (847)835-7700
Co. E-mail: glencoechamber@yahoo.com
URL: http://www.glencoechamber.org
Contact: Sally Sprowl, Executive Director
Description: Promotes business and community development in Glencoe, IL area. **Founded:** 1965.

51115 ■ Glenview Chamber of Commerce
2320 Glenview Rd.
Glenview, IL 60025-2711
Ph: (847)724-0900
Fax: (847)724-0202
Co. E-mail: gcstaff@glenviewchamber.com
URL: http://glenviewchamber.com
Contact: Gregg Goslin, President
Description: Works for the advancement of commercial, industrial, professional and civic interests of Glenview. Provides programs that increase visibility, customers and education. **Founded:** 1923. **Publications:** Community Resource Directory (Biennial); Community Resource Directory (Biennial). **Educational Activities:** Business After Hours (Monthly). **Awards:** Business Person of the Year (Annual).

51116 ■ GLMV Area Chamber of Commerce
1123 S Milwaukee Ave.
Libertyville, IL 60048
Ph: (847)680-0750
Fax: (847)680-0760
Co. E-mail: info@glmvchamber.org
URL: http://www.glmvchamber.org
Contact: Alese Campbell, Executive Director
Description: Promotes business and community development in Green Oaks, Libertyville, Mundelein, and Vernon Hills, Illinois area. **Publications:** Action News (Monthly); Images; GLMV Area Chamber of Commerce--Membership Directory.

51117 ■ Grayslake Area Chamber of Commerce
10 S Seymour Ave.
Grayslake, IL 60030
Ph: (847)223-6888
Fax: (847)223-6895
Co. E-mail: business@grayslakechamber.com
URL: http://www.grayslakechamber.com
Contact: Karen Christian-Smith, Executive Director
Description: Represents commercial, industrial, professional service and retail businesses. Acts as a liaison between the Village of Grayslake, the Township, Lake County, the State and local citizens on matters concerning the well-being of the Grayslake

business community. Plans, organizes and funds community events that are designed to promote the Village and the businesses in it. **Founded:** 1950. **Publications:** Community Resource Guide; Community Resource Guide. **Educational Activities:** Arts (Annual). **Awards:** Joanne W. Lawrence Scholarship (Annual).

51118 ■ Grayville Chamber of Commerce (GCC)
618 W North St.
Grayville, IL 62844-1336
Ph: (618)375-7518
URL: http://www.cityofgrayville.com/info.htm
Description: Promotes business and community development in Grayville, IL. Sponsors annual Grayville Days. **Awards:** Business of Year (Annual); Citizen of the Year (Annual).

51119 ■ Greater Aurora Chamber of Commerce (GACC)
43 W Galena Blvd.
Aurora, IL 60506
Ph: (630)256-3180
Fax: (630)256-3189
Co. E-mail: jhenning@aurorachamber.com
URL: http://www.aurorachamber.com
Contact: Joseph Henning, President
Description: Promotes business and community development in the Aurora, IL area. **Founded:** 1920. **Publications:** Business Monthly (Monthly).

51120 ■ Greater Belleville Chamber of Commerce
216 E A St.
Belleville, IL 62220
Ph: (618)233-2015
Fax: (618)233-2077
Co. E-mail: info@bellevillechamber.org
URL: http://www.bellevillechamber.org
Contact: John Lengerman, Executive Director
Description: Works to support and advance business and community interests, as well as the quality of life.

51121 ■ Greater Centralia Chamber of Commerce
130 S Locust St.
Centralia, IL 62801
Ph: (618)532-6789
Free: 888-533-2600
Fax: (618)533-7305
Co. E-mail: gccoc@centralil.com
URL: http://www.centraliail.com
Contact: Bob Kelsheimer, Executive Director
Description: Improves the Centralia Area Business Climate by working diligently for positive community planning and change. **Publications:** Dateline. **Telecommunication Services:** gccoc@centraliail.com.

51122 ■ Greater Channahon-Minooka Area Chamber of Commerce (GCMACC)
505 Bob Blair Rd.
Minooka, IL 60447
Ph: (815)521-9999
URL: http://www.cmchamber.org
Contact: Jim Zackavec, Chairperson

51123 ■ Greater Decatur Chamber of Commerce
100 S Water St., Ste. 103
Decatur, IL 62523-1048
Ph: (217)422-2200
Fax: (217)422-4576
Co. E-mail: mirinda.rothrock@decaturchamber.com
URL: http://www.decaturchamber.com
Contact: Mirinda Rothrock, President
E-mail: mirinda.rothrock@decaturchamber.com
URL(s): decaturchamber.com. **Description:** Promotes business and community development in Greater Decatur, MI area. **Founded:** 1903. **Publications:** Friday Facts (Weekly); Chamber of Commerce Business Directory (Annual); Organization Directory; Decatur Chamber of Commerce Business Directory. **Awards:** Chamber Member of the Week (Weekly). **Telecommunication Services:** helpdesk@decaturchamber.com; customerservice@decaturchamber.com.

51124 ■ Greater Effingham Chamber of Commerce and Industry (GECCI)
PO Box 643
Effingham, IL 62401
Ph: (217)342-4147
Fax: (217)342-4228
Co. E-mail: chamber@effinghamchamber.org
URL: http://www.effinghamchamber.org
Contact: Norma Lansing, President
Description: Promotes business and community development in the Effingham, IL area. Sponsors rodeo. **Founded:** 1917. **Publications:** *Effingham Business* (Quarterly); *Take Five* (Monthly). **Educational Activities:** Greater Effingham Chamber of Commerce and Industry Luncheon (Monthly). **Awards:** Chamber Community Scholarship (Annual); Member of the Month (Monthly). **Telecommunication Services:** nlansing@effinghamchamber.org.

51125 ■ Greater Fairfield Area Chamber of Commerce (GFACC)
121 E Main St.
Fairfield, IL 62837
Ph: (618)842-6116
Fax: (618)842-5654
Co. E-mail: chamber@fairfieldwireless.net
URL: http://www.fairfieldillinoischamber.com
Contact: Flo Simpson, Executive Secretary
Description: Represents businesses, professionals, and interested others. Promotes agricultural, business, community, and industrial development in the Fairfield, IL area. **Publications:** *Greater Fairfield Area Chamber of Commerce News* (Quarterly).

51126 ■ *Greater Fairfield Area Chamber of Commerce News*
121 E Main St.
Fairfield, IL 62837
Ph: (618)842-6116
Fax: (618)842-5654
Co. E-mail: chamber@fairfieldwireless.net
URL: http://www.fairfieldillinoischamber.com
Contact: Flo Simpson, Executive Secretary
Released: Quarterly

51127 ■ Greater Harvard Area Chamber of Commerce (GHACC)
62 N Ayer St., Ste. B
Harvard, IL 60033
Ph: (815)943-4404
Fax: (815)943-4410
Co. E-mail: info@harvcc.net
URL: http://www.harvcc.net
Contact: Crystal Musgrove, Executive Director
Description: Promotes business and community development in the Harvard, IL area. **Publications:** *Chamber News* (Bimonthly).

51128 ■ Greater Lincolnshire Chamber of Commerce (GLCC)
1 Marriott Dr.
Lincolnshire, IL 60069
Ph: (847)793-2409
Fax: (847)793-2405
Co. E-mail: office.coordinator@lincolnshirechamber. org
URL: http://www.lincolnshirechamber.org
Contact: Stephen Territo, President
Description: Works to serve the needs of businesses in the Greater Lincolnshire area. Provides a community and business guide for all area residents and businesses. **Founded:** 1973.

51129 ■ Greater Salem Chamber of Commerce
615 W Main St.
Salem, IL 62881
Ph: (618)548-3010
Fax: (618)548-3014
Co. E-mail: visitus@salemilchamber.com
URL: http://www.salemilchamber.com
Contact: Laura Daugherty, President
Description: Promotes business and community development in Salem, IL.

51130 ■ Greater Springfield Chamber of Commerce (GSCC)
1011 S 2nd St.
Springfield, IL 62704
Ph: (217)525-1173
Fax: (217)525-8768
Co. E-mail: info@gscc.org
URL: http://www.gscc.org
Contact: Steward Sandstrom, President
Description: Promotes business and community development in the Abbeville, SC area. Sponsors festivals and hall of fame; presents business and service awards. **Publications:** *miniUPDATE e-mail newsletter* (Semimonthly); *Update* (Monthly); *Membership Directory and Buyer's Guide* (Annual). **Awards:** Small Business Person of the Year (Annual).

51131 ■ Greenville Chamber of Commerce
PO Box 283
Greenville, IL 62246
Ph: (618)664-9272
Free: 888-862-8201
Co. E-mail: greenville@newwavecomm.net
URL: http://www.greenvilleusa.org
Contact: Ms. Julia Jenner, Executive Director
Description: Promotes business and community development in Greenville, IL area.

51132 ■ *Guide to Lake Zurich*
1st Bank Plz., Ste. 308
Lake Zurich, IL 60047
Ph: (847)438-5572
Fax: (847)438-5574
Co. E-mail: info@lzacc.com
URL: http://www.lzacc.com
Contact: Dale Perrin, Executive Director
Released: Annual

51133 ■ Hamilton County Chamber of Commerce and Economic Development Commission
PO Box 64
McLeansboro, IL 62859
Ph: (618)643-3971
URL: http://www.mcleansboro.com
Contact: Mark Becker, Chairman
Description: Promotes business and community development in Hamilton County area.

51134 ■ Hampshire Area Chamber of Commerce (HACC)
PO Box 157
Hampshire, IL 60140
Ph: (847)683-1122
Fax: (847)683-1146
Co. E-mail: hampshirecc@fvi.net
URL: http://www.hampshirechamber.org/pages/ default.asp
Contact: Lynn Acker, President
Description: Promotes business and community development in Hampshire, IL. Organizes annual Coon Creek Day.

51135 ■ Havana Area Chamber of Commerce
PO Box 116
Havana, IL 62644
Ph: (309)543-3528
Co. E-mail: havana@scenichavana.com
URL: http://www.scenichavana.com/CoCofficDetail. php
Description: Works with other community resources to promote local tourism, create jobs, and recruit new businesses in Havana, IL. Sponsors community events.

51136 ■ Henry Area Chamber of Commerce
PO Box 211
Henry, IL 61537-0211
Ph: (309)364-3261
Co. E-mail: henrychamber@henrychamber.org
URL: http://www.henrychamber.org
Contact: Chris Laible, President
Description: Promotes business and community development in Henry, IL area. **Founded:** 1959.

51137 ■ Herrin Chamber of Commerce
3 S Park Ave.
Herrin, IL 62948

Ph: (618)942-5163
Co. E-mail: herrincc@herrinillinois.com
URL: http://www.herrinillinois.com
Contact: Kevin Frost, President
Description: Serves and supports the economic good of the greater Herrin area with priority given to economic development and the assistance necessary to acquire and retain business and industry in Herrin and the surrounding region. **Publications:** *Chamber Chat* (Monthly). **Educational Activities:** Herrin Chamber of Commerce Dinner (Annual).

51138 ■ Herscher Chamber of Commerce
PO Box 437
Herscher, IL 60941
Ph: (815)426-2131
Co. E-mail: kim.krygowski@panduit.com
URL: http://www.herscher.net/churchorgs/herscher- ChamberOfCommerce.asp
Contact: Kim Krygowski, President
Description: Provides park improvements and various community projects to the village of Herscher. **Founded:** 1916.

51139 ■ Highland Chamber of Commerce (HCC)
907 Main St.
Highland, IL 62249
Ph: (618)654-3721
Fax: (618)654-8966
Co. E-mail: jami@highlandillinois.com
URL: http://www.highlandillinois.com
Contact: Jami Jansen, Executive Director
Description: Promotes business, tourism, and community development in Highland, IL. **Founded:** 1924. **Publications:** *Available Site Location Guide* (Annual); *Chamber News* (Monthly).

51140 ■ Highland Park Chamber of Commerce (HPCC)
508 Central Ave., Ste. 206
Highland Park, IL 60035
Ph: (847)432-0284
Fax: (847)432-2802
Co. E-mail: info@ehighlandpark.com
URL: http://www.ehighlandpark.com/default2.asp
Contact: Virginia Anzelmo Glasner, Executive Director
Description: Promotes business and community development in Highland Park, IL. Conducts charitable activities. Sponsors festival. **Founded:** 1910.

51141 ■ Hills Chamber of Commerce
PO Box 1164
Bridgeview, IL 60455-0164
Ph: (708)364-7739
Fax: (708)364-7735
Co. E-mail: info@thehillschamber.com
URL: http://www.thehillschamber.com
Contact: Phyllis Majka, President
Description: Promotes business and community development in the communities of Hickory Hills and Palos.

51142 ■ Hinsdale Chamber of Commerce (HCC)
22 E 1st St.
Hinsdale, IL 60521
Ph: (630)323-3952
Fax: (630)323-3953
Co. E-mail: staff@hinsdalechamber.com
URL: http://www.hinsdalechamber.com
Contact: Janet Anderson, Executive Director
Description: Promotes business and community development in Hinsdale, IL. Holds annual Fine Arts Fair, Farmers' Market, and other social events. Sponsors Christmas walk, annual garage, Halloween Parade, sidewalk sales. Operates welcome service. **Founded:** 1925. **Publications:** *Hinsdale Community Directory* (Annual); *Hinsdale Community Directory* (Annual); *Guide Book* (Annual). **Telecommunication Services:** info@hinsdalechamber.com.

51143 ■ *Hinsdale Community Directory*
22 E 1st St.
Hinsdale, IL 60521
Ph: (630)323-3952

Fax: (630)323-3953
Co. E-mail: staff@hinsdalechamber.com
URL: http://www.hinsdalechamber.com
Contact: Janet Anderson, Executive Director
Released: Annual

51144 ■ Hoffman Estates Chamber of Commerce (HECC)
c/o Cheri Sisson, Exec. Dir.
2200 W Higgins Rd., Ste. 201
Hoffman Estates, IL 60169
Ph: (847)781-9100
Fax: (847)781-9172
Co. E-mail: info@hechamber.com
URL: http://www.hechamber.com
Contact: Cheri Sisson, Executive Director
Description: Promotes business and community development in Hoffman Estates, IL area. **Founded:** 1990. **Publications:** *Community Guide* (Annual).

51145 ■ Homewood Area Chamber of Commerce (HACC)
1820 Ridge Rd., Ste. 200
Homewood, IL 60430
Ph: (708)206-3384
Fax: (708)206-3605
Co. E-mail: hacc@homewoodareachamber.com
URL: http://www.homewoodareachamber.com
Contact: Dennis Fare, Executive Director
Description: Promotes business and community development in the area. Sponsors Fine Art Fair; conducts charitable activities. **Founded:** 1962.

51146 ■ Huntley Area Chamber of Commerce and Industry
11419 State Rte. 47
Huntley, IL 60142
Ph: (847)669-0166
Fax: (847)669-0170
Co. E-mail: info@huntleychamber.org
URL: http://www.huntleychamber.org
Contact: Rita Slawek, President
Description: Promotes business and community development in Huntley, IL area. **Founded:** 1992. **Publications:** *The Chamber Review* (Monthly); *Community Guide* (Annual).

51147 ■ IACCE News
215 E Adams St.
Springfield, IL 62701
Ph: (217)522-5512
Fax: (217)522-5518
Co. E-mail: lweitzel@ilchamber.org
URL: http://www.iacce.org
Contact: Elizabeth D. Fiala Kerns, President
Released: Monthly

51148 ■ Illinois Association of Chamber of Commerce Executives (IACCE)
215 E Adams St.
Springfield, IL 62701
Ph: (217)522-5512
Fax: (217)522-5518
Co. E-mail: lweitzel@ilchamber.org
URL: http://www.iacce.org
Contact: Elizabeth D. Fiala Kerns, President
Description: Serves as an access and valued resource for the professional development of Chamber of Commerce executives and staff in Illinois. **Founded:** 1915. **Publications:** *IACCE News* (Monthly); *Resource Guide* (Annual). **Awards:** Distinguished Chamber of the Year (Annual).

51149 ■ Illinois Quad City Chamber of Commerce
622 19th St.
Moline, IL 61265-2142
Ph: (309)757-5416
Fax: (309)757-5435
Co. E-mail: rbaker@quadcitychamber.com
URL: http://www.quadcitychamber.com
Contact: Rick L. Baker, President
Description: Promotes business and community development in Illinois Quad City, IL. **Publications:** *Business News Quarterly* (Quarterly); *QC Direct* (Annual); *Illinois Quad City Chamber of Commerce--Membership Directory* (Annual); *Business News In Depth* (Bimonthly).

51150 ■ Illinois State Chamber of Commerce (ISCC)
Chicago Office
300 S Wacker Dr., Ste. 1600
Chicago, IL 60606-6779
Ph: (312)983-7100
Fax: (312)983-7101
Co. E-mail: dwhitley@ilchamber.org
URL: http://ilchamber.org
Contact: Douglas L. Whitley, President
Description: Promotes business and community development in Illinois. Seeks to reduce operational costs for employers by providing information on state government regulations through seminars, publications and a member helpline. Lobbies on key business issues; holds legislative briefings. **Founded:** 1919. **Publications:** *ISCC Exec Report* (Monthly); *Legislative Directory* (Biennial); *Springfield Scene* (Weekly). **Educational Activities:** Annual Legislative Briefing (Annual); Annual Legislative Conference (Annual).

51151 ■ Illinois Valley Area Chamber of Commerce and Economic Development (IVAC)
300 Bucklin
La Salle, IL 61301-0446
Ph: (815)223-0227
Fax: (815)223-4827
Co. E-mail: ivaced@ivaced.org
URL: http://www.ivaced.org
Contact: Marci Duro, Chief Executive Officer
Description: Promotes business and community development in portions of Bureau, La Salle, Marshall, and Putnam counties, IL. **Founded:** 1911. **Publications:** *Agri-Business Brochure*; *Airport Brochure*; *Major Annual Events*; *Membership Memo* (Monthly); *Transportation Brochure*; *The Illinois Valley*. **Educational Activities:** Small Business Seminar (Monthly).

51152 ■ *Images of Champaign County*
1817 S Neil St., Ste. 201
Champaign, IL 61820-7269
Ph: (217)359-1791
Fax: (217)359-1809
Co. E-mail: info@champaigncounty.org
URL: http://www.champaigncounty.org
Contact: Laura E. Weis, President
Released: Annual

51153 ■ *Industrial Directory*
5002 Oakton St.
Skokie, IL 60077
Ph: (847)673-0240
Fax: (847)673-0249
Co. E-mail: info@skokiechamber.org
URL: http://www.skokiechamber.org
Contact: Howard Meyer, Executive Director
Released: Annual

51154 ■ *Insights*
27 E Main St.
Cary, IL 60013
Ph: (847)639-2800
Fax: (847)639-2168
Co. E-mail: info@carygrovechamber.com
URL: http://www.carygrovechamber.com
Contact: Suzanne Corr, Executive Director
Released: Monthly

51155 ■ *International Marketplace Newsletter*
2540 W Devon Ave.
Chicago, IL 60659
Ph: (773)743-6022
Co. E-mail: westridgechamber@sbcglobal.net
URL: http://westridgechamber.org
Contact: Amie Zander, Executive Director
Price: free.

51156 ■ *ISCC Exec Report*
Chicago Office
300 S Wacker Dr., Ste. 1600
Chicago, IL 60606-6779
Ph: (312)983-7100

Fax: (312)983-7101
Co. E-mail: dwhitley@ilchamber.org
URL: http://ilchamber.org
Contact: Douglas L. Whitley, President
Released: Monthly

51157 ■ Jacksonville Area Chamber of Commerce
c/o Ginny Fanning, Pres.
Jacksonville, IL 62650
Ph: (217)245-2174
Fax: (217)245-0661
Co. E-mail: chamber@jacksonvilleareachamber.org
URL: http://www.jacksonvilleareachamber.org
Contact: Ginny Fanning, President
Description: Promotes business and community development in the Jacksonville, IL area. **Founded:** 1888. **Publications:** *Chamber Review* (Monthly). **Awards:** Business of the Year 25 or More Employees (Annual); Business of the Year Under 25 Employees (Annual); Not-For-Profit Organization of the Year (Annual).

51158 ■ Jasper County Chamber of Commerce (JCCC)
207 1/2 Jourdan St.
Newton, IL 62448
Ph: (618)783-3399
Free: 877-223-0074
Co. E-mail: jasperchamber@psbnewton.com
URL: http://www.newtonillinois.com
Contact: Milissa Weber, Executive Director
Description: Promotes business and community development in Jasper County, IL. **Founded:** 1986.

51159 ■ Jefferson County Chamber of Commerce (JCCC)
200 Potomac Blvd.
Mount Vernon, IL 62864
Ph: (618)242-5725
Fax: (618)242-5130
Co. E-mail: chambermarketing@mvn.net
URL: http://www.southernillinois.com
Contact: Brandon Bullard, Executive Director
Description: Promotes business and community development in Jefferson County, IL. Holds Business After Hours parties and board meetings. **Founded:** 1921. **Publications:** *Business News* (Monthly).

51160 ■ Jefferson Park Chamber of Commerce
5214 W Lawrence Ave., Ste. 5
Chicago, IL 60630
Ph: (773)736-6697
Fax: (773)736-3508
Co. E-mail: jeffparkcoc@sbcglobal.net
URL: http://www.jeffersonpark.net
Contact: Melissa Bukovatz, Executive Director
Description: Helps maintain the viability of the community through promotion and development of business in Jefferson Park. **Founded:** 1934.

51161 ■ Jersey County Business Association (JCBA)
209 N State St.
Jerseyville, IL 62052-1755
Ph: (618)639-5222
Co. E-mail: agilmore@jcba-il.us
URL: http://www.jcba.us
Contact: Alan Gilmore, Chief Executive Officer
Description: Promotes business and community development in Jersey County, IL. Sponsors golf day, car show, and craft shows. **Founded:** 1955. **Publications:** *The Business News* (Monthly). **Telecommunication Services:** carrie@jcba-il.us.

51162 ■ Joliet Region Chamber of Commerce and Industry
PO Box 752
Joliet, IL 60434-0752
Ph: (815)727-5371

Fax: (815)727-5374
Co. E-mail: info@jolietchamber.com
URL: http://www.jolietchamber.com
Contact: Russ Slinkard, President
Description: Promotes business environment to enhance the quality of life in Joliet Region, IL. Serves as the voice in governmental and social affairs in the community. **Founded:** 1914. **Publications:** *Vision* (Monthly).

51163 ■ **Kankakee Regional Chamber of Commerce**
1137 E 5000N Rd.
Bourbonnais, IL 60914
Ph: (815)933-7721
Fax: (815)933-7675
Co. E-mail: david@kankakee.org
URL: http://www.kankakee.org/cwt/external/wcpages/index.aspx
Contact: David Hinderliter, President
Description: Promotes business and community development in the Kankakee County, IL area. **Founded:** 1904. **Publications:** *News and Views* (Monthly). **Awards:** Athena Award (Annual); Citizen of the Year (Annual).

51164 ■ **Kewanee Chamber of Commerce (KCC)**
113 E 2nd St.
Kewanee, IL 61443
Ph: (309)852-2175
Fax: (309)852-2176
Co. E-mail: chamber@kewanee-il.com
URL: http://www.kewanee-il.com
Contact: Mike Fulton, President
Description: Promotes business and community development in Kewanee, IL.

51165 ■ *The Key*
579 First Bank Dr., Ste. 205
Palatine, IL 60067
Ph: (847)359-7200
Fax: (847)359-7246
Co. E-mail: info@palatinechamber.com
URL: http://www.palatinechamber.com
Contact: Mindy Phillips, Director
Released: Bimonthly

51166 ■ **Lake County Chamber of Commerce (LCCC)**
5221 W Grand Ave.
Gurnee, IL 60031
Ph: (847)249-3800
Fax: (847)249-3892
Co. E-mail: info@lakecountychamber.com
URL: http://www.lakecountychamber.com
Contact: Horacio Lopez, Chairman
Description: Businesses and individuals in Lake County, IL. Promotes: tourism; trade between local and foreign businesses; community and county development; friendly relations between local industry and business leaders. **Scope:** business, community development. **Founded:** 1915. **Publications:** *E-Newsletter* (Weekly).

51167 ■ **Lake Forest - Lake Bluff Chamber of Commerce**
272 E Deerpath, Ste. 106
Lake Forest, IL 60045
Ph: (847)234-4282
Co. E-mail: info@lflbchamber.com
URL: http://www.lflbchamber.com/build1/index.cfm
Contact: Joanna Rolek, Executive Director
Description: Promotes the economic and civic interest of the community. **Publications:** *Community Guide* (Annual); *Shopping and Dining Guide* (Annual).

51168 ■ **Lake Zurich Area Chamber of Commerce (LZACC)**
1st Bank Plz., Ste. 308
Lake Zurich, IL 60047
Ph: (847)438-5572

Fax: (847)438-5574
Co. E-mail: info@lzacc.com
URL: http://www.lzacc.com
Contact: Dale Perrin, Executive Director
Description: Retailers, industrial concerns, professionals, and service organizations that promote business and industry in the Lake Zurich Area (including Deer Park, Hawthorn Woods, Kildeer, Long Grove, and North Barrington), IL. Sponsors Business After Hours seminars, retail promotions, and community recognition and beautification programs. Conducts social activities, sponsors scholarships. Sponsors Community Recognition Program and a Community and Business EXPO. **Founded:** 1915. **Publications:** *Chatter* (Monthly); *Guide to Lake Zurich* (Annual). **Educational Activities:** Lake Zurich Area Chamber of Commerce Seminar (Periodic).

51169 ■ *Lakeview Directory & Neighborhood Guide*
3138 N Broadway
Chicago, IL 60657
Ph: (773)348-8608
Fax: (773)348-7409
Co. E-mail: info@lakevieweast.com
URL: http://www.lakevieweast.com
Contact: Maureen Martino, Executive Director
Released: Annual

51170 ■ **Lakeview East Chamber of Commerce (LVECC)**
3138 N Broadway
Chicago, IL 60657
Ph: (773)348-8608
Fax: (773)348-7409
Co. E-mail: info@lakevieweast.com
URL: http://www.lakevieweast.com
Contact: Maureen Martino, Executive Director
Description: Promotes business and community development in the Lakeview area of Chicago. **Publications:** *Chamber Report* (Monthly); *Lakeview Directory & Neighborhood Guide* (Annual); *Official Guide to Lakeview East* (Annual).

51171 ■ **Lawrence County Chamber of Commerce (LCCC)**
619 12th St.
Lawrenceville, IL 62439
Ph: (618)943-3516
Fax: (618)943-4748
Co. E-mail: lccc2@verizon.net
URL: http://www.lawrencecountychamberofcommerce.com
Contact: Rachel Gard, Executive Director
Description: Promotes business and community development in Lawrence County, IL. Conducts annual Basketball Capital Classic. Sponsors the Lawrenceville Fall Festival. **Publications:** *Let Us Point You in the Right Direction* (Annual).

51172 ■ **Lebanon Chamber of Commerce**
221 W St. Louis St.
Lebanon, IL 62254
Ph: (618)537-8420
Co. E-mail: chamber@lebanonil.org
URL: http://www.lebanonil.org
Description: Aims to promote business and resident growth, encourage tourism and shopping, and improve the existing facilities and historical aspects of the city of Lebanon.

51173 ■ *Legislative Directory*
Chicago Office
300 S Wacker Dr., Ste. 1600
Chicago, IL 60606-6779
Ph: (312)983-7100
Fax: (312)983-7101
Co. E-mail: dwhitley@ilchamber.org
URL: http://ilchamber.org
Contact: Douglas L. Whitley, President
Released: Biennial **Price:** $5.

51174 ■ *Legislative Guide to Elected & Appointed Officials*
2775 Algonquin Rd., Ste. 310
Rolling Meadows, IL 60008
Ph: (847)398-3730

Fax: (847)398-3745
Co. E-mail: office@rmchamber.org
URL: http://www.rmchamber.org
Contact: Linda Liles Ballantine, Executive Director

51175 ■ **Lemont Area Chamber of Commerce**
101 Main St.
Lemont, IL 60439-3675
Ph: (630)257-5997
Fax: (630)257-3238
Co. E-mail: info@lemontchamber.com
URL: http://www.lemontchamber.com
Contact: Marlene Miciunas, President
Description: Aims to promote the community and make it a better place to live, work, and conduct business. **Founded:** 1948. **Publications:** *Chamber Chords* (Monthly). **Awards:** Citizen of the Year (Annual).

51176 ■ *Let Us Point You in the Right Direction*
619 12th St.
Lawrenceville, IL 62439
Ph: (618)943-3516
Fax: (618)943-4748
Co. E-mail: lccc2@verizon.net
URL: http://www.lawrencecountychamberofcommerce.com
Contact: Rachel Gard, Executive Director
Released: Annual **Price:** free.

51177 ■ *Leverage*
1690 Newtowne Dr.
Bourbonnais, IL 60914
Ph: (815)932-2222
Fax: (815)932-3294
Co. E-mail: bbcc@bbchamber.com
URL: http://bbchamber.com
Contact: Jaclyn Dugan-Roof, President
Released: Monthly

51178 ■ **Limestone Area Chamber of Commerce (LACOC)**
PO Box 4043
Bartonville, IL 61607
Ph: (309)697-1031
Co. E-mail: email@limestonechamber.com
URL: http://www.limestonechamber.com
Contact: Diana Kelly, President
Description: Promotes business and community development in Limestone area. **Founded:** 1997.

51179 ■ **Lincoln - Logan County Chamber of Commerce**
1555 5th St.
Lincoln, IL 62656
Ph: (217)735-2385
Fax: (217)735-9205
Co. E-mail: chamber@lincolnillinois.com
URL: http://lincolnillinois.com/ABF.aspx
Contact: Andi Hake, Executive Director
Description: Strives to enhance the general welfare and prosperity of the Lincoln and Logan County area. **Founded:** 1903. **Publications:** *Update* (Monthly).

51180 ■ **Lincoln Park Chamber of Commerce (LPCC)**
1925 N Clybourn Ave., Ste. 301
Chicago, IL 60614-7396
Ph: (773)880-5200
Fax: (773)880-0266
Co. E-mail: info@lincolnparkchamber.com
URL: http://www.lincolnparkchamber.com
Contact: Kim Schilf, President
Description: Works to develop and implement membership services and provides essential information. Advocates for the protection and advancement of economic and business development. Promotes the Lincoln Park area and its businesses. Encourages relationships and communication between and among the community and its governmental bodies. **Founded:** 1947. **Publications:** *Resident's Guide to Lincoln Park*; *The Source* (Bimonthly). **Telecommunication Services:** kim@lincolnparkchamber.com.

51181 ■ Lincolnwood Chamber of Commerce and Industry
400 W Touhy Ave.
Lincolnwood, IL 60712
Ph: (847)679-5760
Fax: (847)679-5790
URL: http://www.lincolnwoodchamber.org
Contact: Deanna Minkler, President
Description: Promotes business and community development in Lincolnwood, IL. **Founded:** 1978. **Awards:** Corporate Citizen of the Year (Annual); Madeleine Grant Memorial College Scholarship (Annual).

51182 ■ Lindenhurst - Lake Villa Chamber of Commerce
500 Grand Ave.
Lindenhurst, IL 60046-6075
Ph: (847)356-8446
Fax: (847)356-8561
Co. E-mail: llvchamber@sbcglobal.net
URL: http://www.llvchamber.com/page1.aspx
Contact: Connie Meadie, Executive Director
Description: Helps to promote a sound economic climate in Northeastern Illinois. Helps the members enhance business activity through education, networking opportunities, and cost saving benefits. **Publications:** On the Move (Monthly).

51183 ■ Lisle Area Chamber of Commerce (LCC)
1111 Burlington Ave., Ste. 102
Lisle, IL 60532
Ph: (630)964-0052
Fax: (630)964-2726
Co. E-mail: info@lislechamber.com
URL: http://www.lislechamber.com
Contact: Tom Althoff, President
Description: Promotes business and community development in the Lisle, IL area. **Founded:** 1983. **Publications:** Community Profile on Village of Lisle (Biennial); Membership Directory and Product/Services Guide (Annual).

51184 ■ Litchfield Chamber of Commerce
311 N Madison
Litchfield, IL 62056
Ph: (217)324-2533
Fax: (217)324-3559
Co. E-mail: info@litchfieldchamber.com
URL: http://www.litchfieldchamber.com
Contact: Adrian Baker, President
Description: Aims to promote and stimulate the economic growth within the greater Litchfield area by mobilizing the talents and energies of the chamber's members. **Founded:** 1936. **Publications:** Chamber World (Monthly).

51185 ■ Lockport
921 S State St.
Lockport, IL 60441-3435
Ph: (815)838-3357
Fax: (815)838-2653
Co. E-mail: office@lockportchamber.com
URL: http://www.lockportchamber.com
Contact: Mary Kay Campbell, Executive Director
Released: Biennial

51186 ■ Lockport Chamber of Commerce (LCC)
921 S State St.
Lockport, IL 60441-3435
Ph: (815)838-3357
Fax: (815)838-2653
Co. E-mail: office@lockportchamber.com
URL: http://www.lockportchamber.com
Contact: Mary Kay Campbell, Executive Director
Description: Promotes business and community development in Lockport, IL. Sponsors parades as well as a variety of social and promotional activities. **Founded:** 1974. **Publications:** Lockport (Biennial); Lockport Connections (Monthly); Lockport Map (Biennial). **Educational Activities:** Business After Hours (Annual); Business Expo (Annual); Lockport Chamber of Commerce Meeting (Monthly). **Awards:** Dollars for Scholars (Annual).

51187 ■ Lockport Connections
921 S State St.
Lockport, IL 60441-3435
Ph: (815)838-3357
Fax: (815)838-2653
Co. E-mail: office@lockportchamber.com
URL: http://www.lockportchamber.com
Contact: Mary Kay Campbell, Executive Director
Released: Monthly **Price:** free for members.

51188 ■ Lockport Map
921 S State St.
Lockport, IL 60441-3435
Ph: (815)838-3357
Fax: (815)838-2653
Co. E-mail: office@lockportchamber.com
URL: http://www.lockportchamber.com
Contact: Mary Kay Campbell, Executive Director
Released: Biennial

51189 ■ Lombard Area Chamber of Commerce and Industry
c/o Yvonne Invergo, Exec. Dir.
10 Lilac Ln.
Lombard, IL 60148
Ph: (630)627-5040
Fax: (630)627-5519
Co. E-mail: info@lombardchamber.com
URL: http://www.lombardchamber.com
Contact: Yvonne Invergo, Executive Director
Description: Promotes business and community development in the Lombard, IL area. Sponsors Lilac Festival and Lilac Ball. Sponsors golf outing. **Founded:** 1953. **Publications:** Lombard Community Directory (Annual); Village; The Sourcebook: Directory of Goods and Services. **Awards:** Business Pride Award (Annual); Major Milestone Award (Annual); Property Improvement Award (Annual); Property Stewardship Award (Annual); Jim Bell Distinguished Developer Award (Annual). **Telecommunication Services:** yvonne@lombardchamber.com.

51190 ■ Lombard Community Directory
c/o Yvonne Invergo, Exec. Dir.
10 Lilac Ln.
Lombard, IL 60148
Ph: (630)627-5040
Fax: (630)627-5519
Co. E-mail: info@lombardchamber.com
URL: http://www.lombardchamber.com
Contact: Yvonne Invergo, Executive Director
Released: Annual

51191 ■ Loves Park - Machesney Park Chamber of Commerce—Parks Chamber of Commerce
c/o Diana Johnson, Exec. Dir.
100 Heart Blvd.
Loves Park, IL 61111
Ph: (815)633-3999
Fax: (815)633-4057
Co. E-mail: diana@parkschamber.com
URL: http://www.parkschamber.com
Contact: Diana Johnson, Executive Director
Description: Works to build a healthy economy and improve the quality of life in the community. **Publications:** Chamber Chatter (Monthly).

51192 ■ MaccLink
298 Main St.
Park Forest, IL 60466
Ph: (708)747-6000
Fax: (708)747-6054
Co. E-mail: lauren@mattesonareachamber.com
URL: http://www.macclink.com
Contact: Lauren Alspaugh, Executive Director
Released: Bimonthly

51193 ■ Mahomet Area Chamber of Commerce
PO Box 1031
Mahomet, IL 61853-1031
Ph: (217)586-3165

Fax: (217)586-3774
Co. E-mail: office@mahometchamberofcommerce.com
URL: http://mahometchamber.net
Contact: Mark Kesler, Chairman
Description: Works to advance the general welfare and prosperity of the Mahomet area. **Founded:** 1985. **Publications:** Mahomet Connection (Monthly). **Awards:** Mahomet Chamber of Commerce Scholarship (Annual).

51194 ■ Mahomet Connection
PO Box 1031
Mahomet, IL 61853-1031
Ph: (217)586-3165
Fax: (217)586-3774
Co. E-mail: office@mahometchamberofcommerce.com
URL: http://mahometchamber.net
Contact: Mark Kesler, Chairman
Released: Monthly

51195 ■ Major Annual Events
300 Bucklin
La Salle, IL 61301-0446
Ph: (815)223-0227
Fax: (815)223-4827
Co. E-mail: ivaced@ivaced.org
URL: http://www.ivaced.org
Contact: Marci Duro, Chief Executive Officer

51196 ■ Manhattan Chamber of Commerce
PO Box 357
Manhattan, IL 60442
Ph: (815)478-3811
Fax: (815)478-7761
Co. E-mail: chamber@manhattan-il.com
URL: http://www.manhattan-il.com
Contact: Dianne Huelsman, President
Description: Promotes business and community development in Manhattan, IL.

51197 ■ Manufacturers Directory
308 W State St., Ste. 190
Rockford, IL 61101
Ph: (815)987-8100
Fax: (815)987-8122
Co. E-mail: info@rockfordchamber.com
URL: http://www.rockfordchamber.com
Contact: Einar Forsman, President
Released: Annual

51198 ■ Manufacturer's Guide
633 La Salle St., Ste. 401
Ottawa, IL 61350
Ph: (815)433-0084
Fax: (815)433-2405
Co. E-mail: info@ottawachamberillinois.com
URL: http://www.ottawachamberillinois.com
Contact: Boyd Palmer, Executive Director
Released: Periodic

51199 ■ Marengo-Union Chamber of Commerce
116 S State St.
Marengo, IL 60152
Ph: (815)568-6680
Fax: (815)568-6879
Co. E-mail: chamber@marengo-union.com
URL: http://www.marengo-union.com
Contact: Christine Wienke, Managing Director
Description: Promotes business and community development in McHenry County, IL. Sponsors annual Settlers Day. **Founded:** 1970. **Publications:** Chamber Talk (Monthly). **Telecommunication Services:** assistant@marengo-union.com.

51200 ■ Marion Chamber of Commerce
PO Box 307
Marion, IL 62959
Ph: (618)997-6311
Fax: (618)997-4665
Co. E-mail: marionchamber@marionillinois.com
URL: http://www.marionillinois.com
Contact: Mary Jo McCurdy, Chairperson
Description: Promotes business and community development in the Marion, IL area.

51201 ■ Marshall Area Chamber of Commerce (MACC)
708 Archer Ave.
Marshall, IL 62441
Ph: (217)826-2034
Fax: (217)826-2034
Co. E-mail: marshall.chamber@frontier.com
URL: http://www.marshall-il.com
Contact: George Dallmier, President
URL(s): www.marshallilchamber.com. **Description:** Represents industries and businesses organized to promote agricultural, business, community, and tourism development in the Marshall, IL area. **Founded:** 1940. **Publications:** *Chamber Chatter* (Monthly).

51202 ■ Matteson Area Chamber of Commerce (MACC)
298 Main St.
Park Forest, IL 60466
Ph: (708)747-6000
Fax: (708)747-6054
Co. E-mail: lauren@mattesonareachamber.com
URL: http://www.macclink.com
Contact: Lauren Alspaugh, Executive Director
Description: Promotes business and community development in University Park, IL. **Publications:** *MaccLink* (Bimonthly).

51203 ■ Mattoon Chamber of Commerce
500 Broadway Ave.
Mattoon, IL 61938
Ph: (217)235-5661
Fax: (217)234-6544
Co. E-mail: matchamber@consolidated.net
URL: http://www.mattoonchamber.com
Contact: Brian Titus, President
Description: Business and professional firms. Seeks to support community and economic development in Coles County, IL. Sponsors Bagelfest. **Founded:** 1905. **Publications:** *Briefings* (Monthly); *Business Directory and Buyer's Guide* (Annual); *Mattoon Image Book*. **Awards:** Citizen of the Year (Annual); Education Award (Annual).

51204 ■ Maywood Chamber of Commerce (MCC)
PO Box 172
Maywood, IL 60153
Ph: (708)345-7077
Fax: (708)345-9455
Co. E-mail: info@maywoodchamber.org
URL: http://maywoodchamber.com
Contact: Edwin H. Walker, IV, President
Description: Businesses, churches, organizations, government agencies, and individuals interested in promoting business and community development in Maywood, IL. Conducts charitable activities. **Founded:** 1935. **Publications:** *Business Guide*; *Community Guide* (Annual).

51205 ■ McHenry Area Chamber of Commerce (MACC)
1257 N Green St.
McHenry, IL 60050
Ph: (815)385-4300
Fax: (815)385-9142
Co. E-mail: info@mchenrychamber.com
URL: http://www.mchenrychamber.com
Contact: Kay Rial Bates, President
Description: Represents businesses and professional men and women working together to provide support to the growth and development of the business community and continually improve the quality of life for those who work and live in McHenry. **Founded:** 1952. **Publications:** *Community Guide*; *Up Front* (Monthly). **Educational Activities:** Business Council (Monthly); Country Meadows Craft Show. **Telecommunication Services:** kay@mchenrychamber.com.

51206 ■ McLean County Chamber of Commerce (MCC)
210 S East St.
Bloomington, IL 61701
Ph: (309)829-6344

Fax: (309)827-3940
Co. E-mail: michael@mccleancochamber.org
URL: http://www.mccleancochamber.org
Contact: Dr. Les Mathers, President
Description: Represents businesses and individuals investing time and money in a continual community development program. Improves the economic, civic and cultural well-being of McLean County. **Founded:** 1900. **Publications:** *News, Views & Issues* (Monthly). **Educational Activities:** Business After Hours (Monthly). **Telecommunication Services:** info@mccleancochamber.org.

51207 ■ Melrose Park Chamber of Commerce
900 N 25th Ave.
Melrose Park, IL 60160
Ph: (708)338-1007
Fax: (708)338-9924
Co. E-mail: melroseparkchamber@sbcglobal.net
URL: http://www.melroseparkchamber.org
Contact: Mrs. Cathy K. Stenberg, Executive Director
Description: Helps different companies to recognize their business. **Founded:** 1925. **Publications:** *Chamber Business and Community Guide* (Annual); *Chamber Chit-Chat* (Quarterly).

51208 ■ *Member Directory & Community Guide*
101 E Locust St.
Fairbury, IL 61739
Ph: (815)692-3899
Co. E-mail: fcc@fairburyil.org
URL: http://www.fairburyil.org

51209 ■ *Membership and Business Directory*
308 W State St., Ste. 190
Rockford, IL 61101
Ph: (815)987-8100
Fax: (815)987-8122
Co. E-mail: info@rockfordchamber.com
URL: http://www.rockfordchamber.com
Contact: Einar Forsman, President
Released: Annual

51210 ■ *Membership and Business Services Directory*
101 W 2nd St., Ste. 301
Dixon, IL 61021
Ph: (815)284-3361
Fax: (815)284-3675
Co. E-mail: dchamber@essex1.com
URL: http://www.dixonillinoischamber.com
Contact: John R. Thompson, President
Released: Annual

51211 ■ *Membership Directory and Buyer's Guide*
PO Box 877
Carbondale, IL 62903
Ph: (618)549-2146
Fax: (618)529-5063
Co. E-mail: carbondalechamberofcommerce@gmail.com
URL: http://www.carbondalechamber.com
Contact: Woody Thorne, President
Released: Annual

51212 ■ *Membership Directory and Buyer's Guide*
2002 Walters Ave.
Northbrook, IL 60062
Ph: (847)498-5555
Fax: (847)498-5510
Co. E-mail: info@northbrookchamber.org
URL: http://www.northbrookchamber.org
Contact: Tensley Garris, President

51213 ■ *Membership Directory & Buyers' Guide*
501 Jackson Ave.
Charleston, IL 61920
Ph: (217)345-7041
Fax: (217)345-7042
Co. E-mail: cacc@advant.com
URL: http://www.charlestonchamber.com
Contact: Cindy White, Executive Director
Released: Annual; every January.

51214 ■ *Membership Directory and Buyer's Guide*
55 S Main St., Ste. 351
Naperville, IL 60540
Ph: (630)355-4141
Fax: (630)355-8335
Co. E-mail: chamber@naperville.net
URL: http://www.naperville.net
Contact: Tami Andrew, Chief Executive Officer
Released: Annual

51215 ■ *Membership Directory and Buyer's Guide*
1011 S 2nd St.
Springfield, IL 62704
Ph: (217)525-1173
Fax: (217)525-8768
Co. E-mail: info@gscc.org
URL: http://www.gscc.org
Contact: Steward Sandstrom, President
Released: Annual; distributed every summer. **Price:** $35, for nonmembers; $25, for members.

51216 ■ *Membership Directory and Product/Services Guide*
1111 Burlington Ave., Ste. 102
Lisle, IL 60532
Ph: (630)964-0052
Fax: (630)964-2726
Co. E-mail: info@lislechamber.com
URL: http://www.lislechamber.com
Contact: Tom Althoff, President
Released: Annual

51217 ■ *Membership List*
211 Locust St.
Sterling, IL 61081-3536
Ph: (815)625-2400
Fax: (815)625-9361
Co. E-mail: kewoldsen@saukvalleyareachamber.com
URL: http://www.saukvalleyareachamber.com
Contact: Kimberly Ewoldsen, Executive Director
Released: Periodic

51218 ■ *Membership Memo*
300 Bucklin
La Salle, IL 61301-0446
Ph: (815)223-0227
Fax: (815)223-4827
Co. E-mail: ivaced@ivaced.org
URL: http://www.ivaced.org
Contact: Marci Duro, Chief Executive Officer
Released: Monthly

51219 ■ Mendota Area Chamber of Commerce
PO Box 620
Mendota, IL 61342-0620
Ph: (815)539-6507
Fax: (815)539-6025
Co. E-mail: mendotachamber@yahoo.com
URL: http://mendotachamber.com
Contact: Alison Wasmer, Executive Director
Description: Promotes business and community development in Mendota, IL. **Founded:** 1945.

51220 ■ Metropolis Chamber of Commerce
607 Market St.
Metropolis, IL 62960
Ph: (618)524-2714
Free: 800-949-5740
Fax: (618)524-4780
URL: http://www.metropolischamber.com
Description: Promotes business and community development in Metropolis, IL area. **Publications:** *Chamberlink* (Monthly).

51221 ■ *MGCCI It's Your Business*
6101 Capulina Ave., Lower Level
Morton Grove, IL 60053
Ph: (847)965-0330
Fax: (847)965-0349
Co. E-mail: director@mgcci.org
URL: http://www.mgcci.org
Contact: Christine Sullivan, President
Released: Monthly **Price:** included in membership dues.

51222 ■ *miniUPDATE e-mail newsletter*
1011 S 2nd St.
Springfield, IL 62704
Ph: (217)525-1173
Fax: (217)525-8768
Co. E-mail: info@gscc.org
URL: http://www.gscc.org
Contact: Steward Sandstrom, President
Released: Semimonthly

51223 ■ *Minutes of Board Meeting*
27 E Main St.
Cary, IL 60013
Ph: (847)639-2800
Fax: (847)639-2168
Co. E-mail: info@carygrovechamber.com
URL: http://www.carygrovechamber.com
Contact: Suzanne Corr, Executive Director

51224 ■ Mokena Chamber of Commerce
19820 Wolf Rd.
Mokena, IL 60448-1545
Ph: (708)479-2468
Co. E-mail: mokena@mokena.com
URL: http://www.mokena.com
Contact: Mary Maertin, President
Description: Promotes business and community development in the Mokena, IL area. **Publications:** *Chambergram* (Quarterly).

51225 ■ Momence Chamber of Commerce
203 E River St.
Momence, IL 60954
Ph: (815)472-4620
Fax: (815)472-6453
Co. E-mail: momencechamber@sbcglobal.net
URL: http://www.momence.net
Contact: Jennifer Workman, President
Description: Provides its members with the opportunity to network and make business contacts.

51226 ■ Monmouth Area Chamber of Commerce (MACC)
90 Public Sq.
Monmouth, IL 61462-0857
Ph: (309)734-3181
Co. E-mail: macc@maplecity.com
URL: http://www.monmouthilchamber.com
Contact: Angela McElwee, Executive Director
Description: Represents businesses and professional persons interested in promoting business and community development in the Monmouth, IL area. Sponsors prime beef festival. **Founded:** 1912. **Publications:** *Chamber Chatter* (Monthly); *Chamber Communicator* (Monthly). **Educational Activities:** Good Morning Monmouth (Monthly).

51227 ■ Mont Clare - Elmwood Park Chamber of Commerce
c/o Ms. Barbara Melnyk, Exec. Dir.
Elmwood Park, IL 60707
Ph: (708)456-8000
Fax: (708)456-8680
Co. E-mail: mcepcoc@aol.com
URL: http://www.mcepchamber.org
Contact: Mr. Jonathan Zivojnovic, President
Description: Works on bridging the gap between the business community, political community, community organizations, and the area residents. **Publications:** *The Chamber Chatter* (Bimonthly); *Mont Clare/Elmwood Park Chamber of Commerce Community Guide.* **Telecommunication Services:** info@mcepchamber.org.

51228 ■ Monticello Chamber of Commerce
PO Box 313
Monticello, IL 61856-0313
Ph: (217)762-7921
Free: 800-952-3396
Fax: (217)762-2711
Co. E-mail: info@monticellochamber.org
URL: http://www.monticellochamber.org
Contact: Sue Gortner, Executive Director
URL(s): www.monticelloillinois.net. **Description:** Works to create an environment where businesses can succeed. **Publications:** *Business* (Annual). **Educational Activities:** Lunch with Santa on the Train (Annual).

51229 ■ Morrison Chamber of Commerce
PO Box 8
Morrison, IL 61270
Ph: (815)772-3757
Fax: (815)772-3757
Co. E-mail: morrisonchamber@frontiernet.ne
URL: http://www.morrisonchamber.com
Contact: Susan Gomez, President
Description: Aims to promote Morrison and support its members through structure and events that unite the community. **Founded:** 1927.

51230 ■ Morton Chamber of Commerce (MCC)
415 W Jefferson
Morton, IL 61550-1817
Ph: (309)263-2491
Free: 888-765-6588
Fax: (309)263-2401
Co. E-mail: mkull@mortonillinois.org
URL: http://mortonchamber.org
Contact: Jennifer Daly, Executive Director
Description: Businesses. Promotes business and community development in Morton, IL. Sponsors retail promotions and annual Pumpkin Festival. **Founded:** 1955. **Publications:** *Morton Matters* (Monthly). **Educational Activities:** Pumpkin (Annual). **Telecommunication Services:** jdaly@morton-illinois.org.

51231 ■ Morton Grove Chamber of Commerce and Industry (MGCCI)
6101 Capulina Ave., Lower Level
Morton Grove, IL 60053
Ph: (847)965-0330
Fax: (847)965-0349
Co. E-mail: director@mgcci.org
URL: http://www.mgcci.org
Contact: Christine Sullivan, President
Description: Promotes business and community development in Morton Grove, IL. **Founded:** 1920. **Publications:** *Morton Grove Community Guide* (Biennial); *MGCCI It's Your Business* (Monthly); *Morton Grove Community Guide* (Biennial). **Educational Activities:** Golf Outing (Annual); Business After Hours (Monthly). **Telecommunication Services:** contact@mgcci.org.

51232 ■ *Morton Grove Community Guide*
6101 Capulina Ave., Lower Level
Morton Grove, IL 60053
Ph: (847)965-0330
Fax: (847)965-0349
Co. E-mail: director@mgcci.org
URL: http://www.mgcci.org
Contact: Christine Sullivan, President
Released: Biennial **Price:** $3.

51233 ■ *Morton Matters*
415 W Jefferson
Morton, IL 61550-1817
Ph: (309)263-2491
Free: 888-765-6588
Fax: (309)263-2401
Co. E-mail: mkull@mortonillinois.org
URL: http://mortonchamber.org
Contact: Jennifer Daly, Executive Director
Released: Monthly

51234 ■ Mount Carroll Chamber of Commerce
PO Box 94
Mount Carroll, IL 61053
Ph: (815)244-2255
Free: 800-244-9594
Co. E-mail: info@mtcarrollil.org
URL: http://www.mtcarrollil.org
Contact: Laura Miller-DeSpain, President
Description: Promotes business and community development in Mt. Carroll, IL.

51235 ■ Mount Greenwood Chamber of Commerce
3052 W 111th St.
Chicago, IL 60655

Ph: (773)238-6103
Co. E-mail: info@mgcofc.org
URL: http://www.mgcofc.org
Contact: Darlene Myers, Executive Director
Description: Promotes business and community development in the Mt. Greenwood area of Chicago, IL.

51236 ■ Mount Prospect Chamber of Commerce
107 S Main St.
Mount Prospect, IL 60056
Ph: (847)398-6616
Fax: (847)398-6780
Co. E-mail: info@mountprospectchamber.org
URL: http://www.mountprospectchamber.org
Contact: Dawn Fletcher Collins, Executive Director
Description: Promotes business and community development in Mt. Prospect, IL. **Founded:** 1926. **Publications:** *Chamber Matters* (Bimonthly); *Community Guide and Business Listing* (Annual).

51237 ■ Mount Zion Chamber of Commerce (ZCC)
PO Box 84
Mount Zion, IL 62549
Ph: (217)864-2526
Fax: (217)864-6115
Co. E-mail: askjudy4@aol.com
URL: http://www.mtzionchamber.org
Contact: Judy Kaiser, Administrator
Description: Promotes business and community development in the Mt. Zion, IL area. Participates in Pony Express Days; sponsors Small Business Expo. **Founded:** 1987. **Publications:** *Directory of Members* (Annual).

51238 ■ Murphysboro Chamber of Commerce
203 S 13th Street
Murphysboro, IL 62966
Ph: (618)684-6421
Free: 800-406-8774
Fax: (618)684-2010
Co. E-mail: director@murphysborochamber.com
URL: http://www.murphysboro.com
Contact: Dan Bost, President
Description: Promotes business and community development in Murphysboro, IL. **Founded:** 1923. **Publications:** *Chamber Directory* (Periodic); *City Directory* (Periodic).

51239 ■ Naperville Area Chamber of Commerce
55 S Main St., Ste. 351
Naperville, IL 60540
Ph: (630)355-4141
Fax: (630)355-8335
Co. E-mail: chamber@naperville.net
URL: http://www.naperville.net
Contact: Tami Andrew, Chief Executive Officer
Description: Promotes business and community development in Naperville, IL area. **Founded:** 1913. **Publications:** *Commerce* (Monthly); *Community Resource Guide and Relocation Handbook*; *Membership Directory and Buyer's Guide* (Annual). **Awards:** Anniversary Recognition; Small Business of the Year (Annual). **Telecommunication Services:** mskarr@naperville.net.

51240 ■ National Black Chamber of Commerce (Decatur, Illinois)
132 S Water St., Ste. 430
Decatur, IL 62523
Ph: (217)428-9679
Co. E-mail: info@decaturbcc.org
Contact: Corey Walker, President
Description: Represents Black owned businesses. Seeks to empower and sustain African American communities through entrepreneurship and capitalistic activity. Provides advocacy, training and education to Black communities.

51241 ■ National Black Chamber of Commerce, Champaign County
PO Box 8014
Champaign, IL 61826

Ph: (224)356-1987
Co. E-mail: info@theccbcc.com
URL: http://www.theccbcc.com
Contact: Zernial M. Bogan, President
Description: Represents Black owned businesses. Seeks to empower and sustain African American communities through entrepreneurship and capitalistic activity. Provides advocacy, training and education to Black communities.

51242 ■ National Black Chamber of Commerce, Englewood
PO Box 21453
Chicago, IL 60621
Ph: (773)503-6067
Fax: (773)602-4510
Co. E-mail: info@englewoodbcc.org
Contact: Arness Dancy, President
Description: Represents Black owned businesses. Seeks to empower and sustain African American communities through entrepreneurship and capitalistic activity. Provides advocacy, training and education to Black communities.

51243 ■ National Black Chamber of Commerce, Illinois State
c/o Larry D. Ivory, Pres.
331 Fulton St., Ste. 530
Peoria, IL 61602
Ph: (309)740-4430
Fax: (309)672-1379
Co. E-mail: info@ilbcc.org
URL: http://www.ilbcc.org
Contact: Larry D. Ivory, President
Description: Represents Black owned businesses. Seeks to empower and sustain African American communities through entrepreneurship and capitalistic activity. Provides advocacy, training and education to Black communities.

51244 ■ National Black Chamber of Commerce, Lake County
1020 W Glen Flora Ave., Ste. 104
Waukegan, IL 60085
Ph: (847)599-9510
Fax: (847)599-9534
Co. E-mail: gass@bccoflakecounty.com
URL: http://www.bccoflakecounty.com
Contact: Arthur J. Gass, Sr., President
Description: Represents Black owned businesses. Seeks to empower and sustain African American communities through entrepreneurship and capitalistic activity. Provides advocacy, training and education to Black communities.

51245 ■ Nauvoo Chamber of Commerce
PO Box 41
Nauvoo, IL 62354
URL: http://www.nauvoochamber.org
Contact: Kathy Douglas, Treasurer
Description: Works to advance the general welfare and prosperity of Nauvoo. Promotes the economic, civic, commercial, cultural, industrial, and education interest of the area.

51246 ■ Navigator
800 Roosevelt Rd., Bldg. D, Ste. 108
Glen Ellyn, IL 60137
Ph: (630)469-0907
Fax: (630)469-0426
Co. E-mail: director@glenellynchamber.com
URL: http://www.glenellynchamber.com
Contact: Georgia Koch, Executive Director
Released: Monthly

51247 ■ NCCI Community Guide
8060 W Oakton St.
Niles, IL 60714
Ph: (847)268-8180
Fax: (847)268-8186
Co. E-mail: contactus@nileschamber.com
URL: http://nileschamber.com
Contact: Katie Schneider, Executive Director
Released: Annual

51248 ■ The Networker
5314 W 95th St.
Oak Lawn, IL 60453

Ph: (708)424-8300
Co. E-mail: office@oaklawnchamber.com
URL: http://www.oaklawnchamber.com
Contact: Karen Boll, President

51249 ■ New Lenox Chamber of Commerce
PO Box 42
New Lenox, IL 60451-0042
Ph: (815)485-4241
Fax: (815)485-5001
Co. E-mail: info@newlenoxchamber.com
URL: http://www.newlenoxchamber.com
Contact: Mark Stevens, President
Description: Promotes business and community development in New Lenox Township, IL. Sponsors area festival; conducts community awards, scholarships and partnership with schools. **Founded:** 1960. **Publications:** *Business Bulletin; Welcome to New Lenox; New Lenox, IL: The Community With the Ability to Grow.* **Awards:** Business of the Year (Annual); Citizen of the Year (Annual).

51250 ■ New Lenox, IL: The Community With the Ability to Grow
PO Box 42
New Lenox, IL 60451-0042
Ph: (815)485-4241
Fax: (815)485-5001
Co. E-mail: info@newlenoxchamber.com
URL: http://www.newlenoxchamber.com
Contact: Mark Stevens, President

51251 ■ News and Views
1137 E 5000N Rd.
Bourbonnais, IL 60914
Ph: (815)933-7721
Fax: (815)933-7675
Co. E-mail: david@kankakee.org
URL: http://www.kankakee.org/cwt/external/wcpages/index.aspx
Contact: David Hinderliter, President
Released: Monthly **Price:** $10, /year.

51252 ■ News & Views
427 W Virginia St.
Crystal Lake, IL 60014
Ph: (815)459-1300
Fax: (815)459-0243
Co. E-mail: info@clchamber.com
URL: http://www.clchamber.com
Contact: Gary Reece, President
Released: Monthly

51253 ■ News and Views
1300 Shiloh Blvd.
Zion, IL 60099
Ph: (847)872-5405
URL: http://www.zionchamber.com
Contact: Karen Crane, President
Released: Quarterly **Price:** included in membership dues.

51254 ■ News, Views & Issues
210 S East St.
Bloomington, IL 61701
Ph: (309)829-6344
Fax: (309)827-3940
Co. E-mail: michael@mccleancochamber.org
URL: http://www.mccleancochamber.org
Contact: Dr. Les Mathers, President
Released: Monthly

51255 ■ Newsbriefs
111 S Water St.
Wilmington, IL 60481
Ph: (815)476-7966
Fax: (815)476-7002
Co. E-mail: eric.fisher@cbcast.com
URL: http://wilmingtonilchamber.org/default.aspx
Contact: Eric Fisher, President
Released: Monthly

51256 ■ Nexus
101 Bouthillier St.
Galena, IL 61036
Ph: (815)777-9050

Fax: (815)777-8465
Co. E-mail: office@galenachamber.com
URL: http://www.galenachamber.com
Contact: Ed Schmit, Executive Director
Released: Monthly

51257 ■ Niles Chamber of Commerce and Industry (NCCI)
8060 W Oakton St.
Niles, IL 60714
Ph: (847)268-8180
Fax: (847)268-8186
Co. E-mail: contactus@nileschamber.com
URL: http://nileschamber.com
Contact: Katie Schneider, Executive Director
Description: Promotes business and community development in Niles, IL. **Scope:** audio, written. **Founded:** 1971. **Publications:** *Chamber Scene* (Quarterly); *NCCI Community Guide* (Annual). **Awards:** Business of the Year (Annual); Citizen of the Year (Annual); Employee of the Year (Annual); Ken Scheel Award. **Telecommunication Services:** katie@nileschamber.com

51258 ■ Northbrook Chamber of Commerce and Industry (NCCI)
2002 Walters Ave.
Northbrook, IL 60062
Ph: (847)498-5555
Fax: (847)498-5510
Co. E-mail: info@northbrookchamber.org
URL: http://www.northbrookchamber.org
Contact: Tensley Garris, President
Description: Promotes business and economic development in Northbrook, IL. **Publications:** *Membership Directory and Buyer's Guide; Northbrook Chamber of Commerce and Industry--Membership Directory and Buyer's Guide.*

51259 ■ Norwood Park Chamber of Commerce and Industry
6097 N Northwest Hwy.
Chicago, IL 60631
Ph: (773)763-3606
Fax: (773)763-3620
Co. E-mail: info@norwoodpark.org
URL: http://www.norwoodpark.org
Contact: Ellen Wierzewski, Executive Director
Description: Works to provide leadership, visions and strategy to the business community. **Telecommunication Services:** events@norwoodpark.org.

51260 ■ Oak Forest Chamber of Commerce
15440 S Central Ave.
Oak Forest, IL 60452
Ph: (708)687-4600
Fax: (708)687-7878
Co. E-mail: info@oc-chamber.org
URL: http://oc-chamber.org
Contact: Kim Malecky-Iles, Executive Director
Description: Aims to protect and enhance the investments of the Oak Forest businesses. **Scope:** business, taxes, local area, history. **Founded:** 1964. **Subscriptions:** 50 articles books periodicals. **Publications:** *FYI; Oak Leaf* (Monthly). **Awards:** Scholarship for Oak Forest High School Business Students (Annual).

51261 ■ Oak Lawn Chamber of Commerce
5314 W 95th St.
Oak Lawn, IL 60453
Ph: (708)424-8300
Co. E-mail: office@oaklawnchamber.com
URL: http://www.oaklawnchamber.com
Contact: Karen Boll, President
Description: Works to represent and advance the Oak Lawn business community; strives with constant integrity, fairness and cooperation to promote and to improve the economic atmosphere, business climate and image of Oak Lawn. **Founded:** 1947. **Publications:** *The Networker.*

51262 ■ Oak Leaf
15440 S Central Ave.
Oak Forest, IL 60452
Ph: (708)687-4600

Fax: (708)687-7878
Co. E-mail: info@oc-chamber.org
URL: http://oc-chamber.org
Contact: Kim Malecky-Iles, Executive Director
Released: Monthly

51263 ■ Oak Park-River Forest Chamber of Commerce (OPRFCC)
7727 Lake St.
River Forest, IL 60305
Ph: (708)771-5760
Co. E-mail: info@oprfchamber.org
URL: http://www.oprfchamber.org
Contact: John Lawrence, President
Description: Promotes economic and community development in Oak Park and River Forest, IL. **Founded:** 1895. **Publications:** *Business Connection* (Bimonthly); *Community Guide* (Annual); *Portrait* (Biennial). **Educational Activities:** Consumer Expo (Annual). **Awards:** Athena Award; Blue Chip Business of the year (Annual). **Telecommunication Services:** jdoss@oprdchamber.org.

51264 ■ O'Fallon Chamber of Commerce (OCC)
116 E 1st St.
O'Fallon, IL 62269
Ph: (618)632-3377
Fax: (618)632-8162
Co. E-mail: chamber@ofallonchamber.com
URL: http://www.ofallonchamber.com
Contact: Rick Parks, President
Description: Promotes business and community development in O'Fallon, IL. Sponsors annual Christmas Walk festival. **Founded:** 1946. **Publications:** *O'Fallon Chamber News* (Monthly). **Educational Activities:** Business Luncheon (Monthly).

51265 ■ *O'Fallon Chamber News*
116 E 1st St.
O'Fallon, IL 62269
Ph: (618)632-3377
Fax: (618)632-8162
Co. E-mail: chamber@ofallonchamber.com
URL: http://www.ofallonchamber.com
Contact: Rick Parks, President
Released: Monthly

51266 ■ *Official Guide to Lakeview East*
3138 N Broadway
Chicago, IL 60657
Ph: (773)348-8608
Fax: (773)348-7409
Co. E-mail: info@lakevieweast.com
URL: http://www.lakevieweast.com
Contact: Maureen Martino, Executive Director
Released: Annual

51267 ■ Okawville Chamber of Commerce
PO Box 345
Okawville, IL 62271
Ph: (618)243-5694
Co. E-mail: tourokaw@htc.net
URL: http://www.okawvillecc.com
Description: Promotes business and community development in Okawville.

51268 ■ *On the Move*
500 Grand Ave.
Lindenhurst, IL 60046-6075
Ph: (847)356-8446
Fax: (847)356-8561
Co. E-mail: llvchamber@sbcglobal.net
URL: http://www.llvchamber.com/page1.aspx
Contact: Connie Meadie, Executive Director
Released: Monthly

51269 ■ Oregon Area Chamber of Commerce (OCC)
121 N 4th St.
Oregon, IL 61061
Ph: (815)732-2100
Co. E-mail: ococ@oglecom.com
URL: http://www.oregonil.com
Description: Promotes business and community development in Oregon, IL. Sponsors Autumn on Parade Festival. **Publications:** *The Chamber Update* (Monthly).

51270 ■ Orland Park Area Chamber of Commerce
8799 W 151st St.
Orland Park, IL 60462
Ph: (708)349-2972
Fax: (708)349-7454
Co. E-mail: info@orlandparkchamber.org
URL: http://www.orlandparkchamber.org
Contact: Keloryn Putnam, Executive Director
Description: Serves as the primary resource in helping businesses and the community grow and prosper. **Founded:** 1958. **Publications:** *Chambergram* (Monthly).

51271 ■ Oswego Chamber of Commerce
63 W Washington St.
Oswego, IL 60543-0863
Ph: (630)554-3505
Fax: (630)554-0050
Co. E-mail: info@oswegochamber.org
URL: http://www.oswegochamber.org
Contact: Steve Hatcher, President
Description: Aims to make business in Oswego grow and succeed. **Publications:** *Chamber News* (Monthly).

51272 ■ Ottawa Area Chamber of Commerce and Industry
633 La Salle St., Ste. 401
Ottawa, IL 61350
Ph: (815)433-0084
Fax: (815)433-2405
Co. E-mail: info@ottawachamberillinois.com
URL: http://www.ottawachamberillinois.com
Contact: Boyd Palmer, Executive Director
Description: Retailers, professionals, corporations, and individuals united to promote tourism, generate new business, aid downtown merchants, and improve the quality of life in the Ottawa, IL area. Sponsors Welcomburger festival, Farmers Market, Legislative and State of the City Luncheons, Small Business Seminars and IVLead Leadership Series. **Founded:** 1916. **Subscriptions:** books. **Publications:** *ED Update* (Bimonthly); *Manufacturer's Guide* (Periodic).

51273 ■ *Outlook*
PO Box 315
Savanna, IL 61074
Ph: (815)273-2722
Fax: (815)273-2754
Co. E-mail: savchamber@grics.net
URL: http://www.savanna-il.com
Contact: Pam Brown, Executive Director
Released: Monthly

51274 ■ *Outlook*
9440 Joliet Rd., Ste. B
Hodgkins, IL 60525
Ph: (708)387-7550
Fax: (708)387-7556
Co. E-mail: info@wscci.org
URL: http://www.westsuburbanchamber.org
Contact: Steve Erickson, Executive Director

51275 ■ Palatine Area Chamber of Commerce (PACC)
579 First Bank Dr., Ste. 205
Palatine, IL 60067
Ph: (847)359-7200
Fax: (847)359-7246
Co. E-mail: info@palatinechamber.com
URL: http://www.palatinechamber.com
Contact: Mindy Phillips, Director
Description: Promotes business and community development in Palatine, IL. **Founded:** 1950. **Publications:** *The Chamber Guide* (Annual); *The Chamber Guide* (Annual); *Community Guide* (Monthly); *The Key* (Bimonthly). **Awards:** Ehlenfeldt Memorial Scholarship (Annual). **Telecommunication Services:** mphillips@palatinechamber.com.

51276 ■ Palestine Chamber of Commerce (PCC)
PO Box 155
Palestine, IL 62451
Ph: (618)586-2222

Fax: (618)586-9477
Co. E-mail: palestinecofc@verizon.net
URL: http://www.pioneercity.com/chamberofcommerce
Contact: Jim Clark, Director
Description: Promotes business and community development in Crawford County, IL. Sponsors annual professional rodeo and Labor Day Weekend Festival. **Founded:** 1950.

51277 ■ Palos Hills Chamber of Commerce
10335 S Roberts Rd.
Palos Hills, IL 60465
Ph: (708)598-3400
Co. E-mail: paloshillswebmaster@paloshillsweb.org
URL: http://www.paloshillsweb.org
Contact: Phyllis Majka, President
Description: Promotes business and community development in Palos Hills, IL.

51278 ■ Pana Chamber of Commerce
City Hall
120 E 3rd St.
Pana, IL 62557
Ph: (217)562-4240
Fax: (217)562-3823
Co. E-mail: panachamber@consolidated.net
URL: http://www.panachamber.com
Contact: John Allen, Director
URL(s): www.panaindustrial.com. **Description:** Promotes business and community development in Pana, IL. Sponsors annual Pana Heritage Days, Chamber Week, Downtown Block Party, Car Show, Illinois State Championship Antique Bicycle Show, Blacksmith Hammer in & Antique Tractor Show and Christmas Week. **Founded:** 1943. **Publications:** *Business and Professional Memo* (Quarterly).

51279 ■ Paris Area Chamber of Commerce and Tourism (PACCT)
105 N Central Ave.
Paris, IL 61944
Ph: (217)465-4179
Fax: (217)465-4170
URL: http://www.parisilchamber.com
Contact: Brenda Buckley, Executive Director
Description: Promotes business and community development in Paris, IL. Sponsors Honey Bee Festival. **Founded:** 1903. **Awards:** Parisian (Annual).

51280 ■ Pekin Area Chamber of Commerce
402 Court St.
Pekin, IL 61555-0636
Ph: (309)346-2106
Fax: (309)346-2104
Co. E-mail: chamber@pekin.net
URL: http://www.pekin.net
Contact: Bill Fleming, Executive Director
Description: Promotes the growth of the Pekin area through collective efforts. **Founded:** 1893. **Publications:** *Focus* (Monthly). **Educational Activities:** Business After Hours (Monthly). **Telecommunication Services:** bfleming@pekin.net.

51281 ■ Peoria Area Chamber of Commerce (PACC)
100 SW Water St.
Peoria, IL 61602
Ph: (309)676-0755
Fax: (309)676-7534
Co. E-mail: chamber@mail.h-p.org
URL: http://www.peoriachamber.org
Contact: Roberta M. Parks, President
Description: Promotes business and community development in the Peoria, IL area. **Founded:** 1911. **Publications:** *Chamber Communicator* (Weekly). **Educational Activities:** Business After Hours (Monthly). **Telecommunication Services:** rparks@chamber.h-p.org.

51282 ■ Petersburg Chamber of Commerce (PCC)
122 S 6th Street
Petersburg, IL 62675

Ph: (217)415-4378
Co. E-mail: info@petersburgilchamber.com
URL: http://petersburgilchamber.com
Contact: Alicia Davis-Wade, President
Description: Promotes business and community development in Menard County, IL. Sponsors Petersburg Harvest Fest and Christmas in Petersburg.

51283 ■ Pike County Chamber of Commerce
224 W Washington St.
Pittsfield, IL 62363
Ph: (217)285-2971
Fax: (217)285-5251
Co. E-mail: info@pikeil.org
URL: http://www.pikeil.org
Contact: Kent Hawley, President
Description: Promotes business and community development in Pike County, IL. **Founded:** 1955.

51284 ■ Pinckneyville Chamber of Commerce
4 S Walnut St.
Pinckneyville, IL 62274
Ph: (618)357-3243
Co. E-mail: pvillechamber.execdirector@gmail.com
URL: http://www.pinckneyville.com
Contact: Larry West, President
Description: Provides a venue in which people can take effective action for the progress of the community. Organizes convention, sales meetings and other gatherings.

51285 ■ Plainfield Area Chamber of Commerce (PACC)
24047 W Lockport St., No. 109
Plainfield, IL 60544
Ph: (815)436-4431
Fax: (815)436-0520
Co. E-mail: etcollins@plainfieldchamber.com
URL: http://www.plainfieldchamber.com
Contact: Liz Collins, President
Description: Promotes business and community growth and development. Strives to make the Plainfield area a better place to live, work, worship, learn, and conduct business.

51286 ■ Polo Chamber of Commerce
115 S Franklin Ave.
Polo, IL 61064
Ph: (815)946-3131
Co. E-mail: estessecretarialservice@yahoo.com
URL: http://www.poloil.org
Contact: Chris Phelps, President
Description: Promotes business and community development in Polo, IL. Sponsors festivals.

51287 ■ Pontiac Area Chamber of Commerce (PACC)
PO Box 534
Pontiac, IL 61764
Ph: (815)844-5131
Fax: (815)844-2600
Co. E-mail: clambert@pontiacchamber.org
URL: http://www.pontiacchamber.org
Contact: Cheri Lambert, President
Description: Promotes business and community development in the Pontiac, IL area. Jointly sponsors annual Bluegrass Festival. **Founded:** 1917. **Publications:** *Chamber Plus* (Quarterly).

51288 ■ Portage Park Chamber of Commerce (PPCC)
c/o Tivadar Szabo, Pres.
5758 W Irving Park Rd.
Chicago, IL 60634
Ph: (773)777-2020
Fax: (773)777-0202
Co. E-mail: beebuilding@aol.com
URL: http://www.portageparkchamber.org
Contact: Tivadar Szabo, President
Description: Promotes business and community development in the Portage Park area of Chicago, IL. Markets the six corners business district. Sponsors community events and promotional activities. **Founded:** 1937.

51289 ■ *Portrait*
7727 Lake St.
River Forest, IL 60305

Ph: (708)771-5760
Co. E-mail: info@oprfchamber.org
URL: http://www.oprfchamber.org
Contact: John Lawrence, President
Released: Biennial

51290 ■ Princeton Area Chamber of Commerce and Main Street (PACCMS)
Prouty Community Bldg.
435 S Main St.
Princeton, IL 61356
Ph: (815)875-2616
Free: 877-730-4306
Fax: (815)875-1156
Co. E-mail: kfrey@princeton-il.com
URL: http://www.princetonchamber-il.com
Contact: Kim Frey, Executive Director
Description: Serves as a clearinghouse of business and community information, to legislative issues and reliable business referrals.

51291 ■ Prophetstown-Lyndon Area Chamber of Commerce
335 Washington St.
Prophetstown, IL 61277
Ph: (815)437-5139
Fax: (815)437-5139
Co. E-mail: ptownms@thewisp.net
URL: http://www.prophetstownil.com
Contact: Barb Ballew, Executive Director
Description: Promotes business and community development in the Prophetstown, IL area.

51292 ■ *QC Direct*
622 19th St.
Moline, IL 61265-2142
Ph: (309)757-5416
Fax: (309)757-5435
Co. E-mail: rbaker@quadcitychamber.com
URL: http://www.quadcitychamber.com
Contact: Rick L. Baker, President
Released: Annual

51293 ■ Quincy Area Chamber of Commerce (QACC)
300 Civic Center Plz., Ste. 245
Quincy, IL 62301
Ph: (217)222-7980
Fax: (217)222-3033
Co. E-mail: amy@quincychamber.org
URL: http://www.quincychamber.org
Contact: Amy Looten, Executive Director
Description: Promotes issues and activities for members who enhance the economic well being and quality of life in the Quincy area. **Founded:** 1887. **Publications:** *Update* (Weekly).

51294 ■ Rantoul Area Chamber of Commerce (RACC)
601 S Century Blvd.
Rantoul, IL 61866
Ph: (217)893-3323
Fax: (217)893-3325
URL: http://www.rantoulchamber.com
Contact: Chris Kaler, Executive Director
Description: Promotes business and community development in Rantoul, IL. Sponsors Fourth of July celebration.

51295 ■ *The Reporter*
201-B Canterbury Ln.
Bolingbrook, IL 60440
Ph: (630)226-8420
Fax: (630)759-9937
Co. E-mail: info@bolingbrookchamber.org
URL: http://www.bolingbrookchamber.org
Contact: Mike Evans, Executive Director
Released: Monthly

51296 ■ *Resident's Guide to Lincoln Park*
1925 N Clybourn Ave., Ste. 301
Chicago, IL 60614-7396
Ph: (773)880-5200
Fax: (773)880-0266
Co. E-mail: info@lincolnparkchamber.com
URL: http://www.lincolnparkchamber.com
Contact: Kim Schilf, President

51297 ■ *Resource Guide*
215 E Adams St.
Springfield, IL 62701
Ph: (217)522-5512
Fax: (217)522-5518
Co. E-mail: lweitzel@ilchamber.org
URL: http://www.iacce.org
Contact: Elizabeth D. Fiala Kerns, President
Released: Annual

51298 ■ Richmond/Spring Grove Area Chamber of Commerce
10906 Main St.
Richmond, IL 60071
Ph: (815)678-7742
URL: http://www.rsgchamber.com
Contact: Laura Ferris, Executive Director
Description: Provides favorable business climate by acting as a vehicle to promote the area's economic progress. **Founded:** 1993.

51299 ■ Riverdale Chamber of Commerce (RCC)
208 W 144th St.
Riverdale, IL 60827
Ph: (708)841-3311
Fax: (708)841-1805
Co. E-mail: rdpl2@earthlink.net
URL: http://www.district148.net/rcoc
Contact: John Strauss, President
Description: Promotes business and community development in Riverdale, IL. **Founded:** 1958.

51300 ■ Riverside Chamber of Commerce
PO Box 7
Riverside, IL 60546
Ph: (708)447-8510
Co. E-mail: business@riversidechamberofcommerce.com
URL: http://www.riversidechamberofcommerce.com
Contact: David Moravecek, President
Description: Promotes business and community development in Riverside, IL area.

51301 ■ Rochelle Area Chamber of Commerce
350 May Mart Dr.
Rochelle, IL 61068-0220
Ph: (815)562-4189
Fax: (815)562-4180
Co. E-mail: chamber@rochelle.net
URL: http://www.rochellechamber.org
Contact: Peggy Friday, Chief Executive Officer
Description: Represents, educates and supports member businesses, promoting economic vitality and enhancing the quality of life. **Publications:** *Community Guide* (Annual).

51302 ■ Rock Falls Chamber of Commerce (RFCC)
601 W 10th St.
Rock Falls, IL 61071-1576
Ph: (815)625-4500
Fax: (815)625-4558
Co. E-mail: doug@rockfallschamber.com
URL: http://www.rockfallschamber.com/index.html
Contact: Doug Wiersema, President
Description: Promotes business and community development in Whiteside County, IL. **Founded:** 1956. **Publications:** *Chamber News Highlights* (Monthly). **Awards:** Shoulder to the Wheel (Annual).

51303 ■ *Rockford Area Map*
308 W State St., Ste. 190
Rockford, IL 61101
Ph: (815)987-8100
Fax: (815)987-8122
Co. E-mail: info@rockfordchamber.com
URL: http://www.rockfordchamber.com
Contact: Einar Forsman, President

51304 ■ Rockford Chamber of Commerce
308 W State St., Ste. 190
Rockford, IL 61101
Ph: (815)987-8100

Fax: (815)987-8122
Co. E-mail: info@rockfordchamber.com
URL: http://www.rockfordchamber.com
Contact: Einar Forsman, President
Description: Members help other members increase sales, control costs, network effectively, advocate improvements in the business climate. **Scope:** yearbook, membership directory, manufacturing directory, map. **Founded:** 1910. **Subscriptions:** 4. **Publications:** *Manufacturers Directory* (Annual); *Membership and Business Directory* (Annual); *Rockford Area Map.* **Telecommunication Services:** eforsman@rockfordchamber.com.

51305 ■ Rockford Regional Chamber of Commerce Business Women's Council
308 W State St., Ste. 190
Rockford, IL 61101
Ph: (815)987-8100
Fax: (815)987-8122
Co. E-mail: info@rockfordchamber.com
URL: http://www.rockfordchamber.com
Description: Aims to enhance the economic vitality of its members. **Publications:** *The Voice* (Monthly). **Educational Activities:** Rockford Regional Chamber of Commerce Business Women's Council Luncheon (Annual).

51306 ■ Rockton Chamber of Commerce
330 E Main St., No. 700
Rockton, IL 61072
Ph: (815)624-7625
Fax: (815)624-7385
Co. E-mail: info@rocktonchamber.com
URL: http://www.rocktonchamber.com
Contact: Dennis McCorkle, President
Description: Promotes business and community development in the Rockton, IL area. **Founded:** 1951.

51307 ■ Rolling Meadows Chamber of Commerce (RMCC)
2775 Algonquin Rd., Ste. 310
Rolling Meadows, IL 60008
Ph: (847)398-3730
Fax: (847)398-3745
Co. E-mail: office@rmchamber.org
URL: http://www.rmchamber.org
Contact: Linda Liles Ballantine, Executive Director
Description: Promotes business, industrial, professional, cultural, and civic development in the Rolling Meadows, IL area. Monitors legislation; partners with city to oversee economic development. **Founded:** 1961. **Publications:** *The Connector* (Bimonthly); *Dining Guide* (Semiannual); *Legislative Guide to Elected & Appointed Officials.* **Educational Activities:** Golf Outing (Annual); Networking/Social Function (Periodic).

51308 ■ Romeoville Chamber of Commerce
10 Montrose Dr.
Romeoville, IL 60446-1329
Ph: (815)886-2076
Fax: (815)886-2096
Co. E-mail: info@romeovillechamber.org
URL: http://www.romeovillechamber.org
Contact: Bridget Domberg, President
Description: Serves as communication vehicle of business, professional and service organization in governmental and social affairs in Romeoville. **Founded:** 1975.

51309 ■ *Roselle Chamber Business News*
1350 W Lake St., Ste. A
Roselle, IL 60172
Ph: (630)894-3010
Fax: (630)894-3042
Co. E-mail: executivedirector@rosellechamber.com
URL: http://www.rosellechamber.com
Contact: Gail Croson, Executive Director
Released: Monthly

51310 ■ Roselle Chamber of Commerce and Industry
1350 W Lake St., Ste. A
Roselle, IL 60172
Ph: (630)894-3010

Fax: (630)894-3042
Co. E-mail: executivedirector@rosellechamber.com
URL: http://www.rosellechamber.com
Contact: Gail Croson, Executive Director
Description: Promotes business and community development in Roselle, IL. Conducts networking, social activities and business seminars; sponsors community parade, entertainment tents at annual festival and business expo; participates in or contributes to other business and community projects and events. **Founded:** 1949. **Publications:** *Roselle Chamber Business News* (Monthly). **Awards:** Brian K. Healy Service Award; Business Person of the Year Award (Annual).

51311 ■ Round Lake Area Chamber of Commerce and Industry
2007 Civic Center Way
Round Lake Beach, IL 60073
Ph: (847)546-2002
Fax: (847)546-2254
Co. E-mail: info@rlchamber.org
URL: http://www.rlchamber.org
Contact: Shanna Coakley, Executive Director
Description: Promotes business and community development in the Round Lake, IL area. Conducts annual Home and Trade Fair. **Founded:** 1947. **Publications:** *Chamber News* (Monthly).

51312 ■ St. Charles Chamber of Commerce
3755 E Main St., Ste. 140
St. Charles, IL 60174
Ph: (630)584-8384
Fax: (630)584-6065
Co. E-mail: info@stcharleschamber.com
URL: http://www.stcharleschamber.com
Contact: Lori G. Hewitt, President
Description: Promotes business and community development in St. Charles, IL area. **Founded:** 1922. **Publications:** *Chamber Communique* (Monthly). **Awards:** Charlemagne Award (Annual).

51313 ■ Sandwich Chamber of Commerce
128 E Railroad St.
Sandwich, IL 60548
Ph: (815)312-4963
Fax: (815)786-2505
Co. E-mail: info@sandwich-il.org
URL: http://www.sandwich-il.org
Contact: John R. Lux, President
Description: Works to provide a favorable business climate by acting as a vehicle to help promote the area's economic progress. Supports the development of the business community and to improve the quality of life for those that live and work in the area. **Publications:** *Business Connection* (Monthly).

51314 ■ Sauk Valley Area Chamber of Commerce (SVACC)
211 Locust St.
Sterling, IL 61081-3536
Ph: (815)625-2400
Fax: (815)625-9361
Co. E-mail: kewoldsen@saukvalleyareachamber.com
URL: http://www.saukvalleyareachamber.com
Contact: Kimberly Ewoldsen, Executive Director
Description: Promotes business and community development in the Sauk Valley Area. Conducts Business Expo, Seasonal Sights and Sounds, and Community Carnival. **Founded:** 1912. **Publications:** *Action Report* (Periodic); *Membership List* (Periodic); *Sterling/Rock Falls Restaurant and Lodging Guide* (Periodic).

51315 ■ Savanna Chamber of Commerce (SCC)
PO Box 315
Savanna, IL 61074
Ph: (815)273-2722
Fax: (815)273-2754
Co. E-mail: savchamber@grics.net
URL: http://www.savanna-il.com
Contact: Pam Brown, Executive Director
Description: Promotes business and community development in Savanna, IL. Sponsors annual trade shows and seminars, annual Car Cruise and Beach Party, annual Gingerbread Christmas and Cookie Walk, and other social and promotional activities. **Founded:** 1949. **Publications:** *Outlook* (Monthly).

51316 ■ Shelbyville Area Chamber of Commerce (SCC)
124 N Morgan St.
Shelbyville, IL 62565
Ph: (217)774-2221
Fax: (217)774-2221
Co. E-mail: chamber01@consolidated.net
URL: http://www.shelbyvillechamberofcommerce.com
Contact: Tad Mayhall, President
Description: Promotes business and community development in Shelbyville, IL. **Founded:** 1930. **Publications:** *Chamber Chatter* (Bimonthly); *Chamber of Commerce.*

51317 ■ *Shoppe Talk*
841 Spruce St., Ste. 204
Winnetka, IL 60093
Ph: (847)446-4451
Fax: (847)446-4452
Co. E-mail: wcc@winnetkachamber.com
URL: http://www.winnetkachamber.com
Contact: Terry Dason, Executive Director
Released: Biennial

51318 ■ *Shopping and Dining Guide*
427 W Virginia St.
Crystal Lake, IL 60014
Ph: (815)459-1300
Fax: (815)459-0243
Co. E-mail: info@clchamber.com
URL: http://www.clchamber.com
Contact: Gary Reece, President
Price: free for members.

51319 ■ *Shopping and Dining Guide*
272 E Deerpath, Ste. 106
Lake Forest, IL 60045
Ph: (847)234-4282
Co. E-mail: info@lflbchamber.com
URL: http://www.lflbchamber.com/build1/index.cfm
Contact: Joanna Rolek, Executive Director
Released: Annual

51320 ■ *Shoptalk*
777 Army Trail Rd., Ste. D
Addison, IL 60101
Ph: (630)543-4300
Fax: (630)543-4355
Co. E-mail: addisonchamber@sbcglobal.net
URL: http://www.addisonaic.org
Contact: Bernadette Hanrahan, Executive Director
Released: Bimonthly

51321 ■ Skokie Chamber of Commerce (SCC)
5002 Oakton St.
Skokie, IL 60077
Ph: (847)673-0240
Fax: (847)673-0249
Co. E-mail: info@skokiechamber.org
URL: http://www.skokiechamber.org
Contact: Howard Meyer, Executive Director
Description: Promotes business and community development in the Skokie, IL area. **Founded:** 1925. **Publications:** *Business and Professional Directory* (Annual); *Chamber Connection* (Monthly); *Industrial Directory* (Annual).

51322 ■ *Soundings*
8 S 3rd St.
Geneva, IL 60134-0481
Ph: (630)232-6060
Free: 866-4-GENEVA
Fax: (630)232-6083
Co. E-mail: chamberinfo@genevachamber.com
URL: http://www.genevachamber.com
Contact: Jean Gaines, President
Released: Monthly

51323 ■ *The Source*
1925 N Clybourn Ave., Ste. 301
Chicago, IL 60614-7396
Ph: (773)880-5200
Fax: (773)880-0266
Co. E-mail: info@lincolnparkchamber.com
URL: http://www.lincolnparkchamber.com
Contact: Kim Schilf, President
Released: Bimonthly

51324 ■ The Sourcebook: Directory of Goods and Services
c/o Yvonne Invergo, Exec. Dir.
10 Lilac Ln.
Lombard, IL 60148
Ph: (630)627-5040
Fax: (630)627-5519
Co. E-mail: info@lombardchamber.com
URL: http://www.lombardchamber.com
Contact: Yvonne Invergo, Executive Director

51325 ■ Springfield Scene
Chicago Office
300 S Wacker Dr., Ste. 1600
Chicago, IL 60606-6779
Ph: (312)983-7100
Fax: (312)983-7101
Co. E-mail: dwhitley@ilchamber.org
URL: http://ilchamber.org
Contact: Douglas L. Whitley, President
Released: Weekly

51326 ■ Staunton Chamber of Commerce
PO Box 248
Staunton, IL 62088
Ph: (618)635-8356
Co. E-mail: chamber@stauntonil.com
URL: http://www.stauntonil.com/Home.aspx
Description: Promotes business and community development in Staunton, IL area.

51327 ■ Sterling/Rock Falls Restaurant and Lodging Guide
211 Locust St.
Sterling, IL 61081-3536
Ph: (815)625-2400
Fax: (815)625-9361
Co. E-mail: kewoldsen@saukvalleyareachamber.com
URL: http://www.saukvalleyareachamber.com
Contact: Kimberly Ewoldsen, Executive Director
Released: Periodic

51328 ■ Streamwood Chamber of Commerce (SCC)
22 W Streamwood Blvd.
Streamwood, IL 60107
Ph: (630)837-5200
Fax: (630)837-5251
Co. E-mail: staff@streamwoodchamber.com
URL: http://www.streamwoodchamber.com
Contact: Patrick McKernan, President
Description: Promotes business and community development in Streamwood, IL. Sponsors Summer Celebration, community festivals, and other community events. Founded: 1981. Publications: Chamber News (Bimonthly); Community Guide (Annual). Educational Activities: Business After Hours (Monthly). Awards: Business of the Year (Annual); Business Person of the Year (Annual).

51329 ■ Streator Area Chamber of Commerce and Industry (SACCI)
PO Box 360
Streator, IL 61364
Ph: (815)672-2921
Fax: (815)672-1768
Co. E-mail: sacci@mchsi.com
URL: http://www.streatorchamber.com
Contact: Jack Dzuris, Executive Director
Description: Businesses organized to promote economic and community development in Streator, IL. Founded: 1915.

51330 ■ Sullivan Chamber and Economic Development (SCED)
112 W Harrison St.
Sullivan, IL 61951
Ph: (217)728-4223
Co. E-mail: info@sullivanchamber.com
URL: http://www.sullivanchamber.com
Description: Promotes business and community development in Moultrie County, IL. Promotes tourism. Sponsors annual Christmas parade, Christmas lighting contest, Safe Trick or Treat, and Festival of Stars in May. Founded: 1957. Publications: Sullivan Chamber and Economic Development Newsletter.

51331 ■ Sullivan Chamber and Economic Development Newsletter
112 W Harrison St.
Sullivan, IL 61951
Ph: (217)728-4223
Co. E-mail: info@sullivanchamber.com
URL: http://www.sullivanchamber.com
Released: published if necessary.

51332 ■ Swansea Chamber of Commerce
1400 N Illinois St.
Swansea, IL 62226
Ph: (618)233-3938
Fax: (618)234-0222
Co. E-mail: swansea@swanseachamber.org
URL: http://www.swanseachamber.org
Contact: Tom Tyler, Executive Director
Description: Aims to bring businesses together for the purpose of developing and promoting balanced economic growth and business opportunities that in harmony with the objectives of the entire community. Welcomes all businesses, organizations, and individuals regardless of race, religion, color, or national origin who demonstrate an interest in maintaining and promoting a healthy economic climate in the Village of Swansea, Illinois. Founded: 1969. Publications: E-Chamber Update (Weekly). Awards: Swansea Chamber of Commerce Scholarship Award (Annual).

51333 ■ Swedish-American Chamber of Commerce, Chicago
233 N Michigan Ave., Ste. 3050
Chicago, IL 60601
Ph: (312)772-2252
Co. E-mail: sacc@sacc-chicago.org
URL: http://www.sacc-chicago.org
Contact: Maria Bergman, President

51334 ■ Sycamore Chamber of Commerce
407 W State St., Ste. 10
Sycamore, IL 60178
Ph: (815)895-3456
Fax: (815)895-0125
Co. E-mail: info@sycamorechamber.com
URL: http://www.sycamorechamber.com
Contact: Rose Treml, Executive Director
Description: Promotes economic and social development in Sycamore, IL. Founded: 1915. Publications: Chamber Focus.

51335 ■ Take Five
PO Box 643
Effingham, IL 62401
Ph: (217)342-4147
Fax: (217)342-4228
Co. E-mail: chamber@effinghamchamber.org
URL: http://www.effinghamchamber.org
Contact: Norma Lansing, President
Released: Monthly

51336 ■ Tinley Park Chamber of Commerce (TPCC)
17316 S Oak Park Ave.
Tinley Park, IL 60477
Ph: (708)532-5700
Fax: (708)532-1475
Co. E-mail: info@tinleychamber.org
URL: http://www.tinleychamber.org
Contact: Ms. Kim Scalise, President
Description: Promotes business and community development in Tinley Park, IL. Founded: 1955. Publications: Chamber News and Views (Monthly). Awards: Youth in Business Award (Periodic).

51337 ■ Transportation Brochure
300 Bucklin
La Salle, IL 61301-0446
Ph: (815)223-0227
Fax: (815)223-4827
Co. E-mail: ivaced@ivaced.org
URL: http://www.ivaced.org
Contact: Marci Duro, Chief Executive Officer

51338 ■ Troy Area Chamber of Commerce
647 E US Hwy. 40
Troy, IL 62294
Ph: (618)667-8769
Free: 888-667-8769
Fax: (618)667-8759
Co. E-mail: info@troymaryvillecoc.com
URL: http://www.troycoc.com
Contact: Alice Drobisch, President
Description: Promotes business development and networking in order to enhance the growth and self sufficiency within the community and surrounding areas. Founded: 1984. Telecommunication Services: brase1@sbcglobal.net.

51339 ■ Tuscola Chamber of Commerce
PO Box 434
Tuscola, IL 61953
Ph: (217)253-5013
Co. E-mail: tfdchief@tuscola.org
URL: http://www.tuscola.org
Contact: Jason Maus, President
Description: Promotes business and community development in Tuscola, IL area.

51340 ■ Union County Chamber of Commerce (UCCC)
330 S Main St.
Anna, IL 62906
Ph: (618)833-6311
Fax: (618)833-1903
Co. E-mail: uccc@ajinternet.net
URL: http://www.shawneeheartland.com
Contact: Jeannie Landis, Executive Director
Description: Promotes business and community development in Union County, IL. Sponsors community Christmas decorations and Colorfest. Founded: 1906. Publications: Chamber Notes (Quarterly).

51341 ■ Up Front
1257 N Green St.
McHenry, IL 60050
Ph: (815)385-4300
Fax: (815)385-9142
Co. E-mail: info@mchenrychamber.com
URL: http://www.mchenrychamber.com
Contact: Kay Rial Bates, President
Released: Monthly

51342 ■ Update
1555 5th St.
Lincoln, IL 62656
Ph: (217)735-2385
Fax: (217)735-9205
Co. E-mail: chamber@lincolnillinois.com
URL: http://lincolnillinois.com/ABF.aspx
Contact: Andi Hake, Executive Director
Released: Monthly

51343 ■ Update
300 Civic Center Plz., Ste. 245
Quincy, IL 62301
Ph: (217)222-7980
Fax: (217)222-3033
Co. E-mail: amy@quincychamber.org
URL: http://www.quincychamber.org
Contact: Amy Looten, Executive Director
Released: Weekly

51344 ■ Update
1011 S 2nd St.
Springfield, IL 62704
Ph: (217)525-1173
Fax: (217)525-8768
Co. E-mail: info@gscc.org
URL: http://www.gscc.org
Contact: Steward Sandstrom, President
Released: Monthly Price: included in membership dues.

51345 ■ Uptown Chamber of Commerce
4753 N Broadway St., Ste. 822
Chicago, IL 60640-4992
Ph: (773)878-1184
Fax: (773)878-3678
Co. E-mail: info@uptownbusinesspartners.com
URL: http://www.uptownbusinesspartners.com
Contact: Christie Hahn, Executive Director
Description: Promotes business and community development in the uptown area of Chicago, IL. Publications: Chambergram (Monthly). Awards: Athena Award (Annual); Stone Award (Annual).

51346 ■ Vandalia Chamber of Commerce
PO Box 238
Vandalia, IL 62471
Ph: (618)283-2728
Fax: (618)283-4439
Co. E-mail: info@vandaliachamber.org
URL: http://www.vandaliachamber.org
Contact: Ben Timmermann, President
Description: Aims to advance the interest of business, professional, and service organizations in the Vandalia area through acting as their voice in governmental and social affairs, communicating their needs and enhancing the quality of life. **Founded:** 1914.

51347 ■ Vermilion Advantage-Chamber of Commerce Division (VACC)
28 W North St.
Danville, IL 61832-5729
Ph: (217)442-6201
Fax: (217)442-6228
Co. E-mail: vhaugen@vermilionadvantage.com
URL: http://www.vermilionadvantage.com
Contact: Vicki Haugen, President
Description: Promotes business and community development in the Vermilion County, IL area. **Founded:** 1899. **Publications:** *Commerce Communicator* (Bimonthly); *Danville Is...* (Triennial). **Telecommunication Services:** contact@vermilionadvantage.com.

51348 ■ Villa Park Chamber of Commerce
10 W Park Blvd.
Villa Park, IL 60181
Ph: (630)941-9133
Fax: (630)941-9134
Co. E-mail: vphamber@sbcglobal.net
URL: http://www.villaparkchamber.org
Contact: Alesia Bailey, Executive Director
Description: Promotes business and community development in Villa Park, IL area. **Founded:** 1948. **Publications:** *Chamber Connections* (Monthly).

51349 ■ *Village*
c/o Yvonne Invergo, Exec. Dir.
10 Lilac Ln.
Lombard, IL 60148
Ph: (630)627-5040
Fax: (630)627-5519
Co. E-mail: info@lombardchamber.com
URL: http://www.lombardchamber.com
Contact: Yvonne Invergo, Executive Director

51350 ■ *Village and Business*
The Esplanade at Locust Point
Downers Grove, IL 60515
Ph: (630)968-4050
Fax: (630)968-8368
Co. E-mail: chamber@downersgrove.org
URL: http://www.downersgrove.org
Contact: Laura Crawford, President
Released: Annual

51351 ■ Village of Itasca Chamber of Commerce
550 W Irving Park Rd.
Itasca, IL 60143-1795
Ph: (630)773-0835
Fax: (630)773-2505
Co. E-mail: mayor@itasca.com
URL: http://www.itasca.com
Description: Promotes business and community development in Itasca, IL area.

51352 ■ *Vision*
PO Box 752
Joliet, IL 60434-0752
Ph: (815)727-5371
Fax: (815)727-5374
Co. E-mail: info@jolietchamber.com
URL: http://www.jolietchamber.com
Contact: Russ Slinkard, President
Released: Monthly

51353 ■ *The Voice*
308 W State St., Ste. 190
Rockford, IL 61101
Ph: (815)987-8100

Fax: (815)987-8122
Co. E-mail: info@rockfordchamber.com
URL: http://www.rockfordchamber.com
Released: Monthly

51354 ■ *WACC Report*
110 S 3rd St.
Watseka, IL 60970
Ph: (815)432-2416
Fax: (815)432-2762
Co. E-mail: wacc@att.net
URL: http://www.watsekachamber.org
Contact: Kendra Martin, Executive Director
Released: Monthly

51355 ■ Walnut Chamber of Commerce (WCC)
105 N Main St.
Walnut, IL 61376
Ph: (815)379-2141
Co. E-mail: director@villageofwalnut.com
URL: http://www.villageofwalnut.com
Contact: Ms. Nicole Blessing, Executive Director
Description: Promotes business and community development in the Walnut, IL area. **Founded:** 1972. **Publications:** *Chamber Corner*. **Awards:** Hall of Fame (Annual).

51356 ■ Waterloo Chamber of Commerce
PO Box 1
Waterloo, IL 62298
Ph: (618)939-5300
Fax: (618)939-1805
Co. E-mail: chamber@htc.com
URL: http://www.enjoywaterloo.com
Contact: Debbie Ruggeri, Executive Director
Description: Helps promote a prosperous business climate and quality of life for the businesses and people of Waterloo.

51357 ■ Watseka Area Chamber of Commerce (WACC)
110 S 3rd St.
Watseka, IL 60970
Ph: (815)432-2416
Fax: (815)432-2762
Co. E-mail: wacc@att.net
URL: http://www.watsekachamber.org
Contact: Kendra Martin, Executive Director
Description: Promotes business and community development in the Watseka, IL area. **Founded:** 1945. **Publications:** *WACC Report* (Monthly). **Educational Activities:** Business Showcase (Semiannual).

51358 ■ Wauconda Chamber of Commerce (WCC)
100 N Main St.
Wauconda, IL 60084
Ph: (847)526-5580
Fax: (847)526-3059
Co. E-mail: info@waucondachamber.org
URL: http://www.waucondachamber.org
Contact: Sandy Hartogh, Executive Director
Description: Businesses and industries united to promote and foster the commercial, industrial, professional, civic, and general interests of Wauconda Township, IL. Provides information to the public and business community about the area. Sponsors Miss Wauconda Pageant and the Wauconda Rodeo; holds dinner meetings; conducts Thanksgiving and Christmas community activities. Awards scholarships to local students. **Founded:** 1948. **Publications:** *Wauconda Community Guide* (Annual); *Wauconda Wave* (Bimonthly).

51359 ■ *Wauconda Community Guide*
100 N Main St.
Wauconda, IL 60084
Ph: (847)526-5580
Fax: (847)526-3059
Co. E-mail: info@waucondachamber.org
URL: http://www.waucondachamber.org
Contact: Sandy Hartogh, Executive Director
Released: Annual

51360 ■ *Wauconda Wave*
100 N Main St.
Wauconda, IL 60084

Ph: (847)526-5580
Fax: (847)526-3059
Co. E-mail: info@waucondachamber.org
URL: http://www.waucondachamber.org
Contact: Sandy Hartogh, Executive Director
Released: Bimonthly

51361 ■ *WCC Community Guide*
1150 Wilmette Ave., Ste. A
Wilmette, IL 60091
Ph: (847)251-3800
Fax: (847)251-6321
Co. E-mail: info@wilmettechamber.org
URL: http://www.wilmettechamber.org
Contact: Nada Becker, Executive Director
Released: Annual **Price:** free.

51362 ■ *Welcome to New Lenox*
PO Box 42
New Lenox, IL 60451-0042
Ph: (815)485-4241
Fax: (815)485-5001
Co. E-mail: info@newlenoxchamber.com
URL: http://www.newlenoxchamber.com
Contact: Mark Stevens, President

51363 ■ West Chicago Chamber of Commerce and Industry
306 Main St.
West Chicago, IL 60185
Ph: (630)231-3003
Fax: (630)231-3009
Co. E-mail: info@westchicagochamber.com
URL: http://www.westchicagochamber.com
Contact: David J. Sabathne, President
Description: Works to provide training, networking, community visibility, and government policy engagement. **Founded:** 1952.

51364 ■ West Lawn Chamber of Commerce (WLCC)
4425 W 63rd St., Ste. 208
Chicago, IL 60629
Ph: (773)735-7690
Fax: (773)284-8110
Co. E-mail: westlawnchamber@sbcglobal.net
URL: http://www.westlawnchamber.org
Contact: Mrs. Edie Cavanaugh, Executive Director
Description: Provides technical assistance to local businesses in the areas of marketing, finance, employment, and public relations. **Founded:** 1972.

51365 ■ West Suburban Chamber of Commerce and Industry (WSCCI)
9440 Joliet Rd., Ste. B
Hodgkins, IL 60525
Ph: (708)387-7550
Fax: (708)387-7556
Co. E-mail: info@wscci.org
URL: http://www.westsuburbanchamber.org
Contact: Steve Erickson, Executive Director
Description: Advocates for business by striving to enhance and promote the stability and well-being of the community. Sponsors job fair, golf outing, awards gala, and New Teachers' Welcome Breakfast. **Founded:** 1901. **Publications:** *Outlook*; *Community Resource Guide*; *Regional Map* (Biennial). **Awards:** Business of the Year (Annual); Man of the Year (Annual); Woman of the Year (Annual); Youth of the Year (Annual); Public Servant of the Year (Annual).

51366 ■ Westchester Chamber of Commerce
PO Box 7309
Westchester, IL 60154
Ph: (708)240-8400
Fax: (708)240-8400
Co. E-mail: bruce.horek.bz4d@statefarm.com
URL: http://www.westchesterchamber.org
Contact: Bruce Horek, President
Description: Promotes growth and health of businesses in the community of Westchester. **Founded:** 1954.

51367 ■ Westmont Chamber of Commerce and Tourism Bureau
1 S Cass Ave.
Westmont, IL 60559
Ph: (630)960-5553

Fax: (630)960-5554
Co. E-mail: wcctb@westmontchamber.com
URL: http://www.westmontchamber.com
Contact: Larry Forssberg, Executive Director
Description: Works to improve the economic environment of Westmont by fostering the development of business growth and prosperity of the entire community. **Awards:** Business of the Month (Monthly).

51368 ■ Westridge Chamber of Commerce
2540 W Devon Ave.
Chicago, IL 60659
Ph: (773)743-6022
Co. E-mail: westridgechamber@sbcglobal.net
URL: http://westridgechamber.org
Contact: Amie Zander, Executive Director
Description: Local chamber of commerce. Represents members' interests; holds seminars, workshops, and other promotional activities. **Founded:** 1992. **Publications:** *International Marketplace Newsletter.*

51369 ■ Wheaton Chamber of Commerce (WCC)
108 E Wesley St.
Wheaton, IL 60187
Ph: (630)668-6464
Fax: (630)668-2744
Co. E-mail: info@wheatonchamber.com
URL: http://wheatonchamber.com
Contact: Jill Seijo, President
Description: Fosters meaningful business relationships, advocates on issues impacting the local economy, and develops business education and marketing opportunities. **Publications:** *Wheaton Chamber of Commerce Membership Directory* (Annual); *Advantage* (Monthly); *Business and Community Directory* (Annual); *Wheaton Map* (Annual).

51370 ■ *Wheaton Map*
108 E Wesley St.
Wheaton, IL 60187
Ph: (630)668-6464
Fax: (630)668-2744
Co. E-mail: info@wheatonchamber.com
URL: http://wheatonchamber.com
Contact: Jill Seijo, President
Released: Annual

51371 ■ Wheeling - Prospect Heights Area Chamber of Commerce and Industry (WPHACCI)
2 Community Blvd., Ste. 203
Wheeling, IL 60090-2726
Ph: (847)541-0170
Fax: (847)541-0296
Co. E-mail: info@wphchamber.com
URL: http://www.wphchamber.com
Contact: Catherine Powers, Executive Director
Description: Promotes business and community development in the Wheeling and Prospect Heights, IL area. **Founded:** 1927. **Publications:** *Buying Guide* (Annual); *Chamber Connections* (Bimonthly). **Educational Activities:** Business EXPO (Annual).

51372 ■ Will County Center for Economic Development (CED)
116 N Chicago St.
Two Rialto Sq., Ste. 101
Joliet, IL 60432-4204
Ph: (815)723-1800
Fax: (815)723-6972
Co. E-mail: info@willcountyced.com
URL: http://www.willcountyced.com
Contact: Mr. John E. Greuling, President
Description: Provides information and assistance in locating or expanding a business in Will County. Offers services such as county development data, business incentive programs and government relations. **Founded:** 1981.

51373 ■ Willowbrook - Burr Ridge Chamber of Commerce and Industry
8300 S Madison St.
Burr Ridge, IL 60527
Ph: (630)654-0909

Fax: (630)654-0922
Co. E-mail: info@wbbrchamber.org
URL: http://www.wbbrchamber.org
Contact: Cheryl Collins, Executive Director
Description: Provides community leadership, facilitates communication, promotes education, supports local causes and represents the interest and advancement of its members. **Founded:** 1985.

51374 ■ Wilmette Chamber of Commerce (WCC)
1150 Wilmette Ave., Ste. A
Wilmette, IL 60091
Ph: (847)251-3800
Fax: (847)251-6321
Co. E-mail: info@wilmettechamber.org
URL: http://www.wilmettechamber.org
Contact: Nada Becker, Executive Director
Description: Promotes business and community development in the Wilmette, IL area. Sponsors sidewalk sale. **Founded:** 1957. **Publications:** *WCC Community Guide* (Annual); *Wilmette Chamber Headline News.*

51375 ■ *Wilmette Chamber Headline News*
1150 Wilmette Ave., Ste. A
Wilmette, IL 60091
Ph: (847)251-3800
Fax: (847)251-6321
Co. E-mail: info@wilmettechamber.org
URL: http://www.wilmettechamber.org
Contact: Nada Becker, Executive Director
Released: published if necessary.

51376 ■ Wilmington Chamber of Commerce
111 S Water St.
Wilmington, IL 60481
Ph: (815)476-7966
Fax: (815)476-7002
Co. E-mail: eric.fisher@cbcast.com
URL: http://wilmingtonilchamber.org/default.aspx
Contact: Eric Fisher, President
Description: Promotes business and community development in Wilmington, IL area. **Publications:** *Newsbriefs* (Monthly). **Educational Activities:** Chamber Christmas Party (Annual).

51377 ■ *Win-net-work*
841 Spruce St., Ste. 204
Winnetka, IL 60093
Ph: (847)446-4451
Fax: (847)446-4452
Co. E-mail: wcc@winnetkachamber.com
URL: http://www.winnetkachamber.com
Contact: Terry Dason, Executive Director
Released: Biennial

51378 ■ Winfield Chamber of Commerce (WCC)
PO Box 209
Winfield, IL 60190
Ph: (630)682-3712
Fax: (630)682-3726
Co. E-mail: winfieldchamber@sbcglobal.net
URL: http://www.winfieldchamber.biz
Contact: Rich Bysina, Executive Director
Description: Retail businesses, banks, professional service organizations, and individuals. Promotes business and community development in the Winfield, IL area. Sponsors festival. **Founded:** 1975. **Publications:** *Winfield STUFF!* (Monthly).

51379 ■ *Winfield STUFF!*
PO Box 209
Winfield, IL 60190
Ph: (630)682-3712
Fax: (630)682-3726
Co. E-mail: winfieldchamber@sbcglobal.net
URL: http://www.winfieldchamber.biz
Contact: Rich Bysina, Executive Director
Released: Monthly

51380 ■ Winnetka Chamber of Commerce (WCC)
841 Spruce St., Ste. 204
Winnetka, IL 60093
Ph: (847)446-4451

Fax: (847)446-4452
Co. E-mail: wcc@winnetkachamber.com
URL: http://www.winnetkachamber.com
Contact: Terry Dason, Executive Director
Description: Seeks to serve as the principal representative of area businesses; to ensure a favorable business climate; and to promote economic development. Sponsors Winnetka Days, a recognition luncheon and holiday lighting program. **Founded:** 1923. **Publications:** *Shoppe Talk* (Biennial); *Win-net-work* (Biennial). **Educational Activities:** Recognition Lunches (Monthly).

51381 ■ Wood Dale Chamber of Commerce
PO Box 353
Wood Dale, IL 60191-0353
Ph: (630)595-0505
Fax: (630)595-0677
Co. E-mail: info@wooddalechamber.com
URL: http://www.wooddalechamber.com
Contact: George Ellefsen, President
Description: Works for the advancement of the economic, industrial, professional, cultural and civic welfare of businesses while giving all proper assistance to any new firms or individuals seeking to locate in Wood Dale. Supports beneficial activity for the community. **Publications:** *Chamber Update.*

51382 ■ Woodridge Area Chamber of Commerce (WACC)
6440 Main St., Ste 330
Woodridge, IL 60517-1290
Ph: (630)960-7080
Fax: (630)852-2316
Co. E-mail: chamber@woodridgechamber.com
URL: http://www.woodridgechamber.org
Contact: Amy Melinder, President
Description: Promotes business and community development in the Woodridge, IL area. Sponsors annual Jubilee Festival. **Founded:** 1978. **Publications:** *Chamber Connections* (Monthly); *Chamber Directory* (Annual).

51383 ■ Woodstock Chamber of Commerce and Industry (WCCI)
136 Cass St.
Woodstock, IL 60098
Ph: (815)338-2436
Fax: (815)338-2927
Co. E-mail: info@woodstockilchamber.com
URL: http://www.woodstockilchamber.com
Contact: Todd Kinker, President (Acting)
Description: Promotes business and community development in Woodstock, IL. Sponsors festivals; hosts art fairs, craft fairs, and business exposition. Conducts charitable activities. **Publications:** *Connection* (Monthly).

51384 ■ Yorkville Area Chamber of Commerce
26 W Countryside Pkwy.
Yorkville, IL 60560
Ph: (630)553-6853
Fax: (630)553-0702
Co. E-mail: sherri@yorkvillechamber.org
URL: http://www.yorkvillechamber.org
Contact: Sherri Farley, Executive Director
Description: Promotes the business and community development in Yorkville, IL.

51385 ■ Zion Area Chamber of Commerce
1300 Shiloh Blvd.
Zion, IL 60099
Ph: (847)872-5405
URL: http://www.zionchamber.com
Contact: Karen Crane, President
Description: Enhances the economic environment of its local business community. **Founded:** 1926. **Publications:** *News and Views* (Quarterly).

MINORITY BUSINESS ASSISTANCE PROGRAMS

51386 ■ Chicago Minority Business Opportunity Center
105 W Adams St., Ste. 2300
Chicago, IL 60603
Ph: (312)755-8888

Fax: (312)755-8891
Co. E-mail: business@cmboc.org
URL: http://www.cmboc.org
Contact: Dave Thomas, Executive Director
Description: Works to foster and promote the growth of minority-owned businesses in the Chicago area.

51387 ■ Chicago Minority Supplier Development Council
105 West Adams Ste. 2300
Chicago, IL 60603
Ph: (312)755-8880
Fax: (312)755-8890
Co. E-mail: info@chicagomsdc.org
URL: http://msdc.adaptone.com/cmbdc/
Contact: Shelia C. Hill Morgan, President

51388 ■ Latin American Chamber of Commerce
3512 W Fullerton Ave.
Chicago, IL 60647
Ph: (773)252-5211
Fax: (773)252-7065
Co. E-mail: bsantana@latinamericachamberofcommerce.com
URL: http://www.latinamericanchamberofcommerce.com
Contact: Antonio Guillen, President

FINANCING AND LOAN PROGRAMS

51389 ■ ABN AMRO Private Equity
208 S. La Salle St., 10th Fl.
Chicago, IL 60604
Ph: (312)855-7292
Fax: (312)553-6648
URL: http://www.abnequity.com
Contact: Daniel Foreman, Managing Director
Preferred Investment Size: $1,000,000 to $10,000,000. **Industry Preferences:** Consumer related, computer software and services, other products, communications and media, Internet specific, medical and health, semiconductors and other electronics, and biotechnology. **Geographic Preference:** U.S. and Canada.

51390 ■ Allstate Private Equity
3075 Sanders Rd., Ste. G5D
Northbrook, IL 60062
Ph: (847)402-6709
Fax: (866)695-0483
URL: http://www.allstateinvestments.com
Contact: Ross Posner, Advisor
E-mail: rposner@allstate.com
Preferred Investment Size: $15,000,000-$20,000,000. **Industry Preferences:** Communications and media, computer hardware and software, semiconductors and other electronics, biotechnology, medical and health, consumer related, industrial and energy, financial services, and manufacturing. **Geographic Preference:** U.S.

51391 ■ Alpha Capital Partners, Ltd.
122 S. Michigan Ave., Ste. 1700
Chicago, IL 60603
Ph: (312)322-9800
Fax: (312)322-9808
Co. E-mail: info@alphacapital.com
URL: http://www.alphacapital.com
Contact: Andrew H. Kalnow, President
E-mail: ahkalnow@alphacapital.com
Preferred Investment Size: $500,000 to $5,000,000. **Industry Preferences:** Computer software and services, consumer related, other products, communications and media, medical and health, biotechnology, semiconductors and other electronics, Internet specific, industrial and energy, and computer hardware. **Geographic Preference:** Midwest.

51392 ■ Apex Venture Partners
225 W. Washington, Ste. 1500
Chicago, IL 60606
Ph: (312)857-2800

Fax: (312)857-1800
Co. E-mail: apex@apexvc.com
URL: http://www.apexvc.com
Contact: Amando Pauker, Partner
Preferred Investment Size: $200,000 to $6,000,000. **Industry Preferences:** Internet specific, computer software and services, other products, communications and media, semiconductors and other electronics, consumer related, medical and health, industrial and energy, and biotechnology. **Geographic Preference:** U.S.

51393 ■ Arch Venture Partners
8725 W. Higgins Rd., Ste. 290
Chicago, IL 60631
Ph: (773)380-6600
Fax: (773)380-6606
URL: http://www.archventure.com
Contact: Steven Lazarus, Managing Director
Preferred Investment Size: $500,000 to $10,000,000. **Industry Preferences:** Internet specific, semiconductors and other electronics, computer software and services, medical and health, biotechnology, communications and media, computer hardware, industrial and energy, consumer related, and other products. **Geographic Preference:** Midwest, Mid Atlantic, Northeast, Northern and Southern California, Northwest, Rocky Mountains, Southwest, and West Coast.

51394 ■ Batterson Cross Zakin, LLC (BCZ)
303 W. Madison St., Ste. 1625
Chicago, IL 60606
Ph: (312)269-0300
Fax: (312)269-0021
URL: http://www.battersonvp.com
Contact: Leonard A. Batterson, Chief Executive Officer
Preferred Investment Size: $500,000 to $3,000,000. **Industry Preferences:** Computer software and services, medical and health, Internet specific, communications and media, biotechnology, industrial and energy, computer hardware, other products, semiconductors and other electronics, and consumer related. **Geographic Preference:** U.S.

51395 ■ Beecken Petty O'Keefe & Company
131 S Dearborn St., Ste. 2800
Chicago, IL 60603
Ph: (312)435-0300
Fax: (312)435-0371
Co. E-mail: partners@bpoc.com
URL: http://www.beeckenpetty.com
Contact: Dave K. Beecken, Partner
Preferred Investment Size: $5,000,000 to $500,000,000. **Industry Preferences:** Medical and health, computer software and services, Internet specific, other products, communications and media. **Geographic Preference:** U.S. and Canada.

51396 ■ Bluestar Ventures LP
200 W. Madison St., 37th Fl.
Chicago, IL 60606
Ph: (312)384-5000
Fax: (312)384-5005
Co. E-mail: info@bluestarventures.com
URL: http://www.bluestarventures.com
Contact: Patrick Pollard, Managing Director
E-mail: pat@bluestarventures.com
Preferred Investment Size: $500,000 to $3,000,000. **Industry Preferences:** Communications, computer software, and Internet specific. **Geographic Preference:** Mid Atlantic, Midwest, Northwest, Southeast, and Southwest.

51397 ■ The Capital Strategy Management Co.
233 S. Wacker Dr.
Box 06334
Chicago, IL 60606-0334
Ph: (312)444-1170
URL: http://capitalstrategymanagement.com
Contact: Eric E. von Bauer, President
E-mail: evb@capitalstrategymanagement.com
Preferred Investment Size: $200,000 to $50,000,000. **Industry Preferences:** Communications, computer hardware and software, Internet specific, semiconductors and other electronics, biotechnology, medical and health, consumer related,

industrial and energy, transportation, business service, manufacturing, agriculture, forestry and fishing, environment, and utilities. **Geographic Preference:** Mid Atlantic, Midwest, Rocky Mountains, Southwest, and Southeast.

51398 ■ DN Partners LLC
180 N. LaSalle St., Ste. 3001
Chicago, IL 60601
Ph: (312)332-7960
Fax: (312)332-0856
URL: http://www.dnpartners.com
Contact: Maury J. Bell, Managing Partner
Preferred Investment Size: $3,000,000 to $15,000,000. **Industry Preferences:** Communications, computer hardware, Internet specific, semiconductors and other electronics, medical and health, consumer related, industrial and energy, transportation, financial services, business service, manufacturing, agriculture, forestry and fishing. **Geographic Preference:** Midwest and U.S.

51399 ■ Dresner Capital Resources, Inc.
20 N. Clark St., Ste. 3550
Chicago, IL 60602
Ph: (312)726-3600
Fax: (312)726-7448
Co. E-mail: info@dresnerco.com
URL: http://www.dresnerpartners.com
Contact: Steven M. Dresner, President
E-mail: sdresner@dresnerco.com
Preferred Investment Size: $500,000 to $1,000,000. **Industry Preferences:** Communications, computer hardware and software, Internet specific, semiconductors and other electronics, medical and health, consumer related, industrial and energy, financial services, business service, and manufacturing.

51400 ■ Duchossois Technology Partners LLC (DTEC)
845 Larch Ave.
Elmhurst, IL 60126-1196
Ph: (630)993-6105
Fax: (630)993-8644
Co. E-mail: duchtec@duch.com
URL: http://www.duchtec.com
Contact: Robert L. Fealy, Managing Director
E-mail: rfealy@duch.com
Preferred Investment Size: $2,000,000 to $7,000,000. **Industry Preferences:** Communications, computer software, semiconductors and other electronics,. **Geographic Preference:** U.S.

51401 ■ First Analysis Corp.
1 S. Wacker Dr., Ste. 3900
Chicago, IL 60606
Ph: (312)258-1400
Fax: (312)258-0334
URL: http://www.firstanalysis.com
Contact: Michael Siemplenski, Managing Director
Preferred Investment Size: $3,000,000 to $10,000,000. **Industry Preferences:** Industrial and energy, Internet specific, other products, computer software and services, communications and media, consumer related, medical and health, computer hardware, semiconductors and other electronics, and biotechnology. **Geographic Preference:** U.S.

51402 ■ Frontenac Company
135 S. LaSalle St., Ste. 3800
Chicago, IL 60603
Ph: (312)368-0044
Fax: (312)368-9520
Co. E-mail: info@frontenac.com
URL: http://www.frontenac.com
Contact: Paul D. Carbery, Managing Director
Preferred Investment Size: $10,000,000 to $50,000,000. **Industry Preferences:** Consumer related, other products, Internet specific, computer software and services, medical and health, communications and media, industrial and energy, computer hardware, semiconductors and other electronics, and biotechnology. **Geographic Preference:** U.S.

51403 ■ GTCR Golder Rauner LLC
300 N. LaSalle St., Ste. 5600
Chicago, IL 60654
Ph: (312)382-2200

Fax: (312)382-2201
Co. E-mail: info@gtcr.com
URL: http://www.gtcr.com
Contact: Barry R. Dunn, Principal
E-mail: barry.dunn@gtcr.com
Preferred Investment Size: $10,000,000 to $300,000,000. **Industry Preferences:** Communications, other products, computer software and services, consumer related, semiconductors and other electronics, medical and health, Internet specific, computer hardware. **Geographic Preference:** U.S.

51404 ■ High Street Capital
11 S. LaSalle St., 5th Fl.
Chicago, IL 60603
Ph: (312)423-2650
Fax: (312)267-2861
Co. E-mail: info@HighStreetCapital.com
URL: http://www.highstr.com
Contact: Joseph Katcha, Principal
E-mail: Joe@highstreetcapital.com
Preferred Investment Size: $2,000,000 to $8,000,000. **Industry Preferences:** Communications, computer software, semiconductors and other electronics, medical and health, industrial and energy, business service, and manufacturing. **Geographic Preference:** U.S.

51405 ■ IEG Venture Management, Inc.
70 West Madison St., 14th Fl.
Chicago, IL 60602
Ph: (312)644-0890
Fax: (312)454-0369
URL: http://www.iegventure.com
Contact: Frank Blair, President
E-mail: frankblair@iegventure.com
Industry Preferences: Communications, computer hardware and software, Internet specific, semiconductors and other electronics, biotechnology, medical and health, industrial and energy, transportation, manufacturing, agriculture, forestry and fishing. **Geographic Preference:** Midwest.

51406 ■ JK&B Capital
2 Prudential PLz.
180 N. Stetson Ave., Ste. 4500
Chicago, IL 60601
Ph: (312)946-1200
Fax: (312)946-1103
URL: http://www.jkbcapital.com
Contact: Albert DaValle, Jr., Partner
Preferred Investment Size: $5,000,000 to $30,000,000. **Industry Preferences:** Internet specific, communications and media, computer software and services, semiconductors and other electronics, industrial and energy, and consumer related. **Geographic Preference:** U.S.

51407 ■ KB Partners LLC
1780 Green Bay Rd., Ste. 202
Highland Park, IL 60035
Ph: (847)681-1270
Fax: (847)681-1370
Co. E-mail: ideas@kbpartners.com
URL: http://www.kbpartners.com
Contact: Keith Bank, Managing Director
E-mail: keith@kbpartners.com
Preferred Investment Size: $1,000,000 to $5,000,000. **Industry Preferences:** Internet specific, computer software and services, industrial and energy, communications and media, semiconductors and other electronics, medical and health, and other products. **Geographic Preference:** Midwest and Rocky Mountains.

51408 ■ Lake Capital Partners, Inc.
676 N. Michigan Ave., Ste. 3900
Chicago, IL 60611-2896
Ph: (312)640-7050
Fax: (312)640-7051
Co. E-mail: info@lakecapital.com
URL: http://www.lakecapital.com
Contact: Terence M. Graunke, Principal
Preferred Investment Size: $50,000,000 to $100,000,000. **Industry Preferences:** Technology, financial services, healthcare and business services. **Geographic Preference:** U.S.

51409 ■ LaSalle Capital Group, Inc.
5710 Three First National Plz.
70 W. Madison St.
Chicago, IL 60602
Ph: (312)236-7041
Fax: (312)236-0720
Co. E-mail: contact@lasallecapitalgroup.com
URL: http://www.lasallecapitalgroup.com
Contact: Jeffrey M. Walters, Principal
E-mail: jwalters@lasallecapitalgroup.com
Preferred Investment Size: $5,000,000 to $15,000,000. **Industry Preferences:** Communications, consumer related, semiconductors and other electronics, medical and health, industrial and energy, business service, manufacturing, and agriculture, forestry and fishing. **Geographic Preference:** U.S.

51410 ■ Madison Dearborn Partners LLC
3 First National Plz., Ste. 4600
Chicago, IL 60602
Ph: (312)895-1000
Fax: (312)895-1001
Co. E-mail: info@mdcp.com
URL: http://www.mdcp.com
Contact: Benjamin Chereskin, Managing Director
Preferred Investment Size: $100,000,000 to $600,000,000. **Industry Preferences:** Communications and media, Internet specific, consumer related, semiconductors and other electronics, medical and health, industrial and energy, computer software and services, computer hardware, and other products. **Geographic Preference:** U.S. and Canada.

51411 ■ Marquette Venture Partners
PO Box 1609
Vail, CO 81658
Free: 877-215-3400
Fax: (970)476-2316
URL: http://www.marquetteventures.com
Contact: Lloyd D. Ruth, Partner
E-mail: cruth@marquetteventures.com
Preferred Investment Size: $1,000,000 to $5,000,000. **Industry Preferences:** Medical and health, consumer related, computer software and services, communications and media, biotechnology, Internet specific, semiconductors and other electronics, industrial and energy, and computer hardware. **Geographic Preference:** Mid Atlantic, Midwest, Rocky Mountains, and West Coast.

51412 ■ Mesirow Private Equity Investments, Inc.
353 N. Clark St.
Chicago, IL 60654
Ph: (312)595-6000
Free: 800-453-0600
Fax: (312)595-4246
URL: http://www.meisirowfinancial.com
Contact: Thomas E. Galuhn, Managing Director
E-mail: tgaluhn@mesirowfinancial.com
Preferred Investment Size: $2,000,000 to $10,000,000. **Industry Preferences:** Computer software and services, other products, computer hardware, consumer related, Internet specific, communications and media, industrial and energy, semiconductors and other electronics, medical and health. **Geographic Preference:** U.S. and Canada.

51413 ■ Mosaix Ventures
1822 N. Mohawk St.
Chicago, IL 60614
Ph: (312)274-0988
Fax: (773)913-2792
URL: http://www.mosaixventures.com
Contact: Ranjan Lal, Managing Partner
E-mail: rlal@mosaixventures.com
Preferred Investment Size: $1,000,000 to $4,000,000. **Industry Preferences:** Medical and health, and biotechnology. **Geographic Preference:** U.S. and Canada.

51414 ■ Motorola Ventures
1303 E. Algonquin Rd., 6th Fl.
Schaumburg, IL 60196
Ph: (847)576-0278

Fax: (847)576-2569
URL: http://www.motorola.com/ventures
Contact: Reese Schroeder, Managing Director
Preferred Investment Size: $3,000,000 to $5,000,000. **Industry Preferences:** Communications and media, Internet specific, computer software and services, semiconductors and other electronics, Internet specific, computer hardware, biotechnology, consumer related, and other products. **Geographic Preference:** U.S.

51415 ■ New World Ventures
111 South Wacker Dr., Ste. 4000
Chicago, IL 60606
Ph: (312)447-6000
Fax: (312)447-6006
Co. E-mail: info@newworldvc.com
URL: http://www.newworldvc.com
Contact: Christopher E. Girgenti, Managing Director
Preferred Investment Size: $5,000,000 to $12,000,000. **Industry Preferences:** Internet specific, communications and media, medical and health, and computer software and services. **Geographic Preference:** U.S.

51416 ■ Open Prairie Ventures
400 E. Jefferson
Effingham, IL 62401
Ph: (217)347-1000
Fax: (217)347-1001
Co. E-mail: info@openprairie.com
URL: http://www.openprairie.com
Contact: Dennis Beard, Chief Financial Officer
Preferred Investment Size: $250,000 to $2,500,000. **Industry Preferences:** Communications and media, computer hardware and software, Internet specific, computer related, semiconductors and other electronics, biotechnology, medical and health, industrial and energy. **Geographic Preference:** Midwest.

51417 ■ Polestar Capital, Inc.
180 N. Michigan Ave., Ste. 1905
Chicago, IL 60601
Ph: (312)984-9090
Fax: (312)984-9877
Co. E-mail: info@polestarvc.com
URL: http://www.polestarvc.com
Contact: Derrick K. Collins, Partner
E-mail: dkcollins@polestarvc.com
Industry Preferences: Communications and media, computer software, computer related, and manufacturing. **Geographic Preference:** U.S.

51418 ■ Portage Venture Partners / Graystone Venture Partners
1 Northfield Plz., Ste. 530
Northfield, IL 60093
Ph: (847)446-9460
Fax: (847)446-9470
URL: http://www.portageventures.com
Contact: Mathew McCall, Managing Director
Preferred Investment Size: $500,000 to $20,000,000. **Industry Preferences:** Internet specific, computer software and services, biotechnology, communications and media, medical and health, other products, semiconductors and other electronics, and consumer related. **Geographic Preference:** Midwest.

51419 ■ Prism Capital
444 N. Michigan Ave., Ste. 1910
Chicago, IL 60611
Ph: (312)464-7900
Fax: (312)464-7915
URL: http://www.prismfund.com
Contact: John Hoesley, Partner
E-mail: john@prismfund.com
Preferred Investment Size: $2,000,000 to $15,000,000. **Industry Preferences:** Computer software and services, Internet specific, and consumer related, medical and health, semiconductors and other electronics, computer hardware, and other products. **Geographic Preference:** U.S.

51420 ■ Third Coast Capital
1 N. Franklin St., Ste. 2700
Chicago, IL 60610
Ph: (312)332-6484

Fax: (312)337-2567
URL: http://www.thirdcoastcapital.com
Contact: Kathleen Wilkerson, Managing Director
Preferred Investment Size: $1,000,000 to $5,000,000. **Industry Preferences:** Communications, computer software, Internet specific, biotechnology, medical and health, and consumer related. **Geographic Preference:** U.S.

51421 ■ Thoma Cressey Equity Partners
9200 Sears Tower
233 S. Wacker Dr.
Chicago, IL 60606
Ph: (312)777-4444
Fax: (312)777-4445
URL: http://www.thomacressey.com
Contact: Merrick J. Axel, Principal
E-mail: maxel@cresseyco.com
Preferred Investment Size: $10,000,000 to $100,000,000. **Industry Preferences:** Other products, medical and health, computer software and services, Internet specific, consumer related, computer hardware, and biotechnology. **Geographic Preference:** U.S. and Canada.

51422 ■ Transcap Associates Inc.
900 Skokie Blvd., Ste. 210
Northbrook, IL 60062
Ph: (847)753-9600
Fax: (847)753-9090
Co. E-mail: admin@transcaptrade.com
URL: http://www.transcaptrade.com
Preferred Investment Size: $500,000 to $50,000,000. **Industry Preferences:** Communications, computer hardware, semiconductors and other electronics, medical and health, consumer related, industrial and energy. **Geographic Preference:** U.S.

51423 ■ Tribune Ventures
435 N. Michigan Ave.
Chicago, IL 60611
Ph: (312)222-9100
Fax: (312)222-5993
Co. E-mail: gweitman@tribune.com
URL: http://www.tribuneventures.com
Contact: Andy Oleszczuk, President
Preferred Investment Size: $2,000,000 to $10,000,000. **Industry Preferences:** Internet specific, computer software and services, communications and media, and other products. **Geographic Preference:** Midwest, Northeast, an West Coast.

51424 ■ William Blair Capital Partners
222 W. Adams St.
Chicago, IL 60606
Ph: (312)236-1600
Fax: (312)621-0687
Co. E-mail: info@wmblair.com
URL: http://www.williamblair.com
Contact: Mio Stojkovich, Vice President
Preferred Investment Size: $7,000,000 to $35,000,000. **Industry Preferences:** Consumer related, medical and health, computer software, hardware and services, biotechnology, industrial and energy, communications and media, semiconductors and other electronics. **Geographic Preference:** U.S.

51425 ■ Wind Point Partners (Chicago)
676 N. Michigan Ave., Ste. 3700
Chicago, IL 60611
Ph: (312)255-4800
Fax: (312)255-4820
URL: http://www.wppartners.com
Contact: Nathan Brown, Managing Director
Preferred Investment Size: $30,000,000 to $150,000,000. **Industry Preferences:** Industrial and energy, consumer related, other products, communications and media, medical and health, Internet specific, biotechnology, computer software and services, computer hardware, semiconductors and other electronics. **Geographic Preference:** U.S.

PROCUREMENT ASSISTANCE PROGRAMS

51426 ■ Disa Conus - Defense Information Systems Agency
c/o DITCO/DO4DT
Small Business Administration/PCR
2300 East Dr., Bldg. 3189, R
Scott Air Force B, IL 62225-5406

Ph: (618)220-8840
Co. E-mail: chut@scott.disa.mil
Contact: Tung Shing Chu, Supervisor
Description: Covers activities for Defense Information & Technological Contracting (Scott Air Force Base, IL), 375th Airlift Wing (Scott Air Force Base, IL), and USAF AMC Contracting Flight (Scott Air Force Base, IL).

51427 ■ Illinois Procurement Technical Assistance Center - Black Hawk Community College
4703 16th St., Ste. G
Moline, IL 61265
Ph: (309)797-2806
Co. E-mail: millerv@bhc.edu
URL: http://www.bhc.edu
Contact: Vicky Miller, Director
E-mail: millerv@bhc.edu
Description: Assists entrepreneurs start a new business or expand existing business.

51428 ■ Illinois Procurement Technical Assistance Center - College of DuPage
425 Fawell Blvd.
Glen Ellyn, IL 60137-6599
Ph: (630)942-2184
Fax: (630)942-2771
Co. E-mail: haaker@cod.edu
URL: http://www.cod.edu
Contact: Rita Haake, Director
E-mail: hatcher@cdnet.cod.edu
Description: Assists with doing business with the government, or to improve your current level of government contracting.

51429 ■ Illinois Procurement Technical Assistance Center - College of Lake County
19351 W Washington St.
Grayslake, IL 60030-1198
Ph: (847)543-2580
Fax: (847)223-9371
Co. E-mail: illinoisptac@clcillinois.edu
URL: http://www.clcillinois.edu
Contact: Marc N. Violante, Director
E-mail: mviolante@clcillinois.edu
Description: Assists businesses in competing for contracts with the municipal, state, and federal government.

51430 ■ Illinois Procurement Technical Assistance Center - Illinois Central College
Arbor Hall, Ste. 126
5407 N University
Peoria, IL 61602-1388
Ph: (309)690-6818
Fax: (309)690-6810
Co. E-mail: Linda.krendick@icc.edu
URL: http://www.icc.edu
Contact: Linda Krendick, Director
E-mail: sgorman@icc.edu
Description: Provides government contracting services for small and medium-sized existing businesses in Central Illinois. The Center assists regional companies in doing business with federal, state, and local government agencies, private sector prime contractors, and second-tier suppliers.

51431 ■ Illinois Procurement Technical Assistance Center - Illinois Hispanic Chamber of Commerce
111 W. Washington, Ste. 1660
Chicago, IL 60602
Ph: (312)425-9500
Fax: (312)425-9510
Co. E-mail: ptac@ihccbusiness.net
URL: http://www.ihccbusiness.net
Contact: Gerardo Rodriguez, Director
Description: Promotes the growth and success of Hispanic firms and serves as a strong advocate for business issues.

51432 ■ Illinois Procurement Technical Assistance Center - John A. Logan Community College - Center for Business & Industry
700 Logan College Rd.
Carterville, IL 62918-9802

Ph: (618)985-3741
Fax: (618)985-2867
Co. E-mail: ccrr@jal.cc.il.us
URL: http://www.jal.cc.il.us
Contact: Christopher Barr, Director
E-mail: chrisbarr@jalc.edu
Description: Helps familiarize firms with the government procurement process and provides them the specific marketing and technical assistance required to do business with the government or government prime contractors. Assistance may be in the form of contract preparation, acquisition, or administration.

51433 ■ Illinois Procurement Technical Assistance Center - North Business & Industrial Council (NORBIC)
Pyramid Mouldings Bldg.
5353 W Armstrong Ave., 2nd Fl.
Chicago, IL 60646-6509
Ph: (773)594-9562
Fax: (773)594-9416
Co. E-mail: info@norbic.org
URL: http://www.norbic.org
Contact: James Peters, Director
Description: Advises Illinois companies on procurement opportunities and keeps them abreast of changes in the procurement process at the federal, State of Illinois, and local municipal levels. Technical expertise and assistance are offered in proposal preparation, the procurement process, and contract administration. NORBIC also offers assistance with small business preference programs, including Small Women Owned Businesses, Small Disadvantaged Businesses, Veteran, and 8(a) Certification Assistance.

51434 ■ Illinois Procurement Technical Assistance Center - Rock Valley College
EIGERlab
605 Fulton Ave., Rm. E-108
Rockford, IL 61103
Ph: (815)921-2091
Fax: (815)921-2089
Co. E-mail: j.digiacomo@rockvalleycollege.edu
URL: http://www.rockvalleycollege.com
Contact: John DiGiacomo, Director
E-mail: j.digiacomo@rvc.cc.il.us
Description: Provides such services as trade/export assistance through international trade centers, access to financial and energy management assistance, and job training help.

51435 ■ Illinois Procurement Technical Assistance Center - South Suburban College
15800 S State St.
South Holland, IL 60473
Ph: (708)596-2000
Fax: (708)210-5703
Co. E-mail: procurement@southsuburbancollege.edu
URL: http://www.southsuburbancollege.edu
Contact: David Talbot, Director
E-mail: dtalbot@southsuburbancollege.edu
Description: Provides free counseling and technical assistance to Illinois firms pursuing government contracts.

51436 ■ Illinois Procurement Technical Assistance Center - U.S. General Services Administration (GSA) - Great Lakes (Region 5)
230 S Dearborn St.
Chicago, IL 60604
Ph: (312)353-5395
Fax: (312)886-5595
Co. E-mail: david.hood@gsa.gov
URL: http://www.gsa.gov
Contact: David J. Hood, Administrator
E-mail: james.handley@gsa.gov
Description: Serve its federal agency customers in Illinois, Indiana, Michigan, Minnesota, Ohio, and Wisconsin.

51437 ■ Illinois Procurement Technical Assistance Center - University Entrepreneurship Center
100 N Locust St.
Centralia, IL 62801
Ph: (618)532-1086

Fax: (618)532-2736
Co. E-mail: kimsand@siu.edu
URL: http://www.universityec.com
Contact: Kim Sanders, Director
Description: Provides one-on-one counseling, technical information, marketing assistance and training to existing businesses that are interested in selling their products and/or services to local, state, or federal government agencies.

51438 ■ Illinois Procurement Technical Assistance Center at Western Illinois - Quincy Business & Technology Center
301 Oak St., Rm. 2-27
Quincy, IL 62301
Ph: (217)223-5636
Fax: (217)223-5672
Co. E-mail: qbtc@adams.net
URL: http://www.qbtc.org
Contact: Mary Turner, Director
E-mail: mturner@imec1.org
Description: Nurtures the development of entrepreneurial companies helping them to service and grow during their start up period.

51439 ■ Illinois Procurement Technical Assistance Center - Women's Business Development Center
8 South Michigan, Ste. 400
Chicago, IL 60603-3306
Ph: (312)853-3477
Fax: (312)853-0145
Co. E-mail: wbdc@wbdc.org
URL: http://www.wbdc.org
Contact: Freida Curry, Director
E-mail: mangledc.org
Description: Works with women to launch new businesses and strengthen existing businesses in the Chicago area.

51440 ■ Latin American Chamber of Commerce
3512 W Fullerton Ave.
Chicago, IL 60647
Ph: (773)252-5211
Fax: (773)252-7065
Co. E-mail: lacc@latinamericanchamberofcommerce.com
URL: http://www.latinamericanchamberofcommerce.com
Contact: Jorge Sanchez-Ferrer, Director

INCUBATORS/RESEARCH AND TECHNOLOGY PARKS

51441 ■ Business Center of Decatur
2121 S Imboden Ct.
Decatur, IL 62521
Ph: (217)423-2832
Fax: (217)423-7214
Co. E-mail: bcd@decaturcenter.com
URL: http://www.decaturcenter.com/2home.htm
Contact: Jim Seaberg, General Manager
Description: The Business Center of Decatur is a business incubator for new and growing businesses.

51442 ■ Business and Technology Center (Champaign)
701 Devonshire Dr., C-2
Champaign, IL 61820
Ph: (217)398-5759
Fax: (217)398-0413
Co. E-mail: information@btcservices.net
URL: http://www.btcservices.net
Contact: Cindy Somers, Owner
Description: We are committed to the provision of an affordable, flexible and professional environment in which startup and existing businesses can prosper. We will consistently provide the best possible support services to our clients and will strive to make the latest in business technology available at an affordable price.

51443 ■ Chicago Southland Enterprise Center
1655 Union St
Chicago Heights, IL 60411

Ph: (708)754-6960
Fax: (708)754-8779
Description: Owned by a not-for-profit corporation, this small business incubator fosters collaboration among its tenants, businesses ranging from service to light manufacturing.

51444 ■ Chicago Technology Park Corp.
2201 W Campbell Park Dr., Ste. 1
Chicago, IL 60612-3547
Ph: (312)633-3434
Fax: (312)633-3438
Co. E-mail: info@techpark.com
URL: http://www.techpark.com
Description: A small business incubator serving as a ground for technology companies in early development, as well as expansion facilities for those companies that are growing their operations.

51445 ■ Fulton Carroll Center Incubator
Industrial Council of Northwest Chicago
320 N Damen Ave., Ste. D-100
Chicago, IL 60612
Ph: (312)421-3941
Fax: (312)421-1871
Co. E-mail: info@industrialcouncil.com
URL: http://www.industrialcouncil.com
Contact: Joyce Shanahan, Executive Director
Description: A small business incubator providing no-cost business development services and resources.

51446 ■ Galesburg Business and Technology Center
2051 Tom L. Wilson Blvd.
Galesburg, IL 61401
Ph: (309)345-3501
Fax: (309)345-3526
Co. E-mail: info@galesburgbtc.org
URL: http://www.galesburgbtc.org
Description: A small business incubator is designed to accelerate the growth of entrepreneurial companies through an array of support services.

51447 ■ Greater Sterling Development Corporation
1741 Industrial Dr.
Sterling, IL 61081
Ph: (815)625-5255
Fax: (815)625-5094
Co. E-mail: hsotelo@sterlingdevelopment.org
URL: http://www.sterlingdevelopment.org
Contact: Heather Sotelo, Executive Director
Description: Provides a variety of business development and relocation assistance services.

51448 ■ Macomb Area Economic Development Corporation (MAEDCO)—Western Illinois University
510 N Pearl St., Ste. 300
Macomb, IL 61455
Ph: (309)298-1414
Fax: (309)837-4688
Co. E-mail: maedco@wiu.edu
URL: http://www.wiu.edu
Contact: Dan Cortelyou, President
Description: The Macomb Area Economic Development Corporation (MAEDCO) is a not-for-profit corporation dedicated to the economic growth of the Macomb region. We have crafted an environment that can foster long-term growth, success, and profits for your business. We are capable of arranging a business package tailored to meet your individual requirements. **Publications:** *Western Courier* (3/week); *The Journal of Developing Areas* (Quarterly).

51449 ■ Maple City Business and Technology Center Incubator - Technology Center Incubator
620 S Main St.
Monmouth, IL 61462
Ph: (309)734-8544
Fax: (309)734-8579

51450 ■ Peoria NEXT Innovation Center
801 W Main St.
Peoria, IL 61606
Ph: (309)495-7238

Fax: (309)676-7534
URL: http://www.peorianext.org/index.php
Description: A small business incubator designed to enable leadership in discovery, innovation, and commercialization.

51451 ■ Performance Improvement Institute
Chicago, IL 60606
URL: http://www.zyworld.com/lisandro/IMD1English.htm
Description: A small business incubator focusing on developing and graduating new companies through an incubation process under the leadership of PhD candidates and the supervision of an international faculty.

51452 ■ Quincy Business and Technology Center
301 Oak St.
Quincy, IL 62301
Ph: (217)228-5500
Fax: (217)228-5501
Co. E-mail: qbtc@adams.net
URL: http://www.qbtc.org/
Contact: Les McKenzie, Executive Director
Description: A not-for-profit business incubator encouraging economic development in the Quincy Area by providing a business environment tailored primarily to business start-ups, home-based businesses ready for their first expansion, and businesses requiring assistance in the various management phases of successful entrepreneurship.

51453 ■ Research Park & Enterprise Works
University of Illinois
60 Hazelwood Dr.
Champaign, IL 61820
Ph: (217)333-8324
Co. E-mail: lfrerich@illinois.edu
URL: http://researchpark.illinois.edu/
Contact: Laura A. Frerichs, Associate Director
Description: A small business incubator providing an environment where technology-based businesses can work with the research faculty and students at UIUC to take advantage of opportunities for collaborative research and easy access to University labs, equipment, and services.

51454 ■ Shetland Properties Limited Partnership
5400 W Roosevelt Rd.
Chicago, IL 60644
Ph: (773)921-5400
Fax: (773)921-6680
Co. E-mail: slate@shetland.com
URL: http://www.shetland.com
Contact: Andrew Lappin, President
Description: Creates research parks out of second-generation industrial facilities.

51455 ■ Turner Center for Entrepreneurship
1501 W. Bradley Ave.
141 Jobst Hall
Peoria, IL 61625
Ph: (309)677-4321
Fax: (309)677-3386
Co. E-mail: tce@bradley.edu
URL: http://www.bradley.edu/turnercenter/
Contact: James F. Foley, Director
Description: A not-for-profit program located at Bradley University providing business counseling, technical assistance, training, and educational activities for individuals interested in owning their own businesses. It also helps existing entrepreneurs and businesses who want to expand or take advantage of new opportunities and technologies, are interested in marketing their products and services internationally, or are seeking to commercialize new products and technologies.

51456 ■ University Technology Park - Incubator and ITT Tower
3440 S Dearborn St.
Chicago, IL 60616
Ph: (312)567-3900

Fax: (312)567-3911
Co. E-mail: marselle@utp.iit.edu
URL: http://www.universitytechnologypark.com/
   incubator/index.html
Contact: Daniel F. Marselle, Director
Description: A technology park established to serve technology-based companies in the early product- and customer-development stages that require lab and/or office space as well as convenient access to business development and university-based services.

EDUCATIONAL PROGRAMS

51457 ■ Black Hawk College - Quad-Cities Campus
6600 34th Ave.
Moline, IL 61265
Ph: (309)796-5000
Free: 800-334-1311
Fax: (309)792-5976
URL: http://www.bhc.edu
Description: Two-year college offering a small business management program.

51458 ■ Chicago State University - Office of Continuing Education
9501 S King Dr.
Jacoby Dickens Center Rm 201
Chicago, IL 60628-1598
Ph: (773)995-2545
Fax: (773)995-2941
Co. E-mail: conted@csu.edu
URL: http://www.csu.edu/
Description: Offers mature students career-updating and business-related courses, seminars, and workshops for degree, nondegree, credit, or noncredit status. Conducts course work in advanced business, management, human relations, and small business management. Also provides on-site training and development for employees of small businesses involved in computer operation, budgeting, marketing, and personnel management. Additional courses are presented through the College of Business Administration.

51459 ■ Loyola University Chicago - School of Continuing and Professional Studies
Lewis Towers Ste. 800
820 N Michigan Ave.
Chicago, IL 60611
Ph: (312)915-8900
Fax: (312)915-8905
Co. E-mail: scps@luc.edu
URL: http://www.luc.edu
URL(s): www.luc.edu/adult-education. **Description:** Sponsors several programs of interest to small business professionals: The Weekend College is a concentrated program for men and women who wish to attend college while working full time. The Continuing Education Program serves women interested in beginning or continuing their college careers through day classes. Other courses of study are offered through the Business Administration Department.

51460 ■ Rend Lake College
468 N Ken Gray Pky.
Ina, IL 62846
Ph: (618)437-5321
Fax: (618)437-5677
URL: http://www.rlc.edu/
Description: Two-year college offering a small business management program.

51461 ■ Rock Valley College
3301 N Mulford Rd.
Rockford, IL 61114
Ph: (815)921-7821
Free: 800-973-7821
Fax: (815)636-4074
URL: http://www.rockvalleycollege.edu
Description: Two-year college offering a small business management program.

51462 ■ Sauk Valley Community College
173 IL., Rte. 2
Dixon, IL 61021
Ph: (815)288-5511

Fax: (815)288-1880
Co. E-mail: support@svcc.edu
URL: http://www.svcc.edu
Description: Two-year college offering small business management classes.

PUBLICATIONS

51463 ■ *How to Form Your Own Illinois Corporation Before the Inc. Dries!: A Step by Step Guide, With Forms*
333 S. Taylor Ave.
Oak Park, IL 60302
Ph: (708)524-9033
Fax: (708)524-9038
Ed: Phillip Williams. **Released:** Fourth edition, 1994. **Price:** $26.95. **Description:** Volume 1 of the Small Business Incorporation series. Explains the advantages and disadvantages of incorporation and shows, step-by-step, how the small business owners can incorporate at low cost. Covers Illinois profit and nonprofit corporations, Illinois professional service corporations, subchapter S corporations, and Delaware corporations. Includes forms necessary for incorporation.

51464 ■ *Smart Start your Illinois Business*
PSI Research
300 N. Valley Dr.
Grants Pass, OR 97526
Ph: (503)479-9464
Free: 800-228-2275
Fax: (503)476-1479
Co. E-mail: info@psi-research.com
URL: http://www.psi-research.com
Ed: Michael D. Jenkins. **Released:** Revised edition, 1992. **Price:** $29.95 (looseleaf binder); $24.95 (paper). **Description:** Part of the Successful Business Library series.

51465 ■ *Starting and Operating a Business in Illinois: A Step-by-Step Guide*
PSI Research
300 N. Valley Dr.
Grants Pass, OR 97526
Ph: (503)479-9464
Free: 800-228-2275
Fax: (503)476-1479
Co. E-mail: psi2@magick.net
Ed: Michael D. Jenkins. **Released:** Revised edition, 1992. **Price:** $29.95 (looseleaf binder); $24.95 (paper). **Description:** Part of the Successful Business Library series.

PUBLISHERS

51466 ■ Blackman Kallick
10 S Riverside Plz., 9th Fl.
Chicago, IL 60606-3770
Ph: (312)207-1040
Fax: (312)207-1066
Co. E-mail: info@BlackmanKallick.com
URL: http://www.bkadvice.com
Contact: Evan Bennett, Director
E-mail: ebennett@blackmankallick.com
URL(s): www.blackmankallick.com. **Description:** Description: Publishes on personal taxes and tax information for closely held businesses. Also produces cassettes. Reaches market through direct mail. **Scope:** Provides audit, tax and consulting services for privately held and public companies as well as not-for-profit organizations. Industries served: manufacturing and distribution, construction, family office, food, hospitality, insurance, not-for-profit, private equity and venture capital, real estate and service. **Founded:** 1962. **Publications:** "Changing Law and More Aggressive Attorneys In Fraudulent Transfer Cases," Business Valuation Update, Feb, 2008; "Discourage fraud with smart, tough management," 2002; "4 steps to better decision making," 2002; "How long will your accounting software be around," 2002; "You can grow your own way: Avoid loss with profit-boosting strategies"; "Taming technology: Create effective network services"; "Turn your organization's goals into accomplishments"; "What if Your Not-for-Profit Organization is Audited?"; "How you can benefit from the new domestic production deduction".

51467 ■ Dearborn Trade Publishing Inc.
30 S Wacker Dr., Ste. 2500
Chicago, IL 60606-7481
Ph: (312)836-4400
Free: 800-621-9621
Fax: (312)836-1146
Co. E-mail: trade@dearborn.com
URL: http://www.dearborn.com
Contact: Roy Lipner, President
Description: Description: Publishes books for consumers and professionals on finance, business, real estate, and marketing sales. Accepts proposals for new books. Reaches market through commission representatives, direct mail, and telephone sales. Accepts unsolicited manuscripts. **Founded:** 1959. **Publications:** *100 Best Stocks To Own in America; Mutual Fund Encyclopedia* (Annual); *Hulbert Guide to Financial Newsletters; The 100 Best Technology Stocks for the Long Run.* **Telecommunication Services:** contactkaplanfinancial@kaplan.com.

51468 ■ Institute of Real Estate Management (IREM)
430 N Michigan Ave.
Chicago, IL 60611-4090
Ph: (312)329-6000
Free: 800-837-0706
Fax: (800)338-4736
Co. E-mail: custserv@irem.org
URL: http://www.irem.org
Contact: Ronald Goss, President
Description: Description: Publishes an array of publications, software and a journal geared toward real estate professionals. **Publications:** *Journal of Property Management* (Bimonthly).

51469 ■ McGraw-Hill/Irwin
1333 Burr Ridge Pkwy.
Burr Ridge, IL 60527-6423
Ph: (630)789-5401
Free: 800-338-3987
Fax: (630)789-6944
Co. E-mail: jim_kelly@mcgraw-hill.com
URL: http://www.mhhe.com
Contact: Harold W. McGraw, President
Description: Description: Publishes books on accounting, advertising, business law, business math and statistics, computer information technology, economics, finance, management information systems, marketing and organizational behavior. **Founded:** 1933.

51470 ■ PivotPoint Press
5315 N Clark St., Ste. 124
Chicago, IL 60640-1121
Ph: (773)561-1512
Free: 866-323-9865
Co. E-mail: amedea@pivotpointpress.com
URL: http://www.pivotpointpress.com
Contact: Andra Medea, Publisher
Description: Description: Publishes nonfiction books on business, economics and family. **Founded:** 2005.

51471 ■ Productivity Press (University Park, Illinois)
2427 Bond St.
University Park, IL 60466-3101
Ph: (708)587-4152
Free: 888-319-5852
Fax: (708)534-7803
Co. E-mail: info@productivitypress.com
URL: http://www.productivitypress.com
Contact: Ralph Bernstein, Editor
E-mail: Ralph.bernstein@taylorandfrancis.com
Description: Description: Publishes materials on lean manufacturing and business improvement.

51472 ■ Sourcebooks, Inc.
1935 Brookdale Rd., Ste. 139
Naperville, IL 60563
Ph: (630)961-3900
Free: 800-432-7444

Fax: (630)961-2168
Co. E-mail: info@sourcebooks.com
URL: http://www.sourcebooks.com
Contact: Len Vlahos, President
E-mail: dominique@sourcebooks.com
Description: Description: Publishes on small business, childcare, parenting, self-help, women's issues, history, sports, gift, fiction, family, gifts, entertainment, health and business. Accepts unsolicited manuscripts; query first with a chapter outline and sample chapters. Reaches market through direct mail, trade sales, and wholesalers and distributors, including Baker and Taylor Books, Ingram Book Co., and Quality Books. **Founded:** 1987. **Publications:** *The Complete Scholarship Book*; *505 Weirdest Online Stores*; *The B'* *Student's Complete Scholarship Book*; *The Minority and Women's Complete Scholarship Book*; *The Graduate Student's Complete Scholarship Book*; *U.S. News Ultimate Guide to Medical Schools*; *301 Smart Answers to Tough Interview Questions*; *1000 Best Job Hunting Secrets*; *On Becoming a Doctor*; *First 60 Seconds*.

SMALL BUSINESS DEVELOPMENT CENTERS

51473 ■ Central Indiana Small Business Development Center
Ivy Tech Lawrence Campus
9301 E 59th St., Rm. 147
Indianapolis, IN 46216
Ph: (317)233-7232
Fax: (317)917-7101
Co. E-mail: centralindiana@isbdc.org
URL: http://isbdc.org/location/central-isbdc
Description: Represents and promotes the small business sector. Provides management assistance to current and prospective small business owners. Helps to improve management skills and expand the products and services of members.

51474 ■ East Central Indiana Small Business Development Center
PO Box 1912
Muncie, IN 47308
Ph: (765)282-9950
Free: 866-596-7232
Fax: (765)254-1450
Co. E-mail: eastcentral@isbdc.org
URL: http://isbdc.org/location/east-central-isbdc
Description: Represents and promotes the small business sector. Provides management assistance to current and prospective small business owners. Helps to improve management skills and expand the products and services of members.

51475 ■ Hoosier Heartland Small Business Development Center (HHSBDC)
Burton D. Morgan Center for Entrepreneurship
1201 W State St.
West Lafayette, IN 47907
Ph: (765)496-6491
Free: 866-961-7232
Fax: (765)496-9676
Co. E-mail: sdavis@isbdc.org
URL: http://www.hhsbdc.org
Contact: Susan B. Davis, Regional Director
Description: Represents and promotes the small business sector. Provides management assistance to current and prospective small business owners. Helps to improve management skills and expand the products and services of members.

51476 ■ Indiana Small Business Development Center - Lead Office (ISBDC)
1 N Capitol, Ste. 700
Indianapolis, IN 46204
Ph: (317)234-2082
Free: 888-472-3244
Fax: (317)232-4146
Co. E-mail: leadcenter@isbdc.org
URL: http://isbdc.org
Contact: Jacob Schpok, Director
Description: Provides entrepreneurs with the education, information and tools necessary to build successful businesses. **Founded:** 1985.

51477 ■ Indiana Small Business Development Center Network (ISBDC)
One N Capitol, Ste. 700
Indianapolis, IN 46204
Ph: (317)234-2082
Free: 888-472-3244
Fax: (317)232-4146
Co. E-mail: leadcenter@isbdc.org
URL: http://isbdc.org
Contact: Jacob Schpok, Director
Description: Strives to enhance the success rate of new business formation and contribute to the growth and prosperity of existing businesses in Wayne, Union, Franklin, Fayette, and Rush counties.

51478 ■ Northeast Indiana Small Business Development Center
2101 E Coliseum Blvd.
Fort Wayne, IN 46805
Ph: (260)481-0500
Fax: (260)481-0499
Co. E-mail: northeast@isbdc.org
URL: http://isbdc.org/location/northeast-isbdc
Description: Represents and promotes the small business sector. Provides management assistance to current and prospective small business owners. Helps to improve management skills and expand the products and services of members.

51479 ■ Northwest Indiana Small Business Development Center (NWISBDC)
9800 Connecticut Dr.
Crown Point, IN 46307
Ph: (219)644-3513
Fax: (219)644-3514
Co. E-mail: northwest@isbdc.org
URL: http://www.isbdc.org/location/northwest-isbdc
Contact: LeAnn McCrum, Regional Director
Description: Represents and promotes the small business sector. Provides management assistance to current and prospective small business owners. Helps to improve management skills and expand the products and services of members.

51480 ■ South Bend Small Business Development Center
Commerce Center Bldg.
401 E Colfax Ave., Ste. 120
South Bend, IN 46617
Ph: (574)282-4350
Fax: (574)236-1056
Co. E-mail: sbdcinfo@southbendbcg.com
URL: http://www.southbendbcg.com
Contact: Janet A. Fye, Director
Description: Represents and promotes the small business sector. Provides management assistance to current and prospective small business owners. Helps to improve management skills and expand the products and services of members.

51481 ■ Southeastern Indiana Small Business Development Center
3000 Technology Ave., Ste. N2225
New Albany, IN 47150
Ph: (812)952-9765

Fax: (812)206-8291
Co. E-mail: southeast@isbdc.org
URL: http://isbdc.org/location/southeast-isbdc
Description: Represents and promotes the small business sector. Provides management assistance to current and prospective small business owners. Helps to improve management skills and expand the products and services of members.

51482 ■ Southwestern Indiana Small Business Development Center
318 Main St., Ste. 401
Evansville, IN 47708-1498
Ph: (812)425-8147
Fax: (812)421-5883
Co. E-mail: jko@ccswin.com
URL: http://www.ccswin.com/busndev/swsbdc.asp
Description: Represents and promotes the small business sector. Provides management assistance to current and prospective small business owners. Helps to improve management skills and expand the products and services of members.

51483 ■ West Central Indiana Small Business Development Center
Indiana State University
Scott College of Business, Rm. 510
800 Sycamore St.
Terre Haute, IN 47809
Ph: (812)237-7676
Free: 800-227-7232
Fax: (812)237-7675
Co. E-mail: westcentral@isbdc.org
URL: http://isbdc.org
Contact: Heather Penney, Director
Description: Represents and promotes the small business sector. Provides management assistance to current and prospective small business owners. Helps to improve management skills and expand the products and services of members.

SMALL BUSINESS ASSISTANCE PROGRAMS

51484 ■ Indiana Department of Commerce - Energy Policy Division
1 N Capitol Ave., Ste. 700
Indianapolis, IN 46204-2288
Ph: (317)232-8940
Free: 800-382-4631
Fax: (317)232-8995
URL: http://www.indianacommerce.com
Description: Provides information on energy conservation. Gives free energy audits for small businesses. Provides some loan subsidies for energy conservation measures.

51485 ■ Indiana Department of Commerce - International Development
1 N Capitol Ave., Ste. 700
Indianapolis, IN 46204
Ph: (317)234-2083

Fax: (317)232-4146
URL: http://www.in.gov/iedc
Contact: Stephen Akard, Director
Description: Helps businesses interested in foreign trade to establish contacts and leads. Organizes trade missions.

51486 ■ Indiana Economic Development Corporation
1 N Capitol Ave., Ste. 700
Indianapolis, IN 46204-2288
Ph: (317)232-8800
Free: 800-463-8081
Fax: (317)232-4146
Co. E-mail: sakard@iedc.in.gov
URL: http://www.in.gov/iedc
Contact: Stephen Akard, Director
Description: Coordinates business services offered by the Department of Commerce and other agencies. Serves as a switchboard for access to those services, such as export promotion, defense procurement, minority business development, and regulatory assistance.

51487 ■ Indiana Institute of Technology - McMillen Productivity and Design Center
1600 E Washington Blvd.
Ft. Wayne, IN 46803
Ph: (260)422-5561
Free: 800-937-2448
Fax: (260)422-7696
URL: http://www.indianatech.edu
Description: Offers industrial-quality production-level hardware and software, and staff expertise. Provides consulting and seminars in computer-aided design.

51488 ■ Indiana State University - Small Business Development Center
800 Sycamore St., Rm. 510
Terre Haute, IN 47809
Ph: (812)237-7676
Free: 800-227-7232
Fax: (812)237-7675
Co. E-mail: westcentral@isbdc.org
URL: http://www.isbdc.org/home.aspx
Description: Provides consulting, seminars, training, and access to economic databases.

51489 ■ Indiana University - Indiana Business Research Center
100 S College Ave., Ste. 240
777 Indiana Ave., Ste. 210
Bloomington, IN 47404
Ph: (812)855-5507
Fax: (812)855-7763
Co. E-mail: ibrc@iupui.edu
URL: http://www.ibrc.indiana.edu
Contact: Jerry N. Conover, Director
Description: Collects and analyses business and economic data in the state. Information is accessible through the Indiana Information Retrieval System at libraries, universities, and public agencies. Puts out two bimonthly publications. Presents a Business Outlook Panel annually in several cities.

51490 ■ Indiana University - Indiana Molecular Biology Institute
915 E 3rd St.
Bloomington, IN 47405
Ph: (812)855-4183
Fax: (812)855-6082
Co. E-mail: freemanr@indiana.edu
URL: http://imbi.bio.indiana.edu
Contact: Rhea Freeman, Administrative Assistant
Description: Offers expertise and use of its facilities for industrial research in molecular and cellular biology.

51491 ■ Purdue University - Technical Assistance Program
Vistech 1, Ste. 205
1435 Win Hentschel Blvd., Ste. 205
West Lafayette, IN 47906-4154
Ph: (765)494-9189

Fax: (765)494-9187
Co. E-mail: mckinnis@purdue.edu
URL: http://www.tap.purdue.edu
Contact: David R. McKinnis, Ph.D., Director
Description: Provides technology transfers to businesses free of charge.

SCORE OFFICES

51492 ■ Greater Madison SCORE
Co. E-mail: madisonscore@onlinefusion.net

51493 ■ Greater Wabash Valley SCORE
301 Home Ave.
Terre Haute, IN 47803
Ph: (812)231-6763
Fax: (812)231-6777
Co. E-mail: scorechapter661@aol.com
URL: http://www.scorechapter661.org
Description: Promotes business and community development in the Terre Haute, IN area. Conducts business education seminars and workshops to those wanting to start a business.

51494 ■ Logansport SCORE
Co. E-mail: score@clss.net

51495 ■ Northwest Indiana SCORE
Co. E-mail: nwinscore@aol.com

51496 ■ SCORE Anderson
c/o Anderson Chamber of Commerce
2701 Enterprise Dr., Ste. 202
Anderson, IN 46013
Ph: (765)642-0264
Fax: (765)622-0211
Co. E-mail: postmaster@scoreanderson.org
URL: http://www.scoreanderson.org
Contact: Jim Alexander, Vice Chairperson
URL(s): anderson.score.org/chapters/anderson-score. **Description:** Provides counseling to persons wanting to go into business as well as those already in the business. Sponsors seminars and workshops.

51497 ■ SCORE Bloomington
216 W Allen St., Star Ctr.
Bloomington, IN 47403
Ph: (812)334-2392
Co. E-mail: score527@sbcglobal.net
URL: http://bloomington.score.org
Description: Serves a wide range of clients from the central Indiana area. Conducts business education seminars and workshops to those wanting to start a business.

51498 ■ SCORE Chapter 50
PNC Bank Bldg.
100 W Berry St., Ste. LL101
Fort Wayne, IN 46802
Ph: (260)422-2601
Fax: (260)422-2601
URL: http://fortwayne.score.org
Contact: Les Baggett, Chairperson
Description: Represents volunteer businessmen and women. Provides free small business management assistance to individuals in Northeast Indiana. **Founded:** 1976.

51499 ■ SCORE Dearborn County

51500 ■ SCORE Elkhart
Elkhart Chamber Plz.
418 S Main St.
Elkhart, IN 46516
Ph: (574)293-1531
Fax: (574)294-1859
Co. E-mail: score@elkhartscore.org
URL: http://www.elkhartscore.org
URL(s): elkhart.score.org/chapters/elkhart-score. **Description:** Provides professional guidance and information to America's small businesses. **Founded:** 1991.

51501 ■ *Score eNews*
325 N Main St.
Kokomo, IN 46901
Ph: (765)457-5301

Fax: (765)452-4564
Co. E-mail: kokomoscore@cs.com
URL: http://www.kokomoscore.org
Contact: Mr. Bob Straub, Chairman
Released: Monthly **Price:** free.

51502 ■ SCORE Evansville
c/o Bob Ubelhor, Chair
318 Main St., Ste. 223
Evansville, IN 47708-1417
Ph: (812)426-6144
Fax: (812)492-4301
Co. E-mail: scoreevv@aol.com
URL: http://www.scoreevansville.com
Contact: Bob Ubelhor, Chairperson
Description: Provides general business advice to existing small business.

51503 ■ *SCORE Expert Answers*
325 N Main St.
Kokomo, IN 46901
Ph: (765)457-5301
Fax: (765)452-4564
Co. E-mail: kokomoscore@cs.com
URL: http://www.kokomoscore.org
Contact: Mr. Bob Straub, Chairman
Released: Monthly **Price:** free.

51504 ■ SCORE Kokomo/Howard Counties
325 N Main St.
Kokomo, IN 46901
Ph: (765)457-5301
Fax: (765)452-4564
Co. E-mail: kokomoscore@cs.com
URL: http://www.kokomoscore.org
Contact: Mr. Bob Straub, Chairman
Description: Represents business professionals and counselors. Seeks to provide assistant and counsel to existing and newly opened small businesses. **Founded:** 1984. **Publications:** *Score eNews* (Monthly); *SCORE Expert Answers* (Monthly). **Telecommunication Services:** counselors543@kokomoscore.org.

51505 ■ SCORE Marion/Grant Co
217 S Adams St.
Marion, IN 46952
Ph: (765)664-5107
Co. E-mail: score550@att.net
URL: http://mariongrantcounty.score.org/chapters/mariongrant-co-score
Description: Provides free business counseling and management training programs for small business owners/managers, and for those who plan to start a new business.

51506 ■ SCORE South Bend
401 E Colfax Ave.
Commerce Ctr., Ste. 120
South Bend, IN 46601
Ph: (574)282-4350
Fax: (574)236-1056
Co. E-mail: chair@southbend-score.org
URL: http://www.southbend-score.org
Contact: Gerald Marchetti, Chairperson
Description: Provides counseling to persons wanting to go into business as well as those already in the business. Sponsors seminars and workshops.

51507 ■ SCORE South Central Indiana
719 E 8th St.
New Albany, IN 47150-3215
Ph: (812)944-9178
Co. E-mail: 522score@netpointe.com
URL: http://www.score.socentind.com/content/anm-viewer.asp?a=1&z=2
Contact: Larry W. Burke, Chairman
Description: Provides counseling to persons wanting to go into business as well as those already in the business. Sponsors seminars and workshops.

51508 ■ SCORE South East Indiana
500 Franklin St.
Columbus, IN 47201
Ph: (812)379-4457
Fax: (812)378-7308
Co. E-mail: score419@tls.net
URL: http://southeastindiana.score.org/chapters/south-east-indiana-score

51509 ■ Service Corps of Retired Executives-Chapter 6
8500 Keystone Crossing, Ste. 401
Indianapolis, IN 46240
Ph: (317)226-7264
Co. E-mail: score@indyscore.org
URL: http://www.indyscore.org
Contact: Bob Miramonti, Chairman
Description: Consults those who want to start a new business or grow an existing business.

BETTER BUSINESS BUREAUS

51510 ■ Better Business Bureau of Central Indiana—Better Business Bureau
22 E Washington St., Ste. 200
Indianapolis, IN 46204
Ph: (317)488-2222
Free: 866-463-9222
Fax: (317)488-2224
Co. E-mail: info@indybbb.org
URL: http://indy.bbb.org
Contact: Linda R. Carmody, President
Description: Seeks to promote and foster the highest ethical relationship between businesses and the public through voluntary self-regulation, consumer and business education, and service excellence. Provides information to help consumers and businesses make informed purchasing decisions and avoid costly scams and frauds; settles consumer complaints through arbitration and other means. **Founded:** 1916.

51511 ■ Better Business Bureau of Northern Indiana
4011 Parnell Ave.
Fort Wayne, IN 46805
Ph: (260)423-4433
Free: 800-552-4631
Fax: (260)423-3301
URL: http://fortwayne.bbb.org
Contact: Michael D. Coil, President
Description: Strives to establish a relationship between businesses and the public through self-regulation, service, and consumer and business education.

51512 ■ Central Indiana Better Business Bureau
151 N Delaware St., Ste. 2020
Indianapolis, IN 46204-2506
Ph: (317)488-2222
Free: 866-463-9222
Fax: (317)488-2224
Co. E-mail: info@indybbb.org
URL: http://indy.bbb.org
Contact: Bill Thomas, President
Description: Seeks to promote and foster the highest ethical relationship between businesses and the public through voluntary self-regulation, consumer and business education, and service excellence. Provides information to help consumers and businesses make informed purchasing decisions and avoid costly scams and frauds; settles consumer complaints through arbitration and other means. **Founded:** 1916.

51513 ■ Tri-State Better Business Bureau
3101 N Green River Rd., Ste. 410
Evansville, IN 47715
Ph: (812)473-0202
Free: 800-359-0979
Fax: (812)473-3080
Co. E-mail: info@evansville.bbb.org
URL: http://evansville.bbb.org
Contact: Cathy Eichele, President
Description: Seeks to promote and foster the highest ethical relationship between businesses and the public through voluntary self-regulation, consumer and business education, and service excellence. Provides information to help consumers and businesses make informed purchasing decisions and avoid costly scams and frauds; settles consumer complaints through arbitration and other means.

CHAMBERS OF COMMERCE

51514 ■ Alexandria - Monroe Chamber of Commerce (ACC)
125 N Wayne St.
Alexandria, IN 46001
Ph: (765)724-3144
Fax: (765)683-3504
Co. E-mail: info@alexandriachamber.com
URL: http://alexandriachamber.com
Contact: John Dockrey, Executive Director
Description: Promotes business and community development in Alexandria, IN. Conducts business development and management training courses. **Founded:** 1960.

51515 ■ Angola Area Chamber of Commerce (AACC)
211 E Maumee St., Ste. B
Angola, IN 46703
Ph: (260)665-3512
Fax: (260)665-7418
Co. E-mail: info@angolachamber.org
URL: http://www.angolachamber.org
Contact: Jennifer Rumsey, President
Description: Promotes business and community development in Angola, IN. Maintains industrial committee. **Publications:** *Business to Business* (Monthly); *Industrial Directory* (Periodic).

51516 ■ *Annual Business Directory*
125 N Broadway
Greensburg, IN 47240
Ph: (812)663-2832
Fax: (812)663-4275
Co. E-mail: info@greensburgchamber.com
URL: http://www.greensburgchamber.com
Contact: Jeff Emsweller, Executive Director
Released: Annual

51517 ■ Auburn Chamber of Commerce (ACC)
208 S Jackson St.
Auburn, IN 46706-0168
Ph: (260)925-2100
Fax: (260)925-2199
Co. E-mail: kelly@chamberinauburn.com
URL: http://www.chamberinauburn.com
Contact: Kelly Knox, Executive Director
Description: Promotes business and community development in Auburn, IN. Supports art competitions and annual Auburn-Cord-Duesenberg Festival. Sponsors Auburn Sidewalk Sale Days and Dekalb Free Fall Fair. **Scope:** business, law, training. **Founded:** 1903. **Subscriptions:** 25 articles books periodicals video recordings. **Awards:** Business of the Year (Annual); Citizen of the Year (Annual); College Scholarships; Member of the Month (Monthly); Member of the Year (Annual).

51518 ■ Batesville Area Chamber of Commerce
132 S Main St.
Batesville, IN 47006
Ph: (812)934-3101
Fax: (812)932-0202
Co. E-mail: lwoodward@nalu.net
URL: http://www.batesvillein.com/
Contact: Melissa Tucker, Executive Director
Description: Provides its members with networking, marketing and advertising opportunities, and business counseling and referral services. **Publications:** *Chamber Chatter* (Monthly). **Telecommunication Services:** chamber@batesvillein.com.

51519 ■ *The Beacon*
200 E Michigan Blvd.
Michigan City, IN 46360-3270
Ph: (219)874-6221
Fax: (219)873-1204
Co. E-mail: info@mcachamber.com
URL: http://www.michigancitychamber.com
Contact: Ann Dahm, President
Released: Weekly

51520 ■ Bedford Area Chamber of Commerce
1116 16th St.
Bedford, IN 47421

Ph: (812)275-4493
Fax: (812)279-5889
Co. E-mail: bedford@bedfordchamber.com
URL: http://www.bedfordchamber.com
Description: Promotes business and community development in the Bedford, IN area. **Founded:** 1825. **Publications:** *Chamber Advantage* (Monthly).

51521 ■ Berne Chamber of Commerce (BCC)
205 E Main St.
Berne, IN 46711
Ph: (260)589-8080
Co. E-mail: chamber@bernein.com
URL: http://www.bernein.com
Contact: Connie Potter, Executive Director
Description: Represents industries, professional service firms, and retailers interested in promoting business and community development in Berne, IN. Sponsors Swiss Day Festival. Conducts tours and provides tourist information for sites throughout the U.S. and Switzerland. **Founded:** 1914. **Publications:** *Briefs* (Monthly); *Swiss Days*. **Awards:** Business of the Year (Annual); Citizen of the Year (Annual); Lifetime Achievement (Annual).

51522 ■ *BizVoice*
115 W Washington St., Ste. 850 S
Indianapolis, IN 46204-3420
Ph: (317)264-3110
Free: 800-804-6854
Fax: (317)264-6855
Co. E-mail: kbrinegar@indianachamber.com
URL: http://www.indianachamber.com
Contact: Kevin Brinegar, President
E-mail: kbrinegar@indianachamber.com
Released: Bimonthly

51523 ■ *Book for Business*
c/o The Commerce Center
401 E Colfax Ave., Ste. 310
South Bend, IN 46617
Ph: (574)234-0051
Fax: (574)289-0358
Co. E-mail: info@sjchamber.org
URL: http://www.sjchamber.org
Contact: Paul J. Cafiero, Chairman
Released: Annual

51524 ■ Boone County Chamber of Commerce (BCCC)
221 N Lebanon St.
Lebanon, IN 46052
Ph: (765)482-1320
Fax: (765)482-3114
Co. E-mail: info@boonechamber.org
URL: http://www.boonechamber.org
Contact: Ed Burgin, President
Description: Promotes business and community development in Boone County, IN. **Founded:** 1919. **Publications:** *C of C News* (Bimonthly).

51525 ■ *Briefs*
205 E Main St.
Berne, IN 46711
Ph: (260)589-8080
Co. E-mail: chamber@bernein.com
URL: http://www.bernein.com
Contact: Connie Potter, Executive Director
Released: Monthly **Price:** free for members.

51526 ■ Brown County Chamber of Commerce
PO Box 164
Nashville, IN 47448-0164
Ph: (812)988-6647
Co. E-mail: commerce@browncounty.org
URL: http://www.browncounty.org
Description: Promotes business and community development in Brown County, IL.

51527 ■ Brownsburg Chamber of Commerce (BCoC)
PO Box 82
Brownsburg, IN 46112-0082
Ph: (317)852-7885

Fax: (317)852-8688
Co. E-mail: chamber@brownsburg.com
URL: http://www.brownsburg.com
Contact: Walter Duncan, Executive Director
Description: Promotes business and community development in the Brownsburg, IN area. Sponsors annual Olde Fashioned Fall Festival and annual golf tournament. **Founded:** 1983.

51528 ■ *Business Bulletin*
37 E Main St., Ste. 300
Carmel, IN 46032
Ph: (317)846-1049
Fax: (317)844-6843
Co. E-mail: chamberinfo@carmelchamber.com
URL: http://www.carmelchamber.com
Contact: Mo Merhoff, President
Released: Monthly

51529 ■ *Business to Business*
211 E Maumee St., Ste. B
Angola, IN 46703
Ph: (260)665-3512
Fax: (260)665-7418
Co. E-mail: info@angolachamber.org
URL: http://www.angolachamber.org
Contact: Jennifer Rumsey, President
Released: Monthly **Price:** free.

51530 ■ *Business Directory*
1001 Lillian St.
Hobart, IN 46342
Ph: (219)942-5774
Fax: (219)942-4928
Co. E-mail: info@hobartchamber.com
URL: http://www.hobartchamber.com/
Contact: Mike Adams, Executive Director

51531 ■ *Business Directory and Guide to Buying*
PO Box 204
Griffith, IN 46319
Ph: (219)838-2661
Fax: (219)838-2401
Co. E-mail: griffithchamber1@hotmail.com
URL: http://griffithchamberofcommerce.com
Contact: Kathleen Reed, President
Released: Periodic

51532 ■ *The Business Edge*
2701 Enterprise Dr., Ste. 109
Anderson, IN 46013
Ph: (765)642-0264
Fax: (765)642-0266
Co. E-mail: chamber.rita@ameritech.net
URL: http://www.andersoninchamber.com
Contact: Kyle Morey, President
Released: Monthly

51533 ■ *Business Life*
119 S Main St.
Spencer, IN 47460
Ph: (812)829-3245
Fax: (812)829-0936
Co. E-mail: info@owencountyindiana.org
URL: http://www.owencountyindiana.org
Contact: Denise Shaw, Executive Director
Released: Quarterly

51534 ■ *Business Network*
PO Box 1302
Bloomington, IN 47402
Ph: (812)336-6381
Fax: (812)336-0651
Co. E-mail: info@chamberbloomington.org
URL: http://www.chamberbloomington.org/cwt/external/wcpages/index.aspx
Contact: Christy Gillenwater, President
Released: Monthly

51535 ■ *Business Resource Guide*
418 S Main St.
Elkhart, IN 46515-0428
Ph: (574)293-1531

Fax: (574)294-1859
Co. E-mail: info@elkhart.org
URL: http://www.elkhart.org
Contact: Philip E. Penn, President
Price: free for members (first copy); $25, for members; $50, for nonmembers.

51536 ■ *Business Today*
803 Washington St.
La Porte, IN 46352-0486
Ph: (219)362-3178
Fax: (219)324-7349
Co. E-mail: info@lpchamber.com
URL: http://www.lpchamber.com
Contact: Michael B. Seitz, President
Released: Quarterly

51537 ■ *Buyers Guide*
210 S Wabash St.
Wabash, IN 46992
Ph: (260)563-1168
Fax: (260)563-6920
Co. E-mail: info@wabashchamber.org
URL: http://www.wabashchamber.org
Contact: Ms. Kimberly A. Pinkerton, President
Released: Annual

51538 ■ *C of C News*
221 N Lebanon St.
Lebanon, IN 46052
Ph: (765)482-1320
Fax: (765)482-3114
Co. E-mail: info@boonechamber.org
URL: http://www.boonechamber.org
Contact: Ed Burgin, President
Released: Bimonthly

51539 ■ *Carmel Clay Chamber of Commerce*
37 E Main St., Ste. 300
Carmel, IN 46032
Ph: (317)846-1049
Fax: (317)844-6843
Co. E-mail: chamberinfo@carmelchamber.com
URL: http://www.carmelchamber.com
Contact: Mo Merhoff, President
Description: Enhances members' success, fosters economic growth and contributes to community's quality of life. Sponsors monthly luncheons, networking breakfasts and business after hours events, Taste of the Chamber, Autumn Faire and Golf Classic. **Founded:** 1970. **Publications:** *Business Bulletin* (Monthly); *Community Directory* (Biennial); *Map of Carmel-Clay*.

51540 ■ *Catalyst*
Chase Tower
111 Monument Cir., Ste. 1950
Indianapolis, IN 46204
Ph: (317)464-2200
Fax: (317)464-2217
Co. E-mail: memberservices@indylink.com
URL: http://www.indychamber.com
Contact: Scott W. Miller, President
Released: Quarterly

51541 ■ *Chamber Advantage*
1116 16th St.
Bedford, IN 47421
Ph: (812)275-4493
Fax: (812)279-5889
Co. E-mail: bedford@bedfordchamber.com
URL: http://www.bedfordchamber.com
Released: Monthly

51542 ■ *Chamber Business*
601 Main St., Ste. A
Tell City, IN 47586-0082
Ph: (812)547-2385
Fax: (812)547-8378
Co. E-mail: info@perrycountychamber.com
URL: http://www.perrycountychamber.com
Contact: Cheri Cronin, Administrative Assistant
Released: Monthly

51543 ■ *Chamber Charger*
125 E Monroe St.
Decatur, IN 46733-1732

Ph: (260)724-2604
Co. E-mail: wkuntzman@decaturchamber.org
URL: http://www.decaturchamber.org
Contact: Wes Kuntzman, Executive Director
Released: Monthly

51544 ■ *Chamber Chatter*
132 S Main St.
Batesville, IN 47006
Ph: (812)934-3101
Fax: (812)932-0202
Co. E-mail: lwoodward@nalu.net
URL: http://www.batesvillein.com/
Contact: Melissa Tucker, Executive Director
Released: Monthly

51545 ■ *Chamber Check*
105 N Market St., Ste. A
Rockville, IN 47872
Ph: (765)569-5565
Co. E-mail: info@parkecountychamber.com
URL: http://www.parkecountychamber.com
Contact: Alan Ader, Executive Director
Released: Bimonthly

51546 ■ *Chamber Chimes*
16 S Jackson St.
Greencastle, IN 46135
Ph: (765)653-4517
Fax: (765)848-1015
Co. E-mail: gchamber@gogreencastle.com
URL: http://www.gogreencastle.com
Contact: Tammy Amor, Executive Director
Released: Monthly

51547 ■ *Chamber Commentary*
100 S Main St., Ste. 108
New Castle, IN 47362
Ph: (765)529-5210
Fax: (765)521-7404
Co. E-mail: info@nchcchamber.com
URL: http://www.nchcchamber.com
Contact: Bill Kindig, President
Released: Monthly **Price:** free for members.

51548 ■ *Chamber of Commerce for Anderson and Madison County*
2701 Enterprise Dr., Ste. 109
Anderson, IN 46013
Ph: (765)642-0264
Fax: (765)642-0266
Co. E-mail: chamber.rita@ameritech.net
URL: http://www.andersoninchamber.com
Contact: Kyle Morey, President
Description: Represents retail, commercial, manufacturing, and professional firms promoting community and economic development in the Anderson, IN area. **Founded:** 1914. **Publications:** *The Business Edge* (Monthly).

51549 ■ *Chamber of Commerce Newsletter*
PO Box 208
Linton, IN 47441
Ph: (812)847-4846
Fax: (812)847-0246
Co. E-mail: chamber@joink.com
URL: http://www.lintonchamber.org
Contact: Lynette Shelton, Executive Director
Released: Monthly

51550 ■ *Chamber of Commerce of St. Joseph County*
c/o The Commerce Center
401 E Colfax Ave., Ste. 310
South Bend, IN 46617
Ph: (574)234-0051
Fax: (574)289-0358
Co. E-mail: info@sjchamber.org
URL: http://www.sjchamber.org
Contact: Paul J. Cafiero, Chairman
Description: Seeks to serve the interests of member businesses through progressive leadership, advocacy and services. **Founded:** 1909. **Publications:** *Book for Business* (Annual); *Chamber@Work* (Monthly).

51551 ■ *Chamber Connection*
500 Franklin St.
Columbus, IN 47201-6214
Ph: (812)379-4457

Fax: (812)378-7308
Co. E-mail: info@columbusareachamber.com
URL: http://www.columbusareachamber.com
Contact: Jack Hess, President
Released: Monthly

51552 ■ *Chamber Connection*
122 S Main St.
Kendallville, IN 46755-1716
Ph: (260)347-1554
Free: 877-347-1554
Fax: (260)347-1575
Co. E-mail: kchamber@locl.net
URL: http://www.kendallvillechamber.com
Contact: Mike Walton, Executive Director
Released: Bimonthly

51553 ■ *The Chamber Enterprise*
601 E Conner St.
Noblesville, IN 46060
Ph: (317)773-0086
Fax: (317)773-1966
Co. E-mail: info@noblesvillechamber.com
URL: http://www.noblesvillechamber.com
Contact: Sharon McMahon, President
Released: Monthly

51554 ■ *Chamber Exchange*
PO Box 404
Scottsburg, IN 47170
Ph: (812)752-4080
Fax: (812)752-4307
Co. E-mail: scottcom@c3bb.com
URL: http://www.scottchamber.org/chamber
Contact: Keith Colbert, Executive Director
Released: Monthly

51555 ■ *Chamber Express*
320 Walnut St.
Lawrenceburg, IN 47025
Ph: (812)537-0814
Free: 800-322-8198
Fax: (812)537-0845
URL: http://www.dearborncountychamber.org
Contact: Michael Rozow, Jr., President
Released: Monthly

51556 ■ *The Chamber Impact*
201 N Line St.
Columbia City, IN 46725-0166
Ph: (260)248-8131
Fax: (260)248-8162
Co. E-mail: chamber@columbiacity.org
URL: http://www.columbiacity.org
Contact: Mike DeFreeuw, Chairman
Released: Monthly

51557 ■ *Chamber Insight*
301 E Main St.
Madison, IN 47250
Ph: (812)265-3135
Fax: (812)265-9784
Co. E-mail: info@madisonchamber.org
URL: http://www.madisonchamber.org
Contact: Corey Murphy, Executive Director
Released: Monthly

51558 ■ *Chamber Made*
315 N Main St.
Rushville, IN 46173-1635
Ph: (765)932-2880
Fax: (765)932-4191
Co. E-mail: pamleisure@rushcounty.com
URL: http://www.rushcounty.com/chamber
Contact: Pamela C. Leisure-Svaranowic, Executive
  Director
Released: Quarterly

51559 ■ *The Chamber News*
8536 Kennedy Ave.
Highland, IN 46322
Ph: (219)923-3666
Fax: (219)923-3704
Co. E-mail: info@highlandchamber.com
URL: http://www.highlandchamber.com
Contact: Mary Luptak, Executive Director
Released: Monthly

51560 ■ *Chamber News*
PO Box 340
North Vernon, IN 47265
Ph: (812)346-2339
Fax: (812)346-3805
Co. E-mail: mshepherd@jenningscountychamber.
  com
URL: http://www.jenningscountychamber.com
Contact: Marie Shepherd, Executive Director
Released: Monthly **Price:** free for members.

51561 ■ *Chamber News*
901 S Detroit St., Ste. A
LaGrange, IN 46761
Ph: (260)463-2443
Free: 877-735-0340
Fax: (260)463-2683
Co. E-mail: info@lagrangechamber.org
URL: http://www.lagrangechamber.org
Contact: Beth Sherman, Executive Director
Released: Monthly

51562 ■ *Chamber News*
100 W Waterford St.
Wakarusa, IN 46573
Ph: (574)862-4344
Fax: (574)862-2245
Co. E-mail: chamber@wakarusachamber.com
URL: http://www.wakarusachamber.com
Contact: Deb Shively, Executive Secretary
Released: Monthly

51563 ■ *Chamber News Connection*
13 E Main St.
Peru, IN 46970
Ph: (765)472-1923
Fax: (765)472-7099
Co. E-mail: info@miamicochamber.com
URL: http://www.miamicochamber.com
Contact: Sandy Chittum, President
Released: Quarterly

51564 ■ *Chamber Newsletter*
309 N Green St.
Crawfordsville, IN 47933
Ph: (765)362-6800
Fax: (765)362-6900
URL: http://www.crawfordsvillechamber.com
Contact: S. Dave Long, Executive Vice President
Released: Monthly

51565 ■ *Chamber Newsletter*
1040 Ridge Rd.
Munster, IN 46321
Ph: (219)836-5549
Fax: (219)836-5551
Co. E-mail: info@chambermunster.org
URL: http://www.chambermunster.org
Contact: Wendy Mis, Executive Director
Released: Monthly

51566 ■ *Chamber NewsLink*
33 S 7th St., Ste. 2
Richmond, IN 47374
Ph: (765)962-1511
Fax: (765)966-0882
Co. E-mail: info@rwchamber.org
URL: http://www.rwchamber.org
Contact: Dennis Andrews, President
Released: Monthly

51567 ■ *Chamber Notes*
109 N Market St.
North Manchester, IN 46962-1518
Ph: (260)982-7644
Fax: (260)982-8718
Co. E-mail: nmcc@kconline.com
URL: http://www.northmanchesterchamber.com
Contact: Tim McLaughlin, Executive Director
Released: Monthly

51568 ■ *Chamber Page in the Versailles
Republican*
102 N Main St.
Versailles, IN 47042
Ph: (812)689-6654

Fax: (812)689-3934
Co. E-mail: ripleycc@ripleycountychamber.org
URL: http://ripleycountychamber.org
Contact: Amy Thomas, Director
Released: Quarterly; first Thursday of each quarter.

51569 ■ *Chamber Scene*
305 Warren St.
Huntington, IN 46750-2854
Ph: (260)356-5300
Fax: (260)356-5434
Co. E-mail: info@huntington-chamber.com
URL: http://www.huntington-chamber.com
Contact: Nicole Johnson, Chairperson
Released: Monthly

51570 ■ *Chamber@Work*
c/o The Commerce Center
401 E Colfax Ave., Ste. 310
South Bend, IN 46617
Ph: (574)234-0051
Fax: (574)289-0358
Co. E-mail: info@sjchamber.org
URL: http://www.sjchamber.org
Contact: Paul J. Cafiero, Chairman
Released: Monthly

**51571 ■ Chesterton and Duneland Chamber
of Commerce (DCC)**
220 Broadway
Chesterton, IN 46304
Ph: (219)926-5513
Fax: (219)926-7593
Co. E-mail: info@chestertonchamber.org
URL: http://www.chestertonchamber.org
Contact: Heather Ennnis, Executive Director
Description: Serves its members and foster innovative businesses, educational, cultural and government environment. Represents vibrant business
organization of small and large businesses, professionals, and interested individuals, whose focus is to
market the Duneland area, encourage new growth
and assist existing and expanding businesses. Joining the Chamber is an economical and effective way
to make new contacts and market your business.
Founded: 1955. **Publications:** *Duneland Today*
(Monthly). **Awards:** Duneland Distinguished Woman
Award (Annual); Senior Citizen of the Year (Annual).

51572 ■ *Civic and Organization Guide*
305 Warren St.
Huntington, IN 46750-2854
Ph: (260)356-5300
Fax: (260)356-5434
Co. E-mail: info@huntington-chamber.com
URL: http://www.huntington-chamber.com
Contact: Nicole Johnson, Chairperson
Released: Annual

**51573 ■ Clinton County Chamber of
Commerce (CCCC)**
259 E Walnut St.
Frankfort, IN 46041
Ph: (765)654-5507
Co. E-mail: chamber@ccinchamber.org
URL: http://ccinchamber.org
Contact: Gina L. Sheets, Chief Executive Officer
Description: Promotes business and community
development in Clinton County, IN. **Founded:** 1913.

**51574 ■ Cloverdale Area Chamber of
Commerce (CACC)**
PO Box 83
Cloverdale, IN 46120
Ph: (765)795-3993
Co. E-mail: chamber@ccrtc.com
URL: http://www.cloverdale.in.us/chamber/index.htm
Description: Promotes business and community
development in Cloverdale, IN area. **Founded:** 1985.

**51575 ■ Columbia City Area Chamber of
Commerce (CCACC)**
201 N Line St.
Columbia City, IN 46725-0166
Ph: (260)248-8131

Fax: (260)248-8162
Co. E-mail: chamber@columbiacity.org
URL: http://www.columbiacity.org
Contact: Mike DeFreeuw, Chairman
Description: Promotes business and community development in the Columbia City, IN area. **Founded:** 1952. **Publications:** *The Chamber Impact* (Monthly). **Telecommunication Services:** office@columbiacity. org.

51576 ■ Columbus Area Chamber of Commerce (Columbus, Indiana) (CACC)
500 Franklin St.
Columbus, IN 47201-6214
Ph: (812)379-4457
Fax: (812)378-7308
Co. E-mail: info@columbusareachamber.com
URL: http://www.columbusareachamber.com
Contact: Jack Hess, President
Description: Promotes business and community development in the Columbus, IN area. **Publications:** *Chamber Connection* (Monthly). **Awards:** Achievement of Excellence Award (Annual); Athena Award (Annual); Community Service Award (Annual); Growth and Expansion Award (Annual); Edna V. Folger Outstanding Teacher Award (Annual).

51577 ■ Community Directory
37 E Main St., Ste. 300
Carmel, IN 46032
Ph: (317)846-1049
Fax: (317)844-6843
Co. E-mail: chamberinfo@carmelchamber.com
URL: http://www.carmelchamber.com
Contact: Mo Merhoff, President
Released: Biennial

51578 ■ Community Directory and Buyers Guide
5246 Hohman Ave., Ste. 100
Hammond, IN 46320
Ph: (219)931-1000
Fax: (219)937-8778
Co. E-mail: info@lakeshorechamber.com
URL: http://www.lakeshorechamber.com
Contact: Dave Ryan, Executive Director
Released: Biennial

51579 ■ Community Information Directory
309 N Green St.
Crawfordsville, IN 47933
Ph: (765)362-6800
Fax: (765)362-6900
URL: http://www.crawfordsvillechamber.com
Contact: S. Dave Long, Executive Vice President
Released: Biennial

51580 ■ Community Information Directory
301 E Main St.
Madison, IN 47250
Ph: (812)265-3135
Fax: (812)265-9784
Co. E-mail: info@madisonchamber.org
URL: http://www.madisonchamber.org
Contact: Corey Murphy, Executive Director
Released: Annual

51581 ■ Community Information Directory
601 E Conner St.
Noblesville, IN 46060
Ph: (317)773-0086
Fax: (317)773-1966
Co. E-mail: info@noblesvillechamber.com
URL: http://www.noblesvillechamber.com
Contact: Sharon McMahon, President
Released: Biennial

51582 ■ Community Profile
PO Box 842
Muncie, IN 47308-0842
Ph: (765)288-6681
Free: 800-336-1373
Fax: (765)751-9151
Co. E-mail: info@muncie.com
URL: http://www.muncie.com
Contact: Jay Julian, President
Released: Biennial

51583 ■ Community Service Directory
125 E Monroe St.
Decatur, IN 46733-1732
Ph: (260)724-2604
Co. E-mail: wkuntzman@decaturchamber.org
URL: http://www.decaturchamber.org
Contact: Wes Kuntzman, Executive Director
Released: Periodic

51584 ■ Connection
1 Courthouse Plz.
Greenfield, IN 46140
Ph: (317)477-4188
Fax: (317)477-4189
Co. E-mail: info@greenfieldcc.org
URL: http://www.greenfieldcc.org
Contact: Retta Livengood, President
Released: Monthly

51585 ■ Crawfordsville - Montgomery County Chamber of Commerce (CMCCC)
309 N Green St.
Crawfordsville, IN 47933
Ph: (765)362-6800
Fax: (765)362-6900
URL: http://www.crawfordsvillechamber.com
Contact: S. Dave Long, Executive Vice President
Description: Businesses promoting economic development, tourism, and community and political involvement in Montgomery County, IN. **Founded:** 1918. **Publications:** *Chamber Newsletter* (Monthly); *Community Information Directory* (Biennial).

51586 ■ Culver Chamber of Commerce
PO Box 129
Culver, IN 46511-0129
Ph: (574)842-5253
Co. E-mail: culveradm@millersmerrymanor.com
URL: http://www.culverchamber.com
Contact: Greg Fassett, President
Description: Promotes business and community development in the Culver, IN area. **Founded:** 1925. **Publications:** *Destination Culver* (Semiannual).

51587 ■ Dearborn County Chamber of Commerce (DCC)
320 Walnut St.
Lawrenceburg, IN 47025
Ph: (812)537-0814
Free: 800-322-8198
Fax: (812)537-0845
URL: http://www.dearborncountychamber.org
Contact: Michael Rozow, Jr., President
Description: Promotes business and community development in Dearborn County, IN. Holds monthly board meeting. **Founded:** 1987. **Publications:** *Chamber Express* (Monthly).

51588 ■ Decatur Chamber of Commerce (DCC)
125 E Monroe St.
Decatur, IN 46733-1732
Ph: (260)724-2604
Co. E-mail: wkuntzman@decaturchamber.org
URL: http://www.decaturchamber.org
Contact: Wes Kuntzman, Executive Director
Description: Promotes business, economic, workforce development, and community in Decatur, IN. Sponsors Callithumpian parade, community smorgasbord, Riverside Festival, city-wide sidewalk sale, golf outing, and Holiday Open House. **Founded:** 1903. **Publications:** *Chamber Charger* (Monthly); *Community Service Directory* (Periodic); *Industrial Directory* (Periodic). **Educational Activities:** Industrial Appreciation Dinner (Annual).

51589 ■ Demotte Chamber of Commerce (DCC)
PO Box 721
Demotte, IN 46310
Ph: (219)987-3831
Fax: (219)987-3836
Co. E-mail: demottechamber@netnitco.net
URL: http://www.townofdemotte.com
Contact: Bob Jonkman, President
Description: Promotes business and community development in DeMotte, IN. **Founded:** 1981.

51590 ■ Depot Signal
370 E Jefferson St.
Franklin, IN 46131
Ph: (317)736-6334
Fax: (317)736-9553
Co. E-mail: franklincoc@franklincoc.org
URL: http://www.franklincoc.org/cwt/external/wcpages/index.aspx
Contact: Tricia E. Bechman, Executive Director
Released: Monthly

51591 ■ Destination Culver
PO Box 129
Culver, IN 46511-0129
Ph: (574)842-5253
Co. E-mail: culveradm@millersmerrymanor.com
URL: http://www.culverchamber.com
Contact: Greg Fassett, President
Released: Semiannual

51592 ■ Directions
PO Box 506
Greenwood, IN 46142
Ph: (317)888-4856
Fax: (317)865-2609
Co. E-mail: info@greenwood-chamber.com
URL: http://www.greenwood-chamber.com
Contact: Christian Maslowski, Executive Director
Released: Monthly **Price:** free for members.

51593 ■ Directory/Business Profile Booklet
310 N Elm St.
Corydon, IN 47112
Ph: (812)738-2137
Fax: (812)738-6438
Co. E-mail: dvoelker@harrisonchamber.org
URL: http://www.harrisonchamber.org
Contact: Darrell R. Voelker, Director, Economics
Released: Annual **Price:** free.

51594 ■ Directory of Clubs and Organizations
13 E Main St.
Peru, IN 46970
Ph: (765)472-1923
Fax: (765)472-7099
Co. E-mail: info@miamicochamber.com
URL: http://www.miamicochamber.com
Contact: Sandy Chittum, President
Price: $5.

51595 ■ Directory of Community
PO Box 534
Westfield, IN 46074
Ph: (317)804-3030
Fax: (317)804-3035
Co. E-mail: info@westfield-chamber.org
URL: http://www.westfield-chamber.org
Contact: Julie Sole, Executive Director
Released: Biennial

51596 ■ Duneland Today
220 Broadway
Chesterton, IN 46304
Ph: (219)926-5513
Fax: (219)926-7593
Co. E-mail: info@chestertonchamber.org
URL: http://www.chestertonchamber.org
Contact: Heather Ennnis, Executive Director
Released: Monthly **Price:** included in membership dues.

51597 ■ Elkhart Area Recreational Vehicle Directory
418 S Main St.
Elkhart, IN 46515-0428
Ph: (574)293-1531
Fax: (574)294-1859
Co. E-mail: info@elkhart.org
URL: http://www.elkhart.org
Contact: Philip E. Penn, President
Price: $20, for members; $40, for nonmembers.

51598 ■ Elkhart County Manufacturers Directory
418 S Main St.
Elkhart, IN 46515-0428
Ph: (574)293-1531

Fax: (574)294-1859
Co. E-mail: info@elkhart.org
URL: http://www.elkhart.org
Contact: Philip E. Penn, President
Price: $30, for members; $60, for nonmembers.

51599 ■ *Embrace the Pace*
302 W Market St.
Nappanee, IN 46550
Ph: (574)773-7812
Fax: (574)773-4961
Co. E-mail: inforequest@nappaneechamber.com
URL: http://www.nappaneechamber.com
Contact: Jeff Kitson, Executive Director
Released: Bimonthly

51600 ■ *Emphasis*
826 Ewing St.
Fort Wayne, IN 46802
Ph: (260)424-1435
Fax: (260)426-7232
Co. E-mail: mcallicoat@fwchamber.org
URL: http://www.fwchamber.org
Contact: Mike Landram, President
Released: Periodic

51601 ■ *Executive Quickline*
115 W Washington St., Ste. 850 S
Indianapolis, IN 46204-3420
Ph: (317)264-3110
Free: 800-804-6854
Fax: (317)264-6855
Co. E-mail: kbrinegar@indianachamber.com
URL: http://www.indianachamber.com
Contact: Kevin Brinegar, President
E-mail: kbrinegar@indianachamber.com
Released: Monthly

51602 ■ Ferdinand Chamber of Commerce
PO Box 7
Ferdinand, IN 47532-0101
Ph: (812)367-2280
Co. E-mail: msteczyk@ferdinandindiana.org
URL: http://www.ferdinandinchamber.org
Contact: Marc Steczyk, Executive Director
Description: Promotes business and community development in the Ferdinand, IN area.

51603 ■ Fishers Chamber of Commerce (FCC)
11601 Municipal Dr.
Fishers, IN 46038
Ph: (317)578-0700
Fax: (317)578-1097
Co. E-mail: info@fisherschamber.com
URL: http://www.fisherschamber.com
Contact: Dan Canan, President
Description: Promotes business and community development in Fishers, IN. **Publications:** *Fishers-Chamber.Com* (Monthly). **Awards:** Business of the Year (Annual); Curb Appeal Award (Annual); Emerging Growth (Annual); Small Business of the Year (Annual). **Telecommunication Services:** cwolf@fishers-chamber.com.

51604 ■ *FishersChamber.Com*
11601 Municipal Dr.
Fishers, IN 46038
Ph: (317)578-0700
Fax: (317)578-1097
Co. E-mail: info@fisherschamber.com
URL: http://www.fisherschamber.com
Contact: Dan Canan, President
Released: Monthly **Price:** included in membership dues.

51605 ■ Franklin Chamber of Commerce (FCC)
370 E Jefferson St.
Franklin, IN 46131
Ph: (317)736-6334

Fax: (317)736-9553
Co. E-mail: franklincoc@franklincoc.org
URL: http://www.franklincoc.org/cwt/external/wcpages/index.aspx
Contact: Tricia E. Bechman, Executive Director
Description: Promotes business and community development in the Franklin, IN area. Sponsors Heritage Festival. Convention/Meeting: none. **Founded:** 1920. **Publications:** *Depot Signal* (Monthly); *Franklin Chamber of Commerce Directory* (Annual).

51606 ■ *Franklin Chamber of Commerce Directory*
370 E Jefferson St.
Franklin, IN 46131
Ph: (317)736-6334
Fax: (317)736-9553
Co. E-mail: franklincoc@franklincoc.org
URL: http://www.franklincoc.org/cwt/external/wcpages/index.aspx
Contact: Tricia E. Bechman, Executive Director
Released: Annual

51607 ■ Fremont Area Chamber of Commerce
PO Box 462
Fremont, IN 46737
Ph: (260)495-9010
Fax: (260)495-2446
Co. E-mail: fremontchamber@fremontchamber.org
URL: http://www.fremontchamber.org
Contact: Linda Fulton, Executive Director
Description: Promotes business and economic development in Fremont Area, IN.

51608 ■ French Lick - West Baden Chamber of Commerce (FLWBCC)
PO Box 347
French Lick, IN 47432
Ph: (812)936-2405
Co. E-mail: flwbchamber@psci.net
URL: http://www.frenchlick-westbadencc.com
Description: Promotes business and community development in French Lick, IN.

51609 ■ Gary Chamber of Commerce (GCC)
839 Broadway, Ste. S103
Gary, IN 46402
Ph: (219)885-7407
Fax: (219)885-7408
Co. E-mail: info@garychamber.com
URL: http://www.garychamber.com
Contact: Charles Hughes, Executive Director
Description: Promotes business and community development in the Gary, IN area. **Founded:** 1907. **Publications:** *Potential* (Quarterly).

51610 ■ Goshen Chamber of Commerce (GCC)
232 S Main St.
Goshen, IN 46526-3723
Ph: (574)533-2102
Free: 800-307-4204
Fax: (574)533-2103
Co. E-mail: goshenchamber@goshen.org
URL: http://www.goshen.org
Contact: Raymond J. Quattrini, President
URL(s): www.goshennychamber.com. **Description:** Promotes business and community development in Goshen, IN. **Publications:** *Image*. **Telecommunication Services:** info@goshennychamber.com.

51611 ■ Greater Avon Chamber of Commerce (ACOC)
8244 E U.S. Hwy. 36, Ste. 140
Avon, IN 46123
Ph: (317)272-4333
Fax: (317)272-7217
Co. E-mail: info@avonchamber.org
URL: http://www.avonchamber.org
Contact: Tom Downard, Executive Director
Description: Promotes the continuous improvement of the quality of life in the Avon community through the pursuit of new business, cultural, social and economic education of the citizen by providing accurate and timely assistance to the business community.

51612 ■ Greater Bloomington Chamber of Commerce (GBCC)
PO Box 1302
Bloomington, IN 47402
Ph: (812)336-6381
Fax: (812)336-0651
Co. E-mail: info@chamberbloomington.org
URL: http://www.chamberbloomington.org/cwt/external/wcpages/index.aspx
Contact: Christy Gillenwater, President
Description: Promotes business and community development in the Bloomington, IN area. **Founded:** 1915. **Publications:** *Business Network* (Monthly).

51613 ■ Greater Danville Chamber of Commerce
17 W Marion St.
Danville, IN 46122
Ph: (317)745-0670
Fax: (317)745-0682
URL: http://www.danville-chamber.org
Contact: Brad Eisenhart, President
Description: Promotes business and community development in Danville, IN. Holds monthly board meeting. **Founded:** 1991.

51614 ■ Greater Elkhart County Chamber of Commerce
418 S Main St.
Elkhart, IN 46515-0428
Ph: (574)293-1531
Fax: (574)294-1859
Co. E-mail: info@elkhart.org
URL: http://www.elkhart.org
Contact: Philip E. Penn, President
Description: Represents the business community in problem solving, promoting economic development, transportation issues, and downtown development. **Founded:** 1926. **Publications:** *Elkhart County Manufacturers Directory*; *Business Resource Guide*; *Elkhart County Manufacturers Directory*; *Elkhart County Manufacturers Labels*; *Elkhart Area Recreational Vehicle Directory*; *Elkhart County Major Employers Directory*. **Awards:** Eartha Award; Fairbanks Award; Small Business of the Year (Annual); Outstanding Not for Profit Businesses; Small Business of the Month (Annual).

51615 ■ Greater Fort Wayne Chamber of Commerce
826 Ewing St.
Fort Wayne, IN 46802
Ph: (260)424-1435
Fax: (260)426-7232
Co. E-mail: mcallicoat@fwchamber.org
URL: http://www.fwchamber.org
Contact: Mike Landram, President
Description: Promotes business and community development in the Ft. Wayne, IN area. **Publications:** *Emphasis* (Quarterly); *Emphasis* (Periodic); *Update* (Biweekly). **Telecommunication Services:** mlandram@fwchamber.org.

51616 ■ Greater Greencastle Chamber of Commerce (GGCC)
16 S Jackson St.
Greencastle, IN 46135
Ph: (765)653-4517
Fax: (765)848-1015
Co. E-mail: gchamber@gogreencastle.com
URL: http://www.gogreencastle.com
Contact: Tammy Amor, Executive Director
Description: Promotes and stimulates business, increasing the value of chamber membership to create more opportunities through economic growth and the improved quality of life in the Greencastle, IN area. **Founded:** 1908. **Publications:** *Chamber Chimes* (Monthly). **Educational Activities:** Business After Hours (Monthly).

51617 ■ Greater Greenfield Chamber of Commerce (GGCC)
1 Courthouse Plz.
Greenfield, IN 46140
Ph: (317)477-4188

Fax: (317)477-4189
Co. E-mail: info@greenfieldcc.org
URL: http://www.greenfieldcc.org
Contact: Retta Livengood, President
Description: Promotes business and community development in the Greenfield, IN area. **Founded:** 1957. **Publications:** *Connection* (Monthly). **Educational Activities:** Awards Dinner (Annual). **Awards:** Community Service Award (Annual).

51618 ■ Greater Greenwood Chamber of Commerce (GGCC)
PO Box 506
Greenwood, IN 46142
Ph: (317)888-4856
Fax: (317)865-2609
Co. E-mail: info@greenwood-chamber.com
URL: http://www.greenwood-chamber.com
Contact: Christian Maslowski, Executive Director
Description: Promotes business and community development in the Greenwood, IN area. **Publications:** *Directions* (Monthly). **Awards:** Ernest Mishler Community Service Award (Annual); Pride & Progress Award (Annual).

51619 ■ *Greater Hammond Community Map*
5246 Hohman Ave., Ste. 100
Hammond, IN 46320
Ph: (219)931-1000
Fax: (219)937-8778
Co. E-mail: info@lakeshorechamber.com
URL: http://www.lakeshorechamber.com
Contact: Dave Ryan, Executive Director

51620 ■ *Greater Hammond Transit Map*
5246 Hohman Ave., Ste. 100
Hammond, IN 46320
Ph: (219)931-1000
Fax: (219)937-8778
Co. E-mail: info@lakeshorechamber.com
URL: http://www.lakeshorechamber.com
Contact: Dave Ryan, Executive Director

51621 ■ Greater Indianapolis Chamber of Commerce—Indianapolis Chamber of Commerce
Chase Tower
111 Monument Cir., Ste. 1950
Indianapolis, IN 46204
Ph: (317)464-2200
Fax: (317)464-2217
Co. E-mail: memberservices@indylink.com
URL: http://www.indychamber.com
Contact: Scott W. Miller, President
Description: Promotes business and community development in Indianapolis, IN. **Scope:** demographics. **Founded:** 1890. **Subscriptions:** articles books periodicals. **Publications:** *Catalyst* (Quarterly); *Indianapolis Monthly City Guide* (Annual); *Manufacturers Directory CD*; *Newcomer Booklet*.

51622 ■ Greater La Porte Chamber of Commerce (GLCC)
803 Washington St.
La Porte, IN 46352-0486
Ph: (219)362-3178
Fax: (219)324-7349
Co. E-mail: info@lpchamber.com
URL: http://www.lpchamber.com
Contact: Michael B. Seitz, President
Description: Businesses, professional firms, and individuals who promote business and economic development in La Porte, IN. Seeks to retain and expand business and industry in the area. **Founded:** 1913. **Publications:** *Business Today* (Quarterly); *LaPorte Business Resource Guide* (Annual); *LaPorte Area Industrial Directory*; *LaPorte Clubs and Organizations Directory*; *LaPorte Business Resource Guide* (Annual). **Telecommunication Services:** seitz@lpchamber.com.

51623 ■ Greater Martinsville Chamber of Commerce (MCC)
109 E Morgan St.
Martinsville, IN 46151
Ph: (765)342-8110

Fax: (765)342-5713
Co. E-mail: info@martinsvillechamber.com
URL: http://www.martinsvillechamber.com
Contact: Jamie Thompson, Executive Director
Description: Promotes business and community development in Martinsville, IN.

51624 ■ Greater Monticello Chamber of Commerce and Visitors Bureau
116 N Main St.
Monticello, IN 47960
Ph: (574)583-7220
Co. E-mail: janeto@sugardog.com
URL: http://www.monticelloin.com
Contact: Janet Dold, Executive Director
Description: Strives to build a favorable business government and community environment to enhance the quality of life in Greater Monticello, IN.

51625 ■ Greater Scott County Chamber of Commerce
PO Box 404
Scottsburg, IN 47170
Ph: (812)752-4080
Fax: (812)752-4307
Co. E-mail: scottcom@c3bb.com
URL: http://www.scottchamber.org/chamber
Contact: Keith Colbert, Executive Director
URL(s): scottchamber.org. **Description:** Promotes business, industry, and agriculture through the advancement of education, quality of life, environmental awareness, and tourism in Scott County, IN. **Publications:** *Chamber Exchange* (Monthly).

51626 ■ Greater Seymour Chamber of Commerce (GSCC)
105 S Chestnut St.
Seymour, IN 47274
Ph: (812)522-3681
Fax: (812)524-1800
Co. E-mail: info@seymourchamber.com
URL: http://www.seymourchamber.org
Contact: Bill Bailey, President
Description: Promotes business and community development in the Seymour, IN area. Sponsors art show. **Founded:** 1944.

51627 ■ Greater Valparaiso Chamber of Commerce (GVCC)
PO Box 330
Valparaiso, IN 46384-0330
Ph: (219)462-1105
Fax: (219)462-5710
Co. E-mail: info@valparaisochamber.org
URL: http://www.valparaisochamber.org
Contact: Rex G. Richards, President
Description: Promotes business and community development in the Valparaiso, IN area. **Publications:** *Valparaiso Magazine* (Quarterly).

51628 ■ Greater Zionsville Chamber of Commerce (GZCC)
135 S Elm St.
Zionsville, IN 46077
Ph: (317)873-3836
Co. E-mail: info@zionsvillechamber.org
URL: http://www.zionsvillechamber.org
Contact: Ray Cortopassi, Executive Director
Description: Promotes business and community development in the Zionsville, IN area. Sponsors annual country market, street dance, and village tour of homes. **Founded:** 1961. **Publications:** *Greater Zionsville Chamber of Commerce Newsletter* (Quarterly); *Membership Directory and Research Guide* (Annual).

51629 ■ *Greater Zionsville Chamber of Commerce Newsletter*
135 S Elm St.
Zionsville, IN 46077
Ph: (317)873-3836
Co. E-mail: info@zionsvillechamber.org
URL: http://www.zionsvillechamber.org
Contact: Ray Cortopassi, Executive Director
Released: Quarterly **Price:** free for members.

51630 ■ Greensburg Decatur County Chamber of Commerce (GACC)
125 N Broadway
Greensburg, IN 47240
Ph: (812)663-2832
Fax: (812)663-4275
Co. E-mail: info@greensburgchamber.com
URL: http://www.greensburgchamber.com
Contact: Jeff Emsweller, Executive Director
Description: Local businesses and individuals united to promote economic and community development in the Greensburg, IN area. **Founded:** 1906. **Publications:** *Annual Business Directory* (Annual).

51631 ■ Griffith Chamber of Commerce (GCC)
PO Box 204
Griffith, IN 46319
Ph: (219)838-2661
Fax: (219)838-2401
Co. E-mail: griffithchamber1@hotmail.com
URL: http://griffithchamberofcommerce.com
Contact: Kathleen Reed, President
Description: Promotes business and community development in Griffith, IN. Conducts annual sidewalk sale; sponsors annual golf outing; sponsors school Santa Poster Contest. Also a Family Steak Fry. **Publications:** *Business Directory and Guide to Buying* (Periodic). **Educational Activities:** Griffith Chamber of Commerce Luncheon (Monthly).

51632 ■ Hamilton North Chamber of Commerce
70 N Byron St.
Cicero, IN 46034
Ph: (317)984-4079
Co. E-mail: jane@hamiltonnorthchamber.com
URL: http://www.hamiltonnorthchamber.com
Contact: Debbie Beaudin, President
Description: Promotes business and community development in Hamilton County. **Founded:** 1981.

51633 ■ Harrison County Chamber of Commerce
310 N Elm St.
Corydon, IN 47112
Ph: (812)738-2137
Fax: (812)738-6438
Co. E-mail: dvoelker@harrisonchamber.org
URL: http://www.harrisonchamber.org
Contact: Darrell R. Voelker, Director, Economics
Description: Promotes business and community development in Harrison County, IN. **Founded:** 1933. **Publications:** *Directory/Business Profile Booklet* (Annual). **Awards:** Chamber of Commerce Scholarship Award (Annual); President's Award (Annual).

51634 ■ Highland Chamber of Commerce (HCC)
8536 Kennedy Ave.
Highland, IN 46322
Ph: (219)923-3666
Fax: (219)923-3704
Co. E-mail: info@highlandchamber.com
URL: http://www.highlandchamber.com
Contact: Mary Luptak, Executive Director
Description: Promotes business and community development in Highland, IN. **Publications:** *The Chamber News* (Monthly).

51635 ■ Hobart Chamber of Commerce
1001 Lillian St.
Hobart, IN 46342
Ph: (219)942-5774
Fax: (219)942-4928
Co. E-mail: info@hobartchamber.com
URL: http://www.hobartchamber.com/
Contact: Mike Adams, Executive Director
Description: Strives to support and advance the best interests, commercial and industrial, of the members of this organization; to promote trade; to further industrial, professional and other worthy activities; and to serve constructively for the public welfare of the city, county, state and nation; and for these purposes to cooperate with other agencies and organizations. **Publications:** *Hobart Business Directory* (Annual); *Hobart Business Directory*; *Business*

Directory; *Hobart Horizons* (Monthly); *Business Directory*. **Educational Activities:** General Membership Meeting (Monthly).

51636 ■ *Hobart Horizons*
1001 Lillian St.
Hobart, IN 46342
Ph: (219)942-5774
Fax: (219)942-4928
Co. E-mail: info@hobartchamber.com
URL: http://www.hobartchamber.com/
Contact: Mike Adams, Executive Director
Released: Monthly

51637 ■ *Horizons*
PO Box 842
Muncie, IN 47308-0842
Ph: (765)288-6681
Free: 800-336-1373
Fax: (765)751-9151
Co. E-mail: info@muncie.com
URL: http://www.muncie.com
Contact: Jay Julian, President
Released: Monthly

51638 ■ Huntingburg Chamber of Commerce
309 N Geiger St.
Huntingburg, IN 47542
Ph: (812)683-5699
Free: 866-586-8494
Fax: (812)683-3524
Co. E-mail: info@huntingburgchamber.org
URL: http://www.huntingburgchamber.org
Contact: Christine Prior, Executive Director
Description: Promotes economic and social development in Huntingburg, IN.

51639 ■ *Huntington City and County Map*
305 Warren St.
Huntington, IN 46750-2854
Ph: (260)356-5300
Fax: (260)356-5434
Co. E-mail: info@huntington-chamber.com
URL: http://www.huntington-chamber.com
Contact: Nicole Johnson, Chairperson
Released: Biennial

51640 ■ Huntington County Chamber of Commerce (HCCC)
305 Warren St.
Huntington, IN 46750-2854
Ph: (260)356-5300
Fax: (260)356-5434
Co. E-mail: info@huntington-chamber.com
URL: http://www.huntington-chamber.com
Contact: Nicole Johnson, Chairperson
Description: Promotes community, economic and industrial development in Huntington, IN. Works to retain and improve present business and industry. Sponsors A. B.I.G. Day (golf tournament), annual Heritage Days, Scholarship Recognition, Administrative Assistants Day, and Huntington County EXPO. Works to recruit new business along with partners such as HCUED, and Venture Works. **Founded:** 1924. **Subscriptions:** archival material books business records clippings papers reports. **Publications:** *Chamber Scene* (Monthly); *Civic and Organization Guide* (Annual); *Huntington City and County Map* (Biennial); *Industrial Guide* (Annual); *Program of Action* (Annual); *Visions of Huntington County, Indiana* (Biennial); *Personnel Management Association: Wage and Benefit Study* (Annual).

51641 ■ *Image*
232 S Main St.
Goshen, IN 46526-3723
Ph: (574)533-2102
Free: 800-307-4204
Fax: (574)533-2103
Co. E-mail: goshenchamber@goshen.org
URL: http://www.goshen.org
Contact: Raymond J. Quattrini, President

51642 ■ Indiana Chamber of Commerce (ICC)
115 W Washington St., Ste. 850 S
Indianapolis, IN 46204-3420
Ph: (317)264-3110
Free: 800-804-6854

Fax: (317)264-6855
Co. E-mail: kbrinegar@indianachamber.com
URL: http://www.indianachamber.com
Contact: Kevin Brinegar, President
E-mail: kbrinegar@indianachamber.com
Description: Businesses and other organizations. Promotes free enterprise, and the preservation and advancement of the business climate. Monitors legislative activity. Holds seminars and workshops. **Scope:** business, economics. **Founded:** 1922. **Subscriptions:** 500. **Publications:** *Indiana Chamber of Commerce--Business Directory & Resource Guide*; *Indiana General Assembly Legislative Directory* (Annual); *BizVoice* (Bimonthly); *Executive Quickline* (Monthly); *Outlook* (Bimonthly); *Indiana Chamber of Commerce--Business Directory & Resource Guide* (Annual); *ADA Guide*; *Model Employee Policies for Indiana Employers*. **Telecommunication Services:** tbaumgartner@indianachamber.com; inchamber@indianachamber.com.

51643 ■ *Indianapolis Monthly City Guide*
Chase Tower
111 Monument Cir., Ste. 1950
Indianapolis, IN 46204
Ph: (317)464-2200
Fax: (317)464-2217
Co. E-mail: memberservices@indylink.com
URL: http://www.indychamber.com
Contact: Scott W. Miller, President
Released: Annual

51644 ■ *Industrial and Business Directory*
210 S Wabash St.
Wabash, IN 46992
Ph: (260)563-1168
Fax: (260)563-6920
Co. E-mail: info@wabashchamber.org
URL: http://www.wabashchamber.org
Contact: Ms. Kimberly A. Pinkerton, President
Released: Periodic

51645 ■ *Industrial Directory*
211 E Maumee St., Ste. B
Angola, IN 46703
Ph: (260)665-3512
Fax: (260)665-7418
Co. E-mail: info@angolachamber.org
URL: http://www.angolachamber.org
Contact: Jennifer Rumsey, President
Released: Periodic **Price:** $10.

51646 ■ *Industrial Directory*
125 E Monroe St.
Decatur, IN 46733-1732
Ph: (260)724-2604
Co. E-mail: wkuntzman@decaturchamber.org
URL: http://www.decaturchamber.org
Contact: Wes Kuntzman, Executive Director
Released: Periodic

51647 ■ *Industrial Directory*
13 E Main St.
Peru, IN 46970
Ph: (765)472-1923
Fax: (765)472-7099
Co. E-mail: info@miamicochamber.com
URL: http://www.miamicochamber.com
Contact: Sandy Chittum, President
Price: $15.

51648 ■ *Industrial Directory*
120 N Michigan St.
Plymouth, IN 46563
Ph: (574)936-2323
Fax: (574)936-6584
Co. E-mail: plychamber@plychamber.org
URL: http://www.plychamber.org
Contact: Doug Anspach, Executive Director
Released: Annual **Price:** $25, /year.

51649 ■ *Industrial Directory*
501 N Harrison St.
Shelbyville, IN 46176
Ph: (317)398-6647
Free: 800-318-4083

Fax: (317)392-3901
Co. E-mail: chamberinfo@shelbychamber.net
URL: http://www.shelbychamber.net/cwt/external/wcpages/index.aspx
Contact: Scott Asher, President
Released: Periodic

51650 ■ *Industrial Guide*
305 Warren St.
Huntington, IN 46750-2854
Ph: (260)356-5300
Fax: (260)356-5434
Co. E-mail: info@huntington-chamber.com
URL: http://www.huntington-chamber.com
Contact: Nicole Johnson, Chairperson
Released: Annual

51651 ■ Jasper Chamber of Commerce (JCC)
302 W 6th St.
Jasper, IN 47547-0307
Ph: (812)482-6866
Fax: (812)848-2015
Co. E-mail: chamber@jasperin.org
URL: http://www.jasperin.org
Contact: Nancy Eckerle, Executive Director
Description: Promotes business and community development in Jasper, IN. Sponsors annual Strassenfest. **Founded:** 1954. **Publications:** *Jasper Fact Book/Membership Directory* (Periodic); *Manufacturing and Business Directory* (Periodic).

51652 ■ *Jasper Fact Book/Membership Directory*
302 W 6th St.
Jasper, IN 47547-0307
Ph: (812)482-6866
Fax: (812)848-2015
Co. E-mail: chamber@jasperin.org
URL: http://www.jasperin.org
Contact: Nancy Eckerle, Executive Director
Released: Periodic

51653 ■ Jennings County Chamber of Commerce
PO Box 340
North Vernon, IN 47265
Ph: (812)346-2339
Fax: (812)346-3805
Co. E-mail: mshepherd@jenningscountychamber.com
URL: http://www.jenningscountychamber.com
Contact: Marie Shepherd, Executive Director
Description: Promotes business and community development in Jennings County, IN. **Founded:** 1955. **Publications:** *Chamber News* (Monthly). **Educational Activities:** Business After Hours (Monthly).

51654 ■ Kendallville Area Chamber of Commerce
122 S Main St.
Kendallville, IN 46755-1716
Ph: (260)347-1554
Free: 877-347-1554
Fax: (260)347-1575
Co. E-mail: kchamber@locl.net
URL: http://www.kendallvillechamber.com
Contact: Mike Walton, Executive Director
Description: Promotes business and community development in Kendallville, IN. **Founded:** 1925. **Publications:** *Chamber Connection* (Bimonthly).

51655 ■ Kentland Area Chamber of Commerce
PO Box 273
Kentland, IN 47951-0273
Ph: (219)474-6665
Co. E-mail: knochel@kentlandbank.com
Contact: Sue Knochel, Membership Chairperson Officer, Membership
Description: Promotes business and community development in Kentland, IN.

51656 ■ Knightstown Indiana Chamber of Commerce
PO Box 44
Knightstown, IN 46148-0044
Ph: (765)345-5290

Free: 800-668-1895
Co. E-mail: info@knightstownchamber.org
URL: http://www.knightstownchamber.org
Contact: Amy Blackwell, President
Description: Promotes business and community development in Knightstown, IN area. **Founded:** 1950.

51657 ■ Knox County Chamber of Commerce
316 Main St.
Vincennes, IN 47591-0553
Ph: (812)882-6440
Free: 888-895-6622
Fax: (812)882-6441
Co. E-mail: info@knoxcountychamber.com
URL: http://www.knoxcountychamber.com
Contact: Mark A. McNeece, President
Description: Promotes business and community development in Knox County, IN. **Telecommunication Services:** marc@knoxcountychamber.com; liz@knoxcountychamber.com.

51658 ■ Kokomo - Howard County Chamber of Commerce (KHCCC)
325 N Main St.
Kokomo, IN 46901-4621
Ph: (765)457-5301
Fax: (765)452-4564
Co. E-mail: jconrad@greaterkokomo.com
URL: http://www.kokomochamber.com
Contact: Jeb Conrad, President
Description: Promotes business and community development in Howard County, IN. **Founded:** 1914.

51659 ■ The Kosciusko Business Insights
313 S Buffalo St.
Warsaw, IN 46580-4304
Ph: (574)267-6311
Free: 800-776-6311
Fax: (574)267-7762
URL: http://www.wkchamber.com
Contact: Mark Dobson, President
Released: Monthly

51660 ■ Kouts Chamber of Commerce (KCC)
PO Box 330
Kouts, IN 46347
Ph: (219)246-0934
Co. E-mail: koutschamber@gmail.com
URL: http://www.kouts.info
Contact: Julie Jones, Executive Director
Description: Promotes business and community development in the Kouts, IN area. **Founded:** 1921.

51661 ■ Lafayette - West Lafayette Chamber of Commerce
337 Columbia St.
Lafayette, IN 47902-0348
Ph: (765)742-4044
Fax: (765)742-6276
Co. E-mail: information@lafayettechamber.com
URL: http://www.lafayettechamber.com
Contact: Joseph Seaman, President
Description: Promotes business and community development in the Lafayette, IN area. **Founded:** 1927.

51662 ■ LaGrange County Chamber of Commerce
901 S Detroit St., Ste. A
LaGrange, IN 46761
Ph: (260)463-2443
Free: 877-735-0340
Fax: (260)463-2683
Co. E-mail: info@lagrangechamber.org
URL: http://www.lagrangechamber.org
Contact: Beth Sherman, Executive Director
Description: Provides leadership for the promotion and advancement of economic vitality and quality of life in LaGrange County. **Publications:** Chamber News (Monthly).

51663 ■ Lakeshore Chamber of Commerce (HCC)
5246 Hohman Ave., Ste. 100
Hammond, IN 46320
Ph: (219)931-1000

Fax: (219)937-8778
Co. E-mail: info@lakeshorechamber.com
URL: http://www.lakeshorechamber.com
Contact: Dave Ryan, Executive Director
Description: Promotes business and community development in Hammond, IN. **Founded:** 1912. **Publications:** Community Directory and Buyers Guide (Biennial); Greater Hammond Community Map; Greater Hammond Transit Map; Summer Events Tabloid (Annual).

51664 ■ Lakeview
200 E Michigan Blvd.
Michigan City, IN 46360-3270
Ph: (219)874-6221
Fax: (219)873-1204
Co. E-mail: info@mcachamber.com
URL: http://www.michigancitychamber.com
Contact: Ann Dahm, President
Released: Bimonthly **Price:** free.

51665 ■ LaPorte Business Resource Guide
803 Washington St.
La Porte, IN 46352-0486
Ph: (219)362-3178
Fax: (219)324-7349
Co. E-mail: info@lpchamber.com
URL: http://www.lpchamber.com
Contact: Michael B. Seitz, President
Released: Annual

51666 ■ Ligonier Chamber of Commerce (LCC)
PO Box 121
Ligonier, IN 46767-0121
Ph: (260)894-9909
URL: http://www.ligonierindianachamber.org
Contact: Peggy Daniels, President
Description: Promotes business and community development in Ligonier, IN. Helps sponsor Ligonier festival. **Founded:** 1935. **Awards:** New Business Plaque.

51667 ■ Linton-Stockton Chamber of Commerce (LSCC)
PO Box 208
Linton, IN 47441
Ph: (812)847-4846
Fax: (812)847-0246
Co. E-mail: chamber@joink.com
URL: http://www.lintonchamber.org
Contact: Lynette Shelton, Executive Director
Description: Businesses, civic clubs, fraternal organizations, and interested individuals. Promotes business and community development in Stockton Township, IN. Sponsors Linton Freedom Festival. **Founded:** 1929. **Publications:** Chamber of Commerce Newsletter (Monthly).

51668 ■ Logansport - Cass County Chamber of Commerce
300 E Broadway, Ste. 103
Logansport, IN 46947-3185
Ph: (574)753-6388
Fax: (574)735-0909
Co. E-mail: info@logan-casschamber.com
URL: http://www.logan-casschamber.com
Contact: Brian Shafer, President
Description: Promotes business and community development in Cass County, IN. **Founded:** 1938. **Publications:** On Target (Monthly). **Telecommunication Services:** brian@logan-casschamber.com.

51669 ■ Madison Area Chamber of Commerce (MACC)
301 E Main St.
Madison, IN 47250
Ph: (812)265-3135
Fax: (812)265-9784
Co. E-mail: info@madisonchamber.org
URL: http://www.madisonchamber.org
Contact: Corey Murphy, Executive Director
Description: Retail businesses, educational and professional organizations, and clubs. Promotes business and community development in the Jefferson County, IN area. Sponsors Annual Job Fair, Chamber Annual Golf Outing, Soup, Stew, Chili and; Brew

Festival, Business Expo. **Founded:** 1924. **Publications:** Chamber Insight (Monthly); Community Information Directory (Annual).

51670 ■ Manufacturer Directory for Muncie-Delaware County
PO Box 842
Muncie, IN 47308-0842
Ph: (765)288-6681
Free: 800-336-1373
Fax: (765)751-9151
Co. E-mail: info@muncie.com
URL: http://www.muncie.com
Contact: Jay Julian, President
Released: Annual

51671 ■ Manufacturers Directory CD
Chase Tower
111 Monument Cir., Ste. 1950
Indianapolis, IN 46204
Ph: (317)464-2200
Fax: (317)464-2217
Co. E-mail: memberservices@indylink.com
URL: http://www.indychamber.com
Contact: Scott W. Miller, President
Price: $260, for members; $360, for nonmembers.

51672 ■ Manufacturing and Business Directory
302 W 6th St.
Jasper, IN 47547-0307
Ph: (812)482-6866
Fax: (812)848-2015
Co. E-mail: chamber@jasperin.org
URL: http://www.jasperin.org
Contact: Nancy Eckerle, Executive Director
Released: Periodic

51673 ■ Map of Carmel-Clay
37 E Main St., Ste. 300
Carmel, IN 46032
Ph: (317)846-1049
Fax: (317)844-6843
Co. E-mail: chamberinfo@carmelchamber.com
URL: http://www.carmelchamber.com
Contact: Mo Merhoff, President

51674 ■ Marion-Grant County Chamber of Commerce
217 S Adams St.
Marion, IN 46952-3835
Ph: (765)664-5107
Fax: (765)668-5443
Co. E-mail: info@marionchamber.org
URL: http://www.marionchamber.org
Contact: Michelle Bunker, President
Description: Promotes business and community development in Grant County, IN. **Founded:** 1935. **Publications:** Momentum (Monthly). **Educational Activities:** Business Trade Fair (Annual). **Awards:** Athena Award (Annual); Chairman's Award (Annual); Special Recognition Awards (Annual). **Telecommunication Services:** michelle@marionchamber.org.

51675 ■ Martin County Chamber of Commerce (MCCC)
PO Box 257
Loogootee, IN 47553
Ph: (812)295-4093
Co. E-mail: mccc@martincountyindianachamberofcommerce.org
URL: http://www.martincountyindianachamberofcommerce.org
Contact: Jennifer Wilson, President
Description: Serves as a voice of the business community in Martin County, IN. Supports business development and growth. Provides statistics, historical data and recommendations regarding the climate of business and business trends.

51676 ■ Membership Directory and Research Guide
135 S Elm St.
Zionsville, IN 46077

Ph: (317)873-3836
Co. E-mail: info@zionsvillechamber.org
URL: http://www.zionsvillechamber.org
Contact: Ray Cortopassi, Executive Director
Released: Annual

51677 ■ Mentone Chamber of Commerce
105 E Main St.
Mentone, IN 46539
Ph: (574)353-7417
Co. E-mail: valleyrs11@frontier.com
URL: http://www.mentoneeggcity.com
Contact: Rita Simpson, President
Description: Promotes business and community development in the Mentone, IN area.

51678 ■ Merrillville Chamber of Commerce
255 W 80th Pl.
Merrillville, IN 46410
Ph: (219)769-8180
Fax: (219)736-6223
Co. E-mail: geninq@merrillvillecoc.org
URL: http://www.merrillvillecoc.org
Contact: Edward C. Dernulc, Executive Director
Description: Promotes business and economic development in Merrillville, IN. **Founded:** 1954.

51679 ■ Michigan City Area Chamber of Commerce
200 E Michigan Blvd.
Michigan City, IN 46360-3270
Ph: (219)874-6221
Fax: (219)873-1204
Co. E-mail: info@mcachamber.com
URL: http://www.michigancitychamber.com
Contact: Ann Dahm, President
Description: Promotes business and community development in the Michigan City, IN area. **Founded:** 1918. **Publications:** *The Beacon* (Weekly); *Lakeview* (Bimonthly).

51680 ■ Momentum
217 S Adams St.
Marion, IN 46952-3835
Ph: (765)664-5107
Fax: (765)668-5443
Co. E-mail: info@marionchamber.org
URL: http://www.marionchamber.org
Contact: Michelle Bunker, President
Released: Monthly **Price:** free for members.

51681 ■ Monthly Memo
601 E Conner St.
Noblesville, IN 46060
Ph: (317)773-0086
Fax: (317)773-1966
Co. E-mail: info@noblesvillechamber.com
URL: http://www.noblesvillechamber.com
Contact: Sharon McMahon, President

51682 ■ Muncie-Delaware County Chamber of Commerce (MDCCC)
PO Box 842
Muncie, IN 47308-0842
Ph: (765)288-6681
Free: 800-336-1373
Fax: (765)751-9151
Co. E-mail: info@muncie.com
URL: http://www.muncie.com
Contact: Jay Julian, President
Description: Promotes business and community development in Delaware County, IN. **Founded:** 1937. **Publications:** *Community Profile* (Biennial); *Horizons* (Monthly); *Manufacturer Directory for Muncie-Delaware County* (Annual); *Quality of Life*; *Newcomer's Guide for Muncie-Delaware County Indiana* (Biennial).

51683 ■ Munster Business Handbook
1040 Ridge Rd.
Munster, IN 46321
Ph: (219)836-5549
Fax: (219)836-5551
Co. E-mail: info@chambermunster.org
URL: http://www.chambermunster.org
Contact: Wendy Mis, Executive Director
Released: Annual

51684 ■ Munster Chamber of Commerce
1040 Ridge Rd.
Munster, IN 46321
Ph: (219)836-5549
Fax: (219)836-5551
Co. E-mail: info@chambermunster.org
URL: http://www.chambermunster.org
Contact: Wendy Mis, Executive Director
Description: Business, industry, and professional individuals interested in promoting business and community development in Munster, IN. Sponsors annual Breakfast with Santa, Blues, Jazz and Arts on the Ridge Festival. **Founded:** 1955. **Publications:** *Chamber Newsletter* (Monthly); *Munster Business Handbook* (Annual). **Awards:** Beautification and Appearance (Annual); Citizen of the Year (Annual).

51685 ■ Nappanee Area Chamber of Commerce
302 W Market St.
Nappanee, IN 46550
Ph: (574)773-7812
Fax: (574)773-4961
Co. E-mail: inforequest@nappaneechamber.com
URL: http://www.nappaneechamber.com
Contact: Jeff Kitson, Executive Director
Description: Promotes business, community, and industrial development in the Nappanee, IN area. Sponsors Apple Festival. **Publications:** *Embrace the Pace* (Bimonthly). **Telecommunication Services:** jeff@nappaneechamber.com.

51686 ■ New Castle-Henry County Chamber of Commerce (NC-HC Chamber of Commerce)
100 S Main St., Ste. 108
New Castle, IN 47362
Ph: (765)529-5210
Fax: (765)521-7404
Co. E-mail: info@nchcchamber.com
URL: http://www.nchcchamber.com
Contact: Bill Kindig, President
Description: Promotes business and community development in the New Castle and Henry County, IN area. **Founded:** 1889. **Publications:** *Chamber Commentary* (Monthly). **Awards:** Business of the Year (Annual); Citizen of the Year (Annual).

51687 ■ New Palestine Area Chamber of Commerce (NPACC)
PO Box 541
New Palestine, IN 46163
Ph: (317)861-2345
Fax: (317)861-4201
Co. E-mail: newpalchamber@comcast.net
URL: http://www.newpalchamber.com
Contact: Rebecca Gaines, Secretary
Description: Promotes business and community development in the New Palestine, IN area.

51688 ■ Newcomer Booklet
Chase Tower
111 Monument Cir., Ste. 1950
Indianapolis, IN 46204
Ph: (317)464-2200
Fax: (317)464-2217
Co. E-mail: memberservices@indylink.com
URL: http://www.indychamber.com
Contact: Scott W. Miller, President
Price: free (first copy); $0.50, for members; $1, for nonmembers.

51689 ■ News Letter
119 S Main St.
Spencer, IN 47460
Ph: (812)829-3245
Fax: (812)829-0936
Co. E-mail: info@owencountyindiana.org
URL: http://www.owencountyindiana.org
Contact: Denise Shaw, Executive Director

51690 ■ NewsMonth
120 N Michigan St.
Plymouth, IN 46563
Ph: (574)936-2323

Fax: (574)936-6584
Co. E-mail: plychamber@plychamber.org
URL: http://www.plychamber.org
Contact: Doug Anspach, Executive Director
Released: Monthly **Price:** included in membership dues.

51691 ■ Noblesville Chamber of Commerce (NCC)
601 E Conner St.
Noblesville, IN 46060
Ph: (317)773-0086
Fax: (317)773-1966
Co. E-mail: info@noblesvillechamber.com
URL: http://www.noblesvillechamber.com
Contact: Sharon McMahon, President
Description: Represents businesses, organizations, industries, and individuals promoting business and community development in the Noblesville, IN area. **Founded:** 1935. **Publications:** *The Chamber Enterprise* (Monthly); *Community Information Directory* (Biennial); *Monthly Memo*.

51692 ■ North Manchester Chamber of Commerce (NMCC)
109 N Market St.
North Manchester, IN 46962-1518
Ph: (260)982-7644
Fax: (260)982-8718
Co. E-mail: nmcc@kconline.com
URL: http://www.northmanchesterchamber.com
Contact: Tim McLaughlin, Executive Director
Description: Serves as a community leader fostering projects and programs that will promote the economic health, welfare and development of business in North Manchester area. **Founded:** 1944. **Publications:** *Chamber Notes* (Monthly). **Awards:** Business of the Year (Annual); Citizen of the Year (Annual); Industry of the Year (Annual). **Telecommunication Services:** nmcc@northmanchester-chamber.com; ksroberts@kconline.com

51693 ■ North Webster Tippecanoe Township Chamber of Commerce
301 N Main St.
North Webster, IN 46555
Ph: (574)834-1600
Co. E-mail: nwttchamber@gmail.com
URL: http://www.northwebster.com
Contact: Tonya Bowser, President
Description: Promotes business and community development in the North Webster, IN area.

51694 ■ On Target
300 E Broadway, Ste. 103
Logansport, IN 46947-3185
Ph: (574)753-6388
Fax: (574)735-0909
Co. E-mail: info@logan-casschamber.com
URL: http://www.logan-casschamber.com
Contact: Brian Shafer, President
Released: Monthly

51695 ■ Orleans Chamber of Commerce
PO Box 9
Orleans, IN 47452-0009
Ph: (812)865-9930
Fax: (812)865-3413
Co. E-mail: historicorleans@netsurfusa.net
URL: http://www.historicorleans.com
Contact: Dr. Kelly Kirk, President
Description: Promotes business and community development in Orleans, IN area.

51696 ■ Outlook
115 W Washington St., Ste. 850 S
Indianapolis, IN 46204-3420
Ph: (317)264-3110
Free: 800-804-6854
Fax: (317)264-6855
Co. E-mail: kbrinegar@indianachamber.com
URL: http://www.indianachamber.com
Contact: Kevin Brinegar, President
E-mail: kbrinegar@indianachamber.com
Released: Bimonthly

51697 ■ Owen County Business Directory
119 S Main St.
Spencer, IN 47460

Ph: (812)829-3245
Fax: (812)829-0936
Co. E-mail: info@owencountyindiana.org
URL: http://www.owencountyindiana.org
Contact: Denise Shaw, Executive Director

51698 ■ Owen County Chamber of Commerce and Economic Development Corporation
119 S Main St.
Spencer, IN 47460
Ph: (812)829-3245
Fax: (812)829-0936
Co. E-mail: info@owencountyindiana.org
URL: http://www.owencountyindiana.org
Contact: Denise Shaw, Executive Director
Description: Promotes existing businesses, community & economic development and tourism in Owen County, Indiana. **Founded:** 1816. **Publications:** *Business Life* (Quarterly); *News Letter*; *Owen County Business Directory.*

51699 ■ Paoli Chamber of Commerce
210 W Court St.
Paoli, IN 47454
Ph: (812)723-4769
URL: http://www.paoliindiana.info/pcoc/pcoc.html
Description: Promotes business and industry in and around Paoli, IN. **Founded:** 1984.

51700 ■ Parke County Chamber of Commerce
105 N Market St., Ste. A
Rockville, IN 47872
Ph: (765)569-5565
Co. E-mail: info@parkecountychamber.com
URL: http://www.parkecountychamber.com
Contact: Alan Ader, Executive Director
Description: Promotes business and community development in the Parke County, IN area. **Founded:** 1966. **Publications:** *Chamber Check* (Bimonthly).

51701 ■ Perry County Chamber of Commerce
601 Main St., Ste. A
Tell City, IN 47586-0082
Ph: (812)547-2385
Fax: (812)547-8378
Co. E-mail: info@perrycountychamber.com
URL: http://www.perrycountychamber.com
Contact: Cheri Cronin, Administrative Assistant
Description: Promotes local business and community development in Perry County, IN. **Founded:** 1903. **Publications:** *Chamber Business* (Monthly); *Perry County Community Profile Magazine* (Triennial); *Perry County Community Profile Magazine* (Triennial). **Telecommunication Services:** perry-chamber@psci.net.

51702 ■ *Perry County Community Profile Magazine*
601 Main St., Ste. A
Tell City, IN 47586-0082
Ph: (812)547-2385
Fax: (812)547-8378
Co. E-mail: info@perrycountychamber.com
URL: http://www.perrycountychamber.com
Contact: Cheri Cronin, Administrative Assistant
Released: Triennial

51703 ■ *Personnel Management Association: Wage and Benefit Study*
305 Warren St.
Huntington, IN 46750-2854
Ph: (260)356-5300
Fax: (260)356-5434
Co. E-mail: info@huntington-chamber.com
URL: http://www.huntington-chamber.com
Contact: Nicole Johnson, Chairperson
Released: Annual

51704 ■ Peru - Miami County Chamber of Commerce
13 E Main St.
Peru, IN 46970
Ph: (765)472-1923

Fax: (765)472-7099
Co. E-mail: info@miamicochamber.com
URL: http://www.miamicochamber.com
Contact: Sandy Chittum, President
Description: Promotes business, community development, and tourism in the Miami County, IN area. **Founded:** 1916. **Publications:** *Chamber News Connection* (Quarterly); *Industrial Directory*; *Directory of Clubs and Organizations.* **Educational Activities:** Board Retreat (Annual).

51705 ■ Pike County Chamber of Commerce
714 E Main St.
Petersburg, IN 47567-1231
Ph: (812)354-8155
Co. E-mail: chamber@frontier.com
URL: http://pikecountyin.org
Description: Promotes business and community development in the Pike County, IN.

51706 ■ Plainfield Chamber of Commerce
210 W Main St.
Plainfield, IN 46168-0014
Ph: (317)839-3800
Fax: (317)839-9670
Co. E-mail: chamber@town.plainfield.in.us
URL: http://www.plainfield-in.com
Contact: Kent McPhail, Executive Director
Description: Promotes continuous improvement of commerce in Plainfield by taking leadership in community development through actively supporting and promoting social, economic, cultural, and educational activities. **Founded:** 1967.

51707 ■ Plymouth Area Chamber of Commerce (PACC)
120 N Michigan St.
Plymouth, IN 46563
Ph: (574)936-2323
Fax: (574)936-6584
Co. E-mail: plychamber@plychamber.org
URL: http://www.plychamber.org
Contact: Doug Anspach, Executive Director
Description: Promotes business and community development in the Plymouth, IN area. **Founded:** 1924. **Publications:** *Industrial Directory* (Annual); *NewsMonth* (Monthly). **Awards:** Distinguished Citizen (Annual); Public Servant (Annual); Volunteer (Annual); Youth Service (Annual).

51708 ■ *Potential*
839 Broadway, Ste. S103
Gary, IN 46402
Ph: (219)885-7407
Fax: (219)885-7408
Co. E-mail: info@garychamber.com
URL: http://www.garychamber.com
Contact: Charles Hughes, Executive Director
Released: Quarterly

51709 ■ *Program of Action*
305 Warren St.
Huntington, IN 46750-2854
Ph: (260)356-5300
Fax: (260)356-5434
Co. E-mail: info@huntington-chamber.com
URL: http://www.huntington-chamber.com
Contact: Nicole Johnson, Chairperson
Released: Annual

51710 ■ *Quality of Life*
PO Box 842
Muncie, IN 47308-0842
Ph: (765)288-6681
Free: 800-336-1373
Fax: (765)751-9151
Co. E-mail: info@muncie.com
URL: http://www.muncie.com
Contact: Jay Julian, President

51711 ■ *Report from the Chamber*
4100 Charlestown Rd.
New Albany, IN 47150-9538
Ph: (812)945-0266
Fax: (812)948-4664
Co. E-mail: info@1si.org
URL: http://www.1si.org
Contact: Michael Dalby, President
Released: Monthly

51712 ■ Richmond-Wayne County Chamber of Commerce (RWCCC)
33 S 7th St., Ste. 2
Richmond, IN 47374
Ph: (765)962-1511
Fax: (765)966-0882
Co. E-mail: info@rwchamber.org
URL: http://www.rwchamber.org
Contact: Dennis Andrews, President
Description: Promotes business, industrial, civic, and community development in the Richmond-Wayne County IN area. Maintains small business development, regional manufacturing extension, and export assistance centers; sponsors professional women's network. **Scope:** business. **Founded:** 1955. **Subscriptions:** periodicals. **Publications:** *Chamber NewsLink* (Monthly). **Telecommunication Services:** dennis@rwchamber.org.

51713 ■ Ripley County Chamber of Commerce
102 N Main St.
Versailles, IN 47042
Ph: (812)689-6654
Fax: (812)689-3934
Co. E-mail: ripleycc@ripleycountychamber.org
URL: http://ripleycountychamber.org
Contact: Amy Thomas, Director
Description: Promotes business and community development in Ripley County Versailles, IN area. **Publications:** *Chamber Page in the Versailles Republican* (Quarterly); *Chamber Page in the Versailles Republican* (Quarterly).

51714 ■ Rush County Chamber of Commerce
315 N Main St.
Rushville, IN 46173-1635
Ph: (765)932-2880
Fax: (765)932-4191
Co. E-mail: pamleisure@rushcounty.com
URL: http://www.rushcounty.com/chamber
Contact: Pamela C. Leisure-Svaranowic, Executive Director
Description: Promotes business and community development in Rush County, IN. **Publications:** *Chamber Made* (Quarterly).

51715 ■ St. John Chamber of Commerce (SJCOC)
9495 Keilman St.
St. John, IN 46373
Ph: (219)365-4686
Fax: (219)365-4602
Co. E-mail: info@stjohnchamber.com
URL: http://www.stjohnchamber.com
Contact: Margo Babineaux, President
Description: Promotes business and community development in the St. John, IN area.

51716 ■ Schererville Chamber of Commerce (SCC)
13 W Joliet St.
Schererville, IN 46375
Ph: (219)322-5412
Fax: (219)322-0598
Co. E-mail: info@46375.com
URL: http://www.46375.org
Contact: Mark Hill, President
Description: Promotes business and economic development in Schererville, IN.

51717 ■ Shakamak Area Chamber of Commerce
PO Box 101
Jasonville, IN 47438
Ph: (812)699-1577
URL: http://www.shakamakchamber.org/home/main.php
Contact: Andrea Pierce, President
Description: Promotes community development in Shakamak Area. **Founded:** 1970.

51718 ■ Shelby County Chamber of Commerce (SCCC)
501 N Harrison St.
Shelbyville, IN 46176
Ph: (317)398-6647
Free: 800-318-4083

Fax: (317)392-3901
Co. E-mail: chamberinfo@shelbychamber.net
URL: http://www.shelbychamber.net/cwt/external/
wcpages/index.aspx
Contact: Scott Asher, President
Description: Promotes business and community development in Shelby County, IN. **Founded:** 1948. **Publications:** *Industrial Directory* (Periodic). **Telecommunication Services:** juliemetz@shelbychamber.net.

51719 ■ Southern Indiana Chamber of Commerce (SICC)
4100 Charlestown Rd.
New Albany, IN 47150-9538
Ph: (812)945-0266
Fax: (812)948-4664
Co. E-mail: info@1si.org
URL: http://www.1si.org
Contact: Michael Dalby, President
Description: Promotes economic and community development in Clark and Floyd counties, IN. **Founded:** 1985. **Publications:** *Report from the Chamber* (Monthly). **Telecommunication Services:** michaeld@1si.org.

51720 ■ Spencer County Regional Chamber of Commerce
2792 N U.S. Hwy. 231, Ste. 100
Rockport, IN 47635
Ph: (812)649-2186
Fax: (812)649-2246
Co. E-mail: scrcc@psci.net
URL: http://www.spencercoin.org
Contact: Debbie Barrett, Executive Director
Description: Consists of regional businesses in Spencer County, IN dedicated to the progress and growth of the area.

51721 ■ Starke County Chamber of Commerce
400 N Heaton St.
Knox, IN 46534
Ph: (574)772-5548
Fax: (574)772-0867
Co. E-mail: info@starkechamber.com
URL: http://www.starkecountychamber.com
Contact: Deborah J. Mix, Executive Director
Description: Promotes business and community development in the Knox, IN area. Sponsors annual Business fair. Maintains Starke County Fine Arts Commission. Conducts Harvest Days Festival and Harvest Day Parade. **Founded:** 1984. **Awards:** Henry F. Schricker.

51722 ■ *Summer Events Tabloid*
5246 Hohman Ave., Ste. 100
Hammond, IN 46320
Ph: (219)931-1000
Fax: (219)937-8778
Co. E-mail: info@lakeshorechamber.com
URL: http://www.lakeshorechamber.com
Contact: Dave Ryan, Executive Director
Released: Annual

51723 ■ *Swiss Days*
205 E Main St.
Berne, IN 46711
Ph: (260)589-8080
Co. E-mail: chamber@bernein.com
URL: http://www.bernein.com
Contact: Connie Potter, Executive Director

51724 ■ Syracuse-Wawasee Chamber of Commerce (SWCC)
PO Box 398
Syracuse, IN 46567
Ph: (574)457-5637
Fax: (574)457-5052
Co. E-mail: info@swchamber.com
URL: http://www.swchamber.com
Contact: Tammy Cotton, Executive Director
Description: Promotes business and community development in Syracuse, IN. Sponsors annual Syracuse Days and Holiday Magic. **Founded:** 1972.

51725 ■ Terre Haute Chamber of Commerce
PO Box 689
Terre Haute, IN 47808-0689

Ph: (812)232-2391
Fax: (812)232-2905
Co. E-mail: info@terrehautechamber.com
URL: http://www.terrehautechamber.com/cwt/
external/wcpages/index.aspx
Contact: Ken Brengle, President
Description: Businesses, individuals, and professionals. Promotes business and community development in Wabash Valley, including west central Indiana and east central Illinois. **Founded:** 1906. **Publications:** *Valley Business Review* (Monthly).

51726 ■ Tipton County Chamber of Commerce (TCCC)
136 E Jefferson St.
Tipton, IN 46072
Ph: (765)675-7533
Fax: (765)675-8917
Co. E-mail: ditimm@tds.net
URL: http://www.tiptonchamber.com
Contact: Vicki Warner, Executive Director
Description: Businesses and individuals organized to promote economic and community development in Tipton County, IN. Sponsors community activities. Convention/Meeting: none. **Founded:** 1889. **Publications:** *Tipton County News and Views* (Quarterly). **Telecommunication Services:** jservies@tds.net.

51727 ■ *Tipton County News and Views*
136 E Jefferson St.
Tipton, IN 46072
Ph: (765)675-7533
Fax: (765)675-8917
Co. E-mail: ditimm@tds.net
URL: http://www.tiptonchamber.com
Contact: Vicki Warner, Executive Director
Released: Quarterly

51728 ■ *Update*
826 Ewing St.
Fort Wayne, IN 46802
Ph: (260)424-1435
Fax: (260)426-7232
Co. E-mail: mcallicoat@fwchamber.org
URL: http://www.fwchamber.org
Contact: Mike Landram, President
Released: Biweekly

51729 ■ *Valley Business Review*
PO Box 689
Terre Haute, IN 47808-0689
Ph: (812)232-2391
Fax: (812)232-2905
Co. E-mail: info@terrehautechamber.com
URL: http://www.terrehautechamber.com/cwt/
external/wcpages/index.aspx
Contact: Ken Brengle, President
Released: Monthly **Price:** free.

51730 ■ *Valparaiso Magazine*
PO Box 330
Valparaiso, IN 46384-0330
Ph: (219)462-1105
Fax: (219)462-5710
Co. E-mail: info@valparaisochamber.org
URL: http://www.valparaisochamber.org
Contact: Rex G. Richards, President
Released: Quarterly

51731 ■ *Visions of Huntington County, Indiana*
305 Warren St.
Huntington, IN 46750-2854
Ph: (260)356-5300
Fax: (260)356-5434
Co. E-mail: info@huntington-chamber.com
URL: http://www.huntington-chamber.com
Contact: Nicole Johnson, Chairperson
Released: Biennial

51732 ■ Wabash County Chamber of Commerce (WACC)
210 S Wabash St.
Wabash, IN 46992
Ph: (260)563-1168

Fax: (260)563-6920
Co. E-mail: info@wabashchamber.org
URL: http://www.wabashchamber.org
Contact: Ms. Kimberly A. Pinkerton, President
Description: Promotes business and community development in the Wabash, IN area. Sponsors festival; conducts annual Wabash Showcase - A Business Expo. **Founded:** 1942. **Publications:** *Buyers Guide* (Annual); *Industrial and Business Directory* (Periodic). **Awards:** Business of the Year (Annual); Distinguished Citizen (Annual); Small Business of the Year (Annual). **Telecommunication Services:** kim@wabashchamber.org.

51733 ■ Wakarusa Chamber of Commerce
100 W Waterford St.
Wakarusa, IN 46573
Ph: (574)862-4344
Fax: (574)862-2245
Co. E-mail: chamber@wakarusachamber.com
URL: http://www.wakarusachamber.com
Contact: Deb Shively, Executive Secretary
Description: Strives to render constructive services for the promotion of the welfare of the community and citizens of Wakarusa, Indiana. **Publications:** *Chamber News* (Monthly).

51734 ■ Walkerton Area Chamber of Commerce (WACC)
612 Roosevelt Rd.
Walkerton, IN 46574-1218
Ph: (574)586-3100
Fax: (574)586-3469
Co. E-mail: chamber@walkerton.org
URL: http://www.walkerton.org/business/chamber
Contact: John Small, Jr., President
Description: Promotes business and community development in Walkerton, IN.

51735 ■ Warrick County Chamber of Commerce
224 W Main St., Ste. 203
Boonville, IN 47601-0377
Ph: (812)897-2340
Fax: (812)897-2360
Co. E-mail: ssherman@warrickcounty.us
URL: http://www.warrickcounty.us
Contact: Shari Sherman, Executive Director
Description: Promotes business and community development in Warrick County, IL.

51736 ■ Warsaw - Kosciusko County Chamber of Commerce
313 S Buffalo St.
Warsaw, IN 46580-4304
Ph: (574)267-6311
Free: 800-776-6311
Fax: (574)267-7762
URL: http://www.wkchamber.com
Contact: Mark Dobson, President
Description: Promotes business and community development in Warsaw, IN area. **Founded:** 1911. **Publications:** *The Kosciusko Business Insights* (Monthly).

51737 ■ Wells County Chamber of Commerce
211 W Water St.
Bluffton, IN 46714
Ph: (260)824-0510
Co. E-mail: shuffman@wellscoc.com
URL: http://wellscoc.com
Contact: Suzanne Huffman, Executive Director
Description: Promotes the civic and economic development in Wells County.

51738 ■ Westfield Chamber of Commerce (WCC)
PO Box 534
Westfield, IN 46074
Ph: (317)804-3030
Fax: (317)804-3035
Co. E-mail: info@westfield-chamber.org
URL: http://www.westfield-chamber.org
Contact: Julie Sole, Executive Director
Description: Promotes business and community development in the Westfield-Washington Township, IN area. **Founded:** 1981. **Publications:** *Directory of Community* (Biennial). **Educational Activities:** Community Night (Annual).

51739 ■ Whiting - Robertsdale Chamber of Commerce
1417 119th St.
Whiting, IN 46394
Ph: (219)659-0292
Fax: (219)659-5851
Co. E-mail: marylu.chamber@sbcglobal.net
URL: http://www.whitingindiana.com
Contact: Carol Jacobson, President
Description: Promotes business and community development in Whiting-Robertsdale, IN area.
Founded: 1923. **Publications:** *Write Stuff* (Monthly).

51740 ■ Winchester Area Chamber of Commerce
112 W Washington St.
Winchester, IN 47394
Ph: (765)584-3731
Fax: (765)584-5544
Co. E-mail: chamber@globalsite.net
URL: http://www.winchesterareachamber.org/page/page/5454056.htm
Contact: Sandie Rowe, Executive Director
Description: Promotes business and community development in Winchester, IN area.

51741 ■ *Write Stuff*
1417 119th St.
Whiting, IN 46394
Ph: (219)659-0292
Fax: (219)659-5851
Co. E-mail: marylu.chamber@sbcglobal.net
URL: http://www.whitingindiana.com
Contact: Carol Jacobson, President
Released: Monthly

MINORITY BUSINESS ASSISTANCE PROGRAMS

51742 ■ Fort Wayne's Woman's Bureau - Women's Enterprise
3521 Lake Ave., Ste. 1
Fort Wayne, IN 46805
Ph: (260)424-7977
Fax: (260)426-7576
Co. E-mail: info@womensenterprise.org
URL: http://womensbureau.com/we
Description: Provides business counseling, mentoring, training, and other assistance to promote the growth of women-owned businesses.

51743 ■ Gary Minority Business Opportunity Center
21 Buffington Harbor Dr., Ste. 182
Gary, IN 46406
Ph: (219)977-7071
Fax: (219)977-9668
Co. E-mail: hpuckett@cmbdc.org

51744 ■ Indiana Department of Administration - Minority & Women's Business Enterprises Division
Indiana Government Center S
402 W Washington St., Rm. W479
Indianapolis, IN 46204
Ph: (317)232-3061
Fax: (317)233-6921
Co. E-mail: isoadisparitystudy@idoa.gov
URL: http://www.in.gov/idoa/2352.htm
Description: Supports minority and women's businesses in Indiana.

51745 ■ Indiana Department of Transportation - Economic Opportunity Division - Disadvantaged Business Enterprise Program
State Office Bldg.
100 N Senate Ave.
Rm. IGCN 755
Indianapolis, IN 46204
Ph: (317)232-5089

Fax: (317)233-0891
Co. E-mail: indot@indot.in.gov
URL: http://www.in.gov/indot/2576.htm
Contact: Tiffany Mulligan, Director
Description: Promotes the securing of Department of Highways contracts by minority and women-owned businesses. Provides certification for these companies.

51746 ■ Indiana Minority Supplier Development Council
2126 N Meridian St.
Indianapolis, IN 46202
Ph: (317)921-2680
Fax: (317)923-2204
Co. E-mail: jarode@imsdc.org
URL: http://www.imsdc.org
Contact: Michele R. Howell, Chief Executive Officer
Description: Promotes purchases by corporations from minority businesses through training programs, a Business Opportunity Fair, meetings, and supplier and purchaser directories.

51747 ■ Indiana Small Business Development Center
1 N Capitol Ave., Ste. 900
Indianapolis, IN 46204-2026
Ph: (317)234-2082
Fax: (317)232-8872
Co. E-mail: leadcenter@isdc.org
URL: http://www.isbdc.org
Contact: Jeff Heinzmann, Director
Description: Providing entrepreneurs with the education, information and tools necessary to build successful businesses.

51748 ■ Indianapolis Minority Business Economic Center
402 W Washington St., W69
Indianapolis, IN 46204
Ph: (317)234-5223
Fax: (317)233-6921
Co. E-mail: rhorne@mbec.in.gov

FINANCING AND LOAN PROGRAMS

51749 ■ 1st Source Capital Corp.
100 N Michigan St.
South Bend, IN 46634
Ph: (574)235-2000
Free: 800-513-2360
Fax: (574)235-2227
URL: http://www.1stsource.com
Contact: Eugene L. Cavanaugh, Vice President
Preferred Investment Size: $200,000 to $750,000.
Industry Preferences: Communications and media, computer hardware and software, semiconductors and other electronics, medical and health, consumer related, industrial and energy, and transportation.
Geographic Preference: Indiana and Midwestern states.

51750 ■ Cambridge Ventures, L.P.
4181 E. 96th St., Ste. 200
Indianapolis, IN 46240
Ph: (317)843-9704
Fax: (317)844-9815
URL: http://www.cambridgecapitalmgmt.com
Contact: Jean Wojtowicz, President
Preferred Investment Size: $100,000 to $1,000,000.
Geographic Preference: Midwest.

51751 ■ Gazelle Techventures
11611 N. Meridian St., Ste. 310
Carmel, IN 46032
Ph: (317)275-6800
Fax: (317)275-1100
URL: http://www.gazellevc.com
Contact: Don N. Aquilano, Managing Director
Preferred Investment Size: $1,000,000 to $3,000,000. **Industry Preferences:** Communications and media, computer hardware and software, biotechnology, medical and health, consumer related, industrial and energy, agriculture, forestry, and fishing. **Geographic Preference:** Indiana, Illinois, Kentucky, Michigan, Midwest, and Ohio.

51752 ■ Irwin Ventures LLC / Irwin Ventures Incorporated
500 Washington St.
Columbus, IN 47202
Ph: (812)376-1909
Fax: (812)376-1709
Co. E-mail: info@IrwinFinancial.com
URL: http://www.irwinventures.com
Contact: Will Miller, Chief Executive Officer
Industry Preferences: Communications, computer related, financial services, and business service. **Geographic Preference:** Mid Atlantic, Northeast, Northern California, Northwest, and West Coast.

51753 ■ Monument Advisors Inc.
255 N Alabama
Indianapolis, IN 46204-2619
Ph: (317)656-5065
Fax: (317)656-5060
Co. E-mail: request@monumentadv.com
URL: http://www.monumentadv.com
Contact: Larry S. Wechter, Chief Executive Officer
Founded: 1996. **Preferred Investment Size:** $1,000,000 to $3,000,000. **Industry Preferences:** Computer software and services, other products, industrial and energy, communications and media, consumer related, medical and health. **Geographic Preference:** Indiana and Midwest.

PROCUREMENT ASSISTANCE PROGRAMS

51754 ■ Partners in Contracting Corporation
5217 Hohman Ave., 4th Fl.
Hammond, IN 46320
Ph: (219)931-7561
Fax: (219)931-7594
Co. E-mail: picc@piccorp.org
URL: http://www.piccorp.org
Contact: Mary K. Kaczka, Executive Director
E-mail: kdfox@netnitco.net
Description: Provides marketing and technical assistance and workshop training assisting with all aspects of marketing to the federal, state and local governments.

INCUBATORS/RESEARCH AND TECHNOLOGY PARKS

51755 ■ Chamber of Commerce of Southwestern Indiana - Small Business Development Center (SBDC)
318 Main St., Ste. 401
Evansville, IN 47708
Ph: (812)425-7232
Fax: (812)421-5883
Co. E-mail: chamberinfo@ccswin.com
URL: http://www.ccswin.com/busndev/swsbdc.asp
Contact: Greg Wathen, Executive Director
Description: A small business incubator providing affordable office space, shared services, and business support necessary to create an atmosphere to greatly increase an emerging company's chances for success. Formerly Evansville Small Business Center.

51756 ■ Flagship Enterprise Center
2701 Enterprise Dr.
Anderson, IN 46013
Ph: (765)622-0100
Fax: (765)622-0211
Co. E-mail: ceo@flagshipenterprise.org
URL: http://www.flagshipenterprise.org/
Contact: DeWayne Landwehr, Executive Director
Description: A facility supporting the needs of incubator graduates and qualified early stage companies that are transitioning to a permanent location within Anderson and Madison County.

51757 ■ Innovation Connector
1208 W White River Blvd.
Muncie, IN 47303
Ph: (765)285-4900

Fax: (765)286-0565
Co. E-mail: kfrederick@bsu.edu
URL: http://www.innovationconnector.com/
Contact: Katie Frederick, Executive Director
Description: A small business incubator committed to start-up and spin-off businesses through the nurturing and supportive efforts of its extensive advisory business leaders, Ball State University, and additional experts from across the business spectrum.

51758 ■ Inventrek Technology Park
Greater Kokomo Economic Development Alliance
700 E Firmin St., Ste. 200
Kokomo, IN 46902
Ph: (765)457-2000
Fax: (765)854-0481
Co. E-mail: info@inventrek.org
URL: http://www.inventrek.org/
Description: A small business incubator focusing on long-term economic growth for Kokomo and Howard counties by creating new high-tech companies and supporting the development of new technologies for our existing companies.

51759 ■ Lexington Business Centre
530 E. Lexington Ave.
Elkhart, IN 46516
Ph: (574)522-0390
Fax: (574)295-1711
Co. E-mail: info@thetiedemanngroup.com
URL: http://www.lexingtonbizctr.com/
Description: A small business incubator offering affordable space in a prime location and providing crucial support to new and developing businesses.

51760 ■ Northeast Indiana Innovation Center
3211 Stellhorn Rd.
Fort Wayne, IN 46815
Ph: (260)402-8576
Co. E-mail: dryost@niic.net
URL: http://www.niic.net/
Description: A small business incubator dedicated to developing ideas and growing businesses by fostering an environment of innovation and providing a wealth of essential business resources to accelerate growth.

51761 ■ Purdue Research Park
Kurtz Purdue Technology Center
1281 Win Hentschel Blvd.
West Lafayette, IN 47906
Ph: (765)588-3470
Fax: (765)493-3217
URL: http://www.purdueresearchpark.com/
Description: A small business incubator providing a climate that encourages the development of new high-tech ventures and the growth of established technology firms.

51762 ■ St. Joseph Station
Business Center
300 N Michigan St.
South Bend, IN 46601
Ph: (574)289-5471
Fax: (574)289-7105

51763 ■ Uptown Innovation Center
814 E. Main St.
Richmond, IN 47374
Ph: (765)962-8151

Fax: (765)936-6197
Co. E-mail: uptown@uptownrichmond.com
URL: http://www.rwcstartup.com/
Contact: Renee Oldham, Executive Director
Description: A ten-suite business incubator designed to create an environment which would foster entrepreneurship, allowing not only young companies to grow and develop, but strengthen existing local companies as well, ultimately resulting in a stronger local economy.

51764 ■ Venture Out Business Center
Madison Area Chamber of Commerce
975 Industrial Dr., Ste. 1
Madison, IN 47250
Ph: (812)265-3135
Fax: (812)265-9784
Co. E-mail: info@madisonchamber.org
URL: http://www.madisonchamber.org/business_
center/
Contact: David Collier, Executive Director
Description: A business incubator that offers rental space as well as assistance to new and expanding businesses.

EDUCATIONAL PROGRAMS

51765 ■ Ball State University - Small Business Entrepreneurship Program
2000 W University Ave
Department of Management
Muncie, IN 47306
Ph: (765)289-1241
Free: 800-382-8540
Fax: (765)285-9002
Co. E-mail: askus@bsu.edu
URL: http://www.bsu.edu
Description: Offers a degree program, courses, seminars, and conferences for entrepreneurs and small business professionals. Covers financial and legal aspects of business ownership as well as small business assistance. Includes courses on business plan preparation and microcomputer use. 1-800-382-8540. **Telecommunication Services:** entrepreneur@bsu.edu.

51766 ■ Ivy Tech State College of Indiana - Columbus
4475 Central Ave.
Columbus, IN 47203
Ph: (812)372-9925
Free: 800-922-4838
Fax: (812)372-0311
URL: http://www.ivytech.edu/columbus
Description: Trade and technical college offering a business administration program, and a small business management program.

51767 ■ Ivy Tech State College of Indiana - Fort Wayne
3800 N Anthony Blvd.
Ft. Wayne, IN 46805
Ph: (260)482-9171
Fax: (260)480-4177
URL: http://www.ivytech.edu/fortwayne
URL(s): www.ivytech.edu/northeast. **Description:** Trade and technical school offering a program in small business management. 1-888-489-5463.

51768 ■ Ivy Tech State College of Indiana - Gary
1440 E 35th Ave.
Gary, IN 46409-1499
Ph: (219)981-1111
Free: 800-843-4882
Fax: (219)981-4415
Co. E-mail: cmwillia@ivytech.edu
URL: http://www..ivytech.edu/Northwest
Description: Trade and technical school offering a program in small business management.

LEGISLATIVE ASSISTANCE

51769 ■ Indiana Chamber of Commerce - Indiana Small Business Council - Small Business Legislative Network
115 W Washington St., Ste. 850S
Indianapolis, IN 46204
Ph: (317)264-3110
Fax: (317)264-6855
URL: http://www.indianachamber.com/

51770 ■ Indiana Senate Committee on Agriculture and Small Business
920 Pribble Cir.
Lawrenceburg, IN 47025
Ph: (812)537-0628
Fax: (812)537-0636
Co. E-mail: nugentts@one.net
URL: http://www.in.gov/legislative/
Contact: Johnny Nejent, Chairperson

PUBLICATIONS

51771 ■ *How to Form Your Own Indiana Corporation Before the Inc. Dries!: A Step by Step Guide, With Forms*
333 S. Taylor Ave.
Oak Park, IL 60302
Ph: (708)524-9033
Fax: (708)524-9038
Ed: Phillip Williams. **Released:** 1992. **Price:** $19.95 (paper). **Description:** Volume 4 of the Small Business Incorporation series. Explains the advantages and disadvantages of incorporation and shows, step-by-step, how the small business owners can incorporate at low cost. Covers Indiana profit and nonprofit corporations, Indiana professional service corporations, subchapter S corporations, and Delaware corporations. Includes forms necessary for incorporation.

51772 ■ *Smart Start your Indiana Business*
PSI Research
300 N. Valley Dr.
Grants Pass, OR 97526
Ph: (503)479-9464
Free: 800-228-2275
Fax: (503)476-1479
Co. E-mail: info@psi-research.com
URL: http://www.psi-research.com
Ed: Michael D. Jenkins. **Released:** Revised edition, 1992. **Price:** $29.95 (looseleaf binder); $24.95 (paper). **Description:** Part of the Successful Business Library series.

SMALL BUSINESS DEVELOPMENT CENTERS

51773 ■ Eastern Iowa Small Business Development Center (Davenport, Iowa)
331 W 3rd St., Ste. 100
Davenport, IA 52801
Ph: (563)336-3401
Free: 800-462-3255
Fax: (563)336-3479
Co. E-mail: ahutchinson@eicc.edu
URL: http://www.iowasbdc.org/regional-centers/davenport.aspx
Contact: Ann Hutchinson, Director
Description: Represents and promotes the small business sector. Provides management assistance to current and prospective small business owners. Helps to improve management skills and expand the products and services of members.

51774 ■ Indian Hills Small Business Development Center (Ottumwa, Iowa)
651 Indian Hills Dr., Bldg. 17
Ottumwa, IA 52501
Ph: (641)683-5127
Fax: (641)683-5296
Co. E-mail: bziegler@indianhills.edu
URL: http://www.iowasbdc.org/regional-centers/ottumwa.aspx
Contact: Bryan Ziegler, Director
Description: Represents and promotes the small business sector. Provides management assistance to current and prospective small business owners. Helps to improve management skills and expand the products and services of members.

51775 ■ Iowa Small Business Development Center - Lead Office
Iowa State University
2321 N Loop Dr., Ste. 202
Ames, IA 50010-8218
Ph: (515)294-2030
Fax: (515)294-6522
Co. E-mail: iowasbdc@iastate.edu
URL: http://www.iowasbdc.org
Contact: Jim Heckmann, Director
Description: Represents and promotes the small business sector. Provides management assistance to current and prospective small business owners. Helps to improve management skills and expand the products and services of members.

51776 ■ Iowa State University Small Business Development Center - Ames
2625 N Loop Dr.
Bldg. 2, Ste. 2610
Ames, IA 50010-8635
Ph: (515)296-7828
Fax: (515)296-6714
Co. E-mail: mjupah@iastate.edu
URL: http://www.iowasbdc.org/regional-centers/ames.aspx
Contact: Mike Upah, Director
Description: Represents and promotes the small business sector. Provides management assistance to

current and prospective small business owners. Helps to improve management skills and expand the products and services of members.

51777 ■ Iowa Western Small Business Development Center - Council Bluffs
2700 College Rd.
Council Bluffs, IA 51503
Ph: (712)325-3376
Co. E-mail: spitts@iwcc.edu
URL: http://www.iowasbdc.org/regional-centers/council-bluffs.aspx
Contact: Sue Pitts, Director
Description: Represents and promotes the small business sector. Provides management assistance to current and prospective small business owners. Helps to improve management skills and expand the products and services of members.

51778 ■ Kirkwood Small Business Development Center (Marion, Iowa)
Kirkwood Community College
3375 Armar Dr.
Marion, IA 52302
Ph: (319)377-8256
Fax: (319)398-5698
Co. E-mail: al.beach@kirkwood.edu
URL: http://www.iowasbdc.org/regional-centers/marion-cedar-rapids.aspx
Contact: Al Beach, Director
Description: Represents and promotes the small business sector. Provides management assistance to current and prospective small business owners. Helps to improve management skills and expand the products and services of members.

51779 ■ Mid Iowa Small Business Development Center
2829 Westown Pkwy., Ste. 220
West Des Moines, IA 50266
Ph: (515)331-8954
Fax: (515)252-7828
Co. E-mail: jbruene@iastate.edu
URL: http://www.iowasbdc.org/regional-centers/west-des-moines.aspx
Contact: Sherry Shafer, Director
Description: Represents and promotes the small business sector. Provides management assistance to current and prospective small business owners. Helps to improve management skills and expand the products and services of members.

51780 ■ North Central Iowa Small Business Development Center (Fort Dodge, Iowa)
217 S 25th St., Ste. C12
Fort Dodge, IA 50501
Ph: (515)576-6242
Fax: (515)576-6447
Co. E-mail: ncibusinesscenter@gmail.com
URL: http://www.iowasbdc.org/regional-centers/fort-dodge.aspx
Contact: Lisa Shimkat, Director
Description: Represents and promotes the small business sector. Provides management assistance to current and prospective small business owners. Helps to improve management skills and expand the products and services of members.

51781 ■ North Iowa Area Small Business Development Center (Mason City, Iowa)
500 College Dr.
Mason City, IA 50401
Ph: (641)422-4342
Fax: (641)422-4129
Co. E-mail: bairted@niacc.edu
URL: http://www.iowasbdc.org
Contact: Ted Bair, Director
Description: Represents and promotes the small business sector. Provides management assistance to current and prospective small business owners. Helps to improve management skills and expand the products and services of members. **Founded:** 1985.

51782 ■ Northeast Iowa Small Business Development Center (Dubuque, Iowa)
680 Main St.
Dubuque, IA 52001
Ph: (563)588-3350
Fax: (563)557-0319
Co. E-mail: sullivant@nicc.edu
URL: http://www.iowasbdc.org/regional-centers/dubuque.aspx
Contact: Terry Sullivan, Director
Description: Represents and promotes the small business sector. Provides management assistance to current and prospective small business owners. Helps to improve management skills and expand the products and services of members.

51783 ■ Northwest Iowa Small Business Development Center (Spencer, Iowa)
Iowa Lakes Community College
1900 N Grand Ave., Ste. 8
Spencer, IA 51301
Ph: (712)262-4213
Fax: (712)262-4047
Co. E-mail: kmccarty@iowalakes.edu
URL: http://www.iowasbdc.org/regional-centers/spencer.aspx
Contact: Kelly McCarty, Director
Description: Represents and promotes the small business sector. Provides management assistance to current and prospective small business owners. Helps to improve management skills and expand the products and services of members.

51784 ■ South Central Iowa Small Business Development Center (Creston, Iowa)
1501 W Townline St.
Creston, IA 50801
Ph: (641)782-1483
Fax: (641)782-1334
Co. E-mail: mclaren@swcciowa.edu
URL: http://www.iowasbdc.org/creston.aspx
Contact: Dave McLaren, Director
Description: Represents and promotes the small business sector. Provides management assistance to current and prospective small business owners. Helps to improve management skills and expand the products and services of members.

51785 ▪ Southeastern Iowa Small Business Development Center (Burlington, Iowa)
River Park Pl.
610 N 4th St., Ste. 201
Burlington, IA 52601
Ph: (319)208-5381
Fax: (319)752-3407
Co. E-mail: jclover@scciowa.edu
URL: http://www.iowasbdc.org/regional-centers/burl-ington.aspx
Contact: Janine Clover, Director
Description: Represents and promotes the small business sector. Provides management assistance to current and prospective small business owners. Helps to improve management skills and expand the products and services of members.

51786 ▪ University of Iowa Small Business Development Center (Iowa City, Iowa)
2663 University Capitol Ctr.
Iowa City, IA 52242
Ph: (319)335-3742
Fax: (319)335-4486
Co. E-mail: paul-heath@uiowa.edu
URL: http://www.iowasbdc.org/regional-centers/iowa-city.aspx
Contact: Paul Heath, Director
Description: Represents and promotes the small business sector. Provides management assistance to current and prospective small business owners. Helps to improve management skills and expand the products and services of members.

51787 ▪ University of Northern Iowa Small Business Development Center (Waterloo, Iowa)
8120 Jennings Dr., Ste. 13
Cedar Falls, IA 50613
Ph: (319)236-8123
Co. E-mail: dan.beenken@uni.edu
URL: http://www.iowasbdc.org/regional-centers/waterloo-cedar-falls.aspx
Contact: Dan Beenken, Director
Description: Represents and promotes the small business sector. Provides management assistance to current and prospective small business owners. Helps to improve management skills and expand the products and services of members.

51788 ▪ Western Iowa Tech Small Business Development Center (Sioux City, Iowa)
PO Box 5199
Sioux City, IA 51102-5199
Ph: (712)274-6454
Fax: (712)274-6455
Co. E-mail: wubbend@witcc.edu
URL: http://www.iowasbdc.org/regional-centers/sioux-city.aspx
Contact: Dan Wubbena, Director
Description: Represents and promotes the small business sector. Provides management assistance to current and prospective small business owners. Helps to improve management skills and expand the products and services of members.

SMALL BUSINESS ASSISTANCE PROGRAMS

51789 ▪ Iowa Department of Economic Development - Business Development
200 E Grand Ave.
Des Moines, IA 50309
Ph: (515)725-3000
Free: 800-532-1216
Fax: (515)725-3010
Co. E-mail: info@iowalifechanging.com
URL: http://www.iowalifechanging.com
Description: Works with the private sector to promote policies and implement programs that will expand the economy and increase job opportunities for Iowans.

51790 ▪ Iowa Department of Economic Development - International Div.
200 E Grand Ave.
Des Moines, IA 50309
Ph: (515)242-4743

Fax: (515)242-4918
Co. E-mail: international@ided.state.ia.us
Contact: Bret Mills, Director
Description: Provides information and consulting to companies interested in international trade. Organizes booth space at international trade shows; publishes directories of products to be exported from Iowa. **Publications:** *Iowa Directory of Exporters* (Biennial).

51791 ▪ Iowa Department of Economic Development - Targeted Small Business Assistance
200 E Grand Ave.
Des Moines, IA 50309
Ph: (515)725-3000
Free: 800-532-1216
Fax: (515)725-3010
Co. E-mail: businessfinance@iowalifechanging.com
URL: http://www.iowalifechanging.com
Description: Strives to further the economic well being of Iowa small business and to provide them with growth opportunities by offering services and coordinating efforts with existing programs.

SCORE OFFICES

51792 ▪ Burlington SCORE
Co. E-mail: riverscore@lisco.com

51793 ▪ Cedar Valley SCORE
Regional Business Center
212 E 4th St.
Waterloo, IA 50703
Ph: (319)236-9878
Fax: (319)236-8240
Co. E-mail: score247@consultant.com
URL: http://cedarvalley.score.org/chapters/cedar-valley-score
Description: Provides professional guidance and information to maximize the success of existing and emerging small businesses. Promotes entrepreneur education in Waterloo area, Iowa.

51794 ▪ Central Iowa SCORE
Co. E-mail: info@marshalltown.org

51795 ▪ Council Bluffs SCORE
IWCC Entrepreneurial Center
2700 College Rd., Box 4C
Council Bluffs, IA 51503
Ph: (712)256-6552
Co. E-mail: jmierau@iwcc.edu
Description: Provides consulting services to individuals wishing to start a new business or who have problems with established businesses across Southwest Iowa. Conducts business education seminars. **Founded:** 1981.

51796 ▪ Dubuque Area SCORE

51797 ▪ Muscatine SCORE
102 Walnut St.
Muscatine, IA 52761
Ph: (563)263-8895
Fax: (563)263-7662
Co. E-mail: abull@muscatine.com

51798 ▪ River City SCORE

51799 ▪ SCORE Cedar Rapids
2750 1st Ave. NE, Ste. 350
Cedar Rapids, IA 52402-4831
Ph: (319)362-6405
Fax: (319)362-7861
URL: http://www.scorecr.org
Description: Provides professional guidance and information to maximize the success of existing and emerging small businesses. Offers business assistance to develop business idea or plan and identify problems and potential solutions. Promotes entrepreneur education in Cedar Rapids area.

51800 ▪ SCORE Des Moines
Co. E-mail: score0005@netzero.com

51801 ▪ SCORE Fort Dodge
217 S 25th St., Ste. C12
Fort Dodge, IA 50501

Ph: (515)955-2622
URL: http://www.score.org
Description: Provides professional guidance and information to maximize the success of existing and emerging small businesses. Promotes entrepreneur education in Fort Dodge area, Iowa.

51802 ▪ SCORE Illowa
c/o Clinton Area Chamber of Commerce
333 4th Ave. S
Clinton, IA 52732
Ph: (563)242-5702
URL: http://www.scorecr.org/contact-info.php
Description: Provides professional guidance and information to maximize the success of existing and emerging small businesses. Promotes entrepreneur education in Illowa area.

51803 ▪ SCORE Iowa City
PO Box 1853
Iowa City, IA 52240-1853
Ph: (319)338-1662
URL: http://www.scorecr.org

51804 ▪ SCORE Iowa Lakes
122 W 5th St.
Spencer, IA 51301
Ph: (712)262-3059
URL: http://iowalakes.score.org/chapters/iowa-lakes-score
Description: Provides professional guidance and information to maximize the success of existing and emerging small businesses. Promotes entrepreneur education in Spencer area, Iowa.

51805 ▪ SCORE Northeast Iowa
Decorah Chamber of Commerce
507 W Water St.
Decorah, IA 52101
Ph: (563)382-3990
URL: http://northeastiowa.score.org/chapters/northeast-iowa-score
Description: Provides professional guidance and information to maximize the success of existing and emerging small businesses. Promotes entrepreneur education in Northeast Iowa. **Founded:** 1979.

51806 ▪ SCORE Sioux City
320 6th St.
Federal Bldg., Rm. 186
Sioux City, IA 51101
Ph: (712)277-2324
Fax: (712)277-2325
Co. E-mail: score104@qwestoffice.net
Description: Provides professional guidance and information to maximize the success of existing and emerging small businesses. Promotes entrepreneur education in Sioux area, Iowa.

51807 ▪ SCORE South Central
10 Raynan Rd.
Ottumwa, IA 52501
Ph: (641)683-5127
URL: http://southcentralia.score.org/chapters/south-central-score
Description: Provides professional guidance and information to maximize the success of existing and emerging small businesses. Promotes entrepreneur education in Ottumwa area, Iowa.

51808 ▪ Vista SCORE
Co. E-mail: info@vistascore0617.com

BETTER BUSINESS BUREAUS

51809 ▪ Better Business Bureau of Central and Eastern Iowa
505 5th Ave., Ste. 950
Des Moines, IA 50309-2375
Ph: (515)243-8137
Free: 800-222-1600
Fax: (515)243-2227
Co. E-mail: info@dm.bbb.org
URL: http://iowa.bbb.org
Contact: Chris Coleman, President
Description: Seeks to promote and foster the highest ethical relationship between businesses and the public through voluntary self-regulation, consumer and business education, and service excellence.

Provides information to help consumers and businesses make informed purchasing decisions and avoid costly scams and frauds; settles consumer complaints through arbitration and other means.

CHAMBERS OF COMMERCE

51810 ■ Adel Partners Chamber of Commerce
PO Box 73
Adel, IA 50003
Ph: (515)993-5472
Fax: (515)993-3384
Co. E-mail: rob.burditt@mutualofomaha.com
URL: http://adelpartners.org
Contact: Rob Burditt, President
Description: Promotes business and community development in Adel, IA.

51811 ■ Algona Area Chamber of Commerce (AACC)
123 E State St.
Algona, IA 50511
Ph: (515)295-7201
Fax: (515)295-5920
Co. E-mail: info@algona.org
URL: http://www.algona.org
Contact: Vicki Mallory, Executive Director
Description: Promotes business and community development in the Algona, IA area. **Founded:** 1936.

51812 ■ Alta Chamber of Commerce (ACC)
c/o Real Estate Specialists
106 W Railroad St.
Storm Lake, IA 50588
Ph: (712)732-7594
Co. E-mail: chamber@altaiowa.com
Contact: Joe Aube, President
Description: Promotes business and community development in the Alta, IA area.

51813 ■ Altoona Area Chamber of Commerce (AACC)
119 2nd St.
Altoona, IA 50009
Ph: (515)967-3366
Fax: (515)967-3346
Co. E-mail: altoona@netins.net
URL: http://www.altoonachamber.org
Contact: Melissa Horton, Executive Director
Description: Promotes business and community development in Altoona, IA. Sponsors Altoona Home Show, Pride Day, retail promotions, Christmas lighting contest and community auction. **Founded:** 1970. **Publications:** Chamber Directory (Annual). **Awards:** Bell Nuwell Award (Annual).

51814 ■ Ames Chamber of Commerce (ACC)
1601 Golden Aspen Dr., Ste. 110
Ames, IA 50010
Ph: (515)232-2310
Fax: (515)232-6716
Co. E-mail: dan@ameschamber.com
URL: http://www.ameschamber.com
Contact: Daniel A. Culhane, President
Description: Strives to strengthen the long-term economic vitality of its members and the community. Offers a variety of networking and educational opportunities to help businesses grow and thrive. **Founded:** 1944. **Publications:** Chamber Update (Monthly). **Educational Activities:** Golf Day (Annual).

51815 ■ Anamosa Area Chamber of Commerce
124 E Main St.
Anamosa, IA 52205
Ph: (319)462-4879
Co. E-mail: director@anamosachamber.org
URL: http://www.anamosachamber.org
Description: Promotes business and community development in Anamosa, IA.

51816 ■ Ankeny Area Chamber of Commerce
210 S Ankeny Blvd.
Ankeny, IA 50023
Ph: (515)964-0685

Fax: (515)964-0487
Co. E-mail: chamber@ankeny.org
URL: http://www.ankeny.org/cwt/external/wcpages/index.aspx
Contact: Julie Cooper, Executive Director
Description: Promotes business and community development in Ankeny, IA. **Founded:** 1952. **Publications:** Chamber Action (Monthly).

51817 ■ Area Chamber
424 1st Ave. NE
Cedar Rapids, IA 52401-1196
Ph: (319)398-5317
Fax: (319)398-5228
Co. E-mail: chamber@cedarrapids.org
URL: http://www.cedarrapids.org
Contact: Dee Baird, President
Released: Monthly

51818 ■ Association Directory
700 Locust St., Ste. 100
Des Moines, IA 50309
Ph: (515)286-4950
Fax: (515)286-4974
Co. E-mail: info@desmoinesmetro.com
URL: http://www.desmoinesmetro.com
Contact: Martha A. Willits, Consultant
Released: Annual

51819 ■ At the Lake
205 Main Ave.
Clear Lake, IA 50428
Ph: (641)357-2159
Free: 800-285-5338
Fax: (641)357-8141
Co. E-mail: info@clearlakeiowa.com
URL: http://www.clearlakeiowa.com
Contact: Alice Hanley, President
Released: Monthly **Price:** free.

51820 ■ Atlantic Area Chamber of Commerce (AACC)
102 Chestnut St.
Atlantic, IA 50022-1451
Ph: (712)243-3017
Free: 877-283-2124
Fax: (712)243-4404
Co. E-mail: atlanticchamber@a-m-u.net
URL: http://www.atlanticiowa.com
Contact: Debbie Leistad, President
Description: Promotes business and community development in the Atlantic, IA area. Sponsors Southwest Iowa Focus on Agriculture, Atlantic Fest, Coca-Cola Days, and City Wide Christmas Grand Lighting. **Founded:** 1941. **Publications:** Discover the Chamber (Monthly). **Educational Activities:** Atlanticfest (Annual).

51821 ■ Bedford Chamber of Commerce (BCC)
601 Madison Ave.
Bedford, IA 50833
Ph: (712)523-3637
Fax: (712)523-3384
Co. E-mail: bedfordareadc@frontiernet.net
URL: http://www.bedford-iowa.com
Contact: Randy Kernan, President
Description: Promotes business and community development in Bedford, IA.

51822 ■ Bellevue Area Chamber of Commerce (BCC)
210 N Riverview St.
Bellevue, IA 52031
Ph: (563)872-5830
Fax: (563)872-3611
Co. E-mail: chamber@bellevueia.com
URL: http://www.bellevueia.com
Contact: Deanna Cook, Director
Description: Promotes business and community development in Bellevue, IA. Conducts annual Heritage Days. **Founded:** 1976. **Publications:** Calendar of Events (Annual).

51823 ■ Belmond Area Chamber of Commerce (BACC)
210 E Main St.
Belmond, IA 50421
Ph: (641)444-3937

Fax: (641)444-3944
URL: http://www.belmond.com
Contact: Chris Cox, President
Description: Promotes business and community development in the Belmond, IA area.

51824 ■ Bettendorf Chamber of Commerce (BCC)
2117 State St.
Bettendorf, IA 52722
Ph: (563)355-4753
Co. E-mail: mitzi.hook@bettendorfchamber.com
URL: http://www.uschamber.com/chambers/directory/default.htm?st=ia
Contact: Paul Neuharth, Chairman
Description: Promotes business and community development in the Bettendorf, IA area. Sponsors Program of Action. **Founded:** 1928. **Publications:** The Business Report (Monthly).

51825 ■ Boone Area Chamber of Commerce
903 Story St.
Boone, IA 50036
Ph: (515)432-3342
Free: 800-BOO-NE12
Fax: (515)432-3343
Co. E-mail: boonechamber@iowatelecom.net
URL: http://www.booneiowa.us
Contact: Kurt R. Phillips, Executive Director
Description: Promotes business and community development in the Boone, IA area. Holds annual Pufferbilly Days festival. **Founded:** 1908.

51826 ■ Britt Chamber of Commerce (BCC)
PO Box 63
Britt, IA 50423
Ph: (641)843-3867
Co. E-mail: brittcoc@wctatel.net
URL: http://www.brittiowa.com/chamber/index.htm
Description: Promotes business and community development in Britt, IA. Sponsors draft horse show. **Publications:** Hobo Guide (Annual). **Educational Activities:** National Hobo Convention (Annual).

51827 ■ Burlington/West Burlington Area Chamber of Commerce (BWBCC)
River Park Pl.
610 N 4th St., Ste. 200
Burlington, IA 52601-5069
Ph: (319)752-6365
Free: 800-827-4837
Fax: (319)752-6454
Co. E-mail: info@growburlington.com
URL: http://www.growburlington.com
Contact: Dennis Hinkle, President
URL(s): www.visit.burlington.ia.us. **Description:** Promotes business and community development in Burlington and West Burlington, IA. **Founded:** 1920. **Publications:** The Chamber Newsletter (Monthly); Business Referral Directory (Biennial). **Educational Activities:** Burlington/West Burlington Area Chamber of Commerce Festival (Monthly); Burlington/West Burlington Area Chamber of Commerce Luncheon (Monthly). **Awards:** ABC Award (Annual); Emmy Award (Annual).

51828 ■ The Business Connection
10 Main St.
Cedar Falls, IA 50613-0367
Ph: (319)266-3593
Fax: (319)277-4325
Co. E-mail: info@greatercedarvalleychamber.com
URL: http://www.cedarfalls.com
Contact: Kris Hansen, Chairman
Released: Monthly

51829 ■ Business Connection
10 W 4th St., Ste. 310
Waterloo, IA 50701
Ph: (319)233-8431
Fax: (319)233-4580
Co. E-mail: jstodd2000@aol.com
URL: http://www.waterloochamber.org
Contact: Jay Stoddard, Director
Released: Monthly **Price:** $5, /year.

51830 ■ Business Growth, Community Progress
PO Box 247
Humboldt, IA 50548
Ph: (515)332-1481
Fax: (515)332-1496
Co. E-mail: chamber@hdcchamber.com
URL: http://www.ci.humboldt.ia.us
Contact: Tonya Harklau, Executive Director
Released: Monthly

51831 ■ Business and Industry Insight
515 N Jefferson, Ste. D
Indianola, IA 50125
Ph: (515)961-6269
Co. E-mail: chamber@indianolachamber.com
URL: http://www.indianolachamber.com
Contact: Denise Day, Executive Director
Released: Monthly

51832 ■ Business Monthly
122 W 5th St.
Spencer, IA 51301-7937
Ph: (712)262-5680
Fax: (712)262-5747
Co. E-mail: spencerchamber@smunet.net
URL: http://www.spenceriowachamber.org
Contact: Robert Rose, Executive Director
Released: Monthly **Price:** free.

51833 ■ Business and Professional Directory
424 1st Ave. NE
Cedar Rapids, IA 52401-1196
Ph: (319)398-5317
Fax: (319)398-5228
Co. E-mail: chamber@cedarrapids.org
URL: http://www.cedarrapids.org
Contact: Dee Baird, President
Released: Annual

51834 ■ Business Referral Directory
River Park Pl.
610 N 4th St., Ste. 200
Burlington, IA 52601-5069
Ph: (319)752-6365
Free: 800-827-4837
Fax: (319)752-6454
Co. E-mail: info@growburlington.com
URL: http://www.growburlington.com
Contact: Dennis Hinkle, President
Released: Biennial

51835 ■ The Business Report
2117 State St.
Bettendorf, IA 52722
Ph: (563)355-4753
Co. E-mail: mitzi.hook@bettendorfchamber.com
URL: http://www.uschamber.com/chambers/directory/default.htm?st=ia
Contact: Paul Neuharth, Chairman
Released: Monthly

51836 ■ Caboose on the Loose
100 S 4th St.
Missouri Valley, IA 51555
Ph: (712)642-2553
Fax: (712)642-3771
Co. E-mail: chamberofcommerce1@juno.com
URL: http://www.missourivalleychamber.com
Contact: Mr. Dennis Smith, President
Released: Monthly

51837 ■ Calendar of Events
210 N Riverview St.
Bellevue, IA 52031
Ph: (563)872-5830
Fax: (563)872-3611
Co. E-mail: chamber@bellevueia.com
URL: http://www.bellevueia.com
Contact: Deanna Cook, Director
Released: Annual

51838 ■ Carroll Chamber of Commerce (CCC)
407 W 5th St.
Carroll, IA 51401
Ph: (712)792-4383
Free: 866-586-4383

Fax: (712)792-4384
Co. E-mail: chamber@carrolliowa.com
URL: http://www.carrolliowa.com
Contact: Tom Duff, President
Description: Promotes business and community development in Carroll, IA. **Founded:** 1942. **Telecommunication Services:** k.lawler@carrolliowa.com; r.nees@carrolliowa.com; s.schrad@carrolliowa.com; cadc@carrolliowa.com.

51839 ■ Catalyst
1121 Broadway
Emmetsburg, IA 50536
Ph: (712)852-2283
Fax: (712)852-2156
Co. E-mail: eburgwelcome@kemb.org
URL: http://www.emmetsburg.com
Contact: Deb Hite, Executive Director
Released: Bimonthly

51840 ■ Cedar Falls Chamber of Commerce (CFCC)
10 Main St.
Cedar Falls, IA 50613-0367
Ph: (319)266-3593
Fax: (319)277-4325
Co. E-mail: info@greatercedarvalleychamber.com
URL: http://www.cedarfalls.org
Contact: Kris Hansen, Chairman
Description: Promotes business and community development in Cedar Falls, IA and metropolitan area. **Founded:** 1907. **Publications:** *The Business Connection* (Monthly); *Waterloo-Cedar Falls Business Directory* (Annual).

51841 ■ Cedar Rapids Area Chamber of Commerce (CRACC)
424 1st Ave. NE
Cedar Rapids, IA 52401-1196
Ph: (319)398-5317
Fax: (319)398-5228
Co. E-mail: chamber@cedarrapids.org
URL: http://www.cedarrapids.org
Contact: Dee Baird, President
Description: Promotes business and community development in the Cedar Rapids, IA area. **Founded:** 1918. **Publications:** *Area Chamber* (Monthly); *Business and Professional Directory* (Annual).

51842 ■ Centerville Area Chamber of Commerce
128 N 12th St.
Centerville, IA 52544-1703
Ph: (641)437-4102
Free: 800-611-3800
Fax: (641)437-0527
Co. E-mail: chamber@centervilleia.com
URL: http://www.centervilleia.com
Contact: Joyce Bieber, Executive Director
Description: Promotes business and community development in the Centerville, IA area.

51843 ■ Chamber Action
210 S Ankeny Blvd.
Ankeny, IA 50023
Ph: (515)964-0685
Fax: (515)964-0487
Co. E-mail: chamber@ankeny.org
URL: http://www.ankeny.org/cwt/external/wcpages/index.aspx
Contact: Julie Cooper, Executive Director
Released: Monthly

51844 ■ Chamber Affairs
206 1st Ave.
Rock Rapids, IA 51246
Ph: (712)472-3456
Fax: (712)472-2764
Co. E-mail: chamber@rockrapids.com
URL: http://www.rockrapids.com
Contact: Angie Jager, Executive Director

51845 ■ Chamber Chatter
c/o Julie Schieb, Office Asst.
1102 Willis Ave.
Perry, IA 50220-1556

Ph: (515)465-2481
URL: http://www.perryia.org
Contact: Julie Schieb, Assistant
Released: Monthly

51846 ■ Chamber of Commerce Directory
518 Franklin St.
Pella, IA 50219-1636
Ph: (641)628-2626
Free: 888-746-3882
Fax: (641)628-9697
Co. E-mail: pellacoc@pella.org
URL: http://www.pella.org
Contact: Karen Eischen, Executive Director
Released: Annual

51847 ■ Chamber Communique
303 N Main Ave.
Sioux Center, IA 51250
Ph: (712)722-3457
Free: 800-SXC-ENTR
Fax: (712)722-3465
Co. E-mail: scchambr@mtcnet.net
URL: http://www.siouxcenterchamber.com
Contact: Ardith Lein, Executive Director
Released: Monthly

51848 ■ Chamber Connection
115 E Main St.
Clarinda, IA 51632
Ph: (712)542-2166
Fax: (712)542-4113
Co. E-mail: chamber@clarinda.org
URL: http://www.clarinda.org
Contact: Randy Pullen, II, President
Released: Bimonthly

51849 ■ Chamber Connection
118 W 4th St.
Wilton, IA 52778-0005
Ph: (563)732-2330
Fax: (563)732-2332
URL: http://www.wiltoniowa.org/coc.php
Contact: Lisa Kublik, President
Released: Quarterly

51850 ■ Chamber Directory
119 2nd St.
Altoona, IA 50009
Ph: (515)967-3366
Fax: (515)967-3346
Co. E-mail: altoona@netins.net
URL: http://www.altoonachamber.org
Contact: Melissa Horton, Executive Director
Released: Annual

51851 ■ Chamber-Main Street Sac City (CMSSC)
615 W Main St.
Sac City, IA 50583-1701
Ph: (712)662-7316
Fax: (712)662-7399
Co. E-mail: saccitymainstreet@prairieinet.net
URL: http://www.saccity.org
Contact: Laura Zimmerman, Program Director
Description: Promotes business and community development in Sac City, IA.

51852 ■ Chamber News
c/o Aaron Stangel, Pres.
707 Iowa Ave.
Onawa, IA 51040
Ph: (712)423-1801
Fax: (712)423-4622
Co. E-mail: chamber@onawa.com
URL: http://www.onawa.com
Contact: Aaron Stangel, President
Released: Monthly

51853 ■ Chamber News
101 N Vine St.
West Union, IA 52175-0071
Ph: (563)422-3070
Free: 800-477-5073
Co. E-mail: wuchamber@alpinecom.net
URL: http://www.westunion.com
Contact: Robin Bostrom, Executive Director
Released: Monthly **Price:** free for members.

51854 ■ *Chamber News*
416 W Main St.
Cherokee, IA 51012
Ph: (712)225-6414
Fax: (712)225-2803
Co. E-mail: info@cherokeeiowachamber.com
URL: http://www.cherokeeiowachamber.com
Contact: Julie Hering Kent, Executive Director
Released: Monthly

51855 ■ *The Chamber Newsletter*
River Park Pl.
610 N 4th St., Ste. 200
Burlington, IA 52601-5069
Ph: (319)752-6365
Free: 800-827-4837
Fax: (319)752-6454
Co. E-mail: info@growburlington.com
URL: http://www.growburlington.com
Contact: Dennis Hinkle, President
Released: Monthly

51856 ■ *Chamber Report*
100 Maple St.
Shenandoah, IA 51601
Ph: (712)246-3455
Fax: (712)246-3456
Co. E-mail: chamber@shenandoahiowa.net
URL: http://shenandoahiowa.net
Contact: Shelly Smith, Director, Marketing
Released: Monthly

51857 ■ *Chamber Update*
1601 Golden Aspen Dr., Ste. 110
Ames, IA 50010
Ph: (515)232-2310
Fax: (515)232-6716
Co. E-mail: dan@ameschamber.com
URL: http://www.ameschamber.com
Contact: Daniel A. Culhane, President
Released: Monthly

51858 ■ *Chamber Update*
721 S 2nd St.
Clinton, IA 52732
Ph: (563)242-5702
Co. E-mail: chamber@clintonia.com
URL: http://www.clintonia.com
Contact: Nathan Sondgeroth, President
Released: Monthly

51859 ■ *Chamber Week*
204 W Broadway
Fairfield, IA 52556
Ph: (641)472-2111
Fax: (641)472-6510
Co. E-mail: chamber@fairfieldiowa.com
URL: http://fairfieldiowa.com
Contact: Nancy Morrissey, Executive Director
Released: Weekly

51860 ■ *ChamberEdge*
300 Main St., Ste. 200
Dubuque, IA 52001
Ph: (563)557-9200
Fax: (563)557-1591
Co. E-mail: office@dubuquechamber.com
URL: http://www.dubuquechamber.com
Contact: Molly Grover, President
Released: Monthly

51861 ■ Chariton Chamber and Development Corp.
104 N Grand St.
Chariton, IA 50049
Ph: (641)774-4059
Co. E-mail: ccdc@iowatelecom.net
URL: http://www.charitonchamber.com
Contact: Pat Hartz, President
Description: Seeks to promote tourism, economic development, community betterment, retail development and retention and industrial recruitment and retention. **Founded:** 1986.

51862 ■ Cherokee Chamber of Commerce
416 W Main St.
Cherokee, IA 51012
Ph: (712)225-6414

Fax: (712)225-2803
Co. E-mail: info@cherokeeiowachamber.com
URL: http://www.cherokeeiowachamber.com
Contact: Julie Hering Kent, Executive Director
Description: Promotes business and community development in Cherokee, IA area. **Publications:** *Chamber News* (Monthly).

51863 ■ Clarinda Chamber of Commerce (CABI)
115 E Main St.
Clarinda, IA 51632
Ph: (712)542-2166
Fax: (712)542-4113
Co. E-mail: chamber@clarinda.org
URL: http://www.clarinda.org
Contact: Randy Pullen, II, President
Description: Promotes business and community development in Clarinda, IA. Sponsors retail promotions; promotes tourism. **Founded:** 1929. **Publications:** *Chamber Connection* (Bimonthly).

51864 ■ Clear Lake Area Chamber of Commerce (CLACC)
205 Main Ave.
Clear Lake, IA 50428
Ph: (641)357-2159
Free: 800-285-5338
Fax: (641)357-8141
Co. E-mail: info@clearlakeiowa.com
URL: http://www.clearlakeiowa.com
Contact: Alice Hanley, President
Description: Promotes business and community development in the Clear Lake, IA area. **Founded:** 1906. **Publications:** *At the Lake* (Monthly).

51865 ■ Clinton Area Chamber of Commerce
721 S 2nd St.
Clinton, IA 52732
Ph: (563)242-5702
Co. E-mail: chamber@clintonia.com
URL: http://www.clintonia.com
Contact: Nathan Sondgeroth, President
Description: Promotes business and community development in Clinton, IA. Gathers and disseminates information about the community. **Scope:** small business topics. **Founded:** 1872. **Subscriptions:** articles books periodicals video recordings. **Publications:** *Chamber Update* (Monthly). **Awards:** Clapper Award (Annual).

51866 ■ Colfax Chamber of Commerce
PO Box 62
Colfax, IA 50054
Ph: (515)674-9071
Fax: (515)674-9072
Co. E-mail: colfaxmainstreet@gmail.com
URL: http://www.colfaxiowachamber.com
Contact: George Dickerson, President
Description: Promotes business and community development in Colfax, IA. Assists in funding and development of new and existing business enterprises in Colfax and surrounding areas through the Colfax Betterment Corp. Sponsors Country Christmas Celebration and Mineral Springs Day.

51867 ■ *Commerce Today*
149 W Broadway
Council Bluffs, IA 51503
Ph: (712)325-1000
Free: 800-228-6878
Fax: (712)322-5698
Co. E-mail: bmundt@councilbluffsiowa.com
URL: http://www.councilbluffsiowa.com
Contact: Bob Mundt, President
Released: Monthly

51868 ■ *The Communicator*
1100 16th Ave. Ct. SE
Dyersville, IA 52040
Ph: (563)875-2311
Fax: (563)875-8391
Co. E-mail: dyersvillechamber@dyersville.org
URL: http://www.dyersville.org
Contact: Karla Thompson, Executive Director
Released: Monthly **Price:** free for members.

51869 ■ *Communicator*
124 N Market St.
Oskaloosa, IA 52577-2827
Ph: (641)672-2591
Free: 888-562-6759
Fax: (641)672-2047
Co. E-mail: oskycofc@oacdg.org
URL: http://www.oacdg.org
Contact: Connie Bryan, Manager
Released: Monthly

51870 ■ *Community Insight*
309 E Main St.
Knoxville, IA 50138
Ph: (641)828-7555
Fax: (641)828-7978
Co. E-mail: rxjohnson@iowatelecom.net
URL: http://www.discoverknoxville.com
Contact: Roxanne Johnson, Executive Director
Released: Monthly

51871 ■ *Connections*
217 E Main St.
Ottumwa, IA 52501
Ph: (641)682-3465
Co. E-mail: info@ottumwaiowa.com
URL: http://www.ottumwaiowa.com/chamber/index.
  html
Contact: Terry McNitt, Executive Director
Released: Monthly **Price:** free for members.

51872 ■ Council Bluffs Area Chamber of Commerce (CBACC)
149 W Broadway
Council Bluffs, IA 51503
Ph: (712)325-1000
Free: 800-228-6878
Fax: (712)322-5698
Co. E-mail: bmundt@councilbluffsiowa.com
URL: http://www.councilbluffsiowa.com
Contact: Bob Mundt, President
Description: Promotes business and community development in Council Bluffs, IA. **Founded:** 1912. **Publications:** *Commerce Today* (Monthly).

51873 ■ Cresco Area Chamber of Commerce (CACC)
PO Box 403
Cresco, IA 52136
Ph: (563)547-3434
Fax: (563)547-2056
Co. E-mail: crescochamber@yahoo.com
URL: http://www.crescochamber.com
Contact: Laura Ollendick, Executive Director
Description: Promotes business and community development in Cresco, IA. Sponsors Ag-fest. **Founded:** 1970.

51874 ■ Creston Chamber of Commerce
208 W Taylor St.
Creston, IA 50801
Ph: (641)782-7021
Fax: (641)782-9927
Co. E-mail: chamber@crestoniowachamber.com
URL: http://www.crestoniowachamber.com
Contact: Ellen Gerharz, Executive Director
Description: Promotes business and community development in Creston, IA. **Founded:** 1940.

51875 ■ *Crossroads*
1010 6th Ave.
De Witt, IA 52742
Ph: (563)659-8500
Free: 888-999-5791
Fax: (563)659-2410
Co. E-mail: info@dewitt.org
URL: http://www.dewitt.org
Contact: Tami Petsche, Executive Director
Released: Monthly **Price:** free.

51876 ■ DavenportOne
130 W 2nd St.
Davenport, IA 52801

Ph: (563)322-1706
Co. E-mail: tbarney@davenportone.com
URL: http://www.davenportone.com
Contact: Tara Barney, President
Description: Promotes business and community development in the Davenport, IA area. **Founded:** 1867. **Telecommunication Services:** bbrandsgard@davenportone.com; jsachtleben@davenportone.com.

51877 ■ De Witt Chamber of Commerce
1010 6th Ave.
De Witt, IA 52742
Ph: (563)659-8500
Free: 888-999-5791
Fax: (563)659-2410
Co. E-mail: info@dewitt.org
URL: http://www.dewitt.org
Contact: Tami Petsche, Executive Director
Description: Promotes business and community development in De Witt, IA. **Founded:** 1946. **Publications:** *Crossroads* (Monthly).

51878 ■ Decorah Area Chamber of Commerce (DACC)
507 W Water St.
Decorah, IA 52101
Ph: (563)382-3990
Free: 800-463-4692
Fax: (563)382-5515
Co. E-mail: info@visitdecorah.com
URL: http://www.decoraharea.com
Contact: Brenda Balk, Director
Description: Promotes business and community development in Decorah, IA. Sponsors annual Nordic Fest. **Founded:** 1924.

51879 ■ *Digest*
709 S Center St.
Marshalltown, IA 50158
Ph: (641)753-6645
Fax: (641)752-8373
Co. E-mail: info@marshalltown.org
URL: http://www.marshalltown.org
Contact: Ken Anderson, President
Released: Monthly **Price:** free.

51880 ■ *Discover the Chamber*
102 Chestnut St.
Atlantic, IA 50022-1451
Ph: (712)243-3017
Free: 877-283-2124
Fax: (712)243-4404
Co. E-mail: atlanticchamber@a-m-u.net
URL: http://www.atlanticiowa.com
Contact: Debbie Leistad, President
Released: Monthly

51881 ■ Dubuque Area Chamber of Commerce
300 Main St., Ste. 200
Dubuque, IA 52001
Ph: (563)557-9200
Fax: (563)557-1591
Co. E-mail: office@dubuquechamber.com
URL: http://www.dubuquechamber.com
Contact: Molly Grover, President
Description: Promotes business and community development in Dubuque, IA area. **Publications:** *ChamberEdge* (Monthly).

51882 ■ Dyersville Area Chamber of Commerce
1100 16th Ave. Ct. SE
Dyersville, IA 52040
Ph: (563)875-2311
Fax: (563)875-8391
Co. E-mail: dyersvillechamber@dyersville.org
URL: http://www.dyersville.org
Contact: Karla Thompson, Executive Director
Description: Promotes business and community development in Dyersville, IA area. **Publications:** *The Communicator* (Monthly). **Educational Activities:** Golf Outing (Annual).

51883 ■ Eagle Grove Area Chamber of Commerce (EGACC)
120 N Lucas
Eagle Grove, IA 50533
Ph: (515)448-4821

Fax: (515)448-4821
Co. E-mail: chamber@eaglegrove.com
URL: http://www.eaglegrove.com
Contact: Rachel Cahalan, Executive Director
Description: Promotes business and community development in Eagle Grove, IA. **Founded:** 1927.

51884 ■ *Echo*
1442 Washington St.
Eldora, IA 50627
Ph: (641)939-3241
Fax: (641)939-7555
Co. E-mail: eldoraecondev@heartofiowa.net
URL: http://www.eldoraiowa.com
Contact: Deb Crosser, Executive Director
Released: Monthly **Price:** included in membership dues.

51885 ■ Eldora Area Chamber and Development Council (EACDC)
1442 Washington St.
Eldora, IA 50627
Ph: (641)939-3241
Fax: (641)939-7555
Co. E-mail: eldoraecondev@heartofiowa.net
URL: http://www.eldoraiowa.com
Contact: Deb Crosser, Executive Director
Description: Promotes business and community development in the Eldora, IA area. **Founded:** 1990. **Publications:** *Echo* (Monthly); *Outlook*. **Awards:** CEPP Certification in Industry and Commercial (Periodic).

51886 ■ Elkader Area Chamber of Commerce (EACC)
207 N Main St.
Elkader, IA 52043-0599
Ph: (563)245-2857
Free: 866-334-2857
Fax: (563)245-2857
Co. E-mail: elkader@alpinecom.net
URL: http://www.elkader-iowa.com
Contact: Brian Bruening, President
Description: Promotes business, community development, and tourism in the Elkader, Iowa area. **Founded:** 1964.

51887 ■ Emmetsburg Chamber of Commerce (ECC)
1121 Broadway
Emmetsburg, IA 50536
Ph: (712)852-2283
Fax: (712)852-2156
Co. E-mail: eburgwelcome@kemb.org
URL: http://www.emmetsburg.com
Contact: Deb Hite, Executive Director
Description: Promotes business and community development in Emmetsburg, IA. Sponsors Summerfest. **Publications:** *Catalyst* (Bimonthly).

51888 ■ *Employers Directory*
700 Locust St., Ste. 100
Des Moines, IA 50309
Ph: (515)286-4950
Fax: (515)286-4974
Co. E-mail: info@desmoinesmetro.com
URL: http://www.desmoinesmetro.com
Contact: Martha A. Willits, Consultant
Released: Annual

51889 ■ *Envision*
325 E Washington St.
Iowa City, IA 52240
Ph: (319)337-9637
Fax: (319)338-9958
Co. E-mail: info@iowacityarea.com
URL: http://www.iowacityarea.com
Contact: Nancy Quellhorst, President
Released: Monthly

51890 ■ Estherville Area Chamber of Commerce
620 First Ave. S
Estherville, IA 51334
Ph: (712)362-3541

Fax: (712)362-7742
Co. E-mail: echamber@ncn.net
URL: http://www.estherville.org
Contact: Stephanie Neppl, Executive Director
Description: Promotes business and community development in the Estherville, IA area.

51891 ■ Fairfield Area Chamber of Commerce (FACC)
204 W Broadway
Fairfield, IA 52556
Ph: (641)472-2111
Fax: (641)472-6510
Co. E-mail: chamber@fairfieldiowa.com
URL: http://fairfieldiowa.com
Contact: Nancy Morrissey, Executive Director
Description: Promotes business and community development in the Fairfield, IA area. **Founded:** 1927. **Publications:** *Chamber Week* (Weekly). **Educational Activities:** Art Walk (Monthly).

51892 ■ Fayette Chamber of Commerce
PO Box 28
Fayette, IA 52142-0028
Ph: (563)425-4316
Co. E-mail: fayettecity@iowatelecom.net
URL: http://www.fayetteia.com
Description: Promotes business and community development in Fayette, IA. **Publications:** *Fayette in Focus*.

51893 ■ *Fayette in Focus*
PO Box 28
Fayette, IA 52142-0028
Ph: (563)425-4316
Co. E-mail: fayettecity@iowatelecom.net
URL: http://www.fayetteia.com

51894 ■ Fort Dodge Area Chamber of Commerce
1406 Central Ave.
Fort Dodge, IA 50501
Ph: (515)955-5500
Fax: (515)955-3245
Co. E-mail: info@fortdodgechamber.com
URL: http://www.fortdodgechamber.com
Contact: Amy Bruno, Director
Description: Promotes business and community development in the Ft. Dodge, IA area. **Founded:** 1920. **Awards:** Catalyst and Athena (Biennial).

51895 ■ Fort Madison Area Chamber of Commerce
614 9th St.
Fort Madison, IA 52627
Ph: (319)372-5471
Fax: (319)372-6404
URL: http://www.fortmadison.com
Contact: Ms. Sarah Cantrell, Coordinator
Description: Seeks to provide an environment conducive to community growth and prosperity designed to promote opportunities that will improve the overall economic strength of the membership.

51896 ■ Garner Chamber of Commerce (GCC)
211 State St.
Garner, IA 50438
Ph: (641)923-3993
Fax: (641)923-3993
Co. E-mail: chamber@qwestoffice.net
URL: http://www.garneriachamber.com
Contact: Marline Lewerke, President
Description: Promotes business and community development in Garner, IA. Sponsors festival.

51897 ■ Greater Cedar Valley Chamber of Commerce - Waterloo
10 W 4th St., Ste. 310
Waterloo, IA 50701
Ph: (319)233-8431
Fax: (319)233-4580
Co. E-mail: jstodd2000@aol.com
URL: http://www.waterloochamber.org
Contact: Jay Stoddard, Director
Description: Promotes business and community development in Waterloo, IA. Conducts educational and community service projects. **Founded:** 1928. **Publications:** *Business Connection* (Monthly). **Edu-**

cational **Activities:** Business After Hours (Monthly). **Awards:** Business of the Year (Annual); Citizen of the Year (Annual); Hall of Fame (Annual); Organization of the Year (Annual); Chamber Volunteer of the Year (Annual).

51898 ■ Greater Des Moines Partnership
700 Locust St., Ste. 100
Des Moines, IA 50309
Ph: (515)286-4950
Fax: (515)286-4974
Co. E-mail: info@desmoinesmetro.com
URL: http://www.desmoinesmetro.com
Contact: Martha A. Willits, Consultant
Description: Promotes business and community development in the greater Des Moines, IA area. **Founded:** 1888. **Publications:** *Association Directory* (Annual); *Employers Directory* (Annual); *Media Guide* (Quarterly).

51899 ■ Greater Muscatine Chamber of Commerce and Industry (GMCCI)
102 Walnut St., Ste. 102
Muscatine, IA 52761-4027
Ph: (563)263-8895
Fax: (563)263-8896
Co. E-mail: chamber@muscatine.com
URL: http://www.muscatine.com/gmcci/index.php
Contact: Jane L. Daufeldt, Executive Director
Description: Promotes business and community development in Muscatine, IA. **Publications:** *Pearl City Progress* (Monthly).

51900 ■ Greenfield Chamber/Main Street and Community Development Corporation
c/o Ginny Kuhfus
201 S 1st St.
Greenfield, IA 50849
Ph: (641)743-8444
Co. E-mail: grfld_cc_ms_dev@iowatelecom.net
URL: http://www.greenfieldiowa.com
Description: Seeks to promote business and community development in and for Greenfield. Activities include Easter Party/Egg Hunt, Wings, Wheels and Whistles Weekend Celebration, the Fall Festival/Pancake Supper, Pre-Holiday Open House, Golden Dollar Night, Numbered Newspaper Contest, Senior Citizen Day, Santa Visit and Daddy Shopping Days.

51901 ■ Grinnell Area Chamber of Commerce
833 4th Ave.
Grinnell, IA 50112
Ph: (641)236-6555
Fax: (641)236-3499
Co. E-mail: admin@getintogrinnell.com
URL: http://www.grinnellchamber.org
Contact: Angela Harrington, President
Description: Promotes business and community development in the Grinnell, IA area.

51902 ■ Grundy Center Chamber of Commerce and Development
c/o Kelly Riskedahl, Co-Dir.
705 F Ave.
Grundy Center, IA 50638
Ph: (319)825-3838
Fax: (319)825-6471
Co. E-mail: chamber@gcmuni.net
URL: http://www.grundycenter.com
Contact: Tiffany Carson, President
Description: Promotes business and community development in Grundy Center, IA.

51903 ■ Guthrie Center Chamber of Commerce (GCCC)
PO Box 193
Guthrie Center, IA 50115
Ph: (641)332-2191
URL: http://www.guthriecenter.com
Contact: Geri Thompson, President
Description: Promotes business and community development in Guthrie Center, IA. Conducts charitable activities. **Founded:** 1937.

51904 ■ Hampton Area Chamber of Commerce (HACC)
5 1st St. SW
Hampton, IA 50441
Ph: (641)456-5668

Fax: (641)456-5660
Co. E-mail: hacc@hamptoniowa.org
URL: http://www.hamptoniowa.org
Contact: Jennifer Gruelke, Board Member
Description: Promotes business and community development in Franklin County, IA. **Founded:** 1950.

51905 ■ Hartley Chamber of Commerce
PO Box 146
Hartley, IA 51346
Ph: (712)928-4278
Co. E-mail: hartleychamber@tcaexpress.net
URL: http://www.hartleybusinesses.com
Contact: Dan Sweeney, President
URL(s): www.hartleyiowa.com. **Description:** Promotes business and community development in Hartley, IA.

51906 ■ Hawarden Area Partnership for Progress (HAPP)
1150 Central Ave.
Hawarden, IA 51023
Ph: (712)551-4433
Co. E-mail: happ@cityofhawarden.com
URL: http://www.cityofhawarden.com
Contact: Patty Anderson, President
URL(s): www.happ-online.com. **Description:** Promotes business and community development in Hawarden, IA. Conducts annual Labor Day weekend celebration. **Founded:** 2001.

51907 ■ *Hobo Guide*
PO Box 63
Britt, IA 50423
Ph: (641)843-3867
Co. E-mail: brittcoc@wctatel.net
URL: http://www.brittiowa.com/chamber/index.htm
Released: Annual **Price:** free.

51908 ■ Humboldt/Dakota City Chamber of Commerce
PO Box 247
Humboldt, IA 50548
Ph: (515)332-1481
Fax: (515)332-1496
Co. E-mail: chamber@hdcchamber.com
URL: http://www.ci.humboldt.ia.us
Contact: Tonya Harklau, Executive Director
Description: Promotes business and community development in the Humboldt/Dakota City, IA area. Sponsors 4th of July festival. **Founded:** 1937. **Publications:** *Business Growth, Community Progress* (Monthly).

51909 ■ Independence Area Chamber of Commerce
PO Box 104
Independence, IA 50644
Ph: (319)334-7178
Fax: (319)334-7394
Co. E-mail: indycommerce@indytel.com
URL: http://www.indycommerce.com
Contact: Tammy Rasmussen, Executive Director
Description: Promotes business and community development in the Independence, IA area. Sponsors festival. **Founded:** 1847. **Publications:** *The Promoter* (Quarterly).

51910 ■ Indianola Chamber of Commerce (ICC)
515 N Jefferson, Ste. D
Indianola, IA 50125
Ph: (515)961-6269
Co. E-mail: chamber@indianolachamber.com
URL: http://www.indianolachamber.com
Contact: Denise Day, Executive Director
Description: Promotes business and community development in Indianola, IA. Sponsors the National Balloon Classic Arts and Crafts Festival. **Publications:** *Business and Industry Insight* (Monthly).

51911 ■ Iowa City Area Chamber of Commerce
325 E Washington St.
Iowa City, IA 52240
Ph: (319)337-9637

Fax: (319)338-9958
Co. E-mail: info@iowacityarea.com
URL: http://www.iowacityarea.com
Contact: Nancy Quellhorst, President
Description: Promotes business and community development in Iowa City and Coralville and Johnson counties, IA. Sponsors Iowa Festival. **Founded:** 1921. **Publications:** *Envision* (Monthly); *Reflections* (Monthly).

51912 ■ Iowa Falls Chamber of Commerce - Main Street
520 Rocksylvania
Iowa Falls, IA 50126-2313
Ph: (641)648-5549
Co. E-mail: chamber@iowafallschamber.com
URL: http://www.iowafallsdevelopment.com/iowafalls-chamber
Description: Area businesses and organizations. Seeks to promote the community of Iowa Falls and enhance the quality of life in the community. Activities include seasonal events, business retention and recruitment efforts, and community promotion activities.

51913 ■ Iowa Great Lakes Area Chamber of Commerce (IGLACC)
c/o Okoboji Tourism
PO Box 215
Okoboji, IA 51355
Free: 800-270-2574
Fax: (712)332-2209
Co. E-mail: info@vacationokoboji.com
URL: http://www.vacationokoboji.com/about-us/Default.aspx
Contact: Tom Kuhlman, Executive Vice President
Description: Promotes business, community development, and tourism in the Iowa Great Lakes area of northwestern Iowa. Conducts charitable activities. Sponsors festival. **Founded:** 1973. **Publications:** *Okoboji Spirit* (Annual).

51914 ■ Jefferson Area Chamber of Commerce
220 N Chestnut St.
Jefferson, IA 50129
Ph: (515)386-2155
Fax: (515)386-2156
Co. E-mail: chamber@jeffersoniowa.com
URL: http://www.gojacc.com
Contact: Amy Milligan, Executive Director
Description: Promotes business and community development in Greene County, Iowa. **Founded:** 1936. **Publications:** *The Chamber Connection* (Monthly); *Chamber Update* (Bimonthly). **Educational Activities:** Bell Tower Festival (Annual); Red Barn Craft Show (Annual). **Awards:** Boss of the Year (Annual); Employee of the Year (Annual); Master Growers Awards (Annual); Above and Beyond the Call Award (Annual).

51915 ■ Jesup Chamber of Commerce
PO Box 592
Jesup, IA 50648-0592
Ph: (319)827-1522
Fax: (319)827-3510
Co. E-mail: todd.rohlfsen@fsb1879.com
URL: http://www.jesupiowa.com
Contact: Rodney Duroe, President
Description: Promotes business and community development in Jesup, IA.

51916 ■ Kalona Area Chamber of Commerce
514 B Ave.
Kalona, IA 52247
Ph: (319)656-2660
Co. E-mail: chamber@kctc.net
URL: http://www.kalonachamber.com
Description: Promotes business and community development in Kalona, IA area.

51917 ■ Keokuk Area Chamber of Commerce
329 Main St.
Keokuk, IA 52632
Ph: (319)524-5055

Fax: (319)524-5016
Co. E-mail: keokukcc@iowatelecom.net
URL: http://www.keokukchamber.com
Contact: Chuck Betts, Executive Director
Description: Promotes business and community development in Keokuk, IA. **Founded:** 1920. **Publications:** *LINK* (Periodic). **Educational Activities:** Chamber's Board of Directors Meeting (Monthly).

51918 ■ Knoxville Chamber of Commerce and Economic Development
309 E Main St.
Knoxville, IA 50138
Ph: (641)828-7555
Fax: (641)828-7978
Co. E-mail: rxjohnson@iowatelecom.net
URL: http://www.discoverknoxville.com
Contact: Roxanne Johnson, Executive Director
Description: Strives to create new wealth and growth in Knoxville, IA. **Founded:** 1944. **Publications:** *Community Insight* (Monthly); *Visitors Guide and Economic Development Directory* (Annual).

51919 ■ Lake City Betterment Association (LCBA)
c/o Alissa Blair, Coordinator
PO Box 72
Lake City, IA 51449
Ph: (712)464-7611
Co. E-mail: betterment@lakecityiowa.com
URL: http://www.lakecityiowa.com
Contact: Jenifer Villhauer, Coordinator
Description: Promotes business and community development in Lake City, IA. Sponsors Western Days July 4th Festival.

51920 ■ LINK
329 Main St.
Keokuk, IA 52632
Ph: (319)524-5055
Fax: (319)524-5016
Co. E-mail: keokukcc@iowatelecom.net
URL: http://www.keokukchamber.com
Contact: Chuck Betts, Executive Director
Released: Periodic

51921 ■ MACC Business News
200 E Main St.
Manchester, IA 52057
Ph: (563)927-4141
Fax: (563)927-2958
Co. E-mail: macc@manchesteriowa.org
URL: http://www.manchesteriowa.org
Contact: Susan Broghammer, President
Released: Monthly

51922 ■ Madison County Chamber of Commerce
73 Jefferson St.
Winterset, IA 50273
Ph: (515)462-1185
Free: 800-298-6119
Fax: (515)462-1393
Co. E-mail: chamber@madisoncounty.com
URL: http://www.madisoncounty.com
Contact: Matt Deppe, Co-Chairperson
Description: Promotes business, community development, and tourism in the Winterset, IA area.

51923 ■ Main Street Chamber of Commerce - Adel Partners
PO Box 73
Adel, IA 50003
Ph: (515)993-5472
Fax: (515)993-3384
Co. E-mail: lori@graficsinc.com
URL: http://www.adelpartners.org
Contact: Lori Brocka, President

51924 ■ Manchester Area Chamber of Commerce
200 E Main St.
Manchester, IA 52057
Ph: (563)927-4141

Fax: (563)927-2958
Co. E-mail: macc@manchesteriowa.org
URL: http://www.manchesteriowa.org
Contact: Susan Broghammer, President
Description: Promotes business and community development in the Manchester, IA area. **Founded:** 1944. **Publications:** *Community Resource Guide* (Annual); *Manchester Area Chamber of Commerce-- Community Resource Guide* (Annual); *MACC Business News* (Monthly). **Awards:** Chamber Person of the Year (Annual); Meritorious Service (Annual).

51925 ■ Manning Chamber of Commerce
PO Box 345
Manning, IA 51455-0354
Ph: (712)655-3541
Fax: (712)655-2478
Co. E-mail: ddoyel@templetonsavingsbank.com
URL: http://www.manningia.com
Contact: Kirk Huehn, President
Description: Promotes business and community development in Manning, IA.

51926 ■ Maquoketa Area Chamber of Commerce
117 S Main St.
Maquoketa, IA 52060
Ph: (563)652-4602
Free: 800-989-4602
Fax: (563)652-3020
Co. E-mail: maqchamber@qwestoffice.net
URL: http://www.maquoketachamber.com
Contact: Stacy Driscoll, Director
Description: Promotes business and community development in the Maquoketa, IA area. **Founded:** 1942. **Publications:** *News In Brief* (Bimonthly). **Awards:** Friends of Agriculture Awards (Annual).

51927 ■ Marshalltown Area Chamber of Commerce
709 S Center St.
Marshalltown, IA 50158
Ph: (641)753-6645
Fax: (641)752-8373
Co. E-mail: info@marshalltown.org
URL: http://www.marshalltown.org
Contact: Ken Anderson, President
Description: Promotes business and community development in the Marshalltown, IA area. Operates the Marshalltown Convention and Visitors Bureau. Convention/Meeting: none. **Founded:** 1898. **Publications:** *Digest* (Monthly); *Marshalltown Works* (Monthly).

51928 ■ Marshalltown Works
709 S Center St.
Marshalltown, IA 50158
Ph: (641)753-6645
Fax: (641)752-8373
Co. E-mail: info@marshalltown.org
URL: http://www.marshalltown.org
Contact: Ken Anderson, President
Released: Monthly

51929 ■ Mason City Area Chamber of Commerce (MCACC)
25 W State St.
Mason City, IA 50401
Ph: (641)423-5724
Fax: (641)423-5725
Co. E-mail: chamber@masoncityia.com
URL: http://www.masoncityia.com
Contact: Robin Anderson, Executive Director
Description: Promotes business and community development in the Mason City, IA area. Sponsors North Iowa Band Festival. **Founded:** 1916.

51930 ■ McGregor/Marquette Chamber of Commerce (MCC)
PO Box 105
McGregor, IA 52157-0105
Ph: (563)873-2186
Free: 800-896-0910

Fax: (563)873-2847
Co. E-mail: mac-marq@alpinecom.net
URL: http://www.mcgreg-marq.org
Description: Promotes business and community development in McGregor and Marquette, IA. Sponsors art shows. **Awards:** Special Recognition (Annual); Volunteer (Annual); Activity (Annual); Beautification (Annual); Historical (Annual).

51931 ■ Media Guide
700 Locust St., Ste. 100
Des Moines, IA 50309
Ph: (515)286-4950
Fax: (515)286-4974
Co. E-mail: info@desmoinesmetro.com
URL: http://www.desmoinesmetro.com
Contact: Martha A. Willits, Consultant
Released: Quarterly

51932 ■ Missouri Valley Chamber of Commerce (MVCC)
100 S 4th St.
Missouri Valley, IA 51555
Ph: (712)642-2553
Fax: (712)642-3771
Co. E-mail: chamberofcommerce1@juno.com
URL: http://www.missourivalleychamber.com
Contact: Mr. Dennis Smith, President
Description: Promotes business and community development in Missouri Valley, IA. Sponsors Loess Hills Indian Market, Cultural Exchange, and Harrison County Fair Parade. **Founded:** 1949. **Publications:** *Caboose on the Loose* (Monthly). **Educational Activities:** Chamber Fair Parade (Annual). **Awards:** Business of the Year (Annual); Leadership (Annual); Volunteer of the Year (Annual).

51933 ■ Monticello Area Chamber of Commerce (MACC)
204 E First St.
Monticello, IA 52310
Ph: (319)465-5626
Fax: (319)465-3527
Co. E-mail: chamber@macc-ia.us
URL: http://www.macc-ia.us/Monticello.shtml
Contact: Kelly Postel, President
Description: Promotes business and community development in Monticello, IA area. **Founded:** 1923.

51934 ■ Mount Pleasant Area Chamber of Commerce (MPACC)
124 S Main St.
Mount Pleasant, IA 52641
Ph: (319)385-3101
Free: 877-385-3103
Fax: (319)385-3012
Co. E-mail: mpaca@mountpleasantiowa.org
URL: http://www.mountpleasantiowa.org/alliance
Contact: Kiley Miller, Executive Vice President
Description: Promotes business and community development in the Mt. Pleasant, IA area. **Founded:** 1939. **Publications:** *Newsline* (Monthly). **Awards:** Expansion Award (Annual).

51935 ■ Mount Vernon Area Chamber of Commerce (MVCC)
213 1st St. NW
Mount Vernon, IA 52314
Ph: (319)895-8742
Fax: (319)895-6108
Co. E-mail: cmv@cityofmtvernon-ia.gov
URL: http://www.cityofmtvernon-ia.gov
Description: Promotes improvement of the strong business environment in Mt. Vernon and Lisbon, IA through the recruitment, retention, and expansion of businesses. Seeks to enhance the quality of life in the area.

51936 ■ Nevada Chamber of Commerce
1015 6th St.
Nevada, IA 50201
Ph: (515)382-6538

Fax: (515)382-3803
Co. E-mail: chamber@midiowa.net
URL: http://www.nevadaiowa.org
Contact: Sara Clausen, Executive Director
Description: Promotes business and community development in Nevada, IA. Provides consulting assistance for existing business and new start-up enterprises. Owns and provides sites for business. **Founded:** 1958.

51937 ■ *News In Brief*
117 S Main St.
Maquoketa, IA 52060
Ph: (563)652-4602
Free: 800-989-4602
Fax: (563)652-3020
Co. E-mail: maqchamber@qwestoffice.net
URL: http://www.maquoketachamber.com
Contact: Stacy Driscoll, Director
Released: Bimonthly

51938 ■ *Newsline*
124 S Main St.
Mount Pleasant, IA 52641
Ph: (319)385-3101
Free: 877-385-3103
Fax: (319)385-3012
Co. E-mail: mpaca@mountpleasantiowa.org
URL: http://www.mountpleasantiowa.org/alliance
Contact: Kiley Miller, Executive Vice President
Released: Monthly **Price:** free.

51939 ■ *Nieuwsbrief*
518 Franklin St.
Pella, IA 50219-1636
Ph: (641)628-2626
Free: 888-746-3882
Fax: (641)628-9697
Co. E-mail: pellacoc@pella.org
URL: http://www.pella.org
Contact: Karen Eischen, Executive Director
Released: Monthly

51940 ■ Northwood Area Chamber of Commerce
PO Box 71
Northwood, IA 50459
Ph: (641)381-0035
Co. E-mail: northwoodchamber@gmail.com
URL: http://www.northwoodchamber.org
Description: Promotes business and community development in the Northwood, IA area.

51941 ■ Norwalk Area Chamber of Commerce (NACC)
1039 Sunset Dr.
Norwalk, IA 50211
Ph: (515)981-0619
Fax: (515)981-1890
Co. E-mail: norwalkchamber@smsn.com
URL: http://www.norwalkchamber.org
Contact: Bryan Greiner, President
Description: Provides leadership for the advancement of economic development, promotion of members, and enhances the quality of life for the Norwalk area. **Publications:** *Buyer's Guide* (Annual).

51942 ■ Oelwein Chamber and Area Development (OCAD)
25 W Charles St.
Oelwein, IA 50662
Ph: (319)283-1105
Fax: (319)283-2890
Co. E-mail: ocad@oelwein.com
URL: http://www.oelwein.com
Contact: Sally Falb, Executive Director
Description: Promotes business and community development in Oelwein, IA. **Founded:** 1918. **Publications:** *Oelwein Outlook* (Monthly).

51943 ■ *Oelwein Outlook*
25 W Charles St.
Oelwein, IA 50662
Ph: (319)283-1105
Fax: (319)283-2890
Co. E-mail: ocad@oelwein.com
URL: http://www.oelwein.com
Contact: Sally Falb, Executive Director
Released: Monthly

51944 ■ *Okoboji Spirit*
c/o Okoboji Tourism
PO Box 215
Okoboji, IA 51355
Free: 800-270-2574
Fax: (712)332-2209
Co. E-mail: info@vacationokoboji.com
URL: http://www.vacationokoboji.com/about-us/Default.aspx
Contact: Tom Kuhlman, Executive Vice President
Released: Annual **Price:** free.

51945 ■ Onawa Chamber of Commerce (OCC)
c/o Aaron Stangel, Pres.
707 Iowa Ave.
Onawa, IA 51040
Ph: (712)423-1801
Fax: (712)423-4622
Co. E-mail: chamber@onawa.com
URL: http://www.onawa.com
Contact: Aaron Stangel, President
Description: Promotes business and community development in Onawa, IA. Sponsors Onawa Lewis and Clark Festival. **Founded:** 1949. **Publications:** *Chamber News* (Monthly).

51946 ■ Orange City Chamber of Commerce
PO Box 36
Orange City, IA 51041
Ph: (712)707-4510
Fax: (712)707-4523
Co. E-mail: chamberwindmill@frontiernet.net
URL: http://www.orangecityiowa.com
Contact: Mike Hofman, Executive Director
Description: Seeks to advance the economic, professional, industrial, cultural and civic welfare of the Orange City area.

51947 ■ Osage Chamber of Commerce
808 Main St.
Osage, IA 50461
Ph: (641)732-3163
Fax: (641)732-3163
Co. E-mail: chamber@osage.net
URL: http://www.osage.net/~chamber
Contact: Wendy Heuton, Executive Director
Description: Promotes business and community development in Osage, IA.

51948 ■ Osceola Chamber-Main Street
PO Box 425
Osceola, IA 50213
Ph: (641)342-4200
Fax: (641)342-6353
Co. E-mail: ocms@iowatelecom.net
URL: http://www.osceolachamber.com
Contact: Dave Walkup, President
Description: Promotes business and community development in Osceola, IA.

51949 ■ Oskaloosa Area Chamber and Development Group (OACDG)
124 N Market St.
Oskaloosa, IA 52577-2827
Ph: (641)672-2591
Free: 888-562-6759
Fax: (641)672-2047
Co. E-mail: oskycofc@oacdg.org
URL: http://www.oacdg.org
Contact: Connie Bryan, Manager
Description: Promotes business and community development in the Oskaloosa, IA area. Maintains business referrals. **Founded:** 1863. **Publications:** *Communicator* (Monthly); *Oskaloosa Area Industrial Products and Services Directory* (Periodic).

51950 ■ *Oskaloosa Area Industrial Products and Services Directory*
124 N Market St.
Oskaloosa, IA 52577-2827
Ph: (641)672-2591
Free: 888-562-6759
Fax: (641)672-2047
Co. E-mail: oskycofc@oacdg.org
URL: http://www.oacdg.org
Contact: Connie Bryan, Manager
Released: Periodic

51951 ■ Ottumwa Area Chamber of Commerce (OACC)
217 E Main St.
Ottumwa, IA 52501
Ph: (641)682-3465
Co. E-mail: info@ottumwaiowa.com
URL: http://www.ottumwaiowa.com/chamber/index.html
Contact: Terry McNitt, Executive Director
Description: Promotes business and community development in the Ottumwa, IA area. **Founded:** 1902. **Publications:** *Connections* (Monthly). **Awards:** Gene Shultz Award (Annual).

51952 ■ *Outlook*
1442 Washington St.
Eldora, IA 50627
Ph: (641)939-3241
Fax: (641)939-7555
Co. E-mail: eldoraecondev@heartofiowa.net
URL: http://www.eldoraiowa.com
Contact: Deb Crosser, Executive Director

51953 ■ *Pearl City Progress*
102 Walnut St., Ste. 102
Muscatine, IA 52761-4027
Ph: (563)263-8895
Fax: (563)263-8896
Co. E-mail: chamber@muscatine.com
URL: http://www.muscatine.com/gmcci/index.php
Contact: Jane L. Daufeldt, Executive Director
Released: Monthly

51954 ■ Pella Chamber of Commerce (PCC)
518 Franklin St.
Pella, IA 50219-1636
Ph: (641)628-2626
Free: 888-746-3882
Fax: (641)628-9697
Co. E-mail: pellacoc@pella.org
URL: http://www.pella.org
Contact: Karen Eischen, Executive Director
Description: Promotes business and community development in Pella, IA. Sponsors Fall Festival; bestows annual Community Service Award. **Publications:** *Chamber of Commerce Directory* (Annual); *Nieuwsbrief* (Monthly).

51955 ■ Perry Chamber of Commerce
c/o Julie Schieb, Office Asst.
1102 Willis Ave.
Perry, IA 50220-1556
Ph: (515)465-2446
URL: http://www.perryia.org
Contact: Julie Schieb, Assistant
Description: Strives to promote individual cooperation for the positive advancement of business and community. **Publications:** *Chamber Chatter* (Monthly).

51956 ■ Pocahontas Chamber of Commerce
PO Box 124
Pocahontas, IA 50574
Ph: (712)335-3695
Co. E-mail: pocahontaschamber@gmail.com
URL: http://www.pocahontaschamber.com
Contact: Mary Sturtz, President
Description: Promotes business and community development in Pocahontas, IA.

51957 ■ *Premier Living Guide*
PO Box 65320
West Des Moines, IA 50265
Ph: (515)225-6009
Fax: (515)225-7129
Co. E-mail: info@wdmchamber.org
URL: http://www.wdmchamber.org
Contact: Linda Hulleman, Executive Director
Released: Annual

51958 ■ *The Promoter*
PO Box 104
Independence, IA 50644
Ph: (319)334-7178
Fax: (319)334-7394
Co. E-mail: indycommerce@indytel.com
URL: http://www.indycommerce.com
Contact: Tammy Rasmussen, Executive Director
Released: Quarterly

51959 ■ Red Oak Chamber of Commerce
307 E Reed St.
Red Oak, IA 51566
Ph: (712)623-4821
Fax: (712)623-4822
Co. E-mail: adminasst@redoakiowa.com
URL: http://www.redoakiowa.com
Contact: Jodie Smith, Specialist
Description: Promotes business and community development in Red Oak, IA. **Publications:** *Red Oak Chamber of Commerce ChamberGram* (Monthly).

51960 ■ *Red Oak Chamber of Commerce ChamberGram*
307 E Reed St.
Red Oak, IA 51566
Ph: (712)623-4821
Fax: (712)623-4822
Co. E-mail: adminasst@redoakiowa.com
URL: http://www.redoakiowa.com
Contact: Jodie Smith, Specialist
Released: Monthly

51961 ■ *Reflections*
325 E Washington St.
Iowa City, IA 52240
Ph: (319)337-9637
Fax: (319)338-9958
Co. E-mail: info@iowacityarea.com
URL: http://www.iowacityarea.com
Contact: Nancy Quellhorst, President
Released: Monthly

51962 ■ Rock Rapids Community Affairs Corporation
206 1st Ave.
Rock Rapids, IA 51246
Ph: (712)472-3456
Fax: (712)472-2764
Co. E-mail: chamber@rockrapids.com
URL: http://www.rockrapids.com
Contact: Angie Jager, Executive Director
Description: Promotes social and economic development in Rock Rapid, IA. **Publications:** *Chamber Affairs.*

51963 ■ Rock Valley Chamber of Commerce (RVCC)
PO Box 89
Rock Valley, IA 51247
Ph: (712)476-9300
Fax: (712)476-9116
URL: http://www.rockvalleychamber.com
Contact: Curt Strouth, Director
Description: Promotes business and community development in Rock Valley, IA. Sponsors yearly basketball tournament. Publications: none.

51964 ■ Rockwell City Chamber and Development
3012 270th St.
Rockwell City, IA 50579
Ph: (712)297-8874
Co. E-mail: rcdev@iowatelecom.net
URL: http://www.rockwellcity.com
Description: Promotes business and community development in Rockwell City, IA.

51965 ■ St. Ansgar Chamber of Commerce
PO Box 133
St. Ansgar, IA 50472-0133
Ph: (641)736-4444
Co. E-mail: stagreenhouse@iowatelecom.net
URL: http://www.stansgar.org
Description: Promotes business and community development in St. Ansgar, IA. Sponsors Town and Country Day.

51966 ■ Shelby County Chamber of Commerce
1101 7th St.
Harlan, IA 51537
Ph: (712)755-2114
Free: 888-876-1774

Fax: (712)755-2115
Co. E-mail: info@exploreshelbycounty.com
URL: http://www.exploreshelbycounty.com
Contact: Dawn Cundiff, Executive Director
Description: Promotes business and community development in Harlan, IA.

51967 ■ Sheldon Chamber and Development Corp. (SCDC)
416 9th St.
Sheldon, IA 51201-0276
Ph: (712)324-2813
Fax: (712)324-4602
Co. E-mail: smatus@sheldoniowa.com
URL: http://www.sheldoniowa.com
Contact: Shanelle Matus, Director
Description: Promotes business and tourism in Sheldon, IA. **Telecommunication Services:** mgaul@sheldoniowa.com.

51968 ■ Shenandoah Chamber and Industry Association
100 Maple St.
Shenandoah, IA 51601
Ph: (712)246-3455
Fax: (712)246-3456
Co. E-mail: chamber@shenandoahiowa.net
URL: http://shenandoahiowa.net
Contact: Shelly Smith, Director, Marketing
Description: Promotes business and community development in Shenandoah, IA. Sponsors Master Growers Contest, Shen Fest, Business Horizons program, Teacher Appreciation breakfast, Agriculture Banquet, Administration Staff Luncheon, Legislative Coffees, Industry Coffees, Teen Art Show, Spring Craft Fair, CABA Tournament, and Christmas Parade. **Founded:** 1941. **Publications:** *Chamber Report* (Monthly).

51969 ■ *Shore Line*
119 W 6th St.
Storm Lake, IA 50588
Ph: (712)732-3780
Free: 888-752-4692
Fax: (712)732-1511
Co. E-mail: slc@stormlake.org
URL: http://www.stormlakechamber.com
Contact: Gary Lalone, Executive Director
Released: Monthly

51970 ■ Sibley Chamber of Commerce (SCC)
310 9th St.
Sibley, IA 51249
Ph: (712)754-3212
Fax: (712)754-3212
Co. E-mail: chamber@hickorytech.net
URL: http://www.sibleyiowa.net
Contact: Amy Smith, Executive Director
Description: Promotes business and community development in Sibley, IA. Sponsors annual Good Ole Summertime festival. **Founded:** 1915.

51971 ■ Sidney Chamber of Commerce (SCC)
PO Box 401
Sidney, IA 51652
Ph: (712)374-2023
Co. E-mail: info@sidneyia.net
URL: http://www.sidneyia.net
Contact: Mike Ross, President
Description: Promotes business and community development in Sidney, IA. Sponsors Sidney Iowa Rodeo. **Publications:** *WSJ* (Periodic).

51972 ■ Sioux Center Chamber of Commerce (SCCC)
303 N Main Ave.
Sioux Center, IA 51250
Ph: (712)722-3457
Free: 800-SXC-ENTR
Fax: (712)722-3465
Co. E-mail: scchambr@mtcnet.net
URL: http://www.siouxcenterchamber.com
Contact: Ardith Lein, Executive Director
Description: Promotes business and community development in Sioux Center, IA. **Founded:** 1967. **Publications:** *Chamber Communique* (Monthly).

51973 ■ *Siouxland Business*
101 Pierce St.
Sioux City, IA 51101
Ph: (712)255-7903
Free: 800-228-7903
Fax: (712)258-7578
Co. E-mail: chamber@siouxlandchamber.com
URL: http://www.siouxlandchamber.com
Contact: Chris McGowan, President
Released: Monthly

51974 ■ Siouxland Chamber of Commerce (SCC)
101 Pierce St.
Sioux City, IA 51101
Ph: (712)255-7903
Free: 800-228-7903
Fax: (712)258-7578
Co. E-mail: chamber@siouxlandchamber.com
URL: http://www.siouxlandchamber.com
Contact: Chris McGowan, President
Description: Promotes business and community development in Sioux City, IA. **Publications:** *Siouxland Business* (Monthly). **Educational Activities:** Siouxland Chamber of Commerce Dinner (Annual). **Awards:** W. Edwards Deming Entrepreneurial Excellence Award (Annual).

51975 ■ Spencer Chamber of Commerce
122 W 5th St.
Spencer, IA 51301-7937
Ph: (712)262-5680
Fax: (712)262-5747
Co. E-mail: spencerchamber@smunet.net
URL: http://www.spenceriowachamber.org
Contact: Robert Rose, Executive Director
Description: Promotes business and community development in Spencer, Clay County and Northwest IA. **Founded:** 1890. **Publications:** *Business Monthly* (Monthly).

51976 ■ Storm Lake Chamber of Commerce (SLCC)
119 W 6th St.
Storm Lake, IA 50588
Ph: (712)732-3780
Free: 888-752-4692
Fax: (712)732-1511
Co. E-mail: slc@stormlake.org
URL: http://www.stormlakechamber.com
Contact: Gary Lalone, Executive Director
Description: Promotes business and community development and tourism in the Storm Lake, IA area. **Publications:** *Shore Line* (Monthly). **Awards:** Business Person of the Year (Annual); Chamber Involvement of the Year (Annual); Customer Service of the Year (Annual); Improvement of the Year (Annual).

51977 ■ Story City Chamber of Commerce
602 Broad St.
Story City, IA 50248
Ph: (515)733-4214
Fax: (515)733-4504
Co. E-mail: chamber@storycity.net
URL: http://www.storycity.net
Contact: Carolyn Honeycutt, Director
Description: Promotes business and community development in Story City, IA. Sponsors Scandinavian Days. **Founded:** 1908.

51978 ■ Tama/Toledo Area Chamber of Commerce
PO Box 367
Toledo, IA 52342
Ph: (641)484-6661
Fax: (641)484-6540
Co. E-mail: tama.toledochamber@yahoo.com
URL: http://www.tamatoledo.com
Contact: Carolyn Dolezal, Coordinator
Description: Promotes business and community development in Toledo, IA.

51979 ■ *Urbandale Buyers' Guide*
3600 86th St.
Urbandale, IA 50322
Ph: (515)331-6855

Fax: (515)278-3927
Co. E-mail: info@urbandalechamber.com
URL: http://www.urbandalechamber.com
Contact: Tiffany Menke, Executive Director
Released: Annual **Price:** free.

51980 ■ *Urbandale Chamber Annual Report*
3600 86th St.
Urbandale, IA 50322
Ph: (515)331-6855
Fax: (515)278-3927
Co. E-mail: info@urbandalechamber.com
URL: http://www.urbandalechamber.com
Contact: Tiffany Menke, Executive Director
Released: Annual

51981 ■ Urbandale Chamber of Commerce
3600 86th St.
Urbandale, IA 50322
Ph: (515)331-6855
Fax: (515)278-3927
Co. E-mail: info@urbandalechamber.com
URL: http://www.urbandalechamber.com
Contact: Tiffany Menke, Executive Director
Description: Promotes business and community development in Urbandale, IA. **Publications:** *Urbandale Buyers' Guide* (Annual); *Urbandale Chamber Annual Report* (Annual); *Urbandale Restaurant Guide* (Annual); *Urbandale Buyers Guide* (Annual).

51982 ■ *Urbandale Restaurant Guide*
3600 86th St.
Urbandale, IA 50322
Ph: (515)331-6855
Fax: (515)278-3927
Co. E-mail: info@urbandalechamber.com
URL: http://www.urbandalechamber.com
Contact: Tiffany Menke, Executive Director
Released: Annual

51983 ■ *Visitors Guide and Economic Development Directory*
309 E Main St.
Knoxville, IA 50138
Ph: (641)828-7555
Fax: (641)828-7978
Co. E-mail: rxjohnson@iowatelecom.net
URL: http://www.discoverknoxville.com
Contact: Roxanne Johnson, Executive Director
Released: Annual

51984 ■ Walcott Chamber of Commerce
c/o City of Walcott
128 W Lincoln St.
Walcott, IA 52773-7751
Ph: (563)284-6571
Fax: (563)284-6984
URL: http://www.cityofwalcott.com
Contact: Wendy Minnick, Chairperson

51985 ■ Washington Chamber of Commerce
205 W Main St.
Washington, IA 52353
Ph: (319)653-3272
Fax: (319)653-5805
Co. E-mail: washcofc@iowatelecom.net
URL: http://www.washingtoniowachamber.com
Contact: Tim Coffey, Director
Description: Promotes business and community development in Washington, IA. **Founded:** 1935.

51986 ■ *Waterloo-Cedar Falls Business Directory*
10 Main St.
Cedar Falls, IA 50613-0367
Ph: (319)266-3593
Fax: (319)277-4325
Co. E-mail: info@greatercedarvalleychamber.com
URL: http://www.cedarfalls.org
Contact: Kris Hansen, Chairman
Released: Annual

51987 ■ Waukon Chamber of Commerce
101 W Main St.
Waukon, IA 52172
Ph: (563)568-4110

Fax: (563)568-6990
Co. E-mail: waukoncc@mchsi.com
URL: http://www.waukon.org
Contact: Danny Schlitter, Executive Director
Description: Promotes business and community development in Waukon, IA. Publications: none. **Founded:** 1952. **Subscriptions:** 29000.

51988 ■ Waverly Area Development Group (WADG)
112 W Bremer Ave., Ste. A
Waverly, IA 50677
Ph: (319)352-4526
Fax: (319)352-0136
Co. E-mail: waverly@wl-p.net
URL: http://wadg.waverlyia.com/index.asp
Contact: Kelly Engelken, Executive Director
Description: Encompasses Chamber of Commerce, Main Street, tourism and quality of life. **Founded:** 2000.

51989 ■ West Bend Chamber of Commerce
PO Box 366
West Bend, IA 50597
Ph: (515)887-2181
Co. E-mail: chamber@westbendiowa.com
URL: http://www.westbendiowa.com
Contact: Karen Schwartzkopf, Publisher
Description: Serves the members and community by preserving and encouraging growth and development in the West Bend area.

51990 ■ West Des Moines Chamber of Commerce (WDMCC)
PO Box 65320
West Des Moines, IA 50265
Ph: (515)225-6009
Fax: (515)225-7129
Co. E-mail: info@wdmchamber.org
URL: http://www.wdmchamber.org
Contact: Linda Hulleman, Executive Director
Description: Promotes business and community development in West Des Moines, IA. Sponsors Valley Arts Festival. **Founded:** 1938. **Publications:** *Premier Living Guide* (Annual); *Premier Living Guide* (Annual); *West Side Story* (Monthly). **Educational Activities:** West Des Moines Chamber of Commerce Dinner (Annual); West Des Moines Chamber of Commerce Luncheon (Monthly). **Awards:** Citizen of the Year (Annual).

51991 ■ *West Side Story*
PO Box 65320
West Des Moines, IA 50265
Ph: (515)225-6009
Fax: (515)225-7129
Co. E-mail: info@wdmchamber.org
URL: http://www.wdmchamber.org
Contact: Linda Hulleman, Executive Director
Released: Monthly **Price:** free for members.

51992 ■ West Union Chamber of Commerce (WUCC)
101 N Vine St.
West Union, IA 52175-0071
Ph: (563)422-3070
Free: 800-477-5073
Co. E-mail: wuchamber@alpinecom.net
URL: http://www.westunion.com
Contact: Robin Bostrom, Executive Director
Description: Promotes business and community development in the West Union, IA area. **Publications:** *Chamber News* (Monthly). **Awards:** Citizen of the Year (Annual).

51993 ■ Williamsburg Chamber of Commerce
c/o Barbara Hopp
PO Box 982
Williamsburg, IA 52361
Ph: (319)668-1500
Co. E-mail: jonesweb@iowatelecom.net
URL: http://www.williamsburgiowa.org
Description: Promotes business and community development in Williamsburg, IA. Sponsors annual Kids Day. Provides seasonal promotions for area merchants.

51994 ■ Wilton Chamber of Commerce (WACC)
118 W 4th St.
Wilton, IA 52778-0005
Ph: (563)732-2330
Fax: (563)732-2332
URL: http://www.wiltoniowa.org/coc.php
Contact: Lisa Kublik, President
Description: Strives to make Wilton a better place to live and do business. Seeks to promote commercial, industrial and civic development. Activities include a smorgasbord in May; Wilfundy, a golf day for members and their customers, in June; Founders Day in August; Christmas Activities in December. **Founded:** 1961. **Publications:** *Chamber Connection* (Quarterly).

51995 ■ *WSJ*
PO Box 401
Sidney, IA 51652
Ph: (712)374-2023
Co. E-mail: info@sidneyia.net
URL: http://www.sidneyia.net
Contact: Mike Ross, President
Released: Periodic

MINORITY BUSINESS ASSISTANCE PROGRAMS

51996 ■ Iowans for Social and Economic Development - Iowa Women's Enterprise Center
United Way Human Service Bldg.
1111 9th St., Ste. 380
Des Moines, IA 50314
Ph: (515)283-0940
Co. E-mail: info@isediowa.org
URL: http://www.isedventures.org
Contact: Linda Firkins, President (Acting)
Description: Offers female entrepreneurs business financing, technical assistance, and training to start a small business.

FINANCING AND LOAN PROGRAMS

51997 ■ Aavin Equity Partners, LLC
118 3rd Ave. SE, Ste. 630
Cedar Rapids, IA 52401
Ph: (319)247-1072
Fax: (319)363-9519
URL: http://www.aavin.com
Contact: James D. Thorp, Managing Partner
E-mail: jthorp@aavin.com
Preferred Investment Size: $500,000 to $3,000,000. **Investment Policies:** Early, first, second, and third stage, buyouts, recapitalization, and late stage. **Industry Preferences:** Medical devices and services, telecommunications, financial services, manufacturing and distribution, industrial products and services, and computer and software. **Geographic Preference:** Middle America: the states located between the two major mountain ranges.

51998 ■ Allsop Venture Partners / AAVIN
118 3rd Ave. SE, Ste. 630
Cedar Rapids, IA 52401
Ph: (319)247-1072
Fax: (319)363-9519
URL: http://www.aavin.com
Contact: James D. Thorp, Managing Partner
E-mail: jthorp@aavin.com
Preferred Investment Size: $500,000 to $3,000,000. **Industry Preferences:** communications and media, computer hardware and software, semiconductors and other electronics, medical and health, consumer related, industrial and energy, transportation, financial services, business service, and manufacturing. **Geographic Preference:** Middle America: the states located between the two major mountain ranges.

51999 ■ Berthel Fisher & Company Planning, Inc.
701 Tama St., Bldg. B
Marion, IA 52302-0609
Ph: (319)447-5700

Free: 800-356-5234
Fax: (319)447-4250
URL: http://www.berthel.com
Contact: Thomas J. Berthel, Chief Executive Officer
E-mail: tberthel@berthel.com
Geographic Preference: Midwest.

52000 ■ InvestAmerica Venture Group, Inc.
101 2nd St. SE, Ste. 800
Cedar Rapids, IA 52401
Ph: (319)363-8249
Fax: (319)363-9683
URL: http://www.investamericaventuregroup.com
Contact: David R. Schroder, President
Preferred Investment Size: $1,000,000 to
$2,000,000. **Industry Preferences:** Other products,
industrial and energy, Internet specific, communications and media, consumer related, computer hardware, computer software and services, semiconductors and other electronics, biotechnology, medical
and health. **Geographic Preference:** U.S.

PROCUREMENT ASSISTANCE PROGRAMS

52001 ■ Iowa Procurement Outreach Center
2701 SE Convenience Blvd., Ste. 13
2272 Howe Hall, CIRAS, Ste. 2620
Ankeny, IA 50021
Ph: (515)289-0281
Fax: (515)294-4483
Co. E-mail: bconey@ciras.iastate.edu
URL: http://www.ciras.iastate.edu
Description: Helps small businesses secure federal
government contracts.

**52002 ■ Iowa Procurement Technical
Assistance Center - Iowa State University
Extension Office - Center for Industrial
Research and Service (CIRAS)**
2272 Howe Hall, Ste. 2620
Ames, IA 50011
Ph: (515)294-3420
Fax: (515)294-4925
Co. E-mail: ciras.info@iastate.edu
URL: http://www.ciras.iastate.edu
Description: Provides assistance to business in
marketing products and services to the Federal, state
and local governments.

**52003 ■ Iowa Procurement Technical
Assistance Center - Iowa State University of
Science & Technology - Center For Industrial
Research & Service (CIRAS)**
2272 Howe Hall, Ste. 2620
Ames, IA 50011-2272
Ph: (515)294-3420
Fax: (515)294-4925
Co. E-mail: ciras.info@iastate.edu
URL: http://www.ciras.iastate.edu/procurement
Contact: Ronald A. Cox, Director
E-mail: bogaczyk@iastate.edu
Description: Provide assistance to business in
marketing products and services to the federal, state
and local governments.

**52004 ■ Iowa Procurement Technical
Assistance Center - Outreach Center**
2701 SE Convenience Blvd., Ste. 13
Ankeny, IA 50021
Ph: (515)289-0281
Fax: (515)294-4483
Co. E-mail: bconey@ciras.iastate.edu
URL: http://www.ciras.iastate.edu
Contact: Kathleen Bryan, Director
Description: Helps small businesses secure federal
government contracts.

INCUBATORS/RESEARCH AND TECHNOLOGY PARKS

52005 ■ Iowa State University Research Park
2711 S. Loop Dr., Ste. 4050
Ames, IA 50010-8648
Ph: (515)296-PARK

Fax: (515)296-9924
URL: http://www.isupark.org/
Description: A small business incubator which identifies technology-based concepts and businesses at
early stages of development and provides an environment for their growth.

**52006 ■ John Pappajohn Entrepreneurial
Center**
North Iowa Area Community College
500 College Dr.
Mason City, IA 50401
Ph: (641)422-4111
Free: 888-466-4222
Co. E-mail: zaniojam@niacc.edu
URL: http://www.niacc.edu/pappajohn/
Contact: Mark Olchefske, Director
Description: Provides business consulting, access
to capital, networking events, business acceleration
services, and a variety of educational opportunities.

52007 ■ New Ventures Initiative
331 W. Third St., Ste. 100
Davenport, IA 52801
Ph: (563)327-0160
Co. E-mail: info@newventuresinc.com
URL: http://www.newventuresinc.com/
Contact: Chad Stamper, Director
Description: A small business incubator providing
professionals with real world business experience to
help develop businesses, commercialize technologies, and prepare new companies for the investment
community.

**52008 ■ University of Iowa Research Park -
Business Incubation Program**
2500 Crosspark Rd.
100 Oakdale Campus, Rm. 109 TIC
Coralville, IA 52241
Ph: (319)335-4063
Fax: (319)335-4550
Co. E-mail: diane-gallagher@uiowa.edu
URL: http://enterprise.uiowa.edu/researchpark/index.
php
Description: A small business incubator fostering
the development of new business ventures that make
use of advanced technology, offering services and
facilities to start-up businesses and established
companies eager to initiate new endeavors. Comprised of the BioVentures Center Facility and the
Technology Innovation Center.

EDUCATIONAL PROGRAMS

**52009 ■ Des Moines Area Community
College - Urban Campus**
1100 7th St.
Des Moines, IA 50314
Ph: (515)244-4226
Free: 800-362-2127
Fax: (515)248-7253
URL: http://www.dmacc.org
Description: A wide variety of courses and workshops are offered to the working student wishing to
develop or update specific occupational skills.
Programs emphasize both fundamental concepts and
practical experience to assure thorough competence
in the chosen field. The Small Business Management
Education Program offers a number of courses for
credit and noncredit status--designed to meet the
educational needs of the small business owner.

**52010 ■ Iowa Lakes Community College
(Estherville)**
300 S 18th St.
Estherville, IA 51334
Ph: (712)362-2604
Free: 800-521-5054
Fax: (712)362-8363
Co. E-mail: dreimer@iowalakes.edu
URL: http://www.ilcc.cc.ia.us
Description: Two-year college offering a small business management program.

52011 ■ Marshalltown Community College
3700 S Center St.
Marshalltown, IA 50158
Ph: (641)752-7106

Free: 866-622-4748
Fax: (641)752-8149
Co. E-mail: mccinfo@iavalley.edu
URL: http://www.iavalley.cc.ia.us/mcc
Description: Two-year college offering a small business course through the continuing education program.

LEGISLATIVE ASSISTANCE

**52012 ■ Iowa Senate Committee on Small
Business, Economic Development and
Tourism**
State Capitol Bldg.
E 12th and Grand
Des Moines, IA 50319
Ph: (515)281-5381
Fax: (319)938-2659
URL: http://www.legis.state.ia.us

PUBLICATIONS

52013 ■ *Business Record*
100 4th St.
Des Moines, IA 50309
Ph: (515)288-3336
Fax: (515)288-0309
URL: http://www.businessrecord.com

52014 ■ *Innovation in Iowa*
137 Lynn Ave.
Ames, IA 50014-7198
Free: 800-373-7232
Fax: (515)292-0020
URL: http://www.Iowsbe.org/
Ed: Bryan Ziegler. **Price:** $7.00. **Description:** Offers
information on developing and marketing products.

52015 ■ *Smart Start your Iowa Business*
PSI Research
300 N. Valley Dr.
Grants Pass, OR 97526
Ph: (503)479-9464
Free: 800-228-2275
Fax: (503)476-1479
Co. E-mail: info@psi-research.com
URL: http://www.psi-research.com
Ed: Michael D. Jenkins. **Released:** Revised edition,
1992. **Price:** $29.95 (looseleaf binder); $24.95
(paper). **Description:** Part of the Successful Business Library series.

**52016 ■ *Starting and Operating a Business
in Iowa: A Step-by-Step Guide***
PSI Research
300 N. Valley Dr.
Grants Pass, OR 97526
Ph: (503)479-9464
Free: 800-228-2275
Fax: (503)476-1479
Co. E-mail: psi2@magick.net
Ed: Michael D. Jenkins. **Released:** Revised edition,
1992. **Price:** $29.95 (looseleaf binder); $24.95
(paper). **Description:** Part of the Successful Business Library series.

52017 ■ *Starting a Small Business in Iowa*
Iowa State University
137 Lynn Ave.
Ames, IA 50014-7198
Free: 800-373-7232
Fax: (515)292-0020
Ed: Bryan Ziegler. **Price:** $10.00. **Description:**
Provides details on Iowa resources and requirements,
from marketing surveys to insurance needs and
licensing permits.

SMALL BUSINESS DEVELOPMENT CENTERS

52018 ■ Kansas Small Business Development Center at Fort Hays State University (FHSU KSBDC)
Fort Hays State University
Custer Hall 105
600 Park St.
Hays, KS 67601
Ph: (785)628-5615
Fax: (785)628-4163
Co. E-mail: ksbdc@fhsu.edu
URL: http://www.fhsu.edu/ksbdc
Contact: Ronald Newman, Director
Description: Represents and promotes the small business sector. Provides management assistance to current and prospective small business owners. Helps to improve management skills and expand the products and services of members.

52019 ■ Kansas Small Business Development Center, Lead Office (KSBDC)
214 SW 6th St., Ste. 301
Topeka, KS 66603-3719
Ph: (785)296-6514
Free: 877-625-7232
Fax: (785)291-3261
Co. E-mail: ksbdc.gpanichello@fhsu.edu
URL: http://ksbdc.kansas.gov/Pages/default.aspx
Contact: Mr. Greg Panichello, Director
Description: Provides free, one-on-one counseling designed to find practical solutions to business problems.

SMALL BUSINESS ASSISTANCE PROGRAMS

52020 ■ Business and Technology Institute - Small Business Development Center
Pittsburg State University
1501 S. Joplin St.
Pittsburg, KS 66762
Ph: (620)235-4920
Fax: (620)235-4919
Co. E-mail: ksbdc@pittstate.edu
URL: http://www.pittstate.edu/bti/sbdc/
Contact: Kathryn Richard, Director
Description: Provides one-stop managerial, financial, and technical assistance to new and expanding businesses in Southeast Kansas, Missouri, Oklahoma, and Arkansas.

52021 ■ Kansas Department of Commerce - Agriculture Marketing
1000 SW Jackson St., Ste. 100
Topeka, KS 66612
Ph: (785)296-3737
Fax: (785)296-3776
Co. E-mail: ruraldev@kansascommerce.com
URL: http://www.kansascommerce.com
Description: Provides marketing assistance through food shows, seminars, and media promotions.

52022 ■ Kansas Department of Commerce - Business Development Division
1000 SW Jackson St., Ste. 100
Topeka, KS 66612
Ph: (785)296-5298
Fax: (785)296-3490
Co. E-mail: busdev@kansascommerce.com
URL: http://www.kansascommerce.com/
Description: Promotes the growth, diversification, and retention of business and industry in Kansas. Advocates on behalf of small businesses. Act as a clearinghouse for information on permits and licenses. Maintains six regional offices to provide assistance to small businesses.

52023 ■ Kansas Department of Commerce - Trade Development Division
Curtis State Office Bldg., Ste. 100
1000 SW Jackson St.
Topeka, KS 66612
Ph: (785)296-1866
Fax: (785)296-5263
Co. E-mail: jwatson@kansascommerce.com
URL: http://www.kansascommerce.com
Contact: John Watson, Director
Description: Provides information and assistance to businesses interested in international trade. Services offered include identifying agents and distributors worldwide, assisting in market development, providing technical information, offering world trade statistical data, and trade lead information services.

52024 ■ Kansas Technology Enterprise Corporation
214 SW 6th St., 1st Fl.
Topeka, KS 66603
Ph: (785)296-5272
Fax: (785)296-1160
Co. E-mail: info@ktec.com
URL: http://www.ktec.com
Contact: Kevin Carr, Chief Executive Officer
Description: Provides technical information and referral services. Provides funds for technology-based research.

52025 ■ Wichita State University - College of Education Technology Center
104 Corbin Education Ctr.
Campus Box 131
1845 Fairmount
Wichita, KS 67260-0131
Ph: (316)978-3301
Fax: (316)978-3302
Co. E-mail: day.radenbaugh@wichita.edu
URL: http://webs.wichita.edu/?u=coetechp=/index/
Description: Provides training, seminars, and technical information to engineers, managers, and other employees.

SCORE OFFICES

52026 ■ Emporia SCORE

52027 ■ Golden Belt SCORE
Co. E-mail: mcpmcvlaw@carrollsweb.com

52028 ■ McPherson SCORE
Co. E-mail: gvellwood@cox.net

52029 ■ North Central Kansas SCORE
Co. E-mail: dmswenson@dustdevil.com

52030 ■ SCORE Ark Valley
205 E Ninth St.
Winfield, KS 67156
Ph: (316)221-1617
Co. E-mail: arkvalleyscore317@yahoo.com
Contact: Wally Bell, Chairman
Description: Provides free business counseling and management training programs for small business owners/managers, and for those who plan to start a new business. **Founded:** 1970.

52031 ■ SCORE Hutchinson
One E 9th Ave.
Hutchinson, KS 67501
Ph: (620)665-8468
Fax: (620)665-7619
URL: http://hutchinson.score.org/chapters/hutchinson-score
Description: Provides professional guidance and information to America's small businesses.

52032 ■ SCORE Topeka
120 SE 6th, Ste. 110
Topeka, KS 66603
Ph: (785)234-3049
URL: http://topeka.score.org/chapters/topeka-score
Description: Helps people in planning small business operations. **Founded:** 1982.

52033 ■ SCORE Wichita
271 W 3rd St. N, Ste. 2500
Wichita, KS 67202
Ph: (316)269-6273
Fax: (316)269-6499
Co. E-mail: codgerbob@hotmail.com
URL: http://wichita.score.org/chapters/wichita-score
Description: Provides professional guidance and information to America's small businesses.

52034 ■ Southwest Kansas SCORE
Co. E-mail: dcscore@rurallink.com

BETTER BUSINESS BUREAUS

52035 ■ The BBB Bulletin
345 N Riverview St., Ste. 720
Wichita, KS 67203
Free: 800-856-2417
Fax: (316)263-3063
Co. E-mail: info@kansasplains.bbb.org
URL: http://kansasplains.bbb.org
Contact: Mac Carter, President
Released: Monthly

52036 ■ Better Business Bureau of Kansas
345 N Riverview St., Ste. 720
Wichita, KS 67203
Ph: (316)263-3146
Free: 800-856-2417

Fax: (316)263-3063
Co. E-mail: info@kansasplains.bbb.org
URL: http://kansasplains.bbb.org
Contact: Mac Carter, President
Description: Fosters and promotes the highest ethical relationship between businesses and the public through voluntary self-regulation, consumer and business education, and service excellence. **Founded:** 1928.

52037 ■ Better Business Bureau of Northeast Kansas
345 N Riverview St., Ste. 720
Wichita, KS 67203
Free: 800-856-2417
Fax: (316)263-3063
Co. E-mail: info@kansasplains.bbb.org
URL: http://kansasplains.bbb.org
Contact: Mac Carter, President
Description: Seeks to promote and foster the highest ethical relationship between businesses and the public through voluntary self-regulation, consumer and business education, and service excellence. Provides information to help consumers and businesses make informed purchasing decisions and avoid costly scams and frauds; settles consumer complaints through arbitration and other means. **Founded:** 1968. **Publications:** *The BBB Bulletin* (Monthly).

CHAMBERS OF COMMERCE

52038 ■ Abilene Area Chamber of Commerce
500 N Buckeye
Abilene, KS 67410
Ph: (785)263-1770
Fax: (785)263-1536
Co. E-mail: visitus1@sbcglobal.net
URL: http://www.abileneks.com
Contact: Lynda Lowry, Director
Description: Promotes business and community development in the Abilene, KS area.

52039 ■ Alma Chamber of Commerce
PO Box 234
Alma, KS 66401
Ph: (785)765-3327
Fax: (785)765-3384
URL: http://www.kansaschamber.org/mx/hm.asp?id=home
Contact: Kent Beisner, Chief Executive Officer
Description: Promotes business and community development in the Alma, KS area.

52040 ■ Andover Area Chamber of Commerce and Convention and Visitors' Bureau
1607 E Central Ave.
Andover, KS 67002
Ph: (316)733-0648
Fax: (316)733-8808
Co. E-mail: chamber@andoverinformation.com
Contact: Dave Tingley, President
Description: Promotes business and community development in the Andover, KS area. **Founded:** 1983. **Publications:** *Collaborative Commerce* (Monthly). **Educational Activities:** Andover Area Chamber of Commerce and Convention and Visitors' Bureau Meeting (Monthly). **Awards:** Volunteer of the Year (Annual); Ambassador of the Year (Annual); Expansion and Growth; Greater Andover Days Volunteer; New Business of the Year (Annual).

52041 ■ Anthony Chamber of Commerce (ACC)
PO Box 354
Anthony, KS 67003
Ph: (620)842-5456
Fax: (620)842-3929
Co. E-mail: info@anthonychamber.com
URL: http://www.anthonychamber.com
Contact: Gwen Warner, Executive Director
Description: Promotes business and community development in Anthony, KS.

52042 ■ Arkansas City Area Chamber of Commerce (ACA COC)—Ark City Chamber
106 S Summit
Arkansas City, KS 67005
Ph: (620)442-0230
Co. E-mail: ac-aa@arkcitychamber.org
URL: http://www.arkcity.org/portal/portal.aspx
Contact: Janet Siebert, President
Description: Works to promote economic and community development in the city and the region. **Founded:** 1912. **Awards:** U.S. Chamber Accreditation (Periodic).

52043 ■ Ashland Chamber of Commerce
PO Box 37
Ashland, KS 67831
Ph: (620)635-0427
Co. E-mail: aac@ashlandks.com
URL: http://www.ashlandks.com
Description: Promotes business and community development in Ashland, KS area.

52044 ■ Atchison Area Chamber of Commerce (AACC)
PO Box 126
Atchison, KS 66002
Ph: (913)367-2427
Free: 800-234-1854
Fax: (913)367-2485
Co. E-mail: officemgr@atchisonkansas.net
URL: http://www.atchisonkansas.net
Contact: Jacque Pregont, President
E-mail: president@atchisonkansas.net
Description: Promotes business and community development in the Atchison, KS area. Sponsors local festivals and community activities. **Founded:** 1919. **Subscriptions:** books. **Publications:** *Atchison Area Chamber of Commerce--Membership Directory* (Annual); *Weekly Enews* (Weekly). **Telecommunication Services:** president@atchisonkansas.net.

52045 ■ Atwood Chamber of Commerce (ACC)
PO Box 152
Atwood, KS 67730-0152
Ph: (785)626-9630
Fax: (785)626-9630
Co. E-mail: ripper@ruraltel.net
URL: http://www.atwoodkansas.com
Contact: Richard Rippe, Executive Director
URL(s): www.kansaschamber.org/mx/hm.asp?id=home. **Description:** Promotes business and community development in Atwood, KS. Issues publications. **Publications:** *Chamber Update.*

52046 ■ Baldwin City Chamber of Commerce
720 High St.
Baldwin City, KS 66006-0501
Ph: (785)594-3200
Co. E-mail: info@baldwincitychamber.com
URL: http://baldwincitychamber.com
Contact: Ivan Huntoon, President
Description: Promotes business and community development in Baldwin City, KS.

52047 ■ Baxter Springs Chamber of Commerce
1004 Military Ave.
Baxter Springs, KS 66713-1547
Ph: (620)856-3131
Fax: (620)856-3182
Co. E-mail: info@baxtersprings.us
URL: http://www.baxtersprings.us/index.php?page=city-offices
Description: Promotes business and community development in Baxter Springs, KS. Sponsors annual Cowtown Days festival and Christmas festivities. **Founded:** 1947.

52048 ■ Belle Plaine Area Chamber of Commerce
PO Box 721
Belle Plaine, KS 67013-0721
Co. E-mail: belleplainechamber@gmail.com
URL: http://www.belleplainechamber.com
Contact: Julie Gooch, President
Description: Promotes business and community development in the Belle Plaine, KS area. Sponsors Tulip Time Festival in April. **Founded:** 1955.

52049 ■ Belleville Chamber of Commerce
1309 18th St.
Belleville, KS 66935-0280
Ph: (785)527-5524
Free: 866-527-2355
Co. E-mail: mainstreet@nckcn.com
URL: http://www.bellevilleks.org
Description: Advances the commercial, industrial, civic and general interests of the city of Belleville and the surrounding area.

52050 ■ Beloit Area Chamber of Commerce (BACC)
123 N Mill
Beloit, KS 67420-0582
Ph: (785)738-2717
Co. E-mail: beloitchamber@nckcn.com
URL: http://skyways.lib.ks.us/towns/Beloit
Description: Promotes business and community development in Mitchell County, KS. Conducts annual Consumer and Farm Show. **Founded:** 1902.

52051 ■ Bonner Springs/Edwardsville Area Chamber of Commerce
129 N Nettleton Ave.
Box 403
Bonner Springs, KS 66012-1445
Ph: (913)422-5044
Fax: (913)441-1366
URL: http://www.lifeisbetter.org
Contact: Charlene A. Biles, Executive Vice President Secretary
Description: Promotes business and community development in the Bonner Springs and Edwardsville, KS areas. Sponsors annual Tiblow Days and Autumn Fest celebrations.

52052 ■ *The Bugle Call*
231 E Wall St.
Fort Scott, KS 66701-0205
Ph: (620)223-3566
Free: 800-245-3678
Fax: (620)223-3574
URL: http://www.fortscott.com
Contact: Vicki Pritchett, President
Released: Bimonthly **Price:** included in membership dues.

52053 ■ *The Business Advantage*
311 W Spruce St.
Dodge City, KS 67801-0939
Ph: (620)227-3119
Fax: (620)227-2957
Co. E-mail: info@dodgechamber.com
URL: http://www.dodgechamber.com
Contact: Dan Schenkein, President
Released: Monthly

52054 ■ *Business Advocate*
835 SW Topeka Blvd.
Topeka, KS 66612-1671
Ph: (785)357-6321
Fax: (785)357-4732
Co. E-mail: info@kansaschamber.org
URL: http://www.kansaschamber.org
Contact: Kent Beisner, President

52055 ■ *Business Courier*
3 W Wea St.
Paola, KS 66071-1403
Ph: (913)294-4335
Fax: (913)294-4336
Co. E-mail: mgr@paolachamber.org
URL: http://www.paolachamber.org
Contact: Carol Everhart, Executive Director
Released: Quarterly

52056 ■ *Business Intelligence Report*
350 W Douglas Ave.
Wichita, KS 67202-2970
Ph: (316)265-7771
Fax: (316)265-7502
Co. E-mail: info@wichitachamber.org
URL: http://www.wichitakansas.org
Contact: Gary Plummer, President
Released: Monthly

52057 ■ Business Intelligence Report
9001 W 110th, Ste. 150
Overland Park, KS 66210
Ph: (913)491-3600
Fax: (913)491-0393
Co. E-mail: opcc@opks.org
URL: http://www.opks.org
Contact: Tracey Osborne, President
Released: Monthly

52058 ■ Business Perspective
9001 W 110th, Ste. 150
Overland Park, KS 66210
Ph: (913)491-3600
Fax: (913)491-0393
Co. E-mail: opcc@opks.org
URL: http://www.opks.org
Contact: Tracey Osborne, President
Released: Monthly

52059 ■ Caldwell Area Chamber of Commerce (CACC)
PO Box 42
Caldwell, KS 67022
Ph: (620)845-6666
Co. E-mail: caldwell@kanokla.net
URL: http://caldwellkansas.com
Contact: LuAnn Jamison, Secretary
Description: Promotes business and community development in the Caldwell, KS area. Promotes tourism. Sponsors Chisholm Trail Festival and 4th of July celebration.

52060 ■ Caney Chamber of Commerce
PO Box 211
Caney, KS 67333
Ph: (620)879-5131
Co. E-mail: caneycoc@caneycoc.kscoxmail.com
URL: http://www.caney.com/chamber.htm
Contact: Jackie Freisberg, President
Description: Promotes business and community development in Caney, KS. Sponsors Mayfest, Memorial Day celebration, weekend crafts programs, competitions, annual Christmas parade, and high school reunions.

52061 ■ Chamber Bulletin
c/o Carlota M. Ponds, Dir.
115 E Smith
Hesston, KS 67062
Ph: (620)327-4102
Fax: (620)327-4595
Co. E-mail: chamber@hesstonks.org
URL: http://www.hesstonks.org
Contact: Carlota M. Ponds, Director
Released: Periodic

52062 ■ Chamber Chatter
PO Box 63
Osawatomie, KS 66064
Ph: (913)755-4114
Fax: (913)755-4114
URL: http://www.osawatomiechamber.org
Released: Monthly

52063 ■ Chamber Communique
216 Center Ave.
Oakley, KS 67748
Ph: (785)672-4862
Fax: (785)672-3838
Co. E-mail: oakleycc@ruraltel.net
URL: http://www.oakley-kansas.com/
Contact: Troy Faulkender, President
Released: Monthly **Price:** free for members.

52064 ■ The Chamber Forum
PO Box 576
Meade, KS 67864-0576
Ph: (620)873-2359
URL: http://www.meadechamber.com
Contact: Tiffany Neel, President
Released: Quarterly

52065 ■ Chamber Linc
727 Minnesota Ave.
Kansas City, KS 66117
Ph: (913)371-3070

Fax: (913)371-3732
Co. E-mail: chamber@kckchamber.com
URL: http://www.kckchamber.com
Contact: Cindy Cash, President
Released: Monthly

52066 ■ Chamber News
2700 Vine St.
Hays, KS 67601
Ph: (785)628-8201
Co. E-mail: hayscc@discoverhays.com
URL: http://www.discoverhays.com
Contact: Eric Norris, President
Released: Monthly

52067 ■ Chamber News
208 W Madison Ave.
Iola, KS 66749
Ph: (620)365-5252
Fax: (620)365-8078
URL: http://www.iolachamber.org
Contact: John Baker, President
Released: Quarterly

52068 ■ Chamber Notes
111 W Grand
Hillsboro, KS 67063
Ph: (620)947-3506
URL: http://www.hillsboro-kansas.com
Released: Monthly

52069 ■ The Chamber Outlook
117 N Walnut
Hutchinson, KS 67504-0519
Ph: (620)662-3391
Free: 800-691-4262
Co. E-mail: jond@hutchchamber.com
URL: http://www.hutchchamber.com
Contact: Jon Daveline, President (Acting)
Released: Semimonthly

52070 ■ Chamber Update
PO Box 152
Atwood, KS 67730-0152
Ph: (785)626-9630
Fax: (785)626-9630
Co. E-mail: ripper@ruraltel.net
URL: http://www.atwoodkansas.com
Contact: Richard Rippe, Executive Director

52071 ■ Chamber Updates
114-1/2 N Douglas
Ellsworth, KS 67439
Ph: (785)472-4071
Co. E-mail: ecofc@eaglecom.net
URL: http://ellsworthkschamber.net
Contact: Mr. Nick V. Slechta, Director
Released: Monthly

52072 ■ The Chamber Vision
719 Commercial St.
Emporia, KS 66801-0703
Ph: (620)342-1600
Free: 800-279-3730
URL: http://www.emporiakschamber.org
Contact: Jeanine McKenna, President
Released: Monthly

52073 ■ Chamberline
15100 W 67th St., Ste. 202
Shawnee, KS 66217-9344
Ph: (913)631-6545
Free: 888-550-7282
Fax: (913)631-9628
Co. E-mail: mtaylor@shawneekschamber.com
URL: http://shawneekschamber.com
Contact: Linda Leeper, President
Released: Monthly

52074 ■ Chamberline
113B S Main St.
Ulysses, KS 67880
Ph: (620)356-4700
Fax: (620)424-2437
Co. E-mail: uchamber@pld.com
URL: http://www.ulysseschamber.org/home
Contact: Rae Gorman, Chairman
Released: Monthly

52075 ■ Chanute Area Chamber of Commerce and Office of Tourism
21 N Lincoln Ave.
Chanute, KS 66720
Ph: (620)431-3350
Free: 877-431-3350
Fax: (620)431-7770
Co. E-mail: information@chanutechamber.com
URL: http://www.chanutechamber.com
Contact: Jane Brophy, Executive Director
Description: Promotes business and community development in Chanute, KS area.

52076 ■ Cheney Chamber of Commerce
PO Box 716
Cheney, KS 67025
Ph: (316)540-3151
Co. E-mail: cheneychamber@sktc.net
URL: http://www.cheneychamber.com
Contact: Jeff Albers, President
Description: Promotes business and community development in Cheney, KS. Sponsors Spring Fling and Coming Home for Christmas festivals. Publications: none.

52077 ■ Chetopa Chamber of Commerce
PO Box 182
Chetopa, KS 67336
Ph: (620)236-7511
Fax: (620)236-7025
Co. E-mail: chetopachamber@chetopachamber.org
URL: http://www.chetopachamber.org
Contact: Toni Crumrine, Clerk
Description: Promotes business and community development in Chetopa, KS. Donates proceeds from events to Shriners. Sponsors pro wrestling competitions, Spring Fling, Fourth of July Festival, Dinner Theater, and Halloween Parade.

52078 ■ Cimarron Chamber of Commerce
102 East Ave. A
Cimarron, KS 67835
Ph: (620)855-2507
URL: http://skyways.lib.ks.us/towns/Cimarron
Description: Promotes business and community development in Cimarron, KS area.

52079 ■ Clay Center Area Chamber of Commerce
517 Court St.
Clay Center, KS 67432
Ph: (785)632-5674
Fax: (785)632-5674
Co. E-mail: andy@claycenterkschamber.org
URL: http://www.claycenterkschamber.org
Contact: Andy Contreras, President
Description: Promotes business and community development in Clay Center, KS area.

52080 ■ Coby Chamber Communicator
350 S Range, Ste. 10
Colby, KS 67701
Ph: (785)460-3401
Fax: (785)460-4509
URL: http://oasisontheplains.com
Contact: Holly Whitaker, Executive Director
Released: Monthly

52081 ■ Coffey County Chamber of Commerce
305 Ste. A, Neosho St.
Burlington, KS 66839
Ph: (620)364-2002
Free: 877-364-2002
Co. E-mail: executivedirector@coffeycountychamber.com
URL: http://www.coffeycountychamber.com
Contact: Kelli Higgins, Executive Director
Description: Promotes business and community development in the Burlington, KS area. **Founded:** 1990. **Publications:** Whistle Stop (Monthly).

52082 ■ Coffeyville Chamber of Commerce (CCC)
PO Box 457
Coffeyville, KS 67337-0457
Ph: (620)251-2550

Free: 800-626-3357
URL: http://www.coffeyvillechamber.org
Contact: Ryan Thompson, Chairman
Description: Promotes business and community development in Coffeyville, KS. **Founded:** 1901.

52083 ■ Colby - Thomas County Chamber of Commerce
350 S Range, Ste. 10
Colby, KS 67701
Ph: (785)460-3401
Fax: (785)460-4509
URL: http://oasisontheplains.com
Contact: Holly Whitaker, Executive Director
Description: Promotes business and community development in the Colby, KS area. Sponsors local festivals. **Founded:** 1914. **Publications:** *Coby Chamber Communicator* (Monthly).

52084 ■ Coldwater Chamber of Commerce (CCC)
PO Box 333
Coldwater, KS 67029-0333
Ph: (620)582-2859
Co. E-mail: stalcup@carrollsweb.com
URL: http://www.coldwaterkansas.com/bd.html
Contact: Rita Martin, President
Description: Promotes business and community development in Coldwater, KS. **Founded:** 1962.

52085 ■ Columbus Chamber of Commerce (CCC)
320 E Maple
Columbus, KS 66725
Ph: (620)429-1492
Fax: (620)429-1674
Co. E-mail: columbuschamber@columbus-ks.com
URL: http://www.columbus-kansas.com/chamber
Description: Advances the agricultural, civic, commercial, and industrial interests of the Columbus, KS area. Sponsors Columbus Day Festival and Hot Air Balloon Regatta. **Founded:** 1943. **Publications:** *Discovery* (Monthly).

52086 ■ *Community Profile and Relocation Guide*
646 Vermont St., Ste. 200
Lawrence, KS 66044-0586
Ph: (785)865-4411
Co. E-mail: frontdesk@lawrencechamber.com
URL: http://www.lawrencechamber.com/cwt/external/wcpages/index.aspx
Contact: Tom Kern, President
Released: Annual

52087 ■ Decatur County Area Chamber of Commerce (DCACC)
104 S Penn
Oberlin, KS 67749
Ph: (785)475-3441
Co. E-mail: dcacc@kans.com
URL: http://www.oberlinkansas.org
Contact: Glenva Nichols, Office Manager
Description: Promotes business and community development in Decatur County, KS. **Founded:** 1971. **Telecommunication Services:** dcacc@eaglecom.net.

52088 ■ Derby Chamber of Commerce (DCC)
PO Box 544
Derby, KS 67037
Ph: (316)788-3421
Fax: (316)788-6861
Co. E-mail: info@derbychamber.com
URL: http://www.derbychamber.com
Contact: Alicia Early, President
Description: Promotes business and community development in Derby, KS. Helps sponsor Christmas parade. Participates in organizing Derby Days celebration. **Founded:** 1957. **Publications:** *News* (Monthly). **Educational Activities:** Derby Days (Annual).

52089 ■ *Discovery*
320 E Maple
Columbus, KS 66725
Ph: (620)429-1492

Fax: (620)429-1674
Co. E-mail: columbuschamber@columbus-ks.com
URL: http://www.columbus-kansas.com/chamber
Released: Monthly; distributed last Thursday of month in local paper.

52090 ■ Dodge City Area Chamber of Commerce (DCACC)
311 W Spruce St.
Dodge City, KS 67801-0939
Ph: (620)227-3119
Fax: (620)227-2957
Co. E-mail: info@dodgechamber.com
URL: http://www.dodgechamber.com
Contact: Dan Schenkein, President
Description: Promotes business and community development in the Dodge City, KS area. **Founded:** 1917. **Publications:** *The Business Advantage* (Monthly).

52091 ■ Doniphan County Chamber of Commerce and Economic Development Commission
PO Box 250
Troy, KS 66087-0250
Ph: (785)985-2235
Fax: (785)985-2215
Co. E-mail: edoniphancounty@yahoo.com
URL: http://www.dpcountyks.com/ChamberofCommerce/tabid/2343/Default.aspx
Contact: Lawrence Mays, Executive Director
Description: Promotes business and community development in Doniphan County, KS.

52092 ■ Douglass Chamber of Commerce
PO Box 401
Douglass, KS 67039
Ph: (316)746-3135
Contact: Brenda Davis, Secretary
Description: Promotes business and community development in Douglass, KS.

52093 ■ *E-Post*
701 N Jefferson
Junction City, KS 66441
Ph: (785)762-2632
URL: http://www.junctioncitychamber.org
Contact: Tom Weigand, President
Released: Weekly

52094 ■ Edwards County Chamber of Commerce
PO Box 161
Kinsley, KS 67547
Ph: (620)659-2711
Fax: (620)659-3304
Co. E-mail: ecedc@sbcglobal.net
URL: http://www.edwardscounty.org
Contact: Karen Gilkey, Director
Description: Promotes business in Edwards County.

52095 ■ El Dorado Chamber of Commerce (EDCC)
201 E Central
El Dorado, KS 67042
Ph: (316)321-3150
Fax: (316)321-5419
URL: http://www.eldoradochamber.com
Contact: Shirley R. Patton, Executive Director
Description: Promotes business and community development in El Dorado, KS. Sponsors El Dorado Prairie Port Festival. **Scope:** tourism-related. **Founded:** 1927. **Subscriptions:** 100 articles books. **Awards:** Community Volunteer of the Year (Annual); Volunteer Organization of the Year (Annual).

52096 ■ Ellinwood Area Chamber of Commerce
110 1/2 N Main St.
Ellinwood, KS 67526
Ph: (620)566-7353
Co. E-mail: ellinwoodchamber@hotmail.com
URL: http://www.ellinwoodchamber.com
Contact: Jacque Isern, President
Description: Promotes business and community development in the Ellinwood, KS area.

52097 ■ Ellsworth-Kanopolis Area Chamber of Commerce (EKAC)
114-1/2 N Douglas
Ellsworth, KS 67439
Ph: (785)472-4071
Co. E-mail: ecofc@eaglecom.net
URL: http://ellsworthkschamber.net
Contact: Mr. Nick V. Slechta, Director
Description: Promotes business and community development in the Ellsworth/Kanopolis, KS area. **Founded:** 1947. **Publications:** *Chamber Updates* (Monthly). **Educational Activities:** Cowtown Festival (Annual). **Awards:** Citizen of the Year (Annual).

52098 ■ Emporia Chamber of Commerce and Convention and Visitors Bureau
719 Commercial St.
Emporia, KS 66801-0703
Ph: (620)342-1600
Free: 800-279-3730
URL: http://www.emporiakschamber.org
Contact: Jeanine McKenna, President
Description: Promotes business and community development in the Emporia, KS area. **Publications:** *The Chamber Vision* (Monthly).

52099 ■ Fort Scott Area Chamber of Commerce (FSACC)
231 E Wall St.
Fort Scott, KS 66701-0205
Ph: (620)223-3566
Free: 800-245-3678
Fax: (620)223-3574
URL: http://www.fortscott.com
Contact: Vicki Pritchett, President
Description: Promotes business and community development in the Ft. Scott, KS area. **Publications:** *The Bugle Call* (Bimonthly).

52100 ■ Fredonia Chamber of Commerce
PO Box 449
Fredonia, KS 66736-0449
Ph: (620)378-3221
Fax: (620)378-4833
Co. E-mail: fredoniakschamber@twinmounds.com
URL: http://www.fredoniaks.org/index.asp?NID=168
Contact: Tanya Ostrosky, President
Description: Promotes business and community development in Fredonia, KS. Sponsors the Fredonia Homecoming Festival.

52101 ■ Garden City Area Chamber of Commerce (GCACC)
1511 E Fulton Terr.
Garden City, KS 67846-6165
Ph: (620)276-3264
Fax: (620)276-3290
URL: http://www.gardencitychamber.net
Contact: Reynaldo Mesa, President
Description: Promotes business and community development in the Garden City, KS area. **Founded:** 1888. **Publications:** *The News and Views* (Monthly).

52102 ■ Gardner Area Chamber of Commerce
PO Box 402
Gardner, KS 66030
Ph: (913)856-6464
Fax: (913)856-5274
Co. E-mail: devore@gardnerchamber.com
URL: http://www.gardnerchamber.com
Contact: Steve Devore, President
Description: Promotes business and community development in Gardner, KS. **Telecommunication Services:** audrey@gardnerchamber.com.

52103 ■ Garnett Area Chamber of Commerce (GACC)
419 S Oak St.
Garnett, KS 66032
Ph: (785)448-6767
Fax: (785)448-6767
Co. E-mail: garnettchamber@embarqmail.com
URL: http://www.chamberofgarnettks.com
Contact: Jordan Miller, President
Description: Promotes business and community development in the Garnett, KS area. **Founded:** 1970.

52104 ■ Glasco Chamber Pride (GCP)
PO Box 572
Glasco, KS 67445-0572
Ph: (785)568-2515
Co. E-mail: jnothern334@usd334.org
URL: http://skyways.lib.ks.us/kansas/towns/Glasco
Description: Promotes business and community development in Glasco, KS. **Founded:** 1920.

52105 ■ Goodland Area Chamber of Commerce
PO Box 59
Goodland, KS 67735
Ph: (785)899-7130
URL: http://www.goodlandchamber.com
Contact: Michael Solomon, Director
Description: Promotes business and community development in the Goodland, KS area.

52106 ■ Grant County Chamber of Commerce (GCCC)
113B S Main St.
Ulysses, KS 67880
Ph: (620)356-4700
Fax: (620)424-2437
Co. E-mail: uchamber@pld.com
URL: http://www.ulysseschamber.org/home
Contact: Rae Gorman, Chairman
Description: Promotes business and community development in the Grant County, KS area. Sponsors Home Products Dinner and annual Spring Fling. **Founded:** 1954. **Publications:** *Chamberline* (Monthly).

52107 ■ Great Bend Chamber of Commerce (GBCC)
1125 Williams
Great Bend, KS 67530
Ph: (620)792-2401
Co. E-mail: gbcc@greatbend.org
URL: http://www.greatbend.org
Contact: Jan Peters, President
Description: Promotes programs and projects designed to retain businesses and improve the quality of life in Barton County, KS. Sponsors special events and expositions. **Founded:** 1921. **Publications:** *Outlook* (Monthly). **Educational Activities:** Coffee (Annual).

52108 ■ Greater Topeka Chamber of Commerce (GTCC)
120 SE 6th St., Ste. 110
Topeka, KS 66603-3515
Ph: (785)234-2644
Fax: (785)234-8656
Co. E-mail: topekainfo@topekachamber.org
URL: http://www.topekachamber.org
Contact: Douglas S. Kinsinger, President
Description: Promotes business and community development in the Topeka, KS area. **Publications:** *Topeka Business* (Monthly). **Awards:** Small Business Award (Annual).

52109 ■ Greensburg Chamber of Commerce
315 S Sycamore St.
Greensburg, KS 67054
Ph: (620)723-2400
Free: 800-207-7369
Co. E-mail: dea@corns.us
URL: http://www.bigwell.org
URL(s): skyways.lib.ks.us/towns/Greensburg. **Description:** Promotes business and community development in Greensburg, KS.

52110 ■ *Growing a Business in Johnson County*
9001 W 110th, Ste. 150
Overland Park, KS 66210
Ph: (913)491-3600
Fax: (913)491-0393
Co. E-mail: opcc@opks.org
URL: http://www.opks.org
Contact: Tracey Osborne, President
Released: Periodic

52111 ■ Halstead Chamber of Commerce (HCC)
PO Box 328
Halstead, KS 67056

Ph: (316)835-2662
Co. E-mail: coc@halsteadkansas.com
URL: http://chamberofcommerce.halsteadkansas.com
Contact: Charles Whitt, President
Description: Promotes business and community development in Halstead, KS. **Awards:** Good Neighbor (Annual).

52112 ■ Hays Area Chamber of Commerce
2700 Vine St.
Hays, KS 67601
Ph: (785)628-8201
Co. E-mail: hayscc@discoverhays.com
URL: http://www.discoverhays.com
Contact: Eric Norris, President
Description: Promotes business and community development in the Hays, KS area. **Publications:** *Chamber News* (Monthly).

52113 ■ Haysville Chamber of Commerce
PO Box 372
Haysville, KS 67060
Ph: (316)529-2461
Co. E-mail: haysvillechamber@gmail.com
URL: http://haysvillechamber.com
Contact: Dana Haislett, President
Description: Promotes business and community development in Haysville, KS.

52114 ■ Hesston Community Chamber of Commerce
c/o Carlota M. Ponds, Dir.
115 E Smith
Hesston, KS 67062
Ph: (620)327-4102
Fax: (620)327-4595
Co. E-mail: chamber@hesstonks.org
URL: http://www.hesstonks.org
Contact: Carlota M. Ponds, Director
Description: Promotes economic development, tourism, and community development in the Hesston, Kansas community. **Founded:** 1966. **Publications:** *Chamber Bulletin* (Periodic). **Awards:** Member of the Year (Annual).

52115 ■ Hillsboro Chamber of Commerce (HCC)
111 W Grand
Hillsboro, KS 67063
Ph: (620)947-3506
URL: http://www.hillsboro-kansas.com
Description: Seeks to promote the Hillsboro, KS area by providing leadership which enhances the business climate and quality of life. **Founded:** 1949. **Publications:** *Chamber Notes* (Monthly).

52116 ■ Hoisington Chamber of Commerce (HCC)
123 N Main St.
Hoisington, KS 67544
Ph: (620)653-4311
Co. E-mail: hoisingtoncofc@embarqmail.com
URL: http://www.hoisingtonkansas.com
Contact: Gene Mooney, President
Description: Promotes business and community development in Hoisington, KS. Sponsors annual Labor Day celebration. Makes charitable contributions to Hoisington Main St., Inc. Along with the City of Hoisington, forms the nucleus of local economic development group. Publications: none.

52117 ■ Holton/Jackson County Chamber of Commerce
416 Pennsylvania Ave.
Holton, KS 66436
Ph: (785)364-3963
Co. E-mail: chamber@holtonks.net
URL: http://www.holtonks.net/chamber/index.html
Contact: Katie Ingles, Executive Director
Description: Promotes business and community development in Holton, KS.

52118 ■ Horton Chamber of Commerce (HCC)
PO Box 30
Horton, KS 66439-0030

Ph: (785)486-2681
Co. E-mail: cityofhorton@hortonkansas.net
URL: http://www.hortonkansas.net
Description: Promotes business and community development in Horton, KS. **Founded:** 1925.

52119 ■ Hutchinson/Reno County Chamber of Commerce
117 N Walnut
Hutchinson, KS 67504-0519
Ph: (620)662-3391
Free: 800-691-4262
Co. E-mail: jond@hutchchamber.com
URL: http://www.hutchchamber.com
Contact: Jon Daveline, President (Acting)
Description: Promotes business and community development in the Hutchinson, KS area. **Publications:** *The Chamber Outlook* (Semimonthly).

52120 ■ *Images of the Greater Wichita Area*
350 W Douglas Ave.
Wichita, KS 67202-2970
Ph: (316)265-7771
Fax: (316)265-7502
Co. E-mail: info@wichitachamber.org
URL: http://www.wichitakansas.org
Contact: Gary Plummer, President
Released: Annual **Price:** $3, for members; $5, for nonmembers.

52121 ■ *Impact*
350 W Douglas Ave.
Wichita, KS 67202-2970
Ph: (316)265-7771
Fax: (316)265-7502
Co. E-mail: info@wichitachamber.org
URL: http://www.wichitakansas.org
Contact: Gary Plummer, President
Released: Weekly **Price:** included in membership dues.

52122 ■ Independence Chamber of Commerce (ICC)
322 N Penn Ave.
Independence, KS 67301
Ph: (620)331-1890
Free: 800-882-3606
Fax: (620)331-1899
Co. E-mail: chamber@indkschamber.org
URL: http://www.indkschamber.org
Contact: Gwen Wilburn, President
Description: Promotes business and community development in Independence, KS. **Founded:** 1914.

52123 ■ Iola Area Chamber of Commerce (IACC)
208 W Madison Ave.
Iola, KS 66749
Ph: (620)365-5252
Fax: (620)365-8078
URL: http://www.iolachamber.org
Contact: John Baker, President
Description: Promotes business and community development in Iola, KS. **Publications:** *Chamber News* (Quarterly). **Educational Activities:** Iola Area Chamber of Commerce Board meeting (Monthly).

52124 ■ *Issue*
500 N Main, Ste. 101
Newton, KS 67114
Ph: (316)283-2560
Free: 800-868-2560
Fax: (316)283-8732
Co. E-mail: info@thenewtonchamber.org
URL: http://www.thenewtonchamber.org
Contact: Virgil Penner, Liaison
Released: Monthly

52125 ■ Jewell Chamber of Commerce
PO Box 235
Jewell, KS 66949
Ph: (785)428-3549
Co. E-mail: tshelton@nckcn.com
URL: http://www.kansaschamber.org/mx/hm.asp?id=home
Contact: Thelma Shelton, Secretary Treasurer
Description: Promotes business and community development in the Jewell, KS area.

52126 ■ Junction City Area Chamber of Commerce
701 N Jefferson
Junction City, KS 66441
Ph: (785)762-2632
URL: http://www.junctioncitychamber.org
Contact: Tom Weigand, President
Description: Promotes business and community development in the Junction City, KS area. **Publications:** *E-Post* (Weekly); *Signpost* (Monthly).

52127 ■ Kansas Chamber of Commerce and Industry (KCCI)
835 SW Topeka Blvd.
Topeka, KS 66612-1671
Ph: (785)357-6321
Fax: (785)357-4732
Co. E-mail: info@kansaschamber.org
URL: http://www.kansaschamber.org
Contact: Kent Beisner, President
Description: Promotes business and community development in Kansas. **Publications:** *Business Advocate.*

52128 ■ Kansas City, Kansas Area Chamber of Commerce
727 Minnesota Ave.
Kansas City, KS 66117
Ph: (913)371-3070
Fax: (913)371-3732
Co. E-mail: chamber@kckchamber.com
URL: http://www.kckchamber.com
Contact: Cindy Cash, President
Description: Promotes business and community development in the Kansas City, KS area. **Founded:** 1898. **Publications:** *Chamber Linc* (Monthly); *KCK Business Report* (Monthly).

52129 ■ KCK Business Report
727 Minnesota Ave.
Kansas City, KS 66117
Ph: (913)371-3070
Fax: (913)371-3732
Co. E-mail: chamber@kckchamber.com
URL: http://www.kckchamber.com
Contact: Cindy Cash, President
Released: Monthly

52130 ■ Keeping PACE
PO Box 1115
Pittsburg, KS 66762
Ph: (620)231-1000
Fax: (620)231-3178
Co. E-mail: bbenson@pittsburgareachamber.com
URL: http://pittsburgareachamber.com
Contact: Blake Benson, President
Released: Weekly

52131 ■ Kingman Area Chamber of Commerce (KACC)
322 N Main St.
Kingman, KS 67068
Ph: (620)532-1853
Co. E-mail: kingmanareachamber@gmail.com
URL: http://kingmancc.com
Contact: Wanda Kelsey, Executive Director
Description: Promotes business and community development in Kingman County, KS.

52132 ■ Larned Area Chamber of Commerce (LCC)
502 Broadway St.
Larned, KS 67550
Ph: (620)285-6916
Free: 800-747-6919
Co. E-mail: larnedcofc@gbta.net
URL: http://larned.org/chamber/show.html?id=161
Contact: Linda Henderson, Executive Director
Description: Promotes business and community development in Pawnee County, KS. Sponsors local festivals. **Founded:** 1947.

52133 ■ Lawrence Chamber of Commerce
646 Vermont St., Ste. 200
Lawrence, KS 66044-0586
Ph: (785)865-4411
Co. E-mail: frontdesk@lawrencechamber.com
URL: http://www.lawrencechamber.com/cwt/external/wcpages/index.aspx
Contact: Tom Kern, President
Description: Works to promote and enhance the economic vitality of Lawrence and Douglas County and to be the leading advocate of issues that affect the economic well-being of the members and customers. **Founded:** 1878. **Publications:** *Community Profile and Relocation Guide* (Annual).

52134 ■ Leavenworth-Lansing Area Chamber of Commerce (LLACC)
518 Shawnee
Leavenworth, KS 66048
Ph: (913)682-4112
Fax: (913)682-8170
Co. E-mail: lloffice.chamber@sbcglobal.net
URL: http://www.llchamber.com
Contact: Jennifer Daly, President
Description: Promotes business and community development in Leavenworth County, KS. **Awards:** Citizen of the Year (Annual).

52135 ■ Leawood Chamber of Commerce
13451 Briar, Ste. 201
Leawood, KS 66209
Ph: (913)498-1514
Fax: (913)491-0134
Co. E-mail: chamber@leawoodchamber.org
URL: http://www.leawoodchamber.org
Contact: Kevin Jeffries, President
Description: Promotes business and community development in Leawood, KS area. **Founded:** 1996.

52136 ■ Lenexa Chamber of Commerce (LCC)
11180 Lackman Rd.
Lenexa, KS 66219
Ph: (913)888-1414
Co. E-mail: staff@lenexa.org
URL: http://www.lenexa.org
Contact: Blake Schreck, President
Description: Promotes business and community development in Lenexa, KS. **Founded:** 1925.

52137 ■ Liberal Area Chamber of Commerce (LACC)
4 Rock Island Rd.
Liberal, KS 67905
Ph: (620)624-3855
Fax: (620)624-8851
Co. E-mail: liberalcoc@adelphia.net
URL: http://www.liberalkschamber.com
Contact: Rozelle Webb, Executive Director
Description: Aims to enhance the business climate and to improve the quality of life in Liberal, KS area. **Founded:** 1927.

52138 ■ Lincoln Area Chamber of Commerce
144 E Lincoln Ave.
Lincoln, KS 67455
Ph: (785)524-4934
Fax: (785)524-4934
Co. E-mail: lcoc137@sbcglobal.net
URL: http://www.lincolnkansaschamber.com
Contact: Sandy Adams, Executive Director
Description: Promotes business and community development in Lincoln, KS. **Founded:** 1954.

52139 ■ Lindsborg Chamber of Commerce
125 N Main St.
Lindsborg, KS 67456
Ph: (785)227-3706
Free: 888-227-2227
Co. E-mail: chamber@lindsborg.org
URL: http://www.lindsborg.org
Contact: Ron Johnson, President
Description: Promotes business and community development in Lindsborg, KS.

52140 ■ Little Apple Business Review
501 Poyntz Ave.
Manhattan, KS 66502-6005
Ph: (785)776-8829
Fax: (785)776-0679
Co. E-mail: lyle@manhattan.org
URL: http://www.manhattan.org
Contact: Lyle Butler, III, President
Released: Monthly

52141 ■ Louisburg Chamber of Commerce (LCC)
PO Box 245
Louisburg, KS 66053
Ph: (913)837-2826
Co. E-mail: chamber@louisburgkansas.com
URL: http://louisburgkansas.com
Contact: Julie Baalmann, President
Description: Promotes business and community development in the Louisburg, KS area.

52142 ■ Lucas Area Chamber of Commerce (LACC)
PO Box 186
Lucas, KS 67648
Ph: (785)525-6288
Co. E-mail: lucascoc@wtciweb.com
URL: http://skyways.lib.ks.us/towns/Lucas/index.html
Contact: Connie Dougherty, Director
Description: Promotes business and community development in Lucas, KS. Sponsors charitable functions and festivals. **Founded:** 1970.

52143 ■ Lyndon Chamber of Commerce
PO Box 523
Lyndon, KS 66451
URL: http://www.kansaschamber.org/mx/hm.asp?id=home
Contact: Steve Niemack, President
Description: Promotes business and community development in Lyndon, KS. Conducts charitable programs; sponsors annual Flea Market and Sidewalk Sale, competitions, and local festivals. **Publications:** *Minutes of Lyndon C of C* (Monthly). **Educational Activities:** Lyndon Chamber of Commerce Conference (Monthly).

52144 ■ Madison Area Chamber of Commerce
PO Box 58
Madison, KS 66860-0058
Ph: (620)437-3463
URL: http://www.madisonkschamber.org
Description: Promotes business and community development in the area of Madison, Kansas.

52145 ■ Manhattan Area Chamber of Commerce
501 Poyntz Ave.
Manhattan, KS 66502-6005
Ph: (785)776-8829
Fax: (785)776-0679
Co. E-mail: lyle@manhattan.org
URL: http://www.manhattan.org
Contact: Lyle Butler, III, President
Description: Promotes business and community development in Manhattan, KS. **Founded:** 1918. **Publications:** *Little Apple Business Review* (Monthly).

52146 ■ Mankato Chamber of Commerce (MCC)
202 E Jefferson St.
Mankato, KS 66956
Ph: (785)378-3141
Co. E-mail: mankato@nckcn.com
Contact: Lori Carter, Secretary Treasurer
Description: Promotes business and community development in Mankato, KS.

52147 ■ Marysville Chamber of Commerce
101 N 10th Hwy. 77 and 36
Marysville, KS 66508
Ph: (785)562-3101
Free: 800-752-3965
Co. E-mail: marysvillechamber@sbcglobal.net
URL: http://skyways.lib.ks.us/towns/Marysville
Contact: Jen Sedlacek, President
Description: Promotes business and community development in Marysville, KS area.

52148 ■ McPherson Chamber of Commerce
306 N Main
McPherson, KS 67460-0616
Ph: (620)241-3303
Fax: (620)241-8708
Co. E-mail: cvb@mcphersonks.org
URL: http://www.mcphersonks.org/chamber
Contact: Ms. Jennifer Burch, Executive Director
URL(s): www.mcphersonchamber.org/site/home.php.
Description: Promotes business and community development in McPherson, KS. **Scope:** SBA, Kansas statistical abstract, visitors, tourist. **Founded:** 1921. **Publications:** *The Outlook* (Monthly).

52149 ■ Meade Chamber of Commerce (MCC)
PO Box 576
Meade, KS 67864-0576
Ph: (620)873-2359
URL: http://www.meadechamber.com
Contact: Tiffany Neel, President
URL(s): skyways.lib.ks.us/counties/ME. **Description:** Promotes business and community development in Meade, KS. **Founded:** 1885. **Publications:** *The Chamber Forum* (Quarterly).

52150 ■ Medicine Lodge Area Chamber of Commerce (MLACC)
215 S Iliff St.
Medicine Lodge, KS 67104
Ph: (316)886-3417
URL: http://www.barbercounty.net/medicinelodge.html
Contact: Karen Larson, President
Description: Promotes business and community development in the Medicine Lodge, KS area. Sponsors Indian Summer Days festival.

52151 ■ *Membership Directory and Newcomer's Guide*
500 N Main, Ste. 101
Newton, KS 67114
Ph: (316)283-2560
Free: 800-868-2560
Fax: (316)283-8732
Co. E-mail: info@thenewtonchamber.org
URL: http://www.thenewtonchamber.org
Contact: Virgil Penner, Liaison
Released: Annual **Price:** free.

52152 ■ Minneapolis Area Chamber of Commerce (MACC)
200 W 2nd St.
Minneapolis, KS 67467
Ph: (785)392-3068
Co. E-mail: mplschamber@sbcglobal.net
URL: http://www.minneapoliskrsorg.org
Description: Promotes business and community development in Minneapolis, KS.

52153 ■ *The Morning Sun's*
PO Box 1115
Pittsburg, KS 66762
Ph: (620)231-1000
Fax: (620)231-3178
Co. E-mail: bbenson@pittsburgareachamber.com
URL: http://pittsburgareachamber.com
Contact: Blake Benson, President
Released: Weekly

52154 ■ Mound City Area Chamber of Commerce
PO Box 10
Mound City, KS 66056
Ph: (913)795-2074
Fax: (913)795-3089
Contact: Naomi Childress, Director

52155 ■ Moundridge Community Chamber of Commerce
225 S Christian Ave.
Moundridge, KS 67107
Ph: (620)345-6300
URL: http://www.moundridge.com
Contact: Mike Kaufman, Coordinator
Description: Promotes business and community development in the Moundridge, KS area.

52156 ■ Mulvane Chamber of Commerce
PO Box 67
Mulvane, KS 67110
Ph: (316)777-4850
Co. E-mail: mulvanechamber@gamil.com
URL: http://www.mulvanechamber.com
Contact: Mike Robinson, President
Description: Promotes business and community development in Mulvane, KS.

52157 ■ *Ness Chamber*
102 W Main
Ness City, KS 67560-0262
Ph: (785)798-2413
Co. E-mail: nccofc@gbta.net
URL: http://skyways.lib.ks.us/towns/NessCity/chamber.html
Contact: Yvette Schlegel, Executive Director
Released: Monthly

52158 ■ Ness City Chamber of Commerce (NCCC)
102 W Main
Ness City, KS 67560-0262
Ph: (785)798-2413
Co. E-mail: nccofc@gbta.net
URL: http://skyways.lib.ks.us/towns/NessCity/chamber.html
Contact: Yvette Schlegel, Executive Director
Description: Promotes business and community development in Ness City, KS. **Publications:** *Ness Chamber* (Monthly).

52159 ■ *News*
PO Box 544
Derby, KS 67037
Ph: (316)788-3421
Fax: (316)788-6861
Co. E-mail: info@derbychamber.com
URL: http://www.derbychamber.com
Contact: Alicia Early, President
Released: Monthly

52160 ■ *News Briefs From the Chamber*
PO Box 58
Russell, KS 67665
Ph: (785)483-6960
Free: 800-658-4686
Fax: (785)483-4535
Co. E-mail: kyla@russellchamber.com
URL: http://www.russellks.org
Contact: Kyla Reinhardt, Executive Director
Released: Monthly

52161 ■ *The News and Views*
1511 E Fulton Terr.
Garden City, KS 67846-6165
Ph: (620)276-3264
Fax: (620)276-3290
URL: http://www.gardencitychamber.net
Contact: Reynaldo Mesa, President
Released: Monthly

52162 ■ *News-Voice*
5800 Foxridge Dr., Ste. 100
Mission, KS 66202
Ph: (913)262-2141
Co. E-mail: info@nejcchamber.com
URL: http://www.nejcchamber.com
Contact: Deb Settle, President
Released: Monthly

52163 ■ Newton Area Chamber of Commerce and Visitors Bureau
500 N Main, Ste. 101
Newton, KS 67114
Ph: (316)283-2560
Free: 800-868-2560
Fax: (316)283-8732
Co. E-mail: info@thenewtonchamber.org
URL: http://www.thenewtonchamber.org
Contact: Virgil Penner, Liaison
Description: Works to promote and develop the civic, commercial, industrial, agricultural and professional interest of the City of Newton, Kansas and its vicinity. **Scope:** business, agriculture. **Founded:**

1934. **Subscriptions:** 87000 articles books periodicals video recordings. **Publications:** *Issue* (Monthly); *Membership Directory and Newcomer's Guide* (Annual).

52164 ■ Northeast Johnson County Chamber of Commerce
5800 Foxridge Dr., Ste. 100
Mission, KS 66202
Ph: (913)262-2141
Co. E-mail: info@nejcchamber.com
URL: http://www.nejcchamber.com
Contact: Deb Settle, President
Description: Promotes business and community development in Northeast Johnson County, KS area. **Publications:** *News-Voice* (Monthly). **Awards:** Committee of the Year (Annual); Member Business of the Year (Annual); Small Business of the Year (Annual); Volunteer of the Year (Annual).

52165 ■ Norton Area Chamber of Commerce (NACC)
PO Box 97
Norton, KS 67654
Ph: (785)877-2501
Co. E-mail: nortoncc@ruraltel.net
URL: http://us36.net/nortonkansas
Contact: Karla Reed, Executive Director
URL(s): www.discovernorton.com. **Description:** Promotes business and community development in the Norton, KS area. Sponsors charitable events. Conducts educational programs and competitions.

52166 ■ Oakley Area Chamber of Commerce
216 Center Ave.
Oakley, KS 67748
Ph: (785)672-4862
Fax: (785)672-3838
Co. E-mail: oakleycc@ruraltel.net
URL: http://www.oakley-kansas.com/
Contact: Troy Faulkender, President
Description: Promotes business and community development in Oakley, KS. Sponsors State Corn Husking Festival. **Publications:** *Chamber Communique* (Monthly). **Telecommunication Services:** oakleycc@st-tel.net.

52167 ■ *Olathe Business Report*
18001 W 106 St., Ste. 160
Olathe, KS 66051-0098
Ph: (913)764-1050
Fax: (913)782-4636
Co. E-mail: chamber@olathe.org
URL: http://www.olathe.org/default.asp
Contact: L. Franklin Taylor, President
Released: every six weeks. **Price:** free for members.

52168 ■ Olathe Chamber of Commerce (OCC)
18001 W 106 St., Ste. 160
Olathe, KS 66051-0098
Ph: (913)764-1050
Fax: (913)782-4636
Co. E-mail: chamber@olathe.org
URL: http://www.olathe.org/default.asp
Contact: L. Franklin Taylor, President
Description: Promotes business and community development in the Olathe, KS area. Sponsors annual Olathe Expo and Olathe Night at the Royals. **Founded:** 1921. **Publications:** *Olathe Business Report*; *Relocation and Community Guide to Olathe* (Annual). **Educational Activities:** Blazing New Trails (Annual); Coffee (Weekly). **Awards:** Ambassador of the Year (Annual); Bartlett-Olson Membership Achievement Award (Annual); Citizen of the Year (Annual); Corporate Citizen of the Year (Annual); Volunteer of the Year (Annual).

52169 ■ Osage City Chamber of Commerce
201 S 5th St.
Osage City, KS 66523
Ph: (785)528-3714
Co. E-mail: susanbuenger@gmail.com
URL: http://www.osagecity.com/index.aspx?NID=94
Contact: Susan Buenger, President
Description: Promotes business and community development in Osage City, KS.

52170 ■ Osawatomie Chamber of Commerce
PO Box 63
Osawatomie, KS 66064
Ph: (913)755-4114
Fax: (913)755-4114
URL: http://www.osawatomiechamber.org
Description: Promotes business and community
development in Osawatomie, KS. **Founded:** 1948.
Publications: *Chamber Chatter* (Monthly).

**52171 ■ Osborne Area Chamber of
Commerce (OACC)**
130 N 1st St.
Osborne, KS 67473-2002
Ph: (785)346-2670
Free: 866-346-2670
Fax: (785)346-2522
Co. E-mail: osborneed@ruraltel.net
URL: http://www.discoverosborne.com
Contact: Brian Befort, President
Description: Promotes business and community
development in the Osborne, KS area. Convention/
Meeting: none. Publications: none. **Founded:** 1925.

52172 ■ Ottawa Area Chamber of Commerce
PO Box 580
Ottawa, KS 66067
Ph: (785)242-1000
Fax: (785)242-4792
Co. E-mail: chamber@ottawakansas.org
URL: http://www.ottawakansas.org
Contact: John Coen, President
Description: Promotes business and community
development in the Franklin County, KS area.
Founded: 1929. **Awards:** Entrepreneur Award (An-
nual).

52173 ■ *Outlook*
1125 Williams
Great Bend, KS 67530
Ph: (620)792-2401
Co. E-mail: gbcc@greatbend.org
URL: http://www.greatbend.org
Contact: Jan Peters, President
Released: Monthly

52174 ■ *The Outlook*
306 N Main
McPherson, KS 67460-0616
Ph: (620)241-3303
Fax: (620)241-8708
Co. E-mail: cvb@mcphersonks.org
URL: http://www.mcphersonks.org/chamber
Contact: Ms. Jennifer Burch, Executive Director
Released: Monthly

**52175 ■ Overland Park Chamber of
Commerce**
9001 W 110th, Ste. 150
Overland Park, KS 66210
Ph: (913)491-3600
Fax: (913)491-0393
Co. E-mail: opcc@opks.org
URL: http://www.opks.org
Contact: Tracey Osborne, President
Description: Promotes business and community
development in Johnson County, KS. **Founded:**
1967. **Publications:** *Business Intelligence Report*
(Monthly); *Business Perspective* (Monthly); *Growing
a Business in Johnson County* (Periodic).

52176 ■ Paola Chamber of Commerce
3 W Wea St.
Paola, KS 66071-1403
Ph: (913)294-4335
Fax: (913)294-4336
Co. E-mail: mgr@paolachamber.org
URL: http://www.paolachamber.org
Contact: Carol Everhart, Executive Director
Description: Seeks to promote the commercial,
industrial and civic interests of the Paola area. Spon-
sors six promotions per year. **Founded:** 1920. **Publi-
cations:** *Business Courier* (Quarterly); *Paola's Busi-
ness* (Monthly). **Educational Activities:** Leadership;
Legislative.

52177 ■ *Paola's Business*
3 W Wea St.
Paola, KS 66071-1403

Ph: (913)294-4335
Fax: (913)294-4336
Co. E-mail: mgr@paolachamber.org
URL: http://www.paolachamber.org
Contact: Carol Everhart, Executive Director
Released: Monthly

52178 ■ Parsons Chamber of Commerce
1715 Corning
Parsons, KS 67357
Ph: (620)421-6500
Free: 800-280-6401
Fax: (620)421-6501
Co. E-mail: rikki@parsonschamber.org
URL: http://www.parsonschamber.org
Contact: Debbie Lamb, President
Description: Promotes business and community
development in Parsons, KS. **Founded:** 1921.
Awards: Chamber Citation Award (Annual). **Tele-
communication Services:** whitney@parsonscham-
ber.org.

**52179 ■ Phillipsburg Area Chamber of
Commerce**
PO Box 326
Phillipsburg, KS 67661-0326
Ph: (785)543-2321
Fax: (785)543-0038
Co. E-mail: cvbcham@ruraltel.net
URL: http://www.phillipsburgks.us/development/
chamber
Contact: Jackie L. Swatzell, Office Manager
Description: Promotes business and community
development in the Phillipsburg, KS area.

**52180 ■ Pittsburg Area Chamber of
Commerce**
PO Box 1115
Pittsburg, KS 66762
Ph: (620)231-1000
Fax: (620)231-3178
Co. E-mail: bbenson@pittsburgareachamber.com
URL: http://pittsburgareachamber.com
Contact: Blake Benson, President
Description: Promotes business and community
development in the Pittsburg, KS area. **Publications:**
Keeping PACE (Weekly); *The Morning Sun's*
(Weekly). **Telecommunication Services:** info@pitts-
burgkschamber.com.

52181 ■ Pratt Area Chamber of Commerce
114 N Main
Pratt, KS 67124
Ph: (620)672-5501
Free: 888-886-1164
Co. E-mail: info@prattkan.com
URL: http://www.prattkan.com
Contact: Jan Scarbrough, Executive Director
Description: Promotes business and community
development in Pratt County, KS. **Founded:** 1929.
Subscriptions: 40000 artwork audiovisuals films
papers.

**52182 ■ Russell Area Chamber of Commerce
(RACC)**
PO Box 58
Russell, KS 67665
Ph: (785)483-6960
Free: 800-658-4686
Fax: (785)483-4535
Co. E-mail: kyla@russellchamber.com
URL: http://www.russellks.org
Contact: Kyla Reinhardt, Executive Director
Description: Promotes business, tourism, and com-
munity development in Russell County, KS. Serves
as an information center. Sponsors business after
hours, ambassador calls, legislative coffees, secre-
tary's day luncheon, agricultural appreciation dinner,
ribbon cuttings, rental and employment listings, and
greeter service. **Founded:** 1949. **Publications:** *News
Briefs From the Chamber* (Monthly).

52183 ■ Sabetha Chamber of Commerce
c/o Becca Brown, Exec. Dir.
805 Main St.
Sabetha, KS 66534

Ph: (785)284-2158
Co. E-mail: sabethachamber@gmail.com
URL: http://skyways.lib.ks.us/towns/Sabetha/
chamber.htm
Contact: Becca Brown, Executive Director
Description: Promotes business and community
development in Sabetha, KS. **Subscriptions:** 30000
periodicals.

**52184 ■ St. Francis Area Chamber of
Commerce (SFACC)**
c/o Gloria Bracelin, Sec.
212 E Washington St.
St. Francis, KS 67756
Ph: (785)332-2961
Co. E-mail: coc@cityofstfrancis.net
Contact: Gloria Bracelin, Secretary
Description: Promotes business and community
development in Cheyenne County, KS. **Founded:**
1920. **Publications:** *Cheyenne County*; *Hunting and
Fishing Guide*. **Educational Activities:** St. Francis
Area Chamber of Commerce Meeting (Monthly).

**52185 ■ Salina Area Chamber of Commerce
(SACC)**
120 W Ash St.
Salina, KS 67402-0586
Ph: (785)827-9301
Fax: (785)827-9758
Co. E-mail: scole@salinakansas.org
URL: http://salinakansas.org/index.html
Contact: Mr. Dennis Lauver, President
Description: Promotes business and community
development in the Salina, KS area. **Founded:** 1911.

**52186 ■ Satanta Chamber of Commerce
(SACC)**
PO Box 98
Satanta, KS 67870-0098
Ph: (620)649-3602
Co. E-mail: chamber@satanta.org
URL: http://skyways.lib.ks.us/towns/Satanta/index.
html
Contact: Brent Howie, President
Description: Promotes business and community
development in the Satanta, KS area. Conducts
charitable blood drive. Sponsors annual Satanta Day.
Founded: 1944.

52187 ■ Sedan Area Chamber of Commerce
108 N Sherman
Sedan, KS 67361
Ph: (620)725-4033
Fax: (620)725-4023
Co. E-mail: sedanchamber@yahoo.com
Contact: Lisa Hudson, President
Description: Promotes business and community
development in Sedan, KS.

52188 ■ Seneca Chamber of Commerce
PO Box 135
Seneca, KS 66538-0135
Ph: (785)336-2294
Fax: (785)336-6344
Co. E-mail: seneca_chamber@yahoo.com
URL: http://www.seneca-kansas.us/chamber
Contact: Harry Leem, Executive Director

**52189 ■ Shawnee Area Chamber of
Commerce (SACC)**
15100 W 67th St., Ste. 202
Shawnee, KS 66217-9344
Ph: (913)631-6545
Free: 888-550-7282
Fax: (913)631-9628
Co. E-mail: mtaylor@shawneekschamber.com
URL: http://shawneekschamber.com
Contact: Linda Leeper, President
Description: Promotes business and community
development in the Shawnee, KS area. **Founded:**
1946. **Publications:** *Chamberline* (Monthly).

52190 ■ *Signpost*
701 N Jefferson
Junction City, KS 66441
Ph: (785)762-2632
URL: http://www.junctioncitychamber.org
Contact: Tom Weigand, President
Released: Monthly

52191 ■ Smith Center Chamber of Commerce (SCCC)
c/o Pam Barta, Dir.
219 S Main
Smith Center, KS 66967
Ph: (785)282-3895
Fax: (785)686-4116
Co. E-mail: jnech@smithcenter.net
URL: http://www.smithcenterks.com
Contact: Adam Rentschler, President
Description: Promotes business and community development in Smith Center, KS. **Founded:** 1938.

52192 ■ Sterling Chamber of Commerce
PO Box 56
Sterling, KS 67579
Ph: (620)278-3727
Co. E-mail: lcbuckman@cm.kscoxmail.com
URL: http://sterlingkschamber.com
Contact: Josh Gilmore, Vice President
Description: Promotes business and community development in Sterling, KS.

52193 ■ *Topeka Business*
120 SE 6th St., Ste. 110
Topeka, KS 66603-3515
Ph: (785)234-2644
Fax: (785)234-8656
Co. E-mail: topekainfo@topekachamber.org
URL: http://www.topekachamber.org
Contact: Douglas S. Kinsinger, President
Released: Monthly

52194 ■ Tri-County Area Chamber of Commerce (HTCACC)
106 N Broadway
Herington, KS 67449
Ph: (785)258-2115
URL: http://www.tricountycofc.com
Description: Promotes business and community development in Herington, KS. **Subscriptions:** 15000.

52195 ■ Wamego Area Chamber of Commerce (WCC)
529 Lincoln Ave.
Wamego, KS 66547
Ph: (785)456-7849
Fax: (785)456-7427
Co. E-mail: wchamber@wamego.net
URL: http://www.wamegochamber.com
Contact: Mary Lyn Barnett, Executive Director
Description: Promotes agriculture, business, and community development in Wamego, KS. Sponsors area festivals.

52196 ■ Waterville Chamber of Commerce
PO Box 301
Waterville, KS 66548
Ph: (785)363-2515
URL: http://watervillekansas.com
Description: Promotes business and community development in Waterville, KS.

52197 ■ *Weekly Enews*
PO Box 126
Atchison, KS 66002
Ph: (913)367-2427
Free: 800-234-1854
Fax: (913)367-2485
Co. E-mail: officemgr@atchisonkansas.net
URL: http://www.atchisonkansas.net
Contact: Jacque Pregont, President
E-mail: president@atchisonkansas.net
Released: Weekly

52198 ■ Wellsville Area Chamber of Commerce
PO Box 472
Wellsville, KS 66092
Ph: (785)418-2431
Co. E-mail: wellsvillechamberofcommerce@hotmail.com
URL: http://www.wellsvillechamber.com
Contact: Susan Stueve, President
Description: Promotes business and community development in Wellsville, KS. **Awards:** Citizen of the Year (Annual); Kenneth Hausler Memorial Business Person of the Year (Annual).

52199 ■ *Whistle Stop*
305 Ste. A, Neosho St.
Burlington, KS 66839
Ph: (620)364-2002
Free: 877-364-2002
Co. E-mail: executivedirector@coffeycountychamber.com
URL: http://www.coffeycountychamber.com
Contact: Kelli Higgins, Executive Director
Released: Monthly

52200 ■ Wichita Area Chamber of Commerce (WACC)
350 W Douglas Ave.
Wichita, KS 67202-2970
Ph: (316)265-7771
Fax: (316)265-7502
Co. E-mail: info@wichitachamber.org
URL: http://www.wichitakansas.org
Contact: Gary Plummer, President
Description: Promotes business and community development in the Wichita, KS area. **Founded:** 1917. **Publications:** *Business Intelligence Report* (Monthly); *Images of the Greater Wichita Area* (Annual); *Impact* (Weekly).

52201 ■ Winfield Area Chamber of Commerce (WACC)
PO Box 640
Winfield, KS 67156
Ph: (620)221-2420
Fax: (620)221-2958
Co. E-mail: win@winfieldchamber.org
URL: http://www.winfieldks.org/index.aspx?NID=11
Contact: Diane Rosecrans, Chief Executive Officer
Description: Promotes business and community development in the Winfield, KS area. **Founded:** 1921.

52202 ■ Women's Chamber of Commerce of Kansas City
PO Box 171337
Kansas City, KS 66117
Ph: (913)371-3165
Co. E-mail: kckwcc@gmail.com
URL: http://www.womenschamberkck.org
Contact: Ardith Deason, Corresponding Secretary

52203 ■ Woodson County Chamber of Commerce (WCCC)
108 S Main
Yates Center, KS 66783
Ph: (620)625-3235
Fax: (620)625-2416
Co. E-mail: info@woodsoncountychamber.com
URL: http://www.woodsoncountychamber.com
Contact: Carla Green, Executive Director
Description: Promotes business, community development, and tourism in Woodson County, KS.

MINORITY BUSINESS ASSISTANCE PROGRAMS

52204 ■ Kansas Department of Commerce - Office of Minority and Women Business Development
1000 SW Jackson St., Ste. 100
Topeka, KS 66612-1354
Ph: (785)296-3425
Fax: (785)296-3490
Co. E-mail: rharris@kansascommerce.com
URL: http://www.kansascommerce.com
Contact: Rhonda F. Harris, Director
Description: Provides counseling, technical assistance, and procurement counseling. Conducts low-cost business seminars, workshops, and conferences. Offers business reference materials.

FINANCING AND LOAN PROGRAMS

52205 ■ Child Health Investment Company, LLC
6803 W. 64th St.
Shawnee Mission, KS 66202
Ph: (913)262-1436

Fax: (913)262-1575
Co. E-mail: info@chca.com
URL: http://www.chca.com
Contact: Don Black, President
Industry Preferences: Medical and health, biotechnology, other products, Internet specific, computer software and services, computer hardware, and semiconductors and other electronics. **Geographic Preference:** U.S.

52206 ■ Kansas Technology Enterprise Corporation
214 SW 6th, 1st Fl.
Topeka, KS 66603-3719
Ph: (785)296-5272
Fax: (785)296-1160
Co. E-mail: info@ktec.com
URL: http://www.ktec.com
Contact: Kevin Carr, Chief Executive Officer
E-mail: kcarr@ktec.com
Preferred Investment Size: $250,000 to $500,000. **Industry Preferences:** Communications, computer hardware and software, Internet specifics, semiconductors and other electronics, biotechnology, transportation, medical and health, consumer related, industrial and energy, and business service, and manufacturing. **Geographic Preference:** Midwest.

52207 ■ Kansas Venture Capital, Inc.
10601 Mission Rd., Ste. 250
Leawood, KS 66211
Ph: (913)262-7117
Fax: (913)262-3509
URL: http://www.kvci.com
Contact: Marshall D. Parker, Chief Executive Officer
E-mail: mparker@kvci.com
Preferred Investment Size: $500,000 to $260,000,000. **Industry Preferences:** Communications and media, computer related, semiconductors and other electronics, medical and health, consumer related, industrial and energy, business service, and manufacturing. **Geographic Preference:** Midwest.

PROCUREMENT ASSISTANCE PROGRAMS

52208 ■ Kansas Department of Administration - Division of Purchases
102 N Landon State Office Bldg.
900 SW Jackson St., Rm. 102N
Topeka, KS 66612-1286
Ph: (785)296-2376
Fax: (785)296-7240
Co. E-mail: purchweb@da.state.ks.us
URL: http://www.da.state.ks.us/purch
Contact: Christopher Howe, Director, Purchasing
Description: In cooperation with the Division of Existing Industry Development, provides assistance to businesses seeking procurement opportunities with the state.

INCUBATORS/RESEARCH AND TECHNOLOGY PARKS

52209 ■ Enterprise Center of Johnson County
8527 Bluejacket St.
Lenexa, KS 66214
Ph: (913)438-2282
Fax: (913)888-6928
Co. E-mail: rvaughn@ecjc.com
URL: http://www.ecjc.com/
Description: A small business incubator providing high-growth potential companies with office space, consulting and advisory services, and financing resources in order to help them grow and succeed.

52210 ■ Kansas Technology Enterprise Corporation
109 SW 9th St., Ste. 508
Topeka, KS 66603
Ph: (785)296-5272

Fax: (785)296-1160
Co. E-mail: info@ktec.co
URL: http://www.ktec.com/index_Flash.htm
Description: A private/public partnership established by the state of Kansas to promote technology-based economic development. It serves as a partner to companies bringing economic growth to Kansas.

52211 ■ Lawrence Regional Technology Center
2029 Becker Dr.
Lawrence, KS 66047
Ph: (785)832-2110
Fax: (785)832-8234
Co. E-mail: info@lrtc.biz
URL: http://www.lrtc.biz/
Description: A not-for-profit small business incubator offering resources and services to support the formation and growth of high-technology start-up companies in Lawrence and the surrounding. Its mission is to provide business development assistance to early-stage businesses that have spun off from the University of Kansas, as well as to local entrepreneurs who would like to create their own high-technology firms.

52212 ■ Wichita Technology Corporation
7829 E. Rockhill Rd., Ste. 307
Wichita, KS 67206
Ph: (316)651-5900
Fax: (866)810-6671
Co. E-mail: wtc@wichitatechnology.com
URL: http://www.wichitatechnology.com/
Description: A private commercialization corporation established to create and sustain a formal innovation network that will support technology advancement, transfer, and commercialization in Kansas in order to maintain and facilitate business formation and growth

by enhancing research and development activity, providing business assistance at critical phases of a technology start-up life cycle, and providing access to capital.

EDUCATIONAL PROGRAMS

52213 ■ Coffeyville Community College
400 W 11th St.
Coffeyville, KS 67337
Ph: (620)251-7700
Free: 877-51R-AVEN
Fax: (620)252-7040
Co. E-mail: lmoley@coffeyville.edu
URL: http://www.coffeyville.edu
Contact: Linda Moley, President (Interim)
URL(s): www.ccc.cc.ks.us/, www.coffeyville.edu/forms/request_info.htm. **Description:** Two-year college offering a small business management program. **Founded:** 1923. **Publications:** *The Collegian* (Quarterly).

52214 ■ Labette Community College
200 S 14th St.
Parsons, KS 67357
Ph: (620)421-6700
Free: 888-522-3883
Fax: (620)421-0180
Co. E-mail: admissions@labette.edu
URL: http://www.labette.cc.ks.us
Description: Two-year college offering a small business management program.

52215 ■ Wichita State University - Center for Entrepreneurship
Devlin Hall, 2nd Fl.
1845 Fairmount
Wichita, KS 67260-0147

Ph: (316)978-3000
Fax: (316)978-3687
Co. E-mail: cfe@wichita.edu
URL: http://www.cfe.wichita.edu
Description: Offers degreed courses for entrepreneurs and small business management.

LEGISLATIVE ASSISTANCE

52216 ■ Kansas House Standing Committee on Economic Development and Tourism
Statehouse, Rm. 545 N
Kansas Legis. Research Department
300 SW 10th St.
Topeka, KS 66612
Ph: (785)296-2149
Fax: (785)296-3824
URL: http://www.kslegislature.org

PUBLICATIONS

52217 ■ *Smart Start your Washington D.C. Business*
PSI Research
300 N. Valley Dr.
Grants Pass, OR 97526
Ph: (503)479-9464
Free: 800-228-2275
Fax: (503)476-1479
Co. E-mail: info@psi-research.com
URL: http://www.psi-research.com
Ed: Michael D. Jenkins. **Released:** Revised edition, 1992. **Price:** $29.95 (looseleaf binder); $24.95 (paper). **Description:** Part of the Successful Business Library series.

SMALL BUSINESS DEVELOPMENT CENTERS

52218 ■ Ashland Small Business Development Center - Kentucky
1645 Winchester Ave., 2nd Fl.
Ashland, KY 41101
Ph: (606)329-8011
Fax: (606)324-4570
Co. E-mail: k.jenkins@moreheadstate.edu
URL: http://www.ksbdc.org/locations/ashland
Contact: Kimberly Jenkins, Director
Description: Represents and promotes the small business sector. Provides management assistance to current and prospective small business owners. Helps to improve management skills and expand the products and services of members.

52219 ■ Bluegrass Small Business Development Center
330 E Main St., Ste. 210
Lexington, KY 40507
Ph: (859)257-7666
Free: 888-475-SBDC
Fax: (859)257-1751
Co. E-mail: smack3@uky.edu
URL: http://www.ksbdc.org/locations/lexington
Contact: Shirie Mack, Director
Description: Represents and promotes the small business sector. Provides management assistance to current and prospective small business owners. Helps to improve management skills and expand the products and services of members.

52220 ■ Eastern Kentucky University Small Business Development Center
675 Monticello St., Ste. 1
Somerset, KY 42501
Ph: (606)678-3042
Free: 877-EKU-SBDC
Fax: (606)678-3065
Co. E-mail: johnpreston@windstream.net
URL: http://ekubiz.com
Description: Represents and promotes the small business sector. Provides management assistance to current and prospective small business owners. Helps to improve management skills and expand the products and services of members.

52221 ■ Hopkinsville Small Business Development Center
2800 Ft. Campbell Blvd.
Hopkinsville, KY 42240
Ph: (270)886-8666
Fax: (270)881-9366
Co. E-mail: roy.keller@murraystate.edu
URL: http://www.ksbdc.org/locations/hopkinsville
Contact: Roy Keller, Director
Description: Represents and promotes the small business sector. Provides management assistance to current and prospective small business owners. Helps to improve management skills and expand the products and services of members.

52222 ■ Kentucky Small Business Development Center at Eastern Kentucky University - Richmond
Eastern Kentucky University
College of Business & Technology
Hall Dr., Rm. 145
Richmond, KY 40475
Ph: (859)622-1384
Free: 877-358-7232
Co. E-mail: michael.rodriguez@eku.edu
URL: http://ekubiz.com
Contact: Michael Rodriguez, Director
Description: Represents and promotes the small business sector. Provides management assistance to current and prospective small business owners. Helps to improve management skills and expand the products and services of members.

52223 ■ Kentucky Small Business Development Center - Lead Office (KSBDC)
c/o Becky Naugle, PhD, State Dir.
University of Kentucky
One Quality St., Ste. 635
Lexington, KY 40507
Ph: (859)257-7668
Fax: (859)323-1907
URL: http://www.ksbdc.org
Contact: Becky Naugle, Director
Description: Represents and promotes the small business sector. Provides management assistance to current and prospective small business owners. Helps to improve management skills and expand the products and services of members.

52224 ■ Louisville Small Business Development Center (LSBDC)
2900 W Broadway
Box 315
Louisville, KY 40202
Ph: (502)574-1378
Fax: (502)574-1144
Co. E-mail: david.oetken@uky.edu
URL: http://www.ksbdc.org/locations/louisville
Contact: David Oetken, Director
Description: Represents and promotes the small business sector. Provides management assistance to current and prospective small business owners. Helps to improve management skills and expand the products and services of members.

52225 ■ Maysville Small Business Development Center
201 E Third St.
Maysville, KY 41056
Ph: (606)564-2707
Co. E-mail: m.jackson@moreheadstate.edu
Contact: Mike Jackson, Consultant
Description: Represents and promotes the small business sector. Provides management assistance to current and prospective small business owners. Helps to improve management skills and expand the products and services of members.

52226 ■ Morehead Small Business Development Center
150 E First St.
Morehead, KY 40351
Ph: (606)783-2895
Fax: (606)783-5020
Co. E-mail: m.murphy@moreheadstate.edu
URL: http://www.ksbdc.org/locations/morehead
Contact: Mark Murphy, Consultant
Description: Represents and promotes the small business sector. Provides management assistance to current and prospective small business owners. Helps to improve management skills and expand the products and services of members.

52227 ■ Murray/Paducah Small Business Development Center
926 N 16th St., Ste. 105
Murray, KY 42071-1524
Ph: (270)809-2856
Fax: (270)809-3049
Co. E-mail: chris.wooldridge@murraystate.edu
URL: http://www.ksbdc.org/locations/murray
Contact: Chris Wooldridge, Director
Description: Represents and promotes the small business sector. Provides management assistance to current and prospective small business owners. Helps to improve management skills and expand the products and services of members.

52228 ■ Murray Small Business Development Center
926 N 16th St., Ste. 105
Murray, KY 42071-1524
Ph: (270)809-2856
Fax: (270)809-3049
Co. E-mail: chris.wooldridge@murraystate.edu
URL: http://www.ksbdc.org/locations/murray
Contact: Chris Wooldridge, Director
Description: Represents and promotes the small business sector. Provides management assistance to current and prospective small business owners. Helps to improve management skills and expand the products and services of members.

52229 ■ Northern Kentucky University Small Business Development Center
305 Johns Hill Rd.
Highland Heights, KY 41076-1412
Ph: (859)442-4281
Fax: (859)442-4285
Co. E-mail: cornellc1@nku.edu
URL: http://www.ksbdc.org/locations/highland-heights
Contact: Carol Cornell, Director
Description: Represents and promotes the small business sector. Provides management assistance to current and prospective small business owners. Helps to improve management skills and expand the products and services of members.

52230 ■ Owensboro Small Business Development Center
200 E 3rd St., Ste. 302
Owensboro, KY 42303
Ph: (270)926-8085

Fax: (270)684-0714
Co. E-mail: mickey.johnson@murraystate.edu
URL: http://www.ksbdc.org/locations/owensboro
Contact: Mickey Johnson, Director
Description: Represents and promotes the small business sector. Provides management assistance to current and prospective small business owners. Helps to improve management skills and expand the products and services of members.

52231 ■ Paintsville Small Business Development Center
120 Scott Perry Dr.
Teays Branch Rd.
Paintsville, KY 41240-9000
Ph: (606)788-6008
Fax: (606)789-5623
Co. E-mail: m.morley@moreheadstate.edu
URL: http://www.ksbdc.org/locations/paintsville
Contact: Mike Morley, Director
Description: Represents and promotes the small business sector. Provides management assistance to current and prospective small business owners. Helps to improve management skills and expand the products and services of members.

52232 ■ Pikeville Small Business Development Center
3455 N Mayo Trail, No. 4
Pikeville, KY 41501-3298
Ph: (606)432-5848
Fax: (606)432-8924
Co. E-mail: m.morley@moreheadstate.edu
URL: http://www.ksbdc.org/locations/pikeville
Contact: Mike Morley, Director
Description: Represents and promotes the small business sector. Provides management assistance to current and prospective small business owners. Helps to improve management skills and expand the products and services of members.

52233 ■ Small Business Development Center at Western Kentucky University
1906 College Heights Blvd., No. 61086
Bowling Green, KY 42101
Ph: (270)745-1905
Fax: (270)745-4086
Co. E-mail: chris.bixler@wku.edu
URL: http://wkusmallbiz.com
Contact: Chris Bixler, Assistant Director
Description: Represents and promotes the small business sector. Provides management assistance to current and prospective small business owners. Helps to improve management skills and expand the products and services of members.

52234 ■ Southeast Small Business Development Center
Bell County Campus
1300 Chichester Ave.
Middlesboro, KY 40965-2265
Ph: (606)248-0563
Fax: (606)248-3267
Co. E-mail: samuel.coleman@kctcs.edu
URL: http://www.ksbdc.org/locations/middlesboro
Contact: Sam Coleman, Director
Description: Represents and promotes the small business sector. Provides management assistance to current and prospective small business owners. Helps to improve management skills and expand the products and services of members.

52235 ■ University of Kentucky Small Business Development Center (Elizabethtown, Iowa)
1105 Juliana Ct., Ste. 6
Elizabethtown, KY 42701-7937
Ph: (270)765-6737
Fax: (270)769-5095
Co. E-mail: patricia.krausman@uky.edu
URL: http://www.ksbdc.org/locations/elizabethtown
Contact: Patricia Krausman, Director
Description: Represents and promotes the small business sector. Provides management assistance to current and prospective small business owners. Helps to improve management skills and expand the products and services of members.

52236 ■ West Liberty Small Business Development Center
Morehead State University Regional Enterprise Ctr.
151 University Dr.
West Liberty, KY 41472
Ph: (606)743-4005
Fax: (606)743-4002
Co. E-mail: rcbowe01@moreheadstate.edu
URL: http://www.ksbdc.org/locations/west-liberty
Description: Represents and promotes the small business sector. Provides management assistance to current and prospective small business owners. Helps to improve management skills and expand the products and services of members.

SMALL BUSINESS ASSISTANCE PROGRAMS

52237 ■ Kentucky Cabinet for Economic Development - International Trade Division
Old Capital Annex
300 W Broadway
Frankfort, KY 40601
Ph: (502)564-7140
Free: 800-626-2930
Fax: (502)564-3256
Co. E-mail: econdev@ky.gov
URL: http://www.thinkkentucky.com/kyedc/internationaltrade.aspx
Contact: Mark Peachey, Director
Description: Preserves and increases employment opportunities through foreign investment within the state, and increased export of Kentucky's manufactured products. Operates a Far East office in Japan and a European office in England.

52238 ■ Kentucky Cabinet for Economic Development - New Business Development Division
Old Capital Annex
300 W Broadway
Frankfort, KY 40601
Ph: (502)564-7140
Fax: (502)564-3256
Co. E-mail: econdev@ky.gov
URL: http://www.thinkkentucky.com
Contact: Jum Navolio, Commissioner
Description: Provides site selection assistance and information. Focuses on new job creation and job retention through an Existing Industries Branch, an Industrial Marketing Branch, an Enterprise Zone Program, and a Site Evaluation Branch.

52239 ■ Kentucky Cabinet for Economic Development - Office of Business Technology
2200 Capitol Plaza Tower, 22nd Fl., Rm. 2224
500 Mero St.
Frankfort, KY 40601
Ph: (502)564-4252
Fax: (502)564-5563
URL: http://www.thinkkentucky.com
Description: Serves as a link between businesses and the technological resources and research capabilities of the state universities. Provides coordination of technology transfer to the private sector and works with the federal Small Business Innovation Research program.

52240 ■ Kentucky Cabinet for Economic Development - Small Business Services Division
Old Capital Annex Building
300 W Broadway
Frankfort, KY 40601
Ph: (502)564-2064
Fax: (502)564-6758
Co. E-mail: cedsbsd@ky.gov
URL: http://www.thinkkentucky.com/kyedc/busstart.aspx
Contact: John E. Cole III, Director
Description: Serves as an advocate and ombudsman for small business. Works with the Legislative Small Business Task Force, provides information on programs of interest, and provides information on specialized resource assistance.

52241 ■ Kentucky Cabinet for Economic Development - Small and Minority Business Division - Office of Export Development
Old Capital Annex Building
300 W Broadway
Frankfort, KY 40601
Ph: (502)564-2064
Fax: (502)564-9758
URL: http://www.thinkkentucky.com
Description: Provides exporting assistance to small manufacturers.

SCORE OFFICES

52242 ■ London SCORE
Co. E-mail: london@score.kentucky.org

52243 ■ Louisville SCORE
Federal Bldg., Rm. 188
600 Dr. Martin Luther King Jr. Pl.
Louisville, KY 40202
Ph: (502)582-5976
Fax: (502)582-5819
URL: http://www.score-louisville.org
Contact: Claude King, Chairman
Description: Provides professional guidance, mentoring services and financial assistance to maximize the success of existing and emerging small businesses.

52244 ■ SCORE Ashland
Co. E-mail: bhammond@inicity.net

52245 ■ SCORE Bardstown
Co. E-mail: bardstown@score-kentucky.org

52246 ■ SCORE Bowling Green
Co. E-mail: bowlinggreen@score-kentucky.org

52247 ■ SCORE Elizabethtown
Co. E-mail: etown@score-kentucky.org

52248 ■ SCORE Fort Mitchell
Co. E-mail: score@scorechapter34.org

52249 ■ SCORE LaGrange
Co. E-mail: score@oldhamcountychamber.com

52250 ■ SCORE Lexington
389 Waller Ave., Ste. 130
Lexington, KY 40504-2900
Ph: (859)231-9902
Fax: (859)253-3190
Co. E-mail: info@score-lexington.org
URL: http://www.score-kentucky.org/lexington.html
Contact: Billy Kelley, Chairman
URL(s): lexington.score.org. **Description:** Provides professional guidance and information to America's small businesses. **Founded:** 1976.

52251 ■ SCORE Owensboro
Co. E-mail: scoreowensboro@gmail.com

52252 ■ SCORE Pikeville
Co. E-mail: info@pikecountychamber.org

52253 ■ SCORE Purchase Area
Co. E-mail: paducah@score-kentucky.org

BETTER BUSINESS BUREAUS

52254 ■ Better Business Bureau of Central and Eastern Kentucky
1390 Olivia Ln., Ste. 100
Lexington, KY 40511-1391
Ph: (859)259-1008
Free: 800-866-6668
Fax: (859)259-1639
Co. E-mail: info@bluegrass.bbb.org
URL: http://bluegrass.bbb.org
Description: Promotes and fosters the highest ethical relationship between businesses and the public through voluntary self regulation, consumer and business education and service excellence. **Founded:** 1957. **Publications:** *Give But Give Wisely* (Quarterly); *Taking Care of Business* (Monthly).

52255 ■ Better Business Bureau - Louisville, Southern Indiana and Western Kentucky
844 S 4th St.
Louisville, KY 40203-2186
Ph: (502)583-6546
Free: 800-388-2222
Fax: (502)589-9940
Co. E-mail: info@bbbkyin.org
URL: http://louisville.bbb.org
Contact: Charles Mattingly, President
Description: Promotes ethics in the marketplace, assists businesses and consumers in resolving disputes and provides reliability reports about businesses and charities to help the public make informed decisions on buying and giving. **Founded:** 1917. **Publications:** Business Beat (Monthly). **Educational Activities:** Better Business Bureau - Louisville, Southern Indiana and Western Kentucky Meeting (Annual). **Awards:** Torch Award for Marketplace Ethics (Annual).

52256 ■ Business Beat
844 S 4th St.
Louisville, KY 40203-2186
Ph: (502)583-6546
Free: 800-388-2222
Fax: (502)589-9940
Co. E-mail: info@bbbkyin.org
URL: http://louisville.bbb.org
Contact: Charles Mattingly, President
Released: Monthly

52257 ■ Give But Give Wisely
1390 Olivia Ln., Ste. 100
Lexington, KY 40511-1391
Ph: (859)259-1008
Free: 800-866-6668
Fax: (859)259-1639
Co. E-mail: info@bluegrass.bbb.org
URL: http://bluegrass.bbb.org
Released: Quarterly

52258 ■ Taking Care of Business
1390 Olivia Ln., Ste. 100
Lexington, KY 40511-1391
Ph: (859)259-1008
Free: 800-866-6668
'Fax: (859)259-1639
Co. E-mail: info@bluegrass.bbb.org
URL: http://bluegrass.bbb.org
Released: Monthly

CHAMBERS OF COMMERCE

52259 ■ Anderson County Chamber of Commerce
1090 Glensboro Rd., Ste. 6A
Lawrenceburg, KY 40342-9091
Ph: (502)839-5564
Fax: (502)400-0458
Co. E-mail: accoc@andersonchamberky.org
URL: http://www.andersonchamberky.org
Contact: Cindy Peterson, President
Description: Promotes business and community development in Anderson County, KY. Conducts annual 4th of July celebration. **Founded:** 1959.

52260 ■ Ashland Alliance
1730 Winchester Ave.
Ashland, KY 41105-0830
Ph: (606)324-5111
Fax: (606)325-4607
Co. E-mail: bhammond@inicity.net
URL: http://www.ashlandalliance.com
Contact: Bob Hammond, Director, Business Development
Description: Promotes business and community development in Boyd and Greenup counties, KY.

52261 ■ Bell County Chamber of Commerce
PO Box 788
Middlesboro, KY 40965
Ph: (606)248-1075

Fax: (606)248-8851
Co. E-mail: chamber@bellcountychamber.com
URL: http://www.bellcountychamber.com
Contact: Bo Green, President
Description: Promotes business and community development in Bell County Middlesboro, KY area.
Founded: 1926.

52262 ■ Bowling Green
710 Coll. St.
Bowling Green, KY 42102
Ph: (270)781-3200
Free: 866-330-2422
Fax: (270)843-0458
Co. E-mail: info@bgchamber.com
URL: http://www.bgchamber.com
Contact: Ron Bunch, President
Released: Annual **Price:** $3.

52263 ■ Bowling Green Area Chamber of Commerce
710 Coll. St.
Bowling Green, KY 42102
Ph: (270)781-3200
Free: 866-330-2422
Fax: (270)843-0458
Co. E-mail: info@bgchamber.com
URL: http://www.bgchamber.com
Contact: Ron Bunch, President
Description: Promotes business and community development in Warren County, KY. **Founded:** 1935. **Publications:** Bowling Green (Annual); Chamber Connection (Monthly); Bowling Green (Annual); Demographic. **Educational Activities:** Coffee Hours (Monthly). **Awards:** ATHENA Award (Biennial); ATHENA Young Professional Award (Annual); Bart Hagerman Leadership Award (Biennial); Industry of the Year (Biennial); Small Business Person of the Year (Biennial).

52264 ■ Bullitt County Chamber of Commerce
PO Box 1656
Shepherdsville, KY 40165
Ph: (502)543-6727
Fax: (502)543-1765
Co. E-mail: bcchamber@alltel.net
URL: http://www.bullittchamber.org
Contact: Freida J. Howe, Executive Director
Description: Promotes business and community development in Bullitt County, KY. Issues publications. **Founded:** 1979.

52265 ■ Burkesville Cumberland County Chamber of Commerce
PO Box 312
Burkesville, KY 42717
Ph: (270)864-5890
Co. E-mail: chamber@burkesville.com
URL: http://burkesvillechamber.com/index.htm
Contact: Elijah Wilson, President
Description: Promotes business and community development in Cumberland County, KY.

52266 ■ The Business Bulletin
PO Box 688
Munfordville, KY 42765
Ph: (270)524-2892
Fax: (270)524-1127
Co. E-mail: hart_co@scrtc.com
URL: http://www.hartcountyky.org
Released: Monthly

52267 ■ Business Call
787 Hambley Blvd.
Pikeville, KY 41501
Ph: (270)432-5504
Free: 877-738-4400
Fax: (606)432-7295
Co. E-mail: info@pikecountychamber.org
URL: http://www.sekchamber.com
Contact: Brad N. Hall, President
Released: Monthly

52268 ■ Business Gazette
445 S Hwy. 27, Ste. 101
Somerset, KY 42501
Ph: (606)679-7323

Fax: (606)679-1744
Co. E-mail: info@spcchamber.com
URL: http://www.spcchamber.com
Contact: Kenny Isaacs, Executive Director
Released: Periodic

52269 ■ Business Spotlight
230 2nd St., Ste. 320
Henderson, KY 42420
Ph: (270)826-9531
Fax: (270)827-4461
Co. E-mail: info@hendersonchamber.org
URL: http://www.hendersonky.com
Contact: Brad Schneider, President
Released: Monthly

52270 ■ Buyers' Guide
200 E 3rd St.
Owensboro, KY 42302-0825
Ph: (270)926-1860
Fax: (270)926-3364
Co. E-mail: chamber@owensboro.com
URL: http://www.owensboro.com
Contact: Jody Wassmer, President
Released: Annual

52271 ■ Cadiz-Trigg County Chamber of Commerce
PO Box 647
Cadiz, KY 42211
Ph: (270)522-3892
Fax: (270)522-6343
Co. E-mail: information@cadizchamber.com
URL: http://www.cadizchamber.com
Contact: Mallory Lawrence, President
Description: Promotes business and community development in Trigg County, KY. **Awards:** Ambassador of the Year (Annual); Educator of the Year (Annual); Good Samaritan of the Year (Annual); Small Business of the Year (Annual).

52272 ■ Campbellsville - Taylor County Chamber of Commerce
107 W Broadway
Campbellsville, KY 42718
Ph: (270)465-8601
Fax: (270)465-0607
Co. E-mail: chamber@teamtaylorcounty.com
URL: http://www.campbellsvillechamber.com
Contact: Susie Skaggs, President
Description: Promotes business and community development in Campbellsville, KY area. **Publications:** Chamber Investment Matters (Monthly).

52273 ■ Carroll County Chamber of Commerce
c/o Rhonda S. Crutcher, Admin. Asst.
511 Highland Ave.
Carrollton, KY 41008
Ph: (502)732-7034
Fax: (502)732-7028
Co. E-mail: chamber@carrollcountyky.com
URL: http://www.carrollcountyky.com/coc
Description: Promotes business and community development in Carroll County, KY. **Awards:** Business of the Year (Annual); Community Service and Beautification Award (Annual). **Telecommunication Services:** stephenw.jones@ky.gov.

52274 ■ Chamber Action
111 W Dixie Ave.
Elizabethtown, KY 42701
Ph: (270)765-4334
Fax: (270)737-0690
Co. E-mail: info@hardinchamber.com
URL: http://www.etownchamber.org
Contact: Brad Richardson, President
Released: Monthly

52275 ■ Chamber Briefings
110 S Court St.
Scottsville, KY 42164-1438
Ph: (270)237-4782
Fax: (270)237-5498
Co. E-mail: chamber@scottsvilleky.info
Contact: Sue Shaver, Executive Director
Released: Quarterly **Price:** free.

52276 ■ *Chamber Chatter*
118 E Public Sq.
Glasgow, KY 42141
Ph: (270)651-3161
Fax: (270)651-3122
Co. E-mail: chamber@glasgow-ky.com
URL: http://www.glasgowbarrenchamber.com
Contact: Ernie Myers, Executive Vice President
Released: Bimonthly

52277 ■ *Chamber Chatter*
PO Box 164
Marion, KY 42064
Ph: (270)965-5015
Co. E-mail: susan@crittendenchamber.org
URL: http://www.crittendenchamber.org
Contact: Bob Briley, President
Released: Quarterly

52278 ■ *Chamber of Commerce Newsletter*
508 N Main St.
Nicholasville, KY 40356
Ph: (859)887-4351
Fax: (859)887-1211
Co. E-mail: jessaminechamber@windstream.com
URL: http://www.jessaminechamber.com
Contact: Rob Amburgey, President
Released: Periodic

52279 ■ *Chamber of Commerce Statewide*
464 Chenault Rd.
Frankfort, KY 40601
Ph: (502)695-4700
Fax: (502)695-5051
Co. E-mail: kcc@kychamber.com
URL: http://www.kychamber.com/mx/hm.
  asp?id=home
Contact: Dave Adkisson, President

52280 ■ *Chamber Connection*
710 Coll. St.
Bowling Green, KY 42102
Ph: (270)781-3200
Free: 866-330-2422
Fax: (270)843-0458
Co. E-mail: info@bgchamber.com
URL: http://www.bgchamber.com
Contact: Ron Bunch, President
Released: Monthly

52281 ■ *Chamber Connection*
2800 Ft. Campbell Blvd.
Hopkinsville, KY 42240
Ph: (270)885-9096
Free: 800-842-9959
Fax: (270)886-2059
Co. E-mail: chamber@hopkinsvillechamber.com
URL: http://www.hopkinsvillechamber.com/qcms
Contact: Carter Hendricks, President
Released: Monthly

52282 ■ *Chamber Connection*
239 N Spalding Ave., Ste. 201
Lebanon, KY 40033-1518
Ph: (270)692-9594
Fax: (270)692-2661
Co. E-mail: info@marioncountykychamber.com
URL: http://www.lebanon-ky.com
Contact: Emily Zink, President
Released: Bimonthly **Price:** included in membership dues.

52283 ■ *Chamber Connection*
PO Box 810
Paducah, KY 42002-0810
Ph: (270)443-1746
Fax: (270)442-9152
Co. E-mail: info@paducahchamber.org
URL: http://www.paducahchamber.org
Contact: Elaine Spalding, President
Released: Monthly

52284 ■ *Chamber Courier*
PO Box 566
Monticello, KY 42633-0566
Ph: (606)348-3064

Free: 866-348-3064
Co. E-mail: info@monticellokychamber.com
URL: http://www.monticellokychamber.com
Contact: Charles Peters, Vice President
Released: Quarterly

52285 ■ *Chamber Direct Weekly*
464 Chenault Rd.
Frankfort, KY 40601
Ph: (502)695-4700
Fax: (502)695-5051
Co. E-mail: kcc@kychamber.com
URL: http://www.kychamber.com/mx/hm.
  asp?id=home
Contact: Dave Adkisson, President
Released: Weekly

52286 ■ *Chamber Investment Matters*
107 W Broadway
Campbellsville, KY 42718
Ph: (270)465-8601
Fax: (270)465-0607
Co. E-mail: chamber@teamtaylorcounty.com
URL: http://www.campbellsvillechamber.com
Contact: Susie Skaggs, President
Released: Monthly

52287 ■ *Chamber Membership Directory and Buyer's Guide*
2800 Ft. Campbell Blvd.
Hopkinsville, KY 42240
Ph: (270)885-9096
Free: 800-842-9959
Fax: (270)886-2059
Co. E-mail: chamber@hopkinsvillechamber.com
URL: http://www.hopkinsvillechamber.com/qcms
Contact: Carter Hendricks, President
Released: Annual

52288 ■ *Chamber News*
c/o West Hopkins Industries
PO Box 403
Dawson Springs, KY 42408
Ph: (270)797-2781
Fax: (270)797-2221
Co. E-mail: whi@dawsonspringsky.com
URL: http://www.dawsonspringsky.com/default.aspx
Contact: Rick Hendrickson, President
Released: Quarterly

52289 ■ *Chamber Newsletter*
201 E Main St.
Richmond, KY 40475
Ph: (859)623-1720
Fax: (859)623-0839
Co. E-mail: rchamber@richmondchamber.com
URL: http://www.richmondchamber.com
Contact: Virgil R. Grant, President

52290 ■ *Chamber Notes*
60 Lincoln Sq.
Hodgenville, KY 42748-0176
Ph: (270)358-3411
Co. E-mail: info@laruecounty.org
URL: http://www.laruecounty.org
Contact: Pam Stephens, President
Released: Monthly

52291 ■ *The Chamber Report*
PO Box 513
Franklin, KY 42135-0513
Ph: (270)586-7609
Fax: (270)586-5438
Co. E-mail: cfreese@f-schamber.com
URL: http://www.f-schamber.com
Contact: Cristi Freese, Administrative Assistant
Released: Monthly

52292 ■ *Chamber Spotlight*
409 S Main St.
London, KY 40741
Ph: (606)864-4789
Fax: (606)864-7300
Co. E-mail: info@londonlaurelchamber.com
URL: http://www.londonlaurelchamber.com
Contact: Deanna Herrmann, Executive Director
Released: Monthly **Price:** free.

52293 ■ *Chamber Update*
201 S Main St.
Cynthiana, KY 41031-1801
Ph: (859)234-5236
Fax: (859)234-6647
Co. E-mail: cynchamber@setel.com
URL: http://www.cynthianaky.com/Chamber/cynwork.
  htm
Contact: Pat Grenier, Executive Director
Released: Monthly

52294 ■ *Chamber Wire*
PO Box 725
Hardinsburg, KY 40143-0725
Ph: (270)756-0268
Fax: (270)580-4783
Co. E-mail: chamber@breckinridgecountychamberky.
  com
URL: http://www.breckinridgecountychamberky.com
Contact: Sherry D. Stith, Executive Director
Released: Monthly

52295 ■ *Chamberletter*
2800 Ft. Campbell Blvd.
Hopkinsville, KY 42240
Ph: (270)885-9096
Free: 800-842-9959
Fax: (270)886-2059
Co. E-mail: chamber@hopkinsvillechamber.com
URL: http://www.hopkinsvillechamber.com/qcms
Contact: Carter Hendricks, President
Released: Monthly

52296 ■ *Community Profile*
2 S Maple St.
Winchester, KY 40391
Ph: (859)744-6420
Fax: (859)744-9229
Co. E-mail: chamber@winchesterky.com
URL: http://www.winchesterky.com
Contact: Karen Haley, President

52297 ■ *County Business Directory*
488 Price Ave.
Harrodsburg, KY 40330
Ph: (859)734-2365
Co. E-mail: info@mercerchamber.com
URL: http://www.mercerchamber.com
Contact: Clay Sone, President
Released: Annual

52298 ■ Crittenden County Chamber of Commerce
PO Box 164
Marion, KY 42064
Ph: (270)965-5015
Co. E-mail: susan@crittendenchamber.org
URL: http://www.crittendenchamber.org
Contact: Bob Briley, President
Description: Promotes business and community development in Crittenden County, KY. Sponsors festivals. **Founded:** 1973. **Publications:** *Chamber Chatter* (Quarterly). **Educational Activities:** Backroads Festival (Semiannual). **Awards:** Farmer of the Year (Annual); First Dollar Awards.

52299 ■ Cynthiana-Harrison County Chamber of Commerce
201 S Main St.
Cynthiana, KY 41031-1801
Ph: (859)234-5236
Fax: (859)234-6647
Co. E-mail: cynchamber@setel.com
URL: http://www.cynthianaky.com/Chamber/cynwork.
  htm
Contact: Pat Grenier, Executive Director
Description: Promotes business and community development in Harrison County, KY. **Founded:** 1932. **Publications:** *Chamber Update* (Monthly).

52300 ■ Danville Boyle County
304 S Fourth St.
Danville, KY 40422-2005
Ph: (859)236-2361

Fax: (859)236-3197
Co. E-mail: info@danvilleboylechamber.com
URL: http://www.betterindanville.com/chamber-
    services.aspx
Contact: Paula Fowler, Executive Director
Released: Annual

52301 ■ Danville-Boyle County Chamber of Commerce
304 S Fourth St.
Danville, KY 40422-2005
Ph: (859)236-2361
Fax: (859)236-3197
Co. E-mail: info@danvilleboylechamber.com
URL: http://www.betterindanville.com/chamber-
    services.aspx
Contact: Paula Fowler, Executive Director
Description: Promotes business and community development in Boyle County, KY. **Founded:** 1919. **Publications:** *Danville Boyle County* (Annual); *Foresight* (Monthly). **Educational Activities:** Small Business Roundtable (Quarterly). **Awards:** Business Ethics Award (Periodic); Business of the Year (Periodic); School Bell Award (Periodic); Business Person of the Year (Periodic).

52302 ■ Dawson Springs Chamber of Commerce
c/o West Hopkins Industries
PO Box 403
Dawson Springs, KY 42408
Ph: (270)797-2781
Fax: (270)797-2221
Co. E-mail: whi@dawsonspringsky.com
URL: http://www.dawsonspringsky.com/default.aspx
Contact: Rick Hendrickson, President
Description: Promotes business and community development in Dawson Springs, KY. Sponsors annual city-wide barbecue and annual Industry Appreciation Banquet. Convention/Meeting: none. **Publications:** *Chamber News* (Quarterly).

52303 ■ Edmonton - Metcalfe County Chamber of Commerce
PO Box 42
Edmonton, KY 42129
Ph: (270)432-3222
Fax: (270)432-3222
Co. E-mail: metchamb@scrtc.com
URL: http://www.metcalfechamber.com
Contact: Gaye Shaw, Executive Director
Description: Promotes business and community development in Metcalfe County, KY. **Founded:** 1986.

52304 ■ *Element*
10434 Watterson Trail
Jeffersontown, KY 40299
Ph: (502)267-1674
Fax: (502)267-2070
Co. E-mail: john@jtownchamber.com
URL: http://www.jtownchamber.com
Contact: John Cosby, President
Released: Bimonthly

52305 ■ Elizabethtown-Hardin County Chamber of Commerce
111 W Dixie Ave.
Elizabethtown, KY 42701
Ph: (270)765-4334
Fax: (270)737-0690
Co. E-mail: info@hardinchamber.com
URL: http://www.etownchamber.org
Contact: Brad Richardson, President
Description: Promotes business and community development in Hardin County, KY. **Founded:** 1941. **Publications:** *Chamber Action* (Monthly). **Awards:** ABC Award; Small Business Person Award.

52306 ■ *The Enterprise*
200 E 3rd St.
Owensboro, KY 42302-0825
Ph: (270)926-1860

Fax: (270)926-3364
Co. E-mail: chamber@owensboro.com
URL: http://www.owensboro.com
Contact: Jody Wassmer, President
Released: Monthly **Price:** included in membership dues.

52307 ■ Estill Development Alliance (EDA)
PO Box 421
Irvine, KY 40336
Ph: (606)723-2450
Co. E-mail: info@estillcountyky.net
URL: http://www.estillcountyky.net/index.php/eda
Contact: Kathy Samples, Chairperson
Description: Works to improve the quality of life for citizens of Estill County through conducting, promoting, and supporting civic, cultural, economic, educational, and social activities and programs that maximize citizen and community involvement.

52308 ■ Fleming County Chamber of Commerce
PO Box 24
Flemingsburg, KY 41041
Ph: (606)845-1223
Fax: (606)845-1213
Co. E-mail: crystal@flemingkychamber.com
URL: http://www.flemingkychamber.com
Contact: Crystal L. Ruark, Executive Director
Description: Seeks to promote and encourage the entire business environment of the area. Works with all groups to stimulate the quality of growth of the economy. Activities include member meetings, Business After Hours, Leadership Class and business classes.

52309 ■ *Floyd County*
113 S Central Ave.
Prestonsburg, KY 41653
Ph: (606)886-0364
Fax: (606)886-0422
Co. E-mail: floydchamber@setel.com
URL: http://www.floydcountykentucky.com
Contact: Mandy Stumbo, Executive Director
Released: Annual

52310 ■ Floyd County Chamber of Commerce
113 S Central Ave.
Prestonsburg, KY 41653
Ph: (606)886-0364
Fax: (606)886-0422
Co. E-mail: floydchamber@setel.com
URL: http://www.floydcountykentucky.com
Contact: Mandy Stumbo, Executive Director
Description: Promotes business and community development in Floyd County, KY. **Founded:** 1981. **Publications:** *Floyd County* (Annual); *News and Views* (Monthly). **Awards:** Floyd Countian of the Year (Annual); Floyd County Business Person of the Year (Annual).

52311 ■ *Foresight*
304 S Fourth St.
Danville, KY 40422-2005
Ph: (859)236-2361
Fax: (859)236-3197
Co. E-mail: info@danvilleboylechamber.com
URL: http://www.betterindanville.com/chamber-
    services.aspx
Contact: Paula Fowler, Executive Director
Released: Monthly **Price:** free for members.

52312 ■ Frankfort Area Chamber of Commerce
100 Capital Ave.
Frankfort, KY 40601
Ph: (502)223-8261
Fax: (502)223-5942
Co. E-mail: chamber@frankfortky.info
URL: http://www.frankfortky.info
Contact: Jim Clouse, Secretary Treasurer
Description: Promotes business and community development in Franklin County, KY. **Founded:** 1947.

52313 ■ Franklin-Simpson County Chamber of Commerce
PO Box 513
Franklin, KY 42135-0513

Ph: (270)586-7609
Fax: (270)586-5438
Co. E-mail: cfreese@f-schamber.com
URL: http://www.f-schamber.com
Contact: Cristi Freese, Administrative Assistant
Description: Promotes business and community development in Franklin and Simpson counties, KY. Sponsors charitable activities. Holds competition. **Founded:** 1937. **Publications:** *The Chamber Report* (Monthly).

52314 ■ Garrard County Chamber of Commerce (GCCOC)
PO Box Box 462
Lancaster, KY 40444
Ph: (859)792-2282
Fax: (859)792-2282
Co. E-mail: garrardchamber@gmail.com
URL: http://www.garrardcounty.ky.gov/
    Chamber+of+Commerce
Contact: Tom Hobbs, President
Description: Promotes business, community development and tourism in Garrard County. **Telecommunication Services:** garcocham@windstream.net.

52315 ■ Georgetown-Scott County Chamber of Commerce
160 E Main St.
Georgetown, KY 40324
Ph: (502)863-5424
Fax: (502)863-5756
Co. E-mail: jack@gtown.org
URL: http://www.gtown.org
Contact: Jack Conner, Executive Director
Description: Promotes business and community development in Scott County, KY. **Founded:** 1959. **Publications:** *Quality of Life.*

52316 ■ Glasgow-Barren County Chamber of Commerce
118 E Public Sq.
Glasgow, KY 42141
Ph: (270)651-3161
Fax: (270)651-3122
Co. E-mail: chamber@glasgow-ky.com
URL: http://www.glasgowbarrenchamber.com
Contact: Ernie Myers, Executive Vice President
Description: Promotes business and community development in Barren County, KY. Maintains 4 divisions and 20 committees. Houses the Glasgow/Barren County Tourist and Convention Commission, and the Glasgow/Barren County Community Foundation. **Publications:** *Chamber Chatter* (Bimonthly).

52317 ■ Grand Rivers Tourism Commission
PO Box 181
Grand Rivers, KY 42045
Ph: (270)362-0152
Free: 888-493-0152
Co. E-mail: info@grandrivers.com
URL: http://www.grandrivers.com
Contact: Ms. Kim Kraemer, Director
Description: Promotes Grand Rivers as a tourist destination. Provides visitor services.

52318 ■ Grant County Chamber of Commerce (GCCC)
PO Box 365
Williamstown, KY 41097-0365
Ph: (859)824-3322
Free: 800-824-2858
Fax: (859)824-7082
Co. E-mail: wgutman@grantcommerce.com
URL: http://www.grantcommerce.com
Contact: Wade Gutman, Executive Director
Description: Promotes business and community development in Grant County, KY. **Founded:** 1978.

52319 ■ Grayson Area Chamber of Commerce (GACC)
PO Box 612
Grayson, KY 41143

Ph: (606)474-4401
Co. E-mail: graysonchamber41143@windstream.net
URL: http://www.graysonchamber.org
Contact: Don Combs, President
Description: Promotes business and community development in the Grayson, KY area. **Founded:** 1978.

52320 ■ Greater Breckinridge County Chamber of Commerce
PO Box 725
Hardinsburg, KY 40143-0725
Ph: (270)756-0268
Fax: (270)580-4783
Co. E-mail: chamber@breckinridgecountychamberky.com
URL: http://www.breckinridgecountychamberky.com
Contact: Sherry D. Stith, Executive Director
Description: Strives to create and actively represent a positive business environment for the economic well-being and growth of business, industry, and agriculture in Greater Breckinridge County. **Founded:** 2001. **Publications:** *Chamber Wire* (Monthly).

52321 ■ Greater Corbin Chamber of Commerce
805 S Main St.
Corbin, KY 40701
Ph: (606)528-6390
Fax: (606)528-1583
Co. E-mail: chamberofcommerce@corbinkentucky.us
URL: http://www.corbinkentucky.us
Contact: Joe House, President
URL(s): www.thinkcorbinkentucky.com, www.corbin-ky.org. **Description:** Promotes business and community development in the Corbin, KY area. Promotes convention business and tourism. Sponsors Corbin Nibroc Festival. **Founded:** 1931.

52322 ■ Greater Louisville Inc. - The Metro Chamber of Commerce (GLI)
614 W Main St., Ste. 6000
Louisville, KY 40202
Ph: (502)625-0000
Fax: (502)625-0010
Co. E-mail: info@greaterlouisville.com
URL: http://www.greaterlouisville.com
Contact: Jeff Bringardner, President
Description: Promotes business and community development in Louisville, KY. **Founded:** 1997. **Publications:** *Greater Louisville Ink* (Monthly); *Louisville Fact Book* (Annual); *Major Employers Directory* (Annual).

52323 ■ *Greater Louisville Ink*
614 W Main St., Ste. 6000
Louisville, KY 40202
Ph: (502)625-0000
Fax: (502)625-0010
Co. E-mail: info@greaterlouisville.com
URL: http://www.greaterlouisville.com
Contact: Jeff Bringardner, President
Released: Monthly

52324 ■ Hancock County Chamber of Commerce
PO Box 404
Hawesville, KY 42348
Ph: (270)927-8223
Fax: (270)927-8223
Co. E-mail: erice@hancockky.us
URL: http://www.hancockky.us/Commerce/chamber.htm
Contact: Edna Rice, Executive Director
Description: Promotes business and community development in Hancock County, KY. Issues publications. **Awards:** City of the Year (Annual).

52325 ■ Hart County Chamber of Commerce
PO Box 688
Munfordville, KY 42765
Ph: (270)524-2892
Fax: (270)524-1127
Co. E-mail: hart_co@scrtc.com
URL: http://www.hartcountyky.org
Description: Promotes business and community development in Hart County, KY. **Publications:** *The Business Bulletin* (Monthly).

52326 ■ Henderson County Chamber of Commerce
230 2nd St., Ste. 320
Henderson, KY 42420
Ph: (270)826-9531
Fax: (270)827-4461
Co. E-mail: info@hendersonchamber.org
URL: http://www.hendersonky.com
Contact: Brad Schneider, President
Description: Promotes business and community development in the Henderson, KY area. Sponsors education and drug and alcohol seminars. **Founded:** 1916. **Publications:** *Business Spotlight* (Monthly); *Henderson Highlights* (Weekly); *Images of Henderson-Henderson County* (Annual).

52327 ■ *Henderson Highlights*
230 2nd St., Ste. 320
Henderson, KY 42420
Ph: (270)826-9531
Fax: (270)827-4461
Co. E-mail: info@hendersonchamber.org
URL: http://www.hendersonky.com
Contact: Brad Schneider, President
Released: Weekly **Price:** included in membership dues.

52328 ■ Henry County Chamber of Commerce
PO Box 355
New Castle, KY 40050
Ph: (502)845-0806
Fax: (502)845-5313
Co. E-mail: henrychamber@insightbb.com
URL: http://chamber.henrycountyky.com/index.html
Contact: Ms. Pat Wallace, Executive Director
Description: Promotes business and community development in Henry County, KY area. **Founded:** 1996. **Awards:** Patrick Henry Award (Biennial).

52329 ■ Hickman Chamber of Commerce
808 Moscow Ave.
Hickman, KY 42050
Ph: (270)236-2902
Co. E-mail: hickmanchamber@mygalaxyexpress.com
URL: http://www.hickmankychamber.org
Contact: Velva Yarbro, Executive Director
Description: Promotes business and community development in Hickman, KY. **Founded:** 1988.

52330 ■ Hopkinsville-Christian County Chamber of Commerce
2800 Ft. Campbell Blvd.
Hopkinsville, KY 42240
Ph: (270)885-9096
Free: 800-842-9959
Fax: (270)886-2059
Co. E-mail: chamber@hopkinsvillechamber.com
URL: http://www.hopkinsvillechamber.com/qcms
Contact: Carter Hendricks, President
Description: Promotes business and community development in Christian County, KY. **Founded:** 1888. **Publications:** *Chamber Connection* (Monthly); *Chamberletter* (Monthly); *Chamber Membership Directory and Buyer's Guide* (Annual). **Telecommunication Services:** bshelton@hopkinsvillechamber.com; chendricks@hopkinsvillechamber.com.

52331 ■ *Images of Henderson-Henderson County*
230 2nd St., Ste. 320
Henderson, KY 42420
Ph: (270)826-9531
Fax: (270)827-4461
Co. E-mail: info@hendersonchamber.org
URL: http://www.hendersonky.com
Contact: Brad Schneider, President
Released: Annual

52332 ■ *It's Your Business*
150 E 1st St.
Morehead, KY 40351
Ph: (606)784-6221

Fax: (606)783-1373
Co. E-mail: tcwilliam@moreheadchamber.com
URL: http://www.moreheadchamber.com/cwt/external/wcpages/index.aspx
Contact: Tracy C. Williams, Executive Director

52333 ■ Jeffersontown Chamber of Commerce
10434 Watterson Trail
Jeffersontown, KY 40299
Ph: (502)267-1674
Fax: (502)267-2070
Co. E-mail: john@jtownchamber.com
URL: http://www.jtownchamber.com
Contact: John Cosby, President
Description: Promotes business and community development in Jeffersontown, KY. **Founded:** 1963. **Publications:** *Element* (Bimonthly); *Newsline*. **Educational Activities:** Jeffersontown Gaslight.

52334 ■ Jessamine County Chamber of Commerce
508 N Main St.
Nicholasville, KY 40356
Ph: (859)887-4351
Fax: (859)887-1211
Co. E-mail: jessaminechamber@windstream.com
URL: http://www.jessaminechamber.com
Contact: Rob Amburgey, President
Description: Promotes business and community development in Jessamine County, KY. Conducts Jessamine Jamboree. **Founded:** 1982. **Publications:** *Chamber of Commerce Newsletter* (Periodic); *Jessamine Journal* (Periodic).

52335 ■ *Jessamine Journal*
508 N Main St.
Nicholasville, KY 40356
Ph: (859)887-4351
Fax: (859)887-1211
Co. E-mail: jessaminechamber@windstream.com
URL: http://www.jessaminechamber.com
Contact: Rob Amburgey, President
Released: Periodic

52336 ■ Kentucky Chamber of Commerce
464 Chenault Rd.
Frankfort, KY 40601
Ph: (502)695-4700
Fax: (502)695-5051
Co. E-mail: kcc@kychamber.com
URL: http://www.kychamber.com/mx/hm.asp?id=home
Contact: Dave Adkisson, President
Description: Promotes business and community development in Kentucky. **Scope:** business topics. **Founded:** 1946. **Subscriptions:** books. **Publications:** *Chamber Direct Weekly* (Weekly); *Chamber of Commerce Statewide*; *Kentucky Chamber News* (Bimonthly). **Telecommunication Services:** davida@kychamber.com.

52337 ■ *Kentucky Chamber News*
464 Chenault Rd.
Frankfort, KY 40601
Ph: (502)695-4700
Fax: (502)695-5051
Co. E-mail: kcc@kychamber.com
URL: http://www.kychamber.com/mx/hm.asp?id=home
Contact: Dave Adkisson, President
Released: Bimonthly

52338 ■ Knox County Chamber of Commerce
196 Daniel Boone Dr., Ste. 205
Barbourville, KY 40906
Ph: (606)546-4300
Co. E-mail: chamber@barbourville.com
URL: http://www.knoxcochamber.com
Contact: Eli Broughton, President
Founded: 1943.

52339 ■ LaRue County Chamber of Commerce
60 Lincoln Sq.
Hodgenville, KY 42748-0176

Ph: (270)358-3411
Co. E-mail: info@laruecounty.org
URL: http://www.laruecounty.org
Contact: Pam Stephens, President
Description: Promotes business and community development in LaRue County, KY. **Founded:** 1970. **Publications:** *Chamber Notes* (Monthly). **Educational Activities:** General Membership Meeting (Monthly).

52340 ■ Lebanon-Marion County Chamber of Commerce
239 N Spalding Ave., Ste. 201
Lebanon, KY 40033-1518
Ph: (270)692-9594
Fax: (270)692-2661
Co. E-mail: info@marioncountykychamber.com
URL: http://www.lebanon-ky.com
Contact: Emily Zink, President
Description: Promotes business and community development in Marion County, KY. **Founded:** 1942. **Publications:** *Chamber Connection* (Bimonthly). **Educational Activities:** Marion County Country Ham Days (Annual). **Telecommunication Services:** lebanon@lebanon-ky.com.

52341 ■ Liberty-Casey County Chamber of Commerce
PO Box 278
Liberty, KY 42539
Ph: (606)787-6463
Fax: (606)787-7992
Co. E-mail: chamber@libertykentucky.org
URL: http://www.libertykentucky.org/chamber.html
Contact: Judy Emerson, President
Description: Promotes business and community development in Casey County, KY. **Founded:** 1984.

52342 ■ Lincoln County Chamber of Commerce
201 E Main St., No. 5
Stanford, KY 40484
Ph: (606)365-4118
Fax: (606)365-4118
Co. E-mail: director@lincolncountychamber.com
URL: http://www.lincolncountychamber.com
Contact: Andrea E. Miller, Executive Director
Description: Promotes business and community development in Lincoln County, KY. Encourages industrial development, tourism, and improved education. Conducts charitable activities. Sponsors Parade, and Snow Queen and Snow Princess Contests during Christmas Season. **Scope:** business. **Founded:** 1973. **Awards:** Big Apple (Annual); Earl Butcher (Annual); Farmer of the Year (Annual); Health Care Service Award (Annual); Outstanding Citizen (Annual).

52343 ■ Logan County Chamber of Commerce
116 S Main St.
Russellville, KY 42276
Ph: (270)726-2206
Fax: (270)726-2237
Co. E-mail: logancounty@logantele.com
URL: http://www.loganchamber.com/QCMS_ Chamber
Contact: Lisa Browning, Executive Director
Description: Promotes business and community development in Logan County, KY. Sponsors local festival. **Founded:** 1939. **Publications:** *Logan County Newsline* (Monthly); *Promoting Preservation and Progress.*

52344 ■ *Logan County Newsline*
116 S Main St.
Russellville, KY 42276
Ph: (270)726-2206
Fax: (270)726-2237
Co. E-mail: logancounty@logantele.com
URL: http://www.loganchamber.com/QCMS_ Chamber
Contact: Lisa Browning, Executive Director
Released: Monthly

52345 ■ London-Laurel County Chamber of Commerce
409 S Main St.
London, KY 40741

Ph: (606)864-4789
Fax: (606)864-7300
Co. E-mail: info@londonlaurelchamber.com
URL: http://www.londonlaurelchamber.com
Contact: Deanna Herrmann, Executive Director
Description: Promotes business and community development in Laurel County, KY. **Founded:** 1980. **Publications:** *Chamber Spotlight* (Monthly). **Educational Activities:** Membership Meeting (Monthly).

52346 ■ *Louisville Fact Book*
614 W Main St., Ste. 6000
Louisville, KY 40202
Ph: (502)625-0000
Fax: (502)625-0010
Co. E-mail: info@greaterlouisville.com
URL: http://www.greaterlouisville.com
Contact: Jeff Bringardner, President
Released: Annual

52347 ■ Madisonville-Hopkins County Chamber of Commerce
15 E Center St.
Madisonville, KY 42431
Ph: (270)821-3435
Fax: (270)821-9190
Co. E-mail: chamber@madisonville-hopkinschamber.com
URL: http://www.hopkinschamber.com
Contact: Mary King, Chairperson
Description: Promotes business and community development in the Madisonville, KY area. **Founded:** 1918. **Awards:** Ambassador of the Year (Annual); Educator of the Year (Annual); Volunteer of the Year (Annual); Loman C. Trover Health Care Award (Annual); Small Business Person of the Year (Annual).

52348 ■ *Major Employers Directory*
614 W Main St., Ste. 6000
Louisville, KY 40202
Ph: (502)625-0000
Fax: (502)625-0010
Co. E-mail: info@greaterlouisville.com
URL: http://www.greaterlouisville.com
Contact: Jeff Bringardner, President
Released: Annual

52349 ■ Marshall County Chamber of Commerce
17 U.S. Hwy. 68 W
Benton, KY 42025
Ph: (270)527-7665
Co. E-mail: chamber@marshallcounty.net
URL: http://www.marshallcounty.net
Contact: Gene Gilliland, Chairman
Description: Promotes business and community development in Marshall County, KY. Ensures orderly and progressive economic development. **Founded:** 1950. **Subscriptions:** maps reports.

52350 ■ Mayfield-Graves County Chamber of Commerce
201 E College St.
Mayfield, KY 42066
Ph: (270)247-6101
Fax: (270)247-6110
Co. E-mail: info@mayfieldgraveschamber.com
URL: http://mayfieldgraveschamber.com
Contact: Roger Dillingham, President
Description: Promotes business and community development in Graves County, KY. **Founded:** 1962.

52351 ■ Maysville-Mason County Area Chamber of Commerce
201 E 3rd St.
Maysville, KY 41056
Ph: (606)564-5534
Free: 888-875-6297
Fax: (606)564-5535
Co. E-mail: chamber@maysvilleky.net
URL: http://www.maysvillekentucky.org
Contact: Vicki Steigleder, Executive Director
Description: Promotes business and community development in Mason County, KY.

52352 ■ McCreary County Chamber of Commerce
PO Box 548
Whitley City, KY 42653

Ph: (606)376-5004
Co. E-mail: chamber7@highland.net
URL: http://mccrearychamber.com
Contact: Greg Burdine, President
Description: Promotes business and community development in McCreary County, KY. **Founded:** 1980.

52353 ■ Mercer County Chamber of Commerce
488 Price Ave.
Harrodsburg, KY 40330
Ph: (859)734-2365
Co. E-mail: info@mercerchamber.com
URL: http://www.mercerchamber.com
Contact: Clay Sone, President
Description: Promotes business and community development in the Harrodsburg, KY area. Conducts annual Pioneer Days Festival. **Founded:** 1951. **Publications:** *County Business Directory* (Annual); *New Directions* (Periodic). **Educational Activities:** Mercer County Chamber of Commerce Banquet (Annual); Pioneer Days (Annual).

52354 ■ Middletown Chamber of Commerce
12906 Shelbyville Rd., Ste. 250
Louisville, KY 40243
Ph: (502)244-8086
Fax: (502)244-0185
Co. E-mail: judy@middletownchamber.com
URL: http://www.middletownchamber.com
Contact: Judy Francis, President
Description: Promotes business and community development in Middletown, KY area.

52355 ■ Monticello/Wayne County Chamber of Commerce
PO Box 566
Monticello, KY 42633-0566
Ph: (606)348-3064
Free: 866-348-3064
Co. E-mail: info@monticellokychamber.com
URL: http://www.monticellokychamber.com
Contact: Charles Peters, Vice President
Description: Promotes business and community development in Wayne County, KY. **Founded:** 1967. **Publications:** *Chamber Courier* (Quarterly).

52356 ■ Morehead-Rowan County Chamber of Commerce
150 E 1st St.
Morehead, KY 40351
Ph: (606)784-6221
Fax: (606)783-1373
Co. E-mail: tcwilliam@moreheadchamber.com
URL: http://www.moreheadchamber.com/cwt/ external/wcpages/index.aspx
Contact: Tracy C. Williams, Executive Director
Description: Promotes business and community development in Rowan County, KY. **Founded:** 1955. **Publications:** *It's Your Business.* **Awards:** Business Beautification (Annual); Educator of the Year (Annual); Farm Family of the Year (Annual); New Business of the Year (Annual); Ora Cline Award (Annual); Outstanding Board Member (Annual); Outstanding Community Organization (Annual); Service Above Self (Annual); Manufacturer or Industry of the Year (Annual).

52357 ■ Morgantown-Butler County Chamber of Commerce
PO Box 408
Morgantown, KY 42261
Ph: (270)526-6827
Co. E-mail: bcchamber07@bellsouth.net
URL: http://www.morgantown-ky.com/COMK/ Chamber_of_Commerce.html
Contact: Kay Romans, President
Description: Promotes business and community development in Butler County, KY. Sponsors annual Green River Catfish Festival. Promotes area tourism. Publications: none. **Founded:** 1980.

52358 ■ Mount Sterling-Montgomery County Chamber of Commerce
126 W Main St.
Mount Sterling, KY 40353
Ph: (859)498-5343

Fax: (859)498-3947
Co. E-mail: contact@mtsterlingchamber.com
URL: http://www.mtsterlingchamber.com
Contact: Claude Bentley, President
Description: Promotes business and community development in Montgomery County, KY.

52359 ▪ Murray-Calloway County Chamber of Commerce
805 N 12th St.
Murray, KY 42071-0190
Ph: (270)753-5171
Free: 800-900-5171
Fax: (270)753-0948
Co. E-mail: chamber@mymurray.com
URL: http://www.mymurray.com
Contact: Lance Allison, President
Description: Promotes business, tourism, and community development in Calloway County, KY. **Founded:** 1924. **Publications:** *Murray-Calloway County Magazine* (Biennial); *Murray-Calloway County Magazine.*

52360 ▪ Murray-Calloway County Magazine
805 N 12th St.
Murray, KY 42071-0190
Ph: (270)753-5171
Free: 800-900-5171
Fax: (270)753-0948
Co. E-mail: chamber@mymurray.com
URL: http://www.mymurray.com
Contact: Lance Allison, President
Released: Biennial

52361 ▪ New Directions
488 Price Ave.
Harrodsburg, KY 40330
Ph: (859)734-2365
Co. E-mail: info@mercerchamber.com
URL: http://www.mercerchamber.com
Contact: Clay Sone, President
Released: Periodic

52362 ▪ News and Views
113 S Central Ave.
Prestonsburg, KY 41653
Ph: (606)886-0364
Fax: (606)886-0422
Co. E-mail: floydchamber@setel.com
URL: http://www.floydcountykentucky.com
Contact: Mandy Stumbo, Executive Director
Released: Monthly

52363 ▪ NewsChamber
412 E Main St.
La Grange, KY 40031-0366
Ph: (502)222-1635
Fax: (502)222-3159
Co. E-mail: mail@oldhamcountychamber.com
URL: http://www.oldhamcountychamber.com
Contact: Deana Epperly Karem, Executive Director
Released: Monthly

52364 ▪ Newsline
10434 Watterson Trail
Jeffersontown, KY 40299
Ph: (502)267-1674
Fax: (502)267-2070
Co. E-mail: john@jtownchamber.com
URL: http://www.jtownchamber.com
Contact: John Cosby, President

52365 ▪ The Northern Kentucky Business Journal
PO Box 17416
Fort Mitchell, KY 41017-0416
Ph: (859)578-8800
Fax: (859)578-8802
Co. E-mail: info@nkychamber.com
URL: http://www.nkychamber.com
Contact: Ruth A. Eger, Director
E-mail: reger@nkychamber.com
Released: Monthly

52366 ▪ Northern Kentucky Chamber of Commerce
PO Box 17416
Fort Mitchell, KY 41017-0416
Ph: (859)578-8800

Fax: (859)578-8802
Co. E-mail: info@nkychamber.com
URL: http://www.nkychamber.com
Contact: Ruth A. Eger, Director
E-mail: reger@nkychamber.com
Description: Strives to develop strong businesses and vibrant economy through business advocacy and leadership. **Founded:** 1969. **Publications:** *Northern Kentucky Education Guide* (Annual); *Northern Kentucky: Where We Stand* (Annual); *The Northern Kentucky Business Journal* (Monthly); *Northern Kentucky Industrial Directory* (Annual); *Northern Kentucky Public Officials Directory; Northern Kentucky Local Government Directory* (Annual).

52367 ▪ Oldham County Chamber of Commerce
412 E Main St.
La Grange, KY 40031-0366
Ph: (502)222-1635
Fax: (502)222-3159
Co. E-mail: mail@oldhamcountychamber.com
URL: http://www.oldhamcountychamber.com
Contact: Deana Epperly Karem, Executive Director
Description: Promotes business and community development in Oldham County, KY. Supports community activities. **Founded:** 1962. **Publications:** *NewsChamber* (Monthly); *Oldham County Kentucky* (Periodic). **Educational Activities:** Networking @ Noon (Monthly). **Awards:** Oldham Countian of the Year (Annual); Scholastic Award.

52368 ▪ Oldham County Kentucky
412 E Main St.
La Grange, KY 40031-0366
Ph: (502)222-1635
Fax: (502)222-3159
Co. E-mail: mail@oldhamcountychamber.com
URL: http://www.oldhamcountychamber.com
Contact: Deana Epperly Karem, Executive Director
Released: Periodic **Price:** $1, plus mailing cost.

52369 ▪ Owensboro-Daviess County Chamber of Commerce
200 E 3rd St.
Owensboro, KY 42302-0825
Ph: (270)926-1860
Fax: (270)926-3364
Co. E-mail: chamber@owensboro.com
URL: http://www.owensboro.com
Contact: Jody Wassmer, President
Description: Promotes business and community development in Daviess County, KY. **Founded:** 1913. **Publications:** *Buyers' Guide* (Annual); *The Enterprise* (Monthly); *Owensboro-Daviess County Magazine* (Annual). **Educational Activities:** Chamber Young Professionals (Monthly); Contact Club (Monthly). **Awards:** Entrepreneur of the Year (Annual); Small Business of the Year (Annual).

52370 ▪ Owensboro-Daviess County Magazine
200 E 3rd St.
Owensboro, KY 42302-0825
Ph: (270)926-1860
Fax: (270)926-3364
Co. E-mail: chamber@owensboro.com
URL: http://www.owensboro.com
Contact: Jody Wassmer, President
Released: Annual **Price:** included in membership dues.

52371 ▪ Owingsville-Bath County Chamber of Commerce
PO Box 360
Owingsville, KY 40360
Ph: (606)674-2531
Co. E-mail: info@owingsville.com
URL: http://www.owingsville.com
Contact: Mike Ray, President
Description: Promotes business and community development in Bath County, KY.

52372 ▪ Paducah Area Chamber of Commerce
PO Box 810
Paducah, KY 42002-0810
Ph: (270)443-1746

Fax: (270)442-9152
Co. E-mail: info@paducahchamber.org
URL: http://www.paducahchamber.org
Contact: Elaine Spalding, President
Description: Promotes business and community development in McCracken County, KY. **Founded:** 1938. **Publications:** *Chamber Connection* (Monthly). **Awards:** Business of the Year (Annual); Distinguished Citizen of the Year (Annual); Summit Award (Annual); Volunteer of the Year (Annual).

52373 ▪ Paris-Bourbon County Chamber of Commerce
c/o Lucy Cooper, Exec. Dir.
720 High St.
Paris, KY 40361
Ph: (859)987-3205
Co. E-mail: lcooper@parisky.com
URL: http://www.parisky.com
Contact: Lucy Cooper, Executive Director
Description: Promotes business and community development in Bourbon County, KY. Provides governmental liaison. Conducts community social and promotional activities. **Founded:** 1941. **Publications:** *Paris-Bourbon County Chamber Directory* (Annual). **Educational Activities:** Business after Hours (Periodic).

52374 ▪ Paris-Bourbon County Chamber Directory
c/o Lucy Cooper, Exec. Dir.
720 High St.
Paris, KY 40361
Ph: (859)987-3205
Co. E-mail: lcooper@parisky.com
URL: http://www.parisky.com
Contact: Lucy Cooper, Executive Director
Released: Annual

52375 ▪ Promoting Preservation and Progress
116 S Main St.
Russellville, KY 42276
Ph: (270)726-2206
Fax: (270)726-2237
Co. E-mail: logancounty@logantele.com
URL: http://www.loganchamber.com/QCMS_ Chamber
Contact: Lisa Browning, Executive Director

52376 ▪ Prospect Chamber of Commerce
9509 US Hwy. 42, Ste. 107
Prospect, KY 40059-9291
Ph: (502)228-7493
Fax: (866)802-2544
Co. E-mail: edhovan@insightbb.com
URL: http://www.prospectareachamber.org
Contact: Ed Hovan, President
Description: Promotes business development in Prospect, CT. **Publications:** *Prospect Chamber News* (Monthly).

52377 ▪ Prospect Chamber News
9509 US Hwy. 42, Ste. 107
Prospect, KY 40059-9291
Ph: (502)228-7493
Fax: (866)802-2544
Co. E-mail: edhovan@insightbb.com
URL: http://www.prospectareachamber.org
Contact: Ed Hovan, President
Released: Monthly

52378 ▪ Quality of Life
160 E Main St.
Georgetown, KY 40324
Ph: (502)863-5424
Fax: (502)863-5756
Co. E-mail: jack@gtown.org
URL: http://www.gtown.org
Contact: Jack Conner, Executive Director

52379 ▪ Radcliff-Hardin County Chamber of Commerce
306 N Wilson Rd.
Radcliff, KY 40160
Ph: (270)351-4450

Fax: (270)352-4449
Co. E-mail: jo@radcliffchamber.org
URL: http://www.radcliffchamber.org
Contact: Brad Richardson, President
Description: Promotes business and community development in the Radcliff, KY area. **Founded:** 1965. **Awards:** Ambassador of the Year (Annual); Bronze Business Award (Annual); The Community Service Award (Annual); Double Platinum Business Award (Annual); The Education Award (Annual); The Gold Award (Annual); Gold Business Award (Annual); The Military Award (Annual); President's Awards (Annual); Jonny Holloway Volunteer of the Year (Annual).

52380 ■ Richmond Chamber of Commerce
201 E Main St.
Richmond, KY 40475
Ph: (859)623-1720
Fax: (859)623-0839
Co. E-mail: rchamber@richmondchamber.com
URL: http://www.richmondchamber.com
Contact: Virgil R. Grant, President
Description: Promotes business and community development in Richmond, KY. **Publications:** Chamber Newsletter; Richmond Magazine. **Awards:** Business of the Month (Monthly). **Telecommunication Services:** terri@richmondchamber.com.

52381 ■ Richmond Magazine
201 E Main St.
Richmond, KY 40475
Ph: (859)623-1720
Fax: (859)623-0839
Co. E-mail: rchamber@richmondchamber.com
URL: http://www.richmondchamber.com
Contact: Virgil R. Grant, President

52382 ■ Russell County Chamber of Commerce
PO Box 64
Russell Springs, KY 42642-0064
Ph: (270)866-4333
Fax: (270)866-4304
Co. E-mail: info@russellcountyky.com
URL: http://www.russellcountyky.com
Contact: Joy Fletcher, President
Description: Promotes business and community development in Russell County, KY.

52383 ■ Scottsville-Allen County Chamber of Commerce
110 S Court St.
Scottsville, KY 42164-1438
Ph: (270)237-4782
Fax: (270)237-5498
Co. E-mail: chamber@scottsvilleky.info
Contact: Sue Shaver, Executive Director
Description: Promotes business and community development in Allen County, KY. Collects and disseminates information. Conducts local festivals. **Founded:** 1955. **Publications:** Chamber Briefings (Quarterly).

52384 ■ Somerset-Pulaski County Chamber of Commerce
445 S Hwy. 27, Ste. 101
Somerset, KY 42501
Ph: (606)679-7323
Fax: (606)679-1744
Co. E-mail: info@spcchamber.com
URL: http://www.spcchamber.com
Contact: Kenny Isaacs, Executive Director
Description: Promotes business and community development in Pulaski County, KY. **Founded:** 1925. **Publications:** Business Gazette (Periodic). **Educational Activities:** Chamber Membership Luncheon (Weekly). **Telecommunication Services:** jack@spcchamber.com.

52385 ■ Southeast Kentucky Chamber of Commerce
787 Hambley Blvd.
Pikeville, KY 41501
Ph: (606)432-5504
Free: 877-738-4400

Fax: (606)432-7295
Co. E-mail: info@pikecountychamber.org
URL: http://www.sekchamber.com
Contact: Brad N. Hall, President
Description: Promotes business and community development in Pike County, KY. **Publications:** Business Call (Monthly); Pikeville/Pike County Profile.

52386 ■ Sturgis Chamber of Commerce
513 N Main St.
Sturgis, KY 42459
Ph: (270)333-9316
Fax: (270)333-9319
Co. E-mail: sturgisrally@bellsouth.net
URL: http://www.littlesturgisrally.net
Contact: Paul Hart, President
Description: Promotes business and community development in Sturgis, KY. **Founded:** 1956.

52387 ■ Tompkinsville - Monroe County Chamber of Commerce
PO Box 433
Tompkinsville, KY 42167
Ph: (270)487-1314
Fax: (270)487-0975
Co. E-mail: monroemoney@centernetwork.net
URL: http://www.monroeky.com
Contact: Susan Turner, President
Description: Promotes business and community development in the Tompkinsville, KY area.

52388 ■ Winchester-Clark County Chamber of Commerce
2 S Maple St.
Winchester, KY 40391
Ph: (859)744-6420
Fax: (859)744-9229
Co. E-mail: chamber@winchesterky.com
URL: http://www.winchesterky.com
Contact: Karen Haley, President
URL(s): www.winchesterkychamber.com. **Description:** Promotes business and community development in Clark County, KY. Conducts golf tournament and annual Daniel Boone Pioneer Festival; bestows annual Citizen of the Year and Business of the Year awards. **Founded:** 1941. **Publications:** Community Profile. **Educational Activities:** Business Enhancement (Monthly).

52389 ■ Woodford County Chamber of Commerce
141 N Main St.
Versailles, KY 40383
Ph: (859)873-5122
Fax: (859)873-4576
Co. E-mail: info@woodfordcountyinfo.com
URL: http://woodfordcountyinfo.com
Contact: Tami Vater, Executive Director
Description: Promotes business, tourism, and community development in Woodford County, KY. **Founded:** 1971.

MINORITY BUSINESS ASSISTANCE PROGRAMS

52390 ■ Kentucky Cabinet for Economic Development - Community Development Department - Small and Minority Business Division
Old Capital Annex
300 W Broadway
Frankfort, KY 40601
Ph: (502)564-7140
Free: 800-626-2930
Fax: (502)564-3256
Co. E-mail: MarkL.Johnson@ky.gov
URL: http://www.thinkkentucky.com
Contact: Mark L. Johnson, Branch Manager
Description: Coordinates minority enterprise activities throughout the state's administrative structure. Acts as an advocate. Mobilizes resources and information. Develops marketing resources and provides individual guidance. Also administers a public-sector purchasing assistance program.

52391 ■ Tri-State Minority Supplier Development Council
614 W Main St., Ste. 5500
Louisville, KY 40202
Ph: (502)625-0159
Fax: (502)625-0082
Co. E-mail: info@tsmsdc.com
URL: http://www.tsmsdc.com
Contact: Ty Gettis, Chief Executive Officer
Description: Provides a variety of business development and referral services to minority business owners in Kentucky, West Virginia, and parts of Indiana.

FINANCING AND LOAN PROGRAMS

52392 ■ Chrysalis Ventures
101 S. Fifth St., Ste., 1650
Louisville, KY 40202-3122
Ph: (502)583-7644
Fax: (502)583-7648
Co. E-mail: info@chrysalisventures.com
URL: http://www.chrysalisventures.com
Contact: David A. Jones, Jr., Chairman
Preferred Investment Size: $2,000,000 to $15,000,000. **Industry Preferences:** Internet specific, medical and health, computer software and services, other products, communications and media, consumer related, and biotechnology. **Geographic Preference:** South regions and Midwest.

52393 ■ Iceberg Ventures
124 N. 1st St.
Louisville, KY 40202
Ph: (502)583-6810
Fax: (502)583-5606
Co. E-mail: info@icebergventures.com
URL: http://www.icebergventures.com
Contact: Keith Williams, Chief Operating Officer
Investment Policies: Early stage. **Geographic Preference:** U.S.

52394 ■ K - Kentucky Highlands Investment Corporation
362 Old Whitley Rd.
London, KY 40741
Ph: (606)864-5175
Fax: (606)864-5194
Co. E-mail: khicnet@khic.org
URL: http://www.khic.org
Contact: Brenda McDaniel, Chief Financial Officer
Preferred Investment Size: $500 to $10,000,000. **Investment Policies:** Start-up, second stage, and special situation. **Industry Preferences:** Manufacturing. **Geographic Preference:** Kentucky.

PROCUREMENT ASSISTANCE PROGRAMS

52395 ■ Kentucky Procurement Assistance Program
Old Capitol Annex
300 W. Broadway
Frankfort, KY 40601
Ph: (502)564-2064
Free: 800-626-2930
Fax: (502)564-3256
Co. E-mail: ced.kpap@ky.gov
URL: http://www.thinkkentucky.com
Contact: Debbie McKnight, Branch Manager
Description: Helps Kentucky businesses tap the federal procurement market.

52396 ■ Kentucky & Tennessee Procurement Center
PO Box 59, Rm. 173M
Louisville, KY 40202
Ph: (502)582-6662
Fax: (502)582-5547
Co. E-mail: kathleen.hyatt@sba.gov
URL: http://www.sba.gov
Contact: Kathleen Hyatt
E-mail: kathleen.hyatt@sba.gov
Description: Covers activities for Army Corps of Engineers (Louisville, KY), Fort Knox (Fort Knox, KY), Fort Campbell (Fort Campbell, KY), and Army Corps of Engineers (Nashville, TN).

INCUBATORS/RESEARCH AND TECHNOLOGY PARKS

52397 ■ Center for Economic Development, Entrepreneurship and Technology
Eastern Kentucky University
BTC 147
521 Lancaster Ave.
Richmond, KY 40475
Ph: (859)622-2334
Fax: (859)622-6274
Co. E-mail: Ian.Mooers@eku.edu
URL: http://www.cedet.eku.edu/

Description: A small business incubator providing assistance to businesses, organizations, industries, and communities to aid in their development.

52398 ■ Morgan County Regional Technology Center
151 University Dr.
West Liberty, KY 41472
Free: 877-743-4005
URL: http://www.mcrtc.com/

Description: A small business incubator designed to create a dynamic environment where businesses can focus on product and technology development, sales, and marketing. The Technology Center provides facilities and equipment when available, management assistance, administrative assistance and back office support to its tenants.

52399 ■ University of Kentucky Office of Commercialization and Development - Advanced Science and Technology Commercialization Center
152 ASTeCC Bldg.
Lexington, KY 40503-0286
Ph: (859)218-6563
Fax: (859)257-2489
Co. E-mail: astecc@uky.edu
URL: http://www.econdev.uky.edu/about-astecc.aspx

Description: A faculty research facility and commercialization center established for multidisciplinary research, technology transfer, and new business start-ups.

EDUCATIONAL PROGRAMS

52400 ■ Bowling Green Community College of Western Kentucky University
2355 Nashville Rd., Ste. B
Bowling Green, KY 42101
Ph: (270)780-2550
Fax: (270)745-2011
URL: http://www.wku.edu
Description: Two-year college offering a small business management program.

52401 ■ Morehead State University
Small Business Development Center
College of Business
150 E First St.
Morehead, KY 40351
Ph: (606)783-2895
Fax: (606)783-5020
Co. E-mail: m.murphy@moreheadstate.edu
URL: http://www.moreheadstate.edu
Description: Provides training programs that benefit the small business community.

52402 ■ National College of Business and Technology
7627 Ewing Blvd.
Florence, KY 41042
Ph: (859)525-6510
Free: 888-956-2732
Fax: (859)525-8961
URL: http://www.national-college.edu
Description: Business college offering a small business management program.

LEGISLATIVE ASSISTANCE

52403 ■ Office of the Governor - Legislative Liaison Office
700 Capitol Ave., Ste. 100
Frankfort, KY 40601
Ph: (502)564-2611
Fax: (502)564-2517
URL: http://www.governor.ky.gov/
Description: Assists the governor in formulating small business policies.

PUBLICATIONS

52404 ■ *Business First*
111 W. Washington St.
Louisville, KY 40202
Ph: (502)583-1731
Fax: (502)587-1703
URL: http://www.bizjournals.com/louisville/

52405 ■ *Smart Start your Kentucky Business*
PSI Research
300 N. Valley Dr.
Grants Pass, OR 97526
Ph: (503)479-9464
Free: 800-228-2275
Fax: (503)476-1479
Co. E-mail: info@psi-research.com
URL: http://www.psi-research.com
Ed: Michael D. Jenkins. **Released:** Revised edition, 1992. **Price:** $29.95 (looseleaf binder); $24.95 (paper). **Description:** Part of the Successful Business Library series.

PUBLISHERS

52406 ■ Hatfield House Books
7710 Commonwealth Dr.
Crestwood, KY 40014
Ph: (502)241-5950
Contact: Kenneth F. Hatfield, President
E-mail: kenhat@yahoo.com
Description: Description: Publishes books for small business owners. Reviews books on business related topics and acts as a literary agent. Reaches market through commission representatives and direct mail. Does not accept unsolicited manuscripts. **Founded:** 1984.

52407 ■ Kentucky Cabinet for Economic Development - Small & Minority Business Div.
Old Capitol Annex
300 W Broadway
Frankfort, KY 40601
Ph: (502)564-7140
Free: 800-626-2930
Fax: (502)564-3256
Co. E-mail: econdev@ky.gov
URL: http://www.thinkkentucky.com/smbd
Contact: Deborah Clayton, President
Description: Description: Publishes on Kentucky-based small, minority and women-owned businesses. **Founded:** 1972.

SMALL BUSINESS DEVELOPMENT CENTERS

52408 ■ Louisiana Small Business Development Center - Greater New Orleans Region
UNO Jefferson Center
3330 N Causeway Blvd., Ste. 447
Metairie, LA 70002
Ph: (504)831-3730
Co. E-mail: lsbdc.gnor@lsbdc.org
URL: http://www.lsbdc.org
Description: Represents and promotes the small business sector. Provides management assistance to current and prospective small business owners. Helps to improve management skills and expand the products and services of members.

52409 ■ Louisiana Small Business Development Center - Lead Office (LSBDC)
University of Louisiana at Monroe
700 University Ave., Administration Bldg. 2-123
Monroe, LA 71209-6530
Ph: (318)342-1224
Fax: (318)342-3085
Co. E-mail: lsbdc.ulm@lsbdc.org
URL: http://www.lsbdc.org
Contact: Mary Lynn Wilkerson, Director
Description: Works to provide broad-based management and technical assistance to existing and potential Louisiana businesses through coordinated use of local, state, and federal programs, private sector assets, and resources available at member organizations. Also offers specialized services in technology and international trade.

52410 ■ Louisiana Small Business Development Center at Louisiana State University in Shreveport
LSUS Business Education Bldg., Rm. 103
One University Pl.
Shreveport, LA 71115
Ph: (318)797-5144
Co. E-mail: lsbdc.lsus@lsbdc.org
URL: http://www.lsbdc.org
Contact: Rande Kessler, Director (Acting)
Description: Represents and promotes the small business sector. Provides management assistance to current and prospective small business owners. Helps to improve management skills and expand the products and services of members.

52411 ■ Louisiana Small Business Development Center - LSU South Campus
LBTC Bldg. 3000
8000 GSRI Ave.
Baton Rouge, LA 70820
Ph: (225)578-4842
Co. E-mail: lsbdctc.lsu@lsbdc.org
URL: http://www.lsbdc.org
Description: Represents and promotes the small business sector. Provides management assistance to current and prospective small business owners. Helps to improve management skills and expand the products and services of members.

52412 ■ Louisiana Small Business Development Center at McNeese State University
Burton Business Center
4450 Ryan St.
Lake Charles, LA 70605
Ph: (337)475-5529
Co. E-mail: lsbdc.msu@lsbdc.org
URL: http://www.lsbdc.org
Contact: Donna Little, Director
Description: Represents and promotes the small business sector. Provides management assistance to current and prospective small business owners. Helps to improve management skills and expand the products and services of members.

52413 ■ Louisiana Small Business Development Center at Northwestern State University
Dunbar Plz., Ste. 114C
3600 Jackson St.
Alexandria, LA 71303-3064
Ph: (318)484-2123
Co. E-mail: lsbdc.nsu@lsbdc.org
URL: http://www.lsbdc.org
Contact: Jim Kilcoyne, Director
Description: Represents and promotes the small business sector. Provides management assistance to current and prospective small business owners. Helps to improve management skills and expand the products and services of members.

52414 ■ Louisiana Small Business Development Center at Southeastern Louisiana University
Southeast Louisiana Business Center
1514 Martens Dr.
Hammond, LA 70402-0001
Ph: (985)549-3831
Co. E-mail: lsbdc.slu@lsbdc.org
URL: http://www.lsbdc.org
Contact: William Joubert, Director
Description: Represents and promotes the small business sector. Provides management assistance to current and prospective small business owners. Helps to improve management skills and expand the products and services of members.

52415 ■ Louisiana Small Business Development Center at Southern University
616 Harding Blvd.
Baton Rouge, LA 70807
Ph: (225)922-0998
Co. E-mail: lsbdc.subr@lsbdc.org
URL: http://www.lsbdc.org
Contact: Will M. Campbell, Jr., Director
Description: Represents and promotes the small business sector. Provides management assistance to current and prospective small business owners. Helps to improve management skills and expand the products and services of members.

52416 ■ Louisiana Small Business Development Center at University of Louisiana at Lafayette
635 Cajundome Blvd., Rm. 162
Lafayette, LA 70506
Ph: (337)262-5344
Co. E-mail: lsbdc.ull@lsbdc.org
URL: http://www.lsbdc.org
Contact: Mark Galyean, Director
Description: Represents and promotes the small business sector. Provides management assistance to current and prospective small business owners. Helps to improve management skills and expand the products and services of members.

SCORE OFFICES

52417 ■ Northshore SCORE
Co. E-mail: scorens@scorens.org

52418 ■ Northwest LA SCORE
400 Edwards St.
Shreveport, LA 71101
Ph: (318)677-2500
Fax: (318)677-2541
URL: http://northwestlouisiana.score.org/chapters/northwest-louisiana-score
Description: Provides professional guidance and information to America's small businesses. **Founded:** 1972.

52419 ■ SCORE Baton Rouge
Louisiana Technology Park
7117 Florida Blvd.
Baton Rouge, LA 70806
Ph: (225)381-7130
Free: 877-381-7130
Fax: (225)215-0080
Co. E-mail: scorebr@scorebr.org
URL: http://www.scorebr.org
Contact: James M. Pelton, Chairman
Description: Assists new businesses or businesses facing challenges in the greater Baton Rouge area or in the Northshore area. Provides free and confidential business counseling tailored to meet the needs of small business and their personal objectives.

52420 ■ SCORE Lafayette
Travis Technology Center
110 Travis St., Rm. 89
Lafayette, LA 70503
Ph: (337)889-0214
Fax: (337)889-0212
Co. E-mail: cajun_score@yahoo.com
URL: http://www.lafayettescore.org
Description: Provides public service to America by offering small business advice and training.

52421 ■ SCORE New Orleans
Co. E-mail: nola@scorevolunteer.org

52422 ■ SCORE Northeast Louisiana
1810 Auburn Ave., Ste. 102
Monroe, LA 71201
Ph: (318)323-0878

Fax: (318)323-9492
URL: http://northeastlouisiana.score.org/chapters/
northeast-louisiana-score
Contact: Barney Jones, Administrator
Description: Serves as volunteer program in which
working and retired business management professionals provide free business counseling to men and
women who are considering starting a small business, encountering problems with their business, or
expanding their business. Offers free one-on-one
counseling, online counseling and low cost workshops
on a variety of business topics. **Founded:** 1998.

52423 ■ Southwest Louisiana SCORE
Co. E-mail: score@allianceswla.org

BETTER BUSINESS BUREAUS

**52424 ■ Better Business Bureau (Shreveport,
Louisiana)**
5220-C Rue Verdun
Alexandria, LA 71303
Ph: (318)473-4494
Fax: (318)473-8906
Co. E-mail: info@alexandria-la.bbb.org
URL: http://shreveport.bbb.org
Contact: Andrew Fisher, President
Description: Seeks to promote and foster ethical
relationship between businesses and the public
through voluntary self-regulation, consumer and business education, and service excellence. Provides
information to help consumers and businesses make
informed purchasing decisions and avoid costly
scams and frauds; settles consumer complaints
through arbitration and other means.

52425 ■ Better Business Bureau of Acadiana
4007 W Congress St., Ste. B
Lafayette, LA 70506
Ph: (337)981-3497
Fax: (337)981-7559
Co. E-mail: info@acadiana.bbb.org
URL: http://lafayette.bbb.org
Contact: Sharane A. Gott, President
Description: Seeks to promote and foster the high-
est ethical relationship between businesses and the
public through voluntary self-regulation, consumer
and business education, and service excellence.
Provides information to help consumers and busi-
nesses make informed purchasing decisions and
avoid costly scams and frauds; settles consumer
complaints through arbitration and other means.

**52426 ■ Better Business Bureau of Central
Louisiana**
5220-C Rue Verdun
Alexandria, LA 71303
Ph: (318)473-4494
Fax: (318)473-8906
URL: http://www.alexandria-la.bbb.org
Contact: Ellis Isom, Office Manager
Description: Seeks to promote and foster the high-
est ethical relationship between businesses and the
public through voluntary self-regulation, consumer
and business education, and service excellence.
Provides information to help consumers and busi-
nesses make informed purchasing decisions and
avoid costly scams and frauds; settles consumer
complaints through arbitration and other means.
Founded: 1985.

**52427 ■ Better Business Bureau of Northeast
Louisiana**
212 Walnut St., Ste. 210
Monroe, LA 71201
Ph: (318)387-4600
Free: 800-960-7756
Co. E-mail: info@bbbnela.org
URL: http://nela.bbb.org
Contact: Jo Ann Deal, President
URL(s): www.monroe.bbb.org. **Description:** Seeks
to promote and foster the highest ethical relationship
between businesses and the public through voluntary
self-regulation, consumer and business education,
and service excellence. Provides information to help

consumers and businesses make informed purchasing decisions and avoid costly scams and frauds;
settles consumer complaints through arbitration and
other means.

**52428 ■ Better Business Bureau of South
Central Louisiana**
748 Main St.
Baton Rouge, LA 70802-5526
Ph: (225)346-5222
Fax: (225)346-1029
Co. E-mail: info@batonrouge.bbb.org
URL: http://batonrouge.bbb.org
Description: Seeks to promote and foster the high-
est ethical relationship between businesses and the
public through voluntary self-regulation, consumer
and business education, and service excellence.
Provides information to help consumers and busi-
nesses make informed purchasing decisions and
avoid costly scams and frauds; settles consumer
complaints through arbitration and other means.
Founded: 1950.

**52429 ■ Better Business Bureau of
Southwest Louisiana**
PO Box 7314
Lake Charles, LA 70606
Ph: (337)478-6253
Free: 800-542-7085
Fax: (337)474-8981
Co. E-mail: swlabbb@suddenlinkmail.com
URL: http://lakecharles.bbb.org
Contact: Mrs. Carmen Million, President
Description: Seeks to promote and foster the high-
est ethical relationship between businesses and the
public through voluntary self-regulation, consumer
and business education, and service excellence.
Provides information to help consumers and busi-
nesses make informed purchasing decisions and
avoid costly scams and frauds; settles consumer
complaints through arbitration and other means.

CHAMBERS OF COMMERCE

52430 ■ Annual Report
PO Box 591
Denham Springs, LA 70727
Ph: (225)665-8155
Fax: (225)665-2411
Co. E-mail: info@livingstonparishchamber.org
Contact: Ms. Sherry Mely, Chairperson
Released: Annual

52431 ■ Ascension Chamber of Commerce
1006 W Hwy. 30
Gonzales, LA 70707-1204
Ph: (225)647-7487
Fax: (225)647-5124
Co. E-mail: info@ascensionchamber.com
URL: http://www.ascensionchamber.com
Contact: Sherrie Despino, President
Description: Promotes business and economic
development in Ascension Parish.

**52432 ■ Assumption Area Chamber of
Commerce**
2939 Hwy. 70 S
Pierre Part, LA 70339
Ph: (985)369-2816
Fax: (985)369-4461
Co. E-mail: assumption@bellsouth.net
URL: http://www.assumptionchamber.org
Contact: Misti Johnson, Executive Director
Description: Aims to advance, promote, and improve
the civic, commercial, industrial, agricultural, trade,
educational, and general interests of the Parish of
Assumption. **Founded:** 1994.

52433 ■ Bogalusa Chamber of Commerce
608 Willis Ave.
Bogalusa, LA 70427-3002
Ph: (985)735-5731
Fax: (985)735-6707
Co. E-mail: bogalusachamber@bellsouth.net
URL: http://www.bogalusachamber.org
Description: Promotes business and community
development in Bogalusa, LA. Sponsors Festival in
the Park. **Founded:** 1920. **Publications:** Looking Up

(Bimonthly); Newcomer's Guide (Annual); Facts,
Festivals, Annual events, History, places of interest
for Bogalusa and Washington Parish.

52434 ■ Bossier Chamber of Commerce
710 Benton Rd.
Bossier City, LA 71111-3797
Ph: (318)746-0252
Fax: (318)746-0357
Co. E-mail: info@bossierchamber.com
URL: http://www.bossierchamber.com
Contact: Lisa Johnson, President
Description: Promotes business and community
development in Bossier, LA. **Publications:** Chamber
Update (Monthly). **Awards:** Diplomat of the Year
Award (Annual); Small Business Person of the Year
Award (Annual).

**52435 ■ Breaux Bridge Area Chamber of
Commerce**
314 E Bridge St.
Breaux Bridge, LA 70517
Ph: (337)332-5406
Fax: (337)332-5424
Co. E-mail: info@breauxbridgelive.com
URL: http://www.breauxbridgelive.com
Contact: Tina Begnaud, Executive Director
Description: Promotes business and community
development in Breaux Bridge, LA. **Founded:** 1972.

52436 ■ Cenla Magazine
PO Box 992
Alexandria, LA 71309
Ph: (318)442-6671
Fax: (318)442-6734
Co. E-mail: eltonpody@cenlachamber.org
URL: http://www.cenlachamber.org
Contact: Deborah Randolph, President
Released: Bimonthly

**52437 ■ Central Louisiana Chamber of
Commerce**
PO Box 992
Alexandria, LA 71309
Ph: (318)442-6671
Fax: (318)442-6734
Co. E-mail: eltonpody@cenlachamber.org
URL: http://www.cenlachamber.org
Contact: Deborah Randolph, President
Description: Promotes economic development in the
region. **Founded:** 1914. **Publications:** Cenla Maga-
zine (Bimonthly); The Chamber Means Business
(Monthly).

52438 ■ Chamber
109 W Pine St.
Ponchatoula, LA 70454
Ph: (985)386-2536
Fax: (985)386-2537
Co. E-mail: chamber@ponchatoulachamber.com
URL: http://www.ponchatoulachamber.com
Released: Monthly

52439 ■ Chamber Checklist
PO Box 1383
Ruston, LA 71273-1383
Ph: (318)255-2031
Free: 800-392-9032
Fax: (318)255-3481
Co. E-mail: sterry@rustonlincoln.org
URL: http://www.rustonlincoln.org
Contact: Scott Terry, President
Released: Weekly

**52440 ■ Chamber of Commerce of Lafourche
and the Bayou Region**
PO Box 1462
Larose, LA 70373
Ph: (985)693-6700
Fax: (985)693-6702
URL: http://www.lafourchechamber.com
Contact: Lin Kiger, President
Description: Promotes business and community
development in Larose, LA area. **Founded:** 1994.
Publications: The Chamber Matters (Quarterly).
Awards: Business Person of the Year (Annual).

52441 ■ *Chamber Connection*
118 W Hall Ave.
Slidell, LA 70458
Ph: (985)643-5678
Free: 800-471-3758
Fax: (985)649-2460
Co. E-mail: dawn@estchamber.com
URL: http://www.slidellchamber.com
Contact: Dawn Sharpe, Chief Executive Officer
Released: Monthly

52442 ■ *Chamber Insight*
318 E Bayou Rd.
Thibodaux, LA 70301
Ph: (985)446-1187
Fax: (985)446-1191
Co. E-mail: info@thibodauxchamber.com
URL: http://www.thibodauxchamber.com
Contact: Kathy Benoit, President
Released: Monthly

52443 ■ *The Chamber Matters*
PO Box 1462
Larose, LA 70373
Ph: (985)693-6700
Fax: (985)693-6702
URL: http://www.lafourchechamber.com
Contact: Lin Kiger, President
Released: Quarterly

52444 ■ *The Chamber Means Business*
PO Box 992
Alexandria, LA 71309
Ph: (318)442-6671
Fax: (318)442-6734
Co. E-mail: eltonpody@cenlachamber.org
URL: http://www.cenlachamber.org
Contact: Deborah Randolph, President
Released: Monthly

52445 ■ *Chamber News*
PO Box 591
Denham Springs, LA 70727
Ph: (225)665-8155
Fax: (225)665-2411
Co. E-mail: info@livingstonparishchamber.org
Contact: Ms. Sherry Mely, Chairperson
Released: Monthly

52446 ■ *Chamber News*
400 NW Railroad Ave.
Hammond, LA 70401
Ph: (985)345-4457
Fax: (985)345-4749
URL: http://hammondchamber.org
Contact: Charlotte Lenoir, Executive Director
Released: Weekly

52447 ■ *Chamber ROI*
110 Sibley Rd.
Minden, LA 71058-0819
Ph: (318)377-4240
Fax: (318)377-4215
Co. E-mail: info@mindenchamber.com
URL: http://www.mindenchamber.com
Contact: Mike Moore, President
Released: Monthly

52448 ■ Chamber - Southwest Louisiana
1011 Lakeshore Dr.
Lake Charles, LA 70601-9412
Ph: (337)433-3632
Fax: (337)436-3727
Co. E-mail: gswift@allianceswla.org
URL: http://allianceswla.org/CatSubCat/CatSubCat.
  asp?p9=CSC1
Contact: George Swift, President
Description: Strives to develop Southwest Louisiana by creating economic opportunity, and demanding responsible government and quality education. **Publications:** *Clubs and Organizations Directory; Major Employer's of SWLA Directory; SWLA Business Directory.*

52449 ■ *Chamber Update*
710 Benton Rd.
Bossier City, LA 71111-3797
Ph: (318)746-0252

Fax: (318)746-0357
Co. E-mail: info@bossierchamber.com
URL: http://www.bossierchamber.com
Contact: Lisa Johnson, President
Released: Monthly **Price:** included in membership dues.

52450 ■ *Chamber Updates*
610 Hollycrest Blvd.
Covington, LA 70433
Ph: (985)892-3216
Fax: (985)893-4244
Co. E-mail: info@sttammanychamber.org
URL: http://www.sttammanychamber.org
Contact: Lacey Toledano, President
Released: Weekly

52451 ■ *Chamber Voice*
714 Railroad Ave.
Donaldsonville, LA 70346
Ph: (225)473-4814
Fax: (225)473-4817
Co. E-mail: dvillecoc@bellsouth.net
URL: http://www.donaldsonvillecoc.org
Contact: Becky Katz, Executive Director
Released: Bimonthly **Price:** $10.

52452 ■ *Chaucer News*
PO Box 767
Marksville, LA 71351
Ph: (318)253-0284
Co. E-mail: carrollsanders@bellsouth.net
URL: http://www.marksvillechamberofcommerce.com
Contact: Rene Borrel, President
Released: Monthly **Price:** free.

52453 ■ Claiborne Chamber of Commerce
519 S Main St.
Homer, LA 71040
Ph: (318)927-3271
Fax: (318)927-3271
URL: http://www.claiborneone.org/homer/coc/index.
  html
Contact: Mr. John Watson, Executive Director
Description: Strives to promote, assist, and encourage the advancement of the material prosperity and commercial, industrial, and civic progress of Claiborne Parish, Louisiana.

52454 ■ *Clubs and Organizations Directory*
1011 Lakeshore Dr.
Lake Charles, LA 70601-9412
Ph: (337)433-3632
Fax: (337)436-3727
Co. E-mail: gswift@allianceswla.org
URL: http://allianceswla.org/CatSubCat/CatSubCat.
  asp?p9=CSC1
Contact: George Swift, President
Price: $4, for members; $6, for nonmembers.

52455 ■ *Compass Point*
112 Professional Dr.
West Monroe, LA 71291
Ph: (318)325-1961
Fax: (318)325-4296
Co. E-mail: info@westmonroechamber.org
URL: http://westmonroechamber.org
Contact: Mary Ann Newton, President
Released: Monthly **Price:** included in membership dues.

52456 ■ Coushatta-Red River Chamber of Commerce
PO Box 333
Coushatta, LA 71019
Ph: (318)932-3289
Co. E-mail: redriverchamber@bellsouth.net
URL: http://coushattaredriverchamberofcommerce.
  com/default.aspx
Contact: Mary Ann Wiggins, President
Description: Promotes business and community development in the Red River Parish Coushatta, LA area. Supports local charities; conducts political and business networking forums. **Founded:** 1969.

52457 ■ Donaldsonville Area Chamber of Commerce (DACC)
714 Railroad Ave.
Donaldsonville, LA 70346

Ph: (225)473-4814
Fax: (225)473-4817
Co. E-mail: dvillecoc@bellsouth.net
URL: http://www.donaldsonvillecoc.org
Contact: Becky Katz, Executive Director
Description: Promotes business and community development in the Donaldsonville, LA area. Sponsors festival. **Founded:** 1946. **Publications:** *Chamber Voice* (Bimonthly); *Chamber Voice* (Bimonthly).

52458 ■ *Economic Review*
212 Walnut St., Ste. 100
Monroe, LA 71201-6707
Ph: (318)323-3461
Free: 888-531-9535
Fax: (318)322-7594
Co. E-mail: sedmunds@monroe.org
URL: http://www.monroe.org
Contact: Sue Edmunds, President
Released: Annual

52459 ■ Eunice Chamber of Commerce
200 S CC Duson
Eunice, LA 70535
Ph: (337)457-2565
Fax: (337)546-0278
Co. E-mail: eunicecc@charterinternet.com
URL: http://www.eunicechamber.com
Description: Promotes business and community development in Eunice, LA.

52460 ■ *Facts, Festivals, Annual events, History, places of interest for Bogalusa and Washington Parish*
608 Willis Ave.
Bogalusa, LA 70427-3002
Ph: (985)735-5731
Fax: (985)735-6707
Co. E-mail: bogalusachamber@bellsouth.net
URL: http://www.bogalusachamber.org

52461 ■ French - American Chamber of Commerce - Louisiana Chapter
PO Box 57255
New Orleans, LA 70157
Ph: (504)458-3528
Fax: (504)865-0323
Co. E-mail: info@facc-la.com
URL: http://www.facc-la.com
Contact: Loretta K. Krasnow, Executive Director

52462 ■ *The Front Door*
562 2nd St.
Natchitoches, LA 71457
Ph: (318)352-6894
Free: 800-456-5804
Fax: (318)352-5385
Co. E-mail: chamber@natchitoches.net
URL: http://www.natchitoscheschamber.com
Contact: Nick Pollacia, Jr., President
Released: Monthly

52463 ■ *Gateway News*
23675 Church St.
Plaquemine, LA 70764
Ph: (225)687-3560
Fax: (225)687-3575
URL: http://www.ibervillechamber.com
Contact: Hank Grace, Executive Director
Released: Bimonthly

52464 ■ Greater Abbeville-Vermilion Chamber of Commerce (GACC)
1907 Veterans Memorial Dr.
Abbeville, LA 70510
Ph: (337)893-2491
Fax: (337)893-1807
Co. E-mail: abbevillechamber@abbevillechamber.
  com
URL: http://www.abbevillechamber.com
Contact: Lynn Guillory, Executive Director
Description: Promotes business and community development in the Abbeville, LA area. Sponsors workshops and seminars. Conducts French Market Festival. **Founded:** 1920.

52465 ■ Greater Denham Springs Chamber of Commerce
PO Box 591
Denham Springs, LA 70727
Ph: (225)665-8155
Fax: (225)665-2411
Co. E-mail: info@livingstonparishchamber.org
Contact: Ms. Sherry Mely, Chairperson
Description: Businesses, clergy, and other individuals interested in advancing the general welfare and prosperity of Livingston Parish, LA. Conducts charitable activities. **Founded:** 1966. **Publications:** *Annual Report* (Annual); *Chamber News* (Monthly). **Educational Activities:** Business Expo (Annual).

52466 ■ Greater Lafayette Chamber of Commerce (GLCC)
804 E St. Mary Blvd.
Lafayette, LA 70503-1307
Ph: (337)233-2705
Fax: (337)234-8671
Co. E-mail: rob@lafchamber.org
URL: http://www.lafchamber.org
Contact: Robert M. Guidry, President
Description: Promotes business and community development in the Lafayette, LA area. **Founded:** 1935. **Publications:** *Inforum* (Bimonthly).

52467 ■ Greater Pointe Coupee Chamber of Commerce (GPCCC)
PO Box 555
New Roads, LA 70760
Ph: (225)638-3500
Fax: (225)638-9858
Co. E-mail: pointecoupeechamber@yahoo.com
URL: http://www.pcchamber.org
Contact: Amy Davis, President
Description: Promotes business and community development in the Pointe Coupee Parish, LA area.

52468 ■ Greater Shreveport Chamber of Commerce (GSCC)
400 Edwards St.
Shreveport, LA 71101
Ph: (318)677-2500
Free: 800-448-5432
Fax: (318)677-2541
Co. E-mail: info@shreveportchamber.org
URL: http://www.shreveportchamber.org
Contact: Mr. Richard H. Bremer, President
Description: Promotes business and community development in Shreveport/Bossier City, LA area. Convention/Meeting: none. **Founded:** 1910. **Publications:** *Investor's Update* (Weekly). **Awards:** Athena Award (Annual); Very Important Volunteer Awards (Annual); Walk of Stars Award (Annual); Forum Small Business of the Year Award (Annual); J. Pat Beaird Industry of the Year (Annual). **Telecommunication Services:** dickbremer@shreveportchamber.org.

52469 ■ Greater Slidell Area Chamber of Commerce (GSACC)
118 W Hall Ave.
Slidell, LA 70458
Ph: (985)643-5678
Free: 800-471-3758
Fax: (985)649-2460
Co. E-mail: dawn@estchamber.com
URL: http://www.slidellchamber.com
Contact: Dawn Sharpe, Chief Executive Officer
Description: Promotes business and community development in the Slidell, LA area. Sponsors annual Business Day. **Founded:** 1962. **Publications:** *Chamber Connection* (Monthly); *Slidell City Map* (Periodic); *Slidell Connection* (Annual).

52470 ■ Greater Vernon Chamber of Commerce (GVCC)
PO Box 1228
Leesville, LA 71496-1228
Ph: (337)238-0349
Free: 877-234-0349

Fax: (337)238-0340
Co. E-mail: cofcvernonparish@bellsouth.net
URL: http://www.chambervernonparish.com
Contact: Eddie Wise, Executive Director
Description: Promotes business, community development, and tourism in the Leesville-Vernon Parish, LA area. **Founded:** 1943.

52471 ■ Hammond Chamber of Commerce (HCC)
400 NW Railroad Ave.
Hammond, LA 70401
Ph: (985)345-4457
Fax: (985)345-4749
URL: http://hammondchamber.org
Contact: Charlotte Lenoir, Executive Director
Description: Promotes business and community development in Hammond, LA. **Publications:** *Chamber News* (Weekly). **Educational Activities:** New Member Lead Group (Monthly).

52472 ■ Houma-Terrebonne Chamber of Commerce (HTCC)
6133 Hwy. 311
Houma, LA 70364
Ph: (985)876-5600
Fax: (985)876-5611
Co. E-mail: info@houmachamber.com
URL: http://www.houmachamber.com
Contact: Drake Pothier, President
Description: Promotes business and community development in Terrebonne Parish, LA. **Founded:** 1929. **Awards:** Business of the Year (Annual).

52473 ■ Iberville Chamber of Commerce
23675 Church St.
Plaquemine, LA 70764
Ph: (225)687-3560
Fax: (225)687-3575
URL: http://www.ibervillechamber.com
Contact: Hank Grace, Executive Director
Description: Promotes business and community development in Plaquemine, LA area. **Publications:** *Gateway News* (Bimonthly).

52474 ■ *Images*
212 Walnut St., Ste. 100
Monroe, LA 71201-6707
Ph: (318)323-3461
Free: 888-531-9535
Fax: (318)322-7594
Co. E-mail: sedmunds@monroe.org
URL: http://www.monroe.org
Contact: Sue Edmunds, President
Released: Monthly

52475 ■ *Inforum*
804 E St. Mary Blvd.
Lafayette, LA 70503-1307
Ph: (337)233-2705
Fax: (337)234-8671
Co. E-mail: rob@lafchamber.org
URL: http://www.lafchamber.org
Contact: Robert M. Guidry, President
Released: Bimonthly **Price:** included in membership dues.

52476 ■ *Inside the Chamber*
212 Walnut St., Ste. 100
Monroe, LA 71201-6707
Ph: (318)323-3461
Free: 888-531-9535
Fax: (318)322-7594
Co. E-mail: sedmunds@monroe.org
URL: http://www.monroe.org
Contact: Sue Edmunds, President
Released: Quarterly

52477 ■ *Investor's Update*
400 Edwards St.
Shreveport, LA 71101
Ph: (318)677-2500
Free: 800-448-5432
Fax: (318)677-2541
Co. E-mail: info@shreveportchamber.org
URL: http://www.shreveportchamber.org
Contact: Mr. Richard H. Bremer, President
Released: Weekly

52478 ■ Jefferson Chamber of Commerce
3421 N Causeway Blvd., Ste. 203
Metairie, LA 70002
Ph: (504)835-3880
Fax: (504)835-3828
Co. E-mail: todd@jeffersonchamber.org
URL: http://jeffersonchamber.org
Contact: Todd Murphy, President
Description: Works to improve the quality of life and the economic, civic, and cultural environment in Jefferson Parish. **Founded:** 1998.

52479 ■ Kentwood Chamber of Commerce
PO Box 685
Kentwood, LA 70444
Ph: (985)229-4656
Fax: (985)230-0841
Co. E-mail: kcd@kentwoodla.org
URL: http://www.kentwoodla.org
Description: Promotes business and community development in Kentwood, LA.

52480 ■ *Looking Up*
608 Willis Ave.
Bogalusa, LA 70427-3002
Ph: (985)735-5731
Fax: (985)735-6707
Co. E-mail: bogalusachamber@bellsouth.net
URL: http://www.bogalusachamber.org
Released: Bimonthly

52481 ■ *Major Employer's of SWLA Directory*
1011 Lakeshore Dr.
Lake Charles, LA 70601-9412
Ph: (337)433-3632
Fax: (337)436-3727
Co. E-mail: gswift@allianceswla.org
URL: http://allianceswla.org/CatSubCat/CatSubCat.asp?p9=CSC1
Contact: George Swift, President
Price: $15, for members; $30, for nonmembers.

52482 ■ Marksville Chamber of Commerce (MCC)
PO Box 767
Marksville, LA 71351
Ph: (318)253-0284
Co. E-mail: carrollsanders@bellsouth.net
URL: http://www.marksvillechamberofcommerce.com
Contact: Rene Borrel, President
Description: Promotes business, community development, and tourism in Marksville, LA. **Founded:** 1952. **Publications:** *Chaucer News* (Monthly). **Educational Activities:** Marksville Chamber of Commerce General assembly (Monthly).

52483 ■ Minden/South Webster Chamber of Commerce
110 Sibley Rd.
Minden, LA 71058-0819
Ph: (318)377-4240
Fax: (318)377-4215
Co. E-mail: info@mindenchamber.com
URL: http://www.mindenchamber.com
Contact: Mike Moore, President
Description: Promotes business and community development in South Webster Parish, LA. Sponsors annual Caney-Dorcheat Triathlon. **Founded:** 1942. **Publications:** *Chamber ROI* (Monthly).

52484 ■ Monroe Chamber of Commerce (MCC)
212 Walnut St., Ste. 100
Monroe, LA 71201-6707
Ph: (318)323-3461
Free: 888-531-9535
Fax: (318)322-7594
Co. E-mail: sedmunds@monroe.org
URL: http://www.monroe.org
Contact: Sue Edmunds, President
Description: Promotes business and community development in the Ouachita Parish, LA area. Sponsors annual Riverfest in the spring, annual Winterfest in December, and annual Boat Flotilla, Crabfest, and fireworks display. **Founded:** 1921. **Publications:** *Economic Review* (Annual); *Images* (Monthly); *Inside the Chamber* (Quarterly).

52485 ■ Monthly ZNews
4633 Main St.
Zachary, LA 70791
Ph: (225)654-6777
Fax: (225)654-3957
URL: http://www.zacharychamber.com
Contact: Keith Wahoske, President
Released: Monthly

52486 ■ Natchitoches Area Chamber of Commerce (NACC)
562 2nd St.
Natchitoches, LA 71457
Ph: (318)352-6894
Free: 800-456-5804
Fax: (318)352-5385
Co. E-mail: chamber@natchitoches.net
URL: http://www.natchitocheschamber.com
Contact: Nick Pollacia, Jr., President
Description: Promotes business, community development, and tourism in Natchitoches, LA. Sponsors Festival of Lights. **Publications:** The Front Door (Monthly).

52487 ■ National Black Chamber of Commerce, Baton Rouge
263 3rd St., Ste. 704
Baton Rouge, LA 70801
Ph: (225)381-8480
Fax: (225)343-4247
Co. E-mail: info@brblackchamber.org
URL: http://www.nbrcc.org
Contact: Eric B. Lewis, President
Description: Represents Black owned businesses. Seeks to empower and sustain African American communities through entrepreneurship and capitalistic activity. Provides advocacy, training and education to Black communities.

52488 ■ Newcomer's Guide
608 Willis Ave.
Bogalusa, LA 70427-3002
Ph: (985)735-5731
Fax: (985)735-6707
Co. E-mail: bogalusachamber@bellsouth.net
URL: http://www.bogalusachamber.org
Released: Annual

52489 ■ Opelousas-St. Landry Chamber of Commerce (OSLCC)
109 W Vine St.
Opelousas, LA 70570
Ph: (337)942-2683
Fax: (337)942-2684
Co. E-mail: chamberdesk@charter.net
URL: http://www.opelousaschamber.org
Contact: Gerald Fornoff, President
Description: Promotes business and community development in the St. Landry Parish, LA area. **Founded:** 1919.

52490 ■ Point West
PO Box 448
Addis, LA 70710
Ph: (225)383-3140
Fax: (225)685-1044
URL: http://www.wbrchamber.org
Contact: Kathy Stuart, Executive Director
Released: Monthly

52491 ■ Ponchatoula Chamber of Commerce
109 W Pine St.
Ponchatoula, LA 70454
Ph: (985)386-2536
Fax: (985)386-2537
Co. E-mail: chamber@ponchatoulachamber.com
URL: http://www.ponchatoulachamber.com
Description: Promotes business and community development in Ponchatoula, LA. **Publications:** Chamber (Monthly).

52492 ■ Rayne Chamber of Commerce
PO Box 383
Rayne, LA 70578
Ph: (337)334-2332

Fax: (337)334-8341
Co. E-mail: raynechamber1@bellsouth.net
URL: http://www.rayne.org/chamber.html
Description: Promotes business and community development in Rayne, LA.

52493 ■ Ruston - Lincoln Chamber of Commerce
PO Box 1383
Ruston, LA 71273-1383
Ph: (318)255-2031
Free: 800-392-9032
Fax: (318)255-3481
Co. E-mail: sterry@rustonlincoln.org
URL: http://www.rustonlincoln.org
Contact: Scott Terry, President
Description: Promotes business and community development in the Ruston, LA area. Sponsors annual Louisiana Peach Festival. **Founded:** 1919. **Publications:** Chamber Checklist (Weekly).

52494 ■ Sabine Parish Chamber of Commerce
1601 Texas Hwy.
Many, LA 71449
Ph: (318)256-3523
URL: http://www.sabineparish.com
Contact: Lewis McBryde, President
Description: Promotes business and community development in Sabine Parish, LA. **Founded:** 1947.

52495 ■ St. Martinville Chamber of Commerce
PO Box 436
St. Martinville, LA 70582
Ph: (337)394-7578
Fax: (337)394-4497
URL: http://www.stmartinvillechamber.com
Description: Promotes business and community development in the St. Martinville, LA area. Conducts charitable programs.

52496 ■ St. Tammany West Chamber of Commerce (STWCC)
610 Hollycrest Blvd.
Covington, LA 70433
Ph: (985)892-3216
Fax: (985)893-4244
Co. E-mail: info@sttammanychamber.org
URL: http://www.sttammanychamber.org
Contact: Lacey Toledano, President
Description: Promotes business and community development in Abita Springs, Covington, Folsom, Madisonville, and Mandeville, LA areas. **Founded:** 1963. **Publications:** Chamber Updates (Weekly).

52497 ■ Slidell City Map
118 W Hall Ave.
Slidell, LA 70458
Ph: (985)643-5678
Free: 800-471-3758
Fax: (985)649-2460
Co. E-mail: dawn@estchamber.com
URL: http://www.slidellchamber.com
Contact: Dawn Sharpe, Chief Executive Officer
Released: Periodic

52498 ■ Slidell Connection
118 W Hall Ave.
Slidell, LA 70458
Ph: (985)643-5678
Free: 800-471-3758
Fax: (985)649-2460
Co. E-mail: dawn@estchamber.com
URL: http://www.slidellchamber.com
Contact: Dawn Sharpe, Chief Executive Officer
Released: Annual

52499 ■ Springhill - North Webster Chamber of Commerce
400 N Giles St.
Springhill, LA 71075
Ph: (318)539-4717
Fax: (318)539-2500
Co. E-mail: chamberc@cmaaccess.com
URL: http://www.springhilllouisiana.net
Contact: Thomas Boggs, President
Description: Promotes business and community development in the Springhill, LA area.

52500 ■ SWLA Business Directory
1011 Lakeshore Dr.
Lake Charles, LA 70601-9412
Ph: (337)433-3632
Fax: (337)436-3727
Co. E-mail: gswift@allianceswla.org
URL: http://allianceswla.org/CatSubCat/CatSubCat.asp?p9=CSC1
Contact: George Swift, President
Price: $30, for members; $50, for nonmembers.

52501 ■ Thibodaux Chamber of Commerce (TCC)
318 E Bayou Rd.
Thibodaux, LA 70301
Ph: (985)446-1187
Fax: (985)446-1191
Co. E-mail: info@thibodauxchamber.com
URL: http://www.thibodauxchamber.com
Contact: Kathy Benoit, President
Description: Promotes business and community development in Thibodaux, LA. Sponsors local festival. Holds forums and legislative breakfast. Promotes annual business expo. **Founded:** 1966. **Publications:** Chamber Insight (Monthly); Thibodaux Magazine (Periodic). **Awards:** Chamber's Teenager of the Year (Annual).

52502 ■ Thibodaux Magazine
318 E Bayou Rd.
Thibodaux, LA 70301
Ph: (985)446-1187
Fax: (985)446-1191
Co. E-mail: info@thibodauxchamber.com
URL: http://www.thibodauxchamber.com
Contact: Kathy Benoit, President
Released: Periodic

52503 ■ Union Parish Chamber of Commerce (UPCC)
303 E Water St.
Farmerville, LA 71241-3031
Ph: (318)368-3947
Fax: (318)368-3945
Co. E-mail: upcoc@bayou.com
URL: http://unionparishchamber.org
Contact: Stan Elkins, President
Description: Promotes business and community development in Union Parish. **Founded:** 1996. **Publications:** Union Parish Community Guide (Semiannual); Vision (11/year). **Educational Activities:** General Membership (Bimonthly).

52504 ■ Union Parish Community Guide
303 E Water St.
Farmerville, LA 71241-3031
Ph: (318)368-3947
Fax: (318)368-3945
Co. E-mail: upcoc@bayou.com
URL: http://unionparishchamber.org
Contact: Stan Elkins, President
Released: Semiannual

52505 ■ Vidalia Chamber of Commerce
1401 Carter St.
Vidalia, LA 71373
Ph: (318)336-8223
Co. E-mail: chamber@vidaliala.com
URL: http://www.vidaliala.com
Contact: Jamie Burley, Executive Director
Description: Promotes business and community development in Vidalia, LA.

52506 ■ Vision
303 E Water St.
Farmerville, LA 71241-3031
Ph: (318)368-3947
Fax: (318)368-3945
Co. E-mail: upcoc@bayou.com
URL: http://unionparishchamber.org
Contact: Stan Elkins, President
Released: 11/year

52507 ■ West Baton Rouge Chamber of Commerce (WBRCC)
PO Box 448
Addis, LA 70710
Ph: (225)383-3140

Fax: (225)685-1044
URL: http://www.wbrchamber.org
Contact: Kathy Stuart, Executive Director
Description: Promotes business and community development in Port Allen, LA area. **Publications:** *Point West* (Monthly).

52508 ■ West Monroe-West Ouachita Chamber of Commerce (WMWOCC)
112 Professional Dr.
West Monroe, LA 71291
Ph: (318)325-1961
Fax: (318)325-4296
Co. E-mail: info@westmonroechamber.org
URL: http://westmonroechamber.org
Contact: Mary Ann Newton, President
Description: Promotes business and community development in West Monroe, LA. **Founded:** 1955. **Publications:** *Compass Point* (Monthly). **Awards:** A.O. Evans (Annual). **Telecommunication Services:** mnewton@westmonroechamber.org.

52509 ■ Winn Chamber of Commerce (WCC)
PO Box 565
Winnfield, LA 71483-0565
Ph: (318)628-4461
Fax: (318)628-2551
Co. E-mail: info@winnchamberofcommerce.com
URL: http://www.winnchamberofcommerce.com
Description: Promotes business and community development in Winnfield, LA. Sponsors festival. Encourages tourism. **Founded:** 1949.

52510 ■ Winnsboro - Franklin Parish Chamber of Commerce (WFPCC)
3830 Front St.
Winnsboro, LA 71295
Ph: (318)435-4488
Co. E-mail: info@winnsborochamber.com
URL: http://www.winnsborochamber.com
Contact: Sherry Anders Randall, President
Description: Promotes business and community development in Franklin Parish, LA. Sponsors annual Catfish Festival in April. **Founded:** 1949.

52511 ■ Zachary Chamber of Commerce (ZCC)
4633 Main St.
Zachary, LA 70791
Ph: (225)654-6777
Fax: (225)654-3957
URL: http://www.zacharychamber.com
Contact: Keith Wahoske, President
Description: Promotes business and community development in Zachary, LA. **Founded:** 1968. **Publications:** *Monthly ZNews* (Monthly).

MINORITY BUSINESS ASSISTANCE PROGRAMS

52512 ■ Louisiana Minority Business Opportunity Center
400 Poydras St., Ste. 1350
New Orleans, LA 70130
Ph: (504)229-2960
Fax: (514)299-2961
Co. E-mail: Rfrederick@lamsdc.org
URL: http://www.mboclouisiana.biz
Contact: Rivers Frederick, Director
Description: Provides free developmental services to strategic-growth minority business enterprises in Louisiana.

52513 ■ Louisina MBEC
2714 Canal St., Ste. 300
New Orleans, LA 70119
Ph: (504)821-4811
Fax: (504)324-0217
Co. E-mail: norman@capitalaccessproject.org

52514 ■ Louisina Minority Supplier Development Council
400 Poydras St., Ste. 1960
New Orleans, LA 70130
Ph: (504)293-0400

Fax: (504)293-0401
Co. E-mail: info@lamsdc.org
URL: http://msdc.adaptone.com/lamsdc/
Contact: Phala Kimbrough Mire, President
Description: Assists corporations in developing and expanding minority vendor programs.

52515 ■ Urban League of Greater New Orleans - Women's Business Resource Center
3308 Tulane Ave., Ste. 301
New Orleans, LA 70119
Ph: (504)620-9647
Fax: (504)620-9564
Contact: Angela S. VonDerPool, Director
Description: Provides women business owners with formalized business planning for business expansion.

PROCUREMENT ASSISTANCE PROGRAMS

52516 ■ Louisiana Procurement Technical Assistance Center at Kisatchie-Delta
3516 Parliament Ct.
Alexandria, LA 71303
Ph: (318)487-5454
Fax: (318)487-5451
Co. E-mail: kdptac@kricket.net
URL: http://www.la-ptac.org
Contact: Shelia Wallace, Counselor
E-mail: kdptac@kricket.net
Description: Businesses and individuals interested in learning about government contracting and subcontracting, and/or are actively seeking or currently performing under government contracts and subcontracts with the Department of Defense, federal state and local governments, contact the procurement specialists below covering Allen, Avoyelles, Beauregard, Catahoula, Concordia, Grant, LaSalle, Rapides, Vermon, and Winn Parishes.

52517 ■ Louisiana Procurement Technical Assistance Center at LEDA
211 E Devalcourt St.
Lafayette, LA 70506
Ph: (337)593-1400
Fax: (337)234-3009
Co. E-mail: information@lafayette.org
URL: http://www.lafayette.org
Contact: Billy Lawson, Counselor
E-mail: billy1@lafayette.org
Description: Businesses and individuals interested in learning about government contracting and subcontracting, and/or are actively seeking or currently performing under government contracts and subcontracts with the Department of Defense, federal state and local governments, contact the procurement specialists below covering Acadia, Evangeline, Iberia, Lafayette, St. Landry, St. Martin, St. Mary and Vermilion Parishes.

52518 ■ Louisiana Procurement Technical Assistance Center at New Orleans
PO Box 44172
Lafayette, LA 70504-4172
Ph: (800)206-3545
Free: 800-206-3545
Co. E-mail: noptac@bellsouth.net
URL: http://www.la-ptac.org
Contact: Robert Dempsey, Counselor
E-mail: noptac@bellsouth.net
Description: Businesses and individuals interested in learning about government contracting and subcontracting, and/or are actively seeking or currently performing under government contracts and subcontracts with the Department of Defense, federal state and local governments, contact the procurement specialists below covering Jefferson, Orleans, Plaquemines and St. Bernard Parishes.

52519 ■ Louisiana Procurement Technical Assistance Center at SLEC
PO Box 44172
Lafayette, LA 70504
Ph: (800)206-3545

Free: 800-206-3545
Co. E-mail: noptac@bellsouth.net
URL: http://www.la-ptac.org
Contact: Robert Dempsey, Counselor
E-mail: jan.labat@nicholls.edu
Description: Businesses and individuals interested in learning about government contracting and subcontracting, and/or are actively seeking or currently performing under government contracts and subcontracts with the Department of Defense, federal state and local governments, contact the procurement specialists below covering Assumption, LaFourche, St. Charles, St. James, St. John the Baptist and Terrebonne Parishes.

52520 ■ Louisiana Procurement Technical Assistance Center - University of Louisiana - LAPTAC State Administrative Office
241 E Lewis St., Rm. 110
Lafayette, LA 70504-4172
Ph: (337)482-6422
Free: 800-206-3545
Fax: (337)482-5837
Co. E-mail: la-ptac@louisiana.edu
URL: http://www.la-ptac.org
Contact: Sherrie Mullins, Program Manager
E-mail: sherlm@louisiana.edu
Description: Generates employment and improve the general economy of Louisiana by assisting business firms in obtaining and performing under the U.S. Department of Defense, other federal agencies, state and local government contracts.

52521 ■ Northwest Louisiana Government Procurement Center - Greater Shreveport Chamber of Commerce
400 Edward St.
Shreveport, LA 71101
Ph: (318)677-2530
Fax: (318)677-2534
Co. E-mail: gpc@shreveportchamber.org
URL: http://shreveportla.usachamber.com
Contact: Kelly Ford, Director
E-mail: kellyford@shreveportchamber.org
Description: Increases the number of federal, state, and local government contract award dollars being awarded to businesses thus creating and retaining jobs.

52522 ■ Southeast Louisiana Procurement Technical Assistance Center
PO Box 1771
Denham Springs, LA 70727-1771
Ph: (225)664-2600
Fax: (225)664-0050
Co. E-mail: ccarrier@cox.net
URL: http://www.la-ptac.org
Contact: Cindy Carrier, Counselor
E-mail: ccarrier@cox.net
Description: Businesses and individuals interested in learning about government contracting and subcontracting, and/or are actively seeking or currently performing under government contracts and subcontracts with the Department of Defense, federal state and local governments, contact the procurement specialists below covering Ascension, East Baton Rouge, East Feliciana, Iberville, Livingston, Point Coupee, St. Helena, St. Tammany, Tangipahoa, Washington, West Baton Rouge and West Feliciana Parishes.

52523 ■ Southwest Louisiana Procurement Technical Assistance Center
120 West Pujo St.
Lake Charles, LA 70601
Ph: (337)433-3632
Fax: (337)436-3727
Co. E-mail: la-ptac@louisiana.edu
URL: http://www.la-ptac.org
Contact: Roy Paul, Counselor
E-mail: kmm1928@louisiana.edu
Description: Businesses and individuals interested in learning about government contracting and subcontracting, and/or are actively seeking or currently performing under government contracts and subcontracts with the Department of Defense, federal state

and local governments, contact the procurement specialists below covering Allen, Beauregard, Calcasieu, Cameron, and Jefferson Davis Parishes.

INCUBATORS/RESEARCH AND TECHNOLOGY PARKS

52524 ■ Arts Business Program
Arts Council of New Orleans
818 Howard Ave., Ste. 300
New Orleans, LA 70113
Ph: (504)523-1465
Fax: (504)529-2430
Co. E-mail: gmeneray@artscouncilofneworleans.org
URL: http://www.artscouncilofneworleans.org/
Contact: Dolita Brown, Coordinator
Description: A small business incubator created as an arts management resource center and a professional business environment, serving the creative and administrative growth of individuals and organizations in the arts community; it is a place where individuals and organizations can learn and where they can come together for an exchange of ideas and creative energy.

52525 ■ Central Louisiana Business Incubator
1501-A Wimbledon Dr.
Alexandria, LA 71301
Ph: (318)561-2299
Fax: (318)561-2249
Co. E-mail: info@clbi.org
URL: http://www.clbi.org/
Description: A not-for-profit corporation created as an economic tool designed to accelerate the growth and success of entrepreneurial companies through an array of business support resources and services.

52526 ■ Dixie Business Center
1810 S. Range Ave.
Denham Springs, LA 70726
Ph: (225)665-0809
Fax: (225)665-8171
Co. E-mail: info@dixiebusinesscenter.org
URL: http://www.dixiebusinesscenter.org/
Contact: John Ware, Executive Director
Description: A nonprofit business incubator program dedicated to helping new and emerging businesses develop, grow, and succeed.

52527 ■ Enterprise Center of Louisiana
3419 NW Evangeline Thruway
Carencro, LA 70520
Ph: (337)896-9115
Fax: (337)896-8736
Co. E-mail: rholleman@ecol.org
URL: http://www.ecol.org/
Description: A small business incubator providing an environment in which a new or small emerging business can learn effective business practices while actually engaging in business operations with the end result of creating jobs and diversifying the economy in Acadiana.

52528 ■ InterTech Science Park
2031 Kings Hwy.
Shreveport, LA 71103
Ph: (318)213-0200
Fax: (318)213-0205
Co. E-mail: info@intertechsciencepark.org
URL: http://www.intertechsciencepark.com/
Contact: Sue Doughty, Coordinator
Description: An 800-acre urban science and technology park created to develop the region's human, financial and physical infrastructure required for technology companies to flourish. It provides its tenants with access to academic facilities, researchers, core equipment laboratories, animal care, multitenant wet lab and office space, land for building, venture capital, business planning assistance. and financial incentives.

52529 ■ Jefferson Parish Economic Development Commission - Business Innovation Center and Technology Incubator
700 Churchill Blvd.
Avondale, LA 70092
Ph: (504)833-1881

Fax: (504)833-7676
Co. E-mail: srojas@jedco.org
URL: http://www.jedco.org/business-incubator/
Description: A small business incubator offering affordable services designed to help new businesses grow and thrive.

52530 ■ Louisiana Business & Technology Center
Louisiana State University
E.J. Ourso College of Business
8000 GSRI Ave., Bldg. 3000
Baton Rouge, LA 70820
Ph: (225)578-7555
Fax: (225)578-3975
Co. E-mail: lbtc@lsu.edu
URL: http://www.bus.lsu.edu/lbtc/
Description: A small business incubator located on the campus of Louisiana State University providing space for new business start-ups within its 25,000 square-foot incubator. Companies located in the incubator can concentrate on production and marketing, which directly affects success and profits, while leaving the day-to-day administrative details and overhead problems to the LBTC staff.

52531 ■ Louisiana Emerging Technology Center
PO Box 25128
Baton Rouge, LA 70894
Ph: (225)615-8901
Fax: (225)615-8910
Co. E-mail: acooper@laetc.com
URL: http://www.laetc.com
Contact: Arthur R. Cooper, Executive Director
Description: designed specifically as an incubator for companies with wet-lab needs, serves small and start-up businesses developing and commercializing university technologies.

52532 ■ Louisiana Tech Enterprise Center
509 W Alabama
Ruston, LA 71270
Ph: (318)257-4343
Fax: (318)257-4442
Co. E-mail: dnorris@latech.edu
URL: http://www.lbia.org/members/la_tech_incubator.htm
Contact: Dave N. Norris, Executive Director
Description: A small business incubator established to create successful businesses by providing assistance and facilities to stimulate small business formation, growth and development. It provides administrative assistance and overhead facilities to start-up companies, allowing them to concentrate on research, marketing, and production.

52533 ■ Louisiana Technology Park
7117 Florida Blvd.
Baton Rouge, LA 70806
Ph: (225)218-1100
Fax: (225)218-0101
Co. E-mail: info@latechpark.com
URL: http://www.latechpark.com/
Description: A business incubator formed to create an active and innovative atmosphere for e-business, high-technology and biotechnology. The Park is a comprehensive catalyst for the Internet, e-commerce and biotech economies, focused on growing startup companies; providing high-speed, high-volume commercial data storage and transmission; and offering swift, direct Internet connectivity.

52534 ■ Metro/Regional Business Incubator
Ark-La-Tex Export & Technology Center
7100 W. Park Rd.
Shreveport, LA 71129
Ph: (318)671-1050
Fax: (318)671-9032
Co. E-mail: dsimek@shreve.net
URL: http://www.cdconline.org
Description: A business development project of The Coordinating & Development Corporation providing subsidized rental space for tenants primarily engaged in manufacturing and warehousing/distribution. In addition to the leased space, tenants have access to conference rooms, a training center, shared office

equipment, an employee break room, and full access to the staff for any counseling and technical assistance they may need.

52535 ■ New Orleans BioInnovation Center
134 LaSalle St.
New Orleans, LA 70112
Ph: (504)680-2973
Fax: (504)680-2977
Co. E-mail: aaronm@neworleansbio.com
URL: http://www.neworleansbio.com/
Contact: Aaron Miscenich, Executive Director
Description: A technology business incubator created to foster entrepreneurship within the New Orleans bioscience community by assisting companies commercializing biotechnologies from New Orleans-based universities.

52536 ■ Southeast Louisiana Business Center
1514 Martens Dr.
Hammond, LA 70401
Ph: (985)549-3199
Co. E-mail: wjoubert@selu.edu
URL: http://www.selu.edu/admin/slbc/
Description: A small business incubator whose goal is to extend a nurturing environment to start-up and expanding small businesses in the area. The Center houses area economic development agencies, business counseling resources, and incubator space.

52537 ■ Southwest Louisiana Economic Development Alliance
120 W Pujo St.
Lake Charles, LA 70601
Ph: (337)433-3632
Fax: (337)436-3727
Co. E-mail: gswift@allianceswla.org
URL: http://www.allianceswla.org/
Contact: George Swift, Chief Executive Officer
Description: An alliance established to strengthen the business recruiting and retention efforts for Allen, Beauregard, Calcasieu, Cameron, and Jeff Davis parishes.

52538 ■ Student Business Incubator
Bossier Parish Community College
6220 E. Texas St.
Bossier City, LA 71112
Ph: (318)678-6427
Co. E-mail: tlogan@bpcc.edu
URL: http://www.lbia.org/members/bpcc_incubator.htm
Contact: Tamika Logan, Director
Description: A supportive environment where students' new entrepreneurial start-up businesses are nurtured. Students receive use of fully-equipped office space and office equipment, on-going training and coaching, technical assistance, access to capital, use of meeting rooms, and professional help in launching their own business.

PUBLICATIONS

52539 ■ Smart Start your Connecticut Business
PSI Research
300 N. Valley Dr.
Grants Pass, OR 97526
Ph: (503)479-9464
Free: 800-228-2275
Fax: (503)476-1479
Co. E-mail: info@psi-research.com
URL: http://www.psi-research.com
Ed: Michael D. Jenkins. Released: Revised edition, 1992. Price: $29.95 (looseleaf binder); $24.95 (paper). Description: Part of the Successful Business Library series.

PUBLISHERS

52540 ■ Trost Publishing
400 Poydras St., Ste. 1850
New Orleans, LA 70130

Ph: (504)680-6754
Contact: Tripp Friedler, Manager
Description: Description: Publishes nonfiction books on business and economics. **Founded:** 2004.

SMALL BUSINESS ASSISTANCE PROGRAMS

52541 ■ Maine Department of Economic and Community Development
59 State House Station
Augusta, ME 04333-0059
Ph: (207)624-9800
Fax: (207)287-5701
Co. E-mail: biz.growth@maine.gov
URL: http://www.econdevmaine.com
Contact: Mike Baran, Director
Description: Provides business planning, financing, information, and networking assistance to existing Maine businesses that need financing for expansion purposes. Utilizes programs offered through the Maine WEET and JTPA offices. Assists in identifying funding sources, including federal, state, and private. Also runs the Job Opportunity Zone Program which focuses attention on four designated depressed areas.

52542 ■ Maine Department of Economic and Community Development - Office of Business Development
59 State House Station
Augusta, ME 04333
Ph: (207)624-9804
Fax: (207)287-5701
Co. E-mail: biz.growth@maine.gov
URL: http://www.mainebiz.org
Contact: Mark Ouellette, Director
Description: Encourages investment in new Maine businesses and provides technical assistance to businesses in labor training, financing, site selection, and state licenses, and permits. Includes Maine Products Marketing Program which promotes regional and national awareness of Maine's products.

52543 ■ Maine Development Foundation
295 Water St., Ste. 5
Augusta, ME 04330
Ph: (207)622-6345
Fax: (207)622-6346
Co. E-mail: mdf@mdf.org
URL: http://www.mdf.org
Contact: Kristen Cady, Director
Description: Nonprofit corporation that assists Maine businesses. Services include coordination of joint public-private projects; research and long-range planning for future economic development; and economic education.

52544 ■ Maine International Trade Center
511 Congress St., Ste. 100
Portland, ME 04101-3428
Ph: (207)541-7400
Fax: (207)541-7420
Co. E-mail: info@mitc.com
URL: http://www.mitc.com
Contact: Janine Bisaillon-Cary, Director
Description: A private, nonprofit organization offering extensive export services to Maine businesses. Also includes a library of information on world trade.

SCORE OFFICES

52545 ■ Bangor SCORE
Co. E-mail: info@scorebangor.org

52546 ■ Downeast Maine SCORE
Co. E-mail: scoredowneastmaine@verizon.net

52547 ■ Lewiston-Auburn SCORE
Co. E-mail: contact@lascore.org

52548 ■ SCORE Augusta
68 Sewall St., Rm. 512
Augusta, ME 04330
Ph: (207)622-8509
URL: http://www.scoremaine.org/pages/augusta.htm
Description: Provides entrepreneur education and the formation, growth and success of small business nationwide. Provides free counseling and low-cost workshops.

52549 ■ SCORE Belfast
Co. E-mail: score0305@yahoo.com

52550 ■ SCORE Camden
Co. E-mail: score0305@yahoo.com

52551 ■ SCORE Damariscotta
Co. E-mail: score0305@yahoo.com

52552 ■ SCORE Oxford Hills
2 Market Sq.
South Paris, ME 04281
Ph: (207)743-0499
Co. E-mail: oxscore@megalink.net
URL: http://oxfordhills.score.org
Description: Serves as volunteer program in which working and retired business management professionals provide free business counseling to men and women who are considering starting a small business, encountering problems with their business, or expanding their business. Offers free one-on-one counseling, online counseling and low cost workshops on a variety of business topics.

52553 ■ SCORE Portland
East Tower, 2nd Fl.
100 Middle St.
Portland, ME 04101
Ph: (207)772-1147
Fax: (207)772-5581
Co. E-mail: info@scoremaine.com
URL: http://portlandme.score.org
Description: Delivers expertise and resources to maximize the success of existing and emerging small businesses. Offers 3-hour workshops in how to start own business, writing a business plan, marketing and sales, face to face or email counseling at no cost.

52554 ■ SCORE Rockford
Co. E-mail: score0305@yahoo.com

52555 ■ SCORE Western Mountains
60 Lowell St.
Rumford, ME 04276

Ph: (207)364-3123
Co. E-mail: gkimball2@roadrunner.com
URL: http://www.scoremaine.org/pages/west_mtn.htm
Description: Serves as volunteer program in which working and retired business management professionals provide free business counseling to men and women who are considering starting a small business, encountering problems with their business, or expanding their business. Offers free one-on-one counseling, online counseling and low cost workshops on a variety of business topics.

CHAMBERS OF COMMERCE

52556 ■ Androscoggin County Chamber of Commerce
415 Lisbon St.
Lewiston, ME 04243-0059
Ph: (207)783-2249
Fax: (207)783-4481
Co. E-mail: cmorrison@androscoggincounty.com
URL: http://www.androscoggincounty.com
Contact: Charles Morrison, President
URL(s): www2.androscoggincounty.com. **Description:** Promotes business and community development in Androscoggin County area. **Founded:** 1887. **Awards:** Androscoggin County Chamber of Commerce Adult Scholarships.

52557 ■ *Annual Business and Pleasure Guide*
747 Roosevelt Trail
Windham, ME 04062
Ph: (207)892-8265
Fax: (207)893-0110
Co. E-mail: info@sebagolakeschamber.com
URL: http://www.sebagolakeschamber.com
Contact: Ann Marie Swenson, President
E-mail: aswenson@mainebank.com
Released: Annual **Price:** free.

52558 ■ *Area Guide*
PO Box 236
Bridgton, ME 04009-0236
Ph: (207)647-3472
Co. E-mail: info@mainelakeschamber.com
URL: http://www.mainelakeschamber.com
Released: Annual

52559 ■ *Bangor Region Visitors Guidebook*
208 Main Ave.
Bangor, ME 04401
Ph: (207)947-0307
Fax: (207)990-1427
Co. E-mail: chamber@bangorregion.com
URL: http://www.bangorregion.com
Contact: John Porter, President
Released: Annual

52560 ■ Bangor Regional Chamber of Commerce (BRCC)
208 Main Ave.
Bangor, ME 04401
Ph: (207)947-0307

Fax: (207)990-1427
Co. E-mail: chamber@bangorregion.com
URL: http://www.bangorregion.com
Contact: John Porter, President
Description: Seeks to sustain and promote economic vitality in the Bangor region. **Founded:** 1911. **Publications:** *Bangor Region Visitors Guidebook* (Annual); *Chamber News* (Monthly); *Bangor Region Data Book* (Annual). **Educational Activities:** Early Bird Breakfast (Monthly). **Awards:** Norbert X. Dowd (Annual).

52561 ■ Bar Harbor Chamber of Commerce (BHCC)
1201 Bar Harbor Rd.
Trenton, ME 04605
Ph: (207)288-5103
Free: 800-345-4617
Fax: (207)667-9080
Co. E-mail: visitors@barharborinfo.com
URL: http://www.barharborinfo.com
Contact: Nancy Tibbetts, President
Description: Businesses, organizations, and interested individuals. Promotes economic development and tourism in Bar Harbor, ME. **Founded:** 1969. **Publications:** *Best in Bar Harbor Guide Book.*

52562 ■ *Bath-Brunswick Region Map*
2 Main St.
Topsham, ME 04086
Ph: (207)725-8797
Free: 877-725-8797
Fax: (207)725-9787
Co. E-mail: chamber@midcoastmaine.com
URL: http://www.midcoastmaine.com
Contact: Steven W. Wallace, President
E-mail: president@midcoastmaine.com
Released: Annual

52563 ■ Belfast Area Chamber of Commerce
PO Box 58
Belfast, ME 04915
Ph: (207)338-5900
Co. E-mail: director@belfastmaine.org
URL: http://www.belfastmaine.org
Contact: Jack Driscoll, Executive Director
Description: Promotes business and community development in the Belfast, ME area. Conducts lobbying activities. Sponsors annual fishing contest, 4th of July and downtown Christmas celebrations, Chamber Bay cruise, and historic home tour. **Founded:** 1979. **Publications:** *Belfast Booklet* (Annual).

52564 ■ *Belfast Booklet*
PO Box 58
Belfast, ME 04915
Ph: (207)338-5900
Co. E-mail: director@belfastmaine.org
URL: http://www.belfastmaine.org
Contact: Jack Driscoll, Executive Director
Released: Annual

52565 ■ *Best in Bar Harbor Guide Book*
1201 Bar Harbor Rd.
Trenton, ME 04605
Ph: (207)288-5103
Free: 800-345-4617
Fax: (207)667-9080
Co. E-mail: visitors@barharborinfo.com
URL: http://www.barharborinfo.com
Contact: Nancy Tibbetts, President

52566 ■ Bethel Area Chamber of Commerce (BACC)
PO Box 1247
Bethel, ME 04217-1247
Ph: (207)824-2282
Free: 800-442-5826
Fax: (207)824-7123
Co. E-mail: info@bethelmaine.com
URL: http://www.bethelmaine.com
Contact: Steven Etheridge, President
Description: Businesses, industries, and interested individuals. Promotes business and community development. Provides legislative advocacy. Acts as information center; hosts approximately 15 major local, area, and regional events; offers free lodging

reservation service. **Founded:** 1920. **Awards:** Business Award (Annual); Citizenship Award (Annual); Employees Award (Annual).

52567 ■ Biddeford-Saco Chamber of Commerce and Industry (BSCCI)
138 Main St., Ste. 101
Saco, ME 04072
Ph: (207)282-1567
Fax: (207)282-3149
Co. E-mail: info@biddefordsacochamber.org
URL: http://www.biddefordsacochamber.org
Contact: Craig Pendleton, Executive Director
Description: Promotes business and community development in the Biddeford-Saco, ME area. Sponsors annual golf tournament. **Founded:** 1927. **Publications:** *Chamber News* (Monthly); *Guide Book* (Annual). **Telecommunication Services:** craig@biddefordsacochamber.org.

52568 ■ Blue Hill Peninsula Chamber of Commerce
28 Water St.
Blue Hill, ME 04614
Ph: (207)374-3242
Co. E-mail: chamber@bluehillpeninsula.org
URL: http://www.bluehillpeninsula.org
Contact: Kurt S. Stoll, Executive Director
Description: Individuals interested in the Blue Hill Peninsula and the civic, economic, cultural, commercial, industrial, environmental, and educational interests of the area. **Founded:** 2000. **Awards:** Civic Scholarship (Annual).

52569 ■ Boothbay Harbor Region Chamber of Commerce
PO Box 356
Boothbay Harbor, ME 04538-0356
Ph: (207)633-2353
Fax: (207)633-7448
Co. E-mail: seamaine@boothbayharbor.com
URL: http://www.boothbayharbor.com
Contact: Pamela Riley, President
Description: Promotes business and community development in Boothbay Harbor, ME area. **Founded:** 1962. **Publications:** *Official Boothbay Harbor Region Guide* (Annual); *Boothbay Harbor Region Guide* (Annual). **Awards:** Community Improvement (Annual); Community Service (Annual).

52570 ■ Bucksport Bay Area Chamber of Commerce
52 Main St.
Bucksport, ME 04416
Ph: (207)469-6818
Fax: (207)469-2078
Co. E-mail: director@bucksportbaychamber.com
URL: http://www.bucksportchamber.org
Contact: Tom Goodman, President
Description: Promotes business and community development in the Bucksport Bay area.

52571 ■ *Business Perspectives*
60 Pearl St.
Portland, ME 04101
Ph: (207)772-2811
Fax: (207)772-1179
Co. E-mail: chamber@portlandregion.com
URL: http://www.portlandregion.com/index.
   php?sec=1
Contact: W. Godfrey Wood, Chief Executive Officer
Released: Monthly **Price:** available to members only.

52572 ■ *Cap Area Guide*
21 University Dr.
Augusta, ME 04332-0676
Ph: (207)623-4559
Free: 800-899-5624
Fax: (207)626-9342
Co. E-mail: info@augustamaine.com
URL: http://www.augustamaine.com
Contact: Peter G. Thompson, President
Released: Biennial

52573 ■ Caribou Chamber of Commerce and Industry (CCCI)
24 Sweden St., Ste. 101
Caribou, ME 04736-2132
Ph: (207)498-6156

Free: 800-722-7648
Fax: (207)492-1362
Co. E-mail: info@cariboumaine.net
URL: http://www.cariboumaine.net
Contact: Doug Morrell, President
Description: Promotes business and community development in Caribou, ME. Sponsors Winter Festival and arts and crafts festival; conducts business survey. **Founded:** 2000. **Publications:** *Caribou Information Book* (Biennial); *Caribou Information Book and Chamber of Commerce & Industry Membership Directory: Caribou Map and Guide* (Irregular).

52574 ■ *Caribou Information Book*
24 Sweden St., Ste. 101
Caribou, ME 04736-2132
Ph: (207)498-6156
Free: 800-722-7648
Fax: (207)492-1362
Co. E-mail: info@cariboumaine.net
URL: http://www.cariboumaine.net
Contact: Doug Morrell, President
Released: Biennial

52575 ■ *Chamber Bullet*
4 Western Ave.
South Paris, ME 04281
Ph: (207)743-2281
Fax: (207)743-0687
Co. E-mail: info@oxfordhillsmaine.com
URL: http://www.oxfordhillsmaine.com
Contact: John Williams, Executive Director
Released: Monthly

52576 ■ *The Chamber Chatter*
PO Box 236
Bridgton, ME 04009-0236
Ph: (207)647-3472
Co. E-mail: info@mainelakeschamber.com
URL: http://www.mainelakeschamber.com
Released: Monthly

52577 ■ *Chamber Connections*
2 Main St.
Topsham, ME 04086
Ph: (207)725-8797
Free: 877-725-8797
Fax: (207)725-9787
Co. E-mail: chamber@midcoastmaine.com
URL: http://www.midcoastmaine.com
Contact: Steven W. Wallace, President
E-mail: president@midcoastmaine.com
Released: 10/year **Price:** free for members.

52578 ■ *Chamber News*
138 Main St., Ste. 101
Saco, ME 04072
Ph: (207)282-1567
Fax: (207)282-3149
Co. E-mail: info@biddefordsacochamber.org
URL: http://www.biddefordsacochamber.org
Contact: Craig Pendleton, Executive Director
Released: Monthly **Price:** $50, /year for nonmembers; included in membership dues.

52579 ■ *Chamber News*
208 Main Ave.
Bangor, ME 04401
Ph: (207)947-0307
Fax: (207)990-1427
Co. E-mail: chamber@bangorregion.com
URL: http://www.bangorregion.com
Contact: John Porter, President
Released: Monthly

52580 ■ *Chamber News*
PO Box 740
Kennebunk, ME 04043
Ph: (207)967-0857
Fax: (207)967-8451
Co. E-mail: info@visitthekennebunks.com
URL: http://www.visitthekennebunks.com
Contact: Tina Hewitt-Gordon, Chairperson
Released: Monthly; except summer.

52581 ■ *Chamber Newsletter*
1 Park Dr.
Rockland, ME 04841
Ph: (207)596-0376

Free: 800-562-2529
Fax: (207)596-6549
Co. E-mail: info@therealmaine.com
URL: http://www.therealmaine.com
Contact: Dan Bookham, Executive Director
Released: Monthly **Price:** free.

52582 ■ *Chamber Newsletter*
PO Box 581
Greenville, ME 04441-0581
Ph: (207)695-2702
Free: 888-876-2778
Fax: (207)695-3440
Co. E-mail: info@mooseheadlake.org
URL: http://www.mooseheadlake.org
Contact: Bob Hamer, Executive Director
Released: Monthly

52583 ■ **Cobscook Bay Area Chamber of Commerce (CBACC)**
PO Box 42
Whiting, ME 04691-0042
Ph: (203)871-3714
Co. E-mail: info@cobscookbay.com
URL: http://www.cobscookbay.com
Founded: 2000.

52584 ■ *Community Resource Directory*
2 Main St.
Topsham, ME 04086
Ph: (207)725-8797
Free: 877-725-8797
Fax: (207)725-9787
Co. E-mail: chamber@midcoastmaine.com
URL: http://www.midcoastmaine.com
Contact: Steven W. Wallace, President
E-mail: president@midcoastmaine.com

52585 ■ **Damariscotta Region Chamber of Commerce (DRCC)**
PO Box 13
Damariscotta, ME 04543
Ph: (207)563-8340
Fax: (207)563-8348
Co. E-mail: info@damariscottaregion.com
URL: http://www.damariscottaregion.com
Contact: Val Coolong, President
Description: Seeks to promote business and community development and enhance the relationship between local businesses and professionals with the public.

52586 ■ **Deer Isle - Stonington Chamber of Commerce**
PO Box 490
Deer Isle, ME 04627
Ph: (207)348-6124
Co. E-mail: deerisle@deerisle.com
URL: http://www.deerislemaine.com
Contact: Henry Borntraeger, President
Description: Promotes business and community development in Deer Isle, ME.

52587 ■ *E-Message Board*
4 Western Ave.
South Paris, ME 04281
Ph: (207)743-2281
Fax: (207)743-0687
Co. E-mail: info@oxfordhillsmaine.com
URL: http://www.oxfordhillsmaine.com
Contact: John Williams, Executive Director
Released: Weekly

52588 ■ **Eastport Area Chamber of Commerce**
PO Box 254
Eastport, ME 04631
Ph: (207)853-4644
Co. E-mail: info@eastportchamber.net
URL: http://www.eastportchamber.net
Description: Promotes business and community development in the Eastport, ME area. **Awards:** Harry Mattin Award (Annual).

52589 ■ **Ellsworth Area Chamber of Commerce**
163 High St.
Ellsworth, ME 04605
Ph: (207)667-5584

Fax: (207)667-2617
Co. E-mail: info@ellsworthchamber.org
URL: http://www.ellsworthchamber.org
Contact: Micki Sumpter, Executive Director
Description: Promotes tourism and economic development in the Ellsworth, ME area. Sponsors home and garden show, craft show, Autumn Gold Retail Sale, and business after hours program. Holds monthly board meeting. **Founded:** 1956. **Awards:** Top Drawer Award (Annual).

52590 ■ *Experience Kennebunk-Kennebunkport*
PO Box 740
Kennebunk, ME 04043
Ph: (207)967-0857
Fax: (207)967-8451
Co. E-mail: info@visitthekennebunks.com
URL: http://www.visitthekennebunks.com
Contact: Tina Hewitt-Gordon, Chairperson
Released: Annual

52591 ■ *Explore Maine's Oxford Hills*
4 Western Ave.
South Paris, ME 04281
Ph: (207)743-2281
Fax: (207)743-0687
Co. E-mail: info@oxfordhillsmaine.com
URL: http://www.oxfordhillsmaine.com
Contact: John Williams, Executive Director
Released: Monthly **Price:** free for members.

52592 ■ **Fort Fairfield Chamber of Commerce**
18 Community Center Dr.
Fort Fairfield, ME 04742
Ph: (207)472-3802
Fax: (207)472-3810
Co. E-mail: chamber@fortcc.org
URL: http://fortcc.org
Contact: Michael Bosse, Executive Director
Description: Seeks to advance business and economic growth of Fort Fairfield community.

52593 ■ **Franklin County Chamber of Commerce**
248 Wilton Rd.
Farmington, ME 04938
Ph: (207)778-4215
Fax: (207)778-2438
Co. E-mail: info@franklincountymaine.org
URL: http://www.franklincountymaine.org
Contact: Ivan Gould, President
Description: Seeks to promote business community and individual's interests in Franklin, ME.

52594 ■ **Freeport Merchants Association (FMA)**
23 Depot St.
Freeport, ME 04032-0452
Ph: (207)865-1212
Free: 800-865-1994
Co. E-mail: info@freeportusa.com
URL: http://www.freeportusa.com
Contact: Myra Hopkins, Executive Director
Description: Promotes Freeport area to viable markets, and maximizing beneficial partnerships on a local, state, national and international level. **Publications:** *Visitors Guide.*

52595 ■ **Greater Bridgton-Lakes Region Chamber of Commerce (GBLRCC)**
PO Box 236
Bridgton, ME 04009-0236
Ph: (207)647-3472
Co. E-mail: info@mainelakeschamber.com
URL: http://www.mainelakeschamber.com
Description: Promotes business and community development in Bridgton, ME. **Publications:** *Area Guide* (Annual); *The Chamber Chatter* (Monthly).

52596 ■ **Greater Fort Kent Area Chamber of Commerce**
291 W Main St.
Fort Kent, ME 04743

Ph: (207)834-5354
Co. E-mail: info@fortkentchamber.com
URL: http://www.fortkentchamber.com
Contact: Ann Ouellette, President
Description: Promotes business and community development in Fort Kent, ME. Sponsors area festivals and competitions. Holds Can Am Sled Dog Race. **Founded:** 1946.

52597 ■ **Greater Houlton Chamber of Commerce (HCC)**
109 Main St.
Houlton, ME 04730
Ph: (207)532-4216
Fax: (207)532-4961
Co. E-mail: chamber@greaterhoulton.com
URL: http://www.greaterhoulton.com
Contact: Lori Weston, Executive Director
Description: Promotes business and community development in the Greater Houlton, ME area. Sponsors Potato Feast Days. **Founded:** 1914.

52598 ■ **Greater Madawaska Chamber of Commerce**
356 Main St.
Madawaska, ME 04756
Ph: (207)728-7000
Fax: (207)728-4696
Co. E-mail: valleyvisit@pwless.net
URL: http://www.greatermadawaskachamber.com
Contact: Roger Thibodeau, Executive Director
Description: Promotes business and community development in Madawaska, ME. Sponsors Top O'Maine Trade Show and is home to the Acadian Festival. **Publications:** *LeCoeur de la Val Lee* (Quarterly).

52599 ■ **Greater Portland Chamber of Commerce**
60 Pearl St.
Portland, ME 04101
Ph: (207)772-2811
Fax: (207)772-1179
Co. E-mail: chamber@portlandregion.com
URL: http://www.portlandregion.com/index.php?sec=1
Contact: W. Godfrey Wood, Chief Executive Officer
Description: Promotes business and community development in the Portland, ME area. **Founded:** 1853. **Publications:** *Business Perspectives* (Monthly). **Educational Activities:** Maine Business Expo (Annual).

52600 ■ **Greater Van Buren Chamber of Commerce**
51 Main St., Ste. 101
Van Buren, ME 04785
Ph: (207)868-5059
Fax: (207)868-2222
Co. E-mail: vbchamber@pwless.net
URL: http://www.greatervanburenchamber.com
Contact: Ralph Anderson, Executive Director
Description: Promotes business and community development in Van Buren, ME.

52601 ■ *Guide Book*
138 Main St., Ste. 101
Saco, ME 04072
Ph: (207)282-1567
Fax: (207)282-3149
Co. E-mail: info@biddefordsacochamber.org
URL: http://www.biddefordsacochamber.org
Contact: Craig Pendleton, Executive Director
Released: Annual

52602 ■ *Guide to the Kennebunks*
PO Box 740
Kennebunk, ME 04043
Ph: (207)967-0857
Fax: (207)967-8451
Co. E-mail: info@visitthekennebunks.com
URL: http://www.visitthekennebunks.com
Contact: Tina Hewitt-Gordon, Chairperson
Released: Annual

52603 ■ *Impact*
125 Community Dr., Ste. 101
Augusta, ME 04330
Ph: (207)623-4568

Fax: (207)622-7723
Co. E-mail: dana.f.connors@mainechamber.org
URL: http://www.mainechamber.org/mx/hm.
  asp?id=home
Contact: Dana F. Connors, President
Released: Weekly **Price:** $75, for members.

52604 ■ In Touch
50 Elm St.
Waterville, ME 04901
Ph: (207)873-3315
Fax: (207)877-0087
Co. E-mail: info@midmainechamber.com
URL: http://www.midmainechamber.com
Contact: Kimberly Lindlof, President
Released: Monthly **Price:** free for members.

52605 ■ Katahdin Area Chamber of Commerce
PO Box 426
Millinocket, ME 04462
Ph: (207)723-4443
Co. E-mail: info@katahdinmaine.com
URL: http://www.katahdinmaine.com
Contact: Lee Lamson, President
Description: Promotes business and community development in the Katahdin region. **Founded:** 1995.

52606 ■ Kennebec Valley Chamber of Commerce (KVCC)
21 University Dr.
Augusta, ME 04332-0676
Ph: (207)623-4559
Free: 800-899-5624
Fax: (207)626-9342
Co. E-mail: info@augustamaine.com
URL: http://www.augustamaine.com
Contact: Peter G. Thompson, President
Description: Businesses. Promotes economic development and tourism in the Augusta, ME area. Holds seminars. Sponsors Issues Breakfasts and Whatever Week and Race. **Founded:** 1932. **Publications:** *Cap Area Guide* (Biennial). **Educational Activities:** Whatever Week (Annual). **Awards:** Business of the Year (Annual); Business Person of the Year (Annual); Community Service Award (Annual); Lifetime Achievement Award (Annual); President's Award (Annual); Special Service Award (Annual).

52607 ■ Kennebunk-Kennebunkport Chamber of Commerce (KKCC)
PO Box 740
Kennebunk, ME 04043
Ph: (207)967-0857
Fax: (207)967-8451
Co. E-mail: info@visitthekennebunks.com
URL: http://www.visitthekennebunks.com
Contact: Tina Hewitt-Gordon, Chairperson
Description: Businesses. Promotes business and community development in Kennebunk and Kennebunkport, ME. Sponsors Wedding Expo of the Kennebunks, February is for Lovers, annual Home and Food Show, B&B Inn and Garden Tour, Chamber Golf Tournament, concert and picnic on the green, Kennebearport Teddy Bear Show, Hole in One Contest, annual holiday auction and Downtown Decadence. **Publications:** *Chamber News* (Monthly); *Experience Kennebunk-Kennebunkport* (Annual); *Guide to the Kennebunks* (Annual).

52608 ■ LeCoeur de la Val Lee
356 Main St.
Madawaska, ME 04756
Ph: (207)728-7000
Fax: (207)728-4696
Co. E-mail: valleyvisit@pwless.net
URL: http://www.greatermadawaskachamber.com
Contact: Roger Thibodeau, Executive Director
Released: Quarterly

52609 ■ Maine State Chamber of Commerce
125 Community Dr., Ste. 101
Augusta, ME 04330
Ph: (207)623-4568

Fax: (207)622-7723
Co. E-mail: dana.f.connors@mainechamber.org
URL: http://www.mainechamber.org/mx/hm.
  asp?id=home
Contact: Dana F. Connors, President
URL(s): www.mainechamber.org/. **Description:** Promotes business and community development in Maine. Provides legislative advocacy. Holds seminars. **Founded:** 1984. **Publications:** *Impact* (Weekly).

52610 ■ Mid-Maine Chamber of Commerce
50 Elm St.
Waterville, ME 04901
Ph: (207)873-3315
Fax: (207)877-0087
Co. E-mail: info@midmainechamber.com
URL: http://www.midmainechamber.com
Contact: Kimberly Lindlof, President
Description: Promotes business and community development in the mid-Maine area. Sponsors monthly Business After Hours program and monthly business forum. **Founded:** 1929. **Publications:** *In Touch* (Monthly); *Newsline* (Semimonthly); *Living Better in Mid-Maine Guide* (Semiannual). **Educational Activities:** Annual Awards Banquet (Annual). **Awards:** Business of the Year (Annual); Business Person of the Year (Annual); Distinguished Community Service Award (Annual). **Telecommunication Services:** kimberly@midmainechamber.com.

52611 ■ Moosehead Lake Region Chamber of Commerce
PO Box 581
Greenville, ME 04441-0581
Ph: (207)695-2702
Free: 888-876-2778
Fax: (207)695-3440
Co. E-mail: info@mooseheadlake.org
URL: http://www.mooseheadlake.org
Contact: Bob Hamer, Executive Director
URL(s): mooseheadlake.org/. **Description:** Promotes business and community development in the Moosehead Lake, ME region. Sponsors 4th of July celebration, annual "Moosemainea" in the spring, and annual Winter Festival. **Founded:** 1947. **Publications:** *Chamber Newsletter* (Monthly); *Visitor's Guide*.

52612 ■ Mount Desert Chamber of Commerce
PO Box 675
Northeast Harbor, ME 04662-0675
Ph: (207)276-5040
Co. E-mail: info@mountdesertchamber.org
URL: http://www.mountdesertchamber.org
Contact: Matt Hart, President
Description: Promotes business and community development in Mount Desert, ME. Sponsors seasonal Information Bureau and Yachtman's Reading Room at St. Sea Marina. **Founded:** 1932. **Publications:** *Northeast Harbor Port Directory* (Periodic). **Educational Activities:** Christmas Festival (Annual).

52613 ■ Newsline
50 Elm St.
Waterville, ME 04901
Ph: (207)873-3315
Fax: (207)877-0087
Co. E-mail: info@midmainechamber.com
URL: http://www.midmainechamber.com
Contact: Kimberly Lindlof, President
Released: Semimonthly **Price:** free for members.

52614 ■ Northeast Harbor Port Directory
PO Box 675
Northeast Harbor, ME 04662-0675
Ph: (207)276-5040
Co. E-mail: info@mountdesertchamber.org
URL: http://www.mountdesertchamber.org
Contact: Matt Hart, President
Released: Periodic **Price:** free.

52615 ■ Northern Katahdin Valley Region Chamber of Commerce (NKVRCC)
PO Box 374
Island Falls, ME 04747

Ph: (207)463-4634
Co. E-mail: nkvrcc1@fairpoint.net
URL: http://www.northernmainechamber.com
Contact: Heidi Rigby, President
Description: Supports business communities and encourages new business opportunities in Southern Aroostook and Northern Penobscot county areas.

52616 ■ Official Boothbay Harbor Region Guide
PO Box 356
Boothbay Harbor, ME 04538-0356
Ph: (207)633-2353
Fax: (207)633-7448
Co. E-mail: seamaine@boothbayharbor.com
URL: http://www.boothbayharbor.com
Contact: Pamela Riley, President
Released: Annual **Price:** free.

52617 ■ Ogunquit Chamber of Commerce (OCC)
PO Box 2289
Ogunquit, ME 03907
Ph: (207)646-2939
Fax: (207)641-0856
Co. E-mail: director@ogunquit.org
URL: http://www.ogunquit.org
Description: Promotes business and community development in Ogunquit, ME. Sponsors events such as art shows, fireworks displays, Christmas by the Sea festival, and Patriot's Day celebration. **Founded:** 1966.

52618 ■ Old Orchard Beach Chamber of Commerce
11 1st St.
Old Orchard Beach, ME 04064
Ph: (207)934-2500
Free: 800-365-9386
Co. E-mail: info@oldorchardbeachmaine.com
URL: http://www.oldorchardbeachmaine.com
Description: Promotes business and community development in Old Orchard Beach, ME. Sponsors Beach Olympics to benefit Special Olympics and Adopt a Family Christmas program.

52619 ■ Oxford Hills Chamber of Commerce (OHCC)
4 Western Ave.
South Paris, ME 04281
Ph: (207)743-2281
Fax: (207)743-0687
Co. E-mail: info@oxfordhillsmaine.com
URL: http://www.oxfordhillsmaine.com
Contact: John Williams, Executive Director
Description: Promotes business and community development in Oxford Hills, ME. Sponsors seminars and workshops. Operates year-round visitor's information center. **Founded:** 1971. **Publications:** *Explore Maine's Oxford Hills* (Annual); *Chamber Bullet* (Monthly); *E-Message Board* (Weekly); *Explore Maine's Oxford Hills* (Monthly). **Awards:** Community Service Award (Annual); Employee of the Year (Annual). **Telecommunication Services:** john@oxfordhillsmaine.com.

52620 ■ Penobscot Bay Regional Chamber of Commerce (PBRCC)
1 Park Dr.
Rockland, ME 04841
Ph: (207)596-0376
Free: 800-562-2529
Fax: (207)596-6549
Co. E-mail: info@therealmaine.com
URL: http://www.therealmaine.com
Contact: Dan Bookham, Executive Director
Description: Strives to promote and support members and the economic well being of the area community. **Founded:** 1924. **Publications:** *Chamber Newsletter* (Monthly). **Educational Activities:** Business After Hours (Monthly). **Awards:** Improvement Award (Annual).

52621 ■ Piscataquis County Chamber of Commerce
PO Box 376
Dover Foxcroft, ME 04426
Ph: (207)564-7533

Fax: (207)564-7573
Co. E-mail: exdir@piscataquischamber.com
URL: http://www.piscataquischamber.com
Contact: Erin Warstler, Executive Director
Description: Promotes business and community development in the Southern Piscataquis County, ME.

52622 ■ Rangeley Lakes Region Chamber of Commerce (RLRCC)
PO Box 317
Rangeley, ME 04970
Ph: (207)864-5364
Free: 800-MT-LAKES
Co. E-mail: info@rangeleymaine.com
URL: http://www.rangeleymaine.com
Description: Promotes economic development and tourism in the Rangeley, ME area. **Founded:** 1956.

52623 ■ River Valley Chamber of Commerce (RVCC)
10 Bridge St.
Rumford, ME 04276
Ph: (207)364-3241
Co. E-mail: info@rivervalleychamber.com
URL: http://www.rivervalleychamber.com
Contact: Janet Brennick, President
Description: Promotes business and community development in the Rumford, Mexico, Dixfield, Peru, Canton, Hanover, Andover, Byron and Roxbury areas of Maine. **Founded:** 1912. **Publications:** *River Valley Voice* (Semimonthly). **Educational Activities:** River Valley Chamber of Commerce Dinner (Annual).

52624 ■ River Valley Voice
10 Bridge St.
Rumford, ME 04276
Ph: (207)364-3241
Co. E-mail: info@rivervalleychamber.com
URL: http://www.rivervalleychamber.com
Released: Semimonthly **Price:** free for members.

52625 ■ Rockport-Camden-Lincolnville Chamber of Commerce
PO Box 919
Camden, ME 04843
Ph: (207)236-4404
Free: 800-223-5459
Fax: (207)236-4315
Co. E-mail: chamber@camdenme.org
URL: http://www.visitcamden.com
Contact: Jean Belair, President
Description: Promotes business and community development in the Camden, Lincolnville, and Rockport, ME area. Seeks to function in a manner that enhances the environment, protects resources, and sustains the heritage of the community. Sponsors semiannual arts and crafts shows. Disseminates tourist and relocation information. **Founded:** 1939. **Publications:** *Chamber News* (Monthly); *Guide to Rockport-Camden-Lincolnville* (Annual). **Educational Activities:** Business After Hours (Monthly); Rockport-Camden-Lincolnville Chamber of Commerce Dinner (Annual). **Awards:** Town Person of the Year (Annual).

52626 ■ St. Croix Valley Chamber of Commerce
Wabanaki Culture Center
39 Union St.
Calais, ME 04619
Ph: (207)454-2308
Free: 888-422-3112
Fax: (207)454-2308
Co. E-mail: visitstcroixvalley@myfairpoint.net
URL: http://www.visitcalais.com
Contact: Julie Jordan, Executive Director
Description: Business and professional membership organization working to make the St. Croix Valley, ME area a better place to live, work and to raise a family. **Founded:** 1947.

52627 ■ Schoodic Area Chamber of Commerce
PO Box 381
Winter Harbor, ME 04693

Ph: (207)546-2960
Co. E-mail: lelliott@mainesavings.com
URL: http://www.acadia-schoodic.org
Contact: Linda Elliott, President
Description: Promotes business and community development in on the Schoodic Peninsula, ME. Bestows scholarships. Sponsors annual summer Lobster Festival and annual Trade Day (town-wide yard sale).

52628 ■ Sebago Lakes Region Chamber of Commerce (SLRCC)
747 Roosevelt Trail
Windham, ME 04062
Ph: (207)892-8265
Fax: (207)893-0110
Co. E-mail: info@sebagolakeschamber.com
URL: http://www.sebagolakeschamber.com
Contact: Ann Marie Swenson, President
E-mail: aswenson@mainebank.com
Description: Hosts legislative forums and business programs. Promotes tourism region and supports community events. **Founded:** 1976. **Subscriptions:** artwork business records clippings maps photographs reports. **Publications:** *Soundings* (Quarterly); *Greater Windham Chamber of Commerce--Annual Business and Pleasure Guide* (Annual); *Annual Business and Pleasure Guide* (Annual); *Annual Business and Pleasure Guide* (Annual). **Educational Activities:** Chamber Business Break (Monthly); Director's Meeting (Monthly). **Awards:** Business Person of the Year (Annual); Community Service Leadership Award (Annual); Volunteer of the Year Award (Annual).

52629 ■ Skowhegan Area Chamber of Commerce
23 Commercial St.
Skowhegan, ME 04976
Ph: (207)474-3621
Fax: (207)474-3306
Co. E-mail: exdir@skowheganchamber.com
URL: http://www.skowheganchamber.com
Contact: Gary York, President
Description: Promotes business, commercial, manufacturing, and civic interests of Greater Skowhegan area.

52630 ■ Soundings
747 Roosevelt Trail
Windham, ME 04062
Ph: (207)892-8265
Fax: (207)893-0110
Co. E-mail: info@sebagolakeschamber.com
URL: http://www.sebagolakeschamber.com
Contact: Ann Marie Swenson, President
E-mail: aswenson@mainebank.com
Released: Quarterly

52631 ■ Southern Midcoast Maine Chamber
2 Main St.
Topsham, ME 04086
Ph: (207)725-8797
Free: 877-725-8797
Fax: (207)725-9787
Co. E-mail: chamber@midcoastmaine.com
URL: http://www.midcoastmaine.com
Contact: Steven W. Wallace, President
E-mail: president@midcoastmaine.com
Description: Promotes business and community development in the Bath and Brunswick, ME areas. Operates seasonal tourist information center. **Publications:** *Bath-Brunswick Region Map* (Annual); *Chamber Connections* (10/year); *Community Resource Directory*; *Bath/Brunswick Visitor's Guide* (Annual). **Educational Activities:** Award Ceremony (Annual). **Awards:** Business of the Year (Annual); Citizen of the Year (Annual); Volunteer of the Year (Annual).

52632 ■ Upper Kennebec Valley Chamber of Commerce
PO Box 491
Bingham, ME 04920
Ph: (207)672-4100
Co. E-mail: info@upperkennebecvalley.com
URL: http://www.upperkennebecvalleychamber.com
Contact: Cyndee Gagnon, President

52633 ■ Visitor's Guide
PO Box 581
Greenville, ME 04441-0581
Ph: (207)695-2702
Free: 888-876-2778
Fax: (207)695-3440
Co. E-mail: info@mooseheadlake.org
URL: http://www.mooseheadlake.org
Contact: Bob Hamer, Executive Director

52634 ■ Wells Chamber of Commerce
PO Box 356
Wells, ME 04090-0356
Ph: (207)646-2451
Co. E-mail: wellschamber@wellschamber.org
URL: http://www.wellschamber.org
Contact: Eleanor J. Vadenais, Executive Director
Description: Promotes business and community development in Wells, ME. Sponsors local festivals and annual Christmas parade. **Telecommunication Services:** eleanor@wellschamber.org.

52635 ■ The Yarmouth Chamber
162 Main St.
Yarmouth, ME 04096
Ph: (207)846-3984
Fax: (207)846-5419
Co. E-mail: info@yarmouthmaine.org
URL: http://www.yarmouthmaine.org
Contact: Carolyn Schuster, Executive Director
Released: Monthly

52636 ■ Yarmouth Chamber of Commerce
162 Main St.
Yarmouth, ME 04096
Ph: (207)846-3984
Fax: (207)846-5419
Co. E-mail: info@yarmouthmaine.org
URL: http://www.yarmouthmaine.org
Contact: Carolyn Schuster, Executive Director
Description: Promotes business and community development in Yarmouth, ME. **Founded:** 1956. **Subscriptions:** 40000. **Publications:** *The Yarmouth Chamber* (Monthly). **Educational Activities:** Yarmouth Clam Festival (Annual).

MINORITY BUSINESS ASSISTANCE PROGRAMS

52637 ■ The Maine Women's Business Center at CEI - Coastal Enterprises Inc.
36 Water St.
Wiscasset, ME 04578
Ph: (207)882-7552
Fax: (207)882-7308
Co. E-mail: cei@ceimaine.org
URL: http://www.ceimaine.org/women
Contact: Gretchen Henn, Director
Description: Provides counseling and training services for new and existing women business owners in Maine.

FINANCING AND LOAN PROGRAMS

52638 ■ CEI Ventures, Inc. / CVI
2 Portland Fish Pier, Ste. 206
Portland, ME 04101
Ph: (207)772-5356
Fax: (207)772-5503
URL: http://www.ceiventures.com
Contact: Nathaniel V. Henshaw, Managing Director
E-mail: nvh@ceimaine.org
Preferred Investment Size: $1,000,000 to $4,000,000. **Geographic Preference:** Northeast.

52639 ■ North Atlantic Capital Corporation
2 City Ctr., 5th Fl.
Portland, ME 04101
Ph: (207)772-4470

Fax: (207)772-3257
Co. E-mail: ccoyne@northatlanticcapital.com
URL: http://www.northatlanticcapital.com
Contact: David Coit, Managing Director
Preferred Investment Size: $4,000,000 $8,000,000.
Industry Preferences: Internet specific, computer hardware, other products, consumer related, industrial and energy, computer software and services, communications and media, medical and health, semiconductors and other electronics, and biotechnology. **Geographic Preference:** East Coast.

PROCUREMENT ASSISTANCE PROGRAMS

52640 ■ Maine Procurement Technical Assistance Center - Eastern Maine Development Corporation - Market Development Center
40 Harlow St.
Bangor, ME 04401
Ph: (207)942-6389
Free: 800-339-6389
Fax: (207)942-3548
Co. E-mail: info@emdc.org
URL: http://www.emdc.org
Contact: Patricia Rice, Director
E-mail: ralexander@emdc.org

52641 ■ Maine Procurement Technical Assistance Center - Outreach Center
415 Lisbon St., Ste. 400
Lewiston, ME 04240
Ph: (207)777-5067
URL: http://www.maineptac.org
Contact: Arthur Stolpestad, Director
E-mail: astolpestad@emdc.org
Description: Helps Maine small businesses obtain government contracts with the Department of Defense, other federal agencies, state/local governments, and prime contractors.

52642 ■ Maine Procurement Technical Assistance Center - Outreach Center
403 Hallowell Rd.
Pownal, ME 04069
Ph: (207)653-8625
URL: http://www.maineptac.org
Contact: Ernest Gray, Director
E-mail: egray1@maine.rr.com
Description: Helps Maine small businesses obtain government contracts with the Department of Defense, other federal agencies, state/local governments, and prime contractors.

52643 ■ Maine Procurement Technical Assistance Center - Service Center
17 Main St.
Fairfield, ME 04937-1119
Ph: (207)453-4258
Fax: (207)453-4264
Co. E-mail: jmr@ceimaine.org
URL: http://www.mainesbdc.org
Contact: Janet Roderick, Specialist
E-mail: edahl@emdc.org
Description: Helps Maine small businesses obtain government contracts with the Department of Defense, other federal agencies, state/local governments, and prime contractors.

52644 ■ U.S. SBA Office of Government Contracting for Maine and New Hampshire
68 Sewall St., Rm. 512
Augusta, ME 04330
Ph: (207)622-8379
Fax: (207)481-5513
Co. E-mail: sean.crean@sba.gov
URL: http://www.sba.gov
Contact: Sean F. Crean, Representative
E-mail: sean.crean@sba.gov
Description: Covers activities for the VA Hospital (Togus, ME), the Portsmouth Naval Shipyard (Portsmouth, NH), and the Naval Air Station (Brunswick, ME).

INCUBATORS/RESEARCH AND TECHNOLOGY PARKS

52645 ■ Maine Center for Enterprise Development
University of S Maine
70 Falmouth St.
Portland, ME 04103
Ph: (207)228-8524
Fax: (207)228-8526
Co. E-mail: info@mced.biz
URL: http://www.mced.biz/
Contact: Steven N. Bazinet, Executive Director
Description: A small business incubator providing business incubation services for innovative start-ups.

52646 ■ River Valley Technology Center
60 Lowell St.
Rumford, ME 04276

Ph: (207)369-0396
URL: http://www.rvgc.org/rvtc/home.cfm
Description: A public/private partnership dedicated to nurturing small technology and precision manufacturing businesses during the start-up stage. It provides a variety of business development assistance including low cost space, shared office services, onsite training and managerial and technical assistance in an environment conducive to new small businesses.

52647 ■ Target Technology Center
University of Maine
20 Godfrey Dr.
Orono, ME 04473
Ph: (207)866-6500
Fax: (207)866-6501
URL: http://www.targetincubator.umaine.edu/
Contact: Debbie Neuman, Director
Description: A small business incubator providing information technology companies expertise, tools, resources, and networks.

EDUCATIONAL PROGRAMS

52648 ■ University of Maine at Machias
116 O'Brien Ave.
Machias, ME 04654-1397
Ph: (207)255-1200
Free: 888-468-6866
Fax: (207)255-1419
Co. E-mail: ummadmissions@maine.edu
URL: http://www.umm.maine.edu
Description: Offers programs in small business management.

PUBLICATIONS

52649 ■ *Smart Start your Arizona Business*
PSI Research
300 N. Valley Dr.
Grants Pass, OR 97526
Ph: (503)479-9464
Free: 800-228-2275
Fax: (503)476-1479
Co. E-mail: info@psi-research.com
URL: http://www.psi-research.com
Ed: Michael D. Jenkins. **Released:** Revised edition, 1992. **Price:** $29.95 (looseleaf binder); $24.95 (paper). **Description:** Part of the Successful Business Library series.

SMALL BUSINESS DEVELOPMENT CENTERS

52650 ■ Anne Arundel Small Business Development Center
Anne Arundel Economic Development Corporation
2660 Riva Rd., Ste. 200
Annapolis, MD 21401
Ph: (410)222-4476
Fax: (410)222-7415
Co. E-mail: hminor@ubalt.edu
URL: http://www.centralmdsbdc.org/counseling/an-nearundelcounty.php
Description: Represents and promotes the small business sector. Provides management assistance to current and prospective small business owners. Helps to improve management skills and expand the products and services of members.

52651 ■ Baltimore County Small Business Development Center
University of Baltimore
11 W Mt. Royal Ave.
Baltimore, MD 21201
Ph: (410)837-4973
Co. E-mail: cpanos@ubalt.edu
URL: http://www.centralmdsbdc.org/counseling/balti-morecounty.php
Description: Represents and promotes the small business sector. Provides management assistance to current and prospective small business owners. Helps to improve management skills and expand the products and services of members.

52652 ■ Harford County Maryland Small Business Development Center
Harford Community College
Edgewood Hall
401 Thomas Run Rd.
Bel Air, MD 21015
Ph: (443)412-2237
Fax: (443)412-2353
Co. E-mail: sbdc@harford.edu
URL: http://www.harford.edu/sbdc/Index.asp
Description: Represents and promotes the small business sector. Provides management assistance to current and prospective small business owners. Helps to improve management skills and expand the products and services of members.

52653 ■ Howard County Small Business Development Center
Howard County Economic Development Authority
6751 Columbia Gateway Pwy.
Columbia, MD 21046
Ph: (410)313-6190
Fax: (410)313-7515
Co. E-mail: mredmond@ubalt.edu
URL: http://www.centralmdsbdc.org/counseling/howardcounty.php
Description: Represents and promotes the small business sector. Provides management assistance to current and prospective small business owners. Helps to improve management skills and expand the products and services of members.

52654 ■ Maryland Small Business Development Center - Central Region
11 W Mt. Royal
Baltimore, MD 21201
Ph: (410)837-4928
Free: 877-421-0830
Co. E-mail: ubmdsbdc@ubalt.edu
URL: http://www.centralmdsbdc.org
Contact: Kiesha Haughton Smoots, Regional Director
E-mail: ksmoots@ubalt.edu
Description: Represents and promotes the small business sector. Provides management assistance to current and prospective small business owners. Helps to improve management skills and expand the products and services of members.

52655 ■ Maryland Small Business Development Center - Eastern Region
Perdue School of Business - Salisbury University
215 E Campus Complex
Salisbury, MD 21801
Ph: (410)548-4419
Free: 800-999-7232
Fax: (410)548-5389
Co. E-mail: fahedrick@salisbury.edu
URL: http://www.salisbury.edu/sbdc
Contact: John Hickman, Director
Description: Represents and promotes the small business sector. Provides management assistance to current and prospective small business owners. Helps to improve management skills and expand the products and services of members.

52656 ■ Maryland Small Business Development Center - Southern Region
PO Box 910
La Plata, MD 20646-0910
Ph: (301)934-7583
Fax: (301)934-7681
Co. E-mail: krobertson-slagle@csmd.edu
URL: http://www.sbdchelp.com
Contact: Kelly Robertson-Slagle, Director
E-mail: krobertson-slagle@csmd.edu
Description: Represents and promotes the small business sector. Provides management assistance to current and prospective small business owners. Helps to improve management skills and expand the products and services of members.

52657 ■ Western Region Maryland Small Business Development Center
One Technology Dr., Ste. A
Frostburg, MD 21532
Ph: (301)687-1080
Fax: (301)687-1008
URL: http://www.mdsbdc.umd.edu/region_western.html
Contact: Sandy Mehalko, Regional Director
Description: Represents and promotes the small business sector. Provides management assistance to current and prospective small business owners. Helps to improve management skills and expand the products and services of members.

SMALL BUSINESS ASSISTANCE PROGRAMS

52658 ■ Maryland Department of Business and Economic Development - Business Development Division
401 E Pratt St.
Baltimore, MD 21202-3316
Ph: (410)767-6300
Free: 800-811-0051
Fax: (410)333-4302
Co. E-mail: communications@choosemaryland.org
URL: http://www.choosemaryland.org
Contact: Jayson Knott, Director
Description: attracts new businesses to the state, expands global commerce, cultivates important industry clusters and raises awareness of Maryland as a leader in technology and innovation.

52659 ■ Maryland Economic Development Corp.
100 N Charles St., 6th Fl.
Baltimore, MD 21201
Ph: (410)625-0051
Fax: (410)625-1848
URL: http://www.medco-corp.com
Contact: Robert C. Brennan, Executive Director
Description: Develops vacant or under-utilized industrial sites and other facilities and economic resources that would serve the public interest. Assists in the expansion, modernization, and retention of existing Maryland businesses. Provides marketing, financing, and networking information.

SCORE OFFICES

52660 ■ Frederick County SCORE
Co. E-mail: score@scorefrederick.org

52661 ■ Mid-Shore SCORE
Co. E-mail: score626@goeaston.net

52662 ■ SCORE Greater Baltimore
10 S Howard St., 6th Fl.
Baltimore, MD 21201
Ph: (410)962-2233
Fax: (410)962-1805
Co. E-mail: baltimorescore@verizon.net
URL: http://www.scorebaltimore.org
Contact: Seymour Farbman, Co-Chairperson
URL(s): greaterbaltimore.score.org. **Description:** Serves as volunteer program in which working and retired business management professionals provide free business counseling to men and women who are considering starting a small business, encountering problems with their business, or expanding their business. Offers free one-on-one counseling, online counseling and low cost workshops on a variety of business topics.

52663 ■ SCORE Hagerstown
14 N Potomac St., 2nd Fl., Ste. B
Hagerstown, MD 21740
Ph: (301)766-2043

Fax: (301)766-2000
Co. E-mail: info@scorehagerstown.org
URL: http://www.scorehagerstown.org
Contact: Bob Jones, Chairman
Description: Aims to help emerging businesses succeed and stay active in the local and national small business marketplace.

52664 ■ SCORE Salisbury
Salisbury Area Chamber of Commerce Bldg.
144 E Main St.
Salisbury, MD 21801
Ph: (410)749-0185
Fax: (410)860-9925
Co. E-mail: score@salisburyarea.com
URL: http://www.salisburyscore.org
Contact: Chuck Lemak, Chairman
URL(s): salisbury.score.org. **Description:** Serves as volunteer program in which working and retired business management professionals provide free business counseling to men and women who are considering starting a small business, encountering problems with their business, or expanding their business. Offers free one-on-one counseling, online counseling and low cost workshops on a variety of business topics. **Founded:** 1976.

52665 ■ SCORE Southern Maryland
49 Old Solomons Island Rd., Ste. 204
Annapolis, MD 21401
Ph: (410)266-9553
Co. E-mail: info@score390.org
URL: http://www.score390.org
Contact: Jerry Carlisle, Chairman
Description: Provides no cost business counseling and workshops on starting and growing small businesses to entrepreneurs and individuals interested to start a small business in Anne Arundel, Calvert, Charles, and St. Mary's Counties in Maryland. **Founded:** 1990.

52666 ■ SCORE Upper Shore
122 N Cross St.
Chestertown, MD 21620-1547
Ph: (410)810-0021
Co. E-mail: chapter670@easternshorescore.org
URL: http://www.easternshorescore.org/chapter670.php
Description: Serves as volunteer program in which working and retired business management professionals provide free business counseling to men and women who are considering starting a small business, encountering problems with their business, or expanding their business. Offers free one-on-one counseling, online counseling and low cost workshops on a variety of business topics. **Founded:** 1996.

BETTER BUSINESS BUREAUS

52667 ■ Better Business Bureau of Greater Maryland
1414 Key Hwy., Ste. 100
Baltimore, MD 21230
Ph: (410)347-3990
Fax: (410)347-3936
Co. E-mail: abarnett@greatermd.bbb.org
URL: http://greatermd.bbb.org
Contact: Angie Barnett, President
Description: Promotes and fosters ethical relationships between businesses and the public through voluntary self-regulation, consumer and business education and service excellence.

CHAMBERS OF COMMERCE

52668 ■ Aberdeen Chamber of Commerce (ACC)
214 W Bel Air Ave.
Aberdeen, MD 21001
Ph: (410)272-2580
Fax: (410)272-9357
Co. E-mail: aberdeenchamber@verizon.net
URL: http://www.aberdeencc.com
Contact: Janet Emmons, Director
Description: Seeks to promote the city of Aberdeen and the businesses within. Activities include fund raisers, raffles, carnivals, Business Card Exchanges,

monthly meetings and mailings promoting Aberdeen. **Founded:** 1950. **Publications:** *Chamber News* (Bimonthly). **Educational Activities:** Aberdeen Chamber of Commerce Meeting (Monthly).

52669 ■ Allegany County Chamber of Commerce (ACCC)
Bell Tower Bldg.
24 Frederick St.
Cumberland, MD 21502
Ph: (301)722-2820
Fax: (301)722-5995
Co. E-mail: info@alleganycountychamber.com
URL: http://www.alleganycountychamber.com
Contact: Barbara R. Beebe, Chairman
Description: Promotes business and community development in Allegany County, MD. Sponsors workshops. **Founded:** 1914. **Publications:** *Allegany County Map* (Annual); *Chamber News* (Monthly); *Know Your Chamber*; *Membership Directory and Community Profile*.

52670 ■ *Allegany County Map*
Bell Tower Bldg.
24 Frederick St.
Cumberland, MD 21502
Ph: (301)722-2820
Fax: (301)722-5995
Co. E-mail: info@alleganycountychamber.com
URL: http://www.alleganycountychamber.com
Contact: Barbara R. Beebe, Chairman
Released: Annual **Price:** $0.55, for members; $1, for nonmembers.

52671 ■ Annapolis and Anne Arundel County Chamber of Commerce
49 Old Solomons Island Rd., Ste. 204
Annapolis, MD 21401
Ph: (410)266-3960
Fax: (410)266-8270
Co. E-mail: info@aaaccc.org
URL: http://www.annapolischamber.com
Contact: David Plott, Chairman
Description: Promotes business and community development in Anne Arundel County and Annapolis, MD. Sponsors annual relocation tour, annual trade show, and monthly business mixers and networking breakfasts. Hosts cable television show "It's Good Business". **Founded:** 1918. **Publications:** *Chamber News* (Monthly); *Anne Arundel County - Still Revolutionary*. **Educational Activities:** Business Expo (Annual); Generation Next Happy Hours (Quarterly). **Awards:** Business Leader Award (Annual); Educational Partnerships Award; Environmental Awareness Awards (Annual); Legislator of the Year Award.

52672 ■ Baltimore City Chamber of Commerce
PO Box 4483
Baltimore, MD 21223
Ph: (410)837-7101
Fax: (410)837-7104
Co. E-mail: charlieo@baltimorecitychamber.org
URL: http://www.baltimorecitychamber.org
Contact: Charles R. Owens, President
Description: Promotes business prosperity by nurturing partnerships and identifying resources that maximizes business and economic development in Baltimore City, MD. **Founded:** 1992.

52673 ■ Baltimore County Chamber of Commerce (BCCC)
102 W Pennsylvania Ave., Ste. 101
Towson, MD 21204-4526
Ph: (410)825-6200
Fax: (410)821-9901
Co. E-mail: kscott@baltcountychamber.com
URL: http://www.baltcountycc.com
Contact: Keith Scott, President
Description: Promotes business and community development in Baltimore County, MD. **Founded:** 1971. **Publications:** *Sound Business* (Quarterly); *Membership Directory and Resource Guide* (Periodic). **Awards:** Balto County Business Award; Balto County Police Foundation Award; Excellence in Education (Annual); Merit Scholarship Program (Annual).

52674 ■ Baltimore - Washington Corridor Chamber of Commerce (BWCC)
312 Marshall Ave., Ste. 104
Laurel, MD 20707-4824
Ph: (301)725-4000
Fax: (301)725-0776
Co. E-mail: bwcc@bwcc.org
URL: http://www.baltwashchamber.org
Contact: H. Walter Townshend, III, President
Description: Promotes business and community development along the Baltimore, MD/Washington, D.C. corridor. Sponsors periodic seminars, business mixers and signature events. Manages a regional bus system, Connect-A-Ride, Howard Transit and others. Provides scholarships and hosts an annual symposium for middle and high school math teachers. **Founded:** 1947. **Publications:** *Corridor Chamber Membership Directory* (Annual); *Corridor Chamber News* (Semimonthly). **Educational Activities:** Awards Gala (Annual); Power Networking (Monthly). **Awards:** Foundation Honoree; Business of the Year (Large) (Annual); Business of the Year (Small) (Annual).

52675 ■ *Business*
101 Centennial Ave., Ste. A
La Plata, MD 20646-4208
Ph: (301)932-6500
Fax: (301)932-3945
Co. E-mail: info@charlescountychamber.org
URL: http://www.charlescountychamber.org
Contact: Betsy Burian, Executive Director
Released: Monthly

52676 ■ *Business Advocate*
60 West St., Ste. 100
Annapolis, MD 21401
Ph: (410)269-0642
Fax: (410)269-5247
Co. E-mail: ksnyder@mdchamber.org
URL: http://www.mdchamber.org
Contact: Kathleen T. Snyder, President
Released: Biweekly

52677 ■ *Business and Community Guide*
PO Box 4146
Crofton, MD 21114-4146
Ph: (410)721-9131
Fax: (410)721-0785
Co. E-mail: info@croftonchamber.com
URL: http://www.croftonchamber.com
Contact: Thomas B. Locke, President
Released: Annual

52678 ■ *Business and Community Services Directory*
44200 Airport Rd.
California, MD 20619
Ph: (301)737-3001
Fax: (301)737-0089
Co. E-mail: info@smcchamber.com
URL: http://www.smcchamber.com
Contact: William Scarafia, President
Released: Annual

52679 ■ *Business Directory*
1 Holly Ave.
Severna Park, MD 21146
Ph: (410)647-3900
Fax: (410)647-3999
Co. E-mail: info@severnaparkchamber.com
URL: http://www.severnaparkchamber.com
Contact: Linda S. Zahn, Chief Executive Officer
Released: Annual

52680 ■ *Business Directory and Buyers' Guide*
8601 Georgia Ave., Ste. 203
Silver Spring, MD 20910-3458
Ph: (301)565-3777
Fax: (301)565-3777
Co. E-mail: info@gsscc.org
URL: http://www.silverspringchamber.com
Contact: Jane Redicker, President
Released: Annual

52681 ■ Business Directory and Community Resource Guide
8373 Piney Orchard Pkwy., Ste. 200
Odenton, MD 21113
Ph: (410)672-3422
Fax: (410)672-3475
Co. E-mail: info@westcountychamber.org
URL: http://www.waaccc.org
Contact: Ms. Claire Louder, President
Released: Annual

52682 ■ Business E-News
8601 Georgia Ave., Ste. 203
Silver Spring, MD 20910-3458
Ph: (301)565-3777
Fax: (301)565-3377
Co. E-mail: info@gsscc.org
URL: http://www.silverspringchamber.com
Contact: Jane Redicker, President
Released: Quarterly

52683 ■ Business Exchange
8373 Piney Orchard Pkwy., Ste. 200
Odenton, MD 21113
Ph: (410)672-3422
Fax: (410)672-3475
Co. E-mail: info@westcountychamber.org
URL: http://www.waaccc.org
Contact: Ms. Claire Louder, President
Released: Monthly **Price:** free.

52684 ■ Business Journal
144 E Main St.
Salisbury, MD 21801
Ph: (410)749-0144
Fax: (410)860-9925
Co. E-mail: chamber@salisburyarea.com
URL: http://www.salisburyarea.com
Contact: Bradley A. Bellacicco, Executive Director
Released: Monthly

52685 ■ Calvert County Chamber of Commerce (CCCC)
120 Dares Beach Rd.
Prince Frederick, MD 20678-0009
Ph: (410)535-2577
Fax: (443)295-7213
Co. E-mail: chart@calvertchamber.org
URL: http://www.calvertchamber.org
Contact: Carolyn McHugh, President
Description: Promotes business and community development in Calvert County, MD. **Founded:** 1982. **Publications:** *The Navigator* (Monthly).

52686 ■ Carroll County Chamber of Commerce (CCCC)
9 E Main St., Ste. 105
Westminster, MD 21157
Ph: (410)848-9050
Fax: (410)876-1023
Co. E-mail: info@carrollcountychamber.org
URL: http://www.carrollcountychamber.org
Contact: Mike McMullin, President
Description: Promotes a sound economic environment and business community development in Carroll County, MD. **Founded:** 1924. **Publications:** *Chamber Works* (Monthly); *Carroll County Chamber of Commerce Membership Directory and Buyers' Guide* (Annual). **Educational Activities:** Carroll County Chamber of Commerce Meeting (Monthly).

52687 ■ Carroll County Chamber of Commerce Membership Directory and Buyers' Guide
9 E Main St., Ste. 105
Westminster, MD 21157
Ph: (410)848-9050
Fax: (410)876-1023
Co. E-mail: info@carrollcountychamber.org
URL: http://www.carrollcountychamber.org
Contact: Mike McMullin, President
Released: Annual **Price:** $50.

52688 ■ The Casey Three Chamber Report
122 N Cross St.
Chestertown, MD 21620
Ph: (410)810-2968

Fax: (410)778-1406
Co. E-mail: kentchamber@verizon.net
URL: http://www.kentchamber.org
Contact: Loretta Lodge, Executive Director
Released: Monthly

52689 ■ Cecil County Chamber of Commerce (CCCC)
106 E Main St., Ste. 101A
Elkton, MD 21921-5780
Ph: (410)392-3833
URL: http://www.cecilchamber.org
Contact: Laura Mayse, Executive Director
Description: Promotes business and community development in Cecil County. **Founded:** 1983. **Publications:** *Chamber Matters* (Monthly); *Outlook.*

52690 ■ The Chamber
28 W Washington St., Ste. 200
Hagerstown, MD 21740
Ph: (301)739-2015
Fax: (301)739-1278
Co. E-mail: chamber@hagerstown.org
URL: http://www.hagerstown.org
Contact: Brien J. Poffenberger, President
Released: Monthly

52691 ■ Chamber of Commerce Business Directory
122 N Cross St.
Chestertown, MD 21620
Ph: (410)810-2968
Fax: (410)778-1406
Co. E-mail: kentchamber@verizon.net
URL: http://www.kentchamber.org
Contact: Loretta Lodge, Executive Director
Released: Annual **Price:** free.

52692 ■ Chamber of Commerce of Frederick County (CCFC)
8420-B Gas House Pike
Frederick, MD 21701-4972
Ph: (301)662-4164
Fax: (301)846-4427
Co. E-mail: radams@frederickchamber.org
URL: http://www.frederickchamber.org/cwt/external/
wcpages/index.aspx
Contact: Richard Adams, President
Description: Promotes business and community development in Frederick County, MD. **Founded:** 1912. **Publications:** *Member Directory* (Periodic).

52693 ■ Chamber Matters
106 E Main St., Ste. 101A
Elkton, MD 21921-5780
Ph: (410)392-3833
URL: http://www.cecilchamber.org
Contact: Laura Mayse, Executive Director
Released: Monthly

52694 ■ Chamber News
49 Old Solomons Island Rd., Ste. 204
Annapolis, MD 21401
Ph: (410)266-3960
Fax: (410)266-8270
Co. E-mail: info@aaaccc.org
URL: http://www.annapolischamber.com
Contact: David Plott, Chairman
Released: Monthly **Price:** free for members.

52695 ■ Chamber News
Bell Tower Bldg.
24 Frederick St.
Cumberland, MD 21502
Ph: (301)722-2820
Fax: (301)722-5995
Co. E-mail: info@alleganycountychamber.com
URL: http://www.alleganycountychamber.com
Contact: Barbara R. Beebe, Chairman
Released: Monthly

52696 ■ Chamber News
528 Poplar St.
Cambridge, MD 21613
Ph: (410)228-3575

Fax: (410)228-6848
Co. E-mail: allen@dorchesterchamber.org
URL: http://www.dorchesterchamber.org
Contact: Allen Nelson, Executive Director
Released: Monthly

52697 ■ Chamber Spotlight
28 W Washington St., Ste. 200
Hagerstown, MD 21740
Ph: (301)739-2015
Fax: (301)739-1278
Co. E-mail: chamber@hagerstown.org
URL: http://www.hagerstown.org
Contact: Brien J. Poffenberger, President
Price: $200, for members.

52698 ■ Chamber Update
44200 Airport Rd.
California, MD 20619
Ph: (301)737-3001
Fax: (301)737-0089
Co. E-mail: info@smcchamber.com
URL: http://www.smcchamber.com
Contact: William Scarafia, President
Released: Monthly

52699 ■ Chamber Voice
108 S Bond St.
Bel Air, MD 21014
Ph: (410)838-2020
Free: 800-682-8536
Fax: (410)893-4715
Co. E-mail: info@harfordchamber.org
URL: http://www.harfordchamber.org
Contact: Vanessa Milio, Chief Executive Officer

52700 ■ Chamber Works
9 E Main St., Ste. 105
Westminster, MD 21157
Ph: (410)848-9050
Fax: (410)876-1023
Co. E-mail: info@carrollcountychamber.org
URL: http://www.carrollcountychamber.org
Contact: Mike McMullin, President
Released: Monthly **Price:** included in membership dues.

52701 ■ Chamber Works
100 Owings Ct., Ste. 9
Reisterstown, MD 21136
Ph: (410)356-2888
Fax: (410)356-5112
Co. E-mail: romg@romgchamber.org
URL: http://www.romgchamber.org
Contact: Brian A. Ditto, Executive Director
Released: Quarterly

52702 ■ ChamberLink
28 W Washington St., Ste. 200
Hagerstown, MD 21740
Ph: (301)739-2015
Fax: (301)739-1278
Co. E-mail: chamber@hagerstown.org
URL: http://www.hagerstown.org
Contact: Brien J. Poffenberger, President
Price: $100, for members.

52703 ■ ChamberNews
7910 Woodmont Ave., Ste. 1204
Bethesda, MD 20814-3015
Ph: (301)652-4900
Fax: (301)657-1973
Co. E-mail: staff@bccchamber.org
URL: http://www.bccchamber.org
Contact: Ginanne M. Italiano, President
Released: Monthly

52704 ■ Charles County Chamber of Commerce
101 Centennial Ave., Ste. A
La Plata, MD 20646-4208
Ph: (301)932-6500

Fax: (301)932-3945
Co. E-mail: info@charlescountychamber.org
URL: http://www.charlescountychamber.org
Contact: Betsy Burian, Executive Director
Description: Promotes business and community development in Charles County, MD. **Founded:** 1956. **Publications:** *Business* (Monthly). **Awards:** Emergency Services Award (Annual); Volunteer of the Year (Annual).

52705 ■ *Corridor Chamber Membership Directory*
312 Marshall Ave., Ste. 104
Laurel, MD 20707-4824
Ph: (301)725-4000
Fax: (301)725-0776
Co. E-mail: bwcc@bwcc.org
URL: http://www.baltwashchamber.org
Contact: H. Walter Townshend, III, President
Released: Annual **Price:** free to members.

52706 ■ *Corridor Chamber News*
312 Marshall Ave., Ste. 104
Laurel, MD 20707-4824
Ph: (301)725-4000
Fax: (301)725-0776
Co. E-mail: bwcc@bwcc.org
URL: http://www.baltwashchamber.org
Contact: H. Walter Townshend, III, President
Released: Semimonthly

52707 ■ Crisfield Area Chamber of Commerce (CACC)
906 W Main St.
Crisfield, MD 21817
Ph: (410)968-2500
Free: 800-782-3913
Fax: (410)968-0524
Co. E-mail: info@crisfieldchamber.com
URL: http://www.crisfieldchamber.com
Contact: Tillie Doyle, President
Description: Promotes business and community development in the Crisfield, MD area. **Founded:** 1975.

52708 ■ Dorchester Chamber of Commerce
528 Poplar St.
Cambridge, MD 21613
Ph: (410)228-3575
Fax: (410)228-6848
Co. E-mail: allen@dorchesterchamber.org
URL: http://www.dorchesterchamber.org
Contact: Allen Nelson, Executive Director
Description: Advocacy organization. Seeks to provide quality leadership and facilitate economic growth through responsive member services, political activity and regional partnerships. **Founded:** 1941. **Publications:** *Chamber News* (Monthly). **Telecommunication Services:** nussear@dorchesterchamber.org; shirleyk@dorchesterchamber.org; patj@dorchesterchamber.org.

52709 ■ *The e-Resource*
4 Professional Dr., Ste. 132
Gaithersburg, MD 20879-3426
Ph: (301)840-1400
Fax: (301)963-3918
Co. E-mail: info@ggchamber.org
URL: http://www.ggchamber.org
Contact: Marilyn Balcombe, President
Released: Monthly

52710 ■ Elkton Chamber and Alliance
101 E Main St.
Elkton, MD 21921-6109
Ph: (410)398-5076
Fax: (410)398-4971
Co. E-mail: info@elktonalliance.org
URL: http://www.elktonalliance.org
Contact: Nelson K. Bolender, Chairman
Description: Promotes business and community development in the Elkton, MD area. **Publications:** *Minutes and Memorandum.*

52711 ■ Essex - Middle River - White Marsh Chamber of Commerce (EMRWMCC)
405 Williams Ct., Ste. 108
Middle River, MD 21220
Ph: (443)317-8763

Fax: (443)317-8772
Co. E-mail: info@emrchamber.org
URL: http://www.emrchamber.org
Contact: Hal Ashman, President
Description: Seeks to promote an economic environment in the Baltimore, MD area and to attract new business while allowing established business to prosper. Works for the enhancement of the quality of life in the region by reinvesting resources in all phases of community life. **Founded:** 1948. **Subscriptions:** audio recordings video recordings. **Publications:** *Shore Line* (Quarterly).

52712 ■ Gaithersburg-Germantown Chamber of Commerce (GGCC)
4 Professional Dr., Ste. 132
Gaithersburg, MD 20879-3426
Ph: (301)840-1400
Fax: (301)963-3918
Co. E-mail: info@ggchamber.org
URL: http://www.ggchamber.org
Contact: Marilyn Balcombe, President
Description: Promotes business and community development in Gaithersburg, Maryland. **Publications:** *The e-Resource* (Monthly). **Telecommunication Services:** mbalcombe@ggchamber.org.

52713 ■ Garrett County Chamber of Commerce
15 Visitors Center Dr.
McHenry, MD 21541
Ph: (301)387-4386
Fax: (301)387-2080
Co. E-mail: info@garrettchamber.com
URL: http://www.visitdeepcreek.com
Contact: Nicole Christian, President
Description: Strives to provide supports for small businesses and the tourism industry.

52714 ■ *Getting Down to Business*
1 Holly Ave.
Severna Park, MD 21146
Ph: (410)647-3900
Fax: (410)647-3999
Co. E-mail: info@severnaparkchamber.com
URL: http://www.severnaparkchamber.com
Contact: Linda S. Zahn, Chief Executive Officer
Released: Monthly

52715 ■ Greater Bethesda-Chevy Chase Chamber of Commerce (GBCCCC)
7910 Woodmont Ave., Ste. 1204
Bethesda, MD 20814-3015
Ph: (301)652-4900
Fax: (301)657-1973
Co. E-mail: staff@bccchamber.org
URL: http://www.bccchamber.org
Contact: Ginanne M. Italiano, President
Description: Promotes business and community development in the Bethesda - Chevy Chase communities within Maryland. **Founded:** 1926. **Publications:** *ChamberNews* (Monthly); *Membership Directory and Business Referral* (Annual).

52716 ■ Greater Bowie Chamber of Commerce (GBCC)
1525 Pointer Ridge Pl., Ste. 302
Bowie, MD 20716
Ph: (301)262-0920
Fax: (301)262-0921
Co. E-mail: info@bowiechamber.org
URL: http://www.bowiechamber.org
Contact: Leonard Lucchi, President
Description: Promotes business and community development in Bowie, MD. **Publications:** *Greater Bowie Chamber of Commerce--Business Directory* (Annual).

52717 ■ Greater Crofton Chamber of Commerce (GCCC)
PO Box 4146
Crofton, MD 21114-4146
Ph: (410)721-9131

Fax: (410)721-0785
Co. E-mail: info@croftonchamber.com
URL: http://www.croftonchamber.com
Contact: Thomas B. Locke, President
Description: Promotes business and community development in Crofton, MD area. **Founded:** 1989. **Publications:** *Business and Community Guide* (Annual).

52718 ■ Greater Severna Park Chamber of Commerce (GSPCC)
1 Holly Ave.
Severna Park, MD 21146
Ph: (410)647-3900
Fax: (410)647-3999
Co. E-mail: info@severnaparkchamber.com
URL: http://www.severnaparkchamber.com
Contact: Linda S. Zahn, Chief Executive Officer
Description: Promotes business and community development in the Severna Park, MD area. **Founded:** 1957. **Publications:** *Business Directory* (Annual); *Getting Down to Business* (Monthly).

52719 ■ Greater Silver Spring Chamber of Commerce (GSSCC)
8601 Georgia Ave., Ste. 203
Silver Spring, MD 20910-3458
Ph: (301)565-3777
Fax: (301)565-3377
Co. E-mail: info@gsscc.org
URL: http://www.silverspringchamber.com
Contact: Jane Redicker, President
Description: Connects Silver Spring business to issues, to leaders and to each other. Members benefit from advocacy efforts, access to information, business development and networking events, members-only marketing opportunities, and business services and discounts, including an energy purchasing cooperative. **Founded:** 1996. **Publications:** *Business E-News* (Quarterly); *Weekly Update* (Weekly); *Business Directory and Buyers' Guide* (Annual). **Awards:** Educator of the Year (Annual); Senior of the Year (Annual); Small Business of the Year (Annual); Volunteer of the Year (Annual).

52720 ■ Hagerstown-Washington County Chamber of Commerce (HWCCC)
28 W Washington St., Ste. 200
Hagerstown, MD 21740
Ph: (301)739-2015
Fax: (301)739-1278
Co. E-mail: chamber@hagerstown.org
URL: http://www.hagerstown.org
Contact: Brien J. Poffenberger, President
Description: Promotes business and community development in Washington County, MD. Conducts legislative activities and promotes leadership development. **Scope:** business, tourism. **Founded:** 1919. **Publications:** *The Chamber* (Monthly); *Chamber Spotlight*; *ChamberLink*; *Washington County Business Directory* (Annual). **Educational Activities:** Cumberland Valley Business Expo (Periodic). **Awards:** Educator of the Year (Annual); Washington County Business Awards (Annual); Chamber Business Person of the Year (Annual); Chamber Business Volunteer of the Year (Annual); Chamber Small Business Person of the Year (Annual).

52721 ■ Harford County Chamber of Commerce (HCCC)
108 S Bond St.
Bel Air, MD 21014
Ph: (410)838-2020
Free: 800-682-8536
Fax: (410)893-4715
Co. E-mail: info@harfordchamber.org
URL: http://www.harfordchamber.org
Contact: Vanessa Milio, Chief Executive Officer
Description: Promotes business and community development in Harford County, MD. Maintains 18 committees. Holds business expos and card exchanges. **Founded:** 1977. **Publications:** *Chamber Voice*; *Spokesman* (Monthly). **Awards:** Harford Awards; Member of the Year/Hall of Fame (Annual).

52722 ■ Havre de Grace Chamber of Commerce
450 Pennington Ave.
Havre de Grace, MD 21078

Ph: (410)939-3303
Fax: (410)939-3490
URL: http://www.hdgchamber.com
Contact: Cathy L. Vincenti, Executive Director
Description: Promotes business and community development in Havre De Grace, MD. **Founded:** 1928.

52723 ■ Howard County Chamber of Commerce
5560 Sterrett Pl., Ste. 105
Columbia, MD 21044-2616
Ph: (410)730-4111
Fax: (410)730-4584
Co. E-mail: info@howardchamber.com
URL: http://www.howardchamber.com
Contact: Pamela J. Klahr, President
Description: Promotes business and community development in Howard County, MD. **Founded:** 1969. **Awards:** Business of the Year (Annual). **Telecommunication Services:** president@howardchamber.com; clay@howardchamber.com.

52724 ■ Kent County Chamber of Commerce (KCCC)
122 N Cross St.
Chestertown, MD 21620
Ph: (410)810-2968
Fax: (410)778-1406
Co. E-mail: kentchamber@verizon.net
URL: http://www.kentchamber.org
Contact: Loretta Lodge, Executive Director
Description: Promotes business and community development in Kent County, MD. **Founded:** 1928. **Publications:** *The Casey Three Chamber Report* (Monthly); *Chamber of Commerce Business Directory* (Annual). **Awards:** Citizenship Award (Periodic); Outstanding Community Service Award (Periodic).

52725 ■ *Know Your Chamber*
Bell Tower Bldg.
24 Frederick St.
Cumberland, MD 21502
Ph: (301)722-2820
Fax: (301)722-5995
Co. E-mail: info@alleganycountychamber.com
URL: http://www.alleganycountychamber.com
Contact: Barbara R. Beebe, Chairman
Price: free.

52726 ■ *Legislative Directory*
60 West St., Ste. 100
Annapolis, MD 21401
Ph: (410)269-0642
Fax: (410)269-5247
Co. E-mail: ksnyder@mdchamber.org
URL: http://www.mdchamber.org
Contact: Kathleen T. Snyder, President
Released: Annual

52727 ■ *Legislative Report*
60 West St., Ste. 100
Annapolis, MD 21401
Ph: (410)269-0642
Fax: (410)269-5247
Co. E-mail: ksnyder@mdchamber.org
URL: http://www.mdchamber.org
Contact: Kathleen T. Snyder, President
Released: Weekly; during session.

52728 ■ Maryland Chamber of Commerce
60 West St., Ste. 100
Annapolis, MD 21401
Ph: (410)269-0642
Fax: (410)269-5247
Co. E-mail: ksnyder@mdchamber.org
URL: http://www.mdchamber.org
Contact: Kathleen T. Snyder, President
Description: Promotes business and community development in the state of Maryland. **Founded:** 1968. **Publications:** *Business Advocate* (Biweekly); *Legislative Directory* (Annual); *Legislative Report* (Weekly); *Maryland Guide to Government*.

52729 ■ *Maryland Guide to Government*
60 West St., Ste. 100
Annapolis, MD 21401
Ph: (410)269-0642

Fax: (410)269-5247
Co. E-mail: ksnyder@mdchamber.org
URL: http://www.mdchamber.org
Contact: Kathleen T. Snyder, President

52730 ■ *Member Directory*
8420-B Gas House Pike
Frederick, MD 21701-4972
Ph: (301)662-4164
Fax: (301)846-4427
Co. E-mail: radams@frederickchamber.org
URL: http://www.frederickchamber.org/cwt/external/wcpages/index.aspx
Contact: Richard Adams, President
Released: Periodic

52731 ■ *Membership Directory and Business Referral*
7910 Woodmont Ave., Ste. 1204
Bethesda, MD 20814-3015
Ph: (301)652-4900
Fax: (301)657-1973
Co. E-mail: staff@bccchamber.org
URL: http://www.bccchamber.org
Contact: Ginanne M. Italiano, President
Released: Annual

52732 ■ *Membership Directory and Community Profile*
Bell Tower Bldg.
24 Frederick St.
Cumberland, MD 21502
Ph: (301)722-2820
Fax: (301)722-5995
Co. E-mail: info@alleganycountychamber.com
URL: http://www.alleganycountychamber.com
Contact: Barbara R. Beebe, Chairman
Price: free.

52733 ■ *Membership Directory and Quality of Life Guide*
4640 Forbes Blvd., Ste. 130
Lanham, MD 20706
Ph: (301)731-5000
Fax: (301)731-5011
Co. E-mail: info@pgcoc.org
URL: http://www.pgcoc.org
Contact: Larry R. Spriggs, Chairman
Released: Annual

52734 ■ *Membership Directory and Resource Guide*
102 W Pennsylvania Ave., Ste. 101
Towson, MD 21204-4526
Ph: (410)825-6200
Fax: (410)821-9901
Co. E-mail: kscott@baltcountychamber.com
URL: http://www.baltcountycc.com
Contact: Keith Scott, President
Released: Periodic

52735 ■ *Minutes and Memorandum*
101 E Main St.
Elkton, MD 21921-6109
Ph: (410)398-5076
Fax: (410)398-4971
Co. E-mail: info@elktonalliance.org
URL: http://www.elktonalliance.org
Contact: Nelson K. Bolender, Chairman

52736 ■ Montgomery County Chamber of Commerce (MCCC)
51 Monroe St., Ste. 1800
Rockville, MD 20850
Ph: (301)738-0015
Fax: (301)738-8792
Co. E-mail: ggodwin@mcccmd.com
URL: http://www.montgomerycountychamber.com
Contact: Georgette Godwin, President
Description: Promotes business and community development in Montgomery County, MD.

52737 ■ *The Navigator*
120 Dares Beach Rd.
Prince Frederick, MD 20678-0009
Ph: (410)535-2577

Fax: (443)295-7213
Co. E-mail: chart@calvertchamber.org
URL: http://www.calvertchamber.org
Contact: Carolyn McHugh, President
Released: Monthly

52738 ■ North East Chamber of Commerce
PO Box 787
North East, MD 21901
Ph: (410)287-5252
Co. E-mail: info@northeastchamber.org
URL: http://www.northeastchamber.org
Contact: Carolyn Crouch, President
Description: Promotes business and community development in North East, MD area.

52739 ■ Northern Anne Arundel County Chamber of Commerce (NAACCC)
7477 Baltimore-Annapolis Blvd.
Glen Burnie, MD 21061
Ph: (410)766-8282
Fax: (410)766-5722
Co. E-mail: info@naaccc.com
URL: http://www.naaccc.com
Contact: Barbara Floyd, President
Description: Works with other community resources to promote local tourism, create jobs, and recruit new businesses in Northern Anne Arundel County, MD area. **Founded:** 1947.

52740 ■ Ocean City Chamber of Commerce
12320 Ocean Gateway
Ocean City, MD 21842
Ph: (410)213-0552
Fax: (410)213-7521
Co. E-mail: info@oceancity.org
URL: http://www.oceancity.org
Contact: Melanie A. Pursel, Executive Director
Description: Works to provide community leadership in fostering and supporting economic development and the continued growth of tourism in Ocean City. **Founded:** 1950. **Publications:** *Voice for Business* (Monthly). **Awards:** Outstanding Citizen Award (Annual).

52741 ■ Ocean Pines Area Chamber of Commerce
11031 Cathell Rd.
Ocean Pines, MD 21811
Ph: (410)641-5306
Fax: (410)641-6176
Co. E-mail: info@oceanpineschamber.org
URL: http://www.oceanpineschamber.org
Contact: Elizabeth Kain, Executive Director
Founded: 1975.

52742 ■ Olney Chamber of Commerce (OCC)
PO Box 550
Olney, MD 20830
Ph: (301)774-7117
Fax: (301)774-4944
URL: http://www.olneymd.org
Contact: Trevor Waddington, President
Description: Promotes business and community development in Montgomery County, MD. Sponsors Community Night. **Scope:** business. **Founded:** 1964. **Subscriptions:** articles. **Awards:** State of Maryland (Annual).

52743 ■ *Outlook*
106 E Main St., Ste. 101A
Elkton, MD 21921-5780
Ph: (410)392-3833
URL: http://www.cecilchamber.org
Contact: Laura Mayse, Executive Director

52744 ■ *Pep Talk*
6 Market St.
Pocomoke City, MD 21851-0356
Ph: (410)957-1919
Co. E-mail: pocomokechamber@gmail.com
URL: http://www.pocomoke.com
Contact: Joshua Nordstrom, President
Released: Quarterly

52745 ■ Pikesville Chamber of Commerce
7 Church Ln., Ste. 14
Pikesville, MD 21208
Ph: (410)484-2337

Fax: (410)484-4151
URL: http://www.pikesvillechamber.org
Contact: David Elkes, President
Description: Strives to maintain the quality of life in both residential and commercial areas, draw new businesses, maintain schools, social and religious institutions and enhance the village Pikesville.

52746 ■ Pocomoke City Chamber of Commerce (PCCC)
6 Market St.
Pocomoke City, MD 21851-0356
Ph: (410)957-1919
Co. E-mail: pocomokechamber@gmail.com
URL: http://www.pocomoke.com
Contact: Joshua Nordstrom, President
Description: Promotes business and community development in Pocomoke City, MD. Sponsors festival, parade, and bowl-a-thons and Great Pocomoke Fair in August. **Founded:** 1952. **Publications:** *Pep Talk* (Quarterly). **Educational Activities:** General Membership (Monthly). **Awards:** Business of the Year (Annual); Business Person of the Year (Annual); Employee of the Year (Annual); Recognize the Best (Annual).

52747 ■ Poolesville Area Chamber of Commerce (PACC)
PO Box 256
Poolesville, MD 20837-0256
Ph: (301)349-5753
Co. E-mail: info@poolesvillechamber.com
URL: http://www.pacc.cc
Contact: Maggie Nightingale, Executive Secretary
Description: Promotes business and community development in Poolesville, MD area. **Founded:** 1979.

52748 ■ Potomac Chamber of Commerce (PCC)
PO Box 59160
Potomac, MD 20859-9160
Ph: (301)299-2170
Fax: (301)983-9828
Co. E-mail: adam@potomacpizza.com
URL: http://potomacchamber.org
Contact: Ms. Adam Greenberg, President
Description: Promotes business and community development in Potomac, MD. **Awards:** Business Person of the Year (Annual); Citizen of the Year (Annual); Youth of the Year (Annual).

52749 ■ Prince George's Chamber of Commerce
4640 Forbes Blvd., Ste. 130
Lanham, MD 20706
Ph: (301)731-5000
Fax: (301)731-5011
Co. E-mail: info@pgcoc.org
URL: http://www.pgcoc.org
Contact: Larry R. Spriggs, Chairman
Description: Promotes business and community development in Prince George's County, MD. **Founded:** 1924. **Publications:** *Membership Directory and Quality of Life Guide* (Annual).

52750 ■ Queen Anne's County Chamber of Commerce (QACCC)
PO Box 511
Chester, MD 21619-0511
Ph: (410)643-8530
Fax: (410)643-8477
Co. E-mail: business@qacchamber.com
URL: http://www.qacchamber.com
Contact: David Thompson, Chairman
Description: Promotes business and community development in Queen Annes County, MD.

52751 ■ Reisterstown - Owings Mills - Glyndon Chamber of Commerce (ROMG)
100 Owings Ct., Ste. 9
Reisterstown, MD 21136
Ph: (410)356-2888

Fax: (410)356-5112
Co. E-mail: romg@romgchamber.org
URL: http://www.romgchamber.org
Contact: Brian A. Ditto, Executive Director
Description: Works to serve as a primary business resource and to promote community development. **Founded:** 1949. **Publications:** *Chamber Works* (Quarterly). **Telecommunication Services:** brian@romgchamber.org.

52752 ■ Rockville Chamber of Commerce (RCC)
1 Research Ct., Ste. 450
Rockville, MD 20850-4165
Ph: (301)424-9300
Fax: (301)762-7599
Co. E-mail: rockville@rockvillechamber.org
URL: http://rockvillechamber.org
Contact: Michael Gottlieb, President
Description: Promotes business and community development in Rockville, MD. **Founded:** 1957.

52753 ■ St. Mary's County Chamber of Commerce (SMCCC)
44200 Airport Rd.
California, MD 20619
Ph: (301)737-3001
Fax: (301)737-0089
Co. E-mail: info@smcchamber.com
URL: http://www.smcchamber.com
Contact: William Scarafia, President
Description: Promotes business and community development in St. Mary's County, MD. **Founded:** 1974. **Publications:** *Chamber Update* (Monthly); *Business and Community Services Directory* (Annual).

52754 ■ Salisbury Area Chamber of Commerce (SACC)
144 E Main St.
Salisbury, MD 21801
Ph: (410)749-0144
Fax: (410)860-9925
Co. E-mail: chamber@salisburyarea.com
URL: http://www.salisburyarea.com
Contact: Bradley A. Bellacicco, Executive Director
Description: Promotes business and community development in Salisbury, MD. **Founded:** 1920. **Publications:** *Business Journal* (Monthly).

52755 ■ *Shore Line*
405 Williams Ct., Ste. 108
Middle River, MD 21220
Ph: (443)317-8763
Fax: (443)317-8772
Co. E-mail: info@emrchamber.org
URL: http://www.emrchamber.org
Contact: Hal Ashman, President
Released: Quarterly

52756 ■ Snow Hill Chamber of Commerce (SHCC)
PO Box 176
Snow Hill, MD 21863
Ph: (410)632-0809
URL: http://www.atbeach.com/cities/snowhill/snow-comm.asp
Description: Promotes business and community development in Snow Hill, MD.

52757 ■ *Sound Business*
102 W Pennsylvania Ave., Ste. 101
Towson, MD 21204-4526
Ph: (410)825-6200
Fax: (410)821-9901
Co. E-mail: kscott@baltcountychamber.com
URL: http://www.baltcountycc.com
Contact: Keith Scott, President
Released: Quarterly

52758 ■ *Spokesman*
108 S Bond St.
Bel Air, MD 21014
Ph: (410)838-2020
Free: 800-682-8536

Fax: (410)893-4715
Co. E-mail: info@harfordchamber.org
URL: http://www.harfordchamber.org
Contact: Vanessa Milio, Chief Executive Officer
Released: Monthly

52759 ■ *Voice for Business*
12320 Ocean Gateway
Ocean City, MD 21842
Ph: (410)213-0552
Fax: (410)213-7521
Co. E-mail: info@oceancity.org
URL: http://www.oceancity.org
Contact: Melanie A. Pursel, Executive Director
Released: Monthly

52760 ■ *Washington County Business Directory*
28 W Washington St., Ste. 200
Hagerstown, MD 21740
Ph: (301)739-2015
Fax: (301)739-1278
Co. E-mail: chamber@hagerstown.org
URL: http://www.hagerstown.org
Contact: Brien J. Poffenberger, President
Released: Annual **Price:** free.

52761 ■ *Weekly Update*
8601 Georgia Ave., Ste. 203
Silver Spring, MD 20910-3458
Ph: (301)565-3777
Fax: (301)565-3377
Co. E-mail: info@gsscc.org
URL: http://www.silverspringchamber.com
Contact: Jane Redicker, President
Released: Weekly

52762 ■ West Anne Arundel County Chamber of Commerce (WAACCC)
8373 Piney Orchard Pkwy., Ste. 200
Odenton, MD 21113
Ph: (410)672-3422
Fax: (410)672-3475
Co. E-mail: info@westcountychamber.org
URL: http://www.waaccc.org
Contact: Ms. Claire Louder, President
Description: Promotes business and community development in West Anne Arundel County, MD. **Founded:** 1962. **Publications:** *Business Directory and Community Resource Guide* (Annual); *Business Exchange* (Monthly); *Business Directory and Community Resource Guide* (Annual). **Educational Activities:** West Anne Arundel County Chamber of Commerce Meeting (Annual). **Awards:** Celebrate Community Awards (Annual).

MINORITY BUSINESS ASSISTANCE PROGRAMS

52763 ■ The Center for Minority Business Development - Prince George's Community College
301 Largo Rd., CAT-135
Largo, MD 20774-2199
Ph: (301)583-5205
URL: http://www.cmbd.biz
Contact: Carl E. Brown, Executive Director
Description: Provides business development, educational programs, assessment tools, counseling, and mentoring programs to local minority businesses.

52764 ■ Mayor's Office of Baltimore - Minority & Women-Owned Business Development
City Hall, Rm. 334
Baltimore, MD 21202
Ph: (410)396-3818
Fax: (410)528-1671
Co. E-mail: mombd@baltimorecity.gov
URL: http://www.baltimorecity.gov
Description: Works to improve the opportunites for minority and women-owned businesses to do business with the city of Baltimore.

52765 ■ Women Entrepreneurs of Baltimore Inc.
1118 Light St., Ste. 101
Baltimore, MD 21230
Ph: (410)727-4921
Co. E-mail: jsaltzberg@webinc.org
URL: http://www.webinc.org
Contact: Joanne Saltzberg, Chief Executive Officer
Description: Offers business training and support programs to help women start their own businesses. Primarily serves lower-income women and the unemployed.

FINANCING AND LOAN PROGRAMS

52766 ■ Abell Venture Fund
111 S. Calvert St., Ste. 2300
Baltimore, MD 21202-6164
Ph: (410)547-1300
Fax: (410)539-6579
Co. E-mail: abell@abell.org
URL: http://www.abell.org/abellinvestments
Contact: Robert C. Embry, Jr., President
E-mail: embry@abell.org
Preferred Investment Size: $200,000 to $3,000,000. **Investment Policies:** Early stage and expansion. **Industry Preferences:** Internet specific, semiconductors and other electronics, communications and media, computer software and services, industrial and energy and medical and health. **Geographic Preference:** Maryland.

52767 ■ ABS Ventures
950 Winter St., Ste. 2600
Waltham, MA 02451
Ph: (781)250-0400
Fax: (781)250-0345
Co. E-mail: abs@absventures.com
URL: http://www.absventures.com
Contact: Scott Yaphe, Partner
Preferred Investment Size: $5,000,000 to $15,000,000. **Investment Policies:** Early and later stage, fund of funds, expansion, recapitalization, and special situation. **Industry Preferences:** Computer software and services, medical and health, communications and media, Internet specific, computer hardware, biotechnology, other products, industrial and energy, consumer related, semiconductors and other electronics. **Geographic Preference:** U.S.

52768 ■ Anthem Capital Management LLC
1448 South Rolling Rd., Ste. 200
Baltimore, MD 21227
Ph: (410)625-1510
Fax: (410)625-1735
URL: http://www.anthemcapital.com
Contact: Bill Gust, Partner
E-mail: wgust@anthemcapital.com
Preferred Investment Size: $1,000,000 to $2,000,000. **Industry Preferences:** Computer software and services, Internet specific, biotechnology, industrial and energy, medical and health, communications and media, and other products. **Geographic Preference:** Mid Atlantic.

52769 ■ Boulder Ventures, Ltd.
5425 Wisconsin Ave., Ste. 704
Chevy Chase, MD 20815
Ph: (301)913-0213
Fax: (301)913-0434
URL: http://www.boulderventures.com
Contact: Andrew Jones, Partner
E-mail: andy@boulderventures.com
Preferred Investment Size: $5,000,000 to $10,000,000. **Industry Preferences:** Communications and media, Internet specific, computer software and services, consumer related, semiconductors and other electronics, other products, consumer related, biotechnology, and medical and health. **Geographic Preference:** Colorado and Mid Atlantic.

52770 ■ Catalyst Ventures
1119 St. Paul St.
Baltimore, MD 21202
Ph: (410)244-0123

Fax: (410)752-7721
Co. E-mail: info@catalystventures.com
URL: http://www.catalystventures.com
Preferred Investment Size: $500,000 maximum. **Investment Policies:** Equity. **Industry Preferences:** Data communications, biotechnology, and medical related. **Geographic Preference:** Middle Atlantic.

52771 ■ Grotech Capital Group
230 Schilling Cir., Ste. 362
Hunt Valley, MD 21031
Ph: (703)637-9555
Fax: (410)527-1307
URL: http://www.grotech.com
Contact: Frank Adams, Partner
E-mail: fadams@grotech.com
Preferred Investment Size: $500,000 to $5,000,000. **Industry Preferences:** Internet specific, consumer related, communications and media, other products, computer software, and services, and semiconductors and other electronics, and other products. **Geographic Preference:** Southeast and Mid Atlantic.

52772 ■ Kinetic Ventures LLC
2 Wisconsin Cir., Ste. 620
Chevy Chase, MD 20815-7046
Ph: (301)652-8066
Fax: (301)652-8310
Co. E-mail: kinetic@kineticventures.com
URL: http://www.kineticventures.com
Contact: Nelson Chu, Principal
Preferred Investment Size: $2,000,000 to $7,000,000. **Industry Preferences:** Internet specific, communications and media, computer software and services, industrial and energy, semiconductors and other electronics, and computer hardware. **Geographic Preference:** U.S.

52773 ■ Maryland Venture Capital Trust
401 E. Pratt St.
Baltimore, MD 21202
Ph: (410)767-6300
Free: 888-ChooseMD
URL: http://www.choosemaryland.org
Contact: Elizabeth Good, Managing Director
Industry Preferences: Medical and health, computer software and services, other products, industrial and energy, semiconductors and other electronics, consumer related, biotechnology, and computer hardware. **Geographic Preference:** Maryland.

52774 ■ New Enterprise Associates (Chevy Chase)
5425 Wisconsin Ave., Ste. 800
Chevy Chase, MD 20815
Ph: (301)272-2300
Fax: (301)272-1700
URL: http://www.nea.com
Contact: Peter Barris, Partner
E-mail: pbarris@nea.com
Preferred Investment Size: $200,000 to $20,000,000. **Industry Preferences:** Communications and media, Internet specific, medical and health, computer software and services, semiconductors and other electronics, biotechnology, computer hardware, other products, consumer related, industrial and energy. **Geographic Preference:** U.S.

52775 ■ Novak Biddle Venture Partners, L.P.
7501 Wisconsin Ave., Ste. 1380-E
Bethesda, MD 20814
Ph: (240)497-1910
Fax: (240)223-0255
Co. E-mail: info@novakbiddle.com
URL: http://www.novakbiddle.com
Contact: E. Rogers Novak, Jr., Partner
Preferred Investment Size: $100,000 to $10,000,000. **Industry Preferences:** Internet specific, communications and media, computer software and services, semiconductors and other electronics, computer hardware, other products, and medical and health. **Geographic Preference:** Mid Atlantic, Northeast, and Southeast.

52776 ■ Spring Capital Partners, L.P.
Latrobe Bldg., 5th Fl.
2 E. Read St.
Baltimore, MD 21202
Ph: (410)685-8000

Fax: (410)545-0015
Co. E-mail: mailbox@springcap.com
URL: http://www.springcap.com
Contact: Michael F. Donoghue, Partner
E-mail: mfd@springcap.com
Preferred Investment Size: $2,000,000 to $7,000,000. **Industry Preferences:** Communications and media, computer related, semiconductors and other electronics, medical and health, consumer related, industrial and energy, transportation, and manufacturing. **Geographic Preference:** Eastern half of U.S.

52777 ■ Sterling Partners
650 S. Exeter St., Ste. 1000
Baltimore, MD 21202
Ph: (443)703-1700
Fax: (443)703-1750
URL: http://www.sterlingcap.com
Contact: Eric D. Becker, Managing Director
Preferred Investment Size: Up to $200,000,000. **Industry Preferences:** Communications and media, computer software, medical and health, consumer related, business service, and manufacturing. **Geographic Preference:** Mid Atlantic and Midwest.

52778 ■ T. Rowe Price Threshold Partnerships
100 E. Pratt St.
Baltimore, MD 21202
Ph: (410)345-2000
Free: 800-638-7890
Fax: (410)345-2349
Co. E-mail: usintitinquiries@troweprice.com
URL: http://www.troweprice.com
Preferred Investment Size: $3,000,000 to $5,000,000. **Industry Preferences:** Computer software and services, Internet specific, consumer related, medical and health, other products, semiconductors and other electronics, communications and media, industrial and energy, biotechnology, and other products. **Geographic Preference:** U.S.

52779 ■ Toucan Capital
4800 Montgomery Ln., Ste. 801
Bethesda, MD 20814
Ph: (240)497-4060
Fax: (240)497-4065
Co. E-mail: info@toucancapital.com
URL: http://www.toucancapital.com
Contact: Linda Powers, Managing Director
Preferred Investment Size: $100,000 to $5,000,000. **Industry Preferences:** Biotechnology, industrial and energy. **Geographic Preference:** Mid Atlantic and Northeast.

52780 ■ Walker Ventures SBIC / Walker Ventures
3060 Washington Rd., Ste. 200
Glenwood, MD 21738
Ph: (301)854-6850
Fax: (301)854-6235
Co. E-mail: plans@walkerventures.com
URL: http://www.walkerventures.com
Contact: Rusty Griffith, Principal
Preferred Investment Size: $250,000 to $3,000,000. **Industry Preferences:** Internet specific, computer software and services, communications and media, other products, and semiconductors and other electronics. **Geographic Preference:** Mid Atlantic.

PROCUREMENT ASSISTANCE PROGRAMS

52781 ■ Maryland Department of Business and Economic Development Center - Administration Division - Contracts and Procurement Office
401 E Pratt St.
Baltimore, MD 21202
Ph: (410)767-2211
Fax: (410)767-2216
Co. E-mail: dchronister@mdchoosemaryland.org
URL: http://www.choosemaryland.org
Contact: Debi Chronister, Director

52782 ■ Maryland Procurement Technical Assistance Center
7100 Baltimore Ave., Ste. 402
College Park, MD 20740
Ph: (301)403-2740
Fax: (301)403-2743
Co. E-mail: admin@mdptap.umd.edu
URL: http://www.mdptap.umd.edu
Contact: Mary Lee Kolich, Program Director
E-mail: mkolich@mdptap.umd.edu
Description: Provides marketing, contractual and technical assistance to Maryland small business owners who are interested in marketing their products and services to federal, state and local government agencies.

52783 ■ Office of Government Contacting
National Aeronautics and Space Administration
Goddard Space Flight Center
Bldg. 8, Code 210
Greenbelt, MD 20771
Ph: (301)286-4378
Fax: (202)481-0427
Co. E-mail: bernard.a.durham.1@gfsc.nasa.gov
URL: http://www.sba.gov
Contact: Bernard Durham, Representative
E-mail: bkilyk@pop200.gsfc.nasa.gov
Description: Covers activities for NASA, Goddard Space Flight Center (Greenbelt, MD), NASA Headquarters (Washington, DC), LABCOM Adelphi Lab Center (Adelphi, MD), and Navy Surface Warfare Center (Indian Head, MD).

52784 ■ Regional Contracting Assistance Center - Ranson
322 W Washington St., Ste. 3
Charles Town, WV 25414
Ph: (304)724-7547
Fax: (304)724-7547
Co. E-mail: ctodd@rcacwv.com
URL: http://www.rcacwv.com
Contact: Christine Todd, Specialist
Description: Serves as a clearinghouse for information on contracting/subcontracting opportunities, and as a source for technical resources, information, and training. Offers an electronic bid match, access to government and industry regulations and standards, past procurement histories, technical assistance in understanding bid and contract requirements, assistance in bid proposal preparation, training in various aspects of contracting, and assistance in understanding contract pricing, packaging, and administration.

INCUBATORS/RESEARCH AND TECHNOLOGY PARKS

52785 ■ bwTech@UMBC Research and Technology Park
5523 Research Park Dr., Ste. 310
Baltimore, MD 21228
Ph: (410)455-5900
Fax: (410)455-5901
Co. E-mail: bwtech@umbc.edu
URL: http://www.bwtechumbc.com
Description: A small business incubator supporting technology by providing business development mentoring and assistance, as well as introductions to UMBC researchers and students for early-stage, start-up companies.

52786 ■ Emerging Technology Centers
Factory Bldg., 3rd Fl.
2400 Boston St.
Baltimore, MD 21224
Ph: (410)327-9150
Fax: (410)327-4086
URL: http://www.etcbaltimore.com/contact.html
Description: A non-profit business incubator program focused on growing early-stage technology and bio-technology companies in Baltimore City. It offers fully wired offices and space for participating companies at below market rates, with flexible leases, shared basic services and equipment, tech support, and on-site management.

52787 ■ Frederick Innovative Technology Center
4539 Metropolitan Ct.
Frederick, MD 21704
Ph: (301)694-2999
Fax: (301)360-3554
Co. E-mail: info@fitci.org
URL: http://www.fitci.org/
Description: A small business incubator offering local entrepreneurs facilities, services, and an environment in which they can prosper.

52788 ■ Garrett Information Enterprise Center
685 Mosser Rd., Ste. 1
McHenry, MD 21541
Ph: (301)387-3167
Fax: (301)387-3140
Co. E-mail: Lydia.reiser@garrettcollege.edu
URL: http://www.giecworks.com/
Contact: Lydia G. Reiser, Director
Description: A small business incubator whose goal it is to increase new firms' chances of survival during the early, risky years by providing a low-cost, supportive environment, and a network of assistance that will enable young firms to grow.

52789 ■ Maryland Technology Enterprise Institute
University of Maryland
2120 Potomac Bldg. 092
College Park, MD 20742
Ph: (301)405-3906
Free: 800-245-5810
Fax: (301)403-4105
URL: http://www.mtech.umd.edu
Description: Assists in problem identification, provides support, and formulates solutions. Also performs information searches. Reviews and critiques new ideas, products, and designs.

52790 ■ Montgomery County Department of Economic Development - Business Innovation Network
101 Monroe St., 2nd Fl.
Rockville, MD 20850
Ph: (240)777-2000
Fax: (240)777-2046
Co. E-mail: ded.info@montgomerycountymd.gov
URL: http://www.mcinnovationnetwork.com
Description: A small business incubator and accelerator offering fertile ground for innovations in bioscience, information technology, education, and the arts. Its goal is to nurture and grow young, enterprising businesses into smart and successful companies through its Business Innovation Network.

52791 ■ Mtech Technology Advancement Program
387 Technology Dr., Ste. 1105
College Park, MD 20742
Ph: (301)405-3809
Fax: (301)226-5378
Co. E-mail: smagids@umd.edu
URL: http://www.tap.umd.edu/
Contact: Dean Chang, Director
Description: Mtech TAP is a program of the Engineering Research Center utilizing the extensive resources of the University of Maryland at College Park.

52792 ■ Rockville Innovation Center
95 Monroe St.
Rockville, MD 20850
Ph: (301)315-8096
Fax: (301)315-8097
Co. E-mail: Info@RockvilleREDI.org
URL: http://www.rockvilleredi.org/business/incubator.html
Description: A small business incubator providing space and support for approximately 30 start-up technology companies to grow.

52793 ■ The Rural Development Center
University of Maryland, Eastern Shore
Richard E. Henson Center, Rm. 2147
Princess Anne, MD 21853
Ph: (410)651-6186

Fax: (410)651-6207
Co. E-mail: dskuennen@mail.umes.edu
URL: http://www.skipjack.net/le_shore/rural/
Contact: Daniel Kuennen, Director
Description: The RDC is a community-based incubator serving the needs of people in rural communities. It is located on the campus of the University of Maryland Eastern Shore.

52794 ■ Technical Innovation Center
Hagerstown Community College
11400 Robinwood Dr., Ste. 321
Hagerstown, MD 21742
Ph: (301)790-2800
Fax: (301)797-4808
Co. E-mail: marschnerc@hagerstowncc.edu
URL: http://www.technicalinnovationcenter.com/
Description: A self-sustaining economic development effort fostering the growth of new and expanding businesses by providing access to advanced technologies, business development resources, and collaborative opportunities.

52795 ■ TowsonGlobal - International Incubator
Townson University Business Globalization Center
7801 York Rd., Ste. 342
Towson, MD 21204
Ph: (410)769-6449
Fax: (410)769-6477
Co. E-mail: info@twonsonglobal.com
URL: http://www.townsonglobal.com/dotnetnuke/
Description: An international incubator for early-stage serving as a gateway to international markets for product-oriented Maryland companies and as a magnet for foreign companies looking to market their products in the mid-Atlantic region. It will offer workshops and resources to companies in the greater business community to help them compete in a global marketplace.

52796 ■ Wheaton Business Innovation Center
Montgomery County Business Incubator Network
Wheaton South Bldg.
11002 Veirs Mill Rd., 7th Fl.
Wheaton, MD 20902
Ph: (301)942-4005
Fax: (301)942-4493
Co. E-mail: john.korpela@montgomerycountymd.gov
URL: http://www.montgomerycountymd.gov/content/ded/incub/pdf/wbic.pdf
Contact: John Korpela, Manager
Description: A small business incubator created for current, locally-based business service, government contracting, and/or professional trade businesses looking to grow.

EDUCATIONAL PROGRAMS

52797 ■ University of Baltimore - Merrick School of Business
1420 N Charles St.
Baltimore, MD 21201
Ph: (410)837-4200
Fax: (410)837-5652
Co. E-mail: admissions@ubalt.edu
URL: http://www.ubalt.edu
Description: Undergraduate and graduate business courses, institutes, and conferences are offered in flexible evening and weekend schedules. Programs are designed for persons already in positions of executive responsibility, as well as for those about to enter into managerial positions.

PUBLICATIONS

52798 ■ *Baltimore Business Journal*
111 Market Place, Ste. 720
Baltimore, MD 21202
Ph: (410)576-1161
Fax: (410)752-3112
URL: http://www.bizjournals.com/baltimore/

52799 ■ *Smart Start your Maryland Business*
PSI Research
300 N. Valley Dr.
Grants Pass, OR 97526
Ph: (503)479-9464
Free: 800-228-2275
Fax: (503)476-1479
Co. E-mail: info@psi-research.com
URL: http://www.psi-research.com
Ed: Michael D. Jenkins. **Released:** Revised edition, 1992. **Price:** $29.95 (looseleaf binder); $24.95 (paper). **Description:** Part of the Successful Business Library series.

PUBLISHERS

52800 ■ **Michael Edmond Gray—Rolling Hills Publishing**
242 Eagle Flight
Ozark, MO 65721-7868
Ph: (800)918-7323
Free: 800-918-7323
Fax: (888)329-2747
Co. E-mail: info@rollinghillspublishing.com
URL: http://www.rollinghillspublishing.com
Contact: Michael Gray, Owner
Description: Description: Publishes educational, automobiles. **Founded:** 2003.

52801 ■ **Schreiber Publishing Inc.**
51 Monroe St., Ste. 101
Rockville, MD 20850-2420
Ph: (301)424-7737
Free: 800-822-3213
Fax: (301)424-2336
Co. E-mail: books@schreiberpublishing.com
URL: http://www.schreiberpublishing.com
Contact: Yohanan Manor, Editor
Description: Description: Publishes language and translation books and books relating to art, the Holocaust, history and children. Publishes reference books and fiction books. Accepts unsolicited manuscripts. Reaches market through commission reps, direct mail, reviews, listings, telephone sales as well as distributors. **Founded:** 1994.

SMALL BUSINESS DEVELOPMENT CENTER LEAD OFFICE

52802 ■ University of Massachusetts - Small Business Development Center
227 Isenberg School of Management
121 President's Dr.
Amherst, MA 01003-4935
Ph: (413)545-6301
Fax: (413)545-1273
Co. E-mail: gep@msbdc.umass.edu
URL: http://www.msbdc.org/
Contact: Georgianna Parkin, Director
Description: Provides one-to-one free comprehensive and confidential services focusing on, business growth and strategies, financing and loan assistance as well as strategic, marketing and operational analysis.

SMALL BUSINESS DEVELOPMENT CENTERS

52803 ■ Central Massachusetts Small Business Development Center
950 Main St.
Worcester, MA 01610
Ph: (508)793-7615
Fax: (508)793-8890
Co. E-mail: sbdc@clarku.edu
URL: http://www.clarku.edu/offices/sbdc
Contact: John Rainey, Regional Director
URL(s): www.msbdc.org. **Description:** Represents and promotes the small business sector. Provides management assistance to current and prospective small business owners. Helps to improve management skills and expand the products and services of members.

52804 ■ Massachusetts Small Business Development Center - Berkshire
75 North St., Ste. 360
Pittsfield, MA 01201
Ph: (413)499-0933
Fax: (413)499-3005
Co. E-mail: info@msbdc.umass.edu
URL: http://www.msbdc.org/berkshire
Contact: Keith Girouard, Regional Director
Description: Represents and promotes the small business sector. Provides management assistance to current and prospective small business owners. Helps to improve management skills and expand the products and services of members.

52805 ■ Massachusetts Small Business Development Center Network - Western
Scibelli Enterprise Center
Bldg. 101R
1 Federal St.
Springfield, MA 01105
Ph: (413)737-6712

Fax: (413)737-2312
Co. E-mail: ddoherty@msbdc.umass.edu
URL: http://www.msbdc.org/wmass
Contact: Dianne Fuller Doherty, Director
Description: Represents and promotes the small business sector. Provides management assistance to current and prospective small business owners. Helps to improve management skills and expand the products and services of members.

52806 ■ Massachusetts Small Business Development Center - Northeast
Enterprise Center
121 Loring Ave., Ste. 310
Salem, MA 01970
Ph: (978)542-6343
Fax: (978)542-6345
Co. E-mail: msomer@salemstate.edu
URL: http://sbdc.salemstate.edu
Contact: Margaret Somer, Director
Description: Represents and promotes the small business sector. Provides management assistance to current and prospective small business owners. Helps to improve management skills and expand the products and services of members.

52807 ■ Southeastern Massachusetts Regional Small Business Development Center
200 Pocasset St.
Fall River, MA 02721
Ph: (508)673-9783
Fax: (508)674-1929
Co. E-mail: mlailes@msbdc.umass.edu
URL: http://www.msbdc.org/semass
Contact: Melinda Ailes, Director
Description: Represents and promotes the small business sector. Provides management assistance to current and prospective small business owners. Helps to improve management skills and expand the products and services of members. **Founded:** 1982.

52808 ■ Springfield Business Development Corporation (SBDC)
PO Box 15288
Springfield, MA 01115
Ph: (413)781-1591
Fax: (413)781-1595
Co. E-mail: info@developspringfield.com
URL: http://developspringfield.com
Description: Seeks to promote business through economic and community development. Assists businesses in their expansion and financing needs. Enhances the quality of life and fosters the growth of good jobs within the community.

SMALL BUSINESS ASSISTANCE PROGRAMS

52809 ■ Massachusetts Export Center
State Transportation Bldg.
10 Park Plaza, Ste. 4510
Boston, MA 02116
Ph: (617)973-8664

Fax: (617)973-8681
Co. E-mail: pmurphy@state.ma.us
URL: http://www.mass.gov/export
Contact: Paula Murphy, Director
Description: Provides assistance in market analysis, training, advice on export practices and financing for participation in foreign trade missions, export counseling, and market research. Also identifies foreign contacts for exporting firms and organizes and conducts trade events.

52810 ■ Massachusetts Office of Housing and Economic Development
1 Ashburton Pl., Ste. 2101
Boston, MA 02108
Ph: (617)788-3610
Free: 800-CAPITAL
Fax: (617)788-3605
URL: http://www.mass.gov
Contact: Tina Brooks, Section Chief
Description: Provides assistance and information on relocating and expanding businesses in Massachusetts.

52811 ■ Massachusetts Office of International Trade and Investment
Boston Fish Pier
East Bldg. 1, Ste. 300
212 Northern Ave.
Boston, MA 02210
Ph: (617)973-8650
Fax: (617)227-3488
Co. E-mail: ted.carr@state.ma.us
URL: http://www.mass.gov/moiti
Contact: Ted Carr, Executive Director
Description: Oversees the state's international trade activities. Also monitors the degree of foreign investment in Massachusetts.

SCORE OFFICES

52812 ■ SCORE Agawam

52813 ■ SCORE Amherst
Co. E-mail: info@amherstarea.com

52814 ■ SCORE Boston
Thomas P. O'Neill Federal Bldg.
10 Causeway St., Rm. 265
Boston, MA 02222-1093
Ph: (617)565-5591
Co. E-mail: boston-score-20@verizon.net
URL: http://www.scoreboston.org
Contact: Rodrigo Lopez, Membership Chairperson
Description: Serves as volunteer program in which working and retired business management professionals provide free business counseling to men and women who are considering starting a small business, encountering problems with their business, or expanding their business. Offers free one-on-one counseling, online counseling and low cost workshops on a variety of business topics.

52815 ■ SCORE Cape Cod
270 Communications Way, Ste. 5-B
Hyannis, MA 02601

Ph: (508)775-4884
Fax: (508)790-2540
Co. E-mail: capecodscore@verizon.net
URL: http://www.scorecapecod.com
Description: Serves as volunteer program in which working and retired business management professionals provide free business counseling to men and women who are considering starting a small business, encountering problems with their business, or expanding their business. Offers free one-on-one counseling, online counseling and low cost workshops on a variety of business topics. **Telecommunication Services:** mvscore@verizon.net.

52816 ■ SCORE Greenfield
Co. E-mail: score@franklincc.org

52817 ■ SCORE Northampton

52818 ■ SCORE Northeast Massachusetts
39 Dodge St., Ste. 318
Beverly, MA 01915
Ph: (978)922-9441
Co. E-mail: info@scorenemass.org
URL: http://www.scorenemass.org
Description: Serves as volunteer program in which working and retired business management professionals provide free business counseling to men and women who are considering starting a small business, encountering problems with their business, or expanding their business. Offers free one-on-one counseling, online counseling and low cost workshops on a variety of business topics.

52819 ■ SCORE Pittsfield
Co. E-mail: info@berkshirechamber.com

52820 ■ SCORE Southeastern Massachusetts
60 School St.
Brockton, MA 02301
Ph: (508)587-2673
URL: http://www.scoresema.org
Description: Serves as volunteer program in which working and retired business management professionals provide free business counseling to men and women who are considering starting a small business, encountering problems with their business, or expanding their business. Offers free one-on-one counseling, online counseling and low cost workshops on a variety of business topics. **Founded:** 1978.

52821 ■ SCORE Springfield
Co. E-mail: score@stcc.edu

52822 ■ SCORE Westfield
Co. E-mail: lynn@westfieldbiz.org

52823 ■ SCORE Worcester
c/o Worcester Regional Chamber of Commerce
446 Main St.
Worcester, MA 01608
Ph: (508)753-2929
Co. E-mail: info@scoreworcester.org
URL: http://worcester.score.org
Description: Works to facilitate the formation, success and growth of small business. Provides free, confidential business counseling to individuals just starting a business and to existing small businesses. Offers low cost educational workshops on business topics.

BETTER BUSINESS BUREAUS

52824 ■ Better Business Bureau of Central New England (BBB)
340 Main St., Ste. 802
Worcester, MA 01608
Ph: (508)755-3340
Free: 866-566-1323
Fax: (508)754-4158
Co. E-mail: info@cne.bbb.org
URL: http://central-westernma.bbb.org
Contact: Nancy B. Cahalen, President
Description: Seeks to promote and foster the highest ethical relationship between businesses and the public through voluntary self-regulation, consumer and business education, and service excellence. Provides information to help consumers and businesses make informed purchasing decisions and

avoid costly scams and frauds; settles consumer complaints through arbitration and other means. **Founded:** 1942. **Awards:** Torch Award for Marketplace Ethics (Annual).

52825 ■ Better Business Bureau Serving Eastern Massachusetts, Maine and Vermont
235 W Central St., Ste. 1
Natick, MA 01760-3767
Ph: (508)652-4800
Free: 800-4BB-B811
Fax: (508)652-4820
Co. E-mail: info@bosbbb.org
URL: http://boston.bbb.org
Contact: Mr. Kevin J. Sanders, President
Description: Fosters and promotes the highest ethical relationship between businesses and the public through voluntary self-regulation, consumer and business education, and service excellence. **Founded:** 1921. **Telecommunication Services:** president@boston.bbb.org.

CHAMBERS OF COMMERCE

52826 ■ AdvantageNews
Released: Bimonthly

52827 ■ Affiliated Chambers of Commerce of Greater Springfield (ACCGS)
1441 Main St., Ste. 136
Springfield, MA 01103-1449
Ph: (413)787-1555
Fax: (413)731-8530
Co. E-mail: ciuffreda@myonlinechamber.com
URL: http://www.myonlinechamber.com
Contact: Jeffrey Ciuffreda, President
Description: Promotes, supports and enhances the economic health of the business community and the region.

52828 ■ Alliance for Amesbury
5 Market Sq.
Amesbury, MA 01913
Ph: (978)388-3178
Fax: (978)388-4952
Co. E-mail: steffiemccowan@verizon.net
URL: http://www.amesburychamber.com
Contact: Stefanie McCowan, Executive Director
Description: Aims to maintain working partnership between public officials, the business community and the citizens of Amesbury. Promotes business and community development in the area.

52829 ■ Alliance Newsletter
182 Main St.
Watertown, MA 02471
Ph: (617)926-1017
Fax: (617)926-2322
Co. E-mail: info@wbcc.org
URL: http://www.wbcc.org/home/index.html
Contact: Robert Airasian, President

52830 ■ Amherst Area Chamber of Commerce
28 Amity St.
Amherst, MA 01002
Ph: (413)253-0700
Fax: (413)256-0771
Co. E-mail: info@amherstarea.com
URL: http://www.amherstarea.com
Contact: Tony Maroulis, Executive Director
Description: Promotes business and community development in Amherst, MA. **Scope:** business. **Founded:** 1956. **Subscriptions:** 150 books. **Publications:** Community Beacon (Monthly). **Awards:** Millicent Kauffman Distinguished Service Award (Annual).

52831 ■ Anchor News
PO Box 68
Hanover, MA 02339-0068
Ph: (781)826-8865
Fax: (781)826-7721
Co. E-mail: chamber@hanovermachamber.com
URL: http://www.hanovermachamber.com
Contact: Cathy Follett, President
Released: Monthly **Price:** included in membership dues.

52832 ■ Annual Directory and Guidebook
20 Academy Ln.
Falmouth, MA 02540
Ph: (508)548-8500
Free: 800-526-8532
Fax: (508)548-8521
Co. E-mail: info@falmouthchamber.com
URL: http://www.falmouthchamber.com
Contact: Jay Zavala, President
Released: Annual

52833 ■ Arlington Advocate
611 Massachusetts Ave.
Arlington, MA 02474
Ph: (781)643-4600
Fax: (781)646-5581
Co. E-mail: info@arlcc.org
URL: http://www.arlcc.org
Contact: Jennifer Tripp, Manager
Released: Periodic

52834 ■ Arlington Chamber of Commerce (ACC)
611 Massachusetts Ave.
Arlington, MA 02474
Ph: (781)643-4600
Fax: (781)646-5581
Co. E-mail: info@arlcc.org
URL: http://www.arlcc.org
Contact: Jennifer Tripp, Manager
Description: Promotes business and community development in Arlington, MA. **Founded:** 1916. **Publications:** Arlington Advocate (Periodic).

52835 ■ Assabet Valley Chamber of Commerce
18 Church St.
Hudson, MA 01749
Ph: (978)568-0360
Fax: (978)562-4118
Co. E-mail: info@assabetvalleychamber.org
URL: http://www.assabetvalleychamber.org
Contact: Sarah B. Cressy, President
URL(s): assabetvalleychamber.org. **Description:** Promotes business and community development in Hudson, Maynard, Stow, Bolton and Berlin, MA. **Awards:** Assabet Valley Chamber of Commerce Scholarship (Annual).

52836 ■ Bedford Banner
Town Center Bldg.
12 Mudge Way (2-2)
Bedford, MA 01730-2138
Ph: (781)275-8503
Co. E-mail: bcoc@bedfordchamber.org
URL: http://www.bedfordchamber.org
Contact: Maureen McAulifee Sullivan, Executive Director
Released: Bimonthly

52837 ■ Bedford Chamber of Commerce
Town Center Bldg.
12 Mudge Way (2-2)
Bedford, MA 01730-2138
Ph: (781)275-8503
Co. E-mail: bcoc@bedfordchamber.org
URL: http://www.bedfordchamber.org
Contact: Maureen McAulifee Sullivan, Executive Director
Description: Seeks to promote business and community interests of Bedford area. **Publications:** Bedford Banner (Bimonthly).

52838 ■ Berkshire Chamber of Commerce
6 W Main St.
North Adams, MA 01247
Ph: (413)449-4000
Fax: (413)664-1049
Co. E-mail: info@berkshirechamber.com
URL: http://www.berkshirechamber.com
Contact: Michael Supranowicz, President
Description: Promotes business and community development in Berkshire County.

52839 ■ Berkshires Chamber of Commerce
75 North St., Ste. 360
Pittsfield, MA 01201
Ph: (413)499-4000

Fax: (413)447-9641
Co. E-mail: info@berkshirechamber.com
URL: http://www.berkshirechamber.com
Contact: Michael Supranowicz, President
Description: Seeks to advance economic development and supports the civic, and social welfare of Berkshire county through support and advocacy.

52840 ■ Beverly Chamber of Commerce
100 Cummings Ctr., Ste. 107K
Beverly, MA 01915
Ph: (978)232-9559
Fax: (978)232-9372
Co. E-mail: info@beverlychamber.com
URL: http://www.beverlychamber.com
Contact: John Somes, Executive Director
Description: Promotes business and community development in Beverly, MA.

52841 ■ Blackstone Valley Chamber of Commerce (BVCC)
110 Church St.
Whitinsville, MA 01588-1442
Ph: (508)234-9090
Fax: (508)234-5152
Co. E-mail: dscherer@blackstonevalley.org
URL: http://www.blackstonevalley.org
Contact: Jeannie Hebert, President
Description: Promotes business and community development in Whitinsville, MA. **Founded:** 1979. **Publications:** *Valley Focus* (Monthly). **Telecommunication Services:** jhebert@blackstonevalley.org.

52842 ■ *Brookline Business Report*
251 Harvard St., Ste. 1
Brookline, MA 02446-3202
Ph: (617)739-1330
Fax: (617)739-1200
Co. E-mail: info@brooklinechamber.com
URL: http://www.brooklinechamber.com
Contact: Harry R. Robinson, Executive Director
Released: Quarterly

52843 ■ Brookline Chamber of Commerce (BCC)
251 Harvard St., Ste. 1
Brookline, MA 02446-3202
Ph: (617)739-1330
Fax: (617)739-1200
Co. E-mail: info@brooklinechamber.com
URL: http://www.brooklinechamber.com
Contact: Harry R. Robinson, Executive Director
Description: Acts as a resident and business advocate, provides marketing and networking opportunities, and is focused on improving Brookline and its surroundings. Sponsors an arts and crafts festival; holds seminars, receptions, and networking events. **Founded:** 1917. **Publications:** *Brookline Business Directory: Business Directory* (Annual); *Brookline Business Directory*; *Brookline Business Report* (Quarterly); *Business, Tourist and Shopping Directory* (Annual). **Educational Activities:** Breakfast and Networking (Monthly); Reception and Holiday Party (Annual).

52844 ■ *The Bulletin*
90 New State Hwy., Ste. 1
Raynham, MA 02767
Ph: (508)824-4068
Fax: (508)884-8222
Co. E-mail: info@tauntonareachamber.org
URL: http://www.tauntonareachamber.org
Contact: William D. Lewis, Chairman
Released: Monthly

52845 ■ *Business*
281 Needham St.
Newton, MA 02464
Ph: (617)244-5300
Fax: (617)244-5302
Co. E-mail: info@nnchamber.com
URL: http://www.nnchamber.com/cwt/external/wcpages/index.aspx
Contact: Thomas J. O'Rourke, President
Released: Annual

52846 ■ *Business to Business News*
24 Main St.
Peabody, MA 01960-5593

Ph: (978)531-0384
Fax: (978)532-7227
Co. E-mail: pcc@peabodychamber.com
URL: http://www.peabodychamber.com
Contact: Deanne Healey, President
Released: Monthly **Price:** free.

52847 ■ *Business Calendar*
210 Main St.
Gardner, MA 01440
Ph: (978)632-1780
Fax: (978)630-1767
Co. E-mail: jbellina@gardnerma.com
URL: http://www.gardnerma.com
Contact: James Bellina, President

52848 ■ *Business Directory*
271 Main St., Ste. L-02
Stoneham, MA 02180
Ph: (781)438-0001
Fax: (781)438-0007
Co. E-mail: info@stonehamchamber.org
URL: http://www.stonehamchamber.org
Contact: Sharon A. Iovanni, Executive Director
Released: Annual

52849 ■ *Business Directory/Buyer's Guide*
42 Union St.
Attleboro, MA 02703-2911
Ph: (508)222-0801
Fax: (508)222-1498
URL: http://www.attleborochamber.com
Contact: Jack Lank, President

52850 ■ *Business Directory and Resource Guide*
62 Pleasant St.
Marblehead, MA 01945
Ph: (781)631-2868
Fax: (781)639-8582
Co. E-mail: info@marbleheadchamber.org
URL: http://www.marbleheadchamber.org
Contact: Ann Marie Casey, Executive Director
Released: Annual **Price:** free to members.

52851 ■ *Business Review*
Malden Govt. Center
200 Pleasant St., Ste. 416
Malden, MA 02148-4884
Ph: (781)322-4500
Fax: (781)322-4866
Co. E-mail: info@maldenchamber.org
URL: http://www.maldenchamber.org
Contact: Ted Coates, Executive Director
Released: Monthly

52852 ■ *Business, Tourist and Shopping Directory*
251 Harvard St., Ste. 1
Brookline, MA 02446-3202
Ph: (617)739-1330
Fax: (617)739-1200
Co. E-mail: info@brooklinechamber.com
URL: http://www.brooklinechamber.com
Contact: Harry R. Robinson, Executive Director
Released: Annual

52853 ■ *Business Voice*
210 Main St.
Gardner, MA 01440
Ph: (978)632-1780
Fax: (978)630-1767
Co. E-mail: jbellina@gardnerma.com
URL: http://www.gardnerma.com
Contact: James Bellina, President
Released: Monthly

52854 ■ Cambridge Chamber of Commerce (CCC)
859 Massachusetts Ave.
Cambridge, MA 02139
Ph: (617)876-4100
Fax: (617)354-9874
Co. E-mail: ccinfo@cambridgechamber.org
URL: http://www.cambridgechamber.org
Contact: Kelly Thompson Clark, President
Description: Promotes business and community development in Cambridge, MA area. **Founded:** 1926.

52855 ■ Cape Ann Chamber of Commerce
33 Commercial St.
Gloucester, MA 01930
Ph: (978)283-1601
Fax: (978)283-4740
Co. E-mail: info@capeannchamber.com
URL: http://www.capeannchamber.com
Contact: Mark Grenier, President
URL(s): www.capeannvacations.com. **Description:** Promotes business and community development in Essex, Gloucester, Manchester, and Rockport, MA. **Founded:** 1922. **Publications:** *Soundings* (Monthly).

52856 ■ Cape Cod Canal Regional Chamber of Commerce
70 Main St.
Buzzards Bay, MA 02532
Ph: (508)759-6000
Fax: (508)759-6965
Co. E-mail: info@capecodcanalchamber.org
URL: http://www.capecodcanalchamber.org/cwt/external/wcpages/index.aspx
Contact: Marie Oliva, President
Description: Promotes business and community development in the region. **Publications:** *Chamber E-Connection* (Monthly).

52857 ■ *Chamber Bulletin*
207 Hagman Rd.
Winthrop, MA 02152-0005
Ph: (617)846-9898
Fax: (617)846-9922
Co. E-mail: info@winthropchamber.com
URL: http://www.winthropchamber.com
Contact: Bernice MacIntyre, President

52858 ■ Chamber of Commerce of the Attleboro Area
42 Union St.
Attleboro, MA 02703-2911
Ph: (508)222-0801
Fax: (508)222-1498
URL: http://www.attleborochamber.com
Contact: Jack Lank, President
Description: Promotes business and community development in the Attleboro, MA area. **Publications:** *Keynotes* (Monthly); *Business Directory/Buyer's Guide*. **Awards:** Athena Award (Annual); Person of the Year Award (Annual); Teacher of the Year Award (Annual).

52859 ■ *Chamber Connections*
100 Sherman Ave., Ste. 3
Devens, MA 01434
Ph: (978)772-6976
Fax: (978)772-3503
Co. E-mail: director@nvcoc.com
URL: http://www.nvcoc.com
Contact: Mike Gervais, President
Released: Monthly

52860 ■ *Chamber Currents*
207 Hagman Rd.
Winthrop, MA 02152-0005
Ph: (617)846-9898
Fax: (617)846-9922
Co. E-mail: info@winthropchamber.com
URL: http://www.winthropchamber.com
Contact: Bernice MacIntyre, President
Released: Monthly

52861 ■ *Chamber E-Connection*
70 Main St.
Buzzards Bay, MA 02532
Ph: (508)759-6000
Fax: (508)759-6965
Co. E-mail: info@capecodcanalchamber.org
URL: http://www.capecodcanalchamber.org/cwt/external/wcpages/index.aspx
Contact: Marie Oliva, President
Released: Monthly

52862 ■ *The Chamber Exchange*
264 Exchange St.
Chicopee, MA 01013
Ph: (413)594-2101

Fax: (413)594-2103
Co. E-mail: gailsherman@chicopeechamber.org
URL: http://www.chicopeechamber.org
Contact: Gail A. Sherman, President
Released: Monthly

52863 ■ *Chamber Focus*
794 Purchase St.
New Bedford, MA 02740
Ph: (508)999-5231
Fax: (508)999-5237
Co. E-mail: info@newbedfordchamber.com
URL: http://newbedfordchamber.com
Contact: Roy Nascimento, President
Released: Bimonthly

52864 ■ *Chamber Membership Directory and Community Guide*
108 Beach St.
Revere, MA 02151
Ph: (781)289-8009
Fax: (781)289-2166
Co. E-mail: info@reverechamber.org
URL: http://www.reverechamber.org
Contact: Laura D'Amico, President

52865 ■ *Chamber News*
108 Beach St.
Revere, MA 02151
Ph: (781)289-8009
Fax: (781)289-2166
Co. E-mail: info@reverechamber.org
URL: http://www.reverechamber.org
Contact: Laura D'Amico, President
Released: Quarterly

52866 ■ *Chamber Outlook*
226 Lowell St.
Wilmington, MA 01887-0463
Ph: (978)657-7211
Fax: (978)657-0139
Co. E-mail: wilmingtonchmbr@earthlink.net
URL: http://www.wilmingtonbusiness.com
Contact: Mike Champoux, President
Released: Monthly

52867 ■ *The Chamber Report*
134 Court St.
Plymouth, MA 02360
Ph: (508)830-1620
Fax: (508)830-1621
Co. E-mail: info@plymouthchamber.com
URL: http://www.plymouthchamber.com
Contact: Denis Hanks, Executive Director
Released: Monthly

52868 ■ *The Chamber Speaks*
271 Main St., Ste. L-02
Stoneham, MA 02180
Ph: (781)438-0001
Fax: (781)438-0007
Co. E-mail: info@stonehamchamber.org
URL: http://www.stonehamchamber.org
Contact: Sharon A. Iovanni, Executive Director
Released: Bimonthly

52869 ■ *ChamberNEWS*
258 Main St., Ste. 306
Milford, MA 01757
Ph: (508)473-6700
Fax: (508)473-8467
Co. E-mail: chamber@milfordchamber.org
URL: http://www.milfordchamber.org
Contact: Barry Feingold, President
Released: Monthly

52870 ■ Chatham Chamber of Commerce
PO Box 793
Chatham, MA 02633-0793
Ph: (508)945-5199
Free: 800-715-5567
Fax: (508)430-7919
Co. E-mail: chamber@chathaminfo.com
URL: http://www.chathaminfo.com
Contact: Lisa Franz, Executive Director
URL(s): www.chathamcapecod.org. **Description:** Promotes business and community development in Chatham, MA.

52871 ■ Chicopee Chamber of Commerce
264 Exchange St.
Chicopee, MA 01013
Ph: (413)594-2101
Fax: (413)594-2103
Co. E-mail: gailsherman@chicopeechamber.org
URL: http://www.chicopeechamber.org
Contact: Gail A. Sherman, President
Description: Promotes business and community development in Chicopee, MA. **Publications:** *The Chamber Exchange* (Monthly). **Awards:** Business of the Year (Annual); Chamber Volunteer of the Year (Annual); Citizen of the Year (Annual).

52872 ■ *Chronicle Newsletter*
175 Mcclellan Hwy., Ste. 1
East Boston, MA 02128
Ph: (617)569-5000
Co. E-mail: info@eastbostonchamber.com
URL: http://www.eastbostonchamber.com
Contact: Diane J. Modica, President
Released: Monthly

52873 ■ *Coastlines*
20 Academy Ln.
Falmouth, MA 02540
Ph: (508)548-8500
Free: 800-526-8532
Fax: (508)548-8521
Co. E-mail: info@falmouthchamber.com
URL: http://www.falmouthchamber.com
Contact: Jay Zavala, President
Released: Monthly

52874 ■ Cohasset Chamber of Commerce
PO Box 336
Cohasset, MA 02025-0336
Ph: (781)383-1010
Co. E-mail: info@cohassetchamber.com
URL: http://www.cohassetchamber.org
Description: Promotes business and community development in Cohasset, MA. Sponsors parade; conducts charitable activities. **Founded:** 1982.

52875 ■ *Community Beacon*
28 Amity St.
Amherst, MA 01002
Ph: (413)253-0700
Fax: (413)256-0771
Co. E-mail: info@amherstarea.com
URL: http://www.amherstarea.com
Contact: Tony Maroulis, Executive Director
Released: Monthly

52876 ■ *Community Guide & Business Directory*
PO Box 810
Great Barrington, MA 01230
Ph: (413)528-4284
Free: 800-269-4825
Fax: (413)528-2200
Co. E-mail: info@southernberkshirechamber.com
URL: http://southernberkshirechamber.com
Contact: Betsy Andrus, Executive Director
Released: every 18 months.

52877 ■ Concord Chamber of Commerce
15 Walden St., Ste. 7
Concord, MA 01742-2504
Ph: (978)369-3120
Fax: (978)369-1515
Co. E-mail: info@concordchamberofcommerce.org
URL: http://www.concordchamberofcommerce.org
Contact: Stephanie Stillman, Executive Director
Description: Promotes business and community development in Concord, MA. Conducts charitable programs; sponsors festival. **Founded:** 1953. **Publications:** *Cultural Events Calendar*; *The Grapevine* (Monthly); *Guide Map*; *Lexington Concord Battleroad*; *Women's Group Newsletter* (Periodic); *Concord Chamber of Commerce Directory*.

52878 ■ *County Lines*
PO Box 898
Greenfield, MA 01302-0898
Ph: (413)773-5463

Fax: (413)773-7008
Co. E-mail: fccc@crocker.com
URL: http://www.franklincc.org
Contact: Ann L. Hamilton, President
Released: Monthly

52879 ■ Cranberry Country Chamber of Commerce
PO Box 409
Middleboro, MA 02346-0409
Ph: (508)947-1499
Fax: (508)947-1446
Co. E-mail: info@cranberrycountry.org
URL: http://www.cranberrycountry.org
Contact: Valerie Glynn, President
Description: Seeks to enhance business community and economic environment of Middleboro, MA.

52880 ■ *Cultural Events Calendar*
15 Walden St., Ste. 7
Concord, MA 01742-2504
Ph: (978)369-3120
Fax: (978)369-1515
Co. E-mail: info@concordchamberofcommerce.org
URL: http://www.concordchamberofcommerce.org
Contact: Stephanie Stillman, Executive Director

52881 ■ East Boston Chamber of Commerce
175 Mcclellan Hwy., Ste. 1
East Boston, MA 02128
Ph: (617)569-5000
Co. E-mail: info@eastbostonchamber.com
URL: http://www.eastbostonchamber.com
Contact: Diane J. Modica, President
Description: Promotes business and community development in East Boston, MA. **Publications:** *Chronicle Newsletter* (Monthly).

52882 ■ Eastham Chamber of Commerce
PO Box 1329
Eastham, MA 02642
Ph: (508)240-7211
Co. E-mail: info@easthamchamber.com
URL: http://www.easthamchamber.com
Contact: Lisa Panaccione, President
Description: Promotes and encourages the spirit of fair trade and good business through activities and programs designed to benefit the commercial, cultural and civic welfare of Eastham, MA.

52883 ■ *Economic Development Promotional Brochure*
264 Essex St.
Lawrence, MA 01840-1496
Ph: (978)686-0900
Fax: (978)794-9953
Co. E-mail: office@merrimackvalleychamber.com
URL: http://www.merrimackvalleychamber.com
Contact: Joseph J. Bevilacqua, President
Price: free.

52884 ■ *Fact Finder/Map*
PO Box 357
Williamstown, MA 01267
Ph: (413)458-9077
Free: 800-214-3799
Fax: (413)458-2666
Co. E-mail: info@williamstownchamber.com
URL: http://williamstownchamber.com
Contact: Judy Giamborino, Executive Director
Released: Annual

52885 ■ Fall River Area Chamber of Commerce and Industry Inc. (FRCOC)
200 Pocasset St.
Fall River, MA 02721
Ph: (508)676-8226
Fax: (508)675-5932
Co. E-mail: info@fallriverchamber.com
URL: http://www.fallriverchamber.com
Contact: Robert Mellion, President
Description: Promotes business and community development in the Fall River, MA area. **Founded:** 1911. **Telecommunication Services:** communications@fallriverchamber.com.

52886 ■ *Falmouth Brochure*
20 Academy Ln.
Falmouth, MA 02540

Ph: (508)548-8500
Free: 800-526-8532
Fax: (508)548-8521
Co. E-mail: info@falmouthchamber.com
URL: http://www.falmouthchamber.com
Contact: Jay Zavala, President
Released: Annual

52887 ■ Falmouth Chamber of Commerce
20 Academy Ln.
Falmouth, MA 02540
Ph: (508)548-8500
Free: 800-526-8532
Fax: (508)548-8521
Co. E-mail: info@falmouthchamber.com
URL: http://www.falmouthchamber.com
Contact: Jay Zavala, President
Description: Promotes business and community development in Falmouth, MA. Seeks to preserve and support the aesthetic integrity and character of the area by encouraging cultural, civic, and educational interest in the town. Also organizes Christmas by the Sea weekend and holiday parade during the first weekend of December; conducts annual Cape Cod Antique Market and Show and Sale. **Founded:** 1914. **Publications:** *Annual Directory and Guidebook* (Annual); *Coastlines* (Monthly); *Falmouth Brochure* (Annual). **Educational Activities:** Antique Show (Annual); Falmouth Chamber of Commerce Meeting (Annual). **Awards:** Citizen of the Year (Annual).

52888 ■ *Flagship*
PO Box 100
Hyannis, MA 02601
Ph: (508)775-2201
Free: 877-492-6647
Fax: (508)775-7131
Co. E-mail: guidebook@hyannis.com
URL: http://www.hyannis.com
Contact: Jessica Sylver, President
Released: Monthly **Price:** free.

52889 ■ Franklin County Chamber of Commerce (FCCC)
PO Box 898
Greenfield, MA 01302-0898
Ph: (413)773-5463
Fax: (413)773-7008
Co. E-mail: fccc@crocker.com
URL: http://www.franklincc.org
Contact: Ann L. Hamilton, President
Description: Promotes business and community development in Franklin County, MA. Promotes local tourism. Sponsors music festival, and Home and Leisure Expo. **Founded:** 1919. **Publications:** *County Lines* (Monthly); *Major Employees*; *Guidebooks*.

52890 ■ *The Grapevine*
15 Walden St., Ste. 7
Concord, MA 01742-2504
Ph: (978)369-3120
Fax: (978)369-1515
Co. E-mail: info@concordchamberofcommerce.org
URL: http://www.concordchamberofcommerce.org
Contact: Stephanie Stillman, Executive Director
Released: Monthly

52891 ■ Greater Boston Chamber of Commerce
265 Franklin St., 12th Fl.
Boston, MA 02110
Ph: (617)227-4500
Fax: (617)227-7505
Co. E-mail: info@bostonchamber.com
URL: http://www.bostonchamber.com
Contact: Paul Guzzi, President
Description: Promotes business and community development in Boston, MA area. **Publications:** *Greater Boston Chamber of Commerce--Business Directory* (Continuous); *Major Employers in Greater Boston*; *Greater Boston Directory of Associations* (Biennial).

52892 ■ Greater Gardner Chamber of Commerce (GGCC)
210 Main St.
Gardner, MA 01440
Ph: (978)632-1780

Fax: (978)630-1767
Co. E-mail: jbellina@gardnerma.com
URL: http://www.gardnerma.com
Contact: James Bellina, President
Description: Promotes economic development and tourism in Worcester County, MA. Sponsors Experience Gardner Summer Festival, annual Golf Tournament, and Northeast Clambake. **Founded:** 1898. **Publications:** *Business Calendar*; *Business Voice* (Monthly).

52893 ■ Greater Haverhill Chamber of Commerce
80 Merrimack St.
Haverhill, MA 01830
Ph: (978)373-5663
Fax: (978)373-8060
Co. E-mail: info@haverhillchamber.com
URL: http://www.haverhillchamber.com
Contact: Sven Amirian, President
Description: Promotes business and community development in Haverhill, MA. **Founded:** 1888.

52894 ■ Greater Holyoke Chamber of Commerce
177 High St.
Holyoke, MA 01040-6504
Ph: (413)534-3376
Fax: (413)534-3385
Co. E-mail: info@holycham.com
URL: http://www.holyokechamber.com
Contact: Kathleen Anderson, President
Description: Aims to strengthen the economy of Greater Holyoke by representing and involving the business community in public policy decisions affecting the business climate, by helping individual businesses to prosper, and by creating a community environment conducive to economic opportunity and a positive quality of life. **Founded:** 1890.

52895 ■ Greater Lowell Chamber of Commerce (GLCC)
131 Merrimack St.
Lowell, MA 01852
Ph: (978)459-8154
Fax: (978)452-4145
Co. E-mail: info@greaterlowellchamber.org
URL: http://www.glcc.biz
Contact: Danielle McFadden, President
Description: Seeks to enhance the business community and quality of life of Lowel, MA. area. Supports local charities; conducts political and business networking forums.

52896 ■ Greater Newburyport Chamber of Commerce and Industry
38R Merrimac St.
Newburyport, MA 01950
Ph: (978)462-6680
Fax: (978)465-4145
Co. E-mail: info@newburyportchamber.org
URL: http://www.newburyportchamber.org
Contact: Ann Ormond, President
Description: Seeks to address member needs and to be a leader in economic development. **Founded:** 1966. **Publications:** *Navigator* (Monthly).

52897 ■ Greater Northampton Chamber of Commerce
99 Pleasant St.
Northampton, MA 01060
Ph: (413)584-1900
Fax: (413)584-1934
Co. E-mail: info@explorenorthampton.com
URL: http://www.explorenorthampton.com/chamber/about.htm
Contact: Suzanne Beck, Executive Director
Description: Promotes business and community development in the Northampton, MA area. **Scope:** demographic, tourist, financial. **Founded:** 1918. **Telecommunication Services:** suzanne@explorenorthampton.com.

52898 ■ *Guide*
860 South St.
Fitchburg, MA 01420
Ph: (978)353-7600

Fax: (978)353-4896
Co. E-mail: chamber@massweb.org
URL: http://northcentralmass.com
Contact: David L. McKeehan, President
Released: Semiannual

52899 ■ *Guide to Downtown Plymouth*
134 Court St.
Plymouth, MA 02360
Ph: (508)830-1620
Fax: (508)830-1621
Co. E-mail: info@plymouthchamber.com
URL: http://www.plymouthchamber.com
Contact: Denis Hanks, Executive Director

52900 ■ *Guide Map*
15 Walden St., Ste. 7
Concord, MA 01742-2504
Ph: (978)369-3120
Fax: (978)369-1515
Co. E-mail: info@concordchamberofcommerce.org
URL: http://www.concordchamberofcommerce.org
Contact: Stephanie Stillman, Executive Director

52901 ■ *A Guide to Provincetown*
PO Box 1017
Provincetown, MA 02657-1017
Ph: (508)487-3424
Fax: (508)487-8966
Co. E-mail: info@ptownchamber.com
URL: http://www.ptownchamber.com
Contact: Candice Collins-Boden, Executive Director
Released: Annual **Price:** free.

52902 ■ Hanover Chamber of Commerce
PO Box 68
Hanover, MA 02339-0068
Ph: (781)826-8865
Fax: (781)826-7721
Co. E-mail: chamber@hanovermachamber.com
URL: http://www.hanovermachamber.com
Contact: Cathy Follett, President
Description: Promotes business and community development in Hanover, MA. **Founded:** 1964. **Publications:** *Anchor News* (Monthly). **Awards:** Hanover Chamber of Commerce Scholarship Award (Annual).

52903 ■ Harwich Chamber of Commerce (HCC)
One Schoolhouse Rd.
Harwich Port, MA 02646
Ph: (508)430-1165
Free: 800-442-7942
Fax: (508)430-2105
Co. E-mail: info@harwichcc.com
URL: http://www.harwichcc.com
Contact: Jeremy Gingras, Executive Director
Description: Promotes business and community development in Harwich Port, MA. Sponsors events. **Publications:** *Map and Guide* (Biennial); *Notice* (Monthly). **Awards:** Business Award (Annual); Culinary Arts Award (Annual).

52904 ■ Holden Area Chamber of Commerce
1174 Main St.
Holden, MA 01520-0377
Ph: (508)829-9220
Fax: (508)829-9220
Co. E-mail: info@holdenareachamber.org
URL: http://www.holdenareachamber.org
Contact: Jennifer Stanovich, Executive Director
Description: Promotes business and community development in Holden, Princeton, Paxton and Rutland, MA. **Founded:** 1992. **Publications:** *InTouch* (Quarterly). **Awards:** Business Person of the Year (Annual).

52905 ■ Hyannis Area Chamber of Commerce (HACC)
PO Box 100
Hyannis, MA 02601
Ph: (508)775-2201
Free: 877-492-6647

Fax: (508)775-7131
Co. E-mail: guidebook@hyannis.com
URL: http://www.hyannis.com
Contact: Jessica Sylver, President
Description: Promotes business and community development in the Hyannis, MA area. **Founded:** 1982. **Publications:** *Flagship* (Monthly); *Guidebook* (Periodic).

52906 ■ INBusiness
281 Needham St.
Newton, MA 02464
Ph: (617)244-5300
Fax: (617)244-5302
Co. E-mail: info@nnchamber.com
URL: http://www.nnchamber.com/cwt/external/wcpages/index.aspx
Contact: Thomas J. O'Rourke, President
Released: Monthly

52907 ■ Industrial Directory of Waltham
84 South St.
Waltham, MA 02453
Ph: (781)894-4700
Fax: (781)894-1708
Co. E-mail: info@walthamchamber.com
URL: http://www.walthamchamber.com
Contact: Lisa Lorgeree, Chairman
Released: Periodic

52908 ■ InTouch
1174 Main St.
Holden, MA 01520-0377
Ph: (508)829-9220
Fax: (508)829-9220
Co. E-mail: info@holdenareachamber.org
URL: http://www.holdenareachamber.org
Contact: Jennifer Stanovich, Executive Director
Released: Quarterly

52909 ■ It's Your Business
11 Florence St.
Marlborough, MA 01752-2822
Ph: (508)485-7746
Fax: (508)481-1819
Co. E-mail: marlcham@marlboroughchamber.org
URL: http://www.marlboroughchamber.org
Contact: Martin Levins, Chairman
Released: Monthly

52910 ■ Keynotes
42 Union St.
Attleboro, MA 02703-2911
Ph: (508)222-0801
Fax: (508)222-1498
URL: http://www.attleborochamber.com
Contact: Jack Lank, President
Released: Monthly

52911 ■ The Ledger
Released: Quadrennial

52912 ■ Lenox Chamber of Commerce
12 Housatonic St.
Lenox, MA 01240-0646
Ph: (413)637-3646
Free: 866-515-3669
Fax: (413)637-3626
Co. E-mail: info@lenox.org
URL: http://lenox.org
Contact: Ralph Petillo, Director
Description: Promotes member businesses and community development in Lenox, MA. **Founded:** 1975. **Publications:** *An Official Guide To Lenox* (Annual).

52913 ■ Lexington Chamber of Commerce (LCC)
1875 Massachusetts Ave.
Lexington, MA 02420
Ph: (781)862-2480

Fax: (781)862-5995
Co. E-mail: jterhune@lexingtonchamber.org
URL: http://www.lexingtonchamber.org
Contact: Mary Jo Bohart, Executive Director
Description: Promotes business and community development in Lexington, MA. Sponsors annual Discovery Day Festival, annual Oktoberfest, 10K road race, and other social and promotional activities. **Founded:** 1939. **Publications:** *Visitor's Guide*.

52914 ■ Lexington Concord Battleroad
15 Walden St., Ste. 7
Concord, MA 01742-2504
Ph: (978)369-3120
Fax: (978)369-1515
Co. E-mail: info@concordchamberofcommerce.org
URL: http://www.concordchamberofcommerce.org
Contact: Stephanie Stillman, Executive Director

52915 ■ Local Phone Guide
24 Main St.
Peabody, MA 01960-5593
Ph: (978)531-0384
Fax: (978)532-7227
Co. E-mail: pcc@peabodychamber.com
URL: http://www.peabodychamber.com
Contact: Deanne Healey, President
Released: Annual

52916 ■ Lynn Area Chamber of Commerce (LACC)
583 Chestnut St., Ste. 8
Lynn, MA 01904-2600
Ph: (781)592-2900
Fax: (781)592-2903
Co. E-mail: info@lynnareachamber.com
URL: http://www.lynnareachamber.com
Contact: Leslie Gould, President
Description: Represents the interests of the Lynn area business community at the local, state, and federal levels of government. Provides community programs and public advocacy in the area.

52917 ■ Major Employees
PO Box 898
Greenfield, MA 01302-0898
Ph: (413)773-5463
Fax: (413)773-7008
Co. E-mail: fccc@crocker.com
URL: http://www.franklincc.org
Contact: Ann L. Hamilton, President

52918 ■ Malden Chamber of Commerce
Malden Govt. Center
200 Pleasant St., Ste. 416
Malden, MA 02148-4884
Ph: (781)322-4500
Fax: (781)322-4866
Co. E-mail: info@maldenchamber.org
URL: http://www.maldenchamber.org
Contact: Ted Coates, Executive Director
Description: Promotes business and community development in Malden, MA. **Publications:** *Business Review* (Monthly).

52919 ■ Manufacturers Directory
860 South St.
Fitchburg, MA 01420
Ph: (978)353-7600
Fax: (978)353-4896
Co. E-mail: chamber@massweb.org
URL: http://northcentralmass.com
Contact: David L. McKeehan, President
Released: Annual **Price:** $25.

52920 ■ Map and Guide
One Schoolhouse Rd.
Harwich Port, MA 02646
Ph: (508)430-1165
Free: 800-442-7942
Fax: (508)430-2105
Co. E-mail: info@harwichcc.com
URL: http://www.harwichcc.com
Contact: Jeremy Gingras, Executive Director
Released: Biennial

52921 ■ Marblehead Chamber of Commerce
62 Pleasant St.
Marblehead, MA 01945

Ph: (781)631-2868
Fax: (781)639-8582
Co. E-mail: info@marbleheadchamber.org
URL: http://www.marbleheadchamber.org
Contact: Ann Marie Casey, Executive Director
URL(s): www.visitmarblehead.com. **Description:** Promotes business and community development in Marblehead, MA. Sponsors Christmas Walk and festival. **Publications:** *Business Directory and Resource Guide* (Annual). **Educational Activities:** Business Breakfast Forums (Monthly). **Telecommunication Services:** acasey@marbleheadchamber.org.

52922 ■ Marlborough Regional Chamber of Commerce
11 Florence St.
Marlborough, MA 01752-2822
Ph: (508)485-7746
Fax: (508)481-1819
Co. E-mail: marlcham@marlboroughchamber.org
URL: http://www.marlboroughchamber.org
Contact: Martin Levins, Chairman
Description: Promotes and advocates for business and civic interests in the Marlborough, MA area and collaborates with the community for the overall economic benefit of the region. **Founded:** 1924. **Publications:** *It's Your Business* (Monthly).

52923 ■ Martha's Vineyard Chamber of Commerce (MVCC)
PO Box 1698
Vineyard Haven, MA 02568
Ph: (508)693-0085
Free: 800-505-4815
Co. E-mail: info@mvy.com
URL: http://www.mvy.com
Contact: Nancy Gardella, Executive Director
Description: Promotes tourism, business, and community development on the island of Martha's Vineyard, MA. **Founded:** 1978. **Publications:** *The Visitors Guide*; *The Island Book*. **Awards:** Continuing Education Scholarship (Annual). **Telecommunication Services:** nancy@mvy.com.

52924 ■ Medford Chamber of Commerce
1 Shipyard Way, Ste. 302
Medford, MA 02155
Ph: (781)396-1277
Fax: (781)396-1278
Co. E-mail: director@medfordchamberma.com
URL: http://www.medfordchamberma.com
Contact: Charlotte Scuderi, President
Description: Promotes business and community development in Medford, MA. **Founded:** 1926.

52925 ■ Melrose Chamber of Commerce
1 W Foster St.
Melrose, MA 02176
Ph: (781)665-3033
Fax: (781)665-5595
Co. E-mail: info@melrosechamber.org
URL: http://www.melrosechamber.org
Contact: Joan Ford Mongeau, Executive Director
Description: Seeks to enhance the professional and business communities of Melrose, MA through programs, publicity, and public relations strategies.

52926 ■ Member Directory and Buyer's Guide
1671 Worcester Rd., Ste. 201
Framingham, MA 01701-5400
Ph: (508)879-5600
Fax: (508)875-9325
Co. E-mail: phyllis@metrowest.org
URL: http://www.metrowest.org
Contact: Bonnie P. Biocchi, President
Released: Annual

52927 ■ Merrimack Valley Chamber of Commerce (MVCC)
264 Essex St.
Lawrence, MA 01840-1496
Ph: (978)686-0900

Fax: (978)794-9953
Co. E-mail: office@merrimackvalleychamber.com
URL: http://www.merrimackvalleychamber.com
Contact: Joseph J. Bevilacqua, President
Description: Promotes business and community development in the Merrimack Valley, MA area. **Founded:** 1888. **Publications:** *Economic Development Promotional Brochure.* **Educational Activities:** Business EXPO/Trade Show (Annual). **Awards:** Wilkinson Award (Annual).

52928 ■ Metro South Chamber of Commerce
60 School St.
Brockton, MA 02301
Ph: (508)586-0500
Fax: (508)587-1340
Co. E-mail: info@metrosouthchamber.com
URL: http://www.metrosouthchamber.com
Contact: Christopher Cooney, President
Description: Supports and promotes the local business community through leadership in public advocacy, education, networking, information and community development. **Founded:** 1913.

52929 ■ *MetroWest Business*
1671 Worcester Rd., Ste. 201
Framingham, MA 01701-5400
Ph: (508)879-5600
Fax: (508)875-9325
Co. E-mail: phyllis@metrowest.org
URL: http://www.metrowest.org
Contact: Bonnie P. Biocchi, President
Released: Bimonthly

52930 ■ MetroWest Chamber of Commerce
1671 Worcester Rd., Ste. 201
Framingham, MA 01701-5400
Ph: (508)879-5600
Fax: (508)875-9325
Co. E-mail: phyllis@metrowest.org
URL: http://www.metrowest.org
Contact: Bonnie P. Biocchi, President
Description: Promotes business and community development in South Middlesex County, MA. **Founded:** 1895. **Publications:** *MetroWest Business* (Bimonthly); *MetroWest Chamber of Commerce--Directory; Member Directory and Buyer's Guide* (Annual). **Educational Activities:** Business After Hours (Monthly); Networking Breakfasts (Monthly). **Telecommunication Services:** chamber@metrowest.org.

52931 ■ Middlesex West Chamber of Commerce (MWCoC)
77 Great Rd., Ste. 214
Acton, MA 01720-0212
Ph: (978)263-0010
Fax: (978)264-0303
Co. E-mail: sfletcher@mwcoc.com
URL: http://www.mwcoc.com
Contact: Sarah Fletcher, Executive Director
Description: Promotes business and community development in the region.

52932 ■ Milford Area Chamber of Commerce (MACC)
258 Main St., Ste. 306
Milford, MA 01757
Ph: (508)473-6700
Fax: (508)473-8467
Co. E-mail: chamber@milfordchamber.org
URL: http://www.milfordchamber.org
Contact: Barry Feingold, President
Description: Unites businesses and professionals, and creates central agency to improve business community in Milford area. **Publications:** *ChamberNEWS* (Monthly).

52933 ■ Nantucket Island Chamber of Commerce
Zero Main St., 2nd Fl.
Nantucket, MA 02554-3595
Ph: (508)228-1700

Fax: (508)325-4925
Co. E-mail: info@nantucketchamber.org
URL: http://www.nantucketchamber.org
Contact: P.J. Martin Smith, Executive Director
Description: Promotes business and community development in the Nantucket, MA area. Sponsors festivals, activities, and events to encourage tourism. **Founded:** 1934. **Publications:** *Nantucket Island Chamber of Commerce--Official Guide; Travel and Lodging Brochure* (Annual); *Official Guide to Nantucket* (Annual). **Awards:** Achievement of Merit (Annual).

52934 ■ Nashoba Valley Chamber of Commerce (NVCOC)
100 Sherman Ave., Ste. 3
Devens, MA 01434
Ph: (978)772-6976
Fax: (978)772-3503
Co. E-mail: director@nvcoc.com
URL: http://www.nvcoc.com
Contact: Mike Gervais, President
Description: Promotes business and community development in Nashoba Valley. **Publications:** *Chamber Connections* (Monthly). **Telecommunication Services:** membership@nvcoc.com.

52935 ■ National Black Chamber of Commerce, New England
1127 Main St., 2nd Fl.
Springfield, MA 01103
Ph: (413)731-6444
Fax: (413)731-1011
Co. E-mail: yebyam@neblackchamber.org
URL: http://www.neblackchamber.org
Description: Represents Black owned businesses. Seeks to empower and sustain African American communities through entrepreneurship and capitalistic activity. Provides advocacy, training and education to Black communities.

52936 ■ *Navigator*
38R Merrimac St.
Newburyport, MA 01950
Ph: (978)462-6680
Fax: (978)465-4145
Co. E-mail: info@newburyportchamber.org
URL: http://www.newburyportchamber.org
Contact: Ann Ormond, President
Released: Monthly

52937 ■ *Neponset Valley Business Connection*
190 Vanderbilt Ave.
Norwood, MA 02062-5047
Ph: (781)769-1126
Fax: (781)769-0808
Co. E-mail: denise@nvcc.com
URL: http://www.nvcc.com
Contact: Thomas J. O'Rourke, President
Released: Monthly **Price:** $5; included in membership dues.

52938 ■ Neponset Valley Chamber of Commerce (NVCC)
190 Vanderbilt Ave.
Norwood, MA 02062-5047
Ph: (781)769-1126
Fax: (781)769-0808
Co. E-mail: denise@nvcc.com
URL: http://www.nvcc.com
Contact: Thomas J. O'Rourke, President
Description: Promotes business and community development in Norfolk County, MA. **Founded:** 1894. **Publications:** *Neponset Valley Business Connection* (Monthly). **Educational Activities:** Networking Events-B (Bimonthly). **Awards:** NV Business of Year (Annual); NV Environmental Award (Annual); David P. Mahn Lifetime Achievement Award (Annual); John Gorham Ambassador of Year (Annual); NV Business Person of Year (Annual); NV Corporate Citizen of Year (Annual); Paul Smith Award for Outstanding Volunteerism (Annual).

52939 ■ New Bedford Area Chamber of Commerce
794 Purchase St.
New Bedford, MA 02740
Ph: (508)999-5231

Fax: (508)999-5237
Co. E-mail: info@newbedfordchamber.com
URL: http://newbedfordchamber.com
Contact: Roy Nascimento, President
Description: Seeks to enhance business community and quality of life in South Coast region. **Founded:** 1885. **Publications:** *Chamber Focus* (Bimonthly).

52940 ■ Newton - Needham Chamber of Commerce
281 Needham St.
Newton, MA 02464
Ph: (617)244-5300
Fax: (617)244-5302
Co. E-mail: info@nnchamber.com
URL: http://www.nnchamber.com/cwt/external/wcpages/index.aspx
Contact: Thomas J. O'Rourke, President
Description: Promotes business and community development in Newton, Needham and neighboring areas. **Publications:** *Business* (Annual); *INBusiness* (Monthly). **Telecommunication Services:** torourke@nnchamber.com.

52941 ■ North Attleboro and Plainville Chamber of Commerce
PO Box 1071
North Attleboro, MA 02761
Ph: (508)695-6011
Fax: (508)695-6096
Co. E-mail: info@napcc.org
URL: http://www.napcc.org
Contact: Oreste D'Arconte, Chairman
Description: Promotes economic business and community development in the Greater North Attleboro and Plainville, MA area. Sponsors Fall Festival. **Founded:** 1957. **Publications:** *Chamberlight* (Bimonthly). **Educational Activities:** North Attleboro and Plainville Chamber of Commerce Board meeting (Monthly).

52942 ■ North Central Massachusetts Chamber of Commerce (NCMCC)
860 South St.
Fitchburg, MA 01420
Ph: (978)353-7600
Fax: (978)353-4896
Co. E-mail: chamber@massweb.org
URL: http://northcentralmass.com
Contact: David L. McKeehan, President
Description: Promotes business and community development in North Central Massachusetts. **Founded:** 1984. **Publications:** *Guide* (Semiannual); *Manufacturers Directory* (Annual); *NorthCentralMass.com* (Quarterly).

52943 ■ North Quabbin Chamber of Commerce
427 Main St.
Athol, MA 01331
Ph: (978)249-3849
Fax: (978)249-7151
Co. E-mail: jay@wjdf.com
URL: http://www.northquabbinchamber.com
Contact: Jay Deane, President
Description: Promotes business and community development in the North Quabbin region of Massachusetts. **Founded:** 1982.

52944 ■ *North Shore Business Journal*
5 Cherry Hill Dr., Ste. 100
Danvers, MA 01923-4395
Ph: (978)774-8565
Fax: (978)774-3418
Co. E-mail: info@northshorechamber.org
URL: http://www.northshorechamber.org
Contact: Robert G. Bradford, President
Released: Monthly

52945 ■ North Shore Chamber of Commerce
5 Cherry Hill Dr., Ste. 100
Danvers, MA 01923-4395
Ph: (978)774-8565

Fax: (978)774-3418
Co. E-mail: info@northshorechamber.org
URL: http://www.northshorechamber.org
Contact: Robert G. Bradford, President
Description: Shapes public policy and events to ensure business and government decisions to improve the economy and quality of life of North Shore community. **Founded:** 1918. **Publications:** *North Shore Business Journal* (Monthly); *North Shore Chamber of Commerce--Membership Directory.*

52946 ■ North Suburban Chamber of Commerce (NSCC)
c/o Maureen A. Rogers, Pres.
76R Winn St., No. 3D
Woburn, MA 01801
Ph: (781)933-3499
Fax: (781)933-1071
Co. E-mail: info@northsuburbanchamber.com
URL: http://www.northsuburbanchamber.com
Contact: Maureen A. Rogers, President
Description: Promotes business and community development in the Woburn, MA area.

52947 ■ *NorthCentralMass.com*
860 South St.
Fitchburg, MA 01420
Ph: (978)353-7600
Fax: (978)353-4896
Co. E-mail: chamber@massweb.org
URL: http://northcentralmass.com
Contact: David L. McKeehan, President
Released: Quarterly **Price:** $5, /year; included in membership dues.

52948 ■ *Notice*
One Schoolhouse Rd.
Harwich Port, MA 02646
Ph: (508)430-1165
Free: 800-442-7942
Fax: (508)430-2105
Co. E-mail: info@harwichcc.com
URL: http://www.harwichcc.com
Contact: Jeremy Gingras, Executive Director
Released: Monthly

52949 ■ *An Official Guide To Lenox*
12 Housatonic St.
Lenox, MA 01240-0646
Ph: (413)637-3646
Free: 866-515-3669
Fax: (413)637-3626
Co. E-mail: info@lenox.org
URL: http://lenox.org
Contact: Ralph Petillo, Director
Released: Annual

52950 ■ Peabody Chamber of Commerce (PACC)
24 Main St.
Peabody, MA 01960-5593
Ph: (978)531-0384
Fax: (978)532-7227
Co. E-mail: pcc@peabodychamber.com
URL: http://www.peabodychamber.com
Contact: Deanne Healey, President
Description: Promotes business and community development in the Peabody, MA area. **Publications:** *Business to Business News* (Monthly); *Local Phone Guide* (Annual). **Educational Activities:** Peabody Chamber of Commerce Luncheon (Semimonthly).

52951 ■ Plymouth Area Chamber of Commerce (PACC)
134 Court St.
Plymouth, MA 02360
Ph: (508)830-1620
Fax: (508)830-1621
Co. E-mail: info@plymouthchamber.com
URL: http://www.plymouthchamber.com
Contact: Denis Hanks, Executive Director
Description: Promotes business and community development in Plymouth County, MA. Holds training sessions, board meetings, committee meetings, and more. **Founded:** 1949. **Publications:** *The Chamber Report* (Monthly); *Guide to Downtown Plymouth.*

52952 ■ Provincetown Chamber of Commerce
PO Box 1017
Provincetown, MA 02657-1017
Ph: (508)487-3424
Fax: (508)487-8966
Co. E-mail: info@ptownchamber.com
URL: http://www.ptownchamber.com
Contact: Candice Collins-Boden, Executive Director
Description: Promotes business and community development in Provincetown, MA. Promotes tourism. **Founded:** 1953. **Publications:** *A Guide to Provincetown* (Annual); *Winters Guide to Provincetown* (Annual). **Educational Activities:** Board of Directors (Monthly).

52953 ■ Quaboag Hills Chamber of Commerce
3 Converse St., Ste. 103
Palmer, MA 01069-0269
Ph: (413)283-2418
Fax: (413)289-1355
Co. E-mail: lenny@qhma.com
URL: http://www.quaboag.com
Contact: Carolyn Szarlan, Chairperson
Description: Promotes business and community development in Quaboag Valley area of Massachusetts. Sponsors seminars and workshops and annual Legislators' Night and Citizen of the Year dinners. Provides insurance plan. **Publications:** *Your Business* (Bimonthly).

52954 ■ Reading-North Reading Chamber of Commerce
PO Box 771
Reading, MA 01867
Ph: (781)944-8824
Fax: (781)944-6125
Co. E-mail: rnrchambercom@aol.com
URL: http://www.readingnreadingchamber.org
Contact: Irene Collins, Executive Director
Description: Keeps its members aware of issues concerning them on both the state and local levels, or issues that impact the business community as a whole. **Founded:** 1989.

52955 ■ Revere Chamber of Commerce (RCC)
108 Beach St.
Revere, MA 02151
Ph: (781)289-8009
Fax: (781)289-2166
Co. E-mail: info@reverechamber.org
URL: http://www.reverechamber.org
Contact: Laura D'Amico, President
Description: Businesses, organizations, and interested individuals. Promotes business and community development in Revere, MA. **Founded:** 1979. **Publications:** *Chamber Membership Directory and Community Guide*; *Chamber News* (Quarterly).

52956 ■ Salem Chamber of Commerce
265 Essex St., Ste. 101
Salem, MA 01970
Ph: (978)744-0004
Fax: (978)745-3855
Co. E-mail: info@salem-chamber.org
URL: http://www.salem-chamber.org
Contact: Rinus Oosthoek, Executive Director
Description: Represents the interests of member businesses and works to enhance the business environment of Salem, MA. **Publications:** *Salem Chamber of Commerce--Membership Directory.* **Telecommunication Services:** rinus@salem-chamber.org.

52957 ■ Saugus Chamber of Commerce
394 Lincoln Ave.
Saugus, MA 01906
Ph: (781)233-8407
Fax: (781)231-1145
Co. E-mail: sauguschamber@verizon.net
URL: http://www.sauguschamber.org
Contact: Jim Morin, President
Description: Seeks to improve business community and economic well being of Saugus, MA.

52958 ■ Scituate Chamber of Commerce
PO Box 401
Scituate, MA 02066-0401
Ph: (781)545-4000
Co. E-mail: info@scituatechamber.org
URL: http://www.scituatechamber.org
Contact: Dr. Nico Afanasenko, President
Description: Works to support and promote the well-being of Scituate's business community. Encourages partnership and collaboration among businesses. Provides opportunities for networking, community involvement and professional growth.

52959 ■ Somerville Chamber of Commerce
PO Box 440343
Somerville, MA 02144
Ph: (617)776-4100
Fax: (617)776-1157
Co. E-mail: smackey@somervillechamber.org
URL: http://www.somervillechamber.org
Contact: Stephen Mackey, President
Description: Promotes business and community development in Somerville, MA. **Founded:** 1946.

52960 ■ *Soundings*
33 Commercial St.
Gloucester, MA 01930
Ph: (978)283-1601
Fax: (978)283-4740
Co. E-mail: info@capeannchamber.com
URL: http://www.capeannchamber.com
Contact: Mark Grenier, President
Released: Monthly **Price:** free for members.

52961 ■ South Hadley and Granby Chamber of Commerce
116 Main St., Ste. 4
South Hadley, MA 01075
Ph: (413)532-6451
URL: http://www.southhadleygranbychamber.com
Description: Promotes business and community development in South Hadley, MA. **Founded:** 1959.

52962 ■ South Shore Chamber of Commerce
36 Miller Stile Rd.
Quincy, MA 02269
Ph: (617)479-1111
Fax: (617)479-9274
Co. E-mail: info@southshorechamber.org
URL: http://www.southshorechamber.org
Contact: Peter Forman, President
Description: Seeks to improve the business climate of South Shore region.

52963 ■ Southern Berkshire Chamber of Commerce
PO Box 810
Great Barrington, MA 01230
Ph: (413)528-4284
Free: 800-269-4825
Fax: (413)528-2200
Co. E-mail: info@southernberkshirechamber.com
URL: http://southernberkshirechamber.com
Contact: Betsy Andrus, Executive Director
Description: Promotes business and community development in the southern Berkshire region. **Founded:** 1920. **Publications:** *Community Guide & Business Directory*; *Speaking For Business* (Monthly).

52964 ■ *Speaking For Business*
PO Box 810
Great Barrington, MA 01230
Ph: (413)528-4284
Free: 800-269-4825
Fax: (413)528-2200
Co. E-mail: info@southernberkshirechamber.com
URL: http://southernberkshirechamber.com
Contact: Betsy Andrus, Executive Director
Released: Monthly **Price:** free for members.

52965 ■ Stockbridge Chamber of Commerce
50 Main St.
Stockbridge, MA 01262-0224
Ph: (413)298-5200
Free: 866-626-5327

Fax: (413)931-3128
Co. E-mail: info@stockbridgechamber.org
URL: http://www.stockbridgechamber.org
Contact: Barbara J. Zanetti, Executive Director
Description: Promotes business and community development in Stockbridge, MA. **Publications:** *Welcome to Stockbridge Massachusetts.* **Educational Activities:** Summer Arts and Crafts in Stockbridge Show (Annual).

52966 ■ Stoneham Chamber of Commerce
271 Main St., Ste. L-02
Stoneham, MA 02180
Ph: (781)438-0001
Fax: (781)438-0007
Co. E-mail: info@stonehamchamber.org
URL: http://www.stonehamchamber.org
Contact: Sharon A. Iovanni, Executive Director
Description: Promotes business and community development in Stoneham, MA. **Founded:** 1984. **Publications:** *Business Directory* (Annual); *The Chamber Speaks* (Bimonthly).

52967 ■ Stoughton Chamber of Commerce
PO Box 41
Stoughton, MA 02072
Ph: (781)297-7450
Fax: (781)344-1747
Co. E-mail: chamber@stoughtonma.com
URL: http://www.stoughtonma.com
Contact: Terry Schneider, Executive Director
Description: Promotes business and community development in Stoughton, MA.

52968 ■ Swedish American Chamber of Commerce, New England
c/o Arne Gustafson, Treas.
16 Prescott St.
Wellesley Hills, MA 02481
Ph: (617)419-0171
Co. E-mail: info@sacc-ne.org
URL: http://www.sacc-ne.org
Contact: Per Baverstam, Chairman

52969 ■ Taunton Area Chamber of Commerce (TACC)
90 New State Hwy., Ste. 1
Raynham, MA 02767
Ph: (508)824-4068
Fax: (508)884-8222
Co. E-mail: info@tauntonareachamber.org
URL: http://www.tauntonareachamber.org
Contact: William D. Lewis, Chairman
Description: Promotes business and community development in the Taunton, MA area. **Founded:** 1917. **Publications:** *The Bulletin* (Monthly).

52970 ■ Three Rivers Chamber of Commerce
PO Box 147
Three Rivers, MA 01080
Ph: (413)283-6425
URL: http://www.threeriverschamber.org
Description: Promotes business and community development in Three Rivers, MA.

52971 ■ *Town Map*
226 Lowell St.
Wilmington, MA 01887-0463
Ph: (978)657-7211
Fax: (978)657-0139
Co. E-mail: wilmingtonchmbr@earthlink.net
URL: http://www.wilmingtonbusiness.com
Contact: Mike Champoux, President
Released: Biennial

52972 ■ *Travel and Lodging Brochure*
Zero Main St., 2nd Fl.
Nantucket, MA 02554-3595
Ph: (508)228-1700
Fax: (508)325-4925
Co. E-mail: info@nantucketchamber.org
URL: http://www.nantucketchamber.org
Contact: P.J. Martin Smith, Executive Director
Released: Annual

52973 ■ Tri-Town Chamber of Commerce, Massachusetts—Tri-County Chamber of Commerce
280 School St., Bldg. L100
Mansfield, MA 02048
Ph: (508)339-5655
Fax: (508)339-8333
Co. E-mail: edirector@tri-townchamber.org
URL: http://www.tri-townchamber.org
Contact: Kara Griffin, Executive Director
Description: Promotes business and community development in Foxborough, Mansfield, and Norton, MA. **Founded:** 1986.

52974 ■ United Chamber of Commerce (UCC)
620 Old W Central St., Ste. 202
Franklin, MA 02038
Ph: (508)528-2800
Fax: (508)520-7864
URL: http://www.unitedchamber.org
Contact: Paul Cheli, Director
Description: Promotes business and community development in Franklin, MA. Sponsors golf tournament, networking sessions, and educational seminars. **Founded:** 1977.

52975 ■ *Valley Focus*
110 Church St.
Whitinsville, MA 01588-1442
Ph: (508)234-9090
Fax: (508)234-5152
Co. E-mail: dscherer@blackstonevalley.org
URL: http://www.blackstonevalley.org
Contact: Jeannie Hebert, President
Released: Monthly; every first Sunday. **Price:** free.

52976 ■ *Visitor's Guide*
1875 Massachusetts Ave.
Lexington, MA 02420
Ph: (781)862-2480
Fax: (781)862-5995
Co. E-mail: jterhune@lexingtonchamber.org
URL: http://www.lexingtonchamber.org
Contact: Mary Jo Bohart, Executive Director

52977 ■ *The Visitors Guide*
PO Box 1698
Vineyard Haven, MA 02568
Ph: (508)693-0085
Free: 800-505-4815
Co. E-mail: info@mvy.com
URL: http://www.mvy.com
Contact: Nancy Gardella, Executive Director

52978 ■ Wachusett Chamber of Commerce
PO Box 703
Clinton, MA 01510
Ph: (978)368-7687
Fax: (978)368-7689
Co. E-mail: maegen@wachusettchamber.com
URL: http://www.wachusettchamber.com
Contact: Maegen McCaffrey, Executive Director
Description: Promotes business and community development in the areas of Berlin, Bolton, Boylston, Clinton, Harvard, Lancaster, Sterling, West Boylston and nearby towns. **Founded:** 1884. **Publications:** *Your Chamber at a Glance* (Quarterly).

52979 ■ Wakefield Chamber of Commerce
PO Box 585
Wakefield, MA 01880
Ph: (781)245-0741
Co. E-mail: wakefieldchamberofcommerce@gmail.com
URL: http://www.wakefieldschamber.org
Contact: Kendall Inglese, Executive Director
Description: Promotes business and community development in Wakefield, MA. **Founded:** 1934.

52980 ■ Walpole Chamber of Commerce
PO Box 361
Walpole, MA 02081

Ph: (508)668-0081
Co. E-mail: office@walpolechamber.com
URL: http://www.walpolechamber.org
Contact: Beth Pelick, President
Description: Promotes business and community development in Walpole, MA. **Publications:** *Walpole Chamber of Commerce--Business and Resource Directory.*

52981 ■ *Waltham Map and Guide*
Released: Periodic

52982 ■ Waltham West Suburban Chamber of Commerce (WWSCC)
84 South St.
Waltham, MA 02453
Ph: (781)894-4700
Fax: (781)894-1708
Co. E-mail: info@walthamchamber.com
URL: http://www.walthamchamber.com
Contact: Lisa Lorgeree, Chairman
Description: Promotes business and community development in the Waltham, MA area. **Founded:** 1916. **Publications:** *Industrial Directory of Waltham* (Periodic).

52983 ■ Watertown - Belmont Chamber of Commerce (WBCC)
182 Main St.
Watertown, MA 02471
Ph: (617)926-1017
Fax: (617)926-2322
Co. E-mail: info@wbcc.org
URL: http://www.wbcc.org/home/index.html
Contact: Robert Airasian, President
Description: Promotes business and community development in Watertown, MA. **Publications:** *Alliance Newsletter.*

52984 ■ *Welcome to Stockbridge Massachusetts*
50 Main St.
Stockbridge, MA 01262-0224
Ph: (413)298-5200
Free: 866-626-5327
Fax: (413)931-3128
Co. E-mail: info@stockbridgechamber.org
URL: http://www.stockbridgechamber.org
Contact: Barbara J. Zanetti, Executive Director

52985 ■ Wellesley Chamber of Commerce
1 Hollis St., Ste. 232
Wellesley, MA 02482
Ph: (781)235-2446
Fax: (781)235-7326
Co. E-mail: mobrien@wellesleychamber.org
URL: http://www.wellesleychamber.org
Contact: Maura M. O'Brien, President
Description: Seeks to promote business and community development and enhance the relationship between local businesses and professionals with the public. **Founded:** 1959.

52986 ■ Wellfleet Chamber of Commerce
PO Box 571
Wellfleet, MA 02667-0571
Ph: (508)349-2510
Fax: (508)349-3740
Co. E-mail: info@wellfleetchamber.com
URL: http://www.wellfleetchamber.com
Description: Promotes business and community development in Wellfleet, MA.

52987 ■ Williamstown Chamber of Commerce
PO Box 357
Williamstown, MA 01267
Ph: (413)458-9077
Free: 800-214-3799
Fax: (413)458-2666
Co. E-mail: info@williamstownchamber.com
URL: http://williamstownchamber.com
Contact: Judy Giamborino, Executive Director
Description: Promotes and supports business and tourism in Williamstown, MA and surrounding region. Fosters economic development, new business development, and cultural tourism. Provides advocacy within the town and to the county and state

leadership. **Founded:** 1920. **Publications:** *Fact Finder/Map* (Annual). **Educational Activities:** Membership Meeting (Monthly).

52988 ■ *Wilmington Business Directory*
226 Lowell St.
Wilmington, MA 01887-0463
Ph: (978)657-7211
Fax: (978)657-0139
Co. E-mail: wilmingtonchmbr@earthlink.net
URL: http://www.wilmingtonbusiness.com
Contact: Mike Champoux, President

52989 ■ *Wilmington Chamber of Commerce*
226 Lowell St.
Wilmington, MA 01887-0463
Ph: (978)657-7211
Fax: (978)657-0139
Co. E-mail: wilmingtonchmbr@earthlink.net
URL: http://www.wilmingtonbusiness.com
Contact: Mike Champoux, President
Description: Promotes business and community development in Wilmington, MA. **Founded:** 1961. **Publications:** *Wilmington Business Directory* (Annual); *Chamber Outlook* (Monthly); *Town Map* (Biennial); *Wilmington Business Directory*. **Educational Activities:** Expo - Consumer's Marketplace (Annual). **Telecommunication Services:** wilmingtonchamber@verizon.net.

52990 ■ *Winchester Chamber of Commerce (WCC)*
25 Waterfield St.
Winchester, MA 01890
Ph: (781)729-8870
Co. E-mail: info@winchesterchamber.com
URL: http://www.winchesterchamber.com
Contact: Cathy Alexander, Executive Director
Description: Promotes business and community development in Winchester, MA. **Founded:** 1979.

52991 ■ *Winters Guide to Provincetown*
PO Box 1017
Provincetown, MA 02657-1017
Ph: (508)487-3424
Fax: (508)487-8966
Co. E-mail: info@ptownchamber.com
URL: http://www.ptownchamber.com
Contact: Candice Collins-Boden, Executive Director
Released: Annual

52992 ■ *Winthrop Chamber of Commerce*
207 Hagman Rd.
Winthrop, MA 02152-0005
Ph: (617)846-9898
Fax: (617)846-9922
Co. E-mail: info@winthropchamber.com
URL: http://www.winthropchamber.com
Contact: Bernice MacIntyre, President
Description: Strives to foster a healthy economic climate in Winthrop. **Founded:** 1950. **Publications:** *Chamber Bulletin*; *Chamber Currents* (Monthly).

52993 ■ *Women's Group Newsletter*
15 Walden St., Ste. 7
Concord, MA 01742-2504
Ph: (978)369-3120
Fax: (978)369-1515
Co. E-mail: info@concordchamberofcommerce.org
URL: http://www.concordchamberofcommerce.org
Contact: Stephanie Stillman, Executive Director
Released: Periodic

52994 ■ *Worcester Regional Chamber of Commerce*
446 Main St., Ste. 200
Worcester, MA 01608
Ph: (508)753-2924
Fax: (508)754-8560
Co. E-mail: rkennedy@worcesterchamber.org
URL: http://www.worcesterchamber.org
Contact: Richard B. Kennedy, President
Description: Promotes business and community development in the Worcester region. Sponsors festivals and hall of fame; presents business and service awards. Operates county welcome center and tourism development. Promotes economic development in the Worcester region. **Founded:** 1873.

52995 ■ *Your Business*
3 Converse St., Ste. 103
Palmer, MA 01069-0269
Ph: (413)283-2418
Fax: (413)289-1355
Co. E-mail: lenny@qhma.com
URL: http://www.quaboag.com
Contact: Carolyn Szarlan, Chairperson
Released: Bimonthly

52996 ■ *Your Chamber at a Glance*
PO Box 703
Clinton, MA 01510
Ph: (978)368-7687
Fax: (978)368-7689
Co. E-mail: maegen@wachusettchamber.com
URL: http://www.wachusettchamber.com
Contact: Maegen McCaffrey, Executive Director
Released: Quarterly

MINORITY BUSINESS ASSISTANCE PROGRAMS

52997 ■ **Center for Women and Enterprise**
24 School St., Ste. 700
Boston, MA 02108
Ph: (617)536-0700
Fax: (617)536-7373
Co. E-mail: info@cweonline.org
URL: http://www.cweonline.org
Contact: Susan Rittscher, Chief Executive Officer
Description: Encourages the creation and growth of women-owned businesses through business training, technical assistance, certification, and access to capital.

52998 ■ **MSBDC Boston Regional Office**
University of Massachusetts, Boston
McCormack Bldg., 5th Fl., Rm. 403
100 Morresy Blvd.
Boston, MA 02125-3393
Ph: (617)287-7750
Fax: (617)287-7767
Co. E-mail: mark.allio@umb.edu
URL: http://www.sbdc.umb.edu
Contact: Mark Allio, Director
Description: Committed to helping your business succeed in Massachusetts.

FINANCING AND LOAN PROGRAMS

52999 ■ **ABRY Partners L.L.C.**
111 Huntington Ave.
Boston, MA 02199-7610
Ph: (617)859-2959
Fax: (617)859-8797
Co. E-mail: information@abry.com
URL: http://www.abry.com
Contact: Royce Yudkoff, President
Founded: 1989. **Preferred Investment Size:** $25,000,000 to $150,000,000. **Investment Policies:** Leveraged buyout, expansion, acquisition, recapitalization, roll-ups, and mezzanine. **Industry Preferences:** Communications and media, medical and health, and other products. **Geographic Preference:** U.S.

53000 ■ **Advanced Technology Ventures (ATV)**
500 Boylston St., Ste. 1380
Boston, MA 02116
Ph: (617)850-9700
Co. E-mail: info@atvcapital.com
URL: http://www.atvcapital.com
Contact: Steve Baloff, Partner
E-mail: sbaloff@atvcapital.com
Preferred Investment Size: $15,000,000 to $35,000,000. **Industry Preferences:** Internet specific, computer software and services, computer hardware, other products, semiconductors and other electronics, communications and media, medical and health, biotechnology, industrial and energy, and consumer related. **Geographic Preference:** U.S. and Canada.

53001 ■ **Advent International Corp.**
75 State St.
Boston, MA 02109-1827
Ph: (617)951-9400
Fax: (617)951-0566
Co. E-mail: news@adventinternational.com
URL: http://www.adventinternational.com
Contact: Paul Ferrari, Manager
E-mail: pferrari@adventinternational.com
URL(s): www.adventinternational.com. **Founded:** 1984. **Preferred Investment Size:** $1,000,000 minimum. **Industry Preferences:** Other products, consumer related, communications and media, Internet specific, industrial and energy, medical and health, computer software and services, computer hardware, semiconductors and other electronics, and biotechnology. **Geographic Preference:** U.S. and Canada.

53002 ■ **Ampersand Ventures**
55 William St., Ste. 240
Wellesley, MA 02481
Ph: (781)239-0700
Fax: (781)239-0824
Co. E-mail: info@ampersandventures.com
URL: http://www.ampersandventures.com
Contact: Richard A. Charpie, Partner
Preferred Investment Size: $5,000,000 to $10,000,000. **Industry Preferences:** Healthcare and industrial. **Geographic Preference:** U.S.

53003 ■ **Ascent Venture Partners**
255 State St., 5th Fl.
Boston, MA 02109
Ph: (617)720-9400
Fax: (617)720-9401
Co. E-mail: info@ascentvp.com
URL: http://www.ascentvp.com
Contact: Matt Fates, Partner
Preferred Investment Size: $2,000,000 to $8,000,000. **Industry Preferences:** Internet specific, medical and health, computer software and services, communications and media, medical and health, computer hardware, consumer related, industrial and energy, semiconductors and other electronics. **Geographic Preference:** Eastern U.S.

53004 ■ **Atlantic Capital Corporation**
87 Cambridge St.
Burlington, MA 01803-4115
Ph: (781)272-0088
Free: 800-381-5944
Fax: (781)272-4744
Co. E-mail: scire@atlanticcap.com
URL: http://www.atlanticcap.com
Contact: Peter H. Sprayregen, President
Preferred Investment Size: $300,000 to $500,000. **Industry Preferences:** Diversified. **Geographic Preference:** National.

53005 ■ **Atlas Venture**
25 First St., Ste. 303
Cambridge, MA 02141
Ph: (617)588-2600
Co. E-mail: boston@atlasventure.com
URL: http://www.atlasventure.com
Contact: Peter Shannon, Principal
Preferred Investment Size: $500,000 to $5,000,000. **Industry Preferences:** Internet specific, computer software, hardware and services, biotechnology, communications and media, medical and health, semiconductors and other electronics, industrial and energy. **Geographic Preference:** U.S.

53006 ■ **Axxon Capital**
28 State St., 37th Fl.
Boston, MA 02109
Ph: (617)722-0980
Fax: (617)557-6014
Co. E-mail: info@axxoncapital.com
URL: http://www.axxoncapital.com
Contact: Paula Groves, Founder
Preferred Investment Size: $500,000 to $3,500,000. **Industry Preferences:** Communications, and business service. **Geographic Preference:** Northeast.

53007 ■ **Battery Ventures, L.P.**
2884 Sand Hill Rd., Ste. 101
Menlo Park, CA 94025

Ph: (650)372-3939
Fax: (650)372-3930
URL: http://www.battery.com
Contact: Ken Lawler, Partner
E-mail: ken@battery.com
Preferred Investment Size: $300,000 to $50,000,000. **Industry Preferences:** Internet specific, computer software and services, communications and media, other products, semiconductors and other electronics, computer hardware, industrial and energy. **Geographic Preference:** U.S. and Canada.

53008 ■ Beacon Technology Ventures
8 Saint Mary's St., Ste. 914
Boston, MA 02215
Ph: (617)358-1600
Fax: (617)358-1536
Co. E-mail: info@btehventures.com
URL: http://www.btechventures.com
Contact: Alok Prasad, President
Preferred Investment Size: $250,000 to $3,000,000. **Investment Policies:** Start-up, seed, early, first and second stage. **Industry Preferences:** Communications and media, computer related, semiconductors and other electronics, biotechnology, medical and health. **Geographic Preference:** Northeast.

53009 ■ Berkshires Capital Investors
430 Main St., Ste. 4
Williamstown, MA 01267
Ph: (413)458-9683
Fax: (413)458-5603
Co. E-mail: info@berkshirescap.com
URL: http://www.berkshirescap.com
Contact: Russell Howard, Managing Director
Preferred Investment Size: $250,000 to $1,500,000. **Investment Policies:** Seed and early stage. **Industry Preferences:** Communications, computer software, Internet specific, and business service. **Geographic Preference:** Western Massachusetts.

53010 ■ Bessemer Venture Partners (Cambridge)
196 Broadway, 2nd Fl.
Cambridge, MA 02139
Ph: (617)588-1700
Fax: (617)588-1701
URL: http://www.bessemervp.com
Contact: Christopher Gabrieli, Partner
Preferred Investment Size: $1,000,000 to $10,000,000. **Industry Preferences:** Internet specific, communications and media, computer software and services, semiconductors and other electronics, consumer related, medical and health, industrial and energy, other products, and biotechnology. **Geographic Preference:** U.S.

53011 ■ BioVentures Investors
70 Walnut St., Ste. 302
Cambridge, MA 02481
Ph: (617)252-3443
Fax: (617)621-7993
Co. E-mail: info@bioventuresinvestors.com
URL: http://www.bioventuresinvestors.com
Contact: Anthony Coia, Principal
Preferred Investment Size: $3,000,000 to $7,000,000. **Investment Policies:** Seed, early, first and second stage, balanced, special situation, and private placement. **Industry Preferences:** Biotechnology, and medical and health. **Geographic Preference:** East Coast U.S. and Canada.

53012 ■ Boston Capital Ventures
84 State St., Ste. 320
Boston, MA 02109-2221
Ph: (617)227-6550
Fax: (617)227-3847
Co. E-mail: info@bcv.com
URL: http://www.bcv.com
Contact: Jack Shields, Partner
E-mail: jshields@bcv.com
Preferred Investment Size: $500,000 to $3,000,000. **Industry Preferences:** Internet specific, communications and media, other products, medical and health, computer software and services, consumer related, industrial and energy, semiconductors and other electronics, industrial and energy, biotechnology, and computer hardware. **Geographic Preference:** Northeast and Canada.

53013 ■ Boston Financial & Equity Corporation
1260 Boylston St.
Boston, MA 02215
Ph: (617)267-2900
Fax: (617)437-7601
Co. E-mail: debbie@bfec.com
URL: http://www.bfec.com
Contact: Deborah J. Monosson, Senior Vice President
Preferred Investment Size: $500,000 to $1,000,000. **Industry Preferences:** Diversified. **Geographic Preference:** National.

53014 ■ Boston Millennia Partners
30 Rowes Wharf, Ste. 400
Boston, MA 02110
Ph: (617)428-5150
Co. E-mail: info@millenniapartners.com
URL: http://www.millenniapartners.com
Contact: Dana Callow, Partner
E-mail: dana@milleniapartners.com
Preferred Investment Size: $3,000,000 to $10,000,000. **Industry Preferences:** Internet specific, computer software and services, biotechnology, communications and media, semiconductors and other electronics, other products, computer hardware, consumer related, medical and health. **Geographic Preference:** All U.S., East Coast, and Canada.

53015 ■ Brook Venture Partners
301 Edgewater Pl., 4th Fl.
Wakefield, MA 01880
Ph: (781)295-4000
Fax: (781)295-4007
URL: http://www.brookventure.com
Contact: Andrew Clapp, Partner
E-mail: ewilliams@brookventure.com
Preferred Investment Size: $2,000,000 to $5,000,000. **Industry Preferences:** Communications, computer software, Internet specific, semiconductors and other electronics, medical and health, other products. **Geographic Preference:** Northeast and Mid Atlantic states.

53016 ■ Cambridge Samsung Partners LLC
1 Exeter Plz., 9th Fl.
Boston, MA 02116
Ph: (617)638-0100
Fax: (617)262-5562
URL: http://www.cspartners.com
Contact: Sundar Subramaniam, Managing Director
Geographic Preference: U.S.

53017 ■ CambridgeLight Partners
c/o Cambridge Light & Power
1 Broadway, 14th Fl.
Cambridge, MA 02142
Ph: (617)497-6310
Co. E-mail: info@cambridgelight.com
URL: http://www.cambridgelight.com
Contact: Daniel Alexander, Founder
Preferred Investment Size: $50,000 to $1,000,000. **Investment Policies:** Seed and early stage. **Industry Preferences:** Communications, computer software, Internet specific, and semiconductors and other electronics. **Geographic Preference:** Greater Boston.

53018 ■ Castile Ventures
930 Winter St., Ste. 500
Waltham, MA 02451-1540
Ph: (781)890-0060
Fax: (781)890-0065
Co. E-mail: plans@castileventures.com
URL: http://www.castileventures.com
Contact: Roger Walton, Partner
Preferred Investment Size: $1,000,000 to $10,000,000. **Industry Preferences:** Communications and media, and Internet specific. **Geographic Preference:** Mid Atlantic and Northeast.

53019 ■ Charles River Ventures
1000 Winter St., Ste. 3300
Waltham, MA 02451
Ph: (781)768-6000

Fax: (781)768-6100
URL: http://www.crv.com
Contact: Austin Westerling, Principal
Preferred Investment Size: $25,000 to $5,000,000. **Industry Preferences:** Internet specific, communications and media, computer software and services, computer hardware, other products, industrial and energy, semiconductors and other electronics, medical and health, consumer related, and biotechnology. **Geographic Preference:** U.S.

53020 ■ Commonwealth Capital Ventures
Bay Colony Corporate Ctr.
950 Winter St., Ste. 4100
Waltham, MA 02451
Ph: (781)890-5554
Fax: (781)890-3414
URL: http://www.commonwealthvc.com
Contact: Jeffrey M. Hurst, Partner
Preferred Investment Size: $2,000,000 to $8,000,000. **Industry Preferences:** Computer software and services, Internet specific, communications and media, industrial and energy, medical and health, consumer related, semiconductors and other electronics, biotechnology, and other products. **Geographic Preference:** Northeast U.S.

53021 ■ DFJ New England / Draper Fisher Jurvetson
1 Broadway, 14th Fl.
Cambridge, MA 02142
Ph: (617)758-4275
Free: 758--4234
Fax: (617)758-4101
Co. E-mail: info@dfjne.com
URL: http://www.dfjne.com
Contact: Scott M. Johnson, Managing Director
E-mail: scott1@dfjne.com
Preferred Investment Size: $500,000 to $5,000,000. **Investment Policies:** Start-up, seed, second, early and later stage. **Industry Preferences:** Communications, computer hardware and software, Internet specific, semiconductors and other electronics, consumer related, industrial and energy, and business service. **Geographic Preference:** Northeast.

53022 ■ Downer & Company
60 State St.
Boston, MA 02109
Ph: (617)482-6200
Fax: (617)482-6201
Co. E-mail: info@downer.com
URL: http://www.downer.com
Contact: Charles Downer, Chief Executive Officer
E-mail: cdowner@cwdowner.com
Preferred Investment Size: $300,000 to $500,000. **Industry Preferences:** Computer hardware and software, semiconductors and other electronics, medical and health, consumer related, industrial and energy, and manufacturing. **Geographic Preference:** Northeast and Canada.

53023 ■ Echelon Ventures LLC
303 Wyman St., Ste. 300
Waltham, MA 02451
Ph: (781)530-3707
Fax: (781)530-3717
Co. E-mail: info@echelonventures.com
URL: http://www.echelonventures.com
Contact: Alfred S. Woodworth, Managing Director
Preferred Investment Size: $1,000,000 to $5,000,000. **Investment Policies:** Early, first, and second stage, and expansion. **Industry Preferences:** Computer software, semiconductors and other electronics, biotechnology, and medical and health. **Geographic Preference:** New England-based.

53024 ■ Egan-Managed Capital
30 Federal St.
Boston, MA 02110-2508
Ph: (617)695-2600
Fax: (617)695-2699
Co. E-mail: businessplans@egancapital.com
URL: http://www.egancapital.com
Contact: John R. Egan, Managing Partner
Preferred Investment Size: $2,000,000 to $3,000,000. **Industry Preferences:** Computer software and services, Internet specific, semiconductors

and other electronics, communications and media, and computer hardware. **Geographic Preference:** New England.

53025 ■ Fidelity Ventures
1 Federal St., 27th Fl.
Boston, MA 02110
Ph: (617)830-2100
URL: http://www.fidelityventures.com
Contact: Larry Cheng, Partner
E-mail: lcheng@fidelityventures.com
Preferred Investment Size: $1,000,000 to $10,000,000. **Industry Preferences:** Internet specific, computer software, and services, communications and media, medical and health, financial services, computer hardware, consumer related, semiconductors and other electronics, and other products. **Geographic Preference:** U.S. and Canada.

53026 ■ Flagship Ventures
1 Memorial Dr., 7th Fl.
Cambridge, MA 02142
Ph: (617)868-1888
Fax: (617)868-1115
URL: http://www.flagshipventures.com
Contact: Noubar Afeyan, Chief Executive Officer
Preferred Investment Size: $500,000 to $5,000,000. **Investment Policies:** Start-up, seed, research and development, early and first stage, and balanced. **Industry Preferences:** Computer software and services, communications and media, biotechnology, Internet specific, medical and health, semiconductors and other electronics, other products, computer hardware, and industrial and energy. **Geographic Preference:** Mid Atlantic, Northeast, and West Coast.

53027 ■ Fletcher Spaght Ventures
222 Berkeley St., 20th Fl.
Boston, MA 02116-3761
Ph: (617)247-6700
Fax: (617)247-7757
Co. E-mail: info@fletcherspaght.com
URL: http://www.fletcherspaght.com
Contact: Pearson Spaght, President
E-mail: ps@fletcherspaght.com
Investment Policies: Early stage. **Industry Preferences:** Communications, computer hardware and software, Internet specific, semiconductors and other electronics, medical and health, industrial and energy, transportation, and financial services. **Geographic Preference:** U.S.

53028 ■ Gemini Investors / GMN Investors
20 William St., Ste. 250
Wellesley, MA 02481
Ph: (781)237-7001
Fax: (781)237-7233
URL: http://www.gemini-investors.com
Contact: James Goodman, President
E-mail: jgoodman@gemini-investors.com
Preferred Investment Size: $3,000 to $8,000. **Industry Preferences:** Communications and media, medical and health, computer software and services, Internet specific, other products, computer hardware, industrial and energy, manufacturing, and consumer related. **Geographic Preference:** U.S.

53029 ■ General Catalyst Partners / General Catalyst Group LLC
20 University Rd., 4th Fl.
Cambridge, MA 02138
Ph: (617)234-7000
Fax: (617)234-7040
Co. E-mail: info@generalcatalyst.com
URL: http://www.generalcatalyst.com
Contact: William Fitzgerald, Chief Financial Officer
Preferred Investment Size: $1,000,000 to $25,000,000. **Industry Preferences:** Internet specific, computer software and services, communications and media, other products, industrial and energy, semiconductors and other electronics, and consumer related. **Geographic Preference:** Northeast.

53030 ■ Great Hill Equity Partners, LLC
1 Liberty Sq.
Boston, MA 02109
Ph: (617)790-9400

Fax: (617)790-9401
URL: http://www.greathillpartners.com
Contact: Christopher S. Gaffney, Managing Partner
E-mail: cgaffney@greathillpartners.com
Preferred Investment Size: $50,000,000 to $150,000,000. **Industry Preferences:** Internet specific, communications and media, computer hardware, software and services, semiconductors and other electronics, and other products. **Geographic Preference:** U.S.

53031 ■ Greylock Management Corp. (Boston)
880 Winter St., Ste. 300
Waltham, MA 02451
Ph: (781)622-2300
Fax: (781)622-2300
Co. E-mail: bostongreylock.com
URL: http://www.greylock.com
Contact: Tom Bogan, Partner
Preferred Investment Size: $250,000 minimum. **Industry Preferences:** Diversified. **Geographic Preference:** No preference.

53032 ■ Grove Street Advisors L.L.C.
20 William St., Ste. 230
Wellesley, MA 02481-4131
Ph: (781)263-6100
Fax: (781)263-6101
Co. E-mail: info@grovestreetadvisors.com
URL: http://www.grovestreetadvisors.com
Contact: Clint Harris, Managing Partner
Founded: 1998. **Preferred Investment Size:** $1,000,000 to $7,500,000. **Industry Preferences:** Communications and media, computer software and hardware, Internet specific, semiconductors and other electronics, consumer related, industrial and energy, and business service.

53033 ■ Halpern, Denny & Co.
100 City Hall Plz., Ste. 305
Boston, MA 02108
Ph: (617)536-6602
Fax: (617)536-8535
Co. E-mail: info@HalpernDenny.com
URL: http://www.halperndenny.com
Contact: John D. Halpern, Partner
E-mail: jhalpern@halperndenny.com
Preferred Investment Size: $5,000,000 to $50,000,000. **Industry Preferences:** Consumer related, Internet specific, other products, communications and media, computer software and services, industrial and energy, medical and health, and computer hardware. **Geographic Preference:** U.S.

53034 ■ Harbourvest Partners, LLC
1 Financial Ctr., 44th Fl.
Boston, MA 02111
Ph: (617)348-3707
Fax: (617)350-0305
Co. E-mail: usinfo@barnourvest.com
URL: http://www.harbourvest.com
Contact: Edward W. Kane, Managing Director
Preferred Investment Size: $10,000,000 to $100,000,000. **Industry Preferences:** Other products, Internet specific, communications and media, computer software and services, consumer related, computer hardware, semiconductors and other electronics, industrial and energy, biotechnology, medical and health. **Geographic Preference:** U.S.

53035 ■ High Peaks Venture Partners, LLC / Berkshires Capital Invest
10 2nd St.
Troy, NY 12180
Ph: (518)720-3090
Fax: (518)720-3091
Co. E-mail: info@hpvp.com
URL: http://www.hpvp.com
Contact: Russell Howard, Managing Director
Preferred Investment Size: $100,000 to $2,000,000. **Industry Preferences:** Communications and media, computer hardware, Internet specific, consumer related, semiconductors and other electronics. **Geographic Preference:** New York and Northeast.

53036 ■ Highland Capital Partners
92 Hayden Ave.
Cambridge, MA 02142

Ph: (617)401-4500
Fax: (781)861-5499
Co. E-mail: info@hcp.com
URL: http://www.hcp.com
Contact: Corey Mulloy, Partner
E-mail: cmulloy@hcp.com
Preferred Investment Size: $100,000 to $20,000,000. **Industry Preferences:** Internet specific, computer software and services, communications and media, medical and health, other products, biotechnology, semiconductors and other electronics, computer hardware, and industrial and energy. **Geographic Preference:** U.S. and Canada.

53037 ■ Industry Ventures
750 Battery St., 7th Fl.
San Francisco, CA 94111
Ph: (415)273-4201
Fax: (415)391-7262
Co. E-mail: info@industryventures.com
URL: http://www.industryventures.com
Contact: Hans Swildens, Founder
Preferred Investment Size: $250,000 to $250,000,000. **Industry Preferences:** Communications and media, computer software, Internet specific, consumer related, and business service. **Geographic Preference:** Mid Atlantic, Northeast, Northern California, and West Coast.

53038 ■ Kestrel Venture Management / Corning Venture Management
1 Boston Pl., Ste. 1650
Boston, MA 02108
Ph: (617)451-6722
Fax: (617)451-3322
Co. E-mail: msilva@kestrelvm.com
URL: http://www.kestrelvm.com
Contact: R. Gregg Stone, Principal
Preferred Investment Size: $250,000 minimum. **Investment Policies:** Early stage. **Industry Preferences:** Internet specific, biotechnology, Computer software and services, semiconductors and other electronics, other products, consumer related, computer hardware, communications and media, medical and health, and industrial and energy. **Geographic Preference:** Northeast.

53039 ■ Lee Munder Venture Partners, LLC
John Hancock Tower
200 Clarendon St., 28th Fl.
Boston, MA 02116
Ph: (617)380-5600
Free: 877-241-5191
Fax: (617)380-5601
URL: http://www.leemunder.com
Contact: Lee P. Munder, Chairman
Preferred Investment Size: $500,000 to $3,000,000. **Industry Preferences:** Communications, computer software, industrial and energy, semiconductors and other electronics, and financial services. **Geographic Preference:** Mid Atlantic, Northeast, and Southeast.

53040 ■ Longworth Venture Partners, L.P.
1050 Winter St., Ste. 2600
Waltham, MA 02451
Ph: (781)663-3600
Fax: (781)663-3691
Co. E-mail: businessplans@longworth.com
URL: http://www.longworth.com
Contact: John Lawrence, Chief Financial Officer
Preferred Investment Size: $2,000,000 to $3,000,000. **Industry Preferences:** Computer software, Internet specific, financial services, and business service. **Geographic Preference:** Mid Atlantic, New England, West Coast and elsewhere.

53041 ■ M/C Venture Partners
75 State St., Ste. 2500
Boston, MA 02109
Ph: (617)345-7200
Fax: (617)345-7201
Co. E-mail: mcp@mcpartners.com
URL: http://www.mcventurepartners.com
Contact: David Croll, Managing Partner
Preferred Investment Size: $5,000,000 to $50,000,000. **Industry Preferences:** Communications and media, Internet specific, semiconductors

and other electronics, computer software and services, and consumer related. **Geographic Preference:** U.S. and Canada.

53042 ■ Manulife Capital Corporation
200 Bloor St. E.
North Tower 4
Toronto, ON, Canada M4W 1E5
Ph: (416)926-5727
Fax: (416)926-5737
URL: http://www.manulife.com
Contact: William Euewes, Vice President
Preferred Investment Size: $5,000,000 to $25,000,000. **Investment Policies:** Early stage, mezzanine, buyouts, expansion, and recapitalization. **Industry Preferences:** Biotechnology. **Geographic Preference:** National.

53043 ■ Massachusetts Capital Resource Company
420 Boylston St.
Boston, MA 02116
Ph: (617)536-3900
Fax: (617)536-7930
URL: http://www.masscapital.com
Contact: Richard W. Anderson, President
E-mail: randerson@masscapital.com
Preferred Investment Size: $750,000 to $5,000,000. **Industry Preferences:** Industrial and energy, semiconductors and other electronics, computer software, hardware and services, consumer related, communications and media, medical and health, and Internet specific. **Geographic Preference:** Massachusetts.

53044 ■ Massachusetts Technology Development Corp. (MTDC)
40 Board St., Ste. 230
Boston, MA 02109
Ph: (617)723-4920
Fax: (617)723-5983
Co. E-mail: jhodgman@mtdc.com
URL: http://www.mtdc.com
Contact: Robert J. Crowley, President
E-mail: rcrowley@mtdc.com
Preferred Investment Size: $350,000 to $500,000. **Industry Preferences:** Computer software, hardware and services, semiconductors and other electronics, Internet specific, biotechnology, medical and health, industrial and energy, communications and media. **Geographic Preference:** Massachusetts.

53045 ■ Masthead Venture
55 Cambridge Pky., Ste. 103
Cambridge, MA 02142-1234
Ph: (617)621-3000
Fax: (617)621-3055
Co. E-mail: info@mvpartners.com
URL: http://www.mvpartners.com
Contact: Timothy P. Agnew, Principal
Preferred Investment Size: $500,000 to $5,000,000. **Investment Policies:** Seed and early stage. **Industry Preferences:** Communications, computer software, semiconductors and other electronics, biotechnology, and medical and health. **Geographic Preference:** Northeast.

53046 ■ Matrix Management Corp.
1000 Winter St., Ste. 4500
Waltham, MA 02451-1232
Ph: (781)890-2244
Fax: (781)890-2288
Co. E-mail: info@matrix.com
URL: http://www.matrixpartners.com
Contact: Nicholas F. Beim, Partner
E-mail: nbeim@matrixpartners.com
Founded: 1977. **Preferred Investment Size:** $2,000,000 to $10,000,000. **Industry Preferences:** Communications and media, Internet specific, computer software and services, computer hardware, semiconductors and other electronics. **Geographic Preference:** California and Massachusetts.

53047 ■ MDT Advisers, Inc.
Oliver Street Tower, 21st Fl.
125 High St.
Boston, MA 02110
Ph: (617)235-7100

Fax: (617)235-7199
URL: http://www.mdtai.com
Contact: John B. Fisher, Chief Executive Officer
Preferred Investment Size: $500,000 to $5,000,000. **Industry Preferences:** Consumer related, other products, Internet specific, communications and media, computer software and services, semiconductors and other electronics, industrial and energy, medical and health, computer hardware, and biotechnology. **Geographic Preference:** Northeast.

53048 ■ Mediphase Venture Partners / EHealth Technology Fund
2223 Washington St., Ste. 102
Newton, MA 02462
Ph: (617)332-3408
Fax: (617)332-8463
Co. E-mail: info@mediphaseventure.com
URL: http://www.mediphaseventure.com
Contact: Lawrence G. Miller, Founder
Industry Preferences: Biotechnology, medical and health. **Geographic Preference:** U.S.

53049 ■ Megunticook Management, Inc.
143 Newbury St., 6th Fl.
Boston, MA 02116
Ph: (617)986-3000
Fax: (617)986-3100
Co. E-mail: cvaughan@megunticook.com
URL: http://www.megunticook.com
Contact: Tom Matlack, Managing Partner
Preferred Investment Size: $500,000 to $3,000,000. **Industry Preferences:** Internet specific, communications and media, computer software and services, semiconductors and other electronics, consumer related, computer hardware, and other products. **Geographic Preference:** Northeast.

53050 ■ MPM Capital / MPM Asset Management LLC
The John Hancock Tower
200 Clarendon St., 54th Fl.
Boston, MA 02116
Ph: (617)425-9200
Fax: (617)425-9201
Co. E-mail: info@mpmcapital.com
URL: http://www.mpmcapital.com
Contact: Ken Greenberg, Principal
Preferred Investment Size: $5,000,000 to $50,000,000. **Industry Preferences:** Biotechnology, medical and health, computer software and services, and Internet specific. **Geographic Preference:** U.S.

53051 ■ Navigator Technology Ventures / NTV
1 Broadway, Ste. 1300
Cambridge, MA 02142
Ph: (617)494-0111
Fax: (617)497-1600
Co. E-mail: info@ntven.com
URL: http://www.ntven.com
Contact: Alan Hanover, Chief Executive Officer
E-mail: alain@ntven.com
Preferred Investment Size: $500,000 to $750,000,000. **Investment Policies:** Early and later stage. **Industry Preferences:** Communications, technology, semiconductors and other electronics, and biotechnology. **Geographic Preference:** U.S. .

53052 ■ Neocarta Ventures, Inc.
396 Washington St., Ste. 278
Wellesley Hills, MA 02481
Ph: (781)591-0303
Co. E-mail: info@neocarta.com
URL: http://www.neocarta.com
Contact: D. Jarrett Collins, Managing Director
Preferred Investment Size: $1,000,000 to $5,000,000. **Industry Preferences:** Internet specific, communications and media, computer software and services, semiconductors and other electronics, computer hardware, and other products. **Geographic Preference:** U.S.

53053 ■ North Bridge Venture Partners (NBVP)
950 Winter St., Ste. 4600
Waltham, MA 02451
Ph: (781)290-0004

Fax: (781)290-0999
Co. E-mail: info@northbridge.com
URL: http://nbvp.northbridge.com/Default.asp
Contact: Edward T. Anderson, Partner
URL(s): www.nbvp.com. **Founded:** 1994. **Preferred Investment Size:** $1,000,000 to $10,000,000. **Industry Preferences:** Communications and media, Internet specific, computer software and services, computer hardware, semiconductors and other electronics, medical and health, other products, and biotechnology. **Geographic Preference:** Northeast and Southeast.

53054 ■ North Hill Ventures
10 Post Office Sq., 11th Fl.
Boston, MA 02109
Ph: (617)788-2150
Fax: (617)788-2152
URL: http://www.northhillventures.com
Contact: Benjamin Malka, Principal
E-mail: ben.malka@northhillventures.com
Preferred Investment Size: $2,000,000 to $5,000,000. **Industry Preferences:** Consumer related, financial services, and business service. **Geographic Preference:** U.S.

53055 ■ One Liberty Ventures
150 Cambridge Park Dr., 10th Fl.
Cambridge, MA 02140
Ph: (617)492-7280
Fax: (617)492-7290
Co. E-mail: info@oneliberty.com
URL: http://www.oneliberty.com
Contact: Edwin Kania, Managing Director
Preferred Investment Size: $1,000,000 to $10,000,000. **Industry Preferences:** Communications and media, computer software, hardware and services, Internet specific, biotechnology, medical and health, semiconductors and other electronics, industrial and energy. **Geographic Preference:** Northeast and Southeast.

53056 ■ Osborn Capital LLC
171 Grove St.
Lexington, MA 02420
Ph: (781)402-1790
Fax: (781)402-1793
Co. E-mail: info@osborncapital.com
URL: http://www.osborncapital.com
Contact: Eric Janszen, Managing Director
E-mail: eric@osborncapital.com

53057 ■ Polaris Venture Partners
1000 Winter St., Ste. 3550
Waltham, MA 02451
Ph: (781)290-0770
Fax: (781)290-0880
URL: http://www.polarisventures.com
Contact: Alan G. Spoon, Managing Partner
E-mail: aspoon@polarisventures.com
Preferred Investment Size: $250,000 to $15,000,000. **Industry Preferences:** Internet specific, computer software services, computer hardware, biotechnology, communications and media, business services, manufacturing, medical and health, and other products. **Geographic Preference:** U.S.

53058 ■ Prism Venture Partners
117 Kendrick St., Ste. 200
Needham, MA 02494
Ph: (781)302-4000
Fax: (781)302-4040
URL: http://www.prismventure.com
Contact: Steve D. Weintein, Principal
Preferred Investment Size: $5,000,000 to $15,000,000. **Industry Preferences:** Internet specific, medical and health, communications and media, computer software and services, biotechnology, semiconductors and other electronics, and computer hardware. **Geographic Preference:** Mid Atlantic, Northeast, and West Coast U.S.; and Canada.

53059 ■ Rockport capital Partners
160 Federal St., 18th Fl.
Boston, MA 02110-1700
Ph: (617)912-1420

Fax: (617)912-1449
URL: http://www.rockportcap.com
Contact: David J. Prend, Partner
Preferred Investment Size: $500,000 to $25,000,000. **Investment Policies:** Seed, early, first, second, and later stage. **Industry Preferences:** Semiconductors and other electronics, industrial and energy, utilities, transportation, and environmental. **Geographic Preference:** U.S.

53060 ■ RSA Capital
174 Middlesex Tpke.
Bedford, MA 01730
Ph: (781)515-5000
Free: 877-RSA-4900
Fax: (781)515-5010
URL: http://www.rsasecurity.com
Contact: Arthur W. Coviello, Jr., President
Preferred Investment Size: $2,000,000 to $5,000,000. **Industry Preferences:** Communications, computer software, and Internet specific. **Geographic Preference:** U.S.

53061 ■ Seacoast Capital
55 Ferncroft Rd., Ste. 110
Danvers, MA 01923
Ph: (978)750-1300
Fax: (978)750-1301
URL: http://www.seacoastcapital.com
Contact: Eben S. Moulton, Managing Director
Preferred Investment Size: $2,000,000 to $10,000,000. **Industry Preferences:** Other products, Internet specific, consumer related, semiconductors and other electronics, medical and health, industrial and energy, computer software and services. **Geographic Preference:** U.S.

53062 ■ Seaflower Ventures
Bay Colony Corporate Ctr.
1000 Winter St., Ste. 1000
Waltham, MA 02451
Ph: (781)466-9552
Fax: (781)466-9553
URL: http://www.seaflower.com
Contact: James Sherblom, Partner
Preferred Investment Size: $1,000,000 to $3,000,000. **Industry Preferences:** Medical and health, biotechnology, Internet specific, computer hardware, industrial and energy, and other products. **Geographic Preference:** New England, the Mid Atlantic, the Great Lakes region (Michigan, Wisconsin, Illinois), Easter Canada (Montreal & Toronto), and the Southeast.

53063 ■ Shawmut Capital Partners
75 Federal St., 18th Fl.
Boston, MA 02110
Ph: (617)368-4900
Fax: (617)368-4910
URL: http://www.shawmutcapital.com
Contact: Daniel K. Doyle, Managing Director
Preferred Investment Size: $3,000,000 to $10,000,000. **Industry Preferences:** Financial services. **Geographic Preference:** U.S. and Canada.

53064 ■ Softbank Capital Partners
1188 Centre St.
Newton Center, MA 02459
Ph: (617)928-9300
Fax: (617)928-9304
Co. E-mail: ContactSBCCapital@softbank.com
URL: http://www.sbcap.com
Contact: Ronald D. Fisher, Managing Partner
Industry Preferences: Internet specific, consumer related, computer software and services, communications and media, computer hardware, semiconductors and other electronics, and industrial and energy. **Geographic Preference:** U.S. and Canada.

53065 ■ Solstice Capital
81 Washington St., Ste. 303
Salem, MA 02109-4216
Ph: (617)523-7733
Fax: (617)523-5827
URL: http://www.solcap.com
Contact: Harry George, Partner
Preferred Investment Size: $500,000 to $1,000,000. **Industry Preferences:** Computer software and services, industrial and energy, Internet specific, bio-

technology, medical and health, semiconductors and other electronics, computer hardware, communications and media, consumer related, and other products. **Geographic Preference:** Northeast and Southwest.

53066 ■ Spectrum Equity Investors
333 Middlefield Rd., Ste. 200
Menlo Park, CA 94025
Ph: (415)464-4600
Fax: (415)464-4601
URL: http://www.spectrumequity.com
Contact: Benjamin M. Coughlin, Managing Director
E-mail: ben@spectrumequity.com
Preferred Investment Size: $25,000,000 to $100,000,000. **Industry Preferences:** Communications and media, Internet specific, computer software and services, business services, other products, semiconductors and other electronics, and consumer related. **Geographic Preference:** U.S. and Canada.

53067 ■ Spray Venture Partners
2330 Washington St.
Newton, MA 02462
Ph: (617)332-6060
Fax: (617)332-6070
Co. E-mail: info@spraypartners.com
URL: http://www.spraypartners.com
Contact: Kevin G. Connors, Partner
Preferred Investment Size: $50,000 to $6,000,000. **Industry Preferences:** Medical and health, biotechnology, and Internet specific. **Geographic Preference:** U.S.

53068 ■ The Still River Fund
Reservoir Pl.
1601 Trapelo Rd., Ste. 182
Waltham, MA 02451
Ph: (781)290-5363
Fax: (781)290-0606
URL: http://www.stillriverfund.com
Contact: James A. Saalfield, Partner
E-mail: jim.saalfield@stillriverfund.com
Preferred Investment Size: $500,000 to $5,000,000. **Industry Preferences:** Other products, communications and media, Internet specific, semiconductors and other electronics, computer software and services, biotechnology, and consumer related. **Geographic Preference:** Northeast.

53069 ■ Summit Partners
222 Berkeley St., 18th Fl.
Boston, MA 02116-3733
Ph: (617)824-1000
Fax: (617)824-1100
URL: http://www.summitpartners.com
Contact: John R. Carroll, Managing Director
E-mail: john@summitpartners.com
Founded: 1984. **Preferred Investment Size:** $5,000,000 to $500,000,000. **Industry Preferences:** Other products, computer software and other services, communications and media, Internet specific, computer hardware, semiconductors and other electronics, medical and health, consumer related, biotechnology, business services, industrial and energy. **Geographic Preference:** U.S. and Canada.

53070 ■ TA Associates Inc.
200 Clarendon St., 56th Fl., John Hancock Tower
Boston, MA 02116-5043
Ph: (617)574-6700
Fax: (617)574-6728
URL: http://www.ta.com
Contact: C. Kevin Landry, Chairman of the Board
E-mail: klandry@ta.com
Founded: 1968. **Preferred Investment Size:** $60,000,000 to $500,000,000. **Industry Preferences:** Computer software and services, other products, communications and media, Internet specific, medical and health, semiconductors and other electronics, consumer related, computer hardware, financial and business services, medical and health. **Geographic Preference:** U.S. and Canada.

53071 ■ TTC Ventures
1 Main St., 6th Fl.
Cambridge, CT 02142
Ph: (617)528-3137

Fax: (617)577-1715
URL: http://www.ttcventures.com
Industry Preferences: Internet specific, computer software and services, communications and media, and computer hardware. **Geographic Preference:** U.S.

53072 ■ The Venture Capital Fund of New England
30 Washington St.
Wellesley Hills, MA 02481
Ph: (781)431-8400
Fax: (781)237-6578
Co. E-mail: inquiries@vcfne.com
URL: http://www.vcfne.com
Contact: Kevin J. Dougherty, Managing Director
Preferred Investment Size: $500,000 to $1,500,000. **Industry Preferences:** Computer software and services, communications and media, medical and health, industrial and energy, semiconductors and other electronics, computer hardware, other products, Internet specific, biotechnology, and consumer related. **Geographic Preference:** Northeast.

53073 ■ Venture Investment Management Company LLC (VIMAC)
177 Milk St.
Boston, MA 02190-3410
Ph: (617)350-9800
Fax: (617)350-9899
Co. E-mail: info@vimac.com
URL: http://www.vimac.com
Contact: Robert C. Roeper, Director
E-mail: rroeper@vimac.com
Preferred Investment Size: $5,000,000 to $15,000,000. **Industry Preferences:** Internet specific, computer software, hardware and services, communications and media, semiconductors and other electronics, medical and health, and consumer related. **Geographic Preference:** Ontario and Quebec, Canada.

53074 ■ Ventures
1601 TrapeloRoad, Ste. 170
Waltham, MA 02451
Ph: (978)658-8980
Co. E-mail: info@ventures.com
URL: http://www.ventures.com
Contact: Peter H. Mills, Managing Director
Preferred Investment Size: $1,000,000 to $20,000,000. **Investment Policies:** Early and later stage, expansion, generalist PE, industry rollups, recapitalizations, and special situation. **Industry Preferences:** Internet specific, information technology, consumer related, and industrial and energy. **Geographic Preference:** U.S. and Canada.

53075 ■ Yankee Tek Ventures
1 Memorial Dr., 12th Fl.
Cambridge, MA 01242
Ph: (617)250-0500
Fax: (617)250-0501
Co. E-mail: info@yankeetek.com
URL: http://www.yankeetek.com
Contact: Howard Anderson, Managing Director
Preferred Investment Size: $500,000 to $6,000,000. **Industry Preferences:** Communications, computer software, Internet specific, semiconductors and other electronics, and business service. **Geographic Preference:** Northeast.

53076 ■ Zero Stage Capital Co., Inc.
265 Franklin St.
Boston, MA 02110
Ph: (617)876-5355
Fax: (617)876-1248
Co. E-mail: info@zerostage.com
URL: http://www.zerostage.com
Contact: Ben R. Bronstein, Managing Director
Preferred Investment Size: $2,000 to $10,000,000. **Industry Preferences:** Computer software and services, Internet specific, communications and media, medical and health, biotechnology, semiconductors and other electronics, industrial and energy, consumer related, and other products. **Geographic Preference:** East Coast and Northeast.

PROCUREMENT ASSISTANCE PROGRAMS

53077 ■ Massachusetts Procurement Technical Assistance Center - University of Massachusetts - Small Business Development Center (SBDC)
121 President's Dr., Rm. 227
Amherst, MA 01003
Ph: (413)545-6303
Fax: (413)545-1273
Co. E-mail: ptachelp@msbdc.umass.edu
URL: http://www.msbdc.org/ptac
Contact: Grace Otta, Program Manager
Description: Helps to guide you through the government procurement process and provide you with information on how to become more competitive in the government marketplace.

53078 ■ Small Business Administration
Electronic Systems Center
Hanscom AFB
275 Randolf Rd., Bldg. 1101
Bedford, MA 01731-2818
Ph: (781)377-2737
Fax: (202)481-0340
Co. E-mail: arvind.patel@sba.gov
URL: http://www.sba.gov
Description: Covers activities for Hanscom Air Force Base (Bedford, MA), Army Corps of Engineers (Waltham, MA), Army Soldiers Systems Command (Natick, MA), Transportation Systems Control (Cambridge, MA).

INCUBATORS/RESEARCH AND TECHNOLOGY PARKS

53079 ■ Biogen Idec Innovation Incubator
14 Cambridge Center
Cambridge, MA 02142
Ph: (858)401-8242
Co. E-mail: bi3@biogenidec.com
URL: http://www.bi3.biogenidec.com
Description: A biotech incubator offering a comprehensive set of resources and services to ensure rapid startup and quick progression by supplying all the business and administrative support required to manage day-to-day company operations.

53080 ■ Economic Development & Industrial Corporation of Lynn, Massachusetts - Office of Economic Development
Lynn City Hall
3 City Hall Sq., Rm. 307
Lynn, MA 01901
Ph: (781)581-9399
Fax: (781)581-9731
Co. E-mail: info@ediclynn.org
URL: http://www.ediclynn.org
Contact: James Marsh, Director
Description: The Economic Development & Industrial Corporation of Lynn (EDIC/Lynn) is a non-profit corporation established under a state mandate in 1977 that functions as the City of Lynn's development bank.

53081 ■ Enterprise Center at Salem State College
121 Loring Ave.
Salem, MA 01970
Ph: (978)542-7528
Fax: (978)542-7061
Co. E-mail: sgibney@enterprisectr.org
URL: http://www.enterprisectr.org/
Description: A business incubator and virtual center for entrepreneurs throughout the North Shore of Boston at every stage of business development. The Center leases office space to start up companies, offers free skill-building workshops to the public, and hosts numerous other programs including one hundred twenty-eight Venture North Networking Breakfasts and an annual Business Plan Competition.

53082 ■ Martin Luther King Jr. Business Empowerment Center
237 Chandler St.
Worcester, MA 01609
Ph: (508)756-6330
Fax: (508)751-8591
Co. E-mail: mlkj-bec@rcn.com
URL: http://www.mlkj-bec.org/
Description: A community-based operation focusing on business development, business incubation, and job placement and training; clients are provided technical support and business training skills in the areas of accounting, cash management, employee relations, technology, and business planning. The Center offers quality office space, office equipment, supplies and furniture, conference rooms, internet access, and secretarial staff resources to small, and start-up businesses.

53083 ■ Massachusetts Biomedical Initiatives
Gateway Park
60 Prescott St.
Worcester, MA 01605
Ph: (508)797-4200
Fax: (508)799-4039
Co. E-mail: info@massbiomed.org
URL: http://www.massbiomed.org/
Description: An independent, tax-exempt corporation created to support the growth and expansion of biotechnology and medical device companies throughout the region, enhancing the status of Massachusetts as a world leader in the medical industry.

53084 ■ MassInnovation, LLC
360 Merrimack St., Bldg. 5
Lawrence, MA 01843
Ph: (978)683-2901
Fax: (978)683-2837
Co. E-mail: info@massinnovation.com
URL: http://www.massinnovation.com
Contact: Robert Ansin, Chief Executive Officer
Description: The MIC supports entrepreneurs with facilities for offices, laboratories, and light manufacturing as well as access to venture capital.

53085 ■ Springfield Business Incubator
Springfield Technical Community College
Andrew M. Scibelli Enterprise Center
1 Federal St., Bldg. 101
Springfield, MA 01105
Ph: (413)755-6109
Co. E-mail: marla@admin.umass.edu
URL: http://www.stcc.edu/sbi/
Description: A small business incubator striving to enhance the economic development of the Pioneer Valley by providing entrepreneurs with the opportunity to experience being in business for themselves, while still having a team of advisors guiding them.

EDUCATIONAL PROGRAMS

53086 ■ Becker College
61 Sever St.
Worcester, MA 01609
Ph: (508)791-9241
Free: 877-5-BECKER
Fax: (508)831-7505
Co. E-mail: info@becker.edu
URL: http://www.becker.edu
Description: Four and two year college offering a small business management programs.

53087 ■ Bunker Hill Community College
250 New Rutherford Ave.
Boston, MA 02129-2925
Ph: (617)228-2000
Fax: (617)228-2082
URL: http://www.bhcc.mass.edu
Description: Two-year college offering a small business management course.

53088 ■ Dean College
99 Main St.
Franklin, MA 02038
Ph: (508)541-1508
Free: 800-852-7702

Fax: (508)541-8726
Co. E-mail: admissions@dean.edu
URL: http://www.dean.edu
Description: Two-year college offering a small business management program.

53089 ■ MassBay Community College
50 Oakland St.
Wellesley Hills, MA 02481
Ph: (781)239-3000
Fax: (781)239-2561
Co. E-mail: info@massbay.edu
URL: http://www.massbay.edu
Description: College offering a two-year small business management program.

53090 ■ Mt. Ida College - Division of Continuing Education
777 Dedham St.
Newton Centre, MA 02459
Ph: (617)928-4500
Fax: (617)928-4776
Co. E-mail: continuinged@mountida.edu
URL: http://www.mountida.edu
Description: Offers certificate and/or associate degree programs in business administration and paralegal studies. Also provides noncredit professional development programs to small business owners.

PUBLICATIONS

53091 ■ *Boston Business Journal*
200 High St.
Boston, MA 02110
Ph: (617)330-1000
Fax: (617)330-1016
URL: http://www.amcity.com/boston

53092 ■ *Smart Start your Massachusetts Business*
PSI Research
300 N. Valley Dr.
Grants Pass, OR 97526
Ph: (503)479-9464
Free: 800-228-2275
Fax: (503)476-1479
Co. E-mail: info@psi-research.com
URL: http://www.psi-research.com
Ed: Michael D. Jenkins. **Released:** Revised edition, 1992. **Price:** $29.95 (looseleaf binder); $24.95 (paper). **Description:** Part of the Successful Business Library series.

53093 ■ *Worcester Business Journal*
172 Shrewsbury St.
Worcester, MA 01604
Ph: (508)755-8004
Free: 800-925-8004
Fax: (508)755-8860
URL: http://www.wbjournal.com

PUBLISHERS

53094 ■ Nicholas Brealey Publishing (NB)
20 Park Plz., Ste. 115A
Boston, MA 02108
Ph: (617)523-3801
Free: 888-273-2539
Fax: (617)523-3708
Co. E-mail: info@nicholasbrealey.com
URL: http://www.nicholasbrealey.com
Contact: Jennifer Delaney, Manager
E-mail: jdelaney@nicholasbrealey.com
Description: Description: Publishes trade and professional books in business, intelligent self-help and popular psychology. Accepts unsolicited manuscripts. Reaches market through commission representatives, direct mail, reviews, listings and distributors. **Founded:** 1992.

53095 ■ Charles River Media (CRM)
25 Thomson Pl.
Boston, MA 02210
Ph: (617)757-7900
Free: 800-347-7707

Fax: (617)757-7969
Co. E-mail: info@charlesriver.com
URL: http://www.delmarlearning.com/charlesriver
Contact: Dave Pallai, President
Description: Description: Publishes books and software on game development, web development, networking and computer graphics. Accepts unsolicited manuscripts. Reaches market through commission representatives, as well as wholesalers and distributors. **Founded:** 1994. **Publications:** *Journal of Game Development* (Quarterly).

53096 ■ DBA Books—D Bellavance Agency
291 Beacon St., Ste. 8
Boston, MA 02116-1264
Ph: (617)262-0411
Contact: Diane M. Bellavance, Owner
E-mail: dbellava@lynx.neu.edu
Description: Description: Publishes books for small business owners. Reaches market through direct mail and internet bookstores. Does not accept unsolicited manuscripts. **Founded:** 1979.

53097 ■ HRD Press—Human Resource Development Press Inc.
22 Amherst Rd.
Amherst, MA 01002-9709
Ph: (413)253-3488
Free: 800-822-2801
Fax: (413)253-3490
Co. E-mail: info@hrdpress.com
URL: http://www.hrdpress.com
Contact: Robert W. Carkhuff, President
Description: Description: Publishes textbooks and workshops on human resources development, management and training. Reaches market through direct mail and telephone sales. **Scope:** Publishes print, video, software, and books for consultants, corporate trainers, and educators in the human resource industry. Also provides a wide assortment of administrative, consultative, and technical services. **Founded:** 1972. **Publications:** "The Constant Customer"; "The Manager's Pocket Guide to eCommunication(MPGEC)"; "The Managers Pocket Guide to Emotional Intelligence (MPGEI)"; "Twenty Reproducible Assessment Instruments"; "Establishing the Value of Training". **Seminars:** Planning for Team Results; Preparing the Future Leader; Problem Solving Process; Supervisory Development Series.

53098 ■ JLA Publications—Jeffrey Lant Associates Publications
50 Follen St., Ste. 507
Cambridge, MA 02138
Ph: (617)547-6372
Fax: (617)547-0061
Co. E-mail: drjlant@worldprofit.com
Contact: Jeffrey L. Lant, President
Description: Description: Publishes guides and books on small business topics. Accepts unsolicited manuscripts. **Founded:** 1979.

53099 ■ Jeffrey Lant Associates Inc.
50 Follen St., Ste. 507
Cambridge, MA 02138
Ph: (617)547-6372
Fax: (617)547-0061
URL: http://www.jeffreylant.com
Contact: Dr. Jeffrey L. Lant, President
E-mail: drjlant@worldprofit.com
Description: Description: Publishes technical assistance books for nonprofit organizations, consultants, independent professionals and small and home-based businesses. Offers audio cassettes, workshops and consultation services. Also publishes twice monthly Worlgram newsletter. Reaches market through commission representatives, direct mail, telephone sales and the Internet. Accepts unsolicited manuscripts. **Scope:** Sets up businesses online, design websites and assists with marketing. **Founded:** 1979. **Publications:** "E-mail El Dorado," JLA Publications, 1998; "Web Wealth: How to Turn the World Wide Web Into a Cash Hose for Your Business. Whatever You're Selling," 1997; "Multi-Level Money," JLA Publications, 1994; "No More Cold Calls," JLA Publications, 1997; "Cash Copy"; "How to make at least $100000 a year"; "E-Money". **Seminars:** Business and personal development, including Establishing and Operating Your Successful Consulting Business; Successfully Promoting Your Small Business and Professional Practice; Succeeding in Your Mail Order Business; Successfully Raising Money for Your Nonprofit Organization from Foundations, Corporations and Individuals; Money Making Marketing: Finding the People Who Need What You're Selling and Making Sure They Buy It; Getting Corporations, Foundations, and Individuals to Give You the Money Your Nonprofit Organization Needs.

53100 ■ Standish Press
105 Standish St.
Duxbury, MA 02332
Ph: (781)934-9570
Fax: (781)934-9570
Co. E-mail: standish@verizon.net
Contact: Dick Rothschild, President
Description: Description: Publishes health and fitness for self-help, medical care, writing, home improvement, humor, business, travel and fiction for an adult audience. Does not accept unsolicited manuscripts. Reaches market through reviews and listings as well as wholesalers and distributors. **Founded:** 1999.

SMALL BUSINESS ASSISTANCE PROGRAMS

53101 ■ Michigan Economic Development Corp.
300 N Washington Sq.
Lansing, MI 48913
Ph: (517)373-9808
Free: 888-522-0103
Fax: (517)335-0198
Co. E-mail: MEDCservices@michigan.org
URL: http://www.themedc.org
Contact: Greg Maine, Chief Executive Officer
Description: Advocate for businesses in Michigan that have a conflict with state agencies or that need assistance in getting attention from state agencies.

53102 ■ Michigan Economic Development Corporation - International Development
300 N Washington Sq.
Lansing, MI 48913
Ph: (517)335-5975
Free: 888-522-0103
Fax: (517)241-3689
Co. E-mail: internationaldevinfo@michigan.org
URL: http://www.michigan.org/medc/
Contact: Greg Maine, Chief Executive Officer
Description: Assists firms in developing foreign markets.

53103 ■ Michigan Economic Development Corp. - Small Business Outreach
300 N Washington Sq.
Lansing, MI 48913
Ph: (517)373-9808
Fax: (517)335-0198
URL: http://www.michigan.org/medc
Contact: Greg Maine, Chief Executive Officer
Description: Assists firms in developing foreign markets.

53104 ■ Midland Tomorrow
300 Rodd St., Ste. 201
Midland, MI 48640-6596
Ph: (989)839-0340
Fax: (989)839-7372
Co. E-mail: info@midlandtomorrow.org
URL: http://www.midlandtomorrow.org/
Contact: Scott Walker, Chief Executive Officer

SCORE OFFICES

53105 ■ SCORE Ann Arbor Area Chapter
3601 Plymouth Rd.
Ann Arbor, MI 48105
Ph: (734)929-9091
URL: http://www.annarborscore.com
Contact: Terry Grover, Chairman
Description: Provides public service by offering small business advice and training. **Founded:** 2000.

53106 ■ SCORE Barry County
Co. E-mail: info@mibarry.com

53107 ■ SCORE Cornerstone Alliance
Co. E-mail: score@cstonealliance.org

53108 ■ SCORE Detroit
477 Michigan Ave., Rm. 515
Detroit, MI 48226
Ph: (313)226-7947
Fax: (313)226-3448
Co. E-mail: detscore@sbcglobal.net
URL: http://scoredetroit.org
URL(s): detroit.score.org/chapters/detroit-score. **Description:** Seeks to provide counseling for new and small business. **Scope:** business plans. **Founded:** 1964. **Publications:** SCORE Scribblings (Quarterly). **Awards:** Client of the Year (Annual).

53109 ■ SCORE Grand Rapids
111 Pearl St. NW
Grand Rapids, MI 49503
Ph: (616)771-0305
Co. E-mail: score@grandrapids.org
URL: http://www.scoregr.org
Contact: Bill Leete, Chairman
Description: Dedicated to entrepreneur education and the formation, growth and success of small businesses nationwide.

53110 ■ SCORE Greenville
Co. E-mail: info@greenvillechamber.net

53111 ■ SCORE Holland
Co. E-mail: contactus@scoreholland.org

53112 ■ SCORE Kalamazoo
Co. E-mail: info@scorekazoo.org

53113 ■ SCORE Ludington & Scottville
Co. E-mail: lauran@ludington.org

53114 ■ SCORE Muskegon
c/o Muskegon Chamber of Commerce
380 W Western Ave.
Muskegon, MI 49440
Ph: (231)722-3751
URL: http://www.scoremuskegon.org
Description: Serves as volunteer program in which working and retired business management professionals provide free business counseling to men and women who are considering starting a small business, encountering problems with their business, or expanding their business. Offers free one-on-one counseling, online counseling and low cost workshops on a variety of business topics. **Founded:** 1983.

53115 ■ SCORE Scribblings
477 Michigan Ave., Rm. 515
Detroit, MI 48226
Ph: (313)226-7947
Fax: (313)226-3448
Co. E-mail: detscore@sbcglobal.net
URL: http://scoredetroit.org
Released: Quarterly

53116 ■ SCORE Traverse City
202 E Grandview Pkwy.
Traverse City, MI 49684-0387
Ph: (231)947-5075

Free: 888-796-4913
URL: http://score-tvc.org
Description: Provides entrepreneurs with free, confidential, face-to-face and email business counseling.

53117 ■ Tip of the Mitt SCORE
Co. E-mail: chamber@petoskey.com

BETTER BUSINESS BUREAUS

53118 ■ Better Business Bureau of Detroit and Eastern Michigan
26777 Central Park Blvd., Ste. 100
Southfield, MI 48076-4163
Ph: (248)223-9400
Fax: (248)356-5135
Co. E-mail: info@easternmichiganbbb.org
URL: http://easternmichigan.bbb.org
Contact: Melanie Duquesnel, President
Description: Seeks to promote and foster ethical relationship between businesses and the public through voluntary self-regulation, consumer and business education, and service excellence. Provides information to help consumers and businesses make informed purchasing decisions and avoid costly scams and frauds; settles consumer complaints through arbitration and other means. **Founded:** 1917.

53119 ■ Better Business Bureau of Western Michigan (BBB WMI)
Trust Bldg.
40 Pearl St. NW, Ste. 354
Grand Rapids, MI 49503
Ph: (616)774-8236
Free: 800-684-3222
Fax: (616)774-2014
Co. E-mail: info@westernmichigan.bbb.org
URL: http://westernmichigan.bbb.org
Contact: Phil Catlett, President
Description: Aims to promote through self-regulation, the highest standards of business ethics, and to instill public confidence in business through programs of education and action that inform, protect and assist. **Scope:** company and charity reliability reports. **Founded:** 1937. **Subscriptions:** 18500. **Publications:** Factfinder (Monthly). **Awards:** Best in Business Award (Annual).

53120 ■ Factfinder
Trust Bldg.
40 Pearl St. NW, Ste. 354
Grand Rapids, MI 49503
Ph: (616)774-8236
Free: 800-684-3222
Fax: (616)774-2014
Co. E-mail: info@westernmichigan.bbb.org
URL: http://westernmichigan.bbb.org
Contact: Phil Catlett, President
Released: Monthly **Price:** included in membership dues.

CHAMBERS OF COMMERCE

53121 ■ *ABCC Newsletter*
36341 Front St., Ste. 2
New Baltimore, MI 48047
Ph: (586)725-5148
Free: 866-643-0023
Fax: (586)725-5369
Co. E-mail: info@anchorbaychamber.com
URL: http://www.anchorbaychamber.com
Contact: Lisa M. Edwards, President
Released: Monthly **Price:** available to members only.

53122 ■ *Action*
429 N State St., Ste. 101
Caro, MI 48723
Ph: (989)673-5211
Fax: (989)673-2517
Co. E-mail: executivedirector@carochamber.org
URL: http://www.carochamber.org
Contact: Brenda Caruthers, Executive Director
Released: Monthly **Price:** free.

53123 ■ Alger County Chamber of Commerce
PO Box 405
Munising, MI 49862
Ph: (906)387-2138
Co. E-mail: chamber@algercounty.org
URL: http://www.algercounty.org
Contact: Dr. Katherine Reynolds, Executive Director
Description: Promotes convention business and tourism in the area.

53124 ■ Allegan Area Chamber of Commerce (AACC)
221 Trowbridge St., Ste. B
Allegan, MI 49010
Ph: (269)673-2479
Co. E-mail: info@alleganchamber.com
URL: http://alleganchamber.com
Contact: Brian Corbett, President
Description: Promotes business and community development in the Allegan, MI area.

53125 ■ Anchor Bay Chamber of Commerce (ABCC)
36341 Front St., Ste. 2
New Baltimore, MI 48047
Ph: (586)725-5148
Free: 866-643-0023
Fax: (586)725-5369
Co. E-mail: info@anchorbaychamber.com
URL: http://www.anchorbaychamber.com
Contact: Lisa M. Edwards, President
Description: Promotes business and community development in Anchor Bay area of MI. **Scope:** business topics. **Founded:** 1991. **Publications:** *ABCC Newsletter* (Monthly); *Community Profile and Membership Directory* (Annual). **Educational Activities:** Educational Program (Monthly); Meet the Candidates (Periodic). **Awards:** Gold Medal Award (Annual).

53126 ■ Ann Arbor Area Chamber of Commerce
115 W Huron St., 3rd Fl.
Ann Arbor, MI 48104
Ph: (734)665-4433
Fax: (734)665-4191
Co. E-mail: info@annarborchamber.org
Contact: Jesse Bernstein, President
E-mail: jesse@annarborchamber.org
Description: Promotes business, assists in increasing business revenues and decreasing company expenses, educates businesses, provides a voice for member businesses in matters of public policy issues, assists members in retaining employees and works with other organizations to promote community development in the Ann Arbor region. **Publications:** *Ann Arbor Area Chamber of Commerce--Business Directory; Ann Arbor Business-to-Business* (Periodic); *Chamber Express e-Newsletter* (Bimonthly); *Directory of Firms, Products, and Services* (Periodic); *Ann Arbor Area Chamber of Commerce--Business Directory* (Annual).

53127 ■ *Ann Arbor Business-to-Business*
115 W Huron St., 3rd Fl.
Ann Arbor, MI 48104
Ph: (734)665-4433
Fax: (734)665-4191
Co. E-mail: info@annarborchamber.org
Contact: Jesse Bernstein, President
E-mail: jesse@annarborchamber.org
Released: Periodic

53128 ■ *Area Map*
5300 W US 10
Ludington, MI 49431
Ph: (231)845-0324
Free: 877-420-6618
Fax: (231)845-6857
Co. E-mail: chamberinfo@ludington.org
URL: http://www.ludington.org
Contact: Kathy Maclean, President

53129 ■ Atlanta Area Chamber of Commerce
PO Box 410
Atlanta, MI 49709
Ph: (989)785-3400
Co. E-mail: info@atlantamichiganchamber.com
URL: http://www.atlantamichigan.com
Contact: Phil LaMore, President
Description: Promotes business and community development in Atlanta, MI. **Founded:** 1986.

53130 ■ Au Gres Chamber of Commerce
PO Box 455
Au Gres, MI 48703
Ph: (989)876-6688
Co. E-mail: staff@augreschamber.com
URL: http://www.augreschamber.com

53131 ■ Auburn Area Chamber of Commerce
PO Box 215
Auburn, MI 48611
Ph: (989)662-4001
Co. E-mail: contact@auburnchambermi.org
URL: http://www.auburnchambermi.org
Contact: Cherri Allen, President
Description: Promotes business and community development in the Auburn, MI area.

53132 ■ *Back to Business*
401 E Mitchell St.
Petoskey, MI 49770-2623
Ph: (231)347-4150
Fax: (231)348-1810
Co. E-mail: chamber@petoskey.com
URL: http://www.petoskey.com
Contact: Carlin Smith, President
Released: Monthly

53133 ■ *Back to Business*
368 E Main St.
Harbor Springs, MI 49740
Ph: (231)526-7999
Fax: (231)526-5593
URL: http://www.harborspringschamber.com
Contact: Liz Ahrens, President
Released: Monthly

53134 ■ Barry County Area Chamber of Commerce (BACC)
221 W State St.
Hastings, MI 49058
Ph: (269)945-2454
Fax: (269)945-3839
Co. E-mail: info@mibarry.com
URL: http://www.mibarry.com
Contact: Valerie Byrnes, President
Description: Promotes business and community development in the Hastings, MI area. **Publications:** *Chamber Directory* (Annual); *Chamber Newsletter* (Bimonthly).

53135 ■ Battle Creek Area Chamber of Commerce (BCACC)
One Riverwalk Centre
34 Jackson St. W
Battle Creek, MI 49017
Ph: (269)962-4076
Fax: (269)962-6309
Co. E-mail: kbeer@battlecreek.org
URL: http://www.battlecreek.org
Contact: Kara E. Beer, Executive Director
Description: Promotes business and community development in the Battle Creek, MI area. **Founded:** 1913. **Publications:** *Insight* (Monthly). **Awards:** Athena Award (Annual); Harley Simmons Award (Annual).

53136 ■ *Bay Area Business Journal*
901 Saginaw St.
Bay City, MI 48708
Ph: (989)893-4567
Fax: (989)995-5594
Co. E-mail: chamber@baycityarea.com
URL: http://www.baycityarea.com
Contact: Mike Seward, President
Released: Bimonthly **Price:** free.

53137 ■ Bay Area Chamber of Commerce (BACC)
901 Saginaw St.
Bay City, MI 48708
Ph: (989)893-4567
Fax: (989)995-5594
Co. E-mail: chamber@baycityarea.com
URL: http://www.baycityarea.com
Contact: Mike Seward, President
Description: Promotes business and community development in the Bay City, MI area. **Founded:** 1882. **Publications:** *Bay Area Business Journal* (Bimonthly); *Bay Area Chamber Handbook*. **Awards:** Athena Award (Annual); Leadership Alumni Community Service Award (Annual). **Telecommunication Services:** mseward@baycityarea.com.

53138 ■ *Bay Area Chamber Handbook*
901 Saginaw St.
Bay City, MI 48708
Ph: (989)893-4567
Fax: (989)995-5594
Co. E-mail: chamber@baycityarea.com
URL: http://www.baycityarea.com
Contact: Mike Seward, President

53139 ■ Bellaire Area Chamber of Commerce
PO Box 205
Bellaire, MI 49615
Ph: (231)533-6023
Fax: (231)533-8764
URL: http://www.bellairechamber.org
Contact: Patricia W. Savant, Executive Director
Description: Promotes business and community development in the Bellaire, MI area.

53140 ■ Belleville Area Chamber of Commerce (BCC)
248 Main St.
Belleville, MI 48111
Ph: (734)697-7151
Fax: (734)697-1415
Co. E-mail: bellechamber@bellevillech.org
URL: http://www.bellevillech.org
Contact: Candace Connon, Executive Director
Description: Promotes business and community development in the Belleville, MI area. Participates in annual Strawberry Festival. Holds monthly board meeting. **Founded:** 1963. **Publications:** *Calendar with Directory* (Annual); *Tri-Community Commentator* (Monthly).

53141 ■ Benzie County Chamber of Commerce (BCCC)
826 Michigan Ave.
Benzonia, MI 49616
Ph: (231)882-5801
Free: 800-882-5801
Fax: (231)882-9249
Co. E-mail: chamber@benzie.org
URL: http://www.benzie.org
Contact: Mary Carroll, President
Description: Promotes business, tourism, and community development in Benzie County, MI. Sponsors festivals, including Winterfest; Home & Garden Show; Benzonia Days; Beulah Art Fair; Port City Run; Cherry Field Day; Frankfort Art Fair; and National

Coho Festival. **Founded:** 1981. **Publications:** *Moving Up* (Quarterly). **Telecommunication Services:** director@benzie.org.

53142 ■ Bi-Annual Member Directory
2055 Gratiot Blvd., Ste. D
Marysville, MI 48040
Ph: (810)364-6180
Fax: (810)364-9388
Co. E-mail: chamber@marysvillechamber.com
URL: http://www.marysvillechamber.com
Contact: Laura J. Crawford, Executive Director
Released: Semiannual

53143 ■ Birch Run Area Chamber of Commerce
11600 N Beyer Rd., Ste. 100
Birch Run, MI 48415
Ph: (989)624-9193
Co. E-mail: info@birchrunchamber.com
URL: http://www.birchrunchamber.com
Contact: Manianne Nelson, Secretary
Description: Promotes business and community development in the Birch Run, MI area.

53144 ■ Birmingham-Bloomfield Chamber of Commerce (BBCC)
725 S Adams, Ste. 130
Birmingham, MI 48009
Ph: (248)644-1700
Fax: (248)644-0286
Co. E-mail: thechamber@bbcc.com
URL: http://www.bbcc.com/home
Contact: Joe Bauman, President
Description: Promotes business and community development in Beverly Hills, Bingham Farms, Birmingham, Bloomfield Hills, and Bloomfield Township, MI. **Founded:** 1948. **Publications:** *Business Insight E-News* (Monthly); *IMAGES of Birmingham Bloomfield* (Annual); *Insight* (Monthly). **Telecommunication Services:** carriez@bbcc.com.

53145 ■ Blissfield Area Chamber of Commerce
PO Box 25
Blissfield, MI 49228-0025
Ph: (517)606-0124
Co. E-mail: info@blissfieldchamber.org
URL: http://www.blissfieldchamber.org
Contact: Frank Baker, President
Description: Promotes business and community development in Blissfield, MI area.

53146 ■ Boyne Area City Chamber of Commerce
28 S Lake St.
Boyne City, MI 49712
Ph: (231)582-6222
Fax: (231)582-6963
Co. E-mail: jacklaurent@hotmail.com
URL: http://www.boynecity.com
Contact: Jack Laurent, President
Description: Works to enhance the economic, industrial, professional, cultural, and civic welfare of the Boyne City Area.

53147 ■ Branch County Area Chamber of Commerce
20 Division St.
Coldwater, MI 49036
Ph: (517)278-5985
Fax: (517)278-8369
Co. E-mail: info@branchareachamber.com
URL: http://www.branchareachamber.com
Contact: Jeff Richards, Executive Director
Description: Promotes business and community development in the Branch County, MI area. **Founded:** 1943. **Publications:** *Community* (Annual); *The Connection* (Monthly). **Awards:** Business of the Year (Annual); Citizen of the Year (Annual); Community Organization of the Year (Annual); Teacher of the Year (Annual).

53148 ■ Brooklyn - Irish Hills Chamber of Commerce
131 N Main St., Ste. A
Brooklyn, MI 49230

Ph: (517)592-8907
Co. E-mail: info@brooklynmi.com
URL: http://www.brooklynmi.com
Contact: Cindy Hubbells, Executive Director
Description: Business owners and professional men and women who invest their time and money in a development program for the entire community. Works to improve the economic, social, cultural, commercial, industrial and civic welfare of the Brooklyn-Irish Hills area.

53149 ■ Buchanan Area Chamber of Commerce (BACC)
PO Box 127
Buchanan, MI 49107
Ph: (269)695-3291
Fax: (269)695-3813
Co. E-mail: bacc@buchanan.mi.us
URL: http://www.buchanan.mi.us
Contact: Katie Berry, Board Member
Description: Businesses and individuals promoting economic and community development in the Buchanan, MI area. Conducts annual dinner, area wide promotions, special events and business-related workshops. **Founded:** 1956. **Publications:** *News & Views* (Monthly); *Redbud Area Directory* (Quarterly); *Redbud Area News* (Monthly).

53150 ■ Business Advisor
12900 Hall Rd., Ste. 190
Sterling Heights, MI 48313
Ph: (586)731-5400
Fax: (586)731-3521
Co. E-mail: woehmke@shrcci.com
URL: http://www.suscc.com
Contact: Wayne Oehmke, President
Released: Monthly

53151 ■ Business Beacon
1 S Harbor Dr.
Grand Haven, MI 49417
Ph: (616)842-4910
Fax: (616)842-0379
Co. E-mail: jgaasch@grandhavenchamber.org
URL: http://www.grandhavenchamber.org
Contact: Joy A. Gaasch, President
Price: included in membership dues.

53152 ■ Business Beat
108 N Lafayette St., Ste. A
Greenville, MI 48838
Ph: (616)754-5697
Fax: (616)754-4710
Co. E-mail: info@greenvillechamber.net
URL: http://www.greenvillechamber.net
Contact: Candy Kerschen, Executive Director
Released: Monthly **Price:** free for members.

53153 ■ Business to Business
939 E 12 Mile Rd.
Madison Heights, MI 48071
Ph: (248)542-5010
Fax: (248)542-6821
URL: http://www.madisonheightschamber.com
Released: Periodic

53154 ■ Business to Business
5300 W US 10
Ludington, MI 49431
Ph: (231)845-0324
Free: 877-420-6618
Fax: (231)845-6857
Co. E-mail: chamberinfo@ludington.org
URL: http://www.ludington.org
Contact: Kathy Maclean, President
Released: Monthly

53155 ■ Business to Business Journal
101 W Main St.
Gaylord, MI 49734
Ph: (989)732-6333
Free: 800-345-8621
Fax: (989)732-7990
Co. E-mail: info@gaylordchamber.com
URL: http://www.gaylordchamber.com
Contact: Todd Gregory, Chairman
Released: Quarterly

53156 ■ Business Connection
20600 Eureka Rd.
Taylor, MI 48180-5306
Ph: (734)284-6000
Fax: (734)284-0198
Co. E-mail: sandy@swcrc.com
URL: http://www.swcrc.com
Contact: Sandy Mull, President (Acting)
Released: Monthly **Price:** included in membership dues.

53157 ■ Business Connections
108 W Park St.
Lapeer, MI 48446
Ph: (810)664-6641
Fax: (810)664-4349
Co. E-mail: staff@lapeerareachamber.org
URL: http://www.lapeerareachamber.org
Contact: Neda Payne, Executive Director
Released: Monthly

53158 ■ Business Directory
380 W Western Ave., Ste. 202
Muskegon, MI 49440
Ph: (616)722-3751
Fax: (616)728-7251
Co. E-mail: mlcc@muskegon.org
URL: http://www.muskegon.org
Contact: Michael Hagen, Chairman
Released: Annual

53159 ■ Business Directory
111 Pearl St. NW
Grand Rapids, MI 49503-2831
Ph: (616)771-0300
Fax: (616)771-0318
Co. E-mail: info@grandrapids.org
URL: http://www.grandrapids.org/home
Contact: Rick Baker, President
Released: Annual **Price:** free for members; $25, for nonmembers.

53160 ■ Business Directory
215 N Water St.
Owosso, MI 48867-2875
Ph: (989)723-5149
Fax: (989)723-8353
Co. E-mail: customerservice@shiawasseechamber.org
URL: http://www.shiawasseechamber.org
Contact: Sue Kadlek, President (Acting)
Released: Annual **Price:** $25.

53161 ■ Business Directory
PO Box 175
Romeo, MI 48065-0175
Ph: (586)752-4436
Fax: (586)752-2835
Co. E-mail: contact@rwchamber.com
URL: http://www.rwchamber.com
Contact: Scott Allen, President
Released: Periodic

53162 ■ Business Directory and Buying Guide
317 Union St.
Milford, MI 48381
Ph: (248)685-7129
Fax: (248)685-9047
Co. E-mail: info@huronvcc.com
URL: http://www.huronvcc.com/1/HVCC/index.asp
Contact: Joell Beether, Executive Director
Released: Annual

53163 ■ Business Guide
27601 Jefferson Ave.
St. Clair Shores, MI 48081
Ph: (586)777-2741
Fax: (586)777-4811
Co. E-mail: metroeastchamber@netscape.net
Contact: Heather Lynn, Executive Director
Released: Annual **Price:** free.

53164 ■ The Business Index
512 E Grand Blanc Rd.
Grand Blanc, MI 48439
Ph: (810)695-4222

Fax: (810)695-0053
Co. E-mail: jet@grandblancchamber.org
URL: http://www.grandblancchamber.com
Contact: Jet Kilmer, President
Released: Monthly

53165 ■ *Business Insight E-News*
725 S Adams, Ste. 130
Birmingham, MI 48009
Ph: (248)644-1700
Fax: (248)644-0286
Co. E-mail: thechamber@bbcc.com
URL: http://www.bbcc.com/home
Contact: Joe Bauman, President
Released: Monthly **Price:** free.

53166 ■ *Business News*
200 E Broadway
Mount Pleasant, MI 48858
Ph: (989)772-2396
Fax: (989)773-2656
Co. E-mail: lhadden@mt-pleasant.net
URL: http://www.mt-pleasant.net
Contact: Lisa Hadden, President
Released: Monthly

53167 ■ *Business Perspective*
114 N Leroy St.
Fenton, MI 48430
Ph: (810)629-5447
Fax: (810)629-6608
Co. E-mail: info@fentonchamber.com
URL: http://www.fentonchamber.com
Contact: Mrs. Shelly Day, President
Released: Monthly

53168 ■ *Business Talk*
301 W Michigan Ave., Ste. 101
Ypsilanti, MI 48197-5450
Ph: (734)482-4920
Fax: (734)482-2021
Co. E-mail: info@annarborchamber.org
URL: http://www.ypsichamber.org
Contact: Diane Keller, President
Released: Monthly

53169 ■ *Business Views*
123 E Washington St.
Howell, MI 48843
Ph: (517)546-3920
Fax: (517)546-4115
Co. E-mail: cdonovan@howell.org
URL: http://www.howell.org
Contact: Jessica Clum, Chairperson

53170 ■ *Business and Visitors Guide*
100 Main St., Ste. B
East Jordan, MI 49727
Ph: (231)536-7351
Fax: (231)536-0966
Co. E-mail: info@ejchamber.org
URL: http://www.ejchamber.org
Contact: Mary H. Faculak, President
Released: Annual

53171 ■ *Buyers' Guide*
1 Woodward Ave., Ste. 1900
Detroit, MI 48232-0840
Ph: (313)964-4000
Free: 866-627-5463
Fax: (313)964-0183
Co. E-mail: members@detroitchamber.com
URL: http://www.detroitchamber.com/main/index.asp
Contact: Sandy K. Baruah, President
E-mail: sbaruah@detroitchamber.com
Released: Annual **Price:** $35.

53172 ■ *Buyers Guide*
424 E Michigan Ave.
Marshall, MI 49068
Ph: (269)781-5163
Free: 800-877-5163
Fax: (269)781-6570
Co. E-mail: info@marshallmi.org
URL: http://www.marshallmi.org/index.taf
Contact: Monica Anderson, President
Released: Annual

53173 ■ *Cadillac Area Business Magazine*
222 Lake St.
Cadillac, MI 49601-1874
Ph: (231)775-9776
Fax: (231)775-1440
Co. E-mail: info@cadillac.org
URL: http://www.cadillac.org
Contact: Bill Tencza, President
Released: Bimonthly

53174 ■ *Cadillac Area Chamber of Commerce (CACC)*
222 Lake St.
Cadillac, MI 49601-1874
Ph: (231)775-9776
Fax: (231)775-1440
Co. E-mail: info@cadillac.org
URL: http://www.cadillac.org
Contact: Bill Tencza, President
Description: Promotes business and community development in the Cadillac, MI area. **Founded:** 1899. **Publications:** *Cadillac Area Business Magazine* (Bimonthly).

53175 ■ *Calendar with Directory*
248 Main St.
Belleville, MI 48111
Ph: (734)697-7151
Fax: (734)697-1415
Co. E-mail: bellechamber@bellevillech.org
URL: http://www.bellevillech.org
Contact: Candace Connon, Executive Director
Released: Annual

53176 ■ *Canton Chamber of Commerce (CCC)*
45525 Hanford Rd.
Canton, MI 48187
Ph: (734)453-4040
Fax: (734)453-4503
Co. E-mail: info@cantonchamber.com
URL: http://www.cantonchamber.com
Contact: Dianne Cojei, President
Description: Promotes business and community development in Canton, Michigan. **Founded:** 1972. **Publications:** *Networker* (Monthly). **Telecommunication Services:** diannec@cantonchamber.com.

53177 ■ *Caro Chamber of Commerce*
429 N State St., Ste. 101
Caro, MI 48723
Ph: (989)673-5211
Fax: (989)673-2517
Co. E-mail: executivedirector@carochamber.org
URL: http://www.carochamber.org
Contact: Brenda Caruthers, Executive Director
Description: Promotes business and community development in the Caro, MI area. Sponsors Cars and Crafts Weekend. **Founded:** 1922. **Publications:** *Action* (Monthly). **Awards:** Chamber Business (Annual); Chamber Member (Annual); Chamber Merit (Annual); Citizen of Year (Annual).

53178 ■ *Cass City Chamber of Commerce*
6506 Main St.
Cass City, MI 48726
Ph: (989)872-4618
Free: 866-266-3822
Fax: (989)872-4855
Co. E-mail: chamber@cass-city.net
URL: http://main.casscitychamber.com
Contact: Dee Mulligan, Administrator
Description: Promotes business and community development in Cass City, MI. **Founded:** 1951. **Publications:** *Chamber Chat* (Quarterly).

53179 ■ *Central Lake Chamber of Commerce*
2587 N M-88 Hwy.
Central Lake, MI 49622
Ph: (231)544-3322
Co. E-mail: clcc@torchlake.com
URL: http://www.central-lake.com
Contact: Jackie White, President
Description: Promotes business and community development in Central Lake, MI area.

53180 ■ *Central Macomb County Chamber of Commerce (CMCCC)*
28 First St., Ste. B
Mount Clemens, MI 48043
Ph: (586)493-7600
Fax: (586)493-7602
Co. E-mail: info@macombcountychamber.com
URL: http://macombcountychamber.com
Contact: Grace Shore, Chief Executive Officer
Description: Brings together businesses united to promote economic development and improve the quality of life in Macomb County, MI. Lobbies on economic issues. Participates in annual Farm City Festival. Convention/Meeting: none. **Founded:** 1903. **Publications:** *Membership and Community Directory* (Annual).

53181 ■ *Chamber Buzz*
512 E Grand Blanc Rd.
Grand Blanc, MI 48439
Ph: (810)695-4222
Fax: (810)695-0053
Co. E-mail: jet@grandblancchamber.org
URL: http://www.grandblancchamber.com
Contact: Jet Kilmer, President
Released: Monthly

53182 ■ *Chamber Calling*
200 W Main
Sturgis, MI 49091-0189
Ph: (269)651-5758
Fax: (269)651-4124
Co. E-mail: info@sturgischamber.com
URL: http://www.sturgischamber.com
Contact: Cathi Garn-Abbs, Executive Director
Released: Monthly

53183 ■ *Chamber Chat*
PO Box 45
Ironwood, MI 49938
Ph: (906)932-1122
Fax: (906)932-2756
Co. E-mail: chamber@ironwoodmi.org
URL: http://www.ironwoodmi.org
Contact: Peter Grewe, Director (Acting)
Released: Monthly

53184 ■ *Chamber Chat*
6506 Main St.
Cass City, MI 48726
Ph: (989)872-4618
Free: 866-266-3822
Fax: (989)872-4855
Co. E-mail: chamber@cass-city.net
URL: http://main.casscitychamber.com
Contact: Dee Mulligan, Administrator
Released: Quarterly

53185 ■ *Chamber Chips*
19132 Huron River Dr.
New Boston, MI 48164
Ph: (734)753-4220
Fax: (734)753-4602
Co. E-mail: township@provide.net
URL: http://www.members.tripod.com/htcc48164
Contact: Teresa A. Shearrer-Lewis-Trosin, Executive Secretary
Released: Monthly

53186 ■ *Chamber Communique*
939 E 12 Mile Rd.
Madison Heights, MI 48071
Ph: (248)542-5010
Fax: (248)542-6821
URL: http://www.madisonheightschamber.com
Released: Monthly

53187 ■ *Chamber Connection*
606 Phillips St.
South Haven, MI 49090
Ph: (616)637-5171
Fax: (616)639-1570
Co. E-mail: cofc@southhavenmi.com
URL: http://www.southhavenmi.com
Contact: Kathy Wagaman, Executive Director
Released: Quarterly

53188 ■ *The Chamber Connection*
1396 St. Clair River Dr.
Algonac, MI 48001
Ph: (810)794-5511
Fax: (866)643-0023
Co. E-mail: execdirector@algonacchamber.com
URL: http://www.algonacchamber.com
Released: Bimonthly

53189 ■ *Chamber Connections*
110 W Superior St.
Alma, MI 48801
Ph: (989)463-5525
Fax: (989)463-6588
Co. E-mail: chamber@gratiot.org
URL: http://www.gratiot.org/1/295/index.asp
Contact: Jayne Norris, Executive Director
Released: Monthly

53190 ■ *Chamber Directory*
221 W State St.
Hastings, MI 49058
Ph: (269)945-2454
Fax: (269)945-3839
Co. E-mail: info@mibarry.com
URL: http://www.mibarry.com
Contact: Valerie Byrnes, President
Released: Annual

53191 ■ *Chamber Express e-Newsletter*
115 W Huron St., 3rd Fl.
Ann Arbor, MI 48104
Ph: (734)665-4433
Fax: (734)665-4191
Co. E-mail: info@annarborchamber.org
Contact: Jesse Bernstein, President
E-mail: jesse@annarborchamber.org
Released: Bimonthly

53192 ■ Chamber - Grand Haven, Spring Lake, Ferrysburg
1 S Harbor Dr.
Grand Haven, MI 49417
Ph: (616)842-4910
Fax: (616)842-0379
Co. E-mail: jgaasch@grandhavenchamber.org
URL: http://www.grandhavenchamber.org
Contact: Joy A. Gaasch, President
Description: Works to serve the interests of the local business community. **Publications:** *Business Beacon*; *Clubs and Organizations Directory*; *Industrial Directory*.

53193 ■ *Chamber News*
111 Pearl St. NW
Grand Rapids, MI 49503-2831
Ph: (616)771-0300
Fax: (616)771-0318
Co. E-mail: info@grandrapids.org
URL: http://www.grandrapids.org/home
Contact: Rick Baker, President
Released: Monthly

53194 ■ *Chamber News*
439 W Main St.
Ionia, MI 48846
Ph: (616)527-2560
Co. E-mail: info@ioniachamber.net
URL: http://www.ioniachamber.org
Contact: Dave Cook, President
Released: Monthly **Price:** free.

53195 ■ *Chamber News*
424 E Michigan Ave.
Marshall, MI 49068
Ph: (269)781-5163
Free: 800-877-5163
Fax: (269)781-6570
Co. E-mail: info@marshallmi.org
URL: http://www.marshallmi.org/index.taf
Contact: Monica Anderson, President
Released: Bimonthly

53196 ■ *Chamber News*
c/o Jennifer Heinzman, Exec. Dir.
246 N State St.
Big Rapids, MI 49307
Ph: (231)796-7649

Fax: (231)796-1625
Co. E-mail: info@mecostacounty.com
URL: http://www.mecostacounty.com
Contact: Jennifer Heinzman, Executive Director
Released: Monthly

53197 ■ *Chamber News*
PO Box 61
St. Johns, MI 48879
Ph: (989)224-7248
Fax: (989)224-7667
Co. E-mail: ccchamber@power-net.net
URL: http://www.clintoncountychamber.org
Contact: Brenda Tarpening, Executive Director
Released: Monthly

53198 ■ *Chamber News*
317 Union St.
Milford, MI 48381
Ph: (248)685-7129
Fax: (248)685-9047
Co. E-mail: info@huronvcc.com
URL: http://www.huronvcc.com/1/HVCC/index.asp
Contact: Joell Beether, Executive Director
Released: Monthly

53199 ■ *Chamber News*
57 N Main St.
Three Rivers, MI 49093
Ph: (616)278-8193
Fax: (616)273-1751
Co. E-mail: info@trchamber.com
URL: http://www.trchamber.com
Contact: Christy Trammell, President
Released: Monthly

53200 ■ *Chamber News*
289 Danforth St.
Coopersville, MI 49404
Ph: (616)997-5164
Fax: (616)997-6679
Co. E-mail: ctimmerman@cityofcoopersville.com
URL: http://www.coopersville.com
Contact: Carrie Borchers, President
Released: Monthly

53201 ■ *Chamber Newsletter*
221 W State St.
Hastings, MI 49058
Ph: (269)945-2454
Fax: (269)945-3839
Co. E-mail: info@mibarry.com
URL: http://www.mibarry.com
Contact: Valerie Byrnes, President
Released: Bimonthly

53202 ■ *Chamber Newsletter*
272 E 8th St.
Holland, MI 49423
Ph: (616)392-2389
Fax: (616)392-7379
Co. E-mail: info@hollandchamber.org
URL: http://www.hollandchamber.org
Contact: Jane Clark, President
Released: Monthly

53203 ■ *Chamber Report*
50 E Genesee St.
Iron River, MI 49935
Ph: (906)265-3822
Fax: (906)265-5605
Co. E-mail: info@iron.org
URL: http://www.iron.org
Contact: Bill Leonoff, Executive Director
Released: Quarterly

53204 ■ *Chamber Report*
PO Box 484
Lake Orion, MI 48361-0484
Ph: (248)693-6300
Fax: (248)693-9227
Co. E-mail: info@lakeorionchamber.com
URL: http://orion.lib.mi.us/orion/index.php
Contact: Alaina Campbell, Executive Director
Released: Monthly **Price:** free.

53205 ■ *Chamber Update*
902 College Ave.
Houghton, MI 49931-0336

Ph: (906)482-5240
Free: 866-304-5722
Fax: (906)482-5241
Co. E-mail: info@keweenaw.org
URL: http://www.keweenaw.org
Contact: Johanna Davis, President
Released: Monthly **Price:** included in membership dues.

53206 ■ *Chamber Update*
213 N James St.
Grayling, MI 49738
Ph: (989)348-2921
Fax: (989)348-7315
Co. E-mail: info@graylingchamber.com
URL: http://graylingchamber.com
Contact: Samantha Schnoor, Chairperson
Released: Monthly

53207 ■ Charlevoix Area Chamber of Commerce
109 Mason St.
Charlevoix, MI 49720-1417
Ph: (231)547-2101
Free: 800-951-2101
Fax: (231)547-6633
Co. E-mail: info@charlevoix.org
URL: http://www.charlevoix.org
Contact: Pat McKeown, Chairman
Description: Acts as the energizing and vitalizing force in the community. Aims to unite all individuals, retail, and industrial types of business, for the promotion of commerce and the betterment of the community. Helps businesses to prosper and grow; to increase job opportunities; to encourage an orderly expansion and development of all segments of the community; to contribute to the overall economic stability of the community; to encourage and promote the nation's private enterprise system of competitive marketing.

53208 ■ Cheboygan Area Chamber of Commerce (CACC)
124 N Main St.
Cheboygan, MI 49721
Ph: (231)627-7183
Free: 800-968-3302
Fax: (231)627-2770
Co. E-mail: info@cheboygan.com
URL: http://www.cheboygan.com
Contact: Matthew J. Friday, Executive Director
Description: Promotes business and community development in the Cheboygan, MI area. Sponsors Home Show, Parades, Riverfest, AutumnFest and Buffalo Bash. **Founded:** 1943. **Publications:** *Executive Report* (Monthly); *Cheboygan Area Chamber of Commerce Membership Directory and Buying Guide* (Annual).

53209 ■ *Cheboygan Area Chamber of Commerce Membership Directory and Buying Guide*
124 N Main St.
Cheboygan, MI 49721
Ph: (231)627-7183
Free: 800-968-3302
Fax: (231)627-2770
Co. E-mail: info@cheboygan.com
URL: http://www.cheboygan.com
Contact: Matthew J. Friday, Executive Director
Released: Annual

53210 ■ Chelsea Area Chamber of Commerce
310 N Main St., Ste. 120
Chelsea, MI 48118
Ph: (734)475-1145
Fax: (734)475-6102
Co. E-mail: info@chelseamichamber.org
URL: http://www.chelseamichamber.org
Contact: Bob Pierce, Executive Director
Description: Promotes business and community development in Chelsea, MI area. **Publications:** *Chelsea Area Chamber of Commerce Community Profile & Business Directory*.

53211 ■ Chesaning Chamber of Commerce (CCC)
PO Box 83
Chesaning, MI 48616

Ph: (989)845-3055
Free: 800-255-3055
Fax: (989)845-6006
Co. E-mail: info@chesaningchamber.org
URL: http://www.chesaningchamber.org
Contact: Chris Wood, Vice Chairman of the Board
Description: Promotes business and community development in Chesaning, MI. **Founded:** 1926.

53212 ■ Clare Area Chamber of Commerce
429 N McEwan St.
Clare, MI 48617
Ph: (989)386-2442
Free: 888-ATC-LARE
Fax: (989)386-3173
Co. E-mail: manager@claremichigan.com
URL: http://www.claremichigan.com
Contact: Roger Williams, President
Description: Businesses seeking to promote economic and community development in the Clare, MI area. Sponsors Irish Festival and Summerfest. **Publications:** *The Voice* (Monthly). **Educational Activities:** Crafts in the Park (Annual).

53213 ■ Clarkston Area Chamber of Commerce
5856 S Main St.
Clarkston, MI 48346
Ph: (248)625-8055
Fax: (248)625-8041
Co. E-mail: info@clarkston.org
URL: http://www.clarkston.org
Contact: Penny Shanks, President
Description: Consists of small businesses, community leaders, service clubs and community groups who work together to promote and enhance economic growth and quality of community in the Clarkston Area.

53214 ■ *Clubs and Civic Organizations*
PO Box 10
Niles, MI 49120-0010
Ph: (269)683-3720
URL: http://www.nilesmi.com
Contact: Ronald J. Sather, President
Released: Periodic

53215 ■ *Clubs and Organizations Directory*
1 S Harbor Dr.
Grand Haven, MI 49417
Ph: (616)842-4910
Fax: (616)842-0379
Co. E-mail: jgaasch@grandhavenchamber.org
URL: http://www.grandhavenchamber.org
Contact: Joy A. Gaasch, President
Price: included in membership dues; $5, for nonmembers.

53216 ■ Coloma-Watervliet Area Chamber of Commerce (CWACC)
PO Box 418
Coloma, MI 49038
Ph: (269)468-9160
Fax: (269)468-7088
Co. E-mail: info@coloma-watervliet.org
URL: http://www.coloma-watervliet.org
Contact: Jim Polashak, Chairman
Description: Promotes businesses in the Coloma-Watervliet area. Organizes Business After Hours, Welcome Baskets to new businesses, ribbon cuttings, ground breakings and offers quarterly newsletters and listing on the website to members.

53217 ■ *Commerce Commentary*
36900 Ford Rd.
Westland, MI 48185-2231
Ph: (734)326-7222
Fax: (734)326-6040
Co. E-mail: info@westlandchamber.com
URL: http://www.westlandchamber.com
Contact: Joe Lezotte, Chairman of the Board
Released: Monthly

53218 ■ *Commerce Connection*
506 W Carleton Rd.
Hillsdale, MI 49242
Ph: (517)439-4341

Fax: (517)439-4111
Co. E-mail: info@hillsdalecountychamber.com
URL: http://www.hillsdalecountychamber.com
Contact: Cyndi Young, President

53219 ■ *Communicator*
PO Box 656
Lewiston, MI 49756
Ph: (989)786-2293
Fax: (989)786-4515
Co. E-mail: lewistonchamber@i2k.com
URL: http://www.lewistonchamber.com
Contact: Elaine Dixon, Chairperson
Released: Monthly

53220 ■ *Communicator*
33233 Five Mile Rd.
Livonia, MI 48154
Ph: (734)427-2122
Fax: (734)427-6055
Co. E-mail: chamber@livonia.org
URL: http://www.livonia.org
Contact: Dan West, President
Released: Monthly

53221 ■ *Communicator*
230 Ludington St.
Escanaba, MI 49829
Ph: (906)786-2192
Free: 800-DEL-TAMI
Fax: (906)786-8830
Co. E-mail: info@deltami.org
URL: http://www.deltami.org
Contact: Vickie Micheau, Executive Director
Released: Monthly **Price:** $12, /year.

53222 ■ *Community*
20 Division St.
Coldwater, MI 49036
Ph: (517)278-5985
Fax: (517)278-8369
Co. E-mail: info@branchareachamber.com
URL: http://www.branchareachamber.com
Contact: Jeff Richards, Executive Director
Released: Annual **Price:** $5, for nonmembers; free for members.

53223 ■ *Community Connection*
368 E Main St.
Harbor Springs, MI 49740
Ph: (231)526-7999
Fax: (231)526-5593
URL: http://www.harborspringschamber.com
Contact: Liz Ahrens, President
Released: Bimonthly

53224 ■ *Community Directory*
12900 Hall Rd., Ste. 190
Sterling Heights, MI 48313
Ph: (586)731-5400
Fax: (586)731-3521
Co. E-mail: woehmke@shrcci.com
URL: http://www.suscc.com
Contact: Wayne Oehmke, President
Released: Annual

53225 ■ *Community Profile*
939 E 12 Mile Rd.
Madison Heights, MI 48071
Ph: (248)542-5010
Fax: (248)542-6821
URL: http://www.madisonheightschamber.com

53226 ■ *Community Profile and Business Directory*
401 E Mitchell St.
Petoskey, MI 49770-2623
Ph: (231)347-4150
Fax: (231)348-1810
Co. E-mail: chamber@petoskey.com
URL: http://www.petoskey.com
Contact: Carlin Smith, President
Released: Annual **Price:** free for members.

53227 ■ *Community Profile and Business Directory*
PO Box 484
Lake Orion, MI 48361-0484
Ph: (248)693-6300

Fax: (248)693-9227
Co. E-mail: info@lakeorionchamber.com
URL: http://orion.lib.mi.us/orion/index.php
Contact: Alaina Campbell, Executive Director
Released: Annual **Price:** free.

53228 ■ *Community Profile and Membership Directory*
216 E Central Ave.
Mackinaw City, MI 49701
Ph: (231)436-5574
Free: 888-455-8100
URL: http://www.mackinawchamber.com
Contact: Dawn Edwards, Executive Director
Released: Annual **Price:** included in membership dues.

53229 ■ *Community Profile and Membership Directory*
36341 Front St., Ste. 2
New Baltimore, MI 48047
Ph: (586)725-5148
Free: 866-643-0023
Fax: (586)725-5369
Co. E-mail: info@anchorbaychamber.com
URL: http://www.anchorbaychamber.com
Contact: Lisa M. Edwards, President
Released: Annual **Price:** free.

53230 ■ *Community Resource Guide*
PO Box 521
Manchester, MI 48158
Ph: (734)476-4565
Co. E-mail: president@manchestermi.org
URL: http://www.manchestermi.org
Contact: Janet Larson, President
Released: Annual **Price:** free.

53231 ■ *Connection*
530 S Whittaker, Ste. F
New Buffalo, MI 49117
Ph: (269)469-5409
Fax: (269)469-2257
Co. E-mail: request@harborcountry.org
URL: http://www.harborcountry.org
Contact: Greg Bubb, Vice President
Released: Monthly

53232 ■ *The Connection*
20 Division St.
Coldwater, MI 49036
Ph: (517)278-5985
Fax: (517)278-8369
Co. E-mail: info@branchareachamber.com
URL: http://www.branchareachamber.com
Contact: Jeff Richards, Executive Director
Released: Monthly

53233 ■ *Connection*
4555 Investment Dr., 3rd Fl., Ste. 300
Troy, MI 48098-6338
Ph: (248)641-8151
Fax: (248)641-0545
Co. E-mail: theteam@troychamber.com
URL: http://www.troychamber.com
Contact: Michele Hodges, President

53234 ■ Coopersville Area Chamber of Commerce
289 Danforth St.
Coopersville, MI 49404
Ph: (616)997-5164
Fax: (616)997-6679
Co. E-mail: ctimmerman@cityofcoopersville.com
URL: http://www.coopersville.com
Contact: Carrie Borchers, President
Description: Promotes business and community development in Coopersville, MI. **Publications:** *Chamber News* (Monthly).

53235 ■ *Cornerstone*
PO Box 175
Romeo, MI 48065-0175
Ph: (586)752-4436
Fax: (586)752-2835
Co. E-mail: contact@rwchamber.com
URL: http://www.rwchamber.com
Contact: Scott Allen, President
Released: Bimonthly

53236 ■ *Dearborn Business Journal*
22100 Michigan Ave.
Dearborn, MI 48124
Ph: (313)584-6100
Fax: (313)584-9818
Co. E-mail: info@dearbornchamber.org
URL: http://www.dearbornchamber.org
Contact: Jennifer Giering, President
Released: Monthly

53237 ■ Dearborn Chamber of Commerce
22100 Michigan Ave.
Dearborn, MI 48124
Ph: (313)584-6100
Fax: (313)584-9818
Co. E-mail: info@dearbornchamber.org
URL: http://www.dearbornchamber.org
Contact: Jennifer Giering, President
Description: Aims to promote Dearborn and to help its members to succeed. Promotes business in Dearborn by listing their businesses on the website and on printed directory. Organizes event for networking between members. **Publications:** *Dearborn Business Journal* (Monthly); *Newsbyte* (Biweekly); *Dearborn Business Journal* (Monthly).

53238 ■ Delta County Area Chamber of Commerce
230 Ludington St.
Escanaba, MI 49829
Ph: (906)786-2192
Free: 800-DEL-TAMI
Fax: (906)786-8830
Co. E-mail: info@deltami.org
URL: http://www.deltami.org
Contact: Vickie Micheau, Executive Director
Description: Promotes business and community development in Delta County, MI. **Founded:** 1921. **Publications:** *Communicator* (Monthly). **Educational Activities:** Delta County Area Chamber of Commerce Party (Monthly).

53239 ■ Detroit Regional Chamber (DRC)
1 Woodward Ave., Ste. 1900
Detroit, MI 48232-0840
Ph: (313)964-4000
Free: 866-627-5463
Fax: (313)964-0183
Co. E-mail: members@detroitchamber.com
URL: http://www.detroitchamber.com/main/index.asp
Contact: Sandy K. Baruah, President
E-mail: sbaruah@detroitchamber.com
URL(s): www.detroitchamber.com. **Description:** Promotes business and community development in the southeastern Michigan counties of Lapeer, Livingston, Macomb, Monroe, Oakland, St. Clair, Washtenaw, and Wayne. **Founded:** 1903. **Publications:** *Manufacturers Directory to Southeast Michigan* (Annual); *Discover, Big Business in Metro Detroit*; *Detroit Regional Buyers' Guide* (Annual); *Foreign Companies in Regional Detroit*; *Detroiter: A Publication of the Detroit Regional Chamber*; *Manufacturer's Directory: Manufacturers Directory to Regional Detroit* (Biennial); *Buyers' Guide* (Annual); *Detroiter* (Monthly); *Greater Detroit Manufacturers Directory*; *Greater Detroit Relocation Package*; *Passport to International Detroit*; *Fortune 500 Companies Represented in the Metropolitan Detroit Area*; *Metro Detroit Office Guide* (Annual); *Big Business in Metro Detroit: A Major Employers Directory to Regional Detroit* (Biennial); *Passport to International Detroit-Services: A Directory to International Commerce in Regional Detroit* (Biennial); *Michigan Headquartered Companies: Banking, Industrial, Retail & Utilities*; *Greater Detroit Fact Book*.

53240 ■ *Detroiter*
1 Woodward Ave., Ste. 1900
Detroit, MI 48232-0840
Ph: (313)964-4000
Free: 866-627-5463
Fax: (313)964-0183
Co. E-mail: members@detroitchamber.com
URL: http://www.detroitchamber.com/main/index.asp
Contact: Sandy K. Baruah, President
E-mail: sbaruah@detroitchamber.com
Released: Monthly **Price:** $18, /year for nonmembers.

53241 ■ *Directory of Firms, Products, and Services*
115 W Huron St., 3rd Fl.
Ann Arbor, MI 48104
Ph: (734)665-4433
Fax: (734)665-4191
Co. E-mail: info@annarborchamber.org
Contact: Jesse Bernstein, President
E-mail: jesse@annarborchamber.org
Released: Periodic

53242 ■ *Directory and Planning Calendar*
501 S Front St.
Marquette, MI 49855
Ph: (906)226-6591
Free: 888-578-6489
Fax: (906)226-2099
Co. E-mail: lscp@marquette.org
URL: http://www.marquette.org
Contact: Amy Clickner, Chief Executive Officer
E-mail: aclickner@marquette.org
Released: Annual

53243 ■ *Dowagiac Event and Festival*
c/o Vickie Phillipson, Chair
200 Depot Dr.
Dowagiac, MI 49047
Ph: (269)782-8212
Fax: (269)782-6701
Co. E-mail: vickie@dowagiacchamber.com
URL: http://www.dowagiacchamber.com
Contact: Vickie Phillipson, Chairperson
Released: Annual

53244 ■ *Dowagiac Tourist Guide*
c/o Vickie Phillipson, Chair
200 Depot Dr.
Dowagiac, MI 49047
Ph: (269)782-8212
Fax: (269)782-6701
Co. E-mail: vickie@dowagiacchamber.com
URL: http://www.dowagiacchamber.com
Contact: Vickie Phillipson, Chairperson
Released: Annual **Price:** free.

53245 ■ East Jordan Area Chamber of Commerce (EJACC)
100 Main St., Ste. B
East Jordan, MI 49727
Ph: (231)536-7351
Fax: (231)536-0966
Co. E-mail: info@ejchamber.org
URL: http://www.ejchamber.org
Contact: Mary H. Faculak, President
Description: Businesses, churches, service groups, and individuals interested in promoting business and tourism in the East Jordan, MI area. **Founded:** 1961. **Publications:** *News Capsule* (Quarterly); *Business and Visitors Guide* (Annual). **Awards:** Ambassador of the Year (Annual); Citizen of the Year (Annual); President's Award (Annual).

53246 ■ Eastpointe Area Chamber of Commerce (EACC)
23220 Gratiot Ave.
Eastpointe, MI 48021
Ph: (586)776-5520
Fax: (586)776-7808
URL: http://epchamber.com
Contact: Catherine Green, Executive Director
Description: Promotes business and community development in Eastpointe, MI. **Founded:** 1944. **Publications:** *Newsline* (Monthly).

53247 ■ Edwardsburg Area Chamber of Commerce
PO Box 575
Edwardsburg, MI 49112
Ph: (574)343-3721
Co. E-mail: administration@edwardsburg.biz
URL: http://edwardsburgchamber.org
Contact: David Ball, President
Description: Promotes business and community development in the Edwardsburg, MI area.

53248 ■ Elk Rapids Area Chamber of Commerce (ERACC)
305 US 31 N
Elk Rapids, MI 49629
Ph: (231)264-8202
Fax: (231)264-6591
Co. E-mail: myoungson@elkrapidschamber.org
URL: http://www.elkrapidschamber.org
Contact: Misty Youngson, Executive Director
Description: Promotes business and community development in Antrim County, MI. **Founded:** 1965.

53249 ■ *Enterprise*
346 W Michigan Ave.
Kalamazoo, MI 49007
Ph: (269)381-4000
Fax: (269)343-0430
Co. E-mail: info@kazoochamber.com
URL: http://www.kazoochamber.com
Contact: Steward Sandstrom, President
Released: Monthly

53250 ■ Evart Area Chamber of Commerce (EACC)
PO Box 688
Evart, MI 49631-0668
Ph: (231)734-9799
Fax: (231)734-9799
Co. E-mail: janbooher@yahoo.com
URL: http://www.evartchamberofcommerce.com
Contact: Jan Booher, Secretary
Description: Promotes business and community development in Evart, MI. Sponsors social and promotional events. **Founded:** 1924. **Awards:** Business Person of the Year (Annual).

53251 ■ *Executive Report*
124 N Main St.
Cheboygan, MI 49721
Ph: (231)627-7183
Free: 800-968-3302
Fax: (231)627-2770
Co. E-mail: info@cheboygan.com
URL: http://www.cheboygan.com
Contact: Matthew J. Friday, Executive Director
Released: Monthly

53252 ■ *Executive Report*
402 E Lake St.
Tawas City, MI 48764-0608
Free: 800-55-TAWAS
Co. E-mail: info@tawas.com
URL: http://www.tawas.com
Released: Monthly

53253 ■ *Fall/Winter/Spring Guide*
216 E Central Ave.
Mackinaw City, MI 49701
Ph: (231)436-5574
Free: 888-455-8100
URL: http://www.mackinawchamber.com
Contact: Dawn Edwards, Executive Director
Released: Annual

53254 ■ Farmington/Farmington Hills Chamber of Commerce
33425 Grand River Ave., Ste. 101
Farmington Hills, MI 48335
Ph: (248)919-6917
Fax: (248)919-6921
Co. E-mail: mary@ffhchamber.com
URL: http://gfachamber.com
Contact: Mary Engelman, Executive Director
Description: Strives to enhance the economy and business environment in the Greater Farmington-Farmington Hills area. **Founded:** 1963. **Publications:** *The Voice of Business* (Bimonthly).

53255 ■ Farwell Area Chamber of Commerce (FACC)
PO Box 771
Farwell, MI 48622
Ph: (989)588-0580
Co. E-mail: facc@farwellareachamber.com
URL: http://www.farwellareachamber.com
Description: Promotes economic development and tourism in the Farwell, MI area.

53256 ■ Fenton Area Chamber of Commerce
114 N Leroy St.
Fenton, MI 48430
Ph: (810)629-5447
Fax: (810)629-6608
Co. E-mail: info@fentonchamber.com
URL: http://www.fentonchamber.com
Contact: Mrs. Shelly Day, President
Description: Advocates for member businesses through services and resources, while encouraging a prosperous Fenton Area. **Founded:** 1929. **Publications:** *Business Perspective* (Monthly). **Telecommunication Services:** sday@fentonchamber.com.

53257 ■ Flushing Area Chamber of Commerce
c/o Mary Guzak, Pres.
200 E Main St.
Flushing, MI 48433
Ph: (810)659-9239
Fax: (810)659-9261
URL: http://www.flushingchamber.com
Contact: Mary Guzak, President
Description: Promotes business and community development in the Flushing, MI area. **Founded:** 1948.

53258 ■ *Focus*
500 E Michigan, Ste. 200
Lansing, MI 48901
Ph: (517)487-6340
Fax: (517)484-6910
Co. E-mail: info@lenaweechamber.com
URL: http://www.lansingchamber.org
Contact: Bill Sepic, President
E-mail: wsepic@lansingchamber.org
Released: Monthly

53259 ■ Four Flags Area Chamber of Commerce (FFACC)—Niles Society
PO Box 10
Niles, MI 49120-0010
Ph: (269)683-3720
URL: http://www.nilesmi.com
Contact: Ronald J. Sather, President
Description: Promotes business and community development in the Niles County, MI area. **Founded:** 1919. **Publications:** *Manufacturer's Guide* (Periodic); *Niles Renaissance* (Annual); *Clubs and Civic Organizations* (Periodic). **Awards:** Chamber Scholarship (Annual).

53260 ■ Frankenmuth Chamber of Commerce and Convention and Visitors Bureau
635 S Main St.
Frankenmuth, MI 48734
Ph: (989)652-6106
Free: 800-FUN-TOWN
Fax: (989)652-3841
Co. E-mail: ceo@frankenmuth.org
URL: http://www.frankenmuth.org
Contact: Jamie Furbush, President
Description: Promotes business and community development in Frankenmuth, MI. **Founded:** 1902. **Publications:** *Handleskammer* (Periodic).

53261 ■ Frankfort - Elberta Area Chamber of Commerce
PO Box 566
Frankfort, MI 49635
Ph: (231)352-7251
Fax: (231)352-6750
Co. E-mail: fcofc@frankfort-elberta.com
URL: http://www.frankfort-elberta.com
Contact: Joanne Bartley, Executive Director
Description: Supports the livelihood of Frankfort-Elberta and surrounding area.

53262 ■ Fremont Area Chamber of Commerce (FACC)
7 E Main St.
Fremont, MI 49412
Ph: (231)924-0770

Fax: (231)924-9248
Co. E-mail: info@fremontcommerce.com
URL: http://www.fremontcommerce.com
Contact: Ron Vliem, Executive Director
Description: Promotes business and community development in Fremont, MI. Issues periodic publication. Convention/Meeting: none. **Founded:** 1903. **Publications:** *Community Profile and Business Directory* (Annual). **Telecommunication Services:** ron@fremontcommerce.com.

53263 ■ French - American Chamber of Commerce - Michigan Chapter
c/o Clayton & McKervey P.C.
2000 Town Ctr., Ste. 1800
Southfield, MI 48075
Ph: (248)936-9473
Fax: (248)208-9115
Co. E-mail: info@faccmi.org
URL: http://www.faccmi.org
Contact: Emmanuelle Lavergne, Executive Director

53264 ■ Garden City Chamber of Commerce (GCCC)
30300 Maplewood St.
Garden City, MI 48135
Ph: (734)422-4448
Fax: (734)422-1601
URL: http://www.gardencity.org
Contact: Bob Hunt, President
Description: Promotes business and community development in Garden City, MI. Participates in community festival. **Founded:** 1957. **Awards:** Business Person of the Year (Annual); Firefighter of the Year (Annual); First Citizen Award; Police Officer of the Year (Annual).

53265 ■ Gaylord - Otsego County Chamber of Commerce (GOCCC)
101 W Main St.
Gaylord, MI 49734
Ph: (989)732-6333
Free: 800-345-8621
Fax: (989)732-7990
Co. E-mail: info@gaylordchamber.com
URL: http://www.gaylordchamber.com
Contact: Todd Gregory, Chairman
Description: Promotes business and community development in Otsego County, MI. Sponsors annual Alpenfest. **Founded:** 1948. **Publications:** *Business to Business Journal* (Quarterly); *Gaylord/Otsego County Chamber of Commerce Membership Directory and Community Profile* (Annual). **Educational Activities:** Alpenfest (Annual); Chamber Golf Outing (Annual).

53266 ■ *Gaylord/Otsego County Chamber of Commerce Membership Directory and Community Profile*
101 W Main St.
Gaylord, MI 49734
Ph: (989)732-6333
Free: 800-345-8621
Fax: (989)732-7990
Co. E-mail: info@gaylordchamber.com
URL: http://www.gaylordchamber.com
Contact: Todd Gregory, Chairman
Released: Annual

53267 ■ Grand Blanc Chamber of Commerce (GBCC)
512 E Grand Blanc Rd.
Grand Blanc, MI 48439
Ph: (810)695-4222
Fax: (810)695-0053
Co. E-mail: jet@grandblancchamber.org
URL: http://www.grandblancchamber.com
Contact: Jet Kilmer, President
Description: Businesses and organizations dedicated to advancing the commercial, agricultural, industrial, and civic interests of the community. Offers group health insurance and discounts on charge cards; conducts charitable activities, summer festival and golf outing. **Founded:** 1977. **Publications:** *The Business Index* (Monthly); *Chamber Buzz* (Monthly); *Grand Blanc Community Directory and Buyer's Guide.*

Educational Activities: Issues Committee Meeting (Weekly); Ambassadors Meeting (Monthly). **Telecommunication Services:** info@grandblancchamber.com.

53268 ■ *Grand Blanc Community Directory and Buyer's Guide*
512 E Grand Blanc Rd.
Grand Blanc, MI 48439
Ph: (810)695-4222
Fax: (810)695-0053
Co. E-mail: jet@grandblancchamber.org
URL: http://www.grandblancchamber.com
Contact: Jet Kilmer, President

53269 ■ Grand Ledge Area Chamber of Commerce (GLACC)
220 S Bridge St.
Grand Ledge, MI 48837
Ph: (517)627-2383
Fax: (517)627-9213
Co. E-mail: glaccgl@gmail.com
URL: http://www.grandledgechamber.com
Contact: Dale Bennett, Chairman
Description: Promotes business and community development in Eaton County, MI. Holds monthly board meeting. **Founded:** 1969. **Awards:** Athena and Businessman of the Year (Annual).

53270 ■ Grand Rapids Area Chamber of Commerce (GRACC)
111 Pearl St. NW
Grand Rapids, MI 49503-2831
Ph: (616)771-0300
Fax: (616)771-0318
Co. E-mail: info@grandrapids.org
URL: http://www.grandrapids.org/home
Contact: Rick Baker, President
Description: Creates opportunities for business success in the Grand Rapids, MI area. **Founded:** 1887. **Publications:** *Business Directory* (Annual); *Chamber News* (Monthly).

53271 ■ Grandville Chamber of Commerce
PO Box 175
Grandville, MI 49468
Ph: (616)531-8890
Fax: (616)531-8890
Co. E-mail: sandy@grandjen.com
URL: http://grandvillejenisonchamber.com
Contact: Sandy LeBlanc, Executive Director
Description: Promotes and stimulates long-term, well-planned economic growth, educational opportunities and community resources of Grandville.

53272 ■ Gratiot Area Chamber of Commerce (GACofC)
110 W Superior St.
Alma, MI 48801
Ph: (989)463-5525
Fax: (989)463-6588
Co. E-mail: chamber@gratiot.org
URL: http://www.gratiot.org/1/295/index.asp
Contact: Jayne Norris, Executive Director
Description: Represents businesses in Gratiot County, Michigan united to promote the economic growth of the area. Also home of the Alma Highland Festival and Games. **Founded:** 1994. **Publications:** *Chamber Connections* (Monthly); *Gratiot Area Community Guide* (Annual).

53273 ■ *Gratiot Area Community Guide*
110 W Superior St.
Alma, MI 48801
Ph: (989)463-5525
Fax: (989)463-6588
Co. E-mail: chamber@gratiot.org
URL: http://www.gratiot.org/1/295/index.asp
Contact: Jayne Norris, Executive Director
Released: Annual

53274 ■ *Grayling Community Guide and Membership Directory*
213 N James St.
Grayling, MI 49738
Ph: (989)348-2921

Fax: (989)348-7315
Co. E-mail: info@graylingchamber.com
URL: http://graylingchamber.com
Contact: Samantha Schnoor, Chairperson
Released: Periodic

53275 ■ Grayling Regional Chamber of Commerce (GRCC)
213 N James St.
Grayling, MI 49738
Ph: (989)348-2921
Fax: (989)348-7315
Co. E-mail: info@graylingchamber.com
URL: http://graylingchamber.com
Contact: Samantha Schnoor, Chairperson
Description: Promotes business and community development in Crawford County, MI. Sponsors AuSable River Festival and Canoe Marathon and Grayling's Winter-Fest. **Founded:** 1955. **Publications:** *Chamber Update* (Monthly); *Grayling Community Guide and Membership Directory* (Periodic).

53276 ■ *Greater Albion Business News*
203 S Superior St.
Albion, MI 49224
Ph: (517)629-5533
Fax: (517)629-4284
Co. E-mail: office@greateralbionchamber.org
URL: http://www.greateralbionchamber.org
Contact: Amy DeShon, President
Released: Monthly

53277 ■ Greater Albion Chamber of Commerce (GACC)
203 S Superior St.
Albion, MI 49224
Ph: (517)629-5533
Fax: (517)629-4284
Co. E-mail: office@greateralbionchamber.org
URL: http://www.greateralbionchamber.org
Contact: Amy DeShon, President
Description: Promotes business and community development in the Albion, MI area. **Founded:** 1923. **Publications:** *Greater Albion Business News* (Monthly). **Educational Activities:** Cardboard Classic Sled Race (Annual). **Awards:** Small Business of the Year (Annual).

53278 ■ Greater Algonac Chamber of Commerce
1396 St. Clair River Dr.
Algonac, MI 48001
Ph: (810)794-5511
Fax: (866)643-0023
Co. E-mail: execdirector@algonacchamber.com
URL: http://www.algonacchamber.com
Description: Promotes business and community development in the Algonac, MI area. **Publications:** *The Chamber Connection* (Bimonthly).

53279 ■ Greater Berkley Chamber of Commerce
PO Box 72-1253
Berkley, MI 48072
Ph: (248)414-9157
Fax: (248)691-3174
Co. E-mail: membership@berkleychamber.com
URL: http://berkleychamber.com
Contact: Kees Hiatt, President
Description: Promotes and encourages business in Berkley. Creates favorable commercial climate within the City. Acts as a unified voice and liaison between businesses and others. Assists businesses in the City.

53280 ■ Greater Brighton Area Chamber of Commerce (GBACC)
218 E Grand River
Brighton, MI 48116
Ph: (810)227-5086
Fax: (810)227-5940
Co. E-mail: info@brightoncoc.org
URL: http://www.brightoncoc.org
Contact: Pam McConeghy, President
Description: Promotes business and community development in the Brighton, MI area. Participates in the Great American Folk Art Festival. **Founded:**

1972. **Publications:** *Update Magazine* (Monthly). **Educational Activities:** Livingston Business and Trade Expo (Annual).

53281 ■ Greater Croswell - Lexington Chamber of Commerce
PO Box 142
Lexington, MI 48450
Ph: (810)359-2262
Co. E-mail: croslex@greatlakes.net
URL: http://www.cros-lex-chamber.com
Contact: Jane Lehman, President
Description: Promotes business and community development in Greater Croswell-Lexington, MI.

53282 ■ Greater Decatur Chamber of Commerce
100 S Water St., Ste. 103
Decatur, IL 62523-1048
Ph: (217)422-2200
Fax: (217)422-4576
Co. E-mail: mirinda.rothrock@decaturchamber.com
URL: http://www.decaturchamber.com
Contact: Mirinda Rothrock, President
E-mail: mirinda.rothrock@decaturchamber.com
URL(s): decaturchamber.com. **Description:** Promotes business and community development in Greater Decatur, MI area. **Founded:** 1903. **Publications:** *Friday Facts* (Weekly); *Chamber of Commerce Business Directory* (Annual); *Organization Directory*; *Decatur Chamber of Commerce Business Directory*. **Awards:** Chamber Member of the Week (Weekly). **Telecommunication Services:** helpdesk@decaturchamber.com; customerservice@decaturchamber.com.

53283 ■ *Greater Detroit Manufacturers Directory*
1 Woodward Ave., Ste. 1900
Detroit, MI 48232-0840
Ph: (313)964-4000
Free: 866-627-5463
Fax: (313)964-0183
Co. E-mail: members@detroitchamber.com
URL: http://www.detroitchamber.com/main/index.asp
Contact: Sandy K. Baruah, President
E-mail: sbaruah@detroitchamber.com

53284 ■ *Greater Detroit Relocation Package*
1 Woodward Ave., Ste. 1900
Detroit, MI 48232-0840
Ph: (313)964-4000
Free: 866-627-5463
Fax: (313)964-0183
Co. E-mail: members@detroitchamber.com
URL: http://www.detroitchamber.com/main/index.asp
Contact: Sandy K. Baruah, President
E-mail: sbaruah@detroitchamber.com

53285 ■ Greater Dowagiac Area Chamber of Commerce
c/o Vickie Phillipson, Chair
200 Depot Dr.
Dowagiac, MI 49047
Ph: (269)782-8212
Fax: (269)782-6701
Co. E-mail: vickie@dowagiacchamber.com
URL: http://www.dowagiacchamber.com
Contact: Vickie Phillipson, Chairperson Program Director
Description: Promotes business and community development in the Dowagiac, MI area. **Founded:** 1964. **Publications:** *Dowagiac Tourist Guide* (Annual); *Looking to the Future* (Monthly); *Dowagiac Event and Festival* (Annual).

53286 ■ Greater Durand Area Chamber of Commerce
109 N Saginaw St.
Durand, MI 48429
Ph: (989)288-3715

Fax: (989)288-5177
Co. E-mail: office@durandchamber.com
URL: http://durandchamberofcommerce.com
Contact: Doug Schnell, President
Description: Businesses, service groups, industries, and merchants united to promote commerce in the Durand, MI area. Sponsors festival. **Founded:** 1960. **Publications:** *Railnet* (Quarterly).

53287 ■ *Greater Greenville*
108 N Lafayette St., Ste. A
Greenville, MI 48838
Ph: (616)754-5697
Fax: (616)754-4710
Co. E-mail: info@greenvillechamber.net
URL: http://www.greenvillechamber.net
Contact: Candy Kerschen, Executive Director

53288 ■ Greater Jackson Chamber of Commerce (GJCC)
141 S Jackson St.
Jackson, MI 49201
Ph: (517)782-8221
Fax: (517)780-3688
Co. E-mail: mindy@gjcc.org
URL: http://www.jacksonchamber.org
Contact: Minda Bradish-Orta, President
Description: Promotes business and community development in the Jackson County, MI area. **Founded:** 1909.

53289 ■ *The Greater Mackinaw Area Chamber of Commerce*
216 E Central Ave.
Mackinaw City, MI 49701
Ph: (231)436-5574
Free: 888-455-8100
URL: http://www.mackinawchamber.com
Contact: Dawn Edwards, Executive Director
Price: included in membership dues.

53290 ■ Greater Paw Paw Chamber of Commerce
129 S Kalamazoo St.
Paw Paw, MI 49079
Ph: (269)657-5395
Fax: (269)655-8755
Co. E-mail: ppccdda@btc-bci.com
URL: http://www.pawpawmi.com
Contact: Mary E.H. Springer, Executive Director
Description: Works to promote business interests in the greater Paw Paw area through advocacy and leadership in education, local economic, governmental and community issues.

53291 ■ Greater Romulus Chamber of Commerce
11189 Shook, Ste. C
Romulus, MI 48174
Ph: (734)893-0694
Fax: (734)893-0596
Co. E-mail: info@romuluschamber.com
URL: http://www.romuluschamber.org
Contact: Chuck Zuerner, President
Description: Small businesses interested in fostering and creating a healthy environment to do business. Works to improve business community by providing various promotional and profitable opportunities.

53292 ■ Greater Royal Oak Chamber of Commerce
200 S Washington Ave.
Royal Oak, MI 48067-3821
Ph: (248)547-4000
Fax: (248)547-0504
Co. E-mail: coc@royaloakchamber.com
URL: http://www.royaloakchamber.com
Contact: Mr. Bill Allen, Executive Director
Description: Aims to bring business leaders, civic groups and citizens together to improve and enhance the community. **Founded:** 1936.

53293 ■ Greater South Haven Area Chamber of Commerce (GSHACC)
606 Phillips St.
South Haven, MI 49090
Ph: (616)637-5171

Fax: (616)639-1570
Co. E-mail: cofc@southhavenmi.com
URL: http://www.southhavenmi.com
Contact: Kathy Wagaman, Executive Director
Description: Retail, commercial, industrial, and professional organizations in the South Haven, MI area organized to promote economic and community development. Holds board meetings, luncheons, and annual dinner. **Founded:** 1932. **Publications:** *Chamber Connection* (Quarterly).

53294 ■ Greater West Bloomfield Chamber of Commerce (WBCC)
6668 Orchard Lake Rd., Ste. 207
West Bloomfield, MI 48322
Ph: (248)626-3636
Fax: (248)626-4218
Co. E-mail: wbloomfieldchamber@gmail.com
URL: http://www.westbloomfieldchamber.com
Contact: Suzanne Levine, Executive Director
Description: Promotes business and community development in West Bloomfield, MI. Sponsors West Bloomfield Artfest, Business Person of the Year, Business Beautification Awards, Taste of West Bloomfield, and 6th Annual Golf Classic; conducts charitable activities. **Founded:** 1973. **Publications:** *West Bloomfield Community Directory* (Annual); *West Bloomfield Update* (Monthly). **Educational Activities:** Art Fest (Periodic). **Awards:** Business Beautification (Annual); Business Person of the Year.

53295 ■ Greenville Area Chamber of Commerce (GACC)
108 N Lafayette St., Ste. A
Greenville, MI 48838
Ph: (616)754-5697
Fax: (616)754-4710
Co. E-mail: info@greenvillechamber.net
URL: http://www.greenvillechamber.net
Contact: Candy Kerschen, Executive Director
Description: Promotes business and community development in the Greenville, MI area. **Founded:** 1947. **Publications:** *Business Beat* (Monthly); *Greater Greenville.*

53296 ■ Handleskammer
635 S Main St.
Frankenmuth, MI 48734
Ph: (989)652-6106
Free: 800-FUN-TOWN
Fax: (989)652-3841
Co. E-mail: ceo@frankenmuth.org
URL: http://www.frankenmuth.org
Contact: Jamie Furbush, President
Released: Periodic

53297 ■ Harbor Beach Chamber of Commerce
PO Box 113
Harbor Beach, MI 48441
Ph: (989)479-6477
URL: http://www.harborbeachchamber.com
Contact: Bob Montana, President
Description: Works to advance businesses within Harbor Beach and the surrounding areas.

53298 ■ Harbor Country Chamber of Commerce
530 S Whittaker, Ste. F
New Buffalo, MI 49117
Ph: (269)469-5409
Fax: (269)469-2257
Co. E-mail: request@harborcountry.org
URL: http://www.harborcountry.org
Contact: Greg Bubb, Vice President
Description: Promotes convention business and tourism in area. **Founded:** 1980. **Publications:** *Connection* (Monthly); *Harbor County Guide* (Annual); *Harbor County Guide* (Annual). **Telecommunication Services:** president@harborcountry.org; chamber@harborcountry.org.

53299 ■ Harbor County Guide
530 S Whittaker, Ste. F
New Buffalo, MI 49117
Ph: (269)469-5409

Fax: (269)469-2257
Co. E-mail: request@harborcountry.org
URL: http://www.harborcountry.org
Contact: Greg Bubb, Vice President
Released: Annual

53300 ■ Harbor Springs Chamber of Commerce (HSCC)
368 E Main St.
Harbor Springs, MI 49740
Ph: (231)526-7999
Fax: (231)526-5593
URL: http://www.harborspringschamber.com
Contact: Liz Ahrens, President
Description: Strives to promote, enhance, and contribute to the well-being of the business community, while preserving the character and traditions of Harbor Springs. **Publications:** *Back to Business* (Monthly); *Community Connection* (Bimonthly); *Visitors Guide* (Annual).

53301 ■ Harrison Chamber of Commerce
809 N 1st St.
Harrison, MI 48625-0682
Ph: (989)539-6011
Free: 877-539-6011
Fax: (989)539-6099
Co. E-mail: harrisonchamber@sbcglobal.net
URL: http://harrisonchamber.com
Contact: Barb Hawkins, President
Description: Promotes businesses in Harrison area.

53302 ■ Hillman Area Chamber of Commerce
PO Box 506
Hillman, MI 49746
Ph: (989)742-3739
Fax: (989)742-4757
Co. E-mail: hillman@freeway.net
URL: http://hillmanchamber.org
Contact: Marsha Marquardt, President
URL(s): www.hillmanmichigan.org/chamber.html. **Description:** Promotes business and community development in the Hillman, MI area.

53303 ■ Hillsdale County Chamber of Commerce
506 W Carleton Rd.
Hillsdale, MI 49242
Ph: (517)439-4341
Fax: (517)439-4111
Co. E-mail: info@hillsdalecountychamber.com
URL: http://www.hillsdalecountychamber.com
Contact: Cyndi Young, President
Description: Strives to enhance the economy of Hillsdale County by providing services in identifying local sources for products and services. **Publications:** *Commerce Connection*. **Educational Activities:** Holiday Bazaar (Annual). **Telecommunication Services:** karri@hillsdalecountychamber.com.

53304 ■ Holland Area Chamber of Commerce (HACC)
272 E 8th St.
Holland, MI 49423
Ph: (616)392-2389
Fax: (616)392-7379
Co. E-mail: info@hollandchamber.org
URL: http://www.hollandchamber.org
Contact: Jane Clark, President
Description: Promotes business and community development in the Holland, MI area. **Founded:** 1914. **Publications:** *Chamber Newsletter* (Monthly). **Telecommunication Services:** jclark@hollandchamber.org; bgawlik@hollandchamber.org.

53305 ■ Holly Area Chamber of Commerce
202 S Saginaw St.
Holly, MI 48442
Ph: (248)215-7099
Fax: (248)215-7106
Co. E-mail: info@hollychamber.com
URL: http://www.hollychamber.com
Contact: Sandra Kleven, President
Description: Strives to facilitate new business networking, promote communication among existing business and support the development of the community.

53306 ■ Houghton Lake Chamber of Commerce (HLCC)
1625 W Houghton Lake Dr.
Houghton Lake, MI 48629
Ph: (989)366-5644
Free: 800-248-5253
Fax: (989)366-9472
Co. E-mail: hlcc@houghtonlakemichigan.net
URL: http://houghtonlakechamber.net
Description: Promotes business and community development in Houghton Lake, MI area.

53307 ■ *How Your Chamber Works For You!*
598 Byrne Industrial Dr. NE
Rockford, MI 49341
Ph: (616)866-2000
Fax: (616)866-2141
Co. E-mail: info@rockfordmichamber.com
URL: http://www.rockfordmichamber.com
Contact: Jeannie Gregory, Executive Director
Released: Annual **Price:** free.

53308 ■ Howell Area Chamber of Commerce
123 E Washington St.
Howell, MI 48843
Ph: (517)546-3920
Fax: (517)546-4115
Co. E-mail: cdonovan@howell.org
URL: http://www.howell.org
Contact: Jessica Clum, Chairperson
Description: Works to improve the business community through various programs and services. **Publications:** *Business Views*; *Howell Area Chamber of Commerce--Community Guide and Membership Directory*. **Telecommunication Services:** pconvery@howell.org.

53309 ■ Hudson Area Chamber of Commerce
502 2nd St.
Hudson, WI 54016-1542
Ph: (715)386-8411
Free: 800-657-6775
Fax: (715)386-8432
Co. E-mail: info@hudsonwi.org
URL: http://hudsonwi.org
Contact: Kim Heinemann, President
Description: Supports Hudson Business District.

53310 ■ Hudsonville Area Chamber of Commerce (HACC)
3275 Central Blvd.
Hudsonville, MI 49426
Ph: (616)662-0900
Fax: (616)669-2330
Co. E-mail: keegstra@grar.com
URL: http://hudsonvillechamber.com
Contact: Kris Keegstra, President
Description: Businesses and individuals seeking to promote economic and community development in the Hudsonville, MI area. Convention/Meeting: none. **Founded:** 1979. **Publications:** *Hudsonville Area Chamber of Commerce Profile* (Periodic); *Progress Report* (Bimonthly).

53311 ■ *Hudsonville Area Chamber of Commerce Profile*
3275 Central Blvd.
Hudsonville, MI 49426
Ph: (616)662-0900
Fax: (616)669-2330
Co. E-mail: keegstra@grar.com
URL: http://hudsonvillechamber.com
Contact: Kris Keegstra, President
Released: Periodic

53312 ■ Huron Shores Chamber of Commerce
PO Box 581
Harrisville, MI 48740
Ph: (989)724-5107
Free: 800-432-2823
Fax: (989)724-6656
Co. E-mail: huronshorecc@gmail.com
URL: http://www.huronshoreschamber.com
Contact: Judie Labadie, President
URL(s): www.huronshorescc.com. **Description:** Promotes Alcona County and its communities.

53313 ■ *Huron Township Business Directory*
19132 Huron River Dr.
New Boston, MI 48164
Ph: (734)753-4220
Fax: (734)753-4602
Co. E-mail: township@provide.net
URL: http://www.members.tripod.com/htcc48164
Contact: Teresa A. Shearrer-Lewis-Trosin, Executive Secretary
Released: Semiannual

53314 ■ Huron Township Chamber of Commerce (HTC of C)
19132 Huron River Dr.
New Boston, MI 48164
Ph: (734)753-4220
Fax: (734)753-4602
Co. E-mail: township@provide.net
URL: http://www.members.tripod.com/htcc48164
Contact: Teresa A. Shearrer-Lewis-Trosin, Executive Secretary
Description: Strives to bring community and business together. Promotes business and community development within Huron Township, MI. Sponsors annual Chamber Barn Dance, Scholarship Golf Outing (for local H.S.). Participates in the Huron Toys for Tots & Teens program. Holds monthly board meetings. **Founded:** 1981. **Publications:** *Chamber Chips* (Monthly); *Huron Township Business Directory* (Semiannual). **Awards:** Golf Outing Scholarships (Annual). **Telecommunication Services:** hurontwpchmbrcomm@yahoo.com.

53315 ■ Huron Valley Chamber of Commerce (HVCC)
317 Union St.
Milford, MI 48381
Ph: (248)685-7129
Fax: (248)685-9047
Co. E-mail: info@huronvcc.com
URL: http://www.huronvcc.com/1/HVCC/index.asp
Contact: Joell Beether, Executive Director
Description: Promotes business and community development in the Huron Valley, MI area. **Founded:** 1962. **Publications:** *Chamber News* (Monthly); *Business Directory and Buying Guide* (Annual). **Awards:** Business Improvement Award; Business of the Year (Annual); Citizen of the Year (Annual); Barbara Gavitt Memorial Scholarship Fund.

53316 ■ *IMAGES of Birmingham Bloomfield*
725 S Adams, Ste. 130
Birmingham, MI 48009
Ph: (248)644-1700
Fax: (248)644-0286
Co. E-mail: thechamber@bbcc.com
URL: http://www.bbcc.com/home
Contact: Joe Bauman, President
Released: Annual **Price:** free for members.

53317 ■ *Impact*
12900 Hall Rd., Ste. 190
Sterling Heights, MI 48313
Ph: (586)731-5400
Fax: (586)731-3521
Co. E-mail: woehmke@shrcci.com
URL: http://www.suscc.com
Contact: Wayne Oehmke, President

53318 ■ *In Focus*
27601 Jefferson Ave.
St. Clair Shores, MI 48081
Ph: (586)777-2741
Fax: (586)777-4811
Co. E-mail: metroeastchamber@netscape.net
Contact: Heather Lynn, Executive Director
Released: Monthly

53319 ■ Indian River Chamber of Commerce
PO Box 57
Indian River, MI 49749
Ph: (231)238-9325
Free: 800-394-8310

Fax: (231)238-0949
Co. E-mail: kwegner@irchamber.com
URL: http://www.irchamber.com
Contact: Kevin L. Tucker, President
Description: Promotes business and community development in Indian River, MI. **Awards:** Beautification (Annual); Citizen of the Year (Annual); Lifetime Achievement (Annual); Member of the Year (Annual); Organization of the Year (Annual).

53320 ■ *Industrial Directory*
380 W Western Ave., Ste. 202
Muskegon, MI 49440
Ph: (616)722-3751
Fax: (616)728-7251
Co. E-mail: mlcc@muskegon.org
URL: http://www.muskegon.org
Contact: Michael Hagen, Chairman
Released: Annual

53321 ■ *Industrial Directory*
1 S Harbor Dr.
Grand Haven, MI 49417
Ph: (616)842-4910
Fax: (616)842-0379
Co. E-mail: jgaasch@grandhavenchamber.org
URL: http://www.grandhavenchamber.org
Contact: Joy A. Gaasch, President
Price: $5, for members; $15, for nonmembers.

53322 ■ *Industrial Directory*
33233 Five Mile Rd.
Livonia, MI 48154
Ph: (734)427-2122
Fax: (734)427-6055
Co. E-mail: chamber@livonia.org
URL: http://www.livonia.org
Contact: Dan West, President
Released: Periodic

53323 ■ Inkster Chamber of Commerce
PO Box 596
Inkster, MI 48141-0596
Ph: (734)552-1391
Fax: (734)722-2527
Co. E-mail: info@inksterchamber.org
URL: http://www.inksterchamber.com

53324 ■ *Inside Business*
402 N Telegraph Rd.
Pontiac, MI 48341
Ph: (248)335-9600
Fax: (248)335-9601
Co. E-mail: info@pontiacchamber.com
URL: http://www.pontiacchamber.com
Contact: Kyle Westberg, Chairman
Released: Monthly

53325 ■ *Insight*
One Riverwalk Centre
34 Jackson St. W
Battle Creek, MI 49017
Ph: (269)962-4076
Fax: (269)962-6309
Co. E-mail: kbeer@battlecreek.org
URL: http://www.battlecreek.org
Contact: Kara E. Beer, Executive Director
Released: Monthly

53326 ■ *Insight*
725 S Adams, Ste. 130
Birmingham, MI 48009
Ph: (248)644-1700
Fax: (248)644-0286
Co. E-mail: thechamber@bbcc.com
URL: http://www.bbcc.com/home
Contact: Joe Bauman, President
Released: Monthly

53327 ■ Interlochen Area Chamber of Commerce
PO Box 13
Interlochen, MI 49643
Ph: (231)276-7141
Co. E-mail: interlochenchamber@juno.com
URL: http://www.interlochenchamber.org
Contact: Laura M. Franke, Director
Description: Promotes business and community development in Interlochen, MI area.

53328 ■ Ionia Area Chamber of Commerce (IACC)
439 W Main St.
Ionia, MI 48846
Ph: (616)527-2560
Co. E-mail: info@ioniachamber.net
URL: http://www.ioniachamber.org
Contact: Dave Cook, President
Description: Promotes business and community development in the Ionia, MI area. Sponsors festival. **Founded:** 1937. **Publications:** *Chamber News* (Monthly).

53329 ■ Iron County Chamber of Commerce (ICCOC)
50 E Genesee St.
Iron River, MI 49935
Ph: (906)265-3822
Fax: (906)265-5605
Co. E-mail: info@iron.org
URL: http://www.iron.org
Contact: Bill Leonoff, Executive Director
Description: Industries, retail and wholesale businesses, civic organizations, and individuals organized to promote business and community development in Iron County, MI. Strives to cooperate with units of government, businesses and industries, potential businesses, residents and visitors and to promote the economic development of Iron County in a spirit of unity. Works in the tourism trade in the area by assisting other organizations in their activities and holding annual events, such as the Home and Recreation Show. **Founded:** 1955. **Publications:** *Chamber Report* (Quarterly).

53330 ■ Ironwood Area Chamber of Commerce (IACC)
PO Box 45
Ironwood, MI 49938
Ph: (906)932-1122
Fax: (906)932-2756
Co. E-mail: chamber@ironwoodmi.org
URL: http://www.ironwoodmi.org
Contact: Peter Grewe, Director (Acting)
Description: Businesses and professionals. Promotes business and community development and tourism in the Ironwood, MI area. Conducts annual Jack Frost festival of Lights parade. **Founded:** 1912. **Publications:** *Chamber Chat* (Monthly); *Ironwood - Best of Michigan*.

53331 ■ *Ironwood - Best of Michigan*
PO Box 45
Ironwood, MI 49938
Ph: (906)932-1122
Fax: (906)932-2756
Co. E-mail: chamber@ironwoodmi.org
URL: http://www.ironwoodmi.org
Contact: Peter Grewe, Director (Acting)

53332 ■ Ishpeming Office of Lake Superior Community Partnership
215 W Hematite St.
Ishpeming, MI 49849
Ph: (906)486-4841
Free: 888-578-6489
Co. E-mail: lscp@marquette.org
URL: http://www.marquette.org
Contact: Amy Clickner, Chief Executive Officer
Description: Individuals and commercial, industrial, and professional organizations. Promotes business and community development in the Ishpeming-Negaunee, MI areas. **Founded:** 1951. **Publications:** *The Voice of Business* (Monthly). **Educational Activities:** Business After Hours (Semimonthly). **Awards:** Miss Ishpeming (Annual); Miss Negaunee (Annual).

53333 ■ *Kalamazoo County Connection*
346 W Michigan Ave.
Kalamazoo, MI 49007
Ph: (269)381-4000
Fax: (269)343-0430
Co. E-mail: info@kazoochamber.com
URL: http://www.kazoochamber.com
Contact: Steward Sandstrom, President
Released: Annual

53334 ■ Kalamazoo Regional Chamber of Commerce (KRCC)
346 W Michigan Ave.
Kalamazoo, MI 49007
Ph: (269)381-4000
Fax: (269)343-0430
Co. E-mail: info@kazoochamber.com
URL: http://www.kazoochamber.com
Contact: Steward Sandstrom, President
Description: Companies (1200) representing 2000 individuals. Promotes business and community development in Kalamazoo County, MI. Conducts community affairs. Sponsors festival. **Founded:** 1904. **Publications:** *Enterprise* (Monthly); *Kalamazoo County Connection* (Annual); *Kalamazoo County.* **Educational Activities:** Business Expo (Annual). **Telecommunication Services:** steward@kazoochamber.com.

53335 ■ Kalkaska Area Chamber of Commerce
353 S Cedar St.
Kalkaska, MI 49646
Ph: (231)258-9103
Fax: (231)258-6155
Co. E-mail: annie@tcchamber.org
URL: http://www.tcchamber.org/kalkaska-chamber
Contact: Don Kessel, Chairman
URL(s): kalkaskami.com. **Description:** Strives to improve the community by promoting the economic, civic, commercial, cultural, industrial, and educational interests of the Kalkaska area.

53336 ■ Keweenaw Peninsula Chamber of Commerce
902 College Ave.
Houghton, MI 49931-0336
Ph: (906)482-5240
Free: 866-304-5722
Fax: (906)482-5241
Co. E-mail: info@keweenaw.org
URL: http://www.keweenaw.org
Contact: Johanna Davis, President
Description: Promotes business and community development in Houghton and Keweenaw counties, MI. Promotes tourism. **Publications:** *Chamber Update* (Monthly); *Keweenaw Peninsula Chamber of Commerce Membership Directory* (Annual); *Keweenaw Street Map & Business Guide* (Annual). **Educational Activities:** Business After Hours Forum. **Awards:** Athena (Annual); Honorary (Annual); Person of the Year (Annual); Sparkplug (Annual).

53337 ■ *Keweenaw Peninsula Chamber of Commerce Membership Directory*
902 College Ave.
Houghton, MI 49931-0336
Ph: (906)482-5240
Free: 866-304-5722
Fax: (906)482-5241
Co. E-mail: info@keweenaw.org
URL: http://www.keweenaw.org
Contact: Johanna Davis, President
Released: Annual

53338 ■ *Keweenaw Street Map & Business Guide*
902 College Ave.
Houghton, MI 49931-0336
Ph: (906)482-5240
Free: 866-304-5722
Fax: (906)482-5241
Co. E-mail: info@keweenaw.org
URL: http://www.keweenaw.org
Contact: Johanna Davis, President
Released: Annual

53339 ■ Lake City Area Chamber of Commerce
PO Drawer H
107 S Main St.
Lake City, MI 49651
Ph: (231)839-4969

Fax: (231)839-5991
Co. E-mail: info@lakecitymich.com
URL: http://www.lakecitymich.com
Contact: Penny Lerg, President
Description: Promotes commerce in the Lake City area. **Founded:** 1953. **Publications:** *Lake City Chamber Corner* (Weekly). **Telecommunication Services:** lcacc@centurytel.net.

53340 ■ *Lake City Chamber Corner*
PO Drawer H
107 S Main St.
Lake City, MI 49651
Ph: (231)839-4969
Fax: (231)839-5991
Co. E-mail: info@lakecitymich.com
URL: http://www.lakecitymich.com
Contact: Penny Lerg, President
Released: Weekly

53341 ■ Lake Gogebic Area Chamber of Commerce
PO Box 114
Bergland, MI 49910-0114
Free: 888-464-3242
Co. E-mail: info@lakegogebicarea.com
URL: http://www.lakegogebicarea.com
Contact: Ms. Mary Lou Driesenga, Secretary
Description: Promotes business, tourism and community development in Lake Gogebic, MI area. **Founded:** 1966.

53342 ■ Lakes Area Chamber of Commerce (LACC)
305 N Pontiac Trail, Ste. A
Walled Lake, MI 48390
Ph: (248)624-2826
Fax: (248)624-2892
Co. E-mail: info@lakesareachamber.com
URL: http://www.lakesareachamber.com
Contact: Mark Steinberg, President
Description: Promotes business and community development in the townships of Commerce, Waterford, and White Lake, cities of Walled Lake and Wixom, and village of Wolverine, MI. Sponsors golf and bowling tournaments. **Founded:** 1963. **Publications:** *Lakes Area Chamber of Commerce Membership Directory* (Annual); *Today's Business Choice* (Monthly). **Educational Activities:** Taste of the Lakes (Annual). **Awards:** Lakes Area Chamber of Commerce Scholarship (Annual).

53343 ■ *Lakes Area Chamber of Commerce Membership Directory*
305 N Pontiac Trail, Ste. A
Walled Lake, MI 48390
Ph: (248)624-2826
Fax: (248)624-2892
Co. E-mail: info@lakesareachamber.com
URL: http://www.lakesareachamber.com
Contact: Mark Steinberg, President
Released: Annual

53344 ■ Lakeshore Chamber of Commerce
PO Box 93
Stevensville, MI 49127-0093
Ph: (269)429-1170
Fax: (269)429-8882
Co. E-mail: information@lakeshorechamber.org
URL: http://www.lakeshorechamber.org
Contact: Griffin Ott, President
Description: Works to advance the commercial, industrial, civic and cultural opportunities in the Lakeshore community and surrounding areas.

53345 ■ Lakeview Area Chamber of Commerce (LACC)
PO Box 57
Lakeview, MI 48850
Ph: (989)352-1200
Fax: (989)352-6435
Co. E-mail: info@lakeviewmichigan.com
URL: http://lakeviewmichigan.com
Contact: Brian Brasser, President
Description: Promotes business and community development in the Lakeview, MI area.

53346 ■ Lansing Regional Chamber of Commerce
500 E Michigan, Ste. 200
Lansing, MI 48901
Ph: (517)487-6340
Fax: (517)484-6910
Co. E-mail: info@lenaweechamber.com
URL: http://www.lansingchamber.org
Contact: Bill Sepic, President
E-mail: wsepic@lansingchamber.org
Description: Works to facilitate economic development through the support of existing business and the attraction of new businesses for providing business advocacy and offering membership services. **Founded:** 1897. **Publications:** *Lansing Regional Chamber of Commerce--Membership Directory*; *Focus* (Monthly); *Regional Vision* (Bimonthly). **Educational Activities:** Lansing Regional Chamber of Commerce Conference (Annual); Business Lunch Training Seminar Series (Quarterly). **Awards:** ATHENA Award (Annual); Community Service Award (Annual); Outstanding Small Business Award (Annual); Outstanding Small Business Advocate Award (Annual); Outstanding Small Business Person Award (Annual). **Telecommunication Services:** aberry@lansingchamber.org; tdaman@lansingchamber.org; wsepic@lansingchamber.org.

53347 ■ Lapeer Area Chamber of Commerce (LACC)
108 W Park St.
Lapeer, MI 48446
Ph: (810)664-6641
Fax: (810)664-4349
Co. E-mail: staff@lapeerareachamber.org
URL: http://www.lapeerareachamber.org
Contact: Neda Payne, Executive Director
Description: Works to promote and foster the business community and enhance the quality of life in the area. **Publications:** *Business Connections* (Monthly).

53348 ■ Leelanau Peninsula Chamber of Commerce
5046 SW Bayshore Dr., Ste. G
Suttons Bay, MI 49682
Ph: (231)271-9895
Free: 800-980-9895
Fax: (231)271-9896
Co. E-mail: info@leelanauchamber.com
URL: http://www.leelanauchamber.com
Contact: Sally Guzowski, Executive Director
Description: Promotes business and community development and tourism in Leelanau County, MI. **Founded:** 1960.

53349 ■ Lewiston Area Chamber of Commerce (LACC)
PO Box 656
Lewiston, MI 49756
Ph: (989)786-2293
Fax: (989)786-4515
Co. E-mail: lewistonchamber@i2k.com
URL: http://www.lewistonchamber.com
Contact: Elaine Dixon, Chairperson
Description: Promotes business and community development and tourism in the Lewiston, MI area. Sponsors annual Morel Mushroom and Timberfest events, Car Show, and Arts and Crafts Fairs. **Founded:** 1958. **Publications:** *Communicator* (Monthly). **Educational Activities:** Ambassadors Formation (Monthly).

53350 ■ Litchfield Chamber of Commerce
PO Box 343
Litchfield, MI 49252
Ph: (517)542-2921
Co. E-mail: manager@cityoflitchfield.org
URL: http://www.ci.litchfield.mi.us
Contact: Douglas Terry, Manager
Description: Promotes business and community development in Litchfield, MI. **Founded:** 1967.

53351 ■ *Livonia Business Directory*
33233 Five Mile Rd.
Livonia, MI 48154
Ph: (734)427-2122

Fax: (734)427-6055
Co. E-mail: chamber@livonia.org
URL: http://www.livonia.org
Contact: Dan West, President
Released: Annual

53352 ■ Livonia Chamber of Commerce (LCC)
33233 Five Mile Rd.
Livonia, MI 48154
Ph: (734)427-2122
Fax: (734)427-6055
Co. E-mail: chamber@livonia.org
URL: http://www.livonia.org
Contact: Dan West, President
Description: Business association that promotes economic and community development in the city of Livonia, MI. **Founded:** 1954. **Publications:** *Communicator* (Monthly); *Industrial Directory* (Periodic); *Livonia Business Directory* (Annual).

53353 ■ *Looking to the Future*
c/o Vickie Phillipson, Chair
200 Depot Dr.
Dowagiac, MI 49047
Ph: (269)782-8212
Fax: (269)782-6701
Co. E-mail: vickie@dowagiacchamber.com
URL: http://www.dowagiacchamber.com
Contact: Vickie Phillipson, Chairperson
Released: Monthly **Price:** free.

53354 ■ Lowell Area Chamber of Commerce (LACC)
113 Riverwalk Plz.
Lowell, MI 49331
Ph: (616)897-9161
Fax: (616)897-9101
Co. E-mail: info@lowellchamber.org
URL: http://www.lowellchamber.org
Contact: Liz Baker, Executive Director
Description: Promotes business and community development in the Lowell, MI area. Sponsors semiannual sidewalk sales. Sponsors Riverwalk Arts and Crafts. Christmas festivities, and a golf outing. **Founded:** 1966. **Awards:** Person of the Year (Annual).

53355 ■ Ludington Area Chamber of Commerce (LACC)
5300 W US 10
Ludington, MI 49431
Ph: (231)845-0324
Free: 877-420-6618
Fax: (231)845-6857
Co. E-mail: chamberinfo@ludington.org
URL: http://www.ludington.org
Contact: Kathy Maclean, President
Description: Businesses and individuals interested in promoting business and community development in Ludington area and Mason County, MI. Sponsors Ludington Carferry Festival; Gus Macker 3-on-3 Charity Basketball Tournament; Harbor Festival; Gold Coast Arts and Crafts and Spirit of the Season Parade. **Founded:** 1929. **Publications:** *Area Map*; *Business to Business* (Monthly); *Menu Guide*. **Educational Activities:** Ludington Area Chamber of Commerce Meeting (Annual). **Awards:** Business Leader of the Year (Annual); Citizen of the Year (Annual).

53356 ■ *MAC Connections*
PO Box 521
Manchester, MI 48158
Ph: (734)476-4565
Co. E-mail: president@manchestermi.org
URL: http://www.manchestermi.org
Contact: Janet Larson, President
Released: Bimonthly

53357 ■ Mackinac Island Tourism Bureau
PO Box 451
Mackinac Island, MI 49757

Free: 877-847-0086
Co. E-mail: info@mackinacisland.org
URL: http://www.mackinacisland.org
Contact: Mrs. Mary McGuire Slevin, Executive Director
Description: Promotes business and community development on Mackinac Island, MI. Provides tourism and visitor information. **Publications:** *Discover Mackinac Island Guide Book* (Annual).

53358 ■ Mackinaw City Chamber of Commerce
216 E Central Ave.
Mackinaw City, MI 49701
Ph: (231)436-5574
Free: 888-455-8100
URL: http://www.mackinawchamber.com
Contact: Dawn Edwards, Executive Director
Description: Promotes business and community development and tourism in the Mackinaw City, MI area. Works to create an inviting community dedicated to economic growth and excellence in customer satisfaction. **Publications:** *Fall/Winter/Spring Guide* (Annual); *The Greater Mackinaw Area Chamber of Commerce*; *Summer Visitor's Guide* (Annual); *Community Profile and Membership Directory* (Annual); *Mackinaw City Community Guide and Membership Directory* (Annual).

53359 ■ Macomb County Chamber
28 First St., Ste. B
Chicago Plz.
Warren, MI 48093
Ph: (586)493-7600
Fax: (586)493-7602
Co. E-mail: nicole@macombcountychamber.com
URL: http://www.macombcountychamber.com
Contact: Grace Shore, Chief Executive Officer
Description: Works to encourage the economic development of local businesses by providing information, education, and advocacy and member benefits while making partnerships and investments throughout Macomb County. **Telecommunication Services:** grace@macombcountychamber.com.

53360 ■ Madison Heights - Hazel Park Chamber of Commerce (MHHPCC)
939 E 12 Mile Rd.
Madison Heights, MI 48071
Ph: (248)542-5010
Fax: (248)542-6821
URL: http://www.madisonheightschamber.com
Description: Promotes business and community development in Madison Heights, MI. Sponsors annual Bowl-A-Thon and auction. **Founded:** 1994. **Publications:** *Business to Business* (Periodic); *Chamber Communique* (Monthly); *Community Profile*. **Educational Activities:** Business Expo (Annual).

53361 ■ Mancelona Area Chamber of Commerce
PO Box 558
Mancelona, MI 49659
Ph: (231)587-5500
Fax: (231)587-5500
URL: http://www.mancelonachamber.org
Contact: Joanie Moore, Executive Director
Description: Promotes business and community development in Mancelona, MI.

53362 ■ Manchester Area Chamber of Commerce (MACC)
PO Box 521
Manchester, MI 48158
Ph: (734)476-4565
Co. E-mail: president@manchestermi.org
URL: http://www.manchestermi.org
Contact: Janet Larson, President
Description: Represents businesses and individuals organized to promote economic and community development in the Manchester, MI area. **Founded:** 1984. **Publications:** *Community Resource Guide* (Annual); *MAC Connections* (Bimonthly).

53363 ■ Manistee Area Chamber of Commerce (MACC)
11 Cypress St.
Manistee, MI 49660
Ph: (231)723-2575

Free: 800-288-2286
Co. E-mail: mreed@manisteechamber.com
URL: http://www.manisteechamber.com
Contact: Melissa Reed, Executive Director
Description: Promotes business and community development in Manistee County, MI. Promotes tourism. **Founded:** 1916. **Awards:** Citizen of the Year (Annual); Community Action Award (Annual); Corporate Citizen of the Year (Annual); President's Award (Annual); Volunteer Award (Annual).

53364 ■ *Manufacturer Directory*
921 47th St. SW
Wyoming, MI 49509
Ph: (616)531-5990
Fax: (616)531-0252
Co. E-mail: ken@southkent.org
URL: http://www.southkent.org
Contact: Ken Malik, President
Released: Annual

53365 ■ *Manufacturer's Guide*
PO Box 10
Niles, MI 49120-0010
Ph: (269)683-3720
URL: http://www.nilesmi.com
Contact: Ronald J. Sather, President
Released: Periodic

53366 ■ Marine City Chamber of Commerce
218 S Water St.
Marine City, MI 48039
Ph: (810)765-4501
Fax: (810)765-3077
Co. E-mail: chamberoffice@marinecitychamber.net
URL: http://www.marinecitychamber.net
Contact: Christine Kadey, President
Description: Develops an active organization to promote focus and ensure the economic growth and development of members' business and community at large.

53367 ■ Marquette Area Chamber of Commerce- Lake Superior Community Partnership (LSCP)
501 S Front St.
Marquette, MI 49855
Ph: (906)226-6591
Free: 888-578-6489
Fax: (906)226-2099
Co. E-mail: lscp@marquette.org
URL: http://www.marquette.org
Contact: Amy Clickner, Chief Executive Officer
E-mail: aclickner@marquette.org
Description: Promotes business, tourism, and community development in the Marquette County, MI area. **Founded:** 1930. **Publications:** *Directory and Planning Calendar* (Annual); *Directory and Planning Calendar* (Annual); *Superior Newsletter* (Monthly); *Marquette Area Chamber of Commerce/Lake Superior Community Partnership--Directory and Planning Calendar* (Annual).

53368 ■ Marshall Area Chamber of Commerce (MACC)
424 E Michigan Ave.
Marshall, MI 49068
Ph: (269)781-5163
Free: 800-877-5163
Fax: (269)781-6570
Co. E-mail: info@marshallmi.org
URL: http://www.marshallmi.org/index.taf
Contact: Monica Anderson, President
URL(s): www.marshallmi.org. **Description:** Promotes business and community development in the Marshall, MI area. **Founded:** 1947. **Publications:** *Buyers Guide* (Annual); *Chamber News* (Bimonthly). **Awards:** Athena Award Program (Annual). **Telecommunication Services:** chamber@marshallmi.org.

53369 ■ Marysville Chamber of Commerce
2055 Gratiot Blvd., Ste. D
Marysville, MI 48040
Ph: (810)364-6180

Fax: (810)364-9388
Co. E-mail: chamber@marysvillechamber.com
URL: http://www.marysvillechamber.com
Contact: Laura J. Crawford, Executive Director
Description: Consists of sole proprietors to large manufacturers. Serves as a voice for the business community, offering programs and activities to foster the continued success of the members. Through specific members' services and community events, the Chamber strives to meet its goals. These include: developing and enhancing the marketing of the Marysville area, and recognizing and promoting excellence in education to ensure a sound foundation of human resources for a healthy local economy. **Founded:** 1987. **Publications:** *Bi-Annual Member Directory* (Semiannual); *Marysville Chamber News* (Quarterly); *Bi-Annual Member Directory* (Semiannual).

53370 ■ *Marysville Chamber News*
2055 Gratiot Blvd., Ste. D
Marysville, MI 48040
Ph: (810)364-6180
Fax: (810)364-9388
Co. E-mail: chamber@marysvillechamber.com
URL: http://www.marysvillechamber.com
Contact: Laura J. Crawford, Executive Director
Released: Quarterly

53371 ■ Mason Area Chamber of Commerce (MACC)
148 E Ash St.
Mason, MI 48854-1646
Ph: (517)676-1046
Fax: (517)676-8504
Co. E-mail: masonchamber@masonchamber.org
URL: http://www.masonchamber.org
Contact: Douglas J. Klein, Executive Director
Description: Promotes business and community development in the Mason, MI area. **Founded:** 1972. **Publications:** *Mason in Motion* (Monthly); *Mason in Motion Update* (Monthly). **Educational Activities:** Good Morning, Mason! (Bimonthly). **Awards:** Citizen of the Year (Annual); Excellence in Business (Annual); Excellence in Education (Annual); Presidents Award (Annual). **Telecommunication Services:** dougklein@masonchamber.org.

53372 ■ *Mason in Motion*
148 E Ash St.
Mason, MI 48854-1646
Ph: (517)676-1046
Fax: (517)676-8504
Co. E-mail: masonchamber@masonchamber.org
URL: http://www.masonchamber.org
Contact: Douglas J. Klein, Executive Director
Released: Monthly

53373 ■ *Mason in Motion Update*
148 E Ash St.
Mason, MI 48854-1646
Ph: (517)676-1046
Fax: (517)676-8504
Co. E-mail: masonchamber@masonchamber.org
URL: http://www.masonchamber.org
Contact: Douglas J. Klein, Executive Director
Released: Monthly

53374 ■ Mecosta County Area Chamber of Commerce (MCACC)
c/o Jennifer Heinzman, Exec. Dir.
246 N State St.
Big Rapids, MI 49307
Ph: (231)796-7649
Fax: (231)796-1625
Co. E-mail: info@mecostacounty.com
URL: http://www.mecostacounty.com
Contact: Jennifer Heinzman, Executive Director
Description: Promotes business and community development in the Mecosta County, MI area. **Founded:** 1937. **Publications:** *Chamber News* (Monthly). **Educational Activities:** Labor Day Arts and Crafts (Annual).

53375 ■ *Membership and Business*
301 W Michigan Ave., Ste. 101
Ypsilanti, MI 48197-5450
Ph: (734)482-4920

Fax: (734)482-2021
Co. E-mail: info@annarborchamber.org
URL: http://www.ypsichamber.org
Contact: Diane Keller, President
Released: Annual **Price:** $50.

53376 ■ *Membership and Community Directory*
28 First St., Ste. B
Mount Clemens, MI 48043
Ph: (586)493-7600
Fax: (586)493-7602
Co. E-mail: info@macombcountychamber.com
URL: http://macombcountychamber.com
Contact: Grace Shore, Chief Executive Officer
Released: Annual **Price:** $15, for nonmembers; free for members.

53377 ■ *Membership Roster*
20600 Eureka Rd.
Taylor, MI 48180-5306
Ph: (734)284-6000
Fax: (734)284-0198
Co. E-mail: sandy@swcrc.com
URL: http://www.swcrc.com
Contact: Sandy Mull, President (Acting)
Released: Annual

53378 ■ *Menu Guide*
5300 W US 10
Ludington, MI 49431
Ph: (231)845-0324
Free: 877-420-6618
Fax: (231)845-6857
Co. E-mail: chamberinfo@ludington.org
URL: http://www.ludington.org
Contact: Kathy Maclean, President

53379 ■ Metro East Chamber of Commerce (MECC)
27601 Jefferson Ave.
St. Clair Shores, MI 48081
Ph: (586)777-2741
Fax: (586)777-4811
Co. E-mail: metroeastchamber@netscape.net
Contact: Heather Lynn, Executive Director
Description: Businesses and individuals. Seeks to promote the growth of the business community in Fraser, the Grosse Pointes, Harper Woods, Roseville, and St. Clair Shores, MI. Monitors legislation; holds annual Chamber Cruise and Golf Outing. **Founded:** 1946. **Publications:** *Business Guide* (Annual); *In Focus* (Monthly).

53380 ■ *Metro Guide*
921 47th St. SW
Wyoming, MI 49509
Ph: (616)531-5990
Fax: (616)531-0252
Co. E-mail: ken@southkent.org
URL: http://www.southkent.org
Contact: Ken Malik, President
Released: Annual

53381 ■ Michigan Chamber of Commerce
600 S Walnut St.
Lansing, MI 48933
Ph: (517)371-2100
Free: 800-748-0266
Fax: (517)371-7224
Co. E-mail: rstudley@michamber.com
URL: http://www.michamber.com
Contact: Richard K. Studley, President
Description: Works to represent employer interests in promoting economic development in Michigan. **Founded:** 1959. **Publications:** *Michigan Forward* (Bimonthly).

53382 ■ *Michigan Forward*
600 S Walnut St.
Lansing, MI 48933
Ph: (517)371-2100
Free: 800-748-0266
Fax: (517)371-7224
Co. E-mail: rstudley@michamber.com
URL: http://www.michamber.com
Contact: Richard K. Studley, President
Released: Bimonthly

53383 ■ Midland Area Chamber of Commerce (MACC)
300 Rodd St., Ste. 101
Midland, MI 48640
Ph: (989)839-9901
Fax: (989)835-3701
Co. E-mail: chamber@macc.org
URL: http://www.macc.org
Contact: Mr. Sid Allen, President
Description: Promotes, develop, and support its membership in order to foster a sustainable, prosperous business environment and a high quality, livable community. Supports the vision that Midland can be the best place to work, invest, raise a family and live, in all stages of life. **Awards:** Athena Award (Annual); J. Kermit Campbell Partnership Award (Annual).

53384 ■ Milan Area Chamber of Commerce
PO Box 164
Milan, MI 48160
Ph: (734)439-7932
Fax: (734)241-3520
Co. E-mail: info@milanchamber.org
URL: http://www.milanchamber.org

53385 ■ Monroe County Chamber of Commerce (MCCC)
1645 N Dixie Hwy., Ste. 2
Monroe, MI 48162
Ph: (734)242-3366
Fax: (734)384-3367
Co. E-mail: chamber@monroecountychamber.com
URL: http://monroemi.usachamber.com
Contact: Brian Reicker, Chairperson
Description: Promotes business and community development in Monroe County, MI. **Founded:** 1957. **Awards:** Athena Award (Annual); Small Business Person of the Year (Annual).

53386 ■ Mount Pleasant Area Chamber of Commerce (MPACC)
200 E Broadway
Mount Pleasant, MI 48858
Ph: (989)772-2396
Fax: (989)773-2656
Co. E-mail: lhadden@mt-pleasant.net
URL: http://www.mt-pleasant.net
Contact: Lisa Hadden, President
Description: Promotes business and community development in the Mt. Pleasant, MI area. Participates in area festivals. **Founded:** 1938. **Publications:** *Business News* (Monthly). **Educational Activities:** Business Expo (Annual). **Awards:** Citizen of the Year (Annual); Eagle Awards (Annual).

53387 ■ *Moving Up*
826 Michigan Ave.
Benzonia, MI 49616
Ph: (231)882-5801
Free: 800-882-5801
Fax: (231)882-9249
Co. E-mail: chamber@benzie.org
URL: http://www.benzie.org
Contact: Mary Carroll, President
Released: Quarterly

53388 ■ Muskegon Lakeshore Chamber of Commerce
380 W Western Ave., Ste. 202
Muskegon, MI 49440
Ph: (616)722-3751
Fax: (616)728-7251
Co. E-mail: mlcc@muskegon.org
URL: http://www.muskegon.org
Contact: Michael Hagen, Chairman
Description: Strives to be the voice of businesses in Muskegon area. Promotes the business community, specifically the members. Uses combined resources to provide high quality benefits at the lowest possible price. **Publications:** *Business Directory* (Annual); *Industrial Directory* (Annual); *Muskegon Lakeshore Chamber of Commerce--Business Directory*.

53389 ■ *My Business Advocate*
921 47th St. SW
Wyoming, MI 49509
Ph: (616)531-5990

Fax: (616)531-0252
Co. E-mail: ken@southkent.org
URL: http://www.southkent.org
Contact: Ken Malik, President
Released: Monthly **Price:** included in membership dues.

53390 ■ *Networker*
45525 Hanford Rd.
Canton, MI 48187
Ph: (734)453-4040
Fax: (734)453-4503
Co. E-mail: info@cantonchamber.com
URL: http://www.cantonchamber.com
Contact: Dianne Cojei, President
Released: Monthly

53391 ■ *News Capsule*
100 Main St., Ste. B
East Jordan, MI 49727
Ph: (231)536-7351
Fax: (231)536-0966
Co. E-mail: info@ejchamber.org
URL: http://www.ejchamber.org
Contact: Mary H. Faculak, President
Released: Quarterly

53392 ■ *News Views*
850 W Ann Arbor Trail
Plymouth, MI 48170
Ph: (734)453-1540
Fax: (734)453-1724
URL: http://www.plymouthmich.org
Contact: Wes Graff, President
Released: Monthly

53393 ■ *News & Views*
PO Box 127
Buchanan, MI 49107
Ph: (269)695-3291
Fax: (269)695-3813
Co. E-mail: bacc@buchanan.mi.us
URL: http://www.buchanan.mi.us
Contact: Katie Berry, Board Member
Released: Monthly

53394 ■ *Newsbyte*
22100 Michigan Ave.
Dearborn, MI 48124
Ph: (313)584-6100
Fax: (313)584-9818
Co. E-mail: info@dearbornchamber.org
URL: http://www.dearbornchamber.org
Contact: Jennifer Giering, President
Released: Biweekly

53395 ■ *Newsline*
23220 Gratiot Ave.
Eastpointe, MI 48021
Ph: (586)776-5520
Fax: (586)776-7808
URL: http://epchamber.com
Contact: Catherine Green, Executive Director
Released: Monthly

53396 ■ *Niles Renaissance*
PO Box 10
Niles, MI 49120-0010
Ph: (269)683-3720
URL: http://www.nilesmi.com
Contact: Ronald J. Sather, President
Released: Annual

53397 ■ Northville Chamber of Commerce
195 S Main St.
Northville, MI 48167
Ph: (248)349-7640
Fax: (248)349-8730
Co. E-mail: chamber@northville.org
URL: http://www.northville.org
Contact: Jody Humphries, Executive Director
Description: Promotes business and community development in the Northville, MI area. **Founded:** 1964.

53398 ■ Novi Chamber of Commerce (NCC)
41875 W 11 Mile Rd., Ste. 201
Novi, MI 48375
Ph: (248)349-3743

Fax: (248)349-9719
Co. E-mail: info@novichamber.com
URL: http://www.novichamber.com
Contact: Patricia Zopfi, Director
E-mail: patriciazopfi@la-z-boy.com
Description: Businesses, organizations, and individuals interested in promoting business and community development in Novi, MI. Sponsors 50's Festival in July and Art festival in August. **Founded:** 1967. **Publications:** *Member Business & Community Directory* (Annual); *Novi Chamber of Commerce Newsletter* (Monthly); *Novi Chamber of Commerce-- Business Directory* (Annual). **Educational Activities:** Novi Chamber of Commerce Meeting (Monthly).

53399 ■ *Novi Chamber of Commerce Newsletter*
41875 W 11 Mile Rd., Ste. 201
Novi, MI 48375
Ph: (248)349-3743
Fax: (248)349-9719
Co. E-mail: info@novichamber.com
URL: http://www.novichamber.com
Contact: Patricia Zopfi, Director
E-mail: patriciazopfi@la-z-boy.com
Released: Monthly

53400 ■ *On the Right Track*
124 W Hanson St.
Whitehall, MI 49461
Ph: (231)893-4585
Free: 800-879-9702
Fax: (231)893-0914
Co. E-mail: info@whitelake.org
URL: http://whitelake.org
Contact: Mike Cook, Chairman
Released: Monthly

53401 ■ Ontonagon County Chamber of Commerce
PO Box 266
Ontonagon, MI 49953
Ph: (906)884-4735
Co. E-mail: ontcofc@up.net
URL: http://www.ontonagonmi.org
Contact: Dave Bishop, President
Description: Promotes the county and helps local businesses prosper. **Scope:** tourism information. **Founded:** 1961. **Subscriptions:** business records clippings maps photographs reports. **Awards:** Ambassador Outside the County (Annual); Ontonagon County Action Award (Annual).

53402 ■ Orion Area Chamber of Commerce (OACC)
PO Box 484
Lake Orion, MI 48361-0484
Ph: (248)693-6300
Fax: (248)693-9227
Co. E-mail: info@lakeorionchamber.com
URL: http://orion.lib.mi.us/orion/index.php
Contact: Alaina Campbell, Executive Director
URL(s): www.lakeorionchamber.com. **Description:** Promotes business and community development in the Lake Orion, MI area. **Scope:** starting a business, marketing, resources. **Founded:** 1950. **Subscriptions:** 20. **Publications:** *Chamber Report* (Monthly); *Community Profile and Business Directory* (Annual). **Educational Activities:** Annual Community Business Expo (Annual); Women of the Chamber (Monthly). **Awards:** Business Scholarship (Annual).

53403 ■ Otsego Chamber of Commerce
135 E Allegan St.
Otsego, MI 49078
Ph: (269)694-6880
Co. E-mail: director@otsegochamber.org
URL: http://otsegochamber.org
Contact: Tim Andrus, President
Description: Promotes business and community development in the Otsego, MI area.

53404 ■ Oxford Area Chamber of Commerce (OACC)
PO Box 142
Oxford, MI 48371-0142
Ph: (248)628-0410

Fax: (248)628-0430
Co. E-mail: info@oxfordchamberofcommerce.com
URL: http://www.oxfordchamberofcommerce.com
Contact: Rick Laidler, President
Description: Promotes business and community development in the Oxford, MI area. Conducts business promotions, monthly program, annual golf outing, community awards, and Christmas parade. **Founded:** 1950. **Publications:** *Oxford News* (Monthly). **Educational Activities:** General Membership Meeting (Monthly). **Awards:** Community Awards (Annual).

53405 ■ *Oxford News*
PO Box 142
Oxford, MI 48371-0142
Ph: (248)628-0410
Fax: (248)628-0430
Co. E-mail: info@oxfordchamberofcommerce.com
URL: http://www.oxfordchamberofcommerce.com
Contact: Rick Laidler, President
Released: Monthly **Price:** free.

53406 ■ *Passport to International Detroit*
1 Woodward Ave., Ste. 1900
Detroit, MI 48232-0840
Ph: (313)964-4000
Free: 866-627-5463
Fax: (313)964-0183
Co. E-mail: members@detroitchamber.com
URL: http://www.detroitchamber.com/main/index.asp
Contact: Sandy K. Baruah, President
E-mail: sbaruah@detroitchamber.com

53407 ■ Pentwater Chamber of Commerce
PO Box 614
Pentwater, MI 49449
Ph: (231)869-4150
Free: 866-869-4150
Co. E-mail: travelinfo@pentwater.org
URL: http://www.pentwater.org
Contact: Carol Kitt, Chairperson
Description: Promotes business and community development in Pentwater, MI area.

53408 ■ *Petoskey Harbor Springs Community Profile*
401 E Mitchell St.
Petoskey, MI 49770-2623
Ph: (231)347-4150
Fax: (231)348-1810
Co. E-mail: chamber@petoskey.com
URL: http://www.petoskey.com
Contact: Carlin Smith, President
Released: Annual

53409 ■ Petoskey Regional Chamber of Commerce
401 E Mitchell St.
Petoskey, MI 49770-2623
Ph: (231)347-4150
Fax: (231)348-1810
Co. E-mail: chamber@petoskey.com
URL: http://www.petoskey.com
Contact: Carlin Smith, President
Description: Promotes business, tourism, and community development in the Petoskey, MI area. **Publications:** *Back to Business* (Monthly); *Petoskey Harbor Springs Community Profile* (Annual); *Community Profile and Business Directory* (Annual); *Petoskey Harbor Springs Community Profile* (Annual). **Educational Activities:** Art in the Park (Annual). **Awards:** Mission Award (Annual); Service Excellence Award (Annual).

53410 ■ Pigeon Chamber of Commerce
PO Box 618
Pigeon, MI 48755
Ph: (989)453-7400
Co. E-mail: tracypotter@pigeonchamber.com
URL: http://www.pigeonchamber.com
Contact: Brandis Mallais, President
Description: Promotes business and community development in Pigeon, MI area. **Founded:** 1903.

53411 ■ Plainwell Chamber of Commerce (PCC)
798 E Bridge St., Ste. A
Plainwell, MI 49080

Ph: (269)685-8877
Fax: (269)685-1844
Co. E-mail: greensees@mei.net
URL: http://www.plainwellchamber.com
Contact: Debbie Clark, Treasurer
Description: Promotes business and community development in Plainwell, MI. Sponsors community festival. **Founded:** 1989.

53412 ■ Plymouth Community Chamber of Commerce (PCCC)
850 W Ann Arbor Trail
Plymouth, MI 48170
Ph: (734)453-1540
Fax: (734)453-1724
URL: http://www.plymouthmich.org
Contact: Wes Graff, President
Description: Promotes business and community development in the Plymouth, MI area. **Founded:** 1950. **Publications:** *News Views* (Monthly).

53413 ■ Pontiac Regional Chamber
402 N Telegraph Rd.
Pontiac, MI 48341
Ph: (248)335-9600
Fax: (248)335-9601
Co. E-mail: info@pontiacchamber.com
URL: http://www.pontiacchamber.com
Contact: Kyle Westberg, Chairman
Description: Promotes growth and development of the business community while contributing to a safe, stable, and prosperous environment. **Publications:** *Inside Business* (Monthly).

53414 ■ *Progress Report*
3275 Central Blvd.
Hudsonville, MI 49426
Ph: (616)662-0900
Fax: (616)669-2330
Co. E-mail: keegstra@grar.com
URL: http://hudsonvillechamber.com
Contact: Kris Keegstra, President
Released: Bimonthly

53415 ■ *Railnet*
109 N Saginaw St.
Durand, MI 48429
Ph: (989)288-3715
Fax: (989)288-5177
Co. E-mail: office@durandchamber.com
URL: http://durandchamberofcommerce.com
Contact: Doug Schnell, President
Released: Quarterly

53416 ■ *Redbud Area News*
PO Box 127
Buchanan, MI 49107
Ph: (269)695-3291
Fax: (269)695-3813
Co. E-mail: bacc@buchanan.mi.us
URL: http://www.buchanan.mi.us
Contact: Katie Berry, Board Member
Released: Monthly

53417 ■ Redford Township Chamber of Commerce (RTCC)
26050 5 Mile Rd.
Redford, MI 48239-3289
Ph: (313)535-0960
Fax: (313)535-6356
URL: http://redfordchamber.org
Contact: Leo P. Snage, President
Description: Promotes business and community development in Redford Township, MI. **Founded:** 1950. **Publications:** *Redford Township Directory* (Annual).

53418 ■ *Redford Township Directory*
26050 5 Mile Rd.
Redford, MI 48239-3289
Ph: (313)535-0960
Fax: (313)535-6356
URL: http://redfordchamber.org
Contact: Leo P. Snage, President
Released: Annual

53419 ■ Reed City Area Chamber of Commerce (RCACC)
PO Box 27
Reed City, MI 49677
Ph: (231)832-5431
Free: 877-832-7332
Fax: (231)832-5431
Co. E-mail: chamberdirector@reedcitycrossroads. com
URL: http://www.reedcitycrossroads.com
Contact: Suzie Williams, Executive Director
Description: Helps the business, industry and tourism of Reed City Area to prosper. **Telecommunication Services:** info@reedcity.org.

53420 ■ *Regional Vision*
500 E Michigan, Ste. 200
Lansing, MI 48901
Ph: (517)487-6340
Fax: (517)484-6910
Co. E-mail: info@lenaweechamber.com
URL: http://www.lansingchamber.org
Contact: Bill Sepic, President
E-mail: wsepic@lansingchamber.org
Released: Bimonthly

53421 ■ Richmond Area Chamber of Commerce (RACC)
68371 Oak St.
Richmond, MI 48062
Ph: (586)727-3266
Fax: (586)727-3635
Co. E-mail: info@robn.org
URL: http://www.robn.org
Contact: Kim Galante, Executive Director
Description: Promotes economic growth and development of Richmond, MI. **Founded:** 1979.

53422 ■ Rockford Area Chamber of Commerce (RACC)
598 Byrne Industrial Dr. NE
Rockford, MI 49341
Ph: (616)866-2000
Fax: (616)866-2141
Co. E-mail: info@rockfordmichamber.com
URL: http://www.rockfordmichamber.com
Contact: Jeannie Gregory, Executive Director
Description: Promotes business and community development in the Rockford, MI area. Sponsors annual Start of Summer Celebration and annual Harvest Festival. **Founded:** 1943. **Publications:** *Rockford Living Magazine*; *UPdate* (Bimonthly); *How Your Chamber Works For You!* (Annual).

53423 ■ *Rockford Living Magazine*
598 Byrne Industrial Dr. NE
Rockford, MI 49341
Ph: (616)866-2000
Fax: (616)866-2141
Co. E-mail: info@rockfordmichamber.com
URL: http://www.rockfordmichamber.com
Contact: Jeannie Gregory, Executive Director

53424 ■ Rogers City Chamber of Commerce
292 S Bradley Hwy.
Rogers City, MI 49779
Ph: (989)734-2535
Free: 800-622-4148
Fax: (989)734-7767
Co. E-mail: rcchamber1@charterinternet.com
URL: http://www.rogerscity.com
Contact: David M. Snow, Executive Director
Description: Promotes and develops a vital business environment, considering the needs of the community and preserving the unique identity of the Rogers City, MI area.

53425 ■ Romeo-Washington Chamber of Commerce (RWCC)
PO Box 175
Romeo, MI 48065-0175
Ph: (586)752-4436

Fax: (586)752-2835
Co. E-mail: contact@rwchamber.com
URL: http://www.rwchamber.com
Contact: Scott Allen, President
Description: Promotes business and community development in Macomb County, MI. Sponsors competitions and festival. Conducts charitable activities. **Founded:** 1975. **Publications:** *Business Directory* (Periodic); *Cornerstone* (Bimonthly). **Educational Activities:** Romeo-Washington Chamber of Commerce Luncheon (Quarterly). **Awards:** Ambassador of the Year (Annual); The Brick Award (Annual); Lifetime Achievement Award (Annual); Member of the Month (Monthly); Senior Volunteer of the Year (Annual); Young Female Entrepreneur of the Year (Annual).

53426 ■ Saginaw County Chamber of Commerce
515 N Washington Ave., 2nd Fl.
Saginaw, MI 48607-1370
Ph: (989)752-7161
Fax: (989)752-9055
Co. E-mail: info@saginawchamber.org
URL: http://www.saginawchamber.org
Contact: Bob Van Deventer, President
Description: Manufacturers, agricultural producers, retail stores, service companies and organizations that share a common vision for the community. Strives to develop the business community in Saginaw County. **Publications:** *Saginaw County Chamber of Commerce Business Advocate* (Monthly). **Awards:** ATHENA Award (Annual); Corporate Community Service Award (Annual); Spirit of Saginaw Award (Periodic); Marsh Princing Leadership Saginaw Alumni Award (Annual). **Telecommunication Services:** bob@saginawchamber.org.

53427 ■ *Saginaw County Chamber of Commerce Business Advocate*
515 N Washington Ave., 2nd Fl.
Saginaw, MI 48607-1370
Ph: (989)752-7161
Fax: (989)752-9055
Co. E-mail: info@saginawchamber.org
URL: http://www.saginawchamber.org
Contact: Bob Van Deventer, President
Released: Monthly

53428 ■ St. Ignace Chamber of Commerce
560 N State St.
St. Ignace, MI 49781-1429
Ph: (906)643-8717
Free: 800-970-8717
Co. E-mail: sichamber@lighthouse.net
URL: http://www.saintignace.org
Contact: Janet Peterson, Executive Director
Description: Enhances businesses by building coalitions to build pride and promote the St. Ignace area as a great place to live, work, visit, and do business. **Publications:** *St. Ignace: Mackinac Area's Premier Vacation Guide.* **Awards:** Citizen of the Year (Annual).

53429 ■ *St. Ignace: Mackinac Area's Premier Vacation Guide*
560 N State St.
St. Ignace, MI 49781-1429
Ph: (906)643-8717
Free: 800-970-8717
Co. E-mail: sichamber@lighthouse.net
URL: http://www.saintignace.org
Contact: Janet Peterson, Executive Director

53430 ■ St. Johns Area Chamber of Commerce (SJACC)—Clinton County Chamber of Commerce
PO Box 61
St. Johns, MI 48879
Ph: (989)224-7248
Fax: (989)224-7667
Co. E-mail: ccchamber@power-net.net
URL: http://www.clintoncountychamber.org
Contact: Brenda Tarpening, Executive Director
Description: Promotes business and community development in the St. Johns, MI area. Sponsors St. Johns Mint Festival, annual Christmas House Deco-

rating Contest and Parade. **Publications:** *Chamber News* (Monthly). **Awards:** St. Johns Area Chamber of Commerce/Mint Festival Scholarship (Annual).

53431 ■ Saline Area Chamber of Commerce (SACC)
141 E Michigan Ave.
Saline, MI 48176-1552
Ph: (734)429-4494
Fax: (734)944-6835
Co. E-mail: salinechamber@aol.com
URL: http://www.salinechamber.org
Contact: John Olsen, President
Description: Works to increase the community's economic progress while preserving the high quality of life that makes Saline so unique through its various community events and projects, members services and activities. **Scope:** city, townships, area organizations, area committees, government, state, county, local issues, consumer protection, identity theft, internet fraud, small business, merchant information, insurance, mortgages, real estate information, resumes, area events, activities, projects. **Founded:** 1980. **Subscriptions:** articles periodicals. **Publications:** *Saline Business Advocate* (Monthly); *Saline Chamber Business Directory & Community Profile* (Annual). **Awards:** Business Enterprise Award (Annual); Citizen of the Year (Annual); George A. Anderson Vision Award (Annual); Lifetime Achievement (Annual).

53432 ■ *Saline Business Advocate*
141 E Michigan Ave.
Saline, MI 48176-1552
Ph: (734)429-4494
Fax: (734)944-6835
Co. E-mail: salinechamber@aol.com
URL: http://www.salinechamber.org
Contact: John Olsen, President
Released: Monthly **Price:** $250, /year for nonmembers; free to members.

53433 ■ *Saline Chamber Business Directory & Community Profile*
141 E Michigan Ave.
Saline, MI 48176-1552
Ph: (734)429-4494
Fax: (734)944-6835
Co. E-mail: salinechamber@aol.com
URL: http://www.salinechamber.org
Contact: John Olsen, President
Released: Annual

53434 ■ Sault Area Chamber of Commerce (SACC)
2581 I-75 Business Spur
Sault Ste. Marie, MI 49783
Ph: (906)632-3301
Fax: (906)632-2331
Co. E-mail: office@saultstemarie.org
URL: http://www.saultstemarie.org
Contact: Allan Case, Executive Director
E-mail: director@saultstemarie.org
Description: Business persons, professionals, and individuals interested in promoting business and community development in the Sault Ste. Marie, MI area. Sponsors charitable activities, festivals, and other special events. **Scope:** business. **Founded:** 1889. **Publications:** *Sault Area Business Directory* (Annual). **Telecommunication Services:** director@saultstemarie.org.

53435 ■ Schoolcraft County Chamber of Commerce (SCCC)
c/o Connie Diller, Exec. Dir.
1000 W Lakeshore Dr.
Manistique, MI 49854
Ph: (906)341-5010
Free: 888-819-7420
Fax: (906)341-1549
Co. E-mail: cadillerchamber@hotmail.com
URL: http://www.schoolcraftcountychamber.org
Contact: Connie Diller, Executive Director
Description: Promotes business and community development in Schoolcraft County, MI.

53436 ■ *Shiawassee Business Monthly*
215 N Water St.
Owosso, MI 48867-2875

Ph: (989)723-5149
Fax: (989)723-8353
Co. E-mail: customerservice@shiawasseechamber.org
URL: http://www.shiawasseechamber.org
Contact: Sue Kadlek, President (Acting)
Released: Monthly

53437 ■ Shiawassee Regional Chamber of Commerce (SRCC)
215 N Water St.
Owosso, MI 48867-2875
Ph: (989)723-5149
Fax: (989)723-8353
Co. E-mail: customerservice@shiawasseechamber.org
URL: http://www.shiawasseechamber.org
Contact: Sue Kadlek, President (Acting)
Description: Strives to energize the economic growth of the county through leadership actions. **Founded:** 1902. **Publications:** *Business Directory* (Annual); *Shiawassee Business Monthly* (Monthly); *Business Directory* (Annual). **Educational Activities:** Shiawassee Regional Chamber of Commerce Dinner (Annual). **Awards:** ATHENA Award (Annual); Citizen of the Year (Annual); Mission Award (Annual); Outstanding Small, Medium and Large Business (Annual).

53438 ■ Silver Lake Sand Dunes Area Chamber of Commerce
2388 N Comfort Dr.
Hart, MI 49420
Ph: (231)873-2247
Free: 800-870-9786
Co. E-mail: director@thinkdunes.com
URL: http://www.thinkdunes.com
Contact: Linda Foster, Executive Director
Description: Progressive business people and citizens. Strives to promote the business community and to improve the general welfare and development of Hart, Mears and Silver Lake areas.

53439 ■ South Lyon Area Chamber of Commerce
125 N Lafayette (Pontiac Trail)
South Lyon, MI 48178
Ph: (248)437-3257
Fax: (248)437-4116
Co. E-mail: gene@southlyonchamber.com
URL: http://www.southlyonchamber.com/1/123/index.asp
Contact: Gene Bobic, Executive Director
Description: Promotes business and community development in South Lyon, Lyon Township, Green Oak, and Salem, MI. Conducts annual Taste of South Lyon. **Founded:** 1965. **Awards:** Community Appreciation Awards.

53440 ■ Southern Wayne County Regional Chamber (SWCRC)
20600 Eureka Rd.
Taylor, MI 48180-5306
Ph: (734)284-6000
Fax: (734)284-0198
Co. E-mail: sandy@swcrc.com
URL: http://www.swcrc.com
Contact: Sandy Mull, President (Acting)
Description: Promotes business and community development in southern Wayne County, MI. Conducts business seminars and legislative forums. Maintains numerous committees. **Founded:** 1966. **Publications:** *Business Connection* (Monthly); *Membership Roster* (Annual); *Buyer's Guide* (Annual).

53441 ■ Southfield Area Chamber of Commerce
17515 W 9 Mile Rd., No. 190
Southfield, MI 48075
Ph: (248)557-6661
Fax: (248)557-3931
Co. E-mail: southfieldchamber@yahoo.com
URL: http://www.southfieldchamber.com
Contact: Ed Powers, President
Description: Promotes business and community development in the Southfield, MI area.

53442 ■ Sterling Heights Area Chamber of Commerce (SHACC)
12900 Hall Rd., Ste. 190
Sterling Heights, MI 48313
Ph: (586)731-5400
Fax: (586)731-3521
Co. E-mail: woehmke@shrcci.com
URL: http://www.suscc.com
Contact: Wayne Oehmke, President
Description: Promotes business and community development in the Sterling Heights, Utica, and Shelby Township, MI area. Sponsors Down Home Days and community ball. **Founded:** 1961. **Publications:** *Business Advisor* (Monthly); *Community Directory* (Annual); *Impact.* **Educational Activities:** Business Expo (Semiannual); Sterling Heights Area Chamber of Commerce Seminar (Quarterly).

53443 ■ Sturgis Area Chamber of Commerce (SACC)
200 W Main
Sturgis, MI 49091-0189
Ph: (269)651-5758
Fax: (269)651-4124
Co. E-mail: info@sturgischamber.com
URL: http://www.sturgischamber.com
Contact: Cathi Garn-Abbs, Executive Director
Description: Promotes business and community development in Sturgis, MI. Sponsors Michigan Week Festival and 4th of July celebration. Also sponsors the Sturgis area Business/Education Alliance. **Founded:** 1941. **Publications:** *Chamber Calling* (Monthly).

53444 ■ *Summer Visitor's Guide*
216 E Central Ave.
Mackinaw City, MI 49701
Ph: (231)436-5574
Free: 888-455-8100
URL: http://www.mackinawchamber.com
Contact: Dawn Edwards, Executive Director
Released: Annual

53445 ■ *Superior Newsletter*
501 S Front St.
Marquette, MI 49855
Ph: (906)226-6591
Free: 888-578-6489
Fax: (906)226-2099
Co. E-mail: lscp@marquette.org
URL: http://www.marquette.org
Contact: Amy Clickner, Chief Executive Officer
E-mail: aclickner@marquette.org
Released: Monthly

53446 ■ Suttons Bay Chamber of Commerce
PO Box 46
Suttons Bay, MI 49682-0046
Ph: (231)271-5077
URL: http://www.suttonsbayarea.com
Contact: Amy Peterson, President
Description: Represents the interests of business and organizations in Suttons Bay.

53447 ■ Tawas Area Chamber of Commerce
402 E Lake St.
Tawas City, MI 48764-0608
Free: 800-55-TAWAS
Co. E-mail: info@tawas.com
URL: http://www.tawas.com
Description: Strives to promote a healthy business climate and build a strong community. **Founded:** 1947. **Publications:** *Executive Report* (Monthly).

53448 ■ Three Rivers Area Chamber of Commerce
57 N Main St.
Three Rivers, MI 49093
Ph: (616)278-8193
Fax: (616)273-1751
Co. E-mail: info@trchamber.com
URL: http://www.trchamber.com
Contact: Christy Trammell, President
Description: Works to improve business community and industrial opportunity to enhance the quality of life in the Three River area. **Publications:** *Chamber News* (Monthly).

53449 ■ *Today's Business Choice*
305 N Pontiac Trail, Ste. A
Walled Lake, MI 48390
Ph: (248)624-2826
Fax: (248)624-2892
Co. E-mail: info@lakesareachamber.com
URL: http://www.lakesareachamber.com
Contact: Mark Steinberg, President
Released: Monthly

53450 ■ Traverse City Area Chamber of Commerce
202 E Grandview Pkwy.
Traverse City, MI 49685-0387
Ph: (231)947-5075
Fax: (231)946-2565
Co. E-mail: info@tcchamber.org
URL: http://www.tcchamber.org
Contact: Chad Dutmers, Chairperson
Description: Strives to develop business community by creating collaborations with community vital partners. **Publications:** *Your Chamber News* (Monthly).

53451 ■ *Tri-Community Commentator*
248 Main St.
Belleville, MI 48111
Ph: (734)697-7151
Fax: (734)697-1415
Co. E-mail: bellechamber@bellevillech.org
URL: http://www.bellevillech.org
Contact: Candace Connon, Executive Director
Released: Monthly

53452 ■ Troy Chamber of Commerce
4555 Investment Dr., 3rd Fl., Ste. 300
Troy, MI 48098-6338
Ph: (248)641-8151
Fax: (248)641-0545
Co. E-mail: theteam@troychamber.com
URL: http://www.troychamber.com
Contact: Michele Hodges, President
Description: Promotes business and community development in Troy, MI. **Publications:** *Connection.* **Telecommunication Services:** michele@troychamber.com.

53453 ■ *UPdate*
598 Byrne Industrial Dr. NE
Rockford, MI 49341
Ph: (616)866-2000
Fax: (616)866-2141
Co. E-mail: info@rockfordmichamber.com
URL: http://www.rockfordmichamber.com
Contact: Jeannie Gregory, Executive Director
Released: Bimonthly

53454 ■ *Update Magazine*
218 E Grand River
Brighton, MI 48116
Ph: (810)227-5086
Fax: (810)227-5940
Co. E-mail: info@brightoncoc.org
URL: http://www.brightoncoc.org
Contact: Pam McConeghy, President
Released: Monthly

53455 ■ *Visitors Guide*
368 E Main St.
Harbor Springs, MI 49740
Ph: (231)526-7999
Fax: (231)526-5593
URL: http://www.harborspringschamber.com
Contact: Liz Ahrens, President
Released: Annual

53456 ■ *The Voice*
429 N McEwan St.
Clare, MI 48617
Ph: (989)386-2442
Free: 888-ATC-LARE
Fax: (989)386-3173
Co. E-mail: manager@claremichigan.com
URL: http://www.claremichigan.com
Contact: Roger Williams, President
Released: Monthly

53457 ■ *The Voice of Business*
215 W Hematite St.
Ishpeming, MI 49849
Ph: (906)486-4841
Free: 888-578-6489
Co. E-mail: lscp@marquette.org
URL: http://www.marquette.org
Contact: Amy Clickner, Chief Executive Officer
Released: Monthly **Price:** free for members.

53458 ■ *The Voice of Business*
33425 Grand River Ave., Ste. 101
Farmington Hills, MI 48335
Ph: (248)919-6917
Fax: (248)919-6921
Co. E-mail: mary@ffhchamber.com
URL: http://gfachamber.com
Contact: Mary Engelman, Executive Director
Released: Bimonthly

53459 ■ Wayne Chamber of Commerce (WCC)
34844 W Michigan Ave.
Wayne, MI 48184
Ph: (734)721-0100
Fax: (734)721-3070
Co. E-mail: director@waynechamber.net
URL: http://waynechamber.net
Contact: Scott Cabauatan, President
Description: Promotes business and community development in Wayne, MI. **Founded:** 1939.

53460 ■ *West Bloomfield Community Directory*
6668 Orchard Lake Rd., Ste. 207
West Bloomfield, MI 48322
Ph: (248)626-3636
Fax: (248)626-4218
Co. E-mail: wbloomfieldchamber@gmail.com
URL: http://www.westbloomfieldchamber.com
Contact: Suzanne Levine, Executive Director
Released: Annual

53461 ■ *West Bloomfield Update*
6668 Orchard Lake Rd., Ste. 207
West Bloomfield, MI 48322
Ph: (248)626-3636
Fax: (248)626-4218
Co. E-mail: wbloomfieldchamber@gmail.com
URL: http://www.westbloomfieldchamber.com
Contact: Suzanne Levine, Executive Director
Released: Monthly

53462 ■ West Branch Area Chamber of Commerce (WBACC)
422 W Houghton Ave.
West Branch, MI 48661
Ph: (989)345-2821
Free: 800-755-9091
Fax: (989)345-9075
URL: http://www.wbacc.com
Contact: Christie Blackford, President
Description: Promotes business and community development in West Branch, MI. Sponsors festivals. **Founded:** 1948.

53463 ■ Westland Chamber of Commerce
36900 Ford Rd.
Westland, MI 48185-2231
Ph: (734)326-7222
Fax: (734)326-6040
Co. E-mail: info@westlandchamber.com
URL: http://www.westlandchamber.com
Contact: Joe Lezotte, Chairman of the Board
Description: Promotes business and community development in Westland, MI. **Publications:** *Commerce Commentary* (Monthly).

53464 ■ White Cloud Area Chamber of Commerce
12 N Charles
White Cloud, MI 49349
Ph: (231)689-6607
Co. E-mail: kb8ife@ncats.net
URL: http://www.whitecloudchamber.org
Contact: Ms. Sherry Adams, Secretary
Description: Promotes business and community development in White Cloud, MI.

53465 ■ White Lake Area Chamber of Commerce
124 W Hanson St.
Whitehall, MI 49461
Ph: (231)893-4585
Free: 800-879-9702
Fax: (231)893-0914
Co. E-mail: info@whitelake.org
URL: http://whitelake.org
Contact: Mike Cook, Chairman
Description: Promotes business and community development in Muskegon County, MI. Sponsors festival. **Founded:** 1971. **Publications:** *On the Right Track* (Monthly). **Educational Activities:** Membership Meeting (Monthly). **Awards:** Athena Award; El Award.

53466 ■ Williamston Area Chamber of Commerce
369 W Grand River
Williamston, MI 48895
Ph: (517)655-1549
Fax: (517)655-8859
Co. E-mail: info@williamston.org
URL: http://www.williamston.org
Description: Promotes business and community development in Williamston, MI area.

53467 ■ Wyoming Kentwood Area Chamber of Commerce (WKACC)
921 47th St. SW
Wyoming, MI 49509
Ph: (616)531-5990
Fax: (616)531-0252
Co. E-mail: ken@southkent.org
URL: http://www.southkent.org
Contact: Ken Malik, President
Description: Promotes business and community development in Wyoming, MI. **Founded:** 1980. **Publications:** *Manufacturer Directory* (Annual); *Metro Guide* (Annual); *My Business Advocate* (Monthly). **Awards:** Business of the Year (Annual).

53468 ■ *Your Chamber News*
202 E Grandview Pkwy.
Traverse City, MI 49685-0387
Ph: (231)947-5075
Fax: (231)946-2565
Co. E-mail: info@tcchamber.org
URL: http://www.tcchamber.org
Contact: Chad Dutmers, Chairperson
Released: Monthly

53469 ■ Ypsilanti Area Chamber of Commerce
301 W Michigan Ave., Ste. 101
Ypsilanti, MI 48197-5450
Ph: (734)482-4920
Fax: (734)482-2021
Co. E-mail: info@annarborchamber.org
URL: http://www.ypsichamber.org
Contact: Diane Keller, President
Description: Promotes business and community development in the Ypsilanti, MI area. **Founded:** 1918. **Publications:** *Business Talk* (Monthly); *Membership and Business* (Annual). **Educational Activities:** Brown Bag (Monthly). **Awards:** Athena Award (Annual); Distinguished Service Award (Annual); E3 Award (Annual); Small Business Person of the Year Award (Annual).

53470 ■ Zeeland Chamber of Commerce (ZCC)
149 Main Pl.
Zeeland, MI 49464-1735
Ph: (616)772-2494
Fax: (616)772-0065
Co. E-mail: zchamber@zeelandchamber.org
URL: http://www.zeelandcofc.org
Contact: Ann L. Query, President
Description: Promotes business and community development in Zeeland, MI. **Founded:** 1937. **Publications:** *The Zeelander* (10/year).

53471 ■ *The Zeelander*
149 Main Pl.
Zeeland, MI 49464-1735
Ph: (616)772-2494

Fax: (616)772-0065
Co. E-mail: zchamber@zeelandchamber.org
URL: http://www.zeelandcofc.org
Contact: Ann L. Query, President
Released: 10/year

MINORITY BUSINESS ASSISTANCE PROGRAMS

53472 ■ GROW - Grand Rapids Opportunities for Women
25 Sheldon Blvd. SE, Ste. 210
Grand Rapids, MI 49503
Ph: (616)458-3404
URL: http://www.growbusiness.org
Contact: Bonnie Nawara, Chief Executive Officer
Description: Offers connections, education, and resources to create and grow women-owned businesses in the Grand Rapids area.

53473 ■ Michigan Economic Development Corporation - Office of Small Business Group
300 N Washington Sq.
Lansing, MI 48913
Ph: (517)373-8431
Free: 888-522-0103
Fax: (517)373-9143
Co. E-mail: medcservices@michigan.org
URL: http://www.michiganadvantage.org/
Contact: James Epolito, Chief Executive Officer
Description: Encourages greater minority enterprise development by providing financial and business education programs. Assists in state certification processes, reviews the impact of legislation, and increases awareness of minority businesses.

53474 ■ Michigan Economic Development Corp. - Office of Women Business Owners Services
300 N Washington Sq., 4th Fl.
Lansing, MI 48913
Ph: (517)335-2877
Fax: (517)335-0198
URL: http://www.michigan.org
Contact: James Epolito, Chief Executive Officer
Description: Provides advocacy, technical assistance, and references to outside sources for financial counseling for women entrepreneurs.

53475 ■ Michigan Minority Supplier Development Council
3011 W Grand Blvd., Ste. 230
Detroit, MI 48202-3011
Ph: (313)873-3200
Fax: (313)873-4783
Co. E-mail: ceo@mmbdc.org
URL: http://www.mmbdc.com
Contact: Louis Green, Chief Executive Officer

53476 ■ Michigan Small Business and Technology Development Center—Grand Valley State UniversitySeidman School of Business;
510 West Foltan
Grand Rapids, MI 49504
Ph: (616)331-7480
Fax: (616)331-7485
Co. E-mail: sbtdchq@gvsu.edu
URL: http://misbtdc.org
Contact: Carol Lopucki, Director
Description: Provides a full-range of services for a variety of small businesses including: counseling; training; programs for a variety of needs, from how to get started, to financing; effective selling and e-commerce as well as how to develop business plans. Also provides research help and advocacy.

FINANCING AND LOAN PROGRAMS

53477 ■ Arbor Partners, LLC
130 S. First St.
Ann Arbor, MI 48104
Ph: (734)668-9000

Fax: (734)669-4195
Co. E-mail: info@arborpartners.com
URL: http://www.arborpartners.com
Contact: Donald Walker, Managing Director
Preferred Investment Size: $500,000 to $2,000,000. **Industry Preferences:** Internet specific, computer software and services, consumer related, communications and media. **Geographic Preference:** Michigan and Midwest.

53478 ■ Arboretum Ventures
Market Place Bldg.
303 Detroit St., Ste. 301
Ann Arbor, MI 48104
Ph: (734)998-3688
Fax: (734)988-3689
Co. E-mail: info@arboretumvc.com
URL: http://www.arboretumvc.com
Contact: Jan Garfinkle, Founder
Preferred Investment Size: $1,000,000 to $3,000,000. **Investment Policies:** Seed, early and later stage. **Industry Preferences:** Biotechnology, medical and health. **Geographic Preference:** Illinois, Indiana, Michigan, Midwest, and Ohio.

53479 ■ Camelot Venture Group
27725 Stansbury, Ste. 175
Farmington Hills, MI 48334
Ph: (248)741-5100
URL: http://www.camelotventures.com
Contact: David B. Katzman, Managing Partner
Preferred Investment Size: $5,000,000 to $150,000,000. **Industry Preferences:** Communications and media, computer software and hardware, Internet specific, semiconductors and other electronics, consumer related, financial services, and business service. **Geographic Preference:** U.S. and Canada.

53480 ■ EDF Ventures / Enterprise Development Fund
425 N. Main St.
Ann Arbor, MI 48104-1147
Ph: (734)663-3213
Fax: (734)663-7358
Co. E-mail: bizplans@edfvc.com
URL: http://www.edfvc.com
Contact: Mary Campbell, Founder
Preferred Investment Size: $1,500,000 to $5,000,000. **Industry Preferences:** Internet specific, computer software and services, medical and health, biotechnology, semiconductors and other electronics, communications and media, consumer and related, other products, and computer hardware. **Geographic Preference:** Midwest.

PROCUREMENT ASSISTANCE PROGRAMS

53481 ■ Genesee County Metropolitan Planning Commission
1101 Beach St., Rm. 223
Flint, MI 48502-1420
Ph: (810)257-3010
Fax: (810)257-3185
Co. E-mail: gcmpc@co.genesee.mi.us
URL: http://www.gcmpc.org
Contact: Julie Hinterman, Director

53482 ■ Haworth College of Business - Western Michigan University
3110 Schneider Hall
Kalamazoo, MI 49008-5416
Ph: (269)387-6004
Fax: (269)387-5710
Co. E-mail: sbtdc-kzoo@wmich.edu
URL: http://www.gvsu.edu/misbtdc/region11/
Contact: Tamara Davis, Regional Director
E-mail: sledbett@sabien.net
Description: Provides businesses with marketing know-how and technical tools they need to obtain and perform successfully under federal, state and local government contracts.

53483 ■ Michigan Procurement Technical Assistance Center - Business Development Center
Schoolcraft College
18600 Haggerty Rd.
Livonia, MI 48152-2696
Ph: (734)462-4438
Fax: (734)462-4673
Co. E-mail: inforeq@schoolcraft.edu
URL: http://www.schoolcraft.edu
Contact: Tammy Thomson, Counselor
Description: Provides businesses with marketing know-how and technical tools they need to obtain and perform successfully under federal, state and local government contracts.

53484 ■ Michigan Procurement Technical Assistance Center - Downriver Community Conference
15100 Northline Rd., Ste. 179
Southgate, MI 48195
Ph: (734)362-7070
Fax: (734)281-0265
Co. E-mail: paulaa@dccwf.org
URL: http://www.dccwf.org
Contact: Paula Boase, Director
Description: Provides businesses with marketing know-how and technical tools they need to obtain and perform successfully under federal, state and local government contracts.

53485 ■ Michigan Procurement Technical Assistance Center - Economic Development Alliance of St. Clair County
735 Erie St., Ste. 250
Port Huron, MI 48060
Ph: (810)982-9511
Fax: (810)982-9531
Co. E-mail: adeprez@edascc.com
URL: http://www.edascc.com
Contact: Doug Alexander, Director
Description: Provides businesses with marketing know-how and technical tools they need to obtain and perform successfully under federal, state and local government contracts.

53486 ■ Michigan Procurement Technical Assistance Center - Genesee Regional Chamber of Commerce (Region 6) - Satellite Office
519 S Saginaw St., Ste. 200
Flint, MI 48502
Ph: (810)600-1432
URL: http://www.michigantac.org
Description: Serves as an administrative agent for state and federal employment programs, provides economic development and technical assistance to regional businesses, and coordinates and supports regional planning activities.

53487 ■ Michigan Procurement Technical Assistance Center - Kalamazoo Regional Chamber of Commerce
Chamber Bldg.
346 W Michigan Ave.
Kalamazoo, MI 49007-3737
Ph: (269)381-2977
Fax: (269)381-0430
Co. E-mail: Editor@KazooChamber.com
URL: http://www.kazoochamber.com
Contact: Janice Campbell, Director
E-mail: jcampbell@kazoochamber.com
Description: Assists businesses in their growth and development.

53488 ■ Michigan Procurement Technical Assistance Center - Macomb Community College PTAC
7900 Tank Ave.
Warren, MI 48092
Ph: (586)498-4122
Fax: (586)498-4165
Co. E-mail: oliverr@macomb.edu
URL: http://www.macomb.edu/
Description: Provides businesses with marketing know-how and technical tools they need to obtain and perform successfully under federal, state and local government contracts.

53489 ■ Michigan Procurement Technical Assistance Center - Macomb Community College (Region 4) - Satellite Office
3270 Wilson St.
Marlette, MI 48453
Ph: (989)635-0063
Fax: (989)635-2230
Co. E-mail: cryderman-mossb@macomb.edu
URL: http://www.michigantac.org
Contact: Beth Cryderman Moss, Program Manager
E-mail: mossb@thumbworks.org
Description: Michigan Works! Agency provides job training assistance for Huron, Lapeer, Sanilac and Tuscola County residents.

53490 ■ Michigan Procurement Technical Assistance Center - Muskegon Area First
380 West Ave., Ste. 202
Muskegon, MI 49440
Ph: (231)722-7700
Free: 800-528-8776
Fax: (231)722-6182
Co. E-mail: pport@muskegon.org
URL: http://www.muskegonareafirst.org
Contact: Pamela Vanderlaan-Poort, Program Manager
E-mail: psvander@gte.net
Description: Provides businesses with marketing know-how and technical tools they need to obtain and perform successfully under federal, state and local government contracts.

53491 ■ Michigan Procurement Technical Assistance Center - Northeast Michigan Consortium (Presque Isle Region)
20709 State St.
Onaway, MI 49765
Ph: (989)733-8548
Fax: (989)733-8069
Co. E-mail: general@miworks-nemc.gen.mi.us
URL: http://www.michigantac.org
Contact: Denise Hoffmeyer, Program Manager
E-mail: denise@miworks-nemc.gen.mi.us
Description: Offers services including job training, welfare reform, employment service (including America's Talent Bank/Job Bank automated resume system), TAA/NAFTA programs, assistance in securing federal and state procurement contracts and a variety of youth programs.

53492 ■ Michigan Procurement Technical Assistance Center - Northwest Michigan Council of Governments
1209 S Garfield Ave., Ste. C
Traverse City, MI 49685-0506
Ph: (231)929-5036
Free: 800-692-7774
Fax: (231)929-5042
Co. E-mail: toddolson@nwm.cog.mi.us
URL: http://www.michigantac.org/region1.html
Contact: Todd Olson, Director
E-mail: jhasling@nwm.cog.mi.us
Description: Provides businesses with marketing know-how and technical tools they need to obtain and perform successfully under federal, state and local government contracts.

53493 ■ Michigan Procurement Technical Assistance Center, Saginaw Future Satellite Office (Region 5)
515 N Washington, Ste. 300
Saginaw, MI 48607
Ph: (989)754-8222
Fax: (989)754-1715
Co. E-mail: dsallen@saginawfuture.com
URL: http://www.michigantac.org
Contact: Delena Spates Allen, Director
E-mail: dsallen@saginawfuture.com
Description: Private, non-profit one stop economic development agency helps accomplish business moves and provide a wide array of business services to existing businesses in Saginaw County.

53494 ■ Michigan Procurement Technical Assistance Center - West Central Michigan Employment & Training Consortium
380 W Western Ave., Ste. 202
Big Rapids, MI 49440

Ph: (231)722-7700
Fax: (231)722-6182
Co. E-mail: spolacco@charter.net
URL: http://www.michworkswc.org
Contact: Shelia Polacco, Specialist, Technical Services
Description: Provides businesses with marketing know-how and technical tools they need to obtain and perform successfully under federal, state and local government contracts.

53495 ■ Michigan Procurement Technical Assistant Center - Schoolcraft College
18600 Haggerty Rd.
Livonia, MI 48152-3932
Ph: (734)462-4438
Fax: (734)462-4673
Co. E-mail: bdc@schoolcraft.edu
URL: http://www.schoolcraft.edu/bdc
Contact: Jann Deane, Program Manager
E-mail: tthomson@schoolcraft.edu
Description: Help to locate bidding opportunities for companies and explore what it takes to sell their products and services to the government.

53496 ■ Procurement Technical Assistance Center of South Central Michigan - Enterprise Group of Jackson, Inc.
1 Jackson Sq., Ste. 1100
Jackson, MI 49204
Ph: (517)788-4680
Fax: (517)782-0061
Co. E-mail: pennie@enterprisegroup.org
URL: http://www.enterprisegroup.org/ptac
Contact: Pennie Kay Southwell, Program Manager
E-mail: pennie@enterprisegroup.org
Description: Enhances national defense and economic development of the State of Michigan by assisting Michigan businesses in obtaining and performing on federal, state and local government contracts.

INCUBATORS/RESEARCH AND TECHNOLOGY PARKS

53497 ■ Albion Economic Development Corp.
309 N Superior
Albion, MI 49224
Ph: (517)629-3926
Free: 877-696-8682
Fax: (517)629-3929
Co. E-mail: psindt@albionedc.org
URL: http://www.albionedc.org
Contact: Peggy Sindt, Chief Executive Officer
Description: Works to improve the economic health of the Albion area. Offers an incubator for new businesses with access to equipment and advice.

53498 ■ Altarum Institute
3520 Green Ct., Ste. 300
Ann Arbor, MI 48105
Ph: (734)302-4600
Free: 800-879-6505
Fax: (734)302-4991
Co. E-mail: jeff.moore@altarum.org
URL: http://www.altarum.org
Contact: Lincoln T. Smith, President
E-mail: linc.smith@altarum.org
Description: Research and development facility emphasizing electronics, computer sciences, and optics and their applications. Provides analytical and experimental investigations and technical assistance. **Scope:** Advises government agencies worldwide on health-care and financial management. Drive a shift in the pattern of health care spending in the United States from programs consumed by cost of care to systems centered on the value of health. **Founded:** 1946. **Publications:** "The Role of Partnerships in Community Intervention Programs: New Insights from Case Studies"; "Issue Briefs: What Works in Health Care"; "Strategic Innovations for Affordable, Sustainable Health Care: A Model for Health System Reform"; "Accountable care organizations"; "Disease management"; "Electronic medical records"; "Medical tourism"; "Patient centered medical homes Patient centered medical homes"; "Payment models"; "Performance measurement and health care quality"; "WIC and Obesity Policy Round table Presentations," Mar,

2010; "Learning From State Surveillance Of Childhood Obesity," Mar, 2010; "Access to Oral Health Care During the Prenatal Period," Aug, 2008; "Home Health Care during an Influenza Pandemic: Issues and Resources," Jul, 2008; "An Assessment of the Impact of Medicaid Managed Care on WIC Program Coordination With Primary Care Services," Sep, 2007; "Evaluation to Determine the Effectiveness of the Public Assistance Reporting and Information System," Jun, 2007; Child Health USA 2006," Jul, 2007; Diet-Specific Social Support among rural adolescents," Jun, 2007. **Educational Activities:** International Conference on Applied Geologic Remote Sensing; International Conference on Geospatial Information in Agriculture and Forestry. **Seminars:** Impact on WIC Participants, Feb, 2011; Impact on WIC Vendors and the Food Environment, Feb, 2011; Special Topics, Feb, 2011; Highlights and Updates on Ongoing WIC Food Package Evaluations, Feb, 2011; Can WIC Play a Role In Stemming the Childhood Obesity Epidemic, Mar, 2010; Altarum policy round table on state approaches to covering the uninsured, Jun, 2006; Medical aspects of disaster management conference.

53499 ■ Ann Arbor SPARK Regional Incubator Network
201 S Davison St., Ste. 430
Ann Arbor, MI 48104
Ph: (734)761-9317
Fax: (734)761-9062
Co. E-mail: Lori@AnnArborUSA.org
URL: http://www.annarborspark.org/
Description: A small business incubator committed to advancing the economic development of innovation-based businesses in the Ann Arbor region by offering programs, resources, and proactive support to business at every stage, from start-ups to large organizations looking for expansion opportunities.

53500 ■ Ann Arbor/Ypsilanti Regional Chamber
115 W Huron St., 3rd Fl.
Ann Arbor, MI 48104
Ph: (734)665-4433
Fax: (734)665-4191
Co. E-mail: info@annarborchamber.org
URL: http://www.annarborchamber.org
Description: Promotes commerce in the Ann Arbor/ Ypsilanti region.

53501 ■ Battle Creek Chamber of Commerce Self-Employment Program
77 E. Michigan Ave., Ste. 80
Commerce Pointe Bldg.
Battle Creek, MI 49017
Ph: (269)962-4076
Fax: (269)962-6309
URL: http://www.battlecreek.org/chamber/index2.html
Description: A business assistance center providing existing firms and entrepreneurs with professional assistance in developing business ventures in greater Battle Creek. It combines the resources of various professional and volunteer organizations, enabling it to offer a variety of services at no or a very nominal charge.

53502 ■ Central Michigan University Research Corporation
2625 Denison Dr.
Mount Pleasant, MI 48858
Ph: (989)774-2424
Fax: (989)774-2416
Co. E-mail: cmurc@cmich.edu
URL: http://www.cmurc.com/
Description: A not-for-profit organization established to facilitate innovative research and development opportunities between the university and high technology companies and dedicated to establishing and operating a national center of excellence in the research fields of business intelligence and nanoscale sciences.

53503 ■ Delta Properties
401 Hall St. SW
Box 95
Grand Rapids, MI 49503
Ph: (616)243-9000

Fax: (616)243-1013
Co. E-mail: rick@delta-space.com
URL: http://www.deltapropertiesinc.com
Contact: Rick Ford, Agent
Description: Provides low-cost industrial space to encourage economic development.

53504 ■ Institute for Food Laws and Regulations - Michigan State University
140 G.M. Trout Bldg. (Food Science and Human Nutrition)
East Lansing, MI 48824
Ph: (517)355-8295
Fax: (517)432-1492
Co. E-mail: vhegarty@msu.edu
URL: http://www.iflr.msu.edu
Contact: Dr. Vincent Hegarty, Director
Description: Provides workshops/seminars.

53505 ■ Kettering University - SBDC
1700 University Ave
Flint, MI 48504
Ph: (810)762-9660
Fax: (810)762-9678
Co. E-mail: mlyttle@kettering.edu
Contact: Marsha Lyttle, Director

53506 ■ Lakeshore Business Garden
201. W. Washington Ave., Ste. 410
Zeeland, MI 49464
Ph: (616)772-5226
Co. E-mail: info@lakeshoreadvantage.com
URL: http://www.lakeshoreadvantage.com/garden.asp
Description: A business accelerator facility which acts as a launch pad for early stage companies by supporting entrepreneurs during the creation, start up and early growth stages of development; and by linking entrepreneurs to affordable office space, community resources, expert advice and capital to help increase their chances of success.

53507 ■ Michigan Biotechnology Institute International
3815 Technology Blvd.
Lansing, MI 48910-8596
Ph: (517)337-3181
Fax: (517)337-2122
Co. E-mail: info@mbi.org
URL: http://www.mbi.org
Contact: Bobby Bringi, Chief Executive Officer
Description: Coordinates the development of biotechnology research and technology transfer to businesses; provides in-house research and development; and provides technology transfer to biotechnology businesses.

53508 ■ Michigan Molecular Institute & Impact Analytical
1910 W St Andrews Rd.
Midland, MI 48640
Ph: (989)832-5555
Fax: (989)832-5560
Co. E-mail: mmiinfo@mmi.org
URL: http://mmi.org
Contact: Dr. Robert Nowak, Chief Executive Officer
E-mail: wood@impactanalytical.org
Description: Performs advanced research and development, and graduate-level education in polymer science and composite technology. Provides technical assistance and consulting services. Develops new information on the molecular structure and behavior of non-metallic materials. Also performs proprietary research.

53509 ■ Michigan Tech Enterprise SmartZone
PO Box 395
Houghton, MI 49931
Ph: (906)487-7000
Fax: (906)487-9523
Co. E-mail: jleinonen@mtecsmart.com
URL: http://www.mtecsz.com/default.aspx
Contact: Jonathan Leinonen, Manager
Description: A private, non-profit corporation fostering high-tech business incubation and growth by offering programs and services that encourage entrepreneurial development and that help ensure the success of start-ups and small companies.

53510 ■ MidMichigan Innovation Center
4520 E. Ashman Rd., Ste. M
Midland, MI 48642
Ph: (989)839-2333
Fax: (989)923-1572
Co. E-mail: moultrop@midmichiganinnovationcenter.org
URL: http://www.midmichiganinnovationcenter.org/
Contact: Chris Moultrup, Director
Description: A private, non-profit organization created to provide entrepreneurs and start-up companies with a supportive and collaborative environment, connecting companies with critical resources, valuable services, flexible facilities, and entrepreneurial training and education that will help develop their business ventures.

53511 ■ Southwest Michigan Innovation Center
4717 Campus Dr.
Kalamazoo, MI 49008
Ph: (269)353-1823
Fax: (269)372-3397
Co. E-mail: info@kazoosmic.com
URL: http://www.kazoosmic.com/
Description: A multi-tenant incubator/accelerator providing space and intensive support for life science startup firms in their early stages. There is also space available for graduates of the incubator and for firms that are at a later stage and no longer need the intensive support services of an incubator.

53512 ■ Southwestern Michigan Economic Growth Alliance, Inc.
1950 Industrial Dr.
Niles, MI 49120
Ph: (269)683-1833
Fax: (269)683-7515
Co. E-mail: smega1@sbcglobal.net
URL: http://www.southwesternalliance.org
Contact: Sharon Witt, Executive Director
Description: Works to retain and expand businesses in southwestern Michigan. Formerly the Greater Niles Economic Growth Alliance.

53513 ■ TechTown
440 Burroughs St.
Detroit, MI 48202
Ph: (313)897-5250
Fax: (313)875-5850
Co. E-mail: contact@techtownwsu.org
URL: http://www.techtownwsu.org
Description: A small business incubator providing the support and access to capital needed to build high tech companies in Detroit. It is a community of entrepreneurs, investors, mentors, service providers, and corporate partners committed to empowering entrepreneurs to build successful technology businesses to improve the quality of life for people across the country and around the world.

53514 ■ University of Michigan Tech Transfer - College of Engineering - Office of Technology Transfer - Industrial Development Division
1600 Huron Pky., 2nd Fl., Bldg. 520
Wolverine Tower, Rm. 2071
Ann Arbor, MI 48109-2590
Ph: (734)763-0614
Fax: (734)936-1330
Co. E-mail: techtransfer@umich.edu
URL: http://www.techtransfer.umich.edu
Contact: Ken Nisbet, Executive Director
Description: Involved with industry liaison and direct assistance, conferences, workshops, and economic development. Service programs are designed to retain and create employment by expanding and strengthening industry. Supports the Michigan Industrial Developers Association with practitioners training, community economic profiles, and target industry research using national databases.

53515 ■ West Michigan Science & Technology Initiative
301 Michigan St. NE, Ste. 537
Grand Rapids, MI 49503
Ph: (616)331-5840

Fax: (616)331-5869
Co. E-mail: wmsti@gvsu.edu
URL: http://www.wmsti.org/
Description: A small business incubator dedicating time, product development tools, amenities, and community assets that innovators, entrepreneurs, or small science and technology entrepreneurs need to commercialize their discoveries.

EDUCATIONAL PROGRAMS

53516 ■ Alpena Community College
666 Johnson St.
Alpena, MI 49707-1495
Ph: (989)356-9021
Free: 888-468-6222
Fax: (989)358-7561
URL: http://www.alpenacc.org
Description: Two-year college offering a small business management program.

53517 ■ Baker College - Owosso Campus
1020 S Washington St.
Owosso, MI 48867
Ph: (989)729-3350
Free: 800-879-3797
Fax: (989)729-3330
URL: http://www.baker.edu
Description: Vocational school offering a small business management program.

53518 ■ Mid Michigan Community College
1375 S Clare Ave.
Harrison, MI 48625
Ph: (989)386-6622
Fax: (989)386-9088
Co. E-mail: bmather@midmich.cc.mi.us
URL: http://www.midmich.cc.mi.us
Description: Two-year college offering a small business management program.

53519 ■ Montcalm Community College
2800 College Dr.
Sidney, MI 48885-9723
Ph: (989)328-2111
Free: 877-328-2111
Fax: (989)328-2950
URL: http://www.montcalm.cc.mi.us
Description: Two-year college offering a small business management program.

53520 ■ North Central Michigan College
1515 Howard St.
Petoskey, MI 49770
Ph: (231)348-6600
Free: 888-298-6600
Fax: (231)348-6628
URL: http://www.ncmich.edu/
Description: Two-year college offering a program in small business management.

53521 ■ Southwestern Michigan College - Workforce Education and Business Solutions
2229 U.S. 12 E
Niles, MI 49120
Ph: (269)782-1000
Free: 800-456-8675
Fax: (269)687-5655
Co. E-mail: info@swmich.edu
URL: http://www.swmich.edu
Description: Offers programs/classes in small business/small business management. **Telecommunication Services:** tchilds@swmich.edu.

53522 ■ Wayne State University
Business Management Office
5201 Cass Ave.
Detroit, MI 48202
Ph: (313)577-4515
Fax: (313)993-7664
URL: http://www.wayne.edu
Description: Schedules business and management courses. Also provides free management consulting to small business managers in the metropolitan Detroit area.

TRADE PERIODICALS

53523 ■ *Leader's Edge*
Pub: Michigan Association of CPAs
Contact: Corinne F. Duluk, Assistant Manager
Ed: Marla Janness, Editor, mjanness@ix.netcom.
com. **Released:** Bimonthly, 6/year. **Price:** $20. **Description:** Contains professional and technical
information for certified public accountants.

53524 ■ *MIOSHA News*
Pub: Michigan Department of Consumer and
Industry Services
Contact: Judith M. Shaine, Director, Communications
E-mail: judith.simons@cis.state.mi.us
Released: Quarterly. **Price:** Free. **Description:**
Contains information relevant to occupational safety
and health in relation to Michigan's employers and
employees.

PUBLICATIONS

53525 ■ *How to Form Your Own Michigan
Corporation Before the Inc. Dries!: A Step by
Step Guide, With Forms*
333 S. Taylor Ave.
Oak Park, IL 60302
Ph: (708)524-9033
Fax: (708)524-9038
Ed: Phillip Williams. **Released:** Second edition, 1993.
Price: $24.95. **Description:** Volume 3 of the Small
Business Incorporation series. Explains the advantages and disadvantages of incorporation and shows,
step-by-step, how the small business owners can
incorporate at low cost. Covers Michigan profit and
nonprofit corporations, Michigan professional service
corporations, subchapter S corporations, and Delaware corporations. Includes forms necessary for
incorporation.

53526 ■ *Smart Start your Michigan Business*
PSI Research
300 N. Valley Dr.
Grants Pass, OR 97526
Ph: (503)479-9464
Free: 800-228-2275
Fax: (503)476-1479
Co. E-mail: info@psi-research.com
URL: http://www.psi-research.com
Ed: Michael D. Jenkins. **Released:** Revised edition,
1992. **Price:** $29.95 (looseleaf binder); $24.95
(paper). **Description:** Part of the Successful Business Library series.

PUBLISHERS

53527 ■ **Agnes Press**
6160 Brambleberry Dr.
Howell, MI 48855
Ph: (517)546-3799
Fax: (517)546-9565
Co. E-mail: pete@marelco.com
Contact: Peter H. Burgher, Owner
E-mail: peteburgher@gmail.com
Description: Description: Publishes business books.
offers seminars and consulting. Does not accept
unsolicited manuscripts. Reaches market through
direct mail. **Founded:** 1986.

53528 ■ **Delta Alpha Publishing Ltd.**
35 Ash Dr.
Kimball, MI 48074
Ph: (810)985-1165
Free: 800-292-5544
Fax: (810)985-1168
Co. E-mail: dap@deltaalpha.com
URL: http://www.deltaalpha.com
Contact: Damien Abbott, Editor
E-mail: abbott@deltaalpha.com
Description: Description: Publishes books on real
estate, business and travel. Reaches market through
direct mail, exhibitions and the internet. **Founded:**
2000.

53529 ■ **Humanergy Inc.**
213 W Mansion St.
Marshall, MI 49068
Ph: (269)789-0446
Fax: (269)789-0057
Co. E-mail: info@humanergy.com
URL: http://www.humanergy.com
Contact: Lynn Townsend, Director
E-mail: lynn@humanergy.com
Description: Description: Publishes books on business and leadership.

53530 ■ **Jenkins Group Inc.**
1129 Woodmere Ave., Ste. B
Traverse City, MI 49686
Ph: (231)933-0445
Free: 800-706-4636
Fax: (231)933-0448
Co. E-mail: info@bookpublishing.com
URL: http://www.jenkinsgroupinc.com
Contact: James J. Kalajian, President
E-mail: jjk@bookpublishing.com
URL(s): www.bookpublishing.com. **Description:**
Description: Publishes on business, motivational and
professional improvement, health, fitness, non-fiction
and children's titles. **Founded:** 1988. **Publications:**
*Independent Publisher: Leading the World of Book
Selling in New Directions*; *Publishing Entrepreneur:
Profit Strategies for the Information & Publishing Industry* (Bimonthly); *Independent Publisher Online:
The Voice of The Independent Publishing Industry*
(Monthly). **Awards:** Independent Publisher Book
Awards; Living Now Book Awards; Moonbeam Children's Book Awards; Axiom Business Book Awards.
Telecommunication Services: publish@jenkins-
groupinc.com.

SMALL BUSINESS DEVELOPMENT CENTERS

53531 ■ Central Lakes College Small Business Development Center
501 W College Dr.
Brainerd, MN 56401
Ph: (218)855-8142
Free: 800-933-0346
Fax: (218)855-8141
Co. E-mail: gbergman@clcmn.edu
URL: http://www.clcmn.edu/smallbusiness
Contact: Greg Bergman, Director
Description: Represents and promotes the small business sector. Provides management assistance to current and prospective small business owners. Helps to improve management skills and expand the products and services of members.

53532 ■ Central Minnesota Small Business Development Center
355 5th Ave. S
St. Cloud, MN 56301
Ph: (320)308-4842
Fax: (320)255-4957
Co. E-mail: klross@stcloudstate.edu
URL: http://www.stcloudstate.edu/sbdc
Contact: Barry Kirchoff, Director
Description: Represents and promotes the small business sector. Provides management assistance to current and prospective small business owners. Helps to improve management skills and expand the products and services of members.

53533 ■ Minnesota Small Business Development Center - Northeast
University of Minnesota Duluth
Center for Economic Development
11 E Superior St., Ste. 210
Duluth, MN 55802
Ph: (218)726-7298
Free: 888-387-4594
Fax: (218)726-6338
Co. E-mail: umdced@d.umn.edu
URL: http://www.umdced.com
Contact: Elaine Hansen, Director
Description: Represents and promotes the small business sector. Provides management assistance to current and prospective small business owners. Helps to improve management skills and expand the products and services of members.

53534 ■ Minnesota Small Business Development Center - Northwest
3801 Bemidji Ave., Ste. 4
Bemidji, MN 56601
Ph: (218)755-4255
Fax: (218)755-2718
Co. E-mail: sbdc@bemidjistate.edu
URL: http://www.nwsbdc.com
Contact: Jaimee Meyer, Director (Acting)
Description: Represents and promotes the small business sector. Provides management assistance to current and prospective small business owners. Helps to improve management skills and expand the products and services of members.

53535 ■ Minnesota Small Business Development Center - South Central
120 Alumni Foundation Ctr.
Mankato, MN 56001
Ph: (507)389-8875
Fax: (507)389-1009
Co. E-mail: michael.nolan@mnsu.edu
URL: http://myminnesotabusiness.com
Contact: Michael Nolan, Director
Description: Represents and promotes the small business sector. Provides management assistance to current and prospective small business owners. Helps to improve management skills and expand the products and services of members.

53536 ■ Minnesota Small Business Development Center - Southeast
Rochester Community and Technical College
851 30th Ave. SE
Rochester, MN 55904
Ph: (507)285-7536
Fax: (507)280-5502
Co. E-mail: semnsbdc@gmail.com
URL: http://www.rctc.edu/workforce/smallbusiness
Contact:
Description: Represents and promotes the small business sector. Provides management assistance to current and prospective small business owners. Helps to improve management skills and expand the products and services of members.

53537 ■ Minnesota Small Business Development Center - West Central
Concordia College
Offutt School of Business
901 8th St. S
Moorhead, MN 56562
Ph: (218)299-3037
Fax: (218)299-4277
Co. E-mail: sbdc@cord.edu
URL: http://www.cord.edu/sbdc
Contact: Cathy Lindquist, Regional Director
Description: Represents and promotes the small business sector. Provides management assistance to current and prospective small business owners. Helps to improve management skills and expand the products and services of members.

53538 ■ Small Business Development Center, St. Thomas Metro
Schulze Hall 103
46 S 11th St.
Minneapolis, MN 55403
Ph: (651)962-4500
URL: http://www.stthomas.edu/sbdc
Description: Represents and promotes the small business sector. Provides management assistance to current and prospective small business owners. Helps to improve management skills and expand the products and services of members.

53539 ■ Southwest Small Business Development Center - Minnesota
Southwest Minnesota State University
1501 State St., Ste. 201
Marshall, MN 56258

Ph: (507)537-7386
Free: 800-642-0684
Fax: (507)537-6094
Co. E-mail: sbdc@smsu.edu
URL: http://www.positivelyminnesota.com/Business/Get_Help_from_Our_Experts
Contact: Liz Struve, Director
URL(s): www.smsu.edu/sbdc. **Description:** Represents and promotes the small business sector. Provides management assistance to current and prospective small business owners. Helps to improve management skills and expand the products and services of members.

53540 ■ Twin Cities Small Business Development Center
University of St. Thomas
Opus College of Business
Schulze Hall 103
46 S 11th St.
Minneapolis, MN 55403
Ph: (651)962-4500
Co. E-mail: smallbus@stthomas.edu
URL: http://www.stthomas.edu/business/centers/sbdc
Description: Represents and promotes the small business sector. Provides management assistance to current and prospective small business owners. Helps to improve management skills and expand the products and services of members. **Founded:** 1981.

SMALL BUSINESS ASSISTANCE PROGRAMS

53541 ■ Minnesota Department of Employment and Economic Development
First National Bank Bldg.
332 Minnesota St., Ste. E200
St. Paul, MN 55101-1351
Ph: (651)259-7114
Free: 800-657-3858
Fax: (651)296-1290
URL: http://www.deed.state.mn.us
Contact: Mark Lofthus, Director
Description: Coordinates state government information and resources available to small businesses. Provides information relating to start-up, operation, and expansion of businesses. Offers several free publications.

53542 ■ Minnesota Department of Employment and Economic Development - Business and Community Development Division and Trade
First National Bank Bldg.
332 Minnesota St., Ste. E-200
St. Paul, MN 55101-1351
Ph: (651)259-7114
Free: 800-657-3858
Fax: (651)296-1290
URL: http://www.deed.state.mn.us
Contact: Dan McElroy, Commissioner
Description: Provides grants to cities, townships and counties.

53543 ■ Minnesota Department of Employment and Economic Development - Minnesota Trade Office
First National Bank Bldg.
332 Minnesota St., Ste. E200
St. Paul, MN 55101-1351
Ph: (651)259-7499
Free: 800-657-3858
Fax: (651)296-3555
Co. E-mail: mto@state.mn.us
URL: http://www.exportminnesota.com
Contact: Tony Lorusso, Director
Description: Promotes Minnesota goods and services through export and attraction of foreign investors. Efforts concentrate on small business through several divisions, including Export Development Division, International Marketing and Investment Division, and Export Finance Division.

SCORE OFFICES

53544 ■ SCORE Albert Lea
Co. E-mail: info@score-rochester.og

53545 ■ SCORE Alexandria

53546 ■ SCORE Austin
Co. E-mail: info@score-rochester.org

53547 ■ SCORE Brainerd

53548 ■ SCORE Cannon Falls

53549 ■ SCORE Central Area (St. Cloud, Minnesota)
616 Roosevelt Rd., Ste. 100
St. Cloud, MN 56301-1332
Ph: (320)240-1332
Co. E-mail: chapter@stcloudscore.org
URL: http://www.stcloudscore.org
Contact: Don Schiffler, Chairman
Description: Provides one-on-one confidential business consultation, at no cost. Offers low-cost workshops to current and potential entrepreneurs on business planning, finance, marketing, and similar topics.

53550 ■ SCORE Detroit Lakes
Co. E-mail: mentor@StCloudSCORE.org

53551 ■ SCORE Lake Superior Region

53552 ■ SCORE Minneapolis
Bremer Bank Bldg.
8800 Hwy. 7
Minneapolis, MN 55426
Ph: (952)938-4570
Fax: (952)938-2651
Co. E-mail: minneapolis@score-mn.org
URL: http://minneapolis.score.org
Contact: Marshall Jones, Chairman
URL(s): www.score-mn.org. **Description:** Serves as volunteer program in which working and retired business management professionals provide free business counseling to men and women who are considering starting a small business, encountering problems with their business, or expanding their business. Offers free one-on-one counseling, online counseling and low cost workshops on a variety of business topics. **Founded:** 1964.

53553 ■ SCORE New Ulm Area
c/o New Ulm Chamber of Commerce
1 N Minnesota St.
New Ulm, MN 56073
Ph: (507)233-4300
Fax: (507)354-1504
URL: http://www.score-newulm.org
Description: Serves as volunteer program in which working and retired business management professionals provide free business counseling to men and women who are considering starting a small business, encountering problems with their business, or expanding their business. Offers free one-on-one counseling, online counseling and low cost workshops on a variety of business topics.

53554 ■ SCORE Park Rapids
Co. E-mail: score@hubbardcountyedc.com

53555 ■ SCORE Red Wing
Co. E-mail: redwing@score-mn.org

53556 ■ SCORE St. Paul
176 N Snelling Ave., Ste. 300
St. Paul, MN 55104-4707
Ph: (651)632-8937
Fax: (651)632-8938
Co. E-mail: stpaul@score-mn.org
URL: http://www.score-stpaul.org
Description: Serves as volunteer program in which working and retired business management professionals provide free business counseling to men and women who are considering starting a small business, encountering problems with their business, or expanding their business. Offers free one-on-one counseling, online counseling and low cost workshops on a variety of business topics.

53557 ■ SCORE South Metro
101 W Burnsville Pkwy., Ste. 152
Burnsville, MN 55337
Ph: (952)890-7020
Fax: (952)890-7019
Co. E-mail: southmetro@score-mn.org
URL: http://southmetro.score.org
Description: Serves as volunteer program in which working and retired business management professionals provide free business counseling to men and women who are considering starting a small business, encountering problems with their business, or expanding their business. **Founded:** 1993.

53558 ■ SCORE Willmar

53559 ■ SCORE Worthington
Co. E-mail: wcofc@frontiernet.net

53560 ■ Southeast Minnesota SCORE Chapter 406
c/o Rochester Area Chamber of Commerce
220 S Broadway, Ste. 100
Rochester, MN 55904
Ph: (507)288-8103
Fax: (507)282-8960
Co. E-mail: info@score-rochester.org
URL: http://www.score-rochester.org
Contact: Irvin Plitzuweit, President
Description: Volunteer businessmen and women. Provides free small business management assistance to individuals in the Rochester, MN area. Sponsors workshops. **Founded:** 1974.

BETTER BUSINESS BUREAUS

53561 ■ *BBB Connections*
2706 Gannon Rd.
St. Paul, MN 55116-2600
Ph: (651)699-1111
Free: 800-646-6222
Fax: (651)699-7665
Co. E-mail: ask@bbbmnd.org
URL: http://minnesota.bbb.org
Contact: Dana Badgerow, President
Released: Quarterly **Price:** included in membership dues.

53562 ■ Better Business Bureau Serving Minnesota and North Dakota
2706 Gannon Rd.
St. Paul, MN 55116-2600
Ph: (651)699-1111
Free: 800-646-6222
Fax: (651)699-7665
Co. E-mail: ask@bbbmnd.org
URL: http://minnesota.bbb.org
Contact: Dana Badgerow, President
Description: Provides programs and services to assist consumers and businesses. **Founded:** 1912. **Publications:** *BBB Connections* (Quarterly); *Better Pages* (Annual). **Awards:** Better Business Bureau Integrity Awards (Annual).

53563 ■ *Better Pages*
2706 Gannon Rd.
St. Paul, MN 55116-2600
Ph: (651)699-1111
Free: 800-646-6222

Fax: (651)699-7665
Co. E-mail: ask@bbbmnd.org
URL: http://minnesota.bbb.org
Contact: Dana Badgerow, President
Released: Annual

CHAMBERS OF COMMERCE

53564 ■ *Access*
PO Box 27
Delano, MN 55328-0027
Ph: (763)972-6756
Fax: (763)972-9326
Co. E-mail: info@delanochamber.com
URL: http://www.delanochamber.com
Contact: Lisa Koenecke, Executive Director
Released: Monthly

53565 ■ Aitkin Area Chamber of Commerce (AACC)
PO Box 127
Aitkin, MN 56431-0127
Ph: (218)927-2316
Free: 800-526-8342
Fax: (218)927-4494
Co. E-mail: upnorth@aitkin.com
URL: http://www.aitkin.com
Contact: Jeff Tidholm, President
Description: Promotes business and community development in the Aitkin, MN area. Sponsors Riverboat Heritage Days and Festival of Adventures. Convention/Meeting: none. **Founded:** 1945.

53566 ■ Albany Chamber of Commerce (ACC)
PO Box 634
Albany, MN 56307
Ph: (320)845-7777
Fax: (320)845-2346
Co. E-mail: albanycc@albanytel.com
URL: http://www.albanymnchamber.com
Contact: Kathleen Magel, President
Description: Promotes business and community development in Albany, MN. Sponsors annual Albany Heritage Day. **Publications:** *Chamber Membership Directory* (Annual).

53567 ■ Albert Lea - Freeborn County Chamber of Commerce (ALFCCOC)
701 Marshall St.
Albert Lea, MN 56007
Ph: (507)373-3938
Fax: (507)373-0344
Co. E-mail: alfccoc@albertlea.org
URL: http://www.albertlea.org
Contact: Randy Kehr, Executive Director
Description: Promotes and develops a healthy and positive business climate and improves the quality of life in the Albert Lea-Freeborn County area. **Publications:** *Business Monthly* (Monthly); *E-Biz* (Weekly).

53568 ■ Alexandria Lakes Area Chamber of Commerce (AACC)
206 Broadway
Alexandria, MN 56308
Ph: (320)763-3161
Free: 800-235-9441
Co. E-mail: info@alexandriamn.org
URL: http://www.alexandriamn.org
Contact: Coni McKay, Executive Director
Description: Promotes business and community development in the Alexandria, MN area. **Founded:** 1907. **Publications:** *Alexandria Lakes Area Visitor Guide* (Annual); *Alexandria Lakes Area Visitor Guide* (Annual); *Runeskriber* (Monthly).

53569 ■ *Alexandria Lakes Area Visitor Guide*
206 Broadway
Alexandria, MN 56308
Ph: (320)763-3161
Free: 800-235-9441
Co. E-mail: info@alexandriamn.org
URL: http://www.alexandriamn.org
Contact: Coni McKay, Executive Director
Released: Annual **Price:** free for members.

53570 ■ Anoka Area Chamber of Commerce (AACC)
12 Bridge Sq.
Anoka, MN 55303
Ph: (763)421-7130
Fax: (763)421-0577
Co. E-mail: mail@anokaareachamber.com
URL: http://www.anokaareachamber.com
Contact: Peter Turok, President
Description: Promotes business and community development in Andover, Anoka, Champlin, Dayton, and Ramsey, MN. **Founded:** 1952. **Publications:** *Directory and Map* (Annual).

53571 ■ Apple Valley Chamber of Commerce
14800 Galaxie Ave., Ste. 301
Apple Valley, MN 55124
Ph: (952)432-8422
Free: 800-301-9435
Fax: (952)432-7964
Co. E-mail: info@applevalleychamber.com
URL: http://www.applevalleychamber.com
Contact: Edward Kearney, President
Description: Businesses interested in prospering and creating a healthy, positive environment in which to conduct business. Strives to enhance the business environment and to build a better community by uniting businesses and professional firms. **Publications:** *Newsline* (Monthly).

53572 ■ *At Work*
101 W Burnsville Pkwy., Ste. 150
Burnsville, MN 55337
Ph: (952)435-6000
Fax: (952)435-6972
Co. E-mail: chamber@burnsvillechamber.com
URL: http://www.burnsvillechamber.com
Contact: Bill Corby, President
Released: Monthly

53573 ■ Austin Area Chamber of Commerce
329 N Main St., Ste. 102
Austin, MN 55912
Ph: (507)437-4561
Free: 888-319-5655
Fax: (507)437-4869
Co. E-mail: admin@austincoc.com
URL: http://www.austincoc.com
Contact: Sandy Forstner, Executive Director
Description: Promotes business and community development in the Austin, MN area. **Publications:** *Someplace Special; Someplace Special; Welcome to Austin.* **Educational Activities:** AMIGO Day (Annual); Ladies Night Out (Annual). **Awards:** Business of the Year (Annual). **Telecommunication Services:** execdir@austincoc.com.

53574 ■ Baudette-Lake of the Woods Chamber of Commerce
PO Box 659
Baudette, MN 56623-0659
Ph: (218)634-1174
Free: 800-382-3474
Fax: (218)634-2915
Co. E-mail: info@lakeofthewoodsmn.com
URL: http://www.lakeofthewoodsmn.com
Description: Promotes business and community development in Lake of the Woods County, MN. **Founded:** 1973. **Publications:** *Minnesota's Lake of the Woods Area Vacation Guide* (Annual).

53575 ■ Bemidji Area Chamber of Commerce (BACC)
300 Bemidji Ave.
Bemidji, MN 56601
Ph: (218)444-3541
Free: 800-458-2223
Fax: (218)444-4276
Co. E-mail: info@bemidji.org
URL: http://www.bemidji.org
Contact: Lori Paris, President
Description: Promotes business and community development in the Bemidji, MN area. **Founded:** 1907. **Publications:** *Chamber Report* (Monthly).

53576 ■ Big Stone Lake Area Chamber of Commerce (BSLACC)
987 US Hwy. 12
Ortonville, MN 56278
Ph: (320)839-3284
Free: 800-568-5722
Co. E-mail: chamber@bigstonelake.com
URL: http://bigstonelake.org
Contact: Donnette Herberg, Director
Description: Promotes tourism and economic development in the Big Stone Lake Area.

53577 ■ *The Bottom Line*
PO Box 487
St. Cloud, MN 56302-0487
Ph: (320)251-2940
Fax: (320)251-0081
Co. E-mail: information@stcloudareachamber.com
URL: http://www.stcloudareachamber.com
Contact: Bill Winter, Chairman
Released: Monthly **Price:** $15.

53578 ■ Brainerd Lakes Area Chambers of Commerce
124 N 6th St.
Brainerd, MN 56401-0356
Ph: (218)829-2838
Free: 800-450-2838
Fax: (218)829-8199
Co. E-mail: info@explorebrainerdlakes.com
URL: http://www.explorebrainerdlakes.com
Contact: Lisa Paxton, Chief Executive Officer
Description: Promotes business and community development in the Brainerd, MN area. Sponsors Brainerd Lakes Woods and Irons. **Publications:** *Chamber Connection* (Monthly); *Chamber E-Newsletter* (Weekly); *Vacation Planning Guide* (Annual); *Indoor/Outdoor Activity and Restaurant Guide* (Annual). **Educational Activities:** Commerce and Industry Show (Annual).

53579 ■ Buffalo Area Chamber of Commerce (BACC)
205 Central Ave.
Buffalo, MN 55313
Ph: (763)682-4902
Fax: (763)682-5677
Co. E-mail: info@buffalochamber.org
URL: http://www.buffalochamber.org
Contact: Sally Custer, President
Description: Promotes business and community development in the Buffalo, MN area. Holds annual Buffalo Days, Sidewalk Art and Craft Festival, and Buffalo P.R.C.A. Rodeo. **Founded:** 1969.

53580 ■ Burnsville Chamber of Commerce (BCC)
101 W Burnsville Pkwy., Ste. 150
Burnsville, MN 55337
Ph: (952)435-6000
Fax: (952)435-6972
Co. E-mail: chamber@burnsvillechamber.com
URL: http://www.burnsvillechamber.com
Contact: Bill Corby, President
Description: Promotes business and community development in Burnsville, MN. **Founded:** 1965. **Publications:** *At Work* (Monthly); *Chamber Membership Directory* (Annual).

53581 ■ *Business Advocate*
902 E 2nd St., Ste. 120
Winona, MN 55987
Ph: (507)452-2272
Fax: (507)454-8814
Co. E-mail: info@winonachamber.com
URL: http://www.winonachamber.com
Contact: Della Schmidt, President

53582 ■ *Business Brief*
320 Hoffman Dr.
Owatonna, MN 55060
Ph: (507)451-9700
Free: 800-423-6466
Fax: (507)451-7972
Co. E-mail: oacct@owatonna.org
URL: http://www.owatonna.org
Contact: Brad Meier, President
Released: Monthly

53583 ■ *Business Central*
PO Box 487
St. Cloud, MN 56302-0487
Ph: (320)251-2940
Fax: (320)251-0081
Co. E-mail: information@stcloudareachamber.com
URL: http://www.stcloudareachamber.com
Contact: Bill Winter, Chairman
Released: Bimonthly

53584 ■ *Business Directory*
PO Box 171
Madelia, MN 56062
Ph: (507)642-8822
Free: 888-941-7283
Fax: (507)642-8832
Co. E-mail: chamber@madeliamn.com
URL: http://www.visitmadelia.com
Contact: Karla Grev, Executive Director

53585 ■ *Business Monthly*
701 Marshall St.
Albert Lea, MN 56007
Ph: (507)373-3938
Fax: (507)373-0344
Co. E-mail: alfccoc@albertlea.org
URL: http://www.albertlea.org
Contact: Randy Kehr, Executive Director
Released: Monthly

53586 ■ *Business Perspective*
5782 Blackhire Path
Inver Grove Heights, MN 55076
Ph: (651)451-2266
Fax: (651)451-0846
Co. E-mail: info@riverheights.com
URL: http://www.riverheights.com
Contact: Jennifer Gale, President
Released: Monthly

53587 ■ Cambridge Area Chamber of Commerce
PO Box 343
Cambridge, MN 55008
Ph: (763)689-2505
Fax: (763)552-2505
Co. E-mail: info@cambridge-chamber.com
URL: http://www.cambridge-chamber.com
Contact: Eric Champion, President
Description: Promotes business and community development in the Cambridge, MN area. **Founded:** 1940. **Publications:** *Chamber News Page* (Monthly); *Friday Facts* (Weekly).

53588 ■ Canby Area Chamber of Commerce
PO Box 115
Canby, MN 56220-0115
Ph: (507)223-7775
Co. E-mail: info@canbychamber.com
URL: http://www.canbychamber.com
Contact: Pat Stanley, Chairperson
Description: Provides information on tourist attractions and outdoor activities in the Canby area.

53589 ■ Cannon Falls Area Chamber of Commerce (CFACC)
PO Box 2
Cannon Falls, MN 55009
Ph: (507)263-2289
Fax: (507)263-2785
Co. E-mail: tourism@cannonfalls.org
URL: http://www.cannonfalls.org
Description: Promotes business and community development in the Cannon Falls, MN area. Supports local charities; conducts political and business networking forums. **Founded:** 1979. **Publications:** *Discover Cannon Falls* (Annual); *Chamber News; Discover Cannon Falls* (Annual).

53590 ■ *The Chamber*
PO Box 348
Detroit Lakes, MN 56502-0348
Ph: (218)847-9202
Free: 800-542-3992
Fax: (218)847-9082
Co. E-mail: carrie@visitdetroitlakes.com
URL: http://www.visitdetroitlakes.com
Contact: Carrie Johnston, President
Released: Monthly **Price:** $15.

53591 ■ *Chamber Advantage Newsletter*
220 S Broadway, Ste. 100
Rochester, MN 55904
Ph: (507)288-1122
Fax: (507)282-8960
Co. E-mail: chamber@rochestermnchamber.com
URL: http://www.rochestermnchamber.com
Contact: John Wade, President
Released: Monthly

53592 ■ *Chamber Chatter*
114 3rd St,. Ste. B
Jackson, MN 56143
Ph: (507)847-3867
Fax: (507)847-3869
Co. E-mail: chamber@jacksonmn.com
URL: http://jacksonmn.com
Contact: Pam Heser, Executive Director
Released: Quarterly

53593 ■ *Chamber Chatter*
c/o Marlys Vanderwerf, Exec. Dir.
PO Box 134
Springfield, MN 56087
Ph: (507)723-3508
Fax: (507)723-5213
URL: http://www.springfieldmnchamber.org
Contact: Marlys Vanderwerf, Executive Director
Released: Monthly

53594 ■ *Chamber Chatter*
PO Box 1089
Walker, MN 56484-1089
Ph: (218)547-1313
Free: 800-833-1118
Fax: (218)547-1338
Co. E-mail: info@leech-lake.com
URL: http://www.leech-lake.com
Contact: Cindy Wannarka, President
Released: Monthly

53595 ■ *The Chamber of Commerce News*
200 NW 1st St.
Little Falls, MN 56345
Ph: (320)632-5155
Fax: (320)632-2122
Co. E-mail: assistance@littlefallsmnchamber.com
URL: http://littlefallsmnchamber.com
Contact: Debora K. Boelz, President
Released: Monthly

53596 ■ *Chamber Connection*
PO Box 474
Forest Lake, MN 55025
Ph: (651)464-3200
Fax: (651)464-3201
Co. E-mail: chamber@flacc.org
URL: http://www.flacc.org
Contact: Colleen Eddy, President
Released: Monthly

53597 ■ *The Chamber Connection*
6949 Valley Creek Rd., Ste. 115
Woodbury, MN 55125
Ph: (651)578-0722
Fax: (651)578-7276
Co. E-mail: chamber@woodburychamber.org
URL: http://www.woodburychamber.org
Contact: Liz Fleischhacker, Chairperson

53598 ■ *Chamber Connection*
124 N 6th St.
Brainerd, MN 56401-0356
Ph: (218)829-2838
Free: 800-450-2838
Fax: (218)829-8199
Co. E-mail: info@explorebrainerdlakes.com
URL: http://www.explorebrainerdlakes.com
Contact: Lisa Paxton, Chief Executive Officer
Released: Monthly

53599 ■ *Chamber E-Newsletter*
124 N 6th St.
Brainerd, MN 56401-0356
Ph: (218)829-2838
Free: 800-450-2838

Fax: (218)829-8199
Co. E-mail: info@explorebrainerdlakes.com
URL: http://www.explorebrainerdlakes.com
Contact: Lisa Paxton, Chief Executive Officer
Released: Weekly; every Monday afternoon. **Price:** free for members.

53600 ■ *Chamber Edge*
PO Box 487
St. Cloud, MN 56302-0487
Ph: (320)251-2940
Fax: (320)251-0081
Co. E-mail: information@stcloudareachamber.com
URL: http://www.stcloudareachamber.com
Contact: Bill Winter, Chairman
Released: Monthly

53601 ■ *Chamber Forum*
439 Main St.
Red Wing, MN 55066
Ph: (651)388-4719
Co. E-mail: frontdesk@redwingchamber.com
URL: http://www.redwingchamber.com
Contact: Patty Brown, President
Released: Bimonthly

53602 ■ *Chamber Members Directory*
530 Wilson Ave.
Faribault, MN 55021-4619
Ph: (507)334-4381
Free: 800-658-2354
Fax: (507)334-1003
Co. E-mail: chamber@faribaultmn.org
URL: http://www.faribaultmn.org
Contact: Kymn Anderson, President
Released: Periodic **Price:** $100.

53603 ■ *Chamber Membership Directory*
PO Box 634
Albany, MN 56307
Ph: (320)845-7777
Fax: (320)845-2346
Co. E-mail: albanycc@albanytel.com
URL: http://www.albanymnchamber.com
Contact: Kathleen Magel, President
Released: Annual **Price:** free for members.

53604 ■ *Chamber Membership Directory*
101 W Burnsville Pkwy., Ste. 150
Burnsville, MN 55337
Ph: (952)435-6000
Fax: (952)435-6972
Co. E-mail: chamber@burnsvillechamber.com
URL: http://www.burnsvillechamber.com
Contact: Bill Corby, President
Released: Annual

53605 ■ *The Chamber Network*
1 NW 3rd St.
Grand Rapids, MN 55744
Ph: (218)326-6619
Free: 800-472-6366
Co. E-mail: info@grandmn.com
URL: http://www.grandmn.com
Contact: Bud Stone, President
Released: Monthly

53606 ■ *Chamber News*
PO Box 2
Cannon Falls, MN 55009
Ph: (507)263-2289
Fax: (507)263-2785
Co. E-mail: tourism@cannonfalls.org
URL: http://www.cannonfalls.org

53607 ■ *Chamber News*
4785 Dakota St.
Prior Lake, MN 55372
Ph: (952)440-1000
Fax: (952)440-1611
Co. E-mail: sandi@priorlakechamber.com
URL: http://priorlakechamber.com
Contact: Sandi Fleck, Executive Director
Released: Monthly

53608 ■ *Chamber News Page*
PO Box 343
Cambridge, MN 55008
Ph: (763)689-2505

Fax: (763)552-2505
Co. E-mail: info@cambridge-chamber.com
URL: http://www.cambridge-chamber.com
Contact: Eric Champion, President
Released: Monthly

53609 ■ *Chamber Outlook*
1330 Hwy. 61
Two Harbors, MN 55616
Ph: (218)834-2600
Fax: (218)834-2600
Co. E-mail: donna@twoharborschamber.com
URL: http://www.twoharborschamber.com
Contact: Gordy Anderson, President
Released: Weekly

53610 ■ *Chamber Report*
300 Bemidji Ave.
Bemidji, MN 56601
Ph: (218)444-3541
Free: 800-458-2223
Fax: (218)444-4276
Co. E-mail: info@bemidji.org
URL: http://www.bemidji.org
Contact: Lori Paris, President
Released: Monthly

53611 ■ *Chamber Reporter*
320 Hoffman Dr.
Owatonna, MN 55060
Ph: (507)451-7970
Free: 800-423-6466
Fax: (507)451-7972
Co. E-mail: oacct@owatonna.org
URL: http://www.owatonna.org
Contact: Brad Meier, President
Released: Monthly

53612 ■ *Chamber Reporter Insert*
1801 E County Rd. 101
Shakopee, MN 55379-0717
Ph: (952)445-1660
Free: 800-574-2150
Fax: (952)445-1669
Co. E-mail: chamber@shakopee.org
URL: http://www.shakopee.org/chamber
Contact: Angie Whitcomb, President
Released: Monthly

53613 ■ *Chamber Review*
225 Sunnyside Dr.
Cloquet, MN 55720
Ph: (218)879-1551
Free: 800-554-4350
Fax: (218)878-0223
Co. E-mail: chamber@cloquet.com
URL: http://www.cloquet.com
Contact: Tony Vittorio, Chairman
Released: Monthly **Price:** free with membership.

53614 ■ *Chamber Update*
PO Box 826
Fairmont, MN 56031
Ph: (507)235-5547
Fax: (507)235-8411
Co. E-mail: info@fairmontchamber.org
URL: http://www.fairmont.org/chamber/home.htm
Contact: Bob Wallace, President
Released: Monthly **Price:** free for members.

53615 ■ *Chamber Update*
202 S Court St.
Fergus Falls, MN 56537
Ph: (218)736-6951
Fax: (218)736-6952
Co. E-mail: chamber@prtel.com
URL: http://www.fergusfalls.com
Contact: Lisa Workman, Executive Director
Released: Monthly

53616 ■ *Chamber Update*
PO Box 37
Olivia, MN 56277
Ph: (320)523-1350
Free: 888-265-CORN
Fax: (320)523-1514
URL: http://www.oliviachamber.org
Contact: Nancy Standfuss, Executive Director
Released: Monthly

53617 ■ *Chamber Update*
303 9th St.
Windom, MN 56101
Ph: (507)831-2752
Free: 800-794-6366
Co. E-mail: windomchamber@windomnet.com
URL: http://www.winwacc.com
Contact: Cheryl Hanson, President
Released: Monthly

53618 ■ Chisholm Area Chamber of Commerce (CACC)
223 W Lake St.
Chisholm, MN 55719
Ph: (218)254-7930
Free: 800-422-0806
Co. E-mail: info@chisholmchamber.com
URL: http://www.chisholmchamber.com
Description: Promotes business and community development in the Chisholm, MN area. Sponsors Christmas lighting competition, annual Polar Bear Days, annual Firedays, and All Class Grand Reunion.
Founded: 1933.

53619 ■ *City and County Map*
2104 E Hwy. 12 E
Willmar, MN 56201
Ph: (320)235-0300
Fax: (320)231-1948
Co. E-mail: chamber@willmarareachamber.com
URL: http://www.willmarareachamber.com
Contact: Ken Warner, President

53620 ■ *City Map*
509 Hwy. 10
Elk River, MN 55330-1415
Ph: (763)441-3110
Fax: (763)441-3409
Co. E-mail: eracc@elkriverchamber.org
URL: http://www.elkriverchamber.org
Contact: Debbi Rydberg, President

53621 ■ Cloquet Area Chamber of Commerce
225 Sunnyside Dr.
Cloquet, MN 55720
Ph: (218)879-1551
Free: 800-554-4350
Fax: (218)878-0223
Co. E-mail: chamber@cloquet.com
URL: http://www.cloquet.com
Contact: Tony Vittorio, Chairman
Description: Promotes business and community development in the Cloquet, MN area. Provides business consulting and business plan preparation.
Scope: business. **Founded:** 1952. **Subscriptions:** audio recordings books video recordings. **Publications:** *Chamber Review* (Monthly); *Membership Directory and Buyers Guide* (Annual). **Educational Activities:** Cloquet Carlton Area Chamber of Commerce Dinner (Annual). **Awards:** Business of the Year (Annual); Volunteer of the Year (Annual).

53622 ■ Cokato Chamber of Commerce (CCC)
PO Box 1030
Cokato, MN 55321
Ph: (320)286-5505
Fax: (320)286-5876
Co. E-mail: depclerk@cokato.mn.us
URL: http://www.cokato.mn.us
Contact: Louann Worden, Executive Secretary
Description: Promotes business and community development in Cokato, MN. Supports local charities; conducts political and business networking forums.

53623 ■ *Community Resource Guide*
21st Century Bank Bldg.
9380 Central Ave. NE, Ste. 320
Blaine, MN 55434
Ph: (763)783-3553
Fax: (763)783-3557
Co. E-mail: chamber@metronorthchamber.org
URL: http://www.metronorthchamber.org
Contact: Lori Higgins, President
Released: Annual

53624 ■ *The Connection*
507 Atlantic Ave.
Morris, MN 56267

Ph: (320)589-1242
Co. E-mail: mchamber@fedtel.net
URL: http://www.morrismnchamber.org
Contact: Karen Berget, Chairperson
Released: Monthly

53625 ■ *Connection*
630 10th St. E
Glencoe, MN 55336
Ph: (320)864-3650
Co. E-mail: chamber@glencoemn.org
URL: http://www.glencoechamber.com
Contact: Jason Ryan, Chairman

53626 ■ *Connections*
81 S 9th St., Ste. 200
Minneapolis, MN 55402-3223
Ph: (612)370-9100
Fax: (612)370-9195
Co. E-mail: info@minneapolischamber.org
URL: http://www.minneapolischamber.org
Contact: Todd Klingel, President
Released: Biweekly

53627 ■ Cook Area Chamber of Commerce
PO Box 296
Cook, MN 55723
Ph: (218)666-6093
Free: 877-526-6562
Co. E-mail: ebrunner@cookminnesota.com
URL: http://www.cookminnesota.com
Contact: Ellie Brunner, President
Description: Works to increase awareness of the area, support events, tourism promotion, support economic and community development and business affairs that will benefit the entire community.

53628 ■ Cottage Grove Area Chamber of Commerce
PO Box 16
Cottage Grove, MN 55016-0016
Ph: (651)458-8334
Fax: (651)458-8383
Co. E-mail: office@cottagegrovechamber.org
URL: http://www.cottagegrovechamber.org
Contact: Rhonda Mann, President
Description: Businesses in Cottage Grove, Newport, and St. Paul Park, in South Washington County, Minnesota. Strives to promote economic development and business growth within the Chamber area; develop a strong business-education partnership and identify legislative issues affecting private enterprise.
Founded: 1968.

53629 ■ Crookston Convention and Visitors Bureau
107 2nd St. W
Crookston, MN 56716
Ph: (218)281-4320
Free: 800-809-5997
Fax: (218)281-4349
Co. E-mail: chamber@visitcrookston.com
URL: http://www.visitcrookston.com
Contact: Lori A. Wagner, President
Description: Promotes business and community development in Crookston, MN area.

53630 ■ Dakota County Regional Chamber of Commerce
1121 Town Center Dr., No. 102
Eagan, MN 55123
Ph: (651)452-9872
Fax: (651)452-8978
Co. E-mail: info@ndcchambers.com
URL: http://dcrchamber.com
Contact: Ruthe Batulis, President
Description: Works to unite and strengthen the business community by providing networking, supporting educational opportunities, encouraging business and community development and determining public policy. **Founded:** 1957. **Telecommunication Services:** rbatulis@ndcchambers.com.

53631 ■ Delano Area Chamber of Commerce
PO Box 27
Delano, MN 55328-0027
Ph: (763)972-6756

Fax: (763)972-9326
Co. E-mail: info@delanochamber.com
URL: http://www.delanochamber.com
Contact: Lisa Koenecke, Executive Director
Description: Works to improve the business community of Delano area. **Publications:** *Access* (Monthly). **Educational Activities:** Membership Meeting (Monthly).

53632 ■ Detroit Lakes Regional Chamber of Commerce (DLRCC)
PO Box 348
Detroit Lakes, MN 56502-0348
Ph: (218)847-9202
Free: 800-542-3992
Fax: (218)847-9082
Co. E-mail: carrie@visitdetroitlakes.com
URL: http://www.visitdetroitlakes.com
Contact: Carrie Johnston, President
Description: Promotes business and community development in the Detroit Lakes, MN area.
Founded: 1906. **Publications:** *The Chamber* (Monthly); *Membership Directory/Buyers Guide.*

53633 ■ *Directory of Chamber Members*
6949 Valley Creek Rd., Ste. 115
Woodbury, MN 55125
Ph: (651)578-0722
Fax: (651)578-7276
Co. E-mail: chamber@woodburychamber.org
URL: http://www.woodburychamber.org
Contact: Liz Fleischhacker, Chairperson

53634 ■ *Directory and Map*
12 Bridge Sq.
Anoka, MN 55303
Ph: (763)421-7130
Fax: (763)421-0577
Co. E-mail: mail@anokaareachamber.com
URL: http://www.anokaareachamber.com
Contact: Peter Turok, President
Released: Annual

53635 ■ *Discover Cannon Falls*
PO Box 2
Cannon Falls, MN 55009
Ph: (507)263-2289
Fax: (507)263-2785
Co. E-mail: tourism@cannonfalls.org
URL: http://www.cannonfalls.org
Released: Annual **Price:** free for members.

53636 ■ *Discover Wayzata*
402 E Lake St.
Wayzata, MN 55391-1651
Ph: (952)473-9595
Fax: (952)473-6266
Co. E-mail: info@wayzatachamber.com
URL: http://www.wayzatachamber.com
Contact: Peggy Douglas, President

53637 ■ Duluth Chamber of Commerce
5 W 1st St., Ste. 101
Duluth, MN 55802-2115
Ph: (218)722-5501
Fax: (218)722-3223
Co. E-mail: inquiry@duluthchamber.com
URL: http://www.duluthchamber.com
Contact: David M. Ross, President

Description: Promotes business and community development in Duluth, MN. Supports local charities; conducts political and business networking forums.
Publications: *Xpress*; *The Duluthian* (Bimonthly). **Educational Activities:** Business After Hours (Monthly).

53638 ■ *E-Biz*
701 Marshall St.
Albert Lea, MN 56007
Ph: (507)373-3938
Fax: (507)373-0344
Co. E-mail: alfccoc@albertlea.org
URL: http://www.albertlea.org
Contact: Randy Kehr, Executive Director
Released: Weekly

53639 ■ **Eden Prairie Chamber of Commerce (EPC)**
11455 Viking Dr., Ste. 270
Eden Prairie, MN 55344
Ph: (952)944-2830
Fax: (952)944-0229
Co. E-mail: adminj@epchamber.org
URL: http://www.epchamber.org
Contact: Pat MulQueeny, President
Description: Provides their members opportunities for community leadership. Acts as an advocate for commerce. Promotes community growth and development. **Telecommunication Services:** pat.mulqueeny@epchamber.org.

53640 ■ **Elk River Area Chamber of Commerce (ERACC)**
509 Hwy. 10
Elk River, MN 55330-1415
Ph: (763)441-3110
Fax: (763)441-3409
Co. E-mail: eracc@elkriverchamber.org
URL: http://www.elkriverchamber.org
Contact: Debbi Rydberg, President
Description: Promotes business and community development in the Elk River, MN area. **Founded:** 1968. **Publications:** City Map. **Educational Activities:** Elk River Area Chamber of Commerce Meeting (Monthly).

53641 ■ **Ely Chamber of Commerce (ECC)**
1600 E Sheridan St.
Ely, MN 55731
Ph: (218)365-6123
Free: 800-777-7281
URL: http://www.ely.org
Description: Promotes business and tourism in Ely, MN. Sponsors Blueberry Art Festival and Fall Harvest Moon Festival. **Founded:** 1908. **Publications:** Vacation Guide (Annual).

53642 ■ **Experience the Jackson Area**
114 3rd St,. Ste. B
Jackson, MN 56143
Ph: (507)847-3867
Fax: (507)847-3869
Co. E-mail: chamber@jacksonmn.com
URL: http://jacksonmn.com
Contact: Pam Heser, Executive Director

53643 ■ **Fairmont Area Chamber of Commerce (FACC)**
PO Box 826
Fairmont, MN 56031
Ph: (507)235-5547
Fax: (507)235-8411
Co. E-mail: info@fairmontchamber.org
URL: http://www.fairmont.org/chamber/home.htm
Contact: Bob Wallace, President
Description: Promotes business and community development in the Fairmont, MN area. Supports local charities; conducts political and business networking forums. **Founded:** 1947. **Publications:** Chamber Update (Monthly).

53644 ■ **Faribault Area Chamber of Commerce and Tourism (FACC)**
530 Wilson Ave.
Faribault, MN 55021-4619
Ph: (507)334-4381
Free: 800-658-2354
Fax: (507)334-1003
Co. E-mail: chamber@faribaultmn.org
URL: http://www.faribaultmn.org
Contact: Kymn Anderson, President
Description: Promotes agricultural, business, and community development in the Faribault, MN area. Promotes tourism. Holds annual Heritage Days festival, Balloon Rally and Business Expo. **Founded:** 1920. **Publications:** Manufacturers Directory (Periodic); Organizational Directory (Periodic); Chamber Members Directory (Periodic). **Educational Activities:** Business Farm Luncheon (Annual); Golf Social (Annual). **Awards:** Business of the Year Award (Annual); Partnership in Education Award (Annual).

53645 ■ **Fergus Falls Area Chamber of Commerce (FFACC)**
202 S Court St.
Fergus Falls, MN 56537
Ph: (218)736-6951
Fax: (218)736-6952
Co. E-mail: chamber@prtel.com
URL: http://www.fergusfalls.com
Contact: Lisa Workman, Executive Director
Description: Promotes business and community development in the Fergus Falls, MN area. Holds annual Scandinavian and Frostbite Festivals. **Founded:** 1886. **Publications:** Chamber Update (Monthly). **Educational Activities:** Fergus Falls Area Chamber of Commerce Banquet (Annual). **Awards:** Champion Citizens (Annual).

53646 ■ **The Focus**
705 N 2nd St.
Princeton, MN 55371-1550
Ph: (763)389-1764
Fax: (763)631-1764
Co. E-mail: pacc@sherbtel.net
URL: http://www.princetonmnchamber.org
Contact: Scott Berry, President
Released: Monthly

53647 ■ **Forest Lake Area Chamber of Commerce (FLACC)**
PO Box 474
Forest Lake, MN 55025
Ph: (651)464-3200
Fax: (651)464-3201
Co. E-mail: chamber@flacc.org
URL: http://www.flacc.org
Contact: Colleen Eddy, President
Description: Promotes business and community development in the Forest Lake, MN area. Sponsors Fun in the Forest festival. Convention/Meeting: none. **Founded:** 1963. **Publications:** Chamber Connection (Monthly).

53648 ■ **Friday Facts**
PO Box 343
Cambridge, MN 55008
Ph: (763)689-2505
Fax: (763)552-2505
Co. E-mail: info@cambridge-chamber.com
URL: http://www.cambridge-chamber.com
Contact: Eric Champion, President
Released: Weekly

53649 ■ **Glencoe Area Chamber of Commerce**
630 10th St. E
Glencoe, MN 55336
Ph: (320)864-3650
Co. E-mail: chamber@glencoemn.org
URL: http://www.glencoechamber.com
Contact: Jason Ryan, Chairman
Description: Strives to create, promote, and enhance the business environment and improve the quality of life in the Glencoe area. **Publications:** Connection.

53650 ■ **Glenwood Chamber of Commerce Newsletter**
2 E Minnesota Ave., Ste. 125
Glenwood, MN 56334
Ph: (320)634-3636
Free: 866-634-3636
Fax: (320)634-3637
Co. E-mail: chamber@glenwoodlakesarea.org
URL: http://glenwoodlakesarea.org/index.cfm?pageid=1
Contact: Cody Rogahn, Executive Director
Released: Monthly

53651 ■ **Glenwood Lakes Area Chamber of Commerce (GACC)**
2 E Minnesota Ave., Ste. 125
Glenwood, MN 56334
Ph: (320)634-3636
Free: 866-634-3636

Fax: (320)634-3637
Co. E-mail: chamber@glenwoodlakesarea.org
URL: http://glenwoodlakesarea.org/index.cfm?pageid=1
Contact: Cody Rogahn, Executive Director
Description: Promotes business and community development in Glenwood, MN. Sponsors Waterama festival, Lake Minnewaska Ice Fishing Contest and Physically Limited Golfers Association National Tournament. **Publications:** Glenwood Chamber of Commerce Newsletter (Monthly).

53652 ■ **Grand Marais Chamber of Commerce**
PO Box 805
Grand Marais, MN 55604-0805
Ph: (218)387-9112
Co. E-mail: gmcc@boreal.org
URL: http://www.grandmaraismn.com
Contact: Bev Wolke, Director
Description: Supports member businesses, economic growth, and community events in the Grand Marais Area.

53653 ■ **Grand Rapids Area Chamber of Commerce (GRACC)**
1 NW 3rd St.
Grand Rapids, MN 55744
Ph: (218)326-6619
Free: 800-472-6366
Co. E-mail: info@grandmn.com
URL: http://www.grandmn.com
Contact: Bud Stone, President
Description: Promotes business and community development in the Grand Rapids, MN area. **Founded:** 1902. **Publications:** The Chamber Network (Monthly). **Educational Activities:** Golf Outing (Annual).

53654 ■ **Granite Falls Area Chamber of Commerce (GFACC)**
646 Prentice St.
Granite Falls, MN 56241
Ph: (320)564-4039
Fax: (320)564-3843
Co. E-mail: gfchamber@mvtvwireless.com
URL: http://www.granitefalls.com
Contact: Greg Holmstrom, President
URL(s): www.granitefallschamber.com. **Description:** Promotes business and community development in the Granite Falls, MN area.

53655 ■ **Greater Stillwater Chamber of Commerce**
106 S Main St.
Stillwater, MN 55082
Ph: (651)439-4001
Fax: (651)238-6727
Co. E-mail: info@ilovestillwater.com
URL: http://www.ilovestillwater.com
Contact: Curt Geissler, President
Description: Promotes business and community development in Stillwater, MN.

53656 ■ **Greater Wayzata Area Chamber of Commerce**
402 E Lake St.
Wayzata, MN 55391-1651
Ph: (952)473-9595
Fax: (952)473-6266
Co. E-mail: info@wayzatachamber.com
URL: http://www.wayzatachamber.com
Contact: Peggy Douglas, President
Description: Promotes business and community development in Wayzata, MN. Sponsors trolley rides and concerts in the summer, fall and winter golf outing, and annual festival in September. **Founded:** 1939. **Publications:** Discover Wayzata; Whistle Stop (Monthly). **Educational Activities:** James J. Hill Days (Annual); Holiday Open House and Tree Lighting (Annual).

53657 ■ **Hastings Area Chamber of Commerce and Tourism Bureau**
111 E 3rd St.
Hastings, MN 55033-1211
Ph: (651)437-6775
Free: 888-612-6122

Fax: (651)437-2697
Co. E-mail: info@hastingsmn.org
URL: http://www.hastingsmn.org
Contact: Michelle Jacobs, President
Description: Works together to advance the commercial, financial, industrial, and civic interest of the community.

53658 ■ Hermantown Chamber of Commerce
4940 Lightning Dr.
Hermantown, MN 55811-1447
Ph: (218)729-6843
Fax: (218)729-7132
Co. E-mail: info@hermantownchamber.com
URL: http://www.hermantownchamber.com
Contact: Mike Lundstrom, Executive Director
Description: Promotes business and community development in the Hermantown, MN area. Provides leadership for the community, promotes local resources, enhances local programs, and coordinates development efforts.

53659 ■ Hibbing Area Chamber of Commerce
PO Box 727
Hibbing, MN 55746-0727
Ph: (218)262-3895
Fax: (218)262-3897
Co. E-mail: hibbcofc@hibbing.org
URL: http://www.hibbing.org
Contact: Lory Fedo, President
Description: Promotes business and community development in Hibbing, MN. **Founded:** 1905.

53660 ■ *Hometown Happenings*
2 Main St. S
Hutchinson, MN 55350
Ph: (320)587-5252
Free: 800-572-6689
Fax: (320)587-4752
Co. E-mail: info@explorehutchinson.com
URL: http://www.explorehutchinson.com
Contact: Steve Gasser, Chairman
Released: Monthly

53661 ■ Hutchinson Area Chamber of Commerce, Convention and Visitors Bureau
2 Main St. S
Hutchinson, MN 55350
Ph: (320)587-5252
Free: 800-572-6689
Fax: (320)587-4752
Co. E-mail: info@explorehutchinson.com
URL: http://www.explorehutchinson.com
Contact: Steve Gasser, Chairman
Description: Seeks to promote city of Hutchinson, MN as a place for conventions and business gatherings. **Publications:** *Hometown Happenings* (Monthly).

53662 ■ I-94 West Chamber of Commerce
21370 John Milless Dr.
Rogers, MN 55374
Ph: (763)428-2921
Fax: (763)428-9068
Co. E-mail: requests@i94westchamber.org
URL: http://www.i94westchamber.org
Contact: Rhonda Baack, President
Description: Promotes business and community development in Dayton, MN. Supports local charities; conducts political and business networking forums. **Founded:** 1988.

53663 ■ International Falls Area Chamber of Commerce (IFACC)
301 2nd Ave.
International Falls, MN 56649
Ph: (218)283-9400
Free: 800-325-5766
Fax: (218)283-3572
Co. E-mail: chamber@intlfalls.org
URL: http://ifallschamber.com
Contact: Betsy Jensen, President
Description: Promotes business and community development in the International Falls, MN area. **Founded:** 1953.

53664 ■ Jackson Area Chamber of Commerce (JACC)
114 3rd St,. Ste. B
Jackson, MN 56143
Ph: (507)847-3867
Fax: (507)847-3869
Co. E-mail: chamber@jacksonmn.com
URL: http://jacksonmn.com
Contact: Pam Heser, Executive Director
Description: Promotes business and community development in Jackson, MN. Holds annual Town and Country Day Celebration, Agriculture Day, Craft, Antique, and Toy show. **Publications:** *Chamber Chatter* (Quarterly); *Experience the Jackson Area.*

53665 ■ Kanabec Area Chamber of Commerce (KACC)
200 S Hwy. 65
Mora, MN 55051
Ph: (320)679-5792
Free: 800-291-5792
Co. E-mail: karen@kanabecchamber.org
URL: http://www.kanabecchamber.org
Contact: Karen Onan Amundson, Executive Director
Description: Promotes business and community development in the Mora, MN area. Conducts East Central Home and Leisure Show. **Publications:** *Progress* (Monthly).

53666 ■ La Crescent Chamber of Commerce (LCCC)
109 S Walnut St., Ste. B
La Crescent, MN 55947
Ph: (507)895-2800
Free: 800-926-9480
Fax: (507)895-2619
Co. E-mail: lacrescent.chamber@acegroup.cc
URL: http://www.lacrescentmn.com
Contact: Dewey Severson, President
Description: Promotes business, community development, and tourism in La Crescent, MN. **Founded:** 1975.

53667 ■ Lake Benton Area Chamber of Commerce and Convention and Visitors Bureau
PO Box 205
Lake Benton, MN 56149
Ph: (507)368-9577
URL: http://www.itctel.com/lbenton
Description: Provides information about business opportunities in Lake Benton.

53668 ■ Lake City Area Chamber of Commerce (LCACC)
101 W Center St.
Lake City, MN 55041
Ph: (651)345-4123
Free: 800-369-4123
Fax: (651)345-4195
Co. E-mail: lcchamber@lakecity.org
URL: http://www.lakecity.org
Contact: Mary Huselid, Executive Director
Description: Promotes business and community development in the Lake City, MN area. Sponsors 3 community festivals per year. **Founded:** 1935. **Awards:** Water Ski Days Queen (Annual).

53669 ■ Lake Crystal Area Chamber of Commerce
PO Box 27
Lake Crystal, MN 56055
Ph: (507)726-6088
Co. E-mail: lcchambr@hickorytech.net
URL: http://www.lakecrystalchamber.com
Contact: Judy Meyer, President
Description: Promotes business and community development in Lake Crystal Area, MN.

53670 ■ Lake Minnetonka Chamber of Commerce
2323 Commerce Blvd.
Mound, MN 55364
Ph: (952)472-5622

Fax: (952)472-5624
Co. E-mail: chamber@lakeminnetonkachamber.com
URL: http://www.lakeminnetonkachamber.com
Contact: John B. Waldron, President
Description: Promotes business and community development in the Lake Minnetonka area. **Telecommunication Services:** patsy@lakeminnetonkachamber.com.

53671 ■ Lake Vermilion Area Chamber of Commerce (LVACC)
PO Box 776
Tower, MN 55790
Ph: (218)753-8909
Free: 800-869-3766
Co. E-mail: troy@lakevermilioncommerce.com
URL: http://www.lakevermilioncommerce.com
Contact: Troy Swanson, Executive Director
Description: Promotes business and community development in Tower, MN. Holds annual Fourth of July Celebration.

53672 ■ Laurentian Chamber of Commerce
403 1st St. N
Virginia, MN 55792
Ph: (218)741-2717
Fax: (218)749-4913
Co. E-mail: admin@laurentianchamber.org
URL: http://laurentianchamber.org
Contact: Jim Currie, President
Description: Promotes business and community development in Virginia, Eveleth, Mountain Iron, and Gilbert, MN. Educates on the value and importance of a thriving business community and on business issues impacting them; advocates for issues as appropriate; identifies the needs of the business community and becomes aware of its health; fosters participation and involvement in the chambers to build leaders; and serves as an information and referral resource for members. **Founded:** 1922. **Publications:** *Youth Employment Directory* (Periodic). **Awards:** ATHENA Award (Periodic); Award of Distinction (Periodic).

53673 ■ Le Sueur Area Chamber of Commerce (LSACC)
500 N Main St.
Le Sueur, MN 56058
Ph: (507)665-2501
Fax: (507)665-4372
Co. E-mail: julieb@lesueurchamber.org
URL: http://lesueurchamber.org
Contact: Julie Boyland, Executive Director
Description: Promotes business and community development in the Le Sueur, MN area. Sponsors Legislative Day at the Capitol, garage sales, Farm and Home Show, Giant Celebration, Agriculture Appreciation Affair and Manufacture Expo. **Founded:** 1951. **Publications:** *Voice of Le Sueur Newsletter* (Quarterly). **Educational Activities:** Farm and Home Show (Annual).

53674 ■ Leech Lake Area Chamber of Commerce (LLACC)
PO Box 1089
Walker, MN 56484-1089
Ph: (218)547-1313
Free: 800-833-1118
Fax: (218)547-1338
Co. E-mail: info@leech-lake.com
URL: http://www.leech-lake.com
Contact: Cindy Wannarka, President
Description: Promotes business and community development in the Leech Lake, MN area. **Founded:** 1963. **Publications:** *Chamber Chatter* (Monthly). **Educational Activities:** Ethnic Festival (Annual).

53675 ■ Litchfield Chamber of Commerce (LCC)
219 N Sibley Ave.
Litchfield, MN 55355-0820
Ph: (320)693-8184
Co. E-mail: dee@litch.com
URL: http://www.litch.com
Contact: Dee Schutte, Executive Director
Description: Promotes business and community development in Litchfield, MN.

53676 ■ Little Falls Area Chamber of Commerce (LFACC)
200 NW 1st St.
Little Falls, MN 56345
Ph: (320)632-5155
Fax: (320)632-2122
Co. E-mail: assistance@littlefallsmnchamber.com
URL: http://littlefallsmnchamber.com
Contact: Debora K. Boelz, President
Description: Promotes business and community development in the Little Falls, MN area. Holds arts and crafts fair. **Founded:** 1888. **Publications:** *The Chamber of Commerce News* (Monthly). **Educational Activities:** Little Falls Arts and Crafts Fair (Annual).

53677 ■ Long Prairie Area Chamber of Commerce (LPACC)
42 N 3rd St.
Long Prairie, MN 56347
Ph: (320)732-2514
Fax: (320)732-2514
Co. E-mail: info@longprairie.org
URL: http://www.longprairie.org/chamber/index.html
Contact: Kathleen Nauber, President
Description: Promotes business and community development in the Long Prairie, MN area. Sponsors Prairie Days Festival. **Founded:** 1961. **Publications:** *The Voice of Commerce* (Monthly).

53678 ■ Luverne Area Chamber of Commerce (LCC)
Rock County Courthouse Sq.
213 E Luverne St.
Luverne, MN 56156
Ph: (507)283-4061
Free: 888-283-4061
Fax: (507)283-4061
Co. E-mail: luvernechamber@co.rock.mn.us
URL: http://www.luvernechamber.com
Contact: Jane Wildung Lanphere, Executive Director
Description: Promotes community businesses, organizations, institutions and individuals in Rock County, MN. **Founded:** 1934.

53679 ■ Madelia Area Chamber of Commerce (MACC)
PO Box 171
Madelia, MN 56062
Ph: (507)642-8822
Free: 888-941-7283
Fax: (507)642-8832
Co. E-mail: chamber@madeliamn.com
URL: http://www.visitmadelia.com
Contact: Karla Grev, Executive Director
Description: Promotes business and community development in the Madelia, MN area. **Publications:** *Business Directory*; *Madelia Area Chamber Newsletter* (Monthly).

53680 ■ *Madelia Area Chamber Newsletter*
PO Box 171
Madelia, MN 56062
Ph: (507)642-8822
Free: 888-941-7283
Fax: (507)642-8832
Co. E-mail: chamber@madeliamn.com
URL: http://www.visitmadelia.com
Contact: Karla Grev, Executive Director
Released: Monthly

53681 ■ Madison Area Chamber of Commerce (MACC)
PO Box 70
Madison, MN 56256-0070
Ph: (320)598-7301
Fax: (320)598-7955
Co. E-mail: loutfisk@yahoo.com
URL: http://www.madisonmn.info
Contact: Maynard R. Meyer, Executive Director
Description: Promotes business and community development in the Madison, MN area. **Founded:** 1952.

53682 ■ *Manufacturers Directory*
530 Wilson Ave.
Faribault, MN 55021-4619
Ph: (507)334-4381
Free: 800-658-2354

Fax: (507)334-1003
Co. E-mail: chamber@faribaultmn.org
URL: http://www.faribaultmn.org
Contact: Kymn Anderson, President
Released: Periodic

53683 ■ Marshall Area Chamber of Commerce (MACC)
317 W Main St.
Marshall, MN 56258
Ph: (507)532-4484
Fax: (507)532-4485
Co. E-mail: chamber@marshall-mn.org
URL: http://www.marshall-mn.org
Contact: Cal Brink, Executive Director
Description: Promotes business and community development in the Marshall, MN area. **Founded:** 1932. **Publications:** *Marshall Area Chamber Newsletter* (Monthly). **Educational Activities:** Business After Hours (Monthly).

53684 ■ *Marshall Area Chamber Newsletter*
317 W Main St.
Marshall, MN 56258
Ph: (507)532-4484
Fax: (507)532-4485
Co. E-mail: chamber@marshall-mn.org
URL: http://www.marshall-mn.org
Contact: Cal Brink, Executive Director
Released: Monthly

53685 ■ Melrose Area Chamber of Commerce
223 E Main St.
Melrose, MN 56352
Ph: (320)256-7174
Co. E-mail: chamber@meltel.net
URL: http://www.melrosemn.org
Contact: Craig Schiffler, President
Description: Promotes business and community development in Melrose, MN. Sponsors festival and beauty pageant. **Founded:** 1928.

53686 ■ *Membership Directory and Buyers Guide*
225 Sunnyside Dr.
Cloquet, MN 55720
Ph: (218)879-1551
Free: 800-554-4350
Fax: (218)878-0223
Co. E-mail: chamber@cloquet.com
URL: http://www.cloquet.com
Contact: Tony Vittorio, Chairman
Released: Annual

53687 ■ *Membership Directory/Buyers Guide*
PO Box 348
Detroit Lakes, MN 56502-0348
Ph: (218)847-9202
Free: 800-542-3992
Fax: (218)847-9082
Co. E-mail: carrie@visitdetroitlakes.com
URL: http://www.visitdetroitlakes.com
Contact: Carrie Johnston, President

53688 ■ MetroNorth Chamber of Commerce
21st Century Bank Bldg.
9380 Central Ave. NE, Ste. 320
Blaine, MN 55434
Ph: (763)783-3553
Fax: (763)783-3557
Co. E-mail: chamber@metronorthchamber.org
URL: http://www.metronorthchamber.org
Contact: Lori Higgins, President
Description: Promotes business and community development in Anoka County, MN. Supports local charities; conducts political and business networking forums. **Founded:** 1982. **Publications:** *Community Resource Guide* (Annual). **Educational Activities:** Com-Mark Computer and Marketing Expo (Annual).

53689 ■ Milaca Area Chamber of Commerce
PO Box 155
Milaca, MN 56353
Ph: (320)983-3140

Fax: (320)983-3142
Co. E-mail: info@milacachamber.com
URL: http://milacachamber.com
Description: Works to create, protect and enhance the healthy business environment for the benefit of the area.

53690 ■ Minneapolis Regional Chamber of Commerce
81 S 9th St., Ste. 200
Minneapolis, MN 55402-3223
Ph: (612)370-9100
Fax: (612)370-9195
Co. E-mail: info@minneapolischamber.org
URL: http://www.minneapolischamber.org
Contact: Todd Klingel, President
Description: Promotes business and community development in the Minneapolis, MN area. **Publications:** *Connections* (Biweekly); *Minneapolis Regional Chamber of Commerce--Membership Directory*. **Awards:** Quality of Life Awards (Annual).

53691 ■ *Minnesota Business Views*
400 N Robert St., Ste. 1500
St. Paul, MN 55101
Ph: (651)292-4650
Free: 800-821-2230
Fax: (651)292-4656
Co. E-mail: mail@mnchamber.com
URL: http://www.mnchamber.com
Contact: David Olson, President
Released: Monthly

53692 ■ Minnesota Chamber of Commerce
400 N Robert St., Ste. 1500
St. Paul, MN 55101
Ph: (651)292-4650
Free: 800-821-2230
Fax: (651)292-4656
Co. E-mail: mail@mnchamber.com
URL: http://www.mnchamber.com
Contact: David Olson, President
Description: Promotes business and economic growth throughout the state. **Founded:** 1909. **Publications:** *Minnesota Business Views* (Monthly).

53693 ■ *Minnesota's Lake of the Woods Area Vacation Guide*
PO Box 659
Baudette, MN 56623-0659
Ph: (218)634-1174
Free: 800-382-3474
Fax: (218)634-2915
Co. E-mail: info@lakeofthewoodsmn.com
URL: http://www.lakeofthewoodsmn.com
Released: Annual **Price:** free.

53694 ■ Montevideo Area Chamber of Commerce
202 N 1st St., Ste. 150
Montevideo, MN 56265
Ph: (320)269-5527
Free: 800-269-5527
Fax: (320)269-5696
Co. E-mail: generalinfo@montechamber.com
URL: http://www.montechamber.com
Contact: Diane Sacchariason, President
Description: Promotes business and community development in the Montevideo, MN area. Administers Convention and Visitors' Bureau. **Founded:** 1905.

53695 ■ Monticello Area Chamber of Commerce and Industry
PO Box 192
Monticello, MN 55362
Ph: (763)295-2700
Fax: (763)295-2705
Co. E-mail: info@monticellocci.com
URL: http://www.monticellocci.com
Contact: Sandy Suchy, Executive Director
Description: Promotes business and community development in Monticello, MN. **Founded:** 1967. **Awards:** Business of the Year (Annual); College Scholarship (Annual).

53696 ■ Moose Lake Area Chamber of Commerce
c/o Lisa Cekalla
PO Box 110
Moose Lake, MN 55767
Ph: (218)485-4145
Free: 800-635-3680
Fax: (218)485-4522
Co. E-mail: mlchamber@mooselake-mn.com
URL: http://www.mooselake-mn.com
Contact: Lisa Cekalla, Executive Director
Description: Works with other community resources to promote local tourism, create jobs, and recruit new businesses in Moose Lake, IN area.

53697 ■ Morris Area Chamber of Commerce
507 Atlantic Ave.
Morris, MN 56267
Ph: (320)589-1242
Co. E-mail: mchamber@fedtel.net
URL: http://www.morrismnchamber.org
Contact: Karen Berget, Chairperson
Description: Promotes business and community development in the Morris, MN area. Sponsors Prairie Pioneer Days. **Founded:** 1940. **Publications:** *The Connection* (Monthly). **Educational Activities:** Grand Parade of Lights (Annual).

53698 ■ New Prague Chamber of Commerce (NPCC)
PO Box 191
New Prague, MN 56071
Ph: (952)758-4360
Fax: (952)758-5396
Co. E-mail: info@newprague.com
URL: http://www.newprague.com
Contact: Kristy Mach, Executive Director
Description: Promotes business and community development in New Prague, MN. Conducts charitable activities. Holds annual New Prague Half-Marathon and 5K, Dozinky Czechoslovakian Harvest Festival and Christmas programs. **Founded:** 1977.

53699 ■ New Ulm Area Chamber of Commerce
PO Box 384
New Ulm, MN 56073
Ph: (507)233-4300
Free: 888-463-9856
Fax: (507)354-1504
Co. E-mail: nuchamber@newulmtel.net
URL: http://www.newulm.com
Contact: Audra Shaneman, President
Description: Promotes business and community development in the New Ulm, MN area. Conducts annual Oktoberfest. **Founded:** 1940. **Publications:** *New Ulm Visitors Guide* (Annual); *NU Business Trends* (Monthly); *Program of Work* (Annual).

53700 ■ New Ulm Visitors Guide
PO Box 384
New Ulm, MN 56073
Ph: (507)233-4300
Free: 888-463-9856
Fax: (507)354-1504
Co. E-mail: nuchamber@newulmtel.net
URL: http://www.newulm.com
Contact: Audra Shaneman, President
Released: Annual

53701 ■ Newsline
14800 Galaxie Ave., Ste. 301
Apple Valley, MN 55124
Ph: (952)432-8422
Free: 800-301-9435
Fax: (952)432-7964
Co. E-mail: info@applevalleychamber.com
URL: http://www.applevalleychamber.com
Contact: Edward Kearney, President
Released: Monthly

53702 ■ Nisswa Chamber of Commerce (NCC)
25532 Main St.
Nisswa, MN 56468
Ph: (218)963-2620
Free: 800-950-9610

Fax: (218)963-1420
Co. E-mail: eric.wiltrout@lakewoodbank.com
URL: http://www.nisswa.com
Contact: Eric Wiltrout, President
Description: Promotes business and community development in Nisswa, MN. Sponsors arts and crafts festival. **Founded:** 1946. **Publications:** *The Pulse* (Quarterly). **Awards:** Nisswa Citizen of the Year Award (Annual).

53703 ■ North Branch Area Chamber of Commerce
PO Box 577
North Branch, MN 55056
Ph: (651)674-4077
Co. E-mail: nbachamber@izoom.net
URL: http://www.northbranchchamber.com
Contact: Kathy Lindo, Executive Director
Description: Promotes local business and organizations. Activities include networking opportunities, publication, community celebrations and festivals. **Founded:** 1990.

53704 ■ North Hennepin Area Chamber of Commerce
229 1st Ave. NE
Osseo, MN 55369-1201
Ph: (763)424-6744
Fax: (763)424-6927
Co. E-mail: info@nhachamber.com
URL: http://www.nhachamber.com
Contact: Jill Johnson, Executive Director
Description: Serves members and their communities through identification and advocacy of business issues and the promotion of economic, civic, and educational interests. **Publications:** *North Hennepin Area Chamber of Commerce--Membership Directory & Resource Guide* (Annual). **Awards:** Career Change Scholarship; Star Student Award (Annual). **Telecommunication Services:** jill@nhachamber.com.

53705 ■ Northfield Area Chamber of Commerce
PO Box 198
Northfield, MN 55057-0198
Ph: (507)645-5604
Free: 800-658-2548
Fax: (507)663-7782
Co. E-mail: info@northfieldchamber.com
URL: http://www.northfieldchamber.com
Contact: Mary Schmelzer, Executive Director
Description: Promotes business and community development in the Northfield, MN area. **Awards:** Business of the Year (Annual); Business Person of the Year (Annual).

53706 ■ NU Business Trends
PO Box 384
New Ulm, MN 56073
Ph: (507)233-4300
Free: 888-463-9856
Fax: (507)354-1504
Co. E-mail: nuchamber@newulmtel.net
URL: http://www.newulm.com
Contact: Audra Shaneman, President
Released: Monthly

53707 ■ Olivia Area Chamber of Commerce (OACC)
PO Box 37
Olivia, MN 56277
Ph: (320)523-1350
Free: 888-265-CORN
Fax: (320)523-1514
URL: http://www.oliviachamber.org
Contact: Nancy Standfuss, Executive Director
Description: Works to create, promote and enhance a healthy business environment and image of the Olivia area. **Publications:** *Chamber Update* (Monthly).

53708 ■ Organizational Directory
530 Wilson Ave.
Faribault, MN 55021-4619
Ph: (507)334-4381
Free: 800-658-2354

Fax: (507)334-1003
Co. E-mail: chamber@faribaultmn.org
URL: http://www.faribaultmn.org
Contact: Kymn Anderson, President
Released: Periodic

53709 ■ Owatonna Area Chamber of Commerce and Tourism (OACCT)
320 Hoffman Dr.
Owatonna, MN 55060
Ph: (507)451-7970
Free: 800-423-6466
Fax: (507)451-7972
Co. E-mail: oacct@owatonna.org
URL: http://www.owatonna.org
Contact: Brad Meier, President
Description: Seeks to be the leading partner of the regional center, dedicated to the continuance of its economic prosperity while maintaining community values and pride. Activities include membership, legislative advocacy, communications, information brokering, leadership development, facilitation, networking, cooperative marketing, economic development and tourism promotion. **Founded:** 1924. **Publications:** *Business Brief* (Monthly); *Chamber Reporter* (Monthly). **Educational Activities:** Business After Hours (Monthly); Good Morning Owatonna (Monthly).

53710 ■ Park Rapids Lakes Area Chamber of Commerce (PRACC)
PO Box 249
Park Rapids, MN 56470
Ph: (218)732-4111
Free: 800-247-0054
Fax: (218)732-4112
Co. E-mail: chamber@parkrapids.com
URL: http://www.parkrapids.com
Contact: Bob Seifert, President
Description: Promotes business and community development in the Park Rapids, MN area. **Publications:** *Vacation Guide.*

53711 ■ Paynesville Area Chamber of Commerce (PACC)
PO Box 4
Paynesville, MN 56362
Ph: (320)243-3233
Free: 800-547-9034
Co. E-mail: chamber@lakedalelink.net
URL: http://www.paynesvillechamber.org
Contact: Mike McArthur, President
Description: Promotes business and community development in the Paynesville, MN area.

53712 ■ Pelican Rapids Area Chamber of Commerce (PRACC)
PO Box 206
Pelican Rapids, MN 56572-0206
Ph: (218)863-1221
Co. E-mail: tourism@loretel.net
URL: http://www.pelicanrapidschamber.com
Contact: Everett Ballard, President
Description: Promotes business and community development in Pelican Rapids, MN.

53713 ■ Perham Area Chamber of Commerce (PACC)
185 E Main St.
Perham, MN 56573
Ph: (218)346-7710
Fax: (218)346-7712
Co. E-mail: chamber@perham.com
URL: http://www.perham.com
Contact: Randy Mattfeld, President
Description: Promotes business and community development in the Perham, MN area. Sponsors festival. **Founded:** 1985.

53714 ■ Pine City Area Chamber of Commerce
900 4th St. SE, Ste. 85
Pine City, MN 55063
Ph: (320)629-4565
Co. E-mail: info@pinecitychamber.com
URL: http://www.pinecitychamber.com
Contact: Lara Smetana, President

53715 ■ Pipestone Area Chamber of Commerce (PACC)
PO Box 8
Pipestone, MN 56164
Ph: (507)825-3316
Free: 800-336-6125
Co. E-mail: pipecham@pipestoneminnesota.com
URL: http://www.pipestoneminnesota.com
Contact: Michelle Nelson, President
Description: Promotes business and community development in Pipestone County, MN. **Publications:** none. **Founded:** 1939.

53716 ■ Princeton Area Chamber of Commerce (PACC)
705 N 2nd St.
Princeton, MN 55371-1550
Ph: (763)389-1764
Fax: (763)631-1764
Co. E-mail: pacc@sherbtel.net
URL: http://www.princetonmnchamber.org
Contact: Scott Berry, President
Description: Promotes business and community development in Princeton, MN. Sponsors Rum River Festival. **Founded:** 1926. **Publications:** The Focus (Monthly).

53717 ■ Prior Lake Area Chamber of Commerce
4785 Dakota St.
Prior Lake, MN 55372
Ph: (952)440-1000
Fax: (952)440-1611
Co. E-mail: sandi@priorlakechamber.com
URL: http://priorlakechamber.com
Contact: Sandi Fleck, Executive Director
Description: Strives to foster business development to enhance the quality of life of the community. **Publications:** Chamber News (Monthly).

53718 ■ Program of Work
PO Box 384
New Ulm, MN 56073
Ph: (507)233-4300
Free: 888-463-9856
Fax: (507)354-1504
Co. E-mail: nuchamber@newulmtel.net
URL: http://www.newulm.com
Contact: Audra Shaneman, President
Released: Annual

53719 ■ Progress
200 S Hwy. 65
Mora, MN 55051
Ph: (320)679-5792
Free: 800-291-5792
Co. E-mail: karen@kanabecchamber.org
URL: http://www.kanabecchamber.org
Contact: Karen Onan Amundson, Executive Director
Released: Monthly

53720 ■ The Pulse
25532 Main St.
Nisswa, MN 56468
Ph: (218)963-2620
Free: 800-950-9610
Fax: (218)963-1420
Co. E-mail: eric.wiltrout@lakewoodbank.com
URL: http://www.nisswa.com
Contact: Eric Wiltrout, President
Released: Quarterly

53721 ■ Red Wing Area Chamber of Commerce (RWACC)
439 Main St.
Red Wing, MN 55066
Ph: (651)388-4719
Co. E-mail: frontdesk@redwingchamber.com
URL: http://www.redwingchamber.com
Contact: Patty Brown, President
Description: Promotes business and community development in the Red Wing, MN area. **Publications:** Chamber Forum (Bimonthly).

53722 ■ Redwood Area Chamber and Tourism (RACT)
200 S Mill St.
Redwood Falls, MN 56283

Ph: (507)637-2828
Free: 800-657-7070
Fax: (507)637-5202
Co. E-mail: chamber@redwoodfalls.org
URL: http://www.redwoodfalls.org
Contact: Clint Knorr, Chairman
Description: Promotes business and community development in the Redwood Falls, MN area. **Awards:** First Dollar; Progress (Periodic).

53723 ■ River Heights Chamber of Commerce (RHCC)
5782 Blackhire Path
Inver Grove Heights, MN 55076
Ph: (651)451-2266
Fax: (651)451-0846
Co. E-mail: info@riverheights.com
URL: http://www.riverheights.com
Contact: Jennifer Gale, President
Description: Promotes business and community development in South St. Paul-Inver Grove Heights, MN. **Founded:** 1903. **Publications:** Business Perspective (Monthly). **Educational Activities:** Leadership Conference (Annual). **Awards:** Business of the Year (Annual); Small Business of the Year (Annual); Visions of Excellence.

53724 ■ Robbinsdale Chamber of Commerce
PO Box 22646
Robbinsdale, MN 55422-0646
Ph: (763)531-1279
Co. E-mail: dkiser@twelve.tv
URL: http://www.robbinsdalemn.com/chamber.htm
Contact: D. Kiser, Secretary
Description: Promotes business and community development in the Robinsdale, MN area. **Founded:** 1949.

53725 ■ Rochester Area Chamber of Commerce (RACC)
220 S Broadway, Ste. 100
Rochester, MN 55904
Ph: (507)288-1122
Fax: (507)282-8960
Co. E-mail: chamber@rochestermnchamber.com
URL: http://www.rochestermnchamber.com
Contact: John Wade, President
Description: Promotes business and community development in the Rochester/Olmsted County, MN area. **Founded:** 1866. **Publications:** Rochester Area Chamber of Commerce--Membership Directory (Annual); Chamber Advantage Newsletter (Monthly); Business Reference Guide and Membership Directory (Annual). **Awards:** Lamp of Knowledge Awards (Annual); Small Business of the Year (Annual); Volunteer of the Year (Annual).

53726 ■ Runeskriber
206 Broadway
Alexandria, MN 56308
Ph: (320)763-3161
Free: 800-235-9441
Co. E-mail: info@alexandriamn.org
URL: http://www.alexandriamn.org
Contact: Coni McKay, Executive Director
Released: Monthly **Price:** free for members; $15, /year for nonmembers.

53727 ■ St. Cloud Area Chamber of Commerce (SCACC)
PO Box 487
St. Cloud, MN 56302-0487
Ph: (320)251-2940
Fax: (320)251-0081
Co. E-mail: information@stcloudareachamber.com
URL: http://www.stcloudareachamber.com
Contact: Bill Winter, Chairman
Description: Promotes business and community development in the St. Cloud, MN area. **Founded:** 1869. **Publications:** Business Central (Bimonthly); Chamber Edge (Monthly); The Bottom Line (Monthly). **Educational Activities:** Chamber Connection (Weekly); Chamber Golf Open (Annual).

53728 ■ St. Joseph Chamber of Commerce (SJCC)
PO Box 696
St. Joseph, MN 56374

Ph: (320)271-0274
Co. E-mail: travism@mycmcu.org
URL: http://www.stjosephchamber.com
Contact: Travis Moore, President
Description: Promotes business and community development in the eastern and northern suburbs of St. Paul, MN. Convention/Meeting: none.

53729 ■ St. Paul Area Chamber of Commerce (SPACC)
401 N Robert St., Ste. 150
St. Paul, MN 55101
Ph: (651)223-5000
Fax: (651)223-5119
Co. E-mail: info@saintpaulchamber.com
URL: http://www.saintpaulchamber.com
Contact: Susan Kimberly, President
Description: Voice for business in St. Paul, MN and the east metro area. Strives to influence public policy; provide small business resources; creates economic development; and shapes the future workforce. **Founded:** 1868. **Publications:** St. Paul Area Chamber of Commerce--Membership Directory and Business Resource Guide (Annual).

53730 ■ St. Peter Area Chamber of Commerce
101 S Front St.
St. Peter, MN 56082
Ph: (507)934-3400
Free: 800-473-3404
Fax: (507)934-8960
Co. E-mail: spchamb@hickorytech.net
Description: Strives to provide leadership in order to enhance and promote economic development and quality of life in the St. Peter area.

53731 ■ Sandstone Area Chamber of Commerce
PO Box 23
Sandstone, MN 55072
Ph: (320)245-2271
Co. E-mail: info@sandstonechamber.com
URL: http://www.sandstonechamber.com
Contact: John Kern, President
Description: Promotes business and community development in Sandstone, MN. Encourages tourism. **Awards:** Dollars for Scholars (Annual).

53732 ■ Sauk Centre Area Chamber of Commerce (SCCC)
PO Box 222
Sauk Centre, MN 56378
Ph: (320)352-5201
Fax: (320)352-5202
Co. E-mail: andrea@saukcentrechamber.com
URL: http://www.saukcentrechamber.com
Contact: Andrea Kerfeld, Executive Director
Description: Promotes business and community development in Sauk Centre, MN. Holds festival.

53733 ■ Savage Chamber of Commerce
6050 McColl Dr.
Savage, MN 55378
Ph: (952)894-8876
Fax: (952)894-9906
Co. E-mail: mail@savagechamber.com
URL: http://www.savagechamber.com
Contact: Lori Anderson, Executive Director
Description: Strives to unite business and professional people who are dedicated to the ongoing development and support of business activities, industrial opportunities and civic enhancement of the Savage area. **Founded:** 1964. **Awards:** Business Person of the Year (Annual).

53734 ■ Shakopee Chamber of Commerce
1801 E County Rd. 101
Shakopee, MN 55379-0717
Ph: (952)445-1660
Free: 800-574-2150
Fax: (952)445-1669
Co. E-mail: chamber@shakopee.org
URL: http://www.shakopee.org/chamber
Contact: Angie Whitcomb, President
Description: Promotes convention business and tourism in Shakopee, MN area. Operates tourist information center. **Founded:** 1955. **Publications:** Chamber Reporter Insert (Monthly).

53735 ■ Slayton Area Chamber of Commerce (SACC)
2635 Broadway Ave.
Slayton, MN 56172
Ph: (507)836-6902
Fax: (507)836-6650
Co. E-mail: slaytoncham@iw.net
URL: http://www.slaytonchamber.com
Contact: Eugene Short, President
Description: Promotes business and community development in the Slayton, MN area. Conducts charitable activities.

53736 ■ Sleepy Eye Area Chamber of Commerce (SEACC)
115 2nd Ave. NE
Sleepy Eye, MN 56085
Ph: (507)794-4731
Free: 800-290-0588
Fax: (507)794-4732
Co. E-mail: secofc@sleepyeyetel.net
URL: http://sleepyeye-mn.com
Contact: Mrs. Julie Schmitt, Executive Director
Description: Promotes business and community development in the Sleepy Eye, MN area.

53737 ■ *Someplace Special*
329 N Main St., Ste. 102
Austin, MN 55912
Ph: (507)437-4561
Free: 888-319-5655
Fax: (507)437-4869
Co. E-mail: admin@austincoc.com
URL: http://www.austincoc.com
Contact: Sandy Forstner, Executive Director
Price: included in membership dues.

53738 ■ Springfield Area Chamber of Commerce (SACC)
c/o Marlys Vanderwerf, Exec. Dir.
PO Box 134
Springfield, MN 56087
Ph: (507)723-3508
Fax: (507)723-5213
URL: http://www.springfieldmnchamber.org
Contact: Marlys Vanderwerf, Executive Director
Description: Promotes business and community development in the Springfield, MN area. **Founded:** 1974. **Publications:** *Chamber Chatter* (Monthly).

53739 ■ Swedish-American Chamber of Commerce, Minnesota
c/o American Swedish Institute
2600 Park Ave.
Minneapolis, MN 55407
Ph: (612)991-3001
Co. E-mail: info@saccmn.org
URL: http://www.sacc-minnesota.org
Contact: Aisha Friswold, Chairperson
Founded: 1992.

53740 ■ Thief River Falls Chamber of Commerce
2017 Hwy. 59 SE
Thief River Falls, MN 56701
Ph: (218)681-3720
URL: http://www.trfchamber.com
Description: Works to establish Thief River Falls as the regional center of Northwest Minnesota. Promotes the welfare of all area citizens.

53741 ■ Tracy Area Chamber of Commerce
372 Morgan St.
Tracy, MN 56175
Ph: (507)629-4021
Co. E-mail: tracychamber@iw.net
URL: http://www.tracymnchamber.com
Contact: Trent Fischer, Chairman
Description: Promotes business and community development in the Tracy, MN area. Sponsors Box Car Days festival every Labor Day. **Founded:** 1910.

53742 ■ Twin Cities North Chamber of Commerce
525 Main St., Ste. 200
New Brighton, MN 55112
Ph: (763)571-9781

Fax: (763)572-7950
Co. E-mail: info@twincitiesnorth.org
URL: http://www.twincitiesnorth.org
Contact: Tim Roche, President
Description: Promotes business and community development in the northern Twin Cities suburbs, specifically Arden Hills, Blaine, Columbia Heights, Fridley, Mounds View, New Brighton, Shoreview and Spring Lake Park. **Founded:** 1958.

53743 ■ Twin Cities Quorum
540 N Fairview Ave., Ste. 303
St. Paul, MN 55104
Ph: (651)646-1029
Co. E-mail: julie@twincitiesquorum.com
URL: http://www.twincitiesquorum.com
Contact: Julie Watson, Executive Director

53744 ■ TwinWest Chamber of Commerce
10700 Old County Rd. 15, Ste. 170
Plymouth, MN 55441
Ph: (763)450-2220
Fax: (763)450-2221
Co. E-mail: info@twinwest.com
URL: http://www.twinwest.com
Contact: Bruce Nustad, President
Description: Promotes business and community development in the areas of Brooklyn Center, Brooklyn Park, Crystal, Golden Valley, Hopkins, Medicine Lake, Minnetonka, New Hope, Plymouth, and St. Louis Park. **Publications:** *TwinWest Directions* (Monthly); *TwinWest Chamber of Commerce-- Membership Directory & Business Guide* (Annual); *TwinWest Membership Directory and Business Resource Guide* (Annual). **Awards:** TwinWest Foundation Scholarships (Annual).

53745 ■ *TwinWest Directions*
10700 Old County Rd. 15, Ste. 170
Plymouth, MN 55441
Ph: (763)450-2220
Fax: (763)450-2221
Co. E-mail: info@twinwest.com
URL: http://www.twinwest.com
Contact: Bruce Nustad, President
Released: Monthly

53746 ■ *TwinWest Membership Directory and Business Resource Guide*
10700 Old County Rd. 15, Ste. 170
Plymouth, MN 55441
Ph: (763)450-2220
Fax: (763)450-2221
Co. E-mail: info@twinwest.com
URL: http://www.twinwest.com
Contact: Bruce Nustad, President
Released: Annual

53747 ■ Two Harbors Area Chamber of Commerce (THACC)
1330 Hwy. 61
Two Harbors, MN 55616
Ph: (218)834-2600
Fax: (218)834-2600
Co. E-mail: donna@twoharborschamber.com
URL: http://www.twoharborschamber.com
Contact: Gordy Anderson, President
Description: Promotes business and community development in the Two Harbors, MN area. **Founded:** 1947. **Publications:** *Chamber Outlook* (Weekly).

53748 ■ *Vacation Guide*
1600 E Sheridan St.
Ely, MN 55731
Ph: (218)365-6123
Free: 800-777-7281
URL: http://www.ely.org
Released: Annual **Price:** free.

53749 ■ *Vacation Guide*
PO Box 249
Park Rapids, MN 56470
Ph: (218)732-4111
Free: 800-247-0054
Fax: (218)732-4112
Co. E-mail: chamber@parkrapids.com
URL: http://www.parkrapids.com
Contact: Bob Seifert, President
Price: free.

53750 ■ *Vacation Planning Guide*
124 N 6th St.
Brainerd, MN 56401-0356
Ph: (218)829-2838
Free: 800-450-2838
Fax: (218)829-8199
Co. E-mail: info@explorebrainerdlakes.com
URL: http://www.explorebrainerdlakes.com
Contact: Lisa Paxton, Chief Executive Officer
Released: Annual **Price:** free.

53751 ■ *The Voice of Commerce*
42 N 3rd St.
Long Prairie, MN 56347
Ph: (320)732-2514
Fax: (320)732-2514
Co. E-mail: info@longprairie.org
URL: http://www.longprairie.org/chamber/index.html
Contact: Kathleen Nauber, President
Released: Monthly

53752 ■ *Voice of Le Sueur Newsletter*
500 N Main St.
Le Sueur, MN 56058
Ph: (507)665-2501
Fax: (507)665-4372
Co. E-mail: julieb@lesueurchamber.org
URL: http://lesueurchamber.org
Contact: Julie Boyland, Executive Director
Released: Quarterly

53753 ■ Waconia Area Chamber of Commerce
209 S Vine St.
Waconia, MN 55387
Ph: (952)442-5812
Fax: (952)856-4476
Co. E-mail: ksites@destinationwaconia.org
URL: http://www.waconiachamber.org
Contact: Kellie Sites, President
Description: Seeks to enhance the economic and social health community by improving the business atmosphere of the area.

53754 ■ Waseca Area Chamber of Commerce
111 N State St.
Waseca, MN 56093
Ph: (507)835-3260
Free: 888-820-1243
Fax: (507)835-3267
Co. E-mail: info@wasecachamber.com
URL: http://www.wasecamncc.com
Contact: Kim Foels, President
Description: Promotes business in Waseca, MN. **Founded:** 1923.

53755 ■ *Weekly Facts*
4738 Bald Eagle Ave., Ste. A
White Bear Lake, MN 55110
Ph: (651)429-8593
Fax: (651)429-8592
Co. E-mail: tom@whitebearchamber.com
URL: http://www.whitebearchamber.com
Contact: Tom Snell, Executive Director
Released: Weekly

53756 ■ *Welcome to Austin*
329 N Main St., Ste. 102
Austin, MN 55912
Ph: (507)437-4561
Free: 888-319-5655
Fax: (507)437-4869
Co. E-mail: admin@austincoc.com
URL: http://www.austincoc.com
Contact: Sandy Forstner, Executive Director

53757 ■ Wells Area Chamber of Commerce (WACC)
28 S Broadway
Wells, MN 56097-1633
Ph: (507)553-6450
Free: 866-553-6450
Co. E-mail: wellscc@bevcomm.net
URL: http://wells.govoffice.com
Contact: Andrea Neubauer, Executive Director
Description: Promotes business and community development in the Wells, MN area. Sponsors Wells Kernel Days.

53758 ■ Wheaton Area Chamber of Commerce (WACC)
PO Box 493
Wheaton, MN 56296-0493
URL: http://www.cityofwheaton.com
Contact: Trista Whaley, President
Description: Promotes business and community development in Wheaton, MN.

53759 ■ *Whistle Stop*
402 E Lake St.
Wayzata, MN 55391-1651
Ph: (952)473-9595
Fax: (952)473-6266
Co. E-mail: info@wayzatachamber.com
URL: http://www.wayzatachamber.com
Contact: Peggy Douglas, President
Released: Monthly

53760 ■ White Bear Area Chamber of Commerce
4738 Bald Eagle Ave., Ste. A
White Bear Lake, MN 55110
Ph: (651)429-8593
Fax: (651)429-8592
Co. E-mail: tom@whitebearchamber.com
URL: http://www.whitebearchamber.com
Contact: Tom Snell, Executive Director
Description: Promotes business and community development in the White Bear Lake, MN area.
Founded: 1923. **Publications:** *Weekly Facts* (Weekly). **Awards:** Business of the Year (Annual); Volunteer of the Year (Annual).

53761 ■ Willmar Lakes Area Chamber of Commerce (WLACC)
2104 E Hwy. 12 E
Willmar, MN 56201
Ph: (320)235-0300
Fax: (320)231-1948
Co. E-mail: chamber@willmarareachamber.com
URL: http://www.willmarareachamber.com
Contact: Ken Warner, President
Description: Promotes business and community development in the Willmar, MN area. **Founded:** 1929. **Publications:** *City and County Map.*

53762 ■ Windom Area Chamber of Commerce and Visitors Bureau (WACCVB)
303 9th St.
Windom, MN 56101
Ph: (507)831-2752
Free: 800-794-6366
Co. E-mail: windomchamber@windomnet.com
URL: http://www.winwacc.com
Contact: Cheryl Hanson, President
Description: Promotes business and community development in the Windom, MN area. Serves as a community information center. Sponsors community events including annual summer celebration, Riverfest. **Publications:** *Chamber Update* (Monthly). **Awards:** Community Honoree (Monthly); Rural Stewardship (Annual); WACC & VB Exceptional Achievement (Annual); WACC & VB Volunteer of the Year (Annual).

53763 ■ Winona Area Chamber of Commerce (WACC)
902 E 2nd St., Ste. 120
Winona, MN 55987
Ph: (507)452-2272
Fax: (507)454-8814
Co. E-mail: info@winonachamber.com
URL: http://www.winonachamber.com
Contact: Della Schmidt, President
Description: Promotes business and community development in the Winona, MN area. **Founded:** 1947. **Publications:** *Business Advocate.*

53764 ■ Winthrop Area Chamber of Commerce
PO Box 51
Winthrop, ME 04364
Ph: (207)377-8020

Fax: (207)377-2767
Co. E-mail: info@winthropchamber.org
URL: http://www.winthropchamber.org
Contact: Victoria Christopher, President
Description: Promotes business in Winthrop.

53765 ■ Woodbury Chamber of Commerce
6949 Valley Creek Rd., Ste. 115
Woodbury, MN 55125
Ph: (651)578-0722
Fax: (651)578-7276
Co. E-mail: chamber@woodburychamber.org
URL: http://www.woodburychamber.org
Contact: Liz Fleischhacker, Chairperson
Description: Promotes business and community development in Woodbury, MN. **Publications:** *The Chamber Connection*; *Directory of Chamber Members.* **Awards:** Business of the Year (Annual); Citizen of the Year (Annual); Educational Team of the Year (Annual); Elementary Educator of the Year (Annual); Secondary Educator of the Year (Annual).

53766 ■ Worthington Area Chamber of Commerce
1121 Third Ave.
Worthington, MN 56187-2435
Ph: (507)372-2919
Free: 800-279-2919
Fax: (507)372-2827
Co. E-mail: wcofc@frontiernet.net
URL: http://www.worthingtonmnchamber.com
Description: Promotes business and community development in the Worthington, MN area.

53767 ■ *Xpress*
5 W 1st St., Ste. 101
Duluth, MN 55802-2115
Ph: (218)722-5501
Fax: (218)722-3223
Co. E-mail: inquiry@duluthchamber.com
URL: http://www.duluthchamber.com
Contact: David M. Ross, President

53768 ■ *Youth Employment Directory*
403 1st St. N
Virginia, MN 55792
Ph: (218)741-2717
Fax: (218)749-4913
Co. E-mail: admin@laurentianchamber.org
URL: http://laurentianchamber.org
Contact: Jim Currie, President
Released: Periodic

53769 ■ Zumbrota Chamber of Commerce (ZCC)
PO Box 2
Zumbrota, MN 55992-0002
Ph: (507)732-4282
URL: http://www.co.goodhue.mn.us/visitors/ChambersofCommerce.aspx
Description: Promotes business, community development, and tourism in Zumbrota, MN. Sponsors Covered Bridge Festival.

MINORITY BUSINESS ASSISTANCE PROGRAMS

53770 ■ Metropolitan Economic Development Association (MEDA)
250 2nd Ave. S, Ste. 106
Minneapolis, MN 55401-2168
Ph: (612)332-6332
Fax: (612)317-1002
Co. E-mail: info@meda.net
URL: http://www.meda.net
Contact: Yvonne Cheung Ho, President
E-mail: yho@meda.net
Description: Provides services to entrepreneurs of color in Minnesota. **Scope:** Provider of assistance to businesses owned and managed by ethnic minority residents of Minnesota. Services are directed toward new and existing businesses whose owners are committed to generating long-term profitable growth and employment opportunities. Provides management and leadership training and acts as a communication link between the majority and minority business communities in Minnesota. **Founded:** 1971.

53771 ■ Minnesota Chippewa Tribe - Native American Business Enterprise Center
PO Box 217
Cass Lake, MN 56633
Ph: (218)335-8583
Fax: (218)335-8496
Co. E-mail: mctvhb@paulbunyan.net
URL: http://www.mnchippewatribe.org/economic_development.htm

53772 ■ Women's Business Development Center - Minnesota
250 2nd Ave. S, Ste. 106
Minneapolis, MN 55401
Ph: (612)259-6584
Fax: (612)317-1002
Co. E-mail: wbdc-mn@wbdc.org
URL: http://www.wbdc.org/MN/Defaut.aspx
Description: Offers certification, training, mentoring, networking, and business development services to women's businesses in Minnesota, North Dakota, South Dakota, and Wisconsin.

FINANCING AND LOAN PROGRAMS

53773 ■ Affinity Capital Management
901 Marquette Ave., Ste. 2820
Minneapolis, MN 55402
Ph: (612)252-9900
Fax: (612)252-9911
URL: http://www.affinitycapital.net
Contact: Edson W. Spencer, Jr., Partner
Industry Preferences: Internet specific, medical and health, computer software and services, biotechnology, semiconductors and other electronics. **Geographic Preference:** Midwest.

53774 ■ Bluestream Ventures
221 E. Myrtle St.
Stillwater, MN 55082
Ph: (651)967-5040
Fax: (612)967-5055
URL: http://www.bluestreamventures.com
Contact: Steve Sigmond, Partner
E-mail: steve@bluestreamventures.com
Preferred Investment Size: $2,000,000 to $10,000,000. **Industry Preferences:** Communications, computer software, Internet specific, semiconductors and other electronics. **Geographic Preference:** U.S.

53775 ■ Cherry Tree Investments, Inc.
301 Carlson Pky., Ste. 103
Minnetonka, MN 55305
Ph: (952)893-9012
Fax: (952)893-9036
Co. E-mail: info@cherrytree.com
URL: http://www.cherrytree.com
Contact: Tony Christianson, Managing Partner
Preferred Investment Size: $250,000 to $1,000,000. **Industry Preferences:** Communications, computer hardware and software, Internet specific, semiconductors and other electronics, biotechnology, medical and health, consumer related, financial services, business service, agriculture, forestry and fishing. **Geographic Preference:** Midwest.

53776 ■ Coral Ventures
60 S. 6th St., Ste. 2210
Minneapolis, MN 55402
Ph: (612)335-8666
Fax: (612)335-8668
URL: http://www.coralventures.com
Contact: Yuval Almog, Founder
E-mail: yuval@coralgrp.com
Preferred Investment Size: $1,000,000 to $10,000,000. **Industry Preferences:** Communications and media, medical and media, computer software, hardware and services, Internet specific, biotechnology, semiconductors and other electronics, industrial and energy, and consumer related. **Geographic Preference:** U.S.

53777 ■ Crescendo Venture Management, LLP
480 Cowper St., Ste. 300
Palo Alto, CA 94301
Ph: (650)470-1200
Fax: (650)470-1201
Co. E-mail: businessplans@crescendoventures.com
URL: http://www.crescendoventures.com
Contact: David Spreng, Partner
E-mail: dspreng@crescendoventures.com
Preferred Investment Size: $5,000,000 to $30,000,000. **Industry Preferences:** Internet specific, communications and media, semiconductors and other electronics, other products, computer hardware, computer software and services, medical and health, biotechnology, industrial and energy. **Geographic Preference:** U.S.

53778 ■ Gideon Hixon Fund
800 Anacapa St., Ste. A
Santa Barbara, CA 93101
Ph: (805)963-2277
Fax: (805)565-0929
URL: http://www.gideonhixon.com
Contact: Eric Hixon, Partner
Preferred Investment Size: $500,000 to $1,500,000. **Investment Policies:** Start-up, seed, first and second stage. **Industry Preferences:** Internet specific, medical and health, computer software and services, other products, and semiconductors and other electronics. **Geographic Preference:** U.S.

53779 ■ Mayo Medical Ventures
200 First St. SW
Rochester, MN 55905
Ph: (507)284-2511
Free: 800-323-2688
Fax: (507)284-5410
Co. E-mail: mca.cme@mayo.edu
URL: http://www.mayo.edu
Preferred Investment Size: $250,000 to $1,000,000. **Industry Preferences:** Biotechnology, medical and health, Internet specific, industrial and energy. **Geographic Preference:** U.S.

53780 ■ Norwest Equity Partners
80 S. 8th St., Ste. 3600
Minneapolis, MN 55402
Ph: (612)215-1600
Fax: (612)215-1601
URL: http://www.nep.com
Contact: Andrew Cantwell, Principal
E-mail: acantwell@nep.com
Preferred Investment Size: $30,000,000 to $150,000,000. **Industry Preferences:** Computer software and services, communications and media, consumer related, agriculture, industrial and energy, medical and health, manufacturing, and business service. **Geographic Preference:** U.S.

53781 ■ Oak Investment Partners (Minneapolis)
4550 Wells Fargo Ctr.
90 S. 7th St.
Minneapolis, MN 55402
Ph: (612)339-9322
Fax: (612)337-8017
URL: http://www.oakvc.com
Contact: Scot Javis, Partner
Preferred Investment Size: $25,000,000 to $150,000,000. **Industry Preferences:** Communications and media, Internet specific, computer software and services, semiconductors and other electronics, consumer related, computer hardware, other products, medical and health, biotechnology, industrial and energy. **Geographic Preference:** U.S.

53782 ■ Sherpa Partners LLC
5775 Wayzata Blvd., Ste. 995
St. Louis Park, MN 55416
Ph: (612)803-3169
Co. E-mail: info@sherpapartners.com
URL: http://www.sherpapartners.com
Contact: Richard A. Brimacomb, Partner
Preferred Investment Size: $250,000 to $1,000,000. **Industry Preferences:** Communications and media, computer software, semiconductors and other electronics. **Geographic Preference:** Minnesota.

53783 ■ U.S. Bancorp Piper Jaffray Private Capital
800 Nicollet Mall, Ste. 800
Minneapolis, MN 55402
Ph: (612)303-6000
Fax: (612)303-1350
URL: http://www.piperjaffray.com
Contact: Scott Barrington, Managing Partner
Industry Preferences: Diversified. **Geographic Preference:** U.S.

PROCUREMENT ASSISTANCE PROGRAMS

53784 ■ Metropolitan Economic Development Association (MEDA)
250 2nd Ave. S, Ste. 106
Minneapolis, MN 55401-2168
Ph: (612)332-6332
Fax: (612)317-1002
Co. E-mail: info@meda.net
URL: http://www.meda.net
Contact: Yvonne Cheung Ho, President
E-mail: yho@meda.net
Description: Provides services to entrepreneurs of color in Minnesota. **Scope:** Provider of assistance to businesses owned and managed by ethnic minority residents of Minnesota. Services are directed toward new and existing businesses whose owners are committed to generating long-term profitable growth and employment opportunities. Provides management and leadership training and acts as a communication link between the majority and minority business communities in Minnesota. **Founded:** 1971.

53785 ■ Minnesota Procurement Technical Assistance Center - Metropolitan Economic Development Association (MEDA)
St. Cloud State University
616 Roosevelt Rd., Ste. 100
St. Cloud, MN 56301
Ph: (320)202-6496
Fax: (320)654-5412
Co. E-mail: cnebel@meda.net
URL: http://www.ptac-meda.net
Contact: Christina Nebel-Dickerson, Program Manager
E-mail: rmcgee@mpi.org

53786 ■ Minnesota Procurement Technical Assistance Center - Minnesota Project Innovation, Inc.
250 2nd Ave. S, Ste. 106
Minneapolis, MN 55401
Ph: (612)332-6332
Fax: (612)317-1002
Co. E-mail: skomrosky@meda.net
URL: http://www.ptac-meda.net
Contact: Sherri Komrosky, Program Director

INCUBATORS/RESEARCH AND TECHNOLOGY PARKS

53787 ■ Ceridian Corp.
3311 E Old Shakopee Rd.
Minneapolis, MN 55425-1361
Ph: (952)853-8100
Free: 800-729-7655
Fax: (952)853-5300
URL: http://www.ceridian.com
Contact: Stuart C. Harvey, President
Scope: Serves the human resources, transportation and media markets. Human resources businesses include benefits administration and retirement plans services; human resource management systems and payroll and tax filing services; fully integrated work place effectiveness solutions; payroll and human resources management solutions in the United Kingdom; and computer user training and performance support programs. Also include Com data, which provides transaction processing and information services to the transportation and other industries and arbitration, a research company serving the media industry. **Founded:** 1992. **Publications:** PowerPay. **Special Services:** Comdata®.

53788 ■ Genesis Business Centers, Ltd.
902 1/2 First St. N
Hopkins, MN 55343
Ph: (612)455-2215
Co. E-mail: harlanjacobs@genesiscenters.com
URL: http://www.genesiscenters.com
Contact: Harlan Jacobs, President
Description: An incubator specially designed for emerging high-tech businesses.

53789 ■ Greater Mankato Business Accelerator - Chamber of Commerce & Economic Development
1961 Premier Dr., Ste. 100
Mankato, MN 56001
Ph: (507)385-6649
Free: 800-697-0652
Fax: (507)385-3202
Co. E-mail: jklinger@greatermankato.com
URL: http://www.greatermankato.com
Contact: Jonathan G. Zierdt, Chief Executive Officer
Description: Provides business acceleration and start-up services.

53790 ■ Owatonna Business Incubator
1065 SW 24th Ave.
Owatonna, MN 55060
Ph: (507)451-0517
Fax: (507)455-2788
Co. E-mail: obi@owatonnaincubator.com
URL: http://www.owatonnaincubator.com/
Description: A small business incubator providing a facility in which small and start-up businesses can grow, prosper, and contribute to the surrounding community's economic base.

53791 ■ Time Share Systems
511 11th Ave., Ste. 402
Minneapolis, MN 55415
Ph: (612)332-2071
Fax: (612)332-2249

53792 ■ University of Minnesota Duluth Center for Economic Development - Business Incubator
11 E Superior St., Ste. 210
Duluth, MN 55802
Ph: (218)726-7298
Free: 888-387-4594
Fax: (218)726-6338
Co. E-mail: ced@umdced.com
URL: http://www.umdced.com/
Description: An incubator for technology development companies. Offers access to UMD's Center for Economic Development services.

53793 ■ University Technology Enterprise Center (Minneapolis)
1313 5th St. SE
Minneapolis, MN 55414
Ph: (612)379-3800
Fax: (612)379-3875
Co. E-mail: info@utecinc.com
URL: http://utec-center.com
Description: An enterprise center offering office space and support services for entrepreneurs.

EDUCATIONAL PROGRAMS

53794 ■ Alexandria Technical College
1601 Jefferson St.
Alexandria, MN 56308
Ph: (320)762-0221
Free: 888-234-1222
Fax: (320)762-4501
URL: http://www.alextech.org
Description: Trade and technical school offering a program in small business management.

53795 ■ Central Lakes College
501 W College Dr.
Brainerd, MN 56401
Ph: (218)855-8000
Free: 800-933-0346

Fax: (218)855-8220
URL: http://www.clc.mnscu.edu
Description: Trade and technical school offering a program in entrepreneurship and small business management.

53796 ■ Hibbing Community College
1515 E 25th St.
Hibbing, MN 55746
Ph: (218)262-7200
Free: 800-224-4422
Fax: (218)262-6717
Co. E-mail: admissions@hibbing.edu
URL: http://www.hibbing.edu
Description: Vocational school offering a small business management program.

53797 ■ Minneapolis Community and Technical College - Business Management Program
1501 Hennepin Ave.
Minneapolis, MN 55403-1778
Ph: (612)659-6000
Free: 800-247-0911
Fax: (612)659-6825
Co. E-mail: admissions@minneapolis.edu
URL: http://www.minneapolis.edu/
Description: Offers long-term instruction at an individual's place of business. Conducts seminars and individualized instruction to improve the management skills of prospective and current business owners.

53798 ■ Minnesota State Community and Technical College - Detroit Lakes
900 Hwy. 34 E
Detroit Lakes, MN 56501
Ph: (218)846-3700
Free: 877-450-3322
Fax: (218)846-3794
URL: http://www.minnesota.edu
Description: Trade and technical school offering a program in small business management.

53799 ■ Minnesota State Community and Technical College - Fergus Falls
1414 College Way
Fergus Falls, MN 56537
Ph: (218)736-1500
Free: 877-450-3322
Fax: (218)736-1510
URL: http://www.minnesota.edu
Description: Two-year college offering a small business management program.

53800 ■ Minnesota West Community and Technical College (Pipestone, Minnesota)
1314 N Hiawatha Ave.
Pipestone, MN 56164
Ph: (507)825-6800
Free: 800-658-2330

Fax: (507)825-4656
Co. E-mail: info@mnwest.edu
URL: http://www.mnwest.edu
Contact: Jacqueline Otkin, Dean
Description: Vocational school offering a small business management program. **Founded:** 1967. **Telecommunication Services:** jackie.otkin@mnwest.edu; linda.degriselles@mnwest.edu.

53801 ■ Normandale Community College
9700 France Ave. S
Bloomington, MN 55431
Ph: (952)358-8200
Free: 866-880-8740
Fax: (612)832-6571
URL: http://www.normandale.edu
Description: Two-year college offering a business and marketing management program, covering management skills, cash management, and marketing techniques used in business.

LEGISLATIVE ASSISTANCE

53802 ■ Enterprise Minnesota - Minnesota Department of Trade and Economic Development Center
310 4th Ave. S, Ste. 7050
Minneapolis, MN 55415
Ph: (612)373-2900
Free: 800-325-3073
Fax: (612)373-2901
URL: http://www.enterpriseminnesota.org/
Description: Coordinates and develops technology initiatives and policy recommendations. Advises the legislature, the governor, and the commissioner of trade and economic development on the state's science and technology policy.

PUBLICATIONS

53803 ■ *Smart Start your Arkansas Business*
PSI Research
300 N. Valley Dr.
Grants Pass, OR 97526
Ph: (503)479-9464
Free: 800-228-2275
Fax: (503)476-1479
Co. E-mail: info@psi-research.com
URL: http://www.psi-research.com
Ed: Michael D. Jenkins. **Released:** Revised edition, 1992. **Price:** $29.95 (looseleaf binder); $24.95 (paper). **Description:** Part of the Successful Business Library series.

PUBLISHERS

53804 ■ American Institute of Small Business (AISB)
23075 Hwy. 7, Ste. 200
Shorewood, MN 55331-3168
Ph: (952)545-7001

Free: 800-328-2906
Fax: (952)545-7020
Co. E-mail: info@aisb.biz
URL: http://www.aisb.biz
Contact: Kris Solie-Johnson, President
E-mail: kris@aisb.biz
Description: Publishes books on setting up a small business and entrepreneurship. Offers a bimonthly newsletter, video cassettes and software packages. Accepts unsolicited manuscripts. Reaches market through direct mail, trade sales, telephone sales, wholesalers and distributors. **Founded:** 1986.

53805 ■ Expert Publishing Inc.
14314 Thrush St. NW
Andover, MN 55304
Ph: (763)755-4966
Free: 877-755-4966
Fax: (763)757-8202
Co. E-mail: harry@expertpublishinginc.com
URL: http://www.expertpublishinginc.com
Contact: Sharron Stockhausen, Chief Executive Officer
E-mail: sharron@expertpublishinginc.com
Description: Description: Publishes nonfiction titles on subjects such as business.

53806 ■ Little Leaf Press Inc.
PO Box 187
Milaca, MN 56353
Ph: (651)774-3770
Free: 877-548-2431
Fax: (320)556-3585
Co. E-mail: littleleaf@maxminn.com
Contact: Beth Blasczyk, Chief Executive Officer
Description: Description: Publishes children's, history, hobby and academic books. Accepts unsolicited manuscripts. Reaches market through direct mail, telephone sales, wholesalers and distributors. **Founded:** 1998.

53807 ■ Thomson Legal & Regulatory
610 Opperman Dr.
Eagan, MN 55123-1340
Ph: (651)687-7000
Free: 800-328-9378
Fax: (651)687-5642
Co. E-mail: tlrcorporate.communications@thomson.com
URL: http://www.thomsonreuters.com
Contact: Sharon Rowlands, President
Description: Description: Publishes on legal information, intellectual property, business.

53808 ■ Two-Can Publishing
11571 K-Tel Dr.
Minnetonka, MN 55343
Ph: (952)933-7537
Free: 888-255-9989
Fax: (952)933-3630
Co. E-mail: sales@tnkidsbooks.com
Contact: Robert Nicholson, Manager
Description: Description: Publishes multimedia products and books. Does not accept unsolicited manuscripts. Reaches market through commission representatives, reviews and listings. **Founded:** 2000.

SMALL BUSINESS DEVELOPMENT CENTERS

53809 ■ **East Central Community College Small Business Development Center**
c/o Ronald B. Westbrook, Dir.
PO Box 129
Decatur, MS 39327-0129
Ph: (601)635-6297
Fax: (601)635-4031
Co. E-mail: sbdc@eccc.edu
URL: http://warrior.eccc.edu/workforce/pages/sbdc.
aspx
Contact: Ronald B. Westbrook, Director
URL(s): www.mssbdc.org/center.
aspx?center=47026&subloc=0. **Description:** Represents and promotes the small business sector. Provides management assistance to current and prospective small business owners. Helps to improve management skills and expand the products and services of members.

53810 ■ *Going Into Business in Mississippi: An Entrepreneur's Handbook*
University of Mississippi
122 Jeanette Phillips Dr.
University, MS 38677-1848
Ph: (662)915-5001
Free: 800-725-7232
Fax: (662)915-5650
Co. E-mail: msbdc@olemiss.edu
URL: http://www.mssbdc.org
Contact: Walter D. Gurley, Director

53811 ■ **Jackson State University Small Business Development Center**
Box 500
Jackson, MS 39204
Ph: (601)979-2795
Fax: (601)914-0833
Co. E-mail: jsusbdc@jsums.edu
URL: http://www.jsums.edu/business/sbdc
Contact: Mr. Sydney Brown, Director
Description: Represents and promotes the small business sector. Provides management assistance to current and prospective small business owners. Helps to improve management skills and expand the products and services of members.

53812 ■ **Jones County Junior College Small Business Development Center**
900 S Court St.
Ellisville, MS 39437
Ph: (601)477-4235
Fax: (601)477-4166
Co. E-mail: sbdc@jcjc.edu
URL: http://www.jcjc.edu/atc/smallbusinessdevelop-
mentcenter.php
Contact: Gary Suddith, Director
Description: Represents and promotes the small business sector. Provides management assistance to current and prospective small business owners. Helps to improve management skills and expand the products and services of members.

53813 ■ *The Mississippi Innovator*
University of Mississippi
122 Jeanette Phillips Dr.
University, MS 38677-1848
Ph: (662)915-5001
Free: 800-725-7232
Fax: (662)915-5650
Co. E-mail: msbdc@olemiss.edu
URL: http://www.mssbdc.org
Contact: Walter D. Gurley, Director

53814 ■ **Mississippi Small Business Development Center**
122 Jeanette Phillips Dr.
University, MS 38677-1848
Ph: (662)915-5001
Free: 800-725-7232
Fax: (662)915-5650
Co. E-mail: msbdc@olemiss.edu
URL: http://www.mssbdc.org
Contact: James Harper, Director
Description: Represents and promotes the small business sector. Provides management assistance to current and prospective small business owners. Helps to improve management skills and expand the products and services of members.

53815 ■ **Mississippi Small Business Development Center, Copiah Lincoln Community College (Co-Lin SBDC)**
11 Co-Lin Cir.
Natchez, MS 39120
Ph: (601)446-1168
Fax: (601)643-8277
Co. E-mail: jeff.waller@colin.edu
URL: http://www.mssbdc.org/mapresults.
aspx?showall=y&groupby=area
Contact: Jeff Waller, Director
Description: Represents and promotes the small business sector. Provides management assistance to current and prospective small business owners. Helps to improve management skills and expand the products and services of members.

53816 ■ **Mississippi Small Business Development Center at Delta State University**
PO Box 3235
Cleveland, MS 38733
Ph: (662)846-4236
Fax: (662)846-4235
Co. E-mail: csteele@deltastate.edu
URL: http://staging.deltastate.edu/pages/294.asp
Contact: Cristie D. Sledge, Director
Description: Represents and promotes the small business sector. Provides management assistance to current and prospective small business owners. Helps to improve management skills and expand the products and services of members.

53817 ■ **Mississippi Small Business Development Center - Lead Office (MSBDC)**
University of Mississippi
122 Jeanette Phillips Dr.
University, MS 38677-1848
Ph: (662)915-5001

Free: 800-725-7232
Fax: (662)915-5650
Co. E-mail: msbdc@olemiss.edu
URL: http://www.mssbdc.org
Contact: Walter D. Gurley, Director
Description: Composed of 10 service centers, hosted by five universities and five community colleges in the state of Mississippi. Serves as a one-stop resource center for a variety of counseling, workshops and information for growing businesses and startups. **Founded:** 1981. **Publications:** *Going Into Business in Mississippi: An Entrepreneur's Handbook*; *The Mississippi Innovator*; *SBDC Business Beat* (Quarterly).

53818 ■ **Mississippi State University Small Business Development Center (MSU SBDC)**
PO Box 5288
Mississippi State, MS 39762
Ph: (662)325-8684
Fax: (662)325-4016
Co. E-mail: sbdc@cobilan.msstate.edu
URL: http://business.msstate.edu/sbdc
Contact: Hamp Beatty, Director
Description: Represents and promotes the small business sector. Provides management assistance to current and prospective small business owners. Helps to improve management skills and expand the products and services of members.

53819 ■ *SBDC Business Beat*
University of Mississippi
122 Jeanette Phillips Dr.
University, MS 38677-1848
Ph: (662)915-5001
Free: 800-725-7232
Fax: (662)915-5650
Co. E-mail: msbdc@olemiss.edu
URL: http://www.mssbdc.org
Contact: Walter D. Gurley, Director
Released: Quarterly

53820 ■ **University of Mississippi Small Business Development Center (UMSBDC)**
PO Box 1848
University, MS 38677-1848
Ph: (662)915-1291
Free: 800-725-7232
Fax: (662)915-5650
Co. E-mail: umsbdc@olemiss.edu
URL: http://www.mssbdc.org
Contact: Mr. James Carden, Director
Description: Represents and promotes the small business sector. Provides management assistance to current and prospective small business owners. Helps to improve management skills and expand the products and services of members.

SMALL BUSINESS ASSISTANCE PROGRAMS

53821 ■ **Mississippi Enterprise for Technology - Mississippi Technology Transfer Office**
John C. Stennis Space Center, Bldg. 1103, Rm. 143
Stennis Space Center, MS 39529-6000

Ph: (228)688-3144
Fax: (228)688-1064
Co. E-mail: Charles.E.Beasley@nasa.gov
URL: http://www.mset.org
Contact: Charles E. Beasley, Chief Executive Officer
Description: Helps advanced technology companies locate or expand in Mississippi.

53822 ■ Mississippi University for Women - Career Services
1100 College St., W-1624
Columbus, MS 39701
Ph: (662)241-7619
Fax: (662)329-7192
Co. E-mail: twilliams@ss.muw.edu
URL: http://www.muw.edu/career
Contact: Towanda Williams, Assistant Director
Description: Provides employment-related services to students and organizations.

53823 ■ U.S. Department of Commerce - Mississippi Development Authority
Woolfolk Bldg., Ste. B 01, 501 N West St.
Jackson, MS 39201
Ph: (601)359-3449
Free: 800-340-3323
Fax: (601)359-2832
Co. E-mail: eibus@mississippi.org
URL: http://www.mississippi.org
Contact: Brent Christensen, Executive Director
URL(s): www.visitmississippi.org/. **Description:** Provides assistance to the state's businesses and industries, including loans and loan guarantees to small businesses, and an outreach program. **Telecommunication Services:** tinquiry@mississippi.org; state@mississippi.org.

SCORE OFFICES

53824 ■ SCORE Gulfcoast
Hancock Bank Bldg.
2510 14th St., Ste. 105
Gulfport, MS 39501
Ph: (228)875-0691
URL: http://www.scoregulfport.org
Description: Provides public service to America by offering small business advice and training. **Founded:** 1965.

BETTER BUSINESS BUREAUS

53825 ■ Better Business Bureau of Mississippi
505 Avalon Way, Ste. B
Brandon, MS 39047-7510
Ph: (601)398-1700
Free: 800-987-8280
Fax: (769)251-1054
Co. E-mail: info@ms.bbb.org
URL: http://ms.bbb.org
Contact: David Ormstedt, Chairman
Description: Seeks to promote and foster ethical relationship between businesses and the public through voluntary self-regulation, consumer and business education, and service excellence. Provides information to help consumers and businesses make informed purchasing decisions and avoid costly scams and frauds; settles consumer complaints through arbitration and other means. **Founded:** 1964.

CHAMBERS OF COMMERCE

53826 ■ *Action Line Newsletter*
600 3rd St.
Cleveland, MS 38732
Ph: (662)843-2712
Fax: (662)843-2718
Co. E-mail: judson@clevelandmschamber.com
URL: http://www.clevelandmschamber.com
Contact: Judson Thigpen, Executive Director
Released: Monthly

53827 ■ Area Development Partnership (ADP)
1 Convention Center Plz.
Hattiesburg, MS 39401

Ph: (601)296-7500
Free: 800-238-4288
Fax: (601)296-7505
Co. E-mail: adp@theadp.com
URL: http://www.theadp.com
Contact: Lou Ann Poynter, Chairperson
Description: Strives to improve the quality of life for citizens of the Greater Hattiesburg Area through community and economic development. **Founded:** 1906. **Educational Activities:** Area Development Partnership Breakfast (Monthly).

53828 ■ Belzoni - Humphreys Development Foundation (BHDF)
PO Box 145
Belzoni, MS 39038
Ph: (662)247-4838
Free: 800-408-4838
Fax: (662)247-4805
Co. E-mail: catfish@belzonicable.com
URL: http://www.belzonims.com
Contact: Larson Frey, President
Description: Fosters economic development. Grows all kinds of plants in the Mississippi Delta from cotton, sweet potatoes, and tobacco plants to distribution, manufacturing and processing plants.

53829 ■ Biloxi Chamber of Commerce (BCC)
11975 E Seaway Rd.
Gulfport, MS 39503
Ph: (228)604-0014
Fax: (228)604-0105
Co. E-mail: rachael@mscoastchamber.com
URL: http://biloxi.org
Contact: Bruce Marie, President
Description: Promotes business and community development in Biloxi, MS. Sponsors Biloxi Seafood Festival, Music in May, community activities, and seminars. **Founded:** 1893. **Awards:** Educator Award (Annual).

53830 ■ Booneville Area Chamber of Commerce (BACC)
100 W Church St.
Booneville, MS 38829
Ph: (662)728-4130
Free: 800-300-9302
Fax: (662)728-4134
Co. E-mail: rgreening@boonevillemississippi.com
URL: http://boonevillemississippi.com
Contact: Rhonda Greening, Executive Director
Description: Strives to support businesses, industries and educational entities of Booneville and Prentiss County in order to improve the quality of life of the citizens. **Awards:** BACC Scholarship (Annual).

53831 ■ Brookhaven - Lincoln County Chamber of Commerce
230 S Whitworth Ave.
Brookhaven, MS 39602-0978
Ph: (601)833-1411
Free: 800-613-4667
Fax: (601)833-1412
Co. E-mail: chb@brookhavenchamber.com
URL: http://www.brookhavenchamber.com/index.php
Contact: Cliff Brumfield, Executive Vice President
Description: Strives to enhance the industrial, commercial, tourism, retiree development, civic and general interests of Lincoln County, MS. **Founded:** 1931.

53832 ■ *Business Review*
3010 Goodman Rd. W, Ste. B
Horn Lake, MS 38637
Ph: (662)393-9897
Fax: (662)393-2942
Co. E-mail: info@hornlakechamber.com
URL: http://www.hornlakechamber.com
Contact: Jim Holland, President
Released: Monthly **Price:** included in membership dues.

53833 ■ Calhoun City Chamber of Commerce (CCCC)
102 S Monroe St.
Calhoun City, MS 38916-0161
Ph: (662)628-6990

Fax: (662)628-8931
Co. E-mail: city1@tds.net
URL: http://www.calhouneda.com/calhouncitychamber.html
Contact: Barbara Fox, President
Description: Promotes business and community development in Calhoun County, MS. Sponsors periodic festival. Publications: none. **Founded:** 1969.

53834 ■ Canton Chamber of Commerce
PO Box 74
Canton, MS 39046-0074
Ph: (601)859-5816
Fax: (601)855-0149
Co. E-mail: ccoc@canton-mississippi.com
URL: http://www.canton-mississippi.com/index.php
Contact: Deborah Anderson, Executive Director
Description: Works to improve the growth of business, industry, agriculture and quality of life in the community.

53835 ■ *Chamber Chatter*
201 Hwy. 11 N
Picayune, MS 39466
Ph: (601)798-3122
Fax: (601)798-6984
Co. E-mail: aprillovelace@picayunechamber.org
URL: http://www.picayunechamber.org
Contact: April Parsons, Director
Released: Monthly

53836 ■ *The Chamber Message*
PO Box 272
Columbia, MS 39429
Ph: (601)736-6385
Fax: (601)736-6392
Co. E-mail: info@mcdp.info
URL: http://www.mcdp.info
Contact: Gerald Frazier, President
Released: Quarterly **Price:** free.

53837 ■ *The Chamber Network*
100 E Leake
Clinton, MS 39060-0143
Ph: (601)924-5912
Free: 800-611-9980
Fax: (601)925-4009
Co. E-mail: director@clintonchamber.org
URL: http://www.clintonms.org/index.php
Contact: T.J. McSparrin, Executive Director
Released: Monthly

53838 ■ *Chamber Network*
8700 Northwest Dr.
Southaven, MS 38671
Ph: (662)342-6114
Free: 800-272-6551
Fax: (662)342-6365
Co. E-mail: info@southavenchamber.com
URL: http://www.southavenchamber.com
Contact: Ryan England, President
Released: Monthly

53839 ■ *Chamber News*
c/o Marie Shoemake, Exec. Dir.
500 Korno St.
Collins, MS 39428-1595
Ph: (601)765-6012
Fax: (601)765-1740
Co. E-mail: contact@covingtonchamber.com
URL: http://www.covingtonchamber.com
Contact: Marie Shoemake, Executive Director
Released: Quarterly

53840 ■ *Chamber News*
PO Box 608
Olive Branch, MS 38654-0608
Ph: (662)895-2600
Fax: (662)895-2625
Co. E-mail: info@olivebranchms.com
URL: http://chamber.olivebranchms.com
Contact: Vickie DuPree, Executive Director
Released: Monthly

53841 ■ City of Ridgeland Chamber of Commerce
PO Box 194
Ridgeland, MS 39158-0194
Ph: (601)991-9996

Fax: (601)991-9997
Co. E-mail: admin@ridgelandchamber.com
URL: http://www.ridgelandchamber.com
Contact: Linda T. Bynum, Executive Director
Description: Encourages an economic environment conducive to the continuing development of new and existing business. **Publications:** *Images* (Annual); *Vision* (Quarterly).

53842 ■ *Civic Club and Organizational Directory*
101 Service Dr.
Brandon, MS 39043-0428
Ph: (601)825-2268
Fax: (601)825-1977
Co. E-mail: marinder@rankinchamber.com
URL: http://www.rankinchamber.com/home.aspx
Contact: Mandi Arinder, Executive Director
Released: Periodic

53843 ■ Clarke County Chamber of Commerce
PO Box 172
Quitman, MS 39355
Ph: (601)776-5701
Fax: (601)776-5745
Co. E-mail: clarkechamber@att.net
URL: http://www.clarkecountychamber.com
URL(s): my.att.net/p/s/community.dll?ep=16&groupid=410785&ck=. **Description:** Seeks to unify the citizens of Clarke County, MS to foster growth in leadership, education, and economics. Works to improve the quality of life in the area.

53844 ■ Clarksdale - Coahoma County Chamber of Commerce and Industry Foundation (CCCCCIF)—Coahoma County Industrial Foundation
PO Box 160
Clarksdale, MS 38614
Ph: (662)627-7337
Free: 800-626-3764
Fax: (662)627-1313
Co. E-mail: chamberofcommerce@clarksdale-ms.com
URL: http://www.clarksdale.com/chamber
Contact: Ronald E. Hudson, Executive Director
URL(s): www.clarksdale-ms.com. **Description:** Promotes business and community development in Coahoma County, MS. Sponsors Sunflower River 10-K Run and Delta Jubilee barbecue contest. **Publications:** *Newcomers Guide; On Target* (Quarterly).

53845 ■ Cleveland-Bolivar County Chamber of Commerce (CBCCC)
600 3rd St.
Cleveland, MS 38732
Ph: (662)843-2712
Fax: (662)843-2718
Co. E-mail: judson@clevelandmschamber.com
URL: http://www.clevelandmschamber.com
Contact: Judson Thigpen, Executive Director
Description: Promotes business and community development in Bolivar County, MS. Holds monthly board and committee meeting. **Founded:** 1947. **Publications:** *Action Line Newsletter* (Monthly); *Community Data Book* (Periodic). **Educational Activities:** Membership and Awards Banquet (Annual); Merchants Holiday Open House and White Lights (Annual). **Awards:** Ambassador of the Year (Annual); Chamber Award (Annual); Kossman Award (Annual); The President's Award (Annual).

53846 ■ Clinton Chamber of Commerce (CCC)
100 E Leake
Clinton, MS 39060-0143
Ph: (601)924-5912
Free: 800-611-9980
Fax: (601)925-4009
Co. E-mail: director@clintonchamber.org
URL: http://www.clintonms.org/index.php
Contact: T.J. McSparrin, Executive Director
Description: Promotes business and community development in Clinton, MS. **Founded:** 1962. **Publications:** *The Chamber Network* (Monthly).

53847 ■ *Community Data Book*
600 3rd St.
Cleveland, MS 38732
Ph: (662)843-2712
Fax: (662)843-2718
Co. E-mail: judson@clevelandmschamber.com
URL: http://www.clevelandmschamber.com
Contact: Judson Thigpen, Executive Director
Released: Periodic

53848 ■ Community Development Foundation (CDF)
300 W Main St.
Tupelo, MS 38804
Ph: (662)842-4521
Free: 800-523-3463
Fax: (662)841-0693
Co. E-mail: info@cdfms.org
URL: http://www.cdfms.org
Contact: David Copenhaver, Chairman
Description: Strives to improve the civic, economic, and social welfare of people living in Tupelo and Lee County. **Founded:** 1948. **Publications:** *Northeast Mississippi Business Journal.*

53849 ■ Community Development Partnership—Philadelphia Community Development Partnership
256 W Beacon St.
Philadelphia, MS 39350
Ph: (601)656-1000
Co. E-mail: dvowell@bellsouth.net
URL: http://www.neshoba.org
Contact: David Vowell, President
Description: Promotes business and community development in Neshoba County and Philadelphia, MS. **Founded:** 1954.

53850 ■ *Connections*
412 Hwy. 90, Ste. 6
Bay St. Louis, MS 39520
Ph: (228)467-9048
Fax: (228)467-6033
Co. E-mail: lynne@hancockchamber.org
URL: http://www.hancockchamber.org
Contact: Ms. Tish Haas Williams, Executive Director

53851 ■ Covington County Chamber of Commerce (CCCC)
c/o Marie Shoemake, Exec. Dir.
500 Korno St.
Collins, MS 39428-1595
Ph: (601)765-6012
Fax: (601)765-1740
Co. E-mail: contact@covingtonchamber.com
URL: http://www.covingtonchamber.com
Contact: Marie Shoemake, Executive Director
Description: Promotes business and community development in Covington County, MS. Sponsors annual horse show and Day in the Park. **Founded:** 1987. **Publications:** *Chamber News* (Quarterly).

53852 ■ *Day Care Center Directory*
101 Service Dr.
Brandon, MS 39043-0428
Ph: (601)825-2268
Fax: (601)825-1977
Co. E-mail: marinder@rankinchamber.com
URL: http://www.rankinchamber.com/home.aspx
Contact: Mandi Arinder, Executive Director
Released: Periodic

53853 ■ D'Iberville-St. Martin Chamber of Commerce
PO Box 6054
D'Iberville, MS 39540
Ph: (228)392-2293
Fax: (228)396-3216
URL: http://www.dsmchamber.com
Contact: Sharon Seymour, Executive Director
Description: Promotes business and community development in D'Iberville and St. Martin, MS area. **Founded:** 1974.

53854 ■ *Directions*
PO Box 527
Laurel, MS 39441-0527
Ph: (601)649-3031

Fax: (601)428-2047
Co. E-mail: info@edajones.com
URL: http://www.edajones.com
Released: Quarterly

53855 ■ *Going Our Way*
112 N Railroad Blvd.
McComb, MS 39648
Ph: (601)684-2291
Free: 800-399-4404
Fax: (601)684-4899
Co. E-mail: bherrin2@pikeinfo.com
URL: http://www.pikeinfo.com
Contact: J. Britt Herrin, Executive Director
Released: Monthly

53856 ■ Greater Picayune Area Chamber of Commerce (GPACC)
201 Hwy. 11 N
Picayune, MS 39466
Ph: (601)798-3122
Fax: (601)798-6984
Co. E-mail: aprillovelace@picayunechamber.org
URL: http://www.picayunechamber.org
Contact: April Parsons, Director
Description: Promotes business and community development in the Picayune, MS area. Sponsors festival. **Founded:** 1936. **Publications:** *Chamber Chatter* (Monthly). **Awards:** Citizen of the Year (Annual); Club of the Year (Annual); Volunteer of the Year (Annual).

53857 ■ Greenwood-Leflore Chamber of Commerce (GLCC)
PO Box 848
Greenwood, MS 38935-0848
Ph: (662)453-4152
Co. E-mail: info@greenwoodms.com
URL: http://www.greenwoodms.com/index.php
Contact: Beth Stevens, Executive Vice President
Description: Promotes business and community development in the Greenwood-Leflore, MS area. **Founded:** 1917. **Publications:** *What's Happening* (Bimonthly).

53858 ■ Grenada Area Chamber of Commerce
PO Box 628
Grenada, MS 38902-0628
Ph: (662)226-2571
Free: 800-373-2571
Fax: (662)226-9745
Co. E-mail: buddy@grenadamississippi.com
URL: http://www.grenadamississippi.com
Contact: Buddy Harbin, Executive Director
Description: Promotes business and community development in Grenada County, MS. **Publications:** *Guide to Grenada* (Annual).

53859 ■ *Guide to Grenada*
PO Box 628
Grenada, MS 38902-0628
Ph: (662)226-2571
Free: 800-373-2571
Fax: (662)226-9745
Co. E-mail: buddy@grenadamississippi.com
URL: http://www.grenadamississippi.com
Contact: Buddy Harbin, Executive Director
Released: Annual

53860 ■ Hancock County Chamber of Commerce (HCCC)
412 Hwy. 90, Ste. 6
Bay St. Louis, MS 39520
Ph: (228)467-9048
Fax: (228)467-6033
Co. E-mail: lynne@hancockchamber.org
URL: http://www.hancockchamber.org
Contact: Ms. Tish Haas Williams, Executive Director
Description: Promotes business and community development in Hancock County, MS. **Founded:** 1925. **Publications:** *Connections.* **Educational Activities:** After Hours (Monthly). **Telecommunication Services:** tish@hancockchamber.org; latonja@hancockchamber.org.

53861 ■ Hernando Area Chamber of Commerce
2440 Hwy. 51 S
Hernando, MS 39632
Ph: (662)429-9055
Fax: (662)429-2909
Co. E-mail: chamber@hernandoms.org
URL: http://www.hernandoms.org
Contact: Angie Hick, Director
Description: Promotes business and community development in Hernando, MS area.

53862 ■ *Highlights*
124 N Jackson St.
Kosciusko, MS 39090
Ph: (662)289-2981
Co. E-mail: info@kadcorp.org
URL: http://www.kosciuskotourism.com
Contact: Steve Zea, President
Released: Periodic

53863 ■ Holly Springs Chamber of Commerce (HSCC)
c/o Rebecca Bourgeois, Exec. Dir.
104 E College Ave.
Holly Springs, MS 38635
Ph: (662)252-2943
Co. E-mail: office@hschamber.org
URL: http://www.hschamber.org
Contact: Rebecca Bourgeois, Executive Director
Description: Promotes business and community development in Holly Springs and Marshall County, MS.

53864 ■ Horn Lake Chamber of Commerce
3010 Goodman Rd. W, Ste. B
Horn Lake, MS 38637
Ph: (662)393-9897
Fax: (662)393-2942
Co. E-mail: info@hornlakechamber.com
URL: http://www.hornlakechamber.com
Contact: Jim Holland, President
Description: Works to create jobs by recruiting new business to the area. **Publications:** *Business Review* (Monthly). **Awards:** Business of the Month (Monthly); Community Pride Award.

53865 ■ *Images*
PO Box 194
Ridgeland, MS 39158-0194
Ph: (601)991-9996
Fax: (601)991-9997
Co. E-mail: admin@ridgelandchamber.com
URL: http://www.ridgelandchamber.com
Contact: Linda T. Bynum, Executive Director
Released: Annual

53866 ■ Indianola Chamber of Commerce
PO Box 151
Indianola, MS 38751
Ph: (662)887-4454
Free: 877-816-7581
Fax: (662)887-4454
Co. E-mail: icoc@tecinfo.com
URL: http://www.indianolams.org
Contact: Doug Russell, President
Description: Enhances business environment and contributes to the overall economic well-being and quality of life in Indianola, MS.

53867 ■ *The Innovation Advantage*
Released: Bimonthly

53868 ■ Itawamba County Development Council (ICDC)
PO Box 577
Fulton, MS 38843
Ph: (662)862-4571
Fax: (662)862-5637
Co. E-mail: icdc@itawamba.com
URL: http://www.itawamba.com
Contact: Greg Deakle, Executive Director
Description: Strives to improve and enhance the quality of life for all citizens and promotes orderly business and economic development in Itawamba County. **Founded:** 1953.

53869 ■ *Jackson Commerce*
PO Box 22548
Jackson, MS 39225-2548
Ph: (601)948-7575
Fax: (601)352-5539
Co. E-mail: contact@metrochamber.com
URL: http://www.metrochamber.com
Contact: Duane A. O'Neill, President
Released: Monthly

53870 ■ Jones County Chamber of Commerce
PO Box 527
Laurel, MS 39441-0527
Ph: (601)649-3031
Fax: (601)428-2047
Co. E-mail: info@edajones.com
URL: http://www.edajones.com
Description: Promotes business and economic development in Jones County. **Founded:** 1988. **Publications:** *Directions* (Quarterly).

53871 ■ Kosciusko-Attala Chamber of Commerce (KACC)
124 N Jackson St.
Kosciusko, MS 39090
Ph: (662)289-2981
Co. E-mail: info@kadcorp.org
URL: http://www.kosciuskotourism.com
Contact: Steve Zea, President
Description: Promotes business and community development in the Kosciusko-Attala, MS area. Sponsors local festival. **Founded:** 1935. **Publications:** *Highlights* (Periodic).

53872 ■ Leake County Chamber of Commerce (LCCC)
103 N Pearl St.
Carthage, MS 39051-0209
Ph: (601)267-9231
Fax: (601)267-8123
Co. E-mail: director@leakems.com
URL: http://www.leakems.com
Contact: Renodda Dorman, Executive Director
Description: Promotes business and community development in Leake County, MS. **Founded:** 1953. **Publications:** *News Leakes*. **Educational Activities:** Carthage's Octoberfest (Annual). **Awards:** Man and Woman of the Year (Annual).

53873 ■ Leland Chamber of Commerce
PO Box 67
Leland, MS 38756
Ph: (662)686-2687
Fax: (662)686-2689
Co. E-mail: lcoc@tecinfo.com
URL: http://www.lelandms.org
Contact: Bob Neill, Executive Director
Description: Promotes business and economic development in Leland, MS.

53874 ■ *LOU View*
299 W Jackson Ave.
Oxford, MS 38655
Ph: (662)234-4651
Free: 800-880-6967
Fax: (662)234-4655
Co. E-mail: info@oxfordms.com
URL: http://www.oxfordms.com
Contact: Max D. Hipp, President
Released: Quarterly

53875 ■ Louisville-Winston County Chamber of Commerce (LWCCC)
PO Box 551
Louisville, MS 39339
Ph: (662)773-3921
Fax: (662)773-8909
Co. E-mail: info@winstoncounty.com
URL: http://www.winstoncounty.com
URL(s): www.visitmississippi.org. **Description:** Promotes business and community development in Winston County, MS. **Founded:** 1957.

53876 ■ Madison the City Chamber of Commerce
PO Box 544
Madison, MS 39130
Ph: (601)856-7060

Fax: (601)856-4852
Co. E-mail: information@madisonthecitychamber. com
URL: http://www.madisonthecitychamber.com
Contact: Jane Bell, President
Description: Strives to provide leadership in economic development activities and improve the quality of life in Madison area.

53877 ■ *Manufacturer Directory*
101 Service Dr.
Brandon, MS 39043-0428
Ph: (601)825-2268
Fax: (601)825-1977
Co. E-mail: marinder@rankinchamber.com
URL: http://www.rankinchamber.com/home.aspx
Contact: Mandi Arinder, Executive Director
Released: Periodic

53878 ■ Marion County Development Partnership (MCDP)
PO Box 272
Columbia, MS 39429
Ph: (601)736-6385
Fax: (601)736-6392
Co. E-mail: info@mcdp.info
URL: http://www.mcdp.info
Contact: Gerald Frazier, President
Description: Promotes business and community development in Marion County, MS. **Publications:** *The Chamber Message* (Quarterly).

53879 ■ *Membership Directory and Community Guide*
PO Box 608
Olive Branch, MS 38654-0608
Ph: (662)895-2600
Fax: (662)895-2625
Co. E-mail: info@olivebranchms.com
URL: http://chamber.olivebranchms.com
Contact: Vickie DuPree, Executive Director

53880 ■ *Metro Buyers' Guide*
PO Box 22548
Jackson, MS 39225-2548
Ph: (601)948-7575
Fax: (601)352-5539
Co. E-mail: contact@metrochamber.com
URL: http://www.metrochamber.com
Contact: Duane A. O'Neill, President
Released: Annual

53881 ■ MetroJackson Chamber of Commerce (MJCC)
PO Box 22548
Jackson, MS 39225-2548
Ph: (601)948-7575
Fax: (601)352-5539
Co. E-mail: contact@metrochamber.com
URL: http://www.metrochamber.com
Contact: Duane A. O'Neill, President
Description: Promotes business and community development in Jackson, MS. **Founded:** 1886. **Publications:** *Jackson Commerce* (Monthly); *Metro Buyers' Guide* (Annual).

53882 ■ Mississippi Gulf Coast Chamber of Commerce
11975E Seaway Rd.
Gulfport, MS 39503
Ph: (228)604-0014
Fax: (228)604-0105
Co. E-mail: info@mscoastchamber.com
URL: http://mscoastchamber.com
Contact: Kimberly Nastasi, Chief Executive Officer
Description: Promotes business and community development in the Gulf Coast area of MS. Sponsors civic clearing house, public relations counseling, legislative representation at all levels of government, information bureau, and research and promotion programs. **Publications:** *Relocation Guide* (Annual).

53883 ■ Monroe County Chamber of Commerce
124 W Commerce St.
Aberdeen, MS 39730
Ph: (662)369-6488

Fax: (662)369-6489
Co. E-mail: chamber@gomonroe.org
URL: http://www.gomonroe.org
Contact: Tony Green, Executive Director
Description: Promotes business and community development in Aberdeen-South Monroe, MS. Sponsors Christmas at Blue Bluff and outdoor festivals. **Founded:** 1921. **Publications:** *Monroe Messenger.*

53884 ■ Monroe County Chamber of Commerce
1619 Hwy. 25 N
Amory, MS 38821-0128
Ph: (662)256-7194
Fax: (662)256-9671
Co. E-mail: chamber@gomonroe.org
URL: http://www.gomonroe.org
Contact: Tony Green, President
Description: Promotes business and community development in the Amory, MS area. **Founded:** 1946. **Telecommunication Services:** tony@gomonroe.org.

53885 ■ *Monroe Messenger*
124 W Commerce St.
Aberdeen, MS 39730
Ph: (662)369-6488
Fax: (662)369-6489
Co. E-mail: chamber@gomonroe.org
URL: http://www.gomonroe.org
Contact: Tony Green, Executive Director

53886 ■ Natchez-Adams County Chamber of Commerce (NACCC)
211 Main St.
Natchez, MS 39120
Ph: (601)445-4611
Fax: (601)445-9361
Co. E-mail: natchezchamber@natchezchamber.com
URL: http://natchezchamber.com
Contact: Debbie L. Hudson, President
Description: Promotes business and community development in Natchez-Adams County, MS. **Founded:** 1908. **Awards:** Athena Award (Annual); Natchezian of the Year (Annual).

53887 ■ *Newcomers Guide*
PO Box 160
Clarksdale, MS 38614
Ph: (662)627-7337
Free: 800-626-3764
Fax: (662)627-1313
Co. E-mail: chamberofcommerce@clarksdale-ms.com
URL: http://www.clarksdale.com/chamber
Contact: Ronald E. Hudson, Executive Director

53888 ■ *News Leakes*
103 N Pearl St.
Carthage, MS 39051-0209
Ph: (601)267-9231
Fax: (601)267-8123
Co. E-mail: director@leakems.com
URL: http://www.leakems.com
Contact: Renodda Dorman, Executive Director

53889 ■ Newton Chamber of Commerce (NCC)
PO Box 301
Newton, MS 39345
Ph: (601)683-2201
Fax: (601)683-2201
Co. E-mail: chambernewton@bellsouth.net
URL: http://www.ci.newton.ms.us
Contact: Angie Burkes, Executive Director
Description: Promotes business and community development in the Newton, MS area. Sponsors Open Air A'Fair festival. **Founded:** 1952. **Awards:** Man and Woman of the Year (Annual).

53890 ■ *Northeast Mississippi Business Journal*
300 W Main St.
Tupelo, MS 38804
Ph: (662)842-4521
Free: 800-523-3463
Fax: (662)841-0693
Co. E-mail: info@cdfms.org
URL: http://www.cdfms.org
Contact: David Copenhaver, Chairman

53891 ■ Ocean Springs Chamber of Commerce (OSCC)
1000 Washington Ave.
Ocean Springs, MS 39564
Ph: (228)875-4424
Fax: (228)875-0332
Co. E-mail: mail@oceanspringschamber.com
URL: http://www.oceanspringschamber.com
Contact: Margaret Miller, Executive Director
Description: Promotes business and community development in Ocean Springs, MS.

53892 ■ Okolona Area Chamber of Commerce-Main Street Program
219 Main St.
Okolona, MS 38860
Ph: (662)447-5913
Fax: (662)447-0254
URL: http://www.okolona.org
Contact: Thelma Davis, President
Description: Promotes business and community development in Okolona, MS area. **Founded:** 1934.

53893 ■ Olive Branch Chamber of Commerce (OBCC)
PO Box 608
Olive Branch, MS 38654-0608
Ph: (662)895-2600
Fax: (662)895-2625
Co. E-mail: info@olivebranchms.com
URL: http://chamber.olivebranchms.com
Contact: Vickie DuPree, Executive Director
Description: Promotes business and community development in the Olive Branch, MS area. **Founded:** 1973. **Publications:** *Chamber News* (Monthly); *Membership Directory and Community Guide*; *Coupon Book* (Semiannual). **Educational Activities:** Christmas Parade (Annual); During Hours (Monthly).

53894 ■ *On Target*
PO Box 160
Clarksdale, MS 38614
Ph: (662)627-7337
Free: 800-626-3764
Fax: (662)627-1313
Co. E-mail: chamberofcommerce@clarksdale-ms.com
URL: http://www.clarksdale.com/chamber
Contact: Ronald E. Hudson, Executive Director
Released: Quarterly

53895 ■ Oxford-Lafayette County Chamber of Commerce (OLCCC)
299 W Jackson Ave.
Oxford, MS 38655
Ph: (662)234-4651
Free: 800-880-6967
Fax: (662)234-4655
Co. E-mail: info@oxfordms.com
URL: http://www.oxfordms.com
Contact: Max D. Hipp, President
Description: Promotes business and community development in the Oxford-Lafayette County, MS area. **Founded:** 1940. **Publications:** *LOU View* (Quarterly).

53896 ■ Pearl Chamber of Commerce (PCC)
PO Box 54125
Pearl, MS 39288-4125
Ph: (601)939-3338
Fax: (601)936-5717
Co. E-mail: pearlchamberofcommerce@pearlms.org
URL: http://www.pearlms.org
Contact: Kathy Deer, Executive Director
Description: Promotes business and community development in Pearl, MS. **Founded:** 1979.

53897 ■ Pike County Chamber of Commerce and Economic Development District (PCCCEDD)
112 N Railroad Blvd.
McComb, MS 39648
Ph: (601)684-2291
Free: 800-399-4404

Fax: (601)684-4899
Co. E-mail: bherrin2@pikeinfo.com
URL: http://www.pikeinfo.com
Contact: J. Britt Herrin, Executive Director
Description: Promotes business and community development in Pike County, MS. **Scope:** economic, business, population, demographics. **Subscriptions:** 100 books periodicals reports. **Publications:** *Going Our Way* (Monthly).

53898 ■ Pontotoc County Chamber of Commerce (PCCC)
109 N Main St.
Pontotoc, MS 38863
Ph: (662)489-5042
Fax: (662)489-5263
Co. E-mail: chamber@pontotocchamber.com
URL: http://www.pontotocchamber.com
Contact: Cecilia Derrington, Executive Director
Description: Promotes business and community development in Pontotoc County, MS. Sponsors annual Christmas parade and annual Bodock Festival. **Founded:** 1987.

53899 ■ Port Gibson-Claiborne County Chamber of Commerce (PGCCCC)
1601 Church St.
Port Gibson, MS 39150
Ph: (601)437-4351
Co. E-mail: judyscruggs@bellsouth.net
URL: http://www.portgibsononthemississippi.com/chamber_of_commerce.html
Description: Promotes business and community development in the Port Gibson-Claiborne County, MS area. Provides tourist information on the area.

53900 ■ Rankin County Chamber of Commerce
101 Service Dr.
Brandon, MS 39043-0428
Ph: (601)825-2268
Fax: (601)825-1977
Co. E-mail: marinder@rankinchamber.com
URL: http://www.rankinchamber.com/home.aspx
Contact: Mandi Arinder, Executive Director
Description: Promotes business and community development in Rankin County, MS. Also promotes highway, recreation, agriculture and forestry, and health development. **Founded:** 1959. **Publications:** *Day Care Center Directory* (Periodic); *Manufacturer Directory* (Periodic); *Civic Club and Organizational Directory* (Periodic). **Telecommunication Services:** cburney@rankinchamber.com.

53901 ■ *Relocation Guide*
11975E Seaway Rd.
Gulfport, MS 39503
Ph: (228)604-0014
Fax: (228)604-0105
Co. E-mail: info@mscoastchamber.com
URL: http://mscoastchamber.com
Contact: Kimberly Nastasi, Chief Executive Officer
Released: Annual

53902 ■ Southaven - Horn Lake Area Chamber of Commerce (SHLACC)
8700 Northwest Dr.
Southaven, MS 38671
Ph: (662)342-6114
Free: 800-272-6551
Fax: (662)342-6365
Co. E-mail: info@southavenchamber.com
URL: http://www.southavenchamber.com
Contact: Ryan England, President
Description: Promotes business and community development in Southaven-Horn Lake, MS. **Founded:** 1969. **Publications:** *Chamber Network* (Monthly); *SouthHaven* (Annual); *Visitors Guide* (Annual); *Chamber Digest.* **Awards:** Ambassador Award (Annual); Community Pride (Annual); Business of the Month (Monthly).

53903 ■ *SouthHaven*
8700 Northwest Dr.
Southaven, MS 38671
Ph: (662)342-6114
Free: 800-272-6551

Fax: (662)342-6365
Co. E-mail: info@southavenchamber.com
URL: http://www.southavenchamber.com
Contact: Ryan England, President
Released: Annual

53904 ■ Starkville Area Chamber of Commerce
200 E Main St.
Starkville, MS 39759
Ph: (662)323-3322
Free: 800-649-8687
Fax: (662)323-5815
Co. E-mail: info@starkville.org
URL: http://www.starkville.org
Contact: Melissa Dixon, Chairperson
Description: Promotes business and community development in the Starkville, MS. **Publications:** *The View* (Quarterly). **Awards:** R. Clay Simmons Exemplary Enterprise Award (Annual); T.E. Veitich Community Service Award (Annual).

53905 ■ Tunica County Chamber of Commerce
PO Box 1888
Tunica, MS 38676
Ph: (662)363-2865
Fax: (662)357-0378
Co. E-mail: marketing@tunicachamber.com
URL: http://www.tunicachamber.com
Contact: Brenda Veazey, Manager
Description: Promotes business and community development in Tunica, MS area. **Founded:** 1956.

53906 ■ Union Chamber of Commerce (UCCC)
101 Bank St.
Union, MS 39365
Ph: (601)774-9586
Fax: (601)774-9586
Co. E-mail: unioncommerce@bellsouth.net
URL: http://www.unionms.com
Description: Promotes business and community development in Union, MS. **Founded:** 1962.

53907 ■ Vicksburg-Warren County Chamber of Commerce (VWCCC)
2020 Mission 66
Vicksburg, MS 39180
Ph: (601)636-1012
Fax: (601)636-4422
Co. E-mail: ckilroy@vicksburgchamber.org
URL: http://www.vicksburgchamber.org
Contact: Christi Kilroy, Executive Director
Description: Promotes business and community development in Vicksburg-Warren County, MS. **Founded:** 1894.

53908 ■ *The View*
200 E Main St.
Starkville, MS 39759
Ph: (662)323-3322
Free: 800-649-8687
Fax: (662)323-5815
Co. E-mail: info@starkville.org
URL: http://www.starkville.org
Contact: Melissa Dixon, Chairperson
Released: Quarterly

53909 ■ *Vision*
PO Box 194
Ridgeland, MS 39158-0194
Ph: (601)991-9996
Fax: (601)991-9997
Co. E-mail: admin@ridgelandchamber.com
URL: http://www.ridgelandchamber.com
Contact: Linda T. Bynum, Executive Director
Released: Quarterly

53910 ■ *Visitors Guide*
8700 Northwest Dr.
Southaven, MS 38671
Ph: (662)342-6114
Free: 800-272-6551
Fax: (662)342-6365
Co. E-mail: info@southavenchamber.com
URL: http://www.southavenchamber.com
Contact: Ryan England, President
Released: Annual

53911 ■ Walthall County Chamber of Commerce
PO Box 227
Tylertown, MS 39667
Ph: (601)876-2680
Co. E-mail: walthallchamber@bellsouth.net
URL: http://www.walthallcountychamber.org
Description: Promotes business and community development in Walthall County, MS.

53912 ■ *What's Happening*
PO Box 848
Greenwood, MS 38935-0848
Ph: (662)453-4152
Co. E-mail: info@greenwoodms.com
URL: http://www.greenwoodms.com/index.php
Contact: Beth Stevens, Executive Vice President
Released: Bimonthly

MINORITY BUSINESS ASSISTANCE PROGRAMS

53913 ■ City of Jackson Economic Development Division - Equal Business Opportunity
200 S President St., Rm. 223
Jackson, MS 39201
Ph: (601)960-1055
Fax: (601)960-2403
Co. E-mail: mdavis@city.jackson.ms.us
URL: http://www.jacksonms.gov/government/planning/ebo/
Contact: Mike Davis, Manager
Description: Provides assistance in the development of minority entrepreneurs.

53914 ■ Crudup-Ward Women's Business Center
PO Box 1113
Forest, MS 39074
Ph: (601)469-3357
Fax: (601)469-3357
Co. E-mail: anniewlowery@gmail.com
URL: http://cwainc.org
Contact: Annie Lowery, Executive Director
Description: Provides business information, counseling, management, and technical assistance to women looking to create or expand a business.

53915 ■ Mississippi Development Authority - Minority and Small Business Development Division
501 NW St.
Jackson, MS 39205
Ph: (601)359-3448
Fax: (601)359-5290
Co. E-mail: rcovington@mississippi.org
URL: http://www.mississippi.org
Contact: Bob Covington, Director
Description: Facilitates networking and industry partnerships for minority and women-owned businesses.

53916 ■ Mississippi Minority Business Enterprise Center
John S. and James L. Knight Nonprofit Center
11975 Seaway Rd., Ste. B231
Gulfport, MS 39503
Ph: (228)896-6868
Fax: (228)896-6870
Co. E-mail: info@msmbec.org
URL: http://www.msmbec.org
Contact: Michael Anderson, Director
Description: Provides business development services to minority enterprises, focusing on strategic growth businesses.

PROCUREMENT ASSISTANCE PROGRAMS

53917 ■ Mississippi Contract Procurement Center, Inc. - Delta Contract Procurement Center, Inc. (DCPC)
342 Washington Ave., 2nd Fl.
Greenville, MS 38702
Ph: (662)334-1518

Fax: (662)334-1598
Co. E-mail: dcpc2@suddenlinkmail.com
URL: http://www.mscpc.com
Contact: H.L. "Lee" Woodyard, Director
E-mail: dcpc@juno.com
Description: Assisting Mississippi businesses in obtaining federal, state, local government and commercial contracts.

53918 ■ Mississippi Contract Procurement Center, Inc. - Northeast Mississippi Contract Procurement Center, Inc. (NMCPC)
318 7th St. N
Columbus, MS 39703-1805
Ph: (662)329-1077
Fax: (662)327-6600
Co. E-mail: nmcpc@ebicom.net
URL: http://www.mscpc.com
Contact: Bill Burge, Director
Description: Assisting Mississippi businesses in obtaining federal, state, local government and commercial contracts.

53919 ■ Mississippi Contract Procurement Center, Inc. - South Mississippi Contract Procurement Center, Inc. (SMCPC)
1636 Popps Ferry Rd., Ste. 203
Biloxi, MS 39532
Ph: (228)396-1288
Fax: (228)396-2520
Co. E-mail: mcdowell@mscpc.com
URL: http://www.mscpc.com
Contact: Marcia McDowell, Director
Description: Provides information and direct assistance to firms wishing to do business with the federal government.

53920 ■ Mississippi Contract Procurement Technical Assistance Center, Inc. - East Central Procurement Center (ECCPC)
c/o Meridian Community College
910 Highway 19 N
Meridian, MS 39307
Ph: (601)482-7445
Fax: (601)482-5803
URL: http://www.mscpc.com
Contact: Bill Mabry, Director
Description: Enhances national defense and economic development of the state of Mississippi by assisting Mississippi businesses in obtaining federal, state, local government and commercial contracts serving Clarke, Covington, Jasper, Jones, Kemper, Lauderdale, Leake, Neshoba, Newton, Scott, Smith, and Wayne Counties.

53921 ■ Mississippi Contract Procurement Technical Center, Inc. - Central Mississippi Procurement Center, Inc. (CMPC)
c/o Mississippi Development Authority
501 North West St.
Jackson, MS 39201
Ph: (601)359-3485
Fax: (601)359-5290
Co. E-mail: jhatcher@mississippi.org
URL: http://www.mscpc.com
Contact: Johnithan Hatcher, Director
Description: Enhances national defense and economic development of the state of Mississippi by assisting Mississippi businesses in obtaining federal, state, local government and commercial contracts serving Adams, Claiborne, Copiah, Franklin, Hinds, Jefferson, Jefferson Davis, Lawrence, Lincoln, Madison, Rankin, Simpson, and Warren counties.

53922 ■ Mississippi Procurement Technical Assistance Program - Mississippi Development Authority
PO Box 849
Jackson, MS 39205
Ph: (601)359-3349
Fax: (601)359-2832
URL: http://www.mscpc.com
Contact: Carol Harris, Program Manager
E-mail: charris@mississippi.org

53923 ■ Mississippi Procurement Technical Assistance Program - Mississippi Development Authority - Minority and Small

Business Development Division (MSBDD)
PO Box 849
Jackson, MS 39205
Ph: (601)359-3449
Fax: (601)359-2832
URL: http://www.mscpc.com
Contact: Robert Covington, Deputy Director
Description: To enhance economic development of the state of Mississippi by assisting Mississippi businesses in obtaining federal, state, local government and commercial contracts.

53924 ■ South Mississippi Contract Procurement Center, Inc. (SMCPC)
1636 Popps Ferry Rd., Ste. 203
Biloxi, MS 39532
Ph: (228)396-1288
Fax: (228)396-2520
Co. E-mail: mcdowell@mscpc.com
URL: http://www.mscpc.com
Contact: Marcia McDowell, Director
Description: Enhances national defense and economic development of the state of Mississippi by assisting Mississippi businesses in obtaining federal, state, local government and commercial contracts serving Amite, Forrest, George, Greene, Hancock, Harrison, Jackson, Lamar, Marion, Pearl River, Perry, Pike, Stone, Walthall, Wilkinson.

INCUBATORS/RESEARCH AND TECHNOLOGY PARKS

53925 ■ Coahoma County Business Development Center
1540 DeSoto Ave.
Clarksdale, MS 38614
Ph: (662)627-7337
Fax: (662)627-1313
Co. E-mail: chamberofcommerce@clarksdale-ms.com
URL: http://www.clarksdale-ms.com/
Description: A small business incubator that assists entrepreneurs in the business start-up process and gives aid to new businesses to help ensure their survival.

53926 ■ Gulf Coast Innovation Center
1636 Popps Ferry Rd., Ste. 100
Biloxi, MS 39532
Ph: (228)392-9741

Fax: (228)392-9743
Co. E-mail: contact@innovatems.com
URL: http://www.gcbtc.org/
Contact: Stephen Whitt, Executive Director
Description: A small business incubator providing an atmosphere to encourage the development of small, start-up businesses and enable them to survive.

53927 ■ Jackson Enterprise Center
931 Hwy. 80 W
Jackson, MS 39204
Ph: (601)352-0957
Fax: (601)948-3250
Co. E-mail: leasing@jxnenterprise.com
URL: http://www.jxnenterprise.com
Contact: Fred LaRue, Director
Description: Provides facilities with shared services and networking opportunities for entrepreneurs.

53928 ■ Mississippi Action for Community Education, Inc. (MACE)
119 S Theobald St.
Greenville, MS 38701
Ph: (662)335-3523
Free: 888-812-5837
Fax: (662)334-2939
Co. E-mail: mace03@deltamace.org
URL: http://www.deltamace.org
Description: A non-profit minority, rural development organization Working to improve the economic situation of minorities and the poor.

53929 ■ Mississippi Enterprise for Technology
Bldg. 1103, Ste. 140
Stennis Space Center, MS 39529
Ph: (228)688-3372
Free: 800-746-4699
Fax: (228)688-1064
Co. E-mail: Charles.E.Beasley@nasa.gov
URL: http://www.mset.org/
Description: A small business incubator whose mission is to create, retain, and attract high-skill, high-wage jobs in Mississippi by assisting with the growth and development of young, technology-based companies.

53930 ■ Mississippi Technology Alliance
134 Market Ridge Dr.
Box 600
Ridgeland, MS 39157
Ph: (601)960-3610

Fax: (601)960-3605
Co. E-mail: tjeff@technologyalliance.ms
URL: http://www.technologyalliance.ms/index.php
Contact: Tony Jeff, Chief Executive Officer
Description: A non-profit, public-private partnership whose primary mission is to drive science and technology-based economic development efforts throughout the state, with the end goal being wealth creation through higher paying quality jobs; it focuses on creating wealth by leveraging research capacity and supporting technology business development for Mississippi companies.

53931 ■ North Mississippi Enterprise Initiative, Inc.
9 Industrial Park Dr., Ste. 104
Oxford, MS 38655
Ph: (662)281-0720
Co. E-mail: holly@northmiss.org
URL: http://www.northmiss.org/
Contact: Holly Kelly, Executive Director
Description: A non-profit, public/private regional partnership for entrepreneurial growth. It manages three business incubators - Oxford, Batesville and Grenada - and provides leadership in entrepreneurship within the region.

53932 ■ Renasant Center for IDEAs - Tupelo/Lee County Regional Business Incubator
300 W Main St.
Tupelo, MS 38804
Ph: (662)842-4521
Free: 800-523-3463
Fax: (662)841-0693
Co. E-mail: info@cdfms.org
URL: http://www.cdfms.org/renasant/?id=189
Description: A business incubator helping small businesses grow into global competitors, utilizing a suite of productive services and resources to help design, develop and distribute entrepreneurs and their business goals into the community and global economy.

PUBLICATIONS

53933 ■ *Smart Start your Florida Business*
PSI Research
300 N. Valley Dr.
Grants Pass, OR 97526
Ph: (503)479-9464
Free: 800-228-2275
Fax: (503)476-1479
Co. E-mail: info@psi-research.com
URL: http://www.psi-research.com
Ed: Carl R. Sniffen and Michael D. Jenkins. **Released:** Revised edition, 1992. **Price:** $29.95 (looseleaf binder); $24.95 (paper). **Description:** Part of the Successful Business Library series.

SMALL BUSINESS DEVELOPMENT CENTERS

53934 ■ **Missouri Small Business Development Center - Lead Office (MO SBDC)**
200 Engineering N
410 S 6th St.
Columbia, MO 65211
Ph: (573)884-1555
Fax: (578)884-4298
Co. E-mail: bouchardc@missouri.edu
URL: http://www.missouribusiness.net/sbdc/index.asp
Contact: Chris Bouchard, Director (Acting)

53935 ■ **Missouri Small Business Development Centers - Chillicothe**
715 Washington St.
Chillicothe, MO 64601
Ph: (660)646-6920
Fax: (660)646-6811
Co. E-mail: sbdchill@greenhills.net
URL: http://www.missouribusiness.net/sbdc/centers.asp
Contact: Steve Holt, Director
Description: Represents and promotes the small business sector. Provides management assistance to current and prospective small business owners. Helps to improve management skills and expand the products and services of members.

53936 ■ **Missouri Small Business Development Centers - Northwest Region**
423 N Market St.
Maryville, MO 64468
Ph: (660)562-1701
Fax: (660)582-3071
Co. E-mail: fveeman@nwmissouri.edu
URL: http://www.nwmorcog.org/REGION/sbdc.htm
Contact: Frank Veeman, Regional Director
Description: Represents and promotes the small business sector. Provides management assistance to current and prospective small business owners. Helps to improve management skills and expand the products and services of members.

53937 ■ **Missouri Small Business Development Centers - St. Joseph**
3003 Frederick Ave.
St. Joseph, MO 64506
Ph: (816)232-4461
Fax: (816)364-4873
Co. E-mail: evanssbdc@saintjoseph.com
URL: http://www.missouribusiness.net/sbdc/centers.asp
Contact: Rebecca Evans, Director
URL(s): www.missouri.edu/services/sbtdc. **Description:** Represents and promotes the small business sector. Provides management assistance to current and prospective small business owners. Helps to improve management skills and expand the products and services of members.

53938 ■ **Small Business Development Center - Southeast Missouri State University**
c/o Russell Humphrey
1 University Plz.
MS 0110
Cape Girardeau, MO 63701
Ph: (573)986-6084
Co. E-mail: rahumphrey@semo.edu
URL: http://www2.semo.edu/sesbdc/homepage.html
Description: Represents and promotes the small business sector. Provides management assistance to current and prospective small business owners. Helps to improve management skills and expand the products and services of members.

53939 ■ **Truman State University's Small Business Development Center**
c/o Charlene Boyes, Dir.
100 E Normal Ave.
Kirksville, MO 63501
Ph: (660)785-4307
Fax: (660)785-4357
Co. E-mail: sbdc@truman.edu
URL: http://sbdc.truman.edu
Contact: Charlene Boyes, Director
Description: Represents and promotes the small business sector. Provides management assistance to current and prospective small business owners. Helps to improve management skills and expand the products and services of members.

SMALL BUSINESS ASSISTANCE PROGRAMS

53940 ■ **Missouri Department of Economic Development - Division of Business and Community Services**
301 W. High St., Rms. 720, 770
Jefferson City, MO 65102
Ph: (866)647-3633
Free: 800-523-1434
Fax: (573)751-7384
Co. E-mail: missouridevelopment@ded.mo.gov
URL: http://www.missouridevelopment.org
Contact: Ann Pardalos, Director
Description: Provides assistance to international firms. Works to stimulate direct foreign investment in the state and develop export possibilities.

53941 ■ **University of Central Missouri - Small Business and Technology Development Center**
Dockery Ste. 102
Warrensburg, MO 64093
Ph: (660)543-4402
Fax: (660)543-8159
Co. E-mail: sbtdc@ucmo.edu
URL: http://www.ucmo.edu/sbtdc/
Contact: Wes Savage, Director
Description: Provides assistance to small business owners from start-up to operation processes.

53942 ■ **University of Missouri - Missouri Business Development Program**
W 1026 Lafferre Hall
410 S. Sixth St.
Columbia, MO 65211
Ph: (573)882-7096
Fax: (573)882-9931
Co. E-mail: wilsonv@missouri.edu
URL: http://www.missouribusiness.net
Description: Provides assistance to company officials and local community leaders in their efforts to retain existing jobs and create additional jobs through business expansion. Provides technical assistance and information. People wanting to start small business.

SCORE OFFICES

53943 ■ **Mid-Missouri SCORE**
Co. E-mail: info@midmoscore.org

53944 ■ **Ozark-Gateway SCORE**
Co. E-mail: score438@fid.net

53945 ■ **SCORE Kansas City**
Business Resource Center
4747 Troost Ave., Ste. 128
Kansas City, MO 64110
Ph: (816)235-6675
Fax: (816)235-6590
Co. E-mail: chapter19@scorekc.org
URL: http://kansascity.score.org
Contact: Marvin Weisharr, Chairman
Description: Provides consulting services to individuals wishing to start a new business or who have problems with established businesses. **Founded:** 1964.

53946 ■ **SCORE Lake Ozark**
739 W US Highway 54
Camdenton, MO 65020-6951
Ph: (573)346-5441
Fax: (573)346-3496
Co. E-mail: admin.0493@scorevolunteer.org
URL: http://www.lakeozarkscore.org
Contact: Larry N. Laminger, Chairman
URL(s): lakeoftheozarks.score.org/chapters/lake-ozarks. **Description:** Serves as volunteer program in which working and retired business management professionals provide free business counseling to men and women who are considering starting a small business, encountering problems with their business, or expanding their business. Offers free one-on-one counseling, online counseling and low cost workshops on a variety of business topics. **Founded:** 1981.

53947 ■ **SCORE St. Louis**
1222 Spruce St., Rm. 10.103
St. Louis, MO 63103-2831
Ph: (314)539-6600
Fax: (314)539-3785
Co. E-mail: email_score@stlscore.org
URL: http://www.stlscore.org
Contact: Sam Brown, Branch Manager
Description: Serves as volunteer program in which working and retired business management professionals provide free business counseling to men and

women who are considering starting a small business, encountering problems with their business, or expanding their business. Offers free one-on-one counseling, online counseling and low cost workshops on a variety of business topics. **Founded:** 1965.

53948 ■ SCORE Springfield
830 E Primrose, Ste. 101
Springfield, MO 65809
Ph: (417)890-8501
Fax: (417)889-0074
Co. E-mail: springfieldscore@sbcglobal.net
URL: http://www.springfieldscore.org
Contact: John Fleming, Chairman
Description: Serves as volunteer program in which working and retired business management professionals provide free business counseling to men and women who are considering starting a small business, encountering problems with their business, or expanding their business. Offers free one-on-one counseling, online counseling and low cost workshops on a variety of business topics. **Founded:** 1974.

53949 ■ Southeast Missouri SCORE
Co. E-mail: jbuckenmyer@sbcglobal.net

BETTER BUSINESS BUREAUS

53950 ■ Better Business Bureau of Eastern Missouri and Southern Illinois
15 Sunnen Dr., Ste. 107
St. Louis, MO 63143-1400
Ph: (314)645-3300
Co. E-mail: bbb@stlouisbbb.org
URL: http://stlouis.bbb.org
Contact: Michelle L. Corey, President
Description: Seeks to promote and foster ethical relationship between businesses and the public through voluntary self-regulation, consumer and business education, and service excellence. Provides information to help consumers and businesses make informed purchasing decisions and avoid costly scams and frauds; settles consumer complaints through arbitration and other means.

53951 ■ Better Business Bureau of Greater Kansas City
8080 Ward Pkwy., Ste. 401
Kansas City, MO 64114
Ph: (816)421-7800
Fax: (816)472-5442
Co. E-mail: info@kansascity.bbb.org
URL: http://www.kansascity.bbb.org
Contact: David Buckley, President
Description: Seeks to promote and foster the highest ethical relationship between businesses and the public through voluntary self-regulation, consumer and business education, and service excellence. Provides information to help consumers and businesses make informed purchasing decisions and avoid costly scams and frauds; settles consumer complaints through arbitration and other means.

53952 ■ Better Business Bureau of Southwest Missouri
430 S Glenstone Ave., Ste. A
Springfield, MO 65802
Ph: (417)862-4222
Fax: (417)869-5544
Co. E-mail: info@southwestmissouri.bbb.org
URL: http://southwestmissouri.bbb.org
Contact: Ms. Judy R. Mills, President
Description: Seeks to promote and foster the highest ethical relationship between businesses and the public through voluntary self-regulation, consumer and business education, and service excellence. Provides information to help consumers and businesses make informed purchasing decisions and avoid costly scams and frauds; settles consumer complaints through arbitration and other means.

CHAMBERS OF COMMERCE

53953 ■ *21st Century Update*
3003 Frederick Ave.
St. Joseph, MO 64506
Ph: (816)232-4461
Free: 800-748-7856

Fax: (816)364-4873
Co. E-mail: chamber@saintjoseph.com
URL: http://www.saintjoseph.com
Contact: Ted Allison, President
Released: Quarterly

53954 ■ *Affton Business Connection*
10203 Gravois Rd.
Affton, MO 63123-4029
Ph: (314)849-6499
Fax: (314)849-6399
Co. E-mail: info@afftonchamber.com
URL: http://www.afftonchamber.com
Contact: Ms. Joan Edleson, Executive Director
Released: Monthly **Price:** $15; included in membership dues.

53955 ■ Affton Chamber of Commerce
10203 Gravois Rd.
Affton, MO 63123-4029
Ph: (314)849-6499
Fax: (314)849-6399
Co. E-mail: info@afftonchamber.com
URL: http://www.afftonchamber.com
Contact: Ms. Joan Edleson, Executive Director
Description: Strives to advance the commercial, industrial, and general interests of Affton and its adjacent territory. Promotes trade, industry, and public welfare in the community. **Scope:** community information, 63123 appraised values, land use, building ages. **Founded:** 1947. **Subscriptions:** maps. **Publications:** *Affton Business Connection* (Monthly). **Educational Activities:** Affton Chamber of Commerce Meeting (Monthly). **Awards:** Business Person of the Year (Annual); Citizen of the Year (Annual).

53956 ■ Arnold Chamber of Commerce
1838 Old Lemay Ferry Rd.
Arnold, MO 63010
Ph: (636)296-1910
Fax: (636)555-5555
URL: http://www.arnoldchamber.org
Contact: Mr. Bob Gruenewald, President
Description: Promotes business and community development in Arnold, MO.

53957 ■ Aurora Chamber of Commerce
PO Box 257
Aurora, MO 65605-1666
Ph: (417)678-4150
Fax: (417)678-1387
Co. E-mail: auroracoc@mo-net.com
URL: http://www.auroramochamber.com
Description: Promotes business and community development in Aurora, MO. Sponsors Youth Basketball Tournament, Business Expo, Ye Olde Mining Days, Golf Tournament, Car and Truck Show, Radio Auction, Miss Holly Pageant, Christmas Parade and Santa Train. **Founded:** 1939. **Publications:** *Chamber Communique* (Monthly). **Educational Activities:** Christmas Parade (Annual).

53958 ■ Ava Area Chamber of Commerce (AACC)
PO Box 1103
Ava, MO 65608
Ph: (417)683-4594
Fax: (417)683-9464
Co. E-mail: director@avachamber.org
URL: http://avachamber.org
Contact: Judy Shields, Executive Director
Description: Promotes business and community development in the Ava, MO area. Supports local community projects. Sponsors Poke Salate Days, Glade Top Trail, Christmas Parade, and local contests. **Founded:** 1942. **Publications:** *Community Service Directory* (Periodic).

53959 ■ Barton County Chamber of Commerce
PO Box 577
Lamar, MO 64759
Ph: (417)682-3595

Fax: (417)682-9566
Co. E-mail: nancy@bartoncounty.com
URL: http://www.bartoncounty.com
Contact: Nancy Curless, Executive Director
Description: Promotes business and community development in Lamar and Barton County, MO. **Awards:** Business of the Year (Annual); Educator of the Year (Annual); Employee of the Year (Annual); Truman Award (Annual); Volunteer Spirit of the Year (Annual).

53960 ■ Belton Chamber of Commerce (BCOC)
323 Main St.
Belton, MO 64012-0350
Ph: (816)331-2420
Fax: (816)331-8736
Co. E-mail: chamber@beltonmochamber.com
URL: http://www.beltonmochamber.com/joomla/index.php
Contact: Jeff Fletcher, President
Description: Businesses and individuals in Belton, MO organized to encourage a strong local economy and quality of life by promoting sound government and an informed membership and community. **Awards:** Business Person of the Year (Annual).

53961 ■ Black Chamber of Commerce of Greater Kansas City (BCCGKC)
1501 E 18th St.
Kansas City, MO 64108
Ph: (816)474-9901
Fax: (816)842-1748
URL: http://www.bcckc.org
Description: Seeks to provide leadership in promoting African American businesses and those termed "small and disadvantaged" by federal and local agencies; to act as an advocate for those issues peculiar to the preservation and enhancement of those businesses and their affect on the community as a whole; and to promote and encourage entrepreneurial development in the area. Conducts seminars, management/marketing training, business development, annual trade show and other membership activities. **Founded:** 1984.

53962 ■ Blue Springs Chamber of Commerce
1000 SW Main St.
Blue Springs, MO 64015
Ph: (816)229-8558
Fax: (816)229-1244
Co. E-mail: bschamberinfo@bluespringschamber.com
URL: http://www.bluespringschamber.com
Contact: Lara Vermillion, President
Description: Promotes business and community development in Blue Springs, MO. **Publications:** *Directory and New Resident Guide* (Annual); *New Resident Information*. **Educational Activities:** Fall Fun (Annual).

53963 ■ *Bluff Business Bulletin*
1111 W Pine St.
Poplar Bluff, MO 63901
Ph: (573)785-7761
Fax: (573)785-1901
Co. E-mail: info@poplarbluffchamber.org
URL: http://www.poplarbluffchamber.org
Contact: Steve Halter, President
Released: Monthly

53964 ■ Bolivar Area Chamber of Commerce (BACC)
PO Box 202
Bolivar, MO 65613-0202
Ph: (417)326-4118
Fax: (417)777-9080
Co. E-mail: bolchamb@windstream.net
URL: http://bolivarchamber.com/index.html
Contact: Brenda Harris, President
Description: Promotes business and community development in the Bolivar, MO area. Sponsors annual Country Days, Chicken BBQ, Christmas parade and St. Patrick's Day Auction. **Founded:** 1977. **Publications:** *Chamber Newsletter* (Monthly); *Community Profile*; *Bolivar Area Chamber of Commerce Visitor's Guide and Membership Directory* (Annual).

53965 ■ *Bolivar Area Chamber of Commerce Visitor's Guide and Membership Directory*
PO Box 202
Bolivar, MO 65613-0202
Ph: (417)326-4118
Fax: (417)777-9080
Co. E-mail: bolchamb@windstream.net
URL: http://bolivarchamber.com/index.html
Contact: Brenda Harris, President
Released: Annual **Price:** free.

53966 ■ **Bowling Green Chamber of Commerce**
PO Box 401
Bowling Green, MO 63334-0401
Ph: (573)324-3733
Fax: (573)324-0152
Co. E-mail: bgmocc@att.net
URL: http://www.bgchamber.org
Contact: Elizabeth Kingsley, President
Description: Promotes business and community development in Bowling Green, MO.

53967 ■ **Branson - Lakes Area Chamber of Commerce (BLACC)**
PO Box 1897
Branson, MO 65615
Ph: (417)334-4084
Free: 800-214-3661
Fax: (417)334-4139
Co. E-mail: rsummers@bransoncvb.com
URL: http://www.explorebranson.com
Contact: Ross Summers, President
Description: Promotes business, tourism, and community development in the Branson/Lakes, MO area. **Founded:** 1944. **Publications:** *Keynotes* (Periodic); *The Source* (Monthly); *Slip Away to Branson.* **Awards:** Small Business of the Year Award (Annual).

53968 ■ **Brookfield Area Chamber of Commerce**
101 S Main St.
Brookfield, MO 64628
Ph: (660)258-7255
Fax: (660)258-7255
Co. E-mail: chamber@brookfieldmochamber.com
URL: http://www.brookfieldmochamber.com
Contact: Paul Frey, Executive Director
Description: Promotes and protects the commercial, professional, financial, and general business interests of the City of Brookfield, MO.

53969 ■ **Buckner Chamber of Commerce**
PO Box 287
Buckner, MO 64016
Ph: (816)650-5535
Co. E-mail: sibleyorchards@hotmail.com
URL: http://www.discoverynet.com/~ajsnead/my-comm/chamber.html
Contact: Patrick J. Farrell, President
URL(s): www.ajsmidi.com/mycomm/chamber.html.
Description: Promotes business and community development in Buckner, MO.

53970 ■ **Buffalo Area Chamber of Commerce**
101 N Maple St.
Buffalo, MO 65622
Ph: (417)345-2852
Free: 800-483-5000
Fax: (417)345-2852
Co. E-mail: chamber@buffalococ.com
URL: http://www.buffalococ.com
Contact: Kathy Kesler, Executive Director
Description: Strives to improve and enhance the commercial, industrial, and civic interests of Buffalo, Missouri and its trade area. **Founded:** 1841. **Publications:** *The Members' Messenger* (Monthly).

53971 ■ *Business Barometer*
3003 Frederick Ave.
St. Joseph, MO 64506
Ph: (816)232-4461
Free: 800-748-7856
Fax: (816)364-4873
Co. E-mail: chamber@saintjoseph.com
URL: http://www.saintjoseph.com
Contact: Ted Allison, President
Released: Quarterly **Price:** $15, /year for members.

53972 ■ *Business to Business*
964 S Highway Dr., Ste. 103
Fenton, MO 63026
Ph: (636)717-0200
Fax: (636)717-0214
Co. E-mail: exdir@fentonmochamber.com
URL: http://www.fentonmochamber.com
Contact: Dale Roethemeyer, President
Released: Monthly

53973 ■ *Business and Community*
108 W Adams
Kirkwood, MO 63122
Ph: (314)821-4161
Fax: (314)821-5229
Co. E-mail: jim@thechamber.us
URL: http://www.kirkwooddesperes.com
Contact: Jim Wright, President
Released: Annual

53974 ■ *Business and Community Guide*
357 Marshall Ave., Ste. A
Webster Groves, MO 63119
Ph: (314)962-4142
Fax: (314)962-9398
Co. E-mail: chamberinfo@go-webster.com
URL: http://www.webstershrewsburychamber.com
Contact: Rebecca Olson, President
Released: Annual

53975 ■ *Business Connection*
PO Box 1375
Camdenton, MO 65020-1375
Ph: (573)346-2227
Free: 800-769-1004
Fax: (573)346-3496
Co. E-mail: info@camdentonchamber.com
URL: http://www.camdentonchamber.com
Contact: Trish Creach, Executive Director
Released: Monthly **Price:** free for members; $5, for nonmembers.

53976 ■ *Business Intelligence Report*
3003 Frederick Ave.
St. Joseph, MO 64506
Ph: (816)232-4461
Free: 800-748-7856
Fax: (816)364-4873
Co. E-mail: chamber@saintjoseph.com
URL: http://www.saintjoseph.com
Contact: Ted Allison, President
Released: Monthly

53977 ■ *Business Outlook*
320 E 4th St.
Joplin, MO 64801
Ph: (417)624-4150
Fax: (417)624-4303
Co. E-mail: info@joplincc.com
URL: http://www.joplincc.com
Contact: Rob O'Brian, President
Released: Monthly

53978 ■ *Buyer's Guide and Membership Directory*
15965 Manchester Rd., Ste. 102
Ellisville, MO 63011
Ph: (636)230-9900
Fax: (636)230-9912
URL: http://www.westcountychamber.com
Contact: Lori Kelling, President
Released: Annual

53979 ■ *Calendar of Events*
200 S Main St.
Clinton, MO 64735
Ph: (660)885-8166
Free: 800-222-5251
Fax: (660)885-8168
Co. E-mail: debby@clintonmo.com
URL: http://www.clintonmo.com/ChamberofCommerce/tabid/55/Default.aspx
Contact: Craig Thompson, President

53980 ■ **California Chamber of Commerce**
PO Box 85
California, MO 65018
Ph: (573)796-3040

Fax: (573)796-8309
Co. E-mail: office@calmo.com
URL: http://www.calmo.com
Contact: Diane Eulinger, Executive Secretary
Description: Promotes business and community development in California, MO. Sponsors Ozark Ham and Turkey Festival.

53981 ■ **Camdenton Area Chamber of Commerce (CACC)**
PO Box 1375
Camdenton, MO 65020-1375
Ph: (573)346-2227
Free: 800-769-1004
Fax: (573)346-3496
Co. E-mail: info@camdentonchamber.com
URL: http://www.camdentonchamber.com
Contact: Trish Creach, Executive Director
Description: Promotes business and community development in the Camdenton, MO area. Sponsors festivals, products and services trade show. Promotes tourism. **Founded:** 1946. **Publications:** *Business Connection* (Monthly).

53982 ■ **Cameron Chamber of Commerce**
205 N Main St.
Cameron, MO 64429
Ph: (816)632-2005
Fax: (816)632-2005
Co. E-mail: office@cameronmochamber.com
URL: http://www.cameronmochamber.com/about.htm
Contact: Michelle Fagerstone, Executive Director
Description: Enhances human and economic resources. **Founded:** 1929.

53983 ■ **Cape Girardeau Area Chamber of Commerce**
1267 N Mt. Auburn Rd.
Cape Girardeau, MO 63701
Ph: (573)335-3312
Fax: (573)335-4686
Co. E-mail: info@capechamber.com
URL: http://www.capechamber.com
Contact: John E. Mehner, President
Description: Promotes business and community development in Cape Girardeau, MO. **Founded:** 1917. **Telecommunication Services:** jmehner@capechamber.com.

53984 ■ **Carrollton Chamber of Commerce**
111 N Mason
Carrollton, MO 64633
Ph: (660)542-0922
Fax: (660)542-3489
Co. E-mail: director@carrolltonareachamber.org
URL: http://carrolltonareachamber.org
Contact: Sharon Metz, Executive Director
Description: Promotes business and community development in the Carrollton, MO area. **Founded:** 1912.

53985 ■ **Carthage Chamber of Commerce (CCC)**
402 S Garrison Ave.
Carthage, MO 64836
Ph: (417)358-2373
Fax: (417)358-7479
Co. E-mail: info@carthagechamber.com
URL: http://www.carthagechamber.com
Contact: Mark J. Elliff, President
Description: Promotes business, community development, and tourism in Carthage, MO. **Founded:** 1932. **Publications:** *Spotlight on Carthage* (Monthly).

53986 ■ **Cassville Area Chamber of Commerce**
504 Main St.
Cassville, MO 65625-1418
Ph: (417)847-2814
Co. E-mail: chamber@cassville.com
URL: http://www.cassville.com
Description: Promotes business and community development in Cassville, MO. Conducts annual music/variety show, Christmas parade, semi-annual Trout Derby, industrial golf tournament, and car show.

53987 ■ Centralia Area Chamber of Commerce (CACC)
PO Box 235
Centralia, MO 65240
Ph: (573)682-2272
Fax: (573)682-1111
Co. E-mail: ginny@midamerica.net
URL: http://www.centraliamochamber.com
Contact: Amanda Dawson, President
Description: Promotes business and community development in the Centralia, MO area. Sponsors Anchor Festival. **Founded:** 1939.

53988 ■ Chaffee Chamber of Commerce (CCC)
c/o Pete Dooley, Pres.
State Farm Insurance
231 W Yoakum
Chaffee, MO 63740
Ph: (573)887-3691
Fax: (573)887-4049
Co. E-mail: information@chaffeechamber.com
URL: http://spicecat.com/chaffee_chamber
Contact: Pete Dooley, President
Description: Promotes business and community development in northern Scott County, MO. Sponsors nutrition program.

53989 ■ Chamber Advantage
108 W Adams
Kirkwood, MO 63122
Ph: (314)821-4161
Fax: (314)821-5229
Co. E-mail: jim@thechamber.us
URL: http://www.kirkwooddesperes.com
Contact: Jim Wright, President
Released: Monthly

53990 ■ Chamber Business Line
PO Box 1016
Columbia, MO 65205-1016
Ph: (573)874-1132
Fax: (573)443-3986
Co. E-mail: admin@columbiamochamber.com
URL: http://www.columbiamochamber.com
Contact: Don Laird, President
Released: 11/year

53991 ■ Chamber Chat
16075 Hwy. 160
Forsyth, MO 65653
Ph: (417)546-2741
Co. E-mail: info@forsythmissouri.org
URL: http://forsythmissouri.org
Contact: Bill Bassett, Executive Director
Released: Bimonthly

53992 ■ Chamber Chatter
117 W Booneslick Rd.
Warrenton, MO 63383
Ph: (636)456-2530
Fax: (636)456-2329
Co. E-mail: info@warrentoncoc.com
URL: http://warrentoncoc.com
Contact: Ruth Ebbinghaus, President

53993 ■ Chamber Chronicle
357 Marshall Ave., Ste. A
Webster Groves, MO 63119
Ph: (314)962-4142
Fax: (314)962-9398
Co. E-mail: chamberinfo@go-webster.com
URL: http://www.webstershrewsburychamber.com
Contact: Rebecca Olson, President
Released: Monthly

53994 ■ Chamber Chronicle
PO Box 776
Jefferson City, MO 65101
Ph: (573)634-3616
Fax: (573)634-3805
Co. E-mail: info@jcchamber.org
URL: http://www.jcchamber.org
Contact: Bob Scruggs, Chairman
Released: Bimonthly

53995 ■ Chamber Communique
PO Box 257
Aurora, MO 65605-1666

Ph: (417)678-4150
Fax: (417)678-1387
Co. E-mail: auroracoc@mo-net.com
URL: http://www.auroramochamber.com
Released: Monthly

53996 ■ Chamber Connection
514 Washington St.
Chillicothe, MO 64601
Ph: (660)646-4050
Free: 877-C-CHILLI
Fax: (660)646-3309
Co. E-mail: chamber@chillicothemo.com
URL: http://www.chillicothemo.com
Contact: Kent Peterson, President
Released: Monthly

53997 ■ Chamber Connection
PO Box 632
Excelsior Springs, MO 64024
Ph: (816)630-6161
Co. E-mail: info@exspgschamber.com
URL: http://www.exspgschamber.com
Contact: Mr. Terry Smelcer, Executive Director

53998 ■ Chamber Connection
PO Box 1450
Ozark, MO 65721
Ph: (417)581-6139
Fax: (417)581-0639
Co. E-mail: info@ozarkchamber.com
URL: http://www.ozarkchamber.com
Contact: Dori Grinder, Executive Director
Released: Monthly **Price:** free for members.

53999 ■ Chamber Connections
225 W Austin, Ste. 200
Nevada, MO 64772
Ph: (417)667-5300
Fax: (417)667-3492
Co. E-mail: chamber1@nevada-mo.com
URL: http://www.nevada-mo.com
Contact: Cat McGrath-Farmer, Director
Released: Quarterly

54000 ■ Chamber Directory
1311 Kingshighway St.
Rolla, MO 65401
Ph: (573)364-3577
Free: 888-809-3817
Fax: (573)364-5222
Co. E-mail: rollavc@rollachamber.org
URL: http://www.rollachamber.org
Contact: Stevie Kearse, Executive Director
Released: Annual

54001 ■ Chamber Flash
108 W Adams
Kirkwood, MO 63122
Ph: (314)821-4161
Fax: (314)821-5229
Co. E-mail: jim@thechamber.us
URL: http://www.kirkwooddesperes.com
Contact: Jim Wright, President
Released: Monthly

54002 ■ Chamber Membership
5909 Raytown Trafficway
Raytown, MO 64133-3860
Ph: (816)353-8500
Fax: (816)353-8525
URL: http://raytownchamber.com
Contact: Vicki A. Turnbow, President
Released: Annual **Price:** $10.

54003 ■ The Chamber News
1170 W Kansas St., Ste. H
Liberty, MO 64068
Ph: (816)781-5200
Fax: (816)781-4901
Co. E-mail: info@libertychamber.com
URL: http://www.libertychamber.com
Contact: Gayle Potter, President
Released: Monthly **Price:** included in membership dues.

54004 ■ Chamber News
5 Municipal Dr.
Park Hills, MO 63601-2064

Ph: (573)431-1051
Fax: (573)431-2327
Co. E-mail: phlcoc@sbcglobal.net
URL: http://www.phlcoc.net
Contact: Tamara Coleman, Executive Director
Released: Monthly **Price:** free for members.

54005 ■ Chamber News
PO Box 1077
Independence, MO 64051
Ph: (816)252-4745
Fax: (816)252-4917
Co. E-mail: jhobbs@independencechamber.org
URL: http://www.independencechamber.com
Contact: Teresa Freeland, President
Released: Monthly

54006 ■ Chamber News
1029 Franklin Ave.
Lexington, MO 64067
Ph: (660)259-3082
Fax: (660)259-7776
Co. E-mail: chamber@historiclexington.com
URL: http://www.historiclexington.com
Contact: Penny Grosso, Executive Director
Released: Quarterly

54007 ■ Chamber News
1311 Kingshighway St.
Rolla, MO 65401
Ph: (573)364-3577
Free: 888-809-3817
Fax: (573)364-5222
Co. E-mail: rollavc@rollachamber.org
URL: http://www.rollachamber.org
Contact: Stevie Kearse, Executive Director
Released: Monthly **Price:** free.

54008 ■ Chamber News
11965 St. Charles Rock Rd., Ste. 203
Bridgeton, MO 63044
Ph: (314)291-2131
Fax: (314)291-2153
Co. E-mail: info@northwestchamber.com
URL: http://www.northwestchamber.com/index.php
Contact: Jerry Hart, President
Released: Monthly

54009 ■ Chamber Newsletter
PO Box 202
Bolivar, MO 65613-0202
Ph: (417)326-4118
Fax: (417)777-9080
Co. E-mail: bolchamb@windstream.net
URL: http://bolivarchamber.com/index.html
Contact: Brenda Harris, President
Released: Monthly

54010 ■ Chamber Report
1236 Jungermann Rd., Ste. C
St. Peters, MO 63376
Ph: (636)447-3336
Fax: (636)447-9575
Co. E-mail: info@stpeterschamber.com
URL: http://www.stpeterschamber.com/home/index.html
Contact: Ed Weeks, President
Released: Monthly **Price:** free for members.

54011 ■ Chamber Update
200 S Main St.
Clinton, MO 64735
Ph: (660)885-8166
Free: 800-222-5251
Fax: (660)885-8168
Co. E-mail: debby@clintonmo.com
URL: http://www.clintonmo.com/ChamberofCommerce/tabid/55/Default.aspx
Contact: Craig Thompson, President
Released: Weekly

54012 ■ Charleston Chamber of Commerce
110 E Commercial St.
Charleston, MO 63834
Ph: (573)683-6509

Fax: (573)683-6799
Co. E-mail: chamber@charlestonmo.org
URL: http://www.charlestonmo.org/chamber
Description: Promotes business and community development in Charleston, MO.

54013 ■ Chesterfield Chamber of Commerce (CCC)
101 Chesterfield Business Pkwy.
Chesterfield, MO 63005
Ph: (636)532-3399
Free: 888-242-4262
Fax: (636)532-7446
Co. E-mail: info@chesterfieldmochamber.com
URL: http://www.chesterfieldmochamber.com
Contact: Jennifer Hill, Chairperson
Description: Promotes business and community development in Chesterfield, MO. **Founded:** 1976. **Publications:** *Out and About* (Bimonthly). **Educational Activities:** Golf Tournament (Annual).

54014 ■ Chillicothe Area Chamber of Commerce (CACC)
514 Washington St.
Chillicothe, MO 64601
Ph: (660)646-4050
Free: 877-C-CHILLI
Fax: (660)646-3309
Co. E-mail: chamber@chillicothemo.com
URL: http://www.chillicothemo.com
Contact: Kent Peterson, President
Description: Promotes business and community development in the Chillicothe, MO area. **Founded:** 1855. **Publications:** *Chamber Connection* (Monthly). **Educational Activities:** Boofest (Annual). **Awards:** Agriculture Award (Annual); Outstanding Business Community Service Award (Annual). **Telecommunication Services:** office@chillicothemo.com.

54015 ■ *The City Haller*
2600 Commerce Tower
Kansas City, MO 64105
Ph: (816)221-2424
Fax: (816)221-7440
Co. E-mail: info@kcchamber.com
URL: http://www.kcchamber.com
Contact: James A. Heeter, President
Released: Weekly

54016 ■ Clayton Chamber of Commerce (CCC)
225 S Meramec Ave., Ste. 300
Clayton, MO 63105
Ph: (314)726-3033
Fax: (314)726-0637
Co. E-mail: ccc@claytoncommerce.com
URL: http://www.claytoncommerce.com
Contact: Ellen M. Gale, Executive Director
Description: Promotes business and community development in Clayton, MO. **Founded:** 1952. **Telecommunication Services:** egale@claytoncommerce.com.

54017 ■ *Clinton*
200 S Main St.
Clinton, MO 64735
Ph: (660)885-8166
Free: 800-222-5251
Fax: (660)885-8168
Co. E-mail: debby@clintonmo.com
URL: http://www.clintonmo.com/ChamberofCommerce/tabid/55/Default.aspx
Contact: Craig Thompson, President

54018 ■ Clinton Area Chamber of Commerce
200 S Main St.
Clinton, MO 64735
Ph: (660)885-8166
Free: 800-222-5251
Fax: (660)885-8168
Co. E-mail: debby@clintonmo.com
URL: http://www.clintonmo.com/ChamberofCommerce/tabid/55/Default.aspx
Contact: Craig Thompson, President
Description: Promotes business and community development and tourism in Benton, Henry, and St. Clair counties, MO. **Founded:** 1935. **Publications:** *Calendar of Events*; *Chamber Update* (Weekly); *Clin-*

ton; Spirit. **Educational Activities:** Arts Council (Monthly); Missouri Travel Council (Annual). **Awards:** Academic Excellence Award (Annual); Academic Excellence Scholarship (Periodic); Ag Scholarship (Periodic).

54019 ■ Columbia Chamber of Commerce (CCC)
PO Box 1016
Columbia, MO 65205-1016
Ph: (573)874-1132
Fax: (573)443-3986
Co. E-mail: admin@columbiamochamber.com
URL: http://www.columbiamochamber.com
Contact: Don Laird, President
Description: Promotes business and community development in Columbia, MO. **Founded:** 1905. **Publications:** *Chamber Business Line* (11/year). **Educational Activities:** Agricultural Recognition Banquet (Annual). **Telecommunication Services:** dlaird@columbiamochamber.com.

54020 ■ *Communicator*
323 W Main St.
Washington, MO 63090
Ph: (636)239-2715
Free: 888-7-WASHMO
URL: http://www.washmo.org/chamber/chamber.php
Contact: Mark Wessels, President
Released: Periodic **Price:** free.

54021 ■ *Community Guide*
964 S Highway Dr., Ste. 103
Fenton, MO 63026
Ph: (636)717-0200
Fax: (636)717-0214
Co. E-mail: exdir@fentonmochamber.com
URL: http://www.fentonmochamber.com
Contact: Dale Roethemeyer, President
Released: Annual

54022 ■ *Community Profile*
PO Box 202
Bolivar, MO 65613-0202
Ph: (417)326-4118
Fax: (417)777-9080
Co. E-mail: bolchamb@windstream.net
URL: http://bolivarchamber.com/index.html
Contact: Brenda Harris, President

54023 ■ *Community Service Directory*
PO Box 1103
Ava, MO 65608
Ph: (417)683-4594
Fax: (417)683-9464
Co. E-mail: director@avachamber.org
URL: http://avachamber.org
Contact: Judy Shields, Executive Director
Released: Periodic

54024 ■ Concordia Chamber of Commerce
802 S Gordon St.
Concordia, MO 64020
Ph: (660)463-2454
Co. E-mail: concordiachamber@centurytel.net
URL: http://www.concordiamo.com
Description: Promotes business and community development in Concordia, MO area.

54025 ■ *Connections*
2145 Bryan Valley Commercial
O'Fallon, MO 63366-3496
Ph: (636)240-1818
Co. E-mail: cindy@qcater.com
URL: http://www.ofallonchamber.org
Contact: Erin Williams, President
Released: Monthly

54026 ■ *Connections*
3003 Frederick Ave.
St. Joseph, MO 64506
Ph: (816)232-4461
Free: 800-748-7856
Fax: (816)364-4873
Co. E-mail: chamber@saintjoseph.com
URL: http://www.saintjoseph.com
Contact: Ted Allison, President
Released: Monthly

54027 ■ Crane Area Chamber of Commerce
PO Box 287
Crane, MO 65633
Ph: (417)425-0721
Co. E-mail: cranechamber@aol.com
URL: http://www.cranemo.com
Description: Promotes business and community development in Crane, MO.

54028 ■ Creve Coeur - Olivette Chamber of Commerce (OCC)
10950 Olive Blvd., Ste. 101
Creve Coeur, MO 63141
Ph: (314)569-3536
Fax: (314)569-3073
Co. E-mail: info@ccochamber.com
URL: http://www.ccochamber.com
Contact: Nancy Gray, Executive Vice President
Description: Promotes economic development in Creve Coeur and Olivette, MO. Convention/Meeting: none. **Scope:** community map, quality of life brochures. **Founded:** 1970. **Publications:** *Quality of Life Magazine* (Periodic). **Awards:** C Flag We Can - We Care; Presidential Award for Initiatives from the Private Sector.

54029 ■ *Crossroads Connection*
5909 Raytown Trafficway
Raytown, MO 64133-3860
Ph: (816)353-8500
Fax: (816)353-8525
URL: http://raytownchamber.com
Contact: Vicki A. Turnbow, President
Released: Monthly

54030 ■ Cuba Chamber of Commerce and Visitor Center
PO Box 405
Cuba, MO 65453
Ph: (573)885-2531
Free: 877-212-8429
Co. E-mail: cuba@misn.com
URL: http://cubamochamber.com/chamber-of-commerce
Contact: Tina Hannan, President
Description: Promotes business and community development in the Cuba, MO area. **Founded:** 1953. **Awards:** Beautification Award (Annual); Citizen of the Year (Annual); Entrepreneur Award (Annual); Rookie Award (Annual); Youth in the Spotlight (Annual).

54031 ■ Desloge Chamber of Commerce
207 N Desloge Dr.
Desloge, MO 63601-3533
Ph: (573)431-3006
Fax: (573)431-3006
Co. E-mail: deslogechamber@sbcglobal.net
URL: http://www.deslogechamber.com
Description: Promotes business and community development in Desloge, MO.

54032 ■ Dexter Chamber of Commerce (DCC)
PO Box 21
Dexter, MO 63841
Ph: (573)624-7458
Free: 800-332-8857
Fax: (573)624-7459
Co. E-mail: info@dexterchamber.com
URL: http://www.dexterchamber.com
Contact: Janet Coleman, Executive Director
Description: Promotes business, industrial, and community development in Dexter, MO. **Founded:** 1947. **Awards:** Business of the Year (Annual); Man of the Year (Annual); Organization of the Year (Annual); Woman of the Year (Annual).

54033 ■ *Directory and New Resident Guide*
1000 SW Main St.
Blue Springs, MO 64015
Ph: (816)229-8558
Fax: (816)229-1244
Co. E-mail: bschamberinfo@bluespringschamber.com
URL: http://www.bluespringschamber.com
Contact: Lara Vermillion, President
Released: Annual

54034 ■ East Prairie Chamber of Commerce
106 S Washington
East Prairie, MO 63845
Ph: (573)649-5243
Co. E-mail: bmainord@mrmagservices.com
URL: http://www.eastprairiemo.net
Contact: Bryan Mainord, President
Description: Promotes business and community development in the East Prairie, MO area.

54035 ■ *Economic Forecast*
2600 Commerce Tower
Kansas City, MO 64105
Ph: (816)221-2424
Fax: (816)221-7440
Co. E-mail: info@kcchamber.com
URL: http://www.kcchamber.com
Contact: James A. Heeter, President
Price: free for members; $25, for nonmembers.

54036 ■ El Dorado Springs Chamber of Commerce
1303 S Hwy. 32
El Dorado Springs, MO 64744-2302
Ph: (417)876-4154
Fax: (417)876-4154
Co. E-mail: info@cofc-eldo.org
URL: http://www.eldomo-cofc.org
Contact: Tiffany McGuirk, Executive Director
Description: Promotes business and community development in El Dorado Springs, MO. **Founded:** 1955. **Awards:** Chamber Business of the Year (Annual); Citizen of the Year (Annual); Executive Board Service Award (Annual); Hall of Fame (Annual); Club Group or Organization of the Year (Annual); Local Chamber of Commerce Member of the Year (Annual).

54037 ■ Eldon Chamber of Commerce (ECC)
203 E 1st St.
Eldon, MO 65026
Ph: (573)392-3752
Fax: (573)392-0634
Co. E-mail: eldoninfo@eldonchamber.com
URL: http://www.eldonchamber.com
Contact: John Caine, President
Description: Promotes business and community development in Eldon, MO. Sponsors Eldon Turkey Festival.

54038 ■ Ellington Chamber of Commerce
PO Box 515
Ellington, MO 63638-0515
Ph: (573)663-7997
Fax: (573)663-7873
Co. E-mail: chamber@ellingtonmo.com
URL: http://www.ellingtonmo.com
Contact: Christy Roberts, President
Description: Promotes business and community development in Ellington, MO area.

54039 ■ Elsberry Chamber of Commerce (ECC)
PO Box 32
Elsberry, MO 63343
Ph: (573)898-9124
Co. E-mail: chamber.info@elsberrycofc.org
URL: http://elsberrycofc.org
Contact: Michael Short, President
Description: Promotes business and community development in Elsberry, MO. **Founded:** 1947.

54040 ■ *The Enterprise*
15965 Manchester Rd., Ste. 102
Ellisville, MO 63011
Ph: (636)230-9900
Fax: (636)230-9912
URL: http://www.westcountychamber.com
Contact: Lori Kelling, President
Released: Monthly

54041 ■ Eureka Chamber of Commerce
22 Dreyer Ave.
Eureka, MO 63025
Ph: (636)938-6062

Fax: (636)938-5202
Co. E-mail: kellylubker@eurekachamber.us
URL: http://www.eurekachamber.org
Contact: John Jones, President
Description: Promotes businesses and community development in Eureka area.

54042 ■ Excelsior Springs Area Chamber of Commerce
PO Box 632
Excelsior Springs, MO 64024
Ph: (816)630-6161
Co. E-mail: info@exspgschamber.com
URL: http://www.exspgschamber.com
Contact: Mr. Terry Smelcer, Executive Director
Description: Organized to encourage a strong local economy and quality of life by promoting sound government and an informed membership and community. Promotes business and community development in Excelsior Springs, MO. **Founded:** 1895. **Publications:** *Chamber Connection.* **Awards:** Chamber Member of the Year (Annual); Citizen of the Year (Annual); Volunteer of the Year (Annual).

54043 ■ Farmington Chamber of Commerce (FCC)
PO Box 191
Farmington, MO 63640
Ph: (573)756-3615
Fax: (573)756-1003
Co. E-mail: doug@farmingtonmo.org
URL: http://www.farmingtonmo.org
Contact: Doug McDermott, Executive Director
Description: Promotes business and community development in Farmington, MO. Sponsors Farmington Country Days. **Founded:** 1941. **Publications:** *Your Chamber Connection* (Monthly).

54044 ■ Fenton Area Chamber of Commerce (FACC)
964 S Highway Dr., Ste. 103
Fenton, MO 63026
Ph: (636)717-0200
Fax: (636)717-0214
Co. E-mail: exdir@fentonmochamber.com
URL: http://www.fentonmochamber.com
Contact: Dale Roethemeyer, President
Description: Promotes business and community development in the Fenton, MO area. **Founded:** 1970. **Publications:** *Community Guide* (Annual); *Business to Business* (Monthly); *Community Guide* (Annual); *Fenton Area Chamber of Commerce--Community Guide* (Annual). **Educational Activities:** Membership Meeting (Monthly). **Awards:** Scholarship to High School Seniors (Annual).

54045 ■ Forsyth Chamber of Commerce
16075 Hwy. 160
Forsyth, MO 65653
Ph: (417)546-2741
Co. E-mail: info@forsythmissouri.org
URL: http://forsythmissouri.org
Contact: Bill Bassett, Executive Director
Description: Promotes growth and prosperity of Forsyth and the surrounding communities by leading, attracting, focusing, and encouraging relationships between Chamber members and sponsoring community, civic, and cultural activities. **Publications:** *Chamber Chat* (Bimonthly).

54046 ■ Fredericktown Chamber of Commerce (FCC)
120 W Main St.
Fredericktown, MO 63645
Ph: (573)783-2604
Fax: (573)783-2645
Co. E-mail: chamberdirector@fredericktownmissouri.net
URL: http://fredericktownmissouri.net
Contact: Kyle Wright, Executive Director
Description: Promotes business and community development in the Madison County, MO area. Sponsors seminars. **Founded:** 1946.

54047 ■ *Friday Facts*
2 W Springfield Rd.
Sullivan, MO 63080
Ph: (573)468-3314

Fax: (573)860-2313
Co. E-mail: chamber@sullivanmo.com
URL: http://www.sullivanmo.com
Contact: Jane Epperson, President
Released: Weekly **Price:** free for members.

54048 ■ Grandview Area Chamber of Commerce (GACC)
12500 S Hwy. 71
Grandview, MO 64030
Ph: (816)761-6505
Fax: (816)763-8460
Co. E-mail: ksc@grandview.org
Contact: Kim Curtis, President
Description: Promotes business and community development in the Grandview, MO area. **Scope:** business. **Founded:** 1963. **Subscriptions:** 14. **Publications:** *Business Initiative* (Monthly); *Chamber Directory* (Annual). **Awards:** Business of the Month (Monthly). **Telecommunication Services:** cberberich@grandview.org; abrincefield@grandview.org.

54049 ■ *Greater Kansas City Business*
2600 Commerce Tower
Kansas City, MO 64105
Ph: (816)221-2424
Fax: (816)221-7440
Co. E-mail: info@kcchamber.com
URL: http://www.kcchamber.com
Contact: James A. Heeter, President
Released: Monthly

54050 ■ Greater Kansas City Chamber of Commerce
2600 Commerce Tower
Kansas City, MO 64105
Ph: (816)221-2424
Fax: (816)221-7440
Co. E-mail: info@kcchamber.com
URL: http://www.kcchamber.com
Contact: James A. Heeter, President
Description: Promotes business and community development in the Greater Kansas City, MO area. **Founded:** 1887. **Publications:** *The City Haller* (Weekly); *Economic Forecast*; *Greater Kansas City Business* (Monthly); *Chamber of Commerce of Greater Kansas City--Membership Directory and Buyer's Guide* (Annual). **Telecommunication Services:** heeter@kcchamber.com.

54051 ■ Greater North County Chamber of Commerce
420 W Washington St.
Florissant, MO 63031
Ph: (314)831-3500
Fax: (314)831-9682
Co. E-mail: info@greaternorthcountychamber.com
URL: http://greaternorthcountychamber.chambermaster.com/news/details/welcome
Contact: Carolyn Marty, President
Description: Promotes business and community development in the Florissant, MO area. **Publications:** *Our Town* (Quarterly). **Telecommunication Services:** diana@greaternorthcountychamber.com.

54052 ■ Greater Poplar Bluff Area Chamber of Commerce
1111 W Pine St.
Poplar Bluff, MO 63901
Ph: (573)785-7761
Fax: (573)785-1901
Co. E-mail: info@poplarbluffchamber.org
URL: http://www.poplarbluffchamber.org
Contact: Steve Halter, President
Description: Promotes business and community development in the Greater Poplar Bluff, MO area. **Founded:** 1938. **Publications:** *Bluff Business Bulletin* (Monthly). **Educational Activities:** Greater Poplar Bluff Area Chamber of Commerce Banquet (Annual). **Awards:** Citizen of the Year (Annual).

54053 ■ Greater Warrensburg Area Chamber of Commerce
100 S Holden St.
Warrensburg, MO 64093-2331
Ph: (660)747-3168
Free: 877-OLD-DRUM

Fax: (660)429-5490
Co. E-mail: members@warrensburg.org
URL: http://www.warrensburg.org
Contact: Tamara Long, President
Description: Promotes business and community development in Warrensburg, MO. Sponsors Fall Festival. **Founded:** 1885. **Publications:** *Kaleidoscope* (Monthly). **Telecommunication Services:** chamber@warrensburg.org.

54054 ■ Greater West Plains Area Chamber of Commerce
401 Jefferson Ave.
West Plains, MO 65775-2659
Ph: (417)256-4433
Fax: (417)256-8711
Co. E-mail: info@wpchamber.com
URL: http://wpchamber.com
Description: Promotes business and community development in the Greater West Plains, MO area. Sponsors annual Fur, Fin, and Feather Festival. **Founded:** 1900. **Publications:** *West Plains Ambassador* (Monthly). **Educational Activities:** Business EXPO (Annual).

54055 ■ Hannibal Area Chamber of Commerce (HCC)
PO Box 230
Hannibal, MO 63401
Ph: (573)221-1101
Fax: (573)221-3389
Co. E-mail: info@hannibalchamber.org
URL: http://www.hannibalchamber.org
Contact: McKenzie Disselhorst, Executive Director
Description: Promotes business and community development in Hannibal, MO. **Founded:** 1919. **Publications:** *Hannibal Area Chamber of Commerce--Community Resource Guide* (Annual).

54056 ■ Harrisonville Area Chamber of Commerce (HACC)
2819 Cantrell Rd.
Harrisonville, MO 64701-4006
Ph: (816)380-5271
Fax: (816)884-4291
Co. E-mail: sara@harrisonvillechamber.com
URL: http://www.harrisonvillechamber.com
Contact: Obie Carl, President
Description: Promotes business and community development in the Harrisonville, MO area. **Founded:** 1965.

54057 ■ Hermann Area Chamber of Commerce (HACC)
312 Market St.
Hermann, MO 65041
Ph: (573)486-2313
Free: 800-932-8687
Co. E-mail: tourism@centurytel.net
URL: http://www.visithermann.com
Contact: Raylene Hollrah, President
Description: Promotes business and community development in the Hermann, MO area. **Founded:** 1944.

54058 ■ Higginsville Chamber of Commerce
PO Box 164
Higginsville, MO 64037
Ph: (660)584-3030
Fax: (660)584-3033
Co. E-mail: chamber@ctcis.net
URL: http://www.higginsvillechamber.org
Contact: David Reid, President
Description: Promotes business and community development in Higginsville, MO. Sponsors annual Higginsville Country Fair. **Founded:** 1923. **Awards:** Business of the Month (Monthly); Business of the Year (Annual); Employee of the Month (Monthly); Individual of the Year (Annual).

54059 ■ Holden Chamber of Commerce
100 E 2nd St.
Holden, MO 64040
Ph: (816)732-6844
Co. E-mail: info@holdenchamber.com
URL: http://www.holdenchamber.com
Contact: Diane Klossen, President
Description: Promotes business and community development in Holden, MO.

54060 ■ Houston Area Chamber of Commerce (HACC)
PO Box 374
Houston, MO 65483
Ph: (417)967-2220
Fax: (417)967-2178
Co. E-mail: info@houstonmochamber.com
URL: http://www.houstonmochamber.com
Contact: Velena Ingram, Executive Director
Description: Promotes business and community development in the Houston area. Sponsors the Emmett Kelly Clown Festival, annual golf tournament, Texas County Fair and Old Settler's Reunion, Heritage Days, the Christmas parade and Christmas promotions.

54061 ■ *Images of Sikeston*
One Industrial Dr.
Sikeston, MO 63801-5216
Ph: (573)471-2498
Fax: (573)471-2499
Co. E-mail: chamber@sikeston.net
URL: http://www.sikeston.net
Contact: Susan Glasgow Lawrence, Executive Director
Released: Monthly **Price:** free.

54062 ■ Independence Chamber of Commerce
PO Box 1077
Independence, MO 64051
Ph: (816)252-4745
Fax: (816)252-4917
Co. E-mail: jhobbs@independencechamber.org
URL: http://www.independencechamber.com
Contact: Teresa Freeland, President
Description: Promotes business and community development in Independence, MO. **Founded:** 1920. **Publications:** *Chamber News* (Monthly). **Awards:** Distinguished Board Member of the Year (Annual); Distinguished Citizen of the Year (Annual).

54063 ■ *Industrial Directory*
320 E 4th St.
Joplin, MO 64801
Ph: (417)624-4150
Fax: (417)624-4303
Co. E-mail: info@joplincc.com
URL: http://www.joplincc.com
Contact: Rob O'Brian, President
Released: Annual

54064 ■ Jackson Chamber of Commerce (JCOC)
PO Box 352
Jackson, MO 63755
Ph: (573)243-8131
Free: 888-501-8827
Fax: (573)243-0725
Co. E-mail: assistant@jacksonmochamber.org
URL: http://www.jacksonmochamber.org
Contact: Brian Gerau, Executive Director
Description: Promotes business and community development in Jackson, MO. **Awards:** R. A. Fulenwider Meritorious Community Service Award (Annual). **Telecommunication Services:** director@jacksonmochamber.org.

54065 ■ Jefferson City Area Chamber of Commerce
PO Box 776
Jefferson City, MO 65101
Ph: (573)634-3616
Fax: (573)634-3805
Co. E-mail: info@jcchamber.org
URL: http://www.jcchamber.org
Contact: Bob Scruggs, Chairman
Description: Promotes economic vitality and strength in the Jefferson City area. Participates and partners in activities that improve the economy and quality of life. **Publications:** *Chamber Chronicle* (Bimonthly). **Educational Activities:** Chamber Connections Mixers (Monthly).

54066 ■ Joplin Area Chamber of Commerce (JACC)
320 E 4th St.
Joplin, MO 64801

Ph: (417)624-4150
Fax: (417)624-4303
Co. E-mail: info@joplincc.com
URL: http://www.joplincc.com
Contact: Rob O'Brian, President
Description: Promotes the growth and development of the Joplin, MO area. **Founded:** 1917. **Publications:** *Business Outlook* (Monthly); *Industrial Directory* (Annual). **Awards:** Golden Apple Awards (Annual); Small Business of the Year (Annual). **Telecommunication Services:** robrian@joplincc.com; glamar@joplincc.com; scloyd@joplincc.com.

54067 ■ Kahoka - Clark County Chamber of Commerce
659 Vine St.
Kahoka, MO 63445
Ph: (660)727-2179
Fax: (660)727-3601
URL: http://mochamber.com/mx/hm.asp?id=home
Contact: Tim Ayer, President

54068 ■ *Kaleidoscope*
100 S Holden St.
Warrensburg, MO 64093-2331
Ph: (660)747-3168
Free: 877-OLD-DRUM
Fax: (660)429-5490
Co. E-mail: members@warrensburg.org
URL: http://www.warrensburg.org
Contact: Tamara Long, President
Released: Monthly

54069 ■ Kearney Chamber of Commerce
PO Box 242
Kearney, MO 64060
Ph: (816)628-4229
Co. E-mail: info@kearneychamber.org
URL: http://www.kearneychamber.org
Contact: Ms. Siouxsan Eisen, Executive Director
Description: Promotes business and community development in Kearney, MO area.

54070 ■ Kennett Chamber of Commerce (KCC)
PO Box 61
Kennett, MO 63857
Ph: (573)888-5828
Free: 866-848-5828
Fax: (573)888-9802
Co. E-mail: info@kennettmo.com
URL: http://www.kennettmo.com
Contact: Meg Benson, Executive Director
Description: Promotes business and community development in Kennett, MO. **Founded:** 1946.

54071 ■ *Keynotes*
PO Box 1897
Branson, MO 65615
Ph: (417)334-4084
Free: 800-214-3661
Fax: (417)334-4139
Co. E-mail: rsummers@bransoncvb.com
URL: http://www.explorebranson.com
Contact: Ross Summers, President
Released: Periodic

54072 ■ Kingdom of Callaway Chamber of Commerce (KCCC)
409 Court St.
Fulton, MO 65251-1724
Ph: (573)642-3055
Free: 800-257-3554
Fax: (573)642-5182
Co. E-mail: info@callawaychamber.com
URL: http://www.callawaychamber.com
Contact: Marty Martin-Forman, President
Description: Promotes business and community development in Callaway County, MO. Sponsors Kingdom Days. Conducts charitable activities. **Founded:** 1924.

54073 ■ Kirksville Area Chamber of Commerce
PO Box 251
Kirksville, MO 63501-3581
Ph: (660)665-3766

Fax: (660)665-3767
Co. E-mail: kvacoc@cableone.net
URL: http://www.kirksvillechamber.com
Contact: Sandra Williams, Executive Director
Description: Promotes business and community development in the Kirksville, MO area.

54074 ■ Kirkwood Area Chamber of Commerce
108 W Adams
Kirkwood, MO 63122
Ph: (314)821-4161
Fax: (314)821-5229
Co. E-mail: jim@thechamber.us
URL: http://www.kirkwooddesperes.com
Contact: Jim Wright, President
Description: Promotes business and community development in the Kirkwood, MO area. **Founded:** 1946. **Publications:** *Business and Community* (Annual); *Chamber Advantage* (Monthly); *Chamber Flash* (Monthly). **Educational Activities:** Business Advantage (Monthly). **Awards:** Business Person of the Year (Annual); Citizen of the Year (Annual); Community Spirit Award (Annual); Lifetime Achievement Award. **Telecommunication Services:** iris@thechamber.us; lori@thechamber.us; gina@thechamber.us; beth@thechamber.us.

54075 ■ Lake of the Ozarks West Chamber of Commerce
PO Box 340
Sunrise Beach, MO 65079-0340
Ph: (573)374-5500
Free: 877-227-4086
Fax: (573)374-8576
Co. E-mail: info@lakewestchamber.com
URL: http://www.lakewestchamber.com
Contact: Mr. Michael Kenagy, Executive Director
Description: Works with other community resources to promote local tourism, create jobs, and recruit new businesses in Lake of the Ozarks West, MO area. **Founded:** 1986. **Awards:** Eagle Award (Annual).

54076 ■ Lebanon Area Chamber of Commerce
186 N Adams
Lebanon, MO 65536
Ph: (417)588-3256
Fax: (417)588-3251
Co. E-mail: darrell@lebanonmissouri.com
URL: http://www.lebanonmissouri.com
Contact: Darrell Pollock, Executive Director
Description: Promotes business and community development in the Lebanon, MO area. Sponsors Hillbilly Days Arts and Crafts Festival, and Holiday Festival Parade. **Telecommunication Services:** chamber@lebanonmissouri.com.

54077 ■ Lexington Area Chamber of Commerce (LCC)
1029 Franklin Ave.
Lexington, MO 64067
Ph: (660)259-3082
Fax: (660)259-7776
Co. E-mail: chamber@historiclexington.com
URL: http://www.historiclexington.com
Contact: Penny Grosso, Executive Director
Description: Promotes business, industry, and community development in Lexington, MO. Offers free community Christmas dinner. Conducts volleyball competitions. Sponsors River Festival and Farmer Appreciation Dinner. **Founded:** 1938. **Publications:** *Chamber News* (Quarterly). **Educational Activities:** Apple, Arts and Antique (Annual).

54078 ■ Liberty Area Chamber of Commerce
1170 W Kansas St., Ste. H
Liberty, MO 64068
Ph: (816)781-5200
Fax: (816)781-4901
Co. E-mail: info@libertychamber.com
URL: http://www.libertychamber.com
Contact: Gayle Potter, President
Description: Volunteer partnership of business, civic and professional people working together to build a healthy economy and improve the quality of life in the greater Liberty, Missouri area. **Founded:** 1951. **Publications:** *The Chamber News* (Monthly). **Educational Activities:** Business After Hours (Monthly).

54079 ■ Macon Area Chamber of Commerce
119 N Rollins
Macon, MO 63552
Ph: (660)385-2811
Fax: (660)385-6543
Co. E-mail: director@maconmochamber.com
URL: http://maconmochamber.com
Contact: Sharon Scott, Executive Director
Description: Promotes business and community development in the Macon, MO area. Sponsors competitions and festival. **Founded:** 1935.

54080 ■ *Mainstreet News*
100 W Jackson St.
Mexico, MO 65265
Ph: (573)581-2765
Free: 800-581-2765
URL: http://www.mexico-chamber.org/index.aspx
Contact: Heather DeMint, President
Released: Monthly

54081 ■ Malden Chamber of Commerce (MCC)
607 N Douglass St.
Malden, MO 63863
Ph: (573)276-4519
Fax: (573)276-4925
Co. E-mail: info@maldenchamber.com
URL: http://www.maldenchamber.com
Contact: Brenda Williams, Director
Description: Aids and promotes the business community in the Malden, MO area. Sponsors Miss Missouri Scholarship Pageant preliminaries, Malden Homecoming Festival and 4th of July and Christmas parades. **Founded:** 1951. **Subscriptions:** 45000 articles audiovisuals books papers periodicals. **Publications:** *View Points* (Bimonthly). **Awards:** Business of the Year (Annual).

54082 ■ Marceline Chamber of Commerce
PO Box 93
Marceline, MO 64658
Ph: (660)376-3528
Fax: (660)376-3881
Co. E-mail: goddards@cvalley.net
URL: http://www.marceline.com
Contact: Jed Frost, President
URL(s): mochamber.com/mx/hm.asp?id=sitedoc25#M. **Description:** Promotes business and community development in Marceline, MO.

54083 ■ Mark Twain Lake Chamber of Commerce
PO Box 182
Monroe City, MO 63456-0182
Ph: (573)565-2228
Co. E-mail: mtlcoc@socket.net
URL: http://www.visitmarktwainlake.org
Contact: Dennis Gill, Vice President
Description: Promotes business and community development in Mark Twain Lake, MO area.

54084 ■ Marshall Chamber of Commerce (MCC)
214 N Lafayette Ave.
Marshall, MO 65340-1700
Ph: (660)886-3324
Fax: (660)831-0349
URL: http://www.marshallchamber.com
Contact: Mr. Ken Yowell, Executive Director
Description: Promotes business and community development in Marshall and Saline counties, MO. **Founded:** 1921.

54085 ■ Maryland Heights Chamber of Commerce (MHCC)
547 Westport Plz.
St. Louis, MO 63146-3007
Ph: (314)576-6603

Fax: (314)576-6855
Co. E-mail: kim@mhcc.com
URL: http://www.mhcc.com
Contact: Kim Braddy, Executive Director
Description: Promotes business and community development in Maryland Heights, MO area. **Founded:** 1985. **Awards:** Business Leader of the Year (Annual).

54086 ■ Maryville Chamber of Commerce (MCC)
423 N Market
Maryville, MO 64468
Ph: (660)582-8643
Fax: (660)582-3071
Co. E-mail: chamber@asde.net
URL: http://www.maryvillechamber.com
Contact: Luke Reven, Executive Director
Description: Promotes business and community development in the Maryville, MO area. **Publications:** *Update* (Monthly).

54087 ■ *The Members' Messenger*
101 N Maple St.
Buffalo, MO 65622
Ph: (417)345-2852
Free: 800-483-5000
Fax: (417)345-2852
Co. E-mail: chamber@buffalococ.com
URL: http://www.buffalococ.com
Contact: Kathy Kesler, Executive Director
Released: Monthly

54088 ■ Mexico Area Chamber of Commerce (MACC)
100 W Jackson St.
Mexico, MO 65265
Ph: (573)581-2765
Free: 800-581-2765
URL: http://www.mexico-chamber.org/index.aspx
Contact: Heather DeMint, President
Description: Promotes business and community development in the Mexico, MO area. Focuses on tourism, transportation, and agribusiness. **Founded:** 1917. **Publications:** *Mainstreet News* (Monthly). **Educational Activities:** Agriculture Appreciation and Commerce & Industry Appreciation (Annual).

54089 ■ Monett Chamber of Commerce (MCC)
PO Box 47
Monett, MO 65708
Ph: (417)235-7919
Fax: (417)235-4076
Co. E-mail: chamber@monett-mo.com
URL: http://www.kdbsites.com/chamber
Contact: John Bruner, President
Description: Promotes business and community development in Monett, MO. **Publications:** *Talk of the Towne* (Monthly). **Educational Activities:** Beef Conference. **Awards:** Community Service (Annual); Pride and Progress (Annual). **Telecommunication Services:** chamberdir@monett-mo.com.

54090 ■ Monroe City Area Chamber of Commerce
314 S Main
Monroe City, MO 63456
Ph: (573)735-4391
URL: http://www.marktwainlake.com/monroecity/mc-chamber.html
Description: Promotes business and community development in the Monroe City, MO area.

54091 ■ Montgomery City Area Chamber of Commerce
723 N Sturgeon St.
Montgomery City, MO 63361
Ph: (573)564-3160
Free: 800-242-8829
Fax: (573)564-3802
Co. E-mail: treasurer@mcchamber.org
URL: http://www.montgomerycitymo.org
Contact: Josh Beck, Director
Description: Promotes business and community development in Montgomery City, MO area.

54092 ■ Mound City Chamber of Commerce (MCCC)
PO Box 149
Jefferson City, MO 65102
Ph: (573)634-3511
Fax: (573)634-8855
Co. E-mail: dmehan@mochamber.com
URL: http://mochamber.com
Contact: Daniel P. Mehan, President
Description: Promotes business and community development in Mound City, MO area. **Founded:** 1949.

54093 ■ Mount Vernon Chamber of Commerce
PO Box 373
Mount Vernon, MO 65712
Ph: (417)466-7654
Fax: (417)466-7654
Co. E-mail: mtvchamber@mchsi.com
URL: http://www.mtvernonchamber.com
Contact: Doris McBride, Executive Secretary
Description: Promotes business and community development in Mt. Vernon, MO.

54094 ■ Mountain Grove Chamber of Commerce
PO Box 434
Mountain Grove, MO 65711
Ph: (417)926-4135
Co. E-mail: chamber@mountaingrovechamber.com
URL: http://www.mountaingrovechamber.com
Contact: Robin Allen, President
Description: Promotes business and community development in Mountain Grove, MO. Sponsors Mayfest celebration.

54095 ■ Nevada-Vernon County Chamber of Commerce (NVCCC)
225 W Austin, Ste. 200
Nevada, MO 64772
Ph: (417)667-5300
Fax: (417)667-3492
Co. E-mail: chamber1@nevada-mo.com
URL: http://www.nevada-mo.com
Contact: Cat McGrath-Farmer, Director
Description: Promotes business and community development in Nevada-Vernon County, MO. Sponsors Bushwhacker Days. **Founded:** 1890. **Publications:** *Chamber Connections* (Quarterly).

54096 ■ New Madrid Chamber of Commerce
PO Box 96
New Madrid, MO 63869
Ph: (573)748-5300
Free: 877-748-5300
Fax: (573)748-5402
Co. E-mail: chambernm@yahoo.com
URL: http://www.new-madrid.mo.us
Contact: Christina McWaters, Executive Director
Description: Promotes business and community development in New Madrid, MO area.

54097 ■ *Newcomer's Guide*
2 W Springfield Rd.
Sullivan, MO 63080
Ph: (573)468-3314
Fax: (573)860-2313
Co. E-mail: chamber@sullivanmo.com
URL: http://www.sullivanmo.com
Contact: Jane Epperson, President
Released: Annual

54098 ■ Nixa Area Chamber of Commerce
PO Box 548
Nixa, MO 65714
Ph: (417)725-1545
Fax: (417)725-4532
Co. E-mail: info@nixachamber.com
URL: http://www.nixachamber.com
Contact: Sharon Whitehill Gray, President
Description: Works to provide leadership, to assist growth and development of business, and to enhance the community as a desirable place to live, learn, work, shop and play. **Founded:** 1988.

54099 ■ Northland Regional Chamber of Commerce (NRCC)
634 NW Englewood Rd.
Kansas City, MO 64118
Ph: (816)455-9911
Fax: (816)455-9933
Co. E-mail: northland@northlandchamber.com
URL: http://www.northlandchamber.com
Contact: Sheila Tracy, President
Description: Promotes business and community development in Clay and Platte County, MO. **Founded:** 1992. **Publications:** *The Northland Voice* (Monthly).

54100 ■ *The Northland Voice*
634 NW Englewood Rd.
Kansas City, MO 64118
Ph: (816)455-9911
Fax: (816)455-9933
Co. E-mail: northland@northlandchamber.com
URL: http://www.northlandchamber.com
Contact: Sheila Tracy, President
Released: Monthly

54101 ■ Northwest Chamber of Commerce
11965 St. Charles Rock Rd., Ste. 203
Bridgeton, MO 63044
Ph: (314)291-2131
Fax: (314)291-2153
Co. E-mail: info@northwestchamber.com
URL: http://www.northwestchamber.com/index.php
Contact: Jerry Hart, President
Description: Strives to provide leadership and promote unity through programs and services that stimulate economic growth and enhance the quality of life in the community. **Founded:** 1951. **Publications:** *Chamber News* (Monthly).

54102 ■ Oak Grove Chamber of Commerce
c/o Jordin Mahnke, Exec. Dir.
1212B S Broadway
Oak Grove, MO 64075
Ph: (816)690-4147
Fax: (816)690-4147
Co. E-mail: oakgrovechamber@hotmail.com
URL: http://www.oakgrovechamber.biz
Contact: Jordin Mahnke, Executive Director
Description: Strives to advance wholesome commercial aspects and beneficial directives in the business community.

54103 ■ Odessa Chamber of Commerce
309A Park Ln.
Odessa, MO 64076
Ph: (816)633-4044
Fax: (816)633-4044
Co. E-mail: odessacoc@embarqmail.com
URL: http://www.odessamochamber.com
Contact: Doug Turnbough, President
Description: Strives to provide leadership necessary to promote a favorable economic environment, while improving the quality of life in Odessa, Missouri and the surrounding areas.

54104 ■ O'Fallon Chamber of Commerce (OCC)
2145 Bryan Valley Commercial
O'Fallon, MO 63366-3496
Ph: (636)240-1818
Co. E-mail: cindy@qcater.com
URL: http://www.ofallonchamber.org
Contact: Erin Williams, President
Description: Promotes business and community development in O'Fallon, MO. Conducts charitable activities. Sponsors area festival and Person of the Year competition. **Founded:** 1930. **Publications:** *Connections* (Monthly).

54105 ■ *Our Town*
420 W Washington St.
Florissant, MO 63031
Ph: (314)831-3500
Fax: (314)831-9682
Co. E-mail: info@greaternorthcountychamber.com
URL: http://greaternorthcountychamber.chambermaster.com/news/details/welcome
Contact: Carolyn Marty, President
Released: Quarterly

54106 ■ *Out and About*
101 Chesterfield Business Pkwy.
Chesterfield, MO 63005
Ph: (636)532-3399
Free: 888-242-4262
Fax: (636)532-7446
Co. E-mail: info@chesterfieldmochamber.com
URL: http://www.chesterfieldmochamber.com
Contact: Jennifer Hill, Chairperson
Released: Bimonthly **Price:** free.

54107 ■ Owensville Chamber of Commerce (OCC)
PO Box 77
Owensville, MO 65066
Ph: (573)437-4270
Co. E-mail: chamber1@fidnet.com
URL: http://www.owensvillemissouri.com/chamber.html
Contact: Mr. Robert Niebruegge, Executive Director
Description: Promotes a healthy climate for business, commerce, and industry in Owensville, MO. **Founded:** 1944.

54108 ■ *Ozark Area Chamber of Commerce Professional Directory and Community Information*
PO Box 1450
Ozark, MO 65721
Ph: (417)581-6139
Fax: (417)581-0639
Co. E-mail: info@ozarkchamber.com
URL: http://www.ozarkchamber.com
Contact: Dori Grinder, Executive Director
Released: Annual

54109 ■ Ozark Chamber of Commerce (OCC)
PO Box 1450
Ozark, MO 65721
Ph: (417)581-6139
Fax: (417)581-0639
Co. E-mail: info@ozarkchamber.com
URL: http://www.ozarkchamber.com
Contact: Dori Grinder, Executive Director
Description: Promotes business and community development in Ozark, MO and surrounding areas. Conducts charitable and promotional activities. Sponsors Christmas parade, business education, Adopt-A-School activities, and other community events. **Founded:** 1949. **Publications:** *Chamber Connection* (Monthly); *Ozark Area Chamber of Commerce Professional Directory and Community Information* (Annual).

54110 ■ Pacific Area Chamber of Commerce
333 Chamber Dr.
Pacific, MO 63069
Ph: (636)271-6639
Co. E-mail: exdir@pacificchamber.com
URL: http://www.pacificchamber.com
Contact: Bill McLaren, President
Description: Promotes business and community development in Pacific, MO. **Founded:** 1958.

54111 ■ Paris Area Chamber of Commerce (PACC)
208 N Main St.
Paris, MO 65275-1397
Ph: (660)327-4450
Co. E-mail: chamber@parismo.net
URL: http://www.parismo.net/chamber_of_commerce.htm
Contact: Vanessa Forrest, Executive Director
Description: Promotes business and community development in Paris, MO. **Founded:** 1986. **Awards:** Community Service (Annual).

54112 ■ Park Hills - Leadington Chamber of Commerce
5 Municipal Dr.
Park Hills, MO 63601-2064
Ph: (573)431-1051
Fax: (573)431-2327
Co. E-mail: phlcoc@sbcglobal.net
URL: http://www.phlcoc.net
Contact: Tamara Coleman, Executive Director
Description: Promotes business and community development in St. Francois County, MO. Conducts social and promotional events and assists with

Economic Development. **Founded:** 1942. **Publications:** *Chamber News* (Monthly). **Awards:** Chambers Friend (Annual).

54113 ■ Perryville Chamber of Commerce
2 W St. Maries St.
Perryville, MO 63775
Ph: (573)547-6062
Fax: (573)547-6071
Co. E-mail: melissa@perryvillemo.com
URL: http://www.perryvillemo.com
Contact: Melissa Hemmann, Executive Director
Description: Promotes business and community development in Perryville, MO. Sponsors annual Mayfest and Mother's Day Weekend celebration. **Founded:** 1923. **Telecommunication Services:** cari@perryvillemo.com.

54114 ■ Piedmont Area Chamber of Commerce
215 S Main St.
Piedmont, MO 63957
Ph: (573)223-4046
Co. E-mail: contact@piedmontchamber.com
URL: http://www.piedmontchamber.com
Contact: Scott Combs, President
Description: Promotes business and community development in Piedmont, MO.

54115 ■ Platte City Chamber of Commerce
c/o Jen Robbins, Exec. Dir.
PO Box 650
Platte City, MO 64079-0650
Ph: (816)858-5270
Co. E-mail: info@plattecitymo.com
URL: http://www.plattecitymo.com
Contact: Jen Robbins, Executive Director

54116 ■ Plattsburg Chamber of Commerce (PCC)
101 S Main
Plattsburg, MO 64477
Ph: (816)539-2649
Fax: (816)539-3539
Co. E-mail: chamber@plattsburgmo.com
URL: http://www.plattsburgmo.com/chamber/index.
  htm
Contact: Tonya Sloan, President
Description: Promotes business and community development in the Plattsburg, MO area. Sponsors fall and Christmas festival. Convention/Meeting: none. Publications: none. **Founded:** 1954.

54117 ■ *Quality of Life Magazine*
10950 Olive Blvd., Ste. 101
Creve Coeur, MO 63141
Ph: (314)569-3536
Fax: (314)569-3073
Co. E-mail: info@ccochamber.com
URL: http://www.ccochamber.com
Contact: Nancy Gray, Executive Vice President
Released: Periodic

54118 ■ Raymore Chamber of Commerce
1000 W Foxwood Dr.
Raymore, MO 64083
Ph: (816)322-0599
Fax: (816)322-7127
Co. E-mail: info@raymorechamber.com
URL: http://www.raymorechamber.com
Contact: Jason Matters, President
Description: Works to improve business community and economic growth through leadership, educational or legislative awareness and community interactions. **Telecommunication Services:** cherieturney@ray-morechamber.com.

54119 ■ Raytown Area Chamber of Commerce (RACC)
5909 Raytown Trafficway
Raytown, MO 64133-3860
Ph: (816)353-8500
Fax: (816)353-8525
URL: http://raytownchamber.com
Contact: Vicki A. Turnbow, President
Description: Promotes business and community development in Raytown, MO and surrounding area. Conducts annual Raytown Roundup Days. **Founded:**

1929. **Publications:** *Chamber Membership* (Annual); *Crossroads Connection* (Monthly). **Educational Activities:** Discover Raytown (Monthly).

54120 ■ Republic Area Chamber of Commerce (RACC)
113 W Hwy. 174
Republic, MO 65738
Ph: (417)732-5200
Fax: (417)732-2851
Co. E-mail: rchamber@televar.com
URL: http://www.republicchamber.com
Contact: Deb DeManche, President
Description: Assists all members of the community engaged in retail, wholesale, commercial, industrial, tourism, and trade fields, in the professional, educational, and agricultural fields, and in all other fields where interest is evident to solve the mutual or individual problems in the respective fields. Recognizes and promotes the use of the resources of the area and to work for the improvement and protection of those resources through legislation, or other courses of action when deemed necessary.

54121 ■ Richmond Chamber of Commerce
104 W North Main St.
Richmond, MO 64085
Ph: (816)776-6916
Fax: (816)776-6917
Co. E-mail: cofcommerce@mchsi.com
URL: http://www.richmondchamber.org
Contact: Ellen Franklin, Executive Director
Description: Promotes business and community development in Richmond, MO.

54122 ■ Ripley County Chamber of Commerce
101 Washington St.
Doniphan, MO 63935
Ph: (573)996-2212
Fax: (573)351-1441
Co. E-mail: rcchamber@windstream.net
URL: http://www.ripleycountymissouri.org/Ripley-CountyChamberHome.php
Contact: Ms. Tracey Holden, Executive Director
Description: Strives to foster commercial and industrial development in Doniphan, Missouri and the surrounding areas. Provides technical assistance to its business members. **Founded:** 1963.

54123 ■ Rolla Area Chamber of Commerce
1311 Kingshighway St.
Rolla, MO 65401
Ph: (573)364-3577
Free: 888-809-3817
Fax: (573)364-5222
Co. E-mail: rollavc@rollachamber.org
URL: http://www.rollachamber.org
Contact: Stevie Kearse, Executive Director
Description: Promotes business and community development in the Rolla, MO area. **Founded:** 1928. **Publications:** *Chamber Directory* (Annual); *Chamber News* (Monthly).

54124 ■ St. Charles Chamber of Commerce
2201 1st Capitol Dr.
St. Charles, MO 63301-5805
Ph: (636)946-0633
Free: 888-EZWAY4U
Co. E-mail: info@stcharleschamber.org
URL: http://www.stcharleschamber.org
Contact: Scott Tate, President
Description: Promotes business and community development in St. Charles, MO area. **Publications:** *Quality of Life* (Biennial). **Awards:** Citizen of the Year (Annual); Recognition of Service Excellence Award (Annual); Ring of Excellence Award (Annual); Small Business Person of the Year (Annual).

54125 ■ St. Clair Area Chamber of Commerce
c/o Terry Triphahn, Exec. Dir.
920 St. Clair Plaza Dr., Ste. F
St. Clair, MO 63077
Ph: (636)629-6000

Fax: (636)629-5510
Co. E-mail: chamber@stclairmo.com
URL: http://stclairmo.org/coc
Contact: Angela Crawford, Executive Director
Description: Promotes business and community development in the St. Clair, MO area. Sponsors festival. **Founded:** 1957. **Subscriptions:** articles books periodicals video recordings. **Awards:** Celebrate St. Clair (Annual).

54126 ■ Ste. Genevieve Chamber of Commerce
51 South Third St.
Ste. Genevieve, MO 63670-1601
Ph: (573)883-3686
Fax: (573)883-7092
Co. E-mail: stegenchamber@sbcglobal.net
URL: http://stegenchamber.org
Contact: Ron Klein, President

54127 ■ St. James Chamber of Commerce
PO Box 358
St. James, MO 65559
Ph: (573)265-6649
Co. E-mail: info@stjameschamber.net
URL: http://www.stjameschamber.net
Contact: Jim Fleming, President
Description: Promotes business and community development in St. James, MO area.

54128 ■ St. Joseph Area Chamber of Commerce (SJACC)
3003 Frederick Ave.
St. Joseph, MO 64506
Ph: (816)232-4461
Free: 800-748-7856
Fax: (816)364-4873
Co. E-mail: chamber@saintjoseph.com
URL: http://www.saintjoseph.com
Contact: Ted Allison, President
Description: Promotes business and community development in the St. Joseph, MO area. **Founded:** 1911. **Publications:** *Business Barometer* (Quarterly); *Connections* (Monthly); *21st Century Update* (Quarterly); *Business Intelligence Report* (Monthly); *Toot Your Horn* (Bimonthly).

54129 ■ St. Peters Chamber of Commerce
1236 Jungermann Rd., Ste. C
St. Peters, MO 63376
Ph: (636)447-3336
Fax: (636)447-9575
Co. E-mail: info@stpeterschamber.com
URL: http://www.stpeterschamber.com/home/index.
  html
Contact: Ed Weeks, President
Description: Promotes business and community development in St. Peters, MO area. **Founded:** 1980. **Publications:** *Chamber Report* (Monthly). **Educational Activities:** General Membership Meeting (Monthly). **Telecommunication Services:** eweeks@stpeterschamber.com.

54130 ■ Salem Area Chamber of Commerce
200 S Main St.
Salem, MO 65560
Ph: (573)729-6900
Fax: (573)729-6741
URL: http://www.salemmo.com/chamber/AboutCh-amber.asp
Contact: Genie Zakrzewski, Director
Description: Promotes business, community development, and tourism in Salem, MO. **Founded:** 1930.

54131 ■ Savannah Area Chamber of Commerce (SACC)
PO Box 101
Savannah, MO 64485
Ph: (816)324-3976
Fax: (816)324-5728
Co. E-mail: saccmo@gmail.com
URL: http://www.savannahmochamber.com
Contact: Christy Sipes, Coordinator
Description: Promotes business and community development in Savannah, MO. **Founded:** 1947.

54132 ■ Sedalia Area Chamber of Commerce
600 E 3rd St.
Sedalia, MO 65301-4499

Ph: (660)826-2222
Fax: (660)826-2223
Co. E-mail: mailto:chamber@sedaliamo.org
URL: http://www.sedaliachamber.com
Contact: Doug Benitz, President
Description: Promotes business and community development in the Sedalia, MO area. **Founded:** 1913.

54133 ■ Sikeston Area Chamber of Commerce (SACC)
One Industrial Dr.
Sikeston, MO 63801-5216
Ph: (573)471-2498
Fax: (573)471-2499
Co. E-mail: chamber@sikeston.net
URL: http://www.sikeston.net
Contact: Susan Glasgow Lawrence, Executive Director
Description: Promotes business, tourism, and community development in the Sikeston, MO area. **Founded:** 1929. **Publications:** Images of Sikeston (Monthly).

54134 ■ Slip Away to Branson
PO Box 1897
Branson, MO 65615
Ph: (417)334-4084
Free: 800-214-3661
Fax: (417)334-4139
Co. E-mail: rsummers@bransoncvb.com
URL: http://www.explorebranson.com
Contact: Ross Summers, President

54135 ■ The Source
PO Box 1897
Branson, MO 65615
Ph: (417)334-4084
Free: 800-214-3661
Fax: (417)334-4139
Co. E-mail: rsummers@bransoncvb.com
URL: http://www.explorebranson.com
Contact: Ross Summers, President
Released: Monthly

54136 ■ South Kansas City Chamber of Commerce (SKCCC)
406 E Bannister Rd., Ste. F
Kansas City, MO 64131-3028
Ph: (816)761-7660
Fax: (816)761-7340
Co. E-mail: vwolgast@southkcchamber.com
URL: http://www.southkcchamber.com
Contact: Vickie Wolgast, President
Description: Promotes business and community development in southern Kansas City, MO. **Founded:** 1931.

54137 ■ Spirit
200 S Main St.
Clinton, MO 64735
Ph: (660)885-8166
Free: 800-222-5251
Fax: (660)885-8168
Co. E-mail: debby@clintonmo.com
URL: http://www.clintonmo.com/ChamberofCommerce/tabid/55/Default.aspx
Contact: Craig Thompson, President

54138 ■ Spirit
202 S John Q. Hammons Pkwy.
Springfield, MO 65806
Ph: (417)862-5567
Fax: (417)862-1611
Co. E-mail: jim@springfieldchamber.com
URL: http://www.springfieldchamber.com
Contact: Jim Anderson, President
Released: Monthly

54139 ■ Spotlight on Carthage
402 S Garrison Ave.
Carthage, MO 64836
Ph: (417)358-2373
Fax: (417)358-7479
Co. E-mail: info@carthagechamber.com
URL: http://www.carthagechamber.com
Contact: Mark J. Elliff, President
Released: Monthly **Price:** included in membership dues.

54140 ■ Springfield Area Chamber of Commerce
202 S John Q. Hammons Pkwy.
Springfield, MO 65806
Ph: (417)862-5567
Fax: (417)862-1611
Co. E-mail: jim@springfieldchamber.com
URL: http://www.springfieldchamber.com
Contact: Jim Anderson, President
Description: Promotes business and community development in the Springfield, MO area. **Founded:** 1919. **Publications:** Spirit (Monthly).

54141 ■ Steelville Chamber of Commerce
PO Box 956
Steelville, MO 65565
Ph: (573)775-5533
Co. E-mail: chamber@misn.com
URL: http://chamberofcommerce.steelville.com
Contact: Jeanne Locklear, President
Description: Promotes business and community development in Steelville, MO area. **Founded:** 1982.

54142 ■ Stockton Area Chamber of Commerce
PO Box 410
Stockton, MO 65785
Ph: (417)276-5213
Co. E-mail: stocktonchamber@windstream.net
URL: http://www.stocktonmochamber.com
Contact: Charlotte Haden, Executive Director
Description: Works with other community resources to promote local tourism, create jobs, and recruit new businesses in Stockton, MO area.

54143 ■ Sullivan Area Chamber of Commerce
2 W Springfield Rd.
Sullivan, MO 63080
Ph: (573)468-3314
Fax: (573)860-2313
Co. E-mail: chamber@sullivanmo.com
URL: http://www.sullivanmo.com
Contact: Jane Epperson, President
Description: Promotes business and community development in Sullivan, MO. Participates in charitable programs; sponsors competitions; offers seminars. **Founded:** 1986. **Publications:** Friday Facts (Weekly); Newcomer's Guide (Annual). **Educational Activities:** September Business Showcase (Annual). **Awards:** Beautification (Annual); Man of the Year (Annual); New Business (Annual); Woman of the Year (Annual); Youth of the Year (Annual).

54144 ■ Summersville Chamber of Commerce
PO Box 251
Summersville, MO 65571
Ph: (417)932-4299
Fax: (417)932-4358
URL: http://mochamber.com/mx/hm.asp?id=home
Contact: Ronald Hayes, President

54145 ■ Table Rock Lake - Kimberling City Area Chamber of Commerce (TRLKCACC)
PO Box 495
Kimberling City, MO 65686
Ph: (417)739-2564
Free: 800-595-0393
Fax: (417)739-2580
Co. E-mail: trlchamber@visittablerocklake.com
URL: http://www.visittablerocklake.org
Contact: Ms. Wyli Barnes, President
Description: Promotes business and community development in the Table Rock Lake area and Stone County. **Publications:** Table Rock Lake Vacation Guide (Annual); Table Rock Talk (Monthly). **Awards:** Chamber Volunteer of the Year (Annual); Community Service Award (Annual); Community Volunteer of the Year (Annual); Teacher of the Month (Monthly). **Telecommunication Services:** scarlson@visittablerocklake.com; jhadley@visittablerocklake.com; bpatterson@visittablerocklake.com; sdecker@visittablerocklake.com.

54146 ■ Table Rock Lake Vacation Guide
PO Box 495
Kimberling City, MO 65686
Ph: (417)739-2564
Free: 800-595-0393

Fax: (417)739-2580
Co. E-mail: trlchamber@visittablerocklake.com
URL: http://www.visittablerocklake.org
Contact: Ms. Wyli Barnes, President
Released: Annual **Price:** free.

54147 ■ Table Rock Talk
PO Box 495
Kimberling City, MO 65686
Ph: (417)739-2564
Free: 800-595-0393
Fax: (417)739-2580
Co. E-mail: trlchamber@visittablerocklake.com
URL: http://www.visittablerocklake.org
Contact: Ms. Wyli Barnes, President
Released: Monthly **Price:** free.

54148 ■ Talk of the Towne
PO Box 47
Monett, MO 65708
Ph: (417)235-7919
Fax: (417)235-4076
Co. E-mail: chamber@monett-mo.com
URL: http://www.kdbsites.com/chamber
Contact: John Bruner, President
Released: Monthly **Price:** free.

54149 ■ Tipton Chamber of Commerce (TCC)
PO Box 307
Tipton, MO 65081-0307
Ph: (660)433-6377
Co. E-mail: denny.higgins@commercebank.com
URL: http://www.tiptonmo.com
Contact: Denny Higgins, President
Description: Promotes business and community development in the Tipton, MO area. Sponsors Fremont Days and Christmas Night Parade festivals. **Founded:** 1928. **Awards:** Citizen of the Year (Annual).

54150 ■ Toot Your Horn
3003 Frederick Ave.
St. Joseph, MO 64506
Ph: (816)232-4461
Free: 800-748-7856
Fax: (816)364-4873
Co. E-mail: chamber@saintjoseph.com
URL: http://www.saintjoseph.com
Contact: Ted Allison, President
Released: Bimonthly

54151 ■ Trenton
617 Main St.
Trenton, MO 64683
Ph: (660)359-4324
Fax: (660)359-4606
Co. E-mail: trentonchamber@grundyec.net
URL: http://www.trentonmochamber.com
Contact: Jordan Ferguson, President
Released: Monthly

54152 ■ Trenton Area Chamber of Commerce (TACC)
617 Main St.
Trenton, MO 64683
Ph: (660)359-4324
Fax: (660)359-4606
Co. E-mail: trentonchamber@grundyec.net
URL: http://www.trentonmochamber.com
Contact: Jordan Ferguson, President
Description: Promotes business and community development in north central Missouri. **Founded:** 1938. **Subscriptions:** 30000. **Publications:** Trenton (Monthly).

54153 ■ Troy Area Chamber of Commerce (TCC)
850 E Cherry St., Ste. A
Troy, MO 63379
Ph: (636)462-8769
Fax: (636)528-3731
Co. E-mail: info@troyonthemove.com
URL: http://www.troyonthemove.com
Contact: Kerry M. Klump, Executive Director
Description: Promotes business and community development in Troy, MO. **Publications:** Troy on the Move (Monthly). **Awards:** Man of the Year (Annual); Woman of the Year (Annual).

54154 ■ *Troy on the Move*
850 E Cherry St., Ste. A
Troy, MO 63379
Ph: (636)462-8769
Fax: (636)528-3731
Co. E-mail: info@troyonthemove.com
URL: http://www.troyonthemove.com
Contact: Kerry M. Klump, Executive Director
Released: Monthly

54155 ■ Union Chamber of Commerce (UCC)
PO Box 168
Union, MO 63084
Ph: (636)583-8979
Fax: (636)583-4001
Co. E-mail: tammy@unionmochamber.org
URL: http://www.unionmochamber.org/unionchamber
Contact: Tammy Stowe, Executive Director
Description: Businesses and individuals interested in advancing the civic, cultural, economic, industrial, and professional welfare of the Union, MO area. Sponsors Meet the Candidates Forum. Conducts Founder's Day 10 K Run. **Founded:** 1909.

54156 ■ *Update*
423 N Market
Maryville, MO 64468
Ph: (660)582-8643
Fax: (660)582-3071
Co. E-mail: chamber@asde.net
URL: http://www.maryvillechamber.com
Contact: Luke Reven, Executive Director
Released: Monthly

54157 ■ Van Buren Area Chamber of Commerce
402 Main St.
Van Buren, MO 63965
Ph: (573)323-0800
Co. E-mail: chamber@seevanburen.com
URL: http://www.seevanburen.com
Description: Promotes business and community development in the Van Buren-Big Spring, MO area.

54158 ■ Versailles Area Chamber of Commerce (VACC)
PO Box 256
Versailles, MO 65084
Ph: (573)378-4401
Fax: (573)378-2499
Co. E-mail: info@versailleschamber.com
URL: http://versailleschamber.com
Contact: Jim Dykzeul, President
Description: Promotes business and community development in Versailles, MO. Sponsors Olde Tyme Apple Festival and Christmas Lighting and Parade. **Awards:** Citizen of the Year (Annual).

54159 ■ *View Points*
607 N Douglass St.
Malden, MO 63863
Ph: (573)276-4519
Fax: (573)276-4925
Co. E-mail: info@maldenchamber.com
URL: http://www.maldenchamber.com
Contact: Brenda Williams, Director
Released: Bimonthly **Price:** free.

54160 ■ *Voice*
137 St. Robert Blvd.
St. Robert, MO 65584
Ph: (573)336-5121
Fax: (573)336-5472
Co. E-mail: chamber@wsrchamber.com
URL: http://www.waynesville-strobertchamber.com
Contact: Steve Lynch, Director
Released: Monthly **Price:** included in membership dues.

54161 ■ Warrenton Area Chamber of Commerce
117 W Booneslick Rd.
Warrenton, MO 63383
Ph: (636)456-2530

Fax: (636)456-2329
Co. E-mail: info@warrentoncoc.com
URL: http://warrentoncoc.com
Contact: Ruth Ebbinghaus, President
Description: Promotes the general welfare and prosperity of the Warrenton area. **Publications:** *Chamber Chatter.*

54162 ■ Warsaw Area Chamber of Commerce
PO Box 264
Warsaw, MO 65355
Ph: (660)438-5922
Free: 800-WARSAW-4
Fax: (660)438-3493
Co. E-mail: warsawcc@embarqmail.com
URL: http://www.warsawmo.org
Contact: Ann Porter, President
Description: Promotes business and community development in the Warsaw, MO area.

54163 ■ Washington Area Chamber of Commerce
323 W Main St.
Washington, MO 63090
Ph: (636)239-2715
Free: 888-7-WASHMO
URL: http://www.washmo.org/chamber/chamber.php
Contact: Mark Wessels, President
Description: Promotes business and community development in the Washington, MO area. Sponsors Town and Country Fair; conducts charitable activities. **Founded:** 1939. **Publications:** *Communicator* (Periodic). **Educational Activities:** Chamber Banquet (Annual).

54164 ■ Waynesville-St. Robert Area Chamber of Commerce
137 St. Robert Blvd.
St. Robert, MO 65584
Ph: (573)336-5121
Fax: (573)336-5472
Co. E-mail: chamber@wsrchamber.com
URL: http://www.waynesville-strobertchamber.com
Contact: Steve Lynch, Director
Description: Promotes business and community development in the greater Waynesville-St. Robert, Fort Leonard Wood area. Sponsors summer film festivals, Annual Spring and Fall Golf Tournaments, Annual April Fool's Day Community Trout Fry, and Annual Leader Appreciation Breakfast. **Founded:** 1979. **Publications:** *Voice* (Monthly). **Educational Activities:** Waynesville-St. Robert Area Chamber of Commerce Luncheon (Monthly). **Awards:** Citizen of the Year (Annual); Annual Kathleen Parker Scholarship Award (Annual).

54165 ■ Webb City Area Chamber of Commerce
555 S Main St.
Webb City, MO 64870
Ph: (417)673-1154
Fax: (417)673-2856
Co. E-mail: gwen@webbcitychamber.com
URL: http://www.webbcitychamber.com
Contact: Dixie Meredith, Executive Director
Description: Promotes business and community development in Webb City, MO. Conducts educational activities in local schools. Sponsors area festivals and the Christmas Parade in December. Promotes many activities for the young population such as the DARE program, educational activities in local schools and an annual banquet.

54166 ■ Webster Groves-Shrewsbury Area Chamber of Commerce (WGACC)
357 Marshall Ave., Ste. A
Webster Groves, MO 63119
Ph: (314)962-4142
Fax: (314)962-9398
Co. E-mail: chamberinfo@go-webster.com
URL: http://www.webstershrewsburychamber.com
Contact: Rebecca Olson, President
Description: Promotes business and community development in the Missouri cities of Webster Groves, Shrewsbury and surrounding area. Conducts golf tournament, business expo, community awards banquet and other events to promote its membership and community. **Founded:** 1937. **Publications:**

Chamber Chronicle (Monthly); *Business and Community Guide* (Annual). **Awards:** Heart of the Community Awards (Annual).

54167 ■ Wentzville Chamber of Commerce (WCC)
PO Box 11
Wentzville, MO 63385
Ph: (636)327-6914
Fax: (636)634-2760
Co. E-mail: info@wentzvillechamber.com
URL: http://www.wentzvillechamber.com
Contact: Erin Williams, Executive Director
Description: Promotes business and community development in Wentzville, MO. **Founded:** 1966. **Awards:** Business of the Year; Chamber Person of the Year; Community Service Award; Small Business of the Year. **Telecommunication Services:** erin@wentzvillechamber.com.

54168 ■ *West Plains Ambassador*
401 Jefferson Ave.
West Plains, MO 65775-2659
Ph: (417)256-4433
Fax: (417)256-8711
Co. E-mail: info@wpchamber.com
URL: http://wpchamber.com
Released: Monthly

54169 ■ West St. Louis County Chamber of Commerce (WSLCCC)
15965 Manchester Rd., Ste. 102
Ellisville, MO 63011
Ph: (636)230-9900
Fax: (636)230-9912
URL: http://www.westcountychamber.com
Contact: Lori Kelling, President
Description: Promotes business and community development in western St. Louis County, MO. **Founded:** 1957. **Publications:** *The Enterprise* (Monthly); *Buyer's Guide and Membership Directory* (Annual). **Educational Activities:** General Membership (Monthly).

54170 ■ Windsor Area Chamber of Commerce
102 N Main
Windsor, MO 65360
Ph: (660)647-2318
Co. E-mail: windsorm@iland.net
URL: http://www.windsormo.org
Contact: Terri Kline, President
Description: Promotes business and community development in Windsor, MO. Publications: none.

54171 ■ Wright City Area Chamber of Commerce
PO Box 444
Wright City, MO 63390
Ph: (636)745-7855
Co. E-mail: wcchamber@wrightcitychamber.com
URL: http://www.wrightcitychamber.com
Contact: Phil Cartwright, President
Description: Promotes business and community development in Wright City, MO. Sponsors Strassenbash festival. **Founded:** 1939.

54172 ■ *Your Chamber Connection*
PO Box 191
Farmington, MO 63640
Ph: (573)756-3615
Fax: (573)756-1003
Co. E-mail: doug@farmingtonmo.org
URL: http://www.farmingtonmo.org
Contact: Doug McDermott, Executive Director
Released: Monthly **Price:** included in membership dues.

MINORITY BUSINESS ASSISTANCE PROGRAMS

54173 ■ St. Louis Minority Business Council
308 N 21st St., Ste. 700
St. Louis, MO 63103
Ph: (314)241-1143

Fax: (314)241-1073
Co. E-mail: info@simbc
URL: http://www.slmbc.org
Contact: James Webb, President

Description: Provides ongoing growth opportunities, financial support, and training and education for its corporate members and for Minority Business Enterprises.

54174 ■ University of Missouri--Kansas City - Small Business and Technology Development Center
4747 Troost, Rm. 104A
Kansas City, MO 64110
Ph: (816)235-6063
Fax: (816)235-2947
Co. E-mail: umkcsbdc@umkc.edu
URL: http://sbtdc.umkc.edu
Contact: Carmen DeHart, Director

FINANCING AND LOAN PROGRAMS

54175 ■ A.G. Edwards & Sons
1 N. Jefferson
Saint Louis, MO 63103
Ph: (314)955-3000
Fax: (314)955-2890
URL: http://www.agedwards.com
Contact: Chris Redmond, Managing Director

Investment Policies: Fund of funds. **Industry Preferences:** Agriculture, forestry, and fishing. **Geographic Preference:** Missouri.

54176 ■ Bankers Capital Corporation
3100 Gillham Rd.
Kansas City, MO 64109
Ph: (816)531-1600
Fax: (816)531-1334
Contact: Raymond E. Glasnapp, President

Preferred Investment Size: $100,000 minimum. **Industry Preferences:** Semiconductors and other electronics, consumer related, industrial and energy. **Geographic Preference:** Midwest.

54177 ■ Capital for Business, Inc.
11 S. Meramac St., Ste. 1430
Clayton, MO 63105
Ph: (314)746-7427
Fax: (314)746-8739
Co. E-mail: info@capitalforbusiness.com
URL: http://www.capitalforbusiness.com
Contact: Stephen B. Broun, Managing Partner
E-mail: steve.broun@capitalforbusiness.com

Preferred Investment Size: $500,000 to $5,000,000. **Industry Preferences:** Internet specific, medical and health, consumer related, semiconductors and other electronics, computer hardware, communications and media. **Geographic Preference:** Midwest.

54178 ■ Crown Capital Corporation
12935 N. Forty Dr., Ste. 212
Saint Louis, MO 63141
Ph: (314)590-5100
Fax: (314)590-5105
URL: http://www.crown-cap.com
Contact: R. William Breece, Chief Executive Officer
E-mail: rbreece@crown-cap.com

Preferred Investment Size: $1,000,000 minimum. **Industry Preferences:** Communications, computer software, Internet specific, semiconductors and other electronics, medical and health, consumer related, industrial and energy, financial services, business service, agriculture, forestry and fishing, and other. **Geographic Preference:** U.S.

54179 ■ InvestAmerica Venture Group, Inc. (Kansas City)
Commerce Tower
911 Main St., Ste. 2424
Kansas City, MO 64105
Ph: (816)842-0114

Fax: (816)471-7339
URL: http://www.investamericaventuregroup.com
Contact: Kevin F. Mullane, Senior Vice President

Preferred Investment Size: $1,000,000 to $2,000,000. **Industry Preferences:** Other products, industrial and energy, Internet specific, communications and media, consumer related, computer software, and services, semiconductors and other electronics, computer hardware, biotechnology, medical and health. **Geographic Preference:** U.S.

54180 ■ Kansas City Equity Partners
233 W. 47th St.
Kansas City, MO 64112
Ph: (816)960-1771
Fax: (816)960-1777
Co. E-mail: info@kcep.com
URL: http://www.kcep.com
Contact: Abel Mojica, Principal

Preferred Investment Size: $2,000,000 to $6,000,000. **Industry Preferences:** Internet specific, communications and media, consumer related, industrial and energy, computer software and services, semiconductors and other electronics. **Geographic Preference:** Mid Atlantic, Midwest, Northeast, Rocky Mountains, and West Coast.

54181 ■ RiverVest Venture Partners
7733 Forsyth Blvd., Ste. 1650
Saint Louis, MO 63150
Ph: (314)726-6700
Fax: (314)726-6715
Co. E-mail: info@rivervest.com
URL: http://www.rivervest.com
Contact: Thomas C. Melzer, Managing Director
E-mail: tmelzer@rivervest.com

Preferred Investment Size: $500,000 to $6,000,000. **Industry Preferences:** Biotechnology, medical and health. **Geographic Preference:** U.S.

PROCUREMENT ASSISTANCE PROGRAMS

54182 ■ Heartland Procurement Technical Assistance Center - Institute for Entrepreneurship and Innovation
University of Missouri - Kansas City
4747 Troost Bldg., Rm. 106
Kansas City, MO 64110
Ph: (816)235-2891
Fax: (816)235-2947
Co. E-mail: longdew@umkc.edu
URL: http://www.mssu.edu/heartlandptac/
Contact: Dewayne Long, Director

Description: Assists viable businesses located in Southwest Missouri and the State of Kansas with potential market expansion through procurement opportunities with the government.

54183 ■ Heartland Procurement Technical Assistance Center - Missouri Southern State University - Central Office
Plaster Hall, Rm. 111
3950 Newman Rd.
Joplin, MO 64801-1512
Ph: (417)625-9538
Fax: (417)625-3090
Co. E-mail: heartlandptac@mssu.edu
URL: http://www.heartlandptac.org
Contact: Terri Bennett, Program Manager
E-mail: Bennett-T@mssu.edu

Description: Mission is to assist viable businesses located in Southwest Missouri and the State of Kansas with potential market expansion through procurement opportunities with the government.

54184 ■ Missouri Procurement Technical Assistance Center - Central Region PTAC - University of Missouri-Columbia
W1026 Lafferre Hall
Columbia, MO 65211
Ph: (573)882-9398

Fax: (573)882-9931
Co. E-mail: stubyb@missouri.edu
URL: http://www.missouribusiness.net
Contact: Bill Stuby, Director
E-mail: stubyb@missouri.edu

Description: Assists businesses including small, disadvantaged and women owned firms in obtaining federal, state and local government contracts.

54185 ■ Missouri Procurement Technical Assistance Center - Eastern Region PTAC - University of Missouri at St. Louis
100 N Tucker, Ste. 530
St. Louis, MO 63101
Ph: (314)621-7280
Fax: (314)621-9871
Co. E-mail: frankjo@missouri.edu
URL: http://www.missouribusiness.net
Contact: Joe Frank, Director
E-mail: fyker@missouri.edu

Description: Assists businesses including small, disadvantaged and women owned firms in obtaining federal, state and local government contracts.

54186 ■ Missouri Procurement Technical Assistance Center - Mid-South Region PTAC - Howell County Extension Center - University of Missouri
217 S Aid Ave.
West Plains, MO 65775
Ph: (417)256-2391
Fax: (417)256-8569
Co. E-mail: mushrushw@missouri.edu
URL: http://www.missouribusiness.net
Contact: Willis Mushrush, Specialist
E-mail: mushrushw@missouri.edu

Description: Assists businesses including small, disadvantaged and women owned firms in obtaining federal, state and local government contracts.

54187 ■ Missouri Procurement Technical Assistance Center - South Central Region PTAC - Center for Entrepreneurship and Outreach
203 Centennial Hall
300 W 12th St.
Rolla, MO 65409-1110
Ph: (573)341-4562
Fax: (573)341-6579
Co. E-mail: bwhite@mst.edu
URL: http://ecodevo.mst.edu/

Description: Assists businesses including small, disadvantaged and women owned firms in obtaining federal, state and local government contracts. Formerly University of Missouri-Rolla.

54188 ■ Missouri Procurement Technical Assistance Center - Western Region PTAC - University of Missouri, Kansas City
4747 Troost Bldg., Rm. 105
Kansas City, MO 64110
Ph: (816)235-2891
Fax: (816)235-2947
Co. E-mail: leonardd@umkc.edu
URL: http://www.missouribusiness.net/ptac
Contact: Donna Leonard, Director

Description: Connects small business owners with government agencies in search of products and services at competitive prices.

54189 ■ Missouri Southern State University - Heartland Procurement Technical Assistance Center - Institute for Procurement Assistance
Plaster Hall, Rm. 111
3950 Newman Rd.
Joplin, MO 64801-1512
Ph: (417)625-9538
Fax: (417)625-3090
Co. E-mail: heartlandptac@mssu.edu
URL: http://www.heartlandptac.org
Contact: Terrie Bennett, Program Manager
Description: Covers activities for Kansas.

54190 ■ St. Louis County Economic Council
121 S Meramec Ave., Ste. 900
St. Louis, MO 63105
Ph: (314)615-7663

Fax: (314)615-7666
Co. E-mail: info@SLCEC.com
URL: http://www.slcec.com
Contact: Denny Coleman, Chief Executive Officer

INCUBATORS/RESEARCH AND TECHNOLOGY PARKS

54191 ■ Arts Incubator of Kansas City
115 W. 18th St.
Kansas City, MO 64108
Ph: (816)421-2292
Fax: (816)421-2293
Co. E-mail: info@artsincubatorkc.org
URL: http://artsincubatorkc.org/
Description: A nonprofit organization dedicated to working with emerging artists in the development of their careers by providing affordable, quality studio space in the Crossroads Arts District, a community experiencing extraordinary growth and national recognition as one of the top arts communities in the nation, in addition to providing business workshops and consulting.

54192 ■ Growth Opportunity Connection - Center for Business Innovation
4747 Troost Ave.
Kansas City, MO 64110
Ph: (816)235-6146
Fax: (816)235-6586
Co. E-mail: info@goconnection.org
URL: http://www.goconnection.org

54193 ■ Hispanic Economic Development Corporation
2130 Jefferson St.
Kansas City, MO 64108
Ph: (816)221-3442
Fax: (816)221-6458
Co. E-mail: hedc@kchedc.org
URL: http://www.kchedc.org
Contact: Bernardo Ramirez, Executive Director
Description: not-for-profit community development corporation in the State of Missouri. Founded for the purpose of developing and implementing economic development initiatives that would positively contribute to the quality of life for Latinos in Kansas City, HEDC utilizes its designation as a CDC to access various resources and tools that allow the organization to serve as a catalyst for change within the Latino community.

54194 ■ Joseph Newman Innovation Center
407 Pennsylvania
Joplin, MO 64801
Ph: (417)624-4150
Co. E-mail: steve@joplincc.com
URL: http://www.newmaninnovationcenter.com/
Description: An economic development tool designed to accelerate the growth and success of entrepreneurial companies through an array of business support resources and services. The center's main goal is to produce successful firms that will leave the program financially viable and freestanding.

54195 ■ Life Science Business Incubator at Monsanto Place
1601 S Providence Rd.
University of Missouri
Missouri, MO 65211-3460
Ph: (573)884-0496
Fax: (573)884-3600
Co. E-mail: info@MUincubator.com
URL: http://muincubator.com/index.html
Contact: Jake Halliday, Chief Executive Officer
Description: A small business incubator promoting comprehensive economic development strategy for mid-Missouri by leveraging research and innovation at the University of Missouri-Columbia in order to attract additional life science enterprises to the region and to create new life science ventures around university technologies.

54196 ■ Missouri Enterprise
900 Innovation Dr.
Rolla, MO 65401
Ph: (573)341-0117
Free: 800-956-2682

Fax: (573)341-0135
URL: http://www.missourienterprise.org
Contact: Mary Dean, President
Description: Offers business consulting services to mid-sized manufacturing companies.

54197 ■ Nidus Center for Scientific Enterprise
1005 N Warson rd., Ste. 201
St. Louis, MO 63132
Ph: (314)812-8003
Fax: (314)812-8080
Co. E-mail: susan@niduspartners.com
URL: http://www.niduscenter.com/
Description: An agriculture and energy incubator serving entrepreneur clients who are refining and preparing new technologies for market.

54198 ■ St. Charles County Economic Development Center
5988 Mid Rivers Mall Dr.
St Charles, MO 63304-7195
Ph: (636)441-6880
Free: 877-441-6880
Fax: (636)441-6881
Co. E-mail: info@edcscc.com
URL: http://www.edcscc.com
Description: A small business incubator working in partnership with local governments, community and business leaders, and other regional organizations to offer business financing programs, job creation, and business recruitment and retention.

54199 ■ St. Louis Enterprise Centers
121 S Meramec, Ste. 900
St. Louis, MO 63105
Ph: (314)615-7663
Fax: (314)615-7666
Co. E-mail: Incubators@SLCEC.com
URL: http://www.slcec.com/st-louis-enterprise-centers.html
Description: A small business incubator providing new and growing small businesses with affordable business space, shared support services, access to expert mentors, and valuable networking opportunities. Maintains five state-of-the-art enterprise centers.

54200 ■ Students In Free Enterprise
1959 Kerr St.
900 N. Benton Ave.
Springfield, MO 65803
Ph: (417)575-3509
Free: 800-922-2274
Fax: (417)873-7529
Co. E-mail: dpatterson@sife.org
URL: http://www.sife.org
Description: A global non-profit organization active on more than 1,800 college campuses in more than 43 countries and territories consisting of student teams who develop projects to help create economic opportunity by teaching concepts related to free market economics, business ethics, entrepreneurship, and personal finance and success skills.

54201 ■ Technology Entrepreneur Center
210 N. Tucker Blvd., Ste. 600
St. Louis, MO 63101
Ph: (314)436-3500
Fax: (314)333-0409
Co. E-mail: info@tecstl.org
URL: http://www.tecstl.org/
Description: A small business incubator assisting technology start-up companies in St. Louis to increase their likelihood of success through access to highly qualified mentors, assistance with business planning and strategies, and office services.

54202 ■ The Thomas Hill Enterprise Center
PO Box 276
Macon, MO 63552
Ph: (660)385-6550
URL: http://www.e-center.org
Description: The Center describes itself as an internet/intranet incubator that offers entrepreneurs skills training, government forms, and other services.

EDUCATIONAL PROGRAMS

54203 ■ Jefferson College - Extended Learning
1000 Viking Dr.
Hillsboro, MO 63050
Ph: (636)789-3000
Fax: (636)789-4012
URL: http://www.jeffco.edu
Description: Offers a program/classes in small business/small business management.

54204 ■ St. Louis Community College - Institute for Continuing Education
Cosand Ctr.
300 S Broadway
St. Louis, MO 63102
Ph: (314)539-5000
Fax: (314)984-7960
URL: http://www.stlcc.edu
Description: Small Business Program offers courses designed for small business owners.

LEGISLATIVE ASSISTANCE

54205 ■ Missouri Department of Economic Development - Economic Development Office
301 W. High St.
Jefferson City, MO 65102
Ph: (573)751-4962
Free: 800-523-1434
Fax: (573)526-7700
Co. E-mail: ecodev@ded.mo.gov
URL: http://www.ded.mo.gov
Description: Works to identify and solve problems specific to small business.

PUBLICATIONS

54206 ■ *How to Form Your Own Missouri Corporation Before the Inc. Dries!: A Step by Step Guide, With Forms*
333 S. Taylor Ave.
Oak Park, IL 60302
Ph: (708)524-9033
Fax: (708)524-9038
Ed: Phillip Williams. **Released:** 1992. **Price:** $19.95 (paper). **Description:** Volume 5 of the Small Business Incorporation series. Explains the advantages and disadvantages of incorporation and shows, step-by-step, how the small business owners can incorporate at low cost. Covers Missouri profit and nonprofit corporations, Missouri professional service corporations, subchapter S corporations, and Delaware corporations. Includes forms necessary for incorporation.

54207 ■ *Ingram's*
306 E. 12th St., Ste. 1014
Kansas City, MO 64106
Ph: (816)842-9994
Fax: (816)474-1111
Co. E-mail: subscriptions@ingramsonline.com
URL: http://www.ingramsonline.com

54208 ■ *Kansas City Business Journal*
1101 Walnut, Ste. 800
Kansas City, MO 64106
Ph: (816)421-5900
Fax: (816)472-4010
Co. E-mail: kcbj@unicom.net
URL: http://www.bizjournals.com/kansascity/

54209 ■ *St. Louis Business Journal*
One Metropolitan Sq., Ste. 2170
St. Louis, MO 63102
Ph: (314)421-6200
Fax: (314)621-5031
Co. E-mail: stlouis@amcity.com
URL: http://www.bizjournals.com/stlouis/

54210 ■ *Smart Start your Missouri Business*
PSI Research
300 N. Valley Dr.
Grants Pass, OR 97526
Ph: (503)479-9464
Free: 800-228-2275

Fax: (503)476-1479
Co. E-mail: info@psi-research.com
URL: http://www.psi-research.com
Ed: Michael D. Jenkins. **Released:** Revised edition, 1992. **Price:** $29.95 (looseleaf binder); $24.95 (paper). **Description:** Part of the Successful Business Library series.

PUBLISHERS

54211 ■ Three House Publishing
490 Hillbrook Dr.
Chesterfield, MO 63006-6672

Ph: (314)277-4560
Contact: J. K. Dennis, Manager

Description: Description: Publishes course materials. Also publishes novels and short stories.

SMALL BUSINESS DEVELOPMENT CENTERS

54212 ■ Billings Small Business Development Center
Big Sky Economic Development Authority
222 N 32nd St., Ste. 200
Billings, MT 59101
Ph: (406)256-6871
Fax: (406)256-6877
Co. E-mail: helvik@bigskyeda.org
URL: http://bigskyeda-edc.org/small-business-development.php
Contact: Rebecca Helvik, Advisor
Description: Represents and promotes the small business sector. Provides management assistance to current and prospective small business owners. Helps to improve management skills and expand the products and services of members.

54213 ■ Bozeman Small Business Development Center
222 E Main St., Ste. 202
Bozeman, MT 59715
Ph: (406)728-9234
Fax: (406)582-5855
Co. E-mail: ryanh@mtcdc.org
URL: http://www.mtcdc.org
Contact: Ryan Hansen, Director
Description: Represents and promotes the small business sector. Provides management assistance to current and prospective small business owners. Helps to improve management skills and expand the products and services of members.

54214 ■ Butte Small Business Development Center
65 E Broadway
Butte, MT 59701
Ph: (406)782-7333
Fax: (406)782-9675
Co. E-mail: jjaksha@headwatersrcd.org
Contact: Julie Jaksha, Advisor
Description: Represents and promotes the small business sector. Provides management assistance to current and prospective small business owners. Helps to improve management skills and expand the products and services of members.

54215 ■ Great Falls Small Business Development Center
PO Box 949
Great Falls, MT 59403
Ph: (406)453-8834
Fax: (406)454-2995
Co. E-mail: rengum@gfdevelopment.org
URL: http://sbdc.mt.gov
Contact: Rebecca Engum, Director
URL(s): www.gfdevelopment.org/pages2/p13/sbdc_services.php. **Description:** Represents and promotes the small business sector. Provides management assistance to current and prospective small business owners. Helps to improve management skills and expand the products and services of members.

54216 ■ Havre Small Business Development Center
PO Box 170
Havre, MT 59501
Ph: (406)399-1557
Co. E-mail: jlaplante@bearpaw.org
URL: http://sbdc.mt.gov/default.mcpx
Contact: Joe LaPlante, Director
Description: Represents and promotes the small business sector. Provides management assistance to current and prospective small business owners. Helps to improve management skills and expand the products and services of members.

54217 ■ Helena Small Business Development Center
Montana Business Assistance Connections, Inc.
225 Cruise Ave.
Helena, MT 59601
Ph: (406)447-1510
Fax: (406)447-1514
Co. E-mail: danderson@mbac.biz
URL: http://www.mbac.biz/index.php?pr=Small_Business_Development_Center
Contact: Dan Anderson, Director
Description: Represents and promotes the small business sector. Provides management assistance to current and prospective small business owners. Helps to improve management skills and expand the products and services of members.

54218 ■ Kalispell Small Business Development Center
Kalispell Area Chamber of Commerce
15 Depot Park
Kalispell, MT 59901
Ph: (406)758-2802
Co. E-mail: sbdc@kalispellchamber.com
URL: http://sbdc.mt.gov
Contact: Chris Parson, Director
Description: Represents and promotes the small business sector. Provides management assistance to current and prospective small business owners. Helps to improve management skills and expand the products and services of members.

54219 ■ Missoula Small Business Development Center
PO Box 200505
Helena, MT 59620-0505
Ph: (406)841-2747
Fax: (406)841-2728
Co. E-mail: mtsbdc@mt.gov
URL: http://sbdc.mt.gov
Description: Represents and promotes the small business sector. Provides management assistance to current and prospective small business owners. Helps to improve management skills and expand the products and services of members.

54220 ■ Southeastern Montana Small Business Development Center
6200 Main St.
Colstrip, MT 59323
Ph: (406)748-2990

Fax: (406)748-2900
Co. E-mail: semdc@bhwi.net
URL: http://semdc.org/services/small-business-assistance
Contact: Jim Atchison, Executive Director
Description: Represents and promotes the small business sector. Provides management assistance to current and prospective small business owners. Helps to improve management skills and expand the products and services of members.

54221 ■ Wolf Point Small Business Development Center
233 Cascade St.
Wolf Point, MT 59201
Ph: (406)653-2590
Fax: (406)653-1840
Co. E-mail: sbdc@gndc.org
URL: http://sbdc.mt.gov/2012regionaloffices.mcpx
Contact: Lorene Hintz, Director
Description: Represents and promotes the small business sector. Provides management assistance to current and prospective small business owners. Helps to improve management skills and expand the products and services of members.

SMALL BUSINESS ASSISTANCE PROGRAMS

54222 ■ Big Sky Economic Development Authority
222 N 32nd St., Ste. 200
Billings, MT 59101-1911
Ph: (406)256-6871
Fax: (406)256-6877
Co. E-mail: arveschoug@bigskyeda.org
URL: http://www.bigskyeda.org
Contact: Steve Arveschoug, Chairperson
Description: Offers U.S. Customs services, bonded and general warehouse storage, no inventory tax, and licensing brokerage services to shippers, wholesalers, and manufacturers. Access is provided to international and domestic shippers.

54223 ■ Montana Department of Agriculture - Agriculture Development Division
303 N Roberts St.
Helena, MT 59620-0201
Ph: (406)444-3144
Fax: (406)444-5409
Co. E-mail: agr@mt.gov
URL: http://www.agr.state.mt.us
Contact: Ron DeYong, Director
Description: Provides market research and other assistance to Montana's agricultural producers through identification, analysis, and direction in development of both foreign and domestic markets.

54224 ■ Montana Department of Commerce - Business Resources Division
301 S. Park
Helena, MT 59620-0501
Ph: (406)841-2730

Fax: (406)841-2731
URL: http://businessresources.mt.gov/
Contact: Anthony J. Preite, Director
Description: Publicizes and advertises Montana to firms planning relocations or expansions.

54225 ▪ Montana Department of Commerce - Census and Economic Information Center
301 S Park Ave.
Helena, MT 59620-0505
Ph: (406)841-2740
Fax: (406)841-2731
Co. E-mail: ceic@mt.gov
URL: http://ceic.mt.gov/
Description: Provides population and economic information to businesses, government agencies, and the general public for research, planning, and decision-making purposes.

54226 ▪ Montana Department of Commerce - Community Development Division
301 S Park Ave.
Helena, MT 59601
Ph: (406)841-2770
Fax: (406)841-2771
Co. E-mail: dacole@mt.gov
URL: http://comdev.mt.gov/
Contact: Dave Cole, Administrator
Description: Provides assistance to cities, towns, counties, and tribal governments in planning and carrying out effective economic development programs specifically designed to meet local needs.

54227 ▪ Montana Department of Commerce - Economic Development Division - Marketing Assistance and Made in Montana Program
301 S Park Ave.
Helena, MT 59620-0505
Ph: (406)841-2757
Fax: (406)841-2728
URL: http://www.madeinmontanausa.com/
Contact: Anthony J. Preite, Director
Description: Works with individual small businesses to develop and expand outlets for products manufactured or processed in Montana.

54228 ▪ Montana Department of Commerce - Montana Science and Technology Alliance Division
301 S Park Ave.
Helena, MT 59601
Ph: (406)841-2700
Fax: (406)841-2701
Co. E-mail: apreite@state.mt.us
URL: http://www.commerce.state.mt.us
Contact: Anthony J. Preite, Director
Description: Encourages innovative scientific and technical development within the state. Aids in the creation of new jobs. Assists in financing the establishment of technology-intensive businesses and finances projects that it believes have outstanding technological and commercial potential. Has four complementary investment programs for financial assistance: seed capital investment, applied technology research, technical assistance and technology transfer, and research capability development.

54229 ▪ Montana Department of Commerce - Trade & International Relations Bureau
301 S Park Ave.
Helena, MT 59601
Ph: (406)841-2757
Fax: (406)841-2731
URL: http://businessresources.mt.gov/BRD_TIR.asp
Contact: Mark Bisom, Section Chief
Description: Enhances sales of Montana goods and services in international markets and encourages tourism promotion and reverse investment opportunities. Also offers one-stop technical assistance to businesses wishing to enter foreign markets.

54230 ▪ University of Montana - Montana Business Connections
231 Gallagher Business Bldg.
Missoula, MT 59812-2086
Ph: (406)243-4009

Fax: (406)243-2086
Co. E-mail: mtbc@business.umt.edu
URL: http://www.mbc.umt.edu
Description: Seeks to use the Montana University System to link business owners and entrepreneurs with information, resources, and expertise.

SCORE OFFICES

54231 ▪ Billings SCORE
Co. E-mail: djohnson@crowleylaw.com

54232 ▪ Bitterroot SCORE
Co. E-mail: fishaus@montana.com

54233 ▪ Butte SCORE
Co. E-mail: buttescore@yahoo.com

54234 ▪ Great Falls SCORE
Co. E-mail: score@sofast.net

54235 ▪ Helena SCORE
Co. E-mail: helenascore@yahoo.com

54236 ▪ Missoula SCORE

54237 ▪ Northwest Montana SCORE

54238 ▪ Panhandle SCORE
Co. E-mail: chamber@scottsbluffgering.net

54239 ▪ SCORE Bozeman
2000 Commerce Way
Bozeman, MT 59715
Ph: (406)586-5421
Co. E-mail: scorebozeman@gmail.com
URL: http://www.scorebozeman.org
Description: Serves as volunteer program in which working and retired business management professionals provide free business counseling to men and women who are considering starting a small business, encountering problems with their business, or expanding their business. Offers free one-on-one counseling, online counseling and low cost workshops on a variety of business topics.

CHAMBERS OF COMMERCE

54240 ▪ *The Advantage*
909 S Central Ave.
Sidney, MT 59270
Ph: (406)433-1916
Fax: (406)433-1127
Co. E-mail: schamber@midrivers.com
URL: http://www.sidneymt.com
Contact: Wade VanEvery, Executive Director
Released: Monthly **Price:** included in membership dues.

54241 ▪ Anaconda Chamber of Commerce (ACOC)
306 E Park St.
Anaconda, MT 59711
Ph: (406)563-2400
Fax: (406)563-2400
Co. E-mail: anacondachamber@rfwave.net
URL: http://www.anacondamt.org
Contact: Edith Fransen, Executive Director
Description: Promotes business and community development in Anaconda, MT. Sponsors annual Christmas Stroll, Chocolate Festival, and Wayne Estes Northwest Basketball Championship. **Founded:** 1934.

54242 ▪ Baker Chamber of Commerce and Agriculture
PO Box 849
Baker, MT 59313-0849
Ph: (406)778-2266
Free: 800-862-2537
Co. E-mail: bakerchamberofcommerce@yahoo.com
URL: http://www.bakermt.com
Contact: Mona Madler, Vice President
Description: Promotes business and community development in Baker, MT area. **Founded:** 1910.

54243 ▪ Beaverhead Chamber of Commerce
10 W Reeder
Dillon, MT 59725

Ph: (406)683-5511
Co. E-mail: info@beaverheadchamber.org
URL: http://www.beaverheadchamber.org
Contact: Bernie Childers, Executive Director
Description: Promotes business and community development in Beaverhead County, MT. Sponsors Rancher Roundup festival. **Founded:** 1948. **Publications:** *Beaverhead County, Montana* (Annual); *Welcome Guide* (Annual); *Recreational Opportunities and Information in Dillon and Beaverhead County, Montana.* **Awards:** Ag Business of the Year (Annual); Large Business of the Year (Annual); Medium Business of the Year (Annual); Small Business of the Year (Annual).

54244 ▪ *Beaverhead County, Montana*
10 W Reeder
Dillon, MT 59725
Ph: (406)683-5511
Co. E-mail: info@beaverheadchamber.org
URL: http://www.beaverheadchamber.org
Contact: Bernie Childers, Executive Director
Released: Annual **Price:** free.

54245 ▪ Belgrade Chamber of Commerce (BCC)
10 E Main St.
Belgrade, MT 59714
Ph: (406)388-1616
Fax: (406)388-2090
Co. E-mail: info@belgradechamber.org
URL: http://www.belgradechamber.org
Contact: Debra Youngberg, Executive Director
Description: Strives to serve its members by promoting business, economic, and community development in Belgrade, MT. **Founded:** 1963. **Publications:** *Chamber Update* (Monthly); *Belgrade Montana, Community Profile and Chamber News.* **Educational Activities:** Belgrade Chamber of Commerce Luncheon (Monthly). **Awards:** Employer of the Month (Monthly). **Telecommunication Services:** dyoungberg@belgradechamber.org.

54246 ▪ *Belgrade Montana, Community Profile and Chamber News*
10 E Main St.
Belgrade, MT 59714
Ph: (406)388-1616
Fax: (406)388-2090
Co. E-mail: info@belgradechamber.org
URL: http://www.belgradechamber.org
Contact: Debra Youngberg, Executive Director
Price: included in membership dues.

54247 ▪ Bigfork Area Chamber of Commerce (BACC)
PO Box 237
Bigfork, MT 59911
Ph: (406)837-5888
Fax: (406)837-5808
Co. E-mail: chamber@bigfork.org
URL: http://www.bigfork.org
Contact: Bruce Solberg, Executive Director
Description: Promotes business and community development in the Bigfork, MT area. Encourages tourism. **Founded:** 1970.

54248 ▪ Billings Area Chamber of Commerce
815 S 27th St.
Billings, MT 59107-1177
Ph: (406)245-4111
Fax: (406)245-7333
Co. E-mail: info@billingschamber.com
URL: http://www.billingschamber.com
Contact: John Brewer, President
Description: Promotes business and community development in the Billings, MT area.

54249 ▪ Bitter Root Valley Chamber of Commerce
105 E Main St.
Hamilton, MT 59840
Ph: (406)363-2400

Fax: (406)363-2402
Co. E-mail: localinfo@bvchamber.com
URL: http://www.bitterrootvalleychamber.com
Contact: Richard O'Brien, Executive Director
Description: Promotes business and community development in the Bitterroot Valley, MT area. Sponsors Microbrew Festival and Winterfest. **Founded:** 1913. **Publications:** *Bitterroot Business News* (Bimonthly). **Awards:** Business Person of the Year (Annual).

54250 ■ *Bitterroot Business News*
105 E Main St.
Hamilton, MT 59840
Ph: (406)363-2400
Fax: (406)363-2402
Co. E-mail: localinfo@bvchamber.com
URL: http://www.bitterrootvalleychamber.com
Contact: Richard O'Brien, Executive Director
Released: Bimonthly

54251 ■ Bozeman Area Chamber of Commerce (BACC)
2000 Commerce Way
Bozeman, MT 59715
Ph: (406)586-5421
Free: 800-228-4224
Fax: (406)586-8286
Co. E-mail: info@bozemanchamber.com
URL: http://www.bozemanchamber.com
Contact: Daryl Schliem, President
Description: Promotes business and community development in the Bozeman, MT area. Sponsors festival. **Founded:** 1910. **Publications:** *Bozeman Visitor Guide* (Periodic); *Gallatin Valley Business* (Monthly). **Awards:** Community Excellence Award (Annual). **Telecommunication Services:** dschliem@bozemanchamber.com.

54252 ■ *Bozeman Visitor Guide*
2000 Commerce Way
Bozeman, MT 59715
Ph: (406)586-5421
Free: 800-228-4224
Fax: (406)586-8286
Co. E-mail: info@bozemanchamber.com
URL: http://www.bozemanchamber.com
Contact: Daryl Schliem, President
Released: Periodic

54253 ■ *Business Connection*
PO Box 7577
Missoula, MT 59807
Ph: (406)543-6623
Fax: (406)543-6625
Co. E-mail: info@missoulachamber.com
URL: http://www.missoulachamber.com
Contact: Kim Latrielle, President
Released: Monthly

54254 ■ Butte-Silver Bow Chamber of Commerce
1000 George St.
Butte, MT 59701
Ph: (406)723-3177
Free: 800-735-6814
Fax: (406)723-1215
Co. E-mail: bsbchamber@gmail.com
URL: http://www.buttechamber.org
Contact: Marko Lucich, Executive Director
Description: Promotes business and community development in Silver Bow County, MT. Sponsors competitions. Serves as a Convention and Visitor Bureau for travel in Montana. **Founded:** 1912. **Publications:** *The Progress* (Monthly); *Visitors' Guide* (Annual).

54255 ■ *Chamber Business News*
100 1 Ave. N
Great Falls, MT 59401
Ph: (406)761-4434
Fax: (406)761-6129
Co. E-mail: smalicott@greatfallschamber.org
URL: http://www.greatfallschamber.org
Contact: Steve Malicott, President
Released: Monthly **Price:** free for members.

54256 ■ *Chamber News*
15 Depot Park
Kalispell, MT 59901
Ph: (406)758-2800
Co. E-mail: info@kalispellchamber.com
URL: http://kalispellchamber.com
Contact: Joe Unterreiner, President
Released: Monthly

54257 ■ *Chamber Newsletter*
PO Box 1120
Whitefish, MT 59937
Ph: (406)862-3501
Fax: (406)862-9494
Co. E-mail: visitus@whitefishchamber.org
URL: http://www.whitefishchamber.org
Contact: Kevin Gartland, Executive Director
Released: Monthly

54258 ■ *Chamber Update*
10 E Main St.
Belgrade, MT 59714
Ph: (406)388-1616
Fax: (406)388-2090
Co. E-mail: info@belgradechamber.org
URL: http://www.belgradechamber.org
Contact: Debra Youngberg, Executive Director
Released: Monthly

54259 ■ *The Chambergram*
418 Main St.
Polson, MT 59860
Ph: (406)883-5969
Fax: (406)883-1716
Co. E-mail: info@polsonchamber.com
URL: http://www.polsonchamber.com
Contact: Heather Knutson, President
Released: Monthly

54260 ■ Circle Chamber of Commerce and Agriculture
PO Box 321
Circle, MT 59215
Ph: (406)485-2741
Co. E-mail: chamber@circle-montana.com
URL: http://circle-montana.com
Description: Promotes business and community development in Circle, MT.

54261 ■ Columbia Falls Area Chamber of Commerce
PO Box 312
Columbia Falls, MT 59912
Ph: (406)892-2072
Co. E-mail: info@columbiafallschamber.com
URL: http://www.columbiafallschamber.com
Contact: Paul McKenzie, President
Description: Promotes business and community development in Columbia Falls, MT area.

54262 ■ Columbia Falls Area Chamber Foundation
130 6th St., W, Rm. A
Columbia Falls, MT 59912-3615
Ph: (406)892-4391
Fax: (406)892-4413
Co. E-mail: info@columbiafallschamber.com
URL: http://www.columbiafallschamber.com
Contact: Carol Pike, Executive Director
Description: Promotes the prosperity of its members and the civic, commercial, industrial, and agricultural interests of the community in a way which maintains a small town, family oriented character.

54263 ■ Conrad Area Chamber of Commerce (CACC)
7 6th Ave. SW
Conrad, MT 59425
Ph: (406)271-7791
Fax: (406)221-2924
Co. E-mail: chamber@conradmt.com
URL: http://www.conradmt.com
Contact: Shari Richter, President
Description: Promotes business and community development and tourism in Conrad, MT. Sponsors Art on Main festival and Farm and Ranch Appreciation Day. Organizes retail promotions. **Founded:**

1965. **Publications:** *Live Wire* (Monthly). **Educational Activities:** Conrad Area Chamber of Commerce Meeting (Monthly).

54264 ■ Culbertson Chamber of Commerce
PO Box 351
Culbertson, MT 59218
Ph: (406)787-5271
Fax: (406)787-5271
Co. E-mail: culbertsonmt@hotmail.com
URL: http://www.culbertsonmt.com
Description: Promotes business and community development in Culbertson, MT area.

54265 ■ Cut Bank Area Chamber of Commerce
PO Box 1243
Cut Bank, MT 59427
Ph: (406)873-4041
Co. E-mail: info@cutbankchamber.com
URL: http://www.cutbankchamber.com
Contact: Jeff Billman, President
Description: Promotes business and community development in the Cut Bank, MT area.

54266 ■ Daniels County Chamber of Commerce and Agriculture
PO Box 91
Scobey, MT 59263
Ph: (406)487-2061
Co. E-mail: scobey@nemontel.net
URL: http://www.scobeymt.com
Description: Works to promote a healthy economic environment.

54267 ■ *Deer Lodge Demographics*
1109 Main St.
Deer Lodge, MT 59722
Ph: (406)846-2094
Fax: (406)846-2094
Co. E-mail: chamber@powellcountymontana.com
URL: http://www.powellcountymontana.com

54268 ■ *Deer Lodge Visitor's Guide*
1109 Main St.
Deer Lodge, MT 59722
Ph: (406)846-2094
Fax: (406)846-2094
Co. E-mail: chamber@powellcountymontana.com
URL: http://www.powellcountymontana.com

54269 ■ Ennis Area Chamber of Commerce
PO Box 291
Ennis, MT 59729
Ph: (406)682-4388
Fax: (406)682-4328
Co. E-mail: info@ennischamber.com
URL: http://www.ennischamber.com
Description: Promotes business and community development in Ennis, MT. **Founded:** 1991.

54270 ■ Eureka Area Chamber of Commerce
PO Box 186
Eureka, MT 59917
Ph: (406)889-4636
Fax: (406)297-7794
Co. E-mail: randy@welcome2eureka.com
URL: http://www.welcome2eureka.com
Contact: Randy McIntyre, Executive Director
Description: Promotes business and community development in Eureka, MT area.

54271 ■ *Eye on Business*
PO Box 1730
Helena, MT 59624-1730
Ph: (406)442-2405
Fax: (406)442-2409
Co. E-mail: schaefer@3rivers.net
URL: http://www.montanachamber.com
Contact: Webb Scott Brown, President
Released: Monthly

54272 ■ Fort Benton Chamber of Commerce
PO Box 12
Fort Benton, MT 59442

Ph: (406)622-3864
Co. E-mail: info@forbentonchamber.org
URL: http://www.fortbentonchamber.org
Contact: Earl Taylor, President
Description: Promotes business and community development in Fort Benton, MT area.

54273 ■ Gallatin Valley Business
2000 Commerce Way
Bozeman, MT 59715
Ph: (406)586-5421
Free: 800-228-4224
Fax: (406)586-8286
Co. E-mail: info@bozemanchamber.com
URL: http://www.bozemanchamber.com
Contact: Daryl Schliem, President
Released: Monthly

54274 ■ Gardiner Chamber of Commerce
PO Box 81
Gardiner, MT 59030
Ph: (406)848-7971
Fax: (855)828-2706
Co. E-mail: info@gardinerchamber.com
URL: http://www.gardinerchamber.com
Description: Promotes business and community development in Gardiner, MT.

54275 ■ Garfield County Chamber of Commerce
PO Box 370
Jordan, MT 59337
Ph: (406)557-6158
Fax: (406)557-6158
Co. E-mail: chamber@garfieldcounty.com
URL: http://www.garfieldcounty.com
Contact: Jo Dee Watson, President
Description: Promotes business and community development in Garfield County, MT area.

54276 ■ Glasgow Chamber of Commerce Newsletter
PO Box 832
Glasgow, MT 59230-0832
Ph: (406)228-2222
Co. E-mail: chamber@glasgowmt.net
URL: http://www.glasgowmt.net
Contact: Lisa Olk, Executive Director
Released: Monthly **Price:** chamber membership.

54277 ■ Glasgow Area Chamber of Commerce and Agriculture (GACCA)
PO Box 832
Glasgow, MT 59230-0832
Ph: (406)228-2222
Co. E-mail: chamber@glasgowmt.net
URL: http://www.glasgowmt.net
Contact: Lisa Olk, Executive Director
Description: Promotes agricultural, business, and community development in the Valley County, MT area. Sponsors Montana Governor's Cup Walleye Tournament and longest Dam run. **Publications:** Glascow Chamber of Commerce Newsletter (Monthly).

54278 ■ Glendive Chamber of Commerce and Agriculture (GCCA)
808 N Merrill Ave.
Glendive, MT 59330
Ph: (406)377-5601
Fax: (406)377-5602
Co. E-mail: chamber@midrivers.com
URL: http://www.glendivechamber.com
Description: Promotes business and community development in Glendive, MT.

54279 ■ Great Falls Area Chamber of Commerce (GFCC)
100 1 Ave. N
Great Falls, MT 59401
Ph: (406)761-4434

Fax: (406)761-6129
Co. E-mail: smalicott@greatfallschamber.org
URL: http://www.greatfallschamber.org
Contact: Steve Malicott, President
Description: Supports a strong local economy, promotes the community, represents business to government and provides networking and relationship-building opportunities. **Founded:** 1888. **Publications:** Chamber Business News (Monthly).

54280 ■ Greater Stillwater County Chamber of Commerce (GSCCC)
PO Box 783
Columbus, MT 59019
Ph: (406)322-4505
Co. E-mail: admin@stillwatercountychamber.com
URL: http://www.stillwatercountychamber.com
Contact: Ken Kaiser, President
Description: Promotes business and community development in Columbus, MT. Sponsors festival. **Founded:** 1987.

54281 ■ Guide to Helena Living and Business
225 Cruse Ave.
Helena, MT 59601
Ph: (406)442-4120
Free: 800-743-5362
Fax: (406)447-1532
Co. E-mail: info@helenachamber.com
URL: http://www.helenachamber.com
Contact: Cathy Burwell, President
Released: Annual

54282 ■ Hardin Area Chamber of Commerce and Agriculture (HACC)
PO Box 446
Hardin, MT 59034
Ph: (406)665-1672
Fax: (406)665-3577
Co. E-mail: info@thehardinchamber.org
URL: http://www.thehardinchamber.org
Contact: Shirley Margheim, Secretary
Description: Promotes business and community development in Big Horn County, MT. Operates information center for new residents and tourists. Makes available demographic, legislative, and statistical information. Sponsors community programs. Distributes informational materials regarding tourist attractions in the area. Provides legislative advocacy and promotional activities. Supports Operation Sparkle. Sponsors Little Big Horn Days, Fourth of July events, and Christmas decorations. **Founded:** 1984.

54283 ■ Havre Area Chamber of Commerce (HACC)
130 5th Ave.
Havre, MT 59501-0308
Ph: (406)265-4383
Fax: (406)265-7748
Co. E-mail: chamber@havremt.net
URL: http://www.havremt.com
Contact: Debbie Vandeberg, Executive Director
Description: Promotes business and community development in Havre, MT. **Founded:** 1909.

54284 ■ The Heartbeat
408 NE Main St.
Lewistown, MT 59457-0818
Ph: (406)535-5436
Free: 866-912-3980
Co. E-mail: lewchamb@midrivers.com
URL: http://www.lewistownchamber.com
Released: Monthly **Price:** $25.

54285 ■ Helena Area Chamber of Commerce (HACC)
225 Cruse Ave.
Helena, MT 59601
Ph: (406)442-4120
Free: 800-743-5362

Fax: (406)447-1532
Co. E-mail: info@helenachamber.com
URL: http://www.helenachamber.com
Contact: Cathy Burwell, President
Description: Promotes business and community development in the Helena, MT area. Encourages tourism. **Founded:** 1877. **Publications:** Helena Business (Monthly); Guide to Helena Living and Business (Annual). **Educational Activities:** Membership Banquet (Annual). **Awards:** Business of the Year (Annual); Business Person of the Year (Annual); Diplomat of the Year (Annual); Volunteer of the Year (Annual).

54286 ■ Helena Business
225 Cruse Ave.
Helena, MT 59601
Ph: (406)442-4120
Free: 800-743-5362
Fax: (406)447-1532
Co. E-mail: info@helenachamber.com
URL: http://www.helenachamber.com
Contact: Cathy Burwell, President
Released: Monthly

54287 ■ Kalispell Area Chamber of Commerce (KACC)
15 Depot Park
Kalispell, MT 59901
Ph: (406)758-2800
Co. E-mail: info@kalispellchamber.com
URL: http://kalispellchamber.com
Contact: Joe Unterreiner, President
Description: Promotes business and community development in the Kalispell, MT area. **Founded:** 1904. **Publications:** Chamber News (Monthly).

54288 ■ Lakeside-Somers Chamber of Commerce
PO Box 177
Lakeside, MT 59922-0177
Ph: (406)844-3715
Co. E-mail: fpzanni@msn.com
URL: http://www.lakesidesomers.org
Contact: Francois Zanni, President
Description: Promotes business and community development in Lakeside, MT. Sponsors community fair and Christmas tree lighting/decoration contest. Coordinates winter activities through an event called "Winterfest".

54289 ■ Laurel Chamber of Commerce
108 E Main St.
Laurel, MT 59044-3104
Ph: (406)628-8105
Co. E-mail: lchamber@rbbmt.org
URL: http://www.laurelmontana.org
Contact: John Mataisz, President
Description: Promotes business and community development in Laurel, MT. **Founded:** 1908.

54290 ■ Lewistown Area Chamber of Commerce
408 NE Main St.
Lewistown, MT 59457-0818
Ph: (406)535-5436
Free: 866-912-3980
Co. E-mail: lewchamb@midrivers.com
URL: http://www.lewistownchamber.com
Description: Promotes agriculture, business, and community development in Lewistown and the Central Montana area. **Founded:** 1908. **Publications:** The Heartbeat (Monthly).

54291 ■ Libby Area Chamber of Commerce (LACC)
905 W 9th
Libby, MT 59923
Ph: (406)293-4167
Fax: (406)293-2197
Co. E-mail: libbyacc@libbychamber.org
URL: http://www.libbychamber.org
Description: Promotes natural resource, business, and community development in the Libby, MT area. **Founded:** 1940.

54292 ■ Lincoln Valley Chamber of Commerce
PO Box 985
Lincoln, MT 59639-0985

Ph: (406)362-4949
Co. E-mail: lincolnmontana@linctel.net
URL: http://www.lincolnmontana.com
URL(s): www.visitmt.com. **Description:** Promotes business and community development in the Lincoln, MT area. **Founded:** 1960.

54293 ■ *Live Wire*
7 6th Ave. SW
Conrad, MT 59425
Ph: (406)271-7791
Fax: (406)221-2924
Co. E-mail: chamber@conradmt.com
URL: http://www.conradmt.com
Contact: Shari Richter, President
Released: Monthly

54294 ■ Livingston Area Chamber of Commerce (LACC)
303 E Park St.
Livingston, MT 59047
Ph: (406)222-0850
Co. E-mail: info@livingston-chamber.com
URL: http://www.livingston-chamber.com
Contact: Michelle Jolley, President
Description: Promotes business and community development in the Livingston, MT area. **Founded:** 1944.

54295 ■ Manhattan Area Chamber of Commerce
PO Box 606
Manhattan, MT 59741
Ph: (406)284-4162
Co. E-mail: manhattanmontana@yahoo.com
URL: http://www.manhattanareachamber.com
Contact: Brad Price, President
Description: Fosters the changing environment for business success that enhances the quality of life in the Manhattan, MT area.

54296 ■ Miles City Area Chamber of Commerce
511 Pleasant St.
Miles City, MT 59301
Ph: (406)234-2890
Fax: (406)234-6914
Co. E-mail: mcchamber@mcchamber.com
URL: http://www.milescitychamber.com
Contact: Dannette Cremer, President
Description: Promotes business and community development in Miles City, MT area.

54297 ■ Mineral County Chamber of Commerce
PO Box 483
Superior, MT 59872
Ph: (406)649-6400
Co. E-mail: admin@mineralcountymt.org
URL: http://www.montanarockies.org
Contact: Robert Lyons, President
Description: Promotes business and community development in Mineral county and its surrounding area.

54298 ■ Missoula Area Chamber of Commerce
PO Box 7577
Missoula, MT 59807
Ph: (406)543-6623
Fax: (406)543-6625
Co. E-mail: info@missoulachamber.com
URL: http://www.missoulachamber.com
Contact: Kim Latrielle, President
Description: Promotes business and community development in the Missoula, MT area. **Scope:** business. **Founded:** 1893. **Publications:** *Business Connection* (Monthly). **Telecommunication Services:** kim@missoulachamber.com.

54299 ■ Montana Chamber of Commerce
PO Box 1730
Helena, MT 59624-1730
Ph: (406)442-2405

Fax: (406)442-2409
Co. E-mail: schaefer@3rivers.net
URL: http://www.montanachamber.com
Contact: Webb Scott Brown, President
Description: Seeks to advocate statewide for business in the Legislature and Congress. **Founded:** 1931. **Publications:** *Eye on Business* (Monthly). **Telecommunication Services:** webb@montana-chamber.com.

54300 ■ Philipsburg Chamber of Commerce
PO Box 661
Philipsburg, MT 59858
Ph: (406)859-3388
Co. E-mail: chamber@philipsburgmt.com
URL: http://www.philipsburgmt.com
Description: Promotes business and community development in Philipsburg, MT. Sponsors Flint Creek Valley Days. **Founded:** 1946.

54301 ■ Plains-Paradise Chamber of Commerce (PPCC)
PO Box 1531
Plains, MT 59859
Ph: (406)826-4700
URL: http://www.plainsmtchamber.com
Description: Promotes business and community development in the Plains, MT area.

54302 ■ Polson Chamber of Commerce (PCC)
418 Main St.
Polson, MT 59860
Ph: (406)883-5969
Fax: (406)883-1716
Co. E-mail: info@polsonchamber.com
URL: http://www.polsonchamber.com
Contact: Heather Knutson, President
URL(s): www.visitmt.com. **Description:** Promotes business and community development in the Port Polson, MT area. **Publications:** *The Chambergram* (Monthly). **Telecommunication Services:** chamber@polsonchamber.com.

54303 ■ Powell County Chamber of Commerce
1109 Main St.
Deer Lodge, MT 59722
Ph: (406)846-2094
Fax: (406)846-2094
Co. E-mail: chamber@powellcountymontana.com
URL: http://www.powellcountymontana.com
Description: Promotes businesses, community development and tourism in the city of Deer Lodge and Powell County, MT. Sponsors annual BBQ, annual banquet, Territorial Days, Demolition Derby, Pumpkin Sunday and Christmas Stroll. **Publications:** *Deer Lodge Demographics; Deer Lodge Visitor's Guide; Self Guided Tour of Deer Lodge Historic Buildings.*

54304 ■ *The Progress*
1000 George St.
Butte, MT 59701
Ph: (406)723-3177
Free: 800-735-6814
Fax: (406)723-1215
Co. E-mail: bsbchamber@gmail.com
URL: http://www.buttechamber.org
Contact: Marko Lucich, Executive Director
Released: Monthly

54305 ■ *Recreational Opportunities and Information in Dillon and Beaverhead County, Montana*
10 W Reeder
Dillon, MT 59725
Ph: (406)683-5511
Co. E-mail: info@beaverheadchamber.org
URL: http://www.beaverheadchamber.org
Contact: Bernie Childers, Executive Director

54306 ■ Red Lodge Area Chamber of Commerce
701 N Broadway
Red Lodge, MT 59068
Ph: (406)446-1718

Free: 888-281-0625
Co. E-mail: redlodgechamber@qwestoffice.net
URL: http://www.redlodge.com
Contact: Doug Bailey, President
URL(s): www.redlodgechamber.org. **Description:** Promotes business and community development in the Red Lodge, MT area. Encourages tourism. **Founded:** 1945. **Publications:** *The Red Lodge Insider* (Quarterly). **Educational Activities:** Beartooth (Annual).

54307 ■ *The Red Lodge Insider*
701 N Broadway
Red Lodge, MT 59068
Ph: (406)446-1718
Free: 888-281-0625
Co. E-mail: redlodgechamber@qwestoffice.net
URL: http://www.redlodge.com
Contact: Doug Bailey, President
Released: Quarterly

54308 ■ *Self Guided Tour of Deer Lodge Historic Buildings*
1109 Main St.
Deer Lodge, MT 59722
Ph: (406)846-2094
Fax: (406)846-2094
Co. E-mail: chamber@powellcountymontana.com
URL: http://www.powellcountymontana.com

54309 ■ Shelby Area Chamber of Commerce (SACC)
PO Box 865
Shelby, MT 59474-0865
Ph: (406)434-7184
Co. E-mail: shelbycoc@3rivers.net
URL: http://www.shelbymtchamber.org
Contact: Audie Bancroft, Executive Director
Description: Promotes business and community development in Toole County, MT. **Founded:** 1946.

54310 ■ Sheridan County Chamber of Commerce
PO Box 104
Plentywood, MT 59254-0104
Ph: (406)765-1733
Co. E-mail: chamber@mygreeter.com
URL: http://sheridancountychamber.org
Contact: Richard Rice, President
URL(s): www.visitmt.com. **Description:** Promotes business and community development in Sheridan County, MT.

54311 ■ Sidney Area Chamber of Commerce and Agriculture (SACCA)
909 S Central Ave.
Sidney, MT 59270
Ph: (406)433-1916
Fax: (406)433-1127
Co. E-mail: schamber@midrivers.com
URL: http://www.sidneymt.com
Contact: Wade VanEvery, Executive Director
Description: Promotes business and community development in Sidney, MT. Sponsors Sunrise Festival of the Arts. **Founded:** 1916. **Publications:** *The Advantage* (Monthly).

54312 ■ Sweet Grass County Chamber of Commerce
PO Box 1012
Big Timber, MT 59011
Ph: (406)932-5131
Fax: (406)932-5131
Co. E-mail: info@bigtimber.com
URL: http://www.bigtimber.com
Contact: Connie Kunda, President
Description: Promotes business and community development in Sweet Grass County, MT. **Founded:** 1978.

54313 ■ *Tabloid of Services*
PO Box 1120
Whitefish, MT 59937
Ph: (406)862-3501
Fax: (406)862-9494
Co. E-mail: visitus@whitefishchamber.org
URL: http://www.whitefishchamber.org
Contact: Kevin Gartland, Executive Director
Released: Periodic

54314 ■ Thompson Falls Chamber of Commerce
PO Box 493
Thompson Falls, MT 59873
Ph: (406)827-4930
Co. E-mail: tfchamber@thompsonfallschamber.com
URL: http://www.thompsonfallschamber.com
Description: Promotes business and community development in Thompson Falls, MT. Sponsors Pony Express Days festival.

54315 ■ *Three Fork Telephone Book*
PO Box 1103
Three Forks, MT 59752-1103
Ph: (406)285-4753
Co. E-mail: tfchamber@gmail.com
URL: http://www.threeforksmontana.com
Contact: Bonnie Rate, Executive Secretary
Released: Annual **Price:** for members.

54316 ■ Three Forks Chamber of Commerce (TFCC)
PO Box 1103
Three Forks, MT 59752-1103
Ph: (406)285-4753
Co. E-mail: tfchamber@gmail.com
URL: http://www.threeforksmontana.com
Contact: Bonnie Rate, Executive Secretary
Description: Promotes business and community development in Three Forks, MT. Participates in Rodeo Parade and community picnic. **Founded:** 1964. **Publications:** *Three Fork Telephone Book* (Annual).

54317 ■ *Visitors' Guide*
1000 George St.
Butte, MT 59701
Ph: (406)723-3177
Free: 800-735-6814
Fax: (406)723-1215
Co. E-mail: bsbchamber@gmail.com
URL: http://www.buttechamber.org
Contact: Marko Lucich, Executive Director
Released: Annual

54318 ■ *Welcome Guide*
10 W Reeder
Dillon, MT 59725
Ph: (406)683-5511
Co. E-mail: info@beaverheadchamber.org
URL: http://www.beaverheadchamber.org
Contact: Bernie Childers, Executive Director
Released: Annual; always in May.

54319 ■ West Yellowstone Chamber of Commerce (WYCC)
PO Box 458
West Yellowstone, MT 59758-0458
Ph: (406)646-7701
Fax: (406)646-9691
Co. E-mail: visitorservices@westyellowstonechamber.com
URL: http://www.westyellowstonechamber.com
Contact: Marysue Costello, Executive Director
Description: Promotes business and community development in West Yellowstone, MT. **Telecommunication Services:** director@westyellowstonechamber.com.

54320 ■ Whitefish Chamber of Commerce
PO Box 1120
Whitefish, MT 59937
Ph: (406)862-3501
Fax: (406)862-9494
Co. E-mail: visitus@whitefishchamber.org
URL: http://www.whitefishchamber.org
Contact: Kevin Gartland, Executive Director
Description: Serves as an information bank which supplies valuable community information. Promotes community events to establish a positive image of Whitefish as a great place to work, live and do business. **Founded:** 1947. **Publications:** *Chamber Newsletter* (Monthly); *Tabloid of Services* (Periodic).

PROCUREMENT ASSISTANCE PROGRAMS

54321 ■ Montana Department of Administration - State Procurement Bureau
Mitchell Bldg., Rm. 165
Helena, MT 59620-0135
Ph: (406)444-2575
Fax: (406)444-2529
URL: http://mt.gov/govt/statedir/agency/doa.asp
Contact: Brad Sanders, Bureau Chief
Description: Offers current government procurement information to interested small business bidders. Also provides technical assistance.

54322 ■ Montana Procurement Technical Assistance Center - Government Marketing Assistance Group - Big Sky Economic Development Authority
222 N 32nd St., Ste. 200
Billings, MT 59101
Ph: (406)256-6871
Fax: (406)256-6877
Co. E-mail: jewell@bigskyeda.org
URL: http://www.bigskyeda-edc.org
Contact: Maureen Jewell, Program Manager
E-mail: jewell@bigskyeda.org
Description: Helps to create jobs and grow companies in Montana by helping area businesses win government contracts.

54323 ■ Montana Procurement Technical Assistance Center - Great Falls Development Authority
PO Box 949
Great Falls, MT 59403
Ph: (406)771-9020
Fax: (406)454-2995
Co. E-mail: info@greatfallsdevelopment.org
URL: http://www.gfdevelopment.org
Contact: Brett Doney, Chief Executive Officer
E-mail: karl@mt.net

54324 ■ Montana Procurement Technical Assistance Center - Kalispell Area Chamber of Commerce
Flathead Business Regional Center
15 Depot Park
Kalispell, MT 59901
Ph: (406)755-4221
Co. E-mail: ptac@kalispellchamber.com
URL: http://www.kalispellchamber.com
Contact: Doug Bolender, Manager
Description: Free assistance to help Montana businesses obtain city, county, state, or federal government contracts serving Flathead, Lake, Sanders, and Lincoln Counties.

54325 ■ Montana Procurement Technical Assistance Center - Missoula Area Economic Development Corp. (MAEDC)
1121 E Broadway, Ste. 135
Missoula, MT 59802
Ph: (406)532-3207
Fax: (406)543-2304
Co. E-mail: ptac@maedc.org
URL: http://www.maedc.org
Contact: Doug Bolender, Director
Description: The organization helps employers create quality jobs for area residents, diversify the regional economic base, and improve the economy by taking leadership positions and forming partnerships with other organizations on community issues that affect local economic development. MAEDC helps existing companies expand by providing technical assistance and financing.

54326 ■ Montana Procurement Technical Assistance Center - Montana National Center for American Indian Enterprise Development
219 1st St. E
Polson, MT 59860
Ph: (406)883-4833
Co. E-mail: lou.thompson@ncaied.org
URL: http://www.ncaied.org
Contact: Lou Thompson, Counselor
E-mail: lou.thompson@ncaied.org
Description: Develop and expand an American Indian private sector which employs Indian labor, increases the number of viable tribal and individual Indian businesses, and positively impacts and involves reservation communities, by establishing business relationships between Indian enterprises and private industry.

54327 ■ Montana Procurement Technical Assistance Center - Prospera Business Network
222 E Main St., Ste. 102
Bozeman, MT 59715
Ph: (406)587-3113
Fax: (406)587-9565
Co. E-mail: info@prosperabusinessnetwork.com
URL: http://www.bozeman.org/index.html
Contact: Stuart R. Leidner, Executive Director
E-mail: PRenevier@prosperabusinessnetwork.com
Description: Encourages and supports business expansion, retention and relocation by providing access to guidance, capital, professional development, networking and recognition.

INCUBATORS/RESEARCH AND TECHNOLOGY PARKS

54328 ■ College of Forestry and Conservation - Institute for Tourism and Recreation Research
University of Montana
32 Campus Dr., No. 1234
Missoula, MT 59812-1234
Ph: (406)243-5686
Fax: (406)243-4845
Co. E-mail: request@forestry.umt.edu
URL: http://www.forestry.umt.edu/
Contact: Kate Cenis, Director
Description: Provides research data needed to support the state's tourism industry.

54329 ■ Lake County Community Development Corporation
407 Main St. SW
Ronan, MT 59864
Ph: (406)676-5901
Co. E-mail: lccd@ronan.net
URL: http://www.lakecountycdc.org/
Contact: Billie Lee, Director
Description: A small business incubator working with existing companies to develop and expand their businesses and to structure financial resources appropriate to their situation, and helping recruit new companies which may provide additional and higher wage jobs.

54330 ■ Montana Business Incubator
Montana State University - Billings
100 Poly Dr., Ste. 150
Billings, MT 59101
Ph: (406)657-2138
Fax: (406)657-2006
Co. E-mail: mbinc@mtbiz.org
URL: http://www.mtbiz.org/
Contact: Dave Stoltenberg, Director
Description: A small business incubator committed to creating jobs and wealth in the Billings Montana region by supporting entrepreneurship and innovation. It seeks to assist companies involved in many technical areas, however a special emphasis is placed upon agriculture, medical, and energy related businesses.

54331 ■ Montana Technology Enterprise Center
1121 E. Broadway, Ste. 100
Missoula, MT 59802
Ph: (406)728-3337

Fax: (406)543-2304
Co. E-mail: maedc@maedc.org
URL: http://www.maedc.org/montec
Contact: Dick King, Chief Executive Officer
Description: A technology and business incubator conceived to bolster local start-ups and to encourage the commercialization of university research. Collaborative enterprise between the University of Montana and the Missoula Area Economic Development Foundation.

54332 ■ TechRanch
910 Technology Blvd., Ste. A
Bozeman, MT 59718
Ph: (406)556-0272
Fax: (406)556-0969
Co. E-mail: gbloomer@techranch.org
URL: http://www.techranch.org/

Description: A business incubator created to help Montana-based entrepreneurs launch and build companies that will become long term, profitable operating entities in Montana. Its goal is to create more high-paying, intellectually-stimulating, clean jobs in Montana.

PUBLICATIONS

54333 ■ *Big Sky Business Journal*
PO Box 3262
Billings, MT 59103
Ph: (406)259-2309
Fax: (406)259-7040
Co. E-mail: bsbj@imt.net
URL: http://www.bigskybusiness.com/

54334 ■ *Livingston Enterprise*
PO Box 2000
Livingston, MT 59047
Ph: (406)222-2000
Free: 800-345-8412
Fax: (406)222-8580
Co. E-mail: enterprise@ycsi.net
URL: http://www.livingstonenterprise.com/

54335 ■ *Montana Magazine*
PO Box 5630
Helena, MT 59604
Ph: (406)443-2842
Fax: (406)443-5480
Co. E-mail: magedit@montmang.mt.net
URL: http://www.montanamagazine.com

54336 ■ *Smart Start Your California Business*
PSI Research
300 N. Valley Dr.
Grants Pass, OR 97526
Ph: (503)479-9464
Free: 800-228-2275
Fax: (503)476-1479
Co. E-mail: info@psi-research.com
URL: http://www.psi-research.com

Ed: Michael D. Jenkins. **Released:** Revised edition, 1992. **Price:** $29.95 (looseleaf binder); $24.95 (paper). **Description:** Part of the Successful Business Library series.

SMALL BUSINESS DEVELOPMENT CENTERS

54337 ■ Nebraska Small Business Development Center - Chadron State College
1000 Main St.
Chadron, NE 69337
Ph: (308)432-6282
Co. E-mail: tdonahue@csc.edu
URL: http://nbdc.unomaha.edu
Contact: Tim Donahue, Director
URL(s): www.csc.edu/business/nbdc. **Description:** Represents and promotes the small business sector. Provides management assistance to current and prospective small business owners. Helps to improve management skills and expand the products and services of members.

54338 ■ Nebraska Small Business Development Center - Kearney
c/o Odee Ingersoll, Dir.
University of Nebraska at Kearney
West Center Bldg., Rm. 127E
1917 W 24th St.
Kearney, NE 68849-4440
Ph: (308)865-8344
Fax: (308)865-8153
Co. E-mail: ingersollo@unk.edu
URL: http://nbdc.unomaha.edu/about/kearney.cfm
Contact: Odee Ingersoll, Director
Description: Represents and promotes the small business sector. Provides management assistance to current and prospective small business owners. Helps to improve management skills and expand the products and services of members.

54339 ■ Nebraska Small Business Development Center - Lead Office
University of Nebraska at Omaha
Mammel Hall, Ste. 200
67th and Pine Streets
Omaha, NE 68182
Ph: (402)554-6633
Fax: (402)554-3473
Co. E-mail: cmosteller@unomaha.edu
URL: http://nbdc.unomaha.edu
Contact: Cliff Mosteller, Director
Description: Represents and promotes the small business sector. Provides management assistance to current and prospective small business owners. Helps to improve management skills and expand the products and services of members.

54340 ■ Nebraska Small Business Development Center - Lincoln
c/o Marisol U. Rodriguez, Dir.
UNL Office of Technology Development
1320 Q St., Office 109
Lincoln, NE 68588-0467
Ph: (402)472-5222

Fax: (402)472-0398
Co. E-mail: mrodriguez2@unl.edu
URL: http://nbdc.unomaha.edu/about/lincoln.cfm
Contact: Marisol U. Rodriguez, Director
Description: Represents and promotes the small business sector. Provides management assistance to current and prospective small business owners. Helps to improve management skills and expand the products and services of members.

54341 ■ Nebraska Small Business Development Center - Norfolk
c/o Renee Held, Consultant
Lifelong Learning Center
801 E Benjamin Ave.
Norfolk, NE 68702-0469
Ph: (402)564-0105
Co. E-mail: rheld@mail.unomaha.edu
URL: http://nbdc.unomaha.edu/about/norfolk.cfm
Contact: Renee Held, Consultant
Description: Represents and promotes the small business sector. Provides management assistance to current and prospective small business owners. Helps to improve management skills and expand the products and services of members.

54342 ■ Nebraska Small Business Development Center - North Platte
c/o Jason Tuller, Dir.
300 E 3rd St., Rm. 275
North Platte, NE 69101
Ph: (308)534-5115
Fax: (308)534-5117
Co. E-mail: jtuller@mail.unomaha.edu
URL: http://nbdc.unomaha.edu/about/northplatte.cfm
Contact: Jason Tuller, Director
Description: Represents and promotes the small business sector. Provides management assistance to current and prospective small business owners. Helps to improve management skills and expand the products and services of members.

54343 ■ Nebraska Small Business Development Center - Omaha
University of Nebraska at Omaha
Mammel Hall, Ste. 200
Omaha, NE 68182
Ph: (402)554-2521
Fax: (402)554-3473
Co. E-mail: rbernier@unomaha.edu
URL: http://www.nbdc.unomaha.edu
Contact: Robert E. Bernier, Director
Description: Represents and promotes the Nebraska business sector. Provides management and technical assistance to current and prospective small business owners. Helps businesses qualify for and submit proposals for government contracts. Assists manufacturers and processors in operational improvements and in developing new products. Helps to improve management skills and expand the products and services of members.

54344 ■ Nebraska Small Business Development Center - Scottsbluff
c/o Ingrid Battershell, Dir.
Panhandle Research and Extension Center
4502 Ave. I
Scottsbluff, NE 69361
Ph: (308)635-7513
Co. E-mail: ibattershell@mail.unomaha.edu
URL: http://nbdc.unomaha.edu/about/scottsbluff.cfm
Contact: Ingrid Battershell, Director
Description: Represents and promotes the small business sector. Provides management assistance to current and prospective small business owners. Helps to improve management skills and expand the products and services of members.

54345 ■ Nebraska Small Business Development Center - Wayne
c/o Loren Kucera, Dir.
Wayne State College
Gardner Hall
1111 Main St.
Wayne, NE 68787
Ph: (402)375-7575
Co. E-mail: lokucer1@wsc.edu
URL: http://nbdc.unomaha.edu/about/wayne.cfm
Contact: Loren Kucera, Director
Description: Represents and promotes the small business sector. Provides management assistance to current and prospective small business owners. Helps to improve management skills and expand the products and services of members.

SMALL BUSINESS ASSISTANCE PROGRAMS

54346 ■ Nebraska Ombudsman's Office
State Capitol, Rm. 807
Lincoln, NE 68509-4604
Ph: (402)471-2035
Free: 800-742-7690
Fax: (402)471-4277
Co. E-mail: ombud@leg.ne.gov
URL: http://www.unicam.state.ne.us/web/public/ombudsman
Contact: Marshall Lux, Ombudsman
Description: Receives complaints against state agencies.

SCORE OFFICES

54347 ■ Norfolk SCORE
Co. E-mail: admin@norfolk.ne.us

54348 ■ North Platte SCORE
Co. E-mail: jbfrazier@mail.neb.com

54349 ■ SCORE Central Nebraska
16 W 11th St.
Kearney, NE 68848

Ph: (308)865-5675
Co. E-mail: rhobbs@scorecentralnebraska.org
URL: http://centralnebraska.score.org/chapters/
  central-nebraska-score
Contact: Mr. Robert E. Hobbs, Officer
Description: Provides technical assistance and counseling for new and existing business owners. **Founded:** 1981. **Awards:** Small Business of the Year (Annual).

54350 ■ SCORE Columbus
401 N Front St., Ste. 200
Columbus, NE 43215
Ph: (614)469-2357
Fax: (614)469-5848
Co. E-mail: info@scorecolumbus.org
URL: http://www.scorecolumbus.org
URL(s): columbusoh.score.org/chapters/columbus-score. **Description:** Promotes business and community development in Columbus, NE area.

54351 ■ SCORE Lincoln
285 S 68th Pl., Ste. 530
Lincoln, NE 68510
Ph: (402)437-2409
Co. E-mail: nescore39@aol.com
URL: http://lincoln.score.org/chapters/lincoln-score
Contact: Fred Bailey, Chairman
Description: Provides entrepreneur education for the formation, growth and success of small businesses in the area.

54352 ■ SCORE Omaha
10675 Bedford Ave., Ste. 100
Omaha, NE 68134
Ph: (402)221-3606
Fax: (702)221-7239
Co. E-mail: score0040@gmail.com
URL: http://omaha.score.org
Description: Provides entrepreneur education for the formation, growth and success of small businesses in the area. **Founded:** 1963.

BETTER BUSINESS BUREAUS

54353 ■ Cornhusker Better Business Bureau
11811 P St.
Omaha, NE 68137
Ph: (402)391-7612
Free: 800-649-6814
Fax: (402)391-7535
Co. E-mail: info@bbbnebraska.org
URL: http://www.nebraska.bbb.org
Description: Seeks to promote and foster the highest ethical relationship between businesses and the public through voluntary self-regulation, consumer and business education, and service excellence. Provides information to help consumers and businesses make informed purchasing decisions and avoid costly scams and frauds; settles consumer complaints through arbitration and other means.

CHAMBERS OF COMMERCE

54354 ■ Ainsworth Area Chamber of Commerce and North Central Development Center
335 N Main St.
Ainsworth, NE 69210
Ph: (402)387-2740
Co. E-mail: chamber@threeriver.net
URL: http://www.ainsworthchamber.com/Business_
  Development/index.html
Contact: Roger Lechtenberg, President
Description: Promotes business and community development in the Ainsworth Area, NE.

54355 ■ Albion Chamber of Commerce (ACC)
420 W Market St.
Albion, NE 68620
Ph: (402)395-6012
Fax: (402)395-6723
Co. E-mail: info@cityofalbion-ne.com
URL: http://www.cityofalbion-ne.com
Contact: Dr. Rich Heidemann, President
Description: Promotes business and community development in Albion, NE. **Founded:** 1934.

54356 ■ Alliance Chamber of Commerce (AACC)
305 Box Butte Ave.
Alliance, NE 69301
Ph: (308)762-1520
Free: 800-738-0648
Co. E-mail: chamber@bbc.net
URL: http://www.alliancechamber.com
Contact: Dixie Nelson, Executive Director
Description: Promotes business and community development in the Alliance, NE area.

54357 ■ Alma Chamber of Commerce (ACC)
PO Box 52
Alma, NE 68920-0052
Ph: (308)928-2992
URL: http://www.ci.alma.ne.us/ChamberIndex.htm
Description: Promotes business and community development in Alma, NE.

54358 ■ Arapahoe Chamber of Commerce
PO Box 624
Arapahoe, NE 68922
Ph: (308)962-7777
Co. E-mail: chamber@arapahoe-ne.com
URL: http://www.arapahoe-ne.com
Contact: Jennifer Schroeder, President
Description: Promotes business and community development in Arapahoe, NE.

54359 ■ Ashland Area Chamber of Commerce
PO Box 5
Ashland, NE 68003
Ph: (402)944-2050
URL: http://www.historicashland.com/chamber-of-
  commerce
Contact: Nancy Maack, President
Description: Promotes business and community development in Ashland, NE area.

54360 ■ Auburn Chamber of Commerce (ACC)
1101 J St.
Auburn, NE 68305
Ph: (402)274-3521
Co. E-mail: auburnchamberofcommerce@gmail.com
URL: http://auburn.ne.gov/chamber-of-commerce
Contact: Stephanie Fisher, President
Description: Promotes business and community development in Auburn, NE. Sponsors Calvert Sheridan Days, Fall Foliage Festival, Farmer/Merchant Dinner Dance, Christmas on the Square, and Farm and Home Show.

54361 ■ Aurora Area Chamber and Development (AACD)
PO Box 146
Aurora, NE 68818
Ph: (402)694-6911
Fax: (402)694-5766
Co. E-mail: christian.evans@auroranebraska.com
URL: http://www.auroranebraska.com
Contact: Mr. Christian Evans, Executive Director
Description: Promotes business and community development in Aurora, NE. **Founded:** 1923.

54362 ■ Beatrice Area Chamber of Commerce (BCC)
218 N 5th St.
Beatrice, NE 68310
Ph: (402)223-2338
Fax: (402)223-2339
Co. E-mail: info@beatricechamber.com
URL: http://www.beatricechamber.com
Contact: Deb Meyer, Chairperson
Description: Promotes business and community development in the Beatrice, NE area. **Founded:** 1880. **Publications:** *Chamber News* (Monthly). **Telecommunication Services:** greatone@inebraska.com.

54363 ■ Blair Area Chamber of Commerce (BACC)
1646 Washington St.
Blair, NE 68008
Ph: (402)533-4455

Fax: (402)533-4456
Co. E-mail: mail@blairchamber.org
URL: http://www.blairchamber.org
Contact: Harriet Waite, Executive Director
Description: Promotes business and community development in the Blair, NE area. Sponsors Gateway to the West Days. **Founded:** 1958. **Publications:** *Blair Area Chamber of Commerce--Membership Directory/Buyer's Guide* (Annual).

54364 ■ *Briefs*
7536 S 84th St., Ste. B
La Vista, NE 68128
Ph: (402)339-2078
Fax: (402)339-2026
Co. E-mail: carol@lavistachamber.org
URL: http://www.lavistachamber.org
Contact: Mary Harper, Executive Director

54365 ■ Broken Bow Chamber of Commerce
444 S 8th Ave.
Broken Bow, NE 68822
Ph: (308)872-5691
Fax: (308)872-6137
Co. E-mail: info@brokenbow-ne.com
URL: http://www.brokenbow-ne.com
Contact: Denise Russell, Executive Director
Description: Promotes business and community development in Broken Bow, NE.

54366 ■ Burwell Chamber of Commerce
PO Box 131
Burwell, NE 68823
Ph: (308)346-5210
Free: 888-328-7935
Fax: (308)346-5121
Co. E-mail: burwellecondev@nctc.net
URL: http://www.visitburwell.org
Contact: Lynn Kratky, Director
Description: Works to promote agricultural, commercial, industrial, educational and civic interests of the City of Burwell and its surrounding area.

54367 ■ Butler County Chamber of Commerce
457 D St.
David City, NE 68632
Ph: (402)367-4238
Co. E-mail: director@buildbutlercounty.com
URL: http://www.buildbutlercounty.com
Contact: Wade Rahn, President
Description: Promotes business and community development in Butler County, NE. **Founded:** 1920. **Awards:** Distinguished Service (Annual); Economic Development (Annual).

54368 ■ Cambridge Chamber of Commerce
PO Box Q
Cambridge, NE 69022
Ph: (308)697-3711
Fax: (308)697-3253
Co. E-mail: edcity@swnebr.net
URL: http://www.cambridgene.org
Contact: Derek Downer, President
Description: Promotes business and community development in Cambridge, NE area.

54369 ■ Central City Area Chamber of Commerce
PO Box 418
Central City, NE 68826
Ph: (308)946-3897
Fax: (308)946-3334
Co. E-mail: cchamber@ccablene.com
URL: http://www.centralcitychamber.com
Contact: Kendra Jefferson, Executive Director
Description: Promotes business and community development in Central City, NE area.

54370 ■ Chadron - Dawes County Area Chamber of Commerce (CDCCC)
PO Box 646
Chadron, NE 69337
Ph: (308)432-4401

Free: 800-603-2937
Co. E-mail: director@chadron.com
URL: http://www.chadron.com
Contact: Colette Fernandez, Executive Director
Description: Promotes business and community development in the Chadron, NE area. Sponsors Fur Trade Days. Convention/Meeting: none.

54371 ■ The Chamber Advantage
405 Madison Ave.
Norfolk, NE 68701
Ph: (402)371-4862
Fax: (402)371-0182
Co. E-mail: info@norfolkareachamber.com
URL: http://www.norfolk.ne.us
Contact: Dennis Houston, President
Released: Monthly

54372 ■ Chamber Chatter
PO Box 160
Gordon, NE 69343
Ph: (308)282-0730
Co. E-mail: gcc@gordonchamber.com
URL: http://www.gordonchamber.com
Contact: Bea Lou Hardin, Director
Released: Monthly

54373 ■ The Chamber Informer
122 S Chestnut St.
Kimball, NE 69145
Ph: (308)235-3782
Fax: (308)235-3825
Co. E-mail: kbccc@megavision.com
URL: http://www.ci.kimball.ne.us
Contact: Jeanette Rabender, Executive Director

54374 ■ Chamber News
218 N 5th St.
Beatrice, NE 68310
Ph: (402)223-2338
Fax: (402)223-2339
Co. E-mail: info@beatricechamber.com
URL: http://www.beatricechamber.com
Contact: Deb Meyer, Chairperson
Released: Monthly

54375 ■ Chamber News
Shadow Lake Town Center
Papillion, NE 68046
Ph: (402)339-3050
Fax: (402)339-9968
Co. E-mail: chamber@sarpychamber.org
URL: http://www.sarpychamber.org
Contact: Jane Nielsen, President
Released: Monthly **Price:** $12, /year for nonmembers; free for members.

54376 ■ Chamber Newsletter
918 Washington Ave.
Plattsmouth, NE 68048
Ph: (402)296-6021
Fax: (402)296-6974
Co. E-mail: lisad@plattsmouthchamber.com
URL: http://www.plattsmouthchamber.com
Contact: Lisa Davis, Executive Director
Released: Monthly

54377 ■ The Chamber Vision
PO Box 83006
Lincoln, NE 68501-3006
Ph: (402)436-2350
Fax: (402)436-2360
Co. E-mail: info@lcoc.com
URL: http://www.lcoc.com
Contact: Wendy Birdsall, President
Released: Monthly **Price:** included in membership dues.

54378 ■ Chamber Visions
402 Norris Ave., Ste. 203
McCook, NE 69001
Ph: (308)345-3200
Free: 800-657-2179
Fax: (308)345-3201
Co. E-mail: info@aboutmccook.com
URL: http://aboutmccook.com
Contact: Pamela C. Harsh, Executive Director
Released: Monthly **Price:** free for members.

54379 ■ Chappell Chamber of Commerce
PO Box 121
Chappell, NE 69129-0121
Ph: (308)874-9912
Fax: (308)874-2929
Co. E-mail: chamber69129@yahoo.com
URL: http://www.chappellne.org/chamber.htm
Contact: Cindy Williams, President
Description: Promotes business and community development in Chappell, NE.

54380 ■ Cheyenne County Chamber of Commerce (CCCC)
740 Illinois St.
Sidney, NE 69162-1748
Ph: (308)254-5851
Free: 800-421-4769
Fax: (308)254-3081
Co. E-mail: ccchamber@hamilton.net
URL: http://cheyennecountychamber.com
Contact: Ms. Megan McGown, Executive Director
Description: Promotes business and community development in Cheyenne County and Sidney, NE. **Founded:** 1920. **Telecommunication Services:** mmcgown@hamilton.net.

54381 ■ Columbus Area Chamber of Commerce (Columbus, Nebraska) (CACC)
PO Box 515
Columbus, NE 68601
Ph: (402)564-2769
Fax: (402)564-2026
Co. E-mail: chamber@megavision.com
URL: http://www.thecolumbuspage.com
Contact: K.C. Belitz, President
Description: Promotes business and community development in the Columbus, NE area. **Telecommunication Services:** kbelitz@megavision.com.

54382 ■ Crete Chamber of Commerce (CCC)
PO Box 465
Crete, NE 68333
Ph: (402)826-2136
Co. E-mail: cretechamber@neb.rr.com
URL: http://www.cretechamber.org
Contact: Deb Polacek, Executive Director
Description: Promotes business and community development in the Crete, NE area. **Founded:** 1925.

54383 ■ Direction for Business
PO Box 1486
Grand Island, NE 68802-1486
Ph: (308)382-9210
Fax: (308)382-1154
Co. E-mail: info@gichamber.com
URL: http://www.gichamber.com
Contact: Cindy K. Johnson, President
Released: Monthly

54384 ■ Executive
c/o Barry L. Kennedy, CAE, Pres.
PO Box 95128
Lincoln, NE 68509-5128
Ph: (402)474-4422
Fax: (402)474-5681
Co. E-mail: bkennedy@nechamber.com
URL: http://www.nechamber.com
Contact: Barry L. Kennedy, President
Released: Monthly

54385 ■ Extraordinary News
1514 K St.
Ord, NE 68862
Ph: (308)728-7875
Free: 877-728-7875
Fax: (308)728-7691
Co. E-mail: valleycountyed@frontiernet.net
URL: http://www.ordnebraska.com/chamber.asp
Contact: Caleb Pollard, Executive Director
Released: Monthly **Price:** included in membership dues.

54386 ■ Fairbury Chamber of Commerce
PO Box 274
Fairbury, NE 68352
Ph: (402)729-3000

Fax: (402)729-3076
Co. E-mail: fairburychamber@diodecom.net
URL: http://www.fairburychamber.org
Contact: Sharon Priefert, Executive Director
Description: Promotes business and community development in Fairbury, NE. **Awards:** Community Service Award (Annual); Volunteer of the Year (Annual).

54387 ■ Falls City Area Chamber of Commerce (FCACC)
1705 Stone St.
Falls City, NE 68355
Ph: (402)245-4228
Fax: (402)245-4228
Co. E-mail: fcchamber@sentco.net
URL: http://fallscityareachamber.com
Contact: Billie Jackson, President
Description: Promotes business and community development in the Falls City, NE area. Conducts charitable activities. Sponsors area festivals. **Founded:** 1930.

54388 ■ Fremont Area Chamber of Commerce
PO Box 182
Fremont, NE 68026-0182
Ph: (402)721-2641
Fax: (402)721-9359
Co. E-mail: info@fremontne.org
URL: http://www.fremontne.org
Contact: Ron Tillery, Executive Director
Description: Promotes business and community development in the Fremont, NE area. **Founded:** 1880. **Publications:** Pathfinder (Monthly). **Awards:** Farm Excellence Award (Annual); Honorary Lifetime Membership Award (Annual).

54389 ■ Gordon Chamber of Commerce
PO Box 160
Gordon, NE 69343
Ph: (308)282-0730
Co. E-mail: gcc@gordonchamber.com
URL: http://www.gordonchamber.com
Contact: Bea Lou Hardin, Director
Description: Promotes business and community development in Gordon, NE. Sponsors festival. **Publications:** Chamber Chatter (Monthly).

54390 ■ Gothenburg Area Chamber of Commerce
PO Box 263
Gothenburg, NE 69138
Ph: (308)537-3505
Free: 800-482-5520
Fax: (308)537-2541
Co. E-mail: annea@gothenburgdelivers.com
URL: http://www.gothenburgdelivers.com
Contact: Anne Anderson, Executive Director
Description: Promotes business and community development in the Gothenburg, NE area. Sponsors annual festival. **Founded:** 1967. **Publications:** Pony Express Exchange (Monthly).

54391 ■ Grand Island Area Chamber of Commerce (GIACC)
PO Box 1486
Grand Island, NE 68802-1486
Ph: (308)382-9210
Fax: (308)382-1154
Co. E-mail: info@gichamber.com
URL: http://www.gichamber.com
Contact: Cindy K. Johnson, President
Description: Promotes business and community development in the Grand Island, NE area. Sponsors festival. **Publications:** Direction for Business (Monthly). **Educational Activities:** Ag Appreciation (Annual).

54392 ■ Greater Omaha Chamber of Commerce
1301 Harney St.
Omaha, NE 68102
Ph: (402)346-5000

Fax: (402)346-7050
Co. E-mail: info@omahachamber.org
URL: http://www.omahachamber.org
Contact: David G. Brown, President
URL(s): www.omahachamber.net/. **Description:** Promotes business and community development in the Omaha, NE area. **Founded:** 1893. **Publications:** *Major Employers Directory* (Periodic); *Manufacturer's Directory* (Biweekly); *Profile* (Periodic); *Directory of Major Employers in Omaha* (Biennial); *Directory of Omaha Manufacturers* (Biennial). **Awards:** Small Business Council Awards (Annual).

54393 ■ Greater York Area Chamber of Commerce
603 Lincoln Ave.
York, NE 68467
Ph: (402)362-5531
Fax: (402)362-5953
Co. E-mail: yorkcc@yorkchamber.net
URL: http://yorkchamber.org
Contact: Todd Kirshenbaum, Executive Director
Description: Promotes business and community development in the York, NE area. Sponsors York-fest. **Founded:** 1935. **Publications:** *Surveyor* (Monthly). **Telecommunication Services:** tkirshenbaum@yorkchamber.org.

54394 ■ Happenings
302 E 6th St., Ste. 2
Lexington, NE 68850
Ph: (308)324-5504
Fax: (308)324-5505
URL: http://www.lexcoc.com
Contact: Susan Bennett, Executive Director
Released: Weekly

54395 ■ Hartington Area Chamber of Commerce
PO Box 742
Hartington, NE 68739
Ph: (402)254-6357
Fax: (402)254-6391
Co. E-mail: chamberpres@hartel.net
URL: http://www.ci.hartington.ne.us/chamber.asp
Contact: Karma Schulte, President
Description: Promotes business, agriculture, education, tourism and community development in Hartington, NE area.

54396 ■ Hastings Area Chamber of Commerce (HACC)
PO Box 1104
Hastings, NE 68902-1104
Ph: (402)461-8400
Fax: (402)461-4400
Co. E-mail: info@hastingschamber.com
URL: http://www.hastingschamber.com
Contact: Tom Hastings, President
Description: Promotes business and community development in Hastings, NE. **Founded:** 1903. **Publications:** *Investment Report* (Monthly). **Telecommunication Services:** hastings@hastingschamber.com.

54397 ■ Holdrege Area Chamber of Commerce (HACC)
701 4th Ave., Ste. 10
Holdrege, NE 68949
Ph: (308)995-4444
Fax: (308)995-4445
Co. E-mail: chamber@justtheplacenebraska.com
URL: http://www.holdrege.org
Contact: Monty Vonasek, President
Description: Promotes business and community development in the Holdrege, NE area. **Publications:** *Target* (Monthly).

54398 ■ Impact
1517 Broadway, Ste. 104
Scottsbluff, NE 69361
Ph: (308)632-2133
Free: 800-788-9475
Fax: (308)632-7128
Co. E-mail: chamber@scottsbluffgering.net
URL: http://www.scottsbluffgering.net
Contact: Jean Kearns, Chairman
Released: Monthly

54399 ■ Imperial Chamber of Commerce
PO Box 82
Imperial, NE 69033
Ph: (308)882-5444
Co. E-mail: events@imperialchamber.com
URL: http://imperialchamber.com
Contact: Kris Musick, President
Description: Promotes business and community development in Imperial, NE area.

54400 ■ Investment Report
PO Box 1104
Hastings, NE 68902-1104
Ph: (402)461-8400
Fax: (402)461-4400
Co. E-mail: info@hastingschamber.com
URL: http://www.hastingschamber.com
Contact: Tom Hastings, President
Released: Monthly **Price:** $10, /year.

54401 ■ Kearney Area Chamber of Commerce (KACC)
1007 2nd Ave.
Kearney, NE 68848
Ph: (308)237-3101
Free: 800-227-8340
Fax: (308)237-3103
Co. E-mail: info@kearneycoc.org
URL: http://www.kearneycoc.org
Contact: Roger Jasnoch, President
Description: Serves the needs of the greater Kearney area as an advocate and catalyst in its promotion, growth and quality of life. Works with all segments of the community to facilitate the basic infrastructure by pursuing business and industry, education, agriculture, healthcare, cultural, civic and other common interests. **Founded:** 1918. **Publications:** *Kearney Business Agenda* (Monthly). **Educational Activities:** Cranes Watch (Annual).

54402 ■ Kearney Business Agenda
1007 2nd Ave.
Kearney, NE 68848
Ph: (308)237-3101
Free: 800-227-8340
Fax: (308)237-3103
Co. E-mail: info@kearneycoc.org
URL: http://www.kearneycoc.org
Contact: Roger Jasnoch, President
Released: Monthly **Price:** free.

54403 ■ Kimball - Banner County Chamber of Commerce (KBCCC)
122 S Chestnut St.
Kimball, NE 69145
Ph: (308)235-3782
Fax: (308)235-3825
Co. E-mail: kbccc@megavision.com
URL: http://www.ci.kimball.ne.us
Contact: Jeanette Rabender, Executive Director
Description: Promotes business and community development in Kimball and Banner counties, NE. **Publications:** *The Chamber Informer.*

54404 ■ La Vista Area Chamber of Commerce
7536 S 84th St., Ste. B
La Vista, NE 68128
Ph: (402)339-2078
Fax: (402)339-2026
Co. E-mail: carol@lavistachamber.org
URL: http://www.lavistachamber.org
Contact: Mary Harper, Executive Director
Description: Business, individual, and professional people. Works to develop and improve the economic, industrial, professional, cultural, and civic well-being of the La Vista community. **Founded:** 1982. **Publications:** *Briefs; Links; Pulse.*

54405 ■ Lexington Area Chamber of Commerce
302 E 6th St., Ste. 2
Lexington, NE 68850
Ph: (308)324-5504

Fax: (308)324-5505
URL: http://www.lexcoc.com
Contact: Susan Bennett, Executive Director
Description: Promotes business and community development in the Lexington, NE area. **Founded:** 1940. **Publications:** *Happenings* (Weekly); *Plum Creek Express* (Monthly). **Educational Activities:** The Great Plains Chautauqua (Annual). **Awards:** Scholastic Award (Periodic).

54406 ■ Lincoln Chamber of Commerce
PO Box 83006
Lincoln, NE 68501-3006
Ph: (402)436-2350
Fax: (402)436-2360
Co. E-mail: info@lcoc.com
URL: http://www.lcoc.com
Contact: Wendy Birdsall, President
Description: Promotes business and community development in Lincoln, NE. **Publications:** *The Chamber Vision* (Monthly); *A Directory of Lincoln, Nebraska Manufacturers* (Biennial).

54407 ■ Links
7536 S 84th St., Ste. B
La Vista, NE 68128
Ph: (402)339-2078
Fax: (402)339-2026
Co. E-mail: carol@lavistachamber.org
URL: http://www.lavistachamber.org
Contact: Mary Harper, Executive Director

54408 ■ Loup City Chamber of Commerce
PO Box 24
Loup City, NE 68853-0024
Ph: (308)745-0430
Co. E-mail: lcchamber@cornhusker.net
URL: http://www.loupcity.com
Contact: Pat Swaney, President
Description: Promotes business and community development in the Loup City, NE area.

54409 ■ Major Employers Directory
1301 Harney St.
Omaha, NE 68102
Ph: (402)346-5000
Fax: (402)346-7050
Co. E-mail: info@omahachamber.org
URL: http://www.omahachamber.org
Contact: David G. Brown, President
Released: Periodic

54410 ■ Manufacturer's Directory
1301 Harney St.
Omaha, NE 68102
Ph: (402)346-5000
Fax: (402)346-7050
Co. E-mail: info@omahachamber.org
URL: http://www.omahachamber.org
Contact: David G. Brown, President
Released: Biweekly

54411 ■ McCook Area Chamber of Commerce
402 Norris Ave., Ste. 203
McCook, NE 69001
Ph: (308)345-3200
Free: 800-657-2179
Fax: (308)345-3201
Co. E-mail: info@aboutmccook.com
URL: http://aboutmccook.com
Contact: Pamela C. Harsh, Executive Director
Description: Promotes business and community development in McCook, NE. Conducts charitable activities. **Founded:** 1967. **Publications:** *Chamber Visions* (Monthly). **Educational Activities:** Heritage Days Parade and Craft Show (Annual).

54412 ■ Minden Chamber of Commerce (MCC)
PO Box 375
Minden, NE 68959
Ph: (308)832-1811
Fax: (308)832-1811
Co. E-mail: mindenchamber@gtmc.net
URL: http://www.mindenne.org
Contact: Marcy Brandt, Executive Director
Description: Promotes business and community development in Minden, NE.

54413 ■ Nebraska Chamber of Commerce and Industry (NCCI)
c/o Barry L. Kennedy, CAE, Pres.
PO Box 95128
Lincoln, NE 68509-5128
Ph: (402)474-4422
Fax: (402)474-5681
Co. E-mail: bkennedy@nechamber.com
URL: http://www.nechamber.com
Contact: Barry L. Kennedy, President
Description: Promotes business and community development in Nebraska. **Founded:** 1912. **Publications:** *Executive* (Monthly). **Awards:** Nebraska Business Hall of Fame (Annual); Nebraska Business Hall of Fame Scholarship Foundation (Annual).

54414 ■ Nebraska City Tourism and Commerce (NCTC)
806 1st Ave.
Nebraska City, NE 68410
Ph: (402)873-6654
Free: 800-514-9113
Fax: (402)873-6701
Co. E-mail: tourism@nebraskacity.com
URL: http://www.nebraskacity.com
Contact: Rebecca Turner, Executive Director
Description: Promotes business and community development in Nebraska City, NE. Promotes tourism. Sponsors Applejack Festival, Arbor Day Celebration, and promotional events. **Founded:** 1921. **Publications:** *The View* (Monthly). **Educational Activities:** AppleJack (Annual).

54415 ■ Norfolk Area Chamber of Commerce (NACC)
405 Madison Ave.
Norfolk, NE 68701
Ph: (402)371-4862
Fax: (402)371-0182
Co. E-mail: info@norfolkareachamber.com
URL: http://www.norfolk.ne.us
Contact: Dennis Houston, President
Description: Promotes business and community development in Norfolk, NE. **Founded:** 1885. **Publications:** *The Chamber Advantage* (Monthly).

54416 ■ North Platte Area Chamber of Commerce and Development Corporation
502 S Dewey St.
North Platte, NE 69101
Ph: (308)532-4966
Fax: (308)532-4827
Co. E-mail: cameron@nparea.com
URL: http://www.nparea.com
Contact: Dan Mauk, President
Description: Promotes business and community development in North Platte, NE. **Founded:** 1919. **Publications:** *North Platte Chamber Area News* (Monthly).

54417 ■ *North Platte Chamber Area News*
502 S Dewey St.
North Platte, NE 69101
Ph: (308)532-4966
Fax: (308)532-4827
Co. E-mail: cameron@nparea.com
URL: http://www.nparea.com
Contact: Dan Mauk, President
Released: Monthly

54418 ■ Ogallala - Keith County Chamber of Commerce (OKCCC)
PO Box 628
Ogallala, NE 69153
Ph: (308)284-4066
Free: 800-658-4390
Co. E-mail: info@visitogallala.com
URL: http://www.visitogallala.com
Contact: Brenda Ketcham, Executive Director
Description: Promotes business and community development in Keith County, NE. **Founded:** 1958.

54419 ■ O'Neill Area Chamber of Commerce
125 S 4th St.
O'Neill, NE 68763-1813
Ph: (402)336-2355

Fax: (402)336-4563
Co. E-mail: oneill@telebeep.com
URL: http://www.oneillchamber.org
Contact: Pat Fritz, Executive Director
Description: Promotes business and community development in the O'Neill, NE area.

54420 ■ *Ord Area Business*
1514 K St.
Ord, NE 68862
Ph: (308)728-7875
Free: 877-728-7875
Fax: (308)728-7691
Co. E-mail: valleycountyed@frontiernet.net
URL: http://www.ordnebraska.com/chamber.asp
Contact: Caleb Pollard, Executive Director
Released: Annual

54421 ■ Ord Area Chamber of Commerce (OCC)
1514 K St.
Ord, NE 68862
Ph: (308)728-7875
Free: 877-728-7875
Fax: (308)728-7691
Co. E-mail: valleycountyed@frontiernet.net
URL: http://www.ordnebraska.com/chamber.asp
Contact: Caleb Pollard, Executive Director
Description: Promotes business and community development in the Ord, NE area. **Founded:** 1947. **Publications:** *Extraordinary News* (Monthly); *Ord Area Business* (Annual).

54422 ■ *Pathfinder*
PO Box 182
Fremont, NE 68026-0182
Ph: (402)721-2641
Fax: (402)721-9359
Co. E-mail: info@fremontne.org
URL: http://www.fremontne.org
Contact: Ron Tillery, Executive Director
Released: Monthly

54423 ■ Plainview Chamber of Commerce
PO Box 783
Plainview, NE 68769-0813
Ph: (402)582-7800
URL: http://www.plvwtelco.net/chamber_plvw.html
Contact: Mary Dougherty, Co-President
Description: Promotes business and community development in Plainview, NE area.

54424 ■ Plattsmouth Chamber of Commerce (PCC)
918 Washington Ave.
Plattsmouth, NE 68048
Ph: (402)296-6021
Fax: (402)296-6974
Co. E-mail: lisad@plattsmouthchamber.com
URL: http://www.plattsmouthchamber.com
Contact: Lisa Davis, Executive Director
Description: Promotes business and community development in Plattsmouth, NE. **Founded:** 1953. **Publications:** *Chamber Newsletter* (Monthly). **Educational Activities:** Kass Kounty King Korn Karnival (Annual).

54425 ■ *Plum Creek Express*
302 E 6th St., Ste. 2
Lexington, NE 68850
Ph: (308)324-5504
Fax: (308)324-5505
URL: http://www.lexcoc.com
Contact: Susan Bennett, Executive Director
Released: Monthly **Price:** free.

54426 ■ *Pony Express Exchange*
PO Box 263
Gothenburg, NE 69138
Ph: (308)537-3505
Free: 800-482-5520
Fax: (308)537-2541
Co. E-mail: annea@gothenburgdelivers.com
URL: http://www.gothenburgdelivers.com
Contact: Anne Anderson, Executive Director
Released: Monthly

54427 ■ *Profile*
1301 Harney St.
Omaha, NE 68102
Ph: (402)346-5000
Fax: (402)346-7050
Co. E-mail: info@omahachamber.org
URL: http://www.omahachamber.org
Contact: David G. Brown, President
Released: Periodic

54428 ■ *Pulse*
7536 S 84th St., Ste. B
La Vista, NE 68128
Ph: (402)339-2078
Fax: (402)339-2026
Co. E-mail: carol@lavistachamber.org
URL: http://www.lavistachamber.org
Contact: Mary Harper, Executive Director

54429 ■ Ralston Area Chamber of Commerce
5505 Miller Ave.
Ralston, NE 68127
Ph: (402)339-7737
Fax: (402)339-7954
Co. E-mail: chamber@cityofralston.com
URL: http://www.ralstonareachamber.com
Contact: Marlene L. Hansen, President
Description: Promotes business and community development in Ralston, NE area. **Founded:** 1960.

54430 ■ Ravenna Area Chamber of Commerce
318 Grand Ave.
Ravenna, NE 68869
Ph: (308)452-3344
Co. E-mail: chamber@ravennanebraska.net
URL: http://www.ci.ravenna.ne.us/chamber.htm
Contact: Margaret Treffer, Executive Director
Description: Promotes business and community development in Ravenna, NE area.

54431 ■ Sarpy County Chamber of Commerce (SCCC)
Shadow Lake Town Center
Papillion, NE 68046
Ph: (402)339-3050
Fax: (402)339-9968
Co. E-mail: chamber@sarpychamber.org
URL: http://www.sarpychamber.org
Contact: Jane Nielsen, President
Description: Promotes business and community development in Papillion and the mid-Sarpy County area of Nebraska. Sponsors Papillion Days, Old German Christmas, Business Expo., Monarch Market Place and Grand Give Away Auction. **Founded:** 1955. **Publications:** *Chamber News* (Monthly). **Awards:** Business Hall of Fame Award (Annual). **Telecommunication Services:** jane@sarpychamber.org.

54432 ■ Schuyler Area Chamber of Commerce (SACC)
1107 B St.
Schuyler, NE 68661
Ph: (402)352-5472
Fax: (402)352-5472
Co. E-mail: schuylerchamber@gmail.com
URL: http://www.ci.schuyler.ne.us/chamber.asp
Contact: Marie Myrick, Executive Director
Description: Promotes business and community development in Schuyler, NE. **Founded:** 1932.

54433 ■ Scottsbluff - Gering United Chamber of Commerce (SGCC)
1517 Broadway, Ste. 104
Scottsbluff, NE 69361
Ph: (308)632-2133
Free: 800-788-9475
Fax: (308)632-7128
Co. E-mail: chamber@scottsbluffgering.net
URL: http://www.scottsbluffgering.net
Contact: Jean Kearns, Chairman
Description: Promotes business and community development in Scottsbluff and Gering, NE. **Founded:** 1929. **Publications:** *Impact* (Monthly). **Awards:** Trailblazer of the Year (Annual); Visionary Rising Star (Annual); Visionary Superstar Award (Annual).

54434 ■ Seward Area Chamber of Commerce
616 Bradford
Seward, NE 68434
Ph: (402)643-4189
Co. E-mail: sewcham@sewardne.com
URL: http://www.sewardne.com
Contact: Sharon Pennington, Administrative Assistant
Description: Promotes business and community development in Seward, NE. Assists in presentation of annual 4th of July celebration. **Founded:** 1899.

54435 ■ Superior Area Chamber of Commerce
354 N Commercial Ave.
Superior, NE 68978
Ph: (402)879-3419
Co. E-mail: superiorcc@alltel.net
URL: http://www.ci.superior.ne.us
Description: Promotes business and community development in Superior, NE. **Publications:** *Superior Facts Book.*

54436 ■ *Surveyor*
603 Lincoln Ave.
York, NE 68467
Ph: (402)362-5531
Fax: (402)362-5953
Co. E-mail: yorkcc@yorkchamber.net
URL: http://yorkchamber.org
Contact: Todd Kirshenbaum, Executive Director
Released: Monthly

54437 ■ *Target*
701 4th Ave., Ste. 10
Holdrege, NE 68949
Ph: (308)995-4444
Fax: (308)995-4445
Co. E-mail: chamber@justtheplacenebraska.com
URL: http://www.holdrege.org
Contact: Monty Vonasek, President
Released: Monthly

54438 ■ Tecumseh Chamber of Commerce
PO Box 417
Tecumseh, NE 68450-0126
Ph: (402)335-3570
Co. E-mail: pdarling@windstream.net
URL: http://www.tecumsehne.com
Contact: Steve Mercure, President
Description: Promote economic development and community growth in Tecumseh, NE area.

54439 ■ Tekamah Chamber of Commerce
PO Box 231
Tekamah, NE 68061
Ph: (402)374-2020
Fax: (402)374-1392
Co. E-mail: hshafer@washingtoncountybank.com
URL: http://www.tekamahchamberofcommerce.com
Contact: Harriet Shafer, Secretary
Description: Promotes business and community development in Tekamah, NE.

54440 ■ *Update*
PO Box 125
West Point, NE 68788
Ph: (402)372-2981
Fax: (402)372-1105
Co. E-mail: info@westpointchamber.com
URL: http://www.westpointchamber.com
Contact: Tracy Swanson, President
Released: Monthly

54441 ■ Valentine Chamber of Commerce
PO Box 201
Valentine, NE 69201
Ph: (402)376-2969
Free: 800-658-4024
Co. E-mail: valentinecc@sandhillswireless.net
URL: http://www.visitvalentine.com
Contact: Anne Clark, President
Description: Promotes business and community development in Valentine, NE.

54442 ■ *The View*
806 1st Ave.
Nebraska City, NE 68410
Ph: (402)873-6654

Free: 800-514-9113
Fax: (402)873-6701
Co. E-mail: tourism@nebraskacity.com
URL: http://www.nebraskacity.com
Contact: Rebecca Turner, Executive Director
Released: Monthly

54443 ■ Wahoo Chamber of Commerce and Economic Development
PO Box 154
Wahoo, NE 68066-0154
Ph: (402)443-4001
Fax: (402)443-3077
Co. E-mail: watts@wahoo.ne.us
URL: http://www.wahoo.ne.us/index.asp
Contact: Doug Watts, Executive Director
Description: Promotes business and community development in Wahoo, NE. **Founded:** 1923. **Telecommunication Services:** woita@wahoo.ne.us.

54444 ■ West Point Chamber of Commerce (WPCC)
PO Box 125
West Point, NE 68788
Ph: (402)372-2981
Fax: (402)372-1105
Co. E-mail: info@westpointchamber.com
URL: http://www.westpointchamber.com
Contact: Tracy Swanson, President
Description: Promotes business and community development in West Point, NE. Sponsors Sidewalk Days, Membership Banquet, and Annual Appreciation Barbecue. Holds seminars and workshops. **Publications:** *Update* (Monthly).

54445 ■ Western Douglas County Chamber of Commerce (WDCCC)
20801 Elkhorn Dr.
Elkhorn, NE 68022
Ph: (402)289-9560
Fax: (402)289-9560
Co. E-mail: wdccc@wdccc.org
URL: http://www.wdccc.org
Contact: Jim Tomanek, President
Description: Promotes business and community development in the Western Douglas County.

FINANCING AND LOAN PROGRAMS

54446 ■ Odin Capital Group, LLC
1625 Farnam St., Ste. 700
Omaha, NE 68102
Ph: (402)827-9900
Fax: (402)408-6354
URL: http://www.odincapital.com
Contact: John Gustafson, Principal
E-mail: jgustafson@odincapital.com
Preferred Investment Size: $1,000,000 to $4,000,000. **Industry Preferences:** Communications, computer software, Internet specific, medical and health, industrial and energy, financial services, and business service. **Geographic Preference:** Midwest, Rocky mountains, and Southwest.

PROCUREMENT ASSISTANCE PROGRAMS

54447 ■ Nebraska Procurement Technical Assistance Center - Nebraska Business Development Center - University of Nebraska at Kearney
West Ctr. Bldg., Rm. 127E
1917 W 24th St.
Kearney, NE 68849-4440
Ph: (308)865-8244
Fax: (308)865-8153
Co. E-mail: knappse@unk.edu
URL: http://ptac.unomaha.edu
Contact: Scott Knapp, Counselor
E-mail: knappse@unk.edu
Description: Helps Nebraska businesses grow and generate new business by locating opportunities for business with the government.

54448 ■ Procurement Technical Assistance Center at Lincoln - Nebraska Business Development Center
285 S 68th St. Place, Ste. 550
Lincoln, NE 68510
Ph: (402)472-1177
Fax: (402)472-3363
Co. E-mail: kcarlin@mailunomaha.edu
URL: http://ptac.unomaha.edu
Contact: Kate Carlin, Counselor
E-mail: wrjohnson@mail.unomaha.edu
Description: Helps Nebraska businesses grow and generate new business by locating opportunities for business with the government.

INCUBATORS/RESEARCH AND TECHNOLOGY PARKS

54449 ■ Omaha Small Business Network
2505 N. 24th St.
Omaha, NE 68110
Ph: (402)453-5336
Fax: (402)451-2876
Co. E-mail: info@osbntc.org
URL: http://www.osbnbtc.org/
Description: A small business incubator dedicated to providing the tools needed to have a successful business; helping businesses bridge the gap between survival and independence by offering numerous programs and collaborative relationships with Omaha's leading lenders and support agencies.

54450 ■ University of Nebraska Technology Park
4701 Innovation Dr.
Lincoln, NE 68521-5330
Ph: (402)472-4200
Fax: (402)472-4203
Co. E-mail: info@nutechpark.com
URL: http://www.nutechpark.com/
Contact: Stephen Frayser, President
Description: The first planned business campus in Nebraska. A business incubator serving new and established technology companies.

EDUCATIONAL PROGRAMS

54451 ■ Nebraska Department of Economic Development - Industrial Training Programs
301 Centennial Mall S
Lincoln, NE 68509-4666
Ph: (800)426-6505
Free: 800-426-6505
Fax: (402)471-3778
URL: http://www.neded.org
Description: Customized job training programs.

54452 ■ University of Nebraska at Lincoln - Center for Entrepreneurship
Office of Entrepreneurship
University of Nebraska Lincoln CBA 217
Lincoln, NE 68588-0487
Ph: (402)472-3353
Fax: (402)472-6278
Co. E-mail: entrepreneurship@unl.edu
URL: http://www.cba.unl.edu/outreach/ent
Description: Offers a program/classes in small business/small business management.

PUBLISHERS

54453 ■ GHC Business Books
11202 N Post Rd.
Omaha, NE 68112-1217
Ph: (402)453-1769
Contact: Raymond L. Gustafson, Manager
Description: Description: Publishes book on small business development. services include a business brokerage. Reaches market through direct mail. **Founded:** 1982.

SMALL BUSINESS DEVELOPMENT CENTERS

54454 ■ Carson City Nevada Small Business Development Center
704 W Nye Ln., Ste. 201
Carson City, NV 89703
Ph: (775)883-4413
Fax: (775)883-0494
Co. E-mail: khalbard@clearwire.net
URL: http://www.nsbdc.org/who/offices/carson_city
Description: Represents and promotes the small business sector. Provides management assistance to current and prospective small business owners. Helps to improve management skills and expand the products and services of members.

54455 ■ Carson Valley Nevada Small Business Development Center
1477 Hwy. 395
Gardnerville, NV 89410
Ph: (775)782-8144
Fax: (775)782-1025
Co. E-mail: khalbard@clearwire.net
URL: http://www.nsbdc.org
Description: Represents and promotes the small business sector. Provides management assistance to current and prospective small business owners. Helps to improve management skills and expand the products and services of members.

54456 ■ Churchill County Nevada Small Business Development Center
PO Box 1236
Fallon, NV 89407
Ph: (775)423-8587
Fax: (775)423-1759
Co. E-mail: sbdc@ceda-nv.org
URL: http://www.nsbdc.org/who/offices/fallon
Contact: Rick Lattin, Consultant
Description: Represents and promotes the small business sector. Provides management assistance to current and prospective small business owners. Helps to improve management skills and expand the products and services of members.

54457 ■ Elko Nevada Small Business Development Center
Great Basin College
723 Railroad St.
Elko, NV 89801
Ph: (775)753-2245
Fax: (775)753-2242
Co. E-mail: judye@gwmail.gbcnv.edu
URL: http://www.nsbdc.org/who/offices/elko
Contact: Judy Emerson, Consultant
Description: Represents and promotes the small business sector. Provides management assistance to current and prospective small business owners. Helps to improve management skills and expand the products and services of members.

54458 ■ Ely Nevada Small Business Development Center
1320 E Alultman St.
Ely, NV 89301
Ph: (775)296-1236
Free: 866-404-5204
Co. E-mail: alparker@rndcnv.org
URL: http://www.nsbdc.org/who/offices/ely
Description: Represents and promotes the small business sector. Provides management assistance to current and prospective small business owners. Helps to improve management skills and expand the products and services of members.

54459 ■ Henderson Nevada Small Business Development Center
112 Water St.
Henderson, NV 89015
Ph: (702)992-7208
Fax: (702)992-7245
Co. E-mail: larry.vierra@unlv.edu
URL: http://www.nsbdc.org/who/offices/henderson
Contact: Larry Vierra, Director
Description: Represents and promotes the small business sector. Provides management assistance to current and prospective small business owners. Helps to improve management skills and expand the products and services of members.

54460 ■ Las Vegas Nevada Small Business Development Center
PO Box 456011
Las Vegas, NV 89154
Ph: (702)895-4270
Fax: (702)895-4273
Co. E-mail: nsbdc@unlv.edu
URL: http://www.nsbdc.org/who/offices/las_vegas
Contact: Janis Stevenson, Manager, Business Development
Description: Represents and promotes the small business sector. Provides management assistance to current and prospective small business owners. Helps to improve management skills and expand the products and services of members.

54461 ■ Laughlin Nevada Small Business Development Center
1585 S Casino Dr.
Laughlin, NV 89029
Ph: (702)298-2214
Fax: (702)298-5708
Co. E-mail: director@laughlinchamber.com
URL: http://www.nsbdc.org/who/offices/laughlin
Contact: Janet Medina, Executive Director
Description: Represents and promotes the small business sector. Provides management assistance to current and prospective small business owners. Helps to improve management skills and expand the products and services of members.

54462 ■ Nevada Small Business Development Center - Lead Office (NSBDC)
University of Nevada, Reno
College of Business Administration
Ansari Business Bldg., Rm. 411
Reno, NV 89557-0100
Ph: (775)784-1717
Free: 800-240-7094
Fax: (775)784-4337
Co. E-mail: nsbdc@unr.edu
URL: http://www.nsbdc.org
Contact: Sam Males, Director
Description: Enhances economic growth in Nevada through a network of facilities statewide that provide the expertise, knowledge and innovation necessary to assist startup and existing businesses succeed. Services include business counseling, professional training, environmental and safety assistance, research, geographic information, technology development assistance and disadvantaged business outreach.

54463 ■ Pahrump Nevada Small Business Development Center
Rural Nevada Development Corporation
NSB Bldg., 2nd Fl.
1301 S Hwy. 160
Pahrump, NV 89048
Ph: (775)751-1947
Fax: (775)751-1933
Co. E-mail: alparker@rndcnv.org
URL: http://www.nsbdc.org/who/offices/pahrump
Contact: Allan Parker, Consultant
Description: Represents and promotes the small business sector. Provides management assistance to current and prospective small business owners. Helps to improve management skills and expand the products and services of members.

54464 ■ Winnemucca Nevada Small Business Development Center
90 W Fourth St.
Winnemucca, NV 89445
Ph: (775)623-1064
Fax: (775)623-1664
Co. E-mail: bills@unr.edu
URL: http://www.nsbdc.org/who/offices/winnemucca
Description: Represents and promotes the small business sector. Provides management assistance to current and prospective small business owners. Helps to improve management skills and expand the products and services of members.

SMALL BUSINESS ASSISTANCE PROGRAMS

54465 ■ Nevada Commission on Economic Development
108 E Proctor St.
Carson City, NV 89701
Ph: (775)687-4325
Free: 800-336-1600
Fax: (775)687-4450
Co. E-mail: mskaggs@bizopp.state.nv.us
URL: http://www.expand2nevada.com
Contact: Michael E. Skaggs, Executive Director
Description: Provides assistance to small businesses from start-up to operations.

54466 ■ Nevada Department of Business and Industry
555 E Washington Ave.
Las Vegas, NV 89101
Ph: (702)486-2750
Free: 800-326-5202
Fax: (702)486-2758
Co. E-mail: biinfo@business.nv.gov
URL: http://www.business.nv.gov
Contact: Dianne Cornwall, Director

SCORE OFFICES

54467 ■ SCORE Las Vegas
City Centre Pl.
400 S 4th St., Ste. 250A
Las Vegas, NV 89101
Ph: (702)388-6104
Fax: (702)388-5849
Co. E-mail: info@scorelv.org
URL: http://www.scorelv.org
Contact: Ross Lagattuta, Chairman
Description: Works to help people start and successfully manage their own businesses. **Scope:** business plans, licensing, marketing, financing. **Subscriptions:** 200 audiovisuals books software video recordings.

54468 ■ SCORE Northern Nevada
University of Nevada
College of Business Administration
Nevada Small Business Development Center
Reno, NV 89557
Ph: (775)784-4436
Fax: (775)784-4337
Co. E-mail: info@score-reno.org
URL: http://www.score-reno.org
Contact: Nicole Barde, Counselor
Description: Offers free and confidential business advice, mentoring and information.

BETTER BUSINESS BUREAUS

54469 ■ *BB Views*
6040 S Jones Blvd.
Las Vegas, NV 89118-2619
Ph: (702)320-4500
Fax: (702)320-4560
Co. E-mail: info@sn.bbb.org
URL: http://southernnevada.bbb.org
Contact: George Cartwright, Chief Executive Officer
Released: Quarterly

54470 ■ Better Business Bureau of Southern Nevada
6040 S Jones Blvd.
Las Vegas, NV 89118-2619
Ph: (702)320-4500
Fax: (702)320-4560
Co. E-mail: info@sn.bbb.org
URL: http://southernnevada.bbb.org
Contact: George Cartwright, Chief Executive Officer
Description: Seeks to promote and foster ethical relationship between businesses and the public through voluntary self-regulation, consumer and business education, and service excellence. Provides information to help consumers and businesses make informed purchasing decisions and avoid costly scams and frauds; settles consumer complaints through arbitration and other means. **Scope:** tips for consumers. **Founded:** 1955. **Subscriptions:** books periodicals video recordings. **Publications:** *BB Views* (Quarterly). **Awards:** Golden Apple Award (Annual).

CHAMBERS OF COMMERCE

54471 ■ Beatty Chamber of Commerce
PO Box 956
Beatty, NV 89003
Ph: (775)553-2424
Free: 866-736-3716
Co. E-mail: beattychamber@sbcglobal.net
URL: http://www.beattynevada.org
Description: Strives to improve the economic condition of Beatty, Nevada by promoting its environmental, entertainment and other tourist attractions.

54472 ■ Boulder City Chamber of Commerce
465 Nevada Way
Boulder City, NV 89005-2613
Ph: (702)293-2034
Free: 888-399-2948
Fax: (702)293-0574
Co. E-mail: info@bouldercitychamber.com
URL: http://www.bouldercitychamber.com
Description: Promotes business and community development in Boulder City, NV. Conducts annual spring jamboree and annual Christmas parade and fair. **Founded:** 1932. **Publications:** *Communication Link* (Quarterly).

54473 ■ *Business Directory*
1477 US Hwy. 395, Ste. A
Gardnerville, NV 89410
Ph: (775)782-8144
Free: 800-727-6104
Fax: (775)782-1025
Co. E-mail: info@carsonvalleynv.org
URL: http://www.carsonvalleynv.org
Contact: Cheri Glockner, President
Released: Annual

54474 ■ *Business Roundup*
1405 Idaho St.
Elko, NV 89801
Ph: (775)738-7135
Fax: (775)738-7136
Co. E-mail: chamber@elkonevada.com
URL: http://www.elkonevada.com
Contact: Jennifer Sprout, Chief Executive Officer
Released: Monthly

54475 ■ *The Business Voice*
6671 Las Vegas Blvd. S, Ste. 300
Las Vegas, NV 89119
Ph: (702)735-1616
Fax: (702)735-0406
Co. E-mail: info@lvchamber.com
URL: http://www.lvchamber.com
Contact: Kara Kelley, President
E-mail: kpohl@lvchamber.com
Released: Monthly

54476 ■ Caliente Chamber of Commerce
PO Box 553
Caliente, NV 89008
Ph: (775)726-3129
URL: http://www.lincolncountynevada.com
URL(s): www.lasvegasregion.com/chambers.html.
Description: Promotes business and community development in Caliente, NV. Sponsors annual Homecoming Festival on Memorial Day weekend.

54477 ■ Carson City Area Chamber of Commerce
1900 S Carson St., Ste. 200
Carson City, NV 89701
Ph: (775)882-1565
Fax: (775)882-4179
Co. E-mail: director@carsoncitychamber.com
URL: http://www.carsoncitychamber.com
Contact: Ronni Hannaman, Executive Director
Description: Promotes business and community development in Carson City, NV. **Founded:** 1945. **Publications:** *Voice of Business* (Monthly); *Membership and Business Directory* (Annual).

54478 ■ Carson Valley Chamber of Commerce and Visitors Authority (CVCCVC)
1477 US Hwy. 395, Ste. A
Gardnerville, NV 89410
Ph: (775)782-8144
Free: 800-727-7677
Fax: (775)782-1025
Co. E-mail: info@carsonvalleynv.org
URL: http://www.carsonvalleynv.org
Contact: Cheri Glockner, President
Description: Promotes business, community development and tourism in the Carson Valley area of Nevada. **Founded:** 1945. **Publications:** *Business Directory* (Annual); *Chamber Connection* (Weekly).

54479 ■ *Chamber Business*
1 E 1st St., Ste. 1600
Reno, NV 89501
Ph: (775)337-3030

Fax: (775)337-3038
Co. E-mail: info@renosparkschamber.org
URL: http://www.renosparkschamber.org
Contact: Doug Kurkul, Chief Executive Officer
Released: Monthly

54480 ■ *Chamber Business Directory*
590 S Boulder Hwy.
Henderson, NV 89015-7512
Ph: (702)565-8951
Fax: (702)565-3115
Co. E-mail: info@hendersonchamber.com
URL: http://www.hendersonchamber.com
Contact: Alice Martz, President
Released: Annual

54481 ■ *Chamber Connection*
590 S Boulder Hwy.
Henderson, NV 89015-7512
Ph: (702)565-8951
Fax: (702)565-3115
Co. E-mail: info@hendersonchamber.com
URL: http://www.hendersonchamber.com
Contact: Alice Martz, President
Released: Quarterly

54482 ■ *Chamber Connection*
1477 US Hwy. 395, Ste. A
Gardnerville, NV 89410
Ph: (775)782-8144
Free: 800-727-7677
Fax: (775)782-1025
Co. E-mail: info@carsonvalleynv.org
URL: http://www.carsonvalleynv.org
Contact: Cheri Glockner, President
Released: Weekly

54483 ■ *Chamber News*
PO Box 821
Lovelock, NV 89419-0821
Ph: (775)273-7213
Fax: (775)273-1732
Co. E-mail: pcchamber@sbcglobal.net
URL: http://www.zplace2b.com/pccofc
Contact: Lynn Christofferson, Chairperson
Released: Bimonthly **Price:** included in membership dues.

54484 ■ *Chamber News*
70 N West St.
Fernley, NV 89408
Ph: (775)575-4459
Fax: (775)575-2626
Co. E-mail: fernleychamber@sbcglobal.net
URL: http://www.fernleychamber.org
Contact: Eric Stanger, President
Released: Monthly **Price:** included in membership dues.

54485 ■ *Chamber News*
PO Box 2408
Dayton, NV 89403
Ph: (775)246-7909
Fax: (775)246-5838
Co. E-mail: info@daytonnvchamber.org
URL: http://www.daytonnvchamber.org
Contact: Susan Skaggs, Executive Director
Released: Monthly

54486 ■ *Communication Link*
465 Nevada Way
Boulder City, NV 89005-2613
Ph: (702)293-2034
Free: 888-399-2948
Fax: (702)293-0574
Co. E-mail: info@bouldercitychamber.com
URL: http://www.bouldercitychamber.com
Released: Quarterly

54487 ■ *Comunicacion*
300 N 13th St.
Las Vegas, NV 89101
Ph: (702)385-7367
Fax: (702)385-2614
Co. E-mail: info@lvlcc.com
URL: http://www.lvlcc.com
Contact: Otto Merida, President
Released: Quarterly

54488 ■ Dayton Area Chamber of Commerce
PO Box 2408
Dayton, NV 89403
Ph: (775)246-7909
Fax: (775)246-5838
Co. E-mail: info@daytonnvchamber.org
URL: http://www.daytonnvchamber.org
Contact: Susan Skaggs, Executive Director
Description: Promotes community and business growth in Dayton, Nevada. **Publications:** *Chamber News* (Monthly).

54489 ■ Elko Chamber of Commerce
1405 Idaho St.
Elko, NV 89801
Ph: (775)738-7135
Fax: (775)738-7136
Co. E-mail: chamber@elkonevada.com
URL: http://www.elkonevada.com
Contact: Jennifer Sprout, Chief Executive Officer
Description: Promotes business and community development in Elko County, NV. **Founded:** 1907. **Publications:** *Business Roundup* (Monthly); *Elko Directory* (Periodic).

54490 ■ *Elko Directory*
1405 Idaho St.
Elko, NV 89801
Ph: (775)738-7135
Fax: (775)738-7136
Co. E-mail: chamber@elkonevada.com
URL: http://www.elkonevada.com
Contact: Jennifer Sprout, Chief Executive Officer
Released: Periodic

54491 ■ Fernley Chamber of Commerce
70 N West St.
Fernley, NV 89408
Ph: (775)575-4459
Fax: (775)575-2626
Co. E-mail: fernleychamber@sbcglobal.net
URL: http://www.fernleychamber.org
Contact: Eric Stanger, President
Description: Promotes business and community development in Fernley, NV. Provides visitors' information and sponsors special events. **Founded:** 1981. **Publications:** *Chamber News* (Monthly).

54492 ■ Greater Austin Chamber of Commerce
PO Box 212
Austin, NV 89310-0212
Ph: (775)964-2200
Fax: (775)964-2447
Co. E-mail: austinnvchamber@yahoo.com
URL: http://www.austinnevada.com
Contact: Phillip Williams, President
Description: Promotes business and community development in the Austin, NV area. Promotes tourism throughout the Nevada area.

54493 ■ Greater Fallon Area Chamber of Commerce
85 N Taylor St.
Fallon, NV 89406
Ph: (775)423-2544
Fax: (775)423-0504
Co. E-mail: info@fallonchamber.com
URL: http://www.fallonchamber.com
Contact: Rick Dentino, Executive Director
Description: Promotes business and community development in Churchill County, NV. Encourages tourism. Sponsors annual Hearts of Gold Cantaloupe Festival. **Founded:** 1948. **Awards:** Business Person of the Year (Annual); Pride in the Community Award (Annual).

54494 ■ Henderson Chamber of Commerce
590 S Boulder Hwy.
Henderson, NV 89015-7512
Ph: (702)565-8951
Fax: (702)565-3115
Co. E-mail: info@hendersonchamber.com
URL: http://www.hendersonchamber.com
Contact: Alice Martz, President
Description: Promotes business and community development in Henderson, NV. **Founded:** 1945. **Publications:** *Chamber Business Directory* (Annual); *Chamber Connection* (Quarterly).

54495 ■ Humboldt County Chamber of Commerce
30 W Winnemucca Blvd.
Winnemucca, NV 89445
Ph: (775)623-2225
Free: 877-326-1916
Fax: (775)623-6478
Co. E-mail: chamber@winnemucca.net
URL: http://www.humboldtcountychamber.com
Contact: John Arant, Vice President
Description: Promotes business and community development in Humboldt County, NV. **Founded:** 1920.

54496 ■ Incline Village - Crystal Bay Chamber of Commerce
969 Tahoe Blvd.
Incline Village, NV 89451
Ph: (775)831-4440
Free: 800-519-1584
Fax: (775)832-1625
Co. E-mail: stevet@puretahoenorth.com
URL: http://www.laketahoechamber.com
Contact: Sandy Evans Hall, Executive Director
Description: Promotes business and community development in the Crystal Bay and Incline Village, NV areas. Encourages quality business practices, hospitable treatment of visitors, and community involvement. Maintains business development center. Sponsors theatrical performances. **Founded:** 1976. **Publications:** *The Village Voice* (Monthly). **Educational Activities:** Business Trade Fair (Monthly).

54497 ■ Las Vegas Chamber of Commerce (LVCC)
6671 Las Vegas Blvd. S, Ste. 300
Las Vegas, NV 89119
Ph: (702)735-1616
Fax: (702)735-0406
Co. E-mail: info@lvchamber.com
URL: http://www.lvchamber.com
Contact: Kara Kelley, President
E-mail: kpohl@lvchamber.com
Description: Promotes business and community development in Las Vegas, NV. **Founded:** 1911. **Publications:** *The Business Voice* (Monthly); *Open Door* (Monthly); *Las Vegas Chamber of Commerce--Business Directory*; *Las Vegas Chamber of Commerce--Business Directory* (Annual); *Centennial Business Chronicle*.

54498 ■ Latin Chamber of Commerce of Nevada
300 N 13th St.
Las Vegas, NV 89101
Ph: (702)385-7367
Fax: (702)385-2614
Co. E-mail: info@lvlcc.com
URL: http://www.lvlcc.com
Contact: Otto Merida, President
Description: Businesses, corporations, and Hispanic individuals interested in developing economic, political, and social power for the Hispanic community. Provides scholarships and career, employment, and procurement programs. Offers business counseling. Sponsors annual golf tournament, eight luncheons, five cocktail mixers and two banquets a year. **Founded:** 1976. **Publications:** *Comunicacion* (Quarterly). **Educational Activities:** Awards Banquet (Annual). **Telecommunication Services:** otto@lvlcc.com; membership@lvlcc.com.

54499 ■ Laughlin Chamber of Commerce
1585 S Casino Dr.
Laughlin, NV 89028
Ph: (702)298-2214
Free: 800-227-5245
Fax: (702)298-5708
Co. E-mail: contact@laughlinchamber.com
URL: http://www.laughlinchamber.com
Contact: Janet Medina, Executive Director
Description: Businesses and professional men and women. Works to foster the civic, commercial and industrial development in the community.

54500 ■ *Look North*
3365 W Craig Rd., Ste. 25
North Las Vegas, NV 89032

Ph: (702)642-9595
Fax: (702)642-0439
Co. E-mail: contact@nlvchamber.org
URL: http://www.nlvchamber.org
Contact: Michael V. Varney, President
Released: Monthly **Price:** included in membership dues.

54501 ■ *Look North*
3365 W Craig Rd., Ste. 25
North Las Vegas, NV 89032
Ph: (702)642-9595
Fax: (702)642-0439
Co. E-mail: contact@nlvchamber.org
URL: http://www.nlvchamber.org
Contact: Michael V. Varney, President
Released: Quarterly

54502 ■ Lovelock/Pershing County Chamber of Commerce
PO Box 821
Lovelock, NV 89419-0821
Ph: (775)273-7213
Fax: (775)273-1732
Co. E-mail: pcchamber@sbcglobal.net
URL: http://www.zplace2b.com/pccofc
Contact: Lynn Christofferson, Chairperson
Description: Promotes business and community development in Pershing County, NV. Conducts charitable events. Sponsors competitions. **Publications:** *Chamber News* (Bimonthly). **Telecommunication Services:** info@pershingcountynevada.com.

54503 ■ *Membership and Business Directory*
1900 S Carson St., Ste. 200
Carson City, NV 89701
Ph: (775)882-1565
Fax: (775)882-4179
Co. E-mail: director@carsoncitychamber.com
URL: http://www.carsoncitychamber.com
Contact: Ronni Hannaman, Executive Director
Released: Annual

54504 ■ Mesquite Area Chamber of Commerce
12 W Mesquite Blvd., Ste. 107
Mesquite, NV 89027
Ph: (702)346-2902
Fax: (702)346-6138
Co. E-mail: meschamber@cascadeaccess.com
URL: http://www.mesquite-chamber.com
Contact: Karen Fielding, President
Description: Serves as an agency to address issues relevant to the growth, economic diversification and quality of life in the Mesquite area. Works to bring members and the business community together, conduct activities and provide a forum for views on the development of the area. Promotes Mesquite to others, encouraging awareness and disseminating information about the area to attract visitors. **Founded:** 1974. **Awards:** Business of the Month (Monthly).

54505 ■ Mineral County Chamber of Commerce
314 5th St.
Hawthorne, NV 89415
Ph: (775)945-2507
Co. E-mail: info@mineralcountychamber.com
URL: http://www.mineralcountychamber.com
Contact: Paul MacBeth, President
Description: Encourages tourism; supports education. Sponsors fairs and festivals. Conducts community service activities. Publications: none. **Founded:** 1979.

54506 ■ Moapa Valley Chamber of Commerce
c/o Craig Haderlie, Pres.
PO Box 717
Overton, NV 89040
Ph: (702)397-2136
Fax: (702)397-8756
Co. E-mail: chamber@moapavalley.com
URL: http://www.moapavalley.com
Contact: Craig Haderlie, President
Description: Promotes business and community development in the Moapa Valley area of Nevada. Sponsors Clark County Fair and conducts seminars. **Publications:** *Moapa Valley City Map* (Monthly).

54507 ■ *Moapa Valley City Map*
c/o Craig Haderlie, Pres.
PO Box 717
Overton, NV 89040
Ph: (702)397-2136
Fax: (702)397-8756
Co. E-mail: chamber@moapavalley.com
URL: http://www.moapavalley.com
Contact: Craig Haderlie, President
Released: Monthly

54508 ■ Nevada Chamber of Commerce Association
c/o Reno-Sparks Chamber of Commerce
One E 1st St., No. 1600
Reno, NV 89501
Ph: (775)337-3030
Fax: (775)337-3038
Co. E-mail: info@renosparkschamber.org
URL: http://www.reno-sparkschamber.org
Contact: Douglas R. Kurkul, Chief Executive Officer

54509 ■ North Las Vegas Chamber of Commerce (NLVCC)
3365 W Craig Rd., Ste. 25
North Las Vegas, NV 89032
Ph: (702)642-9595
Fax: (702)642-0439
Co. E-mail: contact@nlvchamber.org
URL: http://www.nlvchamber.org
Contact: Michael V. Varney, President
Description: Promotes business and community development in North Las Vegas, NV and neighboring communities. **Founded:** 1948. **Publications:** *Look North* (Monthly); *Look North* (Quarterly); *North Las Vegas Resource Directory*. **Telecommunication Services:** spowers@nlvchamber.org.

54510 ■ *North Las Vegas Resource Directory*
3365 W Craig Rd., Ste. 25
North Las Vegas, NV 89032
Ph: (702)642-9595
Fax: (702)642-0439
Co. E-mail: contact@nlvchamber.org
URL: http://www.nlvchamber.org
Contact: Michael V. Varney, President

54511 ■ *Open Door*
6671 Las Vegas Blvd. S, Ste. 300
Las Vegas, NV 89119
Ph: (702)735-1616
Fax: (702)735-0406
Co. E-mail: info@lvchamber.com
URL: http://www.lvchamber.com
Contact: Kara Kelley, President
E-mail: kpohl@lvchamber.com
Released: Monthly

54512 ■ Pahrump Valley Chamber of Commerce
1301 S Hwy. 160, 2nd Fl.
Pahrump, NV 89041
Ph: (775)727-5800
Free: 866-722-5800
Fax: (775)727-3909
Co. E-mail: info@pahrumpchamber.com
URL: http://www.pahrumpchamber.com
Contact: Michael Dreyer, President
Description: Promotes business and community development in Pahrump, NV. Encourages tourism. Sponsors the annual Chili Cook Off, Biz Expo, Wild West Extravaganza and Pahrump A Pum Pum. **Founded:** 1975.

54513 ■ Pioche Chamber of Commerce
PO Box 127
Pioche, NV 89043-0127
Ph: (775)962-5544
Co. E-mail: info@piochenevada.com
URL: http://www.piochenevada.com
Contact: Bob Rowe, President
URL(s): www.nevadaweb.com/chambers. **Description:** Promotes business and community development in Pioche, NV.

54514 ■ Reno-Sparks Chamber of Commerce
1 E 1st St., Ste. 1600
Reno, NV 89501
Ph: (775)337-3030

Fax: (775)337-3038
Co. E-mail: info@renosparkschamber.org
URL: http://www.renosparkschamber.org
Contact: Doug Kurkul, Chief Executive Officer
Description: Promotes business and community development in the northern NV area. Sponsors community events. Conducts business seminars and events. **Founded:** 1903. **Publications:** *Chamber Business* (Monthly).

54515 ■ Sparks Chamber of Commerce
PO Box 1176
Sparks, NV 89432
Ph: (775)358-1976
Fax: (775)358-1992
Co. E-mail: info@sparkschamber.org
URL: http://www.sparkschamber.org
Contact: Len Stevens, Executive Director
Description: Promotes business and community development in Reno and Sparks, NV. Operates tourist information center. Sponsors luncheons, mixers and special events. **Founded:** 1976. **Publications:** *Sparks Chamber of Commerce--Business Directory*. **Telecommunication Services:** l.stevens@sparkschamber.org.

54516 ■ *The Village Voice*
969 Tahoe Blvd.
Incline Village, NV 89451
Ph: (775)831-4440
Free: 800-519-1584
Fax: (775)832-1625
Co. E-mail: stevet@puretahoenorth.com
URL: http://www.laketahoechamber.com
Contact: Sandy Evans Hall, Executive Director
Released: Monthly

54517 ■ Virginia City/Gold Hill Chamber of Commerce
178 S C St.
Virginia City, NV 89440
Ph: (775)847-4499
Fax: (775)847-4499
Co. E-mail: vccoc@callatg.com
URL: http://www.virginiacity-nv.com
Description: Promotes tourism and community development in Virginia City, NV. **Founded:** 1996.

54518 ■ *Voice of Business*
1900 S Carson St., Ste. 200
Carson City, NV 89701
Ph: (775)882-1565
Fax: (775)882-4179
Co. E-mail: director@carsoncitychamber.com
URL: http://www.carsoncitychamber.com
Contact: Ronni Hannaman, Executive Director
Released: Monthly

54519 ■ Wells Chamber of Commerce
PO Box 615
Wells, NV 89835
Ph: (775)752-3540
Fax: (775)752-2172
Co. E-mail: coc@californiatrailinterpretivecenter.com
URL: http://wellsnevada.com
Contact: Pat Kelly, President
Description: Promotes business and community development in Wells, NV. Sponsors festival, car shows, chariot races, Jr. rodeo, walk, bike, and run marathon.

54520 ■ White Pine Chamber of Commerce
636 Aultman St.
Ely, NV 89301-1555
Ph: (775)289-8877
Fax: (775)289-6144
Co. E-mail: elycc@whitepinechamber.com
URL: http://www.whitepinechamber.com
Contact: Sherry L. Gaddy, President
Description: Promotes business and community development in the Ely, NV area. **Founded:** 1921.

MINORITY BUSINESS ASSISTANCE PROGRAMS

54521 ■ Nevada Minority Business Enterprise Center - New Ventures Capital Development Corp.
626 S Ninth St.
Las Vegas, NV 89101
Ph: (702)382-9522
Fax: (702)382-0375
Co. E-mail: vershaun_ragland@lvcoxmail.com
URL: http://www.newventurescdc.com
Contact: Vershaun Ragland
Description: Provides business consulting, development, and management services to minority business enterprises in Nevada.

54522 ■ Nevada Women's Business Resource and Assistance Center
2770 S Maryland Pky., Ste. 212
Las Vegas, NV 89109
Ph: (702)732-0414
Fax: (702)732-2705
Co. E-mail: nwbrac@aol.com
Description: Helps low to moderate income women in Nevada to start or grow a small business. Provides advocacy, education, and outreach.

FINANCING AND LOAN PROGRAMS

54523 ■ The Benefit Capital Companies Inc. (BCC)
3235-3245 N Pioneer Rd.
Logandale, NV 89021
Ph: (702)398-3222
Free: 800-922-3767
Fax: (702)398-3700
Co. E-mail: mail@benefitcapital.com
URL: http://www.benefitcapital.com
Contact: Kenneth P. Winslow, President
E-mail: kwinslow@benefitcapital.com
Scope: Counsels on the implementation of management and employee buyouts, especially using ESOPs (Employee Stock Ownership Plans) and related plans. LBO Fund invests equity capital and provides mezzanine financing to facilitate ESOP LBOs. **Founded:** 1984. **Preferred Investment Size:** $2,500,000 minimum. **Industry Preferences:** Diversified. **Geographic Preference:** U.S. **Seminars:** Employee Stock Ownership Plans-New Developments in the Creative Uses of ESOPs.

PROCUREMENT ASSISTANCE PROGRAMS

54524 ■ Nevada Commission on Economic Development - Procurement Outreach Program - Northern Nevada Regional Office
108 E Proctor St.
Carson City, NV 89701-4240
Ph: (775)687-1813
Free: 800-336-1600
Fax: (775)687-4450
Co. E-mail: tbaldassare@bizopp.state.nv.us
URL: http://www.expand2nevada.com/procurement.html
Contact: Kathy Dow, Counselor
Description: Assists small and disadvantaged businesses in Nevada obtain and complete federal government contracts. Also encourages the expansion of the manufacturing and service sectors into government contracting.

54525 ■ Nevada Commission on Economic Development - Procurement Outreach Program - Southern Nevada Regional Office
555 E Washington Ave., Ste. 5400
Las Vegas, NV 89101
Ph: (702)486-2700

Fax: (702)486-2701
Co. E-mail: rhorn@bizopp.state.nv.us
URL: http://www.expand2nevada.com/procurement.
  html
Contact: Rick Horn, Director
Description: Assists small and disadvantaged businesses in Nevada obtain and complete federal government contracts. Also encourages the expansion of the manufacturing and service sectors into government contracting.

54526 ■ Nevada Procurement Technical Assistance Center - Economic Development
108 E Proctor St.
Carson City, NV 89701-4240
Ph: (775)687-4325
Free: 800-336-1600
Fax: (775)687-4450
Co. E-mail: mskaggs@bizopp.state.nv.us
URL: http://www.expand2nevada.com/procurement.
  html
Contact: Michael E. Skaggs, Executive Director
Description: Assists small and disadvantaged businesses in Nevada obtain and complete federal government contracts. Also encourages the expansion of the manufacturing and service sectors into government contracting.

INCUBATORS/RESEARCH AND TECHNOLOGY PARKS

54527 ■ Henderson Business Resource Center
112 Water St.
Henderson, NV 89015
Ph: (702)992-7200
Fax: (702)992-7241
Co. E-mail: hbrc@hendersonchamber.com
URL: http://www.hendersonbizcenter.com/
Description: A small business incubator who develops and supports local businesses and strengthens and diversifies the local economy through entrepreneurship training opportunities, mentoring programs, and introductions to potential capital sources.

EDUCATIONAL PROGRAMS

54528 ■ Community College of Southern Nevada - Cheyenne Campus
3200 E Cheyenne Ave.
North Las Vegas, NV 89030
Ph: (702)651-4000
Free: 800-492-5728
Fax: (702)651-4811
URL: http://www.csn.edu
Description: Offers a program/classes in small business/small business management.

54529 ■ Truckee Meadows Community College - Institute for Business and Industry
5270 Neil Rd.
4001 S Virginia St.
Reno, NV 89502
Ph: (775)829-9000
Fax: (775)829-9009
URL: http://www.tmcc.edu/
Description: Offers a program designed to bring courses to the workplace; in addition, curriculum can be customized for the particular needs of a company.

PUBLICATIONS

54530 ■ *Smart Start your Georgia Business*
PSI Research
300 N. Valley Dr.
Grants Pass, OR 97526
Ph: (503)479-9464
Free: 800-228-2275
Fax: (503)476-1479
Co. E-mail: info@psi-research.com
URL: http://www.psi-research.com
Ed: Michael D. Jenkins. **Released:** Revised edition, 1992. **Price:** $29.95 (looseleaf binder); $24.95 (paper). **Description:** Part of the Successful Business Library series.

PUBLISHERS

54531 ■ GifTech Corp.—TaxMama
2961 Industrial Rd., Ste. 731
Las Vegas, NV 89109
Ph: (818)758-3535
Free: 800-594-9829
Fax: (450)458-1068
Co. E-mail: taxmama@taxmama.com
URL: http://www.taxmama.com
Contact: Eva Rosenberg, Editor
Description: Description: Publishes information about tax, business, women, networking and e-books. Offers video tapes and calendars. Also offers a weekly newsletter. Does not accept unsolicited manuscripts. Reaches market through reviews, listings and the Internet. **Founded:** 1984.

54532 ■ Everett L. Gracey
3288 Alum Creek Ct.
Reno, NV 89509
Ph: (775)324-3290
Fax: (775)324-3289
Co. E-mail: ev@everettgacey.com
URL: http://www.EverettGracey.com
Contact: Everett L. Gracey, Publisher
E-mail: evgracey@charter.net
Description: Description: Publishes business related books. Reaches market through wholesalers Ingram and Baker & Taylor. Does not accept unsolicited manuscripts. **Founded:** 1994.

54533 ■ Long & Silverman Publishing Inc. (L&S)
800 N Rainbow Blvd., Ste. 208
Las Vegas, NV 89107-1103
Ph: (702)948-5073
Free: 888-902-2766
Fax: (509)275-9448
Co. E-mail: sales@lspub.com
URL: http://www.lspub.com
Contact: William Patterson, Principal
Description: Description: Publishes books on business, economics, finances, inspirational, marketing, motivation, success, real estate, self-help and taxes. **Founded:** 2003.

SMALL BUSINESS DEVELOPMENT CENTERS

54534 ■ New Hampshire Small Business Development Center - Lead Office (NHSBDC)
University of NH
The Whittemore School of Business
110 McConnell Hall
Durham, NH 03824
Ph: (603)862-2200
Fax: (603)862-4876
Co. E-mail: mary.collins@unh.edu
URL: http://www.nhsbdc.org
Contact: Mary E. Collins, Director
Description: Provides business management counseling and training seminars. **Founded:** 1984.

54535 ■ Small Business Development Center (Keene, New Hampshire)
Keene State College
Mailstop 2101
Keene, NH 03435
Ph: (603)358-2602
Fax: (603)358-2612
Co. E-mail: goden@keene.edu
URL: http://www.nhsbdc.org/keene-regional-office
Contact: Gary Oden, Regional Manager
Description: Represents and promotes the small business sector. Provides management assistance to current and prospective small business owners. Helps to improve management skills and expand the products and services of members.

54536 ■ Small Business Development Center (Littleton, New Hampshire)
120 Main St.
Littleton, NH 03561
Ph: (603)444-1053
Fax: (603)444-5463
Co. E-mail: stewart.l.gates@mwarep.org
URL: http://www.nhsbdc.org/north-country-regional-office
Description: Represents and promotes the small business sector. Provides management assistance to current and prospective small business owners. Helps to improve management skills and expand the products and services of members.

54537 ■ Small Business Development Center (Manchester, New Hampshire)
33 S Commercial St.
Manchester, NH 03101-1796
Ph: (603)624-2000
Fax: (603)647-4410
Co. E-mail: andrea.obrien@unh.edu
URL: http://www.nhsbdc.org/manchester-regional-office
Contact: Andrea O'Brien, Advisor
Description: Represents and promotes the small business sector. Provides management assistance to current and prospective small business owners. Helps to improve management skills and expand the products and services of members.

54538 ■ Small Business Development Center (Nashua, New Hampshire)
Melanson Heath and Co.
102 Perimeter Rd.
Nashua, NH 03063
Ph: (603)589-2131
Co. E-mail: hollis.mcguire@unh.edu
URL: http://www.nhsbdc.org/nashua-regional-office
Contact: Hollis McGuire, Regional Manager
Description: Represents and promotes the small business sector. Provides management assistance to current and prospective small business owners. Helps to improve management skills and expand the products and services of members.

54539 ■ Small Business Development Center - Seacoast
18 S Main St., Ste. 2A
Rochester, NH 03867
Ph: (603)330-1929
Fax: (603)330-1948
Co. E-mail: susan.browning@unh.edu
URL: http://www.nhsbdc.org/seacoast-regional-office
Contact: Warren Daniel, Regional Manager
Description: Represents and promotes the small business sector. Provides management assistance to current and prospective small business owners. Helps to improve management skills and expand the products and services of members.

SMALL BUSINESS ASSISTANCE PROGRAMS

54540 ■ New Hampshire Department of Resources and Economic Development - Business Resource Center
172 Pembroke Rd.
Concord, NH 03302-1856
Ph: (603)271-2591
Fax: (603)271-6784
Co. E-mail: info@nheconomy.com
URL: http://www.nheconomy.com/
Contact: Roy Duddy, Director
Description: Assists companies considering locating in New Hampshire in their review of staffing and facility requirements, marketing considerations, support services, and other services. Also offers complete, current, and reliable information on those sections of the state best able to support a specific project. Also helps existing businesses.

SCORE OFFICES

54541 ■ Mount Washington Valley SCORE (MWV)
53 Technology Ln., Ste. 101
Conway, NH 03818
Ph: (603)447-4388
Fax: (603)447-9947
Co. E-mail: info@score641.org
URL: http://www.score641.org
Description: Provides professional guidance and information to America's small business in order to strengthen the local and national economy.

54542 ■ SCORE Merrimack Valley, NH, Chapter 199
275 Chestnut St.
Manchester, NH 03101
Ph: (603)666-7561
Fax: (603)666-7925
Co. E-mail: info@score199.mv.com
URL: http://www.score-manchester.org
Description: Represents business people supported by and affiliated with the U.S. Small Business Administration. Provides free, confidential and professional business counseling for small business and those wishing to start their own business. **Founded:** 1975.

54543 ■ SCORE Monadnock
34 Mechanic St.
Keene, NH 03431-3421
Ph: (603)352-0320
Co. E-mail: info@monadnockscore.org
URL: http://www.monadnockscore.org
Contact: Adele Knight, Chairperson
Description: Works to provide quality business counseling without charge to residents and business area. **Founded:** 1969.

54544 ■ Seacoast SCORE Chapter 185
215 Commerce Way, Ste. 420
Portsmouth, NH 03801
Ph: (603)433-0575
Fax: (603)433-0576
Co. E-mail: info@scorehelp.org
URL: http://www.scorehelp.org/chapter_185.html
Description: Represents the interests of retired business professionals who volunteer their experience and knowledge to help small business owners and potential small business owners achieve success. Provides free business counseling and seminars. **Scope:** business, financial. **Founded:** 1967. **Awards:** Distinguished Activity (Annual).

54545 ■ Upper Valley SCORE
Citizens Bank Bldg., Rm. 316
20 W Park St.
Lebanon, NH 03766
Ph: (603)448-3491
Fax: (603)448-1908
Co. E-mail: score@valley.net
URL: http://www.uppervalleyscore.org
Description: Provides free and confidential business counseling tailored to meet the needs of small business and personal objectives. **Founded:** 1967.

BETTER BUSINESS BUREAUS

54546 ■ Better Business Bureau of New Hampshire
48 Pleasant St.
Concord, NH 03301-3483
Ph: (603)224-1991

Fax: (603)228-9035
Co. E-mail: info@bbbnh.org
URL: http://concord.bbb.org
Description: Seeks to promote and foster ethical relationship between businesses and the public through voluntary self-regulation, consumer and business education, and service excellence. Provides information to help consumers and businesses make informed purchasing decisions and avoid costly scams and frauds; settles consumer complaints through arbitration and other means. **Founded:** 1972.

CHAMBERS OF COMMERCE

54547 ■ Activities Guide
PO Box 790
Hampton, NH 03843
Ph: (603)926-8718
Fax: (603)926-9977
Co. E-mail: info@hamptonchamber.com
URL: http://www.hamptonchamber.com
Contact: B.J. Noel, President
Released: Annual

54548 ■ Area Map and Services Directory
PO Box 65
Plymouth, NH 03264
Ph: (603)536-1001
Free: 800-386-3678
Fax: (603)536-4017
Co. E-mail: info@plymouthnh.org
URL: http://www.plymouthnh.org
Contact: Sarah A. Kilfoyle, Executive Director
Released: Annual

54549 ■ Area Visitors Guide
PO Box 65
Plymouth, NH 03264
Ph: (603)536-1001
Free: 800-386-3678
Fax: (603)536-4017
Co. E-mail: info@plymouthnh.org
URL: http://www.plymouthnh.org
Contact: Sarah A. Kilfoyle, Executive Director

54550 ■ Bethlehem Chamber of Commerce
2182 Main St., Rte. 302
Bethlehem, NH 03574-0748
Free: 888-845-1957
Co. E-mail: info@bethlehemwhitemtns.com
URL: http://www.bethlehemwhitemtns.com
Description: Promotes business and community development in Bethlehem, NH.

54551 ■ Brochure and Business Directory/ Recreation Guide
53 S Main St.
Hanover, NH 03755
Ph: (603)643-3115
Fax: (603)643-5606
Co. E-mail: hacc@hanoverchamber.org
URL: http://www.hanoverchamber.org
Contact: Janet Rebman, Executive Director
Released: Annual **Price:** free.

54552 ■ Business and Telephone Directory
PO Box 1
Colebrook, NH 03576
Ph: (603)237-8939
Free: 800-698-8939
Fax: (603)237-4573
Co. E-mail: nccoc@myfairpoint.net
URL: http://www.northcountrychamber.org
Contact: Peter Rouleau, President
Released: Annual

54553 ■ Buyer's Guide
18 S Main St.
Rochester, NH 03867-2702
Ph: (603)332-5080
Fax: (603)332-5216
Co. E-mail: chamber@rochesternh.org
URL: http://www.rochesternh.org
Contact: Laura A. Ring, President
Released: Annual **Price:** $25.

54554 ■ The Chamber Advantage
550 Central Ave.
Dover, NH 03820
Ph: (603)742-2218
Co. E-mail: molly@dovernh.org
URL: http://www.dovernh.org
Contact: Molly Hodgson Smith, Executive Director
Released: Monthly

54555 ■ Chamber Buzz
PO Box 537
Lancaster, NH 03584-0537
Ph: (603)788-2530
Free: 877-788-2530
Co. E-mail: northerngatewaychamber@gmail.com
URL: http://www.northerngatewaychamber.org
Contact: Steven Bissonnette, President
Released: Bimonthly **Price:** included in membership dues.

54556 ■ Chamber Chatter
12 Vintinner Rd.
Campton, NH 03223
Ph: (603)726-3804
Free: 800-237-2307
Fax: (603)726-4058
Co. E-mail: info@watervillevalleyregion.com
URL: http://www.watervillevalleyregion.com
Contact: Chris Bolan, Executive Director
Released: Monthly

54557 ■ Chamber Chatter
2 N Main St.
Newport, NH 03773
Ph: (603)863-1510
Fax: (603)863-9486
Co. E-mail: chamber@newportnhchamber.org
URL: http://www.newportnhchamber.org
Contact: Ella M. Casey, Executive Director
Released: Quarterly

54558 ■ Chamber Chatter Column in the Merrimack News Connection
PO Box 254
Merrimack, NH 03054-0254
Ph: (603)424-3669
Fax: (603)429-4325
Co. E-mail: info@merrimackchamber.org
URL: http://www.merrimackchamber.org
Contact: Eric Brand, President
Released: Weekly

54559 ■ Chamber Chronicles
PO Box 254
Merrimack, NH 03054-0254
Ph: (603)424-3669
Fax: (603)429-4325
Co. E-mail: info@merrimackchamber.org
URL: http://www.merrimackchamber.org
Contact: Eric Brand, President
Released: Bimonthly

54560 ■ Chamber of Commerce Directory
12 Vintinner Rd.
Campton, NH 03223
Ph: (603)726-3804
Free: 800-237-2307
Fax: (603)726-4058
Co. E-mail: info@watervillevalleyregion.com
URL: http://www.watervillevalleyregion.com
Contact: Chris Bolan, Executive Director
Released: Annual

54561 ■ Chamber News
383 S Main St.
Laconia, NH 03246
Ph: (603)524-5531
Fax: (603)524-5534
Co. E-mail: kgifford@lakesregionchamber.org
URL: http://lakesregionchamber.org
Contact: Karmen Gifford, Executive Director
Released: Monthly

54562 ■ Chamber News
10 Wilton Rd., Rte. 101
Peterborough, NH 03458
Ph: (603)924-7234

Fax: (603)924-7235
Co. E-mail: info@greater-peterborough-chamber.com
URL: http://www.greater-peterborough-chamber.com
Contact: Jack Burnett, Executive Director
Released: Monthly

54563 ■ Chamber Update
PO Box 541
Hillsborough, NH 03244-0541
Ph: (603)464-5858
Fax: (603)464-9166
Co. E-mail: hcofc@conknet.com
URL: http://www.hillsboroughnhchamber.com
Released: Monthly

54564 ■ Chamber Update
142 Main St., 5th Fl.
Nashua, NH 03060
Ph: (603)881-8333
Fax: (603)881-7323
Co. E-mail: chamber@nashuachamber.com
URL: http://www.nashuachamber.com
Contact: J. Christopher Williams, President
Released: Quarterly

54565 ■ The Chamber View
1 School St.
Lebanon, NH 03766
Ph: (603)448-1203
Fax: (603)448-6489
Co. E-mail: lebanonchamber@lebanonchamber.com
URL: http://www.lebanonchamber.com
Contact: Paul R. Boucher, President
Released: Monthly

54566 ■ Community Profiles
81 Main St.
Salem, NH 03079
Ph: (603)893-3177
Fax: (603)894-5158
Co. E-mail: donna@gschamber.com
URL: http://gschamber.com
Contact: Donna Morris, Executive Director
Released: Annual

54567 ■ Conway Village Area Chamber of Commerce (CVACC)
PO Box 1019
Conway, NH 03818
Ph: (603)447-2639
Co. E-mail: info@conwaychamber.com
URL: http://www.conwaychamber.com
Contact: Laura Gorman, President
Description: Promotes business and community development in Conway, NH. Conducts charitable programs; sponsors community holiday celebrations. **Founded:** 1903. **Awards:** Conway Village Citizen of the Year (Annual).

54568 ■ Crosswinds
PO Box 278
Exeter, NH 03833
Ph: (603)772-2411
Fax: (603)772-9965
Co. E-mail: info@exeterarea.org
URL: http://www.exeterarea.org
Contact: Michael Schidlovsky, President
Released: Annual **Price:** free.

54569 ■ Dining, Lodging and Visitors' Guide
550 Central Ave.
Dover, NH 03820
Ph: (603)742-2218
Co. E-mail: molly@dovernh.org
URL: http://www.dovernh.org
Contact: Molly Hodgson Smith, Executive Director
Released: Annual

54570 ■ Dividends
PO Box 239
Portsmouth, NH 03802-0239
Ph: (603)436-3988
Fax: (603)436-5118
Co. E-mail: info@portsmouthchamber.org
URL: http://www.portsmouthchamber.org
Contact: Doug Bates, President
Released: Monthly

54571 ■ Exeter Area Chamber of Commerce
PO Box 278
Exeter, NH 03833
Ph: (603)772-2411
Fax: (603)772-9965
Co. E-mail: info@exeterarea.org
URL: http://www.exeterarea.org
Contact: Michael Schidlovsky, President
Description: Promotes business and community development in the Exeter, NH area. **Founded:** 1957. **Publications:** *Crosswinds* (Annual); *Crosswinds* (Annual). **Awards:** Business of the Year (Annual).

54572 ■ *Explore Dover*
550 Central Ave.
Dover, NH 03820
Ph: (603)742-2218
Co. E-mail: molly@dovernh.org
URL: http://www.dovernh.org
Contact: Molly Hodgson Smith, Executive Director
Released: Semiannual

54573 ■ Franconia Notch Chamber of Commerce
PO Box 780
Franconia, NH 03580-0780
Ph: (603)823-5661
Co. E-mail: info@franconianotch.org
URL: http://www.franconianotch.org
Contact: Barbara Ashley, Executive Director
Description: Promotes business and community development in North Central New Hampshire. **Publications:** *Mountain Country* (Annual); *Mountain Country* (Annual).

54574 ■ *Gateways to Greater Nashua: Business, Lifestyle and Relocation Guide*
142 Main St., 5th Fl.
Nashua, NH 03060
Ph: (603)881-8333
Fax: (603)881-7323
Co. E-mail: chamber@nashuachamber.com
URL: http://www.nashuachamber.com
Contact: J. Christopher Williams, President
Released: Annual

54575 ■ Greater Claremont Chamber of Commerce (GCCC)
Moody Bldg., Ste. 102
24 Opera House Sq.
Claremont, NH 03743
Ph: (603)543-1296
Fax: (603)542-1469
Co. E-mail: info@claremontnhchamber.org
URL: http://www.claremontnhchamber.org
Contact: Shelly Hudson, Executive Director
Description: Promotes business and community development in the Claremont, NH area. Sponsors annual Northern Lights in Broadstreet program, a high school career day, and a retail auction. **Scope:** economic development, business references. **Founded:** 1917. **Awards:** Citizen of the Year (Annual).

54576 ■ Greater Derry Chamber of Commerce
29 W Broadway
Derry, NH 03038
Ph: (603)432-8205
Fax: (603)432-7938
Co. E-mail: info@gdlchamber.org
URL: http://www.derry-chamber.org
Contact: William B. Parnell, President
Description: Promotes business and community development in Derry, Hampstead, and Windham, NH. Sponsors Derry Fest Home Days and community decorations and holiday parades. **Founded:** 1964. **Publications:** *Network* (Monthly). **Telecommunication Services:** derrychamber@earthlink.net.

54577 ■ Greater Dover Chamber of Commerce
550 Central Ave.
Dover, NH 03820
Ph: (603)742-2218
Co. E-mail: molly@dovernh.org
URL: http://www.dovernh.org
Contact: Molly Hodgson Smith, Executive Director
Description: Promotes business and community development in the Dover, NH area. Solicits convention and tourism business. Sponsors seminars, workshops, sidewalk sales, summer concerts, street festivals, and other activities. Operates tourist information center. Holds Business After Hours for member businesses. **Founded:** 1920. **Publications:** *The Chamber Advantage* (Monthly); *Explore Dover* (Semiannual); *Greater Dover Chamber of Commerce Business Directory; Dining, Lodging and Visitors' Guide* (Annual); *Greater Dover Chamber of Commerce Business Directory: Explore Dover*. **Telecommunication Services:** info@dovernh.org.

54578 ■ Greater Franklin Chamber of Commerce
c/o Kathy Pevine, Coor.
PO Box 464
Franklin, NH 03235
Ph: (603)934-6909
Co. E-mail: info@franklinnhchamber.com
URL: http://www.laconia-weirs.org
Contact: Sandy Marshall, President
Description: Promotes business and community development in the Greater Franklin, NH area. **Publications:** *Experience Three Rivers* (Monthly).

54579 ■ Greater Hudson Chamber of Commerce (GHCC)—Hudson Chamber of Commerce
71 Lowell Rd.
Hudson, NH 03051
Ph: (603)889-4731
Fax: (603)889-7939
Co. E-mail: info@hudsonchamber.com
URL: http://www.hudsonchamber.com
Contact: Brenda Collins, Executive Director
Description: Promotes business and community development in Hudson, NH. **Founded:** 1969.

54580 ■ Greater Keene Chamber of Commerce (GKCC)
48 Central Sq.
Keene, NH 03431
Ph: (603)352-1303
Fax: (603)358-5341
Co. E-mail: info@keenechamber.com
URL: http://www.keenechamber.com
Contact: Laura Keith King, President
Description: Promotes business and community development in Cheshire County, NH. **Founded:** 1902. **Publications:** *Keene and Cheshire County Profile* (Biennial); *Outlook* (Monthly).

54581 ■ Greater Manchester Chamber of Commerce (GMCC)
54 Hanover St.
Manchester, NH 03101
Ph: (603)666-6600
Fax: (603)626-0910
Co. E-mail: robinc@manchester-chamber.org
URL: http://www.manchester-chamber.org
Contact: Robin Comstock, President
Description: Businesses. Promotes business and community development in northern Hillsborough County, NH. Sponsors educational programs; provides government affairs services. **Founded:** 1911. **Subscriptions:** articles books periodicals.

54582 ■ Greater Nashua Chamber of Commerce
142 Main St., 5th Fl.
Nashua, NH 03060
Ph: (603)881-8333
Fax: (603)881-7323
Co. E-mail: chamber@nashuachamber.com
URL: http://www.nashuachamber.com
Contact: J. Christopher Williams, President
Description: Promotes business and community development in the Nashua, NH area. Conducts lobbying activities; sponsors public affairs programs, golf tournament, and outlook. **Founded:** 1926. **Publications:** *Chamber Update* (Quarterly); *Gateways to Greater Nashua: Business, Lifestyle and Relocation Guide* (Annual); *Gateways Relocation and Quality of Life Magazine* (Annual). **Educational Activities:** Greater Nashua Chamber of Commerce Dinner (Annual). **Awards:** Citizen of the Year Award.

54583 ■ Greater Ossipee Area Chamber of Commerce (GOACC)
PO Box 323
Center Ossipee, NH 03814
Ph: (603)539-6201
Free: 866-683-6295
Co. E-mail: info@ossipeevalley.org
URL: http://www.ossipeevalley.org
Contact: Bill Grover, President
Description: Promotes business and economic development in the Greater Ossipee area. **Awards:** Christine Powers Memorial Fund (Annual).

54584 ■ Greater Peterborough Chamber of Commerce (GPCOC)
10 Wilton Rd., Rte. 101
Peterborough, NH 03458
Ph: (603)924-7234
Fax: (603)924-7235
Co. E-mail: info@greater-peterborough-chamber.com
URL: http://www.greater-peterborough-chamber.com
Contact: Jack Burnett, Executive Director
Description: Promotes business and community development in the Peterborough, NH area. Sponsors annual Festive Days, Holiday Lights, Peterborough Summer Fest, and Business Expo. **Founded:** 1975. **Publications:** *Chamber News* (Monthly); *Guide to Monadnock Region* (Annual); *Lodgings and Accommodations in the Monadnock Region*.

54585 ■ Greater Portsmouth Chamber of Commerce (GPCC)
PO Box 239
Portsmouth, NH 03802-0239
Ph: (603)436-3988
Fax: (603)436-5118
Co. E-mail: info@portsmouthchamber.org
URL: http://www.portsmouthchamber.org
Contact: Doug Bates, President
Description: Promotes business and community development in the Portsmouth, New Hampshire area and southwestern Maine. Sponsors annual Chamber Children's Day and Pumpkinfest. **Founded:** 1920. **Publications:** *Dividends* (Monthly); *Guide to the Seacoast; Leading Employers of the New Hampshire & Southern Maine Seacoast* (Biennial). **Educational Activities:** Mid-Day Meet (Monthly).

54586 ■ Greater Rochester Chamber of Commerce (GRCC)
18 S Main St.
Rochester, NH 03867-2702
Ph: (603)332-5080
Fax: (603)332-5216
Co. E-mail: chamber@rochesternh.org
URL: http://www.rochesternh.org
Contact: Laura A. Ring, President
Description: Promotes business and community development in northern Strafford County, NH. Coordinates annual Holiday parade. Holds annual dinner-dance and annual golf outing. **Founded:** 1928. **Publications:** *Buyer's Guide* (Annual); *Update* (Monthly).

54587 ■ Greater Salem Chamber of Commerce
81 Main St.
Salem, NH 03079
Ph: (603)893-3177
Fax: (603)894-5158
Co. E-mail: donna@gschamber.com
URL: http://gschamber.com
Contact: Donna Morris, Executive Director
Description: Promotes business and community development in the Salem, NH area. Offers networking, cooperative advertising, and referral services. Holds business after hours parties and breakfast and lunch forums. Sponsors Christmas Queen Scholarship Pageant and Business Expo. **Founded:** 1989. **Publications:** *Community Profiles* (Annual); *Impact* (Monthly). **Educational Activities:** Business Expo (Annual). **Awards:** Businessperson of the Year (Annual); High School Scholarships (Annual).

54588 ■ Greater Somersworth Chamber of Commerce (GSCC)
58 High St.
Somersworth, NH 03878
Ph: (603)692-7175
Fax: (603)692-4501
Co. E-mail: jennifer@somersworthchamber.com
URL: http://www.somersworthchamber.com
Contact: Ms. Jennifer Soldati, Executive Director
Description: Promotes business and economic development in Somersworth, NH.

54589 ■ Guide to Monadnock Region
10 Wilton Rd., Rte. 101
Peterborough, NH 03458
Ph: (603)924-7234
Fax: (603)924-7235
Co. E-mail: info@greater-peterborough-chamber.com
URL: http://www.greater-peterborough-chamber.com
Contact: Jack Burnett, Executive Director
Released: Annual

54590 ■ Guide to the Seacoast
PO Box 239
Portsmouth, NH 03802-0239
Ph: (603)436-3988
Fax: (603)436-5118
Co. E-mail: info@portsmouthchamber.org
URL: http://www.portsmouthchamber.org
Contact: Doug Bates, President
Price: free.

54591 ■ Hampton Beach Area Chamber of Commerce
PO Box 790
Hampton, NH 03843
Ph: (603)926-8718
Fax: (603)926-9977
Co. E-mail: info@hamptonchamber.com
URL: http://www.hamptonchamber.com
Contact: B.J. Noel, President
Description: Promotes economic development and tourism in the Hampton, NH area. Operates Visitor Welcome Center. **Founded:** 1915. **Publications:** *Activities Guide* (Annual); *Tidings* (Monthly); *Vacation Guide.*

54592 ■ Hanover Area Chamber of Commerce (HACC)
53 S Main St.
Hanover, NH 03755
Ph: (603)643-3115
Fax: (603)643-5606
Co. E-mail: hacc@hanoverchamber.org
URL: http://www.hanoverchamber.org
Contact: Janet Rebman, Executive Director
Description: Promotes business, tourism, and community relation in Hanover, NH area. Operates information booth in summer. Sponsors annual Street Fest and annual Upper Valley Home and Trade Show. **Founded:** 1961. **Publications:** *Map; Brochure and Business Directory/Recreation Guide* (Annual).

54593 ■ Hillsborough Chamber of Commerce
PO Box 541
Hillsborough, NH 03244-0541
Ph: (603)464-5858
Fax: (603)464-9166
Co. E-mail: hcofc@conknet.com
URL: http://www.hillsboroughnhchamber.com
Description: Represents business people. Promotes business and community development in Hillsborough, NH. **Scope:** tourism, small business. **Founded:** 1971. **Subscriptions:** 250. **Publications:** *Chamber Update* (Monthly). **Awards:** Business of the Year (Annual); Citizen of the Year (Annual).

54594 ■ Impact
81 Main St.
Salem, NH 03079
Ph: (603)893-3177
Fax: (603)894-5158
Co. E-mail: donna@gschamber.com
URL: http://gschamber.com
Contact: Donna Morris, Executive Director
Released: Monthly

54595 ■ Jaffrey Chamber of Commerce (JCC)
7 Main St.
Jaffrey, NH 03452-0002
Ph: (603)532-4549
Fax: (603)532-8823
Co. E-mail: info@jaffreychamber.com
URL: http://www.jaffreychamber.com
Contact: Angela Pelletier, President
Description: Businesses, educational institutions, churches, and interested individuals. Promotes business and community development in the Jaffrey, NH area. Sponsors Festival of Fireworks. **Founded:** 1982.

54596 ■ Keene and Cheshire County Profile
48 Central Sq.
Keene, NH 03431
Ph: (603)352-1303
Fax: (603)358-5341
Co. E-mail: info@keenechamber.com
URL: http://www.keenechamber.com
Contact: Laura Keith King, President
Released: Biennial **Price:** $5.

54597 ■ Lakes Region Chamber of Commerce
383 S Main St.
Laconia, NH 03246
Ph: (603)524-5531
Fax: (603)524-5534
Co. E-mail: kgifford@lakesregionchamber.org
URL: http://lakesregionchamber.org
Contact: Karmen Gifford, Executive Director
Description: Promotes business and community development in the Laconia, NH area. **Founded:** 1920. **Publications:** *Chamber News* (Monthly).

54598 ■ Lebanon Area Street Map
1 School St.
Lebanon, NH 03766
Ph: (603)448-1203
Fax: (603)448-6489
Co. E-mail: lebanonchamber@lebanonchamber.com
URL: http://www.lebanonchamber.com
Contact: Paul R. Boucher, President

54599 ■ Lebanon Chamber of Commerce
1 School St.
Lebanon, NH 03766
Ph: (603)448-1203
Fax: (603)448-6489
Co. E-mail: lebanonchamber@lebanonchamber.com
URL: http://www.lebanonchamber.com
Contact: Paul R. Boucher, President
Description: Promotes business and community development in Lebanon, NH. **Founded:** 1916. **Publications:** *The Chamber View* (Monthly); *Lebanon Area Street Map; Lebanon Area Profile Book* (Periodic). **Educational Activities:** Home and Trade Show (Annual).

54600 ■ Lincoln-Woodstock Chamber of Commerce (LWCC)
PO Box 1017
Lincoln, NH 03251-0358
Ph: (603)745-6621
Co. E-mail: info@lincolnwoodstock.com
URL: http://www.lincolnwoodstock.com/chamber/index.php
Contact: Mark LaClair, Executive Director
Description: Promotes business and community development in Lincoln and Woodstock, NH. Provides referral service and mailing list. Operates Lincoln-Woodstock Central Reservation Service and information booth. **Founded:** 1960. **Publications:** *Lincoln-Woodstock Chamber Newsletter* (Monthly).

54601 ■ Lincoln-Woodstock Chamber Newsletter
PO Box 1017
Lincoln, NH 03251-0358
Ph: (603)745-6621
Co. E-mail: info@lincolnwoodstock.com
URL: http://www.lincolnwoodstock.com/chamber/index.php
Contact: Mark LaClair, Executive Director
Released: Monthly

54602 ■ Lisbon Area Chamber of Commerce
6 S Main St.
Lisbon, NH 03585
Ph: (603)838-6673
Co. E-mail: lisbonnh@adelphia.net
URL: http://www.lisbonnh.org/public_documents/LisbonNH_WebDocs
Contact: John Northrop, President
Description: Promotes business and community development in Lisbon, NH.

54603 ■ Littleton Area Chamber of Commerce (LACC)
PO Box 105
Littleton, NH 03561
Ph: (603)444-6561
Fax: (603)444-2427
Co. E-mail: cstearns@littletonareachamber.com
URL: http://www.littletonareachamber.com
Contact: Chad Stearns, Executive Director
Description: Promotes business and community development in the Littleton, NH area. Maintains hospital, industry, commercial, retail service, and community divisions. Sponsors Business Expo, Home & Trade Show Expo, Frostbite Follies Winter Carnival, Riverfront Art Show, Trout Tournament and Fishing Derby, Taste of Littleton, Concerts in the Park Series, Christmas Parade, Santa Party and Holiday Craft Fair Fourth of July Fireworks, Economic Development Celebration Luncheon. **Founded:** 1921. **Publications:** *Membership Directory and Relocation - Tourism Guide* (Annual). **Educational Activities:** Art Show (Annual). **Awards:** Citizen of the Year; Service Awards.

54604 ■ Lodgings and Accommodations in the Monadnock Region
10 Wilton Rd., Rte. 101
Peterborough, NH 03458
Ph: (603)924-7234
Fax: (603)924-7235
Co. E-mail: info@greater-peterborough-chamber.com
URL: http://www.greater-peterborough-chamber.com
Contact: Jack Burnett, Executive Director

54605 ■ Map
53 S Main St.
Hanover, NH 03755
Ph: (603)643-3115
Fax: (603)643-5606
Co. E-mail: hacc@hanoverchamber.org
URL: http://www.hanoverchamber.org
Contact: Janet Rebman, Executive Director

54606 ■ Map of Merrimack
PO Box 254
Merrimack, NH 03054-0254
Ph: (603)424-3669
Fax: (603)429-4325
Co. E-mail: info@merrimackchamber.org
URL: http://www.merrimackchamber.org
Contact: Eric Brand, President

54607 ■ Membership Directory and Relocation - Tourism Guide
PO Box 105
Littleton, NH 03561
Ph: (603)444-6561
Fax: (603)444-2427
Co. E-mail: cstearns@littletonareachamber.com
URL: http://www.littletonareachamber.com
Contact: Chad Stearns, Executive Director
Released: Annual

54608 ■ Meredith Area Chamber of Commerce
PO Box 732
Meredith, NH 03253-0732
Ph: (603)279-6121
Free: 877-279-6121
Fax: (603)279-4525
Co. E-mail: meredith@lr.net
URL: http://www.meredithareachamber.com
Contact: Susan Cerutti, Executive Director
Description: Promotes business and community development in the Centre Harbor, NH area.

54609 ■ Merrimack Chamber of Commerce
PO Box 254
Merrimack, NH 03054-0254
Ph: (603)424-3669
Fax: (603)429-4325
Co. E-mail: info@merrimackchamber.org
URL: http://www.merrimackchamber.org
Contact: Eric Brand, President
Description: Promotes business and community development in Merrimack, NH. Committed to serve, support and promote its members through networking, community involvement, information services and public awareness. Conducts monthly networking events, seminars, holiday parades, golf tournament, and information booth operation. Services include relocation guide, weekly news articles, Welcome Bag for new residents, map of Merrimack, and ribbon cuttings. **Founded:** 1928. **Publications:** *Chamber Chronicles* (Bimonthly); *Map of Merrimack*; *Chamber Chatter Column in the Merrimack News Connection* (Weekly). **Educational Activities:** Annual Recognition Banquet (Monthly). **Awards:** Annual Student Scholarships (Annual); Business of the Year (Annual); Business Person of the Year (Annual); President's Award (Annual).

54610 ■ *Mountain Country*
PO Box 780
Franconia, NH 03580-0780
Ph: (603)823-5661
Co. E-mail: info@franconianotch.org
URL: http://www.franconianotch.org
Contact: Barbara Ashley, Executive Director
Released: Annual

54611 ■ *Mountain Country Magazine*
12 Vintinner Rd.
Campton, NH 03223
Ph: (603)726-3804
Free: 800-237-2307
Fax: (603)726-4058
Co. E-mail: info@watervillevalleyregion.com
URL: http://www.watervillevalleyregion.com
Contact: Chris Bolan, Executive Director
Released: Periodic

54612 ■ *Network*
29 W Broadway
Derry, NH 03038
Ph: (603)432-8205
Fax: (603)432-7938
Co. E-mail: info@gdlchamber.org
URL: http://www.derry-chamber.org
Contact: William B. Parnell, President
Released: Monthly

54613 ■ New London - Lake Sunapee Region Chamber of Commerce
PO Box 532
New London, NH 03257-0532
Ph: (603)526-6575
Free: 877-526-6575
Co. E-mail: chamberinfo@tds.net
URL: http://www.lakesunapeenh.org
Contact: Rob Bryant, Executive Director
Description: Promotes business and community development in the New London, NH area. Operates information booth. **Founded:** 1970.

54614 ■ Newfound Region Chamber of Commerce
PO Box 454
Bristol, NH 03222
Ph: (603)744-2150
Co. E-mail: newfoundchamber@metrocast.net
URL: http://www.newfoundchamber.com
Contact: Denice DeStefano, President
Description: Seeks to promote business and community development and enhance the relationship between local businesses and professionals with the public.

54615 ■ Newport Area Chamber of Commerce (NACC)
2 N Main St.
Newport, NH 03773
Ph: (603)863-1510

Fax: (603)863-9486
Co. E-mail: chamber@newportnhchamber.org
URL: http://www.newportnhchamber.org
Contact: Ella M. Casey, Executive Director
Description: Promotes business and community development in the Newport, NH area. Sponsors annual Christmas lighting program and beautification projects. Holds weekly band concert during summer. **Publications:** *Chamber Chatter* (Quarterly). **Awards:** Busy Bee Awards.

54616 ■ North Country Chamber of Commerce
PO Box 1
Colebrook, NH 03576
Ph: (603)237-8939
Free: 800-698-8939
Fax: (603)237-4573
Co. E-mail: nccoc@myfairpoint.net
URL: http://www.northcountrychamber.org
Contact: Peter Rouleau, President
Description: Promotes business and community development in the northern New Hampshire area. Promotes tourism. **Publications:** *Business and Telephone Directory* (Annual).

54617 ■ Northern Gateway Chamber of Commerce
PO Box 537
Lancaster, NH 03584-0537
Ph: (603)788-2530
Free: 877-788-2530
Co. E-mail: northerngatewaychamber@gmail.com
URL: http://www.northerngatewaychamber.org
Contact: Steven Bissonnette, President
Description: Promotes business and community development in Lancaster, NH. **Publications:** *Chamber Buzz* (Bimonthly).

54618 ■ *Outlook*
48 Central Sq.
Keene, NH 03431
Ph: (603)352-1303
Fax: (603)358-5341
Co. E-mail: info@keenechamber.com
URL: http://www.keenechamber.com
Contact: Laura Keith King, President
Released: Monthly

54619 ■ Plymouth Chamber of Commerce
PO Box 65
Plymouth, NH 03264
Ph: (603)536-1001
Free: 800-386-3678
Fax: (603)536-4017
Co. E-mail: info@plymouthnh.org
URL: http://www.plymouthnh.org
Contact: Sarah A. Kilfoyle, Executive Director
Description: Promotes business and community development in Plymouth, NH. **Founded:** 1992. **Publications:** *Area Map and Services Directory* (Annual); *Area Visitors Guide*. **Educational Activities:** Business After Hours (Monthly); Business Expo/Job Fair (Annual).

54620 ■ Souhegan Valley Chamber of Commerce (SVCC)
69 Rte. 101A
Amherst, NH 03031
Ph: (603)673-4360
Fax: (603)673-5018
Co. E-mail: chamber@souhegan.net
URL: http://www.souhegan.net
Contact: May Balsama, Executive Director
Description: Promotes business and community development in the Amherst and Milford, NH area. **Founded:** 1988.

54621 ■ *Tidings*
PO Box 790
Hampton, NH 03843
Ph: (603)926-8718
Fax: (603)926-9977
Co. E-mail: info@hamptonchamber.com
URL: http://www.hamptonchamber.com
Contact: B.J. Noel, President
Released: Monthly

54622 ■ *Update*
18 S Main St.
Rochester, NH 03867-2702
Ph: (603)332-5080
Fax: (603)332-5216
Co. E-mail: chamber@rochesternh.org
URL: http://www.rochesternh.org
Contact: Laura A. Ring, President
Released: Monthly

54623 ■ *Vacation Guide*
PO Box 790
Hampton, NH 03843
Ph: (603)926-8718
Fax: (603)926-9977
Co. E-mail: info@hamptonchamber.com
URL: http://www.hamptonchamber.com
Contact: B.J. Noel, President

54624 ■ Waterville Valley Region Chamber of Commerce (WVRCC)
12 Vintinner Rd.
Campton, NH 03223
Ph: (603)726-3804
Free: 800-237-2307
Fax: (603)726-4058
Co. E-mail: info@watervillevalleyregion.com
URL: http://www.watervillevalleyregion.com
Contact: Chris Bolan, Executive Director
Description: Businesses and organizations interested in promoting business and tourism in Plymouth, Campton, Thornton, and Waterville Valley, NH. **Founded:** 1971. **Publications:** *Chamber Chatter* (Monthly); *Chamber of Commerce Directory* (Annual); *Mountain Country Magazine* (Periodic).

MINORITY BUSINESS ASSISTANCE PROGRAMS

54625 ■ WREN - Women's Rural Entrepreneurial Network
2011 Main St.
Bethlehem, NH 03574
Ph: (603)869-9736
Fax: (603)869-9738
Co. E-mail: wren@wrencommunity.org
URL: http://www.wrencommunity.org
Contact: Marilinne Cooper, Executive Director
Description: Provides business development and technical assistance to women who would like to start a business.

FINANCING AND LOAN PROGRAMS

54626 ■ Arete Corporation
PO Box 1299
Center Harbor, NH 03226
Ph: (603)253-9797
Fax: (603)253-9799
Co. E-mail: aretecorp@adelphia.net
URL: http://www.arete-microgen.com
Contact: Robert W. Shaw, President
Preferred Investment Size: $500,000 to $3,000,000. **Industry Preferences:** Industrial and energy. **Geographic Preference:** U.S. and Canada.

PROCUREMENT ASSISTANCE PROGRAMS

54627 ■ New Hampshire Procurement Technical Assistance Center - State of New Hampshire - Economic Development
172 Pembroke Rd.
Concord, NH 03302-1856
Ph: (603)271-7581
Fax: (603)271-6784
Co. E-mail: info@nheconomy.com
URL: http://www.nheconomy.com
Contact: Brad Martin, Program Manager

54628 ■ New Hampshire Procurement Technical Assistance Center - State of New Hampshire - Office of Business & Industrial

Department of Defense
172 Pembroke Rd.
Concord, NH 03302-1856
Ph: (603)271-7581
Fax: (603)271-6784
Co. E-mail: bmartin@dred.state.nh.us
URL: http://www.nheconomy.com/ptac.html
Contact: Brad Martin, Program Manager
E-mail: cway@dred.state.nh.us
Description: The New Hampshire Procurement Technical Assistance Program (NH-PTAP) exists to help New Hampshire client businesses - whether large, small, newly established, minority owned, women-owned, veteran owned, etc obtain information needed to bid competitively on Department of Defense, federal, state and local contracts.

INCUBATORS/RESEARCH AND TECHNOLOGY PARKS

54629 ■ Amoskeag Business Incubator
33 S. Commercial St.
Manchester, NH 03101
Ph: (603)629-9511
Fax: (603)629-9510
Co. E-mail: info@abi-nh.com
URL: http://www.abi-nh.com/
Description: A small business incubator seeking to provide a supportive entrepreneurial environment that stimulates the growth of businesses to ensure economic vitality and encourage job creation by providing affordable office space and technical assistance to early-stage companies.

54630 ■ Dartmouth Regional Technology Center
Centerra Research Park
16 Cavendish Ct.
Lebanon, NH 03766

Ph: (603)676-3300
Fax: (603)646-3670
Co. E-mail: info@thedrtc.com
URL: http://www.thedrtc.com
Contact: Alla Kan, Director
Description: A small business incubator focusing on developing businesses with a proven concept and a solid plan. It offers an educational and infrastructure support program aimed at developing promising technology startups by assisting them in refining their business plans, helping them identify and seek sources of investment and expertise, and providing them with basic business infrastructure and support to make them as productive as possible in as short a time as possible.

EDUCATIONAL PROGRAMS

54631 ■ Hesser College
3 Sundial Ave.
Manchester, NH 03103
Ph: (603)668-6660
Free: 800-935-1824
Fax: (603)621-8994
URL: http://www.hesser.edu
Description: Two-year college offering a small business management program.

PUBLICATIONS

54632 ■ Business NH Magazine
55 S Commercial St.
Manchester, NH 03101
Ph: (603)626-6354
Fax: (603)626-6359
Co. E-mail: businessnh@nh.interwebb.com
URL: http://millyardcommunications.com

54633 ■ New Hampshire Business Review
150 Dow St.
Manchester, NH 03101-1151
Ph: (603)624-1442
Fax: (603)624-1310
URL: http://www.nhbr.com

54634 ■ Smart Start your New Hampshire Business
PSI Research
300 N. Valley Dr.
Grants Pass, OR 97526
Ph: (503)479-9464
Free: 800-228-2275
Fax: (503)476-1479
Co. E-mail: info@psi-research.com
URL: http://www.psi-research.com
Ed: Michael D. Jenkins. **Released:** Revised edition, 1992. **Price:** $29.95 (looseleaf binder); $24.95 (paper). **Description:** Part of the Successful Business Library series.

PUBLISHERS

54635 ■ New Hampshire Small Business Development Center (NHSBDC)
The Whittemore School of Business
University of New Hampshire, 110 McConnell Hall
Durham, NH 03824
Ph: (603)862-2200
Fax: (603)862-4876
URL: http://www.nhsbdc.org
Contact: Mary Collins, Director
Description: Description: Publishes guidebooks of business and marketing data. Reaches market through direct mail. Does not accept unsolicited manuscripts. **Founded:** 1984.

SMALL BUSINESS DEVELOPMENT CENTERS

54636 ■ Bergen Small Business Development Center
Ciarco Learning Center
355 Main St.
Hackensack, NJ 07601
Ph: (201)489-8670
Fax: (201)489-8673
Co. E-mail: sbdc@bergen.edu
URL: http://www.bergen.edu/sbdc/Pages/675.aspx
Contact: Mr. Vincent A. D'Elia, Regional Director
Description: Represents and promotes the small business sector. Provides management assistance to current and prospective small business owners. Helps to improve management skills and expand the products and services of members. **Founded:** 1992.
Awards: Malcolm Baldrige Quality Assurance Assessment (3/year).

54637 ■ Centenary College Small Business Development Center
400 Jefferson St.
Hackettstown, NJ 07840
Ph: (908)852-1400
Free: 800-236-8679
Co. E-mail: info@nw-njsbdc.com
URL: http://www.centenarycollege.edu
Contact: Dolores J. Stammer, Director
Description: Represents and promotes the small business sector. Provides management assistance to current and prospective small business owners. Helps to improve management skills and expand the products and services of members.

54638 ■ Kean University Small Business Development Center
c/o Ms. Mira Kostak, Regional Dir.
301 Morris Ave.
Union, NJ 07083
Ph: (908)737-4220
URL: http://www.njsbdc.com
Contact: Ms. Mira Kostak, Regional Director
Description: Operates in partnership with the U.S. Small Business Administration (SBA) and the New Jersey Commerce and Economic Growth and Tourism Commission; provides free, professional small business consulting and training services. **Founded:** 1989. **Publications:** *Start Up and Business Plan Guides* (Annual). **Awards:** Small Business Success Award (Annual).

54639 ■ Monmouth/Ocean Small Business Development Center
765 Newman Springs Rd.
Lincroft, NJ 07738
Ph: (732)842-8685
Co. E-mail: mosbdc@brookdalecc.edu
URL: http://www.brookdalecc.edu/pages/327.asp
Contact: William Nunnally, Director
Description: Represents and promotes the small business sector. Provides management assistance to current and prospective small business owners. Helps to improve management skills and expand the products and services of members.

54640 ■ New Jersey City University Small Business Development Center
285 Westside Ave., Ste. 189-191
Jersey City, NJ 07305
Ph: (201)200-2156
Fax: (201)200-3404
Co. E-mail: hle2@njcu.edu
URL: http://njsbdc.com/index.php/sbdc/view/9
Contact: Ms. Barbara S. O'Neal, Director
Description: Represents and promotes the small business sector. Provides management assistance to current and prospective small business owners. Helps to improve management skills and expand the products and services of members.

54641 ■ New Jersey Small Business Development Center, Rutgers University (Camden, New Jersey)
419 Cooper St.
Camden, NJ 08102
Ph: (856)225-6221
Fax: (856)225-6621
Co. E-mail: rsbdc@camden.rutgers.edu
URL: http://www.rsbdc.org
Contact: Gary Rago, Director
Description: Represents and promotes the small business sector. Provides management assistance to current and prospective small business owners. Helps to improve management skills and expand the products and services of members.

54642 ■ Rutgers-Newark Small Business Development Center (RNSBDC)
25 James St.
Newark, NJ 07102
Ph: (973)353-5950
Fax: (973)353-5978
Co. E-mail: rnsbdc@newark.rutgers.edu
URL: http://www.business.rutgers.edu/rnsbdc
Contact: Ms. Tendai Ndoro, Director
Description: Represents and promotes the small business sector. Provides management assistance to current and prospective small business owners. Helps to improve management skills and expand the products and services of members.

54643 ■ Small Business Development Center at Raritan Valley Community College
PO Box 3300
Somerville, NJ 08876
Ph: (908)526-1200
Fax: (908)722-4716
Co. E-mail: sbdc@raritanval.edu
URL: http://www.sbdcrvcc.com
Contact: Larry Jenkins, Director
Description: Represents and promotes the small business sector. Provides management assistance to current and prospective small business owners. Helps to improve management skills and expand the products and services of members.

54644 ■ Small Business Development Center - The College of New Jersey
2000 Pennington Ave.
Ewing, NJ 08628
Ph: (609)771-2947
Fax: (609)637-5217
Co. E-mail: info@sbdcnj.com
URL: http://www.tcnj.edu/~sbdc
Contact: Lorraine Allen, Director
Description: Represents and promotes the small business sector. Provides management assistance to current and prospective small business owners. Helps to improve management skills and expand the products and services of members.

54645 ■ *Start Up and Business Plan Guides*
c/o Ms. Mira Kostak, Regional Dir.
301 Morris Ave.
Union, NJ 07083
Ph: (908)737-4220
URL: http://www.njsbdc.com
Contact: Ms. Mira Kostak, Regional Director
Released: Annual **Price:** free.

54646 ■ William Paterson University Small Business Development Center
131 Ellison St.
Paterson, NJ 07505
Ph: (973)754-8695
Co. E-mail: sbdc@wpunj.edu
URL: http://www.wpunj.edu/sbdc
Contact: Kate Muldoon, Director
Description: Represents and promotes the small business sector. Provides management assistance to current and prospective small business owners. Helps to improve management skills and expand the products and services of members.

SMALL BUSINESS ASSISTANCE PROGRAMS

54647 ■ New Jersey Commerce Economic Growth and Tourism Commission - International Trade and Protocol
Mary G. Roebling Bldg.
20 W. State St.
Trenton, NJ 08625-0820
Ph: (609)292-3860
URL: http://www.state.nj.us/njbusiness/wmb/inc/progin/oitp.shtml
Description: Helps New Jersey companies in export development and expansion. Also encourages foreign investment in the state.

54648 ■ New Jersey Commerce Economic Growth and Tourism Commission - Office of Marketing
Mary G. Roebling Bldg.
20 W State St., 4th Fl.
Trenton, NJ 08625-0835
Ph: (609)292-0700
Fax: (609)292-9145
URL: http://www.newjerseycommerce.org
Description: Acts as an ombudsman, handling complaints and problems of small business owners. Also serves as an advocate for small businesses and administers the One Stop Permit Identification System.

54649 ■ **New Jersey Department of Business and Economic Development**
Mary G. Roebling Bldg.
20 W State St.
Trenton, NJ 08625-0990
Ph: (609)292-4431
URL: http://www.newjerseycommerce.org/
Description: Provides complete assistance packages, including financing, site selection, and construction. Package may also include labor recruitment and training.

54650 ■ **New Jersey Economic Development Authority - Office of the Business Advocate**
36 W. State St
P.O Box 990
Trenton, NJ 08625-0820
Ph: (609)292-3863
URL: http://www.njeda.com/web/default.aspx
Contact: Lauren Moore, Director
Description: Certify Minority, women- owned and small businesses. Formerly New Jersey Commerce Commission.

54651 ■ **New Jersey Economic Growth & Tourism - Business Services & Urban Programs**
33 W. State St
P.O Box 026
Trenton, NJ 08625-0820
Ph: (609)292-2146
Fax: (609)292-9145
URL: http://www.state.nj.us/commerce/about_busserv_urbanpro.shtml
Description: Provides a central resource for small, women-owned, and minority-owned businesses in dealing with federal, state, and local governments. Also provides financial, marketing, procurement, technical, and managerial assistance.

SCORE OFFICES

54652 ■ **Central Jersey SCORE**
Co. E-mail: score@raritanval.edu

54653 ■ **Monmouth SCORE**
Co. E-mail: info@score36.org

54654 ■ **North West SCORE**
Co. E-mail: info@njscore24.org

54655 ■ **Ocean County SCORE**
Dover Township Municipal Bldg.
33 Washington St.
Toms River, NJ 08753
Ph: (732)505-6033
Co. E-mail: score150@verizon.net
URL: http://www.oceancountyscore.org
Description: Serves small business community for many years and has a track record of providing small business owners with the advice they need to succeed.

54656 ■ **Princeton SCORE**
Co. E-mail: info@scoreprinceton.org

54657 ■ **SCORE Bergen**
Co. E-mail: contact@scorebergen.org

54658 ■ **SCORE Newark**
Small Business Administration
2 Gateway Ctr., 15th Fl.
Newark, NJ 07102
Ph: (973)645-3982
Co. E-mail: newarkscore@yahoo.com
URL: http://www.scoremetronj.org
Description: Provides personalized, confidential counseling to help people start and operate a successful small business.

54659 ■ **Southern New Jersey SCORE**
Co. E-mail: info@score254.org

54660 ■ **Tri-County SCORE**
Co. E-mail: tri-countyscore@hotmail.com

BETTER BUSINESS BUREAUS

54661 ■ **Better Business Bureau of New Jersey (BBB)**
1700 Whitehorse-Hamilton Sq. Rd., Ste. D-5
Trenton, NJ 08690
Ph: (609)588-0808
Fax: (609)588-0546
Co. E-mail: info@newjersey.bbb.org
URL: http://newjersey.bbb.org
Contact: Melissa Companick, President
URL(s): www.trenton.bbb.org. **Description:** Promotes and fosters ethical relationships between businesses and the public through voluntary self-regulation, consumer and business education, and service excellence. **Founded:** 1962. **Publications:** *Better Business Bureau of New Jersey Consumer Guide* (Annual).

54662 ■ *Better Business Bureau of New Jersey Consumer Guide*
1700 Whitehorse-Hamilton Sq. Rd., Ste. D-5
Trenton, NJ 08690
Ph: (609)588-0808
Fax: (609)588-0546
Co. E-mail: info@newjersey.bbb.org
URL: http://newjersey.bbb.org
Contact: Melissa Companick, President
Released: Annual **Price:** free.

CHAMBERS OF COMMERCE

54663 ■ *Actionline*
Pinho Professional Center
Freehold, NJ 07728-1703
Ph: (732)462-3030
Fax: (732)462-2123
Co. E-mail: admin@wmchamber.com
URL: http://www.wmchamber.com
Contact: Loretta R. Kuhnert, President
Released: Monthly

54664 ■ *Advertising Brochure*
PO Box 22
Avalon, NJ 08202-0022
Ph: (609)967-3936
Co. E-mail: chamber@avalonbeach.com
URL: http://www.avalonbeach.com
Contact: John Allison, President
Released: Annual

54665 ■ *Area Guide*
PO Box 5007
Hazlet, NJ 07730
Ph: (732)203-0340
Fax: (732)203-0341
Co. E-mail: info@northernmonmouthchamber.com
URL: http://www.northernmonmouthchamber.com
Contact: Paul Morris, Executive Director

54666 ■ *Area Info Guide*
2115 S Delsea Dr.
Vineland, NJ 08360
Ph: (856)691-7400
Fax: (856)691-2113
Co. E-mail: info@vinelandchamber.org
URL: http://www.vinelandchamber.org
Contact: Dawn Hunter, Executive Director
Released: Biennial **Price:** free.

54667 ■ **Asbury Park Chamber of Commerce (APCC)**
PO Box 649
Asbury Park, NJ 07712
Ph: (732)775-7676
Fax: (732)775-7675
Co. E-mail: info@asburyparkchamber.com
URL: http://www.asburyparkchamber.com
Contact: Jacqueline L. Pappas, Executive Director
Description: Professionals, non-profit organizations, services, hotels, restaurants, and others. Promotes business and community development in the Asbury Park, NJ area. Sponsors jazz festival, Easter parade, and Columbus Day Landing. **Founded:** 1971.

54668 ■ **Atlantic City Regional Chamber of Commerce**
The Garage at Gordon's Alley
12 S Virginia Ave.
Atlantic City, NJ 08401-4806
Ph: (609)345-4524
Fax: (609)345-1666
Co. E-mail: tthomas@atlanticcitychamber.com
URL: http://www.atlanticcitychamber.com
Contact: Joseph Kelly, President
Description: Promotes business and community development in the Atlantic City, NJ area. **Founded:** 1914.

54669 ■ **Avalon Chamber of Commerce**
PO Box 22
Avalon, NJ 08202-0022
Ph: (609)967-3936
Co. E-mail: chamber@avalonbeach.com
URL: http://www.avalonbeach.com
Contact: John Allison, President
Description: Promotes business and community development in Avalon, NJ. **Publications:** *Advertising Brochure* (Annual).

54670 ■ **Belmar Chamber of Commerce**
1005 1/2 Main St.
Belmar, NJ 07719
Ph: (732)681-2900
Co. E-mail: info@belmarchamber.com
URL: http://www.belmarchamber.com
Contact: Bart Yarnold, President
Description: Promotes business and community development in the Belmar, NJ area. Sponsors festivals and hall of fame; presents business and service awards. Operates county welcome center and tourism development.

54671 ■ *Bergen County Economic Development Book*
PO Box 325
Paramus, NJ 07652-0325
Ph: (201)261-3344
Fax: (201)261-3346
Co. E-mail: staff@paramuschamber.com
URL: http://www.paramuschamber.com
Contact: Dimitri Miaoulis, Chairman
Released: Biennial **Price:** free.

54672 ■ **Bound Brook Area Chamber of Commerce**
PO Box 227
Bound Brook, NJ 08805
Ph: (732)356-7273
Co. E-mail: bbacoc@gmail.com
URL: http://bbareachamber.com
Contact: Sonia Amorim, President
Description: Promotes business and community development in the Bound Brook, NJ area. Sponsors festivals and hall of fame; presents business and service awards. Operates county welcome center and tourism development.

54673 ■ **Brick Township Chamber of Commerce**
270 Chambers Bridge Rd., Ste. 6
Brick, NJ 08723
Ph: (732)477-4949
Fax: (732)477-5788
Co. E-mail: info@brickchamber.com
URL: http://www.brickchamber.org
Contact: Michele Eventoff, Executive Director
Description: Represents the interests of retailers, businesses, and professionals. Promotes business and community development in Brick Township, NJ. Sponsors monthly educational seminars. **Founded:** 1956. **Publications:** *Lifestyles* (Annual). **Awards:** Beautification Awards (Annual); Distinguished Citizens Awards (Annual).

54674 ■ **Bridgeton Area Chamber of Commerce (BACC)**
76 Magnolia Ave.
Bridgeton, NJ 08302
Ph: (856)455-1312

Fax: (856)453-9795
Co. E-mail: bacc@baccnj.com
URL: http://www.baccnj.com
Contact: Anthony Stanzione, Executive Director
Description: Promotes business and economic development in Bridgeton, NJ.

54675 ■ Brigantine Beach Chamber of Commerce
PO Box 484
Brigantine, NJ 08203
Ph: (609)266-3437
Co. E-mail: info@brigantinechamber.com
URL: http://www.brigantinechamber.com
Contact: Emmett Turner, President
Description: Promotes business and community development in Brigantine, NJ. **Founded:** 1926. **Publications:** *Brigantine Beach - Where Mankind and Nature Thrive in Harmony.* **Awards:** Dolly Award (Annual).

54676 ■ *Brigantine Beach - Where Mankind and Nature Thrive in Harmony*
PO Box 484
Brigantine, NJ 08203
Ph: (609)266-3437
Co. E-mail: info@brigantinechamber.com
URL: http://www.brigantinechamber.com
Contact: Emmett Turner, President

54677 ■ Burlington County Chamber of Commerce (BCCC)
100 Technology Way, Ste. 110
Mount Laurel, NJ 08054
Ph: (856)439-2520
Fax: (856)439-2523
Co. E-mail: bccoc@bccoc.com
URL: http://bccoc.com
Contact: Kristi M. Howell-Ikeda, President
Description: Promotes business and community development in Burlington County, NJ. **Founded:** 1964. **Publications:** *The Communicator* (Quarterly). **Awards:** Behind the Scenes (Annual); Mildred and David Gama Scholarship (Annual); Voice of Business (Annual).

54678 ■ *Business Directory*
PO Box 831
Millville, NJ 08332
Ph: (856)825-2600
Fax: (856)825-5333
Co. E-mail: info@millville-nj.com
URL: http://www.millville-nj.com
Contact: Earl Sherrick, Executive Director
Released: Periodic

54679 ■ *Business Directory*
173 Elm St., 3rd Fl.
Westfield, NJ 07090
Ph: (908)233-3021
Fax: (908)654-8183
Co. E-mail: info@westfieldchamber.com
URL: http://www.westfieldareachamber.com
Contact: Neil Pinkman, Executive Director
Released: Biennial

54680 ■ *Business Directory and Map*
195 Change Bridge Rd.
Montville, NJ 07045
Ph: (973)263-3310
Fax: (973)263-3453
Co. E-mail: info@montvillechamber.com
URL: http://montvillechamber.com
Contact: Margaret Miller-Sanders, President
Released: Biennial

54681 ■ *Business Matters*
1033 Rte. 46 E, Ste. A103
Clifton, NJ 07013
Ph: (973)470-9300
Fax: (973)470-9245
Co. E-mail: staff@njrcc.org
URL: http://www.njrcc.org
Contact: Gloria Martini, President
E-mail: gmartini@njrcc.org
Released: Bimonthly

54682 ■ *The Business Network*
395 Rte. 70 W, Ste. 125
Lakewood, NJ 08701
Ph: (732)363-0012
Fax: (732)367-4453
Co. E-mail: staff@mylakewoodchamber.com
URL: http://www.mylakewoodchamber.com
Contact: Kathleen Mead, President
Released: Monthly **Price:** free.

54683 ■ Camden County Regional Chamber of Commerce
1060 Kings Hwy. N, Ste. 200
Cherry Hill, NJ 08034
Ph: (856)667-1600
Fax: (856)667-1464
Co. E-mail: art@camdencountychamber.com
URL: http://www.cherryhillregional.com
Contact: Arthur C. Campbell, President
Description: Promotes business and community development in Cherry Hill, NJ. **Founded:** 1977. **Publications:** *The Commentary* (Monthly); *Cherry Hill Regional Chamber of Commerce--Membership Directory* (Annual).

54684 ■ Cape May County Chamber of Commerce
PO Box 74
Cape May Court House, NJ 08210-0074
Ph: (609)465-7181
Fax: (609)465-5017
Co. E-mail: info@cmcchamber.com
URL: http://www.cmccofc.com
Contact: Vicki Clark, President
Description: Promotes business and community development in Cape May County, NJ. **Founded:** 1944. **Publications:** *Jersey Caper* (Bimonthly); *C.M. Co. St. Maps & Guide*; *Jersey Cape Vacation Guide* (Annual). **Educational Activities:** Business to Business Expo (Periodic).

54685 ■ *Chamber Challenge*
1033 Rte. 46 E, Ste. A103
Clifton, NJ 07013
Ph: (973)470-9300
Fax: (973)470-9245
Co. E-mail: staff@njrcc.org
URL: http://www.njrcc.org
Contact: Gloria Martini, President
E-mail: gmartini@njrcc.org
Released: 11/year **Price:** free.

54686 ■ *Chamber Chatter*
336 Raritan Ctr. Pkwy.
Edison, NJ 08837
Ph: (732)738-9482
Fax: (732)738-9485
Co. E-mail: edisonchamber@att.net
URL: http://www.edisonchamber.com
Contact: Barbara C. Roos, President
Released: Monthly **Price:** free.

54687 ■ *Chamber Chatter*
PO Box 5007
Hazlet, NJ 07730
Ph: (732)203-0340
Fax: (732)203-0341
Co. E-mail: info@northernmonmouthchamber.com
URL: http://www.northernmonmouthchamber.com
Contact: Paul Morris, Executive Director
Released: Quarterly

54688 ■ *Chamber Chatter*
PO Box 2
Wyckoff, NJ 07481-0002
Ph: (201)891-3616
Co. E-mail: info@wyckoffchamber.com
URL: http://www.wyckoffchamber.com
Contact: Jay Vidockler, President
Released: Quarterly

54689 ■ Chamber of Commerce of Greater Cape May (CCGCM)
PO Box 556
Cape May, NJ 08204-0556
Ph: (609)884-5508

Fax: (609)884-2054
Co. E-mail: info@capemaychamber.com
URL: http://www.capemaychamber.com
Contact: Robert Steenrod, President
Description: Promotes business and community development in the Cape May, NJ area. Sponsors festival and competitions; conducts charitable activities. **Founded:** 1951. **Publications:** *Christmas in Cape May*; *Tulip Festival* (Periodic); *Cape May Visitor's Guide* (Annual); *Guidebook of Victorian Cape May* (Annual). **Telecommunication Services:** request@capemaychamber.com.

54690 ■ Chamber of Commerce Serving Old Bridge, Sayerville and South Amboy
PO Box 5241
Old Bridge, NJ 08857
Ph: (732)607-6340
Fax: (732)607-6341
Co. E-mail: info@obssachamber.com
URL: http://www.obssachamber.org
Contact: Greg Camerato, President

54691 ■ Chamber of Commerce Southern New Jersey (CCSNJ)
4015 Main St.
Voorhees, NJ 08043
Ph: (856)424-7776
Fax: (856)424-8180
Co. E-mail: info@chambersnj.com
URL: http://www.chambersnj.com
Contact: Debra P. DiLorenzo, President
Description: Provides its members with opportunities to meet each other and network, resources to enhance their positions in the marketplace, and a collective voice on public policy issues that impact on operations and profitability. **Founded:** 1873. **Publications:** *The Review* (Monthly); *Membership Directory and Buyers' Guide* (Annual).

54692 ■ *Chamber Connection*
25 S Livingston Ave., 2nd Fl., Ste. E
Livingston, NJ 07039
Ph: (973)992-4343
Fax: (973)992-8024
Co. E-mail: info@livingstonchambernj.com
URL: http://www.livingstonchambernj.com
Contact: Beth Lippman, Executive Director
Released: Monthly

54693 ■ *Chamber Connection*
323 Main St., Ste. B
Metuchen, NJ 08840-2433
Ph: (732)548-2964
Fax: (732)548-4094
Co. E-mail: metuchen.chamber@verizon.net
URL: http://www.metuchenchamber.com
Contact: Caroline Woodruff, Office Manager
Released: Quarterly **Price:** free for members.

54694 ■ *Chamber Information Booklet*
PO Box 422
Stone Harbor, NJ 08247
Ph: (609)368-6101
Co. E-mail: joe@wjse.com
URL: http://stoneharborbeach.com
Contact: Philip Barber, President
Released: Periodic

54695 ■ *Chamber News*
456 N Broad St.
Elizabeth, NJ 07208
Ph: (908)355-7600
Fax: (908)436-2054
Co. E-mail: gecc@juno.com
URL: http://www.elizabethchamber.com
Contact: Gordon Haas, President
Released: Quarterly

54696 ■ *Chamberfax*
71 Summit Ave.
Summit, NJ 07901
Ph: (908)522-1700
Fax: (908)522-9252
Co. E-mail: info@suburbanchambers.org
URL: http://www.suburbanchambers.org
Contact: Maureen Kelly, President
Released: Monthly

54697 ■ Chatham Area Chamber of Commerce (CACC)
PO Box 231
Chatham, NJ 07928-0231
Ph: (973)635-2444
Fax: (973)635-2953
Co. E-mail: chathamchamber@gmail.com
URL: http://www.chathamchambernj.org
Contact: Carolyn A. Cherry, Executive Director
Description: Promotes business and community development in Chatham, NJ.

54698 ■ *Christmas in Cape May*
PO Box 556
Cape May, NJ 08204-0556
Ph: (609)884-5508
Fax: (609)884-2054
Co. E-mail: info@capemaychamber.com
URL: http://www.capemaychamber.com
Contact: Robert Steenrod, President

54699 ■ *C.M. Co. St. Maps & Guide*
PO Box 74
Cape May Court House, NJ 08210-0074
Ph: (609)465-7181
Fax: (609)465-5017
Co. E-mail: info@cmcchamber.com
URL: http://www.cmccofc.com
Contact: Vicki Clark, President

54700 ■ *Commentary*
475 Rte. 57 W
Washington, NJ 07882
Ph: (908)835-9200
Fax: (908)835-9296
Co. E-mail: info@warrencountychamber.org
URL: http://www.warrencountychamber.org
Contact: Robert L. Goltz, President
Released: Monthly

54701 ■ *The Commentary*
1060 Kings Hwy. N, Ste. 200
Cherry Hill, NJ 08034
Ph: (856)667-1600
Fax: (856)667-1464
Co. E-mail: art@camdencountychamber.com
URL: http://www.cherryhillregional.com
Contact: Arthur C. Campbell, President
Released: Monthly

54702 ■ *The Communicator*
100 Technology Way, Ste. 110
Mount Laurel, NJ 08054
Ph: (856)439-2520
Fax: (856)439-2523
Co. E-mail: bccoc@bccoc.com
URL: http://bccoc.com
Contact: Kristi M. Howell-Ikeda, President
Released: Quarterly

54703 ■ *Community Directory*
210 Whiteman St.
Fort Lee, NJ 07024
Ph: (201)944-7575
Fax: (201)944-5168
Co. E-mail: assistant@fortleechamber.com
URL: http://www.fortleechamber.com
Contact: Kenneth Bruno, President
Released: Annual

54704 ■ Cranford Chamber of Commerce
PO Box 165
Cranford, NJ 07016
Ph: (908)272-6114
Fax: (908)272-3742
Co. E-mail: cranfordchamber@comcast.net
URL: http://www.cranford.com/chamber
Contact: Eugene Matics, President
Description: Promotes business and community development in Cranford, NJ. **Founded:** 1961.

54705 ■ *Crossroads*
PO Box 325
Paramus, NJ 07652-0325
Ph: (201)261-3344

Fax: (201)261-3346
Co. E-mail: staff@paramuschamber.com
URL: http://www.paramuschamber.com
Contact: Dimitri Miaoulis, Chairman
Released: Monthly

54706 ■ Dennis Township Chamber of Commerce
PO Box 85
Ocean View, NJ 08230
Ph: (609)624-0990
Fax: (609)624-9110
Co. E-mail: info@dennistwpchamber.com
URL: http://www.dennistwpchamber.com
Contact: Kim Gansert, President
Description: Promotes business and community development in Dennis Township, NJ. **Founded:** 1990.

54707 ■ Denville Chamber of Commerce (DCOC)
PO Box 333
Denville, NJ 07834
Ph: (973)625-1171
Fax: (973)575-5795
Co. E-mail: moreinfo@denville-nj.com
URL: http://www.denville-nj.com
Contact: Kristin Pamperin, President
Description: Promotes business and community development in Denville, NJ.

54708 ■ Dover Area Chamber of Commerce
PO Box 506
Dover, NJ 07802
Ph: (973)989-4000
Fax: (973)673-5828
Co. E-mail: email@doverareachamber.com
URL: http://www.doverareachamber.com
Description: Promotes business and community development in the Dover-West Morris, NJ area. **Founded:** 1921.

54709 ■ *e-Chatter*
PO Box 5007
Hazlet, NJ 07730
Ph: (732)203-0340
Fax: (732)203-0341
Co. E-mail: info@northernmonmouthchamber.com
URL: http://www.northernmonmouthchamber.com
Contact: Paul Morris, Executive Director
Released: Monthly

54710 ■ East Brunswick Regional Chamber of Commerce (EBRCC)
PO Box 56
East Brunswick, NJ 08816-0056
Ph: (732)257-3009
Fax: (732)257-0949
Co. E-mail: ebcharitable@gmail.com
URL: http://www.ebchamber.org
Description: Promotes business and community development in the East Brunswick, NJ area. **Awards:** High School Scholarship (Annual).

54711 ■ East Orange Chamber of Commerce (EOCC)
PO Box 2418
East Orange, NJ 07019-2418
Ph: (973)674-0900
Fax: (973)673-5828
Co. E-mail: info@eastorangechamber.biz
URL: http://www.eastorangechamber.biz
Contact: Amir Hashemi, President
Description: Promotes business and community development in East Orange, NJ. **Founded:** 1924.

54712 ■ Eastern Monmouth Area Chamber of Commerce (EMACC)
47 Reckless Pl., Ste. 1
Red Bank, NJ 07701
Ph: (732)741-0055

Fax: (732)741-6778
Co. E-mail: emacc@emacc.org
URL: http://www.emacc.org
Contact: Lynda Rose, President
Description: Promotes business and community development in Eastern Monmouth-Red Bank, NJ area. Sponsors festivals and hall of fame; presents business and service awards. Operates county welcome center and tourism development. **Founded:** 1928.

54713 ■ *Economic Update*
201 Rte. 17 N
Rutherford, NJ 07070
Ph: (201)939-0707
Fax: (201)939-0522
Co. E-mail: office@meadowlands.org
URL: http://www.meadowlands.org/mrcc
Contact: Stephen Orenchuk, Chairman
Released: Monthly

54714 ■ Edison Chamber of Commerce
336 Raritan Ctr. Pkwy.
Edison, NJ 08837
Ph: (732)738-9482
Fax: (732)738-9485
Co. E-mail: edisonchamber@att.net
URL: http://www.edisonchamber.com
Contact: Barbara C. Roos, President
Description: Promotes business and community development in Edison, NJ. Sponsors business/education week, golf classic, Taste of Middlesex, award dinner and Memorial Day parade. **Founded:** 1952. **Publications:** *Chamber Chatter* (Monthly); *Edison Highlights* (Quarterly). **Awards:** Best Golfer; Community Leader; Educator of the Year (Annual); Full Year Scholarship (Annual); Member of the Year (Annual). **Telecommunication Services:** president@edisonchamber.com.

54715 ■ *Edison Highlights*
336 Raritan Ctr. Pkwy.
Edison, NJ 08837
Ph: (732)738-9482
Fax: (732)738-9485
Co. E-mail: edisonchamber@att.net
URL: http://www.edisonchamber.com
Contact: Barbara C. Roos, President
Released: Quarterly **Price:** free for members.

54716 ■ Englewood Chamber of Commerce (ECC)
2-10 N Van Brunt St.
Englewood, NJ 07631-3485
Ph: (201)871-6635
Fax: (201)871-4549
URL: http://www.englewood-chamber.com
Contact: Charles I. Silberman, President
URL(s): www.cityofenglewood.org. **Description:** Promotes business and community development in Englewood, NJ. Sponsors sidewalk sale. **Founded:** 1941. **Publications:** *Shopping Guide* (Biennial).

54717 ■ Fair Lawn Chamber of Commerce
12-45 River Rd.
Fair Lawn, NJ 07410
Ph: (201)796-7050
Fax: (201)475-0619
Co. E-mail: info@fairlawnchamber.org
URL: http://www.fairlawnchamber.org
Contact: Mary A. Marrara, President
Description: Promotes business and community development in Fair Lawn, NJ. **Publications:** *Fair Lawn Focus* (Monthly); *Fair Lawn Chamber of Commerce Membership Directory and Community Guide* (Biennial).

54718 ■ *Fair Lawn Chamber of Commerce Membership Directory and Community Guide*
12-45 River Rd.
Fair Lawn, NJ 07410
Ph: (201)796-7050
Fax: (201)475-0619
Co. E-mail: info@fairlawnchamber.org
URL: http://www.fairlawnchamber.org
Contact: Mary A. Marrara, President
Released: Biennial

54719 ■ *Fair Lawn Focus*
12-45 River Rd.
Fair Lawn, NJ 07410
Ph: (201)796-7050
Fax: (201)475-0619
Co. E-mail: info@fairlawnchamber.org
URL: http://www.fairlawnchamber.org
Contact: Mary A. Marrara, President
Released: Monthly

54720 ■ *Fortleenj.com*
210 Whiteman St.
Fort Lee, NJ 07024
Ph: (201)944-7575
Fax: (201)944-5168
Co. E-mail: assistant@fortleechamber.com
URL: http://www.fortleechamber.com
Contact: Kenneth Bruno, President
Released: Monthly

54721 ■ Franklin Lakes Chamber of Commerce (FLCOC)
PO Box 81
Franklin Lakes, NJ 07417
Ph: (201)891-8790
Co. E-mail: info@flcoc.org
URL: http://www.flcoc.org
Contact: Jeffrey Allan, President
Description: Promotes the economic development of Franklin Lakes, NJ.

54722 ■ Gateway Regional Chamber of Commerce
PO Box 300
Elizabeth, NJ 07207-0300
Ph: (908)352-0900
Fax: (908)352-0865
Co. E-mail: kateconroy@gatewaychamber.com
URL: http://www.gatewaychamber.com
Contact: Edward J. Gunther, President
Description: Promotes business and community development in Central New Jersey. Conducts annual Plainfield Festival of Art. **Founded:** 1921.

54723 ■ Greater Elizabeth Chamber of Commerce (GECC)
456 N Broad St.
Elizabeth, NJ 07208
Ph: (908)355-7600
Fax: (908)436-2054
Co. E-mail: gecc@juno.com
URL: http://www.elizabethchamber.com
Contact: Gordon Haas, President
Description: Promotes business and community development in Elizabeth, NJ. **Founded:** 1997. **Publications:** *Chamber News* (Quarterly).

54724 ■ Greater Fort Lee Chamber of Commerce (GFLCOC)
210 Whiteman St.
Fort Lee, NJ 07024
Ph: (201)944-7575
Fax: (201)944-5168
Co. E-mail: assistant@fortleechamber.com
URL: http://www.fortleechamber.com
Contact: Kenneth Bruno, President
Description: Promotes business and community development in Fort Lee, NJ. **Founded:** 1950. **Publications:** *Community Directory* (Annual); *Fortleenj. com* (Monthly). **Educational Activities:** Business Card Exchange (Annual). **Awards:** Haura Scholarship (Annual); Johansen (Annual); LAB (Annual).

54725 ■ Greater Glassboro Chamber of Commerce (GCC)
PO Box 651
Glassboro, NJ 08028
Ph: (856)589-6600
Co. E-mail: info@glassborochamber.com
URL: http://www.glassborochamber.com
Contact: Chris Painter, President
Description: Promotes business and community development in Glassboro, NJ.

54726 ■ Greater Hammonton Chamber of Commerce
PO Box 554
Hammonton, NJ 08037-0554
Ph: (609)561-9080

Fax: (609)561-9411
URL: http://www.hammontonnj.us
Contact: John Runfolo, Trustee
Description: Promotes business and community development in Hammonton, NJ. Promotes agricultural and cultural interests. Sponsors annual Red, White, and Blueberry Festival. **Founded:** 1926. **Publications:** *Hammonton Business Director* (Annual); *Hammonton Information Guide* (Periodic); *Map of Hammonton, NJ.* **Educational Activities:** Installation and Awards Banquet (Annual).

54727 ■ Greater Long Branch Chamber of Commerce (GLBCC)
PO Box 628
Long Branch, NJ 07740
Ph: (732)222-0400
Fax: (732)571-3385
Co. E-mail: longbranchchamber@verizon.net
URL: http://www.longbranchchamber.org
Contact: Nancy Kleiberg, Executive Director
Description: Promotes business and community development in the Long Branch, NJ area. Sponsors 4th of July Celebration Festival (Oceanfest), Business Expo, Annual Awards Dinner, Golf Outing & Antique Show. **Founded:** 1933.

54728 ■ Greater Mahwah Chamber of Commerce
c/o Sharon Rounds, Exec. Dir.
67 Ramapo Valley Rd., Ste. 211
Mahwah, NJ 07430
Ph: (201)529-5566
Fax: (201)529-8122
Co. E-mail: sharon@mahwah.com
URL: http://www.mahwah.com
Contact: Sharon Rounds, Executive Director
Description: Works to promote and serve the business community of Mahwah area. **Founded:** 1957.

54729 ■ Greater Millville Chamber of Commerce
PO Box 831
Millville, NJ 08332
Ph: (856)825-2600
Fax: (856)825-5333
Co. E-mail: info@millville-nj.com
URL: http://www.millville-nj.com
Contact: Earl Sherrick, Executive Director
Description: Represents professional, industrial, retail, and civic organizations and individuals. Promotes business and community development in Millville, NJ. Sponsors festival. Conducts charitable activities. **Publications:** *Business Directory* (Periodic).

54730 ■ Greater Monmouth Chamber of Commerce (GMCC)
Pinho Professional Center
Freehold, NJ 07728-1703
Ph: (732)462-3030
Fax: (732)462-2123
Co. E-mail: admin@wmchamber.com
URL: http://www.wmchamber.com
Contact: Loretta R. Kuhnert, President
Description: Promotes business and community development in the Western Monmouth County Area. **Publications:** *Actionline* (Monthly). **Telecommunication Services:** info@greatermonmouthchamber.com.

54731 ■ Greater Paramus Chamber of Commerce
PO Box 325
Paramus, NJ 07652-0325
Ph: (201)261-3344
Fax: (201)261-3346
Co. E-mail: staff@paramuschamber.com
URL: http://www.paramuschamber.com
Contact: Dimitri Miaoulis, Chairman
Description: Promotes business and community development in Paramus, NJ. **Founded:** 1951. **Publications:** *Crossroads* (Monthly); *Bergen County Economic Development Book* (Biennial); *Bergen County Economic Development Book* (Biennial). **Telecommunication Services:** office2005@paramuschamber.com.

54732 ■ Greater Paterson Chamber of Commerce (GPCC)
100 Hamilton Plz., Ste. 1201
Paterson, NJ 07505
Ph: (973)881-7300
Fax: (973)881-8233
Co. E-mail: gpcc@greaterpatersoncc.org
URL: http://www.greaterpatersoncc.org
Contact: Jamie Dykes, President
Description: Promotes business and community development in the Paterson, NJ area. **Founded:** 1918. **Publications:** *News Bulletin* (Bimonthly); *Paterson Independent News* (Bimonthly).

54733 ■ Greater Vineland Chamber of Commerce (GVCC)
2115 S Delsea Dr.
Vineland, NJ 08360
Ph: (856)691-7400
Fax: (856)691-2113
Co. E-mail: info@vinelandchamber.org
URL: http://www.vinelandchamber.org
Contact: Dawn Hunter, Executive Director
Description: Promotes business and community development in the Vineland, NJ area. Sponsors Dandelion Festival. **Founded:** 1919. **Publications:** *Area Info Guide* (Biennial); *News and Views* (Monthly); *Vineland* (Periodic).

54734 ■ Greater Wildwood Chamber of Commerce (GWCOC)
3306 Pacific Ave.
Wildwood, NJ 08260-4824
Ph: (609)729-4000
Fax: (609)729-4003
Co. E-mail: info@gwcoc.com
URL: http://www.gwcoc.com
Contact: Tracey Boyle-DuFault, Executive Director
Description: Promotes tourism and economic development in the Wildwood, NJ area. **Founded:** 1938. **Publications:** *Wildwoods Vacation Planner* (Annual). **Educational Activities:** Board of Directors Luncheon Meeting (Monthly). **Awards:** Greater Wildwood Chamber of Commerce Annual Scholarship Award (Annual). **Telecommunication Services:** info@gwcoc.org.

54735 ■ *Guide Book*
517A Arnold Ave.
Point Pleasant Beach, NJ 08742-2501
Ph: (732)899-6878
Free: 888-772-3862
Fax: (732)899-0103
Co. E-mail: info@pointpleasurebeachnj.com
URL: http://www.pointpleasantbeachnj.com
Contact: Patrick English, President
Released: Periodic **Price:** free.

54736 ■ *Guide to Hackensack*
5 University Plaza Dr.
Hackensack, NJ 07601
Ph: (201)489-3700
Fax: (201)489-1741
Co. E-mail: chamberhacknj@aol.com
URL: http://www.hackensackchamber.org
Contact: Darlene Damstrom, Executive Director
Released: Annual

54737 ■ *Hackensack Commerce*
5 University Plaza Dr.
Hackensack, NJ 07601
Ph: (201)489-3700
Fax: (201)489-1741
Co. E-mail: chamberhacknj@aol.com
URL: http://www.hackensackchamber.org
Contact: Darlene Damstrom, Executive Director
Released: Quarterly

54738 ■ Hackensack Regional Chamber of Commerce (HRCC)
5 University Plaza Dr.
Hackensack, NJ 07601
Ph: (201)489-3700

Fax: (201)489-1741
Co. E-mail: chamberhacknj@aol.com
URL: http://www.hackensackchamber.org
Contact: Darlene Damstrom, Executive Director
Description: Promotes business and community development in Hackensack, NJ. **Founded:** 1933. **Publications:** *Guide to Hackensack* (Annual); *Hackensack Commerce* (Quarterly).

54739 ■ *Hackettstown Area Living Magazine*
475 Rte. 57 W
Washington, NJ 07882
Ph: (908)835-9200
Fax: (908)835-9296
Co. E-mail: info@warrencountychamber.org
URL: http://www.warrencountychamber.org
Contact: Robert L. Goltz, President
Released: Biennial

54740 ■ *Hammonton Business Director*
PO Box 554
Hammonton, NJ 08037-0554
Ph: (609)561-9080
Fax: (609)561-9411
URL: http://www.hammontonnj.us
Contact: John Runfolo, Trustee
Released: Annual

54741 ■ *Hammonton Information Guide*
PO Box 554
Hammonton, NJ 08037-0554
Ph: (609)561-9080
Fax: (609)561-9411
URL: http://www.hammontonnj.us
Contact: John Runfolo, Trustee
Released: Periodic **Price:** free.

54742 ■ Howell Chamber of Commerce
PO Box 196
Howell, NJ 07731
Ph: (732)363-4114
Fax: (732)363-8747
Co. E-mail: info@howellchamber.com
URL: http://www.howellchamber.com
Contact: Susan Dominguez, Executive Director
Description: Aims to stimulate economic growth and to enhance the quality of life in the Howell, NJ area.
Awards: Howell Chamber of Commerce Education Foundation (Annual).

54743 ■ *Hudson County Business*
857 Bergen Ave., 3rd Fl.
Jersey City, NJ 07306
Ph: (201)386-0699
Fax: (201)386-8480
Co. E-mail: info@hudsonchamber.org
URL: http://www.hudsonchamber.org
Contact: Joseph F. Scott, Chairman
Released: Bimonthly

54744 ■ Hudson County Chamber of Commerce
857 Bergen Ave., 3rd Fl.
Jersey City, NJ 07306
Ph: (201)386-0699
Fax: (201)386-8480
Co. E-mail: info@hudsonchamber.org
URL: http://www.hudsonchamber.org
Contact: Joseph F. Scott, Chairman
Description: Promotes business and community development in Hudson County, NJ. **Founded:** 1888.
Publications: *Hudson County Business* (Bimonthly).

54745 ■ Hunterdon County Chamber of Commerce
The Century Link Bldg.
14 Mine St., 2nd Fl.
Flemington, NJ 08822
Ph: (908)782-7115
Fax: (908)782-7283
Co. E-mail: info@hunterdon-chamber.org
URL: http://www.hunterdon-chamber.org
Contact: Nick Pellitta, Chairman
Description: Strives to promote a favorable business climate, to support member companies, and to provide business leadership throughout the Hunterdon County.

54746 ■ *In Town*
173 Elm St., 3rd Fl.
Westfield, NJ 07090
Ph: (908)233-3021
Fax: (908)654-8183
Co. E-mail: info@westfieldchamber.com
URL: http://www.westfieldareachamber.com
Contact: Neil Pinkman, Executive Director
Released: Semimonthly

54747 ■ Irvington Chamber of Commerce (ICC)
PO Box 323
Irvington, NJ 07111-0323
Ph: (973)372-4100
Fax: (973)673-5828
Co. E-mail: email@irvington-nj.com
URL: http://www.irvington-nj.com/ICC.html
Contact: Willie White, President
Description: Promotes business and community development in Irvington, NJ.

54748 ■ *It's Your Business*
91 S Virginia Ave., Ste. A
Carneys Point, NJ 08069
Ph: (856)299-6699
Fax: (856)299-0299
Co. E-mail: sccoc@verizon.net
URL: http://salemnjchamber.homestead.com
Contact: Jennifer A. Jones, Executive Director
Released: Monthly

54749 ■ *Jersey Cape Vacation Guide*
PO Box 74
Cape May Court House, NJ 08210-0074
Ph: (609)465-7181
Fax: (609)465-5017
Co. E-mail: info@cmcchamber.com
URL: http://www.cmccofc.com
Contact: Vicki Clark, President
Released: Annual

54750 ■ *Jersey Caper*
PO Box 74
Cape May Court House, NJ 08210-0074
Ph: (609)465-7181
Fax: (609)465-5017
Co. E-mail: info@cmcchamber.com
URL: http://www.cmccofc.com
Contact: Vicki Clark, President
Released: Bimonthly

54751 ■ Lakewood Chamber of Commerce
395 Rte. 70 W, Ste. 125
Lakewood, NJ 08701
Ph: (732)363-0012
Fax: (732)367-4453
Co. E-mail: staff@mylakewoodchamber.com
URL: http://www.mylakewoodchamber.com
Contact: Kathleen Mead, President
Description: Promotes business and community development in Lakewood, NJ. Sponsors Staff Appreciation and Secretary's Day luncheon. **Founded:** 1917. **Publications:** *The Business Network* (Monthly). **Educational Activities:** Lakewood Chamber of Commerce Meeting (Monthly). **Awards:** Citizen of the Year (Annual).

54752 ■ Lambertville Area Chamber of Commerce
59 N Union St., Unit B
Lambertville, NJ 08530
Ph: (609)397-0055
Fax: (609)397-7423
Co. E-mail: info@lambertville.org
URL: http://www.lambertville.org
Contact: Amy Coss, Co-Chairperson
Description: Small business owners. Promotes business and community development in the Lambertville, NJ area. Sponsors annual Shad Festival and arts and crafts show. **Founded:** 1973.

54753 ■ *Lifestyles*
270 Chambers Bridge Rd., Ste. 6
Brick, NJ 08723
Ph: (732)477-4949

Fax: (732)477-5788
Co. E-mail: info@brickchamber.com
URL: http://www.brickchamber.org
Contact: Michele Eventoff, Executive Director
Released: Annual

54754 ■ Livingston Area Chamber of Commerce (LACC)
25 S Livingston Ave., 2nd Fl., Ste. E
Livingston, NJ 07039
Ph: (973)992-4343
Fax: (973)992-8024
Co. E-mail: info@livingstonchambernj.com
URL: http://www.livingstonchambernj.com
Contact: Beth Lippman, Executive Director
Description: Promotes business and community development in Livingston, NJ. **Publications:** *Chamber Connection* (Monthly).

54755 ■ Madison Chamber of Commerce
PO Box 152
Madison, NJ 07940
Ph: (973)377-7830
Fax: (973)822-0451
Co. E-mail: info@madisonnjchamber.org
URL: http://www.spotlitesolutions.com/workin-progress
Contact: Karen Meyer, Executive Director
Description: Aims to support, preserve, and enhance the thriving commercial district of Madison, New Jersey. **Founded:** 1943. **Publications:** *The Madison Marketplace* (Bimonthly).

54756 ■ *The Madison Marketplace*
PO Box 152
Madison, NJ 07940
Ph: (973)377-7830
Fax: (973)822-0451
Co. E-mail: info@madisonnjchamber.org
URL: http://www.spotlitesolutions.com/workin-progress
Contact: Karen Meyer, Executive Director
Released: Bimonthly

54757 ■ *Map of Hammonton, NJ*
PO Box 554
Hammonton, NJ 08037-0554
Ph: (609)561-9080
Fax: (609)561-9411
URL: http://www.hammontonnj.us
Contact: John Runfolo, Trustee

54758 ■ Maplewood Chamber of Commerce
PO Box 423
Maplewood, NJ 07040
Ph: (973)761-4333
Fax: (973)762-9105
Co. E-mail: rene@clawsonarchitects.com
URL: http://www.maplewoodchamber.org
Contact: Rene Clawson, President
Description: Promotes business and community development in Maplewood area, NJ.

54759 ■ Matawan - Aberdeen Chamber of Commerce
PO Box 522
Matawan, NJ 07747-0522
Ph: (732)290-1125
Free: 888-552-5892
Co. E-mail: info@macocnj.com
URL: http://macocnj.com
Contact: Cathy Zavorskas, President

54760 ■ Meadowlands Regional Chamber of Commerce (MRCC)
201 Rte. 17 N
Rutherford, NJ 07070
Ph: (201)939-0707
Fax: (201)939-0522
Co. E-mail: office@meadowlands.org
URL: http://www.meadowlands.org/mrcc
Contact: Stephen Orenchuk, Chairman
Description: Promotes business and community development in Bergen and Hudson counties, NJ. Hosts a Job Bank for member companies help cope with Workforce needs. Conducts educational programs, festivals, and shows. **Founded:** 1974. **Publications:** *Economic Update* (Monthly); *Meadowlands/USA* (Quarterly).

54761 ■ *Meadowlands/USA*
201 Rte. 17 N
Rutherford, NJ 07070
Ph: (201)939-0707
Fax: (201)939-0522
Co. E-mail: office@meadowlands.org
URL: http://www.meadowlands.org/mrcc
Contact: Stephen Orenchuk, Chairman
Released: Quarterly **Price:** $16, /year.

54762 ■ *Member Service Directory*
675 Corliss Ave.
Phillipsburg, NJ 08865-1698
Ph: (908)454-5500
Co. E-mail: info@phillipsburgnj.org
URL: http://www.phillipsburgnj.org
Contact: Deborah N. Russo, Executive Director
Released: Annual

54763 ■ *Membership and Business Directory*
9 Vandeventer Ave.
Princeton, NJ 08542
Ph: (609)924-1776
Fax: (609)924-5776
Co. E-mail: info@princetonchamber.org
URL: http://www.princetonchamber.org
Contact: Peter Crowley, President
Released: Annual **Price:** free for members; $2, for nonmembers.

54764 ■ *Membership Directory and Buyer's Guide*
91 S Virginia Ave., Ste. A
Carneys Point, NJ 08069
Ph: (856)299-6699
Fax: (856)299-0299
Co. E-mail: sccoc@verizon.net
URL: http://salemnjchamber.homestead.com
Contact: Jennifer A. Jones, Executive Director
Price: included in membership dues; $150, for nonmembers.

54765 ■ *Membership Directory and Buyers' Guide*
4015 Main St.
Voorhees, NJ 08043
Ph: (856)424-7776
Fax: (856)424-8180
Co. E-mail: info@chambersnj.com
URL: http://www.chambersnj.com
Contact: Debra P. DiLorenzo, President
Released: Annual

54766 ■ Mercer Regional Chamber of Commerce (MRCC)
1A Quakerbridge Plaza Dr., Ste. 2
Mercerville, NJ 08619
Ph: (609)689-9960
Fax: (609)586-9989
Co. E-mail: info@mercerchamber.org
URL: http://www.mercerchamber.org/
Contact: Michele N. Siekerka, President
Description: Aims to strengthen and enhance the chambers' relation and business aspects. **Publications:** *Mercer Business Magazine* (Monthly).

54767 ■ *Metroline*
52 Main St.
Woodbridge, NJ 07095-2892
Ph: (732)636-4040
Fax: (732)636-3492
Co. E-mail: help@woodbridgechamber.org
URL: http://www.woodbridgechamber.com
Contact: Carole S. Hila, President
Released: Monthly

54768 ■ Metuchen Area Chamber of Commerce
323 Main St., Ste. B
Metuchen, NJ 08840-2433
Ph: (732)548-2964
Fax: (732)548-4094
Co. E-mail: metuchen.chamber@verizon.net
URL: http://www.metuchenchamber.com
Contact: Caroline Woodruff, Office Manager
Description: Promotes business and community development in Metuchen, NJ. **Publications:** *Chamber Connection* (Quarterly).

54769 ■ Middle Township Chamber of Commerce
PO Box 6
Cape May Court House, NJ 08210
Ph: (609)463-1655
Co. E-mail: middletownshipchamberofcom@middle-townshipchamberofcommerce.org
URL: http://www.middletownshipchamberofcom-merce.org
Contact: Bob Noel, President
Description: Business people. Promotes business and community development in Middle Township, NJ.
Founded: 1980.

54770 ■ Middlesex County Regional Chamber of Commerce (MCRCC)
109 Church St.
New Brunswick, NJ 08901
Ph: (732)745-8090
Fax: (732)745-8098
Co. E-mail: info@mcrcc.org
URL: http://www.mcrcc.org
Contact: Lina Llona, Chairman of the Board
Description: Provides opportunities for business growth and prosperity in Middlesex County, New Jersey. **Founded:** 1910.

54771 ■ Millburn-Short Hills Chamber of Commerce
PO Box 651
Millburn, NJ 07041
Ph: (973)379-1198
Fax: (973)376-5678
Co. E-mail: info@millburnchamber.com
URL: http://www.millburnshorthillschamber.com
Contact: Shayne Miller, President
Description: Promotes business and community development in the Millburn-Short Hills, NJ area. Includes activities such as economic development, special events, trade shows, networking, school-business partnership, and retail promotions.
Founded: 1963. **Publications:** *Townscape* (Annual).

54772 ■ *Minutes*
16 E 9th St.
Ocean City, NJ 08226
Ph: (609)399-1412
Fax: (609)398-3932
Co. E-mail: info@oceancitychamber.com
URL: http://www.oceancityvacation.com
Contact: Michele Gillian, Executive Director

54773 ■ Montville Township Chamber of Commerce
195 Change Bridge Rd.
Montville, NJ 07045
Ph: (973)263-3310
Fax: (973)263-3453
Co. E-mail: info@montvillechamber.com
URL: http://montvillechamber.com
Contact: Margaret Miller-Sanders, President
Description: Promotes business and community development in Montville Township, NJ. **Founded:** 1962. **Publications:** *Business Directory and Map* (Biennial). **Educational Activities:** Golf Outing (Annual).

54774 ■ Morris County Chamber of Commerce
325 Columbia Tpke., Ste. 101
Florham Park, NJ 07932
Ph: (973)539-3882
Fax: (973)377-0859
Co. E-mail: paul@morrischamber.org
URL: http://www.morrischamber.org
Contact: Paul Boudreau, President
Description: Promotes business and community development in Morris County, NJ. Maintains speakers' bureau. Sponsors seminars. **Founded:** 1929.

54775 ■ Mount Olive Area Chamber of Commerce (MOACC)
PO Box 192
Budd Lake, NJ 07828-0192

Ph: (973)691-0109
Co. E-mail: info@mtolivechambernj.com
URL: http://www.mtolivechambernj.com
Contact: Jeff Stadelman, President
Description: Promotes business and community development in Morris County, NJ. Sponsors monthly conventions. **Founded:** 1955. **Publications:** *Mt. Olive Today* (Quarterly). **Awards:** Business Person of the Year (Annual); Tom Klecka Humanitarian Award (Annual).

54776 ■ *Mt. Olive Today*
PO Box 192
Budd Lake, NJ 07828-0192
Ph: (973)691-0109
Co. E-mail: info@mtolivechambernj.com
URL: http://www.mtolivechambernj.com
Contact: Jeff Stadelman, President
Released: Quarterly **Price:** free.

54777 ■ *News Bulletin*
100 Hamilton Plz., Ste. 1201
Paterson, NJ 07505
Ph: (973)881-7300
Fax: (973)881-8233
Co. E-mail: gpcc@greaterpatersoncc.org
URL: http://www.greaterpatersoncc.org
Contact: Jamie Dykes, President
Released: Bimonthly

54778 ■ *News and Views*
2115 S Delsea Dr.
Vineland, NJ 08360
Ph: (856)691-7400
Fax: (856)691-2113
Co. E-mail: info@vinelandchamber.org
URL: http://www.vinelandchamber.org
Contact: Dawn Hunter, Executive Director
Released: Monthly

54779 ■ *Newslink*
PO Box 1910
Perth Amboy, NJ 08862
Ph: (732)442-7400
Fax: (908)755-9300
Co. E-mail: pachamerofcommerce@verizon.net
URL: http://www.perthamboychamber.com
Contact: Steve Jobin, President
Released: Monthly

54780 ■ North Essex Chamber of Commerce (NECC)
3 Fairfield Ave.
West Caldwell, NJ 07006-7692
Ph: (973)226-5500
Fax: (973)403-9335
Co. E-mail: email@northessexchamber.com
URL: http://www.northessexchamber.com
Contact: Anthony M. Rainone, President
Description: Promotes business and community development in northern Essex County, NJ. Sponsors golf outing. Operates foundation. Holds business shows. **Founded:** 1969. **Publications:** *North Essex Report* (Bimonthly). **Educational Activities:** BIZ Expo (Annual).

54781 ■ *North Essex Report*
3 Fairfield Ave.
West Caldwell, NJ 07006-7692
Ph: (973)226-5500
Fax: (973)403-9335
Co. E-mail: email@northessexchamber.com
URL: http://www.northessexchamber.com
Contact: Anthony M. Rainone, President
Released: Bimonthly

54782 ■ North Jersey Regional Chamber of Commerce (NJRCC)
1033 Rte. 46 E, Ste. A103
Clifton, NJ 07013
Ph: (973)470-9300

Fax: (973)470-9245
Co. E-mail: staff@njrcc.org
URL: http://www.njrcc.org
Contact: Gloria Martini, President
E-mail: gmartini@njrcc.org
Description: Promotes business and community development in Clifton and Passaic, NJ and surrounding communities. **Founded:** 1980. **Publications:** *Business Matters* (Bimonthly); *Chamber Challenge* (11/year); *Products and Services Guide* (Annual).

54783 ■ Northern Burlington Regional Chamber of Commerce
PO Box 65
Bordentown, NJ 08505
Ph: (609)298-7774
Fax: (609)291-5008
Co. E-mail: info@nbrchamber.org
URL: http://www.nbrchamber.org
Contact: Frederick Gomez, President
Description: Promotes business and community development in the Bordentown, NJ area. **Awards:** Bordentown Regional High (Annual).

54784 ■ Northern Monmouth Chamber of Commerce (NMCC)
PO Box 5007
Hazlet, NJ 07730
Ph: (732)203-0340
Fax: (732)203-0341
Co. E-mail: info@northernmonmouthchamber.com
URL: http://www.northernmonmouthchamber.com
Contact: Paul Morris, Executive Director
Description: Promotes business and community development in the Middletown, NJ area. Sponsors annual Christmas tree lighting ceremony. Sponsors monthly lecture. **Founded:** 1959. **Publications:** *Area Guide*; *Chamber Chatter* (Quarterly); *e-Chatter* (Monthly). **Educational Activities:** Business Expo (Annual).

54785 ■ Nutley Chamber of Commerce
172 Chestnut St.
Nutley, NJ 07110
Ph: (973)667-5300
Fax: (973)667-5300
Co. E-mail: chamber@nutleychamber.com
URL: http://www.nutleychamber.com
Contact: Luther Engler, President
Description: Promotes business and community development in Nutley, NJ. Holds monthly board of directors meeting. Sponsors Sidewalk Sale Days and Santa's arrival. Conducts annual Business After Hours show. **Founded:** 1953.

54786 ■ Oakland Chamber of Commerce
PO Box 8
Oakland, NJ 07436
Ph: (201)337-9282
URL: http://www.oakland-nj.org/chamberofcommerce.html
Description: Promotes business and community development in Oakland, NJ. **Founded:** 1960.

54787 ■ Ocean City Regional Chamber of Commerce (OCRCC)
16 E 9th St.
Ocean City, NJ 08226
Ph: (609)399-1412
Fax: (609)398-3932
Co. E-mail: info@oceancitychamber.com
URL: http://www.oceancityvacation.com
Contact: Michele Gillian, Executive Director
Description: Promotes business and community development in the greater Ocean City, NJ area. Bestows beautification and outstanding citizen awards. Sponsors Night in Venice, job fest, and welcome night. Operates information/welcome centers. **Founded:** 1926. **Publications:** *Minutes*; *Ocean City Relocation Information*; *Ocean City Visitors Guide* (Annual).

54788 ■ *Ocean City Relocation Information*
16 E 9th St.
Ocean City, NJ 08226
Ph: (609)399-1412

Fax: (609)398-3932
Co. E-mail: info@oceancitychamber.com
URL: http://www.oceancityvacation.com
Contact: Michele Gillian, Executive Director

54789 ■ *Ocean City Visitors Guide*
16 E 9th St.
Ocean City, NJ 08226
Ph: (609)399-1412
Fax: (609)398-3932
Co. E-mail: info@oceancitychamber.com
URL: http://www.oceancitychamber.com
Contact: Michele Gillian, Executive Director
Released: Annual **Price:** free.

54790 ■ Ocean Grove Chamber of Commerce
45 Pilgrim Pathway
Ocean Grove, NJ 07756
Ph: (732)774-1391
Free: 800-388-4768
Fax: (732)774-3799
Co. E-mail: info@oceangrovenj.com
URL: http://oceangrovenj.com
Description: Promotes business and community development in Ocean Grove, NJ. **Publications:** *The Teammate* (Quarterly).

54791 ■ Parsippany Area Chamber of Commerce (PACC)
12-14 N Beverwyck Rd.
Lake Hiawatha, NJ 07034
Ph: (973)402-6400
Fax: (973)334-2242
Co. E-mail: robertpeluso@parsippanychamber.org
URL: http://www.njpacc.org
Contact: Robert J. Peluso, President
URL(s): www.parsippanychamber.org. **Description:** Promotes business and community development in the Parsippany, NJ area.

54792 ■ *Paterson Independent News*
100 Hamilton Plz., Ste. 1201
Paterson, NJ 07505
Ph: (973)881-7300
Fax: (973)881-8233
Co. E-mail: gpcc@greaterpatersoncc.org
URL: http://www.greaterpatersoncc.org
Contact: Jamie Dykes, President
Released: Bimonthly

54793 ■ Perth Amboy Chamber of Commerce (PACC)
PO Box 1910
Perth Amboy, NJ 08862
Ph: (732)442-7400
Fax: (908)755-9300
Co. E-mail: pachamberofcommerce@verizon.net
URL: http://www.perthamboychamber.com
Contact: Steve Jobin, President
Description: Promotes business and community development in Perth Amboy, NJ. Sponsors Waterfront Festival, retail sales days, annual Easter and Christmas parades, annual golf/tennis outing and dinner, business expos, after hours and excursions, and seminars. Monitors legislative action. Maintains research and data center. Offers business referrals and tourist information. **Founded:** 1957. **Publications:** *Newslink* (Monthly).

54794 ■ Phillipsburg Area Chamber of Commerce (PACC)
675 Corliss Ave.
Phillipsburg, NJ 08865-1698
Ph: (908)454-5500
Co. E-mail: info@phillipsburgnj.org
URL: http://www.phillipsburgnj.org
Contact: Deborah N. Russo, Executive Director
Description: Promotes business and community development in the Phillipsburg, NJ area. Co-hosts Phillipsburg Ole Towne Festival. Sponsors business expo; seminars; networking functions; informative speaker presentations. **Founded:** 1919. **Publications:** *Member Service Directory* (Annual).

54795 ■ Point Pleasant Beach Chamber of Commerce
517A Arnold Ave.
Point Pleasant Beach, NJ 08742-2501
Ph: (732)899-6878

Free: 888-772-3862
Fax: (732)899-0103
Co. E-mail: info@pointpleasurebeachnj.com
URL: http://www.pointpleasantbeachnj.com
Contact: Patrick English, President
URL(s): www.pointchamber.com/directors.asp. **Description:** Represents business owners. Promotes business and community development in the Point Pleasant, NJ area. Promotes tourism; sponsors Festival of the Sea. **Founded:** 1947. **Publications:** *Guide Book* (Periodic); *Guide Book* (Periodic). **Telecommunication Services:** info@pointpleasant-beachnj.com.

54796 ■ Pompton Lakes Chamber of Commerce
PO Box 129
Pompton Lakes, NJ 07442
Ph: (973)839-0187
Fax: (973)839-0187
Co. E-mail: info@pomptonchamber.com
URL: http://www.pomptonlakeschamber.com
Contact: Art Kaffka, President
Description: Promotes business and community development in Pompton Lakes, NJ.

54797 ■ *Princeton Area Life*
9 Vandeventer Ave.
Princeton, NJ 08542
Ph: (609)924-1776
Fax: (609)924-5776
Co. E-mail: info@princetonchamber.org
URL: http://www.princetonchamber.org
Contact: Peter Crowley, President
Released: Annual **Price:** $1, for members; $2, for nonmembers.

54798 ■ *Princeton Area Map*
9 Vandeventer Ave.
Princeton, NJ 08542
Ph: (609)924-1776
Fax: (609)924-5776
Co. E-mail: info@princetonchamber.org
URL: http://www.princetonchamber.org
Contact: Peter Crowley, President
Price: $2, for members; $3, for nonmembers.

54799 ■ Princeton Regional Chamber of Commerce
9 Vandeventer Ave.
Princeton, NJ 08542
Ph: (609)924-1776
Fax: (609)924-5776
Co. E-mail: info@princetonchamber.org
URL: http://www.princetonchamber.org
Contact: Peter Crowley, President
Description: Represents corporations, small businesses, and independent companies. Promotes business and community development in the Princeton, NJ area. **Founded:** 1959. **Publications:** *Membership and Business Directory* (Annual); *Princeton Area Life* (Annual); *Princeton Area Map*; *Visitor's Guide* (Periodic). **Educational Activities:** Business Council Breakfast Meeting (Monthly); Children's Holiday Show (Annual); General Membership Meeting (Monthly).

54800 ■ *Products and Services Guide*
1033 Rte. 46 E, Ste. A103
Clifton, NJ 07013
Ph: (973)470-9300
Fax: (973)470-9245
Co. E-mail: staff@njrcc.org
URL: http://www.njrcc.org
Contact: Gloria Martini, President
E-mail: gmartini@njrcc.org
Released: Annual

54801 ■ Randolph Area Chamber of Commerce
PO Box 391
Mount Freedom, NJ 07970-0391
Ph: (973)361-3462
Fax: (973)895-3297
URL: http://www.randolphchamber.org
Contact: Lou Nisivoccia, President
Description: Promotes the interests and welfare of its members by fostering and encouraging the advancement of the commercial, industrial, civic, and

general interests of the Township of Randolph and its trade area. Serves as a liaison between local businesses and the township government.

54802 ■ *The Review*
4015 Main St.
Voorhees, NJ 08043
Ph: (856)424-7776
Fax: (856)424-8180
Co. E-mail: info@chambersnj.com
URL: http://www.chambersnj.com
Contact: Debra P. DiLorenzo, President
Released: Monthly

54803 ■ Ridgewood Chamber of Commerce (RCC)
27 Chestnut St., Ste. 1B
Ridgewood, NJ 07450
Ph: (201)445-2600
Fax: (201)251-1958
Co. E-mail: info@ridgewoodchamber.com
URL: http://www.ridgewoodchamber.com
Contact: Joan Groome, Executive Director
Description: Promotes business and community development in Ridgewood, NJ. Sponsors Christmas "Downtown for the Holidays". Holds monthly board and committee meetings. **Founded:** 1927. **Awards:** Volunteer of the Year.

54804 ■ Ringwood Chamber of Commerce
PO Box 62
Ringwood, NJ 07456
Co. E-mail: president@ringwoodchamber.com
URL: http://www.ringwoodchamber.com
Contact: Kathy Heck, Editor
Description: Promotes economic development and represents business professionals, products and services. **Founded:** 1974. **Awards:** Police Officer of the Year (Annual); Volunteer of the Year (Annual).

54805 ■ Roxbury Area Chamber of Commerce (RACC)
PO Box 436
Ledgewood, NJ 07852
Ph: (973)770-0740
Co. E-mail: info@roxburynjchamber.org
URL: http://www.roxburynjchamber.org
Contact: Pam Smith, Secretary
Description: Promotes business and community development in Roxbury area, NJ.

54806 ■ Rutherford Chamber of Commerce
PO Box 215
Rutherford, NJ 07070
Ph: (201)203-4753
Fax: (201)507-7077
Co. E-mail: info@rutherfordchamber.com
URL: http://www.rutherfordchamber.com
Contact: Herbert L. Cutter, Executive Secretary
Description: Promotes business and community development in Rutherford, NJ. Convention/Meeting: none. **Founded:** 1927. **Awards:** Citizen of the Year (Annual).

54807 ■ Salem County Chamber of Commerce
91 S Virginia Ave., Ste. A
Carneys Point, NJ 08069
Ph: (856)299-6699
Fax: (856)299-0299
Co. E-mail: sccoc@verizon.net
URL: http://salemnjchamber.homestead.com
Contact: Jennifer A. Jones, Executive Director
Description: Works to promote the member's businesses; to advocate in government agencies; and to provide services to benefit the members. **Founded:** 1943. **Publications:** *It's Your Business* (Monthly); *Welcome to Historic Salem County*; *Membership Directory and Buyer's Guide*; *Membership Directory and Buyer's Guide*.

54808 ■ *Shopping Guide*
2-10 N Van Brunt St.
Englewood, NJ 07631-3485
Ph: (201)871-6635
Fax: (201)871-4549
URL: http://www.englewood-chamber.com
Contact: Charles I. Silberman, President
Released: Biennial

54809 ■ South Orange Chamber of Commerce
PO Box 621
South Orange, NJ 07079
Ph: (973)762-4333
Fax: (973)763-0943
Co. E-mail: director@southorangechamber.com
URL: http://www.southorangechamber.com
Contact: Leslie Pogany, President
Description: Promotes business and community development in South Orange area, NJ.

54810 ■ *Southern Exposure*
PO Box 1305
Wall, NJ 07719-1305
Ph: (732)280-8800
Fax: (732)280-8505
Co. E-mail: info@smcconline.org
URL: http://www.southernmonmouthchamber.com
Contact: Mr. Jim Dallas, President
Released: Quarterly

54811 ■ Southern Monmouth Chamber of Commerce (SMCC)
PO Box 1305
Wall, NJ 07719-1305
Ph: (732)280-8800
Fax: (732)280-8505
Co. E-mail: info@smcconline.org
URL: http://www.southernmonmouthchamber.com
Contact: Mr. Jim Dallas, President
Description: Promotes business and community development in southern Monmouth County, NJ. Sponsors after-work business card exchanges. Holds business expo, golf outing, and general membership meetings. **Founded:** 1979. **Publications:** *Southern Exposure* (Quarterly); *Southern Monmouth Chamber of Commerce Map and Guide* (Biennial). **Educational Activities:** Business Exposition (Annual); Southern Monmouth Chamber of Commerce Tradeshow (Annual). **Awards:** Golden Osprey Awards (Annual).

54812 ■ *Southern Monmouth Chamber of Commerce Map and Guide*
PO Box 1305
Wall, NJ 07719-1305
Ph: (732)280-8800
Fax: (732)280-8505
Co. E-mail: info@smcconline.org
URL: http://www.southernmonmouthchamber.com
Contact: Mr. Jim Dallas, President
Released: Biennial

54813 ■ Southern Ocean County Chamber of Commerce
265 W 9th St.
Ship Bottom, NJ 08008-4614
Ph: (609)494-7211
Free: 800-292-6372
Fax: (609)494-5807
Co. E-mail: info@discoversouthernocean.com
URL: http://www.visitlbiregion.com
Contact: Chris Swab, President
Description: Aims to foster positive growth, development, and tourism in the Southern Ocean County region.

54814 ■ *Spotlight*
256 Broad St., Rm. 2F
Bloomfield, NJ 07003
Ph: (973)748-2000
Fax: (973)748-2450
Co. E-mail: admin@suburbanessexchamber.com
URL: http://www.suburbanessexchamber.com
Contact: Nestor L. Arce, President
Released: Annual

54815 ■ Stone Harbor Chamber of Commerce
PO Box 422
Stone Harbor, NJ 08247
Ph: (609)368-6101
Co. E-mail: joe@wjse.com
URL: http://stoneharborbeach.com
Contact: Philip Barber, President
URL(s): www.stoneharborbeach.com. **Description:** Promotes business and community development in Stone Harbor, NJ. Sponsors July 4th celebration, an-

nual Merchants Day Sale, annual Boat Show, annual Sail Into Summer Festival, and Christmas At Its Best celebration. **Founded:** 1944. **Publications:** *Chamber Information Booklet* (Periodic); *Welcome to Stone Harbor* (Periodic); *Stone Harbor Chamber of Commerce Vacation Guide*. **Educational Activities:** Stone Harbor Chamber of Commerce Dinner (Quarterly).

54816 ■ Suburban Chamber of Commerce (SCC)
71 Summit Ave.
Summit, NJ 07901
Ph: (908)522-1700
Fax: (908)522-9252
Co. E-mail: info@suburbanchambers.org
URL: http://www.suburbanchambers.org
Contact: Maureen Kelly, President
Description: Promotes business and community development in the Summit, New Providence, and Berkeley Heights, NJ area. **Founded:** 1909. **Publications:** *Chamberfax* (Monthly); *Summit Collection*.

54817 ■ Suburban Essex Chamber of Commerce (SECC)
256 Broad St., Rm. 2F
Bloomfield, NJ 07003
Ph: (973)748-2000
Fax: (973)748-2450
Co. E-mail: admin@suburbanessexchamber.com
URL: http://www.suburbanessexchamber.com
Contact: Nestor L. Arce, President
Description: Promotes business and community development in Bloomfield, NJ. **Founded:** 1917. **Publications:** *Spotlight* (Annual).

54818 ■ *Success*
120 Hampton House Rd.
Newton, NJ 07860
Ph: (973)579-1811
Fax: (973)579-3031
Co. E-mail: mail@sussexcountychamber.org
URL: http://www.sussexcountychamber.org
Contact: Tammie Horsfield, President
Released: Quarterly

54819 ■ *Summit Collection*
71 Summit Ave.
Summit, NJ 07901
Ph: (908)522-1700
Fax: (908)522-9252
Co. E-mail: info@suburbanchambers.org
URL: http://www.suburbanchambers.org
Contact: Maureen Kelly, President

54820 ■ Sussex County Chamber of Commerce
120 Hampton House Rd.
Newton, NJ 07860
Ph: (973)579-1811
Fax: (973)579-3031
Co. E-mail: mail@sussexcountychamber.org
URL: http://www.sussexcountychamber.org
Contact: Tammie Horsfield, President
Description: Promotes business and community development in Sussex County, NJ. Convention/Meeting: none. **Founded:** 1980. **Publications:** *Success* (Quarterly); *Sussex County Magazine* (Annual).

54821 ■ *Sussex County Magazine*
120 Hampton House Rd.
Newton, NJ 07860
Ph: (973)579-1811
Fax: (973)579-3031
Co. E-mail: mail@sussexcountychamber.org
URL: http://www.sussexcountychamber.org
Contact: Tammie Horsfield, President
Released: Annual

54822 ■ *The Teammate*
45 Pilgrim Pathway
Ocean Grove, NJ 07756
Ph: (732)774-1391
Free: 800-388-4768
Fax: (732)774-3799
Co. E-mail: info@oceangrovenj.com
URL: http://oceangrovenj.com
Released: Quarterly

54823 ■ Teaneck Chamber of Commerce
802 Cedar Ln.
Teaneck, NJ 07666
Ph: (201)801-0012
Fax: (201)490-1808
Co. E-mail: info@teaneckchamber.org
URL: http://www.teaneckchamber.org
Contact: Larry Bauer, President
Description: Seeks to foster economic growth and development for the business districts of Teaneck, NJ. **Founded:** 1994.

54824 ■ Toms River - Ocean County Chamber of Commerce
1415 Hooper Ave., Ste. 301
Toms River, NJ 08753
Ph: (732)349-0220
Fax: (732)349-1252
Co. E-mail: info@oc-chamber.com
URL: http://www.oc-chamber.com
Contact: Maureen Stankowitz, President
Description: Promotes business development in Ocean County, New Jersey.

54825 ■ Townscape
PO Box 651
Millburn, NJ 07041
Ph: (973)379-1198
Fax: (973)376-5678
Co. E-mail: info@millburnchamber.com
URL: http://www.millburnshorthillschamber.com
Contact: Shayne Miller, President
Released: Annual

54826 ■ Tri-Town Chamber of Commerce
PO Box 496
Boonton, NJ 07005
Ph: (973)334-4117
Fax: (973)402-0719
Co. E-mail: info@tritownchamber.org
URL: http://www.tritownchamber.org
Contact: Gina Ramich, Executive Director
Description: Seeks to promote business and community development and enhance the relationship between local businesses and professionals with the public. **Founded:** 1948. **Awards:** Business Person of the Year (Annual); 75, 50, 35, 25 Year Citizenship Award (Annual). **Telecommunication Services:** ginaramich@yahoo.com.

54827 ■ Tulip Festival
PO Box 556
Cape May, NJ 08204-0556
Ph: (609)884-5508
Fax: (609)884-2054
Co. E-mail: info@capemaychamber.com
URL: http://www.capemaychamber.com
Contact: Robert Steenrod, President
Released: Periodic

54828 ■ Union Township Chamber of Commerce
355 Chestnut St., 2nd Fl.
Union, NJ 07083-9405
Ph: (908)688-2777
Fax: (908)688-0338
Co. E-mail: info@unionchamber.com
URL: http://www.unionchamber.com
Contact: Sal Dovi, President
Description: Works to unite, strengthen, represent and promote business growth for the members. **Founded:** 1956. **Awards:** President's Award (Annual).

54829 ■ Vernon Chamber of Commerce (VCC)
PO Box 308
Vernon, NJ 07462
Ph: (973)764-0764
Free: 888-663-9989
Co. E-mail: info@vernonchamber.com
URL: http://www.vernonchamber.com
Description: Promotes business and community development in Vernon, NJ.

54830 ■ Visitor's Guide
9 Vandeventer Ave.
Princeton, NJ 08542
Ph: (609)924-1776

Fax: (609)924-5776
Co. E-mail: info@princetonchamber.org
URL: http://www.princetonchamber.org
Contact: Peter Crowley, President
Released: Periodic **Price:** $1. for members; $2, for nonmembers.

54831 ■ Warren County Regional Chamber of Commerce
475 Rte. 57 W
Washington, NJ 07882
Ph: (908)835-9200
Fax: (908)835-9296
Co. E-mail: info@warrencountychamber.org
URL: http://www.warrencountychamber.org
Contact: Robert L. Goltz, President
Description: Promotes business and community development in the Hackettstown, NJ area. **Founded:** 1979. **Publications:** Commentary (Monthly); Hackettstown Area Living Magazine (Biennial). **Educational Activities:** Awards Banquet (Annual); Business Expo (Annual). **Telecommunication Services:** bgoltz@warrencountychamber.org.

54832 ■ Welcome to Historic Salem County
91 S Virginia Ave., Ste. A
Carneys Point, NJ 08069
Ph: (856)299-6699
Fax: (856)299-0299
Co. E-mail: sccoc@verizon.net
URL: http://salemnjchamber.homestead.com
Contact: Jennifer A. Jones, Executive Director

54833 ■ Welcome to Stone Harbor
PO Box 422
Stone Harbor, NJ 08247
Ph: (609)368-6101
Co. E-mail: joe@wjse.com
URL: http://stoneharborbeach.com
Contact: Philip Barber, President
Released: Periodic

54834 ■ West Milford Chamber of Commerce
PO Box 234
West Milford, NJ 07480
Ph: (973)728-3150
URL: http://www.westmilford.com
Contact: Rea Wundrack-Lippner, President
Description: Promotes business and community development in West Milford, NJ. **Founded:** 1949.

54835 ■ Westfield Area Chamber of Commerce (WACC)
173 Elm St., 3rd Fl.
Westfield, NJ 07090
Ph: (908)233-3021
Fax: (908)654-8183
Co. E-mail: info@westfieldchamber.com
URL: http://www.westfieldareachamber.com
Contact: Neil Pinkman, Executive Director
Description: Promotes business and community development in the Westfield, NJ area. Sponsors charitable events. Holds Westfield Spring Fling & FestiFall street fairs. **Founded:** 1950. **Publications:** Business Directory (Biennial); In Town (Semimonthly). **Educational Activities:** Business After Hours Networking (Monthly).

54836 ■ Woodbridge Metro Chamber of Commerce
52 Main St.
Woodbridge, NJ 07095-2892
Ph: (732)636-4040
Fax: (732)636-3492
Co. E-mail: help@woodbridgechamber.org
URL: http://www.woodbridgechamber.com
Contact: Carole S. Hila, President
Description: Promotes business and community development in Woodbridge, NJ. **Founded:** 1964. **Publications:** Metroline (Monthly); Woodbridge Metro Chamber of Commerce--Directory.

54837 ■ Wyckoff Chamber of Commerce
PO Box 2
Wyckoff, NJ 07481-0002

Ph: (201)891-3616
Co. E-mail: info@wyckoffchamber.com
URL: http://www.wyckoffchamber.com
Contact: Jay Vidockler, President
Description: Promotes business and community development in Wyckoff, NJ. Provides information and sponsors social functions. **Founded:** 1926. **Publications:** Chamber Chatter (Quarterly).

MINORITY BUSINESS ASSISTANCE PROGRAMS

54838 ■ Minority Business Enterprise Center of New Jersey
744 Broad St., Ste. 1812
Newark, NJ 07102
Ph: (973)297-1142
Fax: (973)297-1439
Co. E-mail: njmbdc@newjerseymbec.com
URL: http://www.newjerseymbec.com
Contact: Hilda Rayas
Description: Assists in the growth and expansion of minority businesses in New Jersey.

54839 ■ New Jersey Department of Commerce and Economic Development - Division of Small, Women, and Minority Business
20 W State St., 4th Fl.
Mary G. Roebling Bldg. 4th Fl.
Trenton, NJ 08625
Ph: (609)292-2146
Free: 888-239-1288
Fax: (609)292-9145
Co. E-mail: cevramb@commerce.state.nj.us
URL: http://www.newjerseycommerce.org/
Description: Assists minority businesses in financing, procurement, and management training.

54840 ■ New Jersey Division of Revenue - Business Action Center - Small Business Set-Aside
PO Box 455
Trenton, NJ 08846
Ph: (609)292-2146
Fax: (609)292-9145
Co. E-mail: njedia@njeda.com
URL: http://www.state.nj.us/njbusiness/contracting/sbsa
Contact: Caren Franzini, Chief Executive Officer
Description: Responsible for administering the Set-Aside Act for small, women-, and minority-owned businesses. Also helps these businesses compete for government contracts.

FINANCING AND LOAN PROGRAMS

54841 ■ BaseCamp Ventures
1 Executive Dr., Ste. 8
Moorestown, NJ 08057
Ph: (856)813-1100
Fax: (856)813-1148
Co. E-mail: mel@basecampventures.com
URL: http://www.basecampventures.com
Contact: Mel Baiada, Principal
Preferred Investment Size: $500,000 to $2,500,000. **Investment Policies:** Early and first stage. **Industry Preferences:** Communications, computer software, and Internet specific. **Geographic Preference:** Mid Atlantic.

54842 ■ BD Ventures / Becton, Dickinson and Co.
1 Becton Dr.
Franklin Lakes, NJ 07417
Ph: (201)847-6800
Fax: (201)847-4874
Co. E-mail: BDBioVentureCenter@bd.com
URL: http://www.bd.com
Contact: Peter A. Origenes, General Manager
Industry Preferences: Biotechnology.

54843 ■ Cardinal Partners / Cardinal Health Partners
230 Nassau St.
Princeton, NJ 08542
Ph: (609)924-6452
Fax: (609)683-0174
Co. E-mail: info@cardinalpartners.com
URL: http://www.cardinalpartners.com
Contact: John K. Clarke, Managing Partner
Preferred Investment Size: $6,000,000 to $12,000,000. **Industry Preferences:** Computer software and services, medical and health, Internet specific, biotechnology, computer hardware, semiconductors and other electronics, communications and media, industrial and energy, other products, and consumer related. **Geographic Preference:** U.S.

54844 ■ CIT Group / Venture Capital
650 CIT Dr.
Livingston, NJ 07039
Ph: (973)740-5181
Fax: (973)740-5555
URL: http://www.citgroup.com
Contact: Colby W. Collier, Manager
Preferred Investment Size: $3,000,000 minimum. **Industry Preferences:** Diversified. **Geographic Preference:** Entire U.S.

54845 ■ CS Capital Partners, LLC
328 Second St., Ste. 200
Lakewood, NJ 08701
Ph: (732)901-1111
URL: http://www.cs-capital.com
Contact: Solomon Lax, Partner
Preferred Investment Size: $500,000 to $3,000,000. **Industry Preferences:** Internet specific, computer software and services, other products, communications and media, medical and health. **Geographic Preference:** Mid Atlantic, Northeast, and Southeast.

54846 ■ DFW Capital Partners / Demuth, Folger & Wetherill
Glenpointe Ctr. E., 5th Fl.
300 Frank W. Burr Blvd.
Teaneck, NJ 07666
Ph: (201)836-6000
Fax: (201)836-5666
Co. E-mail: info@dfwcapital.com
URL: http://www.dfwcapital.com
Contact: Donald F. DeMuth, Partner
Preferred Investment Size: $5,000,000 to $20,000,000. **Industry Preferences:** Medical and health, consumer related, communications and media, computer hardware, Internet specific, semiconductors and other electronics, computer software and services, other products, industrial and energy. **Geographic Preference:** U.S.

54847 ■ Domain Associates L.L.C.
1 Palmer Sq., Ste. 515
Princeton, NJ 08542
Ph: (609)683-5656
Fax: (609)683-9789
Co. E-mail: more@domainvc.com
URL: http://www.domainvc.com
Contact: Todd C. Brady, Principal
Preferred Investment Size: $1,000,000 to $20,000,000. **Industry Preferences:** Biotechnology, medical and health, Internet specific, computer software and services, industrial and energy, semiconductors and other electronics, and consumer related. **Geographic Preference:** U.S.

54848 ■ Early Stage Enterprises, L.P.
995 Rte. 518
Skillman, NJ 08558
Ph: (609)921-8896
Fax: (609)921-8703
Co. E-mail: jim@esevc.com
URL: http://www.esevc.com
Contact: Ronald R. Hahn, Partner
E-mail: ron@esevc.com
Preferred Investment Size: $500,000 to $1,000,000. **Industry Preferences:** Internet specific, computer software and services, other products, communications and media, medical and health, and biotechnology. **Geographic Preference:** Mid Atlantic.

54849 ■ Edelson Technology Partners
300 Tice Blvd.
Woodcliff Lake, NJ 07677
Ph: (201)930-9898
Fax: (201)930-8899
URL: http://www.edelsontech.com
Contact: Harry Edelson, Partner
E-mail: harry@edelsontech.com
Preferred Investment Size: $1,000,000 to $3,000,000. **Industry Preferences:** Communications and media, industrial and energy, computer software and services, consumer related, computer hardware, semiconductors and other electronics, other products, medical and health, Internet specific, and biotechnology. **Geographic Preference:** U.S. and Canada.

54850 ■ Edison Venture Fund
1009 Lenox Dr., Ste. 4
Lawrenceville, NJ 08648
Ph: (609)896-1900
Fax: (609)896-0066
URL: http://www.edisonventure.com
Contact: John Martinson, Managing Partner
E-mail: jmartinson@edisonventure.com
Preferred Investment Size: $5,000,000 to $8,000,000. **Industry Preferences:** Computer software and services, Internet specific, industrial and energy, communications and media, medical and health, consumer related, other products, computer hardware, semiconductors and other electronics. **Geographic Preference:** Mid Atlantic, Delaware, Maryland, New Jersey, New York, Virginia, Pennsylvania, New England, and North Carolina.

54851 ■ Geocapital Partners, LLC
1 executive Dr., Ste. 160
Fort Lee, NJ 07024
Ph: (201)461-9292
Fax: (201)461-7793
URL: http://www.geocapital.com
Contact: Lawrence W. Lepard, Partner
E-mail: llepard@geocapital.com
Preferred Investment Size: $2,000,000 to $20,000,000. **Industry Preferences:** Internet specific, computer software and services, communications and media, other products, consumer related, industrial and energy, medical and health. **Geographic Preference:** U.S. and Canada.

54852 ■ Healthcare Ventures LLC / Healthcare Investments
55 Cambridge Pky., Ste. 102
Cambridge, MA 02142-1234
Ph: (617)252-4343
Fax: (617)252-4342
URL: http://www.hcven.com
Contact: Harold R. Werner, Managing Director
Preferred Investment Size: $500,000 to $10,000,000. **Industry Preferences:** Biotechnology, medical and health, Internet specific, and consumer related. **Geographic Preference:** Mid Atlantic and Northeast.

54853 ■ Johnston Associates, Inc.
155 Lambert Dr.
Princeton, NJ 08540
Ph: (609)924-2575
Fax: (609)924-3135
Co. E-mail: info@jaivc.com
URL: http://www.jaivc.com
Contact: Robert F. Johnston, President
Preferred Investment Size: $300,000 to $3,000,000. **Industry Preferences:** Biotechnology, medical and health. **Geographic Preference:** Northeast.

54854 ■ New Jersey Technology Council / NJTC Venture Fund
1001 Briggs Rd., Ste. 280
Mount Laurel, NJ 08054
Ph: (856)273-6800
Fax: (856)273-0990
Co. E-mail: info@njtcvc.com
URL: http://www.njtcvc.com
Contact: James Gunton, Partner
E-mail: jim@njtcvc.com
Preferred Investment Size: $1,000,000 to $10,000,000. **Industry Preferences:** Communications, computer software, Internet specific, semicon-ductors and other electronics, biotechnology, medical and health, and financial services. **Geographic Preference:** New Jersey, New York, and Pennsylvania.

54855 ■ New Venture Partners LLC
430 Mountain Ave.
Murray Hill, NJ 07974
Ph: (908)464-0900
Fax: (908)464-8131
Co. E-mail: info@nvpllc.com
URL: http://www.nvpllc.com
Contact: Andrew Garman, Managing Partner
Investment Policies: Seed and early stage. **Industry Preferences:** Communications and media, computer software, and semiconductors and other electronics. **Geographic Preference:** U.S.

54856 ■ Origin Partners
5 Slater Ct.
Hillsborough, NJ 08844
Ph: (908)595-9100
Fax: (908)281-6831
URL: http://www.originpartners.com
Contact: Scott Jones, Managing Director
E-mail: jones@originpartners.com
Preferred Investment Size: $3,000,000 to $5,000,000. **Investment Policies:** Start-up, seed, early and first stage. **Industry Preferences:** Communications and media, computer software, Internet specific, semiconductors and other electronics, and medical and health. **Geographic Preference:** Northeast and Southwest.

54857 ■ Proquest Investments
90 Nassau St., 5th Fl.
Princeton, NJ 08542
Ph: (609)919-3560
Fax: (609)919-3570
URL: http://www.proquestvc.com
Contact: Joyce Tsang, Principal
Preferred Investment Size: $250,000 to $25,000,000. **Industry Preferences:** Medical and health, biotechnology, and Internet specific. **Geographic Preference:** U.S. and Canada.

54858 ■ Ridgewood Capital Management, LLC
14 Philips Pkwy.
Montvale, NJ 07645
Ph: (201)447-9000
Free: 800-942-5550
Fax: (201)447-0474
Co. E-mail: businessplan@ridgewoodcapital.com
URL: http://www.ridgewoodcapital.com
Contact: Robert L. Gold, Chief Executive Officer
E-mail: bgold@ridgewoodcapital.com
Preferred Investment Size: $2,000,000 to $5,000,000. **Industry Preferences:** Internet specific, semiconductors and other electronics, communications and media, computer software and services, computer hardware, other products, industrial and energy, and biotechnology. **Geographic Preference:** Mid Atlantic, Northeast, and West Coast.

54859 ■ The Vertical Group
25 DeForest Ave.
Summit, NJ 07901
Ph: (908)277-3737
Fax: (908)273-9434
Co. E-mail: info@vertical-group.com
URL: http://www.vertical-group.com
Contact: Stephen D. Baksa, Partner
Preferred Investment Size: $250,000 to $10,000,000. **Industry Preferences:** Medical and health, biotechnology, Internet specific, semiconductors and other electronics, computer software and services, communications and media, and industrial and energy.

PROCUREMENT ASSISTANCE PROGRAMS

54860 ■ Air Services Development Office of New Jersey
Newark Liberty International Airport
Bldg. 80
Newark, NJ 07114-3707
Ph: (973)961-4278

Fax: (973)961-4282
Co. E-mail: njasdo@asdoaonline.com
URL: http://www.asdoonline.com
Contact: Helene M. Gibbs, Program Manager
Description: A procurement facility funded by the Port Authority of New York and New Jersey to assist small firms in Essex, Hudson, and Union counties in obtaining contracts with airlines and other businesses at Newark International Airport.

54861 ■ Defense Procurement Technical Assistance Center - New Jersey Institute of Technology
University Heights
Newark, NJ 07102-1982
Ph: (973)596-3105
Fax: (973)596-5806
Co. E-mail: chaplin@njit.edu
URL: http://www.njit.edu/DPTAC/
Contact: Dolcey E. Chaplin, Director
E-mail: chaplin@admin.njit.edu
Description: Provides contractual and technical assistance to small-established New Jersey businesses, who are interested in marketing their products, services to federal, state and local government agencies.

54862 ■ Defense Procurement Technical Assistance Center - New Jersey Institute of Technology - Atlantic Cape Community College - Satellite Office
1535 Bacharach Blvd., Rm. 211
Atlantic City, NJ 08401
Ph: (609)343-4845
Fax: (609)343-4710
Co. E-mail: rrose@njit.edu
URL: http://www.njit.edu/DPTAC
Contact: Sherry Rose, Coordinator, Marketing
Description: Provides contractual and technical assistance to small-established New Jersey businesses, who are interested in marketing their products, services to federal, state and local government agencies.

54863 ■ Defense Procurement Technical Assistance Center - New Jersey Institute of Technology - Business & Career Development Center - Satellite Office
1 High St.
Mount Holly, NJ 08060
Ph: (609)267-5618
Fax: (609)267-5165
Co. E-mail: mirijanian@njit.edu
URL: http://www.njit.edu/DPTAC
Contact: Jan Mirijanian, Coordinator, Marketing
Description: Provides contractual and technical assistance to small-established New Jersey businesses, who are interested in marketing their products, services to federal, state and local government agencies.

54864 ■ Defense Procurement Technical Assistance Center - New Jersey Institute of Technology - New Jersey Commerce & Economic Growth Commission - Satellite Office
Mary G. Roebling Bldg.
20 W State St.
Trenton, NJ 08650
Ph: (609)292-3861
URL: http://www.njit.edu/DPTAC
Description: Provides contractual and technical assistance to small-established New Jersey businesses, who are interested in marketing their products, services to federal, state and local government agencies.

54865 ■ New Jersey Procurement Technical Assistance Center - Union County Economic Development Corporation (UCEDC)
1085 Morris Ave.
Union, NJ 07083
Ph: (908)527-1166

Fax: (908)527-1207
Co. E-mail: info@ucedc.com
URL: http://www.ucedc.com
Contact: Maryann Williams, Director
Description: providing financial, technical, and community assistance to new and existing businesses with emphasis on benefiting under-served people and communities.

54866 ■ Rutgers School of Management - New Jersey Small Business Development Centers - New Jersey Procurement Technical Assistance Center
43 Bleeker St.
Newark, NJ 07102
Ph: (973)353-1927
Fax: (973)353-1110
Co. E-mail: sburroughs@njsbdc.com
URL: http://www.njsbdc.com
Contact: Brenda B. Hopper, Director
E-mail: britman@andromeda.rutgers.edu

54867 ■ United States Small Business Administration
U.S. Army Electronics and Communications Command
ATTN: SBA-PCR, Bldg. 1208
Ft. Monmouth, NJ 07703-5000
Ph: (732)532-3419
Fax: (732)532-8732
Co. E-mail: larry.hanson@sba.gov
URL: http://www.sba.gov
Contact: Larry Hansen, Representative
E-mail: larry.hansen@sba.gov
Description: Covers activities for Communications & Electronics Command (Fort Monmouth, NJ), Army Training Center (Fort Dix, NJ), McGuire Air Force Base (Wrightstown, NJ), and Naval Air Warfare Center (Lakehurst, NJ).

54868 ■ US Small Business Administration
US Army JM&L-LCMC, Bldg. 323
Picatinny Arsenal, NJ 07806-5000
Ph: (973)724-6574
Fax: (973)724-5704
Co. E-mail: michael.cecere@us.army.mil
URL: http://www.sba.gov
Contact: Michael Cecere, Representative
E-mail: michael.cecere@sba.gov
Description: Covers activities for Research and Development Command (Picatinny Arsenal, NJ), Military Traffic Management Command (Bayonne, NJ), and the Medical Center (East Orange, NJ).

INCUBATORS/RESEARCH AND TECHNOLOGY PARKS

54869 ■ ACIN Camden Center for Entrepreneurship in Technology
Waterfront Technology Center, Ste. 300
200 Federal St.
Camden, NJ 08103
Ph: (856)614-5415
Fax: (856)614-5489
Co. E-mail: info@acincenter.org
URL: http://www.acincenter.org
Description: A full-service technology accelerator program designed to assist small companies trying to exploit opportunities within the military through delivering products and services based on emerging technologies that meet an immediate need.

54870 ■ High Technology Small Business Incubator
Burlington County College
601 Pemberton-Browns Mills Rd.
Pemberton, NJ 08068
Ph: (856)222-9311
Co. E-mail: mgenzano@bcc.edu
URL: http://www.bcc.edu/pages/131.asp
Description: An engine for economic growth in New Jersey, creating new jobs, products and services by offering promising start-up companies a nurturing environment for growth. Each tenant company has access to extensive resources, support in developing business and technology plans, and opportunities to exhibit at conferences and venture capital showcases.

Each can tap into a rich network of business resources: legal, venture capital, governmental, scientific, licensing, patent, grant funding, marketing, and e-commerce resources.

54871 ■ The Incubator/The BOSS (Business One Stop Service)
320 Park Ave.
Plainfield, NJ 07060
Ph: (908)757-5155
Fax: (908)757-8398
Co. E-mail: info@thebusinessonestopservice.com
URL: http://www.thebusinessonestopservice.com/main.html
Description: A small business incubator with the resources and solutions to help businesses achieve their short- and long-term goals.

54872 ■ Institute for Entrepreneurial Leadership
211 Warren St.
Newark, NJ 07103
Ph: (973)353-0611
URL: http://www.ifelnj.org/
Description: A small business incubator that takes a holistic, hands-on approach to helping entrepreneurs grow their business. Companies with a strong vision and viable business model can be helped to create wealth for themselves and their community by building a strong foundation for the long-term success of their business.

54873 ■ New Jersey City University Business Development Incubator
285 W. Side Ave.
Jersey City, NJ 07305
Ph: (201)200-2313
Fax: (201)200-2315
Co. E-mail: bdi@njcu.edu
URL: http://web.njcu.edu/sites/profstudies/bdi/Content/default.asp
Description: A small business incubator created to assist young, small companies to commercialize their products, processes and services by providing access to marketing, technical, finance, accounting, sales, legal and management assistance.

54874 ■ NJIT Enterprise Development Center
211 Warren St.
Newark, NJ 07103
Ph: (973)643-4063
Fax: (973)643-4502
Co. E-mail: Jerry.Creighton@njit-edc.org
URL: http://www.njit-edc.org/
Contact: Jerry Creighton, Executive Director
Description: A program committed to the long-term economic vitality and growth of life science and high tech entrepreneurial ventures in the State of New Jersey. The incubator exists to increase the rate of small business formations and to decrease the failure rate of start-ups.

54875 ■ Picatinny Technology Innovation Center
3159 Schrader Rd.
Dover, NJ 07801
Ph: (973)442-6400
Fax: (973)442-6402
Co. E-mail: mmerclean@ccm.edu
URL: http://www.picinnovation.org/
Description: A small business incubator seeking to accelerate the successful commercialization of new products by entrepreneurial technology companies and corporate development teams, by supplying a supportive and resourceful infrastructure and by providing a broad base of support, including business, technical and financing assistance, shared business services to reduce overhead costs, access to the considerable resources and technology of the United States government, and reasonably priced office space.

54876 ■ Rutgers Camden Technology Campus
Waterfront Technology Center
200 Federal St., 2nd Fl., Ste. 244
Camden, NJ 08103
Ph: (856)479-9010

Fax: (856)225-6683
Co. E-mail: fskeith@camden.rutgers.edu
URL: http://www.rutgersbiz.com
Description: A non-profit, mixed-use, small business incubator encouraging entrepreneurs to locate their businesses in Camden by assisting them with low-cost office and conference space, technical support services and mentoring for successful startup. The incubator provides the safety net needed during a new company's most critical and vulnerable period.

54877 ■ Technology Centre of New Jersey
Rte. 1 S and Milltown Rd.
North Brunswick, NJ 08902
Ph: (732)729-0022
Co. E-mail: mwiley@njeda.com
URL: http://www.njtechcentre.com/
Description: A small business incubator offering young, growing firms, as well as large established companies, a way to afford modern laboratory and production facilities that are customized to fit their specific research and development needs. Stand-alone facilities from 5,000 to 60,000 square feet can accommodate state-of-the-art clean rooms and wet labs. Individual wet and dry lab modules of 800 square feet, combinable up to 6,600 square feet, are available in the Commercialization Center for Innovative Technologies. Custom build-to-suit facilities are also available for larger companies that require substantial space on an individual basis.

EDUCATIONAL PROGRAMS

54878 ■ Bergen Community College
400 Paramus Rd.
Paramus, NJ 07652
Ph: (201)447-7100
Fax: (201)493-8974
Co. E-mail: admsoffice@bergen.edu
URL: http://www.bergen.cc.nj.us
Description: Two-year college offering a small business management program.

54879 ■ Brookdale Community College
765 Newman Springs Rd.
Lincroft, NJ 07738-1543
Ph: (732)224-2345
Fax: (732)224-2772
URL: http://www.brookdalecc.edu
Description: Two-year college offering a program in small business management.

54880 ■ Burlington County College
601 Pemberton-Browns Mills Rd.
Pemberton Browns Mills Rd.
Pemberton, NJ 08068
Ph: (609)894-9311
Fax: (609)894-0764
URL: http://www.bcc.edu
Description: Two-year college offering a certificate in small business management.

TRADE PERIODICALS

54881 ■ *Linux Business Week*
Pub: SYS-CON Media
URL(s): linux.sys-con.com/. **Ed:** Jeremy Geelan, Lin Goetz. **Released:** Monthly

PUBLICATIONS

54882 ■ *Mercer Business*
2550 Kuser Rd.
Trenton, NJ 08691
Ph: (609)586-2056
Fax: (609)586-8052
URL: http://www.mercerbusiness.com

54883 ■ *New Jersey Business*
310 Passaic Ave.
Fairfield, NJ 07004
Ph: (973)882-5004
Fax: (973)882-4648
Co. E-mail: njbmag@intac.com
URL: http://www.njbmagazine.com

54884 ■ *New Jersey Monthly*
55 Park Pl.
Morristown, NJ 07963-0920
Ph: (973)539-8230
Fax: (973)538-2953
URL: http://www.njmonthly.com

54885 ■ *Smart Start your New Jersey Business*
PSI Research
300 N. Valley Dr.
Grants Pass, OR 97526
Ph: (503)479-9464
Free: 800-228-2275
Fax: (503)476-1479
Co. E-mail: info@psi-research.com
URL: http://www.psi-research.com
Ed: Michael D. Jenkins. **Released:** Revised edition, 1992. **Price:** $29.95 (looseleaf binder); $24.95 (paper). **Description:** Part of the Successful Business Library series.

PUBLISHERS

54886 ■ Factiva Inc.
4300 Rte. 1 N, Bldg. 5, 2nd Fl.
Princeton, NJ 08543-0300
Ph: (609)627-2000
Free: 800-522-3567
Fax: (609)627-2310
Co. E-mail: moreinfo.americas@factiva.com
URL: http://www.factiva.com
Contact: Todd Larsen, President
Description: Description: Publishes databases listing current financial and investment material and general news and information. Also produces software. Databases accessible through personal computers, communicating word processors and terminals, and teletypewriters. Reaches market through direct mail, telephone sales, advertising, and trade sales. **Founded:** 1974.

54887 ■ Fictionwise Inc.
346 Main St.
Chatham, NJ 07928-2137
Ph: (973)701-6771
Fax: (973)701-6774
Co. E-mail: support@fictionwise.com
URL: http://www.fictionwise.com
Contact: Scott Pendergrast, Owner
E-mail: scott@mindwise.com
Description: Description: Publishes fiction in e-book format and also publishes nonfiction, erotica, humor, horror and romance. **Founded:** 2000.

54888 ■ LexisNexis Matthew Bender (Newark, New Jersey)
744 Broad St.
Newark, NJ 07102-3885
Ph: (973)820-2000
Free: 800-424-4200
Fax: (973)820-2007
Co. E-mail: corpcomm@lexisnexis.com
URL: http://www.lexisnexis.com
Contact: Katherine Downing, Director
Description: Description: Publishes analytical legal information in print, CD-ROM and via the Internet. Works are authored by leading experts in the legal community. **Founded:** 1887.

54889 ■ Passaic County Department of Community and Economic Development
Passaic County Administration Bldg., Freeholder's Office
401 Grand St.
Paterson, NJ 07505-2027
Ph: (973)881-4402
Fax: (973)684-2042
Co. E-mail: pcupdate@passaiccountynj.org
URL: http://www.passaiccountynj.org
Contact: Pat Lepore, Director
E-mail: plepore@passaiccountynj.org
Description: Description: Publishes materials on business, economic development and financing. Offers a newsletter. **Founded:** 1978.

54890 ■ Prentice Hall Business Publishing (PHBP)
1 Lake St.
Upper Saddle River, NJ 07458
Ph: (201)236-7000
Free: 800-227-1816
Fax: (201)236-3400
URL: http://phbusiness.prenhall.com
Contact: Jerome Grant, President
Description: Description: Publishes business books.

54891 ■ Prentice Hall Press
1 Lake St.
Upper Saddle River, NJ 07458-1813
Ph: (201)236-7000
Free: 800-745-8489
Fax: (201)236-3290
URL: http://www.pearsoned.com
Contact: Dame Marjorie M. Scardino, Chief Executive Officer
Description: Description: Publishes books on business, education and self-help in publishing. **Founded:** 1913. **Publications:** *The Best of Everything for Your Baby; Scholarship Book: The Complete Guide to Private Scholarships, Grants, and Loans for Undergraduates* (Annual).

54892 ■ PubEasy
630 Central Ave.
New Providence, NJ 07974
Ph: (908)219-0053
Free: 888-269-5372
Fax: (908)219-0191
Co. E-mail: help@pubeasy.com
URL: http://www.pubeasy.com
Contact: David Campbell, Publisher
Description: Description: Publishes online services to facilitate, speed and connect publishers, booksellers, distributors and wholesalers.

SMALL BUSINESS DEVELOPMENT CENTERS

54893 ■ Alamogordo Small Business Development Center
2400 N Scenic Dr.
Alamogordo, NM 88310
Ph: (575)439-3660
Fax: (575)439-3819
Co. E-mail: infosbdc@nmsua.nmsu.edu
URL: http://www.nmsbdc.org/alamogordo
Contact: Marcus McKay, Director
Description: Represents and promotes the small business sector. Provides management assistance to current and prospective small business owners. Helps to improve management skills and expand the products and services of members.

54894 ■ Albuquerque Small Business Development Center
2501 Yale Blvd. SE, Ste. 302
Albuquerque, NM 87106
Ph: (505)224-5250
Fax: (505)224-5256
Co. E-mail: sbdc@cnm.edu
URL: http://www.nmsbdc.org/albuquerque
Contact: Ray Garcia, Director
Description: Represents and promotes the small business sector. Provides management assistance to current and prospective small business owners. Helps to improve management skills and expand the products and services of members.

54895 ■ Carlsbad Small Business Development Center
221 S Canyon St.
Carlsbad, NM 88220
Ph: (505)885-9531
Fax: (505)885-1515
Co. E-mail: lcoalson@cavern.nmsu.edu
URL: http://www.nmsbdc.org/carlsbad
Contact: Larry Coalson, Director
Description: Represents and promotes the small business sector. Provides management assistance to current and prospective small business owners. Helps to improve management skills and expand the products and services of members.

54896 ■ Clovis Small Business Development Center
Clovis Community College
417 Schepps Blvd.
Clovis, NM 88101-8381
Ph: (575)769-4136
Fax: (575)769-4135
Co. E-mail: sbdc@clovis.edu
URL: http://www.nmsbdc.org/clovis
Contact: Dr. Sandra Taylor-Sawyer, Director
Description: Represents and promotes the small business sector. Provides management assistance to current and prospective small business owners. Helps to improve management skills and expand the products and services of members.

54897 ■ Farmington Small Business Development Center
San Juan College
5101 College Blvd.
Farmington, NM 87402
Ph: (505)566-3528
Fax: (505)566-3698
Co. E-mail: martinezc@sanjuancollege.edu
URL: http://www.nmsbdc.org/farmington
Contact: Carmen Martinez, Director
Description: Represents and promotes the small business sector. Provides management assistance to current and prospective small business owners. Helps to improve management skills and expand the products and services of members.

54898 ■ Las Cruces Small Business Development Center
2345 E Nevada Ave., Ste. 101
Las Cruces, NM 88001-3902
Ph: (575)527-7676
Fax: (575)528-7432
Co. E-mail: fowensby@nmsu.edu
URL: http://www.nmsbdc.org/lascruces/index.html
Contact: Fred K. Owensby, Director
Description: Represents and promotes the small business sector. Provides management assistance to current and prospective small business owners. Helps to improve management skills and expand the products and services of members.

54899 ■ Las Vegas Small Business Development Center
Luna Community College
366 Luna Dr.
Las Vegas, NM 87701
Ph: (505)454-2582
Free: 800-588-7232
Fax: (505)454-5326
Co. E-mail: dbustos@luna.edu
URL: http://www.nmsbdc.org/lasvegas
Contact: Don Bustos, Director
Description: Represents and promotes the small business sector. Provides management assistance to current and prospective small business owners. Helps to improve management skills and expand the products and services of members.

54900 ■ Los Alamos Small Business Development Center
190 Central Park Sq.
Los Alamos, NM 87544
Ph: (505)662-0004
Fax: (505)662-0099
Co. E-mail: sbdc@losalamos.org
URL: http://www.nmsbdc.org/losalamos
Contact: Don Wright, Director
Description: Represents and promotes the small business sector. Provides management assistance to current and prospective small business owners. Helps to improve management skills and expand the products and services of members.

54901 ■ Los Lunas Small Business Development Center
University of New Mexico-Valencia
280 La Entrada Rd.
Los Lunas, NM 87031
Ph: (505)925-8980
Fax: (505)925-8981
Co. E-mail: wayne@unm.edu
URL: http://www.nmsbdc.org/loslunas
Contact: Wayne Abraham, Director
Description: Represents and promotes the small business sector. Provides management assistance to current and prospective small business owners. Helps to improve management skills and expand the products and services of members.

54902 ■ Mesalands Community College Small Business Development Center
911 S 10th St.
Tucumcari, NM 88401
Ph: (575)461-4413
Fax: (575)461-1901
Co. E-mail: sbdc@mesalands.edu
URL: http://www.nmsbdc.org/tucumcari
Contact: Vicki Watson, Director
Description: Represents and promotes the small business sector. Provides management assistance to current and prospective small business owners. Helps to improve management skills and expand the products and services of members.

54903 ■ New Mexico State University-Grants Small Business Development Center
701 E Roosevelt Ave.
Grants, NM 87020-2113
Ph: (505)287-8221
Fax: (505)287-2125
Co. E-mail: clemente@nmsu.edu
URL: http://www.nmsbdc.org/grants
Contact: Clemente Sanchez, Director
Description: Represents and promotes the small business sector. Provides management assistance to current and prospective small business owners. Helps to improve management skills and expand the products and services of members.

54904 ■ Roswell Small Business Development Center
Eastern New Mexico University - Roswell
20 W Mathis
Roswell, NM 88203
Ph: (505)624-7133
Fax: (505)624-7132
Co. E-mail: sbdc@roswell.enmu.edu
URL: http://www.nmsbdc.org/roswell
Contact: Carl Kallansrud, Director
Description: Represents and promotes the small business sector. Provides management assistance to current and prospective small business owners. Helps to improve management skills and expand the products and services of members.

54905 ■ Sandoval County's Small Business Development Center
282 Camino del Pueblo, Ste. 2-A
Bernalillo, NM 87004
Ph: (505)867-5066
Fax: (505)867-3746
Co. E-mail: sandovalsbdc@la.unm.edu
URL: http://www.nmsbdc.org/sandoval
Contact: Ted Trujillo, Director

Description: Represents and promotes the small business sector. Provides management assistance to current and prospective small business owners. Helps to improve management skills and expand the products and services of members.

54906 ■ Santa Fe Small Business Development Center
Santa Fe Community College
6401 Richards Ave.
Santa Fe, NM 87508-4887
Ph: (505)428-1343
Fax: (505)428-1469
Co. E-mail: sfccsbdc@sfcc.edu
URL: http://www.nmsbdc.org/santafe
Contact: Michael Mykris, Director

Description: Represents and promotes the small business sector. Provides management assistance to current and prospective small business owners. Helps to improve management skills and expand the products and services of members.

54907 ■ Small Business Development Center at Northern New Mexico College
1027 N Railroad Ave.
Espanola, NM 87532
Ph: (505)747-2236
Fax: (505)747-2234
Co. E-mail: jbarbee@nnmc.edu
URL: http://www.nmsbdc.org/espanola
Contact: Julianna Barbee, Director

Description: Represents and promotes the small business sector. Provides management assistance to current and prospective small business owners. Helps to improve management skills and expand the products and services of members.

54908 ■ South Valley Small Business Development Center
1309 4th St., Ste. A SW
Albuquerque, NM 87102
Ph: (505)248-0132
Fax: (505)224-5968
Co. E-mail: svsbdc@cnm.edu
URL: http://www.nmsbdc.org/southvalley
Contact: Steven Becerra, Director

Description: Represents and promotes the small business sector. Provides management assistance to current and prospective small business owners. Helps to improve management skills and expand the products and services of members.

54909 ■ Southwest Small Business Development Center - New Mexico
PO Box 680
Silver City, NM 88062
Ph: (575)538-6320
Fax: (575)538-6341
Co. E-mail: sbdc@wnmu.edu
URL: http://www.nmsbdc.org/silvercity
Contact: Bruce Ashburn, Director (Acting)

Description: Represents and promotes the small business sector. Provides management assistance to current and prospective small business owners. Helps to improve management skills and expand the products and services of members.

54910 ■ University of New Mexico-Gallup Small Business Development Center
106 W Hwy. 66
Gallup, NM 87301
Ph: (505)722-2220

Fax: (505)863-6006
Co. E-mail: sbdc@gallup.unm.edu
URL: http://www.nmsbdc.org/gallup
Contact: Dan Sanchez, Director

Description: Represents and promotes the small business sector. Provides management assistance to current and prospective small business owners. Helps to improve management skills and expand the products and services of members.

SMALL BUSINESS ASSISTANCE PROGRAMS

54911 ■ New Mexico Department of Agriculture, Marketing and Economic Development Division
3190 S. Espina
Las Cruces, NM 88003-8005
Ph: (575)646-3007
Fax: (575)646-8120
Co. E-mail: nmagsec@nmda.nmsu.edu
URL: http://www.nmda.nmsu.edu/marketing/
Contact: Jeff Witte, Director
E-mail: ddmd@nmda.nmsu.edu

Description: Provides technical assistance to agricultural producers and processors who export both domestically and internationally.

54912 ■ New Mexico Economic Development Department
1100 St. Francis Dr., Ste. 1060
Santa Fe, NM 87505
Ph: (505)827-0300
Free: 800-374-3060
Fax: (505)827-0328
Co. E-mail: edd.info@state.nm.us
URL: http://www.edd.state.nm.us/

Description: Formulates and implements statewide economic development. Also provides assistance to various individuals and groups.

54913 ■ New Mexico Procurement Assistance Program - General Services Department
PO Box 6850
Santa Fe, NM 87502-6850
Ph: (505)827-0472
Fax: (505)827-2484
URL: http://www.generalservices.state.nm.us/spd/spd.html
Contact: Michael C. Vineyard, Director

Description: Promotes and assists small, minority-owned, and women-owned businesses in marketing their goods and services to government, especially to the state of New Mexico.

54914 ■ New Mexico State University - Arrowhead Center
MSC 3CR
Las Cruces, NM 88003
Ph: (575)646-1434
Fax: (575)646-7037
Co. E-mail: info@arrowheadcenter.org
URL: http://arrowheadcenter.nmsu.edu/
Contact: Dr. Kevin Boberg, Director

Description: Provides research services and a data bank for economic and business related information. Also provides business and economic research to public and private sectors.

SCORE OFFICES

54915 ■ SCORE Albuquerque
Co. E-mail: abq@swcp.com

54916 ■ SCORE Las Cruces
Loretto Towne Center
505 S Main St.
Las Cruces, NM 88001
Ph: (505)523-5627
Fax: (505)524-2101
Co. E-mail: score.397@scorelascruces.org
URL: http://www.scorelascruces.org

URL(s): lascruces.score.org. **Description:** Provides entrepreneur education for the formation, growth and success of small businesses in the area.

54917 ■ SCORE Santa Fe and Northern New Mexico
Montoya Federal Bldg.
120 Federal Pl., Rm. 307
Santa Fe, NM 87501
Ph: (505)988-6302
Fax: (505)988-6300
Co. E-mail: info@santafescore.org
URL: http://www.santafescore.org
Contact: Richard T. Meyer, Chairman

Description: Provides professional guidance, mentoring services and financial assistance to maximize the success of existing and merging small businesses.

BETTER BUSINESS BUREAUS

54918 ■ Better Business Bureau of New Mexico and Southwestern Colorado
2625 Pennsylvania St. NE, Ste. 2050
Albuquerque, NM 87110-3658
Ph: (505)346-0110
Fax: (505)346-0696
Co. E-mail: bbaca@bbbsw.org
URL: http://www.newmexicoandsouthwestcolorado.bbb.org
Contact: Brian E. Baca, President

Description: Seeks to promote and foster ethical relationship between businesses and the public through voluntary self-regulation, consumer and business education, and service excellence. Provides information to help consumers and businesses make informed purchasing decisions and avoid costly scams and frauds; settles consumer complaints through arbitration and other means. **Founded:** 1941.

54919 ■ Better Business Bureau Serving Four Corners and Western Slope
308 N Locke
Farmington, NM 87401-5855
Ph: (505)326-6501
Co. E-mail: jerry@bbbsw.org
URL: http://www.newmexicoandsouthwestcolorado.bbb.org/Home.aspx
Contact: Jerry W. Shipman, President

Description: Provides business reliability reports and complaint handling, including informal mediation, arbitration and alternative dispute resolution, business/consumer education resources and materials, national and local charitable information and the promotion of ethical business standards and voluntary self-regulation. **Founded:** 1976. **Publications:** *Update* (Quarterly). **Educational Activities:** Awareness Workshops (Monthly).

54920 ■ *Update*
308 N Locke
Farmington, NM 87401-5855
Ph: (505)326-6501
Co. E-mail: jerry@bbbsw.org
URL: http://www.newmexicoandsouthwestcolorado.bbb.org/Home.aspx
Contact: Jerry W. Shipman, President
Released: Quarterly

CHAMBERS OF COMMERCE

54921 ■ Alamogordo Chamber of Commerce
1301 N White Sands Blvd.
Alamogordo, NM 88310
Ph: (505)437-6120
Free: 800-826-0294
Fax: (505)437-6334
Co. E-mail: chamber@alamogordo.com
URL: http://www.alamogordo.com
Contact: Mike Espiritu, President

Description: Promotes business and community development in Alamogordo, NM. Sponsors Cottonwood Festival, arts and crafts, Frontier Village (county fair), and White Sands Balloon Fiesta. **Founded:** 1914. **Publications:** *Business Directory* (Periodic); *ChamberChat* (Monthly); *Living in Alamogordo* (Periodic). **Awards:** Business of the Year (Annual); Citizen of the Year (Annual). **Telecommunication Services:** dir@alamogordo.com.

54922 ■ Angel Fire Chamber of Commerce
PO Box 547
Angel Fire, NM 87710
Ph: (505)377-6661
Free: 800-446-8117
Fax: (505)377-3034
Co. E-mail: askus@angelfirechamber.org
URL: http://www.angelfirechamber.org
Contact: Mike Wooley, President
Description: Promotes business and community development in Angel Fire and northern New Mexico.
Founded: 1983. **Publications:** *Chamber In-House.*
Educational Activities: Angel Fire Balloon (Annual).

54923 ■ Aztec Chamber of Commerce
110 N Ash St.
Aztec, NM 87410
Ph: (505)334-7646
Fax: (505)334-7648
Co. E-mail: director@aztecchamber.com
URL: http://www.aztecchamber.com
Contact: Becki Christensen, Executive Director
Description: Promotes business and community development in Aztec, NM. **Publications:** *Aztec Etchings* (Monthly).

54924 ■ Aztec Etchings
110 N Ash St.
Aztec, NM 87410
Ph: (505)334-7646
Fax: (505)334-7648
Co. E-mail: director@aztecchamber.com
URL: http://www.aztecchamber.com
Contact: Becki Christensen, Executive Director
Released: Monthly **Price:** included in membership dues.

54925 ■ Belen Chamber of Commerce
712 Dalies Ave.
Belen, NM 87002-3618
Ph: (505)864-8091
Fax: (505)864-7461
Co. E-mail: belenchamber@belenchamber.com
URL: http://belenchamber.org
Contact: Terri Young, President
Description: Promotes business and community development in Belen, NM. **Founded:** 1895. **Publications:** *Chamber Voice* (Monthly). **Awards:** Business of the Month (Annual); Citizen Business Service Club (Annual).

54926 ■ Bloomfield Chamber of Commerce
224 W Broadway Ave.
Bloomfield, NM 87413
Ph: (505)632-0880
Co. E-mail: askus@bloomfieldchamber.info
URL: http://www.bloomfieldnm.info
Contact: Janet Mackey, President
Description: Promotes business and community development in Bloomfield, NM area.

54927 ■ Bottom Line
760 W Picacho Ave.
Las Cruces, NM 88005
Ph: (505)524-1968
Fax: (505)527-5546
Co. E-mail: ballen@lascruces.org
URL: http://www.lascruces.org
Contact: Bill Allen, President
Released: Monthly

54928 ■ Business Advocate
PO Box 1928
Santa Fe, NM 87507
Ph: (505)988-3279
Fax: (505)984-2205
Co. E-mail: trish@santafechamber.com
URL: http://www.santafechamber.com
Contact: Simon Brackley, President
Released: Monthly

54929 ■ The Business Buzz
PO Box 25100
Albuquerque, NM 87125-0100
Ph: (505)764-3700

Fax: (505)764-3714
Co. E-mail: info@abqchamber.com
URL: http://www.abqchamber.com
Contact: Mrs. Terri L. Cole, President
Released: Monthly

54930 ■ Business Directory
1301 N White Sands Blvd.
Alamogordo, NM 88310
Ph: (505)437-6120
Free: 800-826-0294
Fax: (505)437-6334
Co. E-mail: chamber@alamogordo.com
URL: http://www.alamogordo.com
Contact: Mike Espiritu, President
Released: Periodic **Price:** included in membership dues.

54931 ■ Business Directory and Community Guide
PO Box 1928
Santa Fe, NM 87507
Ph: (505)988-3279
Fax: (505)984-2205
Co. E-mail: trish@santafechamber.com
URL: http://www.santafechamber.com
Contact: Simon Brackley, President
Released: Annual

54932 ■ Capitan Chamber of Commerce
PO Box 441
Capitan, NM 88316
Ph: (505)354-2273
Co. E-mail: capitannm@villageofcapitan.com
URL: http://www.villageofcapitan.com
Description: Promotes business and community development in Capitan, NM. Sponsors annual Smokey Bear Stampede. Holds weekly bingo game. Publications: none. **Founded:** 1980.

54933 ■ Carrizozo Chamber of Commerce
PO Box 567
Carrizozo, NM 88301
Ph: (505)648-2732
Co. E-mail: zozoccc@tularosa.net
URL: http://carrizozochamber.org
Description: Promotes business and community development in Carrizozo, NM.

54934 ■ Chama Valley Chamber of Commerce
PO Box 306-RB
Chama, NM 87520
Ph: (575)756-2306
Free: 800-477-0149
Fax: (575)756-2892
Co. E-mail: info@chamavalley.com
URL: http://www.chamavalley.com
Description: Promotes business and community development in Chama, NM. Sponsors festival.
Founded: 1963.

54935 ■ Chamber Chat
404 W Rte. 66
Tucumcari, NM 88401-7005
Ph: (575)461-1694
Fax: (575)461-3884
Co. E-mail: chamber@tucumcarinm.com
URL: http://www.tucumcarinm.com
Contact: Carole Keith, Board Member
Released: Quarterly

54936 ■ Chamber In-House
PO Box 547
Angel Fire, NM 87710
Ph: (505)377-6661
Free: 800-446-8117
Fax: (505)377-3034
Co. E-mail: askus@angelfirechamber.org
URL: http://www.angelfirechamber.org
Contact: Mike Wooley, President

54937 ■ Chamber News
4001 Southern Blvd. SE
Rio Rancho, NM 87124-2069
Ph: (505)892-1533

Fax: (505)892-6157
Co. E-mail: dmoore@rrchamber.org
URL: http://www.rrchamber.org
Contact: Debbi Moore, President
Released: Monthly **Price:** free.

54938 ■ Chamber News
207 Foch St.
Truth or Consequences, NM 87901
Ph: (505)894-3536
Fax: (505)894-3536
Co. E-mail: contact@truthorconsequenceschamber-ofcommerce.com
URL: http://truthorconsequenceschamberofcom-merce.com
Contact: Jessica Mackenzie, President
Released: Monthly

54939 ■ CHAMBER NEWS
201 S Main
Lovington, NM 88260-4222
Ph: (505)396-5311
Fax: (505)396-2823
Co. E-mail: lovington-nm-chamber@valornet.com
URL: http://lovington.leaco.net
Contact: Leticia Kanmore, Executive Director
Released: Monthly **Price:** free for members.

54940 ■ Chamber Report
131 W 2nd St.
Roswell, NM 88201
Ph: (505)623-5695
Free: 877-849-7679
Fax: (505)624-6870
Co. E-mail: information@roswellnm.org
URL: http://www.roswellnm.org
Contact: Dorrie Faubus, Executive Director
Released: Periodic **Price:** free.

54941 ■ The Chamber Update
105 E Grand Ave.
Clovis, NM 88101
Ph: (505)763-3435
Free: 800-261-7656
Fax: (505)763-7266
Co. E-mail: ernie@clovisnm.org
URL: http://www.clovisnm.org
Contact: Mrs. Ernie Kos, Executive Director
Released: Monthly **Price:** free for members.

54942 ■ Chamber Voice
712 Dalies Ave.
Belen, NM 87002-3618
Ph: (505)864-8091
Fax: (505)864-7461
Co. E-mail: belenchamber@belenchamber.com
URL: http://belenchamber.org
Contact: Terri Young, President
Released: Monthly

54943 ■ ChamberChat
1301 N White Sands Blvd.
Alamogordo, NM 88310
Ph: (505)437-6120
Free: 800-826-0294
Fax: (505)437-6334
Co. E-mail: chamber@alamogordo.com
URL: http://www.alamogordo.com
Contact: Mike Espiritu, President
Released: Monthly

54944 ■ Chamberline
503 6th St.
Las Vegas, NM 87701
Ph: (505)425-8631
Free: 800-832-5947
Fax: (505)425-3057
Co. E-mail: lvexec@qwestoffice.net
URL: http://www.lasvegasnewmexico.com
Contact: Diane Ortiz, Executive Director
Released: Bimonthly

54945 ■ Cimarron Chamber of Commerce
PO Box 604
Cimarron, NM 87714
Ph: (505)376-2417
Free: 888-376-2417

Fax: (505)376-2417
Co. E-mail: cimarronnm@gmail.com
URL: http://www.cimarronnm.com
Contact: Deborah Sanders, President
Description: Promotes business and community development in the Cimarron, NM area.

54946 ■ Clayton-Union County Chamber of Commerce
PO Box 476
Clayton, NM 88415-0476
Ph: (505)374-9253
Free: 800-390-7858
Co. E-mail: cuchamber@plateautel.net
URL: http://www.claytonnewmexico.net
Contact: Rose Ramirez, Executive Director
URL(s): www.claytonnewmexico.org. **Description:** Promotes business and community development in Clayton, NM. **Founded:** 1920.

54947 ■ Cloudcroft Chamber of Commerce (CCC)
PO Box 1290
Cloudcroft, NM 88317
Ph: (505)682-2733
Free: 866-874-4447
Fax: (505)682-6028
Co. E-mail: cloudcroft@cloudcroft.net
URL: http://www.cloudcroft.net
Contact: Teri Scott, President
Description: Promotes business, community development, and tourism in the Cloudcroft-Alamogordo, NM area. **Founded:** 1983.

54948 ■ Clovis - Curry County Chamber of Commerce
105 E Grand Ave.
Clovis, NM 88101
Ph: (505)763-3435
Free: 800-261-7656
Fax: (505)763-7266
Co. E-mail: ernie@clovisnm.org
URL: http://www.clovisnm.org
Contact: Mrs. Ernie Kos, Executive Director
Description: Promotes business and community development in Curry County, NM. **Founded:** 1929. **Publications:** *The Chamber Update* (Monthly).

54949 ■ Deming-Luna County Chamber of Commerce
PO Box 8
Deming, NM 88031-0008
Ph: (505)546-2674
Free: 800-848-4955
Co. E-mail: info@demingchamber.com
URL: http://www.demingchamber.com
Contact: Cyndi Longoria, Executive Director
Description: Promotes business and community development in Deming, NM. Sponsors Great American Duck Race, Rockhound Day, assist with Old Timers' Day. **Founded:** 1910.

54950 ■ *E-Newsletter*
404 W Rte. 66
Tucumcari, NM 88401-7005
Ph: (575)461-1694
Fax: (575)461-3884
Co. E-mail: chamber@tucumcarinm.com
URL: http://www.tucumcarinm.com
Contact: Carole Keith, Board Member
Released: Weekly

54951 ■ Eagle Nest Chamber of Commerce (ENCC)
PO Box 322
Eagle Nest, NM 87718
Ph: (575)377-2420
Co. E-mail: info@eaglenestchamber.org
URL: http://www.eaglenestchamber.org
Contact: Mike Berne, President
Description: Promotes business, community development, and tourism in Eagle Nest, NM. **Founded:** 1975. **Publications:** *Members & Services Directory* (Periodic); *Northern New Mexico's Lakeside Playground* (Periodic). **Educational Activities:** Artsfest (Annual); Fishfest (Annual).

54952 ■ *Economic Profile*
PO Box 25100
Albuquerque, NM 87125-0100
Ph: (505)764-3700
Fax: (505)764-3714
Co. E-mail: info@abqchamber.com
URL: http://www.abqchamber.com
Contact: Mrs. Terri L. Cole, President
Released: Annual

54953 ■ Elephant Butte Chamber of Commerce
PO Box 1355
Elephant Butte, NM 87935
Ph: (505)744-4708
Free: 877-744-4900
Fax: (505)744-0044
Co. E-mail: info@elephantbuttechamberofcommerce.com
URL: http://www.elephantbuttechamberofcommerce.com
Contact: Kim Skinner, President
Description: Seeks to advance the general welfare and prosperity of the Elephant Butte Lake area so that its citizens and all areas of its business community shall prosper. Operates a visitor's center. **Founded:** 1999.

54954 ■ Espanola Valley Chamber of Commerce (EVCC)
PO Box 190
Espanola, NM 87532
Ph: (505)753-2831
Fax: (505)753-1252
Co. E-mail: info@espanolanmchamber.com
URL: http://www.espanolanmchamber.com
Contact: Kelly Duran, President
Description: Promotes business and community development in the Espanola, NM area. **Founded:** 1937. **Publications:** *Espanola Valley Visitors Guide* (Annual); *Noticias Del Valle* (Monthly). **Awards:** Business of the Year (Annual); Man of the Year (Annual); Organization of the Year (Annual); Woman of the Year (Annual); Young Man of the Year (Annual); Young Woman of the Year (Annual).

54955 ■ *Espanola Valley Visitors Guide*
PO Box 190
Espanola, NM 87532
Ph: (505)753-2831
Fax: (505)753-1252
Co. E-mail: info@espanolanmchamber.com
URL: http://www.espanolanmchamber.com
Contact: Kelly Duran, President
Released: Annual **Price:** free.

54956 ■ Farmington Chamber of Commerce
100 W Broadway
Farmington, NM 87401
Ph: (505)325-0279
Free: 888-325-0279
Fax: (505)327-7556
Co. E-mail: chamber@gofarmington.com
URL: http://www.gofarmington.com
Contact: Melissa Bateman-Lane, President
Description: Promotes business and community development in Farmington, NM. **Founded:** 1953.

54957 ■ Fort Sumner Chamber of Commerce
PO Box 28
Fort Sumner, NM 88119-0028
Ph: (505)355-7705
Fax: (505)355-2850
Co. E-mail: ftsumnercoc@plateautel.net
URL: http://www.ftsumnerchamber.com
Description: Promotes business and community development in the De Baca County, NM area. **Telecommunication Services:** info@ftsumnerchamber.com.

54958 ■ Greater Albuquerque Chamber of Commerce
PO Box 25100
Albuquerque, NM 87125-0100
Ph: (505)764-3700

Fax: (505)764-3714
Co. E-mail: info@abqchamber.com
URL: http://www.abqchamber.com
Contact: Mrs. Terri L. Cole, President
Description: Promotes business and community development in Albuquerque, NM. **Publications:** *The Business Buzz* (Monthly); *Economic Profile* (Annual); *Images of Albuquerque* (Annual).

54959 ■ Greater Artesia Chamber of Commerce
107 N 1st St.
Artesia, NM 88210-2101
Ph: (505)746-2744
Free: 800-658-6251
Fax: (505)746-2745
Co. E-mail: hklein@artesiachamber.com
URL: http://www.artesiachamber.com
Contact: Hayley Klein, Executive Director
Description: Promotes business and community development in Artesia, NM. **Founded:** 1924.

54960 ■ Greater Las Cruces Chamber of Commerce (GLCCC)
760 W Picacho Ave.
Las Cruces, NM 88005
Ph: (505)524-1968
Fax: (505)527-5546
Co. E-mail: ballen@lascruces.org
URL: http://www.lascruces.org
Contact: Bill Allen, President
Description: Promotes business and community development in Las Cruces, NM. Assists with the Whole Enchilada Fiesta. **Publications:** *Bottom Line* (Monthly). **Awards:** Business of the Month (Monthly); Business of the Year (Annual); Member of the Year (Annual).

54961 ■ *Group Tours*
PO Box 1028
Silver City, NM 88062-1028
Ph: (575)538-3785
Free: 800-548-9378
Co. E-mail: info@silvercity.org
URL: http://www.silvercity.org
Contact: Jim Nennich, President

54962 ■ Hispano Chamber of Commerce de Las Cruces
3530 Foothills Rd., Ste. E
Las Cruces, NM 88011
Ph: (575)532-9255
Fax: (575)532-9258
URL: http://hispanochamberdelascruces.org
Description: Promotes economic and social development in the Hispanic community of Las Cruces, NM.

54963 ■ Hobbs Chamber of Commerce (HCC)
400 N Marland Blvd.
Hobbs, NM 88240-6330
Ph: (505)397-3202
Free: 800-658-6291
Fax: (505)397-1689
Co. E-mail: hobbschamber@leaconet.com
URL: http://www.hobbschamber.org/html_2002/index.htm
Contact: Kent Waldrop, Chairman
Description: Dedicated to the promotion of the free enterprise system and business in general. Activities include EXPO in the Desert, business fair and Christmas in the Desert, holiday lighting and exhibits throughout the city. Offers relocation packets and information regarding the area. **Founded:** 1929.

54964 ■ *Images of Albuquerque*
PO Box 25100
Albuquerque, NM 87125-0100
Ph: (505)764-3700
Fax: (505)764-3714
Co. E-mail: info@abqchamber.com
URL: http://www.abqchamber.com
Contact: Mrs. Terri L. Cole, President
Released: Annual

54965 ■ Las Vegas-San Miguel Chamber of Commerce (LVSMCC)
503 6th St.
Las Vegas, NM 87701
Ph: (505)425-8631

Free: 800-832-5947
Fax: (505)425-3057
Co. E-mail: lvexec@qwestoffice.net
URL: http://www.lasvegasnewmexico.com
Contact: Diane Ortiz, Executive Director
Description: Promotes business and community development in Las Vegas, NM. **Founded:** 1945. **Publications:** *Chamberline* (Bimonthly).

54966 ■ *Living in Alamogordo*
1301 N White Sands Blvd.
Alamogordo, NM 88310
Ph: (505)437-6120
Free: 800-826-0294
Fax: (505)437-6334
Co. E-mail: chamber@alamogordo.com
URL: http://www.alamogordo.com
Contact: Mike Espiritu, President
Released: Periodic

54967 ■ Los Alamos Chamber of Commerce
109 Central Park Sq.
Los Alamos, NM 87544-0460
Ph: (505)662-8105
Fax: (505)662-8399
Co. E-mail: chamber@losalamos.com
URL: http://www.losalamoschamber.com
Description: Promotes business and community development in the Los Alamos County, NM area.

54968 ■ Los Alamos Commerce and Development Corporation (LACDC)
PO Box 1206
Los Alamos, NM 87544
Ph: (505)662-0001
Fax: (505)662-0099
Co. E-mail: lacdc@losalamos.org
URL: http://www.losalamos.org/lacdc
Contact: Kevin Holsapple, Executive Director
Description: Operates the Los Alamos Chamber of Commerce. Acts as a community economic development and business assistance organization in the Los Alamos area. **Founded:** 1999.

54969 ■ Lovington Chamber of Commerce
201 S Main
Lovington, NM 88260-4222
Ph: (505)396-5311
Fax: (505)396-2823
Co. E-mail: lovington-nm-chamber@valornet.com
URL: http://lovington.leaco.net
Contact: Leticia Kanmore, Executive Director
Description: Promotes business and community development in Lovington, NM. Sponsors Lovington Auto Expo, Southeastern New Mexico Fourth of July Celebration, Lea County Fair and Rodeo, Southeastern New Mexico Arts and Crafts Show, and Electric Light Parade. Awards Miss Lovington Scholarship. Holds directors meeting. **Founded:** 1952. **Publications:** *CHAMBER NEWS* (Monthly). **Awards:** Business of the Year (Annual); Citizen of the Year (Annual).

54970 ■ Magdalena Chamber of Commerce
PO Box 281
Magdalena, NM 87825-0281
Free: 866-854-3217
Co. E-mail: info@magdalena-nm.com
URL: http://www.magdalena-nm.com
Contact: Lee Scholes, President
Description: Seeks to promote business and community development and enhance the relationship between local businesses and professionals with the public.

54971 ■ *Members & Services Directory*
PO Box 322
Eagle Nest, NM 87718
Ph: (575)377-2420
Co. E-mail: info@eaglenestchamber.org
URL: http://www.eaglenestchamber.org
Contact: Mike Berne, President
Released: Periodic

54972 ■ Moriarty Chamber of Commerce (MCC)
PO Box 96
Moriarty, NM 87035

Ph: (505)832-4087
Co. E-mail: info@moriartychamber.com
URL: http://moriartychamber.com
Description: Promotes business and community development in Moriarty, NM and surrounding areas. Sponsors Estancia Valley Bean Fiesta. Conducts Estancia Valley Business Fair. **Founded:** 1948. **Publications:** *Regional Business Directory* (Periodic).

54973 ■ Mountainair Chamber of Commerce (MCC)
PO Box 595
Mountainair, NM 87036-0595
Ph: (505)847-2795
Fax: (505)847-0907
Co. E-mail: mcc@mountainairchamber.com
URL: http://www.mountainairchamber.com
Contact: Scott Remmich, President
Description: Promotes and protects the commercial, professional, financial, general business and residential interests of Mountainair and the surrounding area.

54974 ■ *The Noisy Water Gazette*
720 Sudderth Dr.
Ruidoso, NM 88355-0698
Ph: (505)257-7395
Free: 877-RUI-DOSO
Fax: (505)257-4693
Co. E-mail: info@ruidosonow.com
URL: http://ruidosonow.com
Contact: Sandi Aguilar, Executive Director
Released: Monthly

54975 ■ *Northern New Mexico's Lakeside Playground*
PO Box 322
Eagle Nest, NM 87718
Ph: (575)377-2420
Co. E-mail: info@eaglenestchamber.org
URL: http://www.eaglenestchamber.org
Contact: Mike Berne, President
Released: Periodic

54976 ■ *Noticias Del Valle*
PO Box 190
Espanola, NM 87532
Ph: (505)753-2831
Fax: (505)753-1252
Co. E-mail: info@espanolanmchamber.com
URL: http://www.espanolanmchamber.com
Contact: Kelly Duran, President
Released: Monthly

54977 ■ Red River Chamber of Commerce
PO Box 870
Red River, NM 87558
Ph: (575)754-2366
Free: 800-348-6444
Fax: (575)754-3104
URL: http://www.redrivernewmex.com
Contact: Ron Weathers, President
Description: Promotes business and community development in Red River, NM. **Publications:** *Red River Visitors Guide* (Annual).

54978 ■ *Red River Visitors Guide*
PO Box 870
Red River, NM 87558
Ph: (575)754-2366
Free: 800-348-6444
Fax: (575)754-3104
URL: http://www.redrivernewmex.com
Contact: Ron Weathers, President
Released: Annual

54979 ■ *Regional Business Directory*
PO Box 96
Moriarty, NM 87035
Ph: (505)832-4087
Co. E-mail: info@moriartychamber.com
URL: http://moriartychamber.com
Released: Periodic

54980 ■ Rio Rancho Chamber of Commerce (RRCC)
4001 Southern Blvd. SE
Rio Rancho, NM 87124-2069
Ph: (505)892-1533

Fax: (505)892-6157
Co. E-mail: dmoore@rrchamber.org
URL: http://www.rrchamber.org
Contact: Debbi Moore, President
Description: Promotes business and community development in Rio Rancho, NM. Sponsors Springfest, athletic tournaments, soapbox derby competitions, and other community social events. **Founded:** 1980. **Publications:** *Chamber News* (Monthly). **Telecommunication Services:** dmoore@rrcc.org; info@rrrcc.org.

54981 ■ Roosevelt County Chamber of Commerce
100 S Ave. A
Portales, NM 88130
Ph: (505)356-8541
Free: 800-635-8036
Fax: (505)356-8542
Co. E-mail: chamber@portales.com
URL: http://www.portales.com
Contact: Karl Terry, Executive Director
Description: Promotes business and community development in Roosevelt County, NM area. **Telecommunication Services:** events@portales.com.

54982 ■ Roswell Chamber of Commerce
131 W 2nd St.
Roswell, NM 88201
Ph: (505)623-5695
Free: 877-849-7679
Fax: (505)624-6870
Co. E-mail: information@roswellnm.org
URL: http://www.roswellnm.org
Contact: Dorrie Faubus, Executive Director
Description: Promotes business and community development in Roswell, NM. Works with retired senior volunteer program. **Founded:** 1918. **Publications:** *Chamber Report* (Periodic); *Roswell Magazine* (Annual).

54983 ■ *Roswell Magazine*
131 W 2nd St.
Roswell, NM 88201
Ph: (505)623-5695
Free: 877-849-7679
Fax: (505)624-6870
Co. E-mail: information@roswellnm.org
URL: http://www.roswellnm.org
Contact: Dorrie Faubus, Executive Director
Released: Annual

54984 ■ Ruidoso Valley Chamber of Commerce (RVCC)
720 Sudderth Dr.
Ruidoso, NM 88355-0698
Ph: (505)257-7395
Free: 877-RUI-DOSO
Fax: (505)257-4693
Co. E-mail: info@ruidosonow.com
URL: http://ruidosonow.com
Contact: Sandi Aguilar, Executive Director
Description: Fosters development, growth and prosperity of the business community of Ruidoso, Ruidoso Downs and the surrounding area. **Founded:** 1949. **Publications:** *The Noisy Water Gazette* (Monthly). **Educational Activities:** Art (Annual).

54985 ■ Santa Fe Chamber of Commerce
PO Box 1928
Santa Fe, NM 87507
Ph: (505)988-3279
Fax: (505)984-2205
Co. E-mail: trish@santafechamber.com
URL: http://www.santafechamber.com
Contact: Simon Brackley, President
Description: Promotes business and community development in Santa Fe, NM. **Publications:** *Business Advocate* (Monthly); *Business Directory and Community Guide* (Annual).

54986 ■ Sierra County Chamber of Commerce
207 Foch St.
Truth or Consequences, NM 87901
Ph: (505)894-3536

Fax: (505)894-3536

Co. E-mail: contact@truthorconsequenceschamber-
ofcommerce.com

URL: http://truthorconsequenceschamberofcom-
merce.com

Contact: Jessica Mackenzie, President

Description: Promotes business and community development in Sierra County, NM. Sponsors many local events including Old Fashioned Christmas, Dam It Man Triathalon, Hot Springs Festival & Veterans Day car show. Partners with the Tourism Board, the Main Street Organization and the arts council. **Founded:** 1950. **Publications:** *Chamber News* (Monthly).

54987 ■ Silver City-Grant County Chamber of Commerce

PO Box 1028

Silver City, NM 88062-1028

Ph: (575)538-3785

Free: 800-548-9378

Co. E-mail: info@silvercity.org

URL: http://www.silvercity.org

Contact: Jim Nennich, President

Description: Promotes business and community development in the Old West Country, NM area. **Founded:** 1905. **Publications:** *Group Tours.*

54988 ■ Taos County Chamber of Commerce

515 Gusford Rd., Ste. 6

Taos, NM 87571

Ph: (575)751-8800

Fax: (575)751-8801

Co. E-mail: info@taoschamber.com

URL: http://www.taoschamber.com

Contact: Scott McAdams, Vice Chairperson

Description: Promotes business, tourism, and community development in the Taos County, NM area. Conducts community holiday celebrations; holds annual Taos Arts Festival and annual Taste of Taos food event. **Publications:** *Taos County Vacation Guide* (Periodic).

54989 ■ *Taos County Vacation Guide*

515 Gusford Rd., Ste. 6

Taos, NM 87571

Ph: (575)751-8800

Fax: (575)751-8801

Co. E-mail: info@taoschamber.com

URL: http://www.taoschamber.com

Contact: Scott McAdams, Vice Chairperson

Released: Periodic

54990 ■ Tucumcari-Quay County Chamber of Commerce (TQCCC)

404 W Rte. 66

Tucumcari, NM 88401-7005

Ph: (575)461-1694

Fax: (575)461-3884

Co. E-mail: chamber@tucumcarinm.com

URL: http://www.tucumcarinm.com

Contact: Carole Keith, Board Member

Description: Promotes business and community development in Quay County, NM. Sponsors annual Pinata Festival. **Founded:** 1909. **Publications:** *Chamber Chat* (Quarterly); *E-Newsletter* (Weekly). **Awards:** Business of the Month (Monthly).

MINORITY BUSINESS ASSISTANCE PROGRAMS

54991 ■ NEDA Business Consultants Inc. - New Mexico Minority Business Enterprise Center

718 Central Ave. SW

Albuquerque, NM 87102

Ph: (505)843-7114

Fax: (505)242-2030

Co. E-mail: info@nedainc.net

URL: http://www.nm-mbec.com

Contact: Ann Muller, President

Description: Provides assistance to small and minority businesses in New Mexico.

54992 ■ New Mexico Native American Business Enterprise Center

2401 12th St. NW, Ste. 5-S

Albequerque, NM 87104

Ph: (505)243-6775

Fax: (505)766-9499

Co. E-mail: tedpedro@nmnabec.org

URL: http://www.nmnabec.org

Contact: Theodore M. Pedro, Executive Director

Description: Assists Native American businesses with developmental needs both on and off the reservation.

54993 ■ WESST

609 Broadway Blvd. NE

Albuquerque, NM 87102

Ph: (505)246-6900

Fax: (505)243-3035

URL: http://www.wesst.org

Contact: Agnes Noonan, President

Description: Provides statewide small business development and training in New Mexico. Serves all people, but focus is on women and minorities.

FINANCING AND LOAN PROGRAMS

54994 ■ Technology Ventures Corp.

1155 University Blvd. SE

Albuquerque, NM 87106

Ph: (505)246-2882

Fax: (505)246-2891

URL: http://www.techventures.org

Contact: Sherman McCorkle, Chief Executive Officer

Industry Preferences: Diversified. **Geographic Preference:** Southwest.

PROCUREMENT ASSISTANCE PROGRAMS

54995 ■ New Mexico Procurement Technical Assistance Center

6401 Richards Ave.

Santa Fe, NM 87508

Ph: (505)428-1622

Fax: (505)428-1469

Co. E-mail: wendy.ederer@sfcc.edu

URL: http://www.dla.mil/db/procurem.htm

Contact: Wendy Ederer, Program Manager

E-mail: cmarquez@state.nm.us

INCUBATORS/RESEARCH AND TECHNOLOGY PARKS

54996 ■ Albuquerque SBDC

2501 Yale Blvd. SE, Ste. 302

Albuquerque, NM 87106

Ph: (505)224-5250

Fax: (505)224-5256

Co. E-mail: sbdc@cnm.edu

Contact: Ray Garcia, Director

54997 ■ Economic Development Corporation of Lea County

200 E Broadway, Ste. A201

Hobbs, NM 88241-1376

Ph: (505)397-2039

Free: 800-443-2236

Fax: (505)392-2300

Co. E-mail: edclea@leaco.net

URL: http://www.edclc.org

Contact: Bethe Cunningham, Executive Director

Description: Works to improve the economic condition of Lea County through business expansion, relocation, and retention.

54998 ■ Los Alamos Research Park

190 Central Park Sq.

Los Alamos, NM 87544

Ph: (505)661-4999

Fax: (505)662-0099

Co. E-mail: lacdc@losalamos.org

URL: http://www.la-rp.org

Description: Provides a research and development focused research park.

54999 ■ Quality Center for Business

San Juan College

5101 College Blvd.

Farmington, NM 87402

Ph: (505)566-3700

Co. E-mail: welchj@sanjuancollege.edu

URL: http://www.sjc.cc.nm.us/qcb/

Description: A small business incubator offering an integrated approach to assisting area businesses, industry and organizations with staff or management training; assistance in business planning and technical support; space and office support for growing companies; and the economic development of San Juan County.

55000 ■ Santa Fe Business Incubator

3900 Paseo del Sol

Santa Fe, NM 87507

Ph: (505)424-1140

Fax: (505)424-1144

Co. E-mail: info@sfbi.net

URL: http://www.sfbi.net

Contact: Marie Longserre, Chief Executive Officer

Description: The SFBI seeks to enhance the quality of life in Santa Fe County by supporting emerging businesses through shared resources. Provides office, lab, and light manufacturing space.

55001 ■ South Valley Economic Development Center

318 Isleta Blvd. SW

Albuquerque, NM 87105-3822

Ph: (505)877-0373

Co. E-mail: admin@svedc.com

URL: http://www.bernco.gov/live/departments.asp-
?dept=7147

Description: A small business incubator with processes that accelerate the successful development of start-up and fledgling companies by providing entrepreneurs with an array of targeted resources and services.

55002 ■ WESST Enterprise Center

609 Broadway Blvd., NE

Albuquerque, NM 87102

Ph: (505)246-6900

Free: 800-469-3778

Fax: (505)243-3035

Co. E-mail: jmeyer@wesst.org

URL: http://www.wesst.org/enterprise-center/

Contact: Clare Zurawski, Regional Manager

Description: A mixed-use small business incubator for up to 20 light manufacturing, service, and technology enterprises.

EDUCATIONAL PROGRAMS

55003 ■ Albuquerque Technical-Vocational Institute

525 Buena Vista SE

Albuquerque, NM 87106

Ph: (505)224-3000

Fax: (505)224-3237

Co. E-mail: admissions@cnm.edu

URL: http://www.cnm.edu

Description: Trade and technical school offering a program in entrepreneurship.

55004 ■ Eastern New Mexico University--Roswell

PO Box 6000

Roswell, NM 88202-6000

Ph: (575)624-7000

Fax: (575)624-7119

URL: http://www.roswell.enmu.edu

Description: Part of a small business assistance center system that provides a variety of training programs, including self-paced, evening, and business courses. 1800-243-6687.

55005 ■ New Mexico Junior College - Business Assistance Center

5317 Lovington Hwy.

Hobbs, NM 88240

Ph: (575)392-4510

Free: 800-657-6260

Fax: (575)492-4704
URL: http://www.nmjc.edu
Description: Part of a small business system that provides a variety of training, including self-paced, and business courses. 1-800-657-6260.

55006 ■ Northern New Mexico Community College
921 Paso de Onate
Espanola, NM 87532
Ph: (505)747-2100
Fax: (505)747-2180
URL: http://www.nnmcc.edu
Description: Part of a small business assistance center system that provides a variety of training, including self-paced, evening, and business courses.

55007 ■ Santa Fe Community College
3000 NW 83rd St., Rm. 112
Gainesville, FL 32606
Ph: (352)395-5443
Fax: (352)395-5286
Co. E-mail: info@sfcc.edu
URL: http://www.santafe.edu
URL(s): www.sfcollege.edu, www.sfcc.edu. **Description:** Two-year college offering a program in small business management. **Telecommunication Services:** information@sfcc.edu.

LEGISLATIVE ASSISTANCE

55008 ■ NM Commission on the Status of Women
300 San Mateo Blvd. NE, Ste. 101
Albuquerque, NM 87108
Ph: (505)222-6600
Free: 800-432-9168
Fax: (505)222-6611
URL: http://www.womenscommission.state.nm.us
Description: Assesses the needs of women in business in the state of New Mexico and formulates plans to meet those needs.

PUBLICATIONS

55009 ■ *Smart Start your New Mexico Business*
PSI Research
300 N. Valley Dr.
Grants Pass, OR 97526
Ph: (503)479-9464
Free: 800-228-2275
Fax: (503)476-1479
Co. E-mail: info@psi-research.com
URL: http://www.psi-research.com
Ed: Michael D. Jenkins. **Released:** Revised edition, 1992. **Price:** $29.95 (looseleaf binder); $24.95 (paper). **Description:** Part of the Successful Business Library series.

PUBLISHERS

55010 ■ Sun Books - Sun Publishing
1274 Calle De Comercio
Santa Fe, NM 87502-5588
Ph: (505)471-5177
Free: 877-849-0051
Fax: (505)473-4458
Co. E-mail: info@sunbooks.com
URL: http://www.sunbooks.com
Contact: Skip Whitson, Director
E-mail: info@sunbooks.com
Description: Description: Publishes self-help, motivational, astrology, business, history, art, philosophy and art books. Distributes for Far West Publishing Co. and SunBooks. **Founded:** 1973.

55011 ■ Via Media Publishing Co.
c/o Michael DeMarco
941 Calle Mejia, Ste. 822
Santa Fe, NM 87501
Ph: (505)983-1919
Fax: (814)455-2726
URL: http://www.goviamedia.com
Contact: Michael A. Demarco, Manager
E-mail: md@goviamedia.com
Description: Description: Publishes fiction and nonfiction about martial arts. Accepts unsolicited manuscripts. Reaches market through direct mail, reviews, listings and distributors including Bibliog. **Founded:** 1991. **Publications:** *The Journal of Asian Martial Arts* (Quarterly).

SMALL BUSINESS DEVELOPMENT CENTERS

55012 ■ Albany Small Business Development Center
6 Executive Park Dr.
Albany, NY 12203
Ph: (518)380-5077
Fax: (518)380-5071
Co. E-mail: wbrigham@uamail.albany.edu
URL: http://www.nyssbdc.org/centers/centers.aspx-
  ?centid=10
Contact: William Brigham, Director
Description: Represents and promotes the small business sector. Provides management assistance to current and prospective small business owners. Helps to improve management skills and expand the products and services of members.

55013 ■ Binghamton Small Business Development Center
Binghamton University
The Artco Bldg., 3rd Fl.
218-224 Water St.
Binghamton, NY 13901
Ph: (607)777-4024
Fax: (607)777-4029
Co. E-mail: sbdc@binghamton.edu
URL: http://sbdc.binghamton.edu
Contact: Joanne Jones, Advisor
Description: Represents and promotes the small business sector. Provides management assistance to current and prospective small business owners. Helps to improve management skills and expand the products and services of members.

55014 ■ Brockport Small Business Development Center
350 New Campus Dr.
Brockport, NY 14420
Ph: (585)395-8410
Fax: (585)395-2467
Co. E-mail: sbdc@brockport.edu
URL: http://www.nyssbdc.org
Contact: Jan Pisanczyn, Director
Description: Represents and promotes the small business sector. Provides management assistance to current and prospective small business owners. Helps to improve management skills and expand the products and services of members.

55015 ■ Bronx Small Business Development Center
250 Bedford Park Blvd. W
Bronx, NY 10468-1589
Ph: (718)960-8806
Fax: (718)960-7340
Co. E-mail: sbdc.bronx@lehman.cuny.edu
URL: http://www.nyssbdc.org
Contact: Clarence Stanley, Director
Description: Represents and promotes the small business sector. Provides management assistance to current and prospective small business owners. Helps to improve management skills and expand the products and services of members.

55016 ■ Buffalo State College Small Business Development Center
Buffalo State College
Cleveland Hall 206
1300 Elmwood Ave.
Buffalo, NY 14222
Ph: (716)878-4030
Fax: (716)878-4067
Co. E-mail: smallbus@buffalostate.edu
URL: http://www.buffalostate.edu/sbdc
Contact: Susan A. McCartney, Director
Description: Represents and promotes the small business sector. Provides management assistance to current and prospective small business owners. Helps to improve management skills and expand the products and services of members.

55017 ■ Canton Small Business Development Center
SUNY Canton
34 Cornell Dr.
Canton, NY 13617
Ph: (315)386-7312
Fax: (315)379-3814
Co. E-mail: sbdc@canton.edu
URL: http://www.nyssbdc.org
Contact: Dale Rice, Director
Description: Represents and promotes the small business sector. Provides management assistance to current and prospective small business owners. Helps to improve management skills and expand the products and services of members.

55018 ■ College of Staten Island Small Business Development Center
College of Staten Island
2800 Victory Blvd., Bldg. 2A, Rm. 300
Staten Island, NY 10314-9806
Ph: (718)982-2560
Fax: (718)982-2323
Co. E-mail: sullivane@mail.csi.cuny.edu
URL: http://www.nyssbdc.org
Contact: Dean Balsamini, Director
Description: Represents and promotes the small business sector. Provides management assistance to current and prospective small business owners. Helps to improve management skills and expand the products and services of members.

55019 ■ Farmingdale Small Business Development Center
Farmingdale State College
Campus Commons
2350 Rte. 110
Farmingdale, NY 11735
Ph: (631)420-2765
Fax: (631)370-8895
Co. E-mail: sbdc@farmingdale.edu
URL: http://www.farmingdale.edu/campuspages/
  CAMPUSAFFILIATES/SBDC/homepage.htm
Contact: Lucille Wesnofske, Director
Description: Represents and promotes the small business sector. Provides management assistance to current and prospective small business owners. Helps to improve management skills and expand the products and services of members.

55020 ■ *Fifty-Forty-Ten-News*
101 S Salina St., No. 10, Ste. 1030
Syracuse, NY 13202
Ph: (315)373-0468
Fax: (315)373-0921
Co. E-mail: kcampbell@gsbdc.com
URL: http://www.gsbdc.com
Contact: Peggy A. Adams, Executive Director
Released: Quarterly

55021 ■ Greater Syracuse Business Development Corporation (GSBDC)
101 S Salina St., No. 10, Ste. 1030
Syracuse, NY 13202
Ph: (315)373-0468
Fax: (315)373-0921
Co. E-mail: kcampbell@gsbdc.com
URL: http://www.gsbdc.com
Contact: Peggy A. Adams, Executive Director
Description: Seeks to promote business through economic and community development. Assists businesses in their expansion and financing needs. Enhances the quality of life and fosters the growth of good jobs within the community. **Founded:** 1964. **Publications:** *Fifty-Forty-Ten-News* (Quarterly).

55022 ■ Jamestown Small Business Development Center
Jamestown Community College
525 Falconer St.
Jamestown, NY 14702-0020
Ph: (716)338-1024
Fax: (716)338-1476
Co. E-mail: irenedobies@mail.sunyjcc.edu
URL: http://www.nyssbdc.org
Contact: Irene Dobies, Director
Description: Represents and promotes the small business sector. Provides management assistance to current and prospective small business owners. Helps to improve management skills and expand the products and services of members.

55023 ■ Manhattan Small Business Development Center at Pace University
163 William St., 3rd Fl.
New York, NY 10038
Ph: (212)618-6655
Fax: (212)618-6669
Co. E-mail: sbdc@pace.edu
URL: http://www.nyssbdc.org
Contact: Ira Davidson, Director
Description: Represents and promotes the small business sector. Provides management assistance to current and prospective small business owners. Helps to improve management skills and expand the products and services of members.

55024 ■ Mid-Hudson Small Business Development Center
Business Resource Center
One Development Ct.
Kingston, NY 12401
Ph: (845)339-0025

Fax: (845)339-1631
Co. E-mail: sbdc@sunyulster.edu
URL: http://www.nyssbdc.org/centers/centers.aspx-
  ?centid=94
Contact: Arnaldo Sehwerert, Director
Description: Represents and promotes the small business sector. Provides management assistance to current and prospective small business owners. Helps to improve management skills and expand the products and services of members.

55025 ■ Midtown Manhattan Small Business Development Center at Baruch College
Baruch College, Field Ctr.
55 Lexington Ave., Rm. 2-140
New York, NY 10010-2318
Ph: (646)312-4790
Fax: (646)312-4781
Co. E-mail: sbdc@baruch.cuny.edu
URL: http://www.nyssbdc.org
Contact: Ulas Neftci, Director
Description: Represents and promotes the small business sector. Provides management assistance to current and prospective small business owners. Helps to improve management skills and expand the products and services of members.

55026 ■ Mohawk Valley Small Business Development Center
100 Seymour Rd.
Utica, NY 13502
Ph: (315)792-7547
Fax: (315)792-7554
Co. E-mail: sbdc@sunyit.edu
URL: http://www.sunyit.edu/sbdc
Contact: David C. Mallen, Director
Description: Represents and promotes the small business sector. Provides management assistance to current and prospective small business owners. Helps to improve management skills and expand the products and services of members.

55027 ■ New York State Small Business Development Center (NYS SBDC)
22 Corporate Woods Bldg., 3rd Fl.
Albany, NY 12246
Ph: (518)443-5398
Free: 800-732-SBDC
Co. E-mail: j.king@nyssbdc.org
URL: http://www.nyssbdc.org
Contact: Mr. James King, Director
Description: Regional centers providing information and assistance to small businesses. Makes available training and counseling services. **Founded:** 1984.

55028 ■ Niagara Small Business Development Center
50 Main St.
Lockport, NY 14094
Ph: (716)434-3815
Fax: (716)433-5155
Co. E-mail: sbdc@niagaracc.suny.edu
URL: http://www.nyssbdc.org
Contact: Lynn Oswald, Director
Description: Represents and promotes the small business sector. Provides management assistance to current and prospective small business owners. Helps to improve management skills and expand the products and services of members.

55029 ■ North Country Small Business Development Center
State University of New York College at Plattsburgh
194 US Oval, Rm. 248
Plattsburgh, NY 12903-3900
Ph: (518)564-2042
Fax: (518)564-2043
Co. E-mail: sbdc@plattsburgh.edu
URL: http://www.nyssbdc.org
Contact: Karen Stehlin, Director
Description: Represents and promotes the small business sector. Provides management assistance to current and prospective small business owners. Helps to improve management skills and expand the products and services of members.

55030 ■ Onondaga Small Business Development Center
Onondaga Community College
J. Stanley Coyne
4585 W Seneca Tpke., Ste. 200
Syracuse, NY 13215-4585
Ph: (315)498-6070
Fax: (315)498-2589
Co. E-mail: sbdc@sunyocc.edu
URL: http://www.nyssbdc.org
Contact: Patricia Higgins, Director
Description: Represents and promotes the small business sector. Provides management assistance to current and prospective small business owners. Helps to improve management skills and expand the products and services of members.

55031 ■ Stony Brook Small Business Development Center
Stony Brook University
Research and Development Park
Stony Brook, NY 11794-6016
Ph: (631)632-9070
Fax: (631)632-7176
Co. E-mail: leslie.rurup@stonybrook.edu
URL: http://www.nyssbdc.org
Contact: Jeff Saelens, Director
Description: Represents and promotes the small business sector. Provides management assistance to current and prospective small business owners. Helps to improve management skills and expand the products and services of members.

55032 ■ Westchester Small Business Development Center
Rockland Community College
145 College Rd.
Suffern, NY 10901-3699
Ph: (845)356-6065
Fax: (845)356-6117
Co. E-mail: tmorley@sunyrockland.edu
URL: http://www.nyssbdc.org
Contact: Thomas Morley, Director
Description: Represents and promotes the small business sector. Provides management assistance to current and prospective small business owners. Helps to improve management skills and expand the products and services of members.

55033 ■ York Small Business Development Center
City University of New York, York College
94-50 159th St.
Jamaica, NY 11451-9902
Ph: (718)262-2880
Fax: (718)262-2881
Co. E-mail: sbdc@york.cuny.edu
URL: http://www.nyssbdc.org/centers/centers.aspx-
  ?centid=32
Contact: Harry Wells, Director
Description: Represents and promotes the small business sector. Provides management assistance to current and prospective small business owners. Helps to improve management skills and expand the products and services of members.

SMALL BUSINESS ASSISTANCE PROGRAMS

55034 ■ New Jersey Department of Business and Economic Development
Mary G. Roebling Bldg.
20 W State St.
Trenton, NJ 08625-0990
Ph: (609)292-4431
URL: http://www.newjerseycommerce.org/
Description: Provides complete assistance packages, including financing, site selection, and construction. Package may also include labor recruitment and training.

55035 ■ New York Department of Economic Development - Division of Minority- and Women-owned Business Development
30 S Pearl St.
Albany, NY 12245
Ph: (518)292-5250

Free: 800-STATENY
Fax: (518)292-5803
Co. E-mail: esd@empire.state.nv.us
URL: http://www.empire.state.ny.us/Small_and_
  Growing_Businesses/
Contact: Michael H. Jones-Bey, Executive Director
Description: Certify minority and women owned businesses. Monitor the compliance of state agencies. Meet the goals that the agency sets for the utility of minority and women owned businesses.

55036 ■ New York Department of Economic Development - Division for Small Business - Business Service Ombudsman
30 S Pearl St.
Albany, NY 12245
Ph: (518)292-5220
Free: 800-STATENY
Fax: (518)292-5884
URL: http://www.empire.state.ny.us
Description: Assists businesses in resolving red tape difficulties with all levels of government.

55037 ■ New York State Foundation for Science, Technology and Innovation
30 S Pearl St., 11th Fl.
Albany, NY 12207
Ph: (518)292-5700
Fax: (518)292-5798
Co. E-mail: contact@nystar.state.ny.us
URL: http://www.nystar.state.ny.us
Contact: Edward Reinfurt, Executive Director
Description: Provides major services, including conducting special training programs, awarding research and development grants for university-based research, encouraging high technology, and providing grants and other services to the Centers for Advanced Technology.

55038 ■ New York State Foundation for Science, Technology and Innovation - Incubators & High Technology Economic Development
30 S Pearl St., 11th Fl.
Albany, NY 12207
Ph: (518)292-5700
Fax: (518)292-5780
URL: http://www.nystar.state.ny.us/incubators.htm
Description: Provides established small and medium-sized manufacturing businesses with knowledge, attitudes, and skills so they can address issues of technology based productivity improvements. Assistance is provided on an individualized basis.

55039 ■ State University of New York at Plattsburgh - Economic Development and Technical Assistance
Redcay, Rm. 213
101 Broad St.
Plattsburgh, NY 12901
Ph: (518)564-2214
Fax: (518)564-3220
Co. E-mail: tac@plattsburgh.edu
URL: http://www.tacsuny.com
Contact: Howard Lowe, Director
Description: Provides technical support and data to the business community and develops and promotes new venture capital formation. Specializes in short-term management, marketing, financial packaging, and feasibility analysis services.

SCORE OFFICES

55040 ■ Auburn SCORE
Co. E-mail: scoreauburn@verizon.net

55041 ■ Brooklyn SCORE

55042 ■ Chautauqua Region SCORE
Co. E-mail: rsgolas@localnet.com

55043 ■ Chemung Valley SCORE
Co. E-mail: rshore368@aol.com

55044 ■ Greater Binghamton SCORE
Co. E-mail: chapter0217@stny.rr.com

55045 ■ Orange County SCORE
Co. E-mail: info@orangenyscore.com

55046 ■ Putnam SCORE
Co. E-mail: putnamscore@comcast.net

55047 ■ Rochester SCORE
100 State St., Rm. 410
Rochester, NY 14614
Ph: (585)263-6473
Fax: (585)263-3146
Co. E-mail: admin@scorerochester.org
URL: http://www.scorerochester.org
Description: Provides business owners with information, resources and tools vital to their success. Offers business counseling. **Founded:** 1964.

55048 ■ Rockland SCORE
Co. E-mail: score677@rocklandscore.org

55049 ■ SCORE Brookhaven

55050 ■ SCORE Buffalo - Niagara
130 S Elmwood Ave.
Buffalo, NY 14202
Ph: (716)551-4301
Free: 800-745-0355
Fax: (716)551-4418
Co. E-mail: scorebuffalo1@roadrunner.com
URL: http://www.scorebuffalo.org
Description: Aims to assist entrepreneurs in the startup and growth of small businesses. Includes services such as free, confidential counseling and low-cost management workshops. Acts as a resource partner in association with the Small Business Administration. **Founded:** 1964.

55051 ■ SCORE Clinton Franklin Essex County
Co. E-mail: info@scoreplattsburgh.org

55052 ■ SCORE Dutchess
c/o Dutchess County Regional Chamber of Commerce
1 Civic Ctr. Plz.
Poughkeepsie, NY 12601
Ph: (845)454-1700
Co. E-mail: scoredcny@hotmail.com
URL: http://www.scoredutchessny.org
Contact: Arni Halling, Chairperson
Description: Provides resources and expertise to maximize the success of existing and emerging small businesses. Offers business counseling and workshops. **Founded:** 1964.

55053 ■ SCORE Huntington
Co. E-mail: alabita@aol.com

55054 ■ SCORE Long Island
Co. E-mail: info@scorelongisland.org

55055 ■ SCORE Northeast
1 Computer Dr. S
Albany, NY 12205
Ph: (518)446-1118
Co. E-mail: info@scorealbany.org
URL: http://www.scorealbany.org
Contact: Don Finney, Chairman
Description: Strives for the formation, growth, and success of small businesses. Promotes entrepreneur education in Albany area, New York. **Founded:** 1963.

55056 ■ SCORE NYC
Co. E-mail: ask@scorenyc.org

55057 ■ SCORE Queens County
Co. E-mail: chapter588@aol.com

55058 ■ SCORE Staten Island
Co. E-mail: info@scoresi.org

55059 ■ SCORE Syracuse
224 Harrison St., Ste. 506
Syracuse, NY 13202
Ph: (315)471-9393
Co. E-mail: info@syracusescore.org
URL: http://www.syracusescore.org
Contact: Eric Rogers, President
Founded: 1964.

55060 ■ SCORE Ulster
Co. E-mail: score@sunyulster.org

55061 ■ SCORE Watertown
Co. E-mail: score170@westelcom.com

55062 ■ SCORE Westchester
120 Bloomingdale Rd.
White Plains, NY 10605
Ph: (914)948-3907
Co. E-mail: score306@scorecast.org
URL: http://www.scorewestchester.com
Description: Strives for the formation, growth, and success of small businesses. Promotes entrepreneur education in Westchester area, New York.

55063 ■ Suffolk SCORE
200 Howell Ave.
Riverhead, NY 11901
Ph: (631)727-3200
Co. E-mail: webmaster@easternsuffolkscore.org
URL: http://www.easternsuffolkscore.org
Description: Promotes business and community development in Islip and Eastern Suffolk County. Conducts business education seminars and workshops to those wanting to start a business.

55064 ■ Sullivan SCORE
Co. E-mail: info@sullivanscore.com

55065 ■ Utica SCORE
Co. E-mail: bepapa@adelphia.net

BETTER BUSINESS BUREAUS

55066 ■ Better Business Bureau, Buffalo
100 Bryant Woods S
Buffalo, NY 14228
Ph: (716)881-5222
Free: 800-828-5000
Fax: (716)883-5349
Co. E-mail: geninquiries@upstatenybbb.org
URL: http://www.buffalo.bbb.org
Contact: John G. Doyle, Jr., President
Description: Seeks to promote and foster ethical relationship between businesses and the public through voluntary self-regulation, consumer and business education, and service excellence. Provides information to help consumers and businesses make informed purchasing decisions and avoid costly scams and frauds; settles consumer complaints through arbitration and other means.

55067 ■ Better Business Bureau of Metropolitan New York
30 E 33rd St., 12th Fl.
New York, NY 10016
Ph: (212)533-6200
Fax: (212)477-4912
Co. E-mail: inquiry@newyork.bbb.org
URL: http://www.newyork.bbb.org
Contact: Claire Rosenzweig, President
Description: Seeks to promote and foster ethical relationship between businesses and the public through voluntary self-regulation, consumer and business education, and service excellence. Provides information to help consumers and businesses make informed purchasing decisions and avoid costly scams and frauds; settles consumer complaints through arbitration and other means.

55068 ■ Better Business Bureau, Rochester (BBB)
55 St. Paul St.
Rochester, NY 14604
Free: 800-828-5000
Co. E-mail: geninquiries@upstatenybbb.org
URL: http://www.rochester.bbb.org
Description: Promotes and fosters ethical relationships between businesses and the public.

55069 ■ Long Island Better Business Bureau
399 Conklin St., Ste. 300
Farmingdale, NY 11735
Ph: (516)420-0500
Fax: (516)420-1095
Co. E-mail: longislandbbb@newyork.bbb.org
URL: http://www.newyork.bbb.org
Description: Seeks to promote and foster ethical relationship between businesses and the public through voluntary self-regulation, consumer and business education, and service excellence. Provides

information to help consumers and businesses make informed purchasing decisions and avoid costly scams and frauds; settles consumer complaints through arbitration and other means.

55070 ■ Mid-Hudson Better Business Bureau
150 White Plains Rd., Ste. 107
Tarrytown, NY 10591-5521
Ph: (914)333-0550
Fax: (914)333-7519
Co. E-mail: mhinquiries@newyork.bbb.org
URL: http://www.newyork.bbb.org
Contact: Claire Rosenweig, President
Description: Seeks to promote and foster ethical relationship between businesses and the public through voluntary self-regulation, consumer and business education, and service excellence. Provides information to help consumers and businesses make informed purchasing decisions and avoid costly scams and frauds; settles consumer complaints through arbitration and other means.

CHAMBERS OF COMMERCE

55071 ■ 4 Seasons in the Adirondack Mountains
3847 Main St.
Warrensburg, NY 12885
Ph: (518)623-2161
Fax: (518)623-2184
Co. E-mail: info@warrensburgchamber.com
URL: http://www.warrensburgchamber.com
Contact: Lynn Smith, President
Price: free.

55072 ■ '95 Visitor's Guide to Corning
Released: Annual **Price:** free.

55073 ■ 1000 Islands - Clayton Region Chamber of Commerce
517 Riverside Dr.
Clayton, NY 13624
Ph: (315)686-3771
Free: 800-252-9806
Fax: (315)686-5564
Co. E-mail: info@1000islands-clayton.com
URL: http://www.1000islands-clayton.com
Contact: Karen Goetz, Executive Director
Description: Promotes business, community development, and tourism in the Thousand Island area of New York. **Founded:** 1926. **Publications:** Clayton Vacation Guide (Annual).

55074 ■ Accommodations Directory
193 River St.
Saranac Lake, NY 12983
Ph: (518)891-1990
Free: 800-347-1992
Fax: (518)891-7042
Co. E-mail: info@saranaclake.com
URL: http://www.saranaclake.com
Contact: Katy Van Anden, Executive Director
Released: Periodic

55075 ■ Adirondack Regional Chamber of Commerce (ARCC)
136 Glen St., Ste. 3
Glens Falls, NY 12801
Ph: (518)798-1761
Fax: (518)792-4147
Co. E-mail: frontdesk@adirondackchamber.org
URL: http://www.adirondackchamber.org
Contact: Peter Aust, President
Description: Promotes business and community development in northern Essex, Hamilton, Saratoga, Warren, and Washington counties, NY. **Founded:** 1914. **Publications:** ARCC Regional Report (Monthly); Quality of Life Guide (Annual). **Telecommunication Services:** dburke@nbtbank.com.

55076 ■ Adirondacks-Speculator Region Chamber of Commerce—Adirondacks-Spectacular Region Chamber of Commerce
PO Box 184
Speculator, NY 12164
Ph: (518)548-4521

Fax: (518)548-4905
Co. E-mail: info@speculatorchamber.com
URL: http://www.adrkmts.com
Description: Promotes business and community development in Speculator, NY area.

55077 ■ African American Chamber of Commerce of Westchester and Rockland Counties (AACCWR)
100 Stevens Ave., Ste. 202
Mount Vernon, NY 10550
Ph: (914)699-9050
Fax: (914)699-6279
Co. E-mail: robinlisadouglas@cs.com
URL: http://www.aaccnys.org
Contact: Ms. Robin L. Douglas, President
Description: Promotes business and community development in Westchester and Rockland counties. **Founded:** 1996.

55078 ■ The Agenda
350 Essjay Rd., Ste. 200
Williamsville, NY 14221-8214
Ph: (716)632-6905
Fax: (716)632-0548
Co. E-mail: cdipirro@amherst.org
URL: http://www.amherst.org
Contact: Colleen C. DiPirro, President
Released: Monthly

55079 ■ Albany-Colonie Regional Chamber of Commerce
1 Computer Dr. S
Albany, NY 12205-1631
Ph: (518)431-1400
Fax: (518)431-1402
Co. E-mail: info@acchamber.org
URL: http://acchamber.org
Contact: Mark Eagan, President
URL(s): www.techvalley.org. **Description:** Promotes business, community and economic development in the Albany-Colonie, NY area. Holds numerous networking opportunities and special events and offers its members significant cost-saving benefits. **Founded:** 1900. **Publications:** Friday Fax (Weekly); Visions (Monthly); Albany-Colonie Regional Chamber of Commerce--Business Directory and Relocation Guides.

55080 ■ Alexandria Bay Chamber of Commerce
7 Market St.
Alexandria Bay, NY 13607
Ph: (315)482-9531
Free: 800-541-2110
Co. E-mail: info@alexbay.org
URL: http://www.alexbay.org
Description: Promotes business and community development in Alexandria Bay, NY.

55081 ■ Almanac
Radisson Hotel
200 Genesee St.
Utica, NY 13502
Ph: (315)724-3151
Fax: (315)724-3177
Co. E-mail: info@mvchamber.org
URL: http://www.mvchamber.org
Contact: Thomas Bashant, President
Released: Annual **Price:** $5.

55082 ■ Amherst Chamber of Commerce
350 Essjay Rd., Ste. 200
Williamsville, NY 14221-8214
Ph: (716)632-6905
Fax: (716)632-0548
Co. E-mail: cdipirro@amherst.org
URL: http://www.amherst.org
Contact: Colleen C. DiPirro, President
Description: Aims to create and maintain a positive economic, political, and social climate in Amherst. **Founded:** 1957. **Publications:** The Agenda (Monthly).

55083 ■ Arcade Area Chamber of Commerce
684 Main St.
Arcade, NY 14009
Ph: (585)492-2114

Fax: (585)492-5103
Co. E-mail: aacc278@verizon.net
URL: http://www.arcadechamber.org
Contact: Dorie Clinch, Executive Secretary
Description: Promotes business and community development in the Arcade, NY area. **Founded:** 1952. **Publications:** The Tri-County Business Advocate (Quarterly).

55084 ■ ARCC Regional Report
136 Glen St., Ste. 3
Glens Falls, NY 12801
Ph: (518)798-1761
Fax: (518)792-4147
Co. E-mail: frontdesk@adirondackchamber.org
URL: http://www.adirondackchamber.org
Contact: Peter Aust, President
Released: Monthly

55085 ■ Bainbridge Chamber of Commerce
PO Box 2
Bainbridge, NY 13733
Ph: (607)967-8700
Co. E-mail: bainbridge.chamber@yahoo.com
URL: http://www.bainbridgeny.org
Contact: Barb Mulkins, President
Description: Promotes business and community development in Bainbridge, NY. Sponsors the General Clinton Canoe Regatta.

55086 ■ Baldwin Chamber of Commerce (BCC)
PO Box 804
Baldwin, NY 11510
Ph: (516)223-8080
URL: http://www.baldwinchamber.com
Contact: Kathleen Healy Englehart, Secretary
Description: Promotes business and community development in Baldwin, NY.

55087 ■ Bed and Breakfast Guide
1 Civic Center Plz., Ste. 400
Poughkeepsie, NY 12601
Ph: (845)454-1700
Fax: (845)454-1702
Co. E-mail: charlesnorth@dcrcoc.org
URL: http://www.dutchesscountyregionalchamber.org
Contact: Charles S. North, President

55088 ■ Bedford Hills Chamber of Commerce
PO Box 162
Bedford Hills, NY 10507-0162
Ph: (914)381-3356
Co. E-mail: purpose396@gmail.com
URL: http://www.bedfordhills.org
Contact: Dr. Greg Riley, President
Description: Promotes business and community development in Bedford Hills, NY. Sponsors "Community Day" sidewalk sales. Convention/Meeting: none. **Founded:** 1968.

55089 ■ Bethlehem Chamber of Commerce
318 Delaware Ave., Main Sq.
Delmar, NY 12054-1911
Ph: (518)439-0512
Fax: (518)475-0910
Co. E-mail: info@bethlehemchamber.com
URL: http://www.bethlehemchamber.com
Contact: John McIntyre, Chairman
Description: Aims to promote good business practices, favorable business environment and community prosperity. **Founded:** 1957. **Publications:** In Business for Business (Monthly); Welcome to the Town of Bethlehem. **Educational Activities:** Bethlehem Chamber of Commerce Party (Quarterly). **Telecommunication Services:** marty@bethlehemchamber.com.

55090 ■ Boonville Area Chamber of Commerce
PO Box 163
Boonville, NY 13309
Ph: (315)942-5112

Fax: (315)942-6823
Co. E-mail: info@boonvillechamber.org
URL: http://www.boonvillechamber.com
Contact: Bill Flack, President
Description: Assists businesses, organizations and individuals by providing programs and services that enhance the economic climate and the quality of life for the citizens of the community. **Founded:** 1961.

55091 ■ The Bottom Line
15 Park Ave., Ste. 7
Clifton Park, NY 12065
Ph: (518)371-7748
Fax: (518)371-5025
Co. E-mail: info@southernsaratoga.org
URL: http://www.southernsaratoga.org
Contact: Pete Bardunias, President
Released: Monthly

55092 ■ The Bottom Line
1 Civic Center Plz., Ste. 400
Poughkeepsie, NY 12601
Ph: (845)454-1700
Fax: (845)454-1702
Co. E-mail: charlesnorth@dcrcoc.org
URL: http://www.dutchesscountyregionalchamber.org
Contact: Charles S. North, President
Released: Monthly

55093 ■ Brewster Chamber of Commerce
16 Mt. Ebo Rd. S, Ste. 12A
Brewster, NY 10509-1528
Ph: (845)279-2477
Fax: (845)278-8349
Co. E-mail: info@brewsterchamber.com
URL: http://www.brewsterchamber.com
Contact: Rose Z. Aglieco, Executive Director
Description: Promotes business and community development in Brewster, NY. **Awards:** Student Scholarships (Annual).

55094 ■ Bronx Chamber of Commerce
1200 Waters Pl., Ste. 106
Bronx, NY 10461
Ph: (718)828-3900
Fax: (718)409-3748
Co. E-mail: info@bronxchamber.org
URL: http://www.bronxchamber.org
Contact: Leonard Caro, President
Description: Promotes business and community development in Bronx, NY. Sponsors special events. **Founded:** 1894. **Publications:** Industrial Directory (Periodic).

55095 ■ Bronxville Chamber of Commerce
81 Pondfield Rd., Ste. 7
Bronxville, NY 10708
Ph: (914)337-6040
Fax: (914)337-6040
Co. E-mail: bronxvillechamber@verizon.net
URL: http://www.bronxvillechamber.com
Contact: Susan Miele, Executive Director
Description: Promotes business and community development in Bronxville, NY. **Founded:** 1944.

55096 ■ Brooklyn Chamber of Commerce
25 Elm Pl., Ste. 200, 2nd Fl.
Brooklyn, NY 11201
Ph: (718)875-1000
Fax: (718)237-4274
Co. E-mail: info@brooklynchamber.com
URL: http://www.ibrooklyn.com
Contact: Peter M. Meyer, Chairman
Description: Promotes business and community development in Brooklyn, NY. **Founded:** 1918. **Publications:** Brooklyn Chamber of Commerce--Membership Directory.

55097 ■ Buffalo Niagara Partnership
665 Main St., Ste. 200
Buffalo, NY 14203
Ph: (716)852-7100
Free: 800-241-0474

Fax: (716)852-2761
Co. E-mail: membership@thepartnership.org
URL: http://www.thepartnership.org
Contact: Donald K. Boswell, President
Description: Promotes business and community development in West Seneca, NY. Holds seminars. **Founded:** 1993. **Publications:** *The Focus* (Bimonthly). **Educational Activities:** Business and Community EXPO (Annual). **Awards:** Business of the Year Award (Annual); Citizen of the Year Award (Annual); Educator of the Year Award (Annual); Service Organization of the Year Award (Annual). **Telecommunication Services:** arudnick@thepartnership.org.

55098 ■ *Business to Business*
PO Box 512
Miller Place, NY 11764
Ph: (631)821-1313
Co. E-mail: cdmpresident@yahoo.com
URL: http://www.cdmlongisland.com
Contact: Tom Ianniello, President
Released: Periodic **Price:** for members.

55099 ■ *Business to Business*
PO Box 587
Geneva, NY 14456
Ph: (315)789-1776
Fax: (315)789-3993
Co. E-mail: info@genevany.com
URL: http://www.genevany.com
Contact: Rob Gladden, President
Released: Monthly

55100 ■ *Business and Community Directory*
2050 Western Ave.
Star Plz., No. 109
Guilderland, NY 12084
Ph: (518)456-6611
Fax: (518)456-6690
Co. E-mail: info@guilderlandchamber.com
URL: http://www.guilderlandchamber.com
Contact: Katherine Burbank, Executive Director
Released: Periodic

55101 ■ *Business and Community Service Guide*
1110 Crosspoint Ln., Ste. C
Webster, NY 14580-3280
Ph: (585)265-3960
Fax: (585)265-3702
Co. E-mail: bbernard@websterchamber.com
URL: http://www.websterchamber.com
Contact: Elizabeth Bernard, Administrator
Released: Annual **Price:** free.

55102 ■ *Business Connection*
28 Clinton St.
Saratoga Springs, NY 12866-2143
Ph: (518)584-3255
Fax: (518)587-0318
Co. E-mail: info@saratoga.org
URL: http://www.saratoga.org
Contact: Todd Shimkus, President
Released: Annual **Price:** $50.

55103 ■ Business Council of Westchester
108 Corporate Park Dr., Ste. 101
White Plains, NY 10604
Ph: (914)948-2110
Fax: (914)948-0122
Co. E-mail: mgordon@westchesterny.org
URL: http://www.westchesterny.org
Contact: Dr. Marsha Gordon, President
Description: Promotes business and community development in Westchester-White Plains, NY area. **Founded:** 1904.

55104 ■ *Business Directory*
497 E Main St.
Malone, NY 12953
Ph: (518)483-3760
Free: 877-625-6631
Fax: (518)483-3172
URL: http://visitmalone.com
Contact: Hugh Hill, Executive Director
Released: Annual

55105 ■ *Business Directory*
674 Broadway
Massapequa, NY 11758
Ph: (516)541-1443
Fax: (516)541-8625
Co. E-mail: masscoc@aol.com
URL: http://www.massapequachamber.com
Contact: Patricia Orzano, President
Released: Annual

55106 ■ *Business Directory*
193 River St.
Saranac Lake, NY 12983
Ph: (518)891-1990
Free: 800-347-1992
Fax: (518)891-7042
Co. E-mail: info@saranaclake.com
URL: http://www.saranaclake.com
Contact: Katy Van Anden, Executive Director
Released: Periodic

55107 ■ *Business Directory*
PO Box 726
Schroon Lake, NY 12870-0726
Ph: (518)532-7675
Fax: (518)532-7675
Co. E-mail: chamber@schroonlakeregion.com
URL: http://www.schroonlake.org
Released: Annual

55108 ■ *Business Directory*
214 N Franklin St., Rte. 14
Watkins Glen, NY 14891
Ph: (607)535-4300
Free: 800-607-4552
Fax: (607)535-6243
Co. E-mail: info@watkinsglenchamber.com
URL: http://www.watkinsglenchamber.com
Contact: Rebekah LaMoreaux, President
Released: Annual **Price:** $25.

55109 ■ *Business Directory/Buyer's Guide*
1241 Coffeen St.
Watertown, NY 13601
Ph: (315)788-4400
Fax: (315)788-3369
Co. E-mail: chamber@watertownny.com
URL: http://www.watertownny.com
Contact: Lynne Ferris, Chairman of the Board
Released: Annual

55110 ■ *Business Line*
2050 Western Ave.
Star Plz., No. 109
Guilderland, NY 12084
Ph: (518)456-6611
Fax: (518)456-6690
Co. E-mail: info@guilderlandchamber.com
URL: http://www.guilderlandchamber.com
Contact: Katherine Burbank, Executive Director
Released: Quarterly

55111 ■ *Business and Professional Directory*
1514 Bellmore Ave.
North Bellmore, NY 11710
Ph: (516)679-1875
Fax: (516)409-0544
Co. E-mail: info@bellmorechamber.com
URL: http://bellmorechamber.com
Contact: Tom Valenti, President
Released: Annual **Price:** free.

55112 ■ *Buyer's Guide*
1 W Market St., Ste. 302
Corning, NY 14830
Ph: (607)936-4686
Free: 866-463-6264
Fax: (607)936-4685
Co. E-mail: info@corningny.com
URL: http://www.corningny.com
Contact: Denise K. Ackley, President
Released: Annual

55113 ■ Cairo Chamber of Commerce
PO Box 515
Cairo, NY 12413-0515

Ph: (518)622-3939
Co. E-mail: cairochamberofcommerce@verizon.net
URL: http://www.cairochamberofcommerce.com/page/page/5695726.htm
Contact: Claudia Zucker, President
Description: Promotes goodwill, publicity and development of the commercial welfare of the Cairo area; strives to create a better community spirit among all types of businesses through advancement of activities. **Founded:** 1967.

55114 ■ *Calendar of Events*
94 Montcalm St., Ste. 1
Ticonderoga, NY 12883
Ph: (518)585-6619
Fax: (518)585-9184
Co. E-mail: chamberinfo@ticonderogany.com
URL: http://www.ticonderogany.com
Contact: Matthew J. Courtright, Executive Director
Released: Monthly

55115 ■ Camden Area Chamber of Commerce (CACC)
PO Box 134
Camden, NY 13316
Ph: (315)245-5000
Co. E-mail: contact@camdennychamber.com
URL: http://www.camdennychamber.com
Contact: Ms. Beth Osteen, Executive Director
Description: Promotes business and community development in the Camden, AR area. **Publications:** *Chamber News* (Monthly).

55116 ■ Canandaigua Chamber of Commerce
113 S Main St.
Canandaigua, NY 14424-1903
Ph: (585)394-4400
Fax: (585)394-4546
Co. E-mail: chamber@canandaiguachamber.com
URL: http://www.canandaiguachamber.com
Contact: Alison Grems, President
Description: Promotes business and community development in Canandaigua, NY. **Publications:** *The Chamber Connection* (Monthly); *Canandaigua Area Community Guide & Business Directory* (Annual).

55117 ■ Canastota Chamber of Commerce
PO Box 206
Canastota, NY 13032
Ph: (315)697-3677
Co. E-mail: sales@ricksrags.com
URL: http://www.canastota.org
Description: Aims to promote and assist local businesses, support commercial development, and enhance the general business environment within the Greater Canastota, NY area.

55118 ■ Canton Chamber of Commerce (CCC)
PO Box 369
Canton, NY 13617
Ph: (315)386-8255
Co. E-mail: cantoncc@northnet.org
URL: http://www.cantonnewyork.us/chamber
Contact: Sally Hill, Executive Director
Description: Promotes business and community development in Canton, NY. Holds annual events including Dairy Princess Parade, Peter Rabbit in the Park, Phantoms in the Park, Farmers Market in Village Park, and Winterfest. **Founded:** 1965.

55119 ■ *Cape Vincent*
PO Box 482
Cape Vincent, NY 13618-0482
Ph: (315)654-2481
Co. E-mail: thecape@tds.net
URL: http://www.capevincent.org
Contact: Shelley Higgins, Executive Director
Released: Annual **Price:** free.

55120 ■ Cape Vincent Chamber of Commerce
PO Box 482
Cape Vincent, NY 13618-0482

Ph: (315)654-2481
Co. E-mail: thecape@tds.net
URL: http://www.capevincent.org
Contact: Shelley Higgins, Executive Director
Description: Promotes business, community development, and tourism in Cape Vincent, NY. Sponsors festivals, art shows, fishing contest, tennis tournaments, bike and running races. **Publications:** *Cape Vincent* (Annual); *What's Happening in CV, 13618* (Annual). **Awards:** Citizen of the Year (Annual); Community Achievement (Annual).

55121 ■ Carthage Area Chamber of Commerce
120 S Mechanic St.
Carthage, NY 13619
Ph: (315)493-3590
Co. E-mail: carthagechamber@centralny.twcbc.com
URL: http://www.carthageny.com
Contact: Gino M. Zando, President
Description: Strives to promote civic, economic, and social welfare in Carthage, NY area. **Founded:** 1921.

55122 ■ Cayuga County Chamber of Commerce (CCCOC)
2 State St.
Auburn, NY 13021
Ph: (315)252-7291
Fax: (315)255-3077
Co. E-mail: admin@cayugacountychamber.com
URL: http://www.cayugacountychamber.com
Contact: Andrew Fish, Executive Director
Description: Strives to improve economic vitality and quality of life in Cayuga County. **Founded:** 1908.

55123 ■ CenterState Corporation for Economic Opportunity (CenterState CEO)
572 S Salina St.
Syracuse, NY 13202-3320
Ph: (315)470-1800
Fax: (315)471-8545
Co. E-mail: ceo@centerstateceo.com
URL: http://www.centerstateceo.com
Contact: Rob Simpson, President
Description: Promotes business and community development in the Syracuse, NY area. **Founded:** 1889.

55124 ■ *The Chamber*
652 Main St.
East Aurora, NY 14052-1783
Ph: (716)652-8444
Free: 800-441-2881
Fax: (716)652-8384
Co. E-mail: eanycc@verizon.net
URL: http://www.eanycc.com
Contact: Gary D. Grote, Executive Director
Released: Monthly

55125 ■ *Chamber*
PO Box 576
Pittsford, NY 14534
Ph: (585)234-0308
Co. E-mail: info@pittsfordchamber.org
URL: http://pittsfordchamber.org
Contact: Dr. Shirley Joseph, President

55126 ■ *Chamber Action*
Radisson Hotel
200 Genesee St.
Utica, NY 13502
Ph: (315)724-3151
Fax: (315)724-3177
Co. E-mail: info@mvchamber.org
URL: http://www.mvchamber.org
Contact: Thomas Bashant, President
Released: Monthly

55127 ■ Chamber of Commerce of the Bellmores
1514 Bellmore Ave.
North Bellmore, NY 11710
Ph: (516)679-1875

Fax: (516)409-0544
Co. E-mail: info@bellmorechamber.com
URL: http://bellmorechamber.com
Contact: Tom Valenti, President
URL(s): www.bellmorechamber.com. **Description:** Promotes business and community development in Bellmore and North Bellmore, NY. **Founded:** 1948. **Publications:** *Chamber of Commerce of the Bellmores Business and Professional Directory*; *Business and Professional Directory* (Annual); *Business and Professional Directory* (Annual); *Chamber of Commerce of the Bellmores--Business and Professional Directory* (Annual); *Business and Professional Directory* (Annual). **Educational Activities:** General Membership Meeting (Monthly). **Awards:** Community Person of the Year Award (Annual); Scholarship (Annual); Small Business Person of the Year Award (Annual). **Telecommunication Services:** bellmorecc@aol.com.

55128 ■ Chamber of Commerce of the Borough of Queens
75-20 Astoria Blvd., Ste. 140
East Elmhurst, NY 11370-1131
Ph: (718)898-8500
Fax: (718)898-8599
Co. E-mail: info@queenschamber.org
URL: http://www.queenschamber.org
Contact: Carol Conslato, President
Description: Promotes business and community development in the Borough of Queens.

55129 ■ Chamber of Commerce of Greater Bay Shore
PO Box 5110
Bay Shore, NY 11706
Ph: (631)665-7003
Co. E-mail: bayshorecofcbi@optonline.net
URL: http://www.bayshorecommerce.com
Description: Promotes business and community development in the Greater Bay Shore, NY area. **Founded:** 1946.

55130 ■ Chamber of Commerce of the Greater Ronkonkoma
PO Box 2546
Ronkonkoma, NY 11779
Ph: (631)963-2796
Co. E-mail: info@ronkonkomachamber.com
URL: http://www.ronkonkomachamber.com/rcc
Contact: Steve Browne, President
Description: Promotes business and community development in Ronkonkoma, NY. **Telecommunication Services:** president@ronkonkomachamber.com.

55131 ■ Chamber of Commerce of the Massapequas
674 Broadway
Massapequa, NY 11758
Ph: (516)541-1443
Fax: (516)541-8625
Co. E-mail: masscoc@aol.com
URL: http://www.massapequachamber.com
Contact: Patricia Orzano, President
Description: Promotes business and community development in Massapequa, North Massapequa, and Massapequa Park, NY. **Founded:** 1948. **Publications:** *Business Directory* (Annual); *Meeting Notice*.

55132 ■ Chamber of Commerce of the Mastics and Shirley
PO Box 4
Mastic, NY 11950
Ph: (631)399-2228
Co. E-mail: admin@masticshirleychamber.com
URL: http://www.masticshirleychamber.com
Contact: Mark Smothergill, President
Description: Seeks to promote business and community development and enhance the relationship between local businesses and professionals with the public. **Founded:** 1951.

55133 ■ Chamber of Commerce of the Nyacks (CCN)
PO Box 677
Nyack, NY 10960-0677
Ph: (845)353-2221

Fax: (845)353-4204
Co. E-mail: info@nyack-ny.com
URL: http://www.nyack-ny.com
Contact: Bob Gundersen, President
Description: Promotes business and community development in the Nyacks, NY area. **Founded:** 1956. **Publications:** *The Nyack Guidebook* (Annual). **Educational Activities:** Chamber of Commerce of the Nyacks Board meeting (Bimonthly).

55134 ■ Chamber of Commerce of the Tonawandas
15 Webster St.
North Tonawanda, NY 14120
Ph: (716)692-5120
Fax: (716)692-1867
Co. E-mail: chamber@the-tonawandas.com
URL: http://www.the-tonawandas.com
Contact: Rhonda Ried, President
Description: Highlights and identifies problems, to help develop solutions to better its communities and business climate and to work toward creating the governmental and public support necessary to promote needed improvements and changes.

55135 ■ Chamber of Commerce of Ulster County
55 Albany Ave.
Kingston, NY 12401
Ph: (845)338-5100
Fax: (845)338-0968
Co. E-mail: info@ulsterchamber.org
URL: http://www.ulsterchamber.org
Contact: Ward Todd, President
Description: Promotes business and community development in Ulster County, NY. **Founded:** 1903.

55136 ■ Chamber of Commerce of the Willistons (CCW)
PO Box 207
Williston Park, NY 11596
Ph: (516)739-1943
Fax: (516)294-1444
Co. E-mail: rayhaller@hzinsurance.com
URL: http://www.chamberofthewillistons.org
Contact: Bobby Shannon, President
Description: Promotes business and community development in Williston, NY. Sponsors annual festival and competitions. Conducts charitable activities. **Founded:** 1949.

55137 ■ *Chamber Communicator*
121 Park St.
Tupper Lake, NY 12986
Ph: (518)359-3328
Free: 888-887-5253
Fax: (518)359-2434
Co. E-mail: chamber@tupper-lake.com
URL: http://tupper-lake.com/about/tupper-lake-chamber-of-commerce
Contact: David Tomberlin, President
Released: Quarterly

55138 ■ *Chamber Community*
4635 Millennium Dr.
Geneseo, NY 14454
Ph: (585)243-2222
Fax: (585)243-4824
Co. E-mail: coswald@frontiernet.net
URL: http://livingstoncountychamber.com
Contact: Cynthia Oswald, President
Released: Semiannual

55139 ■ *The Chamber Connection*
113 S Main St.
Canandaigua, NY 14424-1903
Ph: (585)394-4400
Fax: (585)394-4546
Co. E-mail: chamber@canandaiguachamber.com
URL: http://www.canandaiguachamber.com
Contact: Alison Grems, President
Released: Monthly

55140 ■ *Chamber Gazette*
6470 Rte. 20A, Ste. 2
Perry, NY 14530-9798
Ph: (585)237-0230
Free: 800-951-9774

Fax: (585)237-0231
Co. E-mail: info@wycochamber.org
URL: http://www.wycochamber.org
Contact: Laura Lane, President
Released: Bimonthly **Price:** free for members.

55141 ■ *Chamber Letter*
2 Church St.
Ossining, NY 10562
Ph: (914)941-0009
Fax: (914)941-0812
Co. E-mail: info@ossiningchamber.org
URL: http://www.ossiningchamber.org
Contact: Gayle Marchica, President
Released: Bimonthly

55142 ■ *Chamber News*
59 Albany St.
Cazenovia, NY 13035
Ph: (315)655-9243
Free: 888-218-6305
Co. E-mail: info@cazenovia.com
URL: http://www.cazenoviachamber.com
Contact: Gene Gissin, Chairperson
Released: Monthly

55143 ■ *Chamber News*
PO Box 134
Camden, NY 13316
Ph: (315)245-5000
Co. E-mail: contact@camdennychamber.com
URL: http://www.camdennychamber.com
Contact: Ms. Beth Osteen, Executive Director
Released: Monthly

55144 ■ *Chamber News*
114 N Main St.
Wellsville, NY 14895
Ph: (585)593-5080
Fax: (585)593-5088
Co. E-mail: s.havey@wellsvilleareachamber.com
URL: http://www.wellsvilleareachamber.com
Contact: Steven Havey, Executive Director
Released: Monthly

55145 ■ *Chamber News*
1 Bridge St., 2nd Fl.
Catskill, NY 12414
Ph: (518)943-4222
Fax: (518)943-1700
Co. E-mail: tmcnally@greenecounty-chamber.com
URL: http://www.greenecounty-chamber.com
Contact: Tracy McNally, Executive Director
Released: Quarterly

55146 ■ *Chamber Report*
15 Park Ave., Ste. 7
Clifton Park, NY 12065
Ph: (518)371-7748
Fax: (518)371-5025
Co. E-mail: info@southernsaratoga.org
URL: http://www.southernsaratoga.org
Contact: Pete Bardunias, President
Released: Annual

55147 ■ *Chamber Report*
1 Battery Park Plz., 5th Fl.
New York, NY 10004
Ph: (212)493-7400
Fax: (212)344-3344
Co. E-mail: info@pfnyc.org
URL: http://www.nycp.org
Contact: Kathryn S. Wylde, President
Released: Monthly

55148 ■ *The Chamber Report*
1 S Division St.
Peekskill, NY 10566
Ph: (914)737-3600
Fax: (914)737-0541
URL: http://www.hvgatewaychamber.com
Contact: Deborah Milone, Executive Director
Released: Quarterly

55149 ■ *Chamber Review*
4211 N Buffalo St., Ste. 14
Orchard Park, NY 14127-2401
Ph: (716)662-3366

Fax: (716)662-5946
Co. E-mail: opcc@orchardparkchamber.com
URL: http://www.orchardparkchamber.com
Contact: Nancy L. Conley, Executive Director
Released: Monthly

55150 ■ *The Chamber Room*
54 Main St.
Tarrytown, NY 10591
Ph: (914)631-1705
Fax: (914)206-5115
Co. E-mail: info@sleepyhollowchamber.com
URL: http://www.sleepyhollowchamber.com
Contact: John Sardy, Executive Director
Released: Monthly

55151 ■ Chamber of Southern Saratoga County
15 Park Ave., Ste. 7
Clifton Park, NY 12065
Ph: (518)371-7748
Fax: (518)371-5025
Co. E-mail: info@southernsaratoga.org
URL: http://www.southernsaratoga.org
Contact: Pete Bardunias, President
Description: Promotes business and community development in Southern Saratoga County, NY. Provides opportunities for networking, education, personal and professional development, and member benefits. **Founded:** 1967. **Publications:** *The Bottom Line* (Monthly); *Chamber Report* (Annual); *Economic Review.* **Educational Activities:** Business-After-Hours (Monthly). **Awards:** Business of the Year (Annual); Entrepreneur of the Year (Annual); Southern Star (Annual).

55152 ■ *Chamber Vision*
PO Box 310
Plattsburgh, NY 12901
Ph: (518)563-1000
Fax: (518)563-1028
Co. E-mail: info@northcountrychamber.com
URL: http://www.northcountrychamber.com
Contact: Garry Douglas, President
Released: Monthly

55153 ■ *Chamber Visions*
80 North Ave.
Owego, NY 13827
Ph: (607)687-2020
Fax: (607)687-9028
Co. E-mail: business@tiogachamber.com
URL: http://www.tiogachamber.com
Contact: Martha Sauerbrey, President
Released: Bimonthly

55154 ■ *ChamberGram*
904 E Shore Dr.
Ithaca, NY 14850-1026
Ph: (607)273-7080
Fax: (607)272-7617
Co. E-mail: jean@tompkinschamber.org
URL: http://www.tompkinschamber.org
Contact: Tom LiVigne, Chairman
Released: Monthly

55155 ■ *The Chambergram*
4635 Millennium Dr.
Geneseo, NY 14454
Ph: (585)243-2222
Fax: (585)243-4824
Co. E-mail: coswald@frontiernet.net
URL: http://livingstoncountychamber.com
Contact: Cynthia Oswald, President
Released: Monthly

55156 ■ *Chambergram*
5 1/2 Main St.
Delhi, NY 13753
Ph: (607)746-2281
Fax: (607)746-0541
Co. E-mail: info@delawarecounty.org
URL: http://www.delawarecounty.org
Contact: Mary Beth Silano, Executive Director
Released: Quarterly

55157 ■ *Chamberline*
210 E Main St.
Batavia, NY 14020

Ph: (585)343-7440
Free: 800-622-2686
Fax: (585)343-7487
Co. E-mail: chamber@geneseeny.com
URL: http://www.geneseeny.com
Contact: Lynn Freeman, President
Released: Monthly

55158 ■ *Chambernews*
459 Main St.
New Rochelle, NY 10801-6412
Ph: (914)632-5700
Fax: (914)632-0708
Co. E-mail: info@newrochellechamber.org
URL: http://newrochellechamber.org
Contact: Rosemary McLaughlin, President
Released: Monthly

55159 ■ *Chamberviews*
Nussbickel Bldg.
2582 S Ave., Rte. 9D
Wappingers Falls, NY 12590
Ph: (845)296-0001
Fax: (845)296-0006
Co. E-mail: annm@gsdcc.org
URL: http://www.gsdcc.org
Contact: Ann Meagher, President
Released: Monthly

55160 ■ Chautauqua County Chamber of Commerce (CCCC)
10785 Bennett Rd.
Dunkirk, NY 14048
Ph: (716)366-6200
Fax: (716)366-4276
Co. E-mail: cccc@chautauquachamber.org
URL: http://www.chautauquachamber.org
Contact: Todd Tranum, President
Description: Aims to provide strong and effective regional leadership and representation which will unify and promote the interests of Chautauqua County. **Founded:** 2000. **Publications:** *The Voice* (Monthly); *Chautauqua Chamber of Commerce--Membership Directory & Buyer's Guide* (Annual).

55161 ■ Cheektowaga Chamber of Commerce (CCC)
Apple Tree Business Park
2875 Union Rd., Ste. 50
Cheektowaga, NY 14227
Ph: (716)684-5838
Fax: (716)684-5571
Co. E-mail: chamber@cheektowaga.org
URL: http://www.cheektowaga.org
Contact: Debra S. Liegl, President
Description: Promotes business and community development in Cheektowaga, NY. Offers health insurance for small businesses. Sponsors Food Fest. **Founded:** 1939.

55162 ■ Chemung County Chamber of Commerce
400 E Church St.
Elmira, NY 14901-2803
Ph: (607)734-5137
Fax: (607)734-4490
Co. E-mail: info@chemungchamber.org
URL: http://www.chemungchamber.org
Contact: Kevin D. Keeley, President
Description: Promotes business and community development in Chemung County, NY. **Publications:** *Today's Chamber* (Monthly); *Chemung County Chamber of Commerce--Community Profile and Membership Directory.*

55163 ■ Clarence Chamber of Commerce
8899 Main St., Ste. 4
Clarence, NY 14031-0177
Ph: (716)631-3888
Fax: (716)631-3946
Co. E-mail: info@clarence.org
URL: http://www.clarence.org
Contact: Judy Sirianni, President
Description: Aims to support and strengthen the businesses in Clarence, NY area. **Founded:** 1954. **Publications:** *Connections* (Monthly). **Awards:** Busi-

ness of the Year (Annual); Citizen of the Year (Annual); Organization of the Year (Annual); Young Leader of the Year (Annual).

55164 ■ *Clayton Vacation Guide*
517 Riverside Dr.
Clayton, NY 13624
Ph: (315)686-3771
Free: 800-252-9806
Fax: (315)686-5564
Co. E-mail: info@1000islands-clayton.com
URL: http://www.1000islands-clayton.com
Contact: Karen Goetz, Executive Director
Released: Annual

55165 ■ Clifton Springs Area Chamber of Commerce (CSCOC)
PO Box 86
Clifton Springs, NY 14432
Ph: (315)462-8200
Co. E-mail: info@cliftonspringschamber.com
URL: http://www.cliftonspringschamber.com
Contact: Jeff Criblear, President
Description: Promotes business and community development in Clifton Springs, NY.

55166 ■ Clinton Chamber of Commerce (CCC)
c/o Ferris J. Betrus, Exec. VP
PO Box 142
Clinton, NY 13323-0142
Ph: (315)853-1735
Co. E-mail: info@clintonnychamber.org
URL: http://www.clintonnychamber.org
Contact: Ferris J. Betrus, Executive Vice President
Description: Promotes business and community development in Clinton, NY.

55167 ■ *Clubs and Organization Listings*
1241 Coffeen St.
Watertown, NY 13601
Ph: (315)788-4400
Fax: (315)788-3369
Co. E-mail: chamber@watertownny.com
URL: http://www.watertownny.com
Contact: Lynne Ferris, Chairman of the Board
Released: Annual **Price:** free.

55168 ■ *Clubs and Organizations List*
199 Van Buren St.
Newark, NY 14513
Ph: (315)331-2705
Fax: (315)331-4602
Co. E-mail: newarkchamber@rochester.rr.com
URL: http://newarknychamber.org
Contact: Tammra Schiller, President
Released: 10/year **Price:** $15.

55169 ■ Cold Spring - Garrison Area Chamber of Commerce
PO Box 36
Cold Spring, NY 10516
Ph: (845)265-3200
Co. E-mail: chamberdirector@gmail.com
URL: http://www.hvgateway.com/CHAMBER.HTM
Contact: Nat Prentice, President
Description: Promotes business and community development in Cold Spring, NY area.

55170 ■ Colonie Chamber of Commerce
950 New Loudon Rd.
Latham, NY 12110
Ph: (518)785-6995
Fax: (518)785-7173
Co. E-mail: info@coloniechamber.org
URL: http://www.coloniechamber.org
Contact: Tom Nolte, President
Description: Offers members' health insurance, dental insurance, cellular phone service and other discounted services. Hosts monthly networking mixers, a golf tournament, Office Appreciation Luncheon on National Secretaries Day and annual dinner. **Founded:** 1985. **Publications:** *Inside Colonie* (Quarterly).

55171 ■ Columbia County Chamber of Commerce
1 N Front St.
Hudson, NY 12534-2001

Ph: (518)828-4417
Fax: (518)822-9539
Co. E-mail: mail@columbiachamber-ny.com
URL: http://www.columbiachamber-ny.com
Contact: David B. Colby, President
Description: Promotes tourism and economic development in Columbia County, NY. Provides health insurance. Sponsors on-the-job training, seminars, and other events. **Founded:** 1978.

55172 ■ *Commerce Quotes*
Vantage Ctre.
6311 Inducon Corporate Dr.
Sanborn, NY 14132
Ph: (716)285-9141
Fax: (716)285-0941
Co. E-mail: dalteriobrennen@niagarachamber.org
URL: http://www.niagarachamber.org
Contact: Deanna Alterio Brennen, President
Released: Monthly

55173 ■ *Community Audit*
1241 Coffeen St.
Watertown, NY 13601
Ph: (315)788-4400
Fax: (315)788-3369
Co. E-mail: chamber@watertownny.com
URL: http://www.watertownny.com
Contact: Lynne Ferris, Chairman of the Board
Released: Periodic

55174 ■ *Community Economic Profile*
120 N Union St.
Olean, NY 14760
Ph: (716)372-4433
Fax: (716)372-7912
Co. E-mail: info@oleanny.com
URL: http://www.oleanny.com/2
Contact: Larry Sorokes, President

55175 ■ *Community Profile*
199 Van Buren St.
Newark, NY 14513
Ph: (315)331-2705
Fax: (315)331-4602
Co. E-mail: newarkchamber@rochester.rr.com
URL: http://newarknychamber.org
Contact: Tammra Schiller, President

55176 ■ *Connections*
8899 Main St., Ste. 4
Clarence, NY 14031-0177
Ph: (716)631-3888
Fax: (716)631-3946
Co. E-mail: info@clarence.org
URL: http://www.clarence.org
Contact: Judy Sirianni, President
Released: Monthly **Price:** included in membership dues.

55177 ■ Cooperstown Chamber of Commerce (CCC)
31 Chestnut St.
Cooperstown, NY 13326
Ph: (607)547-9983
Fax: (607)547-6006
Co. E-mail: info@cooperstownchamber.org
URL: http://www.cooperstownchamber.org
Contact: Susan O'Handley, Executive Director
Description: Promotes business and community development in Cooperstown, NY. Provides tourist information. **Founded:** 1917. **Publications:** *Cooperstown Chamber Visitors Guide.*

55178 ■ *Cooperstown Chamber Visitors Guide*
31 Chestnut St.
Cooperstown, NY 13326
Ph: (607)547-9983
Fax: (607)547-6006
Co. E-mail: info1@cooperstownchamber.org
URL: http://www.cooperstownchamber.org
Contact: Susan O'Handley, Executive Director

55179 ■ Corning Area Chamber of Commerce (CACC)
1 W Market St., Ste. 302
Corning, NY 14830
Ph: (607)936-4686

Free: 866-463-6264
Fax: (607)936-4685
Co. E-mail: info@corningny.com
URL: http://www.corningny.com
Contact: Denise K. Ackley, President
Description: Promotes business, cultural, community development, and tourism in the Corning, NY area. **Founded:** 1914. **Publications:** *Buyer's Guide* (Annual); *The Link* (Monthly).

55180 ■ Cortland County Chamber of Commerce
37 Church St.
Cortland, NY 13045
Ph: (607)756-2814
Co. E-mail: info@cortlandchamber.com
URL: http://www.cortlandchamber.com
Contact: Bob Haight, Executive Director
Description: Aims to promote the free enterprise system in Cortland, NY area. **Founded:** 1903. **Telecommunication Services:** bob@cortlandchamber.com.

55181 ■ Council of Dedicated Merchants Chamber of Commerce (CDM)
PO Box 512
Miller Place, NY 11764
Ph: (631)821-1313
Co. E-mail: cdmpresident@yahoo.com
URL: http://www.cdmlongisland.com
Contact: Tom Ianniello, President
Description: Represents 225 small business locations within the hamlets of Mt. Sinai, Miller Place, Sound Beach and Rocky Point. Works to bring business and community closer. Promotes the general welfare of the business community through educational programs, tourism, economic development and community enrichment events. Holds bi-monthly general membership meeting, workshops, and festivals. **Founded:** 1970. **Publications:** *Business to Business* (Periodic). **Awards:** Business Advancement Scholarships (Annual).

55182 ■ *Country Travel Guide*
214 N Franklin St., Rte. 14
Watkins Glen, NY 14891
Ph: (607)535-4300
Free: 800-607-4552
Fax: (607)535-6243
Co. E-mail: info@watkinsglenchamber.com
URL: http://www.watkinsglenchamber.com
Contact: Rebekah LaMoreaux, President
Released: Periodic

55183 ■ Dansville Chamber of Commerce (DCC)
126 Main St.
Dansville, NY 14437-0105
Ph: (585)335-6920
Free: 800-949-0174
Fax: (585)335-6296
Co. E-mail: dansvillechamber@hotmail.com
URL: http://www.dansvilleny.net
Contact: William Bacon, President
Description: Works to build and sustain a vibrant economy and a superior quality of life in the community. Serves as an umbrella organization that also includes the NY State Festival of Balloons, the Dansville Economic Development Corporation and the Dansville Business Association. **Founded:** 1795. **Awards:** Outstanding Citizen of the Year (Annual).

55184 ■ Delaware County Chamber of Commerce
5 1/2 Main St.
Delhi, NY 13753
Ph: (607)746-2281
Fax: (607)746-3571
Co. E-mail: info@delawarecounty.org
URL: http://www.delawarecounty.org
Contact: Mary Beth Silano, Executive Director
Description: Seeks to provide leadership to stimulate and support a prosperous economy for the Delaware County, NY area. **Founded:** 1963. **Publications:** *Chambergram* (Quarterly); *Member Update* (Quarterly).

55185 ■ Deposit Chamber of Commerce
PO Box 222
Deposit, NY 13754
Ph: (607)467-1436
Co. E-mail: jdunham@echoes.net
URL: http://www.depositchamber.com
Contact: Nick Barone, President
Description: Promotes business and community development in the Deposit, NY area. Sponsors festivals and hall of fame; presents business and service awards. Operates county welcome center and tourism development.

55186 ■ Dutchess County Regional Chamber of Commerce
1 Civic Center Plz., Ste. 400
Poughkeepsie, NY 12601
Ph: (845)454-1700
Fax: (845)454-1702
Co. E-mail: charlesnorth@dcrcoc.org
URL: http://www.dutchesscountyregionalchamber.org
Contact: Charles S. North, President
Description: Promotes economical growth for business and community development in the Dutchess County area. **Founded:** 1907. **Publications:** *The Bottom Line* (Monthly); *Guide to Government*; *Bed and Breakfast Guide*.

55187 ■ East Hampton Chamber of Commerce (EHCC)
42 Gingerbread Ln.
East Hampton, NY 11937
Ph: (631)324-0362
Co. E-mail: info@easthamptonchamber.com
URL: http://easthamptonchamber.com
Description: Promotes business and community development in East Hampton, NY. **Founded:** 1966.

55188 ■ Eastchester - Tuckahoe Chamber of Commerce
Tuckahoe Village Hall
65 Main St., Ste. 202
Tuckahoe, NY 10707
Ph: (914)779-7344
Co. E-mail: cetcoc@aol.com
URL: http://www.eastchestertuckahoechamberofcommerce.com/c
Contact: Judy Fix, Co-President

55189 ■ *Economic Review*
15 Park Ave., Ste. 7
Clifton Park, NY 12065
Ph: (518)371-7748
Fax: (518)371-5025
Co. E-mail: info@southernsaratoga.org
URL: http://www.southernsaratoga.org
Contact: Pete Bardunias, President

55190 ■ Ellenville - Wawarsing Chamber of Commerce
PO Box 227
Ellenville, NY 12428
Ph: (845)647-4620
Co. E-mail: info@ewcoc.com
URL: http://www.ewcoc.com/Pages/default.aspx
Contact: Dr. Mark Craft, President
Description: Promotes business and community development in Town of Wawarsing, Ulster County, NY. **Founded:** 1953. **Publications:** *Membership Brochure* (Annual). **Educational Activities:** Business Symposium (Annual).

55191 ■ Ellicottville Chamber of Commerce
PO Box 456
Ellicottville, NY 14731
Free: 800-349-9099
Fax: (716)699-5636
Co. E-mail: info@ellicottvillny.com
URL: http://www.ellicottvilleny.com
Contact: Brian McFadden, Executive Director
Description: Promotes economic development in Ellicottville, NY area.

55192 ■ *Enterprise*
1375 Broadway, 3rd Fl.
New York, NY 10018
Ph: (212)479-7772

Fax: (212)473-8074
Co. E-mail: info@manhattancc.org
URL: http://www.manhattancc.org/common/11001/default.cfm?clientID=11001
Contact: Nancy Ploeger, President
Released: Quarterly **Price:** free.

55193 ■ *Escape to Historic Salamanca*
26 Main St.
Salamanca, NY 14779-1516
Ph: (716)945-2034
Fax: (716)945-9143
Co. E-mail: info@salamancachamber.org
URL: http://www.salamancachamber.org
Contact: Jayne L. Fenton, President
Released: Quarterly **Price:** free.

55194 ■ Fair Haven Area Chamber of Commerce
PO Box 13
Fair Haven, NY 13064
Ph: (315)947-6037
Fax: (866)588-4767
Co. E-mail: fairhaveninfo@fairhavenny.com
URL: http://www.fairhavenny.com
Contact: Dan Larson, President
Description: Promotes business and community development in the Fair Haven, NY area. Sponsors Oktoberfest, Fourth of July festival and Arts and Crafts Fair. **Founded:** 1970.

55195 ■ Farmington Chamber of Commerce
c/o Rose M. Kleman, VP
1000 County Rd., No. 8
Farmington, NY 14425
Ph: (315)986-8182
Fax: (315)986-4377
Co. E-mail: cl5827@aol.com
URL: http://www.farmingtoncofc.com
Contact: Rose M. Kleman, Vice President

55196 ■ *FOCUS*
c/o Kathie Gullo, Exec. Dir.
950A Union Rd., Ste. 5
West Seneca, NY 14224
Ph: (716)674-4900
Co. E-mail: cdillchamber@westseneca.org
URL: http://www.westseneca.org
Contact: Kathie Gullo, Executive Director
Released: Monthly

55197 ■ *The Focus*
665 Main St., Ste. 200
Buffalo, NY 14203
Ph: (716)852-7100
Free: 800-241-0474
Fax: (716)852-2761
Co. E-mail: membership@thepartnership.org
URL: http://www.thepartnership.org
Contact: Donald K. Boswell, President
Released: Bimonthly **Price:** free.

55198 ■ Fort Edward Chamber of Commerce
PO Box 267
Fort Edward, NY 12828
Ph: (518)747-3000
Co. E-mail: chamber@fortedwardchamber.org
URL: http://www.fortedwardchamber.org
Contact: Larry P. Moffitt, President

55199 ■ Fredonia Chamber of Commerce (FCC)
5 E Main St.
Fredonia, NY 14063
Ph: (716)679-1565
Fax: (716)672-5240
Co. E-mail: fredcham@netsync.net
URL: http://www.fredoniachamber.org
Description: Promotes business and community development in Fredonia, NY.

55200 ■ *Friday Fax*
1 Computer Dr. S
Albany, NY 12205-1631
Ph: (518)431-1400

Fax: (518)431-1402
Co. E-mail: info@acchamber.org
URL: http://acchamber.org
Contact: Mark Eagan, President
Released: Weekly

55201 ■ Fulton County Regional Chamber of Commerce and Industry (FCRCCI)
2 N Main St.
Gloversville, NY 12078
Ph: (518)725-0641
Free: 800-676-3858
Fax: (518)725-0643
Co. E-mail: info@fultoncountyny.org
URL: http://www.fultoncountyny.org
Contact: Mark Kilmer, President (Acting)
Description: Promotes business and community development in the Fulton County, NY area. Sponsors winter festival, First Night, and home and business expo. Holds seminars. **Founded:** 1919. **Publications:** *Newsline* (Monthly).

55202 ■ Garden City Chamber of Commerce
230 Seventh St.
Garden City, NY 11530
Ph: (516)746-7724
Fax: (516)746-7725
Co. E-mail: gcchamber@verizon.net
URL: http://www.gardencitychamber.org
Contact: Althea Robinson, Executive Director
Description: Promotes business and community development in Garden City, NY. **Founded:** 1926.

55203 ■ Genesee County Chamber of Commerce
210 E Main St.
Batavia, NY 14020
Ph: (585)343-7440
Free: 800-622-2686
Fax: (585)343-7487
Co. E-mail: chamber@geneseeny.com
URL: http://www.geneseeny.com
Contact: Lynn Freeman, President
Description: Strives to lead in the pursuit of creating an environment for business success that will enhance the quality of life for the citizens of Genesee County. Sponsors the Wing Ding Weekend Block Party, Annual Business/Citizen Awards Dinner, Annual Golf Outing and other community events. Official tourism promotion agency for Genesee County. **Founded:** 1972. **Publications:** *Chamberline* (Monthly); *Organization Directory*.

55204 ■ Geneva Area Chamber of Commerce
PO Box 587
Geneva, NY 14456
Ph: (315)789-1776
Fax: (315)789-3993
Co. E-mail: info@genevany.com
URL: http://www.genevany.com
Contact: Rob Gladden, President
Description: Promotes business and community development in the Geneva, NY area. **Founded:** 1902. **Publications:** *Business to Business* (Monthly).

55205 ■ Glen Cove Chamber of Commerce
19 Village Sq.
Glen Cove, NY 11542
Ph: (516)676-6666
Fax: (516)676-5490
Co. E-mail: info@glencovechamber.org
URL: http://www.glencovechamber.org
Contact: Mary Stanco, President
Description: Promotes business and community development in Glen Cove, NY. **Founded:** 1925.

55206 ■ *Good News Travel Fast*
PO Box 272
Lake George, NY 12845-0272
Ph: (518)668-5755
Free: 800-705-0059
Fax: (518)668-4286
Co. E-mail: info@lakegeorgechamber.com
URL: http://www.lakegeorgechamber.com
Contact: Kevin Rosa, President
Released: Monthly

55207 ■ Goshen Chamber of Commerce (GCC)
232 S Main St.
Goshen, IN 46526-3723
Ph: (574)533-2102
Free: 800-307-4204
Fax: (574)533-2103
Co. E-mail: goshenchamber@goshen.org
URL: http://www.goshen.org
Contact: Raymond J. Quattrini, President
URL(s): www.goshennychamber.com. **Description:** Promotes business and community development in Goshen, IN. **Publications:** *Image.* **Telecommunication Services:** info@goshennychamber.com.

55208 ■ Gowanda Area Chamber of Commerce
PO Box 45
Gowanda, NY 14070-0045
Ph: (716)532-2834
URL: http://gowanda-chamber.com
Contact: Jennine Sauriol, President
URL(s): www.gowandanychamber.org. **Description:** Promotes a healthy local economy within Gowanda area by influencing business success, public policy and community development.

55209 ■ Grand Island Chamber of Commerce (GICC)
2257 Grand Island Blvd.
Grand Island, NY 14072
Ph: (716)773-3651
Fax: (716)773-3316
Co. E-mail: info@gichamber.org
URL: http://www.gichamber.org
Contact: Eric Fiebelkorn, President
Description: Promotes business and community development in Grand Island, NY. Sponsors Citizen of the Year award and bicycle race. **Founded:** 1948. **Publications:** *Telephone Directory* (Periodic).

55210 ■ Great Neck Chamber of Commerce
PO Box 220432
Great Neck, NY 11022
Ph: (516)487-2000
Co. E-mail: greatneckinfo@gmail.com
URL: http://www.greatneckchamber.org
Contact: Hooshang Nematzadeh, President
Description: Promotes business and community development in Great Neck, NY.

55211 ■ Greater Baldwinsville Chamber of Commerce
27 Water St., 2nd Fl.
Baldwinsville, NY 13027
Ph: (315)638-0550
Co. E-mail: baldwinsvillechamber@gmail.com
URL: http://www.b-ville.com/content/greater-baldwinsville-chamber-commerce
Contact: Anthony Saraceni, President
Description: Promotes business and community development in the Baldwinsville, NY area. **Founded:** 1961. **Publications:** *News and Views* (Monthly). **Awards:** Business Person of the Year (Annual); Man Volunteer of the Year (Annual); Woman Volunteer of the Year (Annual).

55212 ■ Greater Bath Area Chamber of Commerce (GBACC)
10 Pulteney Sq. W
Bath, NY 14810
Ph: (607)776-7122
Fax: (607)776-7122
Co. E-mail: chamber@bathnychamber.com
URL: http://www.bathnychamber.com
Contact: Bill Caudill, President
Description: Promotes business and community development in the Bath, NY area. **Founded:** 1924. **Publications:** *Greater Bath Area Chamber of Commerce--Business Directory* (Quadrennial). **Telecommunication Services:** email@bathnychamber.com.

55213 ■ Greater Binghamton Chamber of Commerce
PO Box 995
Binghamton, NY 13902-0995
Ph: (607)772-8860

Fax: (607)772-4513
Co. E-mail: chamber@binghamtonchamber.com
URL: http://www.binghamtonchamber.com
Contact: Lou Santoni, President
Description: Promotes business and community development in Binghamton, NY. **Founded:** 1964. **Subscriptions:** articles books. **Publications:** *Greater Binghamton Travel Guide* (Annual); *Planners Guide* (Annual); *Quality of Life Resource Guide* (Annual). **Awards:** Chamber Volunteer of the Year (Annual); Civic Leader of the Year (Annual); Community Advocate of the Year (Annual); Project Pride Award (Annual); Small Business Advocate of the Year (Annual); Small Business Person of the Year (Annual).

55214 ■ *Greater Binghamton Travel Guide*
PO Box 995
Binghamton, NY 13902-0995
Ph: (607)772-8860
Fax: (607)772-4513
Co. E-mail: chamber@binghamtonchamber.com
URL: http://www.binghamtonchamber.com
Contact: Lou Santoni, President
Released: Annual

55215 ■ Greater Brockport Chamber of Commerce (GBCC)
PO Box 119
Brockport, NY 14420
Ph: (585)234-1512
URL: http://www.brockportchamber.org
Contact: Elaine Bader, President
Description: Promotes business and community development in the Brockport, NY area. Conducts charitable activities. **Founded:** 1972.

55216 ■ Greater Cazenovia Area Chamber of Commerce
59 Albany St.
Cazenovia, NY 13035
Ph: (315)655-9243
Free: 888-218-6305
Co. E-mail: info@cazenovia.com
URL: http://www.cazenoviachamber.com
Contact: Gene Gissin, Chairperson
Description: Works to advance and maintain a healthy economic environment in Greater Cazenovia area. **Founded:** 1997. **Publications:** *Chamber News* (Monthly). **Educational Activities:** Membership Meeting (Monthly).

55217 ■ Greater East Aurora Chamber of Commerce (GEACC)
652 Main St.
East Aurora, NY 14052-1783
Ph: (716)652-8444
Free: 800-441-2881
Fax: (716)652-8384
Co. E-mail: eanycc@verizon.net
URL: http://www.eanycc.com
Contact: Gary D. Grote, Executive Director
Description: Promotes business and community development in the East Aurora, NY area. Sponsors area events, including: Roycroft Festival of Arts and Crafts; Toyfest; Business Expo. **Founded:** 1945. **Publications:** *The Chamber* (Monthly). **Educational Activities:** Business Awards (Annual).

55218 ■ Greater Gouverneur Chamber of Commerce
214 E Main St.
Gouverneur, NY 13642
Ph: (315)287-0331
Fax: (315)287-3694
URL: http://www.gouverneurchamber.net
Contact: Donna M. Lawrence, Executive Director
Description: Promotes business and community development in Gouverneur, NY. Sponsors flea market, farmer's market, and other social and promotional events. **Founded:** 1908.

55219 ■ Greater Greenwich Chamber of Commerce (GGCC)
6 Academy St.
Greenwich, NY 12834-1002
Ph: (518)692-7979

Fax: (518)692-7979
Co. E-mail: info@greenwichchamber.org
URL: http://www.greenwichchamber.org
Contact: Renee Bouplon, President
Description: Promotes business and community development in Greenwich, NY.

55220 ■ Greater Harlem Chamber of Commerce (GHCC)
200A W 136th St.
New York, NY 10030
Ph: (212)862-7200
Free: 877-427-5364
Fax: (212)862-8745
Co. E-mail: info@harlemdiscover.com
URL: http://greaterharlemchamber.com
Contact: Lloyd A. Williams, President
Description: Promotes business and community development in the Greater Harlem, NY area. **Founded:** 1896. **Telecommunication Services:** lwilliams@harlemdiscover.com.

55221 ■ Greater Liverpool Chamber of Commerce
314 2nd St.
Liverpool, NY 13088
Ph: (315)457-3895
Fax: (315)234-3227
Co. E-mail: chamber@liverpoolchamber.com
URL: http://www.liverpoolchamber.com
Contact: Lucretia M. Hudzinski, Executive Director
Description: Promotes business and community development in the Liverpool, NY area.

55222 ■ Greater Mahopac-Carmel Chamber of Commerce
953 South Lake Blvd.
Mahopac, NY 10541-0160
Ph: (845)628-5553
Fax: (845)628-5962
Co. E-mail: info@mahopaccarmelchamber.com
URL: http://www.mahopaccarmelonline.com
Contact: Jennifer Maher, President
Description: Seeks to promote business and community development and enhance the relationship between local businesses and professionals with the public. **Founded:** 1948.

55223 ■ Greater Massena Chamber of Commerce
50 Main St.
Massena, NY 13662
Ph: (315)769-3525
Fax: (315)769-5295
Co. E-mail: chamber@massenachamber.com
URL: http://www.massenachamber.com
Contact: Michael Gleason, Executive Director
Description: Promotes business and community development in Massena, NY. Holds monthly board meeting. **Founded:** 1931.

55224 ■ Greater New York Chamber of Commerce
20 W 44th St., 4 Fl.
New York, NY 10036
Ph: (212)686-7220
Fax: (212)686-7232
Co. E-mail: info@chamber.com
URL: http://www.ny-chamber.com
Contact: Mark S. Jaffe, President
Description: Seeks to promote business and community development and enhance the relationship between local businesses and professionals with the public.

55225 ■ Greater Newark Chamber of Commerce
199 Van Buren St.
Newark, NY 14513
Ph: (315)331-2705
Fax: (315)331-4602
Co. E-mail: newarkchamber@rochester.rr.com
URL: http://newarknychamber.org
Contact: Tammra Schiller, President
Description: Represents business and community to further the interests of business within the community. Acts as a clearinghouse of business and community information; interacts with government; sponsors

community events; and works with economic development. **Founded:** 1924. **Publications:** *Clubs and Organizations List* (10/year); *Community Profile*; *Industry List* (Annual). **Awards:** Business of the Year (Annual).

55226 ■ Greater Ogdensburg Chamber of Commerce
330 Ford St.
Ogdensburg, NY 13669
Ph: (315)393-3620
Fax: (315)393-1380
Co. E-mail: chamber@gisco.net
URL: http://www.ogdensburgny.com
Contact: Kevin McDonough, President
Description: Seeks to promote business and community development and enhance the relationship between local businesses and professionals with the public.

55227 ■ Greater Olean Area Chamber of Commerce (GOACC)
120 N Union St.
Olean, NY 14760
Ph: (716)372-4433
Fax: (716)372-7912
Co. E-mail: info@oleanny.com
URL: http://www.oleanny.com/2
Contact: Larry Sorokes, President
Description: Provide business and community development assistance, regional tourism information, and membership benefits. **Founded:** 1906. **Publications:** *Community Economic Profile*. **Telecommunication Services:** tourism@oleanny.com.

55228 ■ Greater Oneida Chamber of Commerce
136 Lenox Ave.
Oneida, NY 13421
Ph: (315)363-4300
Fax: (315)361-4558
Co. E-mail: oneidachamber@cnymail.com
URL: http://oneidachamberny.org
Contact: Henry J. Leo, President
Description: Promotes business and community development in Oneida, NY area.

55229 ■ Greater Ossining Chamber of Commerce
2 Church St.
Ossining, NY 10562
Ph: (914)941-0009
Fax: (914)941-0812
Co. E-mail: info@ossiningchamber.org
URL: http://www.ossiningchamber.org
Contact: Gayle Marchica, President
Description: Promotes business and community development in the Ossining, NY area. Sponsors village fair and holiday activities, business expos, and educational programs. Produces monthly television show. **Founded:** 1945. **Publications:** *Chamber Letter* (Bimonthly).

55230 ■ Greater Oswego Chamber of Commerce
44 E Bridge St.
Oswego, NY 13126
Ph: (315)343-7681
Fax: (315)342-0831
Co. E-mail: gocc@oswegofultonchamber.com
URL: http://oswegochamber.com
Contact: Nick Canale, Jr., President
Description: Promotes business and community development in the Oswego, NY area. **Founded:** 1915.

55231 ■ Greater Patchogue Chamber of Commerce
15 N Ocean Ave.
Patchogue, NY 11772
Ph: (631)207-1000
Fax: (631)475-1599
Co. E-mail: info@patchoguechamber.com
URL: http://www.patchoguechamber.com
Contact: Jacqueline Hensley, President
Description: Promotes business and community development in the Patchogue, NY area. Provides transportation, lodging, and recreation information for the Suffolk county and surrounding area. **Scope:** lo-

cal information, history. **Founded:** 1923. **Subscriptions:** 100. **Publications:** *Patchogue Chamber Business Letter* (Monthly).

55232 ■ Greater Port Jefferson Chamber of Commerce
118 W Broadway
Port Jefferson, NY 11777
Ph: (631)473-1414
Fax: (631)474-4540
Co. E-mail: info@portjeffchamber.com
URL: http://www.portjeffchamber.com
Contact: Suzanne Velazquez, President
Description: Promotes business and community development in the Port Jefferson, NY area.

55233 ■ Greater Smithtown Chamber of Commerce
PO Box 1216
Smithtown, NY 11787
Ph: (631)979-8069
Fax: (631)979-2206
Co. E-mail: info@smithtownchamber.com
URL: http://www.smithtownchamber.org
Contact: Barbara Franco, Executive Director
Description: Promotes business and community development in Smithtown, NY area.

55234 ■ Greater Southern Dutchess Chamber of Commerce (GSDCC)
Nussbickel Bldg.
2582 S Ave., Rte. 9D
Wappingers Falls, NY 12590
Ph: (845)296-0001
Fax: (845)296-0006
Co. E-mail: annm@gsdcc.org
URL: http://www.gsdcc.org
Contact: Ann Meagher, President
Description: Promotes business, community development, and tourism in the Beacon, East Fishkill, Fishkill, and Wappingers Falls, NY area. Issues publications. **Founded:** 1946. **Publications:** *Chamberviews* (Monthly).

55235 ■ Greater Warsaw Chamber of Commerce
PO Box 221
Warsaw, NY 14569
Ph: (585)786-3730
Co. E-mail: info@warsawchamber.com
URL: http://www.warsawchamber.com
Contact: Becky Ryan, President
Description: Promotes business and community development in Warsaw, NY.

55236 ■ Greater Watertown - North Country Chamber of Commerce (GWNC)
1241 Coffeen St.
Watertown, NY 13601
Ph: (315)788-4400
Fax: (315)788-3369
Co. E-mail: chamber@watertownny.com
URL: http://www.watertownny.com
Contact: Lynne Ferris, Chairman of the Board
Description: Promotes business, community development, and tourism in the Jefferson County, NY area. **Founded:** 1903. **Publications:** *Community Audit* (Periodic); *Business Directory/Buyer's Guide* (Annual); *Clubs and Organization Listings* (Annual); *News and Views* (Monthly). **Educational Activities:** Business Fair (Annual).

55237 ■ Greater Westhampton Chamber of Commerce
PO Box 1228
Westhampton Beach, NY 11978
Ph: (631)288-3337
Fax: (631)288-3322
Co. E-mail: info@whbcc.org
URL: http://www.whbcc.com
Contact: John David, President
Description: Organized for the purpose of advancing business relations in the communities of Westhampton, Westhampton Beach, Quiogue, Quogue, East Quogue and Remsenburg-Speonk. Works to improve business within this area, as well as the general economic and cultural welfare of the community. **Founded:** 1948.

55238 ■ Greene County Chamber of Commerce (GCCC)
1 Bridge St., 2nd Fl.
Catskill, NY 12414
Ph: (518)943-4222
Fax: (518)943-1700
Co. E-mail: tmcnally@greenecounty-chamber.com
URL: http://www.greenecounty-chamber.com
Contact: Tracy McNally, Executive Director
Description: Advances the general welfare and prosperity of Greene County by providing a unified voice and effective network for business, civic, cultural, and educational organizations. Helps strengthen and improve the decisions made by local chambers, business, local government and community organizations by providing access to trends, resources and high level expertise from county wide, regional and statewide organizations. **Founded:** 1998. **Publications:** *Chamber News* (Quarterly). **Awards:** Greene County Business Man and Woman of the Year (Annual).

55239 ■ Greenvale Chamber of Commerce
PO Box 123
Greenvale, NY 11548
Ph: (516)484-2550
URL: http://www.greenvalechamber.com
Contact: Michael Lucarelli, Secretary
Description: Promotes business and community development in Greenvale, NY.

55240 ■ Greenwich Village-Chelsea Chamber of Commerce (GVCCC)
37 W 17th St., 2nd Fl.
New York, NY 10011
Ph: (646)470-1773
Fax: (212)924-0714
Co. E-mail: info@villagechamber.com
URL: http://www.villagechelsea.com
Contact: Mr. Tony Juliano, President
Description: Promotes business and community development in Greenwich Village-Chelsea, NY.

55241 ■ *Guide to Government*
1 Civic Center Plz., Ste. 400
Poughkeepsie, NY 12601
Ph: (845)454-1700
Fax: (845)454-1702
Co. E-mail: charlesnorth@dcrcoc.org
URL: http://www.dutchesscountyregionalchamber.org
Contact: Charles S. North, President

55242 ■ Guilderland Chamber of Commerce (GCC)
2050 Western Ave.
Star Plz., No. 109
Guilderland, NY 12084
Ph: (518)456-6611
Fax: (518)456-6690
Co. E-mail: info@guilderlandchamber.com
URL: http://www.guilderlandchamber.com
Contact: Katherine Burbank, Executive Director
Description: Promotes business and community development in the Guilderland, NY area. Conducts educational programs and seminars. Conducts community programs and special events. **Founded:** 1972. **Publications:** *Business and Community Directory* (Periodic); *Business Line* (Quarterly). **Educational Activities:** Recognition Dinner (Annual).

55243 ■ Hamburg Chamber of Commerce
PO Box 848
Hamburg, NY 14075
Ph: (716)649-7917
Free: 877-322-6890
Fax: (716)649-6362
Co. E-mail: hccmail@hamburg-chamber.org
URL: http://www.hamburg-chamber.org
Contact: Betty B. Newell, President
Description: Promotes business and community development in Hamburg, NY. **Founded:** 1926. **Publications:** *The Source* (Periodic). **Educational Activities:** Business After Hours (Monthly).

55244 ■ Hampton Bays Chamber of Commerce (HBCC)
140 W Main St., Ste. 1
Hampton Bays, NY 11946
Ph: (631)728-2211

Fax: (631)728-0308
Co. E-mail: hamptonbayschamber@verizon.net
URL: http://www.hamptonbayschamber.com
Contact: Stan Glinka, President
Description: Promotes business and community development in Hampton Bays, NY.

55245 ■ Hardscrabble News
PO Box 254
Red Hook, NY 12571
Ph: (845)758-0824
Co. E-mail: info@redhookchamber.org
URL: http://www.redhookchamber.org
Contact: Ray Amater, President
Released: Monthly

55246 ■ Heart of Catskill Association - Catskill Chamber of Commerce
PO Box 248
Catskill, NY 12414
Ph: (518)943-0989
Free: 800-603-7737
Co. E-mail: catskillchamber@mhcable.com
URL: http://www.catskillny.org
Contact: Linda Overbaugh, Executive Director
Description: Promotes business and community development in Catskill, NY.

55247 ■ Hempstead Chamber of Commerce
1776 Denton Green Park
Hempstead, NY 11550
Ph: (516)483-2000
Fax: (516)483-2000
Co. E-mail: president@hempsteadchamber.com
Contact: Leo Fernandez, President
Description: Promotes business and community development in Hempstead, NY area. **Founded:** 1902.

55248 ■ Hicksville Chamber of Commerce (HCC)
10 W Marie St.
Hicksville, NY 11801-3804
Ph: (516)931-7170
Fax: (516)931-8546
Co. E-mail: info@hicksvillechamber.com
URL: http://www.hicksvillechamber.com
Contact: Mr. Lionel Chitty, President
Description: Promotes business and community development in Hicksville, NY. **Founded:** 1926. **Educational Activities:** Hicksville Chamber of Commerce Meeting (Monthly). **Awards:** Citizen of the Year (Annual).

55249 ■ Hudson Valley Gateway Chamber of Commerce
1 S Division St.
Peekskill, NY 10566
Ph: (914)737-3600
Fax: (914)737-0541
URL: http://www.hvgatewaychamber.com
Contact: Deborah Milone, Executive Director
Description: Promotes business and community development in the Peekskill and Cortlandt, NY area. **Founded:** 1915. **Publications:** *The Chamber Report* (Quarterly).

55250 ■ Huntington Township Chamber of Commerce
164 Main St.
Huntington, NY 11743-3383
Ph: (631)423-6100
Fax: (631)351-8276
Co. E-mail: info@huntingtonchamber.com
URL: http://www.huntingtonchamber.com
Contact: Ellen O'Brien, Executive Director
Description: Promotes business and community development in Huntington, NY. **Founded:** 1925.

55251 ■ Hyde Park Chamber of Commerce
PO Box 17
Hyde Park, NY 12538
Ph: (845)229-8612

Fax: (845)229-8638
Co. E-mail: info@hydeparkchamber.org
URL: http://www.hydeparkchamber.org
Contact: John Coppola, President
Description: Promotes business and community development in Hyde Park, NY. Sponsors annual Easter Egg Hunt and Halloween Parade.

55252 ■ In Business for Business
318 Delaware Ave., Main Sq.
Delmar, NY 12054-1911
Ph: (518)439-0512
Fax: (518)475-0910
Co. E-mail: info@bethlehemchamber.com
URL: http://www.bethlehemchamber.com
Contact: John McIntyre, Chairman
Released: Monthly **Price:** included in membership dues.

55253 ■ Industrial Directory
1200 Waters Pl., Ste. 106
Bronx, NY 10461
Ph: (718)828-3900
Fax: (718)409-3748
Co. E-mail: info@bronxchamber.org
URL: http://www.bronxchamber.org
Contact: Leonard Caro, President
Released: Periodic

55254 ■ Industry List
199 Van Buren St.
Newark, NY 14513
Ph: (315)331-2705
Fax: (315)331-4602
Co. E-mail: newarkchamber@rochester.rr.com
URL: http://newarknychamber.com
Contact: Tammra Schiller, President
Released: Annual

55255 ■ Inlet Information Office
PO Box 266
Inlet, NY 13360-0266
Ph: (315)357-5501
Free: 866-GOI-NLET
Co. E-mail: info@inletny.com
URL: http://www.inletny.com
Description: Promotes business and community development in Inlet, NY. Sponsors events that draw tourism to the area. Works on economic development issues. Seeks to find a balance between economic development and preservation of the natural surroundings. **Founded:** 1955. **Publications:** *Inlet Lamplighter* (Quarterly); *Vacation Planner* (Annual).

55256 ■ Inlet Lamplighter
PO Box 266
Inlet, NY 13360-0266
Ph: (315)357-5501
Free: 866-GOI-NLET
Co. E-mail: info@inletny.com
URL: http://www.inletny.com
Released: Quarterly **Price:** free.

55257 ■ Inside Colonie
950 New Loudon Rd.
Latham, NY 12110
Ph: (518)785-6995
Fax: (518)785-7173
Co. E-mail: info@coloniechamber.org
URL: http://www.coloniechamber.org
Contact: Tom Nolte, President
Released: Quarterly

55258 ■ Inside The Chamber
214 N Franklin St., Rte. 14
Watkins Glen, NY 14891
Ph: (607)535-4300
Free: 800-607-4552
Fax: (607)535-6243
Co. E-mail: info@watkinsglenchamber.com
URL: http://www.watkinsglenchamber.com
Contact: Rebekah LaMoreaux, President
Released: Bimonthly

55259 ■ Insight
255 River St.
Troy, NY 12180
Ph: (518)274-7020

Fax: (518)272-7729
Co. E-mail: info@renscochamber.com
URL: http://www.renscochamber.com
Contact: Linda Hillman, President
Released: Monthly

55260 ■ Islip Chamber of Commerce
PO Box 112
Islip, NY 11751-0112
Ph: (631)581-2720
Fax: (631)581-2720
Co. E-mail: info@islipchamberofcommerce.com
URL: http://www.islipchamberofcommerce.com
Contact: Angela Parisi, President
Description: Promotes business and economic development in Islip, NY. **Founded:** 1923. **Telecommunication Services:** angelaparisi@hamletrealtyny.com.

55261 ■ Kenmore-Town of Tonawanda Chamber of Commerce
3411 Delaware Ave.
Kenmore, NY 14217-1422
Ph: (716)874-1202
Fax: (716)874-3151
Co. E-mail: info@ken-ton.org
URL: http://www.ken-ton.org
Contact: Ms. Tracey M. Lukasik, Executive Director
Description: Promotes business and community development in the Kenmore/Tonawanda, NY area. **Founded:** 1972. **Telecommunication Services:** tracey@ken-ton.org.

55262 ■ Kings Park Chamber of Commerce
PO Box 322
Kings Park, NY 11754
Ph: (631)269-7678
Fax: (631)656-0024
Co. E-mail: kpcc@kingspark.net
URL: http://www.kingsparkli.com
Contact: Charles Gardner, President
Description: Promotes business and community development in Kings Park, NY.

55263 ■ Lackawanna Area Chamber of Commerce
638 Ridge Rd.
Lackawanna, NY 14218
Ph: (716)823-8841
Fax: (716)823-8848
Co. E-mail: info@lackawannachamber.com
URL: http://www.lackawannachamber.com
Description: Promotes business and community development in the Lackawanna, NY area.

55264 ■ Lake George Regional Chamber of Commerce
PO Box 272
Lake George, NY 12845-0272
Ph: (518)668-5755
Free: 800-705-0059
Fax: (518)668-4286
Co. E-mail: info@lakegeorgechamber.com
URL: http://www.lakegeorgechamber.com
Contact: Kevin Rosa, President
URL(s): lakegeorgechamber.com. **Description:** Promotes business, community development, and tourism in Lake George, NY. **Founded:** 1950. **Publications:** *Good News Travel Fast* (Monthly).

55265 ■ Lancaster Area Chamber of Commerce (LACC)
PO Box 284
Lancaster, NY 14086
Ph: (716)681-9755
Fax: (716)684-3385
Co. E-mail: info@laccny.org
URL: http://www.laccny.org
Contact: Megan Burns-Moran, Executive Director
Description: Promotes business and community development in Depew, Elma, and Lancaster, NY. **Founded:** 1987.

55266 ■ Lewis County Chamber of Commerce
7576 S State St.
Lowville, NY 13367
Ph: (315)376-2213
Free: 800-724-0242

Fax: (315)376-0326
Co. E-mail: info@lewiscountychamber.org
URL: http://www.lewiscountychamber.org
Contact: Anne Merrill, Executive Director
Description: Promotes business and community development in Lewis County, NY. Promotes tourism. **Founded:** 1945.

55267 ■ *The Link*
1 W Market St., Ste. 302
Corning, NY 14830
Ph: (607)936-4686
Free: 866-463-6264
Fax: (607)936-4685
Co. E-mail: info@corningny.com
URL: http://www.corningny.com
Contact: Denise K. Ackley, President
Released: Monthly

55268 ■ Livingston County Chamber of Commerce
4635 Millennium Dr.
Geneseo, NY 14454
Ph: (585)243-2222
Fax: (585)243-4824
Co. E-mail: coswald@frontiernet.net
URL: http://livingstoncountychamber.com
Contact: Cynthia Oswald, President
Description: Promotes business and community development in Livingston County, NY. **Founded:** 1970. **Publications:** *Chamber Community* (Semiannual); *The Chambergram* (Monthly); *Livingston County Travel Guide* (Annual). **Educational Activities:** Chamber After Hours (Monthly). **Awards:** Business and Industry Award (Annual); Farm Award (Annual); Leadership Award (Annual).

55269 ■ *Livingston County Travel Guide*
4635 Millennium Dr.
Geneseo, NY 14454
Ph: (585)243-2222
Fax: (585)243-4824
Co. E-mail: coswald@frontiernet.net
URL: http://livingstoncountychamber.com
Contact: Cynthia Oswald, President
Released: Annual **Price:** free.

55270 ■ Long Beach Chamber of Commerce (LBCC)
350 National Blvd.
Long Beach, NY 11561-3312
Ph: (516)432-6000
Fax: (516)432-0273
URL: http://www.thelongbeachchamber.com
Contact: Lawrence E. Elovich, Chairman of the Board
Description: Promotes business and community development in Long Beach, NY. Sponsors art and crafts festival in July and August. **Founded:** 1938.

55271 ■ Long Island Association (LIA)
300 Broadhollow Rd., Ste. 110W
Melville, NY 11747-4840
Ph: (631)493-3000
Fax: (631)499-2194
Co. E-mail: mcrosson@longislandassociation.org
URL: http://www.longislandassociation.org
Contact: Frank Branchini, President
Description: Seeks to create and retain balanced economic opportunities and jobs in a clean, healthy, and safe environment. **Founded:** 1926.

55272 ■ Lyons Chamber of Commerce
PO Box 39
Lyons, NY 14489
Ph: (315)573-8170
Co. E-mail: lyonsnychamber@gmail.com
URL: http://www.lyonsny.com
Contact: Mark De Cracker, President
Description: Promotes business and community development in Lyons, NY.

55273 ■ Malone Chamber of Commerce (MCC)
497 E Main St.
Malone, NY 12953
Ph: (518)483-3760
Free: 877-625-6631

Fax: (518)483-3172
URL: http://visitmalone.com
Contact: Hugh Hill, Executive Director
Description: Promotes business and community development in the Malone, NY area. Conducts annual Winter Carnival and annual Spring Festival. **Founded:** 1956. **Publications:** *Business Directory* (Annual).

55274 ■ Manhasset Chamber of Commerce (MCC)
PO Box 754
Manhasset, NY 11030
Co. E-mail: leemanhassetcc@aol.com
URL: http://manhassetny.org/chamber/HomePage/tabid/120/Default.aspx
Contact: Les Forrai, President
Description: Promotes business and community development in Manhasset, NY.

55275 ■ Manhattan Chamber of Commerce (MCC)
1375 Broadway, 3rd Fl.
New York, NY 10018
Ph: (212)479-7772
Fax: (212)473-8074
Co. E-mail: info@manhattancc.org
URL: http://www.manhattancc.org/common/11001/default.cfm?clientID=11001
Contact: Nancy Ploeger, President
Description: Promotes business and community development in Manhattan, NY. Sponsors festivals. **Founded:** 1920. **Publications:** *Enterprise* (Quarterly).

55276 ■ Mattituck Chamber of Commerce
PO Box 1056
Mattituck, NY 11952
Ph: (631)734-8301
Co. E-mail: info@mattituckchamber.org
URL: http://www.mattituckchamber.org
Contact: Terry McShane, President
Description: Promotes business and community development in the Mattituck and North Fork, NY area. **Founded:** 1961.

55277 ■ Mayville - Chautauqua Area Chamber of Commerce
PO Box 22
Mayville, NY 14757-0022
Ph: (716)753-3113
Co. E-mail: maychautchamb@yahoo.com
URL: http://mayvillechautauquachamber.org
Contact: Kenneth V. Shearer, Jr., President
Description: Promotes the area as a desirable place to live, conduct business and visit.

55278 ■ *Meeting Notice*

55279 ■ *Meeting Notice*
674 Broadway
Massapequa, NY 11758
Ph: (516)541-1443
Fax: (516)541-8625
Co. E-mail: masscoc@aol.com
URL: http://www.massapequachamber.com
Contact: Patricia Orzano, President

55280 ■ *Member Update*
5 1/2 Main St.
Delhi, NY 13753
Ph: (607)746-2281
Fax: (607)746-3571
Co. E-mail: info@delawarecounty.org
URL: http://www.delawarecounty.org
Contact: Mary Beth Silano, Executive Director
Released: Quarterly

55281 ■ *Members Buyer's Guide*
PO Box 310
Plattsburgh, NY 12901
Ph: (518)563-1000
Fax: (518)563-1028
Co. E-mail: info@northcountrychamber.com
URL: http://www.northcountrychamber.com
Contact: Garry Douglas, President
Released: Annual

55282 ■ *Membership Brochure*
PO Box 227
Ellenville, NY 12428
Ph: (845)647-4620
Co. E-mail: info@ewcoc.com
URL: http://www.ewcoc.com/Pages/default.aspx
Contact: Dr. Mark Craft, President
Released: Annual **Price:** free.

55283 ■ Mineola Chamber of Commerce
PO Box 62
Mineola, NY 11501
Ph: (516)408-3554
Co. E-mail: info@mineolachamber.com
URL: http://www.mineolachamber.com
Contact: Mr. Ray Sikorski, President
Description: Promotes business and community development in Mineola, NY.

55284 ■ Mohawk Valley Chamber of Commerce
Radisson Hotel
200 Genesee St.
Utica, NY 13502
Ph: (315)724-3151
Fax: (315)724-3177
Co. E-mail: info@mvchamber.org
URL: http://www.mvchamber.org
Contact: Thomas Bashant, President
Description: Promotes business and community development in Utica, NY. **Founded:** 1896. **Publications:** *Almanac* (Annual); *Chamber Action* (Monthly). **Awards:** Business of the Year (Annual); John T. O'Toole Person of the Year (Annual).

55285 ■ Mount Kisco Chamber of Commerce (MKCC)
3 N Moger Ave.
Mount Kisco, NY 10549
Ph: (914)666-7525
Fax: (914)666-7663
Co. E-mail: mtkiscochamber@aol.com
URL: http://www.mtkiscochamber.com
Contact: Kathleen Mooney, Executive Director
Description: Promotes business and community development in Mt. Kisco, NY. Sponsors Sidewalk Sales Days and holiday programs. Issues publications. **Founded:** 1965. **Publications:** *Mt. Kisco Lifestyles* (Annual). **Awards:** Citizen of the Year Award (Annual).

55286 ■ *Mt. Kisco Lifestyles*
3 N Moger Ave.
Mount Kisco, NY 10549
Ph: (914)666-7525
Fax: (914)666-7663
Co. E-mail: mtkiscochamber@aol.com
URL: http://www.mtkiscochamber.com
Contact: Kathleen Mooney, Executive Director
Released: Annual

55287 ■ Mount Vernon Chamber of Commerce
PO Box 351
Mount Vernon, NY 10550-2009
Ph: (914)667-7500
Co. E-mail: info@mtvernonchamber.org
URL: http://www.mtvernonchamber.org
Contact: Frank T. Fraley, President
Description: Promotes business and community development in Mt. Vernon, NY. **Founded:** 1912. **Awards:** Chamber Scholarship Award (Annual).

55288 ■ New Hartford Chamber of Commerce
PO Box 372
New Hartford, NY 13413
Ph: (315)735-1974
Fax: (315)266-1231
Co. E-mail: info@newhartfordchamber.com
URL: http://www.newhartfordchamber.com
Contact: Mark A. Turnbull, President
Description: Promotes business and community development in New Hartford, NY.

55289 ■ New Paltz Chamber of Commerce
257 Main St.
New Paltz, NY 12561
Ph: (845)255-0243

Fax: (845)255-5189
Co. E-mail: info@newpaltzchamber.org
URL: http://www.newpaltzchamber.org
Contact: Michael A. Smith, President
Description: Promotes business, community development, and tourism in New Paltz, NY. **Scope:** area's businesses, attractions and services. **Subscriptions:** books business records. **Publications:** *Regional Guide* (Annual); *Update* (Monthly).

55290 ■ New Rochelle Chamber of Commerce (NRCC)
459 Main St.
New Rochelle, NY 10801-6412
Ph: (914)632-5700
Fax: (914)632-0708
Co. E-mail: info@newrochellechamber.org
URL: http://newrochellechamber.org
Contact: Rosemary McLaughlin, President
Description: Promotes business and community development in New Rochelle, NY. Sponsors spring and fall festival, annual Thanksgiving Parade, and annual haunted house. **Founded:** 1922. **Publications:** *New Rochelle Chamber of Commerce--Member Directory* (Annual); *Chambernews* (Monthly). **Telecommunication Services:** chamber@newrochellechamber.org.

55291 ■ New Yorktown Chamber of Commerce
PO Box 632
Yorktown Heights, NY 10598
Ph: (914)245-4599
Fax: (914)734-7171
Co. E-mail: info@yorktownchamber.org
URL: http://www.yorktownchamber.org
Contact: Arlette Rossignol, Director, Operations
Description: Promotes business and community development in Yorktown Heights, NY. **Telecommunication Services:** staff@yorktownchamber.org.

55292 ■ Newcomb Chamber of Commerce
PO Box 222
Newcomb, NY 12852
Ph: (518)582-2274
URL: http://www.newcombny.com/newchamber.html
Description: Promotes business and community development in Newcomb, NY. **Founded:** 1999.

55293 ■ *News and Views*
27 Water St., 2nd Fl.
Baldwinsville, NY 13027
Ph: (315)638-0550
Co. E-mail: baldwinsvillechamber@gmail.com
URL: http://www.b-ville.com/content/greater-baldwinsville-chamber-commerce
Contact: Anthony Saraceni, President
Released: Monthly

55294 ■ *News and Views*
1241 Coffeen St.
Watertown, NY 13601
Ph: (315)788-4400
Fax: (315)788-3369
Co. E-mail: chamber@watertownny.com
URL: http://www.watertownny.com
Contact: Lynne Ferris, Chairman of the Board
Released: Monthly

55295 ■ *Newsline*
2 N Main St.
Gloversville, NY 12078
Ph: (518)725-0641
Free: 800-676-3858
Fax: (518)725-0643
Co. E-mail: info@fultoncountyny.org
URL: http://www.fultoncountyny.org
Contact: Mark Kilmer, President (Acting)
Released: Monthly

55296 ■ Niagara USA Chamber
Vantage Ctre.
6311 Inducon Corporate Dr.
Sanborn, NY 14132
Ph: (716)285-9141

Fax: (716)285-0941
Co. E-mail: dalteriobrennen@niagarachamber.org
URL: http://www.niagarachamber.org
Contact: Deanna Alterio Brennen, President
Description: Promotes business and community development in eastern Niagara County, NY. Provides health insurance. Issues publications. **Founded:** 1903. **Publications:** *Commerce Quotes* (Monthly). **Educational Activities:** Community Expo (Periodic).

55297 ■ Oceanside Chamber of Commerce
PO Box 1
Oceanside, NY 11572
Ph: (516)763-9177
Co. E-mail: info@oceansidechamber.org
URL: http://www.oceansidechamber.org
Contact: Gail Carlin, President
Description: Promotes business and community development in Oceanside, NY.

55298 ■ Orchard Park Chamber of Commerce
4211 N Buffalo St., Ste. 14
Orchard Park, NY 14127-2401
Ph: (716)662-3366
Fax: (716)662-5946
Co. E-mail: opcc@orchardparkchamber.com
URL: http://www.orchardparkchamber.com
Contact: Nancy L. Conley, Executive Director
Description: Develops and encourages the growth and participation of chamber members through actions beneficial to the Orchard Park, NY business community. **Founded:** 1964. **Publications:** *Chamber Review* (Monthly).

55299 ■ *Organization Directory*
210 E Main St.
Batavia, NY 14020
Ph: (585)343-7440
Free: 800-622-2686
Fax: (585)343-7487
Co. E-mail: chamber@geneseeny.com
URL: http://www.geneseeny.com
Contact: Lynn Freeman, President

55300 ■ Orleans County Chamber of Commerce (OCCC)
102 N Main St., Ste. 1
Albion, NY 14411
Ph: (585)589-7727
Fax: (585)589-7326
Co. E-mail: klake@orleanschamber.com
URL: http://www.orleanschamber.com
Contact: Kevim Lake, Executive Director
Description: Seeks to promote business and community development and enhance the relationship between local businesses and professionals with the public. **Publications:** *Orleans County Chamber of Commerce--Membership Directory: Membership Directory and Community Guide.*

55301 ■ Otsego County Chamber of Commerce
189 Main St., Ste. 201
Oneonta, NY 13820
Ph: (607)432-4500
Free: 877-5OT-SEGO
Fax: (607)432-4506
Co. E-mail: tocc@otsegocountychamber.com
URL: http://www.otsegocountychamber.com
Contact: Roxana Hurlburt, Chairman
Description: Promotes business, community development, and tourism in Otsego County, NY. **Founded:** 1906. **Publications:** *Otsego County Travel Guide.*

55302 ■ *Otsego County Travel Guide*
189 Main St., Ste. 201
Oneonta, NY 13820
Ph: (607)432-4500
Free: 877-5OT-SEGO
Fax: (607)432-4506
Co. E-mail: tocc@otsegocountychamber.com
URL: http://www.otsegocountychamber.com
Contact: Roxana Hurlburt, Chairman

55303 ■ Partnership for New York City
1 Battery Park Plz., 5th Fl.
New York, NY 10004
Ph: (212)493-7400

Fax: (212)344-3344
Co. E-mail: info@pfnyc.org
URL: http://www.nycp.org
Contact: Kathryn S. Wylde, President
Description: Promotes business and community development in New York City, NY. Lobbies local, state, and federal government on legislation affecting the city. Provides information and educational programs to members. **Founded:** 1768. **Publications:** *Chamber Report* (Monthly).

55304 ■ *Passport Magazine*
542 E Main St., Ste. 2
Riverhead, NY 11901
Ph: (631)727-7600
Fax: (631)727-7946
Co. E-mail: info@riverheadchamber.com
URL: http://www.riverheadchamber.com
Contact: Robert Lanieri, President
Released: Annual

55305 ■ *Patchogue Chamber Business Letter*
15 N Ocean Ave.
Patchogue, NY 11772
Ph: (631)207-1000
Fax: (631)475-1599
Co. E-mail: info@patchoguechamber.com
URL: http://www.patchoguechamber.com
Contact: Jacqueline Hensley, President
Released: Monthly

55306 ■ Patterson Chamber of Commerce
PO Box 316
Patterson, NY 12563-0316
Ph: (845)363-6304
Fax: (845)363-6304
Co. E-mail: info@pcofc.org
URL: http://www.pcofc.org
Contact: Vince Murphy, President (Acting)
Description: Promotes business and community development in the Town of Patterson, NY.

55307 ■ Pawling Chamber of Commerce
c/o Andrew Carlucci
PO Box 19
Pawling, NY 12564
Ph: (845)855-0500
URL: http://www.pawlingchamber.org
Contact: Peter Cris, Chairman

55308 ■ Pittsford Chamber of Commerce
PO Box 576
Pittsford, NY 14534
Ph: (585)234-0308
Co. E-mail: info@pittsfordchamber.org
URL: http://pittsfordchamber.org
Contact: Dr. Shirley Joseph, President
Description: Promotes business and community development in the Pittsford, NY area. **Founded:** 1789. **Publications:** *Chamber.*

55309 ■ Plank Road Chamber of Commerce
PO Box 324
North Syracuse, NY 13212
Ph: (315)458-4181
Co. E-mail: info@plankroadchamber.com
URL: http://www.northsyracuse.com
Contact: Angela Tucciarone, Secretary
URL(s): www.plankroadchamber.com. **Description:** Seeks to promote business and community development and enhance the relationship between local businesses and professionals with the public.

55310 ■ *Planners Guide*
PO Box 995
Binghamton, NY 13902-0995
Ph: (607)772-8860
Fax: (607)772-4513
Co. E-mail: chamber@binghamtonchamber.com
URL: http://www.binghamtonchamber.com
Contact: Lou Santoni, President
Released: Annual

55311 ■ Plattsburgh - North Country Chamber of Commerce
PO Box 310
Plattsburgh, NY 12901
Ph: (518)563-1000

Fax: (518)563-1028
Co. E-mail: info@northcountrychamber.com
URL: http://www.northcountrychamber.com
Contact: Garry Douglas, President
Description: Promotes business, community development, and tourism in the northeast New York region. **Founded:** 1912. **Publications:** *Chamber Vision* (Monthly); *Members Buyer's Guide* (Annual). **Educational Activities:** Mixer (Monthly).

55312 ■ Potsdam Chamber of Commerce
One Market St.
Potsdam, NY 13676
Ph: (315)274-9000
Fax: (315)274-9222
Co. E-mail: potsdam@slic.com
URL: http://www.potsdamchamber.com
Contact: Robert Bicknell, President
Description: Promotes business and community development in Potsdam, NY area. **Publications:** *The Potsdam Pages* (Bimonthly). **Awards:** Business of the Year Award (Annual); Commitment to the Community Award (Annual).

55313 ■ *The Potsdam Pages*
One Market St.
Potsdam, NY 13676
Ph: (315)274-9000
Fax: (315)274-9222
Co. E-mail: potsdam@slic.com
URL: http://www.potsdamchamber.com
Contact: Robert Bicknell, President
Released: Bimonthly **Price:** $1, for members.

55314 ■ Pulaski - Eastern Shore Chamber of Commerce
PO Box 34
Pulaski, NY 13142
Ph: (315)298-2213
URL: http://www.pulaskinychamber.com
Description: Seeks to promote business and community development and enhance the relationship between local businesses and professionals with the public. **Founded:** 1946.

55315 ■ *Quality of Life*
Released: Periodic

55316 ■ *Quality of Life Guide*
136 Glen St., Ste. 3
Glens Falls, NY 12801
Ph: (518)798-1761
Fax: (518)792-4147
Co. E-mail: frontdesk@adirondackchamber.org
URL: http://www.adirondackchamber.org
Contact: Peter Aust, President
Released: Annual

55317 ■ *Quality of Life Resource Guide*
PO Box 995
Binghamton, NY 13902-0995
Ph: (607)772-8860
Fax: (607)772-4513
Co. E-mail: chamber@binghamtonchamber.com
URL: http://www.binghamtonchamber.com
Contact: Lou Santoni, President
Released: Annual

55318 ■ Red Hook Area Chamber of Commerce
PO Box 254
Red Hook, NY 12571
Ph: (845)758-0824
Co. E-mail: info@redhookchamber.org
URL: http://www.redhookchamber.org
Contact: Ray Amater, President
Description: Promotes business and community development in the Red Hook, NY area. **Founded:** 1960. **Publications:** *Hardscrabble News* (Monthly).

55319 ■ *Regional Guide*
257 Main St.
New Paltz, NY 12561
Ph: (845)255-0243
Fax: (845)255-5189
Co. E-mail: info@newpaltzchamber.org
URL: http://www.newpaltzchamber.org
Contact: Michael A. Smith, President
Released: Annual **Price:** free.

55320 ■ Rensselaer County Regional Chamber of Commerce
255 River St.
Troy, NY 12180
Ph: (518)274-7020
Fax: (518)272-7729
Co. E-mail: info@renscochamber.com
URL: http://www.renscochamber.com
Contact: Linda Hillman, President
Description: Promotes business and community development in Rensselaer County Troy, NY area. **Founded:** 1900. **Publications:** *Insight* (Monthly). **Telecommunication Services:** lhillman@renscochamber.com.

55321 ■ *Resource Guide for the Town of Hunter*
PO Box 177
Hunter, NY 12442
Ph: (518)263-4900
Fax: (518)589-0117
Co. E-mail: chamberinfo@hunterchamber.org
URL: http://www.hunterchamber.org
Contact: Mark Hyer, Chairman
Released: Annual

55322 ■ Rhinebeck Chamber of Commerce
PO Box 42
Rhinebeck, NY 12572
Ph: (845)876-5904
Fax: (845)876-8624
Co. E-mail: info@rhinebeckchamber.com
URL: http://rhinebeckchamber.com
Contact: Colleen Cruikshank, Executive Director
Description: Promotes business and community development in Rhinebeck, NY. **Founded:** 1957.

55323 ■ Riverhead Chamber of Commerce
542 E Main St., Ste. 2
Riverhead, NY 11901
Ph: (631)727-7600
Fax: (631)727-7946
Co. E-mail: info@riverheadchamber.com
URL: http://www.riverheadchamber.com
Contact: Robert Lanieri, President
Description: Promotes commercial, industrial, civic and general interests of the Township of Riverhead and outlying communities within the Central School District No. 2 and within Suffolk County. **Founded:** 1964. **Publications:** *Passport Magazine* (Annual). **Educational Activities:** Chamber Board of Directors Meetings (Monthly).

55324 ■ Rochester Business Alliance, Women's Council
c/o Susan George, Affiliate Mgr.
150 State St.
Rochester, NY 14614
Ph: (585)256-4612
Fax: (585)244-4864
Co. E-mail: susan.george@rballiance.com
URL: http://www.grwc.com
Contact: Susan George, Manager
Description: Enhances the opportunities and knowledge of business and professional women in the civic, commercial, cultural and educational interests of the Greater Rochester Area. **Founded:** 1932. **Awards:** ATHENA Awards (Annual); Young Women of Distinction Award (Annual).

55325 ■ Rockville Centre Chamber of Commerce (RVCCC)
PO Box 226
Rockville Centre, NY 11571
Ph: (516)766-0666
Fax: (516)706-1550
Co. E-mail: mailbox@rvcchamber.org
URL: http://www.rvcchamber.com/index.php
Contact: Lawrence Siegel, President
Description: Promotes business and community development in Rockville Centre, NY. Sponsors 10-K run, Health Fair, spring and fall festivals, and high school mentoring program. Senior Day. **Founded:** 1906.

55326 ■ Rome Area Chamber of Commerce
139 W Dominick St.
Rome, NY 13440-5809
Ph: (315)337-1700

Fax: (315)337-1715
Co. E-mail: info@romechamber.com
URL: http://www.romechamber.com
Contact: William K. Guglielmo, President
Description: Promotes business and community development in the Rome, NY area. **Telecommunication Services:** wkg@romechamber.com.

55327 ■ Roscoe-Rockland Chamber of Commerce
PO Box 443
Roscoe, NY 12776-0443
Ph: (607)498-5765
Co. E-mail: info@roscoeny.com
URL: http://www.roscoeny.com
Description: Promotes business and community development in Roscoe, NY. **Founded:** 1950.

55328 ■ Rye Merchants Association
PO Box 256
Rye, NY 10580
Ph: (914)921-5950
Co. E-mail: wineatfive@verizon.net
URL: http://www.ryemerchantsassociation.com
Description: Promotes business and community development in Rye, NY.

55329 ■ Sag Harbor Chamber of Commerce
PO Box 2810
Sag Harbor, NY 11963
Ph: (631)725-0011
Fax: (631)919-1662
Co. E-mail: info@sagharborchamber.com
URL: http://www.sagharborchamber.com
Contact: Mr. Robert Evjen, President
Description: Promotes business and community development in the greater Sag Harbor, New York area, including Sag Harbor Village, Noyack, North Haven, and the surrounding area. Promotes local events sponsored and hosted by members as well as local non-profit organizations through published and online events calendar. **Awards:** Sag Harbor Chamber of Commerce Award for Graduating Seniors of Pierson High School (Annual). **Telecommunication Services:** robert.evjen@prudentialelliman.com.

55330 ■ St. James Chamber of Commerce
PO Box 286
St. James, NY 11780
Ph: (631)584-8510
Fax: (631)584-8784
Co. E-mail: info@stjameschamber.org
URL: http://www.stjameschamber.org
Contact: Lawrence Glazer, President
Description: Promotes business and community development in St. James, NY. **Founded:** 1853.

55331 ■ St. Lawrence County Chamber of Commerce
101 Main St., 1st Fl.
Canton, NY 13617-1248
Ph: (315)386-4000
Free: 877-228-7810
Co. E-mail: slccoc@northnet.org
URL: http://northcountryguide.com
Contact: Pat McKeown, Executive Director
Description: Seeks to develop, coordinate and implement plans and programs to further the economic development and tourism in St. Lawrence county and the North Country region. **Founded:** 1965. **Publications:** *St. Lawrence County Chamber Members' Directory* (Irregular); *Travel Guide* (Periodic).

55332 ■ Salamanca Area Chamber of Commerce
26 Main St.
Salamanca, NY 14779-1516
Ph: (716)945-2034
Fax: (716)945-9143
Co. E-mail: info@salamancachamber.org
URL: http://www.salamancachamber.org
Contact: Jayne L. Fenton, President
Description: Promotes business and community development in the Salamanca, NY area. Maintains Visitors Welcome Center in office and at Interstate 86. Organize member networking events, community

events and festivals, and enrichment opportunities. **Founded:** 1923. **Publications:** *Escape to Historic Salamanca* (Quarterly); *Visitors Guide Directory* (Periodic).

55333 ■ Saranac Lake Area Chamber of Commerce
193 River St.
Saranac Lake, NY 12983
Ph: (518)891-1990
Free: 800-347-1992
Fax: (518)891-7042
Co. E-mail: info@saranaclake.com
URL: http://www.saranaclake.com
Contact: Katy Van Anden, Executive Director
Description: Promotes business and community development in the Saranac Lake, NY area. Provides sporting events management and tourism information; sponsors concerts. **Founded:** 1921. **Publications:** *Accommodations Directory* (Periodic); *Business Directory* (Periodic).

55334 ■ Saratoga County Chamber of Commerce
28 Clinton St.
Saratoga Springs, NY 12866-2143
Ph: (518)584-3255
Fax: (518)587-0318
Co. E-mail: info@saratoga.org
URL: http://www.saratoga.org
Contact: Todd Shimkus, President
Description: Promotes business and community development in Saratoga County, NY area. **Founded:** 1918. **Publications:** *Business Connection* (Annual); *Update* (Monthly); *Business Connection* (Annual).

55335 ■ Schenectady County Chamber of Commerce
306 State St.
Schenectady, NY 12305-2302
Ph: (518)372-5656
Free: 800-962-8007
Fax: (518)370-3217
Co. E-mail: info@schenectadychamber.org
URL: http://www.schenectadychamber.org
Contact: Charles P. Steiner, President
Description: Seeks to promote business and community development and enhance the relationship between local businesses and professionals with the public.

55336 ■ Schoharie County Chamber of Commerce
PO Box 966
Middleburgh, NY 12122
Ph: (518)827-3900
Free: 800-41V-ISIT
Fax: (518)295-7453
Co. E-mail: info@schohariechamber.com
URL: http://www.schohariechamber.com
Contact: Georgia Van Dyke, President
Description: Seeks to promote business and community development and enhance the relationship between local businesses and professionals with the public. **Founded:** 1989.

55337 ■ Schroon Lake Area Chamber of Commerce
PO Box 726
Schroon Lake, NY 12870-0726
Ph: (518)532-7675
Fax: (518)532-7675
Co. E-mail: chamber@schroonlakeregion.com
URL: http://www.schroonlake.com
Description: Promotes business and community development in the Schroon Lake, NY area. **Publications:** *Business Directory* (Annual). **Educational Activities:** General Meeting (Monthly).

55338 ■ Seneca County Chamber of Commerce
PO Box 70
Seneca Falls, NY 13148-0070
Ph: (315)568-2906

Fax: (315)568-1730
Co. E-mail: info@senecachamber.org
URL: http://www.senecachamber.org
Contact: Lisa Fitzgerald, Chairperson
Description: Seeks to promote business and community development and enhance the relationship between local businesses and professionals with the public. **Founded:** 1968. **Awards:** Business of the Year (Annual).

55339 ■ Sidney Chamber of Commerce
PO Box 2295
Sidney, NY 13838
Ph: (607)561-2642
Fax: (607)561-2644
Co. E-mail: office@sidneychamber.org
URL: http://www.sidneychamber.org
Contact: John Marano, President
Description: Seeks to promote business and community development and enhance the relationship between local businesses and professionals with the public.

55340 ■ Skaneateles Area Chamber of Commerce
22 Jordan St.
Skaneateles, NY 13152
Ph: (315)685-0552
Fax: (315)685-0552
Co. E-mail: info@skaneateles.com
URL: http://www.skaneateles.com
Contact: Susan Dove, Executive Director
Description: Promotes a comprehensive, quality, economic environment in the Skaneateles, NY area with planned growth for continued success of its membership and the community. **Founded:** 1965. **Publications:** *Skaneateles Community Directory* (Annual). **Awards:** Mini-Tourism Grant by Senator John DeFrancesco (Annual).

55341 ■ *Skaneateles Community Directory*
22 Jordan St.
Skaneateles, NY 13152
Ph: (315)685-0552
Fax: (315)685-0552
Co. E-mail: info@skaneateles.com
URL: http://www.skaneateles.com
Contact: Susan Dove, Executive Director
Released: Annual

55342 ■ Sleepy Hollow Tarrytown Chamber of Commerce (SHCC)
54 Main St.
Tarrytown, NY 10591
Ph: (914)631-1705
Fax: (914)206-5115
Co. E-mail: info@sleepyhollowchamber.com
URL: http://www.sleepyhollowchamber.com
Contact: John Sardy, Executive Director
Description: Promotes business and community development in Tarrytown and North Tarrytown, NY. Provides tour information. Holds monthly board of directors meeting. **Founded:** 1927. **Publications:** *The Chamber Room* (Monthly).

55343 ■ Sodus Town Chamber of Commerce
PO Box 187
Sodus, NY 14551-0187
Ph: (315)576-3818
Co. E-mail: chamber14551@yahoo.com
URL: http://sodusny.org
Contact: Mary Jane Mumby, Vice President
Description: Promotes business and community development in Sodus, NY. **Awards:** Annual Citizen of the Year (Annual); Certificates of Appreciation (Annual); Scholarship Award (Annual).

55344 ■ *The Source*
PO Box 848
Hamburg, NY 14075
Ph: (716)649-7917
Free: 877-322-6890
Fax: (716)649-6362
Co. E-mail: hccmail@hamburg-chamber.org
URL: http://www.hamburg-chamber.org
Contact: Betty B. Newell, President
Released: Periodic; every six weeks.

55345 ■ Southampton Chamber of Commerce
76 Main St.
Southampton, NY 11968
Ph: (631)283-0402
Fax: (631)283-8707
Co. E-mail: info@southamptonchamber.com
URL: http://www.southamptonchamber.com
Contact: Micah Schlendorf, President
Description: Promotes business, community development, and tourism in Southampton, Long Island, NY. Sponsors annual Arts and Crafts Festival, annual Golf Tournament, Rag-A-Muffin Parade, annual Business Showcase and annual Southampton Country Holiday Promotion. **Founded:** 1950. **Publications:** *The Southampton Chamber of Commerce Community For All Seasons* (Annual).

55346 ■ Southern Ulster County Chamber of Commerce (SUCCC)
20 Milton Ave., Ste. 3
Highland, NY 12528
Ph: (845)691-6070
Fax: (845)691-9194
Co. E-mail: info@southernulsterchamber.org
URL: http://www.southernulsterchamber.org
Contact: Juliana Burger, President
Description: Promotes agriculture, business and community development in Southern Ulster County, NY. Conducts charitable activities. **Scope:** business, community interests. **Founded:** 1953. **Subscriptions:** 250 articles books periodicals video recordings. **Publications:** *Southern Ulster County Chamber of Commerce Business Directory* (Annual); *Southern Ulster County Chamber of Commerce Newsletter* (Monthly); *Southern Ulster County Chamber of Commerce Business Directory* (Annual). **Awards:** Local Business Scholarship (Annual).

55347 ■ *Southern Ulster County Chamber of Commerce Business Directory*
20 Milton Ave., Ste. 3
Highland, NY 12528
Ph: (845)691-6070
Fax: (845)691-9194
Co. E-mail: info@southernulsterchamber.org
URL: http://www.southernulsterchamber.org
Contact: Juliana Burger, President
Released: Annual

55348 ■ *Southern Ulster County Chamber of Commerce Newsletter*
20 Milton Ave., Ste. 3
Highland, NY 12528
Ph: (845)691-6070
Fax: (845)691-9194
Co. E-mail: info@southernulsterchamber.org
URL: http://www.southernulsterchamber.org
Contact: Juliana Burger, President
Released: Monthly

55349 ■ Staten Island Chamber of Commerce (SICC)
130 Bay St.
Staten Island, NY 10301-2503
Ph: (718)727-1900
Fax: (718)727-2295
Co. E-mail: info@sichamber.com
URL: http://www.sichamber.com
Contact: Ms. Linda Baran, President
Description: Promotes business and community development in Staten Island, NY. **Founded:** 1895. **Awards:** Building Awards (Annual); Louis R. Miller Business Leadership Awards (Annual).

55350 ■ *Students' and Visitors' Tabloid*
Released: Annual

55351 ■ Suffern Chamber of Commerce
PO Box 291
Suffern, NY 10901
Ph: (845)357-8424
Co. E-mail: suffernchamberofcommerce@yahoo.com
URL: http://www.suffernchamberofcommerce.com
Contact: Aury Licata, President

55352 ■ Sullivan County Chamber of Commerce
452 Broadway, Ste. 1
Monticello, NY 12701
Ph: (845)791-4200
Fax: (845)791-4200
Co. E-mail: chamber@catskills.com
URL: http://www.catskills.com
Contact: Terri Ward, President
Description: Works to assure economic growth in Sullivan County. **Founded:** 1974.

55353 ■ Syosset Chamber of Commerce
35 Roosevelt Ave., Ste. 1A
Syosset, NY 11791
Ph: (516)802-4942
URL: http://www.syossetchamber.com
Contact: Dr. Lisa Predmore, President
Description: Business owners/operators in the towns of Syosset, Woodbury, Jericho, Muttontown, and Oyster Bay Cove promoting town beautification, holiday ceremonies, a picnic and golf outing. **Founded:** 1998.

55354 ■ *Telephone Directory*
2257 Grand Island Blvd.
Grand Island, NY 14072
Ph: (716)773-3651
Fax: (716)773-3316
Co. E-mail: info@gichamber.org
URL: http://www.gichamber.org
Contact: Eric Fiebelkorn, President
Released: Periodic

55355 ■ Ticonderoga Area Chamber of Commerce (TACC)
94 Montcalm St., Ste. 1
Ticonderoga, NY 12883
Ph: (518)585-6619
Fax: (518)585-9184
Co. E-mail: chamberinfo@ticonderogany.com
URL: http://www.ticonderogany.com
Contact: Matthew J. Courtright, Executive Director
Description: Promotes business and community development in the Ticonderoga, NY area. Operates information center. Sponsors bass tournament and newcomers reception. **Founded:** 1925. **Publications:** *Calendar of Events* (Monthly); *Ticonderoga, Crown Point, Hague Business Directory* (Annual).

55356 ■ *Ticonderoga, Crown Point, Hague Business Directory*
94 Montcalm St., Ste. 1
Ticonderoga, NY 12883
Ph: (518)585-6619
Fax: (518)585-9184
Co. E-mail: chamberinfo@ticonderogany.com
URL: http://www.ticonderogany.com
Contact: Matthew J. Courtright, Executive Director
Released: Annual

55357 ■ Tioga County Chamber of Commerce (TCCC)
80 North Ave.
Owego, NY 13827
Ph: (607)687-2020
Fax: (607)687-9028
Co. E-mail: business@tiogachamber.com
URL: http://www.tiogachamber.com
Contact: Martha Sauerbrey, President
Description: Promotes business, community development, and tourism in Tioga County, NY. Operates tourist information center. Provides insurance plan. Sponsors seminars. **Founded:** 1969. **Publications:** *Chamber Visions* (Bimonthly). **Educational Activities:** Business Show (Annual).

55358 ■ *Today's Chamber*
400 E Church St.
Elmira, NY 14901-2803
Ph: (607)734-5137
Fax: (607)734-4490
Co. E-mail: info@chemungchamber.org
URL: http://www.chemungchamber.org
Contact: Kevin D. Keeley, President
Released: Monthly **Price:** included in membership dues.

55359 ■ Tompkins County Chamber of Commerce
904 E Shore Dr.
Ithaca, NY 14850-1026
Ph: (607)273-7080
Fax: (607)272-7617
Co. E-mail: jean@tompkinschamber.org
URL: http://www.tompkinschamber.org
Contact: Tom LiVigne, Chairman
Description: Promotes business and community development in Tompkins County, NY. **Publications:** *Tompkins County Chamber of Commerce-- Membership Directory*; *ChamberGram* (Monthly).

55360 ■ Town of Hunter Chamber of Commerce
PO Box 177
Hunter, NY 12442
Ph: (518)263-4900
Fax: (518)589-0117
Co. E-mail: chamberinfo@hunterchamber.org
URL: http://www.hunterchamber.org
Contact: Mark Hyer, Chairman
Description: Promotes business and community development in Hunter, NY. **Publications:** *Resource Guide for the Town of Hunter* (Annual).

55361 ■ *Travel Guide*
101 Main St., 1st Fl.
Canton, NY 13617-1248
Ph: (315)386-4000
Free: 877-228-7810
Co. E-mail: slccoc@northnet.org
URL: http://northcountryguide.com
Contact: Pat McKeown, Executive Director
Released: Periodic **Price:** free.

55362 ■ *The Tri-County Business Advocate*
684 Main St.
Arcade, NY 14009
Ph: (585)492-2114
Fax: (585)492-5103
Co. E-mail: aacc278@verizon.net
URL: http://www.arcadechamber.org
Contact: Dorie Clinch, Executive Secretary
Released: Quarterly

55363 ■ Tupper Lake Chamber of Commerce
121 Park St.
Tupper Lake, NY 12986
Ph: (518)359-3328
Free: 888-887-5253
Fax: (518)359-2434
Co. E-mail: chamber@tupper-lake.com
URL: http://tupper-lake.com/about/tupper-lake-chamber-of-commerce
Contact: David Tomberlin, President
Description: Organized to promote the commercial, recreational, industrial and civic interests of the village of Tupper Lake, town of Altamont and its membership. **Founded:** 1958. **Publications:** *Chamber Communicator* (Quarterly).

55364 ■ *Update*
257 Main St.
New Paltz, NY 12561
Ph: (845)255-0243
Fax: (845)255-5189
Co. E-mail: info@newpaltzchamber.org
URL: http://www.newpaltzchamber.org
Contact: Michael A. Smith, President
Released: Monthly **Price:** free.

55365 ■ *Update*
28 Clinton St.
Saratoga Springs, NY 12866-2143
Ph: (518)584-3255
Fax: (518)587-0318
Co. E-mail: info@saratoga.org
URL: http://www.saratoga.org
Contact: Todd Shimkus, President
Released: Monthly

55366 ■ *Vacation Planner*
PO Box 266
Inlet, NY 13360-0266
Ph: (315)357-5501

Free: 866-GOI-NLET
Co. E-mail: info@inletny.com
URL: http://www.inletny.com
Released: Annual

55367 ■ Victor Chamber of Commerce
37 E Main St.
Victor, NY 14564-1301
Ph: (585)742-1476
Fax: (866)857-6388
Co. E-mail: info@victorchamber.com
URL: http://www.victorchamber.com
Contact: Mitch Donovan, President
Description: Works to advance the commercial, industrial, and civic activities of the town and village of Victor. Enhances the quality of life in the area and preserves the character of the community.

55368 ■ *Visions*
1 Computer Dr. S
Albany, NY 12205-1631
Ph: (518)431-1400
Fax: (518)431-1402
Co. E-mail: info@acchamber.org
URL: http://acchamber.org
Contact: Mark Eagan, President
Released: Monthly

55369 ■ *Visitors Guide Directory*
26 Main St.
Salamanca, NY 14779-1516
Ph: (716)945-2034
Fax: (716)945-9143
Co. E-mail: info@salamancachamber.org
URL: http://www.salamancachamber.org
Contact: Jayne L. Fenton, President
Released: Periodic

55370 ■ *The Voice*
10785 Bennett Rd.
Dunkirk, NY 14048
Ph: (716)366-6200
Fax: (716)366-4276
Co. E-mail: cccc@chautauquachamber.org
URL: http://www.chautauquachamber.org
Contact: Todd Tranum, President
Released: Monthly **Price:** included in membership dues.

55371 ■ Waddington Area Chamber of Commerce
PO Box 291
Waddington, NY 13694-0291
Ph: (315)388-5576
Co. E-mail: waddingtonchamber@gmail.com
URL: http://www.waddingtonny.us/chamber
Contact: Alicia Murphy, President
Description: Promotes business and community development in Waddington, NY.

55372 ■ Warrensburg Chamber of Commerce
3847 Main St.
Warrensburg, NY 12885
Ph: (518)623-2161
Fax: (518)623-2184
Co. E-mail: info@warrensburgchamber.com
URL: http://www.warrensburgchamber.com
Contact: Lynn Smith, President
Description: Promotes business, community development, and tourism in the Warrensburg, NY area. **Founded:** 1975. **Publications:** *4 Seasons in the Adirondack Mountains*; *4 Seasons in the Adirondack Mountains*; *Four Seasons in the Adirondack Mountains*. **Educational Activities:** Chamber Meeting (Monthly).

55373 ■ Warwick Valley Chamber of Commerce (WVCC)
PO Box 202
Warwick, NY 10990
Ph: (845)986-2720
Co. E-mail: info@warwickcc.org
URL: http://www.warwickcc.org
Contact: Michael Johndrow, Executive Director
Description: Fosters cooperative action to advance the common interests of members in the town of Warwick, Orange County, New York and surrounding areas. **Founded:** 1939.

55374 ■ Watkins Glen Area Chamber of Commerce
214 N Franklin St., Rte. 14
Watkins Glen, NY 14891
Ph: (607)535-4300
Free: 800-607-4552
Fax: (607)535-6243
Co. E-mail: info@watkinsglenchamber.com
URL: http://www.watkinsglenchamber.com
Contact: Rebekah LaMoreaux, President
Description: Promotes business and community development in Schuyler County, NY. **Founded:** 1889. **Publications:** *Business Directory* (Annual); *Inside The Chamber* (Bimonthly); *Country Travel Guide* (Periodic). **Telecommunication Services:** rebekah@watkinsglenchamber.com.

55375 ■ Webster Chamber of Commerce (WCC)
1110 Crosspoint Ln., Ste. C
Webster, NY 14580-3280
Ph: (585)265-3960
Fax: (585)265-3702
Co. E-mail: bbernard@websterchamber.com
URL: http://www.websterchamber.com
Contact: Elizabeth Bernard, Administrator
Description: Promotes business and community development in Webster, NY. **Founded:** 1932. **Publications:** *Business and Community Service Guide* (Annual).

55376 ■ *Welcome to Canton*

55377 ■ *Welcome to the Town of Bethlehem*
318 Delaware Ave., Main Sq.
Delmar, NY 12054-1911
Ph: (518)439-0512
Fax: (518)475-0910
Co. E-mail: info@bethlehemchamber.com
URL: http://www.bethlehemchamber.com
Contact: John McIntyre, Chairman

55378 ■ Wellsville Area Chamber of Commerce (WCC)
114 N Main St.
Wellsville, NY 14895
Ph: (585)593-5080
Fax: (585)593-5088
Co. E-mail: s.havey@wellsvilleareachamber.com
URL: http://www.wellsvilleareachamber.com
Contact: Steven Havey, Executive Director
Description: Promotes business and community development in Wellsville, NY. **Founded:** 1909. **Publications:** *Chamber News* (Monthly).

55379 ■ West Seneca Chamber of Commerce
c/o Kathie Gullo, Exec. Dir.
950A Union Rd., Ste. 5
West Seneca, NY 14224
Ph: (716)674-4900
Co. E-mail: cdillchamber@westseneca.org
URL: http://www.westseneca.org
Contact: Kathie Gullo, Executive Director
Description: Promotes business and community development in West Seneca, NY. **Publications:** *FOCUS* (Monthly).

55380 ■ *What's Happening in CV, 13618*
PO Box 482
Cape Vincent, NY 13618-0482
Ph: (315)654-2481
Co. E-mail: thecape@tds.net
URL: http://www.capevincent.org
Contact: Shelley Higgins, Executive Director
Released: Annual **Price:** free.

55381 ■ *Woodstock*
PO Box 36
Woodstock, NY 12498
Ph: (845)679-6234
Co. E-mail: info@woodstockchamber.com
URL: http://woodstockchamber.com
Contact: Nick Altomare, President
Released: Annual **Price:** free.

55382 ■ Woodstock Chamber of Commerce and Arts (WCOCA)
PO Box 36
Woodstock, NY 12498

Ph: (845)679-6234
Co. E-mail: info@woodstockchamber.com
URL: http://woodstockchamber.com
Contact: Nick Altomare, President
Description: Promotes business and community development in Woodstock, NY. Sponsors annual Festival of the Arts, street fairs, and other community events. **Scope:** visitor information. **Subscriptions:** 400. **Publications:** *Woodstock* (Annual).

55383 ■ Wyoming County Chamber of Commerce (WCCC)
6470 Rte. 20A, Ste. 2
Perry, NY 14530-9798
Ph: (585)237-0230
Free: 800-951-9774
Fax: (585)237-0231
Co. E-mail: info@wycochamber.org
URL: http://www.wycochamber.org
Contact: Laura Lane, President
Description: Promotes business and community development in the Perry, NY area. Sponsors Sea Serpent Softball tournament, Sea Serpent Arts festival, and Christmas activities, shuttle to Letchworth Craft Show. **Publications:** *Chamber Gazette* (Bimonthly).

55384 ■ Yonkers Chamber of Commerce
55 Main St., 2nd Fl.
Yonkers, NY 10701
Ph: (914)963-0332
Fax: (914)963-0455
Co. E-mail: info@yonkerschamber.com
URL: http://www.yonkerschamber.com/home.html
Contact: Kevin T. Cacace, President
Description: Promotes business and community development in Yonkers, NY area. **Founded:** 1893.

MINORITY BUSINESS ASSISTANCE PROGRAMS

55385 ■ Empire State Development - Minority and Women's Business Development Division—Empire State Development
633 3rd Ave., 33rd Fl.
New York, NY 10017-6706
Ph: (212)803-2414
Free: 800-STATENY
Fax: (212)803-2459
Co. E-mail: esd@empire.state.ny.us
URL: http://www.nylovesmwbe.ny.gov/
Contact: Dasil Velez, Executive Director
Description: Assists in obtaining statewide certification, financing, business development and technical assistance, permit and regulatory assistance, market and sales expansion, and employment and training.

55386 ■ Jamaica Business Resource Center - Queens, Nassau, Suffolk Minority Business Enterprise Center
90-33 160th St.
Jamaica, NY 11432
Ph: (718)206-2255
Fax: (718)206-3693
Co. E-mail: jbrc@jbrc.org
URL: http://www.queensmbec.org
Contact: Timothy Marshall, Chief Executive Officer

55387 ■ New York State Office of General Services - Minority and Women-Owned Business and Community Relations
Corning Tower, 41st Fl.
Empire State Plaza
Albany, NY 12242
Ph: (518)486-9284
Fax: (518)486-9285
Co. E-mail: omwbeo@ogs.state.ny.us
URL: http://www.ogs.state.ny.us/mwbe/AboutUs.html
Contact: William Clay

55388 ■ Williamsburg (Brooklyn) Minority Business Development Center - Opportunity Development Association (ODA)
12 Heyward St.
Brooklyn, NY 11211
Ph: (718)522-5620

Fax: (718)522-5931
Co. E-mail: odacdc@idt.net
URL: http://www.odabdc.org
Contact: Zvi Kestenbaum, President

55389 ■ Women's Venture Fund
319 W 39th St., 5th Fl.
New York, NY 10018
Ph: (212)563-0499
Fax: (212)284-6951
Co. E-mail: info@wvf-ny.org
URL: http://www.wvf-ny.org
Description: Provides business development services for the creation or expansion of women-owned businesses in New York.

FINANCING AND LOAN PROGRAMS

55390 ■ 4C Ventures / Olivetti Holding, N.V.
21 E. 94th St., 3rd Fl.
New York, NY 10128
Ph: (212)996-3133
Fax: (212)996-1838
URL: http://www.4cventures.com
Contact: Alexandra Giurgiu, Partner
E-mail: agiurgiu@4cventures.com
Preferred Investment Size: $500,000 to $150,000,000. **Industry Preferences:** Computer hardware, computer software and services, communications and media, semiconductors and other electronics, consumer related, Internet specific, other products, and industrial and energy. **Geographic Preference:** U.S. and Canada.

55391 ■ Alimansky Capital Group, Inc.
12 E. 44th St., Penthouse
New York, NY 10017
Ph: (212)832-7300
Co. E-mail: info@alimansky.com
URL: http://www.alimansky.com
Contact: Burt Alimansky, Managing Director
Preferred Investment Size: $2,000,000. **Industry Preferences:** Communications and media, computer, related, semiconductors and other electronics, biotechnology, medical and health, consumer related, industrial and energy, transportation, financial services, business service, manufacturing, agriculture, forestry and fishing. **Geographic Preference:** U.S. and Canada.

55392 ■ Allegra Partners / Lawrence, Smith & Horey
320 Park Ave., 18th Fl.
New York, NY 10022
Ph: (212)277-1526
Fax: (212)277-1533
Co. E-mail: info@allegrapartners.com
URL: http://www.allegrapartners.com
Contact: Larry J. Lawrence, Partner
E-mail: ljl@allegrapartners.com
Preferred Investment Size: $5,000,000 to $20,000,000. **Industry Preferences:** Computer software and services, communications and media, other products, Internet specific, consumer related, medical and health. **Geographic Preference:** Eastern U.S.

55393 ■ The Argentum Group
60 Madison, Ste. 701
New York, NY 10010
Ph: (212)949-6262
Fax: (212)949-8294
URL: http://www.argentumgroup.com
Contact: Walter H. Barandiaran, Managing Partner
E-mail: walter@argentumgroup.com
Preferred Investment Size: $2,000,000-$10,000,000. **Industry Preferences:** Internet specific, medical and health, computer software and services, communications and media, industrial and energy, and computer hardware. **Geographic Preference:** U.S.

55394 ■ Arthur P. Gould & Co.
1 Wilshire Dr.
Lake Success, NY 11020
Ph: (914)723-2560

Fax: (914)723-1756
URL: http://www.gouldco.com
Contact: Andrew G. Gould, President
E-mail: andrew@gouldco.com
Preferred Investment Size: $5,000,000 minimum.
Industry Preferences: Communications, computer hardware and software, semiconductors and other electronics, biotechnology, medical and health, consumer related, industrial and energy, transportation, financial services, manufacturing, agriculture, forestry and fishing.

55395 ■ Baker Capital
575 Madison Ave., 8th Fl.
New York, NY 10022
Ph: (212)848-2000
Fax: (212)486-0660
URL: http://www.bakercapital.com
Contact: Henry G. Baker, Partner
Founded: 1995. **Industry Preferences:** Internet specific, communications and media, computer software and services, computer hardware, semiconductors and other electronics. **Geographic Preference:** U.S.

55396 ■ Bedford Capital Corp.
81 Main St., Ste. 515
White Plains, NY 10601
Ph: (914)948-3840
Fax: (914)285-9282
Co. E-mail: info@bedfordnyc.com
URL: http://www.bedfordnyc.com
Preferred Investment Size: $100,000 to $300,000.
Industry Preferences: Internet specific, medical and health, consumer related, industrial and energy, financial services, and manufacturing. **Geographic Preference:** Midwest.

55397 ■ Bessemer Venture Partners (Larchmont)
1865 Palmer Ave., Ste. 104
Larchmont, NY 10538
Ph: (914)833-5300
Fax: (914)833-5499
Co. E-mail: businessplan@bvp.com
URL: http://www.bessemervp.com
Contact: Jeremy Levine, Partner
Preferred Investment Size: $1,000,000 to $10,000,000. **Industry Preferences:** Internet specific, communications and media, computer software and services, computer hardware, semiconductors and other electronics, consumer related, medical and health, industrial and energy, biotechnology, and other products. **Geographic Preference:** U.S.

55398 ■ BlueCar Partners
The Chrysler Bldg.
405 Lexington Ave., 26th Fl.
New York, NY 10174
Ph: (212)907-6444
Fax: (775)796-3875
Co. E-mail: info@bluecarpartners.com
URL: http://www.bluecarpartners.com
Contact: Granger B. Whitelaw, Managing Director
Investment Policies: Seed and early stage. **Industry Preferences:** Communications, Internet specific, biotechnology, medical and health, and transportation. **Geographic Preference:** U.S.

55399 ■ Bluefish Ventures
990 Avenue of the Americas, Ste., 17J
New York, NY 10018
Ph: (415)614-1161
Fax: (212)695-3449
URL: http://www.bluefishventures.com
Contact: Alex Miller, Partner
E-mail: alex@bluefishventures.com
Preferred Investment Size: $250,000 to $2,000,000.
Investment Policies: Seed, start-up, early, first, and second stage. **Industry Preferences:** Communications, computer software, industrial and energy, and business service. **Geographic Preference:** Northeast and Northwest.

55400 ■ Bristol Capital
110 E. 59th St., 29th Fl.
New York, NY 10022
Ph: (212)593-3157

Fax: (212)202-5022
URL: http://www.bristolcap.com
Contact: Alan Donenfield, President
E-mail: alan@bristolcap.com
Preferred Investment Size: $1,000,000 to $10,000,000.

55401 ■ Carrot Capital Healthcare Ventures
802 6th Ave., Ste. 63
New York, NY 10001
Ph: (212)586-2226
Fax: (212)586-2246
Co. E-mail: sjacobson@carrotcapital.com
URL: http://www.carrotcapitalhealthcareventures.com
Contact: David Geliebter, Managing Partner
Preferred Investment Size: $50,000 to $1,000,000.
Investment Policies: Seed, start-up, and early stage. **Industry Preferences:** Communications, computer hardware and software, semiconductors and other electronics, biotechnology, medical and health, and industrial and energy. **Geographic Preference:** Canada.

55402 ■ CM Equity Partners, L.P.
900 Third Ave., 33rd Fl.
New York, NY 10022
Ph: (212)909-8400
Fax: (212)829-0553
URL: http://www.cmequity.com
Contact: Joel R. Jacks, Founder
Preferred Investment Size: $2,000,000 minimum.
Industry Preferences: Communications and media, and Internet specific. **Geographic Preference:** U.S. and Canada.

55403 ■ Cornerstone Equity Investors, LLC
281 Tresser Blvd., 12th Fl.
Stamford, CT 06901
Ph: (212)753-0901
Fax: (212)826-6798
URL: http://www.cornerstone-equity.com
Contact: Mark Rossi, Managing Director
E-mail: Mrossi@Cornerstone-equity.com
Preferred Investment Size: $15,000,000 to $250,000,000. **Industry Preferences:** Consumer related, medical and health, communications and media, semiconductors and other electronics, computer software and services, Internet specific, semiconductors and other electronics, other products, computer hardware, industrial and energy, and biotechnology.

55404 ■ CW Group, Inc.
910 Harvest Dr., Ste. 105
New York, NY 10021
Ph: (212)308-5266
Fax: (212)644-0354
URL: http://www.cwventures.com
Contact: Walter Channing, Partner
Preferred Investment Size: $500,000 to $5,000,000.
Industry Preferences: Medical and health, biotechnology, Internet specific, computer software and services, industrial and energy, other products, computer hardware, semiconductors and other electronics. **Geographic Preference:** U.S.

55405 ■ Dauphin Capital Partners
108 Forest Ave.
Locust Valley, NY 11560
Ph: (516)759-3339
Fax: (516)759-3322
URL: http://www.dauphincapital.com
Contact: James B. Hoover, Member
E-mail: jhoover@dauphincapital.com
Preferred Investment Size: $1,000,000 to $10,000,000. **Industry Preferences:** Medical and health. **Geographic Preference:** Mid Atlantic, Northeast, and Southeast.

55406 ■ Dawntreader Ventures
1270 Avenue of the Americas, 5th Fl.
New York, NY 10022
Ph: (646)452-6100

Fax: (646)452-6101
Co. E-mail: businessplans@dtventures.com
URL: http://www.dtventures.com
Contact: Sang Ahn, Principal
Preferred Investment Size: $1,000,000 to $15,000,000. **Investment Policies:** Seed, early, first, and second stage. **Industry Preferences:** Internet specific, computer software and services, semiconductors and other electronics, communications and media, other products, and consumer related.

55407 ■ East River Ventures, L.P.
645 Madison Ave., 22nd Fl.
New York, NY 10022
Ph: (212)644-2322
Fax: (212)644-5498
URL: http://www.eastrivervc.com
Contact: Ray Mirza, Principal
E-mail: mray@eastrivervc.com
Industry Preferences: Internet specific, medical and health, computer software and services, computer hardware, communications and media, industrial and energy, semiconductors and other electronics, biotechnology, and other products. **Geographic Preference:** U.S. and Canada.

55408 ■ Easton Hunt Capital Partners, L.P.
767 Third Ave., 7th Fl.
New York, NY 10017
Ph: (212)702-0950
Fax: (212)702-0952
Co. E-mail: info@eastoncapital.com
URL: http://www.eastoncapital.com
Contact: John H. Friedman, Managing Director
E-mail: friedman@eastoncapital.com
Preferred Investment Size: $2,000,000 to $7,500,000. **Industry Preferences:** Computer software, industrial and energy, medical and healthcare devices, business service, and manufacturing. **Geographic Preference:** U.S.

55409 ■ Eastport Partners
204 E. 20th St., 3rd Fl.
New York, NY 10003
Ph: (212)674-1900
Fax: (212)674-6821
URL: http://www.eastportlp.com
Contact: J. Andrew McWethy, Partner
E-mail: amcwethy@eastportlp.com
Investment Policies: Leveraged buyout and management buyouts. **Industry Preferences:** Manufacturing. **Geographic Preference:** U.S.

55410 ■ Elk Associates Funding Corp.
747 3rd Ave., 4th Fl.
New York, NY 10017
Ph: (212)355-2449
Fax: (212)759-3338
URL: http://www.elkassociates.com
Contact: Gary C. Granoff, President
E-mail: garyatelk@aol.com
Preferred Investment Size: $100,000 to $300,000.
Industry Preferences: Communications and media, consumer related, and transportation. **Geographic Preference:** Southeast and Midwest.

55411 ■ EOS Partners, L.P.
320 Park Ave., 9th Fl.
New York, NY 10022
Ph: (212)832-5800
Fax: (212)832-5815
URL: http://www.eospartners.com
Contact: Matt Meehan, Managing Director
E-mail: mmeehan@eospartners.com
Preferred Investment Size: $3,000,000. **Industry Preferences:** Communications and media, other products, consumer related, medical and health, semiconductors and other electronics, computer software and services, Internet specific, industrial and energy. **Geographic Preference:** U.S. and Canada.

55412 ■ Euclidsr Partners
45 Rockefeller Plz., Ste. 1910
New York, NY 10111
Ph: (212)218-6880

Fax: (212)218-6877
URL: http://www.euclidsr.com
Contact: Graham Anderson, Partner
E-mail: graham@euclidsr.com
Industry Preferences: Internet specific, computer software and services, medical and health, biotechnology, semiconductors and other electronics, computer hardware, industrial and energy, communications and media, other products, and consumer related. **Geographic Preference:** U.S.

55413 ■ Exeter Capital Partners
1 Liberty Sq., Ste. 1200
Boston, MA 02109
Ph: (617)224-0100
Fax: (617)892-4311
URL: http://www.exeterfunds.com
Contact: Keith R. Fox, Managing Partner
Preferred Investment Size: $2,000,000 to $20,000,000. **Industry Preferences:** Consumer related, Internet specific, medical and health, computer software and services, communications and media, computer hardware, other products. **Geographic Preference:** U.S.

55414 ■ FA Technology Ventures
100 High St., Ste. 1105
Boston, MA 02110
Ph: (617)757-3883
Fax: (617)757-3881
URL: http://www.fatechventures.com
Contact: George McNamee, Managing Partner
E-mail: George@fatechventures.com
Preferred Investment Size: $3,000,000 to $8,000,000. **Investment Policies:** Early stage and expansion. **Industry Preferences:** Communications, computer software, and industrial and energy. **Geographic Preference:** New York.

55415 ■ Flatiron Partners
1221 Avenue of the Americas, 39th Fl.
New York, NY 10020-1080
Ph: (212)899-3400
Fax: (212)899-3401
URL: http://www.flatironpartners.com
Contact: Philip Summe, Principal
Industry Preferences: Internet specific, computer software and services, communications and media, other products, and consumer related. **Geographic Preference:** New York and Northeast.

55416 ■ Gabelli Multimedia Partners
1 Corporate Ctr.
Rye, NY 10580-1422
Ph: (914)921-5100
Fax: (914)921-5031
Co. E-mail: fsommer@gabelli.com
URL: http://www.gabelli.com
Contact: Robert Zuccaro, Chief Financial Officer
Industry Preferences: Communications and media. **Geographic Preference:** Northeast.

55417 ■ Genesys Partners, Inc.
126 5th Ave.
New York, NY 10011
Ph: (212)686-2828
Fax: (212)686-5155
Co. E-mail: info@genesyspartners.com
URL: http://www.genesyspartners.com
Contact: James G. Kollegger, Chief Executive Officer
Industry Preferences: Internet specific. **Geographic Preference:** U.S.

55418 ■ GlobalNet Partners LP
521 5th Ave., Ste. 1703
New York, NY 10175
Ph: (212)292-4407
Fax: (212)292-4408
Co. E-mail: info@globalnet-advisors.com
URL: http://www.globalnet-advisors.com
Contact: Jonathan B. Adler, Managing Director
Investment Policies: Early and first stage. **Industry Preferences:** Communications and media, computer software, Internet specific, and industrial and energy.

55419 ■ GMG Capital Partners, L.P.
575 Lexington Ave., 28th Fl.
New York, NY 10022
Ph: (212)832-4013

Fax: (212)980-1695
Co. E-mail: info@gmgpartners.net
URL: http://www.gmgpartners.net
Contact: Joachim Gfoeller, Partner
Industry Preferences: Communications and media, and Internet specific. **Geographic Preference:** U.S.

55420 ■ Golub Capital
551 Madison Ave.
New York, NY 10022
Ph: (212)750-6060
Fax: (212)750-5505
URL: http://wwwgolubassoc.com
Contact: Andrew H. Steuerman, Managing Director
E-mail: asteuerman@golubcapital.com
Preferred Investment Size: $4,000,000 to $25,000,000. **Industry Preferences:** Medical and health, consumer related, industrial and energy, transportation, business service, and manufacturing. **Geographic Preference:** U.S.

55421 ■ Harris and Harris Group Inc.
1450 Broadway, 24th Fl.
New York, NY 10018-2224
Ph: (212)582-0900
Fax: (212)582-9563
Co. E-mail: admin@tinytechvc.com
URL: http://www.hhvc.com
Contact: Daniel B. Wolfe, President
Founded: 1981. **Preferred Investment Size:** $100,000 to $2,500,000. **Investment Policies:** Early stage. **Industry Preferences:** Communications, semiconductors and other electronics, biotechnology, medical and health, and industrial and energy. **Geographic Preference:** U.S.

55422 ■ Harvest Partners Inc.
280 Park Ave, 25th Fl.
New York, NY 10017-1264
Ph: (212)599-6300
Fax: (212)812-0100
Co. E-mail: harvestpartners@harvpart.com
URL: http://www.harvpart.com
Contact: Ira D. Klienman, Director
Founded: 1981. **Preferred Investment Size:** $40,000,000 to $600,000,000. **Industry Preferences:** Other products, industrial and energy, consumer related, communications and media, and Internet specific. **Geographic Preference:** U.S.

55423 ■ Holding Capital Group, Inc.
45 W. 45th St., 12th Fl.
New York, NY 10036
Ph: (212)486-6670
Fax: (212)486-0843
Co. E-mail: investmentdirector@holdingcapital.com
URL: http://www.holdingcapital.com
Preferred Investment Size: $2,000,000 to $150,000,000. **Geographic Preference:** U.S.

55424 ■ Hudson Venture Partners
535 5th Ave., 14th Fl.
New York, NY 10017
Ph: (212)644-9797
Fax: (212)644-7430
Co. E-mail: info@hudsonptr.com
URL: http://www.hudsonptr.com
Contact: Lawrence Howard, Managing Director
Preferred Investment Size: $1,000,000 to $3,000,000. **Industry Preferences:** Internet specific, computer software and services, communications and media, computer hardware, biotechnology, medical and health, other products, semiconductors and other electronics. **Geographic Preference:** Mid Atlantic and Northeast.

55425 ■ I-Hatch Ventures, LLC
584 Broadway, Ste. 1103
New York, NY 10012
Ph: (212)651-1750
Fax: (212)208-4590
Co. E-mail: info@i-hatch.com
URL: http://www.i-hatch.com
Contact: Brad Farkas, Principal
Industry Preferences: Internet specific, computer software, hardware and services, consumer related, communications and media. **Geographic Preference:** Northeast.

55426 ■ Impact Venture Partners
2705 Westlake Dr.
Austin, TX 78746
Ph: (512)827-9039
Fax: (512)214-0909
Co. E-mail: eve@impactvp.com
URL: http://www.impactvp.com
Contact: Adam Dell, Partner
Preferred Investment Size: $3,000,000 to $5,000,000. **Investment Policies:** Early stage. **Industry Preferences:** Internet specific, computer software and services, communications and media, and computer hardware. **Geographic Preference:** Northeast and Texas.

55427 ■ Insight Venture Partners / Insight Capital Partners
680 5th Ave., 8th Fl.
New York, NY 10019
Ph: (212)230-9200
Fax: (212)230-9272
URL: http://www.insightpartners.com
Contact: Deven Parekh, Managing Director
Preferred Investment Size: $5,000,000 to $30,000,000. **Industry Preferences:** Internet specific, computer software and services, other products, consumer related, computer hardware, communications and media. **Geographic Preference:** U.S and Canada.

55428 ■ InterEquity Capital Partners, L.P.
220 5th Ave.
New York, NY 10001
Ph: (212)779-2022
Fax: (212)779-2103
URL: http://www.interequity-capital.com
Contact: Irwin Schlass, President
Preferred Investment Size: $1,000,000 to $3,000,000. **Industry Preferences:** Internet specific, medical and health, computer software and services, consumer related, other products, industrial and energy, communications and media. **Geographic Preference:** U.S.

55429 ■ Jegi Capital, LLC
150 E. 52nd St., 18th Fl.
New York, NY 10022
Ph: (212)754-0710
Fax: (212)754-0337
URL: http://www.jegi.com
Contact: David Clark, Managing Director
Preferred Investment Size: $5,000,000 to $10,000,000. **Investment Policies:** Early, first and second stage. **Industry Preferences:** Computer hardware and software, Internet specific, and semiconductors and other electronics. **Geographic Preference:** U.S.

55430 ■ Jerusalem Venture Partners /JVP
156 5th Ave., Ste. 410
New York, NY 10010
Ph: (212)479-5100
Fax: (212)213-1776
URL: http://www.jvpvc.com
Contact: Erel N. Margalit, Founder
Preferred Investment Size: $2,000,000 to $35,000,000. **Industry Preferences:** Internet specific, semiconductors and other electronics, communications and media, computer software and services, and computer hardware.

55431 ■ The Jordan Edmiston Group Inc. / JEGI Capital
150 East 52nd St., 18th Fl.
New York, NY 10022
Ph: (212)754-0710
Fax: (212)754-0337
URL: http://www.jegi.com
Contact: Richard Mead, Managing Director
Preferred Investment Size: $5,000,000 to $10,000,000. **Investment Policies:** Early, first and second stage. **Industry Preferences:** Computer hardware and software, Internet specific, and semiconductors and other electronics. **Geographic Preference:** U.S.

55432 ■ J.P. Morgan Capital Corp.
101 California St., 38th Fl.
San Francisco, CA 94111

Ph: (415)954-4704
Fax: (415)954-4737
URL: http://www.jpmorgan.com
Contact: John Mayer, Chief Executive Officer
Preferred Investment Size: $10,000,000 to $20,000,000. **Industry Preferences:** Other products, communications and media, Internet specific, computer software and services, semiconductors and other electronics, consumer related, medical and health, computer hardware, biotechnology, industrial and energy. **Geographic Preference:** U.S. and Canada.

55433 ■ KBL Healthcare Ventures
52 East 72nd St. - PH
New York, NY 10021
Ph: (212)319-5555
Fax: (212)319-5591
Co. E-mail: inquiries@kblhealthcare.com
URL: http://www.kblhealthcare.com
Contact: Marlene Krauss, Managing Director
E-mail: mkrauss@kblhealthcare.com
Preferred Investment Size: $110,000,000 to $500,000,000. **Industry Preferences:** Medical and health, biotechnology, Internet specific, communications and media, computer software and services. **Geographic Preference:** U.S.

55434 ■ The Lambda Funds
432 E. 84th St.
New York, NY 10028
Ph: (212)774-1812
Fax: (212)230-9886
URL: http://www.lambdafund.com
Contact: Anthony Lamport, Partner
E-mail: alamport@lambdafund.com
Preferred Investment Size: $100,000 to $1,500,000. **Investment Policies:** First stage and management buyouts. **Industry Preferences:** Biotechnology, computer hardware, computer software and services, industrial and energy, consumer related, other products, semiconductors and other electronics, medical and health, communications and media, Internet specific. **Geographic Preference:** Mid Atlantic, Northeast, and West Coast.

55435 ■ Lazard Technology Partners
30 Rockefeller Plz., 48th Fl.
New York, NY 10020
Ph: (212)632-6000
Fax: (212)332-8677
URL: http://www.lazardtp.com
Contact: Russell Planitzer, Principal
Preferred Investment Size: $2,000,000 to $8,000,000. **Industry Preferences:** Internet specific, computer software and services, computer hardware, communications and media, semiconductors and other electronics, and consumer related. **Geographic Preference:** District of Columbia, East Coast, and New York.

55436 ■ Lepercq Capital Management, Inc. / Lepercq de Neuflize & Co., Inc.
156 W. 56th St., 18th Fl.
New York, NY 10019
Ph: (212)698-0700
Fax: (212)262-1055
Co. E-mail: elleng@lepercq.com
URL: http://www.lepercq.com
Contact: Francois Letaconnoux, Chief Executive Officer
Preferred Investment Size: $1,000,000 to $10,000,000. **Industry Preferences:** Communications, computer hardware and software, Internet specific, and consumer related.

55437 ■ Loeb Partners Corp.
61 Broadway
New York, NY 10006
Ph: (212)483-7000
Fax: (212)574-2001
URL: http://www.loebpartners.com
Contact: Thomas Kempner, Chief Executive Officer
Preferred Investment Size: $100,000 minimum. **Industry Preferences:** Internet specific, biotechnology, medical and health, Internet specific, computer software and services, semiconductors and other electronics. **Geographic Preference:** U.S.

55438 ■ McGraw-Hill Ventures /McGraw-Hill Capital Corp.
1221 Avenue of the Americas
New York, NY 10020-1095
Ph: (212)512-2000
Fax: (212)512-3840
URL: http://www.mcgraw-hill.com
Contact: Brian Casey, Vice President
Preferred Investment Size: $500,000 to $5,000,000. **Industry Preferences:** Communications and media, computer software, Internet specific, medical and health, industrial and energy, financial services, business service, and manufacturing. **Geographic Preference:** U.S.

55439 ■ Metropolitan Venture Partners (METVP)
590 Madison Ave., 34th Fl.
New York, NY 10022
Ph: (212)561-1219
Fax: (212)561-1201
Co. E-mail: contact@metvp.com
URL: http://www.metvp.com
Contact: Michael Levin, Managing Director
Preferred Investment Size: $500,000 to $5,000,000. **Industry Preferences:** Communications, computer software, semiconductors and other electronics, and Internet specific. **Geographic Preference:** Northeast.

55440 ■ Milestone Venture Partners
551 Madison Ave., 7th Fl.
New York, NY 10022
Ph: (212)223-7400
Fax: (212)223-0315
Co. E-mail: bplans@milestonevp.com
URL: http://www.milestonevp.com
Contact: Richard J. Dumler, Partner
E-mail: rjd@milestonevp.com
Preferred Investment Size: $250,000 to $2,000,000. **Industry Preferences:** Communications and media, computer software, and Internet specific. **Geographic Preference:** Connecticut, New Jersey, New York, Eastern Pennsylvania, and to a lesser extent, the Northeast and Mid Atlantic.

55441 ■ Mitsui & Co. Venture Partners (MCVP)
200 Park Ave.
New York, NY 10166-0130
Ph: (212)878-4050
Fax: (212)878-4070
URL: http://www.mitsuiventures.com
Contact: Koichi Ando, Chief Executive Officer
Investment Policies: Start-up, seed, early, first and second stage, and research and development. **Industry Preferences:** Communications and media, Internet specific, computer software and services, biotechnology, medical and health, computer hardware, semiconductors and other electronics, and other products. **Geographic Preference:** U.S. and Canada.

55442 ■ Murphy and Partners, L.P.
708 3rd Ave., 6th Fl.
New York, NY 10017
Ph: (212)209-3879
Fax: (212)209-7148
URL: http://www.murphy-partners.com
Contact: John J. Murphy, Jr., Partner
E-mail: john@murphy-partners.com
Preferred Investment Size: $1,000,000 to $10,000,000. **Industry Preferences:** Communications, medical and health, and consumer related. **Geographic Preference:** U.S.

55443 ■ Nazem and Co.
570 Lexington Ave., 15th Fl.
New York, NY 10022
Ph: (212)371-7900
Fax: (212)371-2150
URL: http://www.nazem.com
Contact: Fred F. Nazem, Managing Partner
E-mail: fnazem@nazem.com
Preferred Investment Size: $1,000,000 minimum. **Industry Preferences:** Computer hardware, computer software and services, medical and health, communications and media, biotechnology, semicon-

ductors and other electronics, Internet specific, industrial and energy, other products, and consumer related. **Geographic Preference:** U.S.

55444 ■ Needham Asset Management
445 Park Ave.
New York, NY 10022
Ph: (212)705-0404
Fax: (212)705-0455
Co. E-mail: jgiangrasso@needhamco.com
URL: http://www.needhamfunds.com
Contact: George Needham, Chief Executive Officer
Preferred Investment Size: $2,000,000 to $10,000,000. **Industry Preferences:** Semiconductors and other electronics, computer software and services, communications and media, Internet specific, medical and health, computer hardware, other products, consumer related, industrial and energy. **Geographic Preference:** U.S.

55445 ■ Northwood Ventures
485 Underhill Blvd., Ste. 205
Syosset, NY 11791
Ph: (516)364-5544
Fax: (516)364-0879
URL: http://www.northwoodventures.com
Contact: Peter Schiff, President
E-mail: hwilson@northwoodventures.com
Preferred Investment Size: $1,000,000 to $15,000,000. **Industry Preferences:** Communications and media, Internet specific, consumer related, biotechnology, industrial and energy, semiconductors and other electronics, computer software and services, and computer hardware. **Geographic Preference:** U.S. and Canada.

55446 ■ Norwood Venture Corp.
174 Dezenzo Ln.
West Orange, NJ 107043
Ph: (917)748-5734
Fax: (212)869-5331
Co. E-mail: nvc@norven.com
URL: http://www.norven.com
Contact: Mark R. Littell, Director
Preferred Investment Size: $250,000 to $1,000,000. **Industry Preferences:** Business services. **Geographic Preference:** U.S.

55447 ■ Onondaga Venture Capital Fund, Inc.
241 W. Fayette St.
Syracuse, NY 13202
Ph: (315)478-0157
Fax: (315)478-0158
Co. E-mail: info@ovcfund.com
URL: http://www.ovcfund.com
Contact: Michael Schattner, President
Preferred Investment Size: $50,000 to $300,000. **Industry Preferences:** Communications, computer software, semiconductors and other electronics, biotechnology, medical and health, consumer related, and manufacturing. **Geographic Preference:** Northeast.

55448 ■ Opticality Ventures
29 Country Club Ln., S.
Briarcliff Manor, NY 10510
Ph: (914)923-0003
Fax: (413)487-2114
URL: http://www.opticality.com
Contact: Hadar Pedhazur, Founder
E-mail: hadar@opticality.com
Preferred Investment Size: $1,000,000 to $5,000,000. **Investment Policies:** Early stage. **Industry Preferences:** Computer software and Internet specific.

55449 ■ Ovation Capital Partners
800 3rd Ave., 21st Fl.
New York, NY 10605
Ph: (212)209-3036
Fax: (212)209-3039
URL: http://www.ovationcapital.com
Contact: Greg Frank, Partner
Preferred Investment Size: $1,000,000 to $5,000,000. **Industry Preferences:** Internet related. **Geographic Preference:** Northeast.

55450 ■ Pennell Venture Partners, LLC
332 Bleecker St., Ste. K-67
New York, NY 10014
Ph: (718)855-7087
Fax: (646)365-3195
Co. E-mail: plans@pennell.com
URL: http://www.pennell.com
Contact: Thomas Pennell, President
Preferred Investment Size: $300,000 to $1,500,000.
Investment Policies: Early stage. **Industry Preferences:** Computer software and business services.
Geographic Preference: New York.

55451 ■ Pomona Capital
780 3rd Ave.
New York, NY 10017-7076
Ph: (212)593-3639
Fax: (212)593-3987
Co. E-mail: contactus@pomonacapital.com
URL: http://www.pomonacapital.com
Contact: Mark Marusezewski, Principal
Preferred Investment Size: $1,000,000 minimum.
Industry Preferences: Communications and media, computer hardware and software, biotechnology, medical and health, consumer related, industrial and energy, financial services, and manufacturing. **Geographic Preference:** U.S. and Canada.

55452 ■ Prospect Street Ventures / Prospect Capital Corporation
10 East 40th St., 44th Fl.
New York, NY 10016
Ph: (212)448-0702
Fax: (212)448-9652
Co. E-mail: Deals@prospectstreet.com
URL: http://www.prospectstreet.com
Contact: John Francis Barry, III, Managing Director
Preferred Investment Size: $5,000,000 to $25,000,000. **Industry Preferences:** Internet specific, computer software and services, other products, communications and media, medical and health. **Geographic Preference:** U.S. and Canada.

55453 ■ Rand Capital Corp.—Rand Capital
2200 Rand Bldg.
Buffalo, NY 14203-1922
Ph: (716)853-0802
Fax: (716)854-8480
URL: http://www.randcapital.com
Contact: Allan F. (Pete) Grum, President
Founded: 1969. **Preferred Investment Size:** $500,000 to $1,500,000. **Industry Preferences:** Industrial and energy, other products, communications and media, computer software and services, Internet specific, medical and health, industrial and energy, consumer related, semiconductors and other electronics, computer hardware, and biotechnology.
Geographic Preference: Western and Upstate New York and syndicates outside these areas. York.

55454 ■ Sandler Capital Management
711 5th Ave., 15th Fl.
New York, NY 10022-3111
Ph: (212)754-8100
Fax: (212)826-0280
URL: http://www.sandlercap.com
Contact: Andrew Sandler, Managing Director
Founded: 1979. **Preferred Investment Size:** $20,000,000 minimum. **Investment Policies:** Equity.
Industry Preferences: Internet specific, communications and media, other products, computer software and services, consumer related, medical and health, semiconductors and other electronics. **Geographic Preference:** U.S. and Canada.

55455 ■ Seed Capital Partners/ SoftBank Capital
1 HSBC Ctr., Ste. 3850
Buffalo, NY 14203
Ph: (716)845-7520
Fax: (716)845-7539
URL: http://www.seedcp.com
Contact: Jordan A. Levy, Partner
Preferred Investment Size: $250 to $2,500,000. **Industry Preferences:** Computer software and services, communications and media, Internet specific, semiconductors and other electronics, and other products. **Geographic Preference:** Northeast U.S. and southeastern Canada.

55456 ■ Siguler Guff & Company
825 3rd Ave., 10th Fl.
New York, NY 10022
Ph: (212)332-5100
Fax: (212)332-5120
Co. E-mail: info@sigulerguff.com
URL: http://www.sigulerguff.com
Contact: Drew Guff, Managing Director
Industry Preferences: Communications, computer software and hardware, Internet specific, semiconductors and other electronics, biotechnology, medical and health, consumer related, industrial and energy, transportation, financial services, business service, manufacturing, agriculture, forestry and fishing. **Geographic Preference:** U.S.

55457 ■ Silicon Alley Venture Partners LLC / SAVP
300 Park Ave.
New York, NY 10022
Ph: (212)389-1600
Fax: (212)389-1805
Co. E-mail: partners@savp.com
URL: http://www.savp.com
Contact: Steve Brotman, Managing Director
E-mail: sbrotman@greenhill.com
Preferred Investment Size: $3,000,000 to $6,000,000. **Investment Policies:** Start-up, seed, first, early and second stage. **Industry Preferences:** Computer software, Internet specific, technology, and business services. **Geographic Preference:** Northeast.

55458 ■ Spencer Trask Ventures, Inc. / Spencer Trask Securities
750 3rd Ave., 11th Fl.
New York, NY 10017
Free: 800-622-7078
Co. E-mail: inquiries@spencertrask.com
URL: http://www.spencertrask.com
Contact: William Dioguardi, President
Preferred Investment Size: $1,000,000 to $20,000,000. **Industry Preferences:** Communications and media, computer hardware and software, Internet specific, semiconductors and other electronics, biotechnology, medical and health, consumer related, industrial and energy, financial services, and manufacturing. **Geographic Preference:** U.S.

55459 ■ Sprout Group (New York City)
11 Madison Ave., 13th Fl.
New York, NY 10010
Ph: (212)325-7587
Fax: (212)322-0530
URL: http://www.sproutgroup.com
Contact: Robert Finzi, Managing Partner
Preferred Investment Size: $5,000,000 to $50,000,000. **Industry Preferences:** Medical and health, Internet specific, communications and media, biotechnology, consumer related, computer software and services, semiconductors and other electronics, industrial and energy, other products, and computer hardware. **Geographic Preference:** U.S.

55460 ■ Stamford Financial Consulting
108 Main St.
Stamford, NY 12167
Ph: (607)652-3311
Fax: (607)652-6301
Co. E-mail: dcre@wpe.com
URL: http://www.stamfordfinancial.com
Preferred Investment Size: $2,000,000 to $5,000,000. **Industry Preferences:** Communications, semiconductors and other electronics, consumer related, medical and health, industrial and energy, financial services, and business service. **Geographic Preference:** U.S.

55461 ■ Vencon Management, Inc.
65 W. 55th St.
New York, NY 10019
Ph: (212)581-8787

Fax: (208)955-5165
Co. E-mail: vencon@worldnet.att.net
URL: http://www.venconinc.com
Contact: Irvin Barash, President
Preferred Investment Size: $500,000 to $3,000,000.
Industry Preferences: Communications, computer software, Internet specific, semiconductors and other electronics, biotechnology, medical and health. **Geographic Preference:** U.S. and Canada.

55462 ■ Venrock Associates
530 5th Ave., 22nd Fl.
New York, NY 10036
Ph: (212)444-4100
Fax: (212)444-4101
URL: http://www.venrock.com
Contact: Mike Brooks, Partner
Preferred Investment Size: $5,000,000 to $15,000,000. **Industry Preferences:** Biotechnology, Internet specific, computer software and services, communications and media, medical and health, semiconductors and other electronics, industrial and energy, computer hardware, other products, and consumer related. **Geographic Preference:** U.S.

55463 ■ Venture Capital Fund of America, Inc. / VCFA Group
509 Madison Ave.
New York, NY 10022
Ph: (212)838-5577
Fax: (212)838-7614
URL: http://www.vcfa.com
Contact: Dayton T. Carr, Managing Director
E-mail: carr@vcfa.com
Preferred Investment Size: $1,000,000 to $100,000,000. **Geographic Preference:** U.S and Canada.

55464 ■ Warburg Pincus LLC
450 Lexington Ave.
New York, NY 10017
Ph: (212)878-0600
Fax: (212)878-9351
Co. E-mail: info@warburgpincus.com
URL: http://www.warburgpincus.com
Contact: Scott Arenare, Managing Director
Preferred Investment Size: $1,000,000 minimum.
Industry Preferences: Other products, communications and media, medical and health, Internet specific, computer hardware computer software and services, consumer related, industrial and energy, biotechnology, semiconductors and other electronics. **Geographic Preference:** U.S. and Canada.

55465 ■ Welsh, Carson, Anderson, & Stowe
320 Park Ave., Ste. 2500
New York, NY 10022-6815
Ph: (212)893-9500
Fax: (212)893-9575
URL: http://www.welshcarson.com
Contact: Johnathan Rather, Chief Financial Officer
Preferred Investment Size: $100,000,000 to $500,000,000. **Industry Preferences:** Medical and health, other products, communications and media, Internet specific, computer software and services, computer hardware, consumer related, semiconductors and other electronics.

PROCUREMENT ASSISTANCE PROGRAMS

55466 ■ Empire State Development - Division for Small Business - Procurement Assistance Program
30 S Pearl St.
Albany, NY 12245
Ph: (518)292-5250
Free: 800-STATENY
Fax: (518)592-5884
Co. E-mail: mylovessmbiz@empire.state.ny.us
URL: http://www.empire.state.ny.us
Description: Assists businesses in obtaining contracts and subcontracts from federal and state agencies, departments, and authorities, and from prime contractors in the private sector. Offers training, technical, management, and marketing assistance. Also assists New York state small businesses to

compete for Federal research and development grants. The Procurement Assistance Unit also puts out a publication entitled Selling to Government: Finding New Customers for New York's Businesses.

55467 ■ New York City Department of Business Services - New York City Procurement Outreach Program
110 William St., 7th Fl.
New York, NY 10038
Ph: (212)513-6444
Fax: (212)618-8899
Co. E-mail: bizhelp@nyc.gov
URL: http://www.nyc.gov
Contact: Robert W. Walsh, Commissioner

55468 ■ New York Procurement Center
U.S. Army Corps of Engineers
26 Federal Plaza, Rm. 3100
New York, NY 10278
Ph: (212)264-1762
Fax: (202)481-4286
Co. E-mail: malinda.chen@sba.gov
URL: http://www.sba.gov
Contact: Malinda Chen, Specialist
E-mail: debra.libow@sba.gov
Description: Covers activities for GSA, Federal Supply Service (New York, NY), GSA, Public Buildings Service (New York, NY), Army Corps of Engineers (New York, NY), U.S. Military Academy (West Point, NY).

55469 ■ New York Procurement Technical Assistance Center
50 W Main St., Ste. 8100
Rochester, NY 14614
Ph: (585)753-2015
Co. E-mail: pbirch@monroecounty.gov
URL: http://www.RochesterPTCA.com
Contact: Paulette Birch, Program Director
E-mail: PBirch@MonroeCounty.gov
Description: Assists members in all facets of selling to the government and military.

55470 ■ New York Procurement Technical Assistance Center - Cattaraugus County
303 Court St.
Little Valley, NY 14755
Ph: (716)938-2331
Free: 800-331-0543
Fax: (716)938-2779
Co. E-mail: jjwilliams@cattco.com
URL: http://ww2.cattco.com/procurement-technical-assistance-center/government-marketing
Contact: Joseph Williams, Program Manager
Description: Assist businesses in marketing goods and services to military, federal, state, and local government agencies.

55471 ■ New York Procurement Technical Assistance Center - LaGuardia Community College PTAC
31-10 Thomson Ave.
Long Island City, NY 11101
Ph: (718)482-5315
Fax: (718)609-2091
Co. E-mail: PTAC@lagcc.cuny.edu
URL: http://www.laguardia-ptac.org
Contact: Edgard Hernandez, Director
E-mail: benh@lagcc.cuny.edu
Description: Assists Queens and other New York City firms market their goods and services to the federal, state, and local governments.

55472 ■ New York Procurement Technical Assistance Center - Long Island Development Corporation
45 Seaman Ave.
Bethpage, NY 11714
Free: 866-433-5432
Fax: (516)433-5046
Co. E-mail: info@lidc.org
URL: http://www.lidc.org
Contact: Roslyn D. Goldmacher, Chief Executive Officer
Description: Assistance to small businesses desiring to win contracts to supply the government, both federal and state.

55473 ■ New York Procurement Technical Assistance Center - Rochester Business Alliance
50 W Main St., Ste. 8100
Rochester, NY 14614
Ph: (585)753-2015
Co. E-mail: pbirch@monroecounty.gov
URL: http://www.RochesterPTAC.com
Contact: Paulette Birch, Director
E-mail: paulette.birch@RBAlliance.com
Description: Provides free government contract consulting to diverse business concerns serving Monroe, Genesee, Livingston, Ontario, Orleans, Seneca, and Wayne counties.

55474 ■ New York Procurement Technical Assistance Center - Rockland Economic Development Corporation
Two Blue Hill Plaza
Pearl River, NY 10965
Ph: (845)735-7040
Fax: (845)735-5736
Co. E-mail: info@redc.org
URL: http://www.redc.org
Contact: Liz Kallen, Program Manager
Description: Provides programs and services to make your relocation and expansion decisions easier and cost effective.

55475 ■ New York Procurement Technical Assistance Center - South Bronx Overall Economic Development Corporation
555 Bergen Ave.
Bronx, NY 10455
Ph: (718)292-3113
Fax: (718)292-3153
Co. E-mail: mjohnson@sobro.org
URL: http://www.sobro.org
Description: Assists local businesses in securing government contracts.

55476 ■ Rochester Procurement Technical Assistance Center
50 West Main St., Ste. 8100
Rochester, NY 14614
Ph: (585)753-2015
Co. E-mail: pbirch@monroecounty.gov
URL: http://www.rochesterptac.com
Contact: Paulette Birch, Director
E-mail: PBirch@MonroeCounty.com
Description: Provides free government contract consulting to diverse business concerns. Rochester PTAC serves the counties of Monroe, Genesee, Livingston, Ontario, Orleans, Seneca, and Wayne.

INCUBATORS/RESEARCH AND TECHNOLOGY PARKS

55477 ■ Adirondack Regional Business Incubator
234 Glen St.
Glen Falls, NY 12801
Ph: (518)761-6007
Fax: (518)761-9053
Co. E-mail: pwohl@arbi.biz
URL: http://www.arbi.biz/
Description: A small business incubator seeking to enhance economic development in Warren County by having a state-of-the-art business center offering value-added programs advisory talent, integrated with ACC and the area business community, to unleash the leadership potential and nurture the success of innovative regional businesses.

55478 ■ Albany Center for Economic Success
255 Orange St., Ste. 101
Albany, NY 12210
Ph: (518)427-7804
URL: http://www.acesincubator.org/
Description: A private, non-profit organization focusing on building local business by providing incubator services and technical assistance programs. It provides below market rate office space and supports tenants through shared clerical staff, general office equipment, conference space, and on-going technical service.

55479 ■ Batavia Industrial Center
56 Harvester Ave.
Batavia, NY 14020
Ph: (585)343-2800
Fax: (585)343-7096
Co. E-mail: info@bic4biz.com
URL: http://www.bic4biz.com
Description: A small business incubator focused on the success of small, emerging and established businesses with a large inventory of space, knowledge and experience.

55480 ■ Broome County Industrial Development Agency
Edwin L. Crawford County Office Bldg.
60 Hawley St., 5th Fl.
Binghamton, NY 13902-0995
Ph: (607)584-9000
Free: 800-836-6740
Fax: (607)584-9009
Co. E-mail: info@bcida.com
URL: http://www.bcida.com
Contact: Richard D'Attilio, Executive Director
Description: Provides comprehensive services to companies, including needs assessment, site selection, financial aide, and more.

55481 ■ The Case Center
2-212 Center for Science and Technology
Syracuse University Office of Research
Syracuse, NY 13244
Ph: (315)443-1060
Fax: (315)443-4745
Co. E-mail: case@syr.edu
URL: http://www.case.syr.edu
Contact: Pramod Varshney, Director
Description: An applied research center for advanced technology, Provides R&D collaboration, networking, incubation services, and more.

55482 ■ Center for Environmental Sciences and Technology Management
University at Albany
251 Fuller Rd.
CESTM B110
Albany, NY 12203
Ph: (518)437-8686
Fax: (518)437-8610
URL: http://www.albanynanotech.org
Contact: Jackie DiStefano
Description: This incubator for emerging technology firms offers abundant resources to its tenants, including the University's Nuclear Accelerator Laboratory, electron microscopes, cluster tools, and much more.

55483 ■ Ceramics Corridor Innovation Center
109 Canada Rd.
Painted Post, NY 14870
Ph: (607)962-6387
Fax: (607)962-0645
Co. E-mail: webmaster@ceramicscorridor.org
URL: http://www.ceramicscorridor.org/
Description: A not-for-profit incubation program dedicated to expansion, research and development, and job creation in the ceramics, glass, advanced materials, and materials science technologies in the Ceramics Corridor of New York State. Provides leasing space, technology resources and support, and networking opportunities.

55484 ■ East Side Business Center
1201 E. Fayette St.
Syracuse, NY 13210
Ph: (315)475-8456
Co. E-mail: jkeller@housingvisions.org
URL: http://esbc.housingvisions.org
Description: A small business incubator offering office and light manufacturing/industrial space to new ventures, entrepreneurs and expanding businesses. Formerly the Samuel W. Williams Jr. Business Center.

55485 ■ Hudson Valley Center for Innovation
Hudson Valley Technology Development Center
300 Westage Business Center
Fishkill, NY 12524
Ph: (845)943-5660

Fax: (845)336-8050
Co. E-mail: lneumann@hvcfi.com
URL: http://www.hvcfi.com/index2.aspx
Contact: Les Neumann, Director
Description: A not-for-profit corporation formed to foster the growth and development of emerging high value business and technology development firms, and the creation of high-value jobs throughout the Hudson Valley region of New York State through the implementation, and enhancement, of the cost-effective business incubation model.

55486 ■ Jefferson County Job Development Corporation
800 Starbuck Ave., Ste. 800
Watertown, NY 13601
Ph: (315)782-5865
Free: 800-553-4111
Fax: (315)782-7915
URL: http://www.jcjdc.net/
Description: A small business incubator offering a one-stop-shop for business development assistance, from capital financing to low-cost facility options to economic development incentives.

55487 ■ Lennox Tech Enterprise Center
High Tech Rochester
150 Lucius Gordon Dr., Ste. 100
West Henrietta, NY 14586
Ph: (585)214-2400
Co. E-mail: info@htr.org
URL: http://htr.org/incubator.asp
Description: A catalyst for innovators who plan to build high-growth businesses, offering success services for startup entrepreneurs.

55488 ■ Local Development Corporation of East New York - East Brooklyn Enterprise Center
80 Jamaica Ave., 3rd Fl.
Brooklyn, NY 11207
Ph: (718)385-6700
Fax: (718)385-7505
Co. E-mail: info@ldceny.org
URL: http://www.ldceny.org
Contact: Sherry Roberts, Executive Director
Description: Works to improve the economic situation of East Brooklyn. Operates four divisions: industry, business development, environment, and housing.

55489 ■ Long Island Forum for Technology
510 Grumman Rd. W, Ste. 201
Bethpage, NY 11714
Ph: (631)969-3700
Fax: (631)969-2789
Co. E-mail: info@lift.org
URL: http://www.lift.org
Description: A non-profit development organization offering networking, access to technology, and other business services.

55490 ■ Long Island High Technology Incubator
25 Health Sciences Drive
Box 100
Stony Brook, NY 11790-3350
Ph: (631)444-8800
Fax: (631)444-8825
Co. E-mail: anil.chundale@stonybrook.edu
URL: http://www.lihti.org
Contact: Anil Dhundale, Executive Director
Description: The LIHTI offers tenants a place to start up companies without the difficulties normally associated with emerging businesses. The incubator also provides numerous services through its alliances with both public and private sector organizations.

55491 ■ Mi Kitchen es su Kitchen
370 E. 76th St., Ste. A2004
New York, NY 10021-2550
Ph: (212)452-1866
Fax: (212)452-1767
Co. E-mail: mikitchen1866@aol.com
URL: http://www.mikitchenesukitchen.com/
Contact: Katherine Gregory, Director
Description: A small business incubator offering a time-share rental facility available to up-and-coming food entrepreneurs.

55492 ■ Operation Oswego County
44 W. Bridge St.
Oswego, NY 13126
Ph: (315)343-1545
Fax: (315)343-1546
Co. E-mail: ooc@oswegocounty.org
URL: http://www.oswegocounty.org/
Description: A small business incubator created to establish and implement sound economic development strategies in order to enhance the economic vitality of Oswego County's businesses, industries and citizens leading to an overall better quality of life; its mission is the creation and retention of job opportunities, diversification and strengthening of the economic base, and developing the local economy in a planned, organized and environmentally-friendly atmosphere.

55493 ■ Rensselaer Incubation Program
110 8th St., 3210 J Bldg.
Troy, NY 12180-3590
Ph: (518)276-6658
Fax: (518)276-6380
Co. E-mail: incubator@rpi.edu
URL: http://www.incubator.com
Contact: Ronald M. Kudia, Executive Director
Description: This program, located at Rensselaer Polytechnic Institute, seeks to nurture new technological ventures. It offers tenants affordable offices space, laboratories, and light manufacturing space as well as other services.

55494 ■ Schenectady County Community Business Center
920 Albany St.
Schenectady, NY 12307
Ph: (518)382-3069
Fax: (518)688-2028
Co. E-mail: info@sccbc.org
URL: http://www.sccbc.org/
Description: A small business incubator offering a one-stop resource center for new, growing and challenged small businesses in Schenectady County, New York by providing whatever an entrepreneur needs to build a business.

55495 ■ Second Century Innovation and Ideas Corp
163 William St., 3rd Fl.
New York, NY 10038-2602
Ph: (212)346-1064
Fax: (212)346-1116
Co. E-mail: info@sci2
URL: http://www.sci2.org/
Description: A commercialization accelerator for early stage companies seeking funding, intellectual capital, business development expertise, and potential strategic relationships with Fortune 1000 companies that results in jobs and economic development in Westchester and in lower Manhattan.

55496 ■ SUNY Fredonia Technology Incubator
214 Central Ave.
338 Central Ave., Ste. 340
Dunkirk, NY 14048
Ph: (716)681-6009
Fax: (715)680-6008
Co. E-mail: incubator@fredonia.edu
URL: http://incubator.fredonia.edu
Description: In incubator supporting technology-based businesses. Entrepreneurs also receive help in getting their ideas and businesses up and running, such as through development of business plans, accounting and legal services, office management, financing/venture capital strategies, and marketing plans.

55497 ■ U-Start Business Incubator
4 Nott Terrace
Schenectady, NY 12308
Ph: (518)631-0472
Fax: (518)631-0475
Co. E-mail: execdir@ustartincubator.org
URL: http://www.ustartincubator.org
Contact: William Johnson, Executive Director
Description: A small business incubator whose mission is to support and encourage promising entrepreneurs to grow their ideas in Schenectady County.

55498 ■ UB Technology Incubator
Office of Science, Technology Transfer and Economic Outreach
1576 Sweet Home Rd.
Amherst, NY 14228
Ph: (716)645-5500
Fax: (716)636-5921
Co. E-mail: prv-stor@buffalo.edu
URL: http://www.research.buffalo.edu/stor/incubator/
Description: A small business incubator supporting the creation of new technology-based businesses by providing affordable business services to entrepreneurs.

EDUCATIONAL PROGRAMS

55499 ■ Board of Cooperative Educational Services - Adult and Continuing Education
53 Gibson Rd.
Goshen, NY 10924-9777
Ph: (845)291-0100
Fax: (845)291-0498
Co. E-mail: adulted@ouboces.mhrcc.org
URL: http://www.ouboces.org/
Description: Offers a ten-session class in small business organization.

55500 ■ Bryant and Stratton Business Institute - Henrietta Campus
1225 Jefferson Rd.
Henrietta, NY 14623
Ph: (585)292-5627
Fax: (585)292-6015
URL: http://www.bryantstratton.edu
Description: Business college offering programs in business management and business operations.

55501 ■ Bryant and Stratton Business Institute - Syracuse Campus
953 James St.
Syracuse, NY 13203-2502
Ph: (315)472-6603
Fax: (315)474-4383
Co. E-mail: SyracuseDT@bryanstratton.edu
URL: http://www.bryantstratton.edu
Description: Business college offering programs in business management and business operations.

55502 ■ Bryant and Stratton College - Buffalo Campus
465 Main St., Ste. 400
Buffalo, NY 14203
Ph: (716)884-9120
Free: 866-948-0571
Fax: (716)884-0091
Co. E-mail: buffalo@bryanstratton.edu
URL: http://www.bryantstratton.edu
Description: Business college offering programs in business management and business operations.

55503 ■ C. W Post Campus of Long Island University - Long Island University
720 Northern Blvd.
Brookville, NY 11548
Ph: (516)299-2000
Free: 800-LIU-PLAN
Fax: (516)299-3829
Co. E-mail: enroll@cwpost.liu.edu
URL: http://www.liu.edu
Description: Offers programs in small business management and entrepreneurship.

55504 ■ Erie Community College, City Campus
121 Ellicott St.
Buffalo, NY 14203
Ph: (716)851-1001
Fax: (716)851-1129
URL: http://www.ecc.edu/
Description: Two-year college offering a certificate in small business management.

55505 ■ Fiorello H. LaGuardia Community College of the City University of New York - Division of Adult and Continuing Education - Center for Corporate Education
31-10 Thomson Ave., Rm. B-114
Long Island City, NY 11101

Ph: (718)482-7200
Fax: (718)609-2036
Co. E-mail: acer@lagcc.cuny.edu
URL: http://www.lagcc.cuny.edu
Contact: Timothy Rucinsky, Director
Description: Offers courses in supervisory skills and management, microcomputer applications, communication and interpersonal skills, specialized business workshops, and technical training and workshops in retailing skills for small business owners. Maintains an interest in small business by offering programs at no cost to the community through funding by the New York State Department of Education. Small business courses cover personal selling, customer service, merchandise management, accounting, time and stress management, and microcomputers.

55506 ■ Herkimer County Community College
100 Reservoir Rd.
Herkimer, NY 13350
Ph: (315)866-0300
Fax: (315)866-7253
URL: http://www.hccc.ntcnet.com
Description: Two-year college offering a small business management program.

55507 ■ SUNY Canton College
34 Cornell Dr.
Canton, NY 13617
Ph: (315)386-7011
Free: 800-388-7123
Fax: (315)386-7929
Co. E-mail: admissions@canton.edu
URL: http://www.canton.edu/
Description: Two-year college offering a small business management program.

LEGISLATIVE ASSISTANCE

55508 ■ New York Assembly Standing Committee on Small Business
Legislative Office Bldg., Rm. 202
Albany, NY 12248
Ph: (518)455-4218
Fax: (518)455-3976
Co. E-mail: sweeney@assembly.state.ny.us
URL: http://www.assembly.state.ny.us

55509 ■ New York Senate Standing Committee
Legislative Office Bldg., Rm. 304
Albany, NY 12247
Ph: (518)455-2015
Fax: (518)426-6968
Co. E-mail: alesi@senate.state.ny.us
URL: http://www.senatoralesi.com
Description: Small Business.

TRADE PERIODICALS

55510 ■ *Proof*
Pub: Direct Marketing Club of New York
Released: 10/year. **Description:** Provides information concerning direct marketing to members of the Direct Marketing Club of New York. Recurring features include a calendar of events, news of members, news of educational opportunities, book reviews, and various columns on direct marketing techniques and advancements.

55511 ■ *Queensborough*
Pub: Queens Chamber of Commerce
Released: 5/year. **Price:** Included in membership. **Description:** Focuses on business trends in Queens County, New York.

PUBLICATIONS

55512 ■ *Capital District Business Review*
2 Computer Dr. W.
Albany, NY 12212-5081
Ph: (518)437-9855
Fax: (518)438-9219
URL: http://www.bizjournals.com/albany/

55513 ■ *Crain's New York Business*
220 E. 42nd St.
New York, NY 10017-5846
Ph: (212)210-0100
Fax: (212)210-0799
URL: http://www.crainsny.com

55514 ■ *How to Form Your Own New York Corporation*
950 Parker St.
Berkeley, CA 94710
Ph: (510)549-1976
Free: 800-992-6656
URL: http://www.nolo.com
Ed: Anthony Mancuso. **Released:** 1989. **Price:** $24.95. **Description:** Also available for use on IBM PC 3 (1/4 inch disk), IBM PC 5 (disk), and Macintosh (1/2 inch disk).

55515 ■ *Hudson Valley Business Journal*
86 E Main St.
Wappingers Falls, NY 12590
Ph: (845)298-6236
Fax: (845)298-6238
Co. E-mail: hvbjmail@aol.com
URL: http://hvbizjournal.com/

55516 ■ *Long Island Business News*
2150 Smithtown Ave.
Ronkonkoma, NY 11779-7358
Ph: (516)737-1700
Fax: (516)737-1890
Co. E-mail: editor@libn.com
URL: http://www.libn.com

55517 ■ *Rochester Business Journal*
45 East Ave.
Rochester, NY 14604
Ph: (585)546-8303
Fax: (585)546-3398
Co. E-mail: rbj@rbj.net
URL: http://www.rbj.net/

55518 ■ *Smart Start your New York Business*
PSI Research
300 N. Valley Dr.
Grants Pass, OR 97526
Ph: (503)479-9464
Free: 800-228-2275
Fax: (503)476-1479
Co. E-mail: info@psi-research.com
URL: http://www.psi-research.com
Ed: Michael D. Jenkins. **Released:** Revised edition, 1992. **Price:** $29.95 (looseleaf binder); $24.95 (paper). **Description:** Part of the Successful Business Library series.

55519 ■ *Westchester County Business Journal*
3 Gannett Dr.
White Plains, NY 10604
Ph: (914)694-3600
Fax: (914)694-3699
URL: http://westfaironline.com/

PUBLISHERS

55520 ■ Allworth Press
307 W 36th St., 11th Fl.
New York, NY 10018
Ph: (212)643-6816
Free: 800-491-2808
Fax: (212)643-6819
Co. E-mail: pub@allworth.com
URL: http://www.allworth.com
Contact: Shea Connelly, Manager
E-mail: sconnelly@allworth.com
Description: Description: Publishes practical business and self-help information for photographers, designers, artists, authors, and performing artists. Classic and contemporary critical writings on art and graphic design. Accepts unsolicited manuscripts. Reaches market through direct and special sales programs; the Internet; and Georgetown Publications. **Founded:** 1989. **Publications:** *Business and Legal Forms for Authors and Self-publishers*; *Artists' Communities: A Directory of Residencies that Offer Time and Space for Creativity*; *Starting Your Career as an Interior Designer*; *Starting Your Career as a Freelance Editor*; *Starting Your Career as a Freelance Web Designer*; *Starting Your Career as a Freelance Writer*; *The Education of a Graphic Designer*; *Creative Careers in Photography*; *Starting Your Career in Broadcasting: Working On and Off the Air in Radio and Television*; *Starting Your Career as an Artist: A Guide for Painters, Sculptors, Photographers, and Other Visual Artists*; *Promoting Your Acting Career: Step-by-Step Guide to Opening the Right Doors*; *The Actor's Other Career Book: Using Your Chops to Survive and Thrive*.

55521 ■ American Booksellers Association (ABA)
200 White Plains Rd., Ste. 600
Tarrytown, NY 10591
Ph: (914)591-2665
Free: 800-637-0037
Fax: (914)591-2720
Co. E-mail: info@bookweb.org
URL: http://www.bookweb.org
Contact: Becky Anderson, President
Description: Seeks to meet the needs of members, independently owned bookstores with storefront locations, through education, information dissemination, and advocacy. Supports free speech, literacy, and programs that encourage reading. **Founded:** 1900. **Publications:** *Bookselling this Week*; *ABA Electronic Book Buyer's Handbook*; *ABACUS* (Annual); *Bookselling this Week* (Weekly); *ABA Book Buyer's Handbook*; *ABA Bookselling This Week* (Weekly); *Bookselling This Week*; *American Bookseller: The Official Magazine of The American Booksellers Association* (Monthly). **Educational Activities:** BookExpo America (Annual); BookExpo America (Annual). **Awards:** Indies Choice Book Award; Book Sense Book of the Year Award (Annual).

55522 ■ Center for Entrepreneurial Management Inc. (CEM)
180 Varick St.
New York, NY 10014
Ph: (212)633-0060
Fax: (212)633-0063
Contact: Joseph R. Mancuso, President
Description: Description: Publishes business and management information targeted for officials of small and medium businesses. Many titles available on audio and video cassettes. Also produces newsletters and magazines. Reaches market through direct mail. Does not accept unsolicited manuscripts. **Founded:** 1978. **Publications:** *Chief Executive Officers Newsletter: For the Entrepreneurial Manager and the Pr ofessionals Who Advise Him*.

55523 ■ Doubleday Publishing Group—Knopf Doubleday Publishing Group
1745 Broadway
New York, NY 10019-4368
Ph: (212)782-9000
Free: 800-733-3000
Fax: (212)940-7390
Co. E-mail: ddaypub@randomhouse.com
URL: http://doubleday.com
Contact: Stephen Rubin, President
E-mail: mpalgon@randomhouse.com
Description: Description: Publishes mysteries, romances, westerns, and science fiction. Publishes nonfiction books in many areas including biographies, cookbooks, business, parenting, science, technology, parenting, child care, finance, gay and lesbian studies, money management and psychology. **Founded:** 1897.

55524 ■ Forum Publishing Co.
383 E Main St.
Centerport, NY 11721
Ph: (631)754-5000
Free: 800-635-7654
Co. E-mail: forumpublishing@aol.com
URL: http://www.forum123.com
Contact: Justo Rey, President
Description: Description: Publishes books and directories on business start-ups and expansions. Offers audio cassettes. Accepts unsolicited manuscripts. Reaches market through direct mail. **Founded:** 1981. **Publications:** *Swap Meet Magazine* (Monthly); *Venture Capital Directory* (Annual); *Annual Trade Show*

Directory (Annual); *Closeout Merchandise Directory* (Annual); *Apparel Contractors--Asia Edition*; *Chain Store Guide Dollar Stores*; *Chain Store Guide Wholesale Grocers*; *Hobby and Crafts Suppliers' Guide*; *National Sales Rep Directory*; *RN and WPL Encyclopedia*; *Retailers Forum Magazine* (Monthly); *U.S.A. Closeout Directory* (Annual); *Directory of Leading Chain Tenants*; *Fabrics, Services and Trims*; *Fine Jewelry Wholesalers*; *Gift Buyers' Guide*; *Wholesale Sources Directory*; *Apparel Contractors--U.S.A. Edition*; *Christmas and Holiday Merchandise Guide*; *ABC Art & Craft Event Directory*; *Chain Store Guide Apparel Specialty Stores*; *Chain Store Guide Buyers of Men's & Boy's Apparel*; *Chain Store Guide Buyers of Women's & Children's Apparel*; *Chain Store Guide Chain Restaurant Operators*; *Chain Store Guide Department Store Directory*; *Chain Store Guide Directory of Leading Chain Tenants*; *Chain Store Guide Discount & General Merchandise Stores*; *Chain Store Guide Drug & HBC Stores*; *Chain Store Guide Home Center Operators & Hardware Chains*; *Chain Store Guide Home Furnishings Retailers*; *Chain Store Guide Supermarket, Grocery & Convenience Stores*; *Directory of Brand Name Apparel Manufacturers*; *Directory of Buyers of Men's and Boy's Apparel*; *Directory of Buyers of Women's and Children's Apparel*; *Dollar Store Merchandise Guide: Sources for Dollar Store Operators*.

55525 ■ Genesis Society Inc.—Tree of Life Yoga & WellnessTree of Life;
102-06 Metropolitan Ave.
Forest Hills, NY 11375
Ph: (718)544-5997
Fax: (718)544-5488
Co. E-mail: info@genesissociety.com
URL: http://www.genesissociety.org
Contact: Rene David Alkalay, President
Description: Description: Publishes health-related hand books. **Founded:** 1999.

55526 ■ International Trademark Association (INTA)
655 3rd Ave., 10th Fl.
New York, NY 10017-5617
Ph: (212)642-1700
Fax: (212)768-7796
Co. E-mail: info@inta.org
URL: http://www.inta.org
Contact: Gregg Marrazzo, President
Description: Trademark owners; associate members are lawyers, law firms, advertising agencies, designers, market researchers, and others in the trademark industries. Seeks to: protect the interests of the public in the use of trademarks and trade names; promote the interests of members and of trademark owners generally in the use of their trademarks and trade names; disseminate information concerning the use, registration, and protection of trademarks in the United States, its territories, and in foreign countries. Maintains job bank and speakers' bureau. **Scope:** trademarks. **Founded:** 1878. **Subscriptions:** 3000 books periodicals. **Publications:** *The Trademarker Reporter*; *International Trademark Association--Membership Directory*; *INTA Bulletin* (Biweekly); *The Trademark Reporter* (Bimonthly). **Educational Activities:** International Trademark Association Meeting (Annual). **Awards:** International Trademark Association-Ladas Memorial Awards.

55527 ■ International Wealth Success Inc. (IWS)
24 Canterbury Rd.
Rockville Centre, NY 11570-1310
Ph: (516)766-5850
Free: 800-323-0548
Fax: (516)766-5919
Co. E-mail: admin@iwsmoney.com
URL: http://www.iwsmoney.com
Contact: Tyler G. Hicks, President
E-mail: dhicks@iwsmoney.com
Description: Description: Publishes on capital sources, mail order, import/export and real-estate. Accepts unsolicited manuscripts; include a self-addressed, stamped envelope. Reaches market through commission representatives, direct mail and trade sales. **Founded:** 1967. **Publications:** *Directory of High-Discount Merchandise and Product Sources for Distributors and Mail-Order Wealth Builders* (An-

nual); *Directory of 2,500 Active Real-Estate Lenders* (Annual); *Small Business Investment Company Directory and Handbook* (Annual).

55528 ■ JMW Group Inc.
1 West Ave.
Larchmont, NY 10538-2470
Ph: (914)769-6400
Fax: (914)769-0250
Co. E-mail: bdiedrick@att.net
URL: http://www.jmwgroup.net
Contact: Brice Diedrick, Director
E-mail: bdiedrick@att.net
Description: Description: Publishes both fiction and nonfiction books. **Founded:** 1985.

55529 ■ Macmillan Online USA
c/o Nature America Inc.
345 Park Ave. S
New York, NY 10010-1707
Ph: (212)726-9200
Free: 800-221-2123
Fax: (212)696-9006
Co. E-mail: a.thomas@nature.com
URL: http://www.macmillan.com
Contact: Annette Thomas, Chief Executive Officer
E-mail: annette.thomas@macmillan.com
Description: Description: Publishes scientific and medical journals. **Founded:** 1869.

55530 ■ McGraw-Hill Trade
2 Penn Plz.
New York, NY 10121-0101
Ph: (212)904-2000
Fax: (212)904-4091
Co. E-mail: customer.service@mcgraw-hill.com
URL: http://www.mcgraw-hill.com
Contact: Robert J. Bahash, President
Description: Description: Publishes business and general reference books.

55531 ■ Passion Profit Co.
PO Box 618, Church Street Sta.
New York, NY 10008-0618
Ph: (646)219-3565
Fax: (212)658-9232
Co. E-mail: orders@passionprofit.com
URL: http://www.passionprofit.com
Contact: Walt Goodridge, President
E-mail: walt@passionprofit.com
Description: Description: Publishes how-to books primarily. **Founded:** 1990.

55532 ■ Productivity Press (New York, New York)
270 Madison Ave.
New York, NY 10016
Ph: (212)216-7800
Free: 888-319-5852
Fax: (212)686-5411
Co. E-mail: info@productivitypress.com
URL: http://www.productivitypress.com
Contact: Ed Hanus, Director
E-mail: ehanus@productivitypress.com
Description: Description: Publishes materials on productivity, quality improvement, product development, corporate management, profit management and employee involvement. Publishes translations into English from Japan. **Founded:** 1983.

55533 ■ Rock Beach Press
1255 University Ave.
Rochester, NY 14607
Ph: (716)442-0888
Contact: William J. Stolze, President
Description: Description: Publishes a book about entrepreneurship. Reaches market through direct mail, Baker & Taylor and MacLean Hunter. **Founded:** 1989.

55534 ■ SelectBooks Inc.
1 Union Sq. W, Ste. 909
New York, NY 10003
Ph: (212)206-1997

Fax: (212)206-3815
Co. E-mail: info@selectbooks.com
URL: http://www.selectbooks.com
Contact: Mark W. Hordes, Editor
Description: Description: Publishes non-fiction in the areas of biography, politics, business administration and alternative medicine. **Founded:** 2001.

55535 ■ Standard & Poor's (S&P)
55 Water St.
New York, NY 10041
Ph: (212)438-2000
Free: 800-221-5277
Fax: (212)438-1000
Co. E-mail: questions@standardandpoors.com
URL: http://www.standardandpoors.com
Contact: Deven Sharma, President
Description: Description: Publishes on financial information. Offers more than 50 publications and services, disseminates information electronically and produces historical data on microfiche. Offers periodicals and software. Reaches market through commission representatives, direct mail and telephone sales. **Founded:** 1860. **Publications:** *Standard & Poor's Register of Corporations, Directors and Executives* (Annual); *CreditWeek: The Global Authority on Credit Quality* (Weekly); *Trendline Current Market Perspectives* (Monthly); *Trendline Daily Action Stock Charts* (Weekly); *Standard & Poor's N.Y.S.E. Stock Reports* (Daily); *Small Pension Funds Directory*; *Standard & Poor's Corporation Records*; *CUSIP Master Directory* (Annual); *Standard & Poor's Directory of Bond Agents* (Biennial); *Standard & Poor's Stock Reports--American Stock Exchange*; *Standard and Poor's Bond Guide*; *Standard and Poor's Ratings Handbook*; *Standard and Poor's Semi-Weekly Called Bond Record*; *International Securities Identification Directory* (Annual); *Directory of Bond Agents* (Annual); *Standard and Poor's Daily Stock Price Records*; *The Review of Securities & Commodities Regulation* (Semimonthly); *Mutual Fund Profiles*; *Standard & Poor's Dividend Record* (Daily); *CreditWeek*; *Standard and Poor's Dividend Record* (Daily); *Earnings Guide* (Monthly); *Industry Surveys*; *Bond Guide* (Monthly); *Corporation Records* (Daily); *Stock Guide* (Monthly); *Standard & Poor's MarketScope* (Daily); *Standard & Poor's Security Dealers of North America* (Semiannual); *S & P's Insurance Digest/Life Insurance Edition* (Quarterly); *S & P's Insurance Digest/Property-Casualty & Reinsurance Edition* (Quarterly); *The Review of Banking & Financial Services: An Analysis of Current Laws and Regulations Affecting Banking and Related Industries* (Semimonthly); *Analyst's Handbook: Composite Corporate Per Share Data by Industry*; *Standard & Poor's Stock Reports--New York Stock Exchange, American Stock Exchange, Nasdaq Stock Market and Regional Exchanges*; *Standard & Poor's Stock Reports--Nasdaq and Regional Exchanges*; *Standard & Poor's A.S.E. Stock Reports* (Weekly); *Garden Conservancy's Open Days Directory: The Guide To Visiting America's Best Private Gardens* (Annual); *Trendline Chart Guide* (Monthly); *OTC Chart Manual* (Bimonthly); *Standard & Poor's Nasdaq and Regional Exchange Stock Reports* (Weekly); *Blue List of Current Municipal and Corporate Offerings*. **Telecommunication Services:** clientsupport@standardandpoors.com.

55536 ■ Tokyo Stock Exchange Inc. (TSE)
45 Broadway, Ste. 2103
New York, NY 10006
Ph: (212)363-2350
Fax: (212)363-2354
Co. E-mail: contact@tsenyrep.com
URL: http://www.tse.or.jp/english/about/oversea.html
Contact: Takuo Tsurushima, President
Description: Description: Publishes on business and statistics, stocks and shares. **Founded:** 1870. **Publications:** *Tokyo Stock Exchange Fact Book*.

55537 ■ Vault.com Inc.
150 W 22nd St., 5th Fl.
New York, NY 10011
Ph: (212)366-4212
Free: 888-562-8285

Fax: (212)366-6117
Co. E-mail: questions@staff.vault.com
URL: http://www.vault.com
Contact: Mark Oldman, President
Description: Description: Publishes insider career development books for professionals and recruiters. Accepts unsolicited manuscripts. Reaches market through commission representatives, direct mail, reviews, listing, telephone sales and CDs. **Founded:** 1996. **Publications:** *Vault Guide to Top Internships; Law School Buzz Book; Vault Guide to the Top 100 Law Firms; Vault Guide to the Top Advertising & PR Employers; Vault Guide to the Top Government & Nonprofit Employers; Vault Guide to the Top Health Care Employers; Vault Guide to the Top Hospitality & Tourism Industry Employers; Vault Guide to the Top Manufacturing Employers; Vault Guide to the Top Pharmaceuticals & Biotech Employers; Vault Guide to the Top Real Estate Employers; Vault Guide to the Top Retail Employers; Vault Guide to the Top Tech Employers; Vault Guide to the Top Telecom Employers; Vault Guide to the Top 50 Accounting Firms; Vault*

Guide to the Top 50 Consumer Products Employers; Vault Guide to the Top Boston & Northeast Law Firms; Vault Guide to the Top Business Services Employers; Vault Guide to the Top Chicago & Midwest Law Firms; Vault Guide to the Top Government and Non-Profit Legal Employers; Vault Guide to the Top Insurance Employers; Vault Guide to the Top Internet Industry Employers; Vault Guide to the Top Media & Entertainment Employers; Vault Guide to the Top Mid-Atlantic Law Firms; Vault Guide to the Top New York Law Firms; Vault Guide to the Top Northern California Law Firms; Vault Guide to the Top Northwest & Great Plains Law Firms; Vault Guide to the Top Private Equity Employers; Vault Guide to the Top Southeastern Law Firms; Vault Guide to the Top Texas & Southwest Law Firms; Vault Guide to the Top Transportation Industry Employers; Vault Guide to the Top Washington, D.C. Law Firms; Vault Guide to the Top 25 Technology Consulting Firms.

55538 ■ H.W. Wilson Co.
950 University Ave.
Bronx, NY 10452-4224

Ph: (718)588-8400
Free: 800-367-6770
Fax: (718)590-1617
Co. E-mail: custserv@hwwilson.com
URL: http://www.hwwilson.com
Contact: Harold Regan, President
Description: Description: Publishes reference tools for libraries and book trade. Also offers videotapes, computer software, CD-ROMs and online databases. **Founded:** 1898.

55539 ■ Wise Counsel Press L.L.C.
230 Park Ave., Ste. 1000
New York, NY 10169-1099
Fax: (212)481-4039
Co. E-mail: info@wisecounselpress.com
URL: http://www.wisecounselpress.com
Contact: Nina L. Kaufman, Owner
Description: Description: Publishes legal materials aimed at assisting small businesses and entrepreneurs.